HOW TO ATTEMPT TEST IN TESTCOACH IN 6 SIMPLE STEPS

ON APP

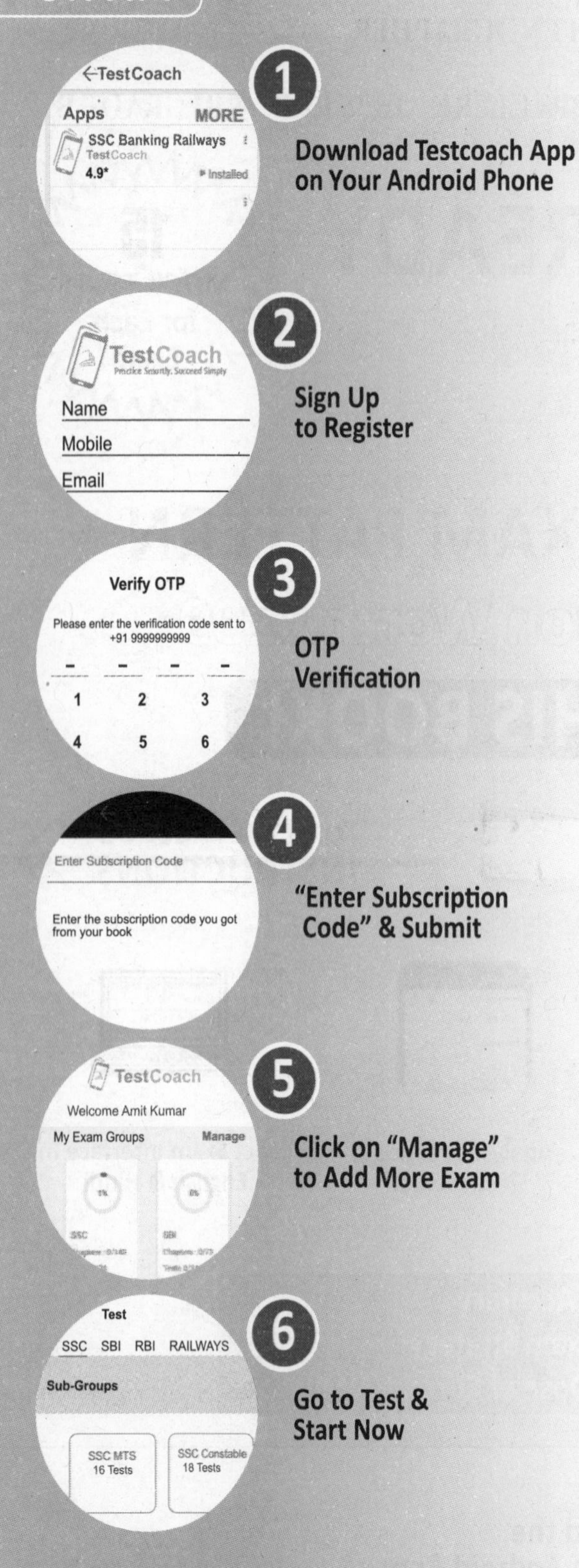

1. Download Testcoach App on Your Android Phone
2. Sign Up to Register
3. OTP Verification
4. "Enter Subscription Code" & Submit
5. Click on "Manage" to Add More Exam
6. Go to Test & Start Now

ON COMPUTER

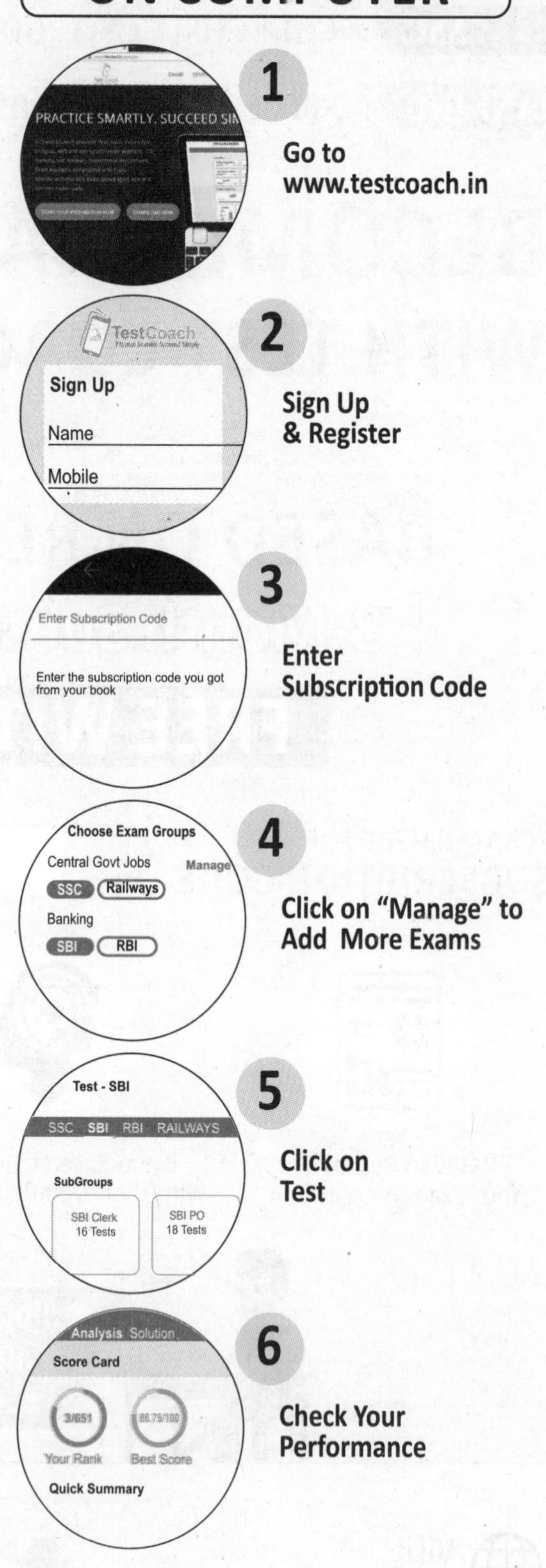

1. Go to www.testcoach.in
2. Sign Up & Register
3. Enter Subscription Code
4. Click on "Manage" to Add More Exams
5. Click on Test
6. Check Your Performance

**Test can be attempted with App or Web.

Contact us: support@testcoach.in, Mob.no.:+919319952655

Quantitative Aptitude

For Competitive Examinations

(Fully Solved)

As per New Examination Pattern

Quantitative Aptitude

For Competitive Examinations

(Fully Solved)

As per New Examination Pattern

An ideal book for :

- Bank PO, SBI-PO, IBPS, RBI Exams
- MBA, MAT, CMAT, GMAT, CAT, IIFT, IGNOU
- SSC Combined Preliminary Exams, Hotel Management
- Sub-Inspectors of Police, CBI, CPO Exams
- UPSC-CSAT, SCRA and other State Services Exams
- Railway Recruitment Board Exams
- Campus Recruitment Tests

Dr. R.S. AGGARWAL

S Chand And Company Limited

(ISO 9001 Certified Company)

S Chand And Company Limited

(ISO 9001 Certified Company)

Head Office: Block B-1, House No. D-1, Ground Floor, Mohan Co-operative Industrial Estate, New Delhi – 110 044 | Phone: 011-66672000

Registered Office: A-27, 2nd Floor, Mohan Co-operative Industrial Estate, New Delhi – 110 044 Phone: 011-49731800

www.**schandpublishing.com**; e-mail: **info@schandpublishing.com**

Branches

Ahmedabad	:	Ph: 27542369, 27541965; ahmedabad@schandpublishing.com
Bengaluru	:	Ph: 22354008, 22268048; bangalore@schandpublishing.com
Bhopal	:	Ph: 4274723, 4209587; bhopal@schandpublishing.com
Bhubaneshwar	:	Ph: 2951580; bhubaneshwar@schandpublishing.com
Chennai	:	Ph: 23632120; chennai@schandpublishing.com
Guwahati	:	Ph: 2738811, 2735640; guwahati@schandpublishing.com
Hyderabad	:	Ph: 40186018; hyderabad@schandpublishing.com
Jaipur	:	Ph: 2291317, 2291318; jaipur@schandpublishing.com
Jalandhar	:	Ph: 4645630; jalandhar@schandpublishing.com
Kochi	:	Ph: 2576207, 2576208; cochin@schandpublishing.com
Kolkata	:	Ph: 23357458, 23353914; kolkata@schandpublishing.com
Lucknow	:	Ph: 4003633; lucknow@schandpublishing.com
Mumbai	:	Ph: 25000297; mumbai@schandpublishing.com
Nagpur	:	Ph: 2250230; nagpur@schandpublishing.com
Patna	:	Ph: 2260011; patna@schandpublishing.com
Ranchi	:	Ph: 2361178; ranchi@schandpublishing.com
Sahibabad	:	Ph: 2771238; info@schandpublishing.com

First Edition 1989

Subsequent Editions and Reprints 1995, 1996 (Twice), 97, 98, 99, 2000, 2001, 2002, 2003, 2004, 2005 (Twice), 2006 (Twice), 2007 (Twice), 2008 (Twice), 2009 (Thrice), 2010 (Twice), 2011 (Thrice), 2012, 2013 (Twice), 2014 (Twice), 2015 (Twice), 2016 (Twice)

Revised and Enlarged Edition 2017*; Reprint 2017; Reprint 2018 (Twice)*

Reprint 2020 (Fourth Time)

ISBN: 978-93-525-3402-9

Product Code: H4QAP49QAPT40ENZX17O

PRINTED IN INDIA

By Vikas Publishing House Private Limited, Plot 20/4, Site-IV, Industrial Area Sahibabad, Ghaziabad – 201 010 and Published by S Chand And Company Limited, A-27, 2nd Floor, Mohan Co-operative Industrial Estate, New Delhi – 110 044

Preface to the Revised Edition

Ever since its release in 1989, *Quantitative Aptitude* has come to acquire a special place of respect and acceptance among students and aspirants appearing for a wide gamut of competitive exams. As a front-runner and a first choice, the book has solidly stood by the students and helped them fulfil their dreams by providing a strong understanding of the subject and even more rigorous practice of it.

Now, more than a quarter of a century later, with the ever changing environment of examinations, the book too reinvents itself while being resolute to its core concept of providing the best content with easily understandable solutions.

Following are the features of this revised and enlarged edition:

1. **Comprehensive:** With more than 5500 questions (supported with answers and solutions—a hallmark of Quantitative Aptitude) the book is more comprehensive than ever before.
2. **Easy to follow:** Chapters begin with easy-to-grasp theory complemented by formulas and solved examples. They are followed by a wide-ranging number of questions for practice.
3. **Latest:** With questions (memory based) from examinations up till year 2016, the book captures the latest examination patterns as well as questions for practice.

With the above enhancements to an already robust book, we fulfil a long-standing demand of the readers to bring out a revised and updated edition, and sincerely hope they benefit immensely from it.

Constructive suggestions for improvement of this book will be highly appreciated and welcomed.

All the Best!

Salient Features of the Book

- A whole lot of objective-type questions, with their solutions by short-cut methods.
- A full coverage of every topic via fully solved examples given at the beginning of each chapter.
- A separate exercise on Data-Sufficiency-Type Questions given in each topic, along with explanatory solutions.
- A more enriched section on Data Interpretation.
- Questions from latest years' examination papers (on memory basis) have been incorporated.

Contents

Contents

Section–I

Arithmetical Ability

1 Number System

FUNDAMENTAL CONCEPTS

I. Numbers

In Hindu-Arabic system, we have ten digits, namely 0, 1, 2, 3, 4, 5, 6, 7, 8 and 9.

*A number is denoted by a group of digits, called **numeral**.*

For denoting a numeral, we use the place-value chart, given below.

	Ten-Crores	Crores	Ten-Lakhs	Lakhs	Ten-Thousands	Thousands	Hundreds	Tens	Ones
(i)				5	2	8	6	7	9
(ii)			4	3	8	0	9	6	7
(iii)		3	5	2	1	8	0	0	9
(iv)	5	6	1	3	0	7	0	9	0

The four numerals shown above may be written in words as:

(i) Five lakh twenty-eight thousand six hundred seventy-nine
(ii) Forty-three lakh eighty thousand nine hundred sixty-seven
(iii) Three crore fifty-two lakh eighteen thousand nine
(iv) Fifty-six crore thirteen lakh seven thousand ninety

Now, suppose we are given the following four numerals in words:

(i) Nine crore four lakh six thousand two
(ii) Twelve crore seven lakh nine thousand two hundred seven
(iii) Four lakh four thousand forty
(iv) Twenty-one crore sixty lakh five thousand fourteen

Then, using the place-value chart, these may be written in figures as under:

	Ten-Crores	Crores	Ten-Lakhs	Lakhs	Ten-Thousands	Thousands	Hundreds	Tens	Ones
(i)		9	0	4	0	6	0	0	2
(ii)	1	2	0	7	0	9	2	0	7
(iii)				4	0	4	0	4	0
(iv)	2	1	6	0	0	5	0	1	4

II. Face value and Place value (or Local Value) of a Digit in a Numeral

(i) The face value of a digit in a numeral is its own value, at whatever place it may be.

Ex. ***In the numeral 6872, the face value of 2 is 2, the face value of 7 is 7, the face value of 8 is 8 and the face value of 6 is 6.***

(ii) In a given numeral:

Place value of ones digit = (ones digit) × 1,
Place value of tens digit = (tens digit) × 10,
Place value of hundreds digit = (hundreds digit) × 100 and so on.

Ex. ***In the numeral 70984, we have***

Place value of 4 = (4 × 1) = 4,
Place value of 8 = (8 × 10) = 80,
Place value of 9 = (9 × 100) = 900,
Place value of 7 = (7 × 10000) = 70000.

Note: Place value of 0 in a given numeral is 0, at whatever place it may be.

III. Various Types of Numbers

1. **Natural Numbers:** *Counting numbers are called natural numbers.*
Thus, 1, 2, 3, 4, ... are all natural numbers.
2. **Whole Numbers:** *All counting numbers, together with 0, form the set of whole numbers.*
Thus, 0, 1, 2, 3, 4, ... are all whole numbers.

3. **Integers:** *All counting numbers, zero and negatives of counting numbers, form the set of integers.*
Thus, ..., – 3, – 2, – 1, 0, 1, 2, 3, ... are all integers.
Set of positive integers = {1, 2, 3, 4, 5, 6, ...}
Set of negative integers = { – 1, – 2, – 3, – 4, – 5, – 6, ...}
Set of all non-negative integers = {0, 1, 2, 3, 4, 5, ...}
4. **Even Numbers:** *A counting number divisible by 2 is called an even number.*
Thus, 0, 2, 4, 6, 8, 10, 12, ... etc. are all even numbers.
5. **Odd Numbers:** *A counting number not divisible by 2 is called an odd number.*
Thus, 1, 3, 5, 7, 9, 11, 13, ... etc. are all odd numbers.
6. **Prime Numbers:** *A counting number is called a prime number if it has exactly two factors, namely itself and 1.*
Ex. All prime numbers less than 100 are:
2, 3, 5, 7, 11, 13, 17, 19, 23, 29, 31, 37, 41, 43, 47, 53, 59, 61, 67, 71, 73, 79, 83, 89, 97
7. **Composite Numbers:** *All counting numbers, which are not prime, are called composite numbers.*
A composite number has more than 2 factors.
8. **Perfect Numbers:** *A number, the sum of whose factors (except the number itself), is equal to the number, is called a perfect number,* e.g. 6, 28, 496
The factors of 6 are 1, 2, 3 and 6. And, 1 + 2 + 3 = 6.
The factors of 28 are 1, 2, 4, 7, 14 and 28. And, 1 + 2 + 4 + 7 + 14 = 28.
9. **Co-primes (or Relative Primes):** *Two numbers whose H.C.F. is 1 are called co-prime numbers,*
Ex. (2, 3), (8, 9) are pairs of co-primes.
10. **Twin Primes:** *Two prime numbers whose difference is 2 are called twin-primes,*
Ex. (3, 5), (5, 7), (11, 13) are pairs of twin-primes.
11. **Rational Numbers:** *Numbers which can be expressed in the form* $\frac{p}{q}$, *where p and q are integers and* $q \neq 0$, *are called rational numbers.*
Ex. $\frac{1}{8}, \frac{-8}{11}, 0, 6, 5\frac{2}{3}$ etc.
12. **Irrational Numbers:** *Numbers which when expressed in decimal would be in non-terminating and non-repeating form, are called irrational numbers.*
Ex. $\sqrt{2}, \sqrt{3}, \sqrt{5}, \sqrt{7}, \pi, e, 0.231764735......$

IV. Important Facts:

1. All natural numbers are whole numbers.
2. All whole numbers are not natural numbers.
0 is a whole number which is not a natural number.
3. Even number + Even number = Even number
Odd number + Odd number = Even number
Even number + Odd number = Odd number
Even number – Even number = Even number
Odd number – Odd number = Even number
Even number – Odd number = Odd number
Odd number – Even number = Odd number
Even number × Even number = Even number
Odd number × Odd number = Odd number
Even number × Odd number = Even number
4. The smallest prime number is 2.
5. The only even prime number is 2.
6. The first odd prime number is 3.
7. 1 is a unique number – neither prime nor composite.
8. The least composite number is 4.
9. The least odd composite number is 9.
10. **Test for a Number to be Prime:**
Let p be a given number and let n be the smallest counting number such that $n^2 \geq p$.
Now, test whether p is divisible by any of the prime numbers less than or equal to n. If yes, then p is not prime otherwise, p is prime.

Ex. ***Test, which of the following are prime numbers?***

(i) 137 ***(ii) 173*** ***(iii) 319*** ***(iv) 437*** ***(v) 811***

Sol. (*i*) We know that $(12)^2 > 137$.
Prime numbers less than 12 are 2, 3, 5, 7, 11.
Clearly, none of them divides 137.
$\therefore$ 137 is a prime number.

(*ii*) We know that $(14)^2 > 173$.
Prime numbers less than 14 are 2, 3, 5, 7, 11, 13.
Clearly, none of them divides 173.
$\therefore$ 173 is a prime number.

(*iii*) We know that $(18)^2 > 319$.
Prime numbers less than 18 are 2, 3, 5, 7, 11, 13, 17.
Out of these prime numbers, 11 divides 319 completely.
$\therefore$ 319 is not a prime number.

(*iv*) We know that $(21)^2 > 437$.
Prime numbers less than 21 are 2, 3, 5, 7, 11, 13, 17, 19.
Clearly, 437 is divisible by 19.
$\therefore$ 437 is not a prime number.

(*v*) We know that $(30)^2 > 811$.
Prime numbers less than 30 are 2, 3, 5, 7, 11, 13, 17, 19, 23, 29.
Clearly, none of these numbers divides 811.
$\therefore$ 811 is a prime number.

V. Important Formulae:

(*i*) $(a + b)^2 = a^2 + b^2 + 2ab$

(*ii*) $(a - b)^2 = a^2 + b^2 - 2ab$

(*iii*) $(a + b)^2 + (a - b)^2 = 2(a^2 + b^2)$

(*iv*) $(a + b)^2 - (a - b)^2 = 4ab$

(*v*) $(a + b)^3 = a^3 + b^3 + 3ab\,(a + b)$

(*vi*) $(a - b)^3 = a^3 - b^3 - 3ab\,(a - b)$

(*vii*) $a^2 - b^2 = (a + b)\,(a - b)$

(*viii*) $(a + b + c)^2 = a^2 + b^2 + c^2 + 2(ab + bc + ca)$

(*ix*) $a^3 + b^3 = (a + b)\,(a^2 + b^2 - ab)$

(*x*) $a^3 - b^3 = (a - b)\,(a^2 + b^2 + ab)$

(*xi*) $a^3 + b^3 + c^3 - 3abc = (a + b + c)\,(a^2 + b^2 + c^2 - ab - bc - ca)$

(*xii*) If $a + b + c = 0$, then $a^3 + b^3 + c^3 = 3abc$

TESTS OF DIVISIBILITY

1. Divisibility By 2:

A number is divisible by 2 if its unit digit is any of 0, 2, 4, 6, 8.

Ex. 58694 is divisible by 2, while 86945 is not divisible by 2.

2. Divisibility By 3:

A number is divisible by 3 only when the sum of its digits is divisible by 3.

Ex. (*i*) In the number 695421, the sum of digits = 27, which is divisible by 3.
$\therefore$ 695421 is divisible by 3.

(*ii*) In the number 948653, the sum of digits = 35, which is not divisible by 3.
$\therefore$ 948653 is not divisible by 3.

3. Divisibility By 9:

A number is divisible by 9 only when the sum of its digits is divisible by 9.

Ex. (*i*) In the number 246591, the sum of digits = 27, which is divisible by 9.
$\therefore$ 246591 is divisible by 9.

(*ii*) In the number 734519, the sum of digits = 29, which is not divisible by 9.
$\therefore$ 734519 is not divisible by 9.

4. Divisibility By 4:

A number is divisible by 4 if the number formed by its last two digits is divisible by 4.

Ex. (*i*) 6879376 is divisible by 4, since 76 is divisible by 4.

(*ii*) 496138 is not divisible by 4, since 38 is not divisible by 4.

5. Divisibility By 8:

A number is divisible by 8 if the number formed by its last three digits is divisible by 8.

Ex. (*i*) In the number 16789352, the number formed by last 3 digits, namely 352 is divisible by 8.
∴ 16789352 is divisible by 8.
(*ii*) In the number 576484, the number formed by last 3 digits, namely 484 is not divisible by 8.
∴ 576484 is not divisible by 8.

6. Divisibility By 10:
A number is divisible by 10 only when its unit digit is 0.
Ex. (*i*) 7849320 is divisible by 10, since its unit digit is 0.
(*ii*) 678405 is not divisible by 10, since its unit digit is not 0.

7. Divisibility By 5:
A number is divisible by 5 only when its unit digit is 0 or 5.
Ex. (*i*) Each of the numbers 76895 and 68790 is divisible by 5.

8. Divisibility By 11:
A number is divisible by 11 if the difference between the sum of its digits at odd places and the sum of its digits at even places is either 0 or a number divisible by 11.
Ex. (*i*) Consider the number 29435417.
(Sum of its digits at odd places) – (Sum of its digits at even places)
= (7 + 4 + 3 + 9) – (1 + 5 + 4 + 2) = (23 – 12) = 11, which is divisible by 11.
∴ 29435417 is divisible by 11.
(*ii*) Consider the number 57463822.
(Sum of its digits at odd places) – (Sum of its digits at even places)
= (2 + 8 + 6 + 7) – (2 + 3 + 4 + 5) = (23 – 14) = 9, which is not divisible by 11.
∴ 57463822 is not divisible by 11.

9. Divisibility By 25:
A number is divisible by 25 if the number formed by its last two digits is either 00 or divisible by 25.
Ex. (*i*) In the number 63875, the number formed by last 2 digits, namely 75 is divisible by 25.
∴ 63875 is divisible by 25.
(*ii*) In the number 96445, the number formed by last 2 digits, namely 45 is not divisible by 25.
∴ 96445 is not divisible by 25.

10. Divisibility By 7 or 13:
Divide the number into groups of 3 digits (starting from right) and find the difference between the sum of the numbers in odd and even places. If the difference is 0 or divisible by 7 or 13 (as the case may be), it is divisible by 7 or 13.
Ex. (*i*) 4537792 → 4 / 537 / 792
(792 + 4) – 537 = 259, which is divisible by 7 but not by 13.
∴ 4537792 is divisible by 7 and not by 13.
(*ii*) 579488 → 579 / 488
579 – 488 = 91, which is divisible by both 7 and 13.
∴ 579488 is divisible by both 7 and 13.

11. Divisibility By 16:
A number is divisible by 16, if the number formed by its last 4 digits is divisible by 16.
Ex. (*i*) In the number 463776, the number formed by last 4 digits, namely 3776, is divisible by 16.
∴ 463776 is divisible by 16.
(*ii*) In the number 895684, the number formed by last 4 digits, namely 5684, is not divisible by 16.
∴ 895684 is not divisible by 16.

12. Divisibility By 6: *A number is divisible by 6, if it is divisible by both 2 and 3.*

13. Divisibility By 12: *A number is divisible by 12, if it is divisible by both 3 and 4.*

14. Divisibility By 15: *A number is divisible by 15, if it is divisible by both 3 and 5.*

15. Divisibility By 18: *A number is divisible by 18, if it is divisible by both 2 and 9.*

16. Divisibility By 14: *A number is divisible by 14, if it is divisible by both 2 and 7.*

17. Divisibility By 24: *A given number is divisible by 24, if it is divisible by both 3 and 8.*

18. Divisibility By 40: *A given number is divisible by 40, if it is divisible by both 5 and 8.*

19. Divisibility By 80: *A given number is divisible by 80, if it is divisible by both 5 and 16.*

Note: *If a number is divisible by p as well as q, where p and q are co-primes, then the given number is divisible by pq.*

If p and q are not co-primes, then the given number need not be divisible by pq, even when it is divisible by both p and q.

Ex. 36 is divisible by both 4 and 6, but it is not divisible by $(4 \times 6) = 24$, since 4 and 6 are not co-primes.

VI. Factorial of a Number

Let n be a positive integer.

Then, the continued product of first n natural numbers is called factorial n, denoted by n ! or $\lfloor n$.

Thus, $n! = n(n-1)(n-2) \ldots\ldots\ldots 3.2.1$

Ex. $5! = 5 \times 4 \times 3 \times 2 \times 1 = 120$.

Note: $0! = 1$

VII. Modulus of a Number

$$|x| = \begin{cases} x, & \text{when } x \geq 0 \\ -x, & \text{when } x < 0 \end{cases}$$

Ex. $|-5| = 5$, $|4| = 4$, $|-1| = 1$, etc.

VIII. Greatest Integral Value

The greatest integral value of an integer x, denoted by [x], is defined as the greatest integer not exceeding x.

Ex. $[1.35] = 1$, $\left[\frac{11}{4}\right] = \left[2\frac{3}{4}\right] = 2$, etc.

IX. Multiplication BY Short cut Methods

1. Multiplication By Distributive Law:

(*i*) $a \times (b + c) = a \times b + a \times c$ (*ii*) $a \times (b - c) = a \times b - a \times c$

Ex. (*i*) $567958 \times 99999 = 567958 \times (100000 - 1) = 567958 \times 100000 - 567958 \times 1$

$= (56795800000) - 567958) = 56795232042.$

(*ii*) $978 \times 184 + 978 \times 816 = 978 \times (184 + 816) = 978 \times 1000 = 978000.$

2. Multiplication of a Number By 5^n: Put n zeros to the right of the multiplicand and divide the number so formed by 2^n.

Ex. $975436 \times 625 = 975436 \times 5^4 = \frac{9754360000}{16} = 609647500.$

X. Division Algorithm or Euclidean Algorithm

If we divide a given number by another number, then:

Dividend = (Divisor × Quotient) + Remainder

Important Facts:

1. (*i*) $(x^n - a^n)$ is divisible by $(x - a)$ for all values of n.

(*ii*) $(x^n - a^n)$ is divisible by $(x + a)$ for all even values of n.

(*iii*) $(x^n + a^n)$ is divisible by $(x + a)$ for all odd values of n.

2. **To find the highest power of a prime number p in n !**

Highest power of p in $n! = \left[\frac{n}{p}\right] + \left[\frac{n}{p^2}\right] + \left[\frac{n}{p^3}\right] + \ldots\ldots + \left[\frac{n}{p^r}\right]$, where $p^r \leq n < p^{r+1}$

SOLVED EXAMPLES

Ex. 1. ***Simplify:*** (*i*) 8888 + 888 + 88 + 8

(*ii*) 715632 − 631104 − 9874 − 999 (LIC, ADO, 2007)

Sol. (*i*)

```
 8888
  888
   88
+   8
 9872
```

(*ii*) Given exp = 715632 − (631104 + 9874 + 99)

= 715632 − 641077 = 74555.

```
  631104
    9874
+     99
  641077
```

```
  715632
- 641077
   74555
```

Ex. 2. *What value will replace the question mark in each of the following questions?*
(i)? – 1936248 = 1635773 ***(ii) 9587 –? = 7429 – 4358***

Sol. *(i)* Let $x - 1936248 = 1635773$. Then, $x = 1635773 + 1936248 = 3572021$.
(ii) Let $9587 - x = 7429 - 4358$.
Then, $9587 - x = 3071 \Rightarrow x = 9587 - 3071 = 6516$.

Ex. 3. *What could be the maximum value of Q in the following equation?*

5P9 + 3R7 + 2Q8 = 1114

Sol. We may analyse the given equation as shown:
Clearly, $2 + P + R + Q = 11$.
So, the maximum value of Q can be $(11 - 2)$, i.e. 9 (when $P = 0$, $R = 0$).

①②
5 P 9
3 R 7
2 Q 8
1 1 1 4

Ex. 4. *Simplify: (i) 5793405 × 9999* ***(ii) 839478 × 625***

Sol. *(i)* $5793405 \times 9999 = 5793405 \times (10000 - 1) = 57934050000 - 5793405 = 57928256595$.

(ii) $839478 \times 625 = 839478 \times 5^4 = 839478 \times \left(\frac{10}{2}\right)^4 = \frac{839478 \times 10^4}{2^4} = \frac{8394780000}{16} = 524673750$.

Ex. 5. *Evaluate: (i) 986 × 137 + 986 × 863* ***(ii) 983 × 207 – 983 × 107***

Sol. *(i)* $986 \times 137 + 986 \times 863 = 986 \times (137 + 863) = 986 \times 1000 = 986000$.
(ii) $983 \times 207 - 983 \times 107 = 983 \times (207 - 107) = 983 \times 100 = 98300$.

Ex. 6. *Simplify: (i) 1605 × 1605* ***(ii) 1398 × 1398***

Sol. *(i)* $1605 \times 1605 = (1605)^2 = (1600 + 5)^2 = (1600)^2 + 5^2 + 2 \times 1600 \times 5$
$= 2560000 + 25 + 16000 = 2576025$.
(ii) $1398 \times 1398 = (1398)^2 = (1400 - 2)^2 = (1400)^2 + 2^2 - 2 \times 1400 \times 2$
$= 1960000 + 4 - 5600 = 1954404$.

Ex. 7. *Evaluate: (i) 475 × 475 + 125 × 125* ***(ii) 796 × 796 – 204 × 204***

Sol. *(i)* We have $(a^2 + b^2) = \frac{1}{2}[(a+b)^2 + (a-b)^2]$

$\therefore (475)^2 + (125)^2 = \frac{1}{2}.[(475+125)^2 + (475-125)^2] = \frac{1}{2}.[(600)^2 + (350)^2]$
$= \frac{1}{2}[360000 + 122500] = \frac{1}{2} \times 482500 = 241250$.

(ii) $796 \times 796 - 204 \times 204 = (796)^2 - (204)^2 = (796 + 204)(796 - 204)$ $[\because (a-b)^2 = (a+b)(a-b)]$
$= (1000 \times 592) = 592000$.

Ex. 8. *Simplify: (i) (387 × 387 + 113 × 113 + 2 × 387 × 113)*
(ii) (87 × 87 + 61 × 61 – 2 × 87 × 61)

Sol. *(i)* Given Exp. $= (387)^2 + (113)^2 + 2 \times 387 \times 113 = (a^2 + b^2 + 2ab)$, where $a = 387$ and $b = 113$
$= (a + b)^2 = (387 + 113)^2 = (500)^2 = 250000$.
(ii) Given Exp. $= (87)^2 + (61)^2 - 2 \times 87 \times 61 = (a^2 + b^2 - 2ab)$, where $a = 87$ and $b = 61$
$= (a - b)^2 = (87 - 61)^2 = (26)^2 = (20 + 6)^2 = (20)^2 + 6^2 + 2 \times 20 \times 6 = (400 + 36 + 240)$
$= (436 + 240) = 676$.

Ex. 9. *Find the square root of 4a² + b² + c² + 4ab – 2bc – 4ac.* **(Campus Recruitment, 2010)**

Sol. $\sqrt{4a^2 + b^2 + c^2 + 4ab - 2bc - 4ac} = \sqrt{(2a)^2 + b^2 + (-c)^2 + 2 \times 2a \times b + 2 \times b \times (-c) + 2 \times (2a) \times (-c)}$
$= \sqrt{(2a + b - c)^2} = (2a + b - c)$.

Ex. 10. *A is counting the numbers from 1 to 31 and B from 31 to 1. A is counting the odd numbers only. The speed of both is the same. What will be the number which will be pronounced by A and B together?*
(Campus Recruitment, 2010)

Sol. The numbers pronounced by A and B in order are:

A	1	3	5	7	9	11	13	15	17	19	21	23	25	27	29	31
B	31	30	29	28	27	26	25	24	23	22	21	20	19	18	17	16

Clearly both A and B pronounce the number 21 together.

Ex. 11. *Simplify:* (*i*) $\dfrac{789 \times 789 \times 789 + 211 \times 211 \times 211}{789 \times 789 - 789 \times 211 + 211 \times 211}$ (*ii*) $\dfrac{658 \times 658 \times 658 - 328 \times 328 \times 328}{658 \times 658 + 658 \times 328 + 328 \times 328}$

Sol. (*i*) Given exp. $= \dfrac{(789)^3 + (211)^3}{(789)^2 - (789 \times 211) + (211)^2} = \dfrac{a^3 + b^3}{a^2 - ab + b^2}$, (where $a = 789$ and $b = 211$)

$= (a + b) = (789 + 211) = 1000.$

(*ii*) Given exp. $= \dfrac{(658)^3 - (328)^3}{(658)^2 + (658 \times 328) + (328)^2} = \dfrac{a^3 - b^3}{a^2 + ab + b^2}$, (where $a = 658$ and $b = 328$)

$= (a - b) = (658 - 328) = 330.$

Ex. 12. *Simplify:* $\dfrac{(893 + 786)^2 - (893 - 786)^2}{(893 \times 786)}$.

Sol. Given exp. $= \dfrac{(a + b)^2 - (a - b)^2}{ab}$ (where $a = 893$, $b = 786$) $= \dfrac{4ab}{ab} = 4.$

Ex. 13. *Which of the following are prime numbers?*

(i) 241 ***(ii) 337*** ***(iii) 391*** ***(iv) 571***

Sol. (*i*) Clearly, $16 > \sqrt{241}$.

Prime numbers less than 16 are 2, 3, 5, 7, 11, 13.

241 is not divisible by any of them.

$\therefore$ 241 is a prime number.

(*ii*) Clearly, $19 > \sqrt{337}$. Prime numbers less than 19 are 2, 3, 5, 7, 11, 13, 17.

337 is not divisible by any one of them.

$\therefore$ 337 is a prime number.

(*iii*) Clearly, $20 > \sqrt{391}$. Prime numbers less than 20 are 2, 3, 5, 7, 11, 13, 17, 19.

We find that 391 is divisible by 17.

$\therefore$ 391 is not a prime number.

(*iv*) Clearly, $24 > \sqrt{571}$. Prime numbers less than 24 are 2, 3, 5, 7, 11, 13, 17, 19,23.

571 is not divisible by any one of them.

$\therefore$ 571 is a prime number.

Ex. 14. *If Δ stands for the operation 'adding first number to twice the second number', then find the value of (1 Δ 2) Δ 3.*

Sol. $(1 \Delta 2) \Delta 3 = (1 + 2 \times 2) \Delta 3 = 5 \Delta 3 = 5 + 2 \times 3 = 5 + 6 = 11.$

Ex. 15. *Given that* $1^2 + 2^2 + 3^2 + \ldots + 10^2 = 385$, ***then find the value of*** $2^2 + 4^2 + 6^2 + \ldots + 20^2$.

Sol. $2^2 + 4^2 + 6^2 + \ldots + 20^2 = 2^2 (1^2 + 2^2 + 3^2 + \ldots + 10^2) = 2^2 \times 385 = 4 \times 385 = 1540.$

Ex.16. *Which of the following numbers is divisible by 3?*

(i) 541326 ***(ii) 5967013***

Sol. (*i*) Sum of digits in 541326 = (5 + 4 + 1 + 3 + 2 + 6) = 21, which is divisible by 3.

Hence, 541326 is divisible by 3.

(*ii*) Sum of digits in 5967013 = (5 + 9 + 6 + 7 + 0 + 1 + 3) = 31, which is not divisible by 3.

Hence, 5967013 is not divisible by 3.

Ex. 17. *What least value must be assigned to * so that the number 197*5462 is divisible by 9?*

Sol. Let the missing digit be x.

Sum of digits = $(1 + 9 + 7 + x + 5 + 4 + 6 + 2) = (34 + x)$.

For $(34 + x)$ to be divisible by 9, x must be replaced by 2.

Hence, the digit in place of * must be 2.

Ex. 18. *Which of the following numbers is divisible by 4?*

(i) 67920594 ***(ii) 618703572***

Sol. (*i*) The number formed by the last two digits in the given number is 94, which is not divisible by 4.

Hence, 67920594 is not divisible by 4.

(*ii*) The number formed by the last two digits in the given number is 72, which is divisible by 4.

Hence, 618703572 is divisible by 4.

Ex. 19. ***Which digits should come in place of * and $ if the number 62684*$ is divisible by both 8 and 5?***

Sol. Since the given number is divisible by 5, so 0 or 5 must come in place of $. But, a number ending with 5 is never divisible by 8. So, 0 will replace $.

Now, the number formed by the last three digits is 4*0, which becomes divisible by 8, if * is replaced by 4.

Hence, digits in place of * and $ are 4 and 0 respectively.

Ex. 20. ***Show that 4832718 is divisible by 11.***

Sol. (Sum of digits at odd places) – (Sum of digits at even places) = (8 + 7 + 3 + 4) – (1 + 2 + 8) = 11, which is divisible by 11.

Hence, 4832718 is divisible by 11.

Ex. 21. ***Is 52563744 divisible by 24?***

Sol. $24 = 3 \times 8$, where 3 and 8 are co-primes.

The sum of the digits in the given number is 36, which is divisible by 3. So, the given number is divisible by 3.

The number formed by the last 3 digits of the given number is 744, which is divisible by 8. So, the given number is divisible by 8. Thus, the given number is divisible by both 3 and 8, where 3 and 8 are co-primes. So, it is divisible by 3×8, i.e. 24.

Ex. 22. ***What are the values of M and N respectively if M39048458N is divisible by both 8 and 11, where M and N are single-digit integers?***

Sol. Since the given number is divisible by 8, it is obvious that the number formed by the last three digits, i.e. 58N is divisible by 8, which is possible only when $N = 4$.

Now, (sum of digits at even places) – (sum of digits at odd places)

$= (8 + 4 + 4 + 9 + M) - (4 + 5 + 8 + 0 + 3)$

$= (25 + M) - 20 = M + 5$, which must be divisible by 11.

So, $M = 6$.

Hence, $M = 6$, $N = 4$.

Ex. 23. ***Find the number of digits in the smallest number which is made up of digits 1 and 0 only and is divisible by 225.***

Sol. $225 = 9 \times 25$, where 9 and 25 are co-primes.

Clearly, a number is divisible by 225 if it is divisible by both 9 and 25.

Now, a number is divisible by 9 if the sum of its digits is divisible by 9 and a number is divisible by 25 if the number formed by the last two digits is divisible by 25.

∴ The smallest number which is made up of digits 1 and 0 and divisible by 225 = 1111111100.

Hence, number of digits = 11.

Ex. 24. ***If the number 3422213pq is divisible by 99, find the missing digits p and q.***

Sol. $99 = 9 \times 11$, where 9 and 11 are co-primes.

Clearly, a number is divisible by 99 if it is divisible by both 9 and 11.

Since the number is divisible by 9, we have:

$(3 + 4 + 2 + 2 + 2 + 1 + 3 + p + q)$ = a multiple of 9

$\Rightarrow 17 + (p + q) = 18$ or 27

$\Rightarrow p + q = 1$ ...(*i*) or $p + q = 10$ ...(*ii*)

Since the number is divisible by 11, we have:

$(q + 3 + 2 + 2 + 3) - (p + 1 + 2 + 4) = 0$ or a multiple of 11

$\Rightarrow (10 + q) - (7 + p) = 0$ or 11

$\Rightarrow 3 + (q - p) = 0$ or 11

$\Rightarrow q - p = -3$ or $q - p = 8$

$\Rightarrow p - q = 3$ ...(*iii*) or $q - p = 8$ ...(*iv*)

Clearly, if (*i*) holds, then neither (*iii*) nor (*iv*) holds. So, (*i*) does not hold.

Also, solving (*ii*) and (*iii*) together, we get: $p = 6.5$, which is not possible.

Solving (*ii*) and (*iv*) together, we get: $p = 1$, $q = 9$.

Ex. 25. ***x is a positive integer such that $x^2 + 12$ is exactly divisible by x. Find all the possible values of x.***

Sol. $\dfrac{x^2+12}{x} = \dfrac{x^2}{x} + \dfrac{12}{x} = x + \dfrac{12}{x}.$

Clearly, 12 must be completely divisible by x.

So, the possible values of x are 1, 2, 3, 4, 6 and 12.

Ex. 26. ***Find the smallest number to be added to 1000 so that 45 divides the sum exactly.***

Sol. On dividing 1000 by 45, we get 10 as remainder.

$\therefore$ Number to be added = (45 – 10) = 35.

Ex. 27. ***What least number must be subtracted from 2000 to get a number exactly divisible by 17?***

Sol. On dividing 2000 by 17, we get 11 as remainder.

$\therefore$ Required number to be subtracted = 11.

Ex. 28. ***Find the number which is nearest to 3105 and is exactly divisible by 21.***

Sol. On dividing 3105 by 21, we get 18 as remainder.

$\therefore$ Number to be added to 3105 = (21 – 18) = 3.

Hence, required number = 3105 + 3 = 3108.

Ex. 29. ***Find the smallest number of five digits which is exactly divisible by 476.***

Sol. Smallest number of 5 digits = 10000.

On dividing 10000 by 476, we get 4 as remainder.

$\therefore$ Number to be added = (476 – 4) = 472.

Hence, required number = 10472.

Ex. 30. ***Find the greatest number of five digits which is exactly divisible by 47.***

Sol. Greatest number of 5 digits is 99999.

On dividing 99999 by 47, we get 30 as remainder.

$\therefore$ Required number = (99999 – 30) = 99969.

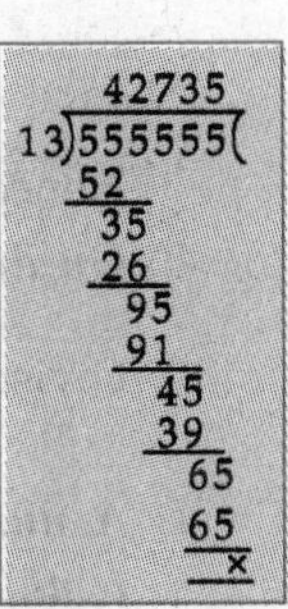

Ex. 31. ***When a certain number is multiplied by 13, the product consists entirely of fives. Find the smallest such number.***

Sol. Clearly, we keep on dividing 55555....... by 13 till we get 0 as remainder.

$\therefore$ Required number = 42735.

Ex. 32. ***When a certain number is multiplied by 18, the product consists entirely of 2's. What is the minimum number of 2's in the product?***

Sol. We keep on dividing 22222......... by 18 till we get 0 as remainder.

Clearly, number of 2's in the product = 9.

```
  12345679
18)222222222(
   18
    42
    36
     62
     54
      82
      72
      102
       90
       122
       108
        142
        126
         162
         162
          ×
```

Ex. 33. ***Find the smallest number which when multiplied by 9 gives the product as 1 followed by a certain number of 7s only.***

Sol. The least number having 1 followed by 7s, which is divisible by 9, is 177777, as 1 + 7 + 7 + 7 + 7 + 7 = 36 (which is divisible by 9).

$\therefore$ Required number = 177777 ÷ 9 = 19753.

Ex. 34. ***What is the unit's digit in the product?***

81 × 82 × 83 × .... 89?

Sol. Required unit's digit = Unit's digit in the product 1 × 2 × 3 ×.......× 9 = 0

[$\because$ 2 × 5 = 10]

Ex. 35. ***Find the unit's digit in the product*** $(2467)^{153} \times (341)^{72}$.

Sol. Clearly, unit's digit in the given product = unit's digit in $7^{153} \times 1^{72}$.

Now, 7^4 gives unit digit 1.

$\therefore$ 7^{152} gives unit digit 1.

$\therefore$ 7^{153} gives unit digit (1 × 7) = 7. Also, 1^{72} gives unit digit 1.

Hence, unit digit in the product = (7 × 1) = 7.

Ex. 36. ***Find the unit's digit in*** $(264)^{102} + (264)^{103}$.

Sol. Required unit's digit = unit's digit in $(4)^{102} + (4)^{103}$.

Now, 4^2 gives unit digit 6.

$\therefore$ $(4)^{102}$ gives unit digit 6.

$(4)^{103}$ gives unit digit of the product (6 × 4) i.e., 4.

Hence, unit's digit in $(264)^{102} + (264)^{103}$ = unit's digit in (6 + 4) = 0.

Ex. 37. ***Find the total number of prime factors in the expression*** $(4)^{11} \times (7)^5 \times (11)^2$.

Sol. $(4)^{11} \times (7)^5 \times (11)^2 = (2 \times 2)^{11} \times (7)^5 \times (11)^2 = 2^{11} \times 2^{11} \times 7^5 \times 11^2 = 2^{22} \times 7^5 \times 11^2$.

$\therefore$ Total number of prime factors = (22 + 5 + 2) = 29.

Ex. 38. ***What is the number of zeros at the end of the product of the numbers from 1 to 100?***

Sol. Let $N = 1 \times 2 \times 3 \times \ldots\ldots\ldots \times 100$.

Clearly, only the multiples of 2 and 5 yield zeros on multiplication.

In the given product, the highest power of 5 is much less than that compared to 2. So, we shall find the highest power of 5 in N.

Highest power of 5 in $N = \left[\frac{100}{5}\right] + \left[\frac{100}{5^2}\right] = 20 + 4 = 24.$

Hence, required number of zeros = 24.

Ex. 39. ***What is the number of zeros at the end of the product $5^5 \times 10^{10} \times 15^{15} \times \ldots\ldots\ldots \times 125^{125}$?***

Sol. Clearly, the highest power of 2 is less than that of 5 in N.

So, the highest power of 2 in N shall give us the number of zeros at the end of N.

Highest power of 2 = Number of multiples of 2 + Number of multiples of 4 (i.e. 2^2) + Number of multiples of 8 (i.e. 2^3) + Number of multiples of 16 (i.e. 2^4)

$= [(10 + 20 + 30 + \ldots\ldots + 120) + (20 + 40 + 60 + \ldots\ldots + 120) + (40 + 80 + 120) + 80]$

$= (780 + 420 + 240 + 80) = 1520.$

Hence, required number of zeros = 1520.

Ex. 40. ***On dividing 15968 by a certain number, the quotient is 89 and the remainder is 37. Find the divisor.***

Sol. Divisor $= \frac{\text{Dividend} - \text{Remainder}}{\text{Quotient}} = \frac{15968 - 37}{89} = 179.$

Ex. 41. ***A number when divided by 114, leaves remainder 21. If the same number is divided by 19, find the remainder.*** (S.S.C., 2010)

Sol. On dividing the given number by 114, let k be the quotient and 21 the remainder.

Then, number $= 114k + 21 = 19 \times 6k + 19 + 2 = 19(6k + 1) + 2.$

$\therefore$ The given number when divided by 19 gives remainder = 2.

Ex. 42. ***A number being successively divided by 3, 5 and 8 leaves remainders 1, 4 and 7 respectively. Find the respective remainders if the order of divisors be reversed.***

Sol.

3	x
5	$y - 1$
8	$z - 4$
	$1 - 7$

$\therefore z = (8 \times 1 + 7) = 15;\ y = (5z + 4) = (5 \times 15 + 4) = 79;$

$x = (3y + 1) = (3 \times 79 + 1) = 238.$

Now,

8	238
5	29 – 6
3	5 – 4
	1 – 2

$\therefore$ Respective remainders are 6, 4, 2.

Ex. 43. ***Three boys A, B, C were asked to divide a certain number by 1001 by the method of factors. They took the factors in the orders 13, 11, 7; 7, 11, 13 and 11, 7, 13 respectively. If the first boy obtained 3, 2, 1 as successive remainders, then find the successive remainders obtained by the other two boys B and C.***

Sol.

13	x
11	$y - 3$
7	$z - 2$
	$1 - 1$

$\therefore z = 7 \times 1 + 1 = 8,$

$y = 11z + 2 = 11 \times 8 + 2 = 90;$

$x = 13y + 3 = 13 \times 90 + 3 = 1173.$

Now,

7	1173
11	167 – 4
13	15 – 2
	1 – 2

So, B obtained 4, 2 and 2 as successive remainders.

And,

11	1173
7	106 – 7
13	15 – 1
	1 – 2

C obtained 7, 1 and 2 as successive remainders.

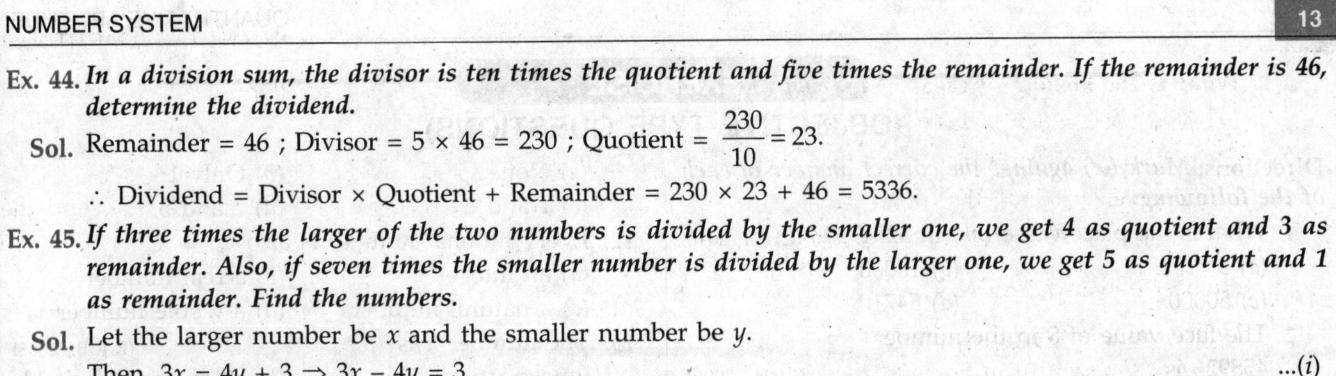

Ex. 44. ***In a division sum, the divisor is ten times the quotient and five times the remainder. If the remainder is 46, determine the dividend.***

Sol. Remainder = 46 ; Divisor = 5 × 46 = 230 ; Quotient = $\frac{230}{10} = 23$.

∴ Dividend = Divisor × Quotient + Remainder = 230 × 23 + 46 = 5336.

Ex. 45. ***If three times the larger of the two numbers is divided by the smaller one, we get 4 as quotient and 3 as remainder. Also, if seven times the smaller number is divided by the larger one, we get 5 as quotient and 1 as remainder. Find the numbers.***

Sol. Let the larger number be x and the smaller number be y.

Then, $3x = 4y + 3 \Rightarrow 3x - 4y = 3$ ...(*i*)

And, $7y = 5x + 1 \Rightarrow -5x + 7y = 1$ ...(*ii*)

Multiplying (*i*) by 5 and (*ii*) by 3, we get:

$15x - 20y = 15$ ...(*iii*) and $-15x + 21y = 3$ ...(*iv*)

Adding (*iii*) and (*iv*), we get: $y = 18$.

Putting $y = 18$ in (*i*), we get: $x = 25$.

Hence, the numbers are 25 and 18.

Ex. 46. ***A number when divided by 6 leaves remainder 3. When the square of the same number is divided by 6, find the remainder.***

Sol. On dividing the given number by 6, let k be the quotient and 3 the remainder.

Then, number = $6k + 3$.

Square of the number $= (6k + 3)^2 = 36k^2 + 9 + 36k = 36k^2 + 36k + 6 + 3$

$= 6(6k^2 + 6k + 1) + 3$, which gives a remainder 3 when divided by 6.

Ex. 47. ***Find the remainder when $9^6 + 7$ is divided by 8.***

Sol. $(x^n - a^n)$ is divisible by $(x - a)$ for all values of n.

So, $(9^6 - 1)$ is divisible by $(9 - 1)$, i.e. $8 \Rightarrow (9^6 - 1) + 8$ is divisible by $8 \Rightarrow (9^6 + 7)$ is divisible by 8.

Hence, required remainder = 0.

Ex. 48. ***Find the remainder when $(397)^{3589} + 5$ is divided by 398.***

Sol. $(x^n + a^n)$ is divisible by $(x + a)$ for all odd values of n.

So, $[(397)^{3589} + 1]$ is divisible by $(397 + 1)$, i.e. 398

$\Rightarrow [\{(397)^{3589} + 1\} + 4]$ gives remainder 4 when divided by 398

$\Rightarrow [(397)^{3589} + 5]$ gives remainder 4 when divided by 398.

Ex. 49. ***If 7^{126} is divided by 48, find the remainder.***

Sol. $7^{126} = (7^2)^{63} = (49)^{63}$.

Now, since $(x^n - a^n)$ is divisible by $(x - a)$ for all values of n,

so $[(49)^{63} - 1]$ or $(7^{126} - 1)$ is divisible by $(49 - 1)$ i.e. 48.

∴ Remainder obtained when $(7)^{126}$ is divided by 48 = 1.

Ex. 50. ***Find the remainder when $(257^{166} - 243^{166})$ is divided by 500.***

Sol. $(x^n - a^n)$ is divisible by $(x + a)$ for all even values of n.

∴ $(257^{166} - 243^{166})$ is divisible by $(257 + 243)$, i.e. 500.

Hence, required remainder = 0.

Ex. 51. ***Find a common factor of $(127^{127} + 97^{127})$ and $(127^{97} + 97^{97})$.***

Sol. $(x^n + a^n)$ is divisible by $(x + a)$ for all odd values of n.

∴ $(127^{127} + 97^{127})$ as well as $(127^{97} + 97^{97})$ is divisible by $(127 + 97)$, i.e. 224.

Hence, required common factor = 224.

Ex. 52. ***A 99–digit number is formed by writing the first 59 natural numbers one after the other as:***

1234567891011121314...........5859

Find the remainder obtained when the above number is divided by 16.

Sol. The required remainder is the same as that obtained on dividing the number formed by the last four digits i.e. 5859 by 16, which is 3.

EXERCISE
(OBJECTIVE TYPE QUESTIONS)

Directions: ***Mark (✔) against the correct answer in each of the following:***

1. What is the place value of 5 in 3254710? (CLAT, 2010)
   (a) 5 (b) 10000
   (c) 50000 (d) 54710
2. The face value of 8 in the number 458926 is (R.R.B., 2006)
   (a) 8 (b) 1000
   (c) 8000 (d) 8926
3. The sum of the place values of 3 in the number 503535 is (M.B.A., 2005)
   (a) 6 (b) 60
   (c) 3030 (d) 3300
4. The difference between the place values of 7 and 3 in the number 527435 is
   (a) 4 (b) 5
   (c) 45 (d) 6970
5. The difference between the local value and the face value of 7 in the numeral 32675149 is
   (a) 5149 (b) 64851
   (c) 69993 (d) 75142
   (e) None of these
6. The sum of the greatest and smallest number of five digits is (M.C.A., 2005)
   (a) 11,110 (b) 10,999
   (c) 109,999 (d) 111,110
7. If the largest three-digit number is subtracted from the smallest five-digit number, then the remainder is
   (a) 1 (b) 9000
   (c) 9001 (d) 90001
8. The smallest number of 5 digits beginning with 3 and ending with 5 will be (R.R.B., 2006)
   (a) 31005 (b) 30015
   (c) 30005 (d) 30025
9. What is the minimum number of four digits formed by using the digits 2, 4, 0, 7? (P.C.S., 2007)
   (a) 2047 (b) 2247
   (c) 2407 (d) 2470
10. All natural numbers and 0 are called the .... numbers. (R.R.B., 2006)
    (a) rational (b) integer
    (c) whole (d) prime
11. Consider the following statements about natural numbers:
    (1) There exists a smallest natural number.
    (2) There exists a largest natural number.
    (3) Between two natural numbers, there is always a natural number.

    Which of the above statements is/are correct?
    (a) None (b) Only 1
    (c) 1 and 2 (d) 2 and 3
12. Every rational number is also
    (a) an integer (b) a real number
    (c) a natural number (d) a whole number
13. The number π is (R.R.B., 2005)
    (a) a fraction (b) a recurring decimal
    (c) a rational number (d) an irrational number
14. $\sqrt{2}$ is a/an
    (a) rational number (b) natural number
    (c) irrational number (d) integer
15. The number $\sqrt{3}$ is
    (a) a finite decimal
    (b) an infinite recurring decimal
    (c) equal to 1.732
    (d) an infinite non-recurring decimal
16. There are just two ways in which 5 may be expressed as the sum of two different positive (non-zero) integers, namely $5 = 4 + 1 = 3 + 2$. In how many ways, 9 can be expressed as the sum of two different positive (non-zero) integers?
    (a) 3 (b) 4
    (c) 5 (d) 6
17. P and Q are two positive integers such that $PQ = 64$. Which of the following cannot be the value of $P + Q$?
    (a) 16 (b) 20
    (c) 35 (d) 65
18. If $x + y + z = 9$ and both y and z are positive integers greater than zero, then the maximum value x can take is (Campus Recruitment, 2006)
    (a) 3 (b) 7
    (c) 8 (d) Data insufficient
19. What is the sum of the squares of the digits from 1 to 9?
    (a) 105 (b) 260
    (c) 285 (d) 385
20. If n is an integer between 20 and 80, then any of the following could be $n + 7$ except
    (a) 47 (b) 58
    (c) 84 (d) 88
21. Which one of the following is the correct sequence in respect of the Roman numerals: C, D, L and M? (Civil Services, 2008)
    (a) $C > D > L > M$ (b) $M > L > D > C$
    (c) $M > D > C > L$ (d) $L > C > D > M$
22. If the numbers from 1 to 24, which are divisible by 2 are arranged in descending order, which number will be at the 8th place from the bottom? (CLAT, 2010)

(a) 10 (b) 12
(c) 16 (d) 18

23. $2 - 2 + 2 - 2 + \ldots\ldots\ldots$ 101 terms =? (P.C.S., 2008)
(a) -2 (b) 0
(c) 2 (d) None of these

24. 98th term of the infinite series 1, 2, 3, 4, 1, 2, 3, 4, 1, 2, ... is (M.C.A., 2005)
(a) 1 (b) 2
(c) 3 (d) 4

25. If x, y, z be the digits of a number beginning from the left, the number is
(a) xyz (b) $x + 10y + 100z$
(c) $10x + y + 100z$ (d) $100x + 10y + z$

26. If x, y, z and w be the digits of a number beginning from the left, the number is
(a) $xyzw$
(b) $wzyx$
(c) $x + 10y + 100z + 1000w$
(d) $10^3x + 10^2y + 10z + w$

27. If n and p are both odd numbers, which of the following is an even number?
(a) $n + p$ (b) $n + p + 1$
(c) $np + 2$ (d) np

28. For the integer n, if n^3 is odd, then which of the following statements are true?
I. n is odd. II. n^2 is odd.
III. n^2 is even.
(a) I only (b) II only
(c) I and II only (d) I and III only

29. If $(n - 1)$ is an odd number, what are the two other odd numbers nearest to it?
(a) $n, n - 1$ (b) $n, n - 2$
(c) $n - 3, n + 1$ (d) $n - 3, n + 5$

30. Which of the following is always odd?
(a) Sum of two odd numbers
(b) Difference of two odd numbers
(c) Product of two odd numbers
(d) None of these

31. If x is an odd integer, then which of the following is true?
(a) $5x - 2$ is even (b) $5x^2 + 2$ is odd
(c) $5x^2 + 3$ is odd (d) None of these

32. If a and b are two numbers such that $ab = 0$, then (R.R.B., 2006)
(a) $a = 0$ and $b = 0$ (b) $a = 0$ or $b = 0$ or both
(c) $a = 0$ and $b \neq 0$ (d) $b = 0$ and $a \neq 0$

33. If A, B, C, D are numbers in increasing order and D, B, E are numbers in decreasing order, then which one of the following sequences need neither be in a decreasing nor in an increasing order?
(a) E, C, D (b) E, B, C
(c) D, B, A (d) A, E, C

34. If m, n, o, p and q are integers, then $m(n + o)(p - q)$ must be even when which of the following is even?
(a) m (b) p
(c) $m + n$ (d) $n + p$

35. If n is a negative number, then which of the following is the least?
(a) 0 (b) $-n$
(c) $2n$ (d) n^2

36. If $x - y = 8$, then which of the following must be true?
I. Both x and y are positive.
II. If x is positive, y must be positive.
III. If x is negative, y must be negative.
(a) I only (b) II only
(c) I and II (d) III only

37. If x and y are negative, then which of the following statements is/are always true?
I. $x + y$ is positive.
II. xy is positive.
III. $x - y$ is positive.
(a) I only (b) II only
(c) III only (d) I and III only

38. If $n = 1 + x$, where x is the product of four consecutive positive integers, then which of the following is/are true?
I. n is odd. II. n is prime.
III. n is a perfect square.
(a) I only (b) I and II only
(c) I and III only (d) None of these

39. If $x = \frac{2}{5}y + 3$, how does y change when x increases from 1 to 2?
(a) y increases from -5 to $-\frac{5}{2}$
(b) y increases from $\frac{2}{5}$ to 5
(c) y increases from $\frac{5}{2}$ to 5
(d) y decreases from -5 to $-\frac{5}{2}$

40. If x is a rational number and y is an irrational number, then
(a) both $x + y$ and xy are necessarily rational
(b) both $x + y$ and xy are necessarily irrational
(c) xy is necessarily irrational, but $x + y$ can be either rational or irrational
(d) $x + y$ is necessarily irrational, but xy can be either rational or irrational

41. The difference between the square of any two consecutive integers is equal to
(a) sum of two numbers
(b) difference of two numbers
(c) an even number
(d) product of two numbers

42. Between two distinct rational numbers a and b, there exists another rational number which is (P.C.S., 2006)
(a) $\frac{a}{2}$ (b) $\frac{b}{2}$
(c) $\frac{ab}{2}$ (d) $\frac{a+b}{2}$

43. If $B > A$, then which expression will have the highest value (given that A and B are positive integers)? (Campus Recruitment, 2007)
(a) $A - B$ (b) AB
(c) $A + B$ (d) Can't say

44. If $0 < x < 1$, which of the following is greatest? (Campus Recruitment, 2007)
(a) x (b) x^2
(c) $\frac{1}{x}$ (d) $\frac{1}{x^2}$

45. If p is a positive fraction less than 1, then
(a) $\frac{1}{p}$ is less than 1 (b) $\frac{1}{p}$ is a positive integer
(c) p^2 is less than p
(d) $\frac{2}{p} - p$ is a positive number

46. If x is a real number, then $x^2 + x + 1$ is
(a) less than $\frac{3}{4}$
(b) zero for at least one value of x
(c) always negative
(d) greater than or equal to $\frac{3}{4}$

47. Let n be a natural number such that $\frac{1}{2}+\frac{1}{3}+\frac{1}{7}+\frac{1}{n}$ is also a natural number. Which of the following statements is not true? (A.A.O. Exam, 2009)
(a) 2 divides n (b) 3 divides n
(c) 7 divides n (d) $n > 84$

48. If n is an integer, how many values of n will give an integral value of $\left(\frac{16n^2+7n+6}{n}\right)$?
(a) 2 (b) 3
(c) 4 (d) None of these

49. If $p > q$ and $r < 0$, then which is true?
(a) $pr < qr$ (b) $p - r < q - r$
(c) $p + r < q + r$ (d) None of these

50. If $X < Z$ and $X < Y$, which of the following is necessarily true?
I. $Y < Z$ II. $X^2 < YZ$
III. $ZX < Y + Z$
(a) Only I (b) Only II
(c) Only III (d) None of these

51. In the relation $x > y + z$, $x + y > p$ and $z < p$, which of the following is necessarily true? (Campus Recruitment, 2008)
(a) $y > p$ (b) $x + y > z$
(c) $y + p > x$ (d) Insufficient data

52. If a and b are positive integers and $\frac{(a-b)}{3.5} = \frac{4}{7}$, then (Campus Recruitment, 2010)
(a) $b > a$ (b) $b < a$
(c) $b = a$ (d) $b \geq a$

53. If $13 = \frac{13w}{(1-w)}$, then $(2w)^2 = ?$ (Campus Recruitment, 2009)
(a) $\frac{1}{4}$ (b) $\frac{1}{2}$
(c) 1 (d) 2

Directions (Questions 54–57): *For a 5–digit number, without repetition of digits, the following information is available.* (B.B.A., 2006)

(i) The first digit is more than 5 times the last digit.
(ii) The two-digit number formed by the last two digits is the product of two prime numbers.
(iii) The first three digits are all odd.
(iv) The number does not contain the digits 3 or 0 and the first digit is also the largest.

54. The second digit of the number is
(a) 5 (b) 7
(c) 9
(d) Cannot be determined

55. The last digit of the number is
(a) 0 (b) 1
(c) 2 (d) 3

56. The largest digit in the number is
(a) 5 (b) 7
(c) 8 (d) 9

57. Which of the following is a factor of the given number?
(a) 2 (b) 3
(c) 4 (d) 9

58. The least prime number is
(a) 0 (b) 1
(c) 2 (d) 3

59. Consider the following statements:
1. If x and y are composite numbers, then $x + y$ is always composite.
2. There does not exist a natural number which is neither prime nor composite.

Which of the above statements is/are correct?
(a) 1 only (b) 2 only
(c) Both 1 and 2 (d) Neither 1 nor 2

60. The number of prime numbers between 0 and 50 is
(a) 14 (b) 15
(c) 16 (d) 17

61. The prime numbers dividing 143 and leaving a remainder of 3 in each case are
(a) 2 and 11 (b) 11 and 13
(c) 3 and 7 (d) 5 and 7

62. The sum of the first four primes is
(a) 10 (b) 11
(c) 16 (d) 17

63. The sum of all the prime numbers from 1 to 20 is
(a) 75 (b) 76
(c) 77 (d) 78

64. A prime number N, in the range 10 to 50, remains unchanged when its digits are reversed. The square of such a number is
(a) 121 (b) 484
(c) 1089 (d) 1936

65. The remainder obtained when any prime number greater than 6 is divided by 6 must be **(Campus Recruitment, 2007)**
(a) either 1 or 2 (b) either 1 or 3
(c) either 1 or 5 (d) either 3 or 5

66. Which of the following is not a prime number? **(CLAT, 2010)**
(a) 21 (b) 23
(c) 29 (d) 43

67. Which of the following is a prime number? **(CLAT, 2010)**
(a) 19 (b) 20
(c) 21 (d) 22

68. Which of the following is a prime number? **(Campus Recruitment, 2008)**
(a) 115 (b) 119
(c) 127 (d) None of these

69. Which of the following is a prime number? **(R.R.B., 2006)**
(a) 143 (b) 289
(c) 117 (d) 359

70. The smallest value of natural number n, for which $2n + 1$ is not a prime number, is
(a) 3 (b) 4
(c) 5 (d) None of these

71. The smallest three-digit prime number is
(a) 101 (b) 103
(c) 107 (d) None of these

72. How many of the integers between 110 and 120 are prime numbers? **(M.B.A., 2006)**
(a) 0 (b) 1
(c) 2 (d) 3
(e) 4

73. Four prime numbers are arranged in ascending order. The product of first three is 385 and that of last three is 1001. The largest prime number is **(R.R.B., 2006)**
(a) 9 (b) 11
(c) 13 (d) 17

74. The sum of three prime numbers is 100. If one of them exceeds another by 36, then one of the numbers is
(a) 7 (b) 29
(c) 41 (d) 67

75. Which one of the following is a prime number?
(a) 161 (b) 221
(c) 373 (d) 437

76. The smallest prime number, that is the fifth term of an increasing arithmetic sequence in which all the four preceding terms are also prime, is
(a) 17 (b) 29
(c) 37 (d) 53

77. The number of prime numbers between 301 and 320 are
(a) 3 (b) 4
(c) 5 (d) 6

78. Consider the following statements:
1. If $p > 2$ is a prime, then it can be written as $4n + 1$ or $4n + 3$ for a suitable natural number n.
2. If $p > 2$ is a prime, then $(p - 1)(p + 1)$ is always divisible by 4.
Of these statements,
(a) (1) is true but (2) is false
(b) (1) is false but (2) is true
(c) (1) and (2) are false
(d) (1) and (2) are true

79. What is the first value of n for which $n^2 + n + 41$ is not a prime?
(a) 1 (b) 10
(c) 20 (d) 40

80. Let $X_k = (p_1 p_2 \ldots\ldots p_k) + 1$, where $p_1, p_2, \ldots\ldots, p_k$ are the first k primes.
Consider the following:
1. X_k is a prime number.
2. X_k is a composite number.
3. $X_k + 1$ is always an even number.
Which of the above is/are correct?
(a) 1 only (b) 2 only
(c) 3 only (d) 1 and 3

81. $6 \times 3 (3 - 1)$ is equal to **(CLAT, 2010)**
(a) 19 (b) 20
(c) 36 (d) 53

82. 1234 + 2345 – 3456 + 4567 =? **(Bank Recruitment, 2010)**
(a) 4590 (b) 4670
(c) 4680 (d) 4690
(e) None of these

83. 5566 – 7788 + 9988 =? + 4444 **(Bank Recruitment, 2010)**
(a) 3223 (b) 3232
(c) 3322 (d) 3333
(e) None of these

84. 38649 − 1624 − 4483 =? (Bank Recruitment, 2009)
(a) 32425 (b) 32452
(c) 34522 (d) 35422
(e) None of these

85. 884697 − 773697 − 102479 =? (Bank Recruitment, 2009)
(a) 8251 (b) 8512
(c) 8521 (d) 8531
(e) None of these

86. 10531 + 4813 − 728 =? × 87 (Bank Recruitment, 2008)
(a) 168 (b) 172
(c) 186 (d) 212
(e) None of these

87. What is 394 times 113?
(a) 44402 (b) 44522
(c) 44632 (d) 44802
(e) None of these

88. 1260 ÷ 14 ÷ 9 =? (Bank P.O., 2009)
(a) 9 (b) 10
(c) 81 (d) 810
(e) None of these

89. 136 × 12 × 8 =? (Bank P.O., 2009)
(a) 12066 (b) 13046
(c) 13064 (d) 13066
(e) None of these

90. 8888 + 848 + 88 −? = 7337 + 737 (Bank P.O., 2009)
(a) 1450 (b) 1550
(c) 1650 (d) 1750
(e) None of these

91. 414 ×? × 7 = 127512 (Bank P.O., 2009)
(a) 36 (b) 40
(c) 44 (d) 48
(e) None of these

92. Product of 82540027 and 43253 is
(a) 3570103787831 (b) 3570103787832
(c) 3570103787833 (d) 3570103787834

93. (46351 − 36418 − 4505) ÷? = 1357 (Bank P.O., 2009)
(a) 2 (b) 3
(c) 4 (d) 6
(e) None of these

94. 6 × 66 × 666 =? (Bank Recruitment, 2007)
(a) 263376 (b) 263763
(c) 263736 (d) 267336
(e) None of these

95. If you subtract − 1 from + 1, what will be the result? (R.R.B., 2006)
(a) − 2 (b) 0
(c) 1 (d) 2

96. 8 + 88 + 888 + 8888 + 88888 + 888888 =?
(a) 897648 (b) 896748
(c) 986748 (d) 987648
(e) None of these

97. From the sum of 17 and − 12, subtract 48. (E.S.I.C., 2006)
(a) − 43 (b) − 48
(c) − 17 (d) − 20

98. 60840 ÷ 234 =?
(a) 225 (b) 255
(c) 260 (d) 310
(e) None of these

99. 3578 + 5729 −? × 581 = 5821
(a) 3 (b) 4
(c) 6 (d) None of these

100. − 95 ÷ 19 =?
(a) − 5 (b) − 4
(c) 0 (d) 5

101. 12345679 × 72 is equal to
(a) 88888888 (b) 888888888
(c) 898989898 (d) 999999998

102. 8899 − 6644 − 3322 =? − 1122
(a) 55 (b) 65
(c) 75 (d) 85
(e) None of these

103. 74844 ÷? = 54 × 63 (Bank P.O., 2009)
(a) 22 (b) 34
(c) 42 (d) 54
(e) None of these

104. 1256 × 3892 =?
(a) 4883852 (b) 4888532
(c) 4888352 (d) 4883582
(e) None of these

105. What is 786 times 964? (Bank P.O., 2008)
(a) 757704 (b) 754164
(c) 759276 (d) 749844
(e) None of these

106. What is 348 times 265? (S.B.I.P.O., 2008)
(a) 88740 (b) 89750
(c) 92220 (d) 95700
(e) None of these

107. (71 × 29 + 27 × 15 + 8 × 4) equals (S.S.C., 2007)
(a) 2496 (b) 3450
(c) 3458 (d) None of these

108. ? × (|a| × |b|) = − ab
(a) 0 (b) −1
(c) 1 (d) None of these

109. $(46)^2 - (?)^2 = 4398 - 3066$
(a) 16 (b) 28
(c) 36 (d) 42
(e) None of these

110. (800 ÷ 64) × (1296 ÷ 36) =?
(a) 420 (b) 460
(c) 500 (d) 540
(e) None of these

111. $5358 \times 51 = ?$
(a) 273258 (b) 273268
(c) 273348 (d) 273358

112. $587 \times 999 = ?$
(a) 586413 (b) 587523
(c) 614823 (d) 615173

113. $3897 \times 999 = ?$
(a) 3883203 (b) 3893103
(c) 3639403 (d) 3791203
(e) None of these

114. $72519 \times 9999 = ?$
(a) 725117481 (b) 674217481
(c) 685126481 (d) 696217481
(e) None of these

115. $2056 \times 987 = ?$
(a) 1936372 (b) 2029272
(c) 1896172 (d) 1923472
(e) None of these

116. $1904 \times 1904 = ?$
(a) 3654316 (b) 3632646
(c) 3625216 (d) 3623436
(e) None of these

117. $1397 \times 1397 = ?$
(a) 1951609 (b) 1981709
(c) 18362619 (d) 2031719
(e) None of these

118. $107 \times 107 + 93 \times 93 = ?$
(a) 19578 (b) 19418
(c) 20098 (d) 21908
(e) None of these

119. $217 \times 217 + 183 \times 183 = ?$ (R.R.B., 2007)
(a) 79698 (b) 80578
(c) 80698 (d) 81268
(e) None of these

120. $106 \times 106 - 94 \times 94 = ?$
(a) 2400 (b) 2000
(c) 1904 (d) 1906
(e) None of these

121. $8796 \times 223 + 8796 \times 77 = ?$
(a) 2736900 (b) 2738800
(c) 2658560 (d) 2716740
(e) None of these

122. $287 \times 287 + 269 \times 269 - 2 \times 287 \times 269 = ?$
(a) 534 (b) 446
(c) 354 (d) 324
(e) None of these

123. $\{(476 + 424)^2 - 4 \times 476 \times 424\} = ?$
(a) 2906 (b) 3116
(c) 2704 (d) 2904
(e) None of these

124. The value of 112×5^4 is
(a) 6700 (b) 70000
(c) 76500 (d) 77200

125. Multiply 574632819 by 125.
(a) 718,290,102,375 (b) 728,490,301,375
(c) 748,290,103,375 (d) 798,290,102,975

126. $935421 \times 625 = ?$
(a) 575648125 (b) 584638125
(c) 584649125 (d) 585628125

127. $(999)^2 - (998)^2 = ?$ (R.R.B., 2008)
(a) 1992 (b) 1995
(c) 1997 (d) 1998

128. $(80)^2 - (65)^2 + 81 = ?$
(a) 306 (b) 2094
(c) 2175 (d) 2256
(e) None of these

129. $(24 + 25 + 26)^2 - (10 + 20 + 25)^2 = ?$
(a) 352 (b) 400
(c) 752 (d) 2600
(e) None of these

130. $(65)^2 - (55)^2 = ?$
(a) 10 (b) 100
(c) 120 (d) 1200

131. If a and b be positive integers such that $a^2 - b^2 = 19$, then the value of a is (S.S.C., 2010)
(a) 9 (b) 10
(c) 19 (d) 20

132. If a and b are positive integers, $a > b$ and $(a + b)^2 - (a - b)^2 > 29$, then the smallest value of a is
(a) 3 (b) 4
(c) 6 (d) 7

133. $397 \times 397 + 104 \times 104 + 2 \times 397 \times 104 = ?$
(a) 250001 (b) 251001
(c) 260101 (d) 261001

134. If $(64)^2 - (36)^2 = 20 \times x$, then $x = ?$
(a) 70 (b) 120
(c) 180 (d) 140
(e) None of these

135. $\dfrac{(489 + 375)^2 - (489 - 375)^2}{(489 \times 375)} = ?$
(a) 144 (b) 864
(c) 2 (d) 4
(e) None of these

136. $\dfrac{(963 + 476)^2 + (963 - 476)^2}{(963 \times 963 + 476 \times 476)} = ?$
(a) 2 (b) 4

(c) 497 (d) 1449
(e) None of these

137. $\frac{768 \times 768 \times 768 + 232 \times 232 \times 232}{786 \times 768 - 768 \times 232 + 232 \times 232} = ?$
(a) 1000 (b) 536
(c) 500 (d) 268
(e) None of these

138. $\frac{854 \times 854 \times 854 - 276 \times 276 \times 276}{854 \times 854 + 854 \times 276 + 276 \times 276} = ?$
(a) 1130 (b) 578
(c) 565 (d) 1156
(e) None of these

139. $\frac{753 \times 753 + 247 \times 247 - 753 \times 247}{753 \times 753 \times 753 + 247 \times 247 \times 247} = ?$
(a) $\frac{1}{1000}$ (b) $\frac{1}{506}$
(c) $\frac{253}{500}$ (d) None of these

140. $\frac{256 \times 256 - 144 \times 144}{112}$ is equal to (S.S.C., 2010)
(a) 420 (b) 400
(c) 360 (d) 320

141. If $a = 11$ and $b = 9$, then the value of $\left(\frac{a^2 + b^2 + ab}{a^3 - b^3}\right)$ is (S.S.C., 2010)
(a) $\frac{1}{2}$ (b) $\frac{1}{20}$
(c) 2 (d) 20

142. If $a + b + c = 0$, $(a + b)(b + c)(c + a)$ equals (M.C.A., 2005)
(a) $ab(a + b)$ (b) $(a + b + c)^2$
(c) $-abc$ (d) $a^2 + b^2 + c^2$

143. If $a = 7$, $b = 5$, $c = 3$, then the value of $a^2 + b^2 + c^2 - ab - bc - ca$ is
(a) -12 (b) 0
(c) 8 (d) 12

144. Both addition and multiplication of numbers are operations which are
(a) neither commutative nor associative
(b) associative but not commutative
(c) commutative but not associative
(d) commutative and associative

145. Which of the following digits will replace the H marks in the following equation?
9H + H8 + H6 = 230
(a) 3 (b) 4
(c) 5 (d) 9
(e) None of these

146. Find the missing number in the following addition problem:

```
      8 3 5
      4 * 8
  +   9 * 4
  ---------
    2 2 * 7
```

(a) 0 (b) 4
(c) 6 (d) 9

147. What number should replace M in this multiplication problem?

```
    3 M 4
  ×     4
  -------
  1 2 1 6
```

(a) 0 (b) 2
(c) 4 (d) 8

148. If p and q represent digits, what is the maximum possible value of q in the statement (S.S.C., 2010)
5p9 + 327 + 2q8 = 1114?
(a) 6 (b) 7
(c) 8 (d) 9

149. What would be the maximum value of Q in the following equation?
5P7 + 8Q9 + R32 = 1928
(a) 6 (b) 8
(c) 9 (d) Data inadequate
(e) None of these

150. What should come in place of * mark in the following equation?
1*5$4 ÷ 148 = 78
(a) 1 (b) 4
(c) 6 (d) 8
(e) None of these

151. If 6*43 – 46@9 = 1904, which of the following should come in place of *?
(a) 4 (b) 6
(c) 9 (d) Cannot be determined
(e) None of these

152. What should be the maximum value of Q in the following equation?
5P9 – 7Q2 + 9R6 = 823
(a) 5 (b) 6
(c) 7 (d) 9
(e) None of these

153. In the following sum, '?' stands for which digit?
? + 1? + 2? +? 3 +? 1 = 21?
(a) 4 (b) 6
(c) 8 (d) 9
(e) None of these

Directions (Questions 154–155): *These questions are based on the following information:*
CBA + CCA = ACD, where A, B, C and D stand for distinct digits and D = 0.

154. B takes the value
(*a*) 0 (*b*) 5
(*c*) 9 (*d*) 0 or 9

155. C takes the value
(*a*) 0 (*b*) 2
(*c*) 2 or 3 (*d*) 5

156. A 3–digit number $4a3$ is added to another 3–digit number 984 to give the four-digit number $13b7$, which is divisible by 11. Then, $(a + b)$ is **(M.B.A., 2006)**
(*a*) 10 (*b*) 11
(*c*) 12 (*d*) 15

157. If $ab\overline{)252(}\,ba$, the values of a and b are **(I.A.M., 2007)**

$$\begin{array}{r} \underline{24} \\ 12 \\ \underline{12} \\ \times \end{array}$$

(*a*) 1, 2 (*b*) 2, 3
(*c*) 1, 3 (*d*) None of these

158.

$$\begin{array}{r} * \;\; * \;\; * \\ \times \;\; * \\ \hline 8 \;\; * \;\; * \;\; 1 \end{array}$$

In the above multiplication problem, * is equal to
(*a*) 1 (*b*) 3
(*c*) 7 (*d*) 9

159. If * means adding 6 times the second number to the first number, then (1 * 2) * 3 equals
(*a*) 21 (*b*) 31
(*c*) 91 (*d*) 93

160. If $1 \times 2 \times 3 \times \ldots\ldots \times n$ is denoted by $\underline{|n}$, then $\underline{|8} - \underline{|7} - \underline{|6}$ is equal to
(*a*) $6 \times 7 \times \underline{|8}$ (*b*) $7 \times 8 \times \underline{|7}$
(*c*) $6 \times 8 \times \underline{|6}$ (*d*) $7 \times 8 \times \underline{|6}$

161. The highest power of 9 dividing 99! completely is
(*a*) 11 (*b*) 20
(*c*) 22 (*d*) 24

162. For an integer n, $n! = n(n - 1)(n - 2)$........... 3.2.1. **(P.C.S., 2008)**
Then, 1! + 2! + 3! + ... + 100! when divided by 5 leaves remainder
(*a*) 0 (*b*) 1
(*c*) 2 (*d*) 3

163. The number of prime factors in the expression $6^{10} \cdot 7^{17} \cdot 11^{27}$ is equal to
(*a*) 54 (*b*) 64
(*c*) 71 (*d*) 81

164. What is the number of prime factors contained in the product $30^7 \times 22^5 \times 34^{11}$?
(*a*) 49 (*b*) 51
(*c*) 52 (*d*) 53

165. What number multiplied by 48 will give the same product as 173 multiplied by 240?
(*a*) 495 (*b*) 545
(*c*) 685 (*d*) 865

166. A positive number, which when added to 1000, gives a sum which is greater than when it is multiplied by 1000. This positive integer is
(*a*) 1 (*b*) 3
(*c*) 5 (*d*) 7

167. 7 is added to a certain number ; the sum is multiplied by 5 ; the product is divided by 9 and 3 is subtracted from the quotient. Thus, if the remainder left is 12, what was the original number? **(S.S.C., 2005)**
(*a*) 20 (*b*) 30
(*c*) 40 (*d*) 60

168. Symbiosis runs a Corporate Training Programme. At the end of running the first programme, its total takings were ₹ 38950. There were more than 45 but less than 100 participants. What was the participant fee for the programme? **(SNAP, 2005)**
(*a*) ₹ 410 (*b*) ₹ 450
(*c*) ₹ 500 (*d*) ₹ 510

169. The sum of four consecutive even numbers A, B, C and D is 180. What is the sum of the set of next four consecutive even numbers? **(Bank Recruitment, 2008)**
(*a*) 196 (*b*) 204
(*c*) 212 (*d*) 214
(*e*) None of these

170. A young girl counted in the following way on the fingers of her left hand. She started calling the thumb 1, the index finger 2, middle finger 3, ring finger 4, little finger 5, then reversed direction, calling the ring finger 6, middle finger 7, index finger 8, thumb 9 and then back to the index figure for 10, middle finger for 11, and so on. She counted upto 1994. She ended on her
(*a*) thumb (*b*) index finger
(*c*) middle finger (*d*) ring finger

171. Given $n = 1 + x$ and x is the product of four consecutive integers. Then which of the following is true?
I. n is an odd integer. II. n is prime.
III. n is a perfect square.
(*a*) Only I is correct
(*b*) Only III is correct
(*c*) Both I and II are correct
(*d*) Both I and III are correct

172. If $x + y = 15$ and $xy = 56$, then what is the value of $x^2 + y^2$? **(L.I.C.A.D.O., 2007)**
(*a*) 110 (*b*) 113
(*c*) 121 (*d*) Cannot be determined
(*e*) None of these

173. Given that $(1^2 + 2^2 + 3^2 + \ldots. + 20^2) = 2870$, the value of $(2^2 + 4^2 + 6^2 + \ldots. + 40^2)$ is
(*a*) 2870 (*b*) 5740
(*c*) 11480 (*d*) 28700

174. The value of $5^2 + 6^2 + ... + 10^2 + 20^2$ is
(*a*) 755 (*b*) 760
(*c*) 765 (*d*) 770

175. Given that 1 + 2 + 3 + 4 + ... + 10 = 55, then the sum 6 + 12 + 18 + 24 + ... + 60 is equal to
(*a*) 300 (*b*) 330
(*c*) 455 (*d*) 655

176. If *m* and *n* are natural numbers such that $2^m - 2^n = 960$, what is the value of *m*? **(M.A.T., 2007)**
(*a*) 10 (*b*) 12
(*c*) 15
(*d*) Cannot be determined

177. On multiplying a number by 7, all the digits in the product appear as 3's. The smallest such number is **(C.P.O., 2006)**
(*a*) 47619 (*b*) 46719
(*c*) 48619 (*d*) 47649

178. The number of digits in the smallest number, which when multiplied by 7 yields all nines, is
(*a*) 3 (*b*) 4
(*c*) 5 (*d*) 6

179. A boy multiplies 987 by a certain number and obtains 559981 as his answer. If in the answer both 9's are wrong but the other digits are correct, then the correct answer will be
(*a*) 553681 (*b*) 555181
(*c*) 555681 (*d*) 556581

180. The numbers 1, 3, 5, ..., 25 are multiplied together. The number of zeros at the right end of the product is **(R.R.B., 2006)**
(*a*) 0 (*b*) 1
(*c*) 2 (*d*) 3

181. The numbers 1, 2, 3, 4, ..., 1000 are multiplied together. The number of zeros at the end (on the right) of the product must be
(*a*) 30 (*b*) 200
(*c*) 211 (*d*) 249

182. First 100 multiples of 10 i.e. 10, 20, 30, ..., 1000 are multiplied together. The number of zeros at the end of the product will be
(*a*) 100 (*b*) 111
(*c*) 124 (*d*) 125

183. The number of zeros at the end of the product $5 \times 10 \times 15 \times 20 \times 25 \times 30 \times 35 \times 40 \times 45 \times 50$ is
(*a*) 5 (*b*) 7
(*c*) 8 (*d*) 10

184. The number of zeros at the end of 60! is
(*a*) 12 (*b*) 14
(*c*) 16 (*d*) 18

185. The numbers 1, 3, 5, 7, ..., 99 and 128 are multiplied together. The number of zeros at the end of the product must be
(*a*) Nil (*b*) 7
(*c*) 19 (*d*) 22

186. The numbers 2, 4, 6, 8, ..., 98, 100 are multiplied together. The number of zeros at the end of the product must be
(*a*) 10 (*b*) 11
(*c*) 12 (*d*) 13

187. Let *S* be the set of prime numbers greater than or equal to 2 and less than 100. Multiply all the elements of *S*. With how many consecutive zeros will the product end?
(*a*) 1 (*b*) 4
(*c*) 5 (*d*) 10

188. Find the number of zeros at the end of the result $3 \times 6 \times 9 \times 12 \times 15 \times .... \times 99 \times 102$.
(*a*) 4 (*b*) 6
(*c*) 7 (*d*) 10

189. The unit's digit of 13^{2003} is **(A.A.O. Exam, 2010)**
(*a*) 1 (*b*) 3
(*c*) 7 (*d*) 9

190. The digit in the unit's place of the number 123^{99} is **(I.A.M., 2007)**
(*a*) 1 (*b*) 4
(*c*) 7 (*d*) 8

191. Match List I with List II and select the correct answer:

List I (Product)	**List II** (Digit in the unit's place)
A. $(1827)^{16}$	(1) 1
B. $(2153)^{19}$	(2) 3
C. $(5129)^{21}$	(3) 5
	(4) 7
	(5) 9

A B C — (*a*) 1 4 3 A B C — (*b*) 4 2 3
A B C — (*c*) 1 4 5 A B C — (*d*) 4 2 5

192. The digit in the unit's place of the number $(67)^{25} - 1$ must be
(*a*) 0 (*b*) 6
(*c*) 8 (*d*) None of these

193. The unit's digit in the product $274 \times 318 \times 577 \times 313$ is
(*a*) 2 (*b*) 3
(*c*) 4 (*d*) 5

194. In the product $459 \times 46 \times 28^* \times 484$, the digit in the unit place is 8. The digit to come in place of * is
(*a*) 3 (*b*) 5
(*c*) 7 (*d*) None of these

195. The digit in the unit place of the number represented by $(7^{95} - 3^{58})$ is
(*a*) 0 (*b*) 4
(*c*) 6 (*d*) 7

196. Unit's digit in $(784)^{126} + (784)^{127}$ is
(*a*) 0 (*b*) 4
(*c*) 6 (*d*) 8

197. The digit in the unit's place of $[(251)^{98} + (21)^{29} - (106)^{100} + (705)^{35} - 16^4 + 259]$ is
(a) 1 (b) 4
(c) 5 (d) 6

198. The digit in the unit's place of the product $(2464)^{1793} \times (615)^{317} \times (131)^{491}$ is
(a) 0 (b) 2
(c) 3 (d) 5

199. If x is an even number, then x^{4n}, where n is a positive integer, will always have
(a) zero in the unit's place
(b) 6 in the unit's place
(c) either 0 or 6 in the unit's place
(d) None of these

200. If m and n are positive integers, then the digit in the unit's place of $5^n + 6^m$ is always
(a) 1 (b) 5
(c) 6 (d) $n + m$

201. The number formed from the last two digits (ones and tens) of the expression $2^{12n} - 6^{4n}$, where n is any positive integer is (S.S.C., 2005)
(a) 10 (b) 00
(c) 30 (d) 02

202. The last digit in the decimal representation of $\left(\frac{1}{5}\right)^{2000}$ is (Hotel Management, 2009)
(a) 2 (b) 4
(c) 5 (d) 6

203. Let x be the product of two numbers 3,659,893,456,789,325,678 and 342,973,489,379,256. The number of digits in x is (A.A.O., 2010)
(a) 32 (b) 34
(c) 35 (d) 36

204. Let a number of three digits have for its middle digit the sum of the other two digits. Then it is a multiple of (C.P.F., 2008)
(a) 10 (b) 11
(c) 18 (d) 50

205. What least value must be given to n so that the number 6135n2 becomes divisible by 9? (L.I.C.A.D.O., 2008)
(a) 1 (b) 2
(c) 3 (d) 4

206. Find the multiple of 11 in the following numbers. (R.R.B., 2006)
(a) 112144 (b) 447355
(c) 869756 (d) 978626

207. 111,111,111,111 is divisible by
(a) 3 and 37 only
(b) 3, 11 and 37 only
(c) 3, 11, 37 and 111 only
(d) 3, 11, 37, 111 and 1001

208. Which of the following numbers is not divisible by 18?
(a) 34056 (b) 50436
(c) 54036 (d) 65043

209. The number 89715938* is divisible by 4. The unknown non-zero digit marked as * will be
(a) 2 (b) 3
(c) 4 (d) 6

210. Which one of the following numbers is divisible by 3?
(a) 4006020 (b) 2345678
(c) 2876423 (d) 9566003

211. A number is divisible by 11 if the difference between the sums of the digits in odd and even places respectively is
(a) a multiple of 3
(b) a multiple of 5
(c) zero or a multiple of 7
(d) zero or a multiple of 11

212. Which one of the following numbers is divisible by 11?
(a) 4823718 (b) 4832718
(c) 8423718 (d) 8432718

213. Which one of the following numbers is divisible by 15?
(a) 17325 (b) 23755
(c) 29515 (d) 30560

214. 7386038 is divisible by
(a) 3 (b) 4
(c) 9 (d) 11

215. Consider the following statements:
The numbers 24984, 26784 and 28584 are
(1) divisible by 3 (2) divisible by 4
(3) divisible by 9
Which of these are correct?
(a) 1 and 2 (b) 2 and 3
(c) 1 and 3 (d) 1, 2 and 3

216. Which of the following numbers is a multiple of 8?
(a) 923872 (b) 923972
(c) 923862 (d) 923962

217. If 78*3945 is divisible by 11, where * is a digit, then * is equal to
(a) 0 (b) 1
(c) 3 (d) 5

218. If m and n are integers divisible by 5, which of the following is not necessarily true?
(a) $m + n$ is divisible by 10
(b) $m - n$ is divisible by 5
(c) $m^2 - n^2$ is divisible by 25
(d) None of these

219. An integer is divisible by 16 if and only if its last X digits are divisible by 16. The value of X would be

(a) 3 (b) 4
(c) 5 (d) 6

220. Which of the following numbers is divisible by 3, 7, 9 and 11?
(a) 639 (b) 2079
(c) 3791 (d) 37911

221. A number 476**0 is divisible by both 3 and 11. The non-zero digits in the hundred's and ten's place respectively are
(a) 7, 4 (b) 5, 3
(c) 5, 2 (d) None of these

222. How many of the following numbers are divisible by 3 but not by 9?
2133, 2343, 3474, 4131, 5286, 5340, 6336, 7347, 8115, 9276
(a) 5 (b) 6
(c) 7 (d) None of these

223. If the number 357*25* is divisible by both 3 and 5, then the missing digits in the unit's place and the thousandth's place respectively are
(a) 0, 6 (b) 5, 1
(c) 5, 4 (d) None of these

224. 6897 is divisible by
(a) 11 only (b) 19 only
(c) both 11 and 19 (d) neither 11 nor 19

225. Which of the following numbers is exactly divisible by 24?
(a) 35718 (b) 63810
(c) 537804 (d) 3125736

226. The number 311311311311311311311 is
(a) neither divisible by 3 nor by 11
(b) divisible by 11 but not by 3
(c) divisible by 3 but not by 11
(d) divisible by both 3 and 11

227. 325325 is a six-digit number. It is divisible by
(a) 7 only (b) 11 only
(c) 13 only (d) all 7, 11 and 13

228. If the seven-figure number 30X0103 is a multiple of 13, then X is
(a) 1 (b) 6
(c) 7 (d) 8

229. If a number is divisible by both 11 and 13, then it must be necessarily
(a) 429 (b) divisible by (11×13)
(c) divisible by $(11 + 13)$ (d) divisible by $(13 - 11)$

230. Which of the following numbers are completely divisible by 7?
I. 195195 II. 181181
III. 120120 IV. 891891
(a) Only I and II (b) Only II and III
(c) Only I and IV (d) Only II and IV
(e) All are divisible

231. If x and y are two digits of the number $653xy$ such that the number is divisible by 80, then $x + y$ is equal to
(a) 3 (b) 4
(c) 5 (d) 6

232. The six-digit number $5ABB7A$ is a multiple of 33 for non-zero digits A and B. Which of the following could be possible value of $A + B$? (A.A.O. Exam, 2010)
(a) 8 (b) 9
(c) 10 (d) 14

233. Which of the following numbers is divisible by 99?
(a) 114345 (b) 913464
(c) 135792 (d) 3572404

234. The digits indicated by * in 3422213** so that this number is divisible by 99 are (R.R.B., 2010)
(a) 1, 9 (b) 3, 7
(c) 4, 6 (d) 5, 5

235. If 37X3 is a four-digit natural number divisible by 7, then the place marked as X must have the value
(a) 0 (b) 3
(c) 5 (d) 9

236. If the seven-digit number $876p37q$ is divisible by 225, then the values of p and q respectively are
(a) 0 and 0 (b) 9 and 0
(c) 0 and 5 (d) 9 and 5

237. If a number $774958A96B$ is divisible by 8 and 9, the respective values of A and B will be
(a) 5 and 8 (b) 7 and 8
(c) 8 and 0 (d) None of these

238. How many of the following numbers are divisible by 132?
264, 396, 462, 792, 968, 2178, 5184, 6336
(a) 4 (b) 5
(c) 6 (d) 7

239. If x and y are positive integers such that $(3x + 7y)$ is a multiple of 11, then which of the following is also a multiple of 11?
(a) $5x - 3y$ (b) $9x + 4y$
(c) $4x + 6y$ (d) $x + y + 6$

240. If n be any natural number then by which largest number $(n^3 - n)$ is always divisible? (S.S.C., 2010)
(a) 3 (b) 6
(c) 12 (d) 18

241. If a and b are two odd positive integers, by which of the following integers is $(a^4 - b^4)$ always divisible? (S.S.C., 2010)
(a) 3 (b) 6
(c) 8 (d) 12

242. The difference between the squares of any two consecutive integers is equal to
(a) an even number
(b) difference of given numbers
(c) sum of given numbers
(d) product of given numbers

243. The number $6n^2 + 6n$ for natural number n is always divisible by **(M.A.T., 2007)**
(a) 6 only (b) 6 and 12
(c) 12 only (d) 18 only

244. The difference of a number consisting of two digits and the number formed by interchanging the digits is always divisible by
(a) 5 (b) 7
(c) 9 (d) 11

245. The sum of a number consisting of two digits and the number formed by interchanging the digits is always divisible by
(a) 7 (b) 9
(c) 10 (d) 11

246. The largest natural number, which exactly divides the product of any four consecutive natural numbers, is **(S.S.C., 2007)**
(a) 6 (b) 12
(c) 24 (d) 120

247. If n is a whole number greater than 1, then $n^2 (n^2 - 1)$ is always divisible by
(a) 8 (b) 10
(c) 12 (d) 16

248. If n is any odd number greater than 1, then $n (n^2 - 1)$ is
(a) divisible by 24 always (b) divisible by 48 always
(c) divisible by 96 always (d) None of these

249. The sum of the digits of a 3-digit number is subtracted from the number. The resulting number is always
(a) not divisible by 9 (b) divisible by 9
(c) not divisible by 6 (d) divisible by 6

250. A number is multiplied by 11 and 11 is added to the product. If the resulting number is divisible by 13, the smallest original number is
(a) 12 (b) 22
(c) 26 (d) 53

251. The product of any three consecutive natural numbers is always divisible by
(a) 3 (b) 6
(c) 9 (d) 15

252. The sum of three consecutive odd numbers is always divisible by
I. 2 II. 3
III. 5 IV. 6
(a) Only I (b) Only II
(c) Only I and II (d) Only I and III

253. The greatest number by which the product of three consecutive multiples of 3 is always divisible is
(a) 54 (b) 81
(c) 162 (d) 243

254. If p is a prime number greater than 3, then $(p^2 - 1)$ is always divisible by
(a) 6 but not 12 (b) 12 but not 24
(c) 24 (d) None of these

255. The difference between the squares of two consecutive odd integers is always divisible by
(a) 3 (b) 6
(c) 7 (d) 8

256. A 4–digit number is formed by repeating a 2–digit number such as 2525, 3232 etc. Any number of this form is exactly divisible by **(S.S.C., 2005, 2010)**
(a) 7 (b) 11
(c) 13
(d) Smallest 3–digit prime number

257. A 6-digit number is formed by repeating a 3-digit number; for example, 256256 or 678678 etc. Any number of this form is always exactly divisible by
(a) 7 only (b) 11 only
(c) 13 only (d) 1001

258. The sum of the digits of a natural number $(10^n - 1)$ is 4707, where n is a natural number. The value of n is **(Hotel Management, 2010)**
(a) 477 (b) 523
(c) 532 (d) 704

259. $(x^n - a^n)$ is divisible by $(x - a)$
(a) for all values of n
(b) only for even values of n
(c) only for odd values of n
(d) only for prime values of n

260. Which one of the following is the number by which the product of 8 consecutive integers is divisible?
(a) 4 ! (b) 6 !
(c) 7 ! (d) 8 !
(e) All of these

261. Consider the following statements:
For any positive integer n, the number $10^n - 1$ is divisible by
(1) 9 for n = odd only (2) 9 for n = even only
(3) 11 for n = odd only (4) 11 for n = even only
Which of the above statements are correct?
(a) 1 and 3 (b) 2 and 3
(c) 1 and 4 (d) 2 and 4

262. If n is any positive integer, $3^{4n} - 4^{3n}$ is always divisible by
(a) 7 (b) 12
(c) 17 (d) 145

263. If the square of an odd natural number is divided by 8, then the remainder will be
(a) 1 (b) 2
(c) 3 (d) 4

264. The largest number that exactly divides each number of the sequence $1^5 - 1, 2^5 - 2, 3^5 - 3, ..., n^5 - n, ...$ is
(a) 1 (b) 15
(c) 30 (d) 120

265. The difference of the squares of two consecutive even integers is divisible by
(a) 3 (b) 4
(c) 6 (d) 7

266. The difference of the squares of two consecutive odd integers is divisible by
(a) 3 (b) 6
(c) 7 (d) 8

267. The smallest 4-digit number exactly divisible by 7 is (P.C.S., 2009)
(a) 1001 (b) 1007
(c) 1101 (d) 1108

268. What least number must be added to 1056 to get a number exactly divisible by 23? (P.C.S., 2009)
(a) 2 (b) 3
(c) 21 (d) 25

269. Which of the following numbers should be added to 8567 to make it exactly divisible by 4? (Bank Recruitment, 2008)
(a) 3 (b) 4
(c) 5 (d) 6
(e) None of these

270. Find the least 6-digit number which is exactly divisible by 349. (R.R.B., 2006)
(a) 100163 (b) 101063
(c) 160063 (d) None of these

271. Which is the greatest 5-digit number exactly divisible by 279? (R.R.B., 2006)
(a) 99603 (b) 99550
(c) 99882 (d) None of these

272. The least number, which must be added to the greatest 6-digit number so that the sum may be exactly divisible by 327 is
(a) 194 (b) 264
(c) 292 (d) 294

273. The least number more than 5000 which is divisible by 73 is
(a) 5009 (b) 5037
(c) 5073 (d) 5099

274. The nearest integer to 58701 which is exactly divisible by 567 is
(a) 55968 (b) 58068
(c) 58968 (d) None of these

275. The smallest number which must be subtracted from 8112 to make it exactly divisible by 99 is
(a) 91 (b) 92
(c) 93 (d) 95

276. The smallest number that must be added to 803642 in order to obtain a multiple of 11 is
(a) 1 (b) 4
(c) 7 (d) 9

277. The number of times 99 is subtracted from 1111 so that the remainder is less than 99 is
(a) 10 (b) 11
(c) 12 (d) 13

278. The smallest number by which 66 must be multiplied to make the result divisible by 18 is
(a) 3 (b) 6
(c) 9 (d) 18

279. The smallest 6-digit number exactly divisible by 111 is
(a) 111111 (b) 110011
(c) 100011 (d) 110101
(e) None of these

280. The sum of all 2-digit numbers divisible by 5 is
(a) 945 (b) 1035
(c) 1230 (d) 1245
(e) None of these

281. How many 3-digit numbers are completely divisible by 6?
(a) 149 (b) 150
(c) 151 (d) 166

282. The number of terms between 11 and 200 which are divisible by 7 but not by 3 are (C.P.F., 2008)
(a) 18 (b) 19
(c) 27 (d) 28

283. Out of the numbers divisible by 3 between 14 and 95 if the numbers with 3 at unit's place are removed, then how many numbers will remain? (R.R.B., 2006)
(a) 22 (b) 23
(c) 24 (d) 25

284. How many numbers less than 1000 are multiples of both 10 and 13?
(a) 6 (b) 7
(c) 8 (d) 9

285. How many integers between 100 and 150, both inclusive, can be evenly divided by neither 3 nor 5?
(a) 26 (b) 27
(c) 28 (d) 33

286. If all the numbers from 501 to 700 are written, what is the total number of times the digit 6 appears? (Civil Services, 2007)
(a) 138 (b) 139
(c) 140 (d) 141

287. How many 3-digit numbers are there in between 100 and 300, having first and the last digit as 2?
(a) 9 (b) 10
(c) 11 (d) 12

288. The total number of integers between 200 and 400, each of which either begins with 3 or ends with 3 or both is (S.S.C., 2007)
(a) 10 (b) 100
(c) 110 (d) 120

289. While writing all the numbers from 700 to 1000, how many numbers occur in which the first digit is greater than the second digit, and the second digit is greater than the third digit?
(a) 61 (b) 64
(c) 78 (d) 85

290. A 9-digit number in which zero does not appear and no digits are repeated has the following properties: The number comprising the left most two digits is divisible by 2, that comprising the left most three digits is divisible by 3, and so on. The number is

(a) 183654729 (b) 381654729
(c) 983654721 (d) 981654723

291. If 11,109,999 is divided by 1111, then what is the remainder? (M.A.T., 2007)

(a) 1098 (b) 1010
(c) 1110 (d) 1188

292. A number divided by 68 gives the quotient 260 and remainder zero. If the same number is divided by 65, the remainder is

(a) 0 (b) 1
(c) 2 (d) 3

293. Which of the following prime numbers while dividing 2176 leaves 9 as remainder?

(a) 17 (b) 29
(c) 167 (d) 197

294. Match List I with List II and select the correct answer:

List I (a, b as given in Euclidean algorithm $a = bq + r$)	List II (Values of q and r)
A. $a = -112, b = -7$	1. $q = -13, r = 1$
B. $a = 118, b = -9$	2. $q = 14, r = 3$
C. $a = -109, b = 6$	3. $q = -19, r = 5$
D. $a = 115, b = 8$	4. $q = 16, r = 0$

A B C D　　A B C D
(a) 3 1 4 2 (b) 3 2 4 1
(c) 4 1 3 2 (d) 4 2 3 1

295. The number 534677 is divided by 777. The difference of divisor and remainder is

(a) 577 (b) 676
(c) 687 (d) 789

296. In a division sum, the quotient, dividend and remainder are 15, 940 and 25 respectively. The divisor is

(a) 31 (b) 50
(c) 60 (d) 61

297. In a division sum, the divisor is 12 times the quotient and 5 times the remainder. If the remainder is 48, then the dividend is

(a) 2404 (b) 3648
(c) 4808 (d) 4848

298. The divisor is 25 times the quotient and 5 times the remainder. If the quotient is 16, then the dividend is

(a) 400 (b) 480
(c) 6400 (d) 6480

299. A number when divided by the sum of 555 and 445 gives two times their difference as quotient and 30 as the remainder. The number is

(a) 1220 (b) 1250
(c) 22030 (d) 220030

300. In doing a question of division with zero remainder, a candidate took 12 as divisor instead of 21. The quotient obtained by him was 35. The correct quotient is

(a) 0 (b) 12
(c) 13 (d) 20

301. In a division problem, the divisor is 7 times of quotient and 5 times of remainder. If the dividend is 6 times of remainder, then the quotient is equal to

(a) 0 (b) 1
(c) 7 (d) None of these

(Hotel Management, 2007)

302. On dividing a number by 19, the difference between quotient and remainder is 9. The number is

(a) 352 (b) 361
(c) 370 (d) 371

303. A number when divided by 136 leaves remainder 36. If the same number is divided by 17, the remainder will be (S.S.C., 2010)

(a) 2 (b) 3
(c) 7 (d) 9

304. A number when divided by 195 leaves a remainder 47. If the same number is divided by 15, the remainder will be (Hotel Management, 2010)

(a) 1 (b) 2
(c) 3 (d) 4

305. A certain number when divided by 899 gives a remainder 63. What is the remainder when the same number is divided by 29? (R.R.B., 2008)

(a) 5 (b) 25
(c) 27 (d) None of these

306. A number when divided by 5 leaves the remainder 3. What is the remainder when the square of the same number is divided by 5?

(a) 0 (b) 3
(c) 4 (d) 9

307. The difference between two numbers is 1365. When the larger number is divided by the smaller one, the quotient is 6 and the remainder is 15. What is the smaller number?

(a) 240 (b) 270
(c) 295 (d) 360

308. When n is divided by 4, the remainder is 3. What is the remainder when $2n$ is divided by 4?

(a) 1 (b) 2
(c) 3 (d) 6

309. When a number is divided by 13, the remainder is 11. When the same number is divided by 17, the remainder is 9. What is the number?

(a) 339 (b) 349
(c) 369 (d) Data inadequate
(e) None of these

310. In a division sum, the remainder was 71. With the same divisor but twice the dividend, the remainder is 43. Which one of the following is the divisor?
(a) 86 (b) 93
(c) 99 (d) 104

311. When a certain positive integer P is divided by another positive integer, the remainder is r_1. When a second positive integer Q is divided by the same integer, the remainder is r_2 and when $(P + Q)$ is divided by the same divisor, the remainder is r_3. Then the divisor may be
(a) $r_1 \; r_2 \; r_3$ (b) $r_1 + r_2 + r_3$
(c) $r_1 - r_2 + r_3$ (d) $r_1 + r_2 - r_3$
(e) Cannot be determined

312. Two numbers when divided by a certain divisor leave the remainders 4375 and 2986 respectively but when the sum of two numbers is divided by the same divisor, the remainder is 2361. The divisor in question is
(a) 4675 (b) 4900
(c) 5000 (d) None of these

313. A number divided by 13 leaves a remainder 1 and if the quotient, thus obtained, is divided by 5, we get a remainder of 3. What will be the remainder if the number is divided by 65?
(a) 16 (b) 18
(c) 28 (d) 40

314. The numbers 2272 and 875 are divided by a three-digit number N, giving the same remainder. The sum of the digits of N is
(a) 10 (b) 11
(c) 12 (d) 13

315. A number when divided by three consecutive numbers 9, 11, 13 leaves the remainders 8, 9 and 8 respectively. If the order of divisors is reversed, the remainders will be **(R.R.B., 2008)**
(a) 10, 8, 9 (b) 10, 1, 6
(c) 8, 9, 8 (d) 9, 8, 8

316. After the division of a number successively by 3, 4 and 7, the remainders obtained are 2, 1 and 4 respectively. What will be the remainder if 84 divides the same number?
(a) 41 (b) 53
(c) 75 (d) 80

317. A number is successively divided by 8, 7 and 3 giving residues 3, 4 and 2 respectively and quotient 31. The number is
(a) 3555 (b) 5355
(c) 5535 (d) 5553

318. A number when divided by 3 leaves a remainder 1. When the quotient is divided by 2, it leaves a remainder 1. What will be the remainder when the number is divided by 6?
(a) 2 (b) 3
(c) 4 (d) 5

319. When the square of any odd number, greater than 1, is divided by 8, it always leaves remainder **(I.A.M., 2007)**
(a) 1 (b) 6
(c) 8
(d) Cannot be determined

320. The numbers from 1 to 29 are written side by side as follows:
1234567891011121314..........2829
If this number is divided by 9, then what is the remainder? **(M.A.T., 2006)**
(a) 0 (b) 1
(c) 3 (d) None of these

321. If 17^{200} is divided by 18, the remainder is
(a) 1 (b) 2
(c) 16 (d) 17

322. What is the remainder when 2^{31} is divided by 5?
(a) 1 (b) 2
(c) 3 (d) 4

323. Consider the following statements:
(1) $a^n + b^n$ is divisible by $a + b$ if $n = 2k + 1$, where k is a positive integer.
(2) $a^n - b^n$ is divisible by $a - b$ if $n = 2k$, where k is a positive integer.
Which of the statements given above is/are correct?
(a) 1 only (b) 2 only
(c) Both 1 and 2 (d) Neither 1 nor 2

324. $(7^{19} + 2)$ is divided by 6. The remainder is
(a) 1 (b) 2
(c) 3 (d) 5

325. If $(10^{12} + 25)^2 - (10^{12} - 25)^2 = 10^n$, then the value of n is
(a) 5 (b) 10
(c) 14 (d) 20

326. $(3^{25} + 3^{26} + 3^{27} + 3^{28})$ is divisible by
(a) 11 (b) 16
(c) 25 (d) 30

327. $(4^{61} + 4^{62} + 4^{63} + 4^{64})$ is divisible by
(a) 3 (b) 11
(c) 13 (d) 17

328. $(9^6 + 1)$ when divided by 8, would leave a remainder of
(a) 0 (b) 1
(c) 2 (d) 3

329. If n is even, $(6^n - 1)$ is divisible by
(a) 6 (b) 30
(c) 35 (d) 37

330. If $(12^n + 1)$ is divisible by 13, then n is
(a) 1 only (b) 12 only
(c) any odd integer (d) any even integer

331. 25^{25} is divided by 26, the remainder is
(*a*) 1 (*b*) 2
(*c*) 24 (*d*) 25

332. If $(67^{67} + 67)$ is divided by 68, the remainder is
(*a*) 1 (*b*) 63
(*c*) 66 (*d*) 67

333. One less than $(49)^{15}$ is exactly divisible by
(*a*) 8 (*b*) 14
(*c*) 50 (*d*) 51

334. The remainder when 7^{84} is divided by 342 is
(*a*) 0 (*b*) 1
(*c*) 49 (*d*) 341

335. The remainder when 2^{60} is divided by 5 equals
(*a*) 0 (*b*) 1
(*c*) 2 (*d*) 3

336. By how many of the following numbers is $2^{12} - 1$ divisible?
2, 3, 5, 7, 10, 11, 13, 14
(*a*) 4 (*b*) 5
(*c*) 6 (*d*) 7

337. The remainder when $(15^{23} + 23^{23})$ is divided by 19, is
(*a*) 0 (*b*) 4
(*c*) 15 (*d*) 18

338. When 2^{256} is divided by 17, the remainder would be
(*a*) 1 (*b*) 14
(*c*) 16 (*d*) None of these

339. $7^{6n} - 6^{6n}$, where n is an integer > 0, is divisible by
(*a*) 13 (*b*) 127
(*c*) 559 (*d*) All of these

340. It is given that $(2^{32} + 1)$ is exactly divisible by a certain number. Which of the following is also definitely divisible by the same number? **(S.S.C., 2007)**
(*a*) $2^{16} + 1$ (*b*) $2^{16} - 1$
(*c*) 7×2^{33} (*d*) $2^{96} + 1$

341. The number $(2^{48} - 1)$ is exactly divisible by two numbers between 60 and 70. The numbers are **(A.A.O. Exam, 2010)**
(*a*) 63 and 65 (*b*) 63 and 67
(*c*) 61 and 65 (*d*) 65 and 67

342. n being any odd number greater than 1, $n^{65} - n$ is always divisible by
(*a*) 5 (*b*) 13
(*c*) 24 (*d*) None of these

343. Let $N = 55^3 + 17^3 - 72^3$. Then, N is divisible by
(*a*) both 7 and 13 (*b*) both 3 and 13
(*c*) both 17 and 7 (*d*) both 3 and 17

Directions (Questions 344–345): *These questions are based on the following information:*
Given $N = \lfloor 1 + \lfloor 2 + \lfloor 3 + \ldots\ldots + \lfloor 99 + \lfloor 100$.

344. Find the last two digits of N.
(*a*) 00 (*b*) 13
(*c*) 19 (*d*) 23

345. Find the remainder when N is divided by 168.
(*a*) 33 (*b*) 67
(*c*) 129 (*d*) 153

346. What is the remainder when 4^{61} is divided by 51?
(*a*) 20 (*b*) 41
(*c*) 50 (*d*) None of these

347. What is the remainder when 17^{36} is divided by 36?
(*a*) 1 (*b*) 7
(*c*) 19 (*d*) 29

348. Which one of the following is the common factor of $(47^{43} + 43^{43})$ and $(47^{47} + 43^{47})$?
(*a*) $(47 - 43)$ (*b*) $(47 + 43)$
(*c*) $(47^{43} + 43^{43})$ (*d*) None of these

349. Find the product of all odd natural numbers less than 5000.
(*a*) $\frac{5000!}{2500 \times 2501}$ (*b*) $\frac{5000!}{2^{2500} \times 2500!}$
(*c*) $\frac{5000!}{2^{5000}}$ (*d*) None of these

350. How many zeros will be required to number the pages of a book containing 1000 pages?
(*a*) 168 (*b*) 184
(*c*) 192 (*d*) 216

351. If $a^2 + b^2 + c^2 = 1$, what is the maximum value of abc?
(*a*) $\frac{1}{3}$ (*b*) $\frac{1}{3\sqrt{3}}$
(*c*) $\frac{2}{\sqrt{3}}$ (*d*) 1

352. Find the unit's digit in the sum of the fifth powers of the first 100 natural numbers.
(*a*) 0 (*b*) 2
(*c*) 5 (*d*) 8

353. If the symbol $[x]$ denotes the greatest integer less than or equal to x, then the value of $\left[\frac{1}{4}\right] + \left[\frac{1}{4} + \frac{1}{50}\right] + \left[\frac{1}{4} + \frac{2}{50}\right] + \ldots\ldots + \left[\frac{1}{4} + \frac{49}{50}\right]$ is
(*a*) 0 (*b*) 9
(*c*) 12 (*d*) 49

354. When $100^{25} - 25$ is written in decimal notation, the sum of its digits is
(*a*) 444 (*b*) 445
(*c*) 446 (*d*) 448

355. What is the number of digits in the number $(1024)^4 \times (125)^{11}$?
(*a*) 35 (*b*) 36
(*c*) 37 (*d*) 38

356. How many numbers will be there between 300 and 500, where 4 comes only one time?
(*a*) 89 (*b*) 99
(*c*) 110 (*d*) 120
[UPSSSC Lower Subordinate (Pre.) Exam, 2016]

357. Which is not a prime number?
[Indian Railways Gr. 'D' Exam, 2014]
(*a*) 13 (*b*) 19
(*c*) 21 (*d*) 17

358. If $x = a(b - c)$, $y = b(c - a)$, $z = c(a - b)$, then the value of $\left(\frac{x}{a}\right)^3 + \left(\frac{y}{b}\right)^3 + \left(\frac{z}{c}\right)^3$ is
[SSC—CHSL (10 + 2) Exam, 2015]
(*a*) $\frac{2xyz}{abc}$ (*b*) $\frac{xyz}{abc}$
(*c*) 0 (*d*) $\frac{3xyz}{abc}$

359. Among the following statements, the statement which is not correct is: **[SSC—CHSL (10 + 2) Exam, 2015]**
(*a*) Every natural number is an integer.
(*b*) Every natural number is a real number.
(*c*) Every real number is a rational number.
(*d*) Every integer is a rational number.

360. If $a + b + c = 6$ and $ab + bc + ca = 10$ then the value of $a^3 + b^3 + c^3 - 3abc$ is
[SSC—CHSL (10 + 2) Exam, 2015]
(*a*) 36 (*b*) 48
(*c*) 42 (*d*) 40

361. If (1001 × 111) = 110000 + (11 × ____), then the number in the blank space is
(*a*) 121 (*b*) 211
(*c*) 101 (*d*) 1111
[CTET, 2016]

Direction (Question 362): The following question consists of a question and two statements I and II given below it. You have to decide whether the data provided in the statement(s) is/are sufficient to answer the question. Given answer

(A) The data in statement I alone is sufficient to answer the question while II alone is not sufficient to answer the questions.
(B) Data in statement II alone is sufficient to answer the question while data in statement I alone is not sufficient to answer the question.
(C) The data in statement I alone or statement II alone is sufficient to answer the question.
(D) The data in both Statement I and II is insufficient to answer the question.
(E) The data in both Statement I and II is sufficient to answer the question.

362. If (the place value of 5 in 15201) + (the place value of 6 in 2659) = 7 × ____, then the number of the blank space is:
(*a*) 800 (*b*) 80
(*c*) 90 (*d*) 900
[CTET, 2016]

363. The sum of digits of a two – digit number is 12 and the difference between the two – digits of the two – digit number is 6. What is the two – digit number?
[IBPS—RRB Office Assistant (Online) Exam, 2015]
(*a*) 39 (*b*) 84
(*c*) 93
(*d*) Other than the given options
(*e*) 75

364. The difference between the greatest and the least four digit numbers that beings with 3 and ends with 5 is
[SSC—CHSL (10 + 2) Exam, 2015]
(*a*) 900 (*b*) 909
(*c*) 999 (*d*) 990

365. The sum of the perfect squares between 120 and 300 is
[SSC—CHSL (10 + 2) Exam, 2015]
(*a*) 1204 (*b*) 1024
(*c*) 1296 (*d*) 1400

366. If $p^3 - q^3 = (p - q)(p - q)^2 - xpq$, then find the value of x **[SSC—CHSL (10 + 2) Exam, 2015]**
(*a*) 1 (*b*) –3
(*c*) 3 (*d*) –1

367. What minimum value should be assigned to *, so that 2361*48 is exactly divisible by 9?
[ESIC—UDC Exam, 2016]
(*a*) 2 (*b*) 3
(*c*) 9 (*d*) 4

368. If p, q, r are all real numbers then $(p-q)^3 + (q-r)^3 + (r-p)^3$ is equal to **[SSC—CAPF/CPOExam, 2016]**
(*a*) $(p-q)(q-r)(r-p)$ (*b*) $3(p-q)(q-r)(r-p)$
(*c*) 1 (*d*) 0

369. If $(a^2 - b^2) \div (a + b) = 25$, then $(a + b)$ = ?
(*a*) 30 (*b*) 25
(*c*) 125 (*d*) 150
[RRB—NTPC Exam, 2016]

370. How many prime numbers are there between 100 to 200? **[CMAT, 2017]**
(*a*) 21 (*b*) 20
(*c*) 16 (*d*) 11

371. The least number of five digit is exactly divisible by 88 is
(*a*) 10032 (*b*) 10132
(*c*) 10088 (*d*) 10023
[SSC Multi-Tasking Staff Exam -2017]

372. The number of three digit numbers which are multiples of 9 are

[CLAT, 2016]

(*a*) 100 (*b*) 99
(*c*) 98 (*d*) 101

373. Two consecutive even positive integers, sum of the squares of which is 1060, are

[CLAT, 2016]

(*a*) 12 and 14 (*b*) 20 and 22
(*c*) 22 and 24 (*d*) 15 and 18

Directions (Question 374): The question below consists of a question and two statements numbered I and II given below it. You have to decide whether the data given in the statements are sufficient to answer the questions. Read both the statements and given answer.

(A) If the data in statement I alone is sufficient to answer the question, while the data in statement II alone is not sufficient to answer the question.
(B) If the data in statement II alone is sufficient to answer the question, while the data in statement I alone is not sufficient to answer the question.
(C) If the data either in statement I alone or statement II alone is sufficient to answer the questions.
(D) If the data given in both Statement I and II together are not sufficient to answer the question.
(E) If the data in both Statement I and II together are necessary to answer the question.

374. What is the number of trees planted in the field in row and column?

[IBPS—Bank Spl. Officer (Marketing) Exam, 2016]

I. Number of columns is more than the number of rows by 4.
II. Number of columns is 20.

375. If n is a natural number and $n = p_1^{x_1} p_2^{x_2} p_3^{x_3}$, where p_1, p_2, p_3 are distinct prime factors, then the number of prime factors for n is

[CDS, 2016]

(*a*) $x_1 + x_2 + x_3$ (*b*) x_1, x_2, x_3
(*c*) $(x_1 + 1)(x_2 + 1)(x_3 + 1)$ (*d*) None of the above

376. Consider the following statements for the sequence of numbers given below:
11, 111, 1111, 11111, ...
1. Each number can be expressed in the form $(4m + 3)$, where m is a natural number.
2. Some numbers are squares.

Which of the above statements is/are correct?

[CDS, 2016]

(*a*) 1 only (*b*) 2 only
(*c*) Both 1 and 2 (*d*) neither 1 nor 2)

377. If the sum of two numbers is 14 and their difference is 10. Find the product of these two numbers.

[UPSSSC Lower Subordinate (Pre.) Exam, 2016]

(*a*) 24 (*b*) 22
(*c*) 20 (*d*) 18

378. If $m = -4$, $n = -2$, then the value of $m^3 - 3m^2 + 3m + 3n + 3n^2 + n^3$ is

(*a*) −120 (*b*) −124
(*c*) −126 (*d*) −128

[SSC—CGL (Tier-I) Exam, 2015]

379. If the sum of two numbers is 14 and their difference is 10, find the product of these two numbers.

[UPSSSC—Lower Subordinate (Pre.) Exam 2016]

(*a*) 18 (*b*) 20
(*c*) 24 (*d*) 22

380. What is the sum of all natural numbers from 1 to 100?

[CLAT-2016]

(*a*) 5050 (*b*) 6000
(*c*) 5000 (*d*) 5052

ANSWERS

1. (*c*)	2. (*a*)	3. (*c*)	4. (*d*)	5. (*c*)	6. (*c*)	7. (*c*)	8. (*c*)	9. (*a*)	10. (*c*)
11. (*b*)	12. (*b*)	13. (*d*)	14. (*c*)	15. (*d*)	16. (*b*)	17. (*c*)	18. (*b*)	19. (*c*)	20. (*d*)
21. (*c*)	22. (*c*)	23. (*c*)	24. (*b*)	25. (*d*)	26. (*d*)	27. (*a*)	28. (*c*)	29. (*c*)	30. (*c*)
31. (*b*)	32. (*b*)	33. (*d*)	34. (*a*)	35. (*c*)	36. (*d*)	37. (*b*)	38. (*c*)	39. (*a*)	40. (*d*)
41. (*a*)	42. (*d*)	43. (*d*)	44. (*d*)	45. (*d*)	46. (*d*)	47. (*d*)	48. (*c*)	49. (*a*)	50. (*b*)
51. (*b*)	52. (*b*)	53. (*c*)	54. (*d*)	55. (*b*)	56. (*d*)	57. (*b*)	58. (*c*)	59. (*d*)	60. (*b*)

61. (d)	62. (d)	63. (c)	64. (a)	65. (c)	66. (a)	67. (a)	68. (c)	69. (d)	70. (b)
71. (a)	72. (b)	73. (c)	74. (d)	75. (c)	76. (b)	77. (b)	78. (b)	79. (d)	80. (d)
81. (c)	82. (d)	83. (c)	84. (e)	85. (c)	86. (a)	87. (b)	88. (b)	89. (e)	90. (d)
91. (c)	92. (a)	93. (c)	94. (c)	95. (d)	96. (d)	97. (a)	98. (c)	99. (c)	100. (a)
101. (b)	102. (a)	103. (a)	104. (c)	105. (a)	106. (c)	107. (a)	108. (b)	109. (b)	110. (e)
111. (a)	112. (a)	113. (b)	114. (a)	115. (b)	116. (c)	117. (a)	118. (c)	119. (b)	120. (a)
121. (e)	122. (d)	123. (c)	124. (b)	125. (a)	126. (b)	127. (c)	128. (d)	129. (d)	130. (d)
131. (b)	132. (b)	133. (b)	134. (d)	135. (d)	136. (a)	137. (a)	138. (b)	139. (a)	140. (b)
141. (a)	142. (c)	143. (d)	144. (d)	145. (e)	146. (c)	147. (a)	148. (b)	149. (c)	150. (a)
151. (e)	152. (c)	153. (c)	154. (c)	155. (b)	156. (a)	157. (a)	158. (d)	159. (b)	160. (c)
161. (d)	162. (d)	163. (b)	164. (d)	165. (d)	166. (a)	167. (a)	168. (a)	169. (c)	170. (b)
171. (d)	172. (b)	173. (c)	174. (a)	175. (b)	176. (a)	177. (a)	178. (d)	179. (c)	180. (a)
181. (d)	182. (c)	183. (c)	184. (b)	185. (b)	186. (c)	187. (a)	188. (c)	189. (c)	190. (c)
191. (c)	192. (b)	193. (a)	194. (a)	195. (b)	196. (a)	197. (b)	198. (a)	199. (c)	200. (a)
201. (b)	202. (d)	203. (b)	204. (b)	205. (a)	206. (d)	207. (d)	208. (d)	209. (c)	210. (a)
211. (d)	212. (b)	213. (a)	214. (d)	215. (d)	216. (a)	217. (d)	218. (a)	219. (b)	220. (b)
221. (c)	222. (b)	223. (d)	224. (c)	225. (d)	226. (a)	227. (d)	228. (d)	229. (b)	230. (e)
231. (d)	232. (b)	233. (a)	234. (a)	235. (a)	236. (c)	237. (c)	238. (a)	239. (a)	240. (b)
241. (c)	242. (c)	243. (b)	244. (c)	245. (d)	246. (c)	247. (c)	248. (a)	249. (b)	250. (a)
251. (b)	252. (b)	253. (c)	254. (c)	255. (d)	256. (d)	257. (d)	258. (b)	259. (a)	260. (e)
261. (d)	262. (c)	263. (a)	264. (c)	265. (b)	266. (d)	267. (a)	268. (a)	269. (e)	270. (a)
271. (c)	272. (d)	273. (b)	274. (c)	275. (c)	276. (c)	277. (b)	278. (a)	279. (c)	280. (a)
281. (b)	282. (a)	283. (c)	284. (b)	285. (b)	286. (c)	287. (b)	288. (c)	289. (d)	290. (b)
291. (c)	292. (a)	293. (d)	294. (c)	295. (b)	296. (d)	297. (d)	298. (d)	299. (d)	300. (d)
301. (b)	302. (d)	303. (a)	304. (b)	305. (a)	306. (c)	307. (b)	308. (b)	309. (b)	310. (c)
311. (d)	312. (c)	313. (d)	314. (a)	315. (b)	316. (b)	317. (b)	318. (c)	319. (a)	320. (c)
321. (a)	322. (c)	323. (c)	324. (c)	325. (c)	326. (d)	327. (d)	328. (c)	329. (c)	330. (c)
331. (d)	332. (c)	333. (a)	334. (b)	335. (b)	336. (a)	337. (a)	338. (a)	339. (d)	340. (d)
341. (a)	342. (c)	343. (d)	344. (b)	345. (a)	346. (d)	347. (a)	348. (b)	349. (b)	350. (c)
351. (b)	352. (a)	353. (c)	354. (a)	355. (b)	356. (b)	357. (c)	358. (d)	359. (c)	360. (a)
361. (c)	362. (a)	363. (d)	364. (d)	365. (d)	366. (b)	367. (b)	368. (b)	369. (b)	370. (a)
371. (a)	372. (a)	373. (c)	374. (d)	375. (b)	376. (a)	377. (a)	378. (c)	379. (c)	380. (a)

SOLUTIONS

1.

TL	L	T-Th	Th	H	T	O
3	2	5	4	7	1	0

Place value of 5 = (5 × 10000) = 50000.

2. The face value of 8 in the given numeral is 8.
3. Sum of the place values of 3 = (3000 + 30) = 3030.
4. Difference between the place values of 7 and 3 in given numeral = (7000 – 30) = 6970.
5. Difference between the local value and the face value of 7 in the given numeral = (70000 – 7) = 69993.
6. Required sum = (99999 + 10000) = 109999.
7. Required difference = (10000 – 999) = 9001.
8. Required number = 30005.
9. Required number = 2047.
10. All natural numbers and 0 are called the whole numbers.
11. Clearly, there exists a smallest natural number, namely 1. So statement (1) is true.
Natural numbers are counting numbers and the counting process never ends. So, the largest nature number is not known. Thus, statement (2) is false.
Thre is no natural number between two consecutive natural numbers. So, statement (3) is false.
12. Clearly, every rational number is also a real number.
13. Clearly, π is an irrational number.
14. Since $\sqrt{2}$ is a non-terminating and non-repeating decimal, so it is an irrational number.
15. $\sqrt{3}$ is an infinite non-recurring decimal.
16. We can write 9 = (1 + 8) ; 9 = (2 + 7) ;
9 = (3 + 6), 9 = (4 + 5).
Thus, it can be done in 4 ways.
17. We may have (64 and 1), (32 and 2), (16 and 4) and (8 and 8).
In any case, the sum is not 35.
18. We may take the least values of y and z as $y = 1$ and $z = 1$.
So, the maximum value of x is 7.
19. We know that: $1^2 + 2^2 + 3^2 + ... + n^2 = \frac{1}{6} n(n+1)(2n+1)$.

$\therefore (1^2 + 2^2 + 3^2 + ... + 9^2) = \left(\frac{1}{6} \times 9 \times 10 \times 19\right) = 285.$

20. $(n + 7) = 88 \Rightarrow n = (88 - 7) = 81$, which is false as $20 < n < 80$.
So, the required number is 88.
21. We have, $M = 1000$; $D = 500$; $C = 100$ and $L = 50$.
$\therefore M > D > C > L$ is the correct sequence.
22. These numbers are 24, 22, 20, 18, 16, 14, 12, 10, 8, 6, 4, 2.
8th number from the bottom is 16.
23. The given series is such that the sum of first hundred terms is zero, and 101st term is 2. So, the sum of 101 terms is 2.
24. Given series is 1, 2, 3, 4, 1, 2, 3, 4, 1, 2, 3, 4, ...
$\therefore$ 96th term is 4. So, $T_{97} = 1$ and $T_{98} = 2$. Hence, the 98th term is 2.
25. Let the hundred's, ten's and one's digits be x, y and z respectively.
Then, the given number is $100x + 10y + z$.
26. Let the thousand's, hundred's, ten's and one's digits be x, y, z, w respectively.
Then, the number is $1000x + 100y + 10z + w = 10^3 x + 10^2 y + 10z + w$.
27. We know that the sum of two odd numbers is even.
$\therefore$ (n is odd, p is odd) $\Rightarrow (n + p)$ is even.
28. n^3 is odd $\Rightarrow n$ is odd and n^2 is odd.
$\therefore$ I and II are true.
29. $(n - 1)$ is odd $\Rightarrow (n - 1) - 2$ and $(n - 1) + 2$ are odd $\Rightarrow (n - 3)$ and $(n + 1)$ are odd.
30. The product of two odd numbers is always odd.
31. x is odd $\Rightarrow x^2$ is odd $\Rightarrow 5x^2$ is odd $\Rightarrow (5x^2 + 2)$ is odd.
32. $ab = 0 \Rightarrow a = 0$ or $b = 0$ or both are zero.
33. $A < B < C < D \Rightarrow D > B > A$
Also, $A < B < C < D$ and $D > B > E \Rightarrow E < B < C < D$ $\Rightarrow E < C < D$ *and* $E < B < C$.
Clearly, we cannot arrange A, E, C is an increasing or decreasing order.
34. When m is even, then $m(n + \text{'o'})(p - q)$ is even.
35. $n < 0 \Rightarrow 2n < 0, -n > 0$ and $n^2 = (-n)^2 > 0$.
Thus, out of the numbers $0, -n, 2n$ and n^2 we find that $2n$ is the least.
36. It is given that $x - y = 8$.
I. We may have $x = 5$ and $y = -3$.
So, it is not necessary that both x and y are positive.
II. If x is positive, then it is not necessary that y is positive, as $x = 5 \Rightarrow y = -3$.
III. If $x < 0$, then $y = x - 8$ which is clearly less than 0.
So, if x is negative, then y must be negative.
37. If $x < 0$ and $y < 0$, then clearly $xy > 0$.
So, whenever x and y are negative, then xy is positive.
Note that $(x < 0, y < 0)$ does not imply that $(x + y)$ is positive.
e.g. If $x = -2$ and $y = -3$, then $(x + y) = -5 < 0$.
Note that $(x < 0, y < 0)$ does not imply that $(x - y) > 0$.
e.g. If $x = -5$ and $y = -2$, then $x - y = -5 - (-2)$ $= -5 + 2 = -3 < 0$.
38. Let $n = 1 + x = 1 + m(m + 1)(m + 2)(m + 3)$, where m is a positive integer.
Then, clearly two of $m, (m + 1), (m + 2), (m + 3)$ are even and so their product is even. Thus, x is even and hence $n = 1 + x$ is odd.
Also, $n = 1 + m(m + 3)(m + 1)(m + 2) = 1 + (m^2 + 3m)(m^2 + 3m + 2)$
$\Rightarrow n = 1 + y(y + 2)$, where $m^2 + 3m = y$
$\Rightarrow n = 1 + y^2 + 2y = (1 + y)^2$, which is a perfect square.
Hence, I and III are true.
39. $1 \le x \le 2 \Rightarrow 1 \le \frac{2}{5} y + 3 \le 2$

$\Rightarrow (1 - 3) \le \frac{2}{5} y \le (2 - 3) \Rightarrow \frac{5}{2}(1 - 3) \le y \le \frac{5}{2}(2 - 3)$

$\Rightarrow -5 \le y \le \frac{-5}{2}$

Hence, y increases from -5 to $\frac{-5}{2}$.
40. (*a*) Let $x = 0$ and $y = \sqrt{2}$. Then, x is rational and y is irrational.
$\therefore \quad x + y = 0 + \sqrt{2} = \sqrt{2}$ which is irrational.
Thus, $x + y$ is not rational.

(*b*) Let $x = 0$ and $y = \sqrt{2}$. Then, x is rational and y is irrational.

$\therefore$ $xy = 0 \times \sqrt{2} = 0$, which is rational.

Hence, xy is not irrational.

(*c*) As shown in (*b*), xy is not necessarily irrational.

(*d*) $x + y$ is necessary irrational. But xy can be either rational or irrational.

Hence, (*d*) is true.

41. Let x and $(x + 1)$ be two consecutive integers. Then $(x + 1)^2 - x^2 = (x + 1 + x)(x + 1 - x) = (x + 1 + x) \times 1 = (x + 1 + x) =$ sum of given numbers.

42. If a and b are two rational numbers, then $\frac{a+b}{2}$ is a rational number lying between a and b.

43. $B > A \Rightarrow A < B \Rightarrow (A - B) < 0$.

Since A and B are both positive integers, we have $(A + B) > 0$ and $AB > 0$.

If ($A = 1$ and $B = 2$), we have $AB < (A + B)$.

If ($A = 2$ and $B = 3$), we have $(A + B) < AB$.

Thus, we cannot say which one of $A + B$ and AB has the highest value.

44. $0 < x < 1 \Rightarrow \quad x^2 < x < 1 \qquad \ldots(i)$

$$\Rightarrow \frac{1}{x^2} > \frac{1}{x} > 1 > x > x^2 \quad \text{[using } (i)]$$

Hence, $\frac{1}{x^2}$ is the greatest.

45. $p < 1 \Rightarrow \frac{1}{p} > 1 \Rightarrow \frac{2}{p} > 2 \Rightarrow \frac{2}{p} - p > 2 - p > 0 \quad [\because p < 1]$

Hence, $\left(\frac{2}{p} - p\right)$ is a positive number.

46. $$(x^2 + x + 1) = \left(x^2 + x + \frac{1}{4}\right) + \frac{3}{4}$$

$$= \left(x + \frac{1}{2}\right)^2 + \frac{3}{4} \geq \frac{3}{4} \qquad \left[\because \left(x + \frac{1}{2}\right)^2 \geq 0\right]$$

Hence, $(x^2 + x + 1)$ is greater than or equal to $\frac{3}{4}$.

47. $$\left(\frac{1}{2} + \frac{1}{3} + \frac{1}{7}\right) + \frac{1}{n} = \frac{(21 + 14 + 6)}{42} + \frac{1}{n} = \left(\frac{41}{42} + \frac{1}{n}\right).$$

This sum is a natural number when $n = 42$.

So, each one of the statements that 2 divides n ; 3 divides n and 7 divides n is true.

Hence, $n > 84$ is false.

48. $$\frac{(16n^2 + 7n + 6)}{n} = \left(\frac{16n^2}{n} + \frac{7n}{n} + \frac{6}{n}\right) = \left(16n + 7 + \frac{6}{n}\right).$$

For $\left(16n + 7 + \frac{6}{n}\right)$ to be an integer, we may have $n = 1$ or $n = 2$ or $n = 3$ or $n = 6$.

Hence, 4 values of n will give the desired result.

49. $(p > q$ and $r < 0) \Rightarrow pr < qr$ is true.

50. $(X < Z$ and $X < Y) \Rightarrow X^2 < YZ$.

51. $x + y > p$ and $p > z \Rightarrow x + y > z$.

52. $$\frac{(a - b)}{3.5} = \frac{4}{7} \Rightarrow (a - b) = \frac{4}{7} \times \frac{7}{2} = 2 \Rightarrow b < a.$$

53. $$\frac{13}{1} = \frac{13w}{(1 - w)} \Rightarrow \frac{w}{(1 - w)} = 1 \Rightarrow w = 1 - w \Rightarrow 2w = 1 \Rightarrow w = \frac{1}{2}.$$

$\therefore (2w)^2 = 4w^2 = 4 \times \frac{1}{4} = 1.$

Questions 54 to 57

Let the digits of the number in order be A, B, C, D, E.

Then, $A > 5\ E \Rightarrow E = 1$.

A, B, C are all odd and none of the digits is $3 \Rightarrow A, B, C$ are the digits from 5, 7, 9.

Since A is the largest digit, so $A = 9$.

$\therefore$ $B = 5$ or 7 and $C = 5$ or 7.

Now, the number DE is the product of two prime numbers. $E = 1$ and $D = 2, 4, 6$ or 8.

41 and 61 are prime numbers and 81 cannot be expressed as product of two primes.

Only 21 can be expressed as the product of two prime numbers ($21 = 3 \times 7$).

So, $D = 2$.

Hence, the number is 95721 or 97521.

54. The second digit of the number is either 5 or 7.

55. The last digit of the number is 1.

56. The largest digit in the number is 9.

57. The number is odd. So, it is not divisible by 2 or 4. Sum of digits $= 9 + 7 + 5 + 2 + 1 = 24$, which is divisible by 3 but not by 9.

So, the given number is divisible by 3.

58. The least prime number is 2.

59. **Statement 1.** Let $x = 4$ and $y = 15$. Then, each one of x and y is a composite number.

But, $x + y = 19$, which is not composite.

$\therefore$ Statement 1 is not true.

Statement 2. We know that 1 is neither prime nor composite.

$\therefore$ Statement 2 is not true.

Thus, neither 1 nor 2 is correct.

60. Prime numbers between 0 and 50 are:

2, 3, 5, 7, 11, 13, 17, 19, 23, 29, 31, 37, 41, 43 and 47.

Their number is 15.

61. Each of the required numbers must divide $(143 - 3) = 140$ exactly.

Now, $140 = 5 \times 7 \times 4$.

Hence, the required prime numbers are 5 and 7.

62. Sum of first four prime numbers $= (2 + 3 + 5 + 7) = 17$.

63. Sum of all prime numbers from 1 to 20 $= (2 + 3 + 5 + 7 + 11 + 13 + 17 + 19) = 77$.

64. Clearly, 11 is a prime number which remains unchanged when its digits are interchanged. And, $(11)^2 = 121$.

Hence, the square of such a number is 121.

65. Let the required prime number be p. Let p when divided by 6 give n as quotient and r as remainder. Then $p = 6n + r$, where $0 \leq r < 6$

Now, $r = 0$, $r = 2$, $r = 3$ and $r = 4$ do not give p as prime.

$\therefore$ $r \neq 0, r \neq 2, r \neq 3$ and $r \neq 4$.

Hence, $r = 1$ or $r = 5$.

66. Clearly, $21 = 3 \times 7$, so 21 is not prime.

67. Clearly, 19 is a prime number.

68. We know that 115 is divisible by 5. So, it is not prime.

119 is divisible by 7. So, it is not prime.

$127 < (12)^2$ and prime numbers less than 12 are 2, 3, 5, 7, 11.

Clearly, 127 is not exactly divisible by any of them. Hence, 127 is a prime number.

69. Clearly, 143 is divisible by 11. So, 143 is not prime.
289 is divisible by 17. So, 289 is not prime.
117 is divisible by 3. So, 117 is not prime.
$359 < (20)^2$ and prime numbers less than 20 are 2, 3, 5, 7, 11, 13, 17, 19.
And, 359 is not exactly divisible by any of them. Hence, 359 is a prime number.

70. Putting $n = 1, 2, 3, 4$ respectively in $(2n + 1)$ we get:
$(2 \times 1 + 1) = 3$, $(2 \times 2 + 1) = 5$, $(2 \times 3 + 1) = 7$ and $(2 \times 4 + 1) = 9$,
where 3, 5, 7 are prime numbers.
$\therefore$ The smallest value of n for which $(2n + 1)$ is not prime, is $n = 4$.

71. Clearly, 100 is divisible by 2. So, 100 is not prime.
$(101) < (11)^2$ and prime numbers less than 11 are 2, 3, 5, 7.
Clearly, 101 is not divisible by any of 2, 3, 5 and 7.
Hence, 101 is the smallest 3-digit prime number.

72. Each one of 112, 114, 116, 118 is divisible by 2. So, none is prime.
Each one of 111, 114, 117 is divisible by 3. So, none is prime.
Clearly, 115 is divisible by 5. So, it is not prime.
Each one of 112 and 119 is divisible by 7. So, none is prime.
Hence, there is only 1 prime number between 110 and 120, which is 113.

73. Let the given prime numbers be p, q, r and s. Then
$p \times q \times r = 385$ and $q \times r \times s = 1001$

$$\Rightarrow \frac{p \times q \times r}{q \times r \times s} = \frac{385}{1001} = \frac{5}{13} \Rightarrow \frac{p}{s} = \frac{5}{13} \Rightarrow p = 5 \text{ and } s = 13.$$

Hence the largest of these prime numbers is 13.

74. Let the required prime numbers be $x, y, y + 36$. Then,
$x + y + y + 36 = 100 \Rightarrow x + 2y = 64$
Let $x = 2$. Then, $2y = 62 \Rightarrow y = 31$.
So, these prime numbers are 2, 31 and 67.
In given choices 67 is the answer.

75. $\sqrt{437} > 20$
All prime numbers less than 20 are 2, 3, 5, 7, 11, 13, 17, 19. 161 is divisible by 7, 221 is divisible by 13 and 437 is divisible by 19. 373 is not divisible by any of the above prime numbers.
$\therefore$ 373 is prime.

76. The required arithmetic sequence of five prime numbers is 5, 11, 17, 23, 29 and therefore, the required 5th term is 29.

77. Each of the numbers 302, 303, 304, 305, 306, 308, 309, 310, 312, 314, 315, 316, 318 and 319 is clearly a composite number.
Out of 307, 311, 313 and 317 clearly every one is prime.
Hence, there are 4 prime numbers between 301 and 320.

78. Clearly, $3 \neq 4n + 1$ and $3 \neq 4n + 3$ for any natural number n.
$\therefore$ Statement (1) is false.
Putting $p = 3, 5, 7, 11, 13, 17$ etc. we get:
$(p - 1)(p + 1) = (2 \times 4), (4 \times 6), (6 \times 8), (10 \times 12), (12 \times 14), (16 \times 18)$ etc., each one of which is divisible by 4.
$\therefore$ Statement (2) is true.
Hence, (1) is false and (2) is true.

79. $n = 1 \Rightarrow (n^2 + n + 41) = (1 + 1 + 41) = 43$, which is prime.
$n = 10 \Rightarrow (n^2 + n + 41) = (100 + 10 + 41) = 151$, which is prime.
$n = 20 \Rightarrow (n^2 + n + 41) = (400 + 20 + 41) = 461$, which is prime.
$n = 40 \Rightarrow (n^2 + n + 41) = (1600 + 40 + 41) = 1681$, which is divisible by 41.
Thus, 1681 is not a prime number.
Hence $n = 40$ for which $(n^2 + n + 41)$ is not prime.

80. $X_2 = (2 \times 3) + 1 = 7$, which is prime and $X_2 + 1 = 8$, which is even.
$X_3 = (2 \times 3 \times 5) + 1 = 31$, which is prime and $X_3 + 1 = 32$, which is even.
$X_4 = (2 \times 3 \times 5 \times 7) + 1 = 211$, which is prime and $X_4 + 1 = 212$, which is even and so on.
Thus X_k is prime and $(X_k + 1)$ is even.
Hence, 1 and 3 are true statements.

81. $6 \times 3 (3 - 1) = 6 \times 3(2) = 6 \times 6 = 36$.

82. Given Expression = (1234 + 2345 + 4567) – 3456
= (8146 – 3456) = 4690.

```
  1234
  2345
+ 4567
  8146
- 3456
  4690
```

83. Let $5566 - 7788 + 9988 = x + 4444$. Then
$(5566 + 9988) - 7788 = x + 4444$
$\Rightarrow 15554 - 7788 = x + 4444 \Rightarrow x + 4444 = 7766$
$\Rightarrow x = (7766 - 4444) = 3322$.

```
  7766
- 4444
  3322
```

84. Given Expression = 38649 – (1624 + 4483)
= (38649 – 6107) = 32542.

85. Given Expression = 884697 – (773697 + 102479)
= 884697 – 876176
= 8521.

```
  884697
- 876176
    8521
```

86. Let $10531 + 4813 - 728 = x \times 87$. Then
$(15344 - 728) = 87 \times x \Rightarrow x = \frac{14616}{87} = 168$.

```
  10531
+  4813
  15344
-   728
  14616
```

```
    168
87)14616(
   87
   591
   522
    696
    696
     ×
```

87. $394 \times 113 = 394 \times (100 + 10 + 3)$
$= (394 \times 100) + (394 \times 10) + (394 \times 3)$
$= 39400 + 3940 + 1182$
$= 44522$.

```
  39400
   3940
+  1182
  44522
```

88. $1260 \div 14 \div 9 = \left(1260 \times \frac{1}{14} \times \frac{1}{9}\right) = 10$.

89. $136 \times 12 \times 8 = 136 \times 96 = 136 \times (100 - 4)$
$= (136 \times 100) - (136 \times 4)$
$= 13600 - 544 = 13056$.

```
  13600
-   544
  13056
```

90. Let $8888 + 848 + 88 - x = 7337 + 737$.
Then $9824 - x = 8074$

$\Rightarrow x = 9824 - 8074 \qquad \Rightarrow x = 1750.$

```
  9824  |  8888  |  7337
- 8074  |   848  | + 737
  1750  |  + 88  |  8074
        |  9824  |
```

91. Let $414 \times x \times 7 = 127512$. Then

$$x = \frac{127512}{414 \times 7} = \frac{18216}{414} = \frac{2024}{46} = \frac{1012}{23} = 44.$$

```
     44
23)1012(
   92
    92
    92
    ×
```

92. $82540027 \times 43253 = 82540027 \times (40000 + 3000 + 200 + 50 + 3)$
$= (82540027 \times 40000) + (82540027 \times 3000) + (82540027 \times 200)$
$+ (82540027 \times 50) + (82540027 \times 3)$

```
  3301601080000
   247620081000
    16508005400
     4127001350
+     247620081
  3570103787831
```

Shortcut Method:
Product of unit's digits of the given numbers = 7 × 3 = 21
Clearly, the required product will have 1 as the unit's digit, which is 3570103787831.

93. Let $\frac{46351 - 36418 - 4505}{x} = 1357$. Then

$$x = \frac{46351 - (36418 + 4505)}{1357}$$

$$\Rightarrow x = \frac{(46351 - 40923)}{1357} = \frac{5428}{1357} = 4.$$

```
  46351  |   36418
- 40923  |  + 4505
   5428  |   40923
```

94. $6 \times 66 \times 666 = 6 \times (6 \times 11) \times (6 \times 111)$
$= (6 \times 6 \times 6) \times (11 \times 111) = (216 \times 1221)$
$= (1221 \times 216) = 1221 \times (200 + 10 + 6)$
$= (1221 \times 200) + (1221 \times 10) + (1221 \times 6)$
$= 244200 + 12210 + 7326 = 263736.$

```
  244200
   12210
+   7326
  263736
```

95. $(+1) - (-1) = (+1 + 1) = 2.$

96.

```
  888888
   88888
    8888
     888
      88
+      8
  987648
```

97. Given Expression = 17 + (– 12) – 48 = 17 – 60 = – 43.

98. $\frac{60840}{234} = \frac{30420}{117} = \frac{3380}{13} = 260.$

99. Let $3578 + 5729 - x \times 581 = 5821$. Then
$x \times 581 = (3578 + 5729) - 5821 \Rightarrow x \times 581 = (9307 - 5821)$
$= 3486 \Rightarrow x = \frac{3486}{581} = 6.$

100. $-95 \div 19 = \frac{-95}{19} = -5.$

101. $12345679 \times 72 = 12345679 \times (70 + 2)$
$= (12345679 \times 70) + (12345679 \times 2)$
$= (864197530 + 24691358)$
$= 888888888.$

```
  864197530
+  24691358
  888888888
```

102. $8899 - 6644 - 3322 = x - 1122 \Rightarrow 2255 - 3322 + 1122 = x$
$\Rightarrow x = 3377 - 3322 = 55.$

103. Let $74844 \div x = 54 \times 63$. Then, $\frac{74844}{x} = 54 \times 63$

$$\Rightarrow x = \frac{74844}{54 \times 63} = \frac{8316}{6 \times 63} = \frac{1386}{63} = \frac{198}{9} = 22.$$

104. $1256 \times 3892 = (1000 + 200 + 50 + 6) \times 3892$
$= (1000 \times 3892) + (200 \times 3892) +$
$(50 \times 3892) + (6 \times 3892)$
$= 3892000 + 778400 + 194600 + 23352$
$= 4888352.$

```
  3892000
   778400
   194600
+   23352
  4888352
```

105. $786 \times 964 = (800 - 14) \times 964$
$= (800 \times 964) - (14 \times 964)$
$= (771200 - 13496) = 757704.$

```
  771200
-  13496
  757704
```

106. $348 \times 265 = (350 - 2) \times 265 = (350 \times 265) - (2 \times 265)$
$= \{(300 + 50) \times 265\} - 530 = (300 \times 265)$
$+ (50 \times 265) - 530$
$= 79500 + 13250 - 530 = 92750 - 530$
$= 92220.$

107. $(71 \times 29 + 27 \times 15 + 8 \times 4) = (80 - 9) \times 29 + 405 + 32 =$
$(80 \times 29) - (9 \times 29) + 437 = 2320 - 261 + 437 = 2757 - 261$
$= 2496.$

108. Let $x \times (|a| \times |b|) = -ab$. Then, $x = \frac{-(ab)}{|ab|} = -1.$

109. Let $(46)^2 - x^2 = 4398 - 3066$
Then, $(46)^2 - x^2 = 1332 \Rightarrow x^2 = (46)^2 - 1332$
$\therefore x^2 = (50 - 4)^2 - 1332 = (50)^2 + 4^2 - 2 \times 50 \times 4 - 1332$
$\Rightarrow x^2 = 2500 + 16 - 400 - 1332 = 2516 - 1732 = 784$
$\Rightarrow x = \sqrt{784} = 28.$

```
 2 | 784 (28       2516
   |  4          - 1732
48 | 384            784
   | 384
   |  ×
```

110. $(800 \div 64) \times (1296 \div 36) = \frac{\overset{50}{\cancel{800}}}{\underset{4}{\cancel{64}}} \times \frac{\overset{\overset{9}{\cancel{27}}}{\cancel{108}}\!\!\!\!\cancel{1296}}{\underset{\cancel{3}}{\cancel{36}}} = 450.$

111. $5358 \times 51 = 5358 \times (50 + 1) = 5358 \times 50 + 5358 \times 1$
$= \frac{5358 \times 100}{2} + 5358$
$= \frac{535800}{2} + 5358 = 267900 + 5358 = 273258.$

112. $587 \times 999 = 587 \times (1000 - 1) = (587 \times 1000) - (587 \times 1)$
$= 587000 - 587 = 586413.$

113. $3897 \times 999 = 3897 \times (1000 - 1) = (3897 \times 1000) - (3897 \times 1)$
$= 3897000 - 3897 = 3893103.$

114. $72519 \times 9999 = 72519 \times (10000 - 1)$
$= (72519 \times 10000) - (72519 \times 1)$
$= 725190000 - 72519 = 725117481.$

725190000
−72519
725117481

115. $2056 \times 987 = 2056 \times (1000 - 13)$
$= (2056 \times 1000) - (2056 \times 13)$
$= 2056000 - 26728 = 2029272.$

116. $1904 \times 1904 = (1904)^2 = (1900 + 4)^2$
$= (1900)^2 + 4^2 + 2 \times 1900 \times 4$
$= 3610000 + 16 + 15200 = 3625216.$

117. $1397 \times 1397 = (1397)^2 = (1400 - 3)^2$
$= (1400)^2 + 3^2 - 2 \times 1400 \times 3 = 1960000 + 9 - 8400$
$= 1951609.$

118. $(107 \times 107) + (93 \times 93) = (107)^2 + (93)^2$
$= (100 + 7)^2 + (100 - 7)^2$
$= (a + b)^2 + (a - b)^2 = 2(a^2 + b^2)$
$= 2[(100)^2 + 7^2] = 2[10000 + 49]$
$= 2 \times 10049 = 20098.$

119. $(217 \times 217) + (183 \times 183) = (217)^2 + (183)^2$
$= (200 + 17)^2 + (200 - 17)^2 = (a + b)^2 + (a - b)^2$
$= 2(a^2 + b^2)$, where $a = 200$, $b = 17$
$= 2 [(200)^2 + (17)^2] = 2 [40000 + 289]$
$= (2 \times 40289) = 80578.$

120. $(106 \times 106 - 94 \times 94) = (106)^2 - (94)^2$
$= (106 + 94) (106 - 94) = (200 \times 12) = 2400.$

121. $(8796 \times 223 + 8796 \times 77) = 8796 \times (223 + 77)$
[by distributive law]
$= (8796 \times 300) = 2638800.$

122. $(287 \times 287 + 269 \times 269 - 2 \times 287 \times 269)$
$= (287)^2 + (269)^2 - (2 \times 287 \times 269)$
$= (287 - 269)^2 = (18)^2 = 324.$
$[\because a^2 + b^2 - 2ab = (a - b)^2]$

123. $(476 + 424)^2 - 4 \times 476 \times 424 = (a + b)^2 - 4ab = (a - b)^2$,
where $a = 476$ & $b = 424 = (476 - 424)^2 = (52)^2 = (50 + 2)^2$
$= (50)^2 + 2^2 + 2 \times 50 \times 2$
$= (2500 + 4 + 200) = 2704.$

124. $(112 \times 5^4) = 112 \times \left(\frac{10}{2}\right)^4 = \frac{112 \times 10000}{16} = 70000.$

125. $(5746320819 \times 125) = \frac{5746320819 \times (125 \times 8)}{8}$
$= \frac{5746320819 \times 1000}{8} = \frac{5746320819000}{8} = 718290102375.$

126. $935421 \times 625 = \frac{935421 \times 625 \times 16}{16} = \frac{935421 \times 10000}{16}$
$= \frac{9354210000}{16} = 584638125.$

127. $(999)^2 - (998)^2 = (999 + 998)(999 - 998) = (1997 \times 1) = 1997.$

128. $(80)^2 - (65)^2 + 81 = (80 + 65)(80 - 65) + 81 = (145 \times 15) + 81 = (2175 + 81) = 2256.$

129. $(24 + 25 + 26)^2 - (10 + 20 + 25)^2 = (75)^2 - (55)^2$
$= (75 + 55)(75 - 55) = (130 \times 20) = 2600.$

130. $(65)^2 - (55)^2 = (65 + 55)(65 - 55) = (120 \times 10) = 1200.$

131. $(a^2 - b^2) = 19 \Rightarrow (a + b)(a - b) = 19.$
Clearly, $a = 10$ and $b = 9$.

132. Since $(a + b)^2 - (a - b)^2 = 4ab$, so the given expression should be a multiple of 4.
So, the least value of $4ab$ is 32 and so the least value of ab is 8.
Hence, the smallest value of a is 4 and that of b is 2.
Hence, $a = 4$.

133. Given Expression $= (397)^2 + (104)^2 + 2 \times 397 \times 104$
$= (397 + 104)^2 = (501)^2 = (500 + 1)^2$
$= (500)^2 + 1^2 + 2 \times 500 \times 1 = 250000 + 1 + 1000 = 251001.$

134. $(64)^2 - (36)^2 = 20 \times x \Rightarrow (64 + 36)(64 - 36) = 20 \times x$
$\Rightarrow x = \frac{100 \times 28}{20} = 140.$

135. Given Expression
$= \frac{(a+b)^2 - (a-b)^2}{ab}$ (where $a = 489$, $b = 375$) $= \frac{4ab}{ab} = 4$

136. Given Expression $= \frac{(a+b)^2 + (a-b)^2}{(a^2+b^2)}$,
(where $a = 963$ and $b = 476$) $= \frac{2(a^2+b^2)}{(a^2+b^2)} = 2.$

137. Given Expression
$= \frac{(a^3+b^3)}{(a^2-ab+b^2)}$, (where $a = 768$ and $b = 232$) $= (a + b)$
$= (768 + 232) = 1000.$

138. Given Expression $= \frac{(854)^3 - (276)^3}{(854)^2 + (854 \times 276) + (276)^2}$
$= \frac{(a^3-b^3)}{(a^2+ab+b^2)}$, where $a = 854$ and $b = 276$
$= (a - b) = (854 - 276) = 578.$

139. Given Expression $= \frac{(753)^2 + (247)^2 - (753 \times 247)}{(753)^3 + (247)^3}$
$= \frac{(a^2+b^2-ab)}{(a^3+b^3)}$, where $a = 753$ and $b = 247$
$= \frac{1}{(a+b)} = \frac{1}{(753+247)} = \frac{1}{1000}.$

140. Given Expression $= \frac{(256)^2 - (144)^2}{112} = \frac{(256+144)(256-144)}{112}$
$= \frac{(400 \times 112)}{112} = 400.$

141. $\frac{(a^2+b^2+ab)}{(a^3-b^3)} = \frac{a^2+b^2+ab}{(a-b)(a^2+b^2+ab)} = \frac{1}{(a-b)} = \frac{1}{(11-9)} = \frac{1}{2}.$

142. $a + b + c = 0 \Rightarrow a + b = -c$, $(b + c) = -a$ and $(c + a) = -b$
$\Rightarrow (a + b)(b + c)(c + a) = (-c) \times (-a) \times (-b) = -(abc).$

143. $(a^2 + b^2 + c^2 - ab - bc - ca) = (a + b + c)^2 - 3(ab + bc + ca)$
$= (7 + 5 + 3)^2 - 3(35 + 15 + 21)$
$= (15)^2 - 3 \times 71$
$= (225 - 213) = 12.$

144. Both addition and multiplication of numbers are commutative and associative.

145. $9H + H8 + H6 = 230 \Rightarrow \{(9 \times 10) + H\} + (10H + 8) + (10H + 6) = 230$

$\Rightarrow 21H + 104 = 230 \Rightarrow 21H = 126$

$\Rightarrow H = 6.$

146. Let the missing digit be x. Then, 1 (carried over) + 3 + x + x = 10 + x $\Rightarrow x = 6$.

147. Clearly, $M = 0$ since $304 \times 4 = 1216$.

148. $5p9 + 327 + 2q8 = 1114 \Rightarrow (500 + 10p + 9) + (327) + (200 + 10q + 8) = 1114$

$\Rightarrow 10(p + q) + 1044 = 1114$

$\Rightarrow 10(p + q) = 70 \Rightarrow (p + q) = 7$

$\Rightarrow$ Maximum value of q is 7

[As minimum value of p = 0]

149. $5P7 + 8Q9 + R32 = 1928 \Rightarrow (500 + 10P + 7) + (800 + 10Q + 9) + (100R + 30 + 2) = 1928$

$\Rightarrow 10P + 10Q + 100R + 1348 = 1928$

$\Rightarrow 10(P + Q + 10R) = 580$

$\Rightarrow P + Q + 10R = 58 \Rightarrow R = 5$ and $P + Q = 8$ or $R = 4$ and $P + Q = 18$

$\Rightarrow$ Maximum value of Q is 9

[for $P = 9$ in second case]

150. Let $\frac{1x\,5y4}{148} = 78$.

Then, $10000 + 1000x + 500 + 10y + 4 = 148 \times 78$

$\Rightarrow 10000 + 1000x + 500 + 10y + 4 = 11544$

$= 10000 + 1000 + 500 + 40 + 4$

$\Rightarrow 1000x = 1000 \Rightarrow x = 1.$

151. Let $6x43 - 46y9 = 1904$.

Clearly, $y = 3$ and $x = 5$.

Hence * must be replaced by 5.

$$\begin{array}{r} ③ \\ 6\,x\,4\,3 \\ -\,4\,6\,y\,9 \\ \hline 1\,9\,0\,4 \end{array}$$

152. $5\,P\,9 - 7\,Q\,2 + 9\,R\,6 = 823$

$\Rightarrow (500 + 10P + 9) - (700 + 10Q + 2) + (900 + 10R + 6) = 823$

$\Rightarrow (500 + 900 - 700) + 10(P + R - Q) + (9 + 6 - 2) = 823$

$\Rightarrow 700 + 10(P + R - Q) = 810 = 700 + 110$

$\Rightarrow 10\,(P + R - Q) = 110$

$\Rightarrow P + R - Q = 11$

$\Rightarrow Q = (P + R - 11).$

To get maximum value of Q we take $P = 9$ and $R = 9$.

This gives $Q = (9 + 9 - 11) = 7$.

Hence, the maximum value of Q is 7.

153. Let the required digit be x. Then

$x + 1x + 2x + x3 + x1 = 21x$

$\Rightarrow x + 10 + x + 20 + x + 10x + 3 + 10x + 1 = 200 + 10 + x$

$\Rightarrow 22x = 210 - 34 = 176 \Rightarrow x = 8.$

Hence, the required digit is 8.

154. It is given that $D = 0$. So, we have $A = 5$.

So, 1 is carried over.

$1 + B + C = 10 + C \Rightarrow 1 + B = 10 \Rightarrow B = 9.$

Now, $1 + C + C = A \Rightarrow 1 + 2C = 5 \Rightarrow 2C = 4 \Rightarrow C = 2.$

Hence $B = 9$.

$$\begin{array}{r} ①① \\ C\,B\,A = 5 \\ +\,C\,C\,A = 5 \\ \hline A\,C\,0 \end{array}$$

155. We have, $C = 2$.

156. Since $13b7$ is divisible by 11, we have

$(7 + 3) - (b + 1) = 0 \Rightarrow 9 - b = 0 \Rightarrow b = 9.$

Putting $b = 9$, $a + 8 = 9$ we get $a = 1$. Hence, $(a + b) = (1 + 9) = 10$.

$$\begin{array}{r} 4\,a\,3 \\ 9\,8\,4 \\ \hline 1\,3\,b\,7 \end{array}$$

157. Clearly, we have $ab \times b = 24$ and $ab \times a = 12$.

$\therefore \frac{ab \times b}{ab \times a} = \frac{24}{12} \Rightarrow \frac{b}{a} = \frac{2}{1} \Rightarrow a = 1, b = 2.$

158. Clearly, $111 \times 1 = 111 \neq 8111$.

But, $999 \times 9 = 8991$. Hence, we have 9 in place of *.

159. $(1 * 2) = 1 + 6 \times 2 = 1 + 12 = 13.$

$(1 * 2) * 3 = 13 * 3 = 13 + 6 \times 3 = 13 + 18 = 31.$

160. $\underline{|8} - \underline{|7} - \underline{|6} = 8 \times 7 \times \underline{|6} - 7 \times \underline{|6} - \underline{|6}$

$= (56 - 7 - 1) \times \underline{|6} = 48 \times \underline{|6} = 6 \times 8 \times \underline{|6}.$

161. Highest power of 3 in 99! $= \left[\frac{99}{3}\right] + \left[\frac{99}{3^2}\right] + \left[\frac{99}{3^3}\right] + \left[\frac{99}{3^4}\right]$

$= \left[\frac{99}{3}\right] + \left[\frac{99}{9}\right] + \left[\frac{99}{27}\right] + \left[\frac{99}{81}\right]$

$= 33 + 11 + 3 + 1 = 48.$

Since $9 = 3^2$, so highest power of 9 dividing 99! $= \frac{48}{2} = 24$.

162. Every number from $\underline{|5}$ onwards is completely divisible by 5.

$\therefore (\underline{|5} + \underline{|6} + \underline{|7} + \ldots\ldots + \underline{|100})$ is completely divisible by 5.

And,

$(\underline{|1} + \underline{|2} + \underline{|3} + \underline{|4}) = (1 + 2 + 3 \times 2 \times 1 + 4 \times 3 \times 2 \times 1) = (1 + 2 + 6 + 24) = 33.$

Clearly, 33 when divided by 5 leaves a remainder 3.

Hence, $(\underline{|1} + \underline{|2} + \underline{|3} + \underline{|4} + \underline{|5} + \ldots\ldots + \underline{|100})$ when divided by 5 leaves a remainder 3.

163. $6^{10} \times 7^{17} \times 11^{27} = (2 \times 3)^{10} \times 7^{17} \times 11^{27} = 2^{10} \times 3^{10} \times 7^{17} \times 11^{27}.$

Number of prime factors in the given expression = (10 + 10 + 17 + 27) = 64.

164. $(30)^7 \times (22)^5 \times (34)^{11} = (2 \times 3 \times 5)^7 \times (2 \times 11)^5 \times (2 \times 17)^{11}$

$= 2^{(7+5+11)} \times 3^7 \times 5^7 \times 11^5 \times 17^{11}$

$= (2^{23} \times 3^7 \times 5^7 \times 11^5 \times 17^{11}).$

Number of prime factors = (23 + 7 + 7 + 5 + 11) = 53.

165. Let $x \times 48 = 173 \times 240$. Then, $x = \frac{173 \times 240}{48} = 173 \times 5 = 865.$

166. $(1000 + x) > (1000 \times x)$. Clearly, $x = 1$.

167. Let the original number be x. Then,

$\frac{(x+7) \times 5}{9} - 3 = 12 \Rightarrow \frac{5x + 35}{9} = 15 \Rightarrow 5x + 35 = 135$

$\Rightarrow 5x = 100 \Rightarrow x = 20.$

168. 38950 is completely divisible by 410 only.

Hence ₹ 410 is the correct answer.

169. Let the four consecutive even numbers be a, $a + 2$, $a + 4$ and $a + 6$.

Then, $a + a + 2 + a + 4 + a + 6 = 180 \Rightarrow 4a = 168$

$\Rightarrow a = 42.$

So, these numbers are 42, 44, 46 and 48.

Sum of next four consecutive even numbers = (50 + 52 + 54 + 56) = 212.

170. Number on thumbs = 1, 9, 17, 25, ...

This is an AP in which $a = 1$ and $d = (9 - 1) = 8$.

$\therefore \quad T_n = a + (n-1)d = 1 + 8(n-1) = (8n-7).$
$8n - 7 = 1994 \Rightarrow 8n = 2001 \Rightarrow n = 250.$
$T_{250} = 1 + (250-1) \times 8 = 1 + 249 \times 8 = 1993.$
So, 1993 lies on thumb and 1994 on index finger.

171. Out of four consecutive integers two are even and therefore, their product is even and on adding 1 to it, we get an odd integer. So, n is odd. Some possible values of n are as under:

$n = 1 + (1 \times 2 \times 3 \times 4) = (1 + 24) = 25 = 5^2,$
$n = 1 + (2 \times 3 \times 4 \times 5) = (1 + 120) = 121 = (11)^2,$
$n = 1 + (3 \times 4 \times 5 \times 6) = (1 + 360) = 361 = (19)^2,$
$n = 1 + (4 \times 5 \times 6 \times 7) = 841 = (29)^2$ and so on.

Hence, n is odd and a perfect square.

172. $(x^2 + y^2) = (x+y)^2 - 2xy = (15)^2 - 2 \times 56$
$= (225 - 112) = 113.$

173. $(2^2 + 4^2 + 6^2 + ... + 40^2) = (1 \times 2)^2 + (2 \times 2)^2 + (2 \times 3)^2 + ... + (2 \times 20)^2 = 2^2 \times (1^2 + 2^2 + 3^2 + ... + 20^2)$
$= (4 \times 2870) = 11480.$

174. $5^2 + 6^2 + ... + 10^2 + 20^2 = (1^2 + 2^2 + 3^2 + ... + 10^2) - (1^2 + 2^2 + 3^2 + 4^2) + 400$

$= \frac{1}{6}n(n+1)(2n+1) - (1+4+9+16) + 400$, where $n = 10$

$= \left(\frac{1}{6} \times 10 \times 11 \times 21\right) - 30 + 400 = (385 - 30 + 400) = 755.$

175. $(6 + 12 + 18 + 24 + ... + 60) = 6 \times (1 + 2 + 3 + 4 + ... + 10) = 6 \times 55 = 330.$

176. $2^m > 960$ when the least value of m is 10.
Then, $2^{10} = 1024$ and $1024 - 960 = 64 = 2^6$.
$\therefore m = 10$ and $n = 6$.

177. We keep on dividing 33333... by 7 till we get 0 as remainder.

```
     47619
  7)333333(
    28
     53
     49
      43
      42
       13
        7
        63
        63
         ×
```

$\therefore$ Required number = 47619

178. We keep on dividing 99999.... by 7 till we get 0 as remainder.

```
     142857
  7)999999(
    7
    29
    28
     19
     14
      59
      56
       39
       35
        49
        49
         ×
```

$\therefore$ Required number = 142857.
Number of digits = 6.

179.

```
        56
  987)559981(
      4935
       6648
       5922
        7261
        2961
          ×
```

Clearly, 7261 must be replaced by 2961, which is possibvle if 6648 is replaced by 6218, which in turn is possible if 5599 is replaced by 5556.
Thus, the correct number is 555681.

180. Clearly, multiples of 2 and 5 together yield 0.
Since the product of odd numbers contains no power of 2, so the given product does not give 0 at the unit place.

181. Let $N = 1 \times 2 \times 3 \times 4 \times .... \times 1000 = 1000!$
Clearly, the highest power of 2 in N is very high as compared to that of 5.
So, the number of zeros in N will be equal to the highest power of 5 in N.
$\therefore$ Required number of zeros

$= \left[\frac{1000}{5}\right] + \left[\frac{1000}{5^2}\right] + \left[\frac{1000}{5^3}\right] + \left[\frac{1000}{5^4}\right]$

$= 200 + 40 + 8 + 1 = 249.$

182. Let $N = 10 \times 20 \times 30 \times ...... \times 1000 = 10^{100} \times (1 \times 2 \times 3 \times 4 \times .... 100) = 10^{100} \times 100!$
Number of zeros in 100 ! = Highest power of 5 in 100 !

$= \left[\frac{100}{5}\right] + \left[\frac{100}{5^2}\right] = 20 + 4 = 24.$

$\therefore$ Number of zeros in $N = 100 + 24 = 124.$

183. Let $N = 5 \times 10 \times 15 \times 20 \times 25 \times 30 \times 35 \times 40 \times 45 \times 50$
$= 5^{10} \times (1 \times 2 \times 3 \times 4 \times .... \times 10) = 5^{10} \times 10!$

Highest power of 2 in 10! $= \left[\frac{10}{2}\right] + \left[\frac{10}{2^2}\right] + \left[\frac{10}{2^3}\right] = 5 + 2 + 1 = 8.$

Highest power of 5 in 10! $= \left[\frac{10}{5}\right] = 2.$

$\therefore N = 2^8 \times 5^{12} \times k.$
Since highest power of 2 is less than that of 5, so required number of zeros = 8.

184. Clearly, highest power of 2 is much higher as compared to that of 5 in 60!, so
Required number of zeros = Highest power of

$5 = \left[\frac{60}{5}\right] + \left[\frac{60}{5^2}\right] = 12 + 2 = 14.$

185. Let $N = (1 \times 3 \times 5 \times 7 \times ... \times 99) \times 128.$
Clearly, N contains 10 multiples of 5 (5, 15, 25, 35, ..., 95) and only one multiple of 2 i.e. 128 or 2^7.
Clearly, highest power of 5 in N is greater than that of 2.
$\therefore$ Number of zeros in N = Highest power of 2 in N = 7.

186. $N = 2 \times 4 \times 6 \times 8 \times .... \times 98 \times 100$
$= 2^{50} \times (1 \times 2 \times 3 \times .... \times 49 \times 50) = 2^{50} \times 50!$
Clearly, the highest power of 2 in N is much higher than that of 5.
$\therefore$ Number of zeros in N = Highest power of 5 in N =

$\left[\frac{50}{5}\right] + \left[\frac{50}{5^2}\right] = 10 + 2 = 12.$

187. Clearly, the list of prime numbers from 2 to 99 has only 1 multiple of 2 and only 1 multiple of 5.
So, number of zeros in the product = 1.

188. Let $N = 3 \times 6 \times 9 \times 12 \times .... \times 102 = 3^{34} \times (1 \times 2 \times 3 \times 4 \times .... \times 34) = 3^{34} \times 34!$
Clearly, highest power of 2 in 34 ! is much greater than that of 5.
So, number of zeros in N = Highest power of 5 in 34! = $\left[\frac{34}{5}\right]+\left[\frac{34}{5^2}\right]=6+1=7.$

189. 3^4 gives unit digit 1. So, $(3^4)^{500}$ gives unit digit 1.
And, 3^3 gives unit digit 7.
$\therefore$ $(13)^{2003}$ gives unit digit = $(1 \times 7) = 7$.

190. 3^4 gives unit digit 1. So, $(3^4)^{24}$ gives unit digit 1.
And, 3^3 gives unit digit 7.
$\therefore$ $3^{99} = (3^4)^{24} \times 3^3$ gives unit digit (1×7) i.e. 7.

191. (*A*) 7^4 gives unit digit 1. So, $7^{16} = (7^4)^4$ gives unit digit 1.
$\therefore$ $(1827)^{16}$ gives unit digit 1. So, $A \rightarrow (1)$.
(*B*) 3^4 gives unit digit 1. So, $(3^4)^4$ gives unit digit 1.
$\therefore$ $3^{19} = 3^{16} \times 3^3$ gives unit digit = $(1 \times 7) = 7$.
$\therefore$ $(2153)^{19}$ gives unit digit 7. So, $B \rightarrow (4)$.
(*C*) 9^2 gives unit digit 1. So, $(9^2)^{10}$ gives unit digit 1.
$\therefore 9^{21} = (9^{20} \times 9)$ gives unit digit = $(1 \times 9) = 9$.
$\therefore (5129)^{21}$ gives unit digit = 9. So, $C \rightarrow (5)$.
Hence, *A B C* is the correct result.
1 4 5

192. Unit digit of $(67)^{25}$ = Unit digit of 7^{25}.
Unit digit of 7^4 is 1 and so the unit digit of $(7^4)^6$ is 1.
$\therefore$ Unit digit of $7^{25} = (1 \times 7) = 7$.
Hence, the unit digit of $(7^{25} - 1)$ is $(7 - 1) = 6$.

193. Unit digit in the given product = Unit digit of $(4 \times 8 \times 7 \times 3)$, which is 2.

194. Unit digit in the given product = 8.
Unit digit of $(9 \times 6 \times x \times 4)$ is 8. So, $x = 3$.

195. Unit digit of 7^4 is 1. So, the unit digit of $(7^4)^{23}$ is 1.
$\therefore$ Unit digit of 7^{95} = Unit digit of $(7^{92} \times 7^3) = (1 \times 3) = 3$.
Unit digit of 3^4 is 1. So, the unit digit of $(3^4)^{14}$ is 1.
$\therefore$ Unit digit of 3^{58} = Unit digit of $(3^{56} \times 3^2) = (1 \times 9) = 9$.
Hence, the unit digit of $(7^{95} - 3^{58}) = (13 - 9) = 4$.

196. Unit digit of 4^2 is 6. So, unit digit in $(4^2)^{63}$ is 6.
$\therefore$ Unit digit of $(784)^{126}$ = Unit digit in 4^{126}, which is 6.
Unit digit in 4^{127} = Unit digit in $(4^{126} \times 4)$ = Unit digit in (6×4), which is 4.
$\therefore$ Unit digit in $(784)^{127}$ is 4.
Hence, unit digit of $\{(784)^{126} + (784)^{127}\}$ = Unit digit of $(6 + 4)$ = Unit digit of 10, which is 0.

197. Unit digit in $[(251)^{98} + (21)^{29} - (106)^{100} + (705)^{35} - (16)^4 + 259]$ = Unit digit in $(1 + 1 - 6 + 5 - 6 + 9) = 4$.

198. Unit digit in the given product
= Unit digit in $(4^{1793} \times 5^{317} \times 1^{491})$
Unit digit in 4^2 is 6 and so the unit digit in $(4^2)^{896}$ is 6.
$\therefore$ Unit digit of 4^{1793} = Unit digit in (6×4) = Unit digit in 24, which is 4.
Unit digit in 5^{317} is 5 and the unit digit in 1^{491} is 1.
$\therefore$ Unit digit in the given product = Unit digit in $(4 \times 5 \times 1)$, which is 0.

199. Let $x = 2y$. Then, $x^{4n} = (2y)^{4n} = \{(2y)^4\}^n = (16\, y^4)^n$.
$y = 1, 2, 3, 4, 5, 6, 7, 8, 9$ gives unit digit as 6 in $(16y^4)^n$.
But, $y = 5$, gives unit digit 0 in $(16\, y^4)^n$.
Hence, the unit digit is 0 or 6.

200. In 5^n we have 5 as unit digit and in 6^m we have 6 as unit digit.
$\therefore$ Unit digit in $(5^n + 6^m)$ = Unit digit in $(5 + 6)$ = Unit digit in 11 = 1.

201. We have: $(2^{12n} - 6^{4n}) = (2^{12n} - 2^{4n} \times 3^{4n}) = 2^{4n}(2^{8n} - 3^{4n})$.
Putting $n = 1$, we get the number $2^4(2^8 - 3^4)$
$= 16(256 - 81) = (16 \times 175) = 2800$
Hence, the number formed by last two digits is 00.

202. $\left(\frac{1}{5}\right)^{2000} = (0.2)^{2000}$.
Last digit of $(0.2)^{2000}$ = Last digit of $(0.2)^4 = 6$.

203. Sum of digits in the two numbers = 19 + 15 = 34.
So, the product will have 33 or 34 digits.
Since $36 \times 34 = 1224$ (i.e. product has 2 + 2 = 4 digits), so the number of digits in x is 34.

204. We know that a number having x,y,z as its digits, is a multiple of 11, if $z + x - y = 0$
Hence, $y = z + x$.

205. $6135n2$ is divisible by 9 if $(6 + 1 + 3 + 5 + n + 2) = (17 + n)$ is divisible by 9.
This happens when the least value of n is 1.

206. In 978626, we have $(6 + 6 + 7) - (2 + 8 + 9) = 0$.
Hence, 978626 is completely divisible by 11.

207. Sum of all digits = 12, which is divisible by 3. So, the given number is divisible by 3.
(Sum of digits at odd places) – (Sum of digits at even places) = 6 – 6 = 0.
So, the given number is divisible by 11.
The given number when divided by 37 gives 3003003003.
So, the given number is divisible by 37.
The given number when divided by 111 gives 1001001001.
Clearly, it is divisible by 111 as well as by 1001.
Hence, the given number is divisible by each one of 3, 11, 37, 111 and 1001.

208. We have $18 = 2 \times 9$, where 2 and 9 are co-primes.
But, 65043 is not divisible by 2. So, it is not divisible by 18.

209. Let the missing digit be x. Then, $(80 + x)$ must be divisible by 4. Hence, $x = 4$.

210. Sum of the digits in 4006020 is 12, which is divisible by 3. Hence, 4006020 is divisible by 3.

211. Clearly, (*d*) is true.

212. For 4823718 we have
$(8 + 7 + 2 + 4) - (1 + 3 + 8) = (21 - 12) = 9$, which is not a multiple of 11.
$\therefore$ 4823718 is not divisible by 11.
Consider the number 4832718.
We have $(8 + 7 + 3 + 4) - (1 + 2 + 8) = (22 - 11) = 11$, which is a multiple of 11.
Hence, 4832718 is divisible by 11.

213. Consider the number 17325.
Its unit digit is 5. So, it is divisible by 5.
Sum of its digits = $(5 + 2 + 3 + 7 + 1) = 18$, which is divisible by 3.
So, the given number is divisible by 3.
And, since 5 and 3 are co-primes, so the given number is divisible by (5×3), i.e. 15.

214. Given number is 7386038.
Sum of its digits = 35, which is not divisible by any of 3 and 9.
So, the given number is not divisible by any of 3 and 9.
Also, 38 is not divisible by 4. So, the given number is not divisible by 4.

Also, $(8 + 0 + 8 + 7) - (3 + 6 + 3) = (23 - 12) = 11$.
So, the given number is divisible by 11.

215. $(2 + 4 + 9 + 8 + 4) = 27$, $(2 + 6 + 7 + 8 + 4) = 27$ and $(2 + 8 + 5 + 8 + 4) = 27$.
So, each one is divisible by 3 and 9 both.
Also, 84 is divisible by 4. So, each one is divisible by 4.
Hence, each given number is divisible by 3, 9 and 4.
So, the statements 1, 2 and 3 are all correct.

216. We know that 872 is divisible by 8. Hence 923872 is divisible by 8.

217. Here $(5 + 9 + x + 7) - (4 + 3 + 8) = 6 + x$. So, we must have $x = 5$.

218. Take $m = 15$ and $n = 20$. Then, each one of m and n is divisible by 5. But, $(m + n)$ is not divisible by 10.
Hence, $(m + n)$ is divisible by 10 is not true.

219. An integer is divisible by 16, if the number formed by last 4 digits is divisible by 16.

220. Clearly, 639 is not divisible by 7.
Consider 2079. Sum of its digits $= (2 + 0 + 7 + 9) = 18$.
So, it is divisible by both 3 and 9.
Also, $(79 - 2) = 77$, which is divisible by 7.
So, 2079 is divisible by 7.
Also, $(9 + 0) - (7 + 2) = 0$. So, 2079 is divisible by 11.
Hence, 2079 is divisible by each one of 3, 7, 9 and 11.

221. Let the given number be $476xy0$. Then
$(0 + x + 7) - (y + 6 + 4) = 0 \Rightarrow x - y - 3 = 0 \Rightarrow x - y = 3$.
Also, $(4 + 7 + 6 + x + y + 0) = (17 + x + y)$ must be divisible by 3.
Since $x \neq 0$, $y \neq 0$, so $x + y \neq 1$.
$\therefore x + y = 4$ or 7 or 10 etc.
$(x + y = 4$ and $x - y = 3) \Rightarrow x = 7/2$, which is not admissible.
$(x + y = 7$ and $x - y = 3) \Rightarrow x = 5$ and $y = 2$.

222. Sum of the digits in respective numbers is:
9, 12, 18, 9, 21, 12, 18, 21, 15 and 24.
Out of these 12, 21, 12, 21, 15, 24 are divisible by 3 but not by 9.
So, the number of required numbers is 6.

223. Let the unit's place be x and the thousand's place be y.
Then, $357y25x$ is divisible by 5 only when $x = 0$ or $x = 5$.
Also, this number is divisible by 3 only when sum of its digits is divisible by 3.
So, $(22 + x + y)$ must be divisible by 3.
$\therefore x + y = 2$
Taking $x = 0$, we get $y = 2$.
So, the unit place = 0 and thousand's place = 2.

224. Clearly, $(7 + 8) - (9 + 6) = 0$. So, 6897 is divisible by 11.
Also, $\frac{6897}{19} = 363$. So, 6897 is divisible by 19.
Hence, 6897 is divisible by both 11 and 19.

225. We have $24 = 3 \times 8$, where 3 and 8 are co-primes.
Clearly, 718 is not divisible by 8. So, 35718 is not divisible by 8.
810 is not divisible by 8. So, 63810 is not divisible by 8.
804 is not divisible by 8. So, 537804 is not divisible by 8.
736 is divisible by 8. So, 3125736 is divisible by 8.
Also, sum of its digits $= (3 + 1 + 2 + 5 + 7 + 3 + 6) = 27$, which is divisible by 3.
So, 3125736 is divisible by 3 also.
Hence, it is divisible by 24.

226. Sum of the digits of the given number $= (7 \times 3) + (14 \times 1) = (21 + 14) = 35$, which is not divisible by 3.
So the given number is not divisible by 3.
Also, $(1 + 3 + 1 + 1 + 3 + 1 + 1 + 3 + 1 + 1 + 3) - (1 + 1 + 3 + 1 + 1 + 3 + 1 + 1 + 3 + 1) = (19 - 16) = 3$, which is neither 0 nor divisible by 11.
So, the given number is not divisible by 11 also.
Hence, it is divisible by neither 3 nor 11.

227. $(325 - 325) = 0$, which is divisible by 7.
So, the given number is divisible by 7.
$(5 + 3 + 2) - (2 + 5 + 3) = 0$. So, the given number is divisible by 11.
And, $\frac{325325}{13} = 25025$. So, 325325 is divisible by 13.
Hence, it is divisible by all 7, 11 and 13.

228. We first divide the number into groups of 3 digits from the right $\rightarrow$ 3 0X0 103
Difference of sum of numbers at odd and even places = $(103 + 3) - 0X0 = 106 - 0X0$, which must be divisible by 13.
$106 - 0X0$ is divisible by 13 only for $X = 8$.

229. We know that 11 and 13 are co-prime.
So, a number divisible by both 11 and 13 will be divisible by (11×13).

230. I. We have$(195 - 195)$ 0
$\therefore$ 195195 is divisible by 7.
II. We have $(181 - 181) = 0$
$\therefore$ 181181 is divisible by 7.
III. We have $(120 - 120) = 0$
$\therefore$ 120120 is divisible by 7.
IV. We have $(891 - 891) = 0$
$\therefore$ 891891 is divisible by 7.
Hence, all are divisible by 7.

231. Since $653xy$ is divisible by 80, we must have $y = 0$.
Now, $653x0$ must be divisible by both 5 and 16.
Clearly, it is divisible by 5 for all values of x.
Now, the number $53x0$ must be divisible by 16.
The least value of x is clearly 6. So, $x + y = 6 + 0 = 6$.

232. We know that $33 = 11 \times 3$, where 11 and 3 are co-primes.
So, the given number must be divisible by both 11 and 3.
Since $5ABB7A$ is divisible by 11, we have
$(A + B + A) - (7 + B + 5) = (2A - 12)$ is either 0 or 11.
$\Rightarrow \quad 2A - 12 = 0$ or $2A - 12 = 11 \Rightarrow A = 6 \left[\because A \neq \frac{23}{2}\right]$
So, the number becomes $56BB76$, which is divisible by 3.
$\therefore (5 + 6 + B + B + 7 + 6) = (24 + 2B)$ must be divisible by 3.
$\therefore 2B = 6 \Rightarrow B = 3 \quad \left[\because B \neq 0 \text{ and } B \neq \frac{3}{2}\right]$
Hence, $(A + B) = (6 + 3) = 9$.

233. We have, $99 = (11 \times 9)$, where 11 and 9 are co-primes.
Consider the number 114345.
Clearly, $(5 + 3 + 1) - (4 + 4 + 1) = 0$. So, 114345 is divisible by 11.
Also, sum of its digits $= (1 + 1 + 4 + 3 + 4 + 5) = 18$, which is divisible by 9.
$\therefore$ 114345 is divisible by 9.
Hence, it is divisible by (11×9), i.e. 99.

234. Let the unit's digit be x and ten's digit be y. Then, the number is $3422213yx$.
Also, $99 = (11 \times 9)$, where 11 and 9 are co-primes.
Since the given number is divisible by 9, it follows that $(3 + 4 + 2 + 2 + 2 + 1 + 3 + y + x) = (17 + y + x)$ must be divisible by 9.
So, $y + x = 1$ or $y + x = 10$.

Again, the given number is divisible by 11.

So, $(x + 3 + 2 + 2 + 3) - (y + 1 + 2 + 4) = x - y + 3$ is either 0 or 11.

$\therefore (x - y + 3 = 0$ or $x - y + 3 = 11) \Rightarrow (y - x = 3$ or $x - y = 8)$

Now, $(y + x = 1$ and $y - x = 3) \Rightarrow y = 2$ and $x = -1$.

$(y + x = 1$ and $x - y = 8) \Rightarrow x = \frac{9}{2}$.

$(y + x = 10$ and $y - x = 3) \Rightarrow y = \frac{13}{2}$.

$(y + x = 10$ and $x - y = 8) \Rightarrow x = 9$ and $y = 1$.

Thus, $x = 9$, $y = 1$. So, the required number is 342221319.

235. 37×3 is divisible by 7

$\Rightarrow$ $(7 \times 3 - 3)$ is either 0 or divisible by 7)

$\Rightarrow$ 7×0 is divisible by 7.

$\Rightarrow$ X = 0 or X = 7.

236. $225 = 9 \times 25$, where 9 and 25 are co-primes.

So, a number is divisible by 225 if it is divisible by both 9 and 25.

Given number is divisible by 25, only if $7q$ is divisible by 25, i.e. if $q = 5$.

Sum of digits of given number = $(8 + 7 + 6 + p + 3 + 7 + 5) = 36 + p$, which must be divisible by 9.

This is possible if $p = 0$.

Hence, $p = 0$, $q = 5$.

237. Since 774958A96B is divisible by 8, so the number 96B must be divisible by 8. So, $B = 0$, as 960 is divisible by 8.

Now, 774958A960 is divisible by 9. So, $(55 + A)$ must be divisible by 9.

This happens when $A = 8$. Hence, $A = 8$ and $B = 0$.

238. $132 = 11 \times 3 \times 4$. So, the required number must be divisible by 3, 4 and 11.

264 → divisible by 3, 4 and 11.
396 → divisible by 3, 4 and 11.
462 → not divisible by 4.
792 → divisible by 3, 4 and 11.
968 → not divisible by 3
2178 → not divisible by 4
5184 → not divisible by 11.
6336 → divisible by 3, 4 and 11.

Hence, out of the given numbers 4 are divisible by 3, 4 and 11.

239. Let $3x + 7y = 11k$. Then, $y = \frac{(11k - 3x)}{7}$.

Then, $5x - 3y = 5x - \frac{3(11k - 3x)}{7} = \frac{35x - 33k + 9x}{7}$

$= \frac{44x - 33k}{7} = \frac{11(4x - 3k)}{7}$, which is divisible by 11.

240. $(1^3 - 1) = 0$, $(2^3 - 2) = 6$, $(3^3 - 3) = 24$, $(4^3 - 4) = 60$ and so on, each one of which is divisible by 6.

241. Let $a = 2k + 1$ & $b = 2m + 1$. Then,

$a^4 - b^4 = (a^2 - b^2)(a^2 + b^2) = (a + b)(a - b)(a^2 + b^2)$

$= (2k + 2m + 2)(2k - 2m)(4k^2 + 4m^2 + 2 + 4k + 4m)$

$= 8(k + m + 1)(k - m)(2k^2 + 2m^2 + 1 + 2k + 2m)$,

which is divisible by 8.

242. Let the two consecutive integers be a and $(a + 1)$. Then, $(a + 1)^2 - a^2 = a^2 + 1 + 2a - a^2 = (2a + 1) = (a + a + 1) =$ sum of given integers.

243. $6n^2 + 6n = 6n(n + 1)$

$(n = 1 \Rightarrow 6n^2 + 6n = 12)$, $(n = 2 \Rightarrow 6n^2 + 6n = 36)$, $(n = 3 \Rightarrow 6n^2 + 6n = 72)$,

each one of which is divisible by 6 and 12 both.

244. Let the ten's digit be x and the unit's digit be y. Then, $(10x + y) - (10y + x) = 9x - 9y = 9(x - y)$, which is divisible by 9.

245. Let the ten's digit be x and the unit's digit be y.

Then, $(10x + y) + (10y + x) = 11(x + y)$, which is divisible by 11.

246. Let $P = n(n + 1)(n + 2)(n + 3)$. Then, $n = 1$ gives $P = (1 \times 2 \times 3 \times 4) = 24$.

Hence, the required number is 24.

247. Let $N = n^2(n^2 - 1) = n^2(n - 1)(n + 1)$.

Then, $n = 2 \Rightarrow N = 2^2 \times (2 - 1) \times (2 + 1) = (4 \times 1 \times 3) = 12$.

Hence, the required number is 12.

248. Let $n = (2m + 1)$. Then,

$N = n(n^2 - 1) = n(n - 1)(n + 1) = (2m + 1)(2m)(2m + 2) = 4m(m + 1)(2m + 1)$.

Now, $m = 1 \Rightarrow N = (4 \times 1 \times 2 \times 3) = 24$.

So, N is always divisible by 24.

249. Let the hundreds, tens and unit digits be x, y and z respectively.

Then, $(100x + 10y + z) - (x + y + z) = 99x + 9y = 9(11x + y)$.

So, the resulting number is divisible by 9.

250. Let the required number be x. Then $\frac{11x + 11}{13}$ = a whole number.

So, $(11x + 11)$ must be divisible by 13. By hit and trial, we get $x = 12$.

Hence, the smallest original number is 12.

251. Let the required product be $n(n + 1)(n + 2)$. Then,

$n = 1 \Rightarrow n(n + 1)(n + 2) = (1 \times 2 \times 3) = 6$.

$n = 2 \Rightarrow n(n + 1)(n + 2) = (2 \times 3 \times 4) = 24$.

$n = 3 \Rightarrow n(n + 1)(n + 2) = (3 \times 4 \times 5) = 60$.

So, each such product is divisible by 6.

252. Let the required odd numbers be n, $(n + 2)$ and $(n + 4)$. Then $n + (n + 2) + (n + 4) = 3n + 6 = 3(n + 2)$, which is always divisible by 3.

But $n = 1 \Rightarrow 3(n + 2) = 3 \times 3 = 9$ which is not divisible by any of 2, 5 and 6.

Hence only II is true.

253. Three consecutive multiples of 3 are $3m$, $3(m + 1)$ and $3(m + 2)$.

Their product $= 3m \times 3(m + 1) \times 3(m + 2) = 27 \times m \times (m + 1) \times (m + 2)$.

Putting $m = 1$, this product is $(27 \times 1 \times 2 \times 3) = 162$.

So, this product is always divisible by 162.

254. $p = 5 \Rightarrow (p^2 - 1) = (25 - 1) = 24$, which is divisible by 24.

$p = 7 \Rightarrow (p^2 - 1) = (49 - 1) = 48$, which is divisible by 24.

$p = 11 \Rightarrow (p^2 - 1) = (121 - 1) = 120$, which is divisible by 24.

Hence, $(p^2 - 1)$ is always divisible by 24.

255. Let the two consecutive odd integers be $(2m + 1)$ and $(2m + 3)$.

Then, $(2m + 3)^2 - (2m + 1)^2 = [(2m + 3) + (2m + 1)][(2m + 3) - (2m + 1)] = (4m + 4) \times 2 = 8m + 8 = 8(m + 1)$, which is always divisible by 8.

256. Clearly, 2525 is not divisible by any of the numbers 7, 11 and 13.
The smallest 3-digit prime number is 101.

```
   25             32
101)2525(      101)3232(
    202            303
    505            202
    505            202
     ×              ×
```

Hence (*d*) is true.

257. Numbers like 2525, 3636 etc. are divisible by 101.
Numbers like 256256, 678678 etc. are divisible by 1001.
Numbers like 32163216, 43754375 etc. are divisible by 10001 and so on.

258. 10^n has $(n + 1)$ digits. Then, 9 will appear n times in $(10^n - 1)$.
So, sum of digits in $(10^n - 1) = 9n$.
$\therefore \quad 9n = 4707 \Rightarrow n = \frac{4707}{9} = 523.$

259. We know that $(x^n - a^n)$ is always divisible by $(x - a)$ for all values of n.

260. The product of 8 consecutive numbers is divisible by each one of 8!, 7!, 6!, 5!, 4!, 3! and 2!

261. We know that $(x^n - a^n)$ is divisible by $(x - a)$, when n is even and $(x^n - a^n)$ is divisible by $(x + a)$, when n is even.
$\therefore$ $(10^n - 1)$ is divisible by $(10 - 1) = 9$, when n is even.
And, $(10^n - 1)$ is divisible by $(10 + 1) = 11$, when n is even.
$\therefore$ Statements 2 and 4 are correct.

262. Putting $n = 1$, we get $(3^{4n} - 4^{3n}) = (3^4 - 4^3) = (81 - 64) = 17$, which is divisible by 17.

263. Let the odd natural number be $(2n + 1)$.
$n = 1$ gives $(2n + 1)^2 = (2 + 1)^2 = 9$.
This when divided by 8 gives 1 as remainder.
$n = 2$ gives $(2n + 1)^2 = 25$.
This when divided by 8 gives 1 as remainder and so on.

264. Required number $= (2^5 - 2) = (32 - 2) = 30$.

265. Two consecutive even integers are $2n$ and $(2n + 2)$.
$\therefore (2n + 2)^2 - (2n)^2 = (4n^2 + 4 + 8n - 4n^2) = 4 + 8n = 4(1 + 2n)$, which is always divisible by 4.

266. Two consecutive odd integers are $(2m + 1)$ and $(2m + 3)$.
$\therefore \quad (2m + 3)^2 - (2m + 1)^2 = (2m + 3 + 2m + 1)(2m + 3 - 2m - 1) = (4m + 4) \times 2 = 8(m + 1)$, which is always divisible by 8.

267. The smallest 4-digit number is 1000.
This when divided by 7 leaves 6 as remainder.
$\therefore$ 1001 is the smallest 4-digit number exactly divisible by 7.

268. On dividing 1056 by 23, we get 21 as remainder.
$\therefore \quad$ Required number to be added $= (23 - 21) = 2$.

```
23)1056(45
   92
   136
   115
    21
```

269. On dividing 8567 by 4, the remainder is 3.
To make it divisible by 4, we must add 1 to it.

270. The least 6-digit number = 100000.
Required number = 100000 + (349 − 186) = 100000 + 163 = 100163.

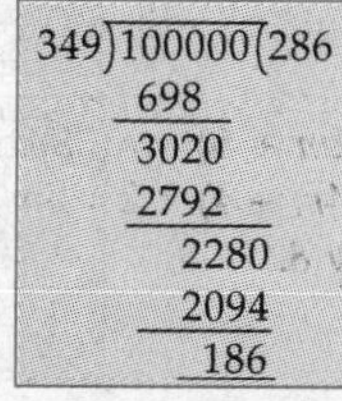

```
349)100000(286
    698
    3020
    2792
     2280
     2094
      186
```

271. The greatest 5-digit number = 99999.
On dividing 99999 by 279, we get 117 as remainder.
$\therefore \quad$ Required number = (99999 − 117) = 99882.

```
279)99999(358
    837
    1629
    1395
     2349
     2232
      117
```

272. The greatest 6-digit number is 999999.
Required number to be added = (327 − 33) = 294.

```
327)999999(3058
    981
     1899
     1635
      2649
      2616
        33
```

273. On dividing 5000 by 73, we get
Required number = 5000 + (73 − 36) = 5037.

```
73)5000(68
   438
    620
    584
     36
```

274. On dividing 58701 by 567, we get 300 as remainder.
$\therefore$ Required number = 58701 + (567 − 300) = 58701 + 267 = 58968.

```
567)58701(103
    567
     2001
     1701
      300
```

275. On dividing 8112 by 99, we get 93 as remainder.
So, the required number to be subtracted is 93.

```
99)8112(81
   792
    192
     99
     93
```

276. On dividing 803642 by 11, we get 4 as remainder.
Required number to be added = (11 − 4) = 7.

277. On dividing 1111 by 99, the quotient is 11 and the remainder is 22.
Hence, the required number is 11.

```
99)1111( 11
   99
   121
    99
    22
```

278. 66 = 11 × 6
In order to get a number divisible by 18, the above product must be multiplied by 3.
Hence 66 must be multiplied by 3.

279. The smallest 6-digit number is 100000. On dividing 100000 by 111, we get 100 as remainder.
So, the number to be added = (111 − 100) = 11.
Hence, the required number = 100011.

```
111)100000(900
    999
     100
```

280. All 2-digit numbers divisible by 5 are 10, 15, 20, 25, ..., 95.
This is an *A.P.* in which $a = 10$, $d = 5$ and $T_n = 95$.
$T_n = 95 \Rightarrow a + (n-1)\,d = 95 \Rightarrow 10 + (n-1) \times 5 = 95$
$\Rightarrow (n-1) = \frac{85}{5} = 17 \Rightarrow n = 18.$
$\therefore$ Sum $= \frac{n}{2}(a+l) = \frac{18}{2}(10+95) = (9 \times 105) = 945.$

281. 3-digit numbers divisible by 6 are 102, 108, 114, ..., 996.
This is an A.P. in which $a = 102$, $d = 6$ and $T_n = 996$.
$\therefore T_n = a + (n-1)\,d \Rightarrow 102 + (n-1) \times 6 = 996 \Rightarrow (n-1) \times 6 = 894$
$\Rightarrow (n-1) = 149 \Rightarrow n = 150.$
Hence, there are 150 such numbers.

282. Multiples of 7 between 11 and 200 are 14, 21, 28, 35, 42, ..., 189, 196.
$T_m = 196 \Rightarrow 14 + (m-1) \times 7 = 196 \Rightarrow (m-1) \times 7 = 182$
$\Rightarrow (m-1) = 26 \Rightarrow m = 27.$
Multiples of 7 and 3 both, i.e. that of 21 are 21, 42, 63, ..., 189
$T_n = 189 \Rightarrow 21 + (n-1) \times 21 = 189 \Rightarrow (n-1) \times 21 = 168$
$\Rightarrow (n-1) = 8 \Rightarrow n = 9.$
$\therefore$ Required number of terms $= (27 - 9) = 18.$

283. Numbers between 14 and 95 and divisible by 3 are 15, 18, 21 24, ..., 93.
$T_m = 93 \Rightarrow 15 + (n-1) \times 3 = 93 \Rightarrow (n-1) \times 3 = 78$
$\Rightarrow (n-1) = 26 \Rightarrow n = 27.$
Numbers to be deleted are 33, 63, 93.
They are 3 in number.
Required number of numbers $= (27 - 3) = 24.$

284. Required numbers are multiples of (10×13), i.e. 130.
These numbers are 130, 260, 390, 520, 650, 780 and 910.
They are 7 in number.

285. Number of integers between 100 and 150 (including both) = 51.
Numbers divisible by 3 are 102, 105, 108, ..., 150.
Let $T_m = 150$. Then, $a + (m-1)\,d = T_m$.
$\therefore 102 + (m-1) \times 3 = 150 \Rightarrow (m-1) \times 3 = 48 \Rightarrow m - 1 = 16 \Rightarrow m = 17.$
Numbers divisible by 5 are 100, 105, 110, 115, ..., 150.
Let $T_n = 150$. Then, $a + (n-1)\,d = T_n$.
$\therefore 100 + (n-1) \times 5 = 150 \Rightarrow (n-1) \times 5 = 50 \Rightarrow (n-1) = 10 \Rightarrow n = 11.$
Numbers divisible by both 3 and 5 are 105, 120, 135, 150.
They are four in number.
Number of numbers divisible by 3 or 5 $= (17 + 11 - 4) = 24.$
Number of numbers neither divisible by 3 nor by 5 are $(51 - 24) = 27.$

286. Numbers from 501 to 599 which have 6 as digit are 506, 516, 526, 536, 546, 556, 560, 561, 562, 563, 564, 565, 566, 567, 568, 569, 576, 586 and 596, i.e. 6 occurs 20 times.
Number of times 6 occurs from 600 to 699 = 100 + 20 = 120.
$\therefore$ Total number of times 6 occurs = 20 + 120 = 140.

287. Such numbers are 202, 212, 222, 232, 242, 252, 262, 272, 282, 292. There are 10 such numbers.

288. Such numbers are 203, 213, 223, 233, 243, 253, 263, 273, 283, 293 and all numbers from 300 to 399. Clearly, number of such numbers = 10 + 100 = 110.

289. When the second digit is 1, third digit can be 0, i.e. there is one such number.
When the second digit is 2, third digit can be 0 or 1, i.e. there are 2 such numbers.
When the second digit is 3, third digit can be 0, 1 or 2 i.e. there are 3 such numbers, and so on.
When the first digit is 7, second digit can be 1, 2, 3, 4, 5 or 6. So, there are
(1 + 2 + 3 + 4 + 5 + 6) = 21 such numbers between 700 and 799.
When the first digit is 8, second digit can be 1, 2, 3, 4, 5, 6 or 7. So, there are
(1 + 2 + 3 + 4 + 5 + 6 + 7) = 28 such numbers between 800 and 899.
When the first digit is 9, second digit can be 1, 2, 3, 4, 5, 6, 7 or 8. So, there are
(1 + 2 + 3 + 4 + 5 + 6 + 7 + 8) = 36 such numbers between 900 and 999.
Hence, the required number = (21 + 28 + 36) = 85.

290. (*a*) In 183654729, 1836547 is not divisible by 7.
(*b*) In 381654729, 38 is divisible by 2, 381 is divisible by 3, 3816 is divisible by 4, 38165 is divisible by 5, 381654 is divisible by 6, 3816547 is divisible by 7, 38165472 is divisible by 8 and 381654729 is divisible by 9.
(*c*) In 983654721, 983 is not divisible by 3.
(*d*) In 981654723, 9816547 is not divisible by 7.

291. On dividing 11109999 by 1111, we get:
So, the required remainder is 1110.

```
1111)11109999(9999
     9999
     11109
      9999
      11109
       9999
       11109
        9999
        1110
```

292. Number = (68 × 260) = 17680. On dividing this number by 65, we get zero as remainder.

```
65)17680(272
   130
    468
    455
     130
     130
      ×
```

293. (2176 – 9) = 2167 = (11 × 197).
So, the required number is 197.

294. (*a*)
```
-7)-112(16
   -112
      0
```
(*b*)
```
-9)118(-13
   9
   28
   27
    1
```
(*c*)
```
6)-109(-19
  -6
  -49
  -54
    5
```
(*d*)
```
8)115(14
  8
  35
  32
   3
```

$q = 16, r = 0$ $\therefore A \to 4$ | $q = -13, r = 1.$ $\therefore B \to 1$

$q = -19, r = 5$ $\therefore C \to 3$ | $q = 14, r = 3$ $\therefore D \to 2$

295. On dividing 534677 by 777 we get 101 as remainder.
$\therefore$ (Divisor) – (Remainder) = (777 – 101) = 676.

```
777)534677(688
    4662
     6847
     6216
      6317
      6216
       101
```

296. $\frac{\text{(Dividend)} - \text{(Remainder)}}{\text{Quotient}} = \text{Divisor}.$

$\therefore \text{Divisor} = \frac{(940 - 25)}{15} = \frac{915}{15} = 61.$

297. Remainder = 48, Divisor = (5 × 48) = 240.
$12 \times \text{Quotient} = \text{Divisor} \Rightarrow \text{Quotient} = \frac{240}{12} = 20.$
Dividend = (240 × 20) + 48 = 4848.

298. Quotient = 16, Divisor = (25 × 16) = 400.
$5 \times \text{Remainder} = \text{Divisor} \Rightarrow \text{Remainder} = \frac{400}{5} = 80.$
Dividend = (400 × 16) + 80 = 6480.

299. Divisor = (555 + 445) = 1000, Quotient = 2(555 – 445) = 2 × 110 = 220 and Remainder = 30.
$\therefore$ Required number = (1000 × 220) + 30 = 220000 + 30 = 220030.

300. Divisor taken = 12, Quotient obtained = 35, Remainder = 0.
$\therefore$ Dividend = (12 × 35) = 420.
Now, dividend = 420, divisor = 21, remainder = 0.
$\therefore \text{Quotient} = \frac{420}{21} = 20.$

301. Divisor = 7 × quotient = 5 × remainder and Dividend = 6 × remainder.

```
5x)6x(1
   5x
    x
```

Let remainder be x. Then, divisor = $5x$ and dividend = $6x$. On dividing $6x$ by $5x$, we get 1 as quotient and x as remainder.
$\therefore$ Quotient = 1.

302. Since the required number is a 3-digit number, so on dividing by 19, it would yield a two-digit quotient which means that the quotient is greater than the remainder.
Let the remainder be x. Then, quotient = $x + 9$.
So, number $N = 19(x + 9) + x = 20x + 171$.
$\therefore$ $(N - 171)$ must be divisible by 20.
Clearly, (371 – 171) = 200, which is divisible by 20.
Hence, the required number = 371.

303. Let the number be x. Let x when divided by 136 give q as quotient and 36 as remainder. Then, $x = 136q + 36 = (17 \times 8q) + (17 \times 2) + 2 = 17 \times (8q + 2) + 2.$
So, the given number when divided by 17 gives 2 as remainder.

304. Let the number be x and the quotient be q.
Then, $x = 195q + 47 = (15 \times 13q) + (15 \times 3) + 2 = 15(13q + 3) + 2.$
So, the given number when divided by 15 gives 2 as remainder.

305. Let the number be x and the quotient be q.
Then, $x = 899q + 63 = (29 \times 31q) + (29 \times 2) + 5 = 29(31q + 2) + 5.$
So, the given number when divided by 29 gives 5 as remainder.

306. Let the number be x and on dividing by 5, we get q as quotient and 3 as remainder.
Then, $x = 5q + 3 \Rightarrow x^2 = (5q + 3)^2 = (25q^2 + 30q + 9)$
$= 5(5q^2 + 6q + 1) + 4.$
Thus, on dividing x^2 by 5, we get 4 as remainder.

307. Let the smaller number be x. Then, larger number $= (x + 1365)$.
$\therefore x + 1365 = 6x + 15 \Rightarrow 5x = 1350 \Rightarrow x = 270.$
Hence, the smaller number = 270.

308. Let $n = 4k + 3$.
Then, $2n = 2(4k + 3) = 8k + 6 = 4 \times 2k + 4 \times 1 + 2 = 4(2k + 1) + 2.$
Thus, on dividing $2n$ by 4, we get 2 as remainder.

309. Let $x = 13p + 11$ and $x = 17q + 9$.
Then, $13p + 11 = 17q + 9 \Rightarrow 17q - 13p = 2 \Rightarrow q = \frac{2 + 13p}{17}$
The least value of p for which $q = \frac{2 + 13p}{17}$ is a whole number, is $p = 26$.
$\therefore x = (13 \times 26 + 11) = 338 + 11 = 349.$

310. Let the dividend be $(x + 71)$ and the divisor be y.
Then, $[2(x + 71) - 43]$ is divisible by $y \Rightarrow (2x + 142 - 43)$ is divisible by y
$\Rightarrow (2x + 99)$ is divisible by y.
$\therefore$ Divisor = 99

Shortcut Method:
Divisor = (2 × 71 – 43) = (142 – 43) = 99.

311. Let $P = x + r_1$ and $Q = y + r_2$, where each of x and y are divisible by the common divisor.
Then, $P + Q = (x + r_1) + (y + r_2) = (x + y) + (r_1 + r_2).$
$(P + Q)$ leaves remainder r_3 when divided by the common divisor.
$\Rightarrow [(x + y) + (r_1 + r_2) - r_3]$ is divisible by the common divisor.
Since $(x + y)$ is divisible by the common divisor, so divisor $= r_1 + r_2 - r_3$.

312. As proved in the above question, divisor = 4375 + 2986 – 2361 = 5000.

313. The number is of the form $(13k + 1)$, where k is of the form $(5m + 3)$.
$\therefore$ Number $= 13k + 1 = 13(5m + 3) + 1 = 65m + 40.$
Clearly when the number is divided by 65, we get 40 as remainder.

314. Clearly, (2272 – 875) = 1397, is exactly divisible by N.
Now, 1397 = 11 × 127.
$\therefore$ The required 3-digit number is 127, the sum of whose digits is 10.

315.

9	x
11	$y - 8$
13	$z - 9$
	$1 - 8$

$z = 13 \times 1 + 8 = 21.$
$y = 11 \times z + 9 = 11 \times 21 + 9 = 240.$
$x = 9 \times y + 8 = 9 \times 240 + 8 = 2168.$

Now, when order of divisors is reversed, we have:

13	2168
11	166 – 10
9	15 – 1
	1 – 6

$\therefore$ Respective remainders are 10, 1 and 6.

316.

3	x
4	$y - 2$
7	$z - 1$
	$1 - 4$

$z = 7 \times 1 + 4 = 11.$

$y = 4 \times z + 1 = 4 \times 11 + 1 = 45.$

$x = 3 \times y + 2 = 3 \times 45 + 2 = 137.$

When 137 is divided by 84, the remainder obtained is 53.

317.

8	x
7	$y - 3$
3	$z - 4$
	$31 - 2$

$z = 3 \times 31 + 2 = 95.$

$y = 7 \times z + 4 = 7 \times 95 + 4 = 669.$

$x = 8 \times y + 3 = 8 \times 669 + 3 = 5355.$

$\therefore$ Required number = 5355.

318.

3	x
2	$y - 1$
	$1 - 1$

$y = 2 \times 1 + 1 = 3$

$x = 3 \times y + 1 = 3 \times 3 + 1 = 10.$

Clearly, 10 when divided by 6, leaves a remainder 4.

319. Let the number be $N = 2x + 1$.

$N^2 = (2x + 1)^2 = 4x^2 + 1 + 4x = 4x(x + 1) + 1.$

Clearly, $4x(x + 1)$ is always divisible by 8 since one of x and $(x + 1)$ is even which when multiplied by 4 is always divisible by 8.

Hence, required remainder = 1.

320. Sum of digits of numbers from 1 to 10 = 46.

Sum of digits of numbers from 11 to 20 = 56.

Sum of digits of numbers from 21 to 29 = 63.

Sum of digits of the given number = 46 + 56 + 63 = 165.

So, the required remainder is the remainder obtained on dividing 165 by 9, which is 3.

321. When n is even, $(x^n - a^n)$ is divisible by $(x + a)$.

$\therefore (17^{200} - 1^{200})$ is divisible by $(17 + 1)$

$\Rightarrow (17^{200} - 1)$ is divisible by 18

$\Rightarrow$ On dividing 17^{200} by 18, we get 1 as remainder.

322. $2^{31} = 2 \times 2^{30} = 2 \times (2^2)^{15} = 2 \times 4^{15}.$

When n is odd, $(x^n + a^n)$ is divisible by $(x + a)$.

$\therefore (4^{15} + 1^{15})$ is divisible by $(4 + 1)$

$\Rightarrow (4^{15} + 1)$ is divisible by 5 $\Rightarrow (2^{30} + 1)$ is divisible by 5

$\Rightarrow$ On dividing 2^{30} by 5, we get $(5 - 1)$ i.e. 4 as remainder.

$\therefore$ Remainder obtained on dividing 2^{31} by 5

= Remainder obtained on dividing (2×4) i.e. 8 by 5 = 3.

323. Clearly,

(1) when n is odd, $(a^n + b^n)$ is divisible by $(a + b)$. So, (1) is true.

(2) $(a^n - b^n)$ is divisible by $(a - b)$ for all values of n. So, (2) is true.

324. $(x^n - a^n)$ is divisible by $(x - a)$ for all values of n.

$\therefore (7^{19} - 1^{19})$ is divisible by $(7 - 1)$

$\Rightarrow (7^{19} - 1)$ is divisible by 6

$\Rightarrow$ On dividing $(7^{19} + 2)$ by 6, remainder obtained = 3.

325. $(10^{12} + 25)^2 - (10^{12} - 25)^2 = 4 \times 10^{12} \times 25$

$[\because (a + b)^2 - (a - b)^2 = 4ab]$

$= 10^{12} \times 100 = 10^{12} \times 10^2 = 10^{14}.$

Hence, $n = 14$.

326. $(3^{25} + 3^{26} + 3^{27} + 3^{28}) = 3^{25}(1 + 3 + 3^2 + 3^3)$

$= 3^{25}(1 + 3 + 9 + 27) = 3^{25} \times 40$

$= (3 \times 10) \times (3^{24} \times 4) = 30 \times (3^{24} \times 4),$

which is divisible by 30.

327. $(4^{61} + 4^{62} + 4^{63} + 4^{64}) = 4^{61}(1 + 4 + 4^2 + 4^3) = 4^{61} \times 85,$ which is divisible by 17.

328. $(x^n - a^n)$ is divisible by $(x - a)$ for all values of n

$\therefore (9^6 - 1^6)$ is divisible by $(9 - 1)$

$\Rightarrow (9^6 - 1)$ is divisible by 8

$\Rightarrow$ On dividing $(9^6 + 1)$ by 8, we get 2 as remainder.

329. When n is even, $(x^n - a^n)$ is divisible by both $(x - a)$ and $(x + a)$.

So, $(6^n - 1)$ is divisible by both $(6 - 1)$ and $(6 + 1)$

$\Rightarrow (6^n - 1)$ is divisible by both 5 and 7

$\Rightarrow (6^n - 1)$ is divisible by (5×7), i.e. 35.

[$\because$ 5 and 7 are co-primes]

330. $(x^n + a^n)$ is divisible by $(x + a)$ when n is odd.

$\therefore (12^n + 1)$ is divisible by $(12 + 1)$ i.e. 13 when n is odd.

331. $(x^n + a^n)$ is divisible by $(x + a)$ when n is odd.

$\therefore (25^{25} + 1^{25})$ is divisible by $(25 + 1)$

$\Rightarrow (25^{25} + 1)$ is divisible by 26

$\Rightarrow$ On dividing 25^{25} by 26, we get $(26 - 1) = 25$ as remainder.

332. $(x^n + a^n)$ is divisible by $(x + a)$ when n is odd.

$\therefore (67^{67} + 1^{67})$ is divisible by $(67 + 1)$

$\Rightarrow (67^{67} + 1)$ is divisible by 68

$\Rightarrow$ On dividing $(67^{67} + 67)$ by 68, we get $(67 - 1) = 66$ as remainder.

333. $(49^{15} - 1) = (7^2)^{15} - 1 = 7^{30} - 1.$

Now, when n is even, $(x^n - a^n)$ is divisible by both $(x - a)$ and $(x + a)$.

$\therefore (7^{30} - 1)$ is divisible by both $(7 - 1)$ and $(7 + 1)$ i.e. by both 6 and 8. Thus, $[(49)^{15} - 1]$ is divisible by both 6 and 8.

334. $7^{84} = (7^3)^{28} = (343)^{28}.$

Now, $(x^n - a^n)$ is divisible by $(x - a)$ for all values of n.

$\therefore [(343)^{28} - 1]$ is divisible by $(343 - 1)$

$\Rightarrow [(343)^{28} - 1]$ is divisible by 342

$\Rightarrow (7^{84} - 1)$ is divisible by 342

$\Rightarrow$ On dividing 7^{84} by 342, we get 1 as remainder.

335. $2^{60} = (2^2)^{30} = 4^{30}.$

When n is even, $(x^n - a^n)$ is divisible by $(x + a)$.

$\therefore (4^{30} - 1^{30})$ is divisible by $(4 + 1)$

$\Rightarrow (4^{30} - 1)$ is divisible by 5 $\Rightarrow (2^{60} - 1)$ is divisible by 5.

$\Rightarrow$ On dividing 2^{60} by 5, we get 1 as remainder.

336. $(2^{12} - 1) = (4096 - 1) = 4095$, which is clearly divisible by 3, 5, 7 and 13 i.e. four numbers in all.

337. $(x^n + a^n)$ is divisible by $(x + a)$ when n is odd.

$\therefore (15^{23} + 23^{23})$ is divisible by $(15 + 23)$

$\Rightarrow (15^{23} + 23^{23})$ is divisible by 38 and hence by 19

$\Rightarrow$ On dividing $(15^{23} + 23^{23})$ by 19, we get 0 as remainder.

338. When n is even, $(x^n - a^n)$ is divisible by $(x + a)$.

Now, $2^{256} = (2^4)^{64} = (16)^{64}$.

$\therefore (16^{64} - 1^{64})$ is divisible by $(16 + 1)$

$\Rightarrow (16^{64} - 1)$ is divisible by 17

$\Rightarrow (2^{256} - 1)$ is divisible by 17

$\Rightarrow$ On dividing 2^{256} by 17, we get 1 as remainder.

339. When n is even, $(x^n - a^n)$ is divisible by both $(x - a)$ as well as $(x + a)$.

Now, $(7^{6n} - 6^{6n}) = [(7^3)^{2n} - (6^3)^{2n}] = [(343)^{2n} - (216)^{2n}]$.

$\therefore (7^{6n} - 6^{6n})$ is divisible by both $(7 - 6)$ and $(7 + 6)$

$\Rightarrow (7^{6n} - 6^{6n})$ is divisible by 13.

And, $[(343)^{2n} - (216)^{2n}]$ is divisible by both $(343 - 216)$ and $(343 + 216)$

$\Rightarrow (7^{6n} - 6^{6n})$ is divisible by both 127 and 559.

340. Let $2^{32} = x$. Then, $(2^{32} + 1) = (x + 1)$.

Let $(x + 1)$ be completely divisible by the natural number N. Then, $(2^{96} + 1) = [(2^{32})^3 + 1] = (x^3 + 1) = (x + 1)(x^2 - x + 1)$, which is completely divisible by N since $(x + 1)$ is divisible by N.

341. $(2^{48} - 1) = [(2^6)^8 - 1] = (64)^8 - 1$.

When n is even, $(x^n - a^n)$ is completely divisible by both $(x - a)$ and $(x + a)$.

$\therefore (64^8 - 1^8)$ is divisible by both $(64 - 1)$ and $(64 + 1)$

$\Rightarrow (2^{48} - 1)$ is divisible by both 63 and 65.

342. $n^{65} - n = n(n^{64} - 1) = n(n^{32} - 1)(n^{32} + 1)$

$= n(n^{16} - 1)(n^{16} + 1)(n^{32} + 1)$

$= n(n^8 - 1)(n^8 + 1)(n^{16} + 1)(n^{32} + 1)$

$= n(n^4 - 1)(n^4 + 1)(n^8 + 1)(n^{16} + 1)(n^{32} + 1)$

$= n(n^2 - 1)(n^2 + 1)(n^4 + 1)(n^8 + 1)(n^{16} + 1)(n^{32} + 1)$

$= (n - 1)\,n\,(n + 1)(n^2 + 1)(n^4 + 1)(n^8 + 1)(n^{16} + 1)(n^{32} + 1)$.

Clearly, $(n - 1)$, n and $(n + 1)$ are three consecutive numbers and they have to be multiples of 2, 3 and 4 as n is odd.

Thus, the given number is definitely a multiple of 24.

343. Let $a = 55$, $b = 17$.

Then, $N = a^3 + b^3 - (a + b)^3 = a^3 + b^3 - [a^3 + b^3 + 3ab(a + b)]$

$= -3ab(a + b) = -3 \times 55 \times 17 \times 72$.

Clearly, N is divisible by both 3 and 17.

344. Taking out $\lfloor 10$ common from $[\lfloor 10 + \lfloor 11 + \ldots\ldots + \lfloor 100]$, we get this expression in the form of a multiple of $\lfloor 10$ which has zeros as its last two digits. So, the last two digits of the expression $[\lfloor 10 + \lfloor 11 + \ldots\ldots + \lfloor 100]$ are zeros.

Thus, the last two digits of N must be the last two digits of the sum $(\lfloor 1 + \lfloor 2 + \ldots\ldots + \lfloor 9)$.

Now, $\lfloor 1 + \lfloor 2 + \ldots\ldots + \lfloor 9 = 1 + 2 + 6 + 24 + 120 + 720 + 5040 + 40320 + 362880$

It has clearly 13 as the last two digits.

So, the last two digits of N are 13.

345. $168 = 2^3 \times 3 \times 7$ and $\lfloor 7 = 7 \times 6 \times 5 \times 4 \times 3 \times 2 \times 1 = 7 \times 5 \times 3^2 \times 2^4 = 168 \times 30$

Hence, $\lfloor 7$ and all the factorials greater than $\lfloor 7$ are divisible by 168.

Now, $N = \lfloor 1 + \lfloor 2 + \lfloor 3 + \ldots\ldots + \lfloor 99 + \lfloor 100$

$= \lfloor 1 + \lfloor 2 + \lfloor 3 + \lfloor 4 + \lfloor 5 + \lfloor 6 +$ a multiple of 168.

So, the remainder obtained on dividing N by 168 is the same as that obtained on dividing $(\lfloor 1 + \lfloor 2 + \lfloor 3 + \lfloor 4 + \lfloor 5 + \lfloor 6)$ by 168.

Now, $\lfloor 1 + \lfloor 2 + \lfloor 3 + \lfloor 4 + \lfloor 5 + \lfloor 6 = 1 + 2 + 6 + 24 + 120 + 720 = 873 = (168 \times 5) + 33$.

Hence, the required remainder is 33.

346. $4^{61} = 4 \times 4^{60} = 4 \times (4^4)^{15} = 4 \times (256)^{15}$.

Now, $(x^n - a^n)$ is divisible by $(x - a)$ for all values of n.

$\therefore (256^{15} - 1)$ is divisible by $(256 - 1)$ i.e. 255 and hence by 51.

$\Rightarrow$ On dividing $(256)^{15}$ by 51, we get 1 as remainder

$\Rightarrow$ On dividing 4^{60} by 51, we get 1 as remainder

$\Rightarrow$ On dividing 4^{61} by 51, remainder obtained $= (4 \times 1) = 4$.

347. $17^{36} = (17^2)^{18} = (289)^{18}$.

Now, $[(289)^{18} - 1]$ is divisible by $(289 - 1)$, i.e. 288

$\Rightarrow (17^{36} - 1)$ is divisible by 288 and hence by 36

$\Rightarrow$ On dividing 17^{36} by 36, we get 1 as remainder.

348. When n is odd, $(x^n + a^n)$ is always divisible by $(x + a)$.

$\therefore$ Each one of $(47^{43} + 43^{43})$ and $(47^{47} + 43^{47})$ is divisible by $(47 + 43)$.

349. Product of all odd natural numbers less than 5000

$= 1 \times 3 \times 5 \times 7 \times \ldots\ldots \times 4999$

$$= \frac{1 \times 2 \times 3 \times 4 \times 5 \times 6 \times \ldots\ldots \times 5000}{2 \times 4 \times 6 \times 8 \times \ldots\ldots \times 5000}$$

$$= \frac{5000!}{2^{2500}(1 \times 2 \times 3 \times 4 \times \ldots\ldots \times 2500)} = \frac{5000!}{2^{2500}.2500!}.$$

350. The pages of the book may be divided into 10 groups: (1 – 100), (101 – 200), (201 – 300),.........., (901 – 1000).

Clearly, for the first group, one needs 11 zeros.

For second to ninth groups, one needs 20 zeros each.

For the tenth group, one needs 21 zeros.

So, total number of zeros required $= 11 + 8 \times 20 + 21 = 192$.

351. $a^2 + b^2 + c^2 = 1$.

So, the maximum value of $a^2 b^2 c^2 = \left(\frac{1}{3} \times \frac{1}{3} \times \frac{1}{3}\right) = \frac{1}{27}$.

($\because$ when sum of three positive quantities is fixed, the product will be maximum when the quantities are equal)

Hence, maximum value of $abc = \frac{1}{\sqrt{27}} = \frac{1}{3\sqrt{3}}$.

352. Let $N = 1^5 + 2^5 + 3^5 + \ldots\ldots + (100)^5$.

Then, $N = (1^5 + 2^5 + 3^5 + \ldots\ldots + 10^5) + (11^5 + 12^5 + \ldots\ldots + 20^5) + (21^5 + 22^5 + \ldots\ldots + 30^5) + \ldots\ldots + (91^5 + 92^5 + \ldots\ldots + 100^5) = N_1 + N_2 + N_3 + \ldots\ldots + N_{10}$.

Since each one of $N_1, N_2, N_3, \ldots\ldots, N_{10}$ has the same unit's digit of its terms, so unit's digit of each one of N_1, N_2,......, N_{10} is also the same.

$\therefore$ Unit's digit in $N = 10 \times$ Unit's digit of $N_1 = 0$.

353. Clearly, each of the 38 terms $\left(\frac{1}{4}\right),\left(\frac{1}{4}+\frac{1}{50}\right),\left(\frac{1}{4}+\frac{2}{50}\right)$..........,$\left(\frac{1}{4}+\frac{37}{50}\right)$ has a value lying between 0 and 1, while each one of the 12 terms $\left(\frac{1}{4}+\frac{38}{50}\right),\left(\frac{1}{4}+\frac{39}{50}\right)$,..........,$\left(\frac{1}{4}+\frac{49}{50}\right)$ has a value lying between 1 and 2.

Hence, the given expression = $(0 \times 38) + (1 \times 12) = 12$.

354. $100^{25} - 25 = (10^2)^{25} - 25 = 10^{50} - 25$

$= \underbrace{1000.....00}_{50\text{ zeros}} - 25 = \underbrace{9999.........}_{48\text{ times}}9975$

$\therefore$ Sum of digits = $(48 \times 9) + 7 + 5 = 432 + 7 + 5 = 444$.

355. $(1024)^4 \times (125)^{11} = (2^{10})^4 \times (5^3)^{11} = 2^{40} \times 5^{33} = 2^7 \times (2^{33} \times 5^{33}) = 2^7 \times 10^{33} = 128 \times 10^{33}$.

Clearly, the number has 1, 2, 8 and thirty-three zeros, i.e. $(3 + 33) = 36$ digits in all.

356. From 300 to 399, we note that when '4' comes only one time = 19 such instances.

From 400 to 499, we note that when '4' comes only one time = 80 such instances.

So, total = (19 + 80) = 99 such instances

357. $21 = 3 \times 7$ is not a prime number because 21 is a composite number.

358. Given $x = a(b - c)$, $y = b(c - a)$; $z = (a - b)$

$x = a(b - c)$

$\Rightarrow \frac{x}{a} = b - c$ ... (i)

Similarly, $y = b(c - a)$

$\Rightarrow \frac{y}{b} = c - a$ (ii) and similarly $z = c(a-b)\frac{z}{c} = c - a$ (iii)

Adding (i), (ii) and (iii) we get

$\because \frac{x}{a}+\frac{y}{b}+\frac{z}{c} = b - c + c - a + a - b = 0$

$\Rightarrow \frac{x}{a}+\frac{y}{b}+\frac{z}{c} = 0$

$\therefore \left(\frac{x}{a}\right)^3+\left(\frac{y}{b}\right)^3+\left(\frac{z}{c}\right)^3$

$= 3\times\frac{x}{a}\times\frac{y}{b}\times\frac{z}{c} = \frac{3xyz}{abc}$

[If $a + b + c = 0$, $a^3 + b^3 + c^3 = 3abc$]

359. Every real number is a rational number is not a correct statement.

360. Given

$a + b + c = 6$

$ab + bc + ca = 10$

$\therefore (a + b + c)^2 = 36$

$\Rightarrow a^2 + b^2 + c^2 + 2ab + 2bc + 2ca = 36$

$\Rightarrow a^2 + b^2 + c^2 + 2(ab + bc + ca) = 36$

$\Rightarrow a^2 + b^2 + c^2 + 2 \times 10 = 36$

$\Rightarrow a^2 + b^2 + c^2 = 16$

As we know $\frac{a^3+b^3+c^3-3abc}{a^2+b^2+c^2-ab-bc-ca} = (a+b+c)$

$\frac{a^3+b^3+c^3-3abc}{16-(ab+bc+ca)} = 6$

$\Rightarrow \frac{a^3+b^3+c^3-3abc}{16-10} = 6$

$\Rightarrow a^3+b^3+c^3-3abc = 6\times6$

$\Rightarrow a^3+b^3+c^3-3abc = 36$

361. Let the blank space is x

$\therefore 1001 \times 111 = 110000 + 11x$

Now find the value of x

$(1000 + 1) \times 111 = 110000 + 11x$

$111000 + 111 = 110000 + 11x$

$111111 = 110000 + 11x$

$11x = 111111 - 110000$

$11x = 1111$

$x = \frac{1111}{11} = 101$

362. The place value of 5 in 15201 = 5000

Place value of 6 in 2659 = 600

$\therefore$ we have $5000 + 600 = 7x$

$7x = 5600$

$x = \frac{5600}{7} = 800$

363. Let the two – digit number be $10a + b$ where $a > b$

According to the question,

$a + b = 12$ ....(i)

$a - b = 6$.....(ii)

On adding equation (i) and (ii).

$2a = 19$

$\Rightarrow a = 9$

From equation (i),

$9 + b = 12$

$\Rightarrow b = 12 - 9 = 3$

$\therefore$ Number is $10a + b$

$= 9 \times 10 + 3 = 93$

$\therefore$ When $a < b$. Then required number is = 39

364. Greatest four digit number that begins with 3 and ends with 5 = 3995

Least four digit number that begins with 3 and ends with 5 = 3005

∴ Required difference = 3995 – 3005 = 990

365. Perfect squares number between 120 and 300

= 121, 144, 169, 196, 225, 256 and 289

Sum of perfect squares between 120 and 300.

= 121 + 144 + 169 + 196 + 225 + 256 + 289 = 1400

366. $p^3 - q^3 = (p-q)\{(p-q)^2 - xpq\}$

$\Rightarrow (p-q)(p^2+q^2+pq) = (p-q)\{(p-q)^2 - xpq\}$

$\{\because a^3 - b^3 = (a-b)(a^2+ab+b^2)\}$

by cancelling same terms of both sides

$\Rightarrow p^2+q^2+pq = p^2+q^2-2pq-xpq$

$\{(a-b^2) = a^2+b^2-2ab\}$

$\Rightarrow 3pq = -xpq$

$\Rightarrow x = -3$

367. 2361*48 will be divisible by 9 if the sum of the digits of the given number is divisible by 9.

2 + 3 + 6 + 1 + * + 4 + 8 i.e. (24 + *) is divisible by 9.

Clearly, * = 3 because 27 is divisible by 9.

368. Let $a = p-q, b = q-r, c = r-p$

$\therefore a+b+c = p-q+q-r+r-p = 0$

$\therefore a^3+b^3+c^3 = 3abc$

$= 3(p-q)(q-r)(r-p)$

369. We know $a^2-b^2 = (a-b)(a+b)$

So $(a^2-b^2) \div (a+b) = 25$

$\Rightarrow \dfrac{(a-b)(a+b)}{a+b} = 25$

370. The number of prime numbers from 100 to 200 is 21.

371. The smallest five digit number is 10000.

```
       113
 88)10000
    88
    120
     88
     320
     264
      56
```

The least number divisible by 88

= 10000 + (88 – 56)

= 10000 + 32 = 10032

372. The first 3-digit number which is divisible by 9 is 108 and last three digit number which is divisible by 9 is 999.

So, we have an AP with a = 108, d = 9 and a_n = 999

$\therefore a_n = a + (n-1)d$

$\Rightarrow 999 = 108 + (n-1)\,9$

$\Rightarrow 999 - 108 = (n-1)\,9$

$\Rightarrow 891 = (n-1)\,9$

$\Rightarrow (n-1) = \dfrac{891}{9} = 99$

$\Rightarrow n + 99 + 1 = 100$

373. Let, the two consecutive even numbers are a and $(a + 2)$, respectively

According to question,

$a^2+(a+2)^2 = 1060 \{\because (a+b)^2 = a^2+b^2+2ab\}$

$\Rightarrow a^2 + a^2 + 4 + 4a = 1060$

$\Rightarrow 2a^2+4a-1056 = 0$

$\Rightarrow a^2+2a-528 = 0$

$\Rightarrow a^2+24a-22a-528 = 0$

$\Rightarrow a(a+24)-22(a+24) = 0$

$\Rightarrow (a-22)(a+24) = 0$

$\Rightarrow a = -24, 22$

374. The data in both the statements I and II are not sufficient to answer the question.

375. Given $n = p_1^{x_1}\, p_2^{x_2}\, p_3^{x_3}$ where p_1, p_2, p_3 are distinct prime factors

Number of prime factors form = $(x_1 \times x_2 \times x_3) = x_1\, x_2\, x_3$

Hence, option (b) is correct

376. 11, 111, 1111, 11111, ...

Let $m = 2 \Rightarrow 4 \times 2 + 3 = 11$

$m = 27 \Rightarrow 4 \times 27 + 3 = 111$

Each number can be expressed in the form $(4m + 3)$ where m is a natural number

Hence, statement 1 is only correct.

377. Let the numbers be a and b

∴ $a + b = 14$ (*i*)

$a - b = 10$ (*i*)

From Eqn. (*i*) and (*ii*)

$2a = 24$

$a = 12$

and $b = 2$

Product = 12 × 2 = 24

⇒ (a – b) = 25

378. $m^3 - 3m^2 + 3m + 3n + 3n^2 + n^3$

$= -64 - 48 - 12 - 6 + 12 - 8$

$= -126$

379. Let the two numbers be are a and b

$\therefore a + b = 14$ ....(i)

$a - b = 10$...(ii)

By adding equation (i) and (ii) we get

$2a = 24$

$\therefore a = 12$ and $b = 2$

$\therefore$ product of these two numbers = $12 \times 2 = 24$

380. Required sum

$= \frac{100}{2}[1+100]$

$= 101 \times 50$

$= 5050$

2 H.C.F. and L.C.M. of Numbers

IMPORTANT FACTS AND FORMULAE

I. Factors and Multiples: If a number a divides another number b exactly, we say that a is a ***factor*** of b. In this case, b is called a ***multiple*** of a.

II. Highest Common Factor (H.C.F.) or Greatest Common Measure (G.C.M.) or Greatest Common Divisor (G.C.D.): The H.C.F. of two or more than two numbers is the greatest number that divides each of them exactly. There are two methods of finding the H.C.F. of a given set of numbers:

1. ***Factorization Method:*** Express each one of the given numbers as the product of prime factors. The product of least powers of common prime factors gives H.C.F.
2. ***Division Method:*** Suppose we have to find the H.C.F. of two given numbers. Divide the larger number by the smaller one. Now, divide the divisor by the remainder. Repeat the process of dividing the preceding number by the remainder last obtained till zero is obtained as remainder. The last divisor is the required H.C.F.

   Finding the H.C.F. of more than two numbers: Suppose we have to find the H.C.F. of three numbers. Then, H.C.F. of [(H.C.F. of any two) and (the third number)] gives the H.C.F. of three given numbers. Similarly, the H.C.F. of more than three numbers may be obtained.

III. Least Common Multiple (L.C.M.): The least number which is exactly divisible by each one of the given numbers is called their L.C.M.

1. ***Factorization Method of Finding L.C.M.:*** Resolve each one of the given numbers into a product of prime factors. Then, L.C.M. is the product of highest powers of all the factors.
2. ***Common Division Method (Short-cut Method) of Finding L.C.M.:*** Arrange the given numbers in a row in any order. Divide by a number which divides exactly at least two of the given numbers and carry forward the numbers which are not divisible. Repeat the above process till no two of the numbers are divisible by the same number except 1. The product of the divisors and the undivided numbers is the required L.C.M. of the given numbers.

IV. Product of two numbers = Product of their H.C.F. and L.C.M.

V. Co-primes: Two numbers are said to be co-primes if their H.C.F. is 1.

VI. H.C.F. and L.C.M. of Fractions:

1. $\text{H.C.F.} = \dfrac{\text{H.C.F. of Numerators}}{\text{L.C.M. of Denominators}}$ 2. $\text{L.C.M.} = \dfrac{\text{L.C.M. of Numerators}}{\text{H.C.F. of Denominators}}$

VII. H.C.F. and L.C.M. of Decimal Fractions: In given numbers, make the same number of decimal places by annexing zeros in some numbers, if necessary. Considering these numbers without decimal point, find H.C.F. or L.C.M. as the case may be. Now, in the result, mark off as many decimal places as are there in each of the given numbers.

VIII. Comparison of Fractions: Find the L.C.M. of the denominators of the given fractions. Convert each of the fractions into an equivalent fraction with L.C.M. as the denominator, by multiplying both the numerator and denominator by the same number. The resultant fraction with the greatest numerator is the greatest.

SOLVED EXAMPLES

Ex. 1. ***Find the H.C.F. of $2^3 \times 3^2 \times 5 \times 7^4$, $2^2 \times 3^5 \times 5^2 \times 7^3$, $2^3 \times 5^3 \times 7^2$.***

Sol. The prime numbers common to given numbers are 2, 5 and 7.

$\therefore$ H.C.F. $= 2^2 \times 5 \times 7^2 = 980$.

Ex. 2. ***Find the H.C.F. of:***

(a) 42, 63 and 140 ***(b) 108, 288 and 360*** **(L.I.C.A.D.O., 2008)**

Sol. (*a*) $42 = 2 \times 3 \times 7$, $63 = 3^2 \times 7$ and $140 = 2^2 \times 5 \times 7$.

$\therefore$ H.C.F. = 7.

(*b*) $108 = 2^2 \times 3^3$, $288 = 2^5 \times 3^2$ and $360 = 2^3 \times 5 \times 3^2$.

$\therefore$ H.C.F. $= 2^2 \times 3^2 = 36$.

Ex. 3. ***Find the H.C.F. of 513, 1134 and 1215.***

Sol.

```
1134 ) 1215 ( 1
       1134
       ----
        81 ) 1134 ( 14
             81
             ----
             324
             324
             ----
              ×
```

$\therefore$ H.C.F. of 1134 and 1215 is 81.

So, required H.C.F. = H.C.F. of 513 and 81.

```
81 ) 513 ( 6
     486
     ---
     27 ) 81 ( 3
          81
          --
          ×
```

$\therefore$ H.C.F. of given numbers = 27.

Ex. 4. ***Reduce*** $\frac{391}{667}$ ***to lowest terms.***

Sol. H.C.F. of 391 and 667 is 23.

On dividing the numerator and denominator by 23, we get:

$$\frac{391}{667} = \frac{391 \div 23}{667 \div 23} = \frac{17}{29}.$$

Ex. 5. ***Find the L.C.M. of*** $2^2 \times 3^3 \times 5 \times 7^2$, $2^3 \times 3^2 \times 5^2 \times 7^4$, $2 \times 3 \times 5^3 \times 7 \times 11$.

Sol. L.C.M. = Product of highest powers of 2, 3, 5, 7 and 11 $= 2^3 \times 3^3 \times 5^3 \times 7^4 \times 11$. **(L.I.C.A.D.O., 2008)**

Ex. 6. ***Find the L.C.M. of***

(a) 87 and 145 ***(b) 72, 108 and 2100***

Sol. (*a*) $87 = 3 \times 29$ and $145 = 5 \times 29$.

$\therefore$ L.C.M. $= 3 \times 5 \times 29 = 435$.

(*b*) $72 = 2^3 \times 3^2$, $108 = 3^3 \times 2^2$, $2100 = 2^2 \times 5^2 \times 3 \times 7$.

$\therefore$ L.C.M. $= 2^3 \times 3^3 \times 5^2 \times 7 = 37800$.

Ex. 7. ***Find the L.C.M. of 16, 24, 36 and 54.***

Sol.

2	16 – 24 – 36 – 54
2	8 – 12 – 18 – 27
2	4 – 6 – 9 – 27
3	2 – 3 – 9 – 27
3	2 – 1 – 3 – 9
	2 – 1 – 1 – 3

$\therefore$ L.C.M. $= 2 \times 2 \times 2 \times 3 \times 3 \times 2 \times 3 = 432$.

Ex. 8. ***Find the H.C.F. and L.C.M. of*** $\frac{2}{3}, \frac{8}{9}, \frac{16}{81}$ ***and*** $\frac{10}{27}$.

Sol. H.C.F. of given fractions $= \frac{\text{H.C.F. of 2, 8, 16, 10}}{\text{L.C.M. of 3, 9, 81, 27}} = \frac{2}{81}$.

L.C.M. of given fractions $= \frac{\text{L.C.M. of 2, 8, 16, 10}}{\text{H.C.F. of 3, 9, 81, 27}} = \frac{80}{3}$.

Ex. 9. ***Find the H.C.F. and L.C.M. of 0.63, 1.05 and 2.1.***

Sol. Making the same number of decimal places, the given numbers are 0.63, 1.05 and 2.10.

Without decimal places, these numbers are 63, 105 and 210.

Now, H.C.F. of 63, 105 and 210 is 21.

$\therefore$ H.C.F. of 0.63, 1.05 and 2.1 is 0.21.

L.C.M. of 63, 105 and 210 is 630.

$\therefore$ L.C.M. of 0.63, 1.05 and 2.1 is 6.30.

Ex. 10. ***Two numbers are in the ratio of 15: 11. If their H.C.F. is 13, find the numbers.***

Sol. Let the required numbers be $15x$ and $11x$.

Then, their H.C.F. is x. So, $x = 13$.

$\therefore$ The numbers are $(15 \times 13$ and $11 \times 13)$, i.e., 195 and 143.

Ex. 11. ***Two numbers are in the ratio of 3: 4. Their L.C.M. is 84. Find the numbers.*** **(S.S.C., 2010)**

Sol. Let the numbers be $3x$ and $4x$. Then, their L.C.M. $= 12x$.

So, $12x = 84$ or $x = 7$.

$\therefore$ The numbers are 21 and 28.

Ex. 12. ***The H.C.F. of two numbers is 11 and their L.C.M. is 693. If one of the numbers is 77, find the other.*** **(P.C.S., 2009)**

Sol. Other number $= \left(\dfrac{11 \times 693}{77}\right) = 99$.

Ex. 13. ***The sum of two numbers is 462 and their highest common factor is 22. What is the minimum number of pairs that satisfy these conditions?*** **(M.A.T., 2004)**

Sol. *Let the required numbers be 22a and 22b.*

Then, $22a + 22b = 462 \Rightarrow a + b = 21$.

Now, co-primes with sum 21 are (1, 20), (2, 19), (4, 17), (5, 16), (8, 13) and (10, 11).

$\therefore$ Required numbers are $(22 \times 1, 22 \times 20)$, $(22 \times 2, 22 \times 19)$,

$(22 \times 4, 22 \times 17)$, $(22 \times 5, 22 \times 16)$, $(22 \times 8, 22 \times 13)$ and $(22 \times 10, 22 \times 11)$.

Clearly, the number of such pairs is 6.

Ex. 14. ***The sum and difference of the L.C.M and H.C.F. of two numbers are 592 and 518 respectively. If the sum of the numbers be 296, find the numbers.*** **(Section Officer's, 2006)**

Sol. Let L and H denote the L.C.M and H.C.F of the two numbers.

Then, $L + H = 592$ ....(*i*) And, $L - H = 518$ ....(*ii*)

Adding (*i*) and (*ii*), we get: $2L = 1110$ or $L = 555$.

$\therefore H = 592 - 555 = 37$.

So, H.C.F. = 37 and L.C.M. = 555.

Let the numbers be x and $(296 - x)$.

Then, $x(296 - x) = 555 \times 37 \Rightarrow x^2 - 296x + 20535 = 0$

$\Rightarrow x^2 - 185x - 111x + 20535 = 0 \Rightarrow x(x - 185) - 111(x - 185) = 0$

$\Rightarrow (x - 185)(x - 111) = 0 \Rightarrow x = 185$ or $x = 111$.

Hence the numbers are 111 and 185.

Ex. 15. ***Find the greatest possible length which can be used to measure exactly the lengths 4 m 95 cm, 9 m and 16 m 65 cm.***

Sol. Required length = H.C.F. of 495 cm, 900 cm and 1665 cm.

$495 = 3^2 \times 5 \times 11$, $900 = 2^2 \times 3^2 \times 5^2$, $1665 = 3^2 \times 5 \times 37$.

$\therefore$ H.C.F. $= 3^2 \times 5 = 45$.

Hence, required length = 45 cm.

Ex. 16. ***Find the greatest number which on dividing 1657 and 2037 leaves remainders 6 and 5 respectively.*** **(Section Officer's, 2006)**

Sol. Required number = H.C.F. of $(1657 - 6)$ and $(2037 - 5)$ = H.C.F. of 1651 and 2032

```
1651 ) 2032 ( 1
       1651
       ----
        381 ) 1651 ( 4
              1524
              ----
               127 ) 381 ( 3
                     381
                     ---
                      ×
```

$\therefore$ Required number = 127.

Ex. 17. ***Find the largest number which divides 62, 132 and 237 to leave the same remainder in each case.***

Sol. Required number = H.C.F. of $(132 - 62)$, $(237 - 132)$ and $(237 - 62)$

= H.C.F. of 70, 105 and 175 = 35.

Ex. 18. ***The H.C.F. of two numbers, each having three digits is 17 and their L.C.M. is 714. Find the sum of the numbers.*** **(C.P.O., 2007)**

Sol. Let the numbers be $17a$ and $17b$.
Then, $17a \times 17b = 17 \times 714 \Rightarrow ab = 42$.
Now, co-primes with product 42 are (1, 42), (2, 21), (3, 14) and (6, 7).
So, the numbers are $(17 \times 1, 17 \times 42)$, $(17 \times 2, 17 \times 21)$, $(17 \times 3, 17 \times 14)$ and $(17 \times 6, 17 \times 7)$.
Since both the numbers are 3-digit numbers, the suitable pair is $(17 \times 6, 17 \times 7)$, i.e., (102, 119).
$\therefore$ Required sum $= 102 + 119 = 221$.

Ex. 19. ***Find the least number which is exactly divisible by 32, 36, 45, 60 and 80.*** **(R.R.B., 2006)**

Sol. Required number = L.C.M. of 32, 36, 45, 60, 80

2	32	36	45	60	80
2	16	18	45	30	40
2	8	9	45	15	20
3	4	9	45	15	10
5	4	3	15	5	10
3	4	3	3	1	2
2	4	1	1	1	2
	2	1	1	1	1

L.C.M. $= 2 \times 2 \times 2 \times 3 \times 5 \times 3 \times 2 \times 2 = 1440$.
Hence, required number = 1440.

Ex. 20. ***Find the least number which when divided by 6, 7, 8, 9 and 12 leaves the same remainder 1 in each case.***

Sol. Required number = (L.C.M. of 6, 7, 8, 9, 12) + 1.

3	6	7	8	9	12
2	2	7	8	3	4
2	1	7	4	3	2
	1	7	2	3	1

$\therefore$ L.C.M. $= 3 \times 2 \times 2 \times 7 \times 2 \times 3 = 504$.
Hence, required number $= (504 + 1) = 505$.

Ex. 21. ***Find the smallest number which when increased by 10 is completely divisible by 12, 15, 18, 20 and 24.*** **(P.C.S., 2008)**

Sol. Required number
$= $ (L.C.M. of 12, 15, 18, 20, 24) $- 10$
$= (2 \times 2 \times 3 \times 5 \times 3 \times 2) - 10$
$= 360 - 10 = 350$.

2	12	15	18	20	24
2	6	15	9	10	12
3	3	15	9	5	6
5	1	5	3	5	2
	1	1	3	1	2

Ex. 22. ***Find the greatest number of five digits which is divisible by 15, 21 and 36.*** **(P.C.S., 2010)**

Sol. Greatest number of five digits = 99999.
Required number must be divisible by L.C.M. of 15, 21, 36, i.e., 1260.
On dividing 99999 by 1260, we get 459 as remainder.
$\therefore$ Required number $= (99999 - 459) = 99540$.

Ex. 23. ***Find the smallest number of five digits exactly divisible by 16, 24, 36 and 54.***

Sol. Smallest number of five digits is 10000.
Required number must be divisible by L.C.M. of 16, 24, 36, 54, i.e., 432.
On dividing 10000 by 432, we get 64 as remainder.
$\therefore$ Required number $= 10000 + (432 - 64) = 10368$.

Ex. 24. ***Find the largest number which when subtracted from 10000, the remainder is divisible by 32, 36, 48 and 50.*** **(R.R.B., 2006)**

Sol. Required number
$= 10000 - $ (L.C.M. of 32, 36, 48, 50)
$= 10000 - (2 \times 2 \times 3 \times 4 \times 3 \times 2 \times 3)$
$= 10000 - 864 = 9136$.

2	32	36	48	54
2	16	18	24	27
3	8	9	12	27
4	8	3	4	9
3	2	3	1	9
	2	1	1	3

Ex. 25. ***Find the largest number of five digits which, when divided by 16, 24, 30 or 36, leaves the same remainder 10 in each case.*** (C.P.O., 2007)

Sol. Largest number of 5 digits = 99999. L.C.M. of 16, 24, 30 and 36 = 720.

On dividing 99999 by 720, remainder obtained is 639.

$\therefore$ Largest number of 5 digits divisible by 16, 24, 30 and 36 = (99999 – 639) = 99360.

Hence, required number = (99360 + 10) = 99370.

Ex. 26. ***Find the least number which when divided by 20, 25, 35 and 40 leaves remainders 14, 19, 29 and 34 respectively.***

Sol. Here, (20 – 14) = 6, (25 – 19) = 6, (35 – 29) = 6 and (40 – 34) = 6.

$\therefore$ Required number = (L.C.M. of 20, 25, 35, 40) – 6 = 1394.

Ex. 27. ***What is the least number which when divided by the numbers 3, 5, 6, 8, 10 and 12 leaves in each case a remainder 2 but when divided by 13 leaves no remainder?*** (S.S.C., 2005)

Sol. L.C.M. of 3, 5, 6, 8, 10 and 12 = 120.

So, the required number is of the form 120 k + 2.

Least value of k for which (120k + 2) is divisible by 13 is k = 8.

$\therefore$ Required number = (120 × 8 + 2) = 962.

Ex. 28. ***The traffic lights at three different road crossings change after every 48 sec., 72 sec. and 108 sec. respectively. If they all change simultaneously at 8:20:00 hours, then at what time will they again change simultaneously?*** (R.R.B., 2006, M.A.T., 2005)

Sol. Interval of change = (L.C.M. of 48, 72, 108) sec. = 432 sec.

So, the lights will again change simultaneously after every 432 seconds, i.e., 7 min. 12 sec.

Hence, next simultaneous change will take place at 8:27:12 hrs.

Ex. 29. ***Seema, Meena and Reema begin to jog around a circular stadium and they complete their revolutions in 54 seconds, 42 seconds and 63 seconds respectively. After how much time will they come together at the starting point?*** (Bank. P.O., 2010)

Sol. L.C.M of 54, 42 and 63 = 378.

So, the three girls will come together at the starting point in 378 seconds i.e., 6 min 18 sec.

Ex. 30. ***Arrange the fractions*** $\frac{17}{18}, \frac{31}{36}, \frac{43}{45}, \frac{59}{60}$ ***in the ascending order.***

Sol. L.C.M. of 18, 36, 45 and 60 = 180. Now,

$$\frac{17}{18} = \frac{17\times10}{18\times10} = \frac{170}{180};\quad \frac{31}{36} = \frac{31\times5}{36\times5} = \frac{155}{180};\quad \frac{43}{45} = \frac{43\times4}{45\times4} = \frac{172}{180};\quad \frac{59}{60} = \frac{59\times3}{60\times3} = \frac{177}{180}.$$

Since, 155 < 170 < 172 < 177, so, $\frac{155}{180} < \frac{170}{180} < \frac{172}{180} < \frac{177}{180}$.

Hence, $\frac{31}{36} < \frac{17}{18} < \frac{43}{45} < \frac{59}{60}$.

EXERCISE

(OBJECTIVE TYPE QUESTIONS)

Directions: ***Mark (✓) against the correct answer:***

1. Find the factors of 330. (CLAT, 2010)
   (*a*) 2 × 4 × 5 × 11 (*b*) 2 × 3 × 7 × 13
   (*c*) 2 × 3 × 5 × 13 (*d*) 2 × 3 × 5 × 11
2. Find the factors of 1122. (CLAT, 2010)
   (*a*) 3 × 9 × 17 × 2 (*b*) 3 × 11 × 17 × 2
   (*c*) 9 × 9 × 17 × 2 (*d*) 3 × 11 × 17 × 3
3. 252 can be expressed as a product of primes as (IGNOU, 2002)
   (*a*) 2 × 2 × 3 × 3 × 7 (*b*) 2 × 2 × 2 × 3 × 7
   (*c*) 3 × 3 × 3 × 3 × 7 (*d*) 2 × 3 × 3 × 3 × 7
4. Which of the following has most number of divisors? (M.B.A. 2002)
   (*a*) 99 (*b*) 101
   (*c*) 176 (*d*) 182
5. A number n is said to be perfect if the sum of all its divisors (excluding n itself) is equal to n. An example of perfect number is
   (*a*) 6 (*b*) 9
   (*c*) 15 (*d*) 21
6. $\frac{1095}{1168}$ when expressed in simplest form is

(a) $\frac{13}{16}$ (b) $\frac{15}{16}$
(c) $\frac{17}{26}$ (d) $\frac{25}{26}$

7. Reduce $\frac{128352}{238368}$ to its lowest terms. **(IGNOU, 2003)**
(a) $\frac{3}{4}$ (b) $\frac{5}{13}$
(c) $\frac{7}{13}$ (d) $\frac{9}{13}$

8. The simplest reduction to the lowest terms of $\frac{116,690,151}{427,863,887}$ is **(SNAP, 2004)**
(a) $\frac{3}{11}$ (b) $\frac{7}{11}$
(c) $\frac{11}{3}$ (d) None of these

9. The highest common factor of 0 and 6 is **(P.C.S., 2008)**
(a) 0 (b) 3
(c) 6 (d) Undefined

10. The H.C.F. of $2^2 \times 3^3 \times 5^5$, $2^3 \times 3^2 \times 5^2 \times 7$ and $2^4 \times 3^4 \times 5 \times 7^2 \times 11$ is
(a) $2^2 \times 3^2 \times 5$ (b) $2^2 \times 3^2 \times 5 \times 7 \times 11$
(c) $2^4 \times 3^4 \times 5^5$ (d) $2^4 \times 3^4 \times 5^5 \times 7 \times 11$

11. The H.C.F. of $2^4 \times 3^2 \times 5^3 \times 7$, $2^3 \times 3^3 \times 5^2 \times 7^2$ and $3 \times 5 \times 7 \times 11$ is
(a) 105 (b) 1155
(c) 2310 (d) 27720

12. H.C.F. of $4 \times 27 \times 3125$, $8 \times 9 \times 25 \times 7$ & $16 \times 81 \times 5 \times 11 \times 49$ is
(a) 180 (b) 360
(c) 540 (d) 1260

13. Find the highest common factor of 36 and 84. **(R.R.B., 2003)**
(a) 4 (b) 6
(c) 12 (d) 18

14. Even numbers are formed by taking at least two at a time from the numbers 0, 4, 8, 9. Their H.C.F. is **(Hotel Management, 2007)**
(a) 2 (b) 4
(c) 10 (d) None of these

15. The H.C.F. of 204, 1190 and 1445 is
(a) 17 (b) 18
(c) 19 (d) 21

16. Which of the following is a pair of co-primes?
(a) (16, 62) (b) (18, 25)
(c) (21, 35) (d) (23, 92)

17. The H.C.F. of 2923 and 3239 is
(a) 37 (b) 47
(c) 73 (d) 79

18. The H.C.F. of 3556 and 3444 is
(a) 23 (b) 25
(c) 26 (d) 28

19. The L.C.M. of $2^3 \times 3^2 \times 5 \times 11$, $2^4 \times 3^4 \times 5^2 \times 7$ and $2^5 \times 3^3 \times 5^3 \times 7^2 \times 11$ is
(a) $2^3 \times 3^2 \times 5$ (b) $2^5 \times 3^4 \times 5^3$
(c) $2^3 \times 3^2 \times 5 \times 7 \times 11$ (d) $2^5 \times 3^4 \times 5^3 \times 7^2 \times 11$

20. Find the lowest common multiple of 24, 36 and 40.
(a) 120 (b) 240
(c) 360 (d) 480

21. The L.C.M. of 22, 54, 108, 135 and 198 is
(a) 330 (b) 1980
(c) 5940 (d) 11880

22. The L.C.M. of 148 and 185 is
(a) 680 (b) 740
(c) 2960 (d) 3700

23. The H.C.F. of $\frac{a}{b}, \frac{c}{d}, \frac{e}{f}$ is equal to **(I.A.M. 2007)**
(a) $\frac{\text{L.C.M. of } a, c, e}{\text{H.C.F. of } b, d, f}$ (b) $\frac{\text{H.C.F. of } a, c, e}{\text{L.C.M. of } b, d, f}$
(c) $\frac{\text{H.C.F. of } a, c, e}{\text{H.C.F. of } b, d, f}$ (d) $\frac{ace}{bdf}$

24. The H.C.F. of $\frac{2}{3}, \frac{8}{9}, \frac{64}{81}$ and $\frac{10}{27}$ is :
(a) $\frac{2}{3}$ (b) $\frac{2}{81}$
(c) $\frac{160}{3}$ (d) $\frac{160}{81}$

25. The H.C.F. of $\frac{9}{10}, \frac{12}{25}, \frac{18}{35}$ and $\frac{21}{40}$ is
(a) $\frac{3}{5}$ (b) $\frac{252}{5}$
(c) $\frac{3}{1400}$ (d) $\frac{63}{700}$

26. The L.C.M. of $\frac{1}{3}, \frac{5}{6}, \frac{2}{9}, \frac{4}{27}$ is
(a) $\frac{1}{54}$ (b) $\frac{10}{27}$
(c) $\frac{20}{3}$ (d) None of these

27. The L.C.M. of $\frac{2}{3}, \frac{3}{5}, \frac{4}{7}, \frac{9}{13}$ is
(a) 36 (b) $\frac{1}{36}$
(c) $\frac{1}{1365}$ (d) $\frac{12}{455}$

28. The L.C.M. of $\frac{3}{4}, \frac{6}{7}, \frac{9}{8}$ is (L.I.C.A.D.O., 2008)
(a) 3 (b) 6
(c) 9 (d) 18

29. The H.C.F. of 1.75, 5.6 and 7 is
(a) 0.07 (b) 0.7
(c) 3.5 (d) 0.35

30. The G.C.D. of 1.08, 0.36 and 0.9 is (Hotel Management, 2002)
(a) 0.03 (b) 0.9
(c) 0.18 (d) 0.108

31. The H.C.F. of 0.54, 1.8 and 7.2 is
(a) 1.8 (b) 0.18
(c) 0.018 (d) 18

32. The L.C.M. of 3, 2.7 and 0.09 is
(a) 2.7 (b) 0.27
(c) 0.027 (d) 27

33. If A, B and C are three numbers, such that the L.C.M. of A and B is B and the L.C.M of B and C is C, then the L.C.M. of A, B and C is
(a) A (b) B
(c) C (d) $\frac{A+B+C}{3}$

34. H.C.F. of 3240, 3600 and a third number is 36 and their L.C.M. is $2^4 \times 3^5 \times 5^2 \times 7^2$. The third number is (M.A.T., 2005)
(a) $2^2 \times 3^5 \times 7^2$ (b) $2^2 \times 5^3 \times 7^2$
(c) $2^5 \times 5^2 \times 7^2$ (d) $2^3 \times 3^5 \times 7^2$

35. Three numbers are in the ratio 1: 2: 3 and their H.C.F. is 12. The numbers are
(a) 4, 8, 12 (b) 5, 10, 15
(c) 10, 20, 30 (d) 12, 24, 36

36. The ratio of two numbers is 3: 4 and their H.C.F. is 4. Their L.C.M. is
(a) 12 (b) 16
(c) 24 (d) 48

37. The sum of two numbers is 216 and their H.C.F. is 27. The numbers are
(a) 27, 189 (b) 81, 189
(c) 108, 108 (d) 154, 162

38. The sum of two numbers is 528 and their H.C.F. is 33. The number of pairs of numbers satisfying the above conditions is
(a) 4 (b) 6
(c) 8 (d) 12

39. The number of number-pairs lying between 40 and 100 with their H.C.F. as 15 is
(a) 3 (b) 4
(c) 5 (d) 6

40. The H.C.F. of two numbers is 12 and their difference is 12. The numbers are
(a) 66, 78 (b) 70, 82
(c) 94, 106 (d) 84, 96

41. The product of two numbers is 4107. If the H.C.F. of these numbers is 37, then the greater number is
(a) 101 (b) 107
(c) 111 (d) 185

42. The product of two numbers is 2028 and their H.C.F. is 13. The number of such pairs is (A.A.O., 2010; P.C.S., 2009)
(a) 1 (b) 2
(c) 3 (d) 4

43. Three numbers which are co-prime to each other are such that the product of the first two is 551 and that of the last two is 1073. The sum of the three numbers is
(a) 75 (b) 81
(c) 85 (d) 89

44. The ratio of two numbers is 13: 15 and their L.C.M. is 39780. The numbers are (P.C.S., 2009)
(a) 884, 1020 (b) 884, 1040
(c) 670, 1340 (d) 2652, 3060

45. Three numbers are in the ratio of 3: 4: 5 and their L.C.M. is 2400. Their H.C.F. is
(a) 40 (b) 80
(c) 120 (d) 200

46. The L.C.M. and ratio of four numbers are 630 and 2: 3: 5: 7 respectively. The difference between the greatest and least numbers is (I.A.M., 2007)
(a) 6 (b) 14
(c) 15 (d) 21

47. The H.C.F. and L.C.M. of two numbers are 12 and 336 respectively. If one of the numbers is 84, the other is (S.S.C., 2010)
(a) 36 (b) 48
(c) 72 (d) 96

48. If the product of two numbers is 324 and their H.C.F. is 3, then their L.C.M. will be (P.C.S., 2008)
(a) 972 (b) 327
(c) 321 (d) 108

49. If H.C.F. of p and q is x and $q = xy$, then the L.C.M. of p and q is (C.D.S., 2004)
(a) pq (b) qy
(c) xy (d) py

50. The sum of two numbers is 2000 and their L.C.M. is 21879. The two numbers are
(a) 1993, 7 (b) 1991, 9
(c) 1989, 11 (d) 1987, 13

51. The H.C.F. and L.C.M. of two numbers are 84 and 21 respectively. If the ratio of the two numbers is 1: 4, then the larger of the two numbers is
(a) 12 (b) 48
(c) 84 (d) 108

52. The L.C.M. of two numbers is 495 and their H.C.F. is 5. If the sum of the numbers is 10, then their difference is
(a) 10 (b) 46
(c) 70 (d) 90

53. The product of the L.C.M. and H.C.F. of two numbers is 24. The difference of two numbers is 2. Find the numbers.
(a) 2 and 4 (b) 6 and 4
(c) 8 and 6 (d) 8 and 10

54. If the sum of two numbers is 36 and their H.C.F. and L.C.M. are 3 and 105 respectively, the sum of the reciprocals of the two numbers is **(S.S.C., 2010)**
(a) $\frac{2}{35}$ (b) $\frac{3}{35}$
(c) $\frac{4}{35}$ (d) None of these

55. The L.C.M. of two numbers is 12 times their H.C.F. The sum of H.C.F. and L.C.M. is 403. If one number is 93, find the other. **(M.B.A., 2007)**
(a) 124 (b) 128
(c) 134 (d) None of these

56. The H.C.F. and L.C.M. of two numbers are 50 and 250 respectively. If the first number is divided by 2, the quotient is 50. The second number is
(a) 50 (b) 100
(c) 125 (d) 250

57. The product of two numbers is 1320 and their H.C.F. is 6. The L.C.M. of the numbers is
(a) 220 (b) 1314
(c) 1326 (d) 7920

58. Product of two co-prime numbers is 117. Their L.C.M. should be
(a) 1 (b) 117
(c) equal to their H.C.F. (d) cannot be calculated

59. The L.C.M. of three different numbers is 120. Which of the following cannot be their H.C.F.? **(Campus Recruitment, 2010)**
(a) 8 (b) 12
(c) 24 (d) 35

60. The H.C.F. of two numbers is 8. Which one of the following can never be their L.C.M.?
(a) 24 (b) 48
(c) 56 (d) 60

61. If the L.C.M. of three numbers is 9570, then their H.C.F. can be
(a) 11 (b) 12
(c) 19 (d) 21

62. The H.C.F. of two numbers is 23 and the other two factors of their L.C.M. are 13 and 14. The larger of the two numbers is
(a) 276 (b) 299
(c) 322 (d) 345

63. About the number of pairs which have 16 as their H.C.F. and 136 as their L.C.M., we can definitely say that
(a) no such pair exists
(b) only one such pair exists
(c) only two such pairs exist
(d) many such pairs exist

64. The H.C.F. and L.C.M. of two numbers are 21 and 4641 respectively. If one of the numbers lies between 200 and 300, the two numbers are **(M.A.T., 2006)**
(a) 273, 357 (b) 273, 359
(c) 273, 361 (d) 273, 363

65. Two numbers, both greater than 29, have H.C.F. 29 and L.C.M. 4147. The sum of the numbers is
(a) 666 (b) 669
(c) 696 (d) 966

66. L.C.M. of two prime numbers x and y $(x > y)$ is 161. The value of $3y - x$ is
(a) -2 (b) -1
(c) 1 (d) 2

67. The greatest number that exactly divides 105, 1001 and 2436 is
(a) 3 (b) 7
(c) 11 (d) 21

68. 21 mango trees, 42 apple trees and 56 orange trees have to be planted in rows such that each row contains the same number of trees of one variety only. Minimum number of rows in which the trees may be planted is **(M.B.A., 2005)**
(a) 3 (b) 15
(c) 17 (d) 20

69. The greatest possible length which can be used to measure exactly the lengths 7 m, 3 m 85 cm, 12 m 95 cm is **(R.R.B., 2008)**
(a) 15 cm (b) 25 cm
(c) 35 cm (d) 42 cm

70. The capacity of two pots is 120 litres and 56 litres respectively. Find the capacity of a container which can exactly measure the contents of the two pots. **(R.R.B., 2005)**
(a) 7500 cc (b) 7850 cc
(c) 8000 cc (d) 9500 cc

71. A daily wage labourer was engaged for a certain number of days for ₹ 5750, but being absent on some of those days he was paid only ₹ 5000. What was his maximum possible daily wage? **(C.P.O., 2006)**
(a) ₹ 125 (b) ₹ 250
(c) ₹ 375 (d) ₹ 500

72. A person has to completely put each of three liquids: 403 litres of petrol, 465 litres of diesel and 496 litres of Mobil Oil in bottles of equal size without mixing any of the above three types of liquids such that

each bottle is completely filled. What is the least possible number of bottles required? **(Civil Services, 2007)**

(*a*) 34 (*b*) 44
(*c*) 46 (*d*) None of these

73. The maximum number of students among whom 1001 pens and 910 pencils can be distributed in such a way that each student gets the same number of pens and same number of pencils is

(*a*) 91 (*b*) 910
(*c*) 1001 (*d*) 1911

74. A rectangular courtyard 3.78 metres long and 5.25 metres wide is to be paved exactly with square tiles, all of the same size. What is the largest size of the tile which could be used for the purpose?

(*a*) 14 cm (*b*) 21 cm
(*c*) 42 cm (*d*) None of these

75. The least number of square tiles required to pave the ceiling of a room 15 m 17 cm long and 9 m 2 cm broad is **(M.B.A., 2006)**

(*a*) 656 (*b*) 738
(*c*) 814 (*d*) 902

76. Three sets of English, Mathematics and Science books containing 336, 240 and 96 books respectively have to be stacked in such a way that all the books are stored subjectwise and the height of each stack is the same. Total number of stacks will be **(S.S.C., 2007)**

(*a*) 14 (*b*) 21
(*c*) 22 (*d*) 48

77. Four metal rods of lengths 78 cm, 104 cm, 117 cm and 169 cm are to be cut into parts of equal length. Each part must be as long as possible. What is the maximum number of pieces that can be cut? **(Civil Services, 2009)**

(*a*) 27 (*b*) 36
(*c*) 43 (*d*) 480

78. Find the greatest number that will divide 43, 91 and 183 so as to leave the same remainder in each case.

(*a*) 4 (*b*) 7
(*c*) 9 (*d*) 13

79. If r is the remainder when each of 7654, 8506 and 9997 is divided by the greatest number d ($d > 1$), then $d - r$ is equal to **(A.A.O., 2010)**

(*a*) 14 (*b*) 18
(*c*) 24 (*d*) 28

80. Let N be the greatest number that will divide 1305, 4665 and 6905, leaving the same remainder in each case. Then sum of the digits in N is **(S.S.C., 2004)**

(*a*) 4 (*b*) 5
(*c*) 6 (*d*) 8

81. A milkman has 3 jars containing 57 litres, 129 litres and 177 litres of pure milk respectively. A measuring can, after a different number of exact measurements of milk in each jar, leaves the same amount of milk unmeasured in each jar. What is the volume of the largest such can? **(J.M.E.T., 2004)**

(*a*) 12 litres (*b*) 16 litres
(*c*) 24 litres (*d*) None of these

82. The greatest number which can divide 1356, 1868 and 2764 leaving the same remainder 12 in each case is

(*a*) 64 (*b*) 124
(*c*) 156 (*d*) 260

83. Which greatest number will divide 3026 and 5053 leaving remainders 11 and 13 respectively? **(C.P.O., 2006)**

(*a*) 15 (*b*) 30
(*c*) 45 (*d*) 60

84. Find the greatest number that will divide 964, 1238 and 1400 leaving remainders 41, 31 and 51 respectively. **(I.I.F.T., 2005)**

(*a*) 61 (*b*) 71
(*c*) 73 (*d*) 81

85. Which of the following fractions is the largest?

(*a*) $\frac{7}{8}$ (*b*) $\frac{13}{16}$
(*c*) $\frac{31}{40}$ (*d*) $\frac{63}{80}$

86. What is the least natural number which leaves no remainder when divided by all the digits from 1 to 9? **(C.D.S., 2004)**

(*a*) 1800 (*b*) 1920
(*c*) 2520 (*d*) 5040

87. What will be the least number which when doubled will be exactly divisible by 12, 18, 21 and 30?

(*a*) 196 (*b*) 630
(*c*) 1260 (*d*) 2520

88. The sum of two numbers is 45. Their difference is $\frac{1}{9}$ of their sum. Their L.C.M. is **(S.S.C., 2007)**

(*a*) 100 (*b*) 150
(*c*) 200 (*d*) 250

89. The smallest fraction, which each of $\frac{6}{7}, \frac{5}{14}, \frac{10}{21}$ will divide exactly is

(*a*) $\frac{30}{7}$ (*b*) $\frac{30}{98}$
(*c*) $\frac{60}{147}$ (*d*) $\frac{50}{294}$

90. The least number of five digits which is exactly divisible by 12, 15 and 18 is

(*a*) 10010 (*b*) 10015
(*c*) 10020 (*d*) 10080

91. The greatest number of four digits which is divisible by 15, 25, 40 and 75 is

(*a*) 9000 (*b*) 9400
(*c*) 9600 (*d*) 9800

92. The number between 4000 and 5000 which is divisible by 12, 18, 21 and 32 is (P.C.S., 2006)
(*a*) 4023 (*b*) 4032
(*c*) 4203 (*d*) 4302

93. The number nearest to 43582 divisible by each of 25, 50 and 75 is (C.P.O., 2007)
(*a*) 43500 (*b*) 43550
(*c*) 43600 (*d*) 43650

94. The least number which should be added to 2497 so that the sum is exactly divisible by 5, 6, 4 and 3 is
(*a*) 3 (*b*) 13
(*c*) 23 (*d*) 33

95. The greatest number which when subtracted from 5834, gives a number exactly divisible by each of 20, 28, 32 and 35 is (S.S.C., 2010)
(*a*) 1120 (*b*) 4714
(*c*) 5200 (*d*) 5600

96. The least number which is a perfect square and is divisible by each of the numbers 16, 20 and 24, is
(*a*) 1600 (*b*) 3600
(*c*) 6400 (*d*) 14400

97. The smallest number which when diminished by 7, is divisible by 12, 16, 18, 21 and 28 is
(*a*) 1008 (*b*) 1015
(*c*) 1022 (*d*) 1032

98. The least number which when increased by 5 is divisible by each one of 24, 32, 36 and 54 is
(*a*) 427 (*b*) 859
(*c*) 869 (*d*) 4320

99. The least number, which when divided by 12, 15, 20 and 54 leaves in each case a remainder of 8 is
(*a*) 504 (*b*) 536
(*c*) 544 (*d*) 548

100. A number less than 500, when divided by 4, 5, 6, 7 leaves remainder 1 in each case. The number is (Hotel Management, 2007)
(*a*) 211 (*b*) 420
(*c*) 421 (*d*) 441

101. What is the greatest number of 3 digits which when divided by 6, 9 and 12 leaves a remainder of 3 in each case? (M.B.A., 2007)
(*a*) 903 (*b*) 939
(*c*) 975 (*d*) 996

102. The largest four-digit number which when divided by 4, 7 or 13 leaves a remainder of 3 in each case, is
(*a*) 8739 (*b*) 9831
(*c*) 9834 (*d*) 9893

103. Let the least number of six digits, which when divided by 4, 6, 10 and 15, leaves in each case the same remainder of 2, be N. The sum of the digits in N is (S.S.C., 2007)
(*a*) 3 (*b*) 4
(*c*) 5 (*d*) 6

104. The least multiple of 13, which on dividing by 4, 5, 6, 7 and 8 leaves remainder 2 in each case is
(*a*) 840 (*b*) 842
(*c*) 2520 (*d*) 2522

105. Find the least number which when divided by 12, leaves a remainder of 7; when divided by 15, leaves a remainder of 10 and when divided by 16, leaves a remainder of 11. (L.D.C., 2006)
(*a*) 115 (*b*) 235
(*c*) 247 (*d*) 475

106. The least number, which when divided by 48, 60, 72, 108 and 140 leaves 38, 50, 62, 98 and 130 as remainders respectively is (P.C.S., 2011)
(*a*) 11115 (*b*) 15110
(*c*) 15120 (*d*) 15210

107. Find the least multiple of 23, which when divided by 18, 21 and 24 leaves remainders 7, 10 and 13 respectively.
(*a*) 3002 (*b*) 3013
(*c*) 3024 (*d*) 3036

108. What is the third term in a sequence of numbers that leave remainders of 1, 2 and 3 when divided by 2, 3 and 4 respectively? (M.A.T., 2004)
(*a*) 11 (*b*) 17
(*c*) 19 (*d*) 35

109. Find the greatest number of 4 digits which when divided by 4, 5, 6, 7 and 8 leaves 1, 2, 3, 4 and 5 as remainders. (M.C.A., 2005)
(*a*) 9237 (*b*) 9240
(*c*) 9840 (*d*) 9999

110. The least number which when divided by 5, 6, 7 and 8 leaves a remainder 3, but when divided by 9 leaves no remainder, is (Section Officers', 2005; L.I.C., 2007)
(*a*) 1677 (*b*) 1683
(*c*) 2523 (*d*) 3363

111. Find the least number which when divided by 16, 18, 20 and 25 leaves 4 as remainder in each case, but when divided by 7 leaves no remainder.
(*a*) 17004 (*b*) 18000
(*c*) 18002 (*d*) 18004

112. A gardener has to plant trees in rows containing equal number of trees. If he plants in rows of 6, 8, 10 or 12, then five trees are left unplanted. But if he plants in rows of 13 trees each, then no tree is left. What is the number of trees that the gardener plants? (J.M.E.T., 2004)
(*a*) 485 (*b*) 725
(*c*) 845 (*d*) None of these

113. When Seeta made necklaces of either 16 beads, 20 beads or 36 beads, not a single bead was left over. What could be the least number of beads Seeta had? (Bank Recruitment, 2008)
(*a*) 700 (*b*) 720
(*c*) 750 (*d*) 780

114. An electronic device makes a beep after every 60 sec. Another device makes a beep after every 62 sec. They beeped together at 10 a.m. The next time, when they would beep together at the earliest is **(M.B.A., 2007)**

(*a*) 10.30 a.m. (*b*) 10.31 a.m.
(*c*) 10.59 a.m. (*d*) 11 a.m.

115. Six bells commence tolling together and toll at intervals of 2, 4, 6, 8, 10 and 12 seconds respectively. In 30 minutes, how many times do they toll together? **(M.B.A., 2006)**

(*a*) 4 (*b*) 10
(*c*) 15 (*d*) 16

116. Four bells begin to toll together and toll respectively at intervals of 6, 7, 8 and 9 seconds. In 1.54 hours, how many times do they toll together and in what interval (seconds)? **(R.R.B., 2006)**

(*a*) 14, 504 (*b*) 14, 480
(*c*) 12, 504 (*d*) 16, 580

117. Four different electronic devices make a beep after every 30 minutes, 1 hour, $1\frac{1}{2}$ hour and 1 hour 45 minutes respectively. All the devices beeped together at 12 noon. They will again beep together at

(*a*) 12 midnight (*b*) 3 a.m.
(*c*) 6 a.m. (*d*) 9 a.m.

118. Three girls start jogging from the same point around a circular track and each one completes one round in 24 seconds, 36 seconds and 48 seconds respectively. After how much time will they meet at one point? **(Specialist Officers', 2009)**

(*a*) 2 minutes 20 seconds (*b*) 2 minutes 24 seconds
(*c*) 3 minutes 36 seconds (*d*) 4 minutes 12 seconds

119. Three persons walking around a circular track complete their respective single revolutions in $15\frac{1}{6}$ seconds, $16\frac{1}{4}$ seconds and $18\frac{2}{3}$ seconds respectively. They will be again together at the common starting point after an hour and

(*a*) 10 seconds (*b*) 20 seconds
(*c*) 30 seconds (*d*) 40 seconds

120. A, B and C start at the same time in the same direction to run around a circular stadium. A completes a round in 252 seconds, B in 308 seconds and C in 198 seconds, all starting at the same point. After what time will they meet again at the starting point?

(*a*) 26 minutes 18 seconds (*b*) 42 minutes 36 seconds
(*c*) 45 minutes (*d*) 46 minutes 12 seconds

121. Three wheels can complete 40, 24 and 16 revolutions per minute respectively. There is a red spot on each wheel that touches the ground at time zero. After how much time, all these spots will simultaneously touch the ground again?

(*a*) $7\frac{1}{2}$ sec (*b*) 18 sec
(*c*) $7\frac{1}{2}$ min (*d*) 18 min

122. A pendulum strikes 5 times in 3 seconds and another pendulum strikes 7 times in 4 seconds. If both pendulums start striking at the same time, how many clear strikes can be listened in 1 minute?

(*a*) 195 (*b*) 199
(*c*) 200 (*d*) 205

123. Find the HCF of 132, 204 and 228. **[Indian Railways—Gr. 'D' Exam, 2014]**

(*a*) 12 (*b*) 18
(*c*) 6 (*d*) 21

124. If three numbers are $2a$, $5a$ and $7a$, what will be their LCM? **[Indian Railways—Gr. 'D' Exam, 2014]**

(*a*) $70a$ (*b*) $65a$
(*c*) $75a$ (*d*) $70a^3$

125. The product of two whole numbers is 1500 and their HCF is 10. Find the LCM. **[Indian Railways—Gr. 'D' Exam, 2014]**

(*a*) 15000 (*b*) 150
(*c*) 150 (*d*) 15

126. A number x is divided by 7. When this number is divided by 8, 12 and 16. It leaves a remainder 3 in each case. The least value of x is: **[SSC—CHSL (10 + 2) Exam, 2015]**

(*a*) 148 (*b*) 149
(*c*) 150 (*d*) 147

127. The number of pair of positive integers whose sum is 99 and HCF is 9 is **[SSC—CHSL (10 + 2) Exam, 2015]**

(*a*) 5 (*b*) 4
(*c*) 3 (*d*) 2

128. The ratio of two numbers is 3 : 4 and their LCM is 120. The sum of numbers is **[SSC—CHSL (10 + 2) Exam, 2015]**

(*a*) 70 (*b*) 140
(*c*) 35 (*d*) 105

129. The greatest four digit number which is exactly divisible by each one of the numbers 12, 18, 21 and 28 **[SSC—CHSL (10 + 2) Exam, 2015]**

(*a*) 9288 (*b*) 9882
(*c*) 9828 (*d*) 9928

130. The traffic lights at three different signal points change after every 45 seconds, 75 seconds and 90 seconds respectively. If all change simultaneously at 7 : 20 : 15 hours, then they will change again simultaneously at **[CLAT, 2016]**

(*a*) 7 : 28 : 00 hours (*b*) 7 : 27 : 45 hours
(*c*) 7 : 27 : 30 hours (*d*) 7 : 27 : 50 hours

ANSWERS

1. (d)	2. (b)	3. (a)	4. (c)	5. (a)	6. (b)	7. (c)	8. (a)	9. (d)	10. (a)
11. (a)	12. (a)	13. (c)	14. (a)	15. (a)	16. (b)	17. (d)	18. (d)	19. (d)	20. (c)
21. (c)	22. (b)	23. (b)	24. (b)	25. (c)	26. (c)	27. (a)	28. (d)	29. (d)	30. (c)
31. (b)	32. (d)	33. (c)	34. (a)	35. (d)	36. (d)	37. (a)	38. (a)	39. (b)	40. (d)
41. (c)	42. (b)	43. (c)	44. (d)	45. (a)	46. (c)	47. (b)	48. (d)	49. (d)	50. (c)
51. (c)	52. (a)	53. (b)	54. (c)	55. (a)	56. (c)	57. (a)	58. (b)	59. (d)	60. (d)
61. (a)	62. (c)	63. (a)	64. (a)	65. (c)	66. (a)	67. (b)	68. (c)	69. (c)	70. (c)
71. (b)	72. (b)	73. (a)	74. (b)	75. (d)	76. (a)	77. (b)	78. (a)	79. (a)	80. (a)
81. (c)	82. (a)	83. (c)	84. (b)	85. (a)	86. (c)	87. (b)	88. (a)	89. (a)	90. (d)
91. (c)	92. (b)	93. (d)	94. (c)	95. (b)	96. (b)	97. (b)	98. (b)	99. (d)	100. (c)
101. (c)	102. (b)	103. (c)	104. (d)	105. (b)	106. (b)	107. (b)	108. (d)	109. (a)	110. (b)
111. (d)	112. (c)	113. (b)	114. (b)	115. (d)	116. (c)	117. (d)	118. (b)	119. (d)	120. (d)
121. (a)	122. (b)	123. (a)	124. (a)	125. (b)	126. (d)	127. (a)	128. (a)	129. (c)	130. (b)

SOLUTIONS

1.
$$\begin{array}{r|l} 2 & 330 \\ \hline 3 & 165 \\ \hline 5 & 65 \\ \hline & 11 \end{array}$$

$\therefore \quad 330 = 2 \times 3 \times 5 \times 11$

2.
$$\begin{array}{r|l} 2 & 1122 \\ \hline 3 & 165 \\ \hline 11 & 187 \\ \hline & 17 \end{array}$$

$\therefore \quad 1122 = 2 \times 3 \times 11 \times 17$

3. Clearly, $252 = 2 \times 2 \times 3 \times 3 \times 7$.

4. $99 = 1 \times 3 \times 3 \times 11$;

$101 = 1 \times 101$;

$176 = 1 \times 2 \times 2 \times 2 \times 2 \times 11$;

$182 = 1 \times 2 \times 7 \times 13$.

So, divisors of 99 are 1, 3, 9, 11, 33 and 99;

divisors of 101 are 1 and 101;

divisors of 176 are 1, 2, 4, 8, 11, 16, 22, 44, 88 and 176;

divisors of 182 are 1, 2, 7, 13, 14, 26, 91 and 182.

Hence, 176 has the most number of divisors.

5.

n	*Divisors excluding n*	*Sum of divisors*
6	1, 2, 3	6
9	1, 3	4
15	1, 3, 5	9
21	1, 3, 7	11

Clearly, 6 is a perfect number.

6.
```
1095) 1168 (1
      1095
      ----
        73) 1095 (15
            73
            ---
            365
            365
            ---
             ×
```

So, H.C.F. of 1095 and 1168 = 73.

$\therefore \quad \frac{1095}{1168} = \frac{1095 \div 73}{1168 \div 73} = \frac{15}{16}$.

7.
```
128352) 238368 (1
        128352
        ------
        110016) 128352 (1
                110016
                ------
                 18336) 110016 (6
                        110016
                        ------
                          ×
```

So, H.C.F. of 128352 and 238368 = 18336.

$\therefore \quad \frac{128352}{238368} = \frac{128352 \div 18336}{238368 \div 18336} = \frac{7}{13}$.

8.
```
116690151) 427863887 (3
           350070453
           ---------
            77793434) 116690151 (1
                       77793434
                       --------
                       38896717) 77793434 (2
                                 77793434
                                 --------
                                    ×
```

So, H.C.F. of 116,690,151 and 427,863,887 = 38896717.

$$\frac{116,690,151}{427,863,887} = \frac{116690151 \div 38896717}{427863887 \div 38896717} = \frac{3}{11}.$$

9. Since division by 0 is undefined, so 0 cannot be a factor of any natural number.

Hence, H.C.F. of 0 and 6 is undefined.

10. H.C.F. = Product of lowest powers of common factors $= 2^2 \times 3^2 \times 5$.

11. H.C.F. = Product of lowest powers of common factors $= 3 \times 5 \times 7 = 105$.

12. $4 \times 27 \times 3125 = 2^2 \times 3^3 \times 5^5$;

$8 \times 9 \times 25 \times 7 = 2^3 \times 3^2 \times 5^2 \times 7$;

$16 \times 81 \times 5 \times 11 \times 49 = 2^4 \times 3^4 \times 5 \times 7^2 \times 11$.

$\therefore$ H.C.F. $= 2^2 \times 3^2 \times 5 = 180$.

13. $36 = 2^2 \times 3^2$; $84 = 2^2 \times 3 \times 7$.

$\therefore$ H.C.F. $= 2^2 \times 3 = 12$.

14. Since all the numbers formed are even, 2 is a common factor.

Also, H.C.F. of two of the numbers i.e., 48 and 490, is 2.

So, the H.C.F. of all the numbers formed is 2.

15. $204 = 2^2 \times 3 \times 17$;

$1190 = 2 \times 5 \times 7 \times 17$; $1445 = 5 \times 17^2$.

$\therefore$ H.C.F. = 17.

16. H.C.F. of 18 and 25 is 1. So, they are co-primes.

17.

```
2923 ) 3239 ( 1
       2923
       ----
        316 ) 2923 ( 9
              2844
              ----
                79 ) 316 ( 4
                     316
                     ---
                      ×
```

$\therefore$ H.C.F. = 79.

18.

```
3444 ) 3556 ( 1
       3444
       ----
        112 ) 3444 ( 30
              3360
              ----
                84 ) 112 ( 1
                      84
                     ---
                      28 ) 84 ( 3
                           84
                           --
                           ×
```

$\therefore$ H.C.F. = 28.

19. L.C.M. = Product of highest powers of prime factors $= 2^5 \times 3^4 \times 5^3 \times 7^2 \times 11$.

20.

2	24	36	40
2	12	18	20
2	6	9	10
3	3	9	5
	1	3	5

L.C.M. $= 2 \times 2 \times 2 \times 3 \times 3 \times 5 = 360$.

21.

2	22	54	108	135	198
3	11	27	54	135	99
3	11	9	18	45	33
3	11	3	6	15	11
11	11	1	2	5	11
	1	1	2	5	1

L.C.M. $= 2 \times 3 \times 3 \times 3 \times 11 \times 2 \times 5 = 5940$.

22. H.C.F. of 148 and 185 is 37. $\therefore$ L.C.M. $= \left(\frac{148 \times 185}{37}\right) = 740$.

23. H.C.F. of fractions $= \frac{\text{H.C.F. of Numerators}}{\text{L.C.M. of Denominators}}$.

H.C.F. of $\frac{a}{b}, \frac{c}{d}, \frac{e}{f} = \frac{\text{H.C.F. of } a, c, e}{\text{L.C.M. of } b, d, f}$.

24. Required H.C.F. $= \frac{\text{H.C.F. of } 2, 8, 64, 10}{\text{L.C.M. of } 3, 9, 81, 27} = \frac{2}{81}$.

25. Required H.C.F. $= \frac{\text{H.C.F. of } 9, 12, 18, 21}{\text{L.C.M. of } 10, 25, 35, 40} = \frac{3}{1400}$.

26. Required L.C.M. $= \frac{\text{L.C.M. of } 1, 5, 2, 4}{\text{H.C.F. of } 3, 6, 9, 27} = \frac{20}{3}$.

27. Required L.C.M. $= \frac{\text{L.C.M. of } 2, 3, 4, 9}{\text{H.C.F. of } 3, 5, 7, 13} = \frac{36}{1} = 36$.

28. Required L.C.M. $= \frac{\text{L.C.M. of } 3, 6, 9}{\text{H.C.F. of } 4, 7, 8} = \frac{18}{1} = 18$.

29. Given numbers with two decimal places are: 1.75, 5.60 and 7.00. Without decimal places, these numbers are: 175, 560 and 700, whose H.C.F. is 35.

$\therefore$ H.C.F. of given numbers = 0.35.

30. Given numbers are 1.08, 0.36 and 0.90. H.C.F. of 108, 36 and 90 is 18.

$\therefore$ H.C.F. of given numbers = 0.18.

31. Given numbers are 0.54, 1.80 and 7.20. H.C.F. of 54, 180 and 720 is 18.

$\therefore$ H.C.F. of given numbers = 0.18.

32. Given numbers are 3.00, 2.70 and 0.09. L.C.M. of 300, 270 and 9 is 2700.

$\therefore$ L.C.M. of given numbers = 27.00 = 27.

33. L.C.M. of A and B is B; L.C.M. of B and C is C $\Rightarrow$ L.C.M. of A, B and C is C.

34. $3240 = 2^3 \times 3^4 \times 5$; $3600 = 2^4 \times 3^2 \times 5^2$;

H.C.F. $= 36 = 2^2 \times 3^2$.

Since H.C.F. is the product of lowest powers of common factors, so the third number must have $(2^2 \times 3^2)$ as its factor.

Since L.C.M. is the product of highest powers of common prime factors, so the third number must have 3^5 and 7^2 as its factors.

$\therefore$ Third number $= 2^2 \times 3^5 \times 7^2$.

35. Let the required numbers be x, $2x$ and $3x$. Then, their H.C.F. = x. So, $x = 12$.

$\therefore$ The numbers are 12, 24 and 36.

36. Let the numbers be $3x$ and $4x$. Then, their H.C.F. = x. So, $x = 4$.
So, the numbers are 12 and 16.
L.C.M. of 12 and 16 = 48.

37. Let the required numbers be $27a$ and $27b$.
Then, $27a + 27b = 216 \Rightarrow a + b = 8$.
Now, co-primes with sum 8 are (1, 7) and (3, 5).
$\therefore$ Required numbers are $(27 \times 1, 27 \times 7)$ and $(27 \times 3, 27 \times 5)$ *i.e.*, (27, 189) and (81, 135).
Out of these, the one available in the given alternatives is the pair (27, 189).

38. Let the required numbers be $33a$ and $33b$.
Then, $33a + 33b = 528 \Rightarrow a + b = 16$.
Now, co-primes with sum 16 are (1, 15), (3, 13), (5, 11) and (7, 9).
$\therefore$ Required numbers are $(33 \times 1, 33 \times 15)$, $(33 \times 3, 33 \times 13)$, $(33 \times 5, 33 \times 11)$, $(33 \times 7, 33 \times 9)$.
The number of such pairs is 4.

39. Numbers with H.C.F. 15 must contain 15 as a factor.
Now, multiples of 15 between 40 and 100 are 45, 60, 75 and 90.
$\therefore$ Number-pairs with H.C.F. 15 are (45, 60), (45, 75), (60, 75) and (75, 90).
[$\because$ H.C.F. of (60, 90) is 30 and that of (45, 90) is 45]
Clearly, there are 4 such pairs.

40. Out of the given numbers, the two with H.C.F. 12 and difference 12 are 84 and 96.

41. Let the numbers be $37a$ and $37b$.
Then, $37a \times 37b = 4107 \Rightarrow ab = 3$.
Now, co-primes with product 3 are (1, 3).
So, the required numbers are $(37 \times 1, 37 \times 3)$ *i.e.*, (1, 111).
$\therefore$ Greater number = 111.

42. Let the numbers be $13a$ and $13b$.
Then, $13a \times 13b = 2028 \Rightarrow ab = 12$.
Now, co-primes with product 12 are (1, 12) and (3, 4).
So, the required numbers are $(13 \times 1, 13 \times 12)$ and $(13 \times 3, 13 \times 4)$.
Clearly, there are 2 such pairs.

43. Since the numbers are co-prime, they contain only 1 as the common factor.
Also, the given two products have the middle number in common.
So, middle number = H.C.F. of 551 and 1073 = 29;

First number = $\left(\frac{551}{29}\right) = 19$;

Third number = $\left(\frac{1073}{29}\right) = 37$.

$\therefore$ Required sum = $(19 + 29 + 37) = 85$.

44. Let the numbers be $13x$ and $15x$.
Then, their L.C.M. = $195x$.
So, $195x = 39780$ or $x = 204$.
$\therefore$ The numbers are 2652 and 3060.

45. Let the numbers be $3x$, $4x$ and $5x$.
Then, their L.C.M. = $60x$.
So, $60x = 2400$ or $x = 40$.
$\therefore$ The numbers are (3×40), (4×40) and (5×40).
Hence, required H.C.F. = 40.

46. Let the numbers be $2x$, $3x$, $5x$ and $7x$ respectively.
Then, their L.C.M. = $(2 \times 3 \times 5 \times 7)\,x = 210x$.
[$\because$ 2, 3, 5, 7 are prime numbers]
So, $210x = 630$ or $x = 3$.
$\therefore$ The numbers are 6, 9, 15 and 21.
Required difference = $21 - 6 = 15$.

47. Other number = $\left(\frac{12 \times 336}{84}\right) = 48$.

48. L.C.M. = $\frac{324}{3} = 108$.

49. Product of numbers = H.C.F. × L.C.M.
$\Rightarrow pq = x \times$ L.C.M.
$\Rightarrow$ L.C.M. = $\frac{pq}{x} = \frac{p(xy)}{x} = py$.

50. Let the numbers be x and $(2000 - x)$.
Then, their L.C.M. = $x(2000 - x)$.
So, $x(2000 - x) = 21879$
$\Leftrightarrow x^2 - 2000x + 21879 = 0$
$\Leftrightarrow (x - 1989)(x - 11) = 0$
$\Leftrightarrow x = 1989$ or $x = 11$.
Hence, the numbers are 1989 and 11.

51. Let the numbers be x and $4x$.
Then, $x \times 4x = 84 \times 21 \Leftrightarrow x^2 = \left(\frac{84 \times 21}{4}\right) \Leftrightarrow x = 21$.
Hence, larger number = $4x = 84$.

52. Let the numbers be x and $(100 - x)$.
Then, $x(100 - x) = 5 \times 495$
$\Leftrightarrow x^2 - 100x + 2475 = 0$
$\Leftrightarrow (x - 55)(x - 45) = 0$
$\Leftrightarrow x = 55$ or $x = 45$.
$\therefore$ The numbers are 45 and 55.
Required difference = $(55 - 45) = 10$.

53. Let the numbers be x and $(x + 2)$.
Then, $x(x + 2) = 24$
$\Leftrightarrow x^2 + 2x - 24 = 0$
$\Leftrightarrow (x - 4)(x + 6) = 0 \Leftrightarrow x = 4$.
So, the numbers are 4 and 6.

54. Let the numbers be a and b.
Then, $a + b = 36$ and $ab = 3 \times 105 = 315$.
$\therefore$ Required sum = $\frac{1}{a} + \frac{1}{b} = \frac{a + b}{ab} = \frac{36}{315} = \frac{4}{35}$.

55. Let H.C.F be h and L.C.M. be l.
Then, $l = 12h$ and $l + h = 403$.
$\therefore 12h + h = 403$ or $h = 31$.
So $l = (403 - 31) = 372$.
Hence, other number = $\left(\frac{31 \times 372}{93}\right) = 124$.

56. First number = $(50 \times 2) = 100$.

Second number = $\left(\frac{50 \times 250}{100}\right) = 125$.

57. L.C.M. = $\frac{\text{Product of numbers}}{\text{H.C.F.}} = \frac{1320}{6} = 220$.

58. H.C.F. of co-prime numbers is 1. So, L.C.M. = $\frac{117}{1} = 117$.

59. Since H.C.F. is always a factor of L.C.M., we cannot have three numbers with H.C.F. 35 and L.C.M. 120.

60. H.C.F. of two numbers divides their L.C.M. exactly. Clearly, 8 is not a factor of 60.

2	9570
3	4785
5	1595
11	319
	29

61. The factors of 9570 are 2, 3, 5, 11 and 29. Clearly, H.C.F. can be any of these factors occurring not more than once and no number other than 2, 3, 5, 11 or 29 or having any factor other than these, can be the H.C.F. So, the only possibility is 11.

62. Clearly, the numbers are (23×13) and (23×14).

$\therefore$ Larger number = $(23 \times 14) = 322$.

63. Since 16 is not a factor of 136, it follows that there does not exist any pair of numbers with H.C.F. 16 and L.C.M. 136.

64. Product of numbers = $21 \times 4641 = 97461$.

Let the numbers be $21a$ and $21b$.

Then, $21a \times 21b = 97461 \Rightarrow ab = 221$.

Now, co-primes with product 221 are (1, 221) and (13, 17).

So, the numbers are $(21 \times 1, 21 \times 221)$ and $(21 \times 13, 21 \times 17)$.

Since one number lies between 200 and 300, the suitable pair is (273, 357).

65. Product of numbers = 29×4147.

Let the numbers be $29a$ and $29b$.

Then, $29a \times 29b = (29 \times 4147) \Rightarrow ab = 143$.

Now, co-primes with product 143 are (1, 143) and (11, 13).

So, the numbers are $(29 \times 1, 29 \times 143)$ and $(29 \times 11, 29 \times 13)$.

Since both numbers are greater than 29, the suitable pair is $(29 \times 11, 29 \times 13)$, i.e., (319, 377).

$\therefore$ Required sum = $(319 + 377) = 696$.

66. H.C.F. of two prime numbers is 1.

Product of numbers = $(1 \times 161) = 161$.

Let the numbers be a and b. Then, $ab = 161$.

Now, co-primes with product 161 are (1, 161) and (7, 23).

Since x and y are prime numbers and $x > y$, we have $x = 23$ and $y = 7$.

$\therefore$ $3y - x = (3 \times 7) - 23 = -2$.

67. H.C.F. of 2436 and 1001 is 7. Also, H.C.F. of 105 and 7 is 7.

$\therefore$ H.C.F. of 105, 1001 and 2436 is 7.

68. For the minimum number of rows, the number of trees in each row must be the maximum.

$\therefore$ Number of trees in each row = H.C.F. of 21, 42, 56 = 7.

Hence, number of rows

$= \left(\frac{21 + 42 + 56}{7}\right) = \frac{119}{7} = 17$.

69. Required length = H.C.F. of 700 cm, 385 cm and 1295 cm = 35 cm.

70. Required capacity

= H.C.F. of 120 litres and 56 litres

= 8 litres = 8000 cc. [$\because$ 1 litre = 1000 cc]

71. Maximum possible daily wage = H.C.F. of ₹ 5750 and ₹ 5000 = ₹ 250.

72. For the least number of bottles, the capacity of each bottle must be maximum.

$\therefore$ Capacity of each bottle = H.C.F. of 403 litres, 465 litres and 496 litres = 31 litres.

Hence, required number of bottles

$= \left(\frac{403 + 465 + 496}{31}\right) = \frac{1364}{31} = 44$.

73. Required number of students = H.C.F. of 1001 and 910 = 91.

74. Largest size of the tile = H.C.F. of 378 cm and 525 cm = 21 cm.

75. For the least number of tiles, the size of the tile must be the maximum.

Maximum size of the tile = H.C.F. of 1517 cm and 902 cm = 41 cm.

Hence, required number of tiles

$= \frac{\text{Area of ceiling}}{\text{Area of each tile}} = \left(\frac{1517 \times 902}{41 \times 41}\right) = 814$.

76. Number of books in each stack = H.C.F. of 336, 240 and 96 = 48.

Hence, total number of stacks = $\left(\frac{336 + 240 + 96}{48}\right) = \frac{672}{48} = 14$.

77. Maximum length of each part = H.C.F. of 78 cm, 104 cm, 117 cm, 169 cm = 13 cm.

$\therefore$ Number of pieces =

$\left(\frac{78 + 104 + 117 + 169}{13}\right) = \frac{468}{13} = 36$.

78. Required number

= H.C.F. of (91 – 43), (183 – 91) and (183 – 43)

= H.C.F. of 48, 92 and 140 = 4.

79. d = H.C.F. of (8506 – 7654), (9997 – 8506) and (9997 – 7654)

= H.C.F. of 852, 1491 and 2343 = 213.

```
213 ) 7654 ( 35
      639
      ----
      1264
      1065
      ----
       199
```

Clearly, $r = 199$.

$\therefore$ $d - r = 213 - 199 = 14$.

80. N = H.C.F. of (4665 – 1305), (6905 – 4665) and (6905 – 1305)

= H.C.F. of 3360, 2240 and 5600 = 1120.

Sum of digits in N = (1 + 1 + 2 + 0) = 4.

81. Required volume

= [H.C.F. of (129 – 57), (177 – 129) and (177 – 57)] litres

= (H.C.F. of 72, 48 and 120) litres = 24 litres.

82. Required number
= H.C.F. of (1356 – 12), (1868 – 12) and (2764 – 12)
= H.C.F. of 1344, 1856 and 2752 = 64.

83. Required number
= H.C.F. of (3026 – 11) and (5053 – 13)
= H.C.F. of 3015 and 5040 = 45.

84. Required number
= H.C.F. of (964 – 41), (1238 – 31) and (1400 – 51)
= H.C.F. of 923, 1207 and 1349 = 71.

85. L.C.M. of 8, 16, 40 and 80 = 80.

$\frac{7}{8}=\frac{70}{80}; \frac{13}{16}=\frac{65}{80}; \frac{31}{40}=\frac{62}{80}.$

Since, $\frac{70}{80}>\frac{65}{80}>\frac{63}{80}>\frac{62}{80}$, so $\frac{7}{8}>\frac{13}{16}>\frac{63}{80}>\frac{31}{40}$. So, $\frac{7}{8}$ is the largest.

86. Required number
= L.C.M. of 1, 2, 3, 4, 5, 6, 7, 8, 9
= 2 × 2 × 3 × 5 × 7 × 2 × 3 = 2520.

2	1	2	3	4	5	6	7	8	9
2	1	1	3	2	5	3	7	4	9
3	1	1	3	1	5	3	7	2	9
	1	1	1	1	5	1	7	2	3

87. L.C.M. of 12, 18, 21, 30
= 2 × 3 × 2 × 3 × 7 × 5
= 1260.
∴ Required number = (1260 ÷ 2) = 630.

2	12	18	21	30
3	6	9	21	15
	2	3	7	5

88. Let the two numbers be a and b.
Then, $a + b = 45$ ...(i)
And, $a - b = 5$ ...(ii)
Adding (i) and (ii), we get: $2a = 50$ or $a = 25$.
Putting $a = 25$ in (i), we get: $b = 20$.
∴ L.C.M. = 5 × 4 × 5 = 100.

5	20	25
	4	5

89. Required fraction
$= \text{L.C.M. of } \frac{6}{7}, \frac{5}{14}, \frac{10}{21} = \frac{\text{L.C.M. of } 6, 5, 10}{\text{H.C.F. of } 7, 14, 21} = \frac{30}{7}.$

90. Least number of 5 digits is 10000. L.C.M. of 12, 15 and 18 is 180.
On dividing 10000 by 180, the remainder is 100.
∴ Required number = 10000 + (180 – 100) = 10080.

91. Greatest number of 4 digits is 9999.

5	15	25	40	75
5	3	5	8	15
3	3	1	8	3
	1	1	8	1

L.C.M. of 15, 25, 40 and 75 = 5 × 5 × 3 × 8 = 600.
On dividing 9999 by 600, the remainder is 399.
∴ Required number = (9999 – 399) = 9600.

92. L.C.M. of 12, 18, 21 and 32 = 2 × 2 × 3 × 3 × 7 × 8 = 2016.

2	12	18	21	32
2	6	9	21	16
3	3	9	21	8
	1	3	7	8

So, the required number is a multiple of 2016 and lies between 4000 and 5000.
Hence, required number = 4032.

93. L.C.M. of 25, 50 and 75 = 5 × 5 × 2 × 3 = 150.

5	25	50	75
5	5	10	15
	1	2	3

On dividing 43582 by 150, the remainder is 82 and quotient is 290.
So, required number = 150 × 291 = 43650.

94. L.C.M. of 5, 6, 4 and 3 = 60. On dividing 2497 by 60, the remainder is 37.
∴ Number to be added = (60 – 37) = 23.

95. L.C.M. of 20, 28, 32, 35 = 2 × 2 × 5 × 7 × 8 = 1120.
Required number = (5834 – 1120) = 4714.

2	20	28	32	35
2	10	14	16	35
5	5	7	8	35
7	1	7	8	7
	1	1	8	1

96. The least number divisible by 16, 20, 24
= L.C.M. of 16, 20, 24 = 240 = 2 × 2 × 2 × 2 × 3 × 5.
To make it a perfect square, it must be multiplied by 3 × 5.
∴ Required number = 240 × 3 × 5 = 3600.

97. Required number = (L.C.M. of 12, 16, 18, 21, 28) + 7
= 1008 + 7 = 1015.

98. Required number = (L.C.M. of 24, 32, 36, 54) – 5
= 864 – 5 = 859.

99. Required number = (L.C.M. of 12, 15, 20, 54) + 8
= 540 + 8 = 548.

100. L.C.M. of 4, 5, 6, 7 = 420.
∴ Required number = 420 + 1 = 421.

101. Greatest number of 3 digits is 999. L.C.M. of 6, 9 and 12 is 36.
On dividing 999 by 36, the remainder obtained is 27.
So, required number = (999 – 27) + 3 = 975.

102. Greatest number of 4 digits is 9999. L.C.M. of 4, 7 and 13 = 364.
On dividing 9999 by 364, the remainder obtained is 171.
∴ Greatest number of 4 digits divisible by 4, 7 and 13 = (9999 – 171) = 9828.
Hence, required number = (9828 + 3) = 9831.

103. Least number of 6 digits is 100000. L.C.M. of 4, 6, 10 and 15 = 60.
On dividing 100000 by 60, the remainder obtained is 40.
∴ Least number of 6 digits divisible by 4, 6, 10 and 15

$= 100000 + (60 - 40) = 100020.$

$\therefore$ $N = (100020 + 2) = 100022.$

Sum of digits in N = (1 + 2 + 2) = 5.

104. L.C.M. of 4, 5, 6, 7 and 8 is 840.

Let the required number be $840k + 2$, which is a multiple of 13.

Least value of k for which $(840k + 2)$ is divisible by 13 is $k = 3$.

$\therefore$ Required number = 840 × 3 + 2 = 2522.

105. Here (12 – 7) = 5, (15 – 10) = 5 and (16 – 11) = 5.

$\therefore$ Required number = (L.C.M. of 12, 15, 16) – 5 = 240 – 5 = 235.

106. Here (48 – 38) = 10, (60 – 50) = 10, (72 – 62) = 10 (108 – 98) = 10 & (140 – 130) = 10.

$\therefore$ Required number = (L.C.M. of 48, 60, 72, 108, 140) – 10 = 15120 – 10 = 15110.

107. Here (18 – 7) = 11, (21 – 10) = 11 and (24 – 13) = 11.

L.C.M. of 18, 21 and 24 is 504.

Let the required number be $504k - 11$.

Least value of k for which $(504k - 11)$ is divisible by 23 is $k = 6$.

$\therefore$ Required number = 504 × 6 – 11 = 3024 – 11 = 3013.

108. Clearly, (2 – 1) = 1, (3 – 2) = 1 and (4 – 3) = 1.

L.C.M. of 2, 3, 4 = 12.

So, the sequence shall have numbers of the form $12k - 1$, where k = 1, 2, 3,......

$\therefore$ Third term of the sequence = 12 × 3 – 1 = 36 – 1 = 35.

109. Clearly, (4 – 1) = 3, (5 – 2) = 3, (6 – 3) = 3, (7 – 4) = 3 and (8 – 5) = 3.

L.C.M. of 4, 5, 6, 7, 8 = 840.

Greatest number of 4 digits = 9999.

On dividing 9999 by 840, the remainder is 759.

So, required number = (9999 – 759) – 3 = 9237.

110. L.C.M. of 5, 6, 7, 8 = 840.

$\therefore$ Required number is of the form $840k + 3$.

Least value of k for which $(840k + 3)$ is divisible by 9 is $k = 2$.

$\therefore$ Required number = (840 × 2 + 3) = 1683.

111. L.C.M of 16, 18, 20, 25 = 3600.

Required number is of the form $3600k + 4$.

Least value of k for which $(3600k + 4)$ is divisible by 7 is $k = 5$.

$\therefore$ Required number = (3600 × 5 + 4) = 18004.

112. L.C.M. of 6, 8, 10, 12 = 120.

$\therefore$ Required number is of the form $120k + 5$.

Least value of k for which $(120k + 5)$ is divisible by 13 is $k = 7$.

$\therefore$ Required number = (120 × 7 + 5) = 845.

113. Required number of beads = L.C.M. of 16, 20, 36 = 720.

114. Interval of change = (L.C.M. of 60 and 62) sec = 1860 sec = 31 min.

So, the devices would beep together 31 min after 10 a.m., i.e., at 10.31 a.m.

115. L.C.M. of 2, 4, 6, 8, 10, 12 is 120.

So, the bells will toll together after every 120 seconds, i.e., 2 minutes.

In 30 minutes, they will toll together $\left[\left(\frac{30}{2}\right)+1\right]$ = 16 times.

116. Interval after which the bells will toll together

= (L.C.M. of 6, 7, 8, 9) sec = 504 sec.

In 1.54 hours, they will toll together $\left[\left(\frac{1.54 \times 60 \times 60}{504}\right)+1\right]$ times = 12 times.

117. Interval after which the devices will beep together

= (L.C.M. of 30, 60, 90, 105) min.

= 1260 min = 21 hrs.

So, the devices will again beep together 21 hrs. after 12 noon i.e., at 9 a.m.

118. L.C.M. of 24, 36, 48 = 144.

So, the three girls will meet at one point in 144 seconds i.e., 2 min 24 sec.

119. L.C.M. of $\frac{91}{6}, \frac{65}{4}$ and $\frac{56}{3} = \frac{\text{L.C.M. of } 91, 65, 56}{\text{H.C.F. of } 6, 4, 3} = 3640.$

So, the three persons will be together at the starting point in 3640 sec

i.e., 1 hour 40 seconds.

120. L.C.M. of 252, 308 and 198 = 2772.

So, A, B and C will again meet at the starting point in 2772 sec. *i.e.*, 46 min. 12 sec.

121. For one complete revolution, the first, second and third wheels take $\frac{60}{40}, \frac{60}{24}, \frac{60}{16}$ seconds i.e., $\frac{3}{2}, \frac{5}{2}, \frac{15}{4}$ seconds respectively.

$\therefore$ Time taken for all red spots to touch the ground again simultaneously.

$= \left(\text{L.C.M. of } \frac{3}{2}, \frac{5}{2}, \frac{15}{4}\right) \text{sec} = \left(\frac{\text{L.C.M. of } 3, 5, 15}{\text{H.C.F. of } 2, 2, 4}\right) \text{sec}$

$= \frac{15}{2} \text{sec} = 7\frac{1}{2} \text{sec}.$

122. First pendulum strikes once in $\frac{3}{5}$ seconds. Second pendulum strikes once in $\frac{4}{7}$ seconds.

L.C.M. of $\frac{3}{5}$ and $\frac{4}{7} = \frac{\text{L.C.M. of 3 and 4}}{\text{H.C.F. of 5 and 7}} = 12.$

So, they strike together after every 12 seconds.

Thus, they strike together $\left(\frac{60}{12}+1\right)$ = 6 times in 1 minute.

$\therefore$ Total number of clear strikes heard

$= \left[\frac{60}{\left(\frac{3}{5}\right)} + \frac{60}{\left(\frac{4}{7}\right)}\right] - 6 = \left(60 \times \frac{5}{3} + 60 \times \frac{7}{4}\right) - 6$

= (100 + 105) – 6 = 199.

123. H.C.F. of 132, 204 and 228.

$132 = 2 \times 2 \times 3 \times 11;$

$204 = 2 \times 2 \times 3 \times 17;$

$228 = 2 \times 2 \times 3 \times 19$

$\therefore$ HCF of 132, 204 and 228 is $2 \times 2 \times 3$ i.e. 12

$\therefore$ Required HCF = 12

Alternative method:

$132)204(1$
$\quad 132$

$72)132(1$
$\quad 72$

$60)72(1$
$\quad 60$

$12)60(5$
$\quad 60$
$\quad \times$

Again HCF of 12 and 228

$12)228(19$
$\quad 12$
$\quad 108$
$\quad 108$
$\quad \times$

$\therefore$ Required HCF = 12

124. The given three numbers are $2a$, $5a$ and $7a$. LCM of $2a$, $5a$ and $7a = 2 \times 5 \times 7 \times a = 70a$

125. Product of two numbers = 1500, HCF = 10

$$\text{LCM} = \frac{\text{Product of two numbers}}{\text{Their HCF}}$$

$$= \frac{1500}{10} = 150$$

Required LCM is 150.

126. LCM of 8, 12 and 16 = 48

2	8 – 12 – 16
2	4 – 6 – 8
2	2 – 3 – 4
	1 – 3 – 2

$2 \times 2 \times 2 \times 2 \times 3 = 48$

$\therefore$ Required number $= 48a + 3$

Which is divisible by 7.

$\therefore x = 48a + 3 = 7 \times 6a + 6a + 3$

$= (7 \times 6a)+(6a + 3)$ which is divisible by 7.

i.e. $6a + 3$ is divisible by 7.

When $a = 3$, $6a + 3 = 18 + 3 = 21$ which is divisible by 7.

$\therefore x = 48 \times 3 + 3 = 144 + 3 = 147$

127. Number of pair of positive integers whose sum is 99 and HCF is 9 is (9, 90; (18, 81); (27, 72); (36, 63) ; (45, 54).

128. Let the numbers are $3x$ and $4x$

So, HCF $= x$

$\because$ HCF × LCM = Product of numbers

$\Rightarrow x \times 120 = 3x \times 4x$

$\Rightarrow x \times 120 = 12x^2$

$\Rightarrow 120 = 12x$

$\Rightarrow x = 10$

$\therefore$ Numbers are 30 and 40.

$\therefore$ Sum of two numbers $= 30 + 40 = 70$

129. The greatest 4 digit number is 9999

The LCM of 12, 18, 21, 28 is 252

On dividing 9999 by 252 the remainder comes out to be 171

$\therefore$ Required number $= 9999 - 171 = 9828$

130.

5	45 – 75 – 90
3	9 – 15 – 18
3	3 – 5 – 6
	1 – 5 – 2

$\Rightarrow 5 \times 3 \times 3 \times 5 \times 2 = 450$

LCM of 45, 75, 90 is 450

$\therefore$ Traffic lights will change simultaneously after 7 minutes 30 seconds i.e. at 7 : 27 : 45 hours.

3 Decimal Fractions

IMPORTANT FACTS AND FORMULAE

I. Decimal Fractions: Fractions in which denominators are powers of 10 are known as ***decimal fractions.***

Thus, $\frac{1}{10}$ = 1 tenth = .1; $\frac{1}{100}$ = 1 hundredth = .01;

$\frac{99}{100}$ = 99 hundredths = .99; $\frac{7}{1000}$ = 7 thousandths = .007, etc.

II. Conversion of a Decimal into Vulgar Fraction: Put 1 in the denominator under the decimal point and annex with it as many zeros as is the number of digits after the decimal point. Now, remove the decimal point and reduce the fraction to its lowest terms.

Thus, $0.25 = \frac{25}{100} = \frac{1}{4}$; $2.008 = \frac{2008}{1000} = \frac{251}{125}$.

III. 1. Annexing zeros to the extreme right of a decimal fraction does not change its value.

Thus, 0.8 = 0.80 = 0.800, etc.

2. If numerator and denominator of a fraction contain the same number of decimal places, then we remove the decimal sign.

Thus, $\frac{1.84}{2.99} = \frac{184}{299} = \frac{8}{13}$; $\frac{.365}{.584} = \frac{365}{584} = \frac{5}{8}$.

IV. Operations on Decimal Fractions:

1. **Addition and Subtraction of Decimal Fractions:** The given numbers are so placed under each other that the decimal points lie in one column. The numbers so arranged can now be added or subtracted in the usual way.

2. **Multiplication of a Decimal Fraction By a Power of 10:** Shift the decimal point to the right by as many places as is the power of 10.

Thus, 5.9632 × 100 = 596.32; 0.073 × 10000 = 0.0730 × 10000 = 730.

3. **Multiplication of Decimal Fractions:** Multiply the given numbers considering them without the decimal point. Now, in the product, the decimal point is marked off to obtain as many places of decimal as is the sum of the number of decimal places in the given numbers.

Suppose we have to find the product (.2 × .02 × .002).

Now, 2 × 2 × 2 = 8. Sum of decimal places = (1 + 2 + 3) = 6.

∴ .2 × .02 × .002 = .000008.

4. **Dividing a Decimal Fraction By a Counting Number:** Divide the given number without considering the decimal point, by the given counting number. Now, in the quotient, put the decimal point to give as many places of decimal as there are in the dividend.

Suppose we have to find the quotient (0.0204 ÷ 17). Now, 204 ÷ 17 = 12.

Dividend contains 4 places of decimal. So, 0.0204 ÷ 17 = 0.0012.

5. **Dividing a Decimal Fraction By a Decimal Fraction:** Multiply both the dividend and the divisor by a suitable power of 10 to make divisor a whole number. Now, proceed as above.

Thus, $\frac{0.00066}{0.11} = \frac{0.00066 \times 100}{0.11 \times 100} = \frac{0.066}{11} = .006$.

V. Comparison of Fractions: Suppose some fractions are to be arranged in ascending or descending order of magnitude. Then, convert each one of the given fractions in the decimal form, and arrange them accordingly.

Suppose, we have to arrange the fractions $\frac{3}{5}, \frac{6}{7}$ and $\frac{7}{9}$ in descending order.

Now, $\frac{3}{5} = 0.6, \frac{6}{7} = 0.857, \frac{7}{9} = 0.777....$

Since $0.857 > 0.777 .... > 0.6$, so $\frac{6}{7} > \frac{7}{9} > \frac{3}{5}$.

VI. Recurring Decimal: If in a decimal fraction, a figure or a set of figures is repeated continuously, then such a number is called a ***recurring decimal.***

In a recurring decimal, if a single figure is repeated, then it is expressed by putting a dot on it. If a set of figures is repeated, it is expressed by putting a bar on the set.

Thus, $\frac{1}{3} = 0.333..... = 0.\dot{3}; \frac{22}{7} = 3.142857142857..... = 3.\overline{142857}$.

Pure Recurring Decimal: A decimal fraction in which all the figures after the decimal point are repeated, is called a pure recurring decimal.

Converting a Pure Recurring Decimal into Vulgar Fraction: Write the repeated figures only once in the numerator and take as many nines in the denominator as is the number of repeating figures.

Thus, $0.\dot{5} = \frac{5}{9}; 0.\overline{53} = \frac{53}{99}; 0.\overline{067} = \frac{67}{999}$; etc.

Mixed Recurring Decimal: A decimal fraction in which some figures do not repeat and some of them are repeated, is called a mixed recurring decimal.

e.g., $0.17333 ..... = 0.17\overline{3}$.

Converting a Mixed Recurring Decimal into Vulgar Fraction: In the numerator, take the difference between the number formed by all the digits after decimal point (taking repeated digits only once) and that formed by the digits which are not repeated. In the denominator, take the number formed by as many nines as there are repeating digits followed by as many zeros as is the number of non-repeating digits.

Thus, $0.1\dot{6} = \frac{16-1}{90} = \frac{15}{90} = \frac{1}{6}; 0.22\overline{73} = \frac{2273-22}{9900} = \frac{2251}{9900}$.

VII. Some Basic Formulae:

1. $(a + b)(a - b) = (a^2 - b^2)$
2. $(a + b)^2 = (a^2 + b^2 + 2ab)$
3. $(a - b)^2 = (a^2 + b^2 - 2ab)$
4. $(a + b + c)^2 = a^2 + b^2 + c^2 + 2(ab + bc + ca)$
5. $(a^3 + b^3) = (a + b)(a^2 - ab + b^2)$
6. $(a^3 - b^3) = (a - b)(a^2 + ab + b^2)$
7. $(a^3 + b^3 + c^3 - 3abc) = (a + b + c)(a^2 + b^2 + c^2 - ab - bc - ac)$
8. When $a + b + c = 0$, then $a^3 + b^3 + c^3 = 3abc$.

SOLVED EXAMPLES

Ex. 1. ***Convert the following into vulgar fractions:***

(i) 0.75 ***(ii) 3.004*** ***(iii) .0056***

Sol. (*i*) $0.75 = \frac{75}{100} = \frac{3}{4}$. (*ii*) $3.004 = \frac{3004}{1000} = \frac{751}{250}$. (*iii*) $.0056 = \frac{56}{10000} = \frac{7}{1250}$.

Ex. 2. ***Arrange the fractions*** $\frac{5}{8}, \frac{7}{12}, \frac{13}{16}, \frac{16}{29}$ ***and*** $\frac{3}{4}$ ***in ascending order of magnitude.***

Sol. Converting each of the given fractions into decimal form, we get:

$\frac{5}{8} = 0.625, \frac{7}{12} = 0.5833, \frac{13}{16} = 0.8125, \frac{16}{29} = 0.5517$ and $\frac{3}{4} = 0.75$.

Now, $0.5517 < 0.5833 < 0.625 < 0.75 < 0.8125$.

$\therefore \frac{16}{29} < \frac{7}{12} < \frac{5}{8} < \frac{3}{4} < \frac{13}{16}$.

Ex. 3. ***Arrange the fractions $\frac{3}{5}, \frac{4}{7}, \frac{8}{9}$ and $\frac{9}{11}$ in their descending order.***

Sol. Clearly, $\frac{3}{5} = 0.6, \frac{4}{7} = 0.571, \frac{8}{9} = 0.88, \frac{9}{11} = 0.818.$

Now, $0.88 > 0.818 > 0.6 > 0.571.$

$\therefore \frac{8}{9} > \frac{9}{11} > \frac{3}{5} > \frac{4}{7}.$

Ex. 4. ***Evaluate: (i) 11.11 + 111.1 + 1111.11*** **(Bank Recruitment, 2009)**

(ii) 6202.5 + 620.25 + 62.025 + 6.2025 + 0.62025

(iii) 5.064 + 3.98 + .7036 + 7.6 + .3 + 2

Sol.

(i)
```
     11.11
    111.10
 + 1111.11
 ---------
   1233.32
```

(ii)
```
   6202.5
    620.25
     62.025
      6.2025
 +    0.62025
 ------------
   6891.59775
```

(iii)
```
   5.064
   3.98
   0.7036
   7.6
   0.3
 + 2.0
 -------
  19.6476
```

Ex. 5. ***Evaluate: (i) 31.004 – 17.2386*** ***(ii) 13 – 5.1967***

Sol.

(i)
```
   31.0040
  -17.2386
  --------
   13.7654
```

(ii)
```
   13.0000
 -  5.1967
  --------
    7.8033
```

Ex. 6. ***Evaluate: (i) 515.15 – 15.51 – 1.51 – 5.11 – 1.11*** **(Bank P.O., 2009)**

(ii) 43.231 – 12.779 – 6.542 – 0.669 **(Bank P.O., 2008)**

Sol. (i) Given expression = 515.15 – (15.51 + 1.51 + 5.11 + 1.11) = 515.15 – 23.24 = 491.91.

```
   15.51          515.15
    1.51        -  23.24
    5.11        --------
 +  1.11          491.91
 -------
   23.24
```

(ii) Given expression = 43.231 – (12.779 + 6.542 + 0.669) = 43.231 – 19.990 = 23.241.

```
   12.779          43.231
    6.542        - 19.990
 +  0.669        --------
 --------          23.241
   19.990
```

Ex. 7. ***What value will replace the question mark in the following equations?***

(i) 5172.49 + 378.352 +? = 9318.678

(ii) ? – 7328.96 = 5169.38

Sol. (i) Let $5172.49 + 378.352 + x = 9318.678$.

Then, $x = 9318.678 - (5172.49 + 378.352) = 9318.678 - 5550.842 = 3767.836$.

(ii) Let $x - 7328.96 = 5169.38$. Then, $x = 5169.38 + 7328.96 = 12498.34$.

Ex. 8. ***Find the products: (i) 6.3204 × 100 (ii) .069 × 10000***

Sol. (i) $6.3204 \times 100 = 632.04$. (ii) $.069 \times 10000 = .0690 \times 10000 = 690$.

Ex. 9. ***Find the products:*** **(Bank P.O., 2008)**

(i) 2.1693 × 1.4

(ii) .4 × .04 × .004 × 40

(iii) 6.66 × 66.6 × 66

Sol. (i) $21693 \times 14 = 303702$. Sum of decimal places = (4 + 1) = 5.

$\therefore 2.1693 \times 1.4 = 3.03702$.

(ii) $4 \times 4 \times 4 \times 40 = 2560$. Sum of decimal places = (1 + 2 + 3) = 6.

$\therefore .4 \times .04 \times .004 \times 40 = .002560$.

(iii) $666 \times 666 \times 66 = 29274696$. Sum of decimal places = (2 + 1) = 3.

$\therefore 6.66 \times 66.6 \times 66 = 29274.696$.

Ex. 10. *Given that 268 × 74 = 19832, find the value of 2.68 × .74.*

Sol. Sum of decimal places = (2 + 2) = 4.

$\therefore$ 2.68 × .74 = 1.9832.

Ex. 11. *Find the quotient:*

(i) 0.63 ÷ 9 (ii) 0.0204 ÷ 17 (iii) 3.1603 ÷ 13

Sol. *(i)* 63 ÷ 9 = 7. Dividend contains 2 places of decimal.

$\therefore$ 0.63 ÷ 9 = .07.

(ii) 204 ÷ 17 = 12. Dividend contains 4 places of decimal.

$\therefore$ 0.0204 ÷ 17 = .0012.

(iii) 31603 ÷ 13 = 2431. Dividend contains 4 places of decimal.

$\therefore$ 3.1603 ÷ 13 = .2431.

Ex. 12. *Evaluate:*

(i) 35 ÷ .07 (ii) 2.5 ÷ 0.0005 (iii) 136.09 ÷ 43.9

Sol. *(i)* $\frac{35}{.07} = \frac{35 \times 100}{.07 \times 100} = \frac{3500}{7} = 500.$

(ii) $\frac{2.5}{0.0005} = \frac{2.5 \times 10000}{0.0005 \times 10000} = \frac{25000}{5} = 5000.$

(iii) $\frac{136.09}{43.9} = \frac{136.09 \times 10}{43.9 \times 10} = \frac{1360.9}{439} = 3.1.$

Ex. 13. *What value will come in place of question mark in the following equations?*

(i) 0.006 ÷? = 0.6 (ii)? ÷ .025 = 80

Sol. *(i)* Let $\frac{0.006}{x} = 0.6$. Then, $x = \frac{0.006}{0.6} = \frac{0.006 \times 10}{0.6 \times 10} = \frac{0.06}{6} = 0.01.$

(ii) Let $\frac{x}{.025} = 80$. Then, $x = 80 \times .025 = 2.$

Ex. 14. *If $\frac{1}{3.718} = .2689$, then find the value of $\frac{1}{.0003718}$.*

Sol. $\frac{1}{.0003718} = \frac{10000}{3.718} = \left(10000 \times \frac{1}{3.718}\right) = 10000 \times .2689 = 2689.$

Ex. 15. *Evaluate:*

(i) 0.5 × 5.6 ÷ 0.5 × 1 (Bank Recruitment, 2010)

(ii) 25 × 3.25 + 50.4 ÷ 24 (Bank P.O., 2010)

(iii) 0.01 × 0.1 – 0.001 ÷ 10 + 0.01 (Bank P.O., 2009)

(iv) 12.28 × 1.5 – 36 ÷ 2.4 (Bank P.O., 2009)

Sol. *(i)* Given expression $= 0.5 \times \frac{5.6}{0.5} \times 12 = \frac{5 \times 56 \times 12}{50} = \frac{3360}{50} = 67.2.$

(ii) Given expression $= 25 \times 3.25 + \frac{50.4}{24} = 81.25 + 2.1 = 83.35.$

(iii) Given expression $= 0.001 - \frac{0.001}{10} + 0.01 = 0.001 - 0.0001 + 0.01. = 0.011 - 0.0001 = 0.0109.$

(iv) Given expression $= 12.28 \times 1.5 - \frac{36}{2.4} = 18.42 - 15 = 3.42.$

Ex. 16. *The product of two numbers is 0.008 and one is $\frac{1}{5}$ of the other. Find the numbers.* (R.R.B., 2009)

Sol. Let the numbers be x and $\frac{x}{5}$. Then,

$x \times \frac{x}{5} = 0.008 \Rightarrow \frac{x^2}{5} = 0.008 \Rightarrow x^2 = 0.008 \times 5 = 0.04 \Rightarrow x = \sqrt{0.04} = 0.2.$

$\therefore$ Greater number = 0.2. Smaller number = $\frac{0.2}{5} = 0.04.$

Hence, the required numbers are 0.2 and 0.04.

Ex. 17. ***Express as vulgar fractions:*** **(S.S.C., 2010)**

(i) $0.\overline{37}$ ***(ii)*** $0.\overline{053}$ ***(iii)*** $0.\overline{001}$ ***(iv)*** $3.\overline{142857}$

Sol. *(i)* $0.\overline{37} = \frac{37}{99}$. *(ii)* $0.\overline{053} = \frac{53}{999}$. *(iii)* $0.\overline{001} = \frac{1}{999}$. *(iv)* $3.\overline{142857} = 3 + 0.\overline{142857} = 3 + \frac{142857}{999999} = 3\frac{142857}{999999}$.

Ex. 18. ***Express as vulgar fractions:***

(i) $0.1\overline{7}$ (ii) $0.12\overline{54}$ (iii) $2.53\overline{6}$

Sol. *(i)* $0.1\overline{7} = \frac{17-1}{90} = \frac{16}{90} = \frac{8}{45}$. *(ii)* $0.12\overline{54} = \frac{1254-12}{9900} = \frac{1242}{9900} = \frac{69}{550}$.

(iii) $2.53\overline{6} = 2 + 0.53\overline{6} = 2 + \frac{536-53}{900} = 2 + \frac{483}{900} = 2 + \frac{161}{300} = 2\frac{161}{300}$.

Ex. 19. ***If*** $\frac{b}{a} = 0.25$***, then what is the value of*** $\frac{2a-b}{2a+b} + \frac{2}{9}$***?*** **(R.R.B., 2005)**

Sol. $\frac{2a-b}{2a+b} + \frac{2}{9} = \frac{2-\frac{b}{a}}{2+\frac{b}{a}} + \frac{2}{9}$ [Dividing numerator and denominator by a]

$= \frac{2-0.25}{2+0.25} + \frac{2}{9} = \frac{1.75}{2.25} + \frac{2}{9} = \frac{7}{9} + \frac{2}{9} = \frac{9}{9} = 1.$

Ex. 20. ***Find the value of*** $(1.99)^2$. **(Campus Recruitment, 2009)**

Sol. $(1.99)^2 = (2 - 0.01)^2 = 2^2 + (0.01)^2 - 2 \times 2 \times 0.01 = 4 + 0.0001 - 0.04 = 3.9601.$

Ex. 21. ***Simplify:*** $\sqrt{\frac{0.009 \times 0.036 \times 0.016 \times 0.08}{0.002 \times 0.0008 \times 0.0002}}$ **(S.S.C., 2010)**

Sol. Since the sum of the decimal places in the numerator and denominator is the same, we have:

Given expression = $\sqrt{\frac{9 \times 36 \times 16 \times 8}{2 \times 8 \times 2}} = \sqrt{1296} = 36.$

Ex. 22. ***Simplify:*** $\frac{(0.35)^2 - (0.03)^2}{0.19}$. **(R.R.B., 2006)**

Sol. Given expression = $\frac{(0.35+0.03)(0.35-0.03)}{0.19} = \frac{0.38 \times 0.32}{0.19} = 2 \times 0.32 = 0.64.$

Ex. 23. ***Find the value of*** $\frac{0.21 \times 0.21 \times 0.21 + 0.021 \times 0.021 \times 0.021}{0.63 \times 0.63 \times 0.63 + 0.063 \times 0.063 \times 0.063}$. **(S.S.C., 2006)**

Sol. Let $a = 0.21$ and $b = 0.021$. Then,

Given expression = $\frac{a^3 + b^3}{(3a)^3 + (3b)^3} = \frac{a^3 + b^3}{27a^3 + 27b^3} = \frac{a^3 + b^3}{27(a^3 + b^3)} = \frac{1}{27}.$

Ex. 24. ***Simplify:***

(i) $\left(\frac{2.75 \times 2.75 \times 2.75 - 2.25 \times 2.25 \times 2.25}{2.75 \times 2.75 + 2.75 \times 2.25 + 2.25 \times 2.25}\right)$ **(C.P.O., 2007)**

(ii) $\left(\frac{0.0347 \times 0.0347 \times 0.0347 + 0.9653 \times 0.9653 \times 0.9653}{0.0347 \times 0.0347 - 0.0347 \times 0.9653 + 0.9653 \times 0.9653}\right)$ **(S.S.C., 2007)**

Sol. (*i*) Given expression $= \left(\dfrac{a^3-b^3}{a^2+ab+b^2}\right)$, where $a = 2.75$, $b = 2.25$

$= (a-b) = (2.75 - 2.25) = 0.5.$

(*ii*) Given expression $= \left(\dfrac{a^3+b^3}{a^2-ab+b^2}\right)$, where $a = 0.0347$, $b = 0.9653$

$= (a+b) = (0.0347 + 0.9653) = 1.$

Ex. 25. ***Find the value of:*** $\dfrac{(0.01)^2+(0.22)^2+(0.333)^2}{(0.001)^2+(0.022)^2+(0.0333)^2}$.

Sol. Given expression $= \dfrac{a^2+b^2+c^2}{\left(\dfrac{a}{10}\right)^2+\left(\dfrac{b}{10}\right)^2+\left(\dfrac{c}{10}\right)^2}$, where $a = 0.01$, $b = 0.022$, $c = 0.0333$ $= \dfrac{100\,(a^2+b^2+c^2)}{(a^2+b^2+c^2)} = 100.$

EXERCISE

(OBJECTIVE TYPE QUESTIONS)

Directions: ***Mark (✓) against the correct answer:***

1. The value of $\dfrac{42}{10000}$ in decimal fraction is (L.I.C.A.D.O., 2008)
 (*a*) .0042 (*b*) .00042
 (*c*) .0420 (*d*) 42000

2. The fraction $101\dfrac{27}{100000}$ in decimal form is
 (*a*) .01027 (*b*) .10127
 (*c*) 101.00027 (*d*) 101.000027

3. When .36 is written in simplest fractional form, the sum of the numerator and the denominator is
 (*a*) 15 (*b*) 34
 (*c*) 114 (*d*) 135

4. The place value of 9 in 0.06945 is (L.I.C.A.D.O., 2008)
 (*a*) 9 (*b*) $\dfrac{9}{10}$
 (*c*) $\dfrac{9}{100}$ (*d*) $\dfrac{9}{1000}$

5. What decimal of an hour is a second?
 (*a*) .0025 (*b*) .0256
 (*c*) .00027 (*d*) .000126

6. If $47.2506 = 4A + \dfrac{7}{B} + 2C + \dfrac{5}{D} + 6E$, then the value of $5A + 3B + 6C + D + 3E$ is
 (*a*) 53.6003 (*b*) 53.6031
 (*c*) 153.6003 (*d*) 213.0003

7. Express $\dfrac{1999}{2111}$ in decimal. (R.R.B., 2006)
 (*a*) 0.893 (*b*) 0.904
 (*c*) 0.946 (*d*) 0.986

8. How many times is 0.1 greater than 0.01?
 (*a*) 1 time (*b*) 10 times
 (*c*) 100 times (*d*) 1000 times

9. Out of the fractions $\dfrac{3}{7}, \dfrac{4}{11}, \dfrac{5}{9}, \dfrac{6}{13}, \dfrac{7}{12}$, which is the second largest? (Bank Recruitment, 2010)
 (*a*) $\dfrac{3}{7}$ (*b*) $\dfrac{4}{11}$
 (*c*) $\dfrac{5}{9}$ (*d*) $\dfrac{6}{13}$
 (*e*) $\dfrac{7}{12}$

10. Which of the following has fractions in ascending order?
 (*a*) $\dfrac{2}{3}, \dfrac{3}{5}, \dfrac{7}{9}, \dfrac{9}{11}, \dfrac{8}{9}$ (*b*) $\dfrac{3}{5}, \dfrac{2}{3}, \dfrac{9}{11}, \dfrac{7}{9}, \dfrac{8}{9}$
 (*c*) $\dfrac{3}{5}, \dfrac{2}{3}, \dfrac{7}{9}, \dfrac{9}{11}, \dfrac{8}{9}$ (*d*) $\dfrac{8}{9}, \dfrac{9}{11}, \dfrac{7}{9}, \dfrac{2}{3}, \dfrac{3}{5}$
 (*e*) $\dfrac{8}{9}, \dfrac{9}{11}, \dfrac{7}{9}, \dfrac{3}{5}, \dfrac{2}{3}$

11. Which of the following are in descending order of their values?
 (*a*) $\dfrac{5}{9}, \dfrac{7}{11}, \dfrac{8}{15}, \dfrac{11}{17}$ (*b*) $\dfrac{5}{9}, \dfrac{8}{15}, \dfrac{11}{17}, \dfrac{7}{11}$
 (*c*) $\dfrac{11}{17}, \dfrac{7}{11}, \dfrac{8}{15}, \dfrac{5}{9}$ (*d*) $\dfrac{11}{17}, \dfrac{7}{11}, \dfrac{5}{9}, \dfrac{8}{15}$

12. What is the difference between the biggest and the smallest fraction among $\dfrac{2}{3}, \dfrac{3}{4}, \dfrac{4}{5}$ and $\dfrac{5}{6}$? (S.S.C., 2006)
 (*a*) $\dfrac{1}{6}$ (*b*) $\dfrac{1}{12}$
 (*c*) $\dfrac{1}{20}$ (*d*) $\dfrac{1}{30}$

13. The least among the following fractions is (S.S.C., 2010)

(a) $\frac{15}{16}$ (b) $\frac{19}{20}$

(c) $\frac{24}{25}$ (d) $\frac{34}{35}$

14. Out of the fractions $\frac{9}{31}, \frac{3}{17}, \frac{6}{23}, \frac{4}{11}$ and $\frac{7}{25}$, which is the largest? (Bank Recruitment, 2010)

(a) $\frac{9}{31}$ (b) $\frac{3}{17}$

(c) $\frac{6}{23}$ (d) $\frac{4}{11}$

(e) None of these

15. If the fractions $\frac{2}{5}, \frac{3}{8}, \frac{4}{9}, \frac{5}{13}$ and $\frac{6}{11}$ are arranged in ascending order of their values, which one will be the fourth? (S.B.I.P.O., 2008)

(a) $\frac{2}{5}$ (b) $\frac{3}{8}$

(c) $\frac{4}{9}$ (d) $\frac{5}{13}$

(e) None of these

16. Which part contains the fractions in ascending order?

(a) $\frac{11}{14}, \frac{16}{19}, \frac{19}{21}$ (b) $\frac{16}{19}, \frac{11}{14}, \frac{19}{21}$

(c) $\frac{16}{19}, \frac{19}{21}, \frac{11}{14}$ (d) $\frac{19}{21}, \frac{11}{14}, \frac{16}{19}$

17. Which of the following fractions is the smallest?

(a) $\frac{13}{16}$ (b) $\frac{15}{19}$

(c) $\frac{17}{21}$ (d) $\frac{7}{8}$

18. Which of the following fractions is greater than $\frac{3}{4}$ and less than $\frac{5}{6}$?

(a) $\frac{1}{2}$ (b) $\frac{2}{3}$

(c) $\frac{4}{5}$ (d) $\frac{9}{10}$

19. Which of the following fractions is less than $\frac{7}{8}$ and greater than $\frac{1}{3}$?

(a) $\frac{1}{4}$ (b) $\frac{23}{24}$

(c) $\frac{11}{12}$ (d) $\frac{17}{24}$

20. Which of the following numbers does not lie between $\frac{4}{5}$ and $\frac{7}{13}$?

(a) $\frac{1}{2}$ (b) $\frac{2}{3}$

(c) $\frac{3}{4}$ (d) $\frac{5}{7}$

21. The arrangement of rational numbers $\frac{-7}{10}, \frac{5}{-8}, \frac{2}{-3}$ in ascending order is

(a) $\frac{2}{-3}, \frac{5}{-8}, \frac{-7}{10}$ (b) $\frac{5}{-8}, \frac{-7}{10}, \frac{2}{-3}$

(c) $\frac{-7}{10}, \frac{5}{-8}, \frac{2}{-3}$ (d) $\frac{-7}{10}, \frac{2}{-3}, \frac{5}{-8}$

22. Which of the following fractions lies between $\frac{2}{3}$ and $\frac{3}{5}$? (C.P.O., 2006)

(a) $\frac{2}{5}$ (b) $\frac{1}{3}$

(c) $\frac{1}{15}$ (d) $\frac{31}{50}$

23. Which of the following fractions is less than $\frac{1}{5}$? (R.R.B., 2006)

(a) $\frac{8}{35}$ (b) $\frac{8}{37}$

(c) $\frac{8}{39}$ (d) $\frac{2}{11}$

24. Which of the following fractions is nearest to $\frac{2}{5}$? (R.R.B., 2006)

(a) $\frac{4}{5}$ (b) $\frac{21}{50}$

(c) $\frac{20001}{50000}$ (d) $\frac{200001}{500000}$

25. The rational numbers lying between $\frac{1}{3}$ and $\frac{3}{4}$ are

(a) $\frac{117}{300}, \frac{287}{400}$ (b) $\frac{95}{300}, \frac{301}{400}$

(c) $\frac{99}{300}, \frac{301}{400}$ (d) $\frac{97}{300}, \frac{299}{500}$

26. Three rational numbers between $\frac{1}{5}$ and $\frac{1}{6}$ are

(a) $\frac{4}{25}, \frac{9}{50}, \frac{17}{100}$ (b) $\frac{4}{25}, \frac{17}{100}, \frac{167}{1000}$

(c) $\frac{4}{25}, \frac{9}{50}, \frac{167}{1000}$ (d) $\frac{9}{50}, \frac{17}{100}, \frac{167}{1000}$

27. 0.3 + 3 + 3.33 + 3.3 + 3.03 + 333 =? (NABARD, 2009)
(a) 345.99 (b) 355.96
(c) 375.66 (d) 375.93
(e) None of these

28. 636.66 + 366.36 + 363.33 =? (Bank Recruitment, 2009)
(a) 1336.35 (b) 1363.25
(c) 1366.25 (d) 1636.25
(e) None of these

29. 24.424 + 5.656 + 1.131 + 0.089 =? (Bank P.O., 2009)
(a) 31.003 (b) 31.3
(c) 31.0003 (d) 31.03
(e) None of these

30. 555.05 + 55.5 + 5.55 + 5 + 0.55 =? (S.B.I.P.O., 2008)
(a) 621.65 (b) 634.85
(c) 647.35 (d) 655.75
(e) None of these

31. 4 + 4.44 + 0.4 + 44.04 + 444 =? (Bank P.O., 2008)
(a) 469.88 (b) 487.66
(c) 496.88 (d) 497.24
(e) None of these

32. 999.99 + 99.99 + 9.99 =? (Bank Recruitment, 2008)
(a) 1019.89 (b) 1099.88
(c) 1108.99 (d) 1109.99
(e) None of these

33. 10.0001 + 9.9999 – 8.9995 =? (E.P.F.O.S.S.A., 2004)
(a) 9.0005 (b) 10.9995
(c) 11.0001 (d) 11.0005
(e) None of these

34. 48.95 – 32.006 =?
(a) 16.089 (b) 16.35
(c) 16.89 (d) 16.944

35. 58.621 – 13.829 – 7.302 – 1.214 =? (Bank P.O., 2009)
(a) 31.254 (b) 35.272
(c) 36.276 (d) 37.281
(e) None of these

36. 341.42 – 53.74 =? – 62.86 (Bank Recruitment, 2010)
(a) 260.44 (b) 340.44
(c) 350.54 (d) 450.54
(e) None of these

37. 534.596 + 61.472 – 496.708 =? + 27.271 (Bank P.O., 2010)
(a) 62.069 (b) 72.089
(c) 126.631 (d) 132.788
(e) None of these

38. 11.71 – 0.86 + 1.78 – 9.20 =? (Bank Recruitment, 2010)
(a) 2.43 (b) 3.13
(c) 3.43 (d) 4.13
(e) None of these

39. 726.34 + 888.12 –? = 1001.88 (Bank P.O., 2009)
(a) 602.64 (b) 618.78
(c) 621.58 (d) 654.54
(e) None of these

40. 832.58 – 242.31 = 779.84 –?
(a) 179.57 (b) 199.57
(c) 295.05 (d) None of these

41. Which one of the following is wrong?
(a) $\frac{9}{4} + 1.75 = 4$ (b) $\frac{9}{5} + 2.2 = 4$
(c) $\frac{6}{5} + 2.8 = 4$ (d) $\frac{3}{2} + 1.5 = 4$

42. If $x = 10$ and $y = 0.1$, which of the following is the greatest?
(a) $x^2 + y^2$ (b) $x^2 - y^2$
(c) $x^2 y^2$ (d) $\frac{x^2}{y^2}$

43. Which of the following is closest to zero? (M.C.A., 2005)
(a) $(0.09)^2$ (b) 0.09
(c) $(1 - 0.9)^2$ (d) $1 - (0.9)^2$

44. One hundredth of centimetre when written in fractions of kilometres, is equal to (M.C.A., 2005)
(a) 0.0000001 (b) 0.000001
(c) 0.0001 (d) 0.001

45. What will come in place of question mark in the following equation?
54.(?)3 + 543 + 5.43 = 603.26
(a) 5 (b) 6
(c) 8 (d) None of these

46. Which of the following is equal to 3.14×10^6? (Hotel Management, 2003)
(a) 314 (b) 3140
(c) 3140000 (d) None of these

47. The number 518,000,000 when expressed in scientific notation, equals
(a) 51.8×10^6 (b) 51.8×10^7
(c) 5.18×10^8 (d) 5.18×10^9

48. 0.000006723 when expressed in scientific notation, is
(a) 6723×10^{-5} (b) 67.23×10^{-7}
(c) 6.723×10^{-6} (d) None of these

49. If $1.125 \times 10^k = 0.001125$, then the value of k is:
(a) – 4 (b) – 3
(c) – 2 (d) – 1

50. $(0.1 \times 0.01 \times 0.001 \times 10^7)$ is equal to (S.S.C., 2010)
(a) $\frac{1}{10}$ (b) $\frac{1}{100}$
(c) 10 (d) 100

51. 383 × 38 × 3.8 =? **(Bank P.O., 2008)**
(*a*) 55305.2 (*b*) 56305.4
(*c*) 57305.6 (*d*) 58305.8
(*e*) None of these

52. The product of 0.09 and 0.007 is **(L.I.C.A.D.O., 2008)**
(*a*) 0.6300 (*b*) 0.00063
(*c*) 0.00630 (*d*) 0.000063

53. 0.1 × 0.01 × 0.001 =? **(M.C.A., 2005)**
(*a*) 0.0001 (*b*) 0.00001
(*c*) 0.000001 (*d*) 0.0000001

54. 3 × 0.3 × 0.03 × 0.003 × 30 =?
(*a*) 0.0000243 (*b*) 0.000243
(*c*) 0.00243 (*d*) 0.0243

55. 14.4 × 16.5 × 8 =? **(Bank P.O., 2009)**
(*a*) 1908.0 (*b*) 1900.8
(*c*) 1912.4 (*d*) 1924.8

56. 47.7 × 12.4 × 8.6 =? **(Bank Recruitment, 2009)**
(*a*) 5086.728 (*b*) 5218.668
(*c*) 5708.428 (*d*) 6180.656
(*e*) None of these

57. 32.4 × 11.5 × 8.5 =? **(Bank Recruitment, 2009)**
(*a*) 3149.5 (*b*) 3129.1
(*c*) 3167.1 (*d*) 3162.5
(*e*) None of these

58. 0.04 × 0.0162 is equal to
(*a*) 6.48×10^{-3} (*b*) 6.48×10^{-4}
(*c*) 6.48×10^{-5} (*d*) 6.48×10^{-6}

59. How many digits will be there to the right of the decimal point in the product of 95.75 and .02554?
(*a*) 5 (*b*) 6
(*c*) 7 (*d*) None of these

60. $\left(.00625 \text{ of } \frac{23}{5}\right)$ when expressed as a vulgar fraction, equals
(*a*) $\frac{23}{80}$ (*b*) $\frac{23}{800}$
(*c*) $\frac{23}{8000}$ (*d*) $\frac{125}{23}$

61. Which is the closest approximation to the following product?
0.3333 × 0.25 × 0.499 × 0.125 × 24
(*a*) $\frac{1}{8}$ (*b*) $\frac{3}{4}$
(*c*) $\frac{3}{8}$ (*d*) $\frac{2}{5}$

62. The number 0.0561 correct to two places of decimals is
(*a*) 0.1 (*b*) 0.06
(*c*) 0.05 (*d*) 0.056

63. (0.05 × 5 – 0.005 × 5) equals **(S.S.C., 2005)**
(*a*) 0.0225 (*b*) 0.225
(*c*) 0.250 (*d*) 0.275

64. 19.99 × 9.9 + 99.9 =? **(NABARD, 2008)**
(*a*) 129.79 (*b*) 297.801
(*c*) 1009 (*d*) 296.910
(*e*) None of these

65. 345 + 25 × 0.80 – 111 =? **(Bank P.O., 2008)**
(*a*) 254 (*b*) 324
(*c*) 666 (*d*) 600
(*e*) None of these

66. 29.92 × 2.4 + 21.28 × 4.5 =? **(Bank P.O., 2009)**
(*a*) 167.568 (*b*) 167.658
(*c*) 176.568 (*d*) 176.658
(*e*) None of these

67. 4.4 × 5.8 × 11.5 – 141.27 =? **(Bank Recruitment, 2009)**
(*a*) 121.17 (*b*) 147.51
(*c*) 152.21 (*d*) 187.95
(*e*) None of these

68. Consider the following quotients:
1. 368.39 divided by 17 2. 170.50 divided by 62
3. 875.65 divided by 83
Their correct sequence in decreasing order is:
(*a*) 1, 3, 2 (*b*) 2, 1, 3
(*c*) 2, 3, 1 (*d*) 3, 1, 2

69. 0.213 ÷ 0.00213 =?
(*a*) 1 (*b*) 10
(*c*) 100 (*d*) None of these

70. $\frac{25.025}{0.025}$ is equal to **(R.R.B., 2004)**
(*a*) 1.01 (*b*) 10.1
(*c*) 101 (*d*) 1001

71. 4.036 divided by 0.04 gives **(Hotel Management, 2003)**
(*a*) 1.009 (*b*) 10.09
(*c*) 100.9 (*d*) None of these

72. $\frac{1}{0.04}$ is equal to
(*a*) $\frac{1}{40}$ (*b*) $\frac{2}{5}$
(*c*) 2.5 (*d*) 25

73. (833.25 – 384.45) ÷ 24 =? **(Bank P.O., 2010)**
(*a*) 1.87 (*b*) 2.01
(*c*) 18.7 (*d*) 20.1
(*e*) None of these

74. 6425 ÷ 125 × 8 =? **(Bank Recruitment, 2009)**
(*a*) 41.12 (*b*) 64.25
(*c*) 411.2 (*d*) 421.25
(*e*) None of these

75. 7777 ÷ 77 ÷ 5 =? **(Bank Recruitment, 2009)**
(*a*) 15.2 (*b*) 18.5
(*c*) 22.4 (*d*) 50.5
(*e*) None of these

76. (0.75 × 4.4 × 2.4) ÷ 0.6 =? **(Bank Recruitment, 2009)**
(*a*) 4.752 (*b*) 12
(*c*) 13.2 (*d*) 15.84
(*e*) None of these

77. $\left(\frac{0.05}{0.25}+\frac{0.25}{0.05}\right)^3 = ?$
(*a*) 139.4 (*b*) 140
(*c*) 140.6 (*d*) 143.9

78. The value of 0.0396 ÷ 2.51 correct to 2 significant figures is
(*a*) 0.015 (*b*) 0.0157
(*c*) 0.016 (*d*) 0.017

79. 3927 + 5526 ÷ 12.5 =? **(L.I.C.A.D.O., 2007)**
(*a*) 750.24 (*b*) 756.24
(*c*) 4369.08 (*d*) 4369.24
(*e*) None of these

80. (11.6 ÷ 0.8) (13.5 ÷ 2) =? **(R.R.B., 2008)**
(*a*) 98 (*b*) 99
(*c*) 100 (*d*) None of these

81. (0.05 × 6.25) ÷ 2.5 =? **(Bank P.O., 2008)**
(*a*) 0.95 (*b*) 0.105
(*c*) 0.115 (*d*) 1.25
(*e*) None of these

82. 0.5 × 0.5 + 0.5 ÷ 5 is equal to **(L.I.C.A.D.O., 2008)**
(*a*) 0.15 (*b*) 0.25
(*c*) 0.35 (*d*) 0.45

83. 400 ÷ 0.1 × 0.2 =?
(*a*) 0.8 (*b*) 8
(*c*) 80 (*d*) 8000
(*e*) None of these

84. $5.5 - [6.5 - \{3.5 \div (6.5 - \overline{5.5 - 2.5})\}]$ is equal to
(*a*) – 1 (*b*) 0
(*c*) 0.1 (*d*) 1

85. .04 ×? = .000016
(*a*) 0.0004 (*b*) 0.04
(*c*) 4 (*d*) None of these

86. $\frac{.009}{?} = .01$
(*a*) .0009 (*b*) .09
(*c*) .9 (*d*) 9

87. If $\frac{144}{0.144} = \frac{14.4}{x}$, then the value of x is
(*a*) 0.0144 (*b*) 1.44
(*c*) 14.4 (*d*) 144

88. 40.04 ÷ 0.4 =? × 0.05
(*a*) 20.02 (*b*) 20.2
(*c*) 200.2 (*d*) 2002

89. 48 ÷ 75 × 84.5 ÷ 20 =? **(Bank P.O., 2006)**
(*a*) 1.527 (*b*) 1.834
(*c*) 2.704 (*d*) 2.914
(*e*) None of these

90. (5420 + 3312 +?) ÷ 600 = 25.93 **(Bank Recruitment, 2009)**
(*a*) 6286 (*b*) 6584
(*c*) 6826 (*d*) 6830
(*e*) None of these

91. $[(?)^2 + (18)^2] \div 125 = 3.56$ **(Bank Recruitment, 2009)**
(*a*) 11 (*b*) 12
(*c*) 14 (*d*) 15
(*e*) None of these

92. 786 ÷ 24 ×? = 6.55
(*a*) 0.2 (*b*) 0.4
(*c*) 4 (*d*) 5
(*e*) None of these

93. A maximum of how many pieces of 12.6 cm can be cut from a 857 cm long rod?
(*a*) 58 (*b*) 62
(*c*) 64 (*d*) 68

94. Vishal donates blood thrice in 2 years – each time 350 ml. How many litres of blood will he donate in 6 years? **(Bank Recruitment, 2010)**
(*a*) 1.2 (*b*) 3.15
(*c*) 4.5 (*d*) 6.3
(*e*) None of these

95. Terry consumes 1600 ml of milk everyday. How many litres of milk will she consume in 4 weeks? **(Bank Recruitment, 2010)**
(*a*) 41.6 (*b*) 42.6
(*c*) 43.4 (*d*) 44.8
(*e*) None of these

96. A tailor has 37.5 metres of cloth and he has to make 8 pieces out of a metre of cloth. How many pieces can be make out of this cloth?
(*a*) 320 (*b*) 360
(*c*) 400 (*d*) None of these

97. The price of commodity X increases by 40 paise every year, while the price of commodity Y increases by 15 paise every year. If in 2004, the price of commodity X was ₹ 4.20 and that of Y was ₹ 6.30, in which year commodity X will cost 40 paise more than the commodity Y?
(*a*) 2013 (*b*) 2014
(*c*) 2015 (*d*) 2016

98. A sum of ₹ 6.25 is made up of 80 coins which are either 10P or 5P. How many are there of each kind? (A.T.M.A., 2006)

(*a*) 45, 35 (*b*) 40, 40
(*c*) 35, 45 (*d*) 25, 55

99. The number 0.121212 ...... in the form $\frac{p}{q}$ is equal to (S.S.C., 2010)

(*a*) $\frac{2}{11}$ (*b*) $\frac{4}{11}$
(*c*) $\frac{2}{33}$ (*d*) $\frac{4}{33}$

100. The rational number for the recurring decimal 0.125125 ..... is

(*a*) $\frac{63}{487}$ (*b*) $\frac{119}{993}$
(*c*) $\frac{125}{999}$ (*d*) None of these

101. When $0.\overline{47}$ is converted into a fraction, the result is (Section Officers', 2003)

(*a*) $\frac{46}{90}$ (*b*) $\frac{46}{99}$
(*c*) $\frac{47}{90}$ (*d*) $\frac{47}{99}$

102. $0.\overline{36}$ expressed in the form $\frac{p}{q}$ equals

(*a*) $\frac{4}{11}$ (*b*) $\frac{4}{13}$
(*c*) $\frac{35}{90}$ (*d*) $\frac{35}{99}$

103. The least among the following is

(*a*) 0.2 (*b*) 1 ÷ 0.2
(*c*) $0.\overline{2}$ (*d*) $(0.2)^2$

104. $1.\overline{27}$ in the form $\frac{p}{q}$ is equal to (S.S.C., 2010)

(*a*) $\frac{127}{100}$ (*b*) $\frac{14}{11}$
(*c*) $\frac{73}{100}$ (*d*) $\frac{11}{14}$

105. $0.4\overline{23}$ is equivalent to the fraction (C.P.O., 2005)

(*a*) $\frac{94}{99}$ (*b*) $\frac{49}{99}$
(*c*) $\frac{491}{990}$ (*d*) $\frac{419}{990}$

106. Express $0.29\overline{56}$ in the form $\frac{p}{q}$ (vulgar fraction) (R.R.B., 2005)

(*a*) $\frac{2956}{1000}$ (*b*) $\frac{2956}{10000}$
(*c*) $\frac{2927}{9900}$ (*d*) None of these

107. Let F = $0.841\overline{81}$. When F is written as a fraction in lowest terms, the denominator exceeds the numerator by

(*a*) 13 (*b*) 14
(*c*) 29 (*d*) 87

108. The value of $4.1\overline{2}$ is

(*a*) $4\frac{11}{90}$ (*b*) $4\frac{11}{99}$
(*c*) $\frac{371}{900}$ (*d*) None of these

109. $2.8\overline{768}$ is equal to (C.P.O., 2006)

(*a*) $2\frac{878}{999}$ (*b*) $2\frac{9}{10}$
(*c*) $2\frac{292}{333}$ (*d*) $2\frac{4394}{4995}$

110. The value of $(0.\overline{2} + 0.\overline{3} + 0.\overline{32})$ is (S.S.C., 2005)

(*a*) $0.\overline{77}$ (*b*) $0.\overline{82}$
(*c*) $0.\overline{86}$ (*d*) $0.\overline{87}$

111. $0.\overline{142857} \div 0.\overline{285714}$ is equal to (S.S.C., 2007)

(*a*) $\frac{1}{2}$ (*b*) $\frac{1}{3}$
(*c*) 2 (*d*) 10

112. $3.\overline{87} - 2.\overline{59}$ =?

(*a*) 1.20 (*b*) $1.\overline{2}$
(*c*) $1.\overline{27}$ (*d*) $1.\overline{28}$

113. The simplification of $3.\overline{36} - 2.\overline{05} + 1.\overline{33}$ equals

(*a*) 2.60 (*b*) 2.64
(*c*) $2.\overline{61}$ (*d*) $2.\overline{64}$

114. $(0.\overline{09} \times 7.\overline{3})$ is equal to: (S.S.C., 2003)

(*a*) $.\overline{6}$ (*b*) $.\overline{657}$
(*c*) $.\overline{67}$ (*d*) $.6\overline{57}$

115. $(0.34\overline{67} + 0.13\overline{33})$ is equal to (Hotel Management, 2002)

(*a*) $0.4\overline{8}$ (*b*) $0.\overline{48}$
(*c*) $0.48\overline{01}$ (*d*) 0.48

116. $(8.3\overline{1} + 0.\overline{6} + 0.00\overline{2})$ is equal to (S.S.C., 2005)

(*a*) $8.9\overline{12}$ (*b*) $8.\overline{912}$
(*c*) $8.9\overline{79}$ (*d*) $8.97\overline{9}$

117. The sum of $\overline{2}.75$ and $\overline{3}.78$ is

(*a*) $\overline{1}.03$ (*b*) $\overline{1}.53$
(*c*) $\overline{4}.53$ (*d*) $\overline{5}.53$

118. If $\frac{547.527}{0.0082} = x$, then the value of $\frac{547527}{82}$ is

(a) $\frac{x}{10}$ (b) $10x$
(c) $100x$ (d) None of these

119. If $2994 \div 14.5 = 172$, then $29.94 \div 1.45 = ?$

(a) 0.172 (b) 1.72
(c) 17.2 (d) 172

120. If $213 \times 16 = 3408$, then 1.6×21.3 is equal to

(a) 0.3408 (b) 3.408
(c) 34.08 (d) 340.8

121. If $\frac{1}{6.198} = 0.16134$, then the value of $\frac{1}{0.0006198}$ is

(a) 0.016134 (b) 0.16134
(c) 1613.4 (d) 16134

122. When 52416 is divided by 312, the quotient is 168. What will be the quotient when 52.416 is divided by 0.0168?

(a) 3.12 (b) 312
(c) 3120 (d) None of these

123. Given $168 \times 32 = 5376$, then $5.376 \div 16.8$ is equal to

(a) 0.032 (b) 0.32
(c) 3.2 (d) 32

124. $54.327 \times 357.2 \times 0.0057$ is the same as

(a) $5.4327 \times 3.572 \times 5.7$
(b) $5.4327 \times 3.572 \times 0.57$
(c) $54327 \times 3572 \times 0.0000057$
(d) None of these

125. $\frac{5.3472 \times 324.23}{3.489 \times 5.42}$ is the same as

(a) $\frac{53472 \times 3.2423}{3.489 \times 54.2}$ (b) $\frac{53472 \times 32423}{3489 \times 542}$
(c) $\frac{534.72 \times 324.23}{34.89 \times 5.42}$ (d) $\frac{53472 \times 3242.3}{3489 \times 542}$

126. $\frac{96.54 - 89.63}{96.54 + 89.63} \div \frac{965.4 - 896.3}{9.654 + 8.963} = ?$

(a) 10^{-2} (b) 10^{-1}
(c) 10 (d) None of these

127. If $1^3 + 2^3 + ... + 9^3 = 2025$, then the value of $(0.11)^3 + (0.22)^3 + ... + (0.99)^3$ is close to:

(a) 0.2695 (b) 0.3695
(c) 2.695 (d) 3.695

128. The value of $\frac{1}{4} + \frac{1}{4 \times 5} + \frac{1}{4 \times 5 \times 6}$ correct to 4 decimal places is

(a) 0.3075 (b) 0.3082
(c) 0.3083 (d) 0.3085

129. Find the value of the following expression upto four places of decimals.

$$\left[1 + \frac{1}{1 \times 2} + \frac{1}{1 \times 2 \times 4} + \frac{1}{1 \times 2 \times 4 \times 8} + \frac{1}{1 \times 2 \times 4 \times 8 \times 16}\right]$$

(a) 1.6414 (b) 1.6415
(c) 1.6416 (d) 1.6428

130. The sum of the first 20 terms of the series $\frac{1}{5 \times 6} + \frac{1}{6 \times 7} + \frac{1}{7 \times 8} + ...$ is

(a) 0.16 (b) 1.6
(c) 16 (d) None of these

131. The last digit in the decimal representation of $\left(\frac{1}{5}\right)^{2000}$ is **(Hotel Management, 2010)**

(a) 2 (b) 4
(c) 5 (d) 6

132. Which of the following is equal to 1?

(a) $\frac{(0.11)^2}{(1.1)^2 \times 0.1}$ (b) $\frac{(1.1)^2}{11^2 \times (0.01)^2}$
(c) $\frac{(0.011)^2}{(1.1)^2 \times (0.01)^2}$ (d) $\frac{(0.11)^2}{11^2 \times 0.01}$

133. The expression $\frac{3}{4} + \frac{5}{36} + \frac{7}{144} + \cdots + \frac{17}{5184} + \frac{19}{8100}$ is equal to **(A.A.O. Exam, 2010)**

(a) 0.9 (b) 0.95
(c) 0.99 (d) 1.91

134. If $1.5x = 0.04y$, then the value of $\left(\frac{y-x}{y+x}\right)$ is **(N.M.A.T. 2006; M.B.A. 2007; S.S.C. 2010)**

(a) $\frac{730}{77}$ (b) $\frac{73}{77}$
(c) $\frac{7.3}{77}$ (d) None of these

135. The value of $\left[35.7 - \left(3 + \frac{1}{3 + \frac{1}{3}}\right) - \left(2 + \frac{1}{2 + \frac{1}{2}}\right)\right]$ is

(a) 30 (b) 34.8
(c) 36.6 (d) 41.4

136. $\frac{(0.1667)(0.8333)(0.3333)}{(0.2222)(0.6667)(0.1250)}$ is approximately equal to

(a) 2 (b) 2.40
(c) 2.43 (d) 2.50

137. $\frac{3.5 \times 1.4}{0.7} = ?$ (L.I.C.A.D.O., 2007)

(a) 0.7 (b) 2.4
(c) 3.5 (d) 7.1
(e) None of these

138. $\frac{1.6 \times 3.2}{0.08} = ?$ (Bank Recruitment, 2007)

(a) 0.8 (b) 6.4
(c) 8 (d) 64
(e) None of these

139. $\frac{4.41 \times 0.16}{2.1 \times 1.6 \times 0.21}$ is simplified to (S.S.C., 2010)

(a) 1 (b) 0.1
(c) 0.01 (d) 10

140. $\frac{.625 \times .0729 \times 28.9}{.0081 \times .025 \times 1.7} = ?$ (I.I.F.T. 2005)

(a) 382.5 (b) 3625
(c) 3725 (d) 3825
(e) None of these

141. The value of $\frac{3.6 \times 0.48 \times 2.50}{0.12 \times 0.09 \times 0.5}$ is

(a) 80 (b) 800
(c) 8000 (d) 80000

142. $\frac{0.0203 \times 2.92}{0.0073 \times 14.5 \times 0.7} = ?$

(a) 0.8 (b) 1.45
(c) 2.40 (d) 3.25

143. The value of $\frac{3.157 \times 4126 \times 3.198}{63.972 \times 2835.121}$ is closest to

(a) 0.002 (b) 0.02
(c) 0.2 (d) 2

144. The value of $\frac{489.1375 \times 0.0483 \times 1.956}{0.0873 \times 92.581 \times 99.749}$ is closet to

(a) 0.006 (b) 0.06
(c) 0.6 (d) 6

145. The value of $\frac{241.6 \times 0.3814 \times 6.842}{0.4618 \times 38.25 \times 73.65}$ is close to

(a) 0.2 (b) 0.4
(c) 0.6 (d) 1

146. $(0.2 \times 0.2 + 0.01)(0.1 \times 0.1 + 0.02)^{-1}$ is equal to (Section Officers', 2003)

(a) $\frac{5}{3}$ (b) $\frac{9}{5}$
(c) $\frac{41}{4}$ (d) $\frac{41}{12}$

147. $\frac{5 \times 1.6 - 2 \times 1.4}{1.3} = ?$

(a) 0.4 (b) 1.2
(c) 1.4 (d) 4

148. The value of $(4.7 \times 13.26 + 4.7 \times 9.43 + 4.7 \times 77.31)$ is: (IGNOU, 2003)

(a) 0.47 (b) 47
(c) 470 (d) 4700

149. Simplify : $\frac{0.2 \times 0.2 + 0.2 \times 0.02}{0.044}$.

(a) 0.004 (b) 0.4
(c) 1 (d) 2

150. The value of $\left(\frac{8.6 \times 5.3 + 8.6 \times 4.7}{4.3 \times 9.7 - 4.3 \times 8.7}\right)$ is

(a) 3.3 (b) 6.847
(c) 13.9 (d) 20

151. The value of $\left(\frac{.896 \times .763 + .896 \times .237}{.7 \times .064 + .7 \times .936}\right)$ is

(a) .976 (b) 9.76
(c) 1.28 (d) 12.8

152. The value of $(1.25)^3 - 2.25\,(1.25)^2 + 3.75\,(0.75)^2 - (0.75)^3$ is

(a) 1 (b) $\frac{1}{2}$
(c) $\frac{1}{4}$ (d) $\frac{1}{8}$

153. $(78.95)^2 - (43.35)^2 = ?$ (S.B.I.P.O., 2008)

(a) 4148 (b) 4235.78
(c) 4305 (d) 4353.88
(e) None of these

154. The value of $\frac{(75.8)^2 - (55.8)^2}{20}$ is

(a) 20 (b) 40
(c) 121.6 (d) 131.6

155. $\frac{(3.63)^2 - (2.37)^2}{3.63 + 2.37}$ is simplified to (C.P.O., 2006)

(a) 1.26 (b) 1.36
(c) 2.26 (d) 6

156. $\frac{(36.54)^2 - (3.46)^2}{?} = 40$

(a) 3.308 (b) 4
(c) 33.08 (d) 330.8

157. The value of $\frac{(67.542)^2 - (32.458)^2}{75.458 - 40.374}$ is

(a) 1 (b) 10
(c) 100 (d) None of these

158. $\left(\dfrac{1.49\times14.9-0.51\times5.1}{14.9-5.1}\right)$ is equal to (S.S.C., 2004)
(*a*) 0.20 (*b*) 2.00
(*c*) 20 (*d*) 22

159. $\dfrac{4.2\times4.2-1.9\times1.9}{2.3\times6.1}=?$
(*a*) 0.5 (*b*) 1
(*c*) 1.9 (*d*) 4.2

160. Simplify: $\dfrac{5.32\times56+5.32\times44}{(7.66)^2-(2.34)^2}$.
(*a*) 7.2 (*b*) 8.5
(*c*) 10 (*d*) 12

161. $\dfrac{(0.6)^4-(0.5)^4}{(0.6)^2+(0.5)^2}$ is equal to
(*a*) 0.1 (*b*) 0.11
(*c*) 1.1 (*d*) 11

162. (7.5 × 7.5 + 37.5 + 2.5 × 2.5) is equal to
(*a*) 30 (*b*) 60
(*c*) 80 (*d*) 100

163. The simplification of $\dfrac{0.2\times0.2+0.02\times0.02-0.4\times0.02}{0.36}$ gives
(*a*) 0.009 (*b*) 0.09
(*c*) 0.9 (*d*) 9

164. $(99.75)^2 - 2250.0625 = ?$ (Bank P.O., 2008)
(*a*) 6545.625 (*b*) 7700
(*c*) 8875 (*d*) 9900.625
(*e*) None of these

165. $(55.25)^2 - 637.5625 = ?$ (Bank P.O., 2008)
(*a*) 25.25 (*b*) 625
(*c*) 1375 (*d*) 2415
(*e*) None of these

166. $\dfrac{3.25\times3.20-3.20\times3.05}{0.064}$ is equal to (S.S.C., 2010)
(*a*) 1 (*b*) $\dfrac{1}{2}$
(*c*) $\dfrac{1}{10}$ (*d*) 10

167. The value of $(.98)^3 + (.02)^3 + 3 \times .98 \times .02 - 1$ is (S.S.C., 2005)
(*a*) 0 (*b*) 1
(*c*) 1.09 (*d*) 1.98

168. The expression (11.98 × 11.98 + 11.98 × x + 0.02 × 0.02) will be a perfect square for x equal to:
(*a*) 0.02 (*b*) 0.2
(*c*) 0.04 (*d*) 0.4

169. The value of $\dfrac{(2.697-0.498)^2+(2.697+0.498)^2}{2.697\times2.697+0.498\times0.498}$ is
(*a*) 0.5 (*b*) 2
(*c*) 2.199 (*d*) 3.195

170. The value of $\dfrac{(0.137+0.098)^2-(0.137-0.098)^2}{0.137\times0.098}$ is
(*a*) 0.039 (*b*) 0.235
(*c*) 0.25 (*d*) 4

171. The value of
$\left(\dfrac{0.051\times0.051\times0.051+0.041\times0.041\times0.041}{0.051\times0.051-0.051\times0.041+0.041\times0.041}\right)$ is (S.S.C., 2003)
(*a*) 0.00092 (*b*) 0.0092
(*c*) 0.092 (*d*) 0.92

172. The value of $\dfrac{5.71\times5.71\times5.71-2.79\times2.79\times2.79}{5.71\times5.71+5.71\times2.79+2.79\times2.79}$ is (S.S.C., 2005)
(*a*) 2.82 (*b*) 2.92
(*c*) 8.5 (*d*) 8.6

173. The value of
$\left(\dfrac{0.943\times0.943-0.943\times0.057+0.057\times0.057}{0.943\times0.943\times0.943+0.057\times0.057\times0.057}\right)$ is (M.B.A., 2005)
(*a*) 0.32 (*b*) 0.886
(*c*) 1.1286 (*d*) None of these

174. The value of $\left(\dfrac{0.125+0.027}{0.5\times0.5+0.09-0.15}\right)$ is (S.S.C., 2010)
(*a*) 0.08 (*b*) 0.2
(*c*) 0.8 (*d*) 1

175. $\left(\dfrac{10.3\times10.3\times10.3+1}{10.3\times10.3-10.3+1}\right)$ is equal to:: (S.S.C., 2004)
(*a*) 9.3 (*b*) 10.3
(*c*) 11.3 (*d*) 12.3

176. $\left[\dfrac{8(3.75)^3+1}{(7.5)^2-6.5}\right]$ is equal to:: (S.S.C., 2003)
(*a*) $\dfrac{9}{5}$ (*b*) 2.75
(*c*) 4.75 (*d*) 8.5

177. The value of $\left(\dfrac{0.1\times0.1\times0.1+0.02\times0.02\times0.02}{0.2\times0.2\times0.2+0.04\times0.04\times0.04}\right)$ is (Hotel Management 2003; S.S.C., 2005)
(*a*) 0.0125 (*b*) 0.125
(*c*) 0.25 (*d*) 0.5

178. $\frac{(0.013)^3 + 0.000000343}{(0.013)^2 - 0.000091 + 0.000049} = ?$ (I.I.F.T., 2005)

(a) 0.002 (b) 0.020
(c) 0.021 (d) 0.023
(e) None of these

179. The value of $\frac{(2.3)^3 - .027}{(2.3)^2 + .69 + .09}$ is (R.R.B., 2005)

(a) 0 (b) 1.6
(c) 2 (d) 3.4

180. The value of $\frac{(0.06)^2 + (0.47)^2 + (0.079)^2}{(0.006)^2 + (0.047)^2 + (0.0079)^2}$ is

(N.M.A.T. 2006; G.B.O. 2007)

(a) 0.1 (b) 10
(c) 100 (d) 1000

181. $\frac{(4.53-3.07)^2}{(3.07-2.15)(2.15-4.53)} + \frac{(3.07-2.15)^2}{(2.15-4.53)(4.53-3.07)} + \frac{(2.15-4.53)^2}{(4.53-3.07)(3.07-2.15)}$

is simplified to (C.P.O., 2004)

(a) 0 (b) 1
(c) 2 (d) 3

182. The fraction equivalent to $\frac{2}{5}\%$ is

[Indian Railways Gr. 'D' Exam, 2014]

(a) $\frac{1}{40}$ (b) $\frac{1}{125}$
(c) $\frac{1}{250}$ (d) $\frac{1}{500}$

183. The vulgar fraction of $0.39\overline{39}$ is

[SSC—CHSL (10+2) Exam, 2015]

(a) $\frac{15}{33}$ (b) $\frac{11}{39}$
(c) $\frac{17}{39}$ (d) $\frac{13}{33}$

184. Solve $(41.99^2 - 18.04^2) \div ? = 13.11^2 - 138.99$

[IBPS—Bank Spl. Officers (IT) Exam, 2015]

(a) 48 (b) 12
(c) 72 (d) 84
(e) 128

185. Solve $\frac{3}{5}$ of $\frac{4}{7}$ of $\frac{5}{12}$ of 1015 = ?

[United India Insurance Co. Ltd. (UIICL) Assistant (Online) Exam, 2015]

(a) 220 (b) 340
(c) 240 (d) 145
(e) 190

186. Solve $1\frac{1}{8} + 1\frac{6}{7} + 3\frac{3}{5} = ?$

[United India Insurance Co. Ltd. (UIICL) Assistant (Online) Exam, 2015]

(a) $8\frac{121}{140}$ (b) $6\frac{163}{280}$
(c) $9\frac{197}{280}$ (d) $7\frac{117}{140}$
(e) None of these

187. $2\frac{1.5}{5} + 2\frac{1}{6} - 1\frac{3.5}{15} = \left(\frac{(?)^{1/3}}{4}\right) + 1\frac{7}{30}$

[IDBI Bank Executive Officers Exam, 2015]

(a) 2 (b) 8
(c) 512 (d) 324
(e) None of these

188. Solve 323.46 + 23.04 – 43.17 – ? = 303

[NICL—AAO Exam, 2015]

(a) 0.33 (b) 1.33
(c) 1.23 (d) 0.21
(e) 0.51

189. Solve $1\frac{1}{2} + 2\frac{2}{7} = 3\frac{1}{2} + ?$ [NICL—AAO Exam, 2015]

(a) 2/3 (b) 2/7
(c) 5/8 (d) 7/2
(e) 1/7

190. Solve 48.2 × 2.5 × 2.2 + ? = 270

[NICL—AAO Exam, 2015]

(a) 6.5 (b) 2.8
(c) 4.9 (d) 3.4
(e) 1.2

191. Solve $4\frac{2}{3} + 3\frac{1}{2} - 1\frac{2}{3} = ?$ [NICL—AAO Exam, 2015]

(a) $2\frac{1}{5}$ (b) $2\frac{5}{3}$
(c) $1\frac{3}{4}$ (d) $1\frac{1}{2}$
(e) $6\frac{1}{2}$

192. Solve: 17292/33 ÷ 8 = ? [NICL—AAO Exam, 2015]

(a) 23.5 (b) 53.5
(c) 65.5 (d) 33.5
(e) 45.5

193. Solve 1599 ÷ 39.99 + $\frac{4}{5} \times 2449 - 120.05 = ?$

[IBPS—BANK PO/MT (Pre.) Exam, 2015]

(a) 1680 (b) 1940
(c) 1640 (d) 1880
(e) 1780

194. Solve $1576 \div 45.02 + 23.99 \times \sqrt{255} = ?$

[IBPS—BANK PO/MT (Pre.) Exam, 2015]

(*a*) 340 (*b*) 420
(*c*) 380 (*d*) 460
(*e*) 360

195. Solve $3899 \div 11.99 - 2379 \div 13.97 = ?$

[IBPS—BANK PO/MT (Pre.) Exam, 2015]

(*a*) 125 (*b*) 250
(*c*) 155 (*d*) 135
(*e*) 225

196. Solve $2\frac{2}{9}+4\frac{1}{18}-1\frac{1}{2}=?$

[IBPS—RRB Office Assistant (Online) Exam, 2015]

(*a*) $4\frac{5}{9}$ (*b*) $4\frac{7}{9}$
(*c*) $5\frac{8}{9}$ (*d*) $6\frac{1}{2}$
(*e*) $5\frac{2}{3}$

197. Solve $\frac{294 \div 14 \times 5 + 11}{?} = 8^2 \div 5 + 1.7$

[IBPS—RRB Office Assistant (Online) Exam, 2015]

(*a*) 8 (*b*) 6
(*c*) 12 (*d*) 5
(*e*) 10

198. Solve $2.5 \times 4.8 + 7.2 \times 1.5 - 1.2 \times 14 = ?$

[IBPS—RRB Office Assistant (Online) Exam, 2015]

(*a*) 1.2 (*b*) 6.5
(*c*) 4 (*d*) 4.8
(*e*) 6

199. Solve $\sqrt{197} \times 6.99 + 626.96 = ?$

[IBPS—Bank PO/PT Exam, 2015]

(*a*) 885 (*b*) 725
(*c*) 825 (*d*) 650
(*e*) 675

200. Which of the following fractions is the largest?

$\frac{3}{2}, \frac{7}{3}, \frac{5}{4}, \frac{7}{2}$ [ESIC—UDC Exam, 2016]

(*a*) $\frac{7}{3}$ (*b*) $\frac{5}{4}$
(*c*) $\frac{7}{2}$ (*d*) $\frac{3}{2}$

201. Solve $\frac{?}{529} = \frac{329}{?}$ [SBI Jr. Associates (Pre.) Exam, 2016]

(*a*) 404 (*b*) 408
(*c*) 410 (*d*) 414
(*e*) 416

202. The numerator of a fraction is decreased by 25% and the denominator is increased by 250%. If the resultant fraction is $\frac{6}{5}$, what is the original fraction? [SBI Jr. Associates (Pre.) Exam, 2016]

(*a*) $\frac{22}{5}$ (*b*) $\frac{24}{5}$
(*c*) $\frac{27}{6}$ (*d*) $\frac{28}{5}$
(*e*) $\frac{30}{11}$

203. Solve $\frac{21.5}{5}+\frac{21}{6}-\frac{13.5}{15}=\left(\frac{(?)^{\frac{1}{3}}}{4}\right)+\frac{17}{30}$

[IBPS—Bank Sp. Officer (Marketing) Exam, 2016]

(*a*) 2 (*b*) 8
(*c*) 512 (*d*) 324
(*e*) None of these

204. Solve $\left(\frac{18}{4}\right)^2 \times \left(\frac{455}{19}\right) \div \left(\frac{61}{799}\right) = ?$

[IBPS—Bank Sp. Officer (Marketing) Exam, 2016]

(*a*) 6320 (*b*) 6400
(*c*) 6350 (*d*) 6430
(*e*) 6490

205. $\frac{5}{9}$ of a number is equal to twenty five percent of second number. Second number is equal to $\frac{1}{4}$ of third number. The value of third number is 2960. What is 30% of first number ?

[DMRC—Customer Relationship Assistant (CRA) Exam, 2016]

(*a*) 99.9 (*b*) 88.8
(*c*) 77.7 (*d*) None of these

206. Solve $7\frac{1}{2}-\left[2\frac{1}{4}+\left\{1\frac{1}{4}-\frac{1}{2}\left(1\frac{1}{2}-\frac{1}{3}-\frac{1}{6}\right)\right\}\right]=?$

[UPSSSC—Lower Subordinate (Pre.) Exam, 2016]

(*a*) $\frac{2}{9}$ (*b*) $4\frac{1}{2}$
(*c*) $9\frac{1}{2}$ (*d*) $1\frac{77}{228}$

ANSWERS

1. (a)	2. (c)	3. (b)	4. (d)	5. (c)	6. (c)	7. (c)	8. (b)	9. (c)	10. (c)
11. (d)	12. (a)	13. (a)	14. (d)	15. (c)	16. (a)	17. (b)	18. (c)	19. (d)	20. (a)
21. (d)	22. (d)	23. (d)	24. (d)	25. (a)	26. (d)	27. (e)	28. (e)	29. (b)	30. (a)
31. (c)	32. (e)	33. (d)	34. (d)	35. (c)	36. (c)	37. (b)	38. (c)	39. (e)	40. (d)
41. (d)	42. (d)	43. (a)	44. (a)	45. (c)	46. (c)	47. (c)	48. (c)	49. (b)	50. (c)
51. (a)	52. (b)	53. (c)	54. (c)	55. (b)	56. (a)	57. (c)	58. (b)	59. (b)	60. (b)
61. (a)	62. (b)	63. (b)	64. (b)	65. (a)	66. (a)	67. (c)	68. (a)	69. (c)	70. (d)
71. (c)	72. (d)	73. (c)	74. (c)	75. (e)	76. (c)	77. (c)	78. (c)	79. (c)	80. (d)
81. (e)	82. (c)	83. (e)	84. (b)	85. (a)	86. (c)	87. (a)	88. (d)	89. (c)	90. (c)
91. (a)	92. (a)	93. (d)	94. (b)	95. (d)	96. (d)	97. (b)	98. (a)	99. (d)	100. (c)
101. (d)	102. (a)	103. (d)	104. (b)	105. (d)	106. (c)	107. (d)	108. (a)	109. (c)	110. (d)
111. (a)	112. (d)	113. (d)	114. (a)	115. (c)	116. (d)	117. (c)	118. (a)	119. (c)	120. (c)
121. (c)	122. (c)	123. (b)	124. (a)	125. (d)	126. (a)	127. (c)	128. (c)	129. (c)	130. (a)
131. (d)	132. (c)	133. (c)	134. (b)	135. (a)	136. (d)	137. (e)	138. (d)	139. (a)	140. (d)
141. (b)	142. (a)	143. (c)	144. (b)	145. (b)	146. (a)	147. (d)	148. (c)	149. (c)	150. (d)
151. (c)	152. (d)	153. (d)	154. (d)	155. (a)	156. (c)	157. (c)	158. (b)	159. (b)	160. (c)
161. (b)	162. (d)	163. (b)	164. (b)	165. (d)	166. (d)	167. (a)	168. (c)	169. (b)	170. (d)
171. (c)	172. (b)	173. (d)	174. (c)	175. (c)	176. (d)	177. (b)	178. (b)	179. (c)	180. (c)
181. (d)	182. (c)	183. (d)	184. (a)	185. (d)	186. (b)	187. (c)	188. (a)	189. (b)	190. (c)
191. (e)	192. (c)	193. (d)	194. (b)	195. (c)	196. (b)	197. (a)	198. (e)	199. (b)	200. (c)
201. (e)	202. (d)	203. (e)	204. (c)	205. (a)	206. (b)				

SOLUTIONS

1. $\frac{42}{10000} = .0042.$

2. $101\frac{27}{100000} = 101 + \frac{27}{100000} = 101 + .00027 = 101.00027.$

3. $0.36 = \frac{36}{100} = \frac{9}{25}.$

   Sum of numerator and denominator = 9 + 25 = 34.

4. 9 is at thousandths place in 0.06945.

   So, place value of 9 = $\frac{9}{1000}.$

5. Required decimal = $\frac{1}{60 \times 60} = \frac{1}{3600} = .00027.$

6. $4A + \frac{7}{B} + 2C + \frac{5}{D} + 6E = 47.2506$

   $\Rightarrow \quad 4A + \frac{7}{B} + 2C + \frac{5}{D} + 6E = 40 + 7 + 0.2 + 0.05 + 0.0006$

   Comparing the terms on both sides, we get:

   $4A = 40, \frac{7}{B} = 7, 2C = 0.2, \frac{5}{D} = 0.05, 6E = 0.0006$

   or $A = 10, B = 1, C = 0.1, D = 100, E = 0.0001.$

   $\therefore \quad 5A + 3B + 6C + D + 3E$

   $= (5 \times 10) + (3 \times 1) + (6 \times 0.1) + 100 + (3 \times 0.0001)$

   $= 50 + 3 + 0.6 + 100 + 0.0003 = 153.6003.$

7. 2111) 19990 (0.946 $\quad \therefore \frac{1999}{2111} = 0.946$

```
18999
 9910
 8444
 14660
 12666
  1994
```

8. 0.1 = 10 × 0.01

9. Converting each of the given fractions into decimal form, we get:

$\frac{3}{7}=0.428, \frac{4}{11}=0.363, \frac{5}{9}=0.555, \frac{6}{13}=0.461, \frac{7}{12}=0.583$

Clearly, 0.583 > 0.555 > 0.461 > 0.428 > 0.363.

So, $\frac{7}{12}>\frac{5}{9}>\frac{6}{13}>\frac{3}{7}>\frac{4}{11}$.

10. Converting each of the given fractions into decimal form, we get:

$\frac{2}{3}=0.66, \frac{3}{5}=0.6, \frac{7}{9}=0.77, \frac{9}{11}=0.81, \frac{8}{9}=0.88.$

Clearly, 0.6 < 0.66 < 0.77 < 0.81 < 0.88.

So, $\frac{3}{5}<\frac{2}{3}<\frac{7}{9}<\frac{9}{11}<\frac{8}{9}$.

11. Converting each of the given fractions into decimal form, we get:

$\frac{5}{9}=0.55, \frac{7}{11}=0.63, \frac{8}{15}=0.533, \frac{11}{17}=0.647.$

Clearly, 0.647 > 0.63 > 0.55 > 0.533.

So, $\frac{11}{17}>\frac{7}{11}>\frac{5}{9}>\frac{8}{15}$.

12. Converting each of the given fractions into decimal form, we get:

$\frac{2}{3}=0.66, \frac{3}{4}=0.75, \frac{4}{5}=0.8, \frac{5}{6}=0.833.$

Since 0.833 > 0.8 > 0.75 > 0.66, so $\frac{5}{6}>\frac{4}{5}>\frac{3}{4}>\frac{2}{3}$.

∴ Required difference $=\left(\frac{5}{6}-\frac{2}{3}\right)=\frac{1}{6}$.

13. Converting each of the given fractions into decimal form, we get:

$\frac{15}{16}=0.9375, \frac{19}{20}=0.95, \frac{24}{25}=0.96, \frac{34}{35}=0.971$

Clearly, 0.9375 < 0.95 < 0.96 < 0.971. So, $\frac{15}{16}<\frac{19}{20}<\frac{24}{25}<\frac{34}{35}$.

14. Converting each of the given fractions into decimal form, we get:

$\frac{9}{31}=0.29, \frac{3}{17}=0.176, \frac{6}{23}=0.26, \frac{4}{11}=0.363, \frac{7}{25}=0.28.$

Clearly, 0.363 > 0.29 > 0.28 > 0.26 > 0.176.

So, $\frac{4}{11}>\frac{9}{31}>\frac{7}{25}>\frac{6}{23}>\frac{3}{17}$.

15. Converting each of the given fractions into decimal form, we get:

$\frac{2}{5}=0.4, \frac{3}{8}=0.375, \frac{4}{9}=0.444, \frac{5}{13}=0.384, \frac{6}{11}=0.545$

Clearly, 0.375 < 0.384 < 0.4 < 0.444 < 0.545.

So, $\frac{3}{8}<\frac{5}{13}<\frac{2}{5}<\frac{4}{9}<\frac{6}{11}$.

16. Clearly, $\frac{11}{14}=0.785, \frac{16}{19}=0.842, \frac{19}{21}=0.904.$

Now, 0.785 < 0.842 < 0.904. So, $\frac{11}{14}<\frac{16}{19}<\frac{19}{21}$.

17. We have:

$\frac{13}{16}=0.8125, \frac{15}{19}=0.7894, \frac{17}{21}=0.8095$ and $\frac{7}{8}=0.875.$

Since 0.7894 is the smallest, so $\frac{15}{19}$ is the smallest.

18. $\frac{3}{4}=0.75, \frac{5}{6}=0.833, \frac{1}{2}=0.5, \frac{2}{3}=0.66, \frac{4}{5}=0.8, \frac{9}{10}=0.$

Clearly, 0.8 lies between 0.75 and 0.833.

∴ $\frac{4}{5}$ lies between $\frac{3}{4}$ and $\frac{5}{6}$.

19. $\frac{7}{8}=0.875, \frac{1}{3}=0.333, \frac{1}{4}=0.25, \frac{23}{24}=0.958,$

$\frac{11}{12}=0.916, \frac{17}{24}=0.708.$

Clearly, 0.708 lies between 0.333 and 0.875.

∴ $\frac{17}{24}$ lies between $\frac{1}{3}$ and $\frac{7}{8}$.

20. $\frac{4}{5}=0.8, \frac{7}{13}=0.53, \frac{1}{2}=0.5, \frac{2}{3}=0.66, \frac{3}{4}=0.75, \frac{5}{7}=0.714.$

Clearly, 0.5 does not lie between 0.53 and 0.8.

∴ $\frac{1}{2}$ does not lie between $\frac{4}{5}$ and $\frac{7}{13}$.

21. $\frac{-7}{10}=-0.7, \frac{5}{-8}=-\frac{5}{8}=-0.625, \frac{2}{-3}=-\frac{2}{3}=-0.66.$

Since −0.7 < −0.66 < −0.625, so $\frac{-7}{10}<\frac{2}{-3}<\frac{5}{-8}$.

22. $\frac{2}{3}=0.666, \frac{3}{5}=0.6, \frac{2}{5}=0.4, \frac{1}{3}=0.333, \frac{1}{15}=0.066, \frac{31}{50}=0.62.$

Clearly, 0.62 lies between 0.6 and 0.666. So, $\frac{31}{50}$ lie between $\frac{2}{3}$ and $\frac{3}{5}$.

23. $\frac{1}{5}=0.2, \frac{8}{35}=0.228, \frac{8}{37}=0.216, \frac{8}{39}=0.205, \frac{2}{11}=0.181.$

Clearly, 0.181 < 0.2. So, $\frac{2}{11}<\frac{1}{5}$.

24. $\frac{2}{5}=0.4, \frac{4}{5}=0.8, \frac{21}{50}=0.42, \frac{20001}{50000}=0.40002,$

$\frac{200001}{500000}=0.400002.$

Clearly, 0.400002 is nearest to 0.4.

So, $\frac{200001}{500000}$ is nearest to $\frac{2}{5}$.

25. $\frac{1}{3}=0.333, \frac{3}{4}=0.75, \frac{117}{300}=0.39, \frac{287}{400}=0.7175,$

$\frac{95}{300}=0.316, \frac{301}{400}=0.7525, \frac{99}{300}=0.33,$

$\frac{97}{300} = 0.323, \frac{299}{500} = 0.598.$

Clearly, each one of 0.39 and 0.7175 lies between 0.333 and 0.75.

So, $\frac{117}{300}$ and $\frac{287}{400}$ lie between $\frac{1}{3}$ and $\frac{3}{4}$.

26. $\frac{1}{5} = 0.2$ and $\frac{1}{6} = 0.166.$

(a) $\frac{4}{25} = 0.16, \frac{9}{50} = 0.18, \frac{17}{100} = 0.17$

(b) $\frac{4}{25} = 0.16, \frac{17}{100} = 0.17, \frac{167}{1000} = 0.167$

(c) $\frac{4}{25} = 0.16, \frac{9}{50} = 0.18, \frac{167}{1000} = 0.167$

(d) $\frac{9}{50} = 0.18, \frac{17}{100} = 0.17, \frac{167}{1000} = 0.167$

27.
$$\begin{array}{r} 0.3 \\ 3.0 \\ 3.33 \\ 3.03 \\ +\ 333.0 \\ \hline 345.96 \\ \hline \end{array}$$

28.
$$\begin{array}{r} 636.66 \\ 366.36 \\ +\ 363.33 \\ \hline 1366.35 \\ \hline \end{array}$$

29.
$$\begin{array}{r} 24.424 \\ 5.656 \\ 1.131 \\ +\ 0.089 \\ \hline 31.300 \\ \hline \end{array}$$

30.
$$\begin{array}{r} 555.05 \\ 55.5 \\ 5.55 \\ 5.0 \\ +\ 0.55 \\ \hline 621.65 \\ \hline \end{array}$$

31.
$$\begin{array}{r} 4\ .0 \\ 4.44 \\ 0.4 \\ 44.04 \\ +\ 444.0 \\ \hline 496.88 \\ \hline \end{array}$$

32.
$$\begin{array}{r} 9\ 9\ 9.9\ 9 \\ 9\ 9.9\ 9 \\ +\ 9.9\ 9 \\ +\ 9.9\ 9 \\ \hline 1\ 1\ 0\ 9.9\ 7 \\ \hline \end{array}$$

33.
$$\begin{array}{r} 10.0\ 0\ 0\ 1 \\ +\ 9.9\ 9\ 9\ 9 \\ \hline 20.0\ 0\ 0\ 0 \\ \hline \end{array} \qquad \begin{array}{r} 20.0000 \\ -\ 8.9995 \\ \hline 11.0005 \\ \hline \end{array}$$

34.
$$\begin{array}{r} 48.95 \\ -\ 32.0\ 0\ 6 \\ \hline 16.9\ 4\ 4 \\ \hline \end{array}$$

35. Given expression = 58.621 – (13.829 + 7.302 + 1.214)
= 58.621 – 22.345 = 36.276.

36. Let 341.42 – 53.74 = x – 62.86.
Then, x = (341.42 + 62.86) – 53.74
= 404.28 – 53.74 = 350.54.

37. Let 534.596 + 61.472 – 496.708 = x + 27.271
Then, x = (534.596 + 61.472) – (496.708 + 27.271)
= 596.068 – 523.979 = 72.089.

38. Given expression = (11.71 + 1.78) – (0.86 + 9.20)
= 13.49 – 10.06 = 3.43.

39. Let 726.34 + 888.12 – x = 1001.88.
Then, x = (726.34 + 888.12) – 1001.88
= 1614.46 – 1001.88 = 612.58.

40. Let 832.58 – 242.31 = 779.84 – x.
Then, x = (779.84 + 242.31) – 832.58
= 1022.15 – 832.58 = 189.57.

41. (a) $\frac{9}{4} + 1.75 = 2.25 + 1.75 = 4.$

(b) $\frac{9}{5} + 2.2 = 1.8 + 2.2 = 4.$

(c) $\frac{6}{5} + 2.8 = 1.2 + 2.8 = 4.$

(d) $\frac{3}{2} + 1.5 = 1.5 + 1.5 = 3.$

42. (a) $x^2 + y^2 = (10)^2 + (0.1)^2 = 100 + 0.01 = 100.01.$
(b) $x^2 - y^2 = (10)^2 - (0.1)^2 = 100 - 0.01 = 99.99.$
(c) $x^2 y^2 = (10)^2 \times (0.1)^2 = 100 \times 0.01 = 1.$
(d) $\frac{x^2}{y^2} = \frac{(10)^2}{(0.1)^2} = \frac{100}{0.01} = 10000.$

Clearly, $\frac{x^2}{y^2}$ is the greatest.

43. (a) $(0.09)^2 = 0.0081$
(b) 0.09
(c) $(1 - 0.9)^2 = (0.1)^2 = 0.01$
(d) $1 - (0.9)^2 = 1 - 0.81 = 0.19$

Clearly, 0.0081 < 0.01 < 0.09 < 0.19.
So, 0.0081 is closest to zero.

44. Required fraction $= \frac{\frac{1}{100}\text{ cm}}{1\text{ km}} = \frac{\left(\frac{1}{100}\right)\text{cm}}{(1000 \times 100)\text{ cm}}$
$= \frac{1}{100 \times 1000 \times 100}$
$= \frac{1}{10000000} = 0.0000001.$

45. Let x + 543 + 5.43 = 603.26.
Then, x = 603.26 – (543 + 5.43)
= 603.26 – 548.43 = 54.83.

∴ Missing digit = 8.

46. $3.14 \times 10^6 = 3.140000 \times 1000000 = 3140000.$

47. $518{,}000{,}000 = 5.18 \times 100000000 = 5.18 \times 10^8.$

48. $0.000006723 = \frac{0.000006723 \times 10^6}{10^6}$
$= \frac{6.723}{10^6} = 6.723 \times 10^{-6}.$

49. $10^k = \frac{0.001125}{1.125} = \frac{1.125}{1125} = \frac{1.125 \times 10^3}{1125 \times 10^3} = \frac{1}{10^3} = 10^{-3}.$

∴ $k = -3.$

50. Given expression $= \left(\frac{1}{10} \times \frac{1}{100} \times \frac{1}{1000} \times 10^7\right)$
$= \left(\frac{10^7}{10^6}\right) = 10^{(7-6)} = 10.$

51. 383 × 38 × 38 = 553052.
Number of decimal places = 1.
∴ 383 × 38 × 3.8 = 55305.2.

52. 9 × 7 = 63.
Sum of decimal places = 5. ∴ 0.09 × 0.007 = 0.00063.

53. Sum of decimal places = 6. ∴ 0.1 × 0.01 × 0.001 = 0.000001.

54. 3 × 3 × 3 × 3 × 30 = 2430.

Sum of decimal places = 6.

$\therefore$ $3 \times 0.3 \times 0.03 \times 0.003 \times 30 = 0.00243$.

55. $144 \times 165 \times 8 = 190080$.

Sum of decimal places = 2.

$\therefore$ $14.4 \times 16.5 \times 8 = 1900.80$.

56. $477 \times 124 \times 86 = 5086728$.

Sum of decimal places = 3.

$\therefore$ $47.7 \times 12.4 \times 8.6 = 5086.728$.

57. $324 \times 115 \times 85 = 3167100$.

Sum of decimal places = 3.

$\therefore$ $32.4 \times 11.5 \times 8.5 = 3167.1$.

58. $4 \times 162 = 648$.

Sum of decimal places = 6.

$\therefore$ $0.04 \times 0.0162 = 0.000648 = 6.48 \times 10^{-4}$.

59. Sum of decimal places = 7.

Since the last digit to the extreme right will be zero ($\because 5 \times 4 = 20$), so there will be 6 significant digits to the right of the decimal point.

60. $\left(.00625 \text{ of } \frac{23}{5}\right) = \left(\frac{625}{100000} \times \frac{23}{5}\right) = \frac{23}{800}$.

61. Given product $= 0.3 \times 0.25 \times 0.5 \times 0.125 \times 24$

$= \left(\frac{3}{10} \times \frac{25}{100} \times \frac{5}{10} \times \frac{125}{1000} \times 24\right)$

$= \frac{9}{80} = \frac{1}{8}$ (app.)

62. The digit at the third decimal place is 6, which is greater than 5.

So, 0.0561, rounded to two decimal places, is 0.06.

63. Given expression $= 0.25 - 0.025 = 0.225$.

64. Given expression $= 197.901 + 99.9 = 297.801$.

65. Given expression $= 345 + 20 - 111 = 365 - 111 = 254$.

66. Given expression $= 71.808 + 95.76 = 167.568$.

67. Given expression $= 293.48 - 141.27 = 152.21$.

68. 1. $36839 \div 17 = 2167$.

Dividend contains 2 places of decimal.

$\therefore$ $368.39 \div 17 = 21.67$.

2. $17050 \div 62 = 275$. Dividend contains 2 places of decimal.

$\therefore$ $170.50 \div 62 = 2.75$.

3. $87565 \div 83 = 1055$.

Dividend contains 2 places of decimal.

$\therefore$ $875.65 \div 83 = 10.55$.

Since $21.67 > 10.55 > 2.75$, the desired order is 1, 3, 2.

69. $\frac{0.213}{0.00213} = \frac{0.213 \times 100000}{0.00213 \times 100000} = \frac{213 \times 100}{213} = 100$.

70. $\frac{25.025}{0.025} = \frac{25025}{25} = 1001$.

71. $\frac{4.036}{0.04} = \frac{403.6}{4} = 100.9$.

72. $\frac{1}{0.04} = \frac{100}{4} = 25$.

73. Given expression $= 448.8 \div 24 = 18.7$.

74. Given expression $= 51.4 \times 8 = 411.2$.

75. Given expression $= 101 \div 5 = 20.2$.

76. Given expression $= 7.92 \div 0.6 = 79.2 \div 6 = 13.2$.

77. $\left(\frac{0.05}{0.25} + \frac{0.25}{0.05}\right)^3 = \left(\frac{5}{25} + \frac{25}{5}\right)^3$

$= \left(\frac{1}{5} + 5\right)^3 = \left(\frac{26}{5}\right)^3 = (5.2)^3 = 140.608$.

78. $\frac{0.0396}{2.51} = \frac{3.96}{251} = \left(\frac{396}{251 \times 100}\right) = \frac{1.577}{100} = 0.01577 \approx 0.016$.

79. Given expression $= 3927 + \frac{5526}{12.5} = 3927 + \frac{55260}{125}$

$= 3927 + 442.08 = 4369.08$.

80. Given expression $= \frac{116}{8} \times \frac{13.5}{2} = 14.5 \times 6.75 = 97.875$.

81. Given expression $= \frac{0.05 \times 6.25}{2.5} = \frac{0.3125}{2.5} = \frac{3.125}{25} = 0.125$.

82. Given expression $= 0.5 \times 0.5 + \frac{0.5}{5} = 0.25 + 0.1 = 0.35$.

83. Given expression $= \frac{400}{0.1} \times 0.2 = 4000 \times 0.2 = 800$.

84. Given expression $= 5.5 - [6.5 - \{3.5 \div (6.5 - 3)\}]$

$= 5.5 - [6.5 - \{3.5 \div 3.5\}]$

$= 5.5 - [6.5 - 1] = 5.5 - 5.5 = 0$.

85. Let $.04 \times x = .000016$.

Then, $x = \frac{.000016}{.04} = \frac{.0016}{4} = .0004$.

86. Let $\frac{.009}{x} = .01$. Then, $x = \frac{.009}{.01} = \frac{.9}{1} = .9$.

87. $\frac{144}{0.144} = \frac{14.4}{x} \Leftrightarrow \frac{144 \times 1000}{144} = \frac{14.4}{x} \Leftrightarrow x = \frac{14.4}{1000} = 0.0144$.

88. Let $40.04 \div 0.4 = x \times 0.05$.

Then, $\frac{40.04}{0.4} = 0.05x \Rightarrow \frac{400.4}{4} = 0.05x$

$\Rightarrow$ $0.05x = 100.1 \Rightarrow x = \frac{100.1}{0.05} = \frac{10010}{5} = 2002$.

89. Given expression $= \frac{48}{75} \times \frac{84.5}{20} = 0.64 \times 4.225 = 2.704$.

90. Let $(5420 + 3312 + x) \div 600 = 25.93$.

Then, $\frac{8732 + x}{600} = 25.93$

$\Rightarrow$ $8732 + x = 25.93 \times 600$

$\Rightarrow$ $8732 + x = 15558 \Rightarrow x = 6826$.

91. Let $\frac{x^2 + (18)^2}{125} = 3.56$.

Then, $x^2 + 324 = 125 \times 3.56 = 445$

$\Rightarrow$ $x^2 = 121 \Rightarrow x = 11$.

92. Let $786 \div 24 \times x = 6.55$.

Then, $\frac{786}{24} \times x = 6.55 \Rightarrow 32.75\,x = 6.55$

$\Rightarrow \quad x = \frac{6.55}{32.75} = \frac{655}{3275} = \frac{1}{5} = 0.2.$

93. Number of pieces $= \frac{857}{12.6} = \frac{8570}{126} = 68.01 \approx 68.$

94. Quantity of blood donated in 2 years $= (350 \times 3)$ ml $= 1050$ ml $= 1.05$ litres.

$\therefore$ Quantity of blood donated in 6 years $= \left(\frac{1.05}{2} \times 6\right)$ litres $= 3.15$ litres.

95. Daily consumption $= 1600$ ml $= 1.6$ litres.

Consumption in 4 weeks $= (1.6 \times 4 \times 7)$ litres $= 44.8$ litres.

96. Length of each piece $= \left(\frac{1}{8}\right)$ m $= 0.125$ m.

$\therefore$ Required number of pieces $= \left(\frac{37.5}{0.125}\right) = \left(\frac{375 \times 100}{125}\right) = 300.$

97. Suppose commodity X will cost 40 paise more than Y after z years. Then,

$(4.20 + 0.40z) - (6.30 + 0.15z) = 0.40$

$\Leftrightarrow \quad 0.25z = 0.40 + 2.10 \quad \Leftrightarrow \quad z = \frac{2.50}{0.25} = \frac{250}{25} = 10.$

$\therefore$ X will cost 40 paise more than Y 10 years after 2004 i.e., in 2014.

98. Let the number of 10P coins be x.

Then, number of 5P coins $= (80 - x)$.

$\therefore \quad 0.1x + 0.05\,(80 - x) = 6.25$

$\Rightarrow \quad 0.1x + 4 - 0.05x = 6.25 \Rightarrow 0.05x = 2.25$

$\Rightarrow \quad x = \frac{2.25}{0.05} = \frac{225}{5} = 45.$

Hence, number of 10P coins = 45. And, number of 5P coins = (80 – 45) = 35.

99. $0.121212..... = 0.\overline{12} = \frac{12}{99} = \frac{4}{33}.$

100. $0.125125\,..... = 0.\overline{125} = \frac{125}{999}.$

101. $0.\overline{47} = \frac{47}{99}.$

102. $0.\overline{36} = \frac{36}{99} = \frac{4}{11}.$

103. $1 \div 0.2 = \frac{1}{0.2} = \frac{10}{2} = 5;\ 0.\bar{2} = 0.222\,.....;\ (0.2)^2 = 0.04.$

$0.04 < 0.2 < 0.22..... < 5.$

Since 0.04 is the least, so $(0.2)^2$ is the least.

104. $1.\overline{27} = 1 + 0.\overline{27} = 1 + \frac{27}{99} = 1 + \frac{3}{11} = \frac{11+3}{11} = \frac{14}{11}.$

105. $0.4\overline{23} = \frac{423 - 4}{990} = \frac{419}{990}.$

106. $0.29\overline{56} = \frac{2956 - 29}{9900} = \frac{2927}{9900}.$

107. $0.841\overline{81} = \frac{84181 - 841}{99000} = \frac{83340}{99000} = \frac{463}{550}.$

$\therefore$ Required difference $= (550 - 463) = 87.$

108. $4.1\bar{2} = 4 + 0.1\bar{2} = 4 + \frac{12 - 1}{90} = 4\frac{11}{90}.$

109. $2.8\overline{768} = 2 + 0.8\overline{768} = 2 + \frac{8768 - 8}{9990} = 2 + \frac{8760}{9990} = 2\frac{292}{333}.$

110. $0.\bar{2} + 0.\bar{3} + 0.\overline{32} = \left(\frac{2}{9} + \frac{3}{9} + \frac{32}{99}\right) = \left(\frac{22 + 33 + 32}{99}\right) = \frac{87}{99} = 0.\overline{87}.$

111. $0.\overline{142857} \div 0.\overline{285714} = \frac{142857}{999999} \div \frac{285714}{999999}$

$= \left(\frac{142857}{999999} \times \frac{999999}{285714}\right) = \frac{1}{2}.$

112. $3.\overline{87} - 2.\overline{59} = (3 + 0.\overline{87}) - (2 + 0.\overline{59}) = \left(3 + \frac{87}{99}\right) - \left(2 + \frac{59}{99}\right)$

$= 1 + \left(\frac{87}{99} - \frac{59}{99}\right) = 1 + \frac{28}{99} = 1.\overline{28}.$

113. $3.\overline{36} - 2.\overline{05} + 1.\overline{33} = [(3 + 0.\overline{36}) + (1 + 0.\overline{33})] - (2 + 0.\overline{05})$

$= \left[4 + \left(\frac{36}{99} + \frac{33}{99}\right)\right] - \left[2 + \frac{5}{99}\right]$

$= 2 + \left(\frac{36}{99} + \frac{33}{99} - \frac{5}{99}\right) = 2 + \frac{64}{99} = 2.\overline{64}.$

114. $0.\overline{09} \times 7.\bar{3} = \frac{9}{99} \times 7\frac{3}{9} = \frac{1}{11} \times \frac{66}{9} = \frac{2}{3} = 0.\bar{6}.$

115. $0.34\overline{67} + 0.13\overline{33} = \frac{3467 - 34}{9900} + \frac{1333 - 13}{9900} = \frac{3433 + 1320}{9900}$

$= \frac{4753}{9900} = \frac{4801 - 48}{9900} = 0.48\overline{01}.$

116. $(8.3\bar{1} + 0.\bar{6} + 0.00\bar{2}) = 8 + \frac{31 - 3}{90} + \frac{6}{9} + \frac{2}{900}$

$= \frac{7200 + 280 + 600 + 2}{900}$

$= \frac{8082}{900} = 8\frac{882}{900} = 8 + \frac{979 - 97}{900} = 8.97\bar{9}.$

117. $\bar{2}.75 + \bar{3}.78 = (-2 + 0.75) + (-3 + 0.78)$

$= -5 + (0.75 + 0.78) = -5 + 1.53$

$= -5 + 1 + 0.53 = -4 + 0.53 = \bar{4}.53.$

118. $\frac{547527}{82} = \frac{54.7527}{0.0082} = \left(\frac{547.527}{0.0082} \times \frac{1}{10}\right) = \frac{x}{10}.$

119. $\frac{29.94}{1.45} = \frac{299.4}{14.5} = \left(\frac{2994}{14.5} \times \frac{1}{10}\right) = \frac{172}{10} = 17.2.$

120. $1.6 \times 21.3 = \left(\frac{16}{10} \times \frac{213}{10}\right) = \left(\frac{16 \times 213}{100}\right) = \frac{3408}{100} = 34.08.$

121. $\frac{1}{0.0006198} = \frac{10000}{6.198} = \left(10000 \times \frac{1}{6.198}\right)$

$= (10000 \times 0.16134) = 1613.4.$

122. Given, $\frac{52416}{312} = 168 \Leftrightarrow \frac{52416}{168} = 312.$

Now, $\frac{52.416}{0.0168} = \frac{524160}{168} = \left(\frac{52416}{168} \times 10\right) = (312 \times 10) = 3120.$

123. Given, 168 × 32 = 5376 or 5376 ÷ 168 = 32.

Now, $\frac{5.376}{16.8} = \frac{53.76}{168} = \left(\frac{5376}{168} \times \frac{1}{100}\right) = \frac{32}{100} = 0.32.$

124. Number of decimal places in the given expression = 8.

Number of decimal places in (*a*) = 8.

Number of decimal places in (*b*) = 9.

Number of decimal places in (*c*) = 7.

Clearly, the expression in (*a*) is the same as the given expression.

125. For the expressions to be equivalent, the difference between the sum of the decimal places in the numerator and that in the denominator must be equal.

This difference is 1 in the given expression and 1 in (*d*).

So, (*d*) is the answer.

126. Given expression $= \frac{(96.54 - 89.63)}{(96.54 + 89.63)} \times \frac{(9.654 + 8.963)}{(965.4 - 896.3)}$

$= \frac{(96.54 - 89.63)}{(965.4 - 896.3)} \times \frac{(9.654 + 8.963)}{(96.54 + 89.63)}$

$= \frac{(96.54 - 89.63)}{10\,(96.54 - 89.63)} \times \frac{(96.54 + 89.63)}{10\,(96.54 + 89.63)}$

$= \frac{1}{10} \times \frac{1}{10} = \frac{1}{100} = \frac{1}{10^2} = 10^{-2}.$

127. $(0.11)^3 + (0.22)^3 + \ldots + (0.99)^3 = (0.11)^3 (1^3 + 2^3 + \ldots + 9^3)$

$= 0.001331 \times 2025 = 2.695275 \approx 2.695.$

128. $\frac{1}{4} + \frac{1}{4 \times 5} + \frac{1}{4 \times 5 \times 6} = \frac{1}{4}\left(1 + \frac{1}{5} + \frac{1}{30}\right)$

$= \frac{1}{4}\left(\frac{30 + 6 + 1}{30}\right) = \frac{1}{4} \times \frac{37}{30}$

$= \frac{37}{120} = 0.3083.$

129. Given expression $= \frac{2 \times 4 \times 8 \times 16 + 4 \times 8 \times 16 + 8 \times 16 + 16 + 1}{2 \times 4 \times 8 \times 16}$

$= \frac{1024 + 512 + 128 + 16 + 1}{1024}$

$= \frac{1681}{1024} = 1.6416.$

130. Given expression $= \frac{1}{5 \times 6} + \frac{1}{6 \times 7} + \frac{1}{7 \times 8} + \ldots + \frac{1}{24 \times 25}$

$= \left(\frac{1}{5} - \frac{1}{6}\right) + \left(\frac{1}{6} - \frac{1}{7}\right) + \left(\frac{1}{7} - \frac{1}{8}\right) + \ldots + \left(\frac{1}{24} - \frac{1}{25}\right)$

$= \left(\frac{1}{5} - \frac{1}{25}\right) = \frac{4}{25} = 0.16.$

131. $\frac{1}{5} = 0.2;\ \left(\frac{1}{5}\right)^2 = (0.2)^2 = 0.04;\ \left(\frac{1}{5}\right)^3 = (0.2)^3 = 0.008;$

$\left(\frac{1}{5}\right)^4 = (0.2)^4 = 0.0016.$

Clearly, for every power which is a multiple of 4, the expression would have 6 as the last digit.

So, $\left(\frac{1}{5}\right)^{2000}$ would have 6 as the last digit.

132. To get 1 as the answer, the expression must have the same number of decimal places in the numerator and denominator.

The number of decimal places in the given expressions are as under:

(*a*) Numerator → 4; Denominator → 3

(*b*) Numerator → 2; Denominator → 4

(*c*) Numerator → 6; Denominator → 6

(*d*) Numerator → 4; Denominator → 2

∴ The correct answer is (*c*).

133. Given expression

$= \left(1 - \frac{1}{4}\right) + \left(\frac{1}{4} - \frac{1}{9}\right) + \left(\frac{1}{9} - \frac{1}{16}\right) + \ldots + \left(\frac{1}{81} - \frac{1}{100}\right)$

$= 1 - \frac{1}{100} = \frac{99}{100} = 0.99.$

134. $\frac{x}{y} = \frac{0.04}{1.5} = \frac{4}{150} = \frac{2}{75} \Rightarrow \frac{y - x}{y + x} = \frac{1 - \frac{x}{y}}{1 + \frac{x}{y}} = \frac{1 - \frac{2}{75}}{1 + \frac{2}{75}} = \frac{73}{77}.$

135. Given expression

$= 35.7 - \left(\frac{3 + \frac{1}{10}}{3}\right) - \left(\frac{2 + \frac{1}{5}}{2}\right) = 35.7 - \left(3 + \frac{3}{10}\right) - \left(2 + \frac{2}{5}\right)$

$= 35.7 - \frac{33}{10} - \frac{12}{5} = 35.7 - \left(\frac{33}{10} + \frac{12}{5}\right)$

$= 35.7 - \frac{57}{10} = 35.7 - 5.7 = 30.$

136. Given expression $= \frac{(0.3333)}{(0.2222)} \times \frac{(0.1667)\,(0.8333)}{(0.6667)\,(0.1250)}$

$= \frac{3333}{2222} \times \frac{\frac{1}{6} \times \frac{5}{6}}{\frac{2}{3} \times \frac{125}{1000}}$

$= \left(\frac{3}{2} \times \frac{1}{6} \times \frac{5}{6} \times \frac{3}{2} \times 8\right) = \frac{5}{2} = 2.50.$

137. Given expression $= \frac{35 \times 1.4}{7} = 5 \times 1.4 = 7.$

138. Given expression $= \frac{16 \times 32}{8} = 16 \times 4 = 64.$

139. Given expression $= \frac{441 \times 16}{21 \times 16 \times 21} = 1.$

140. Given expression $= \dfrac{625 \times 729 \times 289}{81 \times 25 \times 17} = 3825.$

141. $\dfrac{3.6 \times 0.48 \times 2.50}{0.12 \times 0.09 \times 0.5} = \dfrac{36 \times 48 \times 250}{12 \times 9 \times 5} = 800.$

142. $\dfrac{0.0203 \times 2.92}{0.0073 \times 14.5 \times 0.7} = \dfrac{203 \times 292}{73 \times 145 \times 7} = \dfrac{4}{5} = 0.8.$

143. $\dfrac{3.157 \times 4126 \times 3.198}{63.972 \times 2835.121} \approx \dfrac{3.2 \times 4126 \times 3.2}{64 \times 2835}$

$= \dfrac{32 \times 4126 \times 32}{64 \times 2835} \times \dfrac{1}{100}$

$= \dfrac{66016}{2835} \times \dfrac{1}{100} = \dfrac{23.28}{100} = 0.23 \approx 0.2.$

144. $\dfrac{489.1375 \times 0.0483 \times 1.956}{0.0873 \times 92.581 \times 99.749} \approx \dfrac{489 \times 0.05 \times 2}{0.09 \times 93 \times 100} = \dfrac{489}{9 \times 93 \times 10}$

$= \dfrac{163}{279} \times \dfrac{1}{10} = \dfrac{0.58}{10} = 0.058 \approx 0.06.$

145. $\dfrac{241.6 \times 0.3814 \times 6.842}{0.4618 \times 38.25 \times 73.65} \approx \dfrac{240 \times 0.38 \times 6.9}{0.46 \times 38 \times 75}$

$= \dfrac{240 \times 38 \times 69}{46 \times 38 \times 75} \times \dfrac{1}{10} = \left(\dfrac{24}{5} \times \dfrac{1}{10}\right) = \dfrac{4.8}{10} = 0.48.$

So, the value is close to 0.4.

146. Given expression $= \dfrac{(0.2 \times 0.2 + 0.01)}{(0.1 \times 0.1 + 0.02)} = \dfrac{0.04 + 0.01}{0.01 + 0.02} = \dfrac{0.05}{0.03} = \dfrac{5}{3}.$

147. Given expression $= \dfrac{8 - 2.8}{1.3} = \dfrac{5.2}{1.3} = \dfrac{52}{13} = 4.$

148. Given expression $= 4.7 \times (13.26 + 9.43 + 77.31)$

$= 4.7 \times 100 = 470.$

149. Given expression $= \dfrac{0.2\,(0.2 + 0.02)}{0.044} = \dfrac{0.2 \times 0.22}{0.044} = \dfrac{0.044}{0.044} = 1.$

150. Given expression $= \dfrac{8.6 \times (5.3 + 4.7)}{4.3 \times (9.7 - 8.7)} = \dfrac{8.6 \times 10}{4.3 \times 1} = 20.$

151. Given expression $= \dfrac{.896 \times (.763 + .237)}{.7 \times (.064 + .936)}$

$= \dfrac{.896 \times 1}{.7 \times 1} = \dfrac{8.96}{7} = 1.28.$

152. Given expression $= (1.25)^3 - (0.75)^3 - 3 \times (1.25)^2 \times 0.75 + 3 \times 1.25 \times (0.75)^2$

$= (1.25 - 0.75)^3 = (0.5)^3 = \left(\dfrac{1}{2}\right)^3 = \dfrac{1}{8}.$

$[\because (a - b)^3 = a^3 - b^3 - 3a^2b + 3ab^2]$

153. $(78.95)^2 - (43.35)^2 = (78.95 + 43.35)(78.95 - 43.35)$

$= 122.3 \times 35.6 = 4353.88.$

$[\because a^2 - b^2 = (a + b)(a - b)]$

154. Given expression $= \dfrac{(a^2 - b^2)}{(a - b)}$, where $a = 75.8$, $b = 55.8$

$= \dfrac{(a - b)(a + b)}{(a - b)} = a + b$

$= 75.8 + 55.8 = 131.6.$

155. Given expression $= \dfrac{(a^2 - b^2)}{(a + b)}$, where $a = 3.63$, $b = 2.37$

$= \dfrac{(a - b)(a + b)}{(a + b)} = (a - b)$

$= 3.63 - 2.37 = 1.26.$

156. Let $\dfrac{(36.54)^2 - (3.46)^2}{x} = 40.$ Then,

$x = \dfrac{(36.54)^2 - (3.46)^2}{40} = \dfrac{(36.54)^2 - (3.46)^2}{36.54 + 3.46}$

$= \dfrac{a^2 - b^2}{a + b} = (a - b) = (36.54 - 3.46) = 33.08.$

157. Given expression $= \dfrac{(67.542)^2 - (32.458)^2}{(67.542 + 7.196) - (32.458 + 7.916)}$

$= \dfrac{(67.542)^2 - (32.458)^2}{67.542 - 32.458}$

$= (67.542 + 32.458) = 100.$

158. Given expression $= \left(\dfrac{1.49 \times 1.49 \times 10 - 0.51 \times 0.51 \times 10}{1.49 \times 10 - 0.51 \times 10}\right)$

$= \dfrac{10\,[(1.49)^2 - (0.51)^2]}{10\,(1.49 - 0.51)}$

$= (1.49 + 0.51) = 2.$

159. Given expression $= \dfrac{(a^2 - b^2)}{(a + b)(a - b)} = \dfrac{(a^2 - b^2)}{(a^2 - b^2)} = 1.$

160. Given expression $= \dfrac{5.32 \times (56 + 44)}{(7.66 + 2.34)(7.66 - 2.34)}$

$= \dfrac{5.32 \times 100}{10 \times 5.32} = 10.$

161. Given expression $= \dfrac{[(0.6)^2]^2 - [(0.5)^2]^2}{(0.6)^2 + (0.5)^2}$

$= \dfrac{[(0.6)^2 + (0.5)^2]\,[(0.6)^2 - (0.5)^2]}{(0.6)^2 + (0.5)^2}$

$= (0.6)^2 - (0.5)^2 = (0.6 + 0.5)(0.6 - 0.5)$

$= (1.1 \times 0.1) = 0.11.$

162. Given expression $= (7.5 \times 7.5 + 2 \times 7.5 \times 2.5 + 2.5 \times 2.5)$

$= (a^2 + 2ab + b^2) = (a + b)^2$

$= (7.5 + 2.5)^2 = 10^2 = 100.$

163. $0.2 \times 0.2 + 0.02 \times 0.02 - 0.4 \times 0.02$

$= 0.2 \times 0.2 + 0.02 \times 0.02 - 2 \times 0.2 \times 0.02$

$= (a^2 + b^2 - 2ab) = (a - b)^2 = (0.2 - 0.02)^2 = (0.18)^2.$

$\therefore$ Given expression $= \dfrac{(0.18 \times 0.18)}{0.36} = 0.09.$

164. Given expression $= (100 - 0.25)^2 - 2250.0625$

$= (100)^2 + (0.25)^2 - 2 \times 100 \times 0.25 - 2250.0625$

$= 10000.0625 - 50 - 2250.0625 = 10000.0625 - 2300.0625$

$= 7700.$

165. Given expression $= (55.25)^2 - (25.25)^2$

$= (55.25 + 25.25)\ (55.25 - 25.25)$

$= 80.5 \times 30 = 2415.$

166. Given expression $= \dfrac{3.20\ (3.25 - 3.05)}{0.064} = \dfrac{3.20 \times 0.2}{0.064}$

$= \dfrac{0.64}{0.064} = \dfrac{64}{6.4} = 10.$

167. Given expression $= [(.98)^3 + (.02)^3 + 3 \times .98 \times .02$ $(.98 + .02)] - 1 = (.98 + .02)^3 - 1 = (1)^3 - 1 = 0.$

168. Given expression $= (11.98)^2 + (0.02)^2 + 11.98 \times x.$

For the given expression to be a perfect square, we must have:

$11.98 \times x = 2 \times 11.98 \times 0.02$ or $x = 0.04.$

169. Given expression $= \dfrac{(a-b)^2 + (a+b)^2}{a^2+b^2} = \dfrac{2\ (a^2+b^2)}{(a^2+b^2)} = 2.$

170. Given expression $= \dfrac{(a+b)^2 - (a-b)^2}{ab} = \dfrac{4ab}{ab} = 4.$

171. Given expression $= \dfrac{(0.051)^3 + (0.041)^3}{(0.051)^2 - (0.051 \times 0.041) + (0.041)^2}$

$= \left(\dfrac{a^3+b^3}{a^2-ab+b^2}\right)$

$= (a + b) = (0.051 + 0.041) = 0.092.$

172. Given expression $= \dfrac{(5.71)^3 - (2.79)^3}{(5.71)^2 + 5.71 \times 2.97 + (2.79)^2}$

$= \left(\dfrac{a^3-b^3}{a^2+ab+b^2}\right)$

$= (a - b) = (5.71 - 2.79) = 2.92.$

173. Given expression $= \dfrac{(0.943)^2 - (0.943 \times 0.057) + (0.057)^2}{(0.943)^3 + (0.057)^3}$

$= \dfrac{a^2-ab+b^2}{a^3+b^3} = \dfrac{1}{a+b}$

$= \dfrac{1}{0.943+0.057} = 1.$

174. Given expression $= \dfrac{(0.5)^3 + (0.3)^3}{(0.5)^2 + (0.3)^2 - (0.5 \times 0.3)}$

$= \left(\dfrac{a^3+b^3}{a^2+b^2-ab}\right)$

$= (a + b) = (0.5 + 0.3) = 0.8.$

175. Given expression $= \dfrac{(10.3)^3 + (1)^3}{(10.3)^2 - (10.3 \times 1) + (1)^2} = \left(\dfrac{a^3+b^3}{a^2-ab+b^2}\right)$

$= (a + b) = (10.3 + 1) = 11.3.$

176. Given expression $= \dfrac{(2 \times 3.75)^3 + (1)^3}{(7.5)^2 - (7.5 \times 1) + (1)^2}$

$= \dfrac{(7.5)^3 + (1)^3}{(7.5)^2 - (7.5 \times 1) + (1)^2}$

$= \left(\dfrac{a^3+b^3}{a^2-ab+b^2}\right) = (a+b) = (7.5+1) = 8.5.$

177. Given expression $= \dfrac{(0.1)^3 + (0.02)^3}{2^3\ [(0.1)^3 + (0.02)^3]} = \dfrac{1}{8} = 0.125.$

178. Given expression $= \dfrac{(0.013)^3 + (0.007)^3}{(0.013)^2 - (0.013 \times 0.007) + (0.007)^2}$

$= \left(\dfrac{a^3+b^3}{a^2-ab+b^2}\right)$

$= a + b = 0.013 + 0.007 = 0.020.$

179. Given expression $= \dfrac{(2.3)^3 - (0.3)^3}{(2.3)^2 + (2.3 \times 0.3) + (0.3)^2}$

$= \left(\dfrac{a^3-b^3}{a^2+ab+b^2}\right)$

$= (a - b) = (2.3 - 0.3) = 2.$

180. Given expression $= \dfrac{a^2+b^2+c^2}{\left(\frac{a}{10}\right)^2 + \left(\frac{b}{10}\right)^2 + \left(\frac{c}{10}\right)^2},$

where $a = 0.06$, $b = 0.47$ and $c = 0.079.$

$= \dfrac{100\ (a^2+b^2+c^2)}{(a^2+b^2+c^2)} = 100.$

181. Given expression

$= \dfrac{(4.53 - 3.07)^3 + (3.07 - 2.15)^3 + (2.15 - 4.53)^3}{(4.53 - 3.07)\ (3.07 - 2.15)\ (2.15 - 4.53)}$

$= \dfrac{a^3+b^3+c^3}{abc} = \dfrac{3abc}{abc} = 3.$

$[\because$ if $a + b + c = 0,\ a^3 + b^3 + c^3 = 3abc]$

182. $\dfrac{2}{5}\% = \dfrac{2}{5} \times \dfrac{1}{100} = \dfrac{1}{250}$

183. The given expression can be written in this form also

$N = 0.39\overline{39}$ ...(i)

Multiply equation (i) with 100 on both sides.

$100N = 39.\overline{39}$ ...(ii)

Subtracting equation (i) from (ii) we get

$\Rightarrow 100N - N = 39.\overline{39} - 0.\overline{39}$

$99N = 39$

$\Rightarrow N = \dfrac{39}{99} = \dfrac{13}{33}$

184. $\{(41.99)^2 - (18.04)^2\} \div ? = (13.11)^2 - 138.99$

$\Rightarrow \{(42)^2 - (18)^2\} \div ? = (13)^2 - 139\ \{\because a^2 - b^2 = (a+b)(a-b)\}$

$\Rightarrow \{(42+18)(42-18)\} \div ? = 169 - 139$

$\Rightarrow 60 \times 24 \div ? = 30$

$\Rightarrow ? = \dfrac{60 \times 24}{30} = 48$

185. Given $\frac{3}{5}$ of $\frac{4}{7}$ of $\frac{5}{12}$ of 1015

$\Rightarrow x = \frac{3}{5} \times \frac{4}{7} \times \frac{5}{12} \times 1015 = 145$

186. Given $1\frac{1}{8} + 1\frac{6}{7} + 3\frac{3}{5}$

$\frac{9}{8} + \frac{13}{7} + \frac{18}{5} = x$

By taking the LCM of 8, 7 and 5 is 280.

$\frac{315 + 520 + 1008}{280} = \frac{1843}{280} = 6\frac{163}{280}$

187. $2\frac{1.5}{5} + 2\frac{1}{6} - 1\frac{3.5}{15} = \frac{x^{1/3}}{4} + 1\frac{7}{30}$

$\Rightarrow \frac{11.5}{5} + \frac{13}{6} - \frac{18.5}{15} = \frac{x^{1/3}}{4} + \frac{37}{30}$

LCM of 5, 6 and 15 is 30.

$\Rightarrow \frac{69 + 65 - 37}{30} = \frac{x^{1/3}}{4} + \frac{37}{30}$

$\Rightarrow \frac{97}{30} = \frac{x^{\frac{1}{3}}}{4} + \frac{37}{30}$

$\Rightarrow \frac{x^{1/3}}{4} = \frac{97}{30} - \frac{37}{30}$

$\Rightarrow x^{1/3} = \frac{60}{30} \times 4$

$\Rightarrow x^{1/3} = 8 \Rightarrow x = (8)^3$

$\Rightarrow x = 512$

Hence, the number is 512.

188. Let the missing number be x.

Given $323.46 + 23.04 - 43.17 - x = 303$

$x = 323.46 + 23.04 - 43.17 - 303$

$= 0.33$

189. Let the missing number be x.

Given $1\frac{1}{2} + 2\frac{2}{7} = 3\frac{1}{2} + x$

$x = 1\frac{1}{2} + 2\frac{2}{7} - 3\frac{1}{2}$

$x = \frac{3}{2} + \frac{16}{7} - \frac{7}{2}$

$x = \frac{21 + 32 - 49}{14}$

$x = \frac{4}{14} = \frac{2}{7}$

Hence, the number is $\frac{2}{7}$.

190. Let the missing number be x.

Given $48.2 \times 2.5 \times 2.2 + x = 270$

$\Rightarrow x = 270 - 48.2 \times 2.5 \times 2.2$

$x = 270 - 265.1 = 4.9$

Hence, the number is 4.9.

191. Given $4\frac{2}{3} + 3\frac{1}{2} + 1\frac{2}{3}$

$= \frac{14}{3} + \frac{7}{2} - \frac{5}{3}$

By taking LCM of 3, 2 and 3 is 6.

$= \frac{28 + 21 - 10}{6}$

$= \frac{39}{6} = \frac{13}{2} = 6\frac{1}{2}$

192. $\frac{17292}{33} \times \frac{1}{8}$

$= \frac{17292}{33 \times 8} = 65.5$

193. Given $= 1599 \div 39.99 + \frac{4}{5} \times 2449 - 120.05$

$= 1600 \div 40 + \frac{4}{5} \times 2450 - 120$

$= 1600 \div 40 + 1960 - 120$

$= 40 + 1960 - 120 = 1880$

194. Given expression

$= 1576 \div 45.02 + 23.99 \times \sqrt{255}$

$= 1575 \div 45 + 24 \times \sqrt{256}$

$= 35 + 24 \times 16 = 35 + 384 = 419$

195. $= 3899 \div 11.99 - 2379 \div 13.97$

$= 3900 \div 12 - 2380 \div 14$

$\approx 325 - 170 \approx 155$

196. $2\frac{2}{9} + 4\frac{1}{18} - 1\frac{1}{2} = ?$

Let the missing number be x

$x = \frac{20}{9} + \frac{73}{18} - \frac{3}{2}$

LCM of 9, 18 and 2 is 18.

$= \frac{40 + 73 - 27}{18} = \frac{86}{18}$

$= \frac{43}{9} = 4\frac{7}{9}$

197. Let the missing number be x.

$\frac{294 \div 14 \times 5 + 11}{x} = 8^2 \div 5 + 1.7$

$\Rightarrow \frac{\frac{294}{14} \times 5 + 11}{x} = \frac{64}{5} + 1.7$

$\Rightarrow \frac{21 \times 5 + 11}{x} = 12.8 + 1.7$

$\Rightarrow \frac{105 + 11}{x} = 12.8 + 1.7$

$\Rightarrow \frac{116}{x} = 14.5$

$\Rightarrow x = \frac{116}{14.5} = \frac{116 \times 10}{145} = 8$

Hence, the number is 8.

198. Let the missing number be x

$x = 2.5 \times 4.8 + 7.2 \times 1.5 - 1.2 \times 14$

$= (12 + 10.8 - 16.8) = 6$

199. Given $\sqrt{197} \times 6.99 + 626.96$

$= \sqrt{196} \times 7 + 627$

$= 14 \times 7 + 627 = 98 + 627 = 725$

200. Each fraction is equivalent to decimal

$\frac{3}{2} = 1.5$; $\frac{7}{3} = 2.3$

$\frac{5}{4} = 1.25; \frac{7}{2} = 3.5$

Hence, $\frac{7}{2}$ is largest fraction.

201. Let the missing number be x; $\frac{x}{529} = \frac{329}{x}$

$x \times x = 529 \times 329$

$x = \sqrt{174041} = 417.18 \approx 416$

Hence, the number is 416.

202. Let original fraction be $\frac{a}{b}$.

Now, according to the question

$$\frac{a - a \times \frac{25}{100}}{b + b \times \frac{250}{100}} = \frac{6}{5}$$

$$\frac{0.75a}{3.50b} = \frac{6}{5}$$

$$\Rightarrow \frac{a}{b} = \frac{6}{5} \times \frac{3.50}{0.75} = \frac{6 \times 350 \times 100}{5 \times 75 \times 100} = \frac{28}{5}$$

203. Let the missing number be x.

$$\frac{21.5}{5} + \frac{21}{6} - \frac{13.5}{15} = \frac{(x)^{\frac{1}{3}}}{4} + \frac{17}{30}$$

$$\frac{21.5}{5} + \frac{21}{6} - \frac{13.5}{15} - \frac{17}{30} = \frac{(x)^{\frac{1}{3}}}{4}$$

LCM of 5, 6, 15 and 30 is 30.

$$\frac{129 + 105 - 27 - 17}{30} = \frac{\sqrt[3]{x}}{4}$$

$$\sqrt[3]{x} = \frac{190 \times 4}{30} = 25.33 \approx 25$$

$x = 25^3$

$x = 15625$

Hence, the numbers 15625.

204. $\left(\frac{18}{4}\right)^2 \times \left(\frac{455}{19}\right) \div \left(\frac{61}{799}\right)$

$$= \frac{324}{16} \times \frac{455}{19} \times \frac{799}{61} = 6350$$

205. Let the third number be 2960

$\because$ Second number $= \frac{1}{4}$ of third number $= \frac{1}{4} \times 2960 = 740$

$\frac{5}{9}$ of first number = 25% of second number

$\frac{5}{9}$ first number $= \frac{25 \times 740}{100} = 185$

$\Rightarrow$ First number $= \frac{185 \times 9}{5} = 333$

$\therefore$ 30% of 333 $= \frac{30}{100} \times 333 = 999$

206. $7\frac{1}{2} - \left[2\frac{1}{4} \div \left\{1\frac{1}{4} - \frac{1}{2}\left(1\frac{1}{2} - \frac{1}{3} - \frac{1}{6}\right)\right\}\right]$

$$= \frac{15}{2} - \left[\frac{9}{4} \div \left\{\frac{5}{4} - \frac{1}{2}\left(\frac{3}{2} - \frac{1}{3} - \frac{1}{6}\right)\right\}\right]$$

$$= \frac{15}{2}\left[\frac{9}{4} \div \left\{\frac{5}{4} - \frac{1}{2}\left(\frac{9-2-1}{6}\right)\right\}\right]$$

$$= \frac{15}{2}\left[\frac{9}{4} \div \left(\frac{5}{4} - \frac{1}{2}\right)\right] = \frac{15}{2}\left[\frac{9}{4} \div \left(\frac{5-2}{4}\right)\right]$$

$$= \frac{15}{2} - \left[\frac{9}{4} \div \frac{3}{4}\right] = \frac{15}{2} - \left[\frac{9}{4} \times \frac{4}{3}\right]$$

$$= \frac{15}{2} - 3 = \frac{15-6}{2} = \frac{9}{2} = 4\frac{1}{2}$$

4 Simplification

IMPORTANT FACTS AND FORMULAE

I. 'BODMAS' Rule: This rule depicts the correct sequence in which the operations are to be executed, so as to find out the value of a given expression.

Here, '*B*' stands for 'Bracket', '*O*' for 'of', '*D*' for 'Division', '*M*' for 'Multiplication', '*A*' for 'Addition' and '*S*' for 'Subtraction'.

Thus, in simplifying an expression, first of all the brackets must be removed, strictly in the order ( ), { } and [ ].

After removing the brackets, we must use the following operations strictly in the order:

(*i*) of (*ii*) Division (*iii*) Multiplication (*iv*) Addition (*v*) Subtraction

II. Modulus of a Real Number: Modulus of a real number a is defined as

$$|a| = \begin{cases} a, & \text{if } a > 0 \\ -a, & \text{if } a < 0 \end{cases}$$

Thus, $|5| = 5$ and $|-5| = -(-5) = 5$.

III. Virnaculum (or Bar): When an expression contains Virnaculum, before applying the 'BODMAS' rule, we simplify the expression under the Virnaculum.

IV. Some Important Formulae:

(*i*) $(a + b)^2 = (a^2 + b^2 + 2ab)$

(*ii*) $(a - b)^2 = (a^2 + b^2 - 2ab)$

(*iii*) $(a + b)^2 + (a - b)^2 = 2(a^2 + b^2)$

(*iv*) $(a + b)^2 - (a - b)^2 = 4ab$

(*v*) $(a^2 - b^2) = (a + b)(a - b)$

(*vi*) $(a + b)^3 = a^3 + b^3 + 3ab(a + b)$

(*vii*) $(a - b)^3 = a^3 - b^3 - 3ab(a - b)$

(*viii*) $(a^3 + b^3) = (a + b)(a^2 - ab + b^2)$

(*ix*) $(a^3 - b^3) = (a - b)(a^2 + ab + b^2)$

(*x*) $(a + b + c)^2 = a^2 + b^2 + c^2 + 2(ab + bc + ca)$

(*xi*) $a^3 + b^3 + c^3 - 3abc = (a + b + c)(a^2 + b^2 + c^2 - ab - bc - ca)$

V. For any two sets *A* and *B*, we have:

(*i*) $n(A - B) + n(A \cap B) = n(A)$

(*ii*) $n(B - A) + n(A \cap B) = n(B)$

(*iii*) $n(A \cup B) = n(A - B) + n(A \cap B) + n(B - A)$

(*iv*) $n(A \cup B) = n(A) + n(B) - n(A \cap B)$.

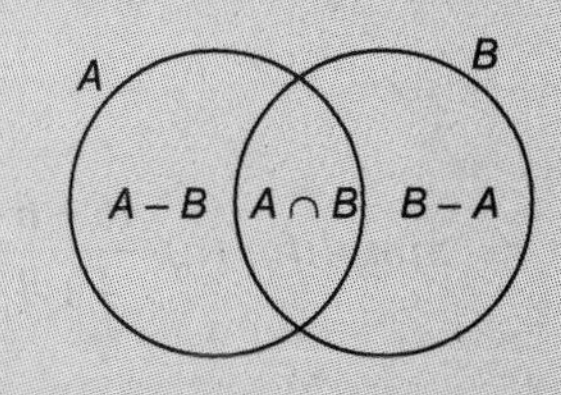

SOLVED EXAMPLES

Ex. 1. $\boldsymbol{4368 + 2158 - 596 - ? = 3421 + 1262}$ **(Bank P.O., 2009)**

Sol. Let $4368 + 2158 - 596 - x = 3421 + 1262$

$\Rightarrow x + 596 = (4368 + 2158) - (3421 + 1262)$

$\Rightarrow x + 596 = 6526 - 4683 = 1843$

$\Rightarrow x = 1843 - 596 = 1247.$

Hence, required number = 1247.

Ex. 2. $\boldsymbol{3456 \div 12 \div 8 = ?}$ **(Bank Recruitment, 2008)**

Sol. Given expression $= \dfrac{3456}{12} \div 8 = 288 \div 8 = 36.$

Ex. 3. ***13 × 252 ÷ 42 + 170 =? + 47*** (Bank P.O., 2010)

Sol. Let 13 × 252 ÷ 42 + 170 = x + 47. Then,

$$13 \times \frac{252}{42} + 170 = x + 47 \Rightarrow 13 \times 6 + 170 = x + 47 \Rightarrow x + 47 = 78 + 170 = 248$$

$$\Rightarrow x = 248 - 47 = 201.$$

Hence, required number = 201.

Ex. 4. ***Simplify: (a) 460 × 15 – 5 × 20*** (Bank P.O., 2010)

(b) 1 ÷ [1 + 1 ÷ {1 + 1 ÷ 1(1 + 1 ÷ 2)}] + 1 (A.A.O., 2009)

Sol. (*a*) Given expression = 6900 – 100 = 6800.

(*b*) Given expression $= 1 \div \left[1 + 1 \div \left\{1 + 1 \div 1\left(1 + \frac{1}{2}\right)\right\}\right] + 1$

$$= 1 \div \left[1 + 1 \div \left\{1 + 1 \div \frac{3}{2}\right\}\right] + 1 = 1 \div \left[1 + 1 \div \left\{1 + 1 \times \frac{2}{3}\right\}\right] + 1$$

$$= 1 \div \left[1 + 1 \div \left\{1 + \frac{2}{3}\right\}\right] + 1 = 1 \div \left[1 + 1 \div \frac{5}{3}\right] + 1$$

$$= 1 \div \left[1 + 1 \times \frac{3}{5}\right] + 1 = 1 \div \left[1 + \frac{3}{5}\right] + 1 = 1 \div \frac{8}{5} + 1 = 1 \times \frac{5}{8} + 1 = \frac{5}{8} + 1 = \frac{13}{8}.$$

Ex. 5. ***Find the missing numeral:***

(a) (? – 2763) ÷ 86 × 13 = 208 (L.I.C.A.D.O., 2007)

(b) 3565 ÷ 23 + 4675 ÷? = 430 (Bank Recruitment, 2008)

Sol. (*a*) Let (x – 2763) ÷ 86 × 13 = 208.

Then, $\frac{(x - 2763)}{86} \times 13 = 208 \Rightarrow \frac{(x - 2763)}{86} = \frac{208}{13} = 16$

$$\Rightarrow (x - 2763) = 16 \times 86 = 1376$$

$$\Rightarrow x = 1376 + 2763 = 4139.$$

(*b*) Let 3565 ÷ 23 + 4675 ÷ x = 430.

Then, $\frac{3565}{23} + \frac{4675}{x} = 430 \Rightarrow 155 + \frac{4675}{x} = 430$

$$\Rightarrow \frac{4675}{x} = 430 - 155 = 275 \Rightarrow x = \frac{4675}{275} = 17.$$

Ex. 6. ***Simplify: (a)*** $\frac{(6+6+6+6) \div 6}{4+4+4+4 \div 4}$ ***(b)*** $\frac{(2+3) \times 5 + 3 \div \frac{1}{2}}{6 + 5 \times 4 \div \frac{4}{5}}$ (R.R.B., 2006)

Sol. (*a*) Given expression $= \frac{24 \div 6}{4+4+4+1} = \frac{4}{13}.$

(*b*) Given expression $= \frac{5 \times 5 + 3 \times 2}{6 + 5 \times 4 \times \frac{5}{4}} = \frac{25 + 6}{6 + 25} = \frac{31}{31} = 1.$

Ex. 7. ***What should come in place of both the question marks in the following equation?***

$$\frac{128 \div 16 \times ? - 7 \times 2}{7^2 - 8 \times 6 + ?^2} = 1$$

Sol. Let $\frac{128 \div 16 \times x - 7 \times 2}{7^2 - 8 \times 6 + x^2} = 1.$

Then, $8x - 7 \times 2 = 49 - 48 + x^2 \Leftrightarrow 8x - 14 = 1 + x^2 \Leftrightarrow x^2 - 8x + 15 = 0$

$$\Leftrightarrow x^2 - 3x - 5x + 15 = 0 \Leftrightarrow x(x - 3) - 5(x - 3) = 0$$

$$\Leftrightarrow (x - 3)(x - 5) = 0 \Leftrightarrow x = 3 \text{ or } x = 5.$$

Hence, missing number is 3 or 5.

Ex. 8. ***Simplify:*** *(a)* $108 \div 36 \text{ of } \frac{1}{4} + \frac{2}{5} \times 3\frac{1}{4}$

(b) $\frac{2}{3} \times \frac{5}{6} + \frac{4}{9} - \frac{3}{4} + \frac{2}{9} \times \frac{5}{9} \div \frac{2}{9}$ (P.C.S., 2009)

Sol. (*a*) Given expression $= 108 \div 9 + \frac{2}{5} \times \frac{13}{4} = \frac{108}{9} + \frac{13}{10} = \left(12 + \frac{13}{10}\right) = \frac{133}{10} = 13\frac{3}{10}.$

(*b*) Given expression $= \frac{2}{3} \times \frac{5}{6} + \frac{4}{9} - \frac{3}{4} + \frac{2}{9} \times \frac{5}{9} \times \frac{9}{2}$

$= \frac{5}{9} + \frac{4}{9} - \frac{3}{4} + \frac{5}{9} = \frac{14}{9} - \frac{3}{4} = \frac{56 - 27}{36} = \frac{29}{36}.$

Ex. 9. ***What value will replace the question mark in the following equation?***

$4\frac{1}{2} + 3\frac{1}{6} + ? + 2\frac{1}{3} = 13\frac{2}{5}.$

Sol. Let $\frac{9}{2} + \frac{19}{6} + x + \frac{7}{3} = \frac{67}{5}.$

Then, $x = \frac{67}{5} - \left(\frac{9}{2} + \frac{19}{6} + \frac{7}{3}\right) \Leftrightarrow x = \frac{67}{5} - \left(\frac{27 + 19 + 14}{6}\right) = \left(\frac{67}{5} - \frac{60}{6}\right)$

$\Leftrightarrow x = \left(\frac{67}{5} - 10\right) = \frac{17}{5} = 3\frac{2}{5}.$

Hence, missing fraction $= 3\frac{2}{5}.$

Ex. 10. ***Simplify:*** $\left[3\frac{1}{4} \div \left\{1\frac{1}{4} - \frac{1}{2}\left(2\frac{1}{2} - \overline{\frac{1}{4} - \frac{1}{6}}\right)\right\}\right].$

Sol. Given exp. $= \left[\frac{13}{4} \div \left\{\frac{5}{4} - \frac{1}{2}\left(\frac{5}{2} - \frac{3-2}{12}\right)\right\}\right] = \left[\frac{13}{4} \div \left\{\frac{5}{4} - \frac{1}{2}\left(\frac{5}{2} - \frac{1}{12}\right)\right\}\right]$

$= \left[\frac{13}{4} \div \left\{\frac{5}{4} - \frac{1}{2}\left(\frac{30-1}{12}\right)\right\}\right] = \left[\frac{13}{4} \div \left\{\frac{5}{4} - \frac{29}{24}\right\}\right]$

$= \left[\frac{13}{4} \div \left\{\frac{30-29}{24}\right\}\right] = \left[\frac{13}{4} \div \frac{1}{24}\right] = \left[\frac{13}{4} \times 24\right] = 78.$

Ex. 11. ***Simplify:*** $\dfrac{\frac{7}{2} \div \frac{5}{2} \times \frac{3}{2}}{\frac{7}{2} \div \frac{5}{2} \text{ of } \frac{3}{2}} \div 5.25$

Sol. Given exp. $= \dfrac{\frac{7}{2} \times \frac{2}{5} \times \frac{3}{2}}{\frac{7}{2} \div \frac{15}{4}} \div 5.25 = \dfrac{\frac{21}{10}}{\frac{7}{2} \times \frac{4}{15}} \div \frac{525}{100} = \frac{21}{10} \times \frac{15}{14} \times \frac{100}{525} = \frac{6}{14} = \frac{3}{7}.$

Ex. 12. ***Simplify:*** $b - [b - (a + b) - \{b - (b - \overline{a - b})\} + 2a].$

Sol. Given exp. $= b - [b - (a + b) - \{b - (b - a + b)\} + 2a]$

$= b - [b - a - b - \{b - (2b - a)\} + 2a]$

$= b - [- a - \{b - 2b + a\} + 2a]$

$= b - [- a - \{- b + a\} + 2a]$

$= b - [- a + b - a + 2a] = b - b = 0.$

Ex. 13. ***If $x + y = 23$ and $xy = 126$, what is the value of $x^2 + y^2$?*** **(Bank Recruitment, 2010)**

Sol. $(x + y) = 23 \Rightarrow (x + y)^2 = (23)^2 = 529 \Rightarrow x^2 + y^2 + 2xy = 529$

$\Rightarrow x^2 + y^2 + 2 \times 126 = 529 \Rightarrow x^2 + y^2 = 529 - 252 = 277.$

Ex. 14. ***If $\frac{a}{b} = \frac{4}{5}$ and $\frac{b}{c} = \frac{15}{16}$, find the value of $\frac{c^2 - a^2}{c^2 + a^2}$.*** **(M.B.A., 2007)**

Sol. $\frac{a}{b} = \frac{4}{5}$ and $\frac{b}{c} = \frac{15}{16} \Rightarrow \frac{a}{b} \times \frac{b}{c} = \frac{4}{5} \times \frac{15}{16} = \frac{3}{4} \Rightarrow \frac{a}{c} = \frac{3}{4} \Rightarrow \frac{c}{a} = \frac{4}{3}.$

$$\therefore \frac{c^2 - a^2}{c^2 + a^2} = \frac{\frac{c^2}{a^2} - 1}{\frac{c^2}{a^2} + 1} = \frac{\left(\frac{c}{a}\right)^2 - 1}{\left(\frac{c}{a}\right)^2 + 1} = \frac{\left(\frac{4}{3}\right)^2 - 1}{\left(\frac{4}{3}\right)^2 + 1} = \frac{\left(\frac{16}{9} - 1\right)}{\left(\frac{16}{9} + 1\right)} = \frac{7}{9} \times \frac{9}{25} = \frac{7}{25}.$$

Ex. 15. ***If $a = \frac{4xy}{x + y}$, find the value of $\frac{a + 2x}{a - 2x} + \frac{a + 2y}{a - 2y}$.*** **(M.C.A., 2007)**

Sol.
$$\frac{a + 2x}{a - 2x} + \frac{a + 2y}{a - 2y} = \frac{\frac{4xy}{x + y} + 2x}{\frac{4xy}{x + y} - 2x} + \frac{\frac{4xy}{x + y} + 2y}{\frac{4xy}{x + y} - 2y} = \frac{4xy + 2x(x + y)}{4xy - 2x(x + y)} + \frac{4xy + 2y(x + y)}{4xy - 2y(x + y)}$$

$$= \frac{2x(2y + x + y)}{2x(2y - x - y)} + \frac{2y(2x + x + y)}{2y(2x - x - y)} = \frac{(3y + x)}{(y - x)} + \frac{(3x + y)}{(x - y)}$$

$$= \frac{(3x + y)}{(x - y)} - \frac{(3y + x)}{(x - y)} = \frac{(3x + y) - (3y + x)}{(x - y)} = \frac{2x - 2y}{x - y} = 2.$$

Ex. 16. ***Find the value of $4 - \cfrac{5}{1 + \cfrac{1}{3 + \cfrac{1}{2 + \cfrac{1}{4}}}}$.***

Sol. Given exp. $= 4 - \cfrac{5}{1 + \cfrac{1}{3 + \cfrac{1}{(9/4)}}} = 4 - \cfrac{5}{1 + \cfrac{1}{3 + \cfrac{4}{9}}} = 4 - \cfrac{5}{1 + \cfrac{1}{(31/9)}}$

$= 4 - \cfrac{5}{1 + \cfrac{9}{31}} = 4 - \frac{5}{(40/31)} = 4 - \frac{5 \times 31}{40} = 4 - \frac{31}{8} = \frac{1}{8}.$

Ex. 17. ***If $\cfrac{2x}{1 + \cfrac{1}{1 + \cfrac{x}{1 - x}}} = 1$, then find the value of x.***

Sol. We have: $\cfrac{2x}{1 + \cfrac{1}{\cfrac{(1 - x) + x}{1 - x}}} = 1 \Leftrightarrow \cfrac{2x}{1 + \cfrac{1}{[1/(1 - x)]}} = 1 \Leftrightarrow \frac{2x}{1 + (1 - x)} = 1$

$\Leftrightarrow 2x = 2 - x \Leftrightarrow 3x = 2 \Leftrightarrow x = \frac{2}{3}.$

Ex. 18. ***(i) If $4x + 5y = 83$ and $\frac{3x}{2y} = \frac{21}{22}$, then what is the value of $y - x$?*** **(Bank P.O., 2008)**

(ii) If $\frac{x}{4} - \frac{x - 3}{6} = 1$, then find the value of x.

Sol. (*i*) $\frac{3x}{2y}=\frac{21}{22}\Rightarrow\frac{x}{y}=\frac{21}{22}\times\frac{2}{3}=\frac{7}{11}\Rightarrow x=\frac{7}{11}y.$

$4x+5y=83\Rightarrow 4\times\frac{7}{11}y+5y=83\Rightarrow\frac{28}{11}y+5y=83$

$\Rightarrow\frac{83}{11}y=83\Rightarrow y=83\times\frac{11}{83}=11.$

$\therefore\quad x=\left(\frac{7}{11}\times 11\right)=7.$ So, $y-x=11-7=4$.

(*ii*) $\frac{x}{4}-\frac{x-3}{6}=1\Leftrightarrow\frac{3x-2(x-3)}{12}=1\Leftrightarrow 3x-2x+6=12\Leftrightarrow x=6.$

Ex. 19. ***If $2x+3y=34$ and $\frac{x+y}{y}=\frac{13}{8}$, then find the value of $5y+7x$.***

Sol. The given equations are:

$2x+3y=34$ ...(*i*) and, $\frac{x+y}{y}=\frac{13}{8}\Rightarrow 8x+8y=13y\Rightarrow 8x-5y=0$ ...(*ii*)

Multiplying (*i*) by 5, (*ii*) by 3 and adding, we get: $34x=170$ or $x=5$.

Putting $x=5$ in (*i*), we get: $y=8$.

$\therefore$ $5y+7x=(5\times 8+7\times 5)=40+35=75$.

Ex. 20. ***The cost of 4 bags and 3 boxes is ₹ 555 and the cost of 3 bags and 4 boxes is ₹ 460. What is the cost of one bag?*** **(Bank P.O., 2009)**

Sol. Let the cost of 1 bag be ₹ x and that of 1 box be ₹ y.

Then, $4x+3y=555$ ...(*i*) and $3x+4y=460°$ ...(*ii*)

Adding (*i*) and (*ii*), we get: $7x+7y=1015$ or $x+y=145$ ...(*iii*)

Subtracting (*ii*) from (*i*), we get: $x-y=95$ ...(*iv*)

Adding (*iii*) and (*iv*), we get: $2x=240$ or $x=120$.

Hence, cost of 1 bag = ₹ 120.

Ex. 21. ***If $2x+3y+z=55$, $x+z-y=4$ and $y-x+z=12$, then what are the values of x, y and z?***

Sol. The given equations are:

$2x+3y+z=55$ ...(*i*); $x+z-y=4$ ...(*ii*); $y-x+z=12$ ...(*iii*)

Subtracting (*ii*) from (*i*), we get: $x+4y=51$ ...(*iv*)

Subtracting (*iii*) from (*i*), we get: $3x+2y=43$ ...(*v*)

Multiplying (*v*) by 2 and subtracting (*iv*) from it, we get: $5x=35$ or $x=7$.

Putting $x=7$ in (*iv*), we get: $4y=44$ or $y=11$.

Putting $x=7$, $y=11$ in (*i*), we get: $z=8$.

Ex. 22. ***If $x^2-7x=-12$, what is the value of x?*** **(M.B.A., 2006)**

Sol. $x^2-7x=-12\Leftrightarrow x^2-7x+12=0\Leftrightarrow x^2-3x-4x+12=0$

$\Leftrightarrow x(x-3)-4(x-3)=0\Leftrightarrow(x-3)(x-4)=0\Leftrightarrow x=3$ or $x=4$.

Ex. 23. ***Find the value of $\left(1-\frac{1}{3}\right)\left(1-\frac{1}{4}\right)\left(1-\frac{1}{5}\right)\ldots\ldots\left(1-\frac{1}{100}\right)$.***

Sol. Given expression $=\frac{2}{3}\times\frac{3}{4}\times\frac{4}{5}\times\ldots\ldots\times\frac{99}{100}=\frac{2}{100}=\frac{1}{50}.$

Ex. 24. ***Find the value of $\frac{1}{2\times 3}+\frac{1}{3\times 4}+\frac{1}{4\times 5}+\frac{1}{5\times 6}+\ldots\ldots+\frac{1}{9\times 10}$.***

Sol. Given expression $=\left(\frac{1}{2}-\frac{1}{3}\right)+\left(\frac{1}{3}-\frac{1}{4}\right)+\left(\frac{1}{4}-\frac{1}{5}\right)+\left(\frac{1}{5}-\frac{1}{6}\right)+\ldots\ldots+\left(\frac{1}{9}-\frac{1}{10}\right)$

$=\left(\frac{1}{2}-\frac{1}{10}\right)=\frac{4}{10}=\frac{2}{5}.$

Ex. 25. ***Simplify :*** $99\frac{48}{49} \times 245$.

Sol. Given expression $= \left(100 - \frac{1}{49}\right) \times 245 = \frac{4899}{49} \times 245 = 4899 \times 5 = 24495$.

Ex. 26. ***Find the value of:*** $\frac{1}{30} + \frac{1}{42} + \frac{1}{56} + \frac{1}{72} + \frac{1}{90} + \frac{1}{110}$. **(A.A.O. Exam, 2009)**

Sol. Given expression $= \left(\frac{1}{5} - \frac{1}{6}\right) + \left(\frac{1}{6} - \frac{1}{7}\right) + \left(\frac{1}{7} - \frac{1}{8}\right) + \left(\frac{1}{8} - \frac{1}{9}\right) + \left(\frac{1}{9} - \frac{1}{10}\right) + \left(\frac{1}{10} - \frac{1}{11}\right)$

$= \left(\frac{1}{5} - \frac{1}{11}\right) = \frac{6}{55}$.

Ex. 27. ***A board 7 ft. 9 inches long is divided into 3 equal parts. What is the length of each part?***

Sol. Length of board = 7 ft. 9 inches = (7 × 12 + 9) inches = 93 inches.

∴ Length of each part = $\left(\frac{93}{3}\right)$ inches = 31 inches = 2 ft. 7 inches.

Ex. 28. ***Ram went to a shop to buy 50 kg of rice. He buys two varieties of rice which cost him ₹ 4.50 per kg and ₹ 5 per kg. He spends a total of ₹ 240. What was the quantity of rice bought which cost him ₹ 4.50 per kg?*** **(M.A.T., 2007)**

Sol. Let the quantity of rice bought at ₹ 4.50 per kg be x kg.

Then, quantity of rice bought at ₹ 5 per kg = $(50 - x)$ kg.

∴ $4.50x + 5(50 - x) = 240 \Rightarrow 250 - 0.5x = 240 \Rightarrow 0.5x = 10 \Rightarrow x = 20$.

Hence, quantity of rice bought at ₹ 4.50 per kg = 20 kg.

Ex. 29. ***A boy was asked to multiply a certain number by 53. He multiplied it by 35 and got his answer less than the correct one by 1206. Find the number to be multiplied.*** **(SNAP, 2005)**

Sol. Let the required number be x.

Then, $53x - 35x = 1206 \Leftrightarrow 18x = 1206 \Leftrightarrow x = \frac{1206}{18} = 67$.

Hence, number to be multiplied = 67.

Ex. 30. $\frac{4}{15}$ ***of*** $\frac{5}{7}$ ***of a number is greater than*** $\frac{4}{9}$ ***of*** $\frac{2}{5}$ ***of the same number by 8. What is half of that number?***

Sol. Let the number be x.

Then, $\frac{4}{15}$ of $\frac{5}{7}$ of $x - \frac{4}{9}$ of $\frac{2}{5}$ of $x = 8 \Leftrightarrow \frac{4}{21}x - \frac{8}{45}x = 8$

$\Leftrightarrow \left(\frac{4}{21} - \frac{8}{45}\right)x = 8 \Leftrightarrow \left(\frac{60 - 56}{315}\right)x = 8 \Leftrightarrow \frac{4}{315}x = 8$

$\Leftrightarrow x = \left(\frac{8 \times 315}{4}\right) = 630 \Leftrightarrow \frac{1}{2}x = 315$.

Hence, required number = 315.

Ex. 31. ***A man owns*** $\frac{2}{3}$ ***of the market research bureau business and sells*** $\frac{3}{4}$ ***of his shares for ₹ 75000. What is the value of business?*** **(Campus Recruitment, 2010)**

Sol. Let the total value be ₹ x.

Then, $\frac{3}{4}$ of $\frac{2}{3}$ of $x = 75000 \Leftrightarrow \frac{x}{2} = 75000 \Leftrightarrow x = 150000$.

∴ Value of business = ₹ 150000.

Ex. 32. ***A man spends $\frac{2}{5}$ of his salary on house rent, $\frac{3}{10}$ of his salary on food and $\frac{1}{8}$ of his salary on conveyance. If he has ₹ 1400 left with him, find his expenditure on food and conveyance.***

Sol. Part of the salary left $= 1-\left(\frac{2}{5}+\frac{3}{10}+\frac{1}{8}\right)=1-\frac{33}{40}=\frac{7}{40}$.

Let the monthly salary be ₹ x.

Then, $\frac{7}{40}$ of $x = 1400 \Leftrightarrow x=\left(\frac{1400\times 40}{7}\right)=8000$.

$\therefore$ Expenditure on food = ₹$\left(\frac{3}{10}\times 8000\right)$ = ₹ 2400.

Expenditure on conveyance = ₹$\left(\frac{1}{8}\times 8000\right)$ = ₹ 1000.

Ex. 33. ***A third of Arun's marks in Mathematics exceeds a half of his marks in English by 30. If he got 240 marks in the two subjects together, how many marks did he get in English?***

Sol. Let Arun's marks in Mathematics and English be x and y respectively.

Then, $\frac{1}{3}x-\frac{1}{2}y=30 \Leftrightarrow 2x-3y=180$ ...(*i*) and $x+y=240$ ...(*ii*)

Solving (*i*) and (*ii*), we get: x = 180 and y = 60.

$\therefore$ Arun's marks in English = 60.

Ex. 34. ***A tin of oil was $\frac{4}{5}$ full. When 6 bottles of oil were taken out and four bottles of oil were poured into it, it was $\frac{3}{4}$ full. How many bottles of oil can the tin contain?***

Sol. Suppose x bottles can fill the tin completely.

Then, $\frac{4}{5}x-\frac{3}{4}x=(6-4) \Leftrightarrow \frac{x}{20}=2 \Leftrightarrow x=40$.

$\therefore$ Required number of bottles = 40.

Ex. 35. ***If $\frac{1}{8}$ of a pencil is black, $\frac{1}{2}$ of the remaining is white and the remaining $3\frac{1}{2}$ cm is blue, find the total length of the pencil.***

Sol. Let the total length of the pencil be x cm. Then,

Black part = $\left(\frac{x}{8}\right)$ cm. Remaining part = $\left(x-\frac{x}{8}\right)$ cm = $\left(\frac{7x}{8}\right)$ cm.

White part = $\left(\frac{1}{2}\times\frac{7x}{8}\right)$ cm = $\left(\frac{7x}{16}\right)$ cm. Remaining part = $\left(\frac{7x}{8}-\frac{7x}{16}\right)$ cm = $\frac{7x}{16}$ cm.

$\therefore \frac{7x}{16}=\frac{7}{2}$ or $x=\frac{16}{2}=8$ cm.

Hence, total length of the pencil = 8 cm.

Ex. 36. ***At a college football game, $\frac{4}{5}$ of the seats in the lower deck of the stadium were sold. If $\frac{1}{4}$ of all the seating in the stadium is located in the lower deck, and if $\frac{2}{3}$ of all the seats in the stadium were sold, what fraction of the unsold seats in the stadium was in the lower deck?***

Sol. Let the total number of seats in the stadium be x.

Then, number of seats in the lower deck = $\frac{x}{4}$.

Number of seats sold $= \frac{2x}{3}$. Number of seats unsold $= \left(x - \frac{2x}{3}\right) = \frac{x}{3}$.

Number of sold seats in lower deck $= \frac{4}{5}$ of $\frac{x}{4} = \frac{x}{5}$.

Number of unsold seats in lower deck $= \left(\frac{x}{4} - \frac{x}{5}\right) = \frac{x}{20}$.

$\therefore$ Required fraction $= \frac{x/20}{x/3} = \frac{3}{20}$.

Ex. 37. ***In a certain office, $\frac{1}{3}$ of the workers are women, $\frac{1}{2}$ of the women are married and $\frac{1}{3}$ of the married women have children. If $\frac{3}{4}$ of the men are married and $\frac{2}{3}$ of the married men have children, what part of workers are without children?***

Sol. Let the total number of workers be x. Then,

Number of women $= \frac{x}{3}$ and number of men $= \left(x - \frac{x}{3}\right) = \frac{2x}{3}$.

Number of women having children $= \frac{1}{3}$ of $\frac{1}{2}$ of $\frac{x}{3} = \frac{x}{18}$.

Number of men having children $= \frac{2}{3}$ of $\frac{3}{4}$ of $\frac{2x}{3} = \frac{x}{3}$.

Number of workers having children $= \left(\frac{x}{18} + \frac{x}{3}\right) = \frac{7x}{18}$.

$\therefore$ Workers having no children $= \left(x - \frac{7x}{18}\right) = \frac{11x}{18} = \frac{11}{18}$ of all workers.

Ex. 38. ***A crate of mangoes contains one bruised mango for every 30 mangoes in the crate. If 3 out of every 4 bruised mangoes are considered unsaleable, and there are 12 unsaleable mangoes in the crate, then how many mangoes are there in the crate?***

Sol. Let the total number of mangoes in the crate be x. Then,

Number of bruised mangoes $= \frac{1}{30}x$.

Number of unsaleable mangoes $= \left(\frac{3}{4} \times \frac{1}{30}x\right) = \frac{1}{40}x$.

$\therefore \frac{1}{40}x = 12$ or $x = (12 \times 40) = 480$.

Hence, total number of mangoes in the crate = 480.

Ex. 39. ***The cost of 4 rings and 2 bangles is ₹ 57200. What is the cost of 6 rings and 3 bangles?*** **(Bank Recruitment, 2009)**

Sol. We have: $4R + 2B = 57200 \Rightarrow \frac{3}{2}(4R + 2B) = \frac{3}{2} \times 57200 \Rightarrow 6R + 3B = 85800$.

Hence, cost of 6 rings and 3 bangles = ₹ 85800.

Ex. 40. ***The cost of 15 kg of sugar is ₹ 255, the cost of 17 kg of tea is ₹ 1615 and the cost of 22 kg of rice is ₹ 572. What is the total cost of 18 kg of sugar, 21 kg of tea and 27 kg of rice?*** **(Bank P.O., 2008)**

Sol. Cost of 1 kg sugar = ₹ $\left(\frac{255}{15}\right)$ = ₹ 17; Cost of 1 kg tea = ₹ $\left(\frac{1615}{17}\right)$ = ₹ 95;

Cost of 1 kg rice = ₹ $\left(\frac{572}{22}\right)$ = ₹ 26.

$\therefore$ Required cost = ₹ (17 × 18 + 95 × 21 + 26 × 27) = ₹ (306 + 1995 + 702) = ₹ 3003.

Ex. 41. ***If * is an operation such that x * y = 3x + 2y, find the value of 2 * 3 + 3 * 4.***

Sol. $2 * 3 + 3 * 4 = (3 \times 2 + 2 \times 3) + (3 \times 3 + 2 \times 4) = (6 + 6) + (9 + 8)$
$= 12 + 17 = 29.$

Ex. 42. ***If*** $a^2 + b^2 = 117$ ***and*** $ab = 54$***, then find the value of*** $\dfrac{a+b}{a-b}$.

Sol. $(a + b)^2 = a^2 + b^2 + 2ab = 117 + 2 \times 54 = 225 \Rightarrow a + b = 15.$
$(a - b)^2 = a^2 + b^2 - 2ab = 117 - 2 \times 54 = 9 \Rightarrow a - b = 3.$

$\therefore \quad \dfrac{a+b}{a-b} = \dfrac{15}{3} = 5.$

Ex. 43. ***Find the value of*** $\left(\dfrac{75983 \times 75983 - 45983 \times 45983}{30000}\right)$.

Sol. Given expression $= \dfrac{(75983)^2 - (45983)^2}{(75983 - 45983)} = \dfrac{(a^2 - b^2)}{(a - b)}$, where $a = 75983, b = 45983$

$= \dfrac{(a+b)(a-b)}{(a-b)} = (a + b) = (75983 + 45983) = 121966.$

Ex. 44. ***Find the value of*** $\left(\dfrac{343 \times 343 \times 343 - 113 \times 113 \times 113}{343 \times 343 + 343 \times 113 + 113 \times 113}\right)$. **(B.Ed. Entrance, 2010)**

Sol. Given expression $= \dfrac{(a^3 - b^3)}{(a^2 + ab + b^2)}$, where $a = 343, b = 113$

$= (a - b) = (343 - 113) = 230.$

Ex. 45. ***If*** $(x - 4)^3 + (x - 9)^3 + (x - 8)^3 = 3(x - 4)(x - 9)(x - 8)$***, find the value of x.***

Sol. If $a^3 + b^3 + c^3 = 3abc$, then $a + b + c = 0$.

So, we have: $(x - 4) + (x - 9) + (x - 8) = 0 \Rightarrow 3x - 21 = 0 \Rightarrow 3x = 21 \Rightarrow x = 7.$

Ex. 46. ***There are certain number of benches in a classroom. If four students sit on each bench then three benches remain unoccupied. If, however, three students sit on each bench then three students remain standing in the class. Find the number of students in the class.*** **(P.C.S., 2009)**

Sol. Let the total number of benches in the class be x.

Case I. When 4 students sit on each bench

In this case, total number of students $= 4(x - 3)$.

Case II. When 3 students sit on each bench

In this case, total number of students $= 3x + 3$.

$\therefore \quad 4(x - 3) = 3x + 3 \Leftrightarrow 4x - 12 = 3x + 3 \Leftrightarrow x = 15.$

Hence, number of students in the class $= 4(x - 3) = 4 \times 12 = 48.$

Ex. 47. ***A man divides ₹ 8600 among 5 sons, 4 daughters and 2 nephews. If each daughter receives four times as much as each nephew, and each son receives five times as much as each nephew, how much does each daughter receive?***

Sol. Let the share of each nephew be ₹ x.

Then, share of each daughter = ₹ $(4x)$; share of each son = ₹ $(5x)$.

So, $5 \times 5x + 4 \times 4x + 2 \times x = 8600 \Leftrightarrow 25x + 16x + 2x = 8600$
$\Leftrightarrow 43x = 8600 \Leftrightarrow x = 200.$

$\therefore$ Share of each daughter = ₹ (4×200) = ₹ 800.

Ex. 48. ***₹ 6500 were divided equally among a certain number of persons. Had there been 15 more persons, each would have got ₹ 30 less. Find the original number of persons.*** **(M.A.T., 2005)**

Sol. Let the original number of persons be x.

Then, $\dfrac{6500}{x} - \dfrac{6500}{(x+15)} = 30 \Leftrightarrow 6500\left[\dfrac{x+15-x}{x(x+15)}\right] = 30 \Leftrightarrow 30x(x + 15) = 6500 \times 15$

$\Leftrightarrow x^2 + 15x = 3250 \Leftrightarrow x^2 + 15x - 3250 = 0$

$\Leftrightarrow x^2 + 65x - 50x - 3250 = 0$

$\Leftrightarrow x(x + 65) - 50(x + 65) = 0$

$\Leftrightarrow (x + 65)(x - 50) = 0 \Leftrightarrow x = 50.$

Hence, original number of persons = 50.

Ex. 49. ***Village X has a population of 68000, which is decreasing at the rate of 1200 per year. Village Y has a population of 42000, which is increasing at the rate of 800 per year. In how many years will the population of the two villages be equal?***

Sol. Let the population of villages X and Y be equal after p years.

Then, $68000 - 1200p = 42000 + 800p \Rightarrow 2000p = 26000 \Rightarrow p = 13.$

So, their population will be equal after 13 years.

Ex. 50. ***From a group of boys and girls, 15 girls leave. There are then left 2 boys for each girl. After this, 45 boys leave. There are then 5 girls for each boy. Find the number of girls in the beginning.***

Sol. Let at present there be x boys. Then, number of girls at present = $5x$.

Before the boys had left: Number of boys = $x + 45$ and number of girls = $5x$.

$\therefore \quad x + 45 = 2 \times 5x \Leftrightarrow 9x = 45 \Leftrightarrow x = 5.$

Hence, number of girls in the beginning = $5x + 15 = 25 + 15 = 40$.

Ex. 51. ***If x is an integer such that*** $x + \frac{1}{x} = \frac{17}{4}$, ***find the value of*** $x - \frac{1}{x}$. **(M.B.A., 2008)**

Sol. $x + \frac{1}{x} = \frac{17}{4} \Leftrightarrow \left(x + \frac{1}{x}\right)^2 = \left(\frac{17}{4}\right)^2 \Leftrightarrow x^2 + \frac{1}{x^2} + 2 \cdot x \cdot \frac{1}{x} = \frac{289}{16}$

$\Leftrightarrow x^2 + \frac{1}{x^2} = \frac{289}{16} - 2 = \frac{257}{16} \Leftrightarrow x^2 + \frac{1}{x^2} - 2 \cdot x \cdot \frac{1}{x} = \frac{257}{16} - 2$

$\Leftrightarrow \left(x - \frac{1}{x}\right)^2 = \frac{225}{16} = \left(\frac{15}{4}\right)^2 \Leftrightarrow x - \frac{1}{x} = \frac{15}{4}.$

Ex. 52. ***A zoo keeper counted the heads of the animals in a zoo and found it to be 80. When he counted the legs of the animals he found it to be 260. If the zoo had either pigeons or horses, how many horses were there in the zoo?*** **(R.R.B., 2009)**

Sol. Let the number of pigeons be x and the number of horses be y.

Then, total number of heads = $x + y$.

total number of legs = $2x + 4y$.

$\therefore \quad x + y = 80$ ...(*i*)

And, $2x + 4y = 260$ or $x + 2y = 130$ ...(*ii*)

Subtracting (*i*) from (*ii*), we get: $y = 50$.

Putting $y = 50$ in (*i*), we get: $x = 30$.

Hence, number of horses in the zoo = 50.

Ex. 53. ***In a caravan, in addition to 50 hens there are 45 goats and 8 camels with some keepers. If the total number of feet be 224 more than the number of heads, find the number of keepers.***

Sol. Let the number of keepers be x. Then,

Total number of heads = $(50 + 45 + 8 + x) = (103 + x)$.

Total number of feet = $(45 + 8) \times 4 + (50 + x) \times 2 = (312 + 2x)$.

$\therefore \quad (312 + 2x) - (103 + x) = 224 \Leftrightarrow x = 15.$

Hence, number of keepers = 15.

Ex. 54. ***When an amount was distributed among 14 boys, each of them got ₹ 80 more than the amount received by each boy when the same amount is distributed equally among 18 boys. What was the amount?***

Sol. Let the total amount be ₹ x. Then,

$\frac{x}{14} - \frac{x}{18} = 80 \Leftrightarrow \frac{2x}{126} = 80 \Leftrightarrow \frac{x}{63} = 80 \Leftrightarrow x = 63 \times 80 = 5040.$

Hence, total amount = ₹ 5040.

Ex. 55. ***Mr. Bhaskar is on tour and he has ₹ 360 for his expenses. If he exceeds his tour by 4 days, he must cut down his daily expenses by ₹ 3. For how many days is Mr. Bhaskar on tour?***

Sol. Suppose Mr. Bhaskar is on tour for x days. Then,

$$\frac{360}{x} - \frac{360}{x+4} = 3 \Leftrightarrow \frac{1}{x} - \frac{1}{x+4} = \frac{1}{120} \Leftrightarrow x(x+4) = 4 \times 120 = 480$$

$$\Leftrightarrow x^2 + 4x - 480 = 0 \Leftrightarrow (x + 24)(x - 20) = 0 \Leftrightarrow x = 20.$$

Hence, Mr. Bhaskar is on tour for 20 days.

Ex. 56. ***A railway half-ticket costs half the full fare. But the reservation charge on half-ticket is the same as that on full ticket. One reserved first-class ticket for a journey between two stations is ₹ 525 and the cost of one full and one half reserved first-class tickets is ₹ 850. What is the reservation charge?*** (Bank P.O., 2008)

Sol. Let the full fare be ₹ x and the reservation charge per ticket be ₹ y.

Then, $x + y = 525$ ...(*i*)

And, $\frac{3x}{2} + 2y = 850$ or $3x + 4y = 1700$ ...(*ii*)

Multiplying (*i*) by 3 and subtracting from (*ii*), we get: $y = 125$.

Hence, reservation charge = ₹ 125.

Ex. 57. ***Tom reads at an average rate of 30 pages per hour, while Jane reads at an average rate of 40 pages per hour. If Tom starts reading a novel at 4: 30 and Jane begins reading an identical copy of the same book at 5: 20, then at what time will they be reading the same page?*** (M.A.T., 2007)

Sol. Suppose they are reading the same page x hours after 5: 20.

Time from 4: 30 to 5: 20 = 50 min = $\frac{5}{6}$ hr.

Then, $30\left(x + \frac{5}{6}\right) = 40x \Leftrightarrow 30x + 25 = 40x \Leftrightarrow 10x = 25 \Leftrightarrow x = 2.5.$

Hence, Tom and Jane will be reading the same page $2\frac{1}{2}$ hrs i.e., 2 hr 30 min after 5: 20 i.e., at 7: 50.

Ex. 58. ***In an objective examination of 90 questions, 5 marks are allotted for every correct answer and 2 marks are deducted for every wrong answer. After attempting all the 90 questions a student got a total of 387 marks. Find the number of questions that he attempted wrong.*** (M.A.T. 2007)

Sol. Let the number of questions attempted correctly be x.

Then, number of questions attempted wrong = $(90 - x)$

$\therefore \quad 5x - 2(90 - x) = 387 \Leftrightarrow 7x = 387 + 180 = 567 \Leftrightarrow x = 81.$

Hence, number of questions attempted wrong = $(90 - 81) = 9$.

Ex. 59. ***Kiran had 85 currency notes in all, some of which were of ₹ 100 denomination and the remaining of ₹ 50 denomination. The total amount of all these currency notes was ₹ 5000. How much amount did she have in the denomination of ₹ 50?***

Sol. Let the number of 50-rupee notes be x.

Then, the number of 100-rupee notes = $(85 - x)$.

$\therefore \quad 50x + 100(85 - x) = 5000 \Leftrightarrow x + 2(85 - x) = 100 \Leftrightarrow x = 70.$

So, required amount = ₹ (50×70) = ₹ 3500.

Ex. 60. ***In a group of 70 people, 37 like coffee, 52 like tea and each person likes at least one of the two drinks. Find the number of people who like both coffee and tea.*** (P.C.S., 2007)

Sol. Let A and B represent the set of people who like coffee and tea respectively.

Then, $n(A) = 37$, $n(B) = 52$, $n(A \cup B) = 70$.

$\therefore \quad n(A \cap B) = n(A) + n(B) - n(A \cup B)$

$= 37 + 52 - 70 = 89 - 70 = 19.$

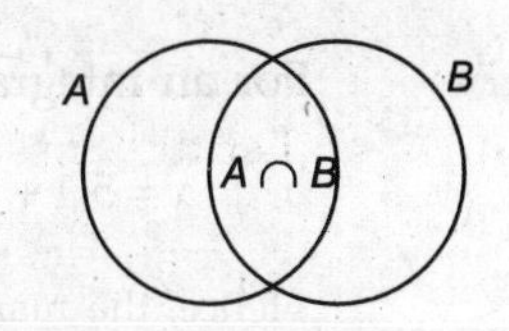

Hence, number of people who like both coffee and tea = 19.

Ex. 61. ***A train starts full of passengers. At the first station, it drops one-third of the passengers and takes 280 more. At the second station, it drops one-half of the new total and takes 12 more. On arriving at the third station, it is found to have 248 passengers. Find the number of passengers in the beginning.***

Sol. Let the number of passengers in the beginning be x.

After 1st station, number of passengers $= \left(x - \frac{x}{3}\right) + 280 = \left(\frac{2x}{3} + 280\right)$.

After 2nd station, number of passengers $= \frac{1}{2}\left(\frac{2x}{3} + 280\right) + 12$.

$\therefore \quad \frac{1}{2}\left(\frac{2x}{3} + 280\right) + 12 = 248 \Leftrightarrow \frac{2x}{3} + 280 = 2 \times 236 \Leftrightarrow \frac{2x}{3} = 192$

$\Leftrightarrow \quad x = \left(192 \times \frac{3}{2}\right) = 288.$

$\therefore$ Required number of passengers = 288.

Ex. 62. ***Arun and Sajal are friends. Each has some money. If Arun gives ₹ 30 to Sajal, then Sajal will have twice the money left with Arun. But, if Sajal gives ₹ 10 to Arun, then Arun will have thrice as much as is left with Sajal. How much money does each have?***

Sol. Suppose Arun has ₹ x and Sajal has ₹ y. Then,

$2(x - 30) = y + 30 \Rightarrow 2x - y = 90$ ...(*i*)

and $x + 10 = 3(y - 10) \Rightarrow x - 3y = -40$ ...(*ii*)

Solving (*i*) and (*ii*), we get: $x = 62$ and $y = 34$.

$\therefore$ Arun has ₹ 62 and Sajal has ₹ 34.

Ex. 63. ***An executive goes on a business trip. His daily schedule has a definite pattern. If he is busy with a meeting in the morning, he is free in the afternoon. When he returns, he realises that he attended 15 meetings altogether. There were 12 free mornings and 13 free afternoons. What was the duration of his trip?***

Sol. Let M and A represent the number of busy mornings and busy afternoons respectively.

Then, total number of mornings in the trip $= 12 + M$.

And, total number of afternoons in the trip $= 13 + A$.

Clearly, $12 + M = 13 + A$ or $M - A = 1$ ...(*i*)

Total number of meetings $= M + A$

So, $M + A = 15$ ...(*ii*)

Adding (*i*) and (*ii*), we get: $2M = 16$ or $M = 8$.

Hence, duration of the trip = (12 + 8) = 20 days.

Ex. 64. ***A man received a cheque. The rupees had been transposed for paise and vice- versa. After spending 5 rupees 42 paise, he discovered that he now had exactly six times the value of the correct cheque amount. What amount should he have received?*** **(M.A.T., 2005)**

Sol. Let the amount received be x rupees and y paise.

Then, amount written on cheque $= (100x + y)$ paise.

Actual amount to be received $= (100y + x)$ paise.

$\therefore \quad (100x + y) - 542 = 6(100y + x)$

$\Leftrightarrow \quad 100x + y - 542 = 600y + 6x \Leftrightarrow 94x - 599y = 542$

$\Leftrightarrow \quad 94x = 542 + 599y$

$\Leftrightarrow \quad x = \frac{542 + 599y}{94} = \frac{470 + 470y + 72 + 129y}{94} = 5(1 + y) + \frac{72 + 129y}{94}.$

For an integral value of x, $(72 + 129y)$ must be divisible by 94. This happens when $y = 6$.

$\therefore \quad x = 5(1 + 6) + \frac{72 + 129 \times 6}{94} = 35 + 9 = 44.$

Hence, the man should have received ₹ 6.44.

EXERCISE
(OBJECTIVE TYPE QUESTIONS)

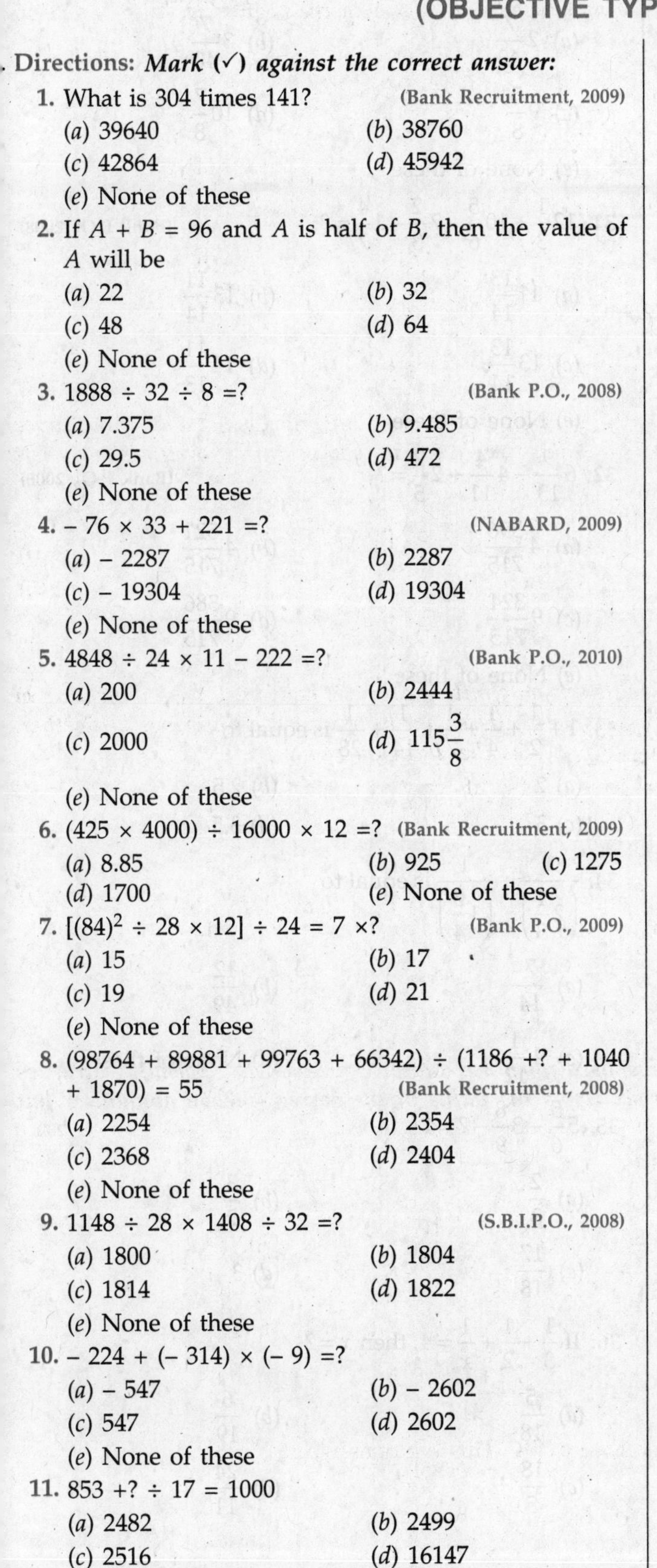

Directions: ***Mark (✓) against the correct answer:***

1. What is 304 times 141? **(Bank Recruitment, 2009)**
(*a*) 39640 (*b*) 38760
(*c*) 42864 (*d*) 45942
(*e*) None of these

2. If $A + B = 96$ and A is half of B, then the value of A will be
(*a*) 22 (*b*) 32
(*c*) 48 (*d*) 64
(*e*) None of these

3. 1888 ÷ 32 ÷ 8 =? **(Bank P.O., 2008)**
(*a*) 7.375 (*b*) 9.485
(*c*) 29.5 (*d*) 472
(*e*) None of these

4. – 76 × 33 + 221 =? **(NABARD, 2009)**
(*a*) – 2287 (*b*) 2287
(*c*) – 19304 (*d*) 19304
(*e*) None of these

5. 4848 ÷ 24 × 11 – 222 =? **(Bank P.O., 2010)**
(*a*) 200 (*b*) 2444
(*c*) 2000 (*d*) $115\frac{3}{8}$
(*e*) None of these

6. (425 × 4000) ÷ 16000 × 12 =? **(Bank Recruitment, 2009)**
(*a*) 8.85 (*b*) 925 (*c*) 1275
(*d*) 1700 (*e*) None of these

7. $[(84)^2 \div 28 \times 12] \div 24 = 7 \times ?$ **(Bank P.O., 2009)**
(*a*) 15 (*b*) 17
(*c*) 19 (*d*) 21
(*e*) None of these

8. (98764 + 89881 + 99763 + 66342) ÷ (1186 +? + 1040 + 1870) = 55 **(Bank Recruitment, 2008)**
(*a*) 2254 (*b*) 2354
(*c*) 2368 (*d*) 2404
(*e*) None of these

9. 1148 ÷ 28 × 1408 ÷ 32 =? **(S.B.I.P.O., 2008)**
(*a*) 1800 (*b*) 1804
(*c*) 1814 (*d*) 1822
(*e*) None of these

10. – 224 + (– 314) × (– 9) =?
(*a*) – 547 (*b*) – 2602
(*c*) 547 (*d*) 2602
(*e*) None of these

11. 853 +? ÷ 17 = 1000
(*a*) 2482 (*b*) 2499
(*c*) 2516 (*d*) 16147
(*e*) None of these

12. (? – 968) ÷ 79 × 4 = 512 **(Bank Recruitment, 2007)**
(*a*) 10185 (*b*) 10190
(*c*) 11075 (*d*) 11080
(*e*) None of these

13. $[(125)^2 \div 50 \times 20] \div 25 = ?$
(*a*) 11 (*b*) 100
(*c*) 150 (*d*) 250
(*e*) None of these

14. 999 × 99 × 9 ÷ 99 ÷ 9 ÷ 3 =? **(Bank P.O., 2009)**
(*a*) 99 (*b*) 111
(*c*) 333 (*d*) 999
(*e*) None of these

15. If $a, b, c, \ldots\ldots, x, y, z$ are 26 natural numbers, then the value of
$(x - a)(x - b)(x - c) \ldots\ldots (x - y)(x - z)$ is
(*a*) 0 (*b*) 1
(*c*) 13 (*d*) 26

16. Simplify: $1 - [1 - \{1 - (1 - \overline{1 - 1})\}]$
(*a*) 0 (*b*) 1
(*c*) 2 (*d*) 3

17. What mathematical operation should come at the place of '?' in the equation:
2? 6 – 12 ÷ 4 + 2 = 11.
(*a*) + (*b*) –
(*c*) × (*d*) ÷

18. If 45 – [28 – {37 – (15 – *)}] = 58, then * is equal to:
(*a*) – 29 (*b*) – 19
(*c*) 19 (*d*) 29

19. $\frac{343 \times 49}{216 \times 16 \times 81} = ?$ **(Bank P.O., 2010)**
(*a*) $\frac{7^5}{6^7}$ (*b*) $\frac{7^5}{6^8}$
(*c*) $\frac{7^4}{6^8}$ (*d*) $\frac{7^6}{6^7}$
(*e*) None of these

20. The value of x in the equation $\frac{113 \times 4 - x \times 2}{13 \times 9 - 5 \times 7} = 5$ is **(P.C.S., 2008)**
(*a*) 21 (*b*) 27
(*c*) 35 (*d*) 42

21. $\frac{18 \times 14 - 6 \times 8}{488 \div 4 - 20} = ?$ **(L.I.C.A.D.O., 2007)**
(*a*) $\frac{1}{2}$ (*b*) $\frac{3}{4}$
(*c*) 2 (*d*) 4
(*e*) None of these

22. $\frac{5+5+5}{7+7+7} - \frac{5+5}{7+7} + \frac{5}{7} = ?$

(a) $\frac{1}{7}$ (b) $\frac{3}{7}$
(c) $\frac{5}{7}$ (d) $\frac{13}{14}$

23. $\frac{3+4\div 2\times 3}{4+3\times 2\div 3} = ?$

(a) $\frac{7}{36}$ (b) $\frac{11}{18}$
(c) $\frac{3}{2}$ (d) $\frac{9}{4}$

24. $\frac{4+4\times 18-6-8}{123\times 6-146\times 5} = ?$

(a) 1 (b) 2
(c) 6.65 (d) 7.75

25. $\frac{180\times 15-12\times 20}{140\times 8+2\times 55} = ?$

(a) $\frac{1}{7}$ (b) $\frac{4}{5}$
(c) 2 (d) 4
(e) None of these

26. Evaluate: $\frac{8-[5-(-3+2)]\div 2}{|5-3|-|5-8|\div 3}$

(a) 2 (b) 3
(c) 4 (d) 5

27. Given that $(1^2 + 2^2 + 3^2 + ... + 10^2) = 385$, the value of $(2^2 + 4^2 + 6^2 + ... + 20^2)$ is equal to (M.B.A., 2006)

(a) 770 (b) 1155
(c) 1540 (d) $(385)^2$

28. $2\frac{1}{4} + 1\frac{1}{3} - 4\frac{1}{2} = ?$ (Bank Recruitment, 2010)

(a) $-1\frac{1}{12}$ (b) $\frac{11}{12}$
(c) $-\frac{11}{12}$ (d) $1\frac{1}{12}$
(e) None of these

29. $4\frac{3}{7} - 1\frac{3}{14} = ? + 2\frac{3}{28}$ (Bank P.O., 2010)

(a) $1\frac{3}{28}$ (b) $3\frac{1}{14}$
(c) $3\frac{3}{14}$ (d) $3\frac{1}{28}$
(e) None of these

30. $1\frac{3}{4} - 1\frac{1}{5} + 1\frac{5}{8} = ?$ (Bank Recruitment, 2010)

(a) $2\frac{7}{40}$ (b) $3\frac{7}{40}$
(c) $9\frac{5}{8}$ (d) $10\frac{7}{8}$
(e) None of these

31. $12\frac{1}{3} + 10\frac{5}{6} - 7\frac{2}{3} - 1\frac{4}{7} = ?$ (Bank P.O., 2008)

(a) $11\frac{13}{14}$ (b) $13\frac{11}{14}$
(c) $13\frac{13}{14}$ (d) $14\frac{11}{13}$
(e) None of these

32. $6\frac{9}{13} - 4\frac{4}{11} + 2\frac{2}{5} = ?$ (Bank P.O., 2006)

(a) $4\frac{596}{715}$ (b) $4\frac{521}{715}$
(c) $9\frac{324}{715}$ (d) $9\frac{386}{715}$
(e) None of these

33. $1 + \frac{1}{2} + \frac{1}{4} + \frac{1}{7} + \frac{1}{14} + \frac{1}{28}$ is equal to

(a) 2 (b) 2.5
(c) 3 (d) 3.5

34. $\frac{1}{\left(2\frac{1}{3}\right)} + \frac{1}{\left(1\frac{3}{4}\right)}$ is equal to

(a) $\frac{7}{14}$ (b) $\frac{12}{49}$
(c) $4\frac{1}{12}$ (d) None of these

35. $5\frac{5}{6} - 3\frac{8}{9} - ? = 1$

(a) $\frac{2}{3}$ (b) $\frac{3}{2}$
(c) $\frac{17}{18}$ (d) 3

36. If $\frac{1}{3} + \frac{1}{2} + \frac{1}{x} = 4$, then $x = ?$

(a) $\frac{5}{18}$ (b) $\frac{6}{19}$
(c) $\frac{18}{5}$ (d) $\frac{24}{11}$

37. $\frac{532}{648} \times \frac{432}{588} = ?$ (L.I.C.A.D.O., 2007)

(a) $\frac{2}{21}$ (b) $\frac{38}{63}$

(c) $\frac{21}{64}$ (d) $\frac{19}{21}$

(e) None of these

38. $1\frac{10}{11} \times 17\frac{2}{7} \times 36\frac{1}{6} = ?$

(a) $397\frac{5}{6}$ (b) $397\frac{1}{2}$

(c) $1193\frac{5}{6}$ (d) $1193\frac{1}{2}$

(e) None of these

39. $\frac{3}{7}$ of $455 + \frac{5}{8}$ of $456 = ?$ (Bank Recruitment, 2009)

(a) 448 (b) 464

(c) 476 (d) 480

(e) None of these

40. $\frac{3}{5}$ of $\frac{4}{7}$ of $\frac{5}{9}$ of $\frac{21}{24}$ of $504 = ?$

(a) 63 (b) 69

(c) 96 (d) 109

(e) None of these

41. $6\frac{5}{6} \times 5\frac{1}{3} + 17\frac{2}{3} \times 4\frac{1}{2} = ?$

(a) $112\frac{1}{3}$ (b) $116\frac{2}{3}$

(c) 240 (d) 663

(e) None of these

42. $4\frac{4}{5} \div 6\frac{2}{5} = ?$ (Bank Recruitment, 2009)

(a) $\frac{3}{4}$ (b) $\frac{5}{7}$

(c) $\frac{5}{8}$ (d) $\frac{7}{11}$

(e) None of these

43. $1\frac{1}{4} + 1\frac{5}{9} \times 1\frac{5}{8} \div 6\frac{1}{2} = ?$ (Bank P.O., 2009)

(a) 17 (b) 27

(c) 18 (d) 42

(e) None of these

44. $\frac{225}{836} \times \frac{152}{245} \div 1\frac{43}{77} = ?$ (Bank Recruitment, 2009)

(a) $\frac{6}{49}$ (b) $\frac{6}{11}$

(c) $\frac{3}{28}$ (d) $\frac{1}{7}$

(e) None of these

45. $\left(16\frac{2}{5} - 12\frac{1}{15}\right) \div 3\frac{4}{81} = ?$

(a) $1\frac{9}{19}$ (b) $1\frac{9}{13}$

(c) $2\frac{8}{13}$ (d) $3\frac{2}{19}$

(e) None of these

46. $18\frac{3}{4} \times ? \div \frac{6}{37} = 1480$

(a) $11\frac{7}{12}$ (b) $11\frac{4}{5}$

(c) $12\frac{5}{12}$ (d) $12\frac{4}{5}$

(e) None of these

47. $\frac{3}{2} \times \frac{11}{5} \div \left(\frac{25}{44} \times \frac{11}{5}\right) \div \frac{33}{15} = ?$

(a) $\frac{1}{2}$ (b) $\frac{2}{3}$

(c) $\frac{126}{125}$ (d) $5\frac{101}{125}$

(e) None of these

48. If $3\frac{x}{7} \times 2\frac{y}{5} = 10$, then the values of x and y respectively, would be

(a) 3, 4 (b) 5, 7

(c) 4, 3 (d) 4, 4

49. $1 + 2 \div \left\{1 + 2 \div \left(1 + \frac{1}{3}\right)\right\}$ is equal to

(a) $1\frac{4}{5}$ (b) $2\frac{1}{4}$

(c) $4\frac{1}{5}$ (d) $5\frac{1}{4}$

50. Simplify: $10\frac{1}{8}$ of $\frac{12}{15} \div \frac{35}{36}$ of $\frac{20}{49}$.

(a) $17\frac{5}{12}$ (b) $17\frac{8}{17}$

(c) $20\frac{3}{25}$ (d) $20\frac{103}{250}$

51. $\dfrac{-\frac{1}{2} - \frac{2}{3} + \frac{4}{5} - \frac{1}{3} + \frac{1}{5} + \frac{3}{4}}{\frac{1}{2} + \frac{2}{3} - \frac{4}{3} + \frac{1}{3} - \frac{1}{5} - \frac{4}{5}}$ is simplified to

(a) $-\frac{3}{10}$ (b) $-\frac{10}{3}$

(c) -2 (d) 1

52. When $\left(\frac{1}{2}-\frac{1}{4}+\frac{1}{5}-\frac{1}{6}\right)$ is divided by $\left(\frac{2}{5}-\frac{5}{9}+\frac{3}{5}-\frac{7}{18}\right)$, the result is

(a) $2\frac{1}{18}$ (b) $3\frac{1}{6}$
(c) $3\frac{3}{10}$ (d) $5\frac{1}{10}$

53. Which of the following can be used to compute $\left(34\times4\frac{1}{2}\right)$?

(a) $(30\times4)+\left(4\times4\frac{1}{2}\right)$
(b) $(34\times40)+\left(34\times\frac{1}{2}\right)$
(c) $\left(30\times4\frac{1}{2}\right)+(4\times4)$
(d) $\left(34\times\frac{1}{2}\right)+(30\times4)+(4\times4)$

54. $\frac{3}{8}$ of $168\times15\div5+?=549\div9+235$

(a) 107 (b) 174
(c) 189 (d) 296
(e) None of these

55. Find the value of * in the following

$1\frac{2}{3}\div\frac{2}{7}\times\frac{*}{7}=1\frac{1}{4}\times\frac{2}{3}\div\frac{1}{6}$ (S.S.C., 2002)

(a) 0.006 (b) $\frac{1}{6}$
(c) 0.6 (d) 6

56. $5\frac{2}{3}\div?\frac{5}{6}=2$

(a) 2 (b) 3
(c) 4 (d) None of these

57. Supply the two missing figures in order indicated by x and y in the given equation, the fractions being in their lowest terms. (IGNOU, 2003)

$5\frac{1}{x}\times y\frac{3}{4}=20$

(a) 3, 1 (b) 3, 3
(c) 4, 1 (d) 5, 3

58. The difference of $1\frac{3}{16}$ and its reciprocal is equal to (M.A.T., 2002)

(a) $1\frac{1}{8}$ (b) $\frac{4}{3}$
(c) $\frac{15}{16}$ (d) None of these

59. How many $\frac{1}{8}$s are there in $37\frac{1}{2}$?

(a) 300 (b) 400
(c) 500 (d) Cannot be determined

60. Let $a=(4\div3)\div3\div4$, $b=4\div(3\div3)\div4$, $c=4\div3\div(3\div4)$. The maximum value among the above three is (I.A.M., 2007)

(a) a (b) b
(c) c (d) All equal

61. If I $=\frac{3}{4}\div\frac{5}{6}$, II $=3\div[(4\div5)\div6]$, III $=[3\div(4\div5)]\div6$, IV $=3\div4\div(5\div6)$, then (A.A.O., 2009)

(a) I and II are equal (b) I and III are equal
(c) I and IV are equal (d) All are equal

62. The value of $\left(\frac{5}{7}\text{ of }1\frac{6}{13}\right)\div\left(2\frac{5}{7}\div3\frac{1}{4}\right)$ is

(a) $\frac{20}{169}$ (b) 1
(c) $\frac{5}{4}$ (d) $1\frac{119}{180}$

63. $2\frac{3}{4}\div2\frac{2}{3}\div1\frac{1}{12}=?$

(a) $\frac{39}{48}$ (b) $1\frac{1}{4}$
(c) $\frac{169}{144}$ (d) None of these

64. The value of $\frac{2}{3}\times\frac{3}{\frac{5}{6}\div\frac{2}{3}\text{ of }1\frac{1}{4}}$ is

(a) $\frac{1}{2}$ (b) $\frac{2}{3}$
(c) 1 (d) 2

65. $\frac{4335}{4(?)24}\div1\frac{7}{8}=\frac{289}{528}$

(a) 1 (b) 2
(c) 8 (d) None of these

66. $5\frac{1}{3}-3\frac{2}{3}\div1\frac{1}{3}\div?+3\frac{1}{5}\div1\frac{1}{5}=7$

(a) $1\frac{1}{2}$ (b) $2\frac{1}{3}$
(c) $3\frac{1}{4}$ (d) None of these

67. $9-1\frac{2}{9}\text{ of }3\frac{3}{11}\div5\frac{1}{7}\text{ of }\frac{7}{9}=?$ (S.S.C., 2002)

(a) $\frac{5}{4}$ (b) 8
(c) $8\frac{32}{81}$ (d) 9

68. $\frac{5}{6} \div \frac{6}{7} \times ? - \frac{8}{9} \div 1\frac{3}{5} + \frac{3}{4} \times 3\frac{1}{3} = 2\frac{7}{9}$

(a) $\frac{7}{6}$ (b) $\frac{6}{7}$
(c) 1 (d) None of these

69. $\frac{3}{4} \div 2\frac{1}{4}$ of $\frac{2}{3} - \frac{\frac{1}{2} - \frac{1}{3}}{\frac{1}{2} + \frac{1}{3}} \times 3\frac{1}{3} + \frac{5}{6} = ?$

(a) $\frac{7}{18}$ (b) $\frac{49}{54}$
(c) $\frac{2}{3}$ (d) $\frac{1}{6}$

70. A student was asked to solve the fraction $\frac{\frac{7}{3} + 1\frac{1}{2} \text{ of } \frac{5}{3}}{2 + 1\frac{2}{3}}$ and his answer was $\frac{1}{4}$. By how much was his answer wrong?

(a) 1 (b) $\frac{1}{55}$
(c) $\frac{1}{220}$ (d) None of these

71. Simplify: $\frac{\frac{1}{3} + \frac{3}{4}\left(\frac{2}{5} - \frac{1}{3}\right)}{1\frac{2}{3} \text{ of } \frac{3}{4} - \frac{1}{4} \text{ of } \frac{4}{5}}$.

(a) $\frac{1}{63}$ (b) $\frac{23}{40}$
(c) $\frac{23}{55}$ (d) $\frac{23}{63}$

72. Find the value of $1 - \left(\frac{1\frac{2}{3}}{3\frac{1}{2}} + \frac{1\frac{1}{6}}{3\frac{1}{2}}\right)$.

(a) $\frac{3}{20}$ (b) $\frac{4}{21}$
(c) $\frac{8}{21}$ (d) $\frac{13}{21}$

73. If the expression $2\frac{1}{2}$ of $\frac{3}{4} \times \frac{1}{2} \div \frac{3}{2} + \frac{1}{2} \div \frac{3}{2}\left[\frac{2}{3} - \frac{1}{2} \text{ of } \frac{2}{3}\right]$ is simplified, we get (R.R.B., 2006)

(a) $\frac{1}{2}$ (b) $\frac{7}{8}$
(c) $1\frac{5}{8}$ (d) $2\frac{3}{5}$

74. The value of $\frac{1\frac{1}{7} - \frac{2}{3} + \frac{\frac{2}{5}}{1 - \frac{1}{25}}}{1 - \frac{1}{7}\left[\frac{1}{3} + \frac{\frac{2}{5}}{1 - \frac{2}{5}}\right]}$ is (I.I.F.T., 2005)

(a) $\frac{3}{4}$ (b) $\frac{24}{25}$
(c) 1 (d) $1\frac{1}{24}$

75. $\frac{6}{5 - \frac{5}{3}} \div \frac{4 - \frac{2}{4 - \frac{1}{2}}}{5 - \frac{3}{2}} - \frac{2}{5}$ of $\left\{\frac{6}{9} + \frac{2}{3} \text{ of } \frac{1}{2}\right\} = ?$ (M.C.A., 2005)

(a) $1\frac{1}{3}$ (b) $2\frac{13}{49}$
(c) $1\frac{7}{16}$ (d) $2\frac{3}{5}$

76. The expression $\frac{5\frac{5}{8}}{6\frac{3}{7}}$ of $\frac{6\frac{7}{11}}{9\frac{1}{8}} \div \frac{8}{9}\left(2\frac{3}{11} + \frac{13}{22}\right)$ of $\frac{3}{5}$ equals

(a) 1 (b) $\frac{1}{2}$
(c) $\frac{7}{9}$ (d) $\frac{5}{12}$

77. The simplified value of $\frac{\frac{1}{3} \div \frac{1}{3} \times \frac{1}{3}}{\frac{1}{3} \div \frac{1}{3} \text{ of } \frac{1}{3}} - \frac{1}{9}$ is

(a) 0 (b) $\frac{1}{9}$
(c) $\frac{1}{3}$ (d) 1

78. The value of $\frac{\frac{1}{2} \div \frac{1}{2} \text{ of } \frac{1}{2}}{\frac{1}{2} + \frac{1}{2} \text{ of } \frac{1}{2}}$ is

(a) 1 (b) $1\frac{1}{3}$
(c) $2\frac{2}{3}$ (d) 3

79. $\frac{3\frac{1}{4} - \frac{4}{5} \text{ of } \frac{5}{6}}{4\frac{1}{3} \div \frac{1}{5} - \left(\frac{3}{10} + 21\frac{1}{5}\right)}$ is equal to

(a) $\frac{1}{6}$ (b) $2\frac{7}{12}$

(c) $15\frac{1}{2}$ (d) $21\frac{1}{2}$

80. $\frac{7\frac{1}{2}-5\frac{3}{4}}{3\frac{1}{2}+?} \div \frac{\frac{1}{2}+1\frac{1}{4}}{1\frac{1}{5}+3\frac{1}{2}} = 0.6$

(a) $4\frac{1}{3}$ (b) $4\frac{1}{2}$

(c) $4\frac{2}{3}$ (d) None of these

81. Which of the following pairs of fractions adds up to a number greater than 5?

(a) $\frac{5}{3}, \frac{3}{4}$ (b) $\frac{7}{3}, \frac{11}{5}$

(c) $\frac{11}{4}, \frac{8}{3}$ (d) $\frac{13}{5}, \frac{11}{6}$

82. $5 - \left[\frac{3}{4} + \left\{2\frac{1}{2} - \left(0.5 + \overline{\frac{1}{6} - \frac{1}{7}}\right)\right\}\right]$ is equal to

(a) $1\frac{19}{84}$ (b) $2\frac{61}{84}$

(c) $2\frac{23}{84}$ (d) $2\frac{47}{84}$

83. If [p] means the greatest integer less than or equal to p, then $\left[-\frac{1}{4}\right] + \left[4\frac{1}{4}\right] + [3]$ is equal to:

(a) 4 (b) 5
(c) 6 (d) 7

84. If $x = -3$, then $x^3 - x^2 - x$ will be equal to **(U.P.G.I.C., 2009)**

(a) – 33 (b) – 27
(c) 15 (d) 54

85. Let $R = gS - 4$, when $S = 8$ and $R = 16$. If $S = 10$, then R is equal to

(a) 11 (b) 14
(c) 20 (d) 21

86. If $x = 5$, $y = 3$ and $z = 2$, then $\frac{x(y-z)}{y(x+y+z)} = ?$

(a) $\frac{1}{6}$ (b) $\frac{1}{30}$

(c) 1 (d) 5

87. If $a = 7$, $b = 5$, then the value of $a^3 - b^3 + 3a^2b$ is

(a) 218 (b) 307
(c) 735 (d) 953

88. $-7m - [3n - \{8m - (4n - 10m)\}]$ simplifies to **(R.R.B., 2006)**

(a) $11m - 5n$ (b) $11m - 7n$
(c) $11n - 7m$ (d) $13n - 11m$

89. If $a + 2b = 6$ and $ab = 4$, then what is $\frac{2}{a} + \frac{1}{b}$? **(M.B.A., 2006)**

(a) $\frac{1}{2}$ (b) $\frac{1}{3}$

(c) $\frac{3}{2}$ (d) 2

(e) $\frac{5}{2}$

90. If $\frac{a}{3} = \frac{b}{4} = \frac{c}{7}$, the value of $(a + b + c) \div c$ is

(a) $\frac{1}{7}$ (b) $\frac{1}{2}$

(c) 2 (d) 7

91. The value of $2a^3 - [3a^3 + 4b^3 - \{2a^3 + (-7a^3)\} + 5a^3 - 7b^3]$ is **(Teacher's Exam, 2007)**

(a) $-11a^3 + 3b^3$ (b) $7b^3 + 3a^3$
(c) $11a^3 - 3b^3$ (d) $-(11a^3 + 3b^3)$

92. If $\frac{x}{y+z} = a$; $\frac{y}{z+x} = b$ and $\frac{z}{x+y} = c$, then $\frac{1}{1+a} + \frac{1}{1+b} + \frac{1}{1+c}$ is equal to

(a) 2 (b) 3
(c) 6 (d) $x + y + z$

93. If $y = (x + 3)^2$, then $(-2x - 6)^2$ is equal to

(a) $-4y^2$ (b) $-2y^2$
(c) $-4y$ (d) $2y$
(e) $4y$

94. Which among the following is the correct value of $(x + a)(x + b)$? **(R.R.B., 2007)**

(a) $x^2 + abx + ab$ (b) $x^2 - (a + b)x + ab$
(c) $x^2 + (a + b)x + ab$ (d) $x^2 + (a - b)x + ab$

95. The value of $\left[1 + \frac{1}{x+1}\right]\left[1 + \frac{1}{x+2}\right]\left[1 + \frac{1}{x+3}\right]\left[1 + \frac{1}{x+4}\right]$ is

(a) $\frac{x+5}{x+1}$ (b) $\frac{x+1}{x+5}$

(c) $1 + \frac{1}{x+5}$ (d) $\frac{1}{x+5}$

96. If $(a - b)$ is 6 more than $(c + d)$ and $(a + b)$ is 3 less than $(c - d)$, then $(a - c)$ is

(a) 0.5 (b) 1
(c) 1.5 (d) None of these

97. If $\frac{a}{b} = \frac{4}{3}$, then $\frac{3a + 2b}{3a - 2b} = ?$ **(M.B.A., 2007)**

(a) – 1 (b) 3
(c) 5 (d) 6

98. If $\frac{x}{y} = \frac{6}{5}$, then the value of $\left(\frac{6}{7} - \frac{5x - y}{5x + y}\right)$ is equal to

(a) $\frac{1}{7}$ (b) $\frac{2}{7}$

(c) $\frac{3}{7}$ (d) $\frac{4}{7}$

99. If $\frac{x}{y} = \frac{1}{3}$, then $\frac{x^2 + y^2}{x^2 - y^2} = ?$ (R.R.B., 2006)

(a) $-\frac{10}{9}$ (b) $\frac{5}{4}$

(c) $-\frac{5}{4}$ (d) $-\frac{5}{3}$

100. If $\frac{x}{2y} = \frac{6}{7}$, the value of $\frac{x - y}{x + y} + \frac{14}{19}$ is

(a) $\frac{13}{19}$ (b) $\frac{15}{19}$

(c) 1 (d) $1\frac{1}{19}$

101. If $\frac{a}{b} = \frac{4}{5}$ and $\frac{b}{c} = \frac{15}{16}$, then $\frac{c^2 - a^2}{c^2 + a^2}$ is (M.B.A., 2007)

(a) $\frac{1}{7}$ (b) $\frac{7}{25}$

(c) $\frac{3}{4}$ (d) None of these

102. If $x = 1 - q$ and $y = 2q + 1$, then for what value of q, x is equal to y?

(a) -1 (b) 0

(c) $\frac{1}{2}$ (d) 2

103. Find x if $\frac{x}{5} - \frac{x}{6} = 4$.

(a) -120 (b) -100

(c) 100 (d) 120

104. If $4x + 5y = 83$ and $\frac{3x}{2y} = \frac{21}{22}$, then $y - x = ?$

(a) 3 (b) 4

(c) 7 (d) 11

105. If $a = \frac{x}{x + y}$ and $b = \frac{y}{x - y}$, then $\frac{ab}{a + b}$ is equal to

(a) $\frac{xy}{x^2 + y^2}$ (b) $\frac{x^2 + y^2}{xy}$

(c) $\frac{x}{x + y}$ (d) $\left(\frac{y}{x + y}\right)^2$

106. If $\frac{a}{b} = \frac{1}{3}, \frac{b}{c} = 2, \frac{c}{d} = \frac{1}{2}, \frac{d}{e} = 3$ and $\frac{e}{f} = \frac{1}{4}$, then what is the value of $\frac{abc}{def}$? (C.A.T., 2006)

(a) $\frac{1}{4}$ (b) $\frac{3}{4}$

(c) $\frac{3}{8}$ (d) $\frac{27}{4}$

(e) $\frac{27}{8}$

107. If $\frac{m}{n} = \frac{4}{3}$ and $\frac{r}{t} = \frac{9}{14}$, the value of $\frac{3mr - nt}{4nt - 7mr}$ is (M.B.A. 2011)

(a) $-5\frac{1}{2}$ (b) $-\frac{11}{14}$

(c) $-1\frac{1}{4}$ (d) $\frac{11}{14}$

108. If $a + \frac{1}{b} = 1$ and $b + \frac{1}{c} = 1$, then $c + \frac{1}{a}$ is equal to (S.S.C., 2007)

(a) 0 (b) $\frac{1}{2}$

(c) 1 (d) 2

109. If $y + \frac{1}{z} = 1$ and $x + \frac{1}{y} = 1$, then what is the value of xyz?

(a) -1 (b) 0

(c) $\frac{1}{2}$ (d) 1

110. If $\frac{x}{(2x + y + z)} = \frac{y}{(x + 2y + z)} = \frac{z}{(x + y + 2z)} = a$, then find a if $x + y + z \neq 0$. (M.A.T., 2005)

(a) $\frac{1}{3}$ (b) $\frac{1}{4}$

(c) $\frac{1}{2}$ (d) $\frac{1}{8}$

111. If $\frac{a}{b + c} = \frac{b}{c + a} = \frac{c}{a + b} = K$, then the value of K is

(a) $\pm\frac{1}{2}$ (b) $\frac{1}{2}$ or -1

(c) -1 (d) $\frac{1}{2}$

112. If $a - 8 = b$, then determine the value of $|a - b| - |b - a|$.

(a) 0 (b) 2

(c) 4 (d) 16

113. If $x = \frac{a}{a-1}$ and $y = \frac{1}{a-1}$, then

(a) x is equal to y
(b) x is equal to y only if $a < 1$
(c) x is greater than y
(d) x is greater than y only if $a < 1$
(e) y is greater than x only if $a < 1$

114. If $0 < a < 1$, then the value of $a + \frac{1}{a}$ is

(a) less than 2 (b) greater than 2
(c) less than 4 (d) greater than 4

115. If $\frac{a}{x} + \frac{y}{b} = 1$ and $\frac{b}{y} + \frac{z}{c} = 1$, then $\frac{x}{a} + \frac{c}{z}$ will be equal to:

(a) 0 (b) $\frac{b}{y}$
(c) 1 (d) $\frac{y}{b}$

116. If a, b, c are integers; $a^2 + b^2 = 45$ and $b^2 + c^2 = 40$, then the values of a, b and c respectively are

(a) 2, 6, 3 (b) 3, 2, 6
(c) 5, 4, 3 (d) None of these

117. If $x + y = 15$ and $xy = 56$, then what is the value of $x^2 + y^2$? (L.I.C.A.D.O., 2007)

(a) 110 (b) 113
(c) 121 (d) Cannot be determined
(e) None of these

118. If $(a - b) = 4$ and $ab = 2$, then $(a^2 + b^2) = ?$

(a) 18 (b) 20
(c) 25 (d) None of these

119. If $a = bc$ and $c = a - b$, then the value of a is (R.R.B., 2008)

(a) $b^2 - 1$ (b) $\frac{b^2}{b-1}$
(c) $\frac{b}{b-1}$ (d) None of these

120. If $a + b + c = 0$, find the value of

$$\frac{a^2}{(a^2 - bc)} + \frac{b^2}{(b^2 - ca)} + \frac{c^2}{(c^2 - ab)}.$$ (M.A.T., 2005)

(a) 0 (b) 1
(c) 2 (d) 4

121. If $\frac{x}{y} = \frac{a+2}{a-2}$, then $\frac{x^2 - y^2}{x^2 + y^2}$ is equal to

(a) $\frac{8a}{a^2+4}$ (b) $\frac{4a}{a^2-4}$
(c) $\frac{4}{a^2}$ (d) $\frac{4a}{a^2+4}$

122. If $3x + 7 = x^2 + P = 7x + 5$, what is the value of P?

(a) $\frac{1}{2}$ (b) $8\frac{1}{4}$
(c) $8\frac{1}{2}$ (d) Cannot be determined

123. If $\frac{2a+b}{a+4b} = 3$, then find the value of $\frac{a+b}{a+2b}$.

(a) $\frac{2}{7}$ (b) $\frac{5}{9}$
(c) $\frac{10}{7}$ (d) $\frac{10}{9}$

124. If $(2a + 3b)(2c - 3d) = (2a - 3b)(2c + 3d)$, then

(a) $\frac{a}{b} = \frac{c}{d}$ (b) $\frac{a}{d} = \frac{c}{b}$
(c) $\frac{a}{b} = \frac{d}{c}$ (d) $\frac{b}{a} = \frac{c}{d}$

125. If $(a + b + 2c + 3d)(a - b - 2c + 3d) = (a - b + 2c - 3d)(a + b - 2c - 3d)$, then $2bc$ is equal to

(a) $\frac{3}{2}$ (b) $\frac{3a}{2d}$
(c) $3ad$ (d) a^2d^2

126. The expression $\frac{x+y}{x-y} \div \frac{(x+y)^2}{(x^2-y^2)}$ is equal to

(a) -1 (b) $x - y$
(c) 1 (d) $x + y$

127. $\frac{a^2 - b^2 - 2bc - c^2}{a^2 + b^2 + 2ab - c^2}$ is equivalent to

(a) $\frac{a-b+c}{a+b+c}$ (b) $\frac{a-b-c}{a-b+c}$
(c) $\frac{a-b-c}{a+b-c}$ (d) $\frac{a+b+c}{a-b+c}$

128. If $x + y + z = 0$, then $x^2 + xy + y^2$ equals

(a) $y^2 + yz + z^2$ (b) $y^2 - yz + z^2$
(c) $z^2 - zx + x^2$ (d) $z^2 + zx + x^2$

129. If $a + b + c = 2s$, then the value of $(s - a)^2 + (s - b)^2 + (s - c)^2 + s^2$ will be

(a) $s^2 - a^2 - b^2 - c^2$ (b) $s^2 + a^2 + b^2 + c^2$
(c) $a^2 + b^2 + c^2$ (d) $4s^2 - a^2 - b^2 - c^2$

130. If $(x + y)^2 - z^2 = 4$, $(y + z)^2 - x^2 = 9$, $(z + x)^2 - y^2 = 36$, what is/are the value(s) of $x + y + z$?

(a) 0 (b) ± 1
(c) ± 3 (d) ± 7

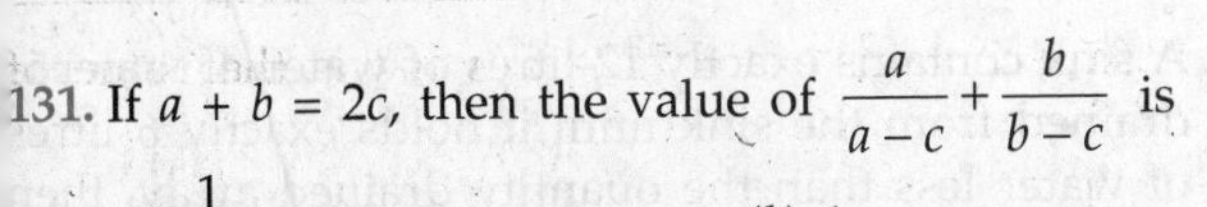

131. If $a + b = 2c$, then the value of $\frac{a}{a-c} + \frac{b}{b-c}$ is

(a) $\frac{1}{2}$ (b) 1
(c) 2 (d) 3

132. $\frac{x}{x-1} + \frac{1}{x+1} + \frac{2x}{1-x^2} = ?$

(a) 1 (b) 2
(c) 3 (d) 4

133. The value of $\frac{(a+b)^2}{(a^2-b^2)}$ is **(R.R.B., 2006)**

(a) $\frac{ab}{a+b}$ (b) $\frac{2ab}{a-b}$
(c) $\frac{a+b}{a-b}$ (d) None of these

134. If $ab + bc + ca = 0$, then what is the value of $\left(\frac{1}{a^2-bc} + \frac{1}{b^2-ca} + \frac{1}{c^2-ab}\right)$?

(a) 0 (b) 1
(c) 3 (d) $a + b + c$

135. How many boxes are required for filling 15 kg of sweet if each box is filled with 250 grams of sweet? **(Bank Recruitment, 2010)**

(a) 30 (b) 70
(c) 80 (d) 120
(e) None of these

136. The bus fare for one person is ₹ 420 from Agra to Aligarh and the train fare between the same places for one person is equal to three-fourths the bus fare for two persons between the same places. What is the total fare paid by 3 persons travelling by bus and 4 persons travelling by train between the two places? **(Bank P.O., 2010)**

(a) ₹ 3360 (b) ₹ 3406
(c) ₹ 3440 (d) ₹ 3460
(e) None of these

137. The cost of 6 pens and 3 pencils is ₹ 84. One-third of the cost of one pen is equal to the cost of one pencil. What is the total cost of 4 pens and 5 pencils? **(Bank Recruitment, 2010)**

(a) ₹ 66 (b) ₹ 68
(c) ₹ 72 (d) ₹ 78
(e) None of these

138. If an amount of ₹ 4,36,563 is distributed equally amongst 69 persons, how much amount would each person get? **(Bank Recruitment, 2009)**

(a) ₹ 5876 (b) ₹ 5943
(c) ₹ 6148 (d) ₹ 6327
(e) None of these

139. 32 shirt pieces of 120 cm each can be cut from a reel of cloth. After cutting these pieces 80 cm of cloth remains. What is the length of reel of cloth in metres? **(Bank Recruitment, 2009)**

(a) 38.70 metres (b) 39.20 metres
(c) 3870 metes (d) 3920 metres
(e) None of these

140. A canteen requires 798 bananas for a week. Total how many bananas did it require for the months of January, February and March 2008? **(Bank Recruitment, 2008)**

(a) 10277 (b) 10374 (c) 10480
(d) 10586 (e) None of these

141. Ram has ₹ 6 more than Mohan and ₹ 9 more than Sohan. All the three have ₹ 33 in all. Ram has a share of **(R.R.B., 2006)**

(a) ₹ 7 (b) ₹ 10
(c) ₹ 13 (d) ₹ 16

142. What is the maximum number of half-pint bottles of cream that can be filled with a 4-gallon can of cream? (2pt. = 1qt. and 4qt. = 1gal.) **(Campus Recruitment, 2010)**

(a) 16 (b) 24
(c) 30 (d) 64

143. The sum of the weights of *A* and *B* is 80 kg. Half of the weight of *A* is equal to $\frac{5}{6}$ times the weight of *B*. Find the weight of *B*.

(a) 20 kg (b) 30 kg
(c) 40 kg (d) 60 kg

144. *a* is greater than *b* by 2 and *b* is greater than *c* by 10. If $a + b + c = 130$, then $(b + c) - a = ?$

(a) 34 (b) 38
(c) 42 (d) 44
(e) None of these

145. The price of item *X* rises by ₹ 40 per year and that of item *Y* by ₹ 15 per year. If the price of item *X* and *Y* in the year 2002 was ₹ 420 and ₹ 630 respectively, in which year the price of item *X* will be ₹ 40 more than the price of item *Y*?

(a) 2010 (b) 2011
(c) 2012 (d) 2013

146. How many pieces of 85 cm length can be cut from a rod 42.5 metres long?

(a) 30 (b) 40
(c) 60 (d) None of these

147. On Sports Day, if 30 children were made to stand in a column, then 16 columns could be formed. If 24 children were made to stand in a column, then how many columns could be formed?

(a) 20 (b) 22
(c) 29 (d) 45

148. The number of students in each section of a school is 24. After admitting new students, three new sections were started. Now, the total number of sections is 16 and there are 21 students in each section. The number of new students admitted is
(a) 14 (b) 24
(c) 48 (d) 114

149. A man earns ₹ 20 on the first day and spends ₹ 15 on the next day. He again earns ₹ 20 on the third day and spends ₹ 15 on the fourth day. If he continues to save like this, how soon will he have ₹ 60 in hand? (M.A.T., 2006)
(a) On 17th day (b) On 27th day
(c) On 30th day (d) On 40th day

150. A car company sold 150 cars in a special 6-day sale. Each day, the company sold 6 more than the previous day. How many cars were sold on the 6th day?
(a) 35 (b) 40
(c) 50 (d) 60
(e) 70

151. A group of 1200 persons consisting of captains and soldiers is travelling in a train. If for every 15 soldiers there is one captain, then the number of captains in the group is
(a) 70 (b) 75
(c) 80 (d) 82

152. It costs ₹ x each to make the first thousand copies of a compact disc and ₹ y to make each subsequent copy. If z is greater than 1000, how much will it cost to make z copies of the compact disc?
(a) $zx - zy$ (b) $1000x + yz$
(c) $1000(x - y) + yz$ (d) $1000(z - y) + xz$

153. The total monthly salary of 4 men and 2 women is ₹ 46,000. If a woman earns ₹500 more than a man, what is the monthly salary of a woman?
(a) ₹ 6500 (b) ₹ 7500
(c) ₹ 8000 (d) ₹ 9000

154. A pineapple costs ₹ 7 each. A watermelon costs ₹ 5 each. X spends ₹ 38 on these fruits. The number of pineapples purchased is
(a) 2 (b) 3
(c) 4 (d) Data inadequate

155. Water boils at 212°F or 100°C and melts at 32°F or 0°C. If the temperature of a particular day is 35°C, it is equivalent to
(a) 85°F (b) 90°F
(c) 95°F (d) 99°F

156. 74 is divided into two parts so that 5 times one part and 11 times the other part are together equal to 454. The parts are (R.R.B., 2006)
(a) 14, 60 (b) 60, 14
(c) 30, 44 (d) 44, 30

157. A sink contains exactly 12 litres of water. If water is drained from the sink until it holds exactly 6 litres of water less than the quantity drained away, then how many litres of water were drained away? (M.A.T., 2006)
(a) 2 (b) 3
(c) 6 (d) 9

158. A family has several children. Each boy in the family has as many sisters as brothers and each girl has twice as many brothers as sisters.. How many brothers and sisters are there? (SNAP, 2005)
(a) 4 brothers, 3 sisters (b) 4 brothers, 4 sisters
(c) 3 brothers, 4 sisters (d) Cannot say

159. If 1 Japanese Yen = 0.01 US Dollars, 100 US Dollars = 5000 Indian Rupees (INR), how many Japanese Yens are 100 INR? (JMET, 2008)
(a) 20 (b) 200
(c) 500 (d) 2000

160. 12 buckets of water fill a tank when the capacity of each bucket is 13.5 litres. How many buckets will be needed to fill the same tank, if the capacity of each bucket is 9 litres?
(a) 8 (b) 15
(c) 16 (d) 18

161. $\left[1+\dfrac{1}{1+\dfrac{1}{1+\dfrac{1}{3}}}\right] \div 1\dfrac{4}{7}$ is equal to (M.B.A., 2007)
(a) 1 (b) $1\frac{1}{3}$
(c) $1\frac{1}{4}$ (d) $1\frac{1}{7}$

162. $\dfrac{13}{48}$ is equal to (C.P.O., 2006)
(a) $\dfrac{1}{3+\dfrac{1}{1+\dfrac{1}{16}}}$ (b) $\dfrac{1}{2+\dfrac{1}{1+\dfrac{1}{8}}}$
(c) $\dfrac{1}{3+\dfrac{1}{1+\dfrac{1}{1+\dfrac{1}{8}}}}$ (d) $\dfrac{1}{3+\dfrac{1}{1+\dfrac{1}{2+\dfrac{1}{4}}}}$

163. Find the value of $\dfrac{1}{1+\dfrac{1}{3-\dfrac{4}{2+\dfrac{1}{3-\dfrac{1}{2}}}}}+\dfrac{3}{3-\dfrac{4}{3+\dfrac{1}{2-\dfrac{1}{2}}}}$.
(a) $\dfrac{13}{7}$ (b) $\dfrac{15}{7}$
(c) $\dfrac{11}{21}$ (d) $\dfrac{17}{28}$

164. If $2 = x + \cfrac{1}{1+\cfrac{1}{3+\cfrac{1}{4}}}$, then the value of x is

(a) $\frac{12}{17}$ (b) $\frac{13}{17}$
(c) $\frac{18}{17}$ (d) $\frac{21}{17}$

165. If $\dfrac{2+\cfrac{1}{3\frac{4}{5}}}{2+\cfrac{1}{3+\cfrac{1}{1+\cfrac{1}{4}}}} = x$, then the value of x is

(a) $\frac{1}{7}$ (b) $\frac{3}{7}$
(c) 1 (d) $\frac{8}{7}$

166. $8 - 8 \times \dfrac{2\frac{1}{5} - 1\frac{2}{7}}{2 - \cfrac{1}{6 - \cfrac{1}{6}}}$ is equal to

(a) 2 (b) 4
(c) 6 (d) 8

167. $\dfrac{2}{2 + \cfrac{2}{3 + \cfrac{2}{3 + \frac{2}{3}}} \times 0.39}$ is simplified to

(a) $\frac{1}{3}$ (b) 2
(c) 6 (d) None of these

168. Simplify: $\dfrac{1}{1 + \cfrac{\frac{2}{3}}{1 + \frac{2}{3} + \cfrac{\frac{8}{9}}{1 - \frac{2}{3}}}}$.

(a) $\frac{11}{13}$ (b) $\frac{13}{15}$
(c) $\frac{13}{11}$ (d) $\frac{15}{13}$

169. If $\dfrac{2}{2 + \cfrac{2}{2 + \frac{2}{x}}} = 3$, then x is equal to

(a) $-\frac{4}{7}$ (b) $\frac{4}{7}$
(c) $-\frac{4}{9}$ (d) $\frac{4}{9}$

170. If $\frac{37}{13} = 2 + \cfrac{1}{x + \cfrac{1}{y + \frac{1}{z}}}$, where x, y, z are natural numbers, then x, y, z are

(a) 1, 2, 5 (b) 1, 5, 2
(c) 5, 2, 11 (d) 11, 2, 5

171. Let $x = 1 + \cfrac{1}{1 + \cfrac{1}{1 + \cfrac{1}{1 + \ldots \infty}}}$. Which of the following is correct?

(a) $x^2 + x + 1 = 0$ (b) $x^2 - x + 1 = 0$
(c) $x^2 + x - 1 = 0$ (d) $x^2 - x - 1 = 0$

172. Let $P = \cfrac{1}{1 + \cfrac{1}{1 + \cfrac{1}{3 + \cfrac{1}{4 + \ldots \cdots + \cfrac{1}{1008}}}}}$ and $Q = \cfrac{1}{2 + \cfrac{1}{3 + \cfrac{1}{4 + \ldots \cdots + \cfrac{1}{1008}}}}$.

Then, $P + Q$ when calculated, gives

(a) 1 (b) 2
(c) 3 (d) 4

173. $\dfrac{\left[\left(1 + \cfrac{1}{10 + \frac{1}{10}}\right)\left(1 + \cfrac{1}{10 + \frac{1}{10}}\right) - \left(1 - \cfrac{1}{10 + \frac{1}{10}}\right)\left(1 - \cfrac{1}{10 + \frac{1}{10}}\right)\right]}{\left[\left(1 + \cfrac{1}{10 + \frac{1}{10}}\right) + \left(1 - \cfrac{1}{10 + \frac{1}{10}}\right)\right]}$

simplifies to

(a) $\frac{20}{101}$ (b) $\frac{90}{101}$
(c) $\frac{100}{101}$ (d) $\frac{101}{100}$

174. Which of the following values of x and y satisfy the following equations I and II?

I. $3x + y = 19$ II. $x - y = 9$

(a) $-7, -2$ (b) $-7, 2$
(c) $7, -2$ (d) $7, 2$

175. If $4x = p(x + 3) + q(x - 1)$ is an identity, then the values of p and q are (I.A.M., 2007)

(a) $1, -3$ (b) 1, 3
(c) 1, 1 (d) 3, 1

176. If $x = y = 2z$ and $xyz = 256$, then x =? **(Campus Recruitment, 2005)**

(a) 2 (b) 4
(c) 8 (d) None of these

177. If $3y + 9x = 54$ and $\frac{28x}{13y} = \frac{140}{39}$, then what is the value of $y - x$? **(Bank P.O., 2009)**

(a) – 2 (b) – 1
(c) 1 (d) 2 (e) None of these

178. If $3x + 7y = 75$ and $5x - 5y = 25$, then what is the value of $x + y$? **(Bank P.O., 2007)**

(a) 14 (b) 15
(c) 16 (d) 17
(e) None of these

179. If $a + b = 5$ and $3a + 2b = 20$, then $(3a + b)$ will be:

(a) 10 (b) 15
(c) 20 (d) 25

180. If $2p + 3q = 18$ and $2p - q = 2$, then $2p + q$ =?

(a) 6 (b) 7
(c) 10 (d) 20

181. If $2x + y = 5$ and $3x - 4y = 2$, then the value of $2xy$ is

(a) 4 (b) 6
(c) 8 (d) 10

182. If $3x - 5y = 5$ and $\frac{x}{x+y} = \frac{5}{7}$, then what is the value of $2xy$ is

(a) 3 (b) 4
(c) 6 (d) 9
(e) None of these

183. If $4x + 3y = 18xy$ and $2x - 5y + 4xy = 0$, then the values of x and y will be respectively

(a) $-\frac{1}{2}$ and $-\frac{1}{3}$ (b) – 1 and – 3
(c) $\frac{1}{2}$ and $\frac{1}{3}$ (d) $\frac{1}{4}$ and $\frac{1}{3}$

184. If $2x + y = 17$; $y + 2z = 15$ and $x + y = 9$, then what is the value of $4x + 3y + z$?

(a) 41 (b) 43
(c) 45 (d) 55
(e) None of these

185. If $3x - 4y + z = 7$; $2x - z + 3y = 19$; $x + 2y + 2z = 24$, then what is the value of z?

(a) 4 (b) 5
(c) 6 (d) 8

186. If $2x + y = 15$, $2y + z = 25$ and $2z + x = 26$, what is the value of z?

(a) 4 (b) 7
(c) 9 (d) 11

187. If $2x + 3y = 31$, $y - z = 4$ and $x + 2z = 11$, then what is the value of $x + y + z$?

(a) 12 (b) 13
(c) 15 (d) 16

188. The price of 10 chairs is equal to that of 4 tables. The price of 15 chairs and 2 tables together is ₹ 4000. The total price of 12 chairs and 3 tables is

(a) ₹ 3500 (b) ₹ 3750
(c) ₹ 3840 (d) ₹ 3900

189. If two jeans and three shirts cost ₹ 4000 and three jeans and two shirts cost ₹ 3500, how much does a jean cost? **(P.C.S., 2009)**

(a) ₹ 500 (b) ₹ 1000
(c) ₹ 1500 (d) ₹ 2000

190. Cost of 8 pens and 4 pencils is ₹ 176 and the cost of 2 pens and 2 pencils is ₹ 48. What is the cost of one pen? **(Bank P.O., 2009)**

(a) ₹ 12 (b) ₹ 14
(c) ₹ 16 (d) ₹ 18
(e) None of these

191. The cost of two dozen apples and three dozen bananas is ₹ 136. The cost of 5 dozen bananas and one dozen apples is ₹ 110. What is the price of one dozen bananas? **(Bank Recruitment, 2009)**

(a) ₹ 16 (b) ₹ 18
(c) ₹ 20 (d) ₹ 24
(e) None of these

192. The cost of one pencil, two pens and four erasers is ₹ 22 while the cost of five pencils, four pens and two erasers is ₹ 32. How much will three pencils, three pens and three erasers cost? **(Campus Recruitment, 2010)**

(a) ₹ 21 (b) ₹ 24
(c) ₹ 27 (d) ₹ 30

193. Ram Singh goes to Pushkar Mela with ₹ 10000 to buy exactly 100 animals. He finds that cows are sold at ₹ 1000, horses at ₹ 300 and chicken at ₹ 50. How many chicken should he buy to meet his target of 100 animals? **(SNAP, 2005)**

(a) 88 (b) 90
(c) 92 (d) 94

194. 3 men and 4 boys can earn ₹ 756 in 7 days. 11 men and 13 boys can earn ₹ 3008 in 8 days. In what time will 7 men with 9 boys earn ₹ 2480? **(P.C.S., 2006)**

(a) 8 days (b) 9 days
(c) 10 days (d) 11 days

195. At a certain fast food restaurant, Brian can buy 3 burgers, 7 shakes and one order of fries for ₹ 120 exactly. At the same place, it would cost ₹ 164.50 for 4 burgers, 10 shakes and one order of fries. How much would it cost for an ordinary meal of one burger, one shake and one fries?

(a) ₹ 21 (b) ₹ 31
(c) ₹ 41 (d) Cannot be determined

196. If $2x^2 + 12x + 18 = 0$, what is the value of x? (Bank P.O., 2006)

(a) -3 (b) -2
(c) 2 (d) 3
(e) More than one answer

197. If $x^2 - 7x = -12$, what is the value of x? (C.E.T., 2006)

(a) -3 or -4 (b) 3 or 4
(c) 3 or -4 (d) Cannot be determined
(e) None of these

198. The roots of the equation $2x^2 - 11x + 15 = 0$ are (Campus Recruitment, 2008)

(a) $3, \frac{5}{2}$ (b) $5, \frac{3}{2}$
(c) $-3, -\frac{5}{2}$ (d) None of these

199. The value of $\left(1-\frac{1}{2}\right)\left(1-\frac{1}{3}\right)\left(1-\frac{1}{4}\right)\cdots\left(1-\frac{1}{m}\right)$ is (P.C.S., 2008)

(a) 1 (b) $\frac{1}{m}$
(c) $\frac{1}{2m}$ (d) $\frac{1}{1\cdot2\cdot3\cdots(m-1)\,m}$

200. The expression $\left(1+\frac{1}{3}\right)\left(1+\frac{1}{4}\right)\left(1+\frac{1}{5}\right)\cdots\left(1+\frac{1}{n}\right)$ simplifies to (M.B.A. 2006, 2008)

(a) $\frac{n+1}{3}$ (b) $\frac{n}{n+1}$
(c) $\frac{3}{n}$ (d) $1+\frac{1}{3}\cdot\frac{1}{4}\cdot\frac{1}{5}\cdots\frac{1}{n}$

201. When simplified, the product $\left(2-\frac{1}{3}\right)\left(2-\frac{3}{5}\right)\left(2-\frac{5}{7}\right)\cdots\left(2-\frac{997}{999}\right)$ is equal to (R.R.B., 2007)

(a) $\frac{5}{999}$ (b) $\frac{1001}{999}$
(c) $\frac{1}{1001}$ (d) $\frac{1001}{3}$

202. $\frac{3}{4}\left(1+\frac{1}{3}\right)\left(1+\frac{2}{3}\right)\left(1-\frac{2}{5}\right)\left(1+\frac{6}{7}\right)\left(1-\frac{12}{13}\right)=?$

(a) $\frac{1}{5}$ (b) $\frac{1}{6}$
(c) $\frac{1}{7}$ (d) None of these

203. The value of $\left(1-\frac{1}{3^2}\right)\left(1-\frac{1}{4^2}\right)\left(1-\frac{1}{5^2}\right)\cdots\left(1-\frac{1}{11^2}\right)\left(1-\frac{1}{12^2}\right)$ is

(a) $\frac{11}{20}$ (b) $\frac{13}{15}$
(c) $\frac{13}{18}$ (d) $\frac{15}{16}$
(e) None of these

204. What is the value of the following expression?

$$\frac{1}{(2^2-1)}+\frac{1}{(4^2-1)}+\frac{1}{(6^2-1)}+\cdots+\frac{1}{(20^2-1)}$$

(a) $\frac{9}{19}$ (b) $\frac{10}{19}$
(c) $\frac{10}{21}$ (d) $\frac{11}{21}$

205. Find the sum : $\frac{1}{2}+\frac{1}{6}+\frac{1}{12}+\frac{1}{20}+\frac{1}{30}+\frac{1}{42}+\frac{1}{56}+\frac{1}{72}+\frac{1}{90}+\frac{1}{110}+\frac{1}{132}$.

(a) $\frac{7}{8}$ (b) $\frac{11}{12}$
(c) $\frac{15}{16}$ (d) $\frac{17}{18}$

206. The sum of the first 35 terms of the series $\frac{1}{2}+\frac{1}{3}-\frac{1}{4}-\frac{1}{2}-\frac{1}{3}+\frac{1}{4}+\frac{1}{2}+\frac{1}{3}-\frac{1}{4}\ldots$ is :

(a) $-\frac{1}{2}$ (b) $-\frac{1}{4}$
(c) $\frac{1}{4}$ (d) None of these

207. $\left(1\frac{1}{2}+11\frac{1}{2}+111\frac{1}{2}+1111\frac{1}{2}\right)$ is equal to (S.S.C., 2010)

(a) 617 (b) 618
(c) $1234\frac{1}{2}$ (d) 1236

208. $\left(999\frac{999}{1000}\times7\right)$ is equal to (C.P.O., 2007)

(a) $6633\frac{7}{1000}$ (b) $6993\frac{7}{1000}$
(c) $6999\frac{993}{1000}$ (d) $7000\frac{7}{1000}$

209. The value of $999\frac{995}{999}\times999$ is

(a) 990809 (b) 998996
(c) 998999 (d) 999824

210. $\left(999\frac{1}{7}+999\frac{2}{7}+999\frac{3}{7}+999\frac{4}{7}+999\frac{5}{7}+999\frac{6}{7}\right)$ is simplified to

(a) 2997 (b) 5979
(c) 5994 (d) 5997

211. The value of $998\frac{2}{17}+998\frac{3}{17}+998\frac{5}{17}+998\frac{8}{17}+998\frac{16}{17}$ is (I.A.M., 2007)

(a) 4990 (b) 4992
(c) 9998 (d) 10000

212. The simplest value of $\frac{1}{1\times2}+\frac{1}{2\times3}+\frac{1}{3\times4}+....+\frac{1}{9\times10}$ is (P.C.S., 2008)

(a) $\frac{1}{10}$ (b) $\frac{9}{10}$
(c) 1 (d) 10

213. $\left(\frac{1}{1.4}+\frac{1}{4.7}+\frac{1}{7.10}+\frac{1}{10.13}+\frac{1}{13.16}\right)$ is equal to (S.S.C., 2007)

(a) $\frac{1}{3}$ (b) $\frac{3}{8}$
(c) $\frac{5}{16}$ (d) $\frac{41}{7280}$

214. When simplified, the sum $\frac{1}{2}+\frac{1}{6}+\frac{1}{12}+\frac{1}{20}+\frac{1}{30}+....+\frac{1}{n(n+1)}$ is equal to (S.S.C., 2006)

(a) $\frac{1}{n}$ (b) $\frac{1}{n+1}$
(c) $\frac{n}{n+1}$ (d) $\frac{2(n-1)}{n}$

215. The value of $1+\frac{1}{4\times3}+\frac{1}{4\times3^2}+\frac{1}{4\times3^3}$ is

(a) $\frac{121}{108}$ (b) $\frac{3}{2}$
(c) $\frac{31}{2}$ (d) None of these

216. $\frac{1}{1\cdot2\cdot3}+\frac{1}{2\cdot3\cdot4}+\frac{1}{3\cdot4\cdot5}+\frac{1}{4\cdot5\cdot6}$ is equal to

(a) $\frac{7}{30}$ (b) $\frac{11}{30}$
(c) $\frac{13}{30}$ (d) $\frac{17}{30}$

217. The value of $\frac{3}{1^2\cdot2^2}+\frac{5}{2^2\cdot3^2}+\frac{7}{3^2\cdot4^2}+\frac{9}{4^2\cdot5^2}+\frac{11}{5^2\cdot6^2}+\frac{13}{6^2\cdot7^2}+\frac{15}{7^2\cdot8^2}+\frac{17}{8^2\cdot9^2}+\frac{19}{9^2\cdot10^2}$ is (S.S.C., 2004)

(a) $\frac{1}{100}$ (b) $\frac{99}{100}$
(c) 1 (d) $\frac{101}{100}$

218. The sum of the first 99 terms of the series $\frac{3}{4}+\frac{5}{36}+\frac{7}{144}+\frac{9}{400}+....$

(a) $\frac{99}{100}$ (b) $\frac{999}{1000}$
(c) $\frac{9999}{10000}$ (d) 1

219. Mayank, Mirza, Little and Jaspal bought a motorbike for ₹ 60000. Mayank paid one-half of the sum of the amounts paid by the other boys, Mirza paid one-third of the sum of the amounts paid by the other boys and Little paid one-fourth of the sum of the amounts paid by the other boys. How much did Jaspal have to pay?

(a) ₹ 13000 (b) ₹ 15000
(c) 17000 (d) None of these

220. Income of a company doubles after every one year. If the initial income was ₹ 4 lakhs, what would be the income after 5 years? (Bank P.O., 2003)

(a) ₹ 1.24 crores (b) ₹ 1.28 crores
(c) ₹ 2.52 crores (d) ₹ 2.56 crores
(e) None of these

221. Breeding of a certain species of insects is incredible everyday the total number of such insects in a closed glass jar is double the number on the previous day. There was just one insect in the jar on 1/2/2007, and the jar was full to the brim with these insects on 28/2/2007. On which date of February was the jar quarter-full? (P.C.S., 2008)

(a) 7 (b) 14
(c) 26 (d) None of these

222. The flowers in a basket double every minute and the basket gets full in one hour. In how much time, the basket was $\frac{1}{32}$ full?

(a) 12 minutes (b) 32 minutes
(c) 45 minutes (d) 55 minutes

223. A man's investment doubles in every 5 years. If he invested ₹ 5000 in each of the years 1990, 1995, 2000 and 2005, then what was the total amount received by him in 2010?

(a) ₹ 30000 (b) ₹ 70000
(c) ₹ 140000 (d) ₹ 150000

224. After measuring 120 metres of a rope, it was discovered that the measuring metre rod was 3 cm longer. The true length of the rope measured is (S.S.C., 2007)

(a) 116 m 40 cm (b) 121 m 20 cm
(c) 123 m (d) 123 m 60 cm

225. Smita was asked to multiply a certain number by 36. She multiplied it by 63 instead and got an answer 3834 more than the correct one. What was the number to be multiplied? (Bank P.O., 2008)

(a) 126 (b) 142
(c) 148 (d) 152
(e) None of these

226. A boy multiplied 423 by a number and obtained 65589 as his answer. If both the fives in the answer are wrong and all other figures are correct, the correct answer is:
(a) 60489 (b) 61189
(c) 62189 (d) 62389

227. A candidate was asked to find $\frac{7}{8}$ of a positive number. He found $\frac{7}{18}$ of the same by mistake. If his answer was 770 less than the correct one, then the original given number was (Campus Recruitment, 2010)
(a) 1260 (b) 1548
(c) 6160 (d) None of these

228. A student was asked to divide a number by $\frac{17}{8}$. Instead, he actually multiplied it by $\frac{17}{8}$ and hence got 225 more than the expected answer. What was the expected answer?
(a) 64 (b) 126
(c) 136 (d) None of these

229. One junior student is asked to divide half a number by 6 and the other half by 4 and then add the quantities. Instead of doing so, the student divides the given number by 5. If the answer is 4 short of the correct answer, then the number is
(a) 320 (b) 360
(c) 400 (d) 480 (M.B.A., 2008)

230. If $3\frac{2}{3}$ is subtracted from $9\frac{1}{9}$ and the difference is multiplied by 450, what is the final answer? (Bank P.O., 2009)
(a) 2045 (b) 2250
(c) 2540 (d) Cannot be determined
(e) None of these

231. By how much is $\frac{3}{4}$ of 968 less than $\frac{7}{8}$ of 1008? (Bank P.O., 2010)
(a) 146 (b) 154
(c) 158 (d) 165
(e) None of these

232. If $x = y - \frac{y}{10}$, where y is a positive integer which increases in value, then x (P.C.S., 2009)
(a) first increases in value then decreases
(b) decreases in value
(c) increases in value
(d) first decreases then increases in value

233. The difference between $\frac{3}{4}$th of $\frac{4}{5}$th of a number and $\frac{1}{6}$th of $\frac{2}{5}$th of the same number is 648. What is the number? (Bank P.O., 2009)
(a) 1110 (b) 1215
(c) 1325 (d) 1440
(e) None of these

234. Which number gives the same result when added to $1\frac{1}{2}$ and when multiplied by $1\frac{1}{2}$?
(a) 1 (b) 3
(c) 5 (d) 7

235. $\frac{5}{12}$ of which sum is equal to $3\frac{3}{4}$ of ₹ 100?
(a) ₹ 750 (b) ₹ 800
(c) ₹ 900 (d) ₹ 1000

236. $\frac{3}{8}$ is what part of $\frac{1}{12}$?
(a) $\frac{3}{7}$ (b) $\frac{1}{12}$
(c) $\frac{4}{3}$ (d) None of these

237. The smallest fraction which should be subtracted from the sum of $1\frac{3}{4}$, $2\frac{1}{2}$, $5\frac{7}{12}$, $3\frac{1}{3}$ and $2\frac{1}{4}$ to make the result a whole number is
(a) $\frac{5}{12}$ (b) $\frac{7}{12}$
(c) $\frac{1}{2}$ (d) 7

238. What fraction should be added to the sum of $5\frac{3}{4}$, $4\frac{4}{5}$ and $7\frac{3}{8}$ to make the result a whole number? (M.B.A., 2006)
(a) $\frac{1}{40}$ (b) $\frac{2}{40}$
(c) $\frac{3}{40}$ (d) $\frac{4}{40}$

239. If x is a positive number, then which of the following fractions has the greatest value?
(a) $\frac{x}{x}$ (b) $\frac{x}{x+1}$
(c) $\frac{x+1}{x}$ (d) $\frac{x+2}{x+3}$

240. By how much does $\frac{6}{7/8}$ exceed $\frac{6/7}{8}$?

(a) $6\frac{1}{8}$ (b) $6\frac{3}{4}$

(c) $7\frac{3}{4}$ (d) $7\frac{5}{6}$

241. If $\frac{4}{5}$ of an estate be worth ₹ 16,800, then the value of $\frac{3}{7}$ of the estate is

(a) ₹ 9000 (b) ₹ 21,000

(c) ₹ 72,000 (d) ₹ 90,000

242. Two-fifth of one-fourth of three-seventh of a number is 15. What is half of that number?

(a) 94 (b) 96

(c) 188 (d) 196

(e) None of these

243. What fraction of an hour is a second?

(a) $\frac{1}{24}$ (b) $\frac{1}{60}$

(c) $\frac{1}{120}$ (d) $\frac{1}{3600}$

244. When a ball bounces, it rises to $\frac{3}{4}$ of the height from which it fell. If the ball is dropped from a height of 32 m, how high will it rise at the third bounce?

(a) 13 m (b) $13\frac{1}{2}$ m

(c) $14\frac{1}{2}$ m (d) None of these

245. Sanket earns twice as much in the month of March as in each of the other months of the year. What part of his entire annual earnings was earned in March?

(a) $\frac{1}{7}$ (b) $\frac{1}{6}$

(c) $\frac{2}{11}$ (d) $\frac{2}{13}$

246. If one-third of a tank holds 80 litres of water, then the quantity of water that half of the tank holds is

(a) $\frac{80}{3}$ litres (b) 100 litres

(c) 120 litres (d) 240 litres

247. A person travels 3.5 km from place *A* to place *B*. Out of this distance, he travels $1\frac{2}{3}$ km on bicycle, $1\frac{1}{6}$ km on scooter and the rest on foot. What portion of the whole distance does he cover on foot?

(a) $\frac{3}{19}$ (b) $\frac{4}{11}$

(c) $\frac{4}{21}$ (d) $\frac{5}{6}$

248. What fraction of $\frac{4}{7}$ must be added to itself to make the sum $1\frac{1}{14}$?

(a) $\frac{1}{2}$ (b) $\frac{4}{7}$

(c) $\frac{7}{8}$ (d) $\frac{15}{14}$

249. Express $\frac{2}{3}$ of $\frac{1}{4}$ of ₹ 25.20 as a fraction of $1\frac{1}{2}$ of ₹ 36.

(a) $\frac{5}{8}$ (b) $\frac{5}{42}$

(c) $\frac{7}{90}$ (d) $\frac{11}{90}$

250. A 70 cm long wire is to be cut into two pieces such that one piece will be $\frac{2}{5}$ as long as the other. How many centimetres will the shorter piece be?

(a) 10 (b) 14

(c) 20 (d) 28

251. A certain amount is distributed among *A*, *B* and *C*. *A* gets $\frac{3}{16}$ and *B* gets $\frac{1}{4}$ of the whole amount. If *C* gets ₹ 81, then *B* gets

(a) ₹ 30 (b) ₹ 32

(c) ₹ 36 (d) ₹ 40

252. $\frac{1}{10}$ of a pole is coloured red, $\frac{1}{20}$ white, $\frac{1}{30}$ blue, $\frac{1}{40}$ black, $\frac{1}{50}$ violet, $\frac{1}{60}$ yellow and the rest is green. If the length of the green portion of the pole is 12.08 metres, then the length of the pole is

(S.S.C., 2004)

(a) 16 m (b) 18 m

(c) 20 m (d) 30 m

253. If we multiply a fraction by itself and divide the product by its reciprocal, the fraction thus obtained is $18\frac{26}{27}$. The original fraction is

(a) $\frac{8}{27}$ (b) $1\frac{1}{3}$

(c) $2\frac{2}{3}$ (d) None of these

254. The marks scored in an examination are converted from 50 to 10 for the purpose of internal assessment. The highest marks were 47 and the lowest were 14. The difference between the maximum and the minimum internal assessment scores is

(*a*) 3.3 (*b*) 4.8
(*c*) 6.6 (*d*) 7.4

255. One-third of Rahul's savings in National Savings Certificate is equal to one-half of his savings in Public Provident Fund. If he has ₹ 1,50,000 as total savings, how much has he saved in Public Provident Fund?

(*a*) ₹ 30,000 (*b*) ₹ 50,000
(*c*) ₹ 60,000 (*d*) ₹ 90,000

256. In a family, the father took $\frac{1}{4}$ of the cake and he had 3 times as much as each of the other members had. The total number of family members is

(*a*) 3 (*b*) 7
(*c*) 10 (*d*) 12

257. A waiter's salary consists of his salary and tips. During one week his tips were $\frac{5}{4}$ of his salary. What fraction of his income came from tips?

(*a*) $\frac{4}{9}$ (*b*) $\frac{5}{4}$
(*c*) $\frac{5}{8}$ (*d*) $\frac{5}{9}$

258. A sum of ₹ 1360 has been divided among *A*, *B* and *C* such that *A* gets $\frac{2}{3}$ of what *B* gets and *B* gets $\frac{1}{4}$ of what *C* gets. *B*'s share is **(M.A.T., 2002)**

(*a*) ₹ 120 (*b*) ₹ 160
(*c*) ₹ 240 (*d*) ₹ 300

259. Three friends had dinner at a restaurant. When the bill was received, Amita paid $\frac{2}{3}$ as much as Veena paid and Veena paid $\frac{1}{2}$ as much as Tanya paid. What fraction of the bill did Veena pay? **(SNAP, 2005)**

(*a*) $\frac{1}{3}$ (*b*) $\frac{3}{11}$
(*c*) $\frac{12}{31}$ (*d*) $\frac{5}{8}$

260. $\frac{1}{4}$ of a tank holds 135 litres of water. What part of the tank is full if it contains 180 litres of water?

(*a*) $\frac{1}{6}$ (*b*) $\frac{1}{3}$
(*c*) $\frac{2}{3}$ (*d*) $\frac{2}{5}$

261. A tank is $\frac{2}{5}$ full. If 16 litres of water is added to the tank, it becomes $\frac{6}{7}$ full. The capacity of the tank is

(*a*) 28 litres (*b*) 32 litres
(*c*) 35 litres (*d*) 42 litres

262. A drum of kerosene is $\frac{3}{4}$ full. When 30 litres of kerosene is drawn from it, it remains $\frac{7}{12}$ full. The capacity of the drum is **(S.S.C., 2010)**

(*a*) 120 litres (*b*) 135 litres
(*c*) 150 litres (*d*) 180 litres

263. A tin of oil was $\frac{5}{8}$ full. When 10 bottles of oil was taken out and 8 bottles of oil was poured into it, it was $\frac{3}{5}$ full. How many bottles of oil can the tin contain?

(*a*) 20 (*b*) 30
(*c*) 40 (*d*) 80

264. 1 m of an object is to be represented by 10 cm on the drawing scale. The representative fraction (R.F.) of the scale is

(*a*) $\frac{1}{10}$ (*b*) $\frac{1}{20}$
(*c*) $\frac{1}{100}$ (*d*) None of these

265. An area of 100 sq. cm on the map represents an area of 49 sq. km on the field. The R.F. of the scale to be used is

(*a*) $\frac{1}{10000}$ (*b*) $\frac{1}{20000}$
(*c*) $\frac{1}{49000}$ (*d*) $\frac{1}{70000}$

266. The fluid contained in a bucket can fill four large bottles or seven small bottles. A full large bottle is used to fill an empty small bottle. What fraction of the fluid is left over in the large bottle when the small one is full?

(*a*) $\frac{2}{7}$ (*b*) $\frac{3}{7}$
(*c*) $\frac{4}{7}$ (*d*) $\frac{5}{7}$

267. To fill a tank, 25 buckets of water is required. How many buckets of water will be required to fill the same tank if the capacity of the bucket is reduced to two-fifth of its present?

(*a*) 10 (*b*) 35
(*c*) $62\frac{1}{2}$ (*d*) Cannot be determined
(*e*) None of these

268. A stationary engine has enough fuel to run 12 hours when its tank is $\frac{4}{5}$ full. How long will it run when the tank is $\frac{1}{3}$ full? **(Campus Recruitment, 2009)**

(*a*) Less than 2 hours (*b*) 2 hours
(*c*) 3 hours (*d*) 4 hours
(*e*) 5 hours

269. A tree grows only $\frac{3}{5}$ as fast as the one beside it. In four years the combined growth of the trees is eight feet. How much does the shorter tree grow in 2 years? **(Campus Recruitment, 2008)**

(*a*) Less than 2 feet (*b*) 2 feet
(*c*) $2\frac{1}{2}$ feet (*d*) 3 feet
(*e*) More than 3 feet

270. A car is filled with four and a half gallons of fuel for a round trip. If the amount of fuel taken while going is $\frac{1}{4}$ more than the amount taken for coming, what is the amount of fuel consumed while coming back? **(Campus Recruitment, 2009)**

(*a*) Less than 2 gallons (*b*) 2 gallons
(*c*) $2\frac{1}{2}$ gallons (*d*) 3 gallons
(*e*) More than 3 gallons

271. The lowest temperature in the night in a city is one-third more than $\frac{1}{2}$ the highest during the day. Sum of the lowest temperature and the highest temperature is 100 degrees. Then what is the lowest temperature? **(Campus Recruitment, 2010)**

(*a*) 30 degrees (*b*) 40 degrees
(*c*) 36 degrees (*d*) None of these

272. In a class there are 18 boys who are over 160 cm tall. If these boys constitute three-fourths of the boys and the total number of boys is two-thirds of the number of students in the class, then what is the number of girls in the class?

(*a*) 6 (*b*) 12
(*c*) 18 (*d*) 24

273. Peter gave one-fourth of the amount he had to Michael. Michael in turn gave half of what he received from Peter to Sam. If the difference between the remaining amount with Peter and the amount received by Sam is ₹ 500, how much money did Michael receive from Peter?

(*a*) ₹ 100 (*b*) ₹ 200
(*c*) ₹ 400 (*d*) Data inadequate
(*e*) None of these

274. Four children *A*, *B*, *C* and *D* divide a bag of sweets. *A* takes $\frac{1}{3}$ of them, *B* $\frac{2}{5}$th of the remainder and the rest is equally shared between *C* and *D*. What fraction of the sweets did *C* or *D* get?

(*a*) $\frac{1}{4}$ (*b*) $\frac{1}{5}$
(*c*) $\frac{1}{6}$ (*d*) $\frac{1}{17}$

275. Rita travelled 1200 km by air, which formed $\frac{2}{5}$th of her journey. One-third of the whole journey she travelled by car and the remaining journey by train. Find the distance travelled by the train. **(R.R.B., 2006)**

(*a*) 480 km (*b*) 800 km
(*c*) 1600 km (*d*) 1800 km

276. A man spends one-quarter of his income on food, one-fifth of it on rent and remaining, which is ₹ 231, on other commodities. Find his total income.

(*a*) ₹ 400 (*b*) ₹ 410
(*c*) ₹ 420 (*d*) ₹ 460

277. A boy read $\frac{3}{8}$th of a book on one day and $\frac{4}{5}$th of the remainder on another day. If there were 30 pages unread, how many pages did the book contain? **(I.M.T. 2002; XAT, 2006)**

(*a*) 240 (*b*) 300
(*c*) 600 (*d*) None of these

278. An institute organised a fete and $\frac{1}{5}$ of the girls and $\frac{1}{8}$ of the boys participated in the same. What fraction of the total number of students took part in the fete?

(*a*) $\frac{2}{13}$ (*b*) $\frac{13}{40}$
(*c*) Data inadequate (*d*) None of these

279. At an International Dinner, $\frac{1}{5}$ of the people attending were French men. If the number of French women at the dinner was $\frac{2}{3}$ greater than the number of French men, and there were no other French people at the dinner, then what fraction of the people at the dinner were not French? **(M.B.A., 2003)**

(*a*) $\frac{1}{5}$ (*b*) $\frac{2}{5}$
(*c*) $\frac{2}{3}$ (*d*) $\frac{7}{15}$

280. In a class, $\frac{3}{5}$ of the students are girls and rest are boys. If $\frac{2}{9}$ of the girls and $\frac{1}{4}$ of the boys are absent, what part of the total number of students is present?

(a) $\frac{17}{25}$ (b) $\frac{18}{49}$

(c) $\frac{23}{30}$ (d) $\frac{23}{36}$

281. One-third of the boys and one-half of the girls of a college participated in a social work project. If the number of participating students is 300 out of which 100 are boys, what is the total number of students in the college?

(a) 500 (b) 600

(c) 700 (d) 800

282. To win an election, a candidate needs $\frac{3}{4}$ of the votes cast. If after $\frac{2}{3}$ of the votes have been counted, a candidate has $\frac{5}{6}$ of what he needs, then what part of the remaining votes does he still need?

(M.A.T., 2008)

(a) $\frac{1}{8}$ (b) $\frac{3}{8}$

(c) $\frac{1}{10}$ (d) $\frac{1}{4}$

283. A fires 5 shots to B's 3 but A kills only once in 3 shots while B kills once in 2 shots. When B has missed 27 times, A has killed

(a) 30 birds (b) 60 birds

(c) 72 birds (d) 90 birds

284. If every 2 out of 3 readymade shirts need alterations in the collar, every 3 out of 4 need alterations in the sleeves, and every 4 out of 5 need it in the body, how many alterations will be required for 60 shirts?

(a) 24 (b) 123

(c) 133 (d) 143

285. The sum of three fractions is $2\frac{11}{24}$. When the largest fraction is divided by the smallest, the fraction thus obtained is $\frac{7}{6}$ which is $\frac{1}{3}$ more than the middle one. The fractions are

(a) $\frac{3}{5}, \frac{4}{7}, \frac{2}{3}$ (b) $\frac{7}{8}, \frac{5}{6}, \frac{3}{4}$

(c) $\frac{7}{9}, \frac{2}{3}, \frac{3}{5}$ (d) None of these

286. A millionaire bought a lot of hats $\frac{1}{4}$ of which were brown. The millionaire sold $\frac{2}{3}$ of the hats including $\frac{4}{5}$ of the brown hats. What fraction of the unsold hats were brown?

(Campus Recruitment, 2010)

(a) $\frac{1}{60}$ (b) $\frac{1}{15}$

(c) $\frac{3}{20}$ (d) $\frac{3}{5}$

(e) $\frac{3}{4}$

287. Equal amounts of water were poured into two empty jars of different capacities, which made one jar $\frac{1}{4}$ full and the other jar $\frac{1}{3}$ full. If the water in the jar with lesser capacity is, then poured into the jar with the greater capacity, what fraction of the larger jar will be filled with water?

(M.A.T., 2005)

(a) $\frac{1}{2}$ (b) $\frac{2}{3}$

(c) $\frac{3}{4}$ (d) $\frac{2}{7}$

288. Mr. X spends $\frac{1}{4}$ of his income on food and $\frac{1}{3}$ less than what he spent on food, on the education of his children. What fraction of his income did he spend on food and education?

(a) $\frac{2}{7}$ (b) $\frac{1}{2}$

(c) $\frac{5}{12}$ (d) $\frac{7}{12}$

289. A body of 7300 troops is formed of 4 battalions so that $\frac{1}{2}$ of the first, $\frac{2}{3}$ of the second, $\frac{3}{4}$ of the third and $\frac{4}{5}$ of the fourth are all composed of the same number of men. How many men are there in the second battalion?

(M.A.T., 2008)

(a) 1500 (b) 1600

(c) 1800 (d) 2400

290. After reading $\frac{3}{5}$ of the biology homework on Monday night, Sanjay read $\frac{1}{3}$ of the remaining homework on Tuesday night. What fraction of the original homework would Sanjay have to read on Wednesday night to complete the assignment?

(a) $\frac{1}{5}$ (b) $\frac{1}{15}$

(c) $\frac{2}{15}$ (d) $\frac{4}{15}$

291. The highest score in an inning was $\frac{3}{11}$ of the total and the next highest was $\frac{3}{11}$ of the remainder. If the scores differed by 9, the total score was

(a) 110 (b) 121

(c) 132 (d) 143

292. Mechanics are paid twice the hourly wages of sales people. Custodial workers are paid one-third the hourly wages of mechanics. What fraction of the hourly wages of custodial workers are sales people paid? **(M.B.A., 2006)**

(a) $\frac{1}{3}$ (b) $\frac{1}{2}$

(c) $\frac{2}{3}$ (d) $\frac{3}{2}$

(e) $\frac{4}{3}$

293. Ganeshi's monthly income is twice Jassi's monthly income. Two-third of Jassi's monthly income is equal to Sukhvinder's monthly income. If Sukhvinder's annual income is ₹ 2.34 lakhs, what is Ganeshi's monthly income? **(Bank Recruitment, 2010)**

(a) ₹ 14625 (b) ₹ 29250

(c) ₹ 28230 (d) ₹ 58500

(e) None of these

294. The cost of 36 kg of rice last year was ₹ 1044 and the cost of 24 kg of rice this year is ₹ 768. What is the difference between the cost per kg of rice last year and the cost per kg of rice this year? **(Bank Recruitment, 2008)**

(a) ₹ 3 (b) ₹ 4

(c) ₹ 5 (d) ₹ 6

(e) None of these

295. The cost of 12 belts and 30 wallets is ₹ 8940. What is the cost of 4 belts and 10 wallets? **(Bank Recruitment, 2009)**

(a) ₹ 2780 (b) ₹ 2870

(c) ₹ 2890 (d) ₹ 2980

(e) None of these

296. The cost of 5 pendants and 8 chains is ₹ 1,45,785. What would be the cost of 15 pendants and 24 chains? **(Bank P.O., 2009)**

(a) ₹ 3,25,285 (b) ₹ 4,39,355

(c) ₹ 5,50,000 (d) Cannot be determined

(e) None of these

297. The cost of 21 tables and 35 chairs is ₹ 41825. What is the cost of 9 tables and 15 chairs?

(a) ₹ 17775 (b) ₹ 17925

(c) ₹ 18075 (d) ₹ 18725

(e) None of these

298. The cost of 13 kg of sugar is ₹ 195, the cost of 17 kg of rice is ₹ 544 and the cost of 21 kg of wheat is ₹ 336. What is the total cost of 21 kg of sugar, 26 kg of rice and 19 kg of wheat? **(M.A.T., 2009)**

(a) ₹ 1306 (b) ₹ 1451

(c) ₹ 1500 (d) ₹ 1636

299. The most economical price among the following is **(Campus Recruitment, 2008)**

(a) 10 kilo for ₹ 160 (b) 2 kilo for ₹ 30

(c) 4 kilo for ₹ 70 (d) 20 kilo for ₹ 340

(e) 8 kilo for ₹ 130

300. There are 200 questions on a 3 hour examination. Among these questions are 50 Mathematics problems. It is suggested that twice as much time be spent on each Maths problem as for each other question. How many minutes should be spent on Mathematics problems? **(Campus Recruitment, 2010)**

(a) 36 (b) 60

(c) 72 (d) 100

301. What part of an hour elapses from 4.56 P.M. to 5.32 P.M.? **(R.R.B., 2006)**

(a) $\frac{1}{4}$ (b) $\frac{1}{2}$

(c) $\frac{3}{5}$ (d) $\frac{3}{4}$

302. 72 hours 6 minutes ÷ 14 =?

(a) 59 minutes (b) 5 hours 9 minutes

(c) 6 hours 9 minutes (d) 7 hours 8 minutes

303. A class starts at 10 a.m. and lasts till 1.27 p.m. Four periods are held during this interval. After every period, 5 minutes are given free to the students. The exact duration of each period is

(a) 42 minutes (b) 48 minutes

(c) 51 minutes (d) 53 minutes

304. A light was seen at intervals of 13 seconds. It was seen for the first time at 1 hr. 54 min. 50 secs. a.m. and the last time at 3 hrs. 17 min. 49 secs. a.m. How many times was the light seen? **(A.A.O. Exam., 2003)**

(a) 360 (b) 375

(c) 378 (d) 384

305. A woman works continuously for 7 days in the kitchen and refuses to work on the 8th day when her husband takes over. If she starts her work on a Sunday, then the 10th time she rests will be on which day of the week?

(a) Sunday (b) Monday

(c) Tuesday (d) Friday

306. If $x * y = x^2 + y^2 - xy$, then the value of $9 * 11$ is
(a) 93 (b) 103
(c) 113 (d) 121

307. If $a * b = \frac{ab}{a+b}$, find the value of $3 * (3 * -1)$.
(a) – 3 (b) – 1.5
(c) – 1 (d) $\frac{2}{3}$

308. If $a * b = 2a - 3b + ab$, then $3 * 5 + 5 * 3$ is equal to
(a) 22 (b) 24
(c) 26 (d) 28

309. If $x \oplus y = x^2 + 2y$, what is the value of p if $4 \oplus (3 \oplus p) = 50$?
(a) 4 (b) 7
(c) 8 (d) 12.5

310. If $a * b * c$ means $\frac{a+b}{c}$ for all numbers except 0, then $(a * b * c) * a * b$ is equal to
(a) 0 (b) 1
(c) $\frac{a+b+c}{ab}$ (d) $\frac{a+b+ac}{bc}$
(e) $\frac{ab+bc+ca}{a+b+c}$

Directions (*Questions 311 to 313*): ***Each question below consists of a number. Your task is to follow the following steps in order to find the result from the given alternatives.*** **(M.C.A., 2005)**

Step I: Multiply the number by 3 and add the square of the number.
Step II: Divide the result obtained after Step I by 5 and add 6.
Step III: Divide the result obtained after Step II by 3 and then square the resulting number.

311. 6 (a) 13 (b) 30
(c) 31.03 (d) 31.36

312. 2.5 (a) 8.10 (b) 8.51 (approx.)
(c) 18.05 (d) 80.50 (approx.)

313. 5 (a) 2.80 (b) 12.80
(c) 20.08 (approx.) (d) 21.80 (approx.)

314. If the operation $\wedge$ is defined by the equation $x \wedge y = 2x + y$, what is the value of a in $2 \wedge a = a \wedge 3$? **(Campus Recruitment, 2009)**
(a) 0 (b) – 1
(c) 1 (d) 4

315. If $\oplus$ is an operation such that $a \oplus b = \begin{cases} 2a, \text{ when } a > b \\ a+b, \text{ when } a < b \\ a^2, \text{ when } a = b \end{cases}$,

then $\left[\frac{(5 \oplus 7) + (4 \oplus 4)}{3(5 \oplus 5) - (15 \oplus 11) - 3}\right]$ is equal to **(C.P.O., 2007)**
(a) $\frac{1}{3}$ (b) $\frac{2}{3}$
(c) $\frac{14}{13}$ (d) $\frac{14}{23}$

316. At Srinagar, starting at 9 a.m. on a certain day, snow began to fall at a rate of $1\frac{1}{4}$ inches every two hours until 3 p.m. If there was already $2\frac{1}{4}$ inches of snow on the ground at 9 a.m., how many inches of snow was on the ground at 3 p.m. that day?
(a) $3\frac{3}{4}$ (b) 6
(c) 7 (d) $7\frac{1}{2}$

317. A squirrel starts climbing up a tree at the speed of 6 metres a minute but after every 6 metres it slips down 4 metres in the next minute. It will be able to reach the top 120 metres high in **(R.R.B., 2006)**
(a) 20 minutes (b) 60 minutes
(c) 115 minutes (d) $1\frac{1}{2}$ hours

318. Ram had ₹ 1000 in his Savings Bank Account. Every month in the first week he needs money, so he withdraws ₹ 500, but by the end of the month, he deposits ₹ 750. After how many months the original amount will grow three times? **(R.R.B., 2005)**
(a) 6 months (b) 7 months
(c) 8 months (d) 9 months

319. The growth of a medicinal plant of height 1 metre, is 1 cm/day and it is growing straight vertically upward. A man cuts 6 cm from the top, at a regular interval of every 11 days. Its height will be 2 metres after **(I.A.M., 2007)**
(a) 220 days (b) 250 days
(c) 275 days (d) None of these

320. A stairway 10 ft. high is such that each step accounts for half a foot upward and one foot forward. What distance will an ant travel if it starts from ground level to reach the top of the stairway? **(R.R.B., 2009)**
(a) 30 ft. (b) 33 ft.
(c) 10 ft. (d) 29 ft.

321. The sum of all proper fractions whose denominators are less than or equal to 100, is
(a) $22\frac{1}{4}$ (b) 1925
(c) 2475 (d) None of these

322. The value of $\frac{1-x^4}{1+x} \div \frac{1+x^2}{x} \times \frac{1}{x(1-x)}$ is
(a) 1 (b) $1 - x^2$
(c) $\frac{1}{x}$ (d) $1 + x$
(e) None of these

323. $\frac{17}{15}\times\frac{17}{15}+\frac{2}{15}\times\frac{2}{15}-\frac{17}{15}\times\frac{4}{15}$ is equal to

(a) 0 (b) 1
(c) 10 (d) 11

324. $2\times 13\frac{3}{4}\times 5\frac{1}{4}+5\frac{1}{4}\times 5\frac{1}{4}+13\frac{3}{4}\times 13\frac{3}{4}=?$

(a) 311 (b) 316
(c) 361 (d) 380

325. The simplification of $\left(\frac{75983\times 75983-45983\times 45983}{30000}\right)$ yields the result

(a) 121796 (b) 121866
(c) 121956 (d) 121966

326. Simplify: $\frac{13\frac{4}{7}\times 13\frac{4}{7}+8\frac{3}{7}\times 8\frac{3}{7}}{13\frac{4}{7}+8\frac{3}{7}}$ (R.R.B., 2006)

(a) 18 (b) 20
(c) 22 (d) 24

327. $\frac{(a-b)^2-(a+b)^2}{-4a}=\frac{x}{y}$. On simplifying the given equation, which of the following equations will be obtained? (Bank P.O., 2009)

(a) $xy = b$ (b) $bx = y$
(c) $ab = x$ (d) $yb = x$
(e) $ay = x$

328. What is $\frac{\frac{7}{8}\times\frac{7}{8}+\frac{5}{6}\times\frac{5}{6}+\frac{7}{8}\times\frac{5}{3}}{\frac{7}{8}\times\frac{7}{8}-\frac{5}{6}\times\frac{5}{6}}$ equal to? (S.S.C., 2007)

(a) $\frac{41}{24}$ (b) $\frac{1}{24}$
(c) 41 (d) None of these

329. The simplified value of $1998^2 - 1997^2 + 1996^2 - 1995^2 + 1994^2 - 1993^2$ is

(a) 11953 (b) 11958
(c) 11963 (d) 11973

330. $\frac{(856+167)^2+(856-167)^2}{856\times 856+167\times 167}=?$

(a) 1 (b) 2
(c) 689 (d) 1023

331. $\frac{(469+174)^2-(469-174)^2}{469\times 174}=?$ (M.B.A., 2002)

(a) 2 (b) 4
(c) 295 (d) 643

332. If $a - b = 3$ and $a^2 + b^2 = 29$, find the value of ab. (R.R.B., 2003)

(a) 10 (b) 12
(c) 15 (d) 18

333. If $\frac{x^2-1}{x+1}=4$, $x = ?$

(a) 0 (b) 1
(c) 5 (d) Cannot be determined
(e) None of these

334. $\frac{\left(3\frac{2}{3}\right)^2-\left(2\frac{1}{2}\right)^2}{\left(4\frac{3}{4}\right)^2-\left(3\frac{1}{3}\right)^2}\div\frac{3\frac{2}{3}-2\frac{1}{2}}{4\frac{3}{4}-3\frac{1}{3}}=?$

(a) $\frac{37}{97}$ (b) $\frac{74}{97}$
(c) $1\frac{23}{74}$ (d) None of these

335. The simplified value of

$$\frac{\left(1+\frac{1}{1+\frac{1}{100}}\right)\left(1+\frac{1}{1+\frac{1}{100}}\right)-\left(1-\frac{1}{1+\frac{1}{100}}\right)\left(1-\frac{1}{1+\frac{1}{100}}\right)}{\left(1+\frac{1}{1+\frac{1}{100}}\right)+\left(1-\frac{1}{1+\frac{1}{100}}\right)}$$ is

(a) 100 (b) $\frac{200}{101}$
(c) 200 (d) $\frac{202}{100}$

336. The value of $\frac{769435\times 770001-566}{769435+770001\times 769434}$ is

(a) -1 (b) -2
(c) 1 (d) 2

337. If $a - b = 1$, then the value of $a^3 - b^3 - 3ab$ will be

(a) -3 (b) -1
(c) 1 (d) 3

338. If $x - y = 1$ and $x^2 + y^2 = 41$, then the value of $x + y$ will be

(a) 5 or 4 (b) -5 or -4
(c) ± 9 (d) ± 1

339. If $x^4 + y^4 = 17$ and $x + y = 1$, then what is the value of $x^2y^2 - 2xy$?

(a) 8 (b) 10
(c) 12 (d) 16

340. If $x = a + m$, $y = b + m$, $z = c + m$, the value of $\frac{x^2+y^2+z^2-yz-zx-xy}{a^2+b^2+c^2-ab-bc-ca}$ is

(a) 1 (b) $\frac{x+y+z}{a+b+c}$
(c) $\frac{a+b+c}{x+y+z}$ (d) not possible to find

341. If $a + b + c = 13$, $a^2 + b^2 + c^2 = 69$, then find $ab + bc + ca$.

(a) – 50 (b) 50
(c) 69 (d) 75

342. If $\frac{x^2+y^2+z^2-64}{xy-yz-zx} = -2$ and $x+y=3z$, then the value of z is

(a) 2 (b) 3
(c) 4 (d) None of these

343. $\left(\frac{785\times785\times785+435\times435\times435}{785\times785+435\times435-785\times435}\right)$ simplifies to

(a) 350 (b) 785
(c) 1220 (d) 1320

344. $\left(\frac{147\times147+147\times143+143\times143}{147\times147\times147-143\times143\times143}\right) = ?$

(a) $\frac{1}{4}$ (b) 290
(c) $\frac{1}{290}$ (d) 4

345. $\frac{(13)^3+7^3}{(13)^2+7^2-?} = 20$

(a) 6 (b) 20
(c) 91 (d) None of these

346. The value of $\frac{\left(\frac{3}{5}\right)^3-\left(\frac{2}{5}\right)^3}{\left(\frac{3}{5}\right)^2-\left(\frac{2}{5}\right)^2}$ is (S.S.C., 2003)

(a) $\frac{1}{5}$ (b) $\frac{19}{25}$
(c) $\frac{21}{25}$ (d) 1

347. $\frac{38\times38\times38+34\times34\times34+28\times28\times28-38\times34\times84}{38\times38+34\times34+28\times28-38\times34-34\times28-38\times28}$ is equal to

(a) 24 (b) 32
(c) 44 (d) 100

348. The value of $\frac{(x-y)^3+(y-z)^3+(z-x)^3}{9(x-y)(y-z)(z-x)}$ is equal to

(a) 0 (b) $\frac{1}{9}$
(c) $\frac{1}{3}$ (d) 1

349. If $x = 5$, $y = 3$, the value of $\frac{x^3-y^3}{x^2-y^2}-\frac{3xy}{x+y}$ will be (P.C.S., 2009)

(a) 1 (b) $\frac{1}{2}$
(c) $\frac{3}{2}$ (d) $\frac{5}{2}$

350. If $a + b + c = 11$ and $ab + bc + ca = 20$, then the value of the expression $a^3 + b^3 + c^3 - 3abc$ will be

(a) 121 (b) 341
(c) 671 (d) 781

351. The value of $\frac{(x-y)^3+(y-z)^3+(z-x)^3}{(x^2-y^2)^3+(y^2-z^2)^3+(z^2-x^2)^3}$ is

(a) 0
(b) 1
(c) $[2(x+y+z)]^{-1}$
(d) $[(x+y)(y+z)(z+x)]^{-1}$

352. If $a + b + c = 0$, the value of $\frac{a^2}{bc}+\frac{b^2}{ca}+\frac{c^2}{ab}$ is

(a) $3abc$ (b) $\frac{1}{3}$
(c) 1 (d) 3

353. If $a = 29$, $b = 24$, $c = 27$, the value of $a^3 + b^3 + c^3 - 3abc$ is

(a) 1420 (b) 1520
(c) 1620 (d) 1920

354. If $\frac{x^2-1}{x} = 4$, then $\frac{x^6-1}{x^3}$ is

(a) 63 (b) 66
(c) 75 (d) 76

355. $(32)^3 + (79)^3 - (111)^3 + 3 \times 32 \times 79 \times 111$ is equal to

(a) 0 (b) 1
(c) 10000 (d) 30007

356. If $(x + y) = 3$, $xy = 2$, then what is the value of $x^3 + y^3$?

(a) 6 (b) 7
(c) 8 (d) 9
(e) None of these

357. The value of $\frac{x^2-(y-z)^2}{(x+z)^2-y^2}+\frac{y^2-(x-z)^2}{(x+y)^2-z^2}+\frac{z^2-(x-y)^2}{(y+z)^2-x^2}$ is (M.B.A., 2006)

(a) – 1 (b) 0
(c) 1 (d) None of these

358. If $\frac{p}{a}+\frac{q}{b}+\frac{r}{c}=1$ and $\frac{a}{p}+\frac{b}{q}+\frac{c}{r}=0$ where a, b, c, p, q, r are non-zero real numbers, then $\frac{p^2}{a^2}+\frac{q^2}{b^2}+\frac{r^2}{c^2}$ is equal to

(a) 0 (b) 1
(c) 3 (d) 9

359. If $x^4 - y^4 = 15$, then find the value of $x^4 + y^4$, where x and y are natural numbers.
(a) 17 (b) 31
(c) 71 (d) 113

360. Along a yard 225 metres long, 26 trees are planted at equal distances, one tree being at each end of the yard. What is the distance between two consecutive trees?
(a) 8 metres (b) 9 metres
(c) 10 metres (d) 15 metres

361. In a garden, there are 10 rows and 12 columns of mango trees. The distance between the two trees is 2 metres and a distance of one metre is left from all sides of the boundary of the garden. The length of the garden is
(a) 20 m (b) 22 m
(c) 24 m (d) 26 m

362. A farmer has decided to build a wire fence along one straight side of his property. For this, he planned to place several fence-posts at 6 m intervals, with posts fixed at both ends of the side. After he bought the posts and wire, he found that the number of posts he had bought was 5 less than required. However, he discovered that the number of posts he had bought would be just sufficient if he spaced them 8 m apart. What is the length of the side of his property and how many posts did he buy? (M.A.T., 2007)
(a) 100 m, 15 (b) 100 m, 16
(c) 120 m, 15 (d) 120 m, 16

363. On a 2 km road, a total number of 201 trees are planted on each side of the road at equal distances. How many such trees in all will be planted on both sides of a 50 km road such that the distance between two consecutive trees is the same as that of the consecutive trees on the 2 km road?
(a) 501 (b) 5000
(c) 5001 (d) 5025
(e) 5050

364. When all the students in a school are made to stand in rows of 54, 30 such rows are formed. If the students are made to stand in rows of 45, how many such rows will be formed? (Bank P.O., 2010)
(a) 25 (b) 32
(c) 36 (d) 42
(e) None of these

365. There are x trees and y parrots. If in each tree only one parrot is sitting, then one parrot remains without a tree. If in each tree, two parrots are sitting, then one tree remains without a parrot. Therefore, x and y are respectively
(a) 3 and 4 (b) 4 and 5
(c) 5 and 6 (d) 6 and 7

366. In a classroom, there are certain number of benches. If 6 students are made to sit on a bench, then to accommodate all of them, one more bench is needed. However, if 7 students are made to sit on a bench, then after accommodating all of them, space for 5 students is left. What is the total number of students in the class?
(a) 30 (b) 42
(c) 72 (d) None of these

367. There are benches in a classroom. If 4 students sit on each bench, then three benches are left vacant and if 3 students sit on each bench, then 3 students are left standing. The total number of students in the class is
(a) 36 (b) 42
(c) 48 (d) 54

368. Students of a class are preparing for a drill and are made to stand in rows. If 4 students are extra in a row, then there would be 2 rows less. But there would be 4 more rows if 4 students are less in a row. The number of students in the class is (M.A.T., 2006)
(a) 56 (b) 65
(c) 69 (d) 96

369. If a sum of ₹ 275 is to be divided between Ram and Shyam so that Ram gets $\frac{3}{4}$th more of what Shyam gets, then the share of Ram will be
(a) ₹ 100 (b) ₹ 160
(c) ₹ 175 (d) ₹ 200

370. Sweets were distributed equally among 64 children. After giving 7 sweets to each child 15 sweets were left out. Total how many sweets were there? (Bank P.O., 2009)
(a) 436 (b) 446
(c) 448 (d) 463
(e) None of these

371. X gives $\frac{1}{2}$ of his property to his wife and $\frac{1}{2}$ of the rest to his son. The remainder is divided equally between his two daughters. The share of each daughter is
(a) $\frac{1}{4}$ (b) $\frac{1}{6}$
(c) $\frac{1}{8}$ (d) $\frac{2}{3}$

372. If each child is given 10 sweets, there are 3 sweets left over. But if each is given 11, then the number of sweets is 4 less. Find the number of sweets. (R.R.B., 2009)
(a) 37 (b) 57
(c) 73 (d) 75

373. 180 oranges are distributed among 70 boys and girls such that each boy gets 2 and each girl gets 3 oranges. The number of boys are

(*a*) 25 (*b*) 30
(*c*) 40 (*d*) 70

374. A farmer divides his herd of cows among his four sons so that first son gets one-half of the herd, the second son gets one-fourth, the third son one-fifth and the fourth son 7 cows. The total number of cows in the herd is **(R.R.B., 2006)**

(*a*) 100 (*b*) 140
(*c*) 180 (*d*) 240

375. A man had two sons. To the elder, he left $\frac{5}{11}$ of his property, to the younger $\frac{5}{11}$ of the remainder, the rest to the widow. Find the share of the sons if the widow gets ₹ 3600. **(M.B.A. 2007)**

(*a*) ₹ 1200, ₹ 1000 (*b*) ₹ 6600, ₹ 2000
(*c*) ₹ 7500, ₹ 1000 (*d*) None of these

376. If ₹ 370 are divided among 10 men, 12 women and 20 boys such that each man gets an amount equal to that received by one woman and one boy together and each woman gets twice the amount received by a boy, then the amount received by 10 men would be

(*a*) ₹ 100 (*b*) ₹ 120
(*c*) ₹ 130 (*d*) ₹ 150

377. A sum of ₹ 750 is distributed among *A*, *B*, *C* and *D* in such a manner that *A* gets as much as *B* and C together, *B* gets ₹ 125 more than C and *D* gets as much as C. What is *A*'s share?

(*a*) ₹ 100 (*b*) ₹ 225
(*c*) ₹ 275 (*d*) ₹ 325

378. A bonus of ₹ 1000 is to be divided among three people so that Rohit receives twice as much as Sachin, who receives one-fifth as much as Gagan. How much money should Gagan receive?

(*a*) ₹ 100 (*b*) ₹ 250
(*c*) ₹ 375 (*d*) ₹ 625

379. Three boys agree to divide a bag of marbles in the following manner. The first boy takes one more than half the marbles. The second takes a third of the number remaining. The third boy finds that he is left with twice as many marbles as the second boy. The original number of marbles **(M.B.A., 2011)**

(*a*) is 8 or 38
(*b*) is 14 or 32
(*c*) is 20 or 26
(*d*) Cannot be determined from the given data

380. A man has divided his total money in his will in such a way that half of it goes to his wife, $\frac{2}{3}$rd of the remaining among his three sons equally and the rest among his four daughters equally. If each daughter gets ₹ 20,000, how much money will each son get?

(*a*) ₹ 48,233.33 (*b*) ₹ 50,333.33
(*c*) ₹ 53,333.33 (*d*) Data inadequate
(*e*) None of these

381. Anand, Bijoy, Chetan and Dharma together have ₹ 47 with them. Anand and Bijoy together have ₹ 27; Chetan and Anand have ₹ 25 and Dharma and Anand have ₹ 23. How much money does Bijoy have?

(*a*) ₹ 9 (*b*) ₹ 11
(*c*) ₹ 13 (*d*) ₹ 28

382. When a sum of money was distributed to 12 persons instead of 16 persons, each person got ₹ 400 more. What was the sum?

(*a*) ₹ 14400 (*b*) ₹ 16000
(*c*) ₹ 19200 (*d*) Data inadequate
(*e*) None of these

383. After distributing the sweets equally among 25 children, 8 sweets remain. Had the number of children been 28, 22 sweets would have been left after equally distributing. What was the total number of sweets?

(*a*) 328 (*b*) 348
(*c*) 358 (*d*) Data inadequate

384. On a school's Annual Day sweets were to be equally distributed amongst 112 children. But on that particular day, 32 children were absent. Thus the remaining children got 6 extra sweets. How many sweets was each child originally supposed to get? **(Bank P.O., 2009)**

(*a*) 15 (*b*) 18
(*c*) 24 (*d*) Cannot be determined
(*e*) None of these

385. A sum of money is equally divided among a number of children. Had there been 16 children more, each would have received ₹ 2 less and had there been 16 fewer, each would have received ₹ 3 more. Find the sum of the money distributed.

(*a*) ₹ 880 (*b*) ₹ 896
(*c*) ₹ 928 (*d*) ₹ 960

386. Vidushi and Sanya distributed ₹ 100 each in charity. Vidushi distributes money to 5 more people than Sanya and Sanya gives each ₹ 1 more than Vidushi. How many people are recipients of the charity?

(*a*) 45 (*b*) 60
(*c*) 90 (*d*) None of these

387. In a classroom the number of boys is three times the number of girls. Which of the following numbers does not represent the total number of students in the classroom?

(*a*) 40 (*b*) 42
(*c*) 44 (*d*) 48

388. There are some boys and girls in a room. The square of the number of girls is less than the square of the number of boys by 28. If there were two more girls, the number of boys would have been the same as that of the girls. The total number of boys and girls in the room is (C.P.O., 2007)

(a) 7 (b) 10
(c) 14 (d) 56

389. A classroom has equal number of boys and girls. Eight girls left to play kho-kho, leaving twice as many boys as girls in the classroom. What was the total number of girls and boys present initially?

(a) 16 (b) 24
(c) 32 (d) Cannot be determined
(e) None of these

390. What is the value of the expression $(1 + x)(1 + x^2)(1 + x^4)(1 + x^8)(1 - x)$?

(a) $x^8 + 1$ (b) $x^{16} - 1$
(c) $1 + x^{16}$ (d) $1 - x^{16}$

391. The expression $\frac{1}{x-1} - \frac{1}{x+1} - \frac{2}{x^2+1} - \frac{4}{x^4+1}$ is equal to

(a) $\frac{8}{x^8+1}$ (b) $\frac{8}{x^8-1}$
(c) $\frac{8}{x^7-1}$ (d) $\frac{8}{x^7+1}$

392. $\left(x+\frac{1}{x}\right)\left(x-\frac{1}{x}\right)\left(x^2+\frac{1}{x^2}-1\right)\left(x^2+\frac{1}{x^2}+1\right)$ is equal to (S.S.C., 2006)

(a) $x^6 - \frac{1}{x^6}$ (b) $x^8 - \frac{1}{x^8}$
(c) $x^6 + \frac{1}{x^6}$ (d) $x^8 + \frac{1}{x^8}$

393. If $\left(x+\frac{1}{x}\right) = 3$, then $\left(x^2+\frac{1}{x^2}\right) = ?$

(a) 7 (b) 9
(c) 10 (d) 27

394. If $\left(a-\frac{1}{a}\right) = p$, then $\left(a^2+\frac{1}{a^2}\right)$ is equal to

(a) p (b) $p - 2$
(c) $p + 2$ (d) None of these

395. If $\frac{x-1}{x} = 3$, then the value of $1+\frac{1}{x^2}$ is

(a) 9 (b) 10
(c) 11 (d) None of these

396. If $\left(x^2+\frac{1}{x^2}\right) = 34$, then $\left(x+\frac{1}{x}\right)$ is equal to

(a) 3 (b) 4
(c) 5 (d) None of these

397. If $\left(x+\frac{1}{x}\right) = 2$, then $\left(x-\frac{1}{x}\right)$ is equal to (R.R.B., 2006)

(a) 0 (b) 1
(c) 2 (d) 5

398. If $\left(a+\frac{1}{a}\right) = 6$, then $\left(a^4+\frac{1}{a^4}\right) = ?$ (R.R.B., 2008)

(a) 1154 (b) 1158
(c) 1160 (d) 1164

399. If $\left(x-\frac{1}{x}\right) = 2$, then the value of $\left(x^4+\frac{1}{x^4}\right)$ is

(a) 4 (b) 8
(c) 12 (d) 34

400. If $\left(x-\frac{1}{x}\right) = \sqrt{21}$; the value of $\left(x^2+\frac{1}{x^2}\right)\left(x+\frac{1}{x}\right)$ is

(a) 42 (b) 63
(c) 115 (d) 120
(e) 125

401. If $\left(x^4+\frac{1}{x^4}\right) = 322$, the value of $\left(x-\frac{1}{x}\right)$ is

(a) 4 (b) $3\sqrt{2}$
(c) 6 (d) 8

402. If $x+\frac{1}{x} = p$, the value of $x^3+\frac{1}{x^3}$ is

(a) $p^3+\frac{1}{p^3}$ (b) $p^3 - 3p$
(c) p^3 (d) $p^3 + 3p$

403. If $x-\frac{1}{x} = 1$, then the value of $x^3-\frac{1}{x^3}$ is equal to

(a) 2 (b) 3
(c) 4 (d) 8

404. If $\left(a^4+\frac{1}{a^4}\right) = 1154$, then the value of $\left(a^3+\frac{1}{a^3}\right) = ?$

(a) 198 (b) 200
(c) 216 (d) None of these

405. If $\left(x+\frac{1}{x}\right) = 3$, then the value of $\left(x^6+\frac{1}{x^6}\right)$ is

(a) 322 (b) 364
(c) 414 (d) 927

406. If $\left(x+\frac{1}{x}\right) = \sqrt{13}$, then the value of $\left(x^3-\frac{1}{x^3}\right)$ is (Delhi Police, 2010)

(a) 26 (b) 27
(c) 30 (d) 36

407. If $\left(4b^2+\frac{1}{b^2}\right) = 2$, then $\left(8b^3+\frac{1}{b^3}\right) = ?$ (S.S.C., 2008)

(a) 0 (b) 1
(c) 2 (d) 5

08. If $\left(2p+\frac{1}{p}\right)=4$, the value of $\left(p^3+\frac{1}{8p^3}\right)$ is (S.S.C., 2010)

(a) 4 (b) 5
(c) 8 (d) 15

09. In a herd of cows, the number of legs are 14 more than twice the number of heads. The number of cows in the herd is (P.C.S., 2009)

(a) 5 (b) 7
(c) 10 (d) 12

10. In a group of buffaloes and ducks, the number of legs is 24 more than twice the number of heads. What is the number of buffaloes in the group?

(a) 6 (b) 8
(c) 10 (d) 12

11. Krishan has some hens and some cows. If the total number of animal heads is 59 and the total number of feet is 190, how many cows does Krishan have? (M.A.T., 2009)

(a) 23 (b) 32
(c) 36 (d) Cannot be determined

12. There are some parrots and some tigers in a forest. If the total number of animal heads in the forest is 858 and the total number of animal legs is 1846, what is the number of parrots in the forest? (Bank P.O., 2010)

(a) 800 (b) 833
(c) 845 (d) Cannot be determined
(e) None of these

13. A certain number of horses and an equal number of men are going somewhere. Half of the owners are on their horses' back while the remaining ones are walking along leading their horses. If the number of legs walking on the ground is 70, then how many horses are there?

(a) 10 (b) 12
(c) 14 (d) 16

14. A railway half-ticket costs half the full fare and the reservation charge is the same on half ticket as on full ticket. One reserved first class ticket from Chennai to Trivandrum costs ₹ 216 and one full reserved and one half reserved first class tickets cost ₹ 327. What is the basic first class full fare and what is the reservation charge? (R.R.B., 2009)

(a) ₹ 105, ₹ 6 (b) ₹ 216, ₹ 12
(c) ₹ 210, ₹ 6 (d) ₹ 210, ₹ 12

5. An employee may claim ₹ 7 for each km when he travels by taxi and ₹ 6 for each km if he drives his own car. If in one week he claimed ₹ 675 for travelling 90 km, how many kms did he travel by taxi? (L.I.C.A.A.O., 2007)

(a) 135 (b) 155
(c) 162 (d) 170

416. In a party 15 people shake their hands with each other. How many times did the hand-shakes take place? (R.R.B., 2009)

(a) 105 (b) 120
(c) 135 (d) 165

417. In a group of children, each child exchanges a gift with every other child. If the number of gifts is 132, then the number of children in the group is

(a) 10 (b) 11
(c) 12 (d) 13

418. A man has 1044 candles. After burning, he can make a new candle from 9 stubs left behind. Find the maximum number of candles that can be made.

(a) 116 (b) 120
(c) 130 (d) 140

419. A computer printed 176400 lines in a given day. If the printer was in operation for 7 hours during the day, how many lines did it print per minute? (Campus Recruitment, 2008)

(a) 280 (b) 360
(c) 420 (d) 440

420. A man takes 8 minutes to type a page. If 1710 pages are to be typed in the afternoon between 1 o' clock to 2 o' clock, how many men are required? (R.R.B., 2009)

(a) 221 (b) 249
(c) 256 (d) None of these

421. Ashu reads at an average rate of 30 pages per hour while Neeru reads at an average rate of 40 pages per hour. If Ashu starts reading a novel at 2: 30 and Neeru begins reading an identical copy of the same book at 3: 20, at what time will they be reading the same page?

(a) 5: 00 (b) 5: 50
(c) 6: 40 (d) 7: 00
(e) 7: 30

422. In a test, a candidate secured 336 marks out of maximum marks x. If the maximum marks x had been converted into 400 marks, he would have secured 192 marks. What was the maximum marks of the test? (Bank P.O., 2009)

(a) 500 (b) 650
(c) 700 (d) 750
(e) 800

423. The marks scored in an examination are converted from 50 to 10 for the purpose of internal assessment. The highest marks were 47 and the lowest were 14. The difference between the maximum and the minimum internal assessment scores is

(a) 3.3 (b) 4.8
(c) 6.6 (d) 7.4

424. In an examination, a student scores 4 marks for every correct answer and loses 1 mark for every wrong answer. A student attempted all the 200 questions and scored in all 200 marks. The number of questions he answered correctly was **(S.S.C., 2010)**

(*a*) 60 (*b*) 68
(*c*) 80 (*d*) 82

425. On a 26 question test, five points were deducted for each wrong answer and eight points were credited for each correct answer. If all the questions were answered, how many were correct if the score was zero?

(*a*) 6 (*b*) 9
(*c*) 10 (*d*) 13

426. In an examination, a student attempted 15 questions correctly and secured 40 marks. If there were two types of questions (2 marks and 4 marks questions), how many questions of 2 marks did he attempt correctly?

(*a*) 5 (*b*) 10
(*c*) 20 (*d*) 40

427. In an examination there are 30 questions. 1 mark is given for each correct answer and 0.25 is deducted for every incorrect answer. Ankur attempted all the questions and scored 13.75. How many incorrect answers did he have? **(XAT, 2009)**

(*a*) 10 (*b*) 11
(*c*) 12 (*d*) 15
(*e*) None of these

428. For aiming at a target a person gets one rupee each time when he hits it and loses one rupee when he misses it. If he gets ₹ 30 after aiming at the target one hundred times, then how many times did he miss the target? **(P.C.S., 2009)**

(*a*) 25 (*b*) 35
(*c*) 40 (*d*) 45

429. There are some cows, bulls and 45 hens in a group. One caretaker looks after 15 animals. The number of bulls is twice the number of cows. If the number of heads is less than the total number of feet by 186 (including the caretakers), how many caretakers are there?

(*a*) 5 (*b*) 6
(*c*) 8 (*d*) 9
(*e*) None of these

430. A man's basic pay for a 40 hours' week is ₹ 200. Overtime is paid at 25% above the basic rate. In a certain week, he worked overtime and his total was ₹ 300. He, therefore, worked for a total of (in hours) **(L.I.C.A.A.O., 2007)**

(*a*) 52 (*b*) 56
(*c*) 58 (*d*) 62

431. In a regular week, there are 5 working days and fo each day, the working hours are 8. A man gets ₹ 24 per hour for regular work and ₹ 32 per hour fo overtime. If he earns ₹ 4320 in 4 weeks, then hov many hours does he work for?

(*a*) 160 (*b*) 175
(*c*) 180 (*d*) 195

432. David gets on the elevator at the 11th floor of building and rides up at the rate of 57 floors pe minute. At the same time, Albert gets on an elevato at the 51st floor of the same building and rides dow at the rate of 63 floors per minute. If they continu travelling at these rates, then at which floor will thei paths cross? **(M.B.A., 2008**

(*a*) 19th (*b*) 28th
(*c*) 30th (*d*) 37th

433. Mr. Shah decided to walk down the escalator of tube station. He found that if he walks down 2 steps, he requires 30 seconds to reach the botton However, if he steps down 34 stairs he would onl require 18 seconds to get to the bottom. If the tim is measured from the moment the top step begin to descend to the time he steps off the last step a the bottom, find out the height of the stairway i steps. **(Campus Recruitment, 2009**

(*a*) 42 (*b*) 46
(*c*) 52 (*d*) 54

434. Mohan engaged a servant on the condition that h would pay him ₹ 200 and a uniform after 10 day The servant served only for 5 days and got ₹ 20 an a uniform. Find the price of the uniform. **(R.R.B. 200**

(*a*) ₹ 80 (*b*) ₹ 120
(*c*) ₹ 140 (*d*) ₹ 160

435. A labourer was engaged for 20 days on the conditio that he will receive ₹ 60 for each day he works an he will be fined ₹ 5 for each day he is absent. If h received ₹ 745 in all, then the number of days o which he remained absent is

(*a*) 3 (*b*) 5
(*c*) 7 (*d*) 9

436. The taxi charges in a city comprise of a fixed charg together with the charge of the distance covere For a journey of 16 km, the charges paid are ₹ 15 and for a journey of 24 km, the charges paid ar ₹ 204. What will a person have to pay for travellir a distance of 30 km?

(*a*) ₹ 236 (*b*) ₹ 240
(*c*) ₹ 248 (*d*) ₹ 252

437. M men agree to purchase a gift for ₹ D. If thre men drop out how much more will each have t contribute towards the purchase of the gift? **(Campus Recruitment, 200**

(*a*) $\frac{D}{M-3}$ (*b*) $\frac{MD}{3}$

(*c*) $\frac{M}{D-3}$ (*d*) $\frac{3D}{M^2-3M}$

38. N number of persons decided to raise ₹ 3 lakhs by equal contributions from each. Had they contributed ₹ 50 each extra, the contribution would have been ₹ 3.25 lakhs. How many persons are there?
(a) 400 (b) 450
(c) 600 (d) Cannot be determined
(e) None of these

39. Each boy contributed rupees equal to the number of girls and each girl contributed rupees equal to the number of boys in a class of 60 students. If the total contribution thus collected is ₹ 1600, how many boys are there in the class? (M.B.A., 2006)
(a) 25 (b) 30
(c) 50 (d) Data inadequate

40. Eight people are planning to share equally the cost of a rental car. If one person withdraws from the arrangement and the others share equally the entire cost of the car, then the share of each of the remaining persons increased by
(a) $\frac{1}{7}$ (b) $\frac{1}{8}$
(c) $\frac{1}{9}$ (d) $\frac{7}{8}$

41. A person on tour has ₹ 360 for his daily expenses. If he extends his tour for 4 days, he has to cut his daily expenses by ₹ 3. Find the original duration of the tour.
(a) 15 days (b) 20 days
(c) 24 days (d) 30 days

42. Some students planned a picnic. The budget for food was ₹ 500. But, 5 of them failed to go and thus the cost of food for each member increased by ₹ 5. How many students attended the picnic? (M.A.T., 2006)
(a) 15 (b) 20
(c) 25 (d) 30

43. A class decided to have a party at a total cost of ₹ 720. Four students decided to stay out of the party. To meet the expenses the remaining students had to increase their share by ₹ 9. What is the original cost per student? (M.A.T., 2010)
(a) ₹ 18 (b) ₹ 20
(c) ₹ 24 (d) ₹ 36

44. A group of boys decided to buy a few CDs whose total price was between ₹ 200 and ₹ 250. But at the time of purchase, two of the boys declined to contribute as a result of which the remaining boys had to pay Re 1 more than they had originally planned. What was the price of the CDs if the boys contributed equally and in whole number of rupees?
(a) ₹ 210 (b) ₹ 220
(c) ₹ 230 (d) ₹ 240

445. Rahul owes ₹ X and gives a ₹ 50 note in payment. He receives the following change: $3X$ fifty-paise coins, 14 ten-paise coins and $4X$ five-paise coins. X is equal to:
(a) 12 (b) 16
(c) 18 (d) 22

446. A total of 324 coins of 20 paise and 25 paise make a sum of ₹ 71. The number of 25-paise coins is
(a) 120 (b) 124
(c) 144 (d) 200

447. A man has one-rupee, 5-rupee and 10-rupee currency notes of worth ₹ 480. If the number of notes of each denomination be same, then the total number of notes will be (R.R.B., 2007)
(a) 45 (b) 60
(c) 75 (d) 90

448. The total value of a collection of coins of denominations Re 1, 50-paise, 25-paise, 10-paise and 5-paise is ₹ 380. If the number of coins of each denomination is the same, then the number of one-rupee coins is
(a) 160 (b) 180
(c) 200 (d) 220

449. A bag contains three types of coins — 1-rupee coins, 50 p-coins and 25 p-coins totalling 175 coins. If the total value of the coins of each kind be the same, the total amount in the bag is
(a) ₹ 75 (b) ₹ 126
(c) ₹ 175 (d) ₹ 300

450. In a box, there are a certain number of coins which amount to ₹ 25. There are 2-rupee coins, 50-paise coins and 25-paise coins. If there are at least one 2-rupee coin, two 50-paise coins and two 25-paise coins, then what could be the minimum number of coins in the box?
(a) 12 (b) 14
(c) 16 (d) 18

Directions (*Questions 451 to 452*): *These questions are based on the following information:* (Campus Recruitment, 2008)

85 children went to an amusement park where they could ride on merry-go-round, roller coaster and Ferris wheel. It was known that 20 of them took all the three rides and 55 of them have taken at least two of the three rides. Each ride costs Re 1, and the total receipt of the amusement park was ₹ 145.

451. How many children took exactly one ride?
(a) 5 (b) 10
(c) 15 (d) 20

452. How many children did not try any of the rides?
(a) 5 (b) 10
(c) 15 (d) 20

453. In a class of 50 students, 25 take Bengali, 16 take Hindi, 12 students take no language. How many take both Bengali and Hindi? (P.C.S., 2008)
(a) 3 (b) 4
(c) 9 (d) 13

454. Out of 100 students in a class, 60 take tea, 40 take coffee and 25 take both. The number of students not taking either tea or coffee is (P.C.S., 2009)
(*a*) 25 (*b*) 28
(*c*) 30 (*d*) 32

455. In a class of 25 students, 12 have taken Mathematics, 8 have taken Mathematics but not Biology. The number of students who have taken both Mathematics and Biology is (R.R.B., 2006)
(*a*) 4 (*b*) 8
(*c*) 24 (*d*) 36

456. In a group of 52 persons, 16 drink tea but not coffee and 33 drink tea. How many drink coffee but not tea? (M.B.A., 2008)
(*a*) 3 (*b*) 7
(*c*) 17 (*d*) 19

457. In a town with population of 4000, 3000 people are egg eaters, 2000 meat eaters and 1500 eat both eggs and meat. How many are pure vegetarians?
(*a*) 400 (*b*) 500
(*c*) 1000 (*d*) 1500

458. There are 50 students admitted to a nursery class. Some students can speak only English and some can speak only Hindi. Ten students can speak both English and Hindi. If the number of students who can speak English is 21, then how many students can speak Hindi, how many can speak only Hindi and how many can speak only English?
(*a*) 21, 11 and 29 respectively
(*b*) 28, 18 and 22 respectively
(*c*) 37, 27 and 13 respectively
(*d*) 39, 29 and 11 respectively

459. In an office, $\frac{3}{4}$ of the staff can neither type nor take shorthand. However, $\frac{1}{5}$th can type and $\frac{1}{3}$rd can take shorthand. What part of the whole staff can do both?
(*a*) $\frac{1}{5}$ (*b*) $\frac{3}{40}$
(*c*) $\frac{13}{40}$ (*d*) $\frac{17}{60}$

460. In a group of players in a college, 20 are in the basketball team, 24 in the hockey team and 27 in the cricket team. If 12 play hockey and basketball, 10 play cricket and basketball, 14 play hockey and cricket and 7 play all the three games, then the total number of players in the group is
(*a*) 42 (*b*) 43
(*c*) 45 (*d*) 49

461. In the cinema set of a movie, 125 mechanical aliens were created. Some of these aliens had peculiar features. 40 had two noses, 30 had three legs, 20 had four ears, 10 had two noses and three legs, 12 had three legs and four ears, 5 had two noses and four ears and 3 had all the three unusual features. How many were there without any of these unusual features?
(*a*) 5 (*b*) 35
(*c*) 80 (*d*) None of these

Directions (*Questions 462 to 466*): *These questions are based on the following information:* (S.B.I.P.O., 2007)

Children in a class play only one or two or all of the three games – badminton, football and cricket. 5 children play only cricket, 8 children play only football and 7 children play only badminton. 3 children play only two games – badminton and football, 4 children play only two games – cricket and football, and another 4 children play only two games – badminton and cricket. 2 children play all the three games.

462. How many children play football as well as cricket?
(*a*) 4 (*b*) 6
(*c*) 7 (*d*) 15
(*e*) None of these

463. In all, how many children play badminton?
(*a*) 12 (*b*) 13
(*c*) 14 (*d*) 17
(*e*) None of these

464. In all, how many children play football?
(*a*) 8 (*b*) 14
(*c*) 15 (*d*) 17
(*e*) None of these

465. How many children play badminton as well as cricket?
(*a*) 4 (*b*) 6
(*c*) 9 (*d*) 10
(*e*) None of these

466. Total how many children are there in the class?
(*a*) 31 (*b*) 33
(*c*) 35 (*d*) 36
(*e*) None of these

467. A survey on a sample of 25 new cars being sold at a local auto dealer was conducted to see which of the three popular options – air-conditioning, radio and power windows – were already installed. (M.A.T., 200

The survey found:
15 had air-conditioning
2 had air-conditioning and power windows but no radios
12 had radio
6 had air-conditioning and radio but no power-windows
11 had power-windows
4 had radio and power windows
3 had all three options

What is the number of cars that had none of the options?

(*a*) 1 (*b*) 2
(*c*) 3 (*d*) 4

468. In a class of 50 students, 23 speak English, 15 speak Hindi and 18 speak Punjabi. 3 speak only English and Hindi, 6 speak only Hindi and Punjabi and 6 speak only English and Punjabi. If 9 speak only English, then how many speak all the three?

(*a*) 1 (*b*) 2
(*c*) 3 (*d*) 5

469. In a hospital, there were 200 Diabetes, 150 Hyperglycaemia and 150 Gastro-enteritis patients. Of these, 80 patients were treated for both Diabetes and Hyperglycaemia. Sixty patients were treated for Gastro-enteritis and Hyperglycaemia, while 70 were treated for Diabetes and Gastro-enteritis. Some of these patients have all the three diseases. Doctor Dennis treats patients with only Diabetes. Doctor Hormis treats patients with only Hyperglycaemia and Doctor Gerard treats patients with only Gastro-enteritis. Doctor Paul is a Generalist. Therefore, he can treat patients with multiple diseases. Patients always prefer a specialist for their disease. If Dr. Dennis had 80 patients, then the other three doctors can be arranged in terms of the number of patients treated as

(*a*) Paul > Hormis > Gerard
(*b*) Gerard > Paul > Hormis
(*c*) Paul > Gerard > Hormis
(*d*) None of these

470. In a joint family of 18 members, 10 take milk, 8 take tea and 6 take coffee; 5 take milk as well as tea but none takes milk and coffee. The number of members who take tea as well as coffee is

(*a*) None (*b*) 1
(*c*) 2 (*d*) 3

Directions ***(Questions 471 to 475): Study the following information carefully to answer the given questions:*** **(Bank P.O., 2006)**

The teachers' colony has 2800 members, out of which 650 members read only English newspaper. 550 members read only Hindi newspaper and 450 members read only Marathi newspaper. The number of members reading all the 3 newspapers is 100. Members reading Hindi as well as English newspaper are 200. 400 members read Hindi as well as Marathi newspaper and 300 members read English as well as Marathi newspaper.

471. Find the number of members reading Hindi newspaper.

(*a*) 750 (*b*) 980 (*c*) 1000
(*d*) 1020 (*e*) None of these

472. How many members read only one newspaper?

(*a*) 1540 (*b*) 1560
(*c*) 1640 (*d*) 1650
(*e*) None of these

473. Find the number of members reading no newspaper.

(*a*) 150 (*b*) 460
(*c*) 550 (*d*) 750 (*e*) None of these

474. How many members read at least two newspapers?

(*a*) 500 (*b*) 600
(*c*) 800 (*d*) 1000
(*e*) None of these

475. Find the difference between the number of members reading English as well as Marathi newspaper and the number of members reading English as well as Hindi newspaper.

(*a*) 50 (*b*) 100
(*c*) 200 (*d*) 300
(*e*) None of these

476. In a garrison, there was some pilferage of ration everyday. If the pilferage was 12 kg a day, the ration would have lasted for 75 days. If the pilferage was restricted to 8 kg per day, the ration would have lasted for 90 days. For how many days would the ration have lasted, if there was no pilferage?

(*a*) 105 (*b*) 120
(*c*) 150 (*d*) 180

477. Two candles having the same lengths are such that one burns out completely in 3 hours at a uniform rate and the other in 4 hours. At what time should both the candles be lighted together so that at 4 P.M. the length of one is twice the length of the other? **(A.A.O. Exam, 2010)**

(*a*) 1: 24 P.M. (*b*) 1: 30 P.M.
(*c*) 1: 36 P.M. (*d*) 1: 42 P.M.

478. A man purchased 40 fruits – apples and oranges – for ₹ 17. Had he purchased as many oranges as apples and as many apples as oranges, he would have paid ₹ 15. Find the cost of one pair of an apple and an orange. **(SNAP, 2007)**

(*a*) 60 paise (*b*) 70 paise
(*c*) 80 paise (*d*) 1 rupee

479. A buyer purchased few books of equal value for a total cost of ₹ 720. If the value of each were ₹ 2 less than the price at which the buyer originally bought, she could have purchased 4 more books than what she had bought. How many books did she originally purchase? **(M.A.T., 2006)**

(*a*) 18 (*b*) 20
(*c*) 34 (*d*) 36

480. A small confectioner bought a certain number of pastries flavoured pineapple, mango and black-forest from the bakery, giving for each pastry as many rupees as there were pastry of that kind; altogether he bought 23 pastries and spent ₹ 211. Find the number of each kind of pastry that he bought, if mango pastry is cheaper than pineapple pastry and dearer than black-forest pastry. **(I.I.F.T., 2010)**

(*a*) (10, 9, 4) (*b*) (11, 9, 3)
(*c*) (10, 8, 5) (*d*) (11, 8, 4)

481. One test tube contains some acid and another test tube contains an equal quantity of water. To prepare a solution, 20 grams of the acid is poured into the second test tube. Then, two-thirds of the so-formed solution is poured from the second tube into the first. If the fluid in first test tube is four times that in the second, what quantity of water was taken initially? **(M.A.T. 2009; N.M.A.T., 2005)**

(*a*) 40 grams (*b*) 60 grams
(c) 80 grams (*d*) 100 grams

482. One bottle is half-full of milk and another bottle with twice the capacity is one-quarter full of milk. If water is added so that both the bottles are full and the contents of both are then poured into a third bottle that is empty and large enough to hold the contents of both, what fraction of the contents in the third bottle is milk? **(Campus Recruitment, 2008)**

(*a*) $\frac{1}{4}$ (*b*) $\frac{1}{3}$
(c) $\frac{2}{3}$ (*d*) $\frac{3}{8}$

483. A train started with 540 passengers. At the first stop $\frac{1}{9}$ of them got down and 24 got up. On its second stop $\frac{1}{8}$ of the passengers then existing got down and 9 got up. With how many passengers did it reach the third stop? **(R.R.B., 2008)**

(*a*) 450 (*b*) 500
(c) 540 (*d*) 550

484. A train started from a station with a certain number of passengers. At the first halt, half of the passengers got down and 125 passengers got in. At the second halt, half of the passengers left and 100 entered. Then the train left for its destination with 250 passengers. The number of passengers in the train at the start was

(*a*) 250 (*b*) 350
(c) 450 (*d*) 550

485. The total number of digits used in numbering the pages of a book having 366 pages, is **(R.R.B., 2008)**

(*a*) 732 (*b*) 990
(c) 1098 (*d*) 1305

486. A printer numbers the pages of a book starting with 1 and uses 3189 digits in all. How many pages does the book have?

(*a*) 1000 (*b*) 1074
(c) 1075 (*d*) 1080

487. In a class, there are two sections *A* and *B*. If 10 students of section *B* shift over to section *A*, the strength of *A* becomes three times the strength of *B*. But if 10 students shift over from *A* to *B*, both *A* and *B* become equal in strength. How many students are there in sections *A* and *B*? **(R.R.B., 2006)**

(*a*) 80, 40 (*b*) 90, 40
(c) 45, 15 (*d*) 50, 30

488. Recently my brother and I played chess for chocolates. Whoever lost the game gave the other a chocolate. After the last game we counted the chocolates. I had 20 more chocolates than I started with, although he won 7 games. There were no draws. How many games did we play?

(*a*) 27 (*b*) 34
(c) 37 (*d*) 54

489. Robin says, "If Jai gives me ₹ 40, he will have half as much as Atul, but if Atul gives me ₹ 40, then the three of us will have the same amount." What is the total amount of money that Robin, Jai and Atul have between them?

(*a*) ₹ 240 (*b*) ₹ 320
(c) ₹ 360 (*d*) ₹ 420

490. *A*, *B*, *C* and *D* play a game of cards. *A* says to *B*, "If I give you 8 cards, you will have as many as *C* has and I shall have 3 less than what *C* has. Also, if I take 6 cards from *C*, I shall have twice as many as *D* has." If *B* and *D* together have 50 cards, how many cards has *A* got?

(*a*) 23 (*b*) 27
(c) 37 (*d*) 40

491. *A*, *B*, *C*, *D* and *E* play a game of cards. *A* says to *B*, "If you give me 3 cards, you will have as many as *E* has and if I give you 3 cards, you will have as many as *D* has." *A* and *B* together have 10 cards more than what *D* and *E* together have. If *B* has 2 cards more than what *C* has and the total number of cards be 133, how many cards does *B* have?

(*a*) 22 (*b*) 23
(c) 25 (*d*) 35

492. *A* gives *B* as many rupees as *B* has and *C* as many rupees as *C* has. Similarly, *B* then gives *A* and *C* as many rupees as each then has. *C*, similarly, then gives *A* and *B* as many rupees as each then has. If each finally has ₹ 16, with how many rupees does *A* start? **(M.B.A., 2010)**

(*a*) 26 (*b*) 28
(c) 30 (*d*) 32

493. Iqbal dealt some cards to Mushtaq and himself from a pack of playing cards and laid the rest aside. Iqbal then said to Mushtaq, "If you give me a certain number of your cards, I will have four times as many cards as you have. If I give you the same number of cards, I will have thrice as many cards as you." How many cards did Iqbal have?

(a) 9 (b) 12
(c) 31 (d) 35
(e) None of these

494. While out on picnic, a group of boys came upon an apple tree. One of the boys climbed the tree and picked enough apples for each boy to have three, with none left over. Then along came three boys, making it impossible to divide the picked apples evenly. However, after picking one more apple and adding it to the total, every boy had two apples, with none left over. How many apples were finally divided?

(a) 10 (b) 12
(c) 16 (d) 18

495. A teacher bought a certain number of friendship bands for the students in the classroom for Friendship Day celebrations. Each student gives a friendship band to every other student. However, on the Friendship Day, 2 students were absent as a result of which 122 friendship bands were not utilized. But one out of the two absent students came late. Find the number of friendship bands which finally remained unutilized.

(a) 57 (b) 59
(c) 62 (d) 64

496. Reena bought chocolates to distribute among her friends on her 18th birthday. If she gives 3 chocolates to each friend, one friend will get only 2 chocolates. Also, if she gives 2 chocolates to each friend, she will be left with 15 chocolates. How many chocolates did she buy?

(a) 44 (b) 47
(c) 50 (d) None of these

497. A certain organisation has three committees. Only two persons are members of all committees, but every pair of committees have three members in common. What is the least possible number of members on any one committee? **(Campus Recruitment, 2008)**

(a) 4 (b) 5
(c) 6 (d) None of these

498. In a certain game, each player scores either 2 points or 5 points. If n players score 2 points and m players score 5 points, and the total number of points scored is 50, what is the least possible difference between m and n?

(a) 1 (b) 3
(c) 5 (d) 7

499. A school has to buy at least 15 chairs within a budgetary ceiling of ₹ 2000. A chair with arms costs ₹ 160 and one without arms costs ₹ 100. What is the maximum number of chairs with arms that the school can buy?

(a) 7 (b) 8
(c) 9 (d) 12

500. On Monday, a certain animal shelter housed 55 cats and dogs. By Friday, exactly $\frac{1}{5}$ of the cats and $\frac{1}{4}$ of the dogs had been adopted; no new cats or dogs were brought to the shelter during this period. What is the greatest possible number of pets that could have been adopted from the animal shelter between Monday and Friday?

(a) 11 (b) 12
(c) 13 (d) 14

501. Out of two-thirds of the total number of basketball matches, a team has won 17 matches and lost 3 of them. What is the maximum number of matches that the team can lose and still win more than three-fourth of the total number of matches if it is true that no match can end in a tie?

(a) 3 (b) 4
(c) 5 (d) 6

502. Manick visited his cousin Aniket during the summer vacation. In the mornings, they both would go for swimming. In the evenings, they would play tennis. They would engage in at most one activity per day i.e., either they went swimming or played tennis each day. There were days when they took rest and stayed home all day long. There were 32 mornings when they did nothing, 18 evenings when they stayed at home, and a total of 28 days when they swam or played tennis. What duration of the summer vacation did Manick stay with Aniket? **(M.B.A. 2011)**

(a) 36 days (b) 39 days
(c) 46 days (d) 58 days

503. 10 cows can graze in a field for 15 days and 20 cows can graze in the same field for 10 days. For how many days can 30 cows graze in the field?

(a) 5 days (b) $7\frac{1}{2}$ days
(c) $7\frac{2}{3}$ days (d) $8\frac{1}{3}$ days
(e) Cannot be determined

504. Grass in a lawn grows equally thick and at a uniform rate. It takes 24 days for 70 cows and 60 days for 30 cows to eat the whole of the grass. How many cows are needed to eat the grass in 96 days?

(a) 18 (b) 20
(c) 24 (d) 36
(e) None of these

Directions *(Questions 505-506)***: *These questions are based on the following information:***

In a holy city, there are ten shrines and a certain number of holy lakes. A group of pilgrims stayed in the city for a few days and visited the shrines and lakes during their stay. At the end of the stay it turned out that in all each shrine was visited exactly by 4 pilgrims and each lake was visited exactly by 6 pilgrims. Each pilgrim visited exactly 5 shrines and 3 lakes.

505. The number of lakes in the holy city is

(*a*) 4 (*b*) 6
(*c*) 8 (*d*) 10

506. The number of pilgrims in the group is

(*a*) 4 (*b*) 6
(*c*) 8 (*d*) 10

507. From a number of apples, a man sells half the number of existing apples plus 1 to the first customer, sells $\frac{1}{3}$rd of the remaining apples plus 1 to the second customer and $\frac{1}{5}$th of the remaining apples plus 1 to the third customer. He then finds that he has 3 apples left. How many apples did he have originally?

(*a*) 15 (*b*) 18
(*c*) 20 (*d*) 25

508. Ravi has two examinations on Wednesday – Engineering Mathematics in the morning and Engineering Drawing in the afternoon. He has a fixed amount of time to read the textbooks of both these subjects on Tuesday. During this time he can read 80 pages of Engineering Mathematics and 100 pages of Engineering Drawing. Alternatively, he can also read 50 pages of Engineering Mathematics and 250 pages of Engineering Drawing. Assume that the amount of time it takes to read one page of the textbook of either subject is constant. Ravi is confident about Engineering Drawing and wants to devote full time to reading Engineering Mathematics. The number of Engineering Mathematics text book pages he can read on Tuesday is **(M.B.A., 2007)**

(*a*) 60 (*b*) 100
(*c*) 300 (*d*) 500

509. Rohan went to the post-office to buy five-rupee, two-rupee and one-rupee stamps. He paid the clerk ₹ 20, and since he had no change, he gave Rohan three more one-rupee stamps. If the number of stamps of each type that he had ordered initially was more than one, what was the total number of stamps that he bought?

(*a*) 8 (*b*) 9
(*c*) 10 (*d*) 12

510. Aditya went to a stationery shop to buy some Parker pens. Gel pens cost ₹ 300 each while fountain pens cost ₹ 400 each. Aditya spent a total of ₹ 3600 on pens. If he had bought as many fountain pens as the number of gel pens he actually bought and vice versa, he would have saved an amount equal to half the cost of one pen of one of the two types. Find the total number of pens he bought.

(*a*) 8 (*b*) 9
(*c*) 10 (*d*) 12

Directions *(Questions 511-513)***: *Study the following information carefully to answer these questions:***

A young girl Roopa leaves home with x flowers and goes to the bank of a nearby river. On the bank of the river, there are four places of worship, standing in a row. She dips all the x flowers into the river, the number of flowers doubles. Then, she enters the first place of worship and offers y flowers to the deity. She dips the remaining flowers into the river, and again the number of flowers doubles. She goes to the second place of worship and offers y flowers to the deity. She dips the remaining flowers into the river and again the number of flowers doubles. She goes to the third place of worship and offers y flowers to the deity. She dips the remaining flowers into the river and again the number of flowers doubles. She goes to the fourth place of worship and offers y flowers to the deity. Now she is left with no flowers in hand.

511. If Roopa leaves home with 30 flowers, the number of flowers she offers to each deity is

(*a*) 30 (*b*) 31
(*c*) 32 (*d*) 33

512. The minimum number of flowers that could be offered to each deity is

(*a*) 0 (*b*) 15
(*c*) 16 (*d*) Cannot be determined

513. The minimum number of flowers with which Roopa leaves home is

(*a*) 0 (*b*) 15
(*c*) 16 (*d*) Cannot be determined

514. The owner of a local jewellery store hired 3 watchmen to guard his diamonds, but a thief still got in and stole some diamonds. On the way out the thief met each watchman, one at a time. To each he gave $\frac{1}{2}$ of the diamonds he had then, and 2 more besides. He escaped with one diamond. How many did he steal originally?

(*a*) 25 (*b*) 36
(*c*) 40 (*d*) None of these

515. Three friends returning from a movie, stopped to eat at a restaurant. After dinner, they paid their bill and noticed a bowl of mints, at the front counter. Divya took $\frac{1}{3}$ of the mints, but returned four because she had a momentary pang of guilt. Reema then took one-fourth of what was left but returned three for similar reasons. Shweta then took half of the remainder but threw two back into the bowl. The bowl had only 17 mints left when the raid was over. How many mints were originally in the bowl?

(a) 31 (b) 38
(c) 41 (d) None of these

516. At a stationery shop it costs ₹ 185 for 4 gel-pens, 8 ball-point pens and one marker pen and ₹ 315 for 7 gel-pens, 15 ball-point pens and one marker pen. Then what would be the cost of one gel-pen, one ball-point pen and one marker pen?

(a) ₹ 45 (b) ₹ 55
(c) ₹ 60 (d) ₹ 70

517. In a cricket match, Team A scored 232 runs without losing a wicket. The score consisted of byes, wides and runs scored by two opening batsmen, Ram and Shyam. The runs scored by the two batsmen are 26 times wides. There are 8 more byes than wides. If the ratio of runs scored by Ram and Shyam is 6: 7, then the runs scored by Ram is (M.B.A., 2008)

(a) 88 (b) 96
(c) 102 (d) 112
(e) None of these

518. Balls are arranged in rows to form an equilateral triangle. The first row consists of one ball, the second row consists of two balls and so on. If 669 more balls are added, then all the balls can be arranged in the shape of a square and each of the sides then contains 8 balls less than each side of the triangle had. The initial number of balls is

(a) 1500 (b) 1540
(c) 1600 (d) 1690

Directions (*Questions 519 and 520*): *Refer to the data below and answer these questions:*

It took a group of men 5 days to shift 545 crates. Every day after the first, 6 more men than the previous day were put on the job. Also, every day after the first, each man, by arrangement, shifted 5 fewer crates than the earlier day. The result was that during the latter part of the period, the number of crates shifted per day began to go down.

519. What was the number of crates shifted on the third day?

(a) 26 (b) 137
(c) 152 (d) 169
(e) None of these

520. What was the number of men on the fifth day?

(a) 1 (b) 7
(c) 13 (d) 19
(e) None of these

521. $\frac{20+8\times0.5}{20-?}=12$. Find the value in place of (?)
[Indian Railway Group 'D' Exam, 2014]

(a) 2 (b) 8
(c) 18 (d) None of these

522. If $\frac{a}{b}+\frac{b}{a}=2$, then the value of $(a-b)$ is
[SSC—CHSL (10 + 2) Exam, 2015]

(a) 1 (b) 2
(c) –1 (d) 0

523. $24.96^2 \div (34.11 \div 20.05) + 67.96 - 89.11 = ?$
[IBPS—Bank Spl. Officers (IT) Exam, 2015]

(a) 884 (b) 346
(c) 252 (d) 424
(e) 366

524. If $\frac{x+1}{x-1}=\frac{a}{b}$ and $\frac{1-y}{1+y}=\frac{b}{a}$, then the value of $\frac{x-y}{1+xy}$ is
[SSC—CHSL (10+2) Exam, 2015]

(a) $\frac{2ab}{a^2-b^2}$ (b) $\frac{a^2-b^2}{2ab}$
(c) $\frac{a^2+b^2}{2ab}$ (d) $\frac{a^2-b^2}{ab}$

525. $200 \div 25 \times 4 + 12 - 3 = ?$
[United India Insurance Co. Ltd. (UIICL) Assistant (Online) Exam, 2015]

(a) 35 (b) 40
(c) 30 (d) 41
(e) 50

526. $14 \times 627 \div \sqrt{1089}=(?)^3+141$
[IDBI Bank Executive Officers Exam, 2015]

(a) $5\sqrt{5}$ (b) $(125)^3$
(c) 25 (d) 5
(e) None of these

527. Evaluate: (923 – 347) / ? = 32 [NICL—AAO Exam, 2015]

(a) 35 (b) 20
(c) 18 (d) 15
(e) 40

Direction: What approximate value will come in place of the question mark (?) in the following question? *(You are not expected to calculate the exact value).*

528. $1559.95 - 7.99 \times 24.96 - ?^2 = 1154$

[IBPS Bank PO/MT (Pre.) Exam, 2015]

(a) 14 (b) 24
(c) 32 (d) 18
(e) 8

529. Solve $1\frac{4}{5} + 20 - 280 \div 25 = ?$

[IBPS—RRB Office Assistant (Online) Exam, 2015]

(a) $8\frac{1}{5}$ (b) $9\frac{1}{2}$
(c) $11\frac{1}{2}$ (d) $10\frac{3}{5}$
(e) $12\frac{1}{5}$

530. $((64 - 38) \times 4) \div 13 = ?$

[IBPS—RRB Office Assistant (Online) Exam, 2015]

(a) 4 (b) 1
(c) 8 (d) 2
(e) 5

531. If $x + y = 2a$ then the value of $\frac{a}{x-a} + \frac{a}{y-a}$ is

[SSC—CHSL (10+2) Exam, 2015]

(a) 2 (b) 0
(c) –1 (d) 1

Directions (*Questions 532 to 533*): What approximate value should come in place of question mark(?) in the following questions? (*NOTE: You are not expected to calculate the exact value).*

532. $421 \div 35 \times 299.97 \div 25.05 = ?^2$

[IBPS—Bank PO/MT Exam, 2015]

(a) 22 (b) 24
(c) 28 (d) 12
(e) 18

533. $19.99 \times 15.98 + 224.98 + 125.02 = ?$

[IBPS—Bank PO/MT Exam, 2015]

(a) 620 (b) 580
(c) 670 (d) 560
(e) 520

534. $3625 \times ? = 1450$

[United India Insurance (UIICL) Assistant (Online) Exam, 2015]

(a) $\frac{1}{3}$ (b) $\frac{2}{5}$
(c) $\frac{1}{5}$ (d) $\frac{4}{5}$
(e) $\frac{3}{5}$

535. Solve: $128.43 + 30.21 + ? = 173$

[NICL—AAO Exam, 2015

(a) 35.66 (b) 29.66
(c) 43.66 (d) 24.66
(e) 14.36

536. Evaluate :$123 \times 999 + 123$

(a) 246999 (b) 123000
(c) 246000 (d) 123999

[ESIC—UDC Exam, 2016]

537. Simplify $\frac{(359+256)^2 + (359-256)^2}{359\times359 + 256\times256}$

[ESIC—UDC Exam, 2016]

(a) 1089 (b) 615
(c) 516 (d) 2

538. $84368 + 65466 - 72009 - 13964 = ?$

[SBI—Jr. Associates (Pre.) Exam, 2016]

(a) 61481 (b) 62921
(c) 63861 (d) 64241
(e) None of these

539. Solve $4376 + 3209 - 1784 + 97 = 3125 + ?$

[SBI—Jr. Associates (Pre.) Exam, 2016]

(a) 2713 (b) 2743
(c) 2773 (d) 2793
(e) 2737

540. Solve $14 \times 627 \div \sqrt{(1089)} = (?)^3 + 141$

[IBPS—Bank Spl. Officer (Marketing) Exam, 2016]

(a) $5\sqrt{5}$ (b) $(125)^3$
(c) 25 (d) 5
(e) None of these

541. If $\left(x + \frac{1}{x}\right) = 3$, then $\left(x^2 + \frac{1}{x^2}\right)$ is

[UPSSSC—Lower Subordinate (Pre.) Exam, 2016]

(a) $\frac{10}{3}$ (b) $\frac{82}{9}$
(c) 7 (d) 11

542. If $x + y + z = 0$, then, $x^3 + y^3 + z^3 + 3xyz$ is equal to

[CDS 2016]

(a) 0 (b) $6xyz$
(c) $12xyz$ (d) xyz

543. What is the remainder when 4^{96} is divided by 6?

[CDS 2016]

(a) 4 (b) 3
(c) 2 (d) 1

Direction: In the question given below, if the given mathematical symbols are changed from '+' to '÷', '–' to '×', '÷', to '–' and from '×' to '+', then choose your answers from the following options.

544. 67 × 119 + 17 – 27 ÷ 259 = ?

[DMRC—Customer Relationship Assistant (CRA) Exam, 2016]

(*a*) –13 (*b*) –3

(*c*) 4 (*d*) 7

545. $\dfrac{(0.73)^3+(0.27)^3}{(0.73)^2+(0.27)^2-0.73\times0.27}=?$

[UPSSSC—Lower Subordinate (Pre.) Exam, 2016]

(*a*) 0.27 (*b*) 0.4087

(*c*) 0.73 (*d*) 1

ANSWERS

1. (*c*)	2. (*b*)	3. (*a*)	4. (*a*)	5. (*c*)	6. (*c*)	7. (*e*)	8. (*b*)	9. (*b*)	10. (*d*)
11. (*b*)	12. (*d*)	13. (*d*)	14. (*c*)	15. (*a*)	16. (*a*)	17. (*c*)	18. (*c*)	19. (*a*)	20. (*a*)
21. (*c*)	22. (*c*)	23. (*c*)	24. (*d*)	25. (*c*)	26. (*d*)	27. (*c*)	28. (*c*)	29. (*a*)	30. (*a*)
31. (*c*)	32. (*b*)	33. (*a*)	34. (*d*)	35. (*c*)	36. (*b*)	37. (*b*)	38. (*d*)	39. (*d*)	40. (*e*)
41. (*e*)	42. (*a*)	43. (*e*)	44. (*c*)	45. (*e*)	46. (*d*)	47. (*e*)	48. (*d*)	49. (*a*)	50. (*d*)
51. (*a*)	52. (*d*)	53. (*d*)	54. (*a*)	55. (*d*)	56. (*a*)	57. (*b*)	58. (*d*)	59. (*a*)	60. (*c*)
61. (*c*)	62. (*c*)	63. (*d*)	64. (*d*)	65. (*b*)	66. (*d*)	67. (*b*)	68. (*b*)	69. (*c*)	70. (*d*)
71. (*d*)	72. (*b*)	73. (*c*)	74. (*d*)	75. (*c*)	76. (*d*)	77. (*a*)	78. (*c*)	79. (*c*)	80. (*a*)
81. (*c*)	82. (*c*)	83. (*c*)	84. (*a*)	85. (*d*)	86. (*a*)	87. (*d*)	88. (*b*)	89. (*c*)	90. (*c*)
91. (*a*)	92. (*a*)	93. (*e*)	94. (*c*)	95. (*a*)	96. (*c*)	97. (*b*)	98. (*a*)	99. (*c*)	100. (*c*)
101. (*b*)	102. (*b*)	103. (*d*)	104. (*b*)	105. (*a*)	106. (*c*)	107. (*b*)	108. (*c*)	109. (*a*)	110. (*b*)
111. (*d*)	112. (*a*)	113. (*c*)	114. (*b*)	115. (*c*)	116. (*d*)	117. (*b*)	118. (*b*)	119. (*b*)	120. (*c*)
121. (*d*)	122. (*b*)	123. (*d*)	124. (*a*)	125. (*c*)	126. (*c*)	127. (*c*)	128. (*d*)	129. (*c*)	130. (*d*)
131. (*c*)	132. (*a*)	133. (*c*)	134. (*a*)	135. (*e*)	136. (*e*)	137. (*b*)	138. (*d*)	139. (*b*)	140. (*b*)
141. (*d*)	142. (*d*)	143. (*b*)	144. (*a*)	145. (*c*)	146. (*d*)	147. (*a*)	148. (*b*)	149. (*a*)	150. (*b*)
151. (*b*)	152. (*c*)	153. (*c*)	154. (*c*)	155. (*c*)	156. (*b*)	157. (*d*)	158. (*a*)	159. (*b*)	160. (*d*)
161. (*a*)	162. (*d*)	163. (*b*)	164. (*d*)	165. (*c*)	166. (*b*)	167. (*d*)	168. (*b*)	169. (*a*)	170. (*b*)
171. (*d*)	172. (*a*)	173. (*a*)	174. (*c*)	175. (*b*)	176. (*c*)	177. (*a*)	178. (*d*)	179. (*d*)	180. (*c*)
181. (*a*)	182. (*a*)	183. (*c*)	184. (*e*)	185. (*b*)	186. (*d*)	187. (*c*)	188. (*d*)	189. (*a*)	190. (*e*)
191. (*e*)	192. (*c*)	193. (*d*)	194. (*c*)	195. (*b*)	196. (*a*)	197. (*b*)	198. (*a*)	199. (*b*)	200. (*a*)
201. (*d*)	202. (*c*)	203. (*c*)	204. (*c*)	205. (*b*)	206. (*b*)	207. (*d*)	208. (*c*)	209. (*b*)	210. (*d*)
211. (*b*)	212. (*b*)	213. (*c*)	214. (*c*)	215. (*a*)	216. (*a*)	217. (*b*)	218. (*c*)	219. (*a*)	220. (*b*)
221. (*c*)	222. (*d*)	223. (*d*)	224. (*d*)	225. (*b*)	226. (*a*)	227. (*d*)	228. (*a*)	229. (*d*)	230. (*e*)
231. (*e*)	232. (*c*)	233. (*b*)	234. (*b*)	235. (*c*)	236. (*d*)	237. (*a*)	238. (*c*)	239. (*c*)	240. (*b*)
241. (*a*)	242. (*e*)	243. (*d*)	244. (*b*)	245. (*d*)	246. (*c*)	247. (*c*)	248. (*c*)	249. (*c*)	250. (*c*)
251. (*c*)	252. (*a*)	253. (*c*)	254. (*c*)	255. (*c*)	256. (*c*)	257. (*d*)	258. (*c*)	259. (*b*)	260. (*b*)
261. (*c*)	262. (*d*)	263. (*d*)	264. (*a*)	265. (*d*)	266. (*b*)	267. (*c*)	268. (*e*)	269. (*a*)	270. (*b*)
271. (*b*)	272. (*b*)	273. (*b*)	274. (*b*)	275. (*b*)	276. (*c*)	277. (*a*)	278. (*a*)	279. (*d*)	280. (*c*)
281. (*c*)	282. (*b*)	283. (*a*)	284. (*c*)	285. (*b*)	286. (*c*)	287. (*a*)	288. (*c*)	289. (*c*)	290. (*d*)

291. (b)	292. (d)	293. (d)	294. (a)	295. (d)	296. (e)	297. (b)	298. (b)	299. (b)	300. (c)
301. (c)	302. (b)	303. (b)	304. (d)	305. (c)	306. (b)	307. (a)	308. (a)	309. (a)	310. (d)
311. (d)	312. (b)	313. (d)	314. (c)	315. (b)	316. (b)	317. (c)	318. (c)	319. (d)	320. (d)
321. (c)	322. (a)	323. (b)	324. (c)	325. (d)	326. (c)	327. (d)	328. (c)	329. (d)	330. (b)
331. (b)	332. (a)	333. (c)	334. (b)	335. (b)	336. (c)	337. (c)	338. (c)	339. (a)	340. (a)
341. (b)	342. (c)	343. (c)	344. (a)	345. (c)	346. (b)	347. (d)	348. (c)	349. (b)	350. (c)
351. (d)	352. (d)	353. (b)	354. (d)	355. (a)	356. (d)	357. (c)	358. (b)	359. (a)	360. (b)
361. (c)	362. (d)	363. (c)	364. (c)	365. (a)	366. (c)	367. (c)	368. (d)	369. (c)	370. (d)
371. (c)	372. (c)	373. (b)	374. (b)	375. (d)	376. (d)	377. (d)	378. (d)	379. (d)	380. (c)
381. (c)	382. (c)	383. (c)	384. (a)	385. (d)	386. (a)	387. (b)	388. (c)	389. (c)	390. (d)
391. (b)	392. (a)	393. (a)	394. (d)	395. (d)	396. (d)	397. (a)	398. (a)	399. (d)	400. (c)
401. (a)	402. (b)	403. (c)	404. (a)	405. (a)	406. (d)	407. (a)	408. (b)	409. (b)	410. (d)
411. (c)	412. (e)	413. (c)	414. (c)	415. (a)	416. (a)	417. (c)	418. (c)	419. (c)	420. (d)
421. (b)	422. (c)	423. (c)	424. (c)	425. (c)	426. (b)	427. (e)	428. (b)	429. (b)	430. (b)
431. (b)	432. (c)	433. (b)	434. (d)	435. (c)	436. (b)	437. (d)	438. (e)	439. (d)	440. (a)
441. (b)	442. (b)	443. (d)	444. (b)	445. (c)	446. (b)	447. (d)	448. (c)	449. (a)	450. (d)
451. (c)	452. (c)	453. (a)	454. (a)	455. (a)	456. (d)	457. (b)	458. (d)	459. (d)	460. (a)
461. (d)	462. (b)	463. (e)	464. (d)	465. (b)	466. (b)	467. (b)	468. (d)	469. (c)	470. (b)
471. (e)	472. (d)	473. (e)	474. (e)	475. (b)	476. (c)	477. (c)	478. (c)	479. (d)	480. (b)
481. (d)	482. (b)	483. (a)	484. (b)	485. (b)	486. (b)	487. (d)	488. (b)	489. (c)	490. (d)
491. (c)	492. (a)	493. (c)	494. (c)	495. (c)	496. (b)	497. (a)	498. (b)	499. (b)	500. (c)
501. (b)	502. (b)	503. (b)	504. (b)	505. (a)	506. (c)	507. (c)	508. (b)	509. (c)	510. (c)
511. (c)	512. (c)	513. (b)	514. (b)	515. (d)	516. (b)	517. (b)	518. (b)	519. (d)	520. (e)
521. (c)	522. (d)	523. (b)	524. (a)	525. (d)	526. (d)	527. (c)	528. (a)	529. (d)	530. (c)
531. (b)	532. (d)	533. (c)	534. (b)	535. (e)	536. (b)	537. (d)	538. (c)	539. (c)	540. (d)
541. (c)	542. (b)	543. (a)	544. (b)	545. (a)					

SOLUTIONS

1. $304 \times 141 = 42864$.

2. $A + B = 96 \Rightarrow \frac{1}{2}B + B = 96 \Rightarrow \frac{3}{2}B = 96 \Rightarrow B = \left(96 \times \frac{2}{3}\right) = 64.$

   $\therefore\ A = \left(\frac{1}{2} \times 64\right) = 32.$

3. $1888 \div 32 \div 8 = \frac{1888}{32} \div 8 = 59 \div 8 = \frac{59}{8} = 7.375.$

4. Given exp. $= -2508 + 221 = -2287$.

5. Given exp. $= \frac{4848}{24} \times 11 - 222 = 202 \times 11 - 222$

   $= 2222 - 222 = 2000.$

6. Given exp. $= \frac{425 \times 4000}{16000} \times 12 = \frac{425}{4} \times 12 = 425 \times 3 = 1275.$

7. Let $[(84)^2 \div 28 \times 12] \div 24 = 7 \times x$.

   Then, $\left[\frac{84 \times 84}{28} \times 12\right] \div 24 = 7x \Leftrightarrow [84 \times 3 \times 12] \div 24 = 7x$

   $\Leftrightarrow 7x = \frac{3024}{24} = 126 \Leftrightarrow x = 18.$

8. Let the missing number be x.

   Then, $\frac{354750}{4096 + x} = 55 \Leftrightarrow 55(4096 + x) = 354750$

   $\Leftrightarrow 55x = 354750 - 225280$

   $\Leftrightarrow 55x = 129470 \Leftrightarrow x = 2354.$

9. Given expression = 41 × 44 = 1804.

10. Given expression = (– 224) + 2826 = 2602.

11. Let 853 + x ÷ 17 = 1000.

Then, $853+\frac{x}{17}=1000 \Leftrightarrow \frac{x}{17}=1000-853=147$

$\Leftrightarrow x = 147 \times 17 = 2499.$

12. Let (x – 968) ÷ 79 × 4 = 512.

Then, $\frac{x-968}{79}\times 4=512 \Leftrightarrow x-968=\frac{512\times 79}{4}=10112$

$\Leftrightarrow x = 10112 + 968 = 11080.$

13. Given exp. $=\left[\frac{125\times 125}{50}\times 20\right]\div 25 = 6250 \div 25 = 250.$

14. Given exp. $=999\times 99\times\frac{9}{99}\div 9\div 3 = 999\times 99\times\frac{9}{99}\times\frac{1}{9}\div 3$

$=999\times 99\times\frac{9}{99}\times\frac{1}{9}\times\frac{1}{3} = 333.$

15. $(x - a)(x - b)(x - c) \ldots (x - y)(x - z)$

$= (x - a)(x - b)(x - c) \ldots (x - x)(x - y)(x - z)$

$= \{(x - a)(x - b)(x - c) \ldots (x - w)\} \times 0 \times [(x - y)(x - z)]$

$= 0.$

16. Given exp. = 1 – [1 – {1 – (1 – 0)}] = 1 – [1 – {1 – 1}]

= 1 – [1 – 0] = 1 – 1 = 0.

17. Let 2 x 6 – 12 ÷ 4 + 2 = 11.

Then, 2 x 6 – 3 + 2 = 11 ⇔ 2 x 6 = 11 + 3 – 2 = 12.

So 'x' must be replaced by '×'.

18. Let 45 – [28 – {37 – (15 – x)}] = 58.

Then, 45 – [28 – {37 – 15 + x}] = 58

⇔ 45 – [28 – {22 + x}] = 58

⇔ 45 – [28 – 22 – x] = 58 ⇔ 45 – [6 – x] = 58

⇔ 45 – 6 + x = 58

⇔ 39 + x = 58 ⇔ x = 58 – 39 = 19.

19. Given exp. $=\frac{7^3\times 7^2}{6^3\times 2^4\times 3^4}=\frac{7^{(3+2)}}{6^3\times(2\times 3)^4}=\frac{7^5}{6^3\times 6^4}$

$=\frac{7^5}{6^{(3+4)}}=\frac{7^5}{6^7}.$

20. $\frac{113\times 4-x\times 2}{13\times 9-5\times 7}=5 \Leftrightarrow \frac{452-2x}{117-35}=5 \Leftrightarrow \frac{452-2x}{82}=5$

$\Leftrightarrow 452 - 2x = 410$

$\Leftrightarrow 2x = 452 - 410 = 42 \Leftrightarrow x = 21.$

21. Given expression $=\frac{252-48}{122-20}=\frac{204}{102}=2.$

22. Given expression $=\frac{15}{21}-\frac{10}{14}+\frac{5}{7}=\frac{5}{7}-\frac{5}{7}+\frac{5}{7}=\frac{5}{7}.$

23. Given expression $=\frac{3+2\times 3}{4+3\times\frac{2}{3}}=\frac{3+6}{4+2}=\frac{9}{6}=\frac{3}{2}.$

24. Given expression $=\frac{4+72-14}{738-730}=\frac{76-14}{8}=\frac{62}{8}=7.75.$

25. Given expression $=\frac{2700-240}{1120+110}=\frac{2460}{1230}=2.$

26. Given exp. $=\frac{8-[5-(-1)]\div 2}{|2|-|-3|\div 3}=\frac{8-[5+1]\div 2}{2-3\div 3}=\frac{8-6\div 2}{2-1}$

$= 8 - 3 = 5.$

27. $(2^2 + 4^2 + 6^2 + \ldots + 20^2) = 2^2(1^2 + 2^2 + 3^2 + \ldots + 10^2)$

$= 4 \times 385 = 1540.$

28. Given exp. $=\frac{9}{4}+\frac{4}{3}-\frac{9}{2}=\frac{27+16-54}{12}=-\frac{11}{12}.$

29. Let $4\frac{3}{7}-1\frac{3}{14}=x+2\frac{3}{28}.$

Then, $\frac{31}{7}-\frac{17}{14}=x+\frac{59}{28} \Leftrightarrow x=\frac{31}{7}-\frac{17}{14}-\frac{59}{28}$

$\Leftrightarrow x=\frac{124-34-59}{28}=\frac{31}{28}=1\frac{3}{28}.$

30. Given exp. $=\frac{7}{4}-\frac{6}{5}+\frac{13}{8}=\frac{70-48+65}{40}=\frac{87}{40}=2\frac{7}{40}.$

31. Given exp. $=\frac{37}{3}+\frac{65}{6}-\frac{23}{3}-\frac{11}{7}=\frac{518+455-322-66}{42}$

$=\frac{585}{42}=\frac{195}{14}=13\frac{13}{14}.$

32. Given exp. $=\frac{87}{13}-\frac{48}{11}+\frac{12}{5}=\frac{4785-3120+1716}{715}$

$=\frac{3381}{715}=4\frac{521}{715}.$

33. Given exp. $=\frac{28+14+7+4+2+1}{28}=\frac{56}{28}=2.$

34. Given exp. $=\frac{1}{(7/3)}+\frac{1}{(7/4)}=\frac{3}{7}+\frac{4}{7}=\frac{7}{7}=1.$

35. Let $\frac{35}{6}-\frac{35}{9}-x=1.$

Then, $x=\frac{35}{6}-\frac{35}{9}-1=\frac{35}{6}-\left(\frac{35}{9}+1\right)$

$=\frac{35}{6}-\frac{44}{9}=\frac{105-88}{18}=\frac{17}{18}.$

36. $\frac{1}{x}=4-\left(\frac{1}{3}+\frac{1}{2}\right)=4-\left(\frac{2+3}{6}\right)=4-\frac{5}{6}$

$=\frac{24-5}{6}=\frac{19}{6} \Rightarrow x=\frac{6}{19}.$

37. $\frac{\overset{19}{\cancel{\overset{133}{\cancel{532}}}}}{\underset{3}{\cancel{\underset{81}{\cancel{648}}}}}\times\frac{\overset{2}{\cancel{\overset{54}{\cancel{432}}}}}{\underset{21}{\cancel{\underset{147}{\cancel{588}}}}}=\frac{38}{63}.$

38. Given expression $=\frac{\overset{3}{\cancel{21}}}{\cancel{11}}\times\frac{\overset{11}{\cancel{121}}}{\cancel{7}}\times\frac{217}{\underset{2}{\cancel{6}}}=\frac{2387}{2}=1193\frac{1}{2}.$

39. Given expression $=\left(\frac{3}{7}\times 455+\frac{5}{8}\times 456\right)=(3\times 65+5\times 57)$

= 195 + 285 = 480.

40. Given expression $=\left(\frac{3}{5}\times\frac{4}{7}\times\frac{5}{9}\times\frac{21}{24}\times 504\right)=84.$

41. Given exp. $= \left(\frac{41}{6}\times\frac{16}{3}+\frac{53}{3}\times\frac{9}{2}\right)=\left(\frac{328}{9}+\frac{159}{2}\right)$

$= \frac{656+1431}{18}=\frac{2087}{18}=115\frac{17}{18}.$

42. Given exp. $= \frac{24}{5}\div\frac{32}{5}=\frac{24}{5}\times\frac{5}{32}=\frac{3}{4}.$

43. Given exp. $= \frac{5}{4}+\frac{14}{9}\times\frac{13}{8}\times\frac{2}{13}=\frac{5}{4}+\frac{7}{18}=\frac{45+14}{36}=\frac{59}{36}=1\frac{23}{36}.$

44. Given exp. $= \frac{225}{836}\times\frac{152}{245}\div\frac{120}{77}=\frac{225}{836}\times\frac{152}{245}\times\frac{77}{120}=\frac{3}{28}.$

45. Given exp. $= \left(\frac{82}{5}-\frac{181}{15}\right)\div\frac{247}{81}=\left(\frac{246-181}{15}\right)\times\frac{81}{247}$

$= \frac{65}{15}\times\frac{81}{247}=\frac{27}{19}=1\frac{8}{19}.$

46. Let $18\frac{3}{4}\times x\div\frac{6}{37}=1480.$

Then, $\frac{75}{4}\times x\times\frac{37}{6}=1480 \Leftrightarrow x=\frac{1480\times4\times6}{75\times37}=\frac{64}{5}=12\frac{4}{5}.$

47. Given exp. $= \frac{3}{2}\times\frac{11}{5}\div\frac{5}{4}\div\frac{33}{15}=\frac{3}{2}\times\frac{11}{5}\times\frac{4}{5}\div\frac{33}{15}$

$= \frac{3}{2}\times\frac{11}{5}\times\frac{4}{5}\times\frac{15}{33}=\frac{6}{5}=1\frac{1}{5}.$

48. $3\frac{x}{7}\times2\frac{y}{5}=10 \Leftrightarrow \frac{21+x}{7}\times\frac{10+y}{5}=10$

$\Leftrightarrow (21+x)(10+y)=350$ ...(*i*)

Clearly, $x = 4$, $y = 4$ satisfy the equation (*i*).

49. Given exp. $= 1+2\div\left\{1+2\div\frac{4}{3}\right\}=1+2\div\left\{1+2\times\frac{3}{4}\right\}$

$= 1+2\div\left\{1+\frac{3}{2}\right\}=1+2\div\frac{5}{2}=1+2\times\frac{2}{5}$

$= 1+\frac{4}{5}=\frac{9}{5}=1\frac{4}{5}.$

50. Given exp. $= \frac{\overset{27}{\cancel{81}}}{\underset{2}{\cancel{8}}}\text{ of }\frac{\overset{3}{\cancel{12}}}{\underset{5}{\cancel{15}}}\div\frac{\overset{5}{\cancel{35}}}{\underset{9}{\cancel{36}}}\text{ of }\frac{\overset{5}{\cancel{20}}}{\underset{7}{\cancel{49}}}=\frac{81}{10}\div\frac{25}{63}$

$= \frac{81}{10}\times\frac{63}{25}=\frac{5103}{250}=20\frac{103}{250}.$

51. Given exp. $= \frac{\left(-\frac{2}{3}-\frac{1}{3}\right)+\left(\frac{4}{5}+\frac{1}{5}\right)+\left(\frac{3}{4}-\frac{1}{2}\right)}{\left(\frac{2}{3}-\frac{4}{3}+\frac{1}{3}\right)-\left(\frac{1}{5}+\frac{4}{5}\right)+\frac{1}{2}}$

$= \frac{-1+1+\frac{1}{4}}{-\frac{1}{3}-1+\frac{1}{2}}=\frac{\frac{1}{4}}{\frac{-2-6+3}{6}}=\frac{\frac{1}{4}}{-\frac{5}{6}}$

$= \frac{1}{4}\times\left(-\frac{6}{5}\right)=\frac{-3}{10}.$

52. $\frac{\left(\frac{1}{2}-\frac{1}{4}+\frac{1}{5}-\frac{1}{6}\right)}{\left(\frac{2}{5}-\frac{5}{9}+\frac{3}{5}-\frac{7}{18}\right)}=\frac{\left(\frac{30-15+12-10}{60}\right)}{\left(\frac{2}{5}+\frac{3}{5}\right)-\left(\frac{5}{9}+\frac{7}{18}\right)}$

$= \frac{\left(\frac{17}{60}\right)}{1-\frac{17}{18}}=\left(\frac{17}{60}\times18\right)=\frac{51}{10}=5\frac{1}{10}.$

53. $\left(34\times4\frac{1}{2}\right)=34\times\left(4+\frac{1}{2}\right)=(34\times4)+\left(34\times\frac{1}{2}\right)$

$= (30+4)\times4+\left(34\times\frac{1}{2}\right)$

$= (30\times4)+(4\times4)+\left(34\times\frac{1}{2}\right).$

54. Let $\frac{3}{8}$ of $168\times15\div5+x=549\div9+235.$

Then, $63\times15\div5+x=61+235 \Leftrightarrow 63\times3+x=296$

$\Leftrightarrow 189+x=296$

$\Leftrightarrow x=107.$

55. Let $\frac{5}{3}\div\frac{2}{7}\times\frac{x}{7}=\frac{5}{4}\times\frac{2}{3}\div\frac{1}{6}.$

Then, $\frac{5}{3}\times\frac{7}{2}\times\frac{x}{7}=\frac{5}{4}\times\frac{2}{3}\times6$

$\Leftrightarrow \frac{5}{6}x=5 \Leftrightarrow x=\left(\frac{5\times6}{5}\right)=6.$

56. Let $5\frac{2}{3}\div x\frac{5}{6}=2.$

Then, $\frac{17}{3}\div x\frac{5}{6}=2 \Leftrightarrow x\frac{5}{6}=\frac{17}{3}\times\frac{1}{2}=\frac{17}{6} \Leftrightarrow x\frac{5}{6}=2\frac{5}{6}.$

$\therefore \quad x=2.$

57. Given equation is : $\frac{(5x+1)}{x}\times\frac{(4y+3)}{4}=20$

$\Leftrightarrow (5x+1)(4y+3)=80x$ ...(*i*)

Clearly, $x = 3$ and $y = 3$ satisfy (*i*).

58. Required difference $= \frac{19}{16}-\frac{16}{19}=\frac{19^2-16^2}{304}$

$= \frac{(19+16)(19-16)}{304}=\frac{35\times3}{304}=\frac{105}{304}.$

59. Required number $= \frac{37\frac{1}{2}}{1/8}=\frac{75/2}{1/8}=\frac{75}{2}\times8=300.$

60. $a=(4\div3)\div3\div4=\frac{4}{3}\times\frac{1}{3}\times\frac{1}{4}=\frac{1}{9}.$

$b=4\div(3\div3)\div4=4\div1\div4=1.$

$c=4\div3\div(3\div4)=4\div3\div\frac{3}{4}=\frac{4}{3}\times\frac{4}{3}=\frac{16}{9}.$

Clearly, c is the greatest.

61. I. $\frac{3}{4}\div\frac{5}{6}=\frac{3}{4}\times\frac{6}{5}=\frac{9}{10}.$

II. $3\div[(4\div5)\div6]=3\div\left(\frac{4}{5}\times\frac{1}{6}\right)=3\div\frac{4}{30}=3\times\frac{30}{4}=\frac{45}{2}.$

III. $[3\div(4\div5)]\div6=\left[3\div\frac{4}{5}\right]\div6=\left[3\times\frac{5}{4}\right]\div6=\frac{15}{4}\times\frac{1}{6}=\frac{5}{8}.$

IV. $3\div4\div(5\div6)=3\div4\div\frac{5}{6}=\frac{3}{4}\times\frac{6}{5}=\frac{9}{10}.$

So, I and IV are equal.

62. Given exp. $= \left(\frac{5}{7}\times\frac{19}{13}\right)\div\left(\frac{19}{7}\times\frac{4}{13}\right)=\frac{5\times19}{7\times13}\times\frac{7\times13}{19\times4}=\frac{5}{4}.$

63. Given exp. $=\frac{11}{4}\div\frac{8}{3}\div\frac{13}{12}=\frac{11}{4}\times\frac{3}{8}\times\frac{12}{13}=\frac{99}{104}.$

64. Given exp. $=\frac{2}{3}\times\frac{3}{\frac{5}{6}\div\frac{2}{3}\text{ of }\frac{5}{4}}=\frac{2}{3}\times\frac{3}{\frac{5}{6}\div\frac{5}{6}}=\frac{2}{3}\times3=2.$

65. Let $\frac{4335}{x}\div\frac{15}{8}=\frac{289}{528}.$

Then, $\frac{4335}{x}=\frac{289}{528}\times\frac{15}{8}\Leftrightarrow\frac{4335}{x}=\frac{289\times5}{176\times8}$

$\Leftrightarrow x=\left(\frac{4335\times176\times8}{289\times5}\right)=4224.$

$\therefore$ Missing digit = 2.

66. Let $\frac{16}{3}-\frac{11}{3}\div\frac{4}{3}\div x+\frac{16}{5}\div\frac{6}{5}=7.$ Then,

$\frac{16}{3}-\frac{11}{3}\times\frac{3}{4}\times\frac{1}{x}+\frac{16}{5}\times\frac{5}{6}=7$

$\Leftrightarrow\frac{16}{3}-\frac{11}{4x}+\frac{8}{3}=7$

$\Leftrightarrow\frac{24}{3}-\frac{11}{4x}=7$

$\Leftrightarrow\frac{11}{4x}=8-7=1$

$\Leftrightarrow 4x=11\Leftrightarrow x=\frac{11}{4}=2\frac{3}{4}.$

67. Given exp. $=9-\frac{11}{9}\text{ of }\frac{36}{11}\div\frac{36}{7}\text{ of }\frac{7}{9}=9-4\div4=9-1=8.$

68. Let $\frac{5}{6}\div\frac{6}{7}\times x-\frac{8}{9}\div\frac{8}{5}+\frac{3}{4}\times\frac{10}{3}=\frac{25}{9}.$ Then,

$\frac{5}{6}\times\frac{7}{6}\times x-\frac{8}{9}\times\frac{5}{8}+\frac{3}{4}\times\frac{10}{3}=\frac{25}{9}\Leftrightarrow\frac{35}{36}x-\frac{5}{9}+\frac{5}{2}=\frac{25}{9}$

$\Leftrightarrow\frac{35}{36}x=\frac{25}{9}+\frac{5}{9}-\frac{5}{2}=\frac{10}{3}-\frac{5}{2}$

$\Leftrightarrow\frac{35}{36}x=\frac{5}{6}\Leftrightarrow x=\left(\frac{5}{6}\times\frac{36}{35}\right)=\frac{6}{7}.$

69. Given exp. $=\frac{3}{4}\div\frac{9}{4}\text{ of }\frac{2}{3}-\frac{\left(\frac{3-2}{6}\right)}{\left(\frac{3+2}{6}\right)}\times\frac{10}{3}+\frac{5}{6}$

$=\frac{3}{4}\div\frac{3}{2}-\frac{1}{6}\times\frac{6}{5}\times\frac{10}{3}+\frac{5}{6}$

$=\frac{3}{4}\times\frac{2}{3}-\frac{2}{3}+\frac{5}{6}=\left(\frac{1}{2}-\frac{2}{3}+\frac{5}{6}\right)$

$=\left(\frac{3-4+5}{6}\right)=\frac{4}{6}=\frac{2}{3}.$

70. $\frac{\frac{7}{3}+1\frac{1}{2}\text{ of }\frac{5}{3}}{2+1\frac{2}{3}}=\frac{\frac{7}{3}+\frac{3}{2}\text{ of }\frac{5}{3}}{2+\frac{5}{3}}=\frac{\frac{7}{3}+\frac{5}{2}}{\frac{11}{3}}=\frac{29}{6}\times\frac{3}{11}=\frac{29}{22}.$

$\therefore$ Required answer $=\frac{29}{22}-\frac{1}{4}=\frac{58-11}{44}=\frac{47}{44}=1\frac{3}{44}.$

71. Given exp. $=\frac{\frac{1}{3}+\frac{3}{4}\left(\frac{6-5}{15}\right)}{\frac{5}{3}\text{ of }\frac{3}{4}-\frac{1}{5}}=\frac{\frac{1}{3}+\frac{3}{4}\times\frac{1}{15}}{\frac{5}{4}-\frac{1}{5}}$

$=\frac{\frac{1}{3}+\frac{1}{20}}{\frac{25-4}{20}}=\frac{23}{60}\times\frac{20}{21}=\frac{23}{63}.$

72. Given exp. $=1-\left(\frac{\frac{5}{3}}{\frac{7}{2}}+\frac{\frac{7}{6}}{\frac{7}{2}}\right)=1-\left(\frac{5}{3}\times\frac{2}{7}+\frac{7}{6}\times\frac{2}{7}\right)$

$=1-\left(\frac{10}{21}+\frac{1}{3}\right)=1-\frac{17}{21}=\frac{4}{21}.$

73. Given exp. $=\frac{5}{2}\text{ of }\frac{3}{4}\times\frac{1}{2}\div\frac{3}{2}+\frac{1}{2}\div\frac{3}{2}\left[\frac{2}{3}-\frac{1}{3}\right]$

$=\frac{5}{2}\text{ of }\frac{3}{4}\times\frac{1}{2}\div\frac{3}{2}+\frac{1}{2}\div\left(\frac{3}{2}\times\frac{1}{3}\right)$

$=\frac{15}{8}\times\frac{1}{2}\div\frac{3}{2}+\frac{1}{2}\div\frac{1}{2}$

$=\frac{15}{8}\times\frac{1}{2}\times\frac{2}{3}+\frac{1}{2}\times2=\frac{5}{8}+1=1\frac{5}{8}.$

74. Given exp. $=\frac{\frac{8}{7}-\frac{2}{3}+\frac{2}{5}\times\frac{25}{24}}{1-\frac{1}{7}\left[\frac{1}{3}+\frac{2}{5}\times\frac{5}{3}\right]}=\frac{\frac{8}{7}-\frac{2}{3}+\frac{5}{12}}{1-\frac{1}{7}\left[\frac{1}{3}+\frac{2}{3}\right]}$

$=\frac{\frac{96-56+35}{84}}{\left(1-\frac{1}{7}\right)}=\frac{75}{84}\times\frac{7}{6}=\frac{25}{24}=1\frac{1}{24}.$

75. Given exp. $=\frac{6}{\left(\frac{10}{3}\right)}\div\frac{4-\frac{2}{\left(\frac{7}{2}\right)}}{\left(\frac{7}{2}\right)}-\frac{2}{5}\text{ of }\left\{\frac{6}{9}+\frac{1}{3}\right\}$

$=\frac{6\times3}{10}\div\frac{4-\frac{2\times2}{7}}{\left(\frac{7}{2}\right)}-\frac{2}{5}\text{ of }1$

$=\frac{9}{5}\div\frac{\left(4-\frac{4}{7}\right)}{\left(\frac{7}{2}\right)}-\frac{2}{5}=\frac{9}{5}\div\left(\frac{24}{7}\times\frac{2}{7}\right)-\frac{2}{5}$

$=\frac{9}{5}\times\frac{49}{48}-\frac{2}{5}=\frac{147}{80}-\frac{2}{5}=\frac{147-32}{80}=\frac{115}{80}=\frac{23}{16}=1\frac{7}{16}.$

76. Given exp. $=\left(\frac{45}{8}\times\frac{7}{45}\right)\text{ of }\left(\frac{73}{11}\times\frac{8}{73}\right)\div\frac{8}{9}\left(\frac{25}{11}+\frac{13}{22}\right)\text{ of }\frac{3}{5}$

$=\frac{7}{8}\text{ of }\frac{8}{11}\div\left(\frac{8}{9}\times\frac{63}{22}\right)\text{ of }\frac{3}{5}$

$=\frac{7}{11}\div\frac{28}{11}\textit{ of }\frac{3}{5}=\frac{7}{11}\div\frac{84}{55}=\frac{7}{11}\times\frac{55}{84}=\frac{5}{12}.$

77. Given exp. $= \dfrac{\frac{1}{3}\times 3\times\frac{1}{3}}{\frac{1}{3}\div\frac{1}{9}} - \dfrac{1}{9} = \dfrac{\frac{1}{3}}{\frac{1}{3}\times 9} - \dfrac{1}{9} = \dfrac{1}{3}\times\dfrac{1}{3} - \dfrac{1}{9} = \dfrac{1}{9} - \dfrac{1}{9} = 0.$

78. Given exp. $= \dfrac{\frac{1}{2}\div\frac{1}{4}}{\frac{1}{2}+\frac{1}{4}} = \dfrac{\frac{1}{2}\times 4}{\frac{2+1}{4}} = 2\times\dfrac{4}{3} = \dfrac{8}{3} = 2\dfrac{2}{3}.$

79. Given exp. $= \dfrac{\frac{13}{4}-\frac{4}{5}\text{ of }\frac{5}{6}}{\frac{13}{3}\div\frac{1}{5}-\left(\frac{3}{10}+\frac{106}{5}\right)} = \dfrac{\frac{13}{4}-\frac{2}{3}}{\frac{13}{3}\times 5-\frac{215}{10}}$

$= \dfrac{\frac{31}{12}}{\frac{65}{3}-\frac{43}{2}} = \left(\dfrac{31}{12}\times 6\right) = \dfrac{31}{2} = 15\dfrac{1}{2}.$

80. Let $\dfrac{\frac{15}{2}-\frac{23}{4}}{\frac{7}{2}+x} \div \dfrac{\frac{1}{2}+\frac{5}{4}}{\frac{6}{5}+\frac{7}{2}} = \dfrac{6}{10}.$

Then, $\left[\dfrac{7}{4}\times\dfrac{2}{(7+2x)}\right]\div\left[\dfrac{7}{4}\times\dfrac{10}{47}\right] = \dfrac{3}{5}$

$\Leftrightarrow \dfrac{7}{2(7+2x)} = \dfrac{3}{5}\times\dfrac{7}{4}\times\dfrac{10}{47} = \dfrac{21}{94}$

$\Leftrightarrow 7+2x = \left(\dfrac{7}{2}\times\dfrac{94}{21}\right) = \dfrac{47}{3}$

$\Leftrightarrow 2x = \dfrac{47}{3} - 7 = \dfrac{26}{3} \quad \Leftrightarrow x = \left(\dfrac{26}{3}\times\dfrac{1}{2}\right) = \dfrac{13}{3} = 4\dfrac{1}{3}.$

81. $\dfrac{5}{3}+\dfrac{3}{4} = \dfrac{20+9}{12} = \dfrac{29}{12} = 2\dfrac{5}{12} < 5;\ \dfrac{7}{3}+\dfrac{11}{5}$

$= \dfrac{35+33}{15} = \dfrac{68}{15} = 4\dfrac{8}{15} < 5;$

$\dfrac{11}{4}+\dfrac{8}{3} = \dfrac{33+32}{12} = \dfrac{65}{12} = 5\dfrac{5}{12} > 5;\ \dfrac{13}{5}+\dfrac{11}{6}$

$= \dfrac{78+55}{30} = \dfrac{133}{30} = 4\dfrac{13}{30} < 5.$

82. Given exp. $= 5 - \left[\dfrac{3}{4}+\left\{\dfrac{5}{2}-\left(\dfrac{1}{2}+\dfrac{7-6}{42}\right)\right\}\right]$

$= 5 - \left[\dfrac{3}{4}+\left\{\dfrac{5}{2}-\left(\dfrac{1}{2}+\dfrac{1}{42}\right)\right\}\right]$

$= 5 - \left[\dfrac{3}{4}+\left\{\dfrac{5}{2}-\dfrac{22}{42}\right\}\right] = 5 - \left[\dfrac{3}{4}+\dfrac{83}{42}\right] = 5 - \dfrac{229}{84}$

$= \left(\dfrac{420-229}{84}\right) = \dfrac{191}{84} = 2\dfrac{23}{84}.$

83. Given exp. $= -1 + 4 + 3 = 6.$

84. $x^3 - x^2 - x = (-3)^3 - (-3)^2 - (-3) = -27 - 9 + 3 = -33.$

85. Putting $S = 8$ and $R = 16$, we have:

$R = gS - 4 \Leftrightarrow 16 = 8g - 4$

$\Leftrightarrow 8g = 20 \Leftrightarrow g = \dfrac{20}{8} = \dfrac{5}{2}.$

$\therefore$ When $S = 10$, $R = gS - 4$

$\Leftrightarrow R = \dfrac{5}{2}\times 10 - 4 = 25 - 4 = 21.$

86. $\dfrac{x(y-z)}{y(x+y+z)} = \dfrac{5(3-2)}{3(5+3+2)} = \dfrac{5}{3\times 10} = \dfrac{1}{6}.$

87. $a^3 - b^3 + 3a^2b = 7^3 - 5^3 + 3\times 7^2\times 5$
$= 343 - 125 + 735 = 953.$

88. Given exp. $= -7m - [3n - \{8m - 4n + 10m\}]$
$= -7m - [3n - \{18m - 4n\}]$
$= -7m - [3n - 18m + 4n] = -7m - [7n - 18m]$
$= -7m - 7n + 18m = 11m - 7n.$

89. $\dfrac{2}{a}+\dfrac{1}{b} = \dfrac{2b+a}{ab} = \dfrac{6}{4} = \dfrac{3}{2}.$

90. Let $\dfrac{a}{3} = \dfrac{b}{4} = \dfrac{c}{7} = k.$ Then, $a = 3k$, $b = 4k$, $c = 7k$.

$\therefore \dfrac{(a+b+c)}{c} = \dfrac{3k+4k+7k}{7k} = \dfrac{14k}{7k} = 2.$

91. Given exp. $= 2a^3 - [3a^3 + 4b^3 - \{-5a^3\} + 5a^3 - 7b^3]$
$= 2a^3 - [3a^3 + 4b^3 + 5a^3 + 5a^3 - 7b^3]$
$= 2a^3 - [13a^3 - 3b^3] = 2a^3 - 13a^3 + 3b^3$
$= -11a^3 + 3b^3.$

92. $\dfrac{1}{1+a}+\dfrac{1}{1+b}+\dfrac{1}{1+c} = \dfrac{1}{1+\frac{x}{y+z}}+\dfrac{1}{1+\frac{y}{z+x}}+\dfrac{1}{1+\frac{z}{x+y}}$

$= \dfrac{y+z}{x+y+z}+\dfrac{z+x}{x+y+z}+\dfrac{x+y}{x+y+z}$

$= \dfrac{2(x+y+z)}{(x+y+z)} = 2.$

93. $(-2x-6)^2 = [-2(x+3)]^2 = 4(x+3)^2 = 4y.$

94. $(x+a)(x+b) = x^2 + ax + bx + ab = x^2 + (a+b)x + ab.$

95. $\left[1+\dfrac{1}{x+1}\right]\left[1+\dfrac{1}{x+2}\right]\left[1+\dfrac{1}{x+3}\right]\left[1+\dfrac{1}{x+4}\right]$

$= \left[\dfrac{(x+1)+1}{x+1}\right]\left[\dfrac{(x+2)+1}{x+2}\right]\left[\dfrac{(x+3)+1}{x+3}\right]\left[\dfrac{(x+4)+1}{x+4}\right]$

$= \left(\dfrac{x+2}{x+1}\right)\left(\dfrac{x+3}{x+2}\right)\left(\dfrac{x+4}{x+3}\right)\left(\dfrac{x+5}{x+4}\right) = \dfrac{x+5}{x+1}.$

96. $(a-b)-(c+d) = 6$ and $(c-d)-(a+b) = 3$

$\Rightarrow (a-c)-(b+d) = 6$ and $(c-a)-(b+d) = 3$

$\Rightarrow (b+d) = (a-c)-6$ and $(b+d) = (c-a)-3$

$\Rightarrow (a-c)-6 = (c-a)-3 \Rightarrow 2(a-c) = 3$

$\Rightarrow (a-c) = \dfrac{3}{2} = 1.5.$

97. $\dfrac{3a+2b}{3a-2b} = \dfrac{3\frac{a}{b}+2}{3\frac{a}{b}-2} = \dfrac{3\times\frac{4}{3}+2}{3\times\frac{4}{3}-2} = \dfrac{6}{2} = 3.$

98. $\left(\dfrac{6}{7}-\dfrac{5x-y}{5x+y}\right) = \dfrac{6}{7}-\left(\dfrac{5\frac{x}{y}-1}{5\frac{x}{y}+1}\right) = \dfrac{6}{7}-\left(\dfrac{5\times\frac{6}{5}-1}{5\times\frac{6}{5}+1}\right)$

$= \dfrac{6}{7}-\left(\dfrac{6-1}{6+1}\right) = \dfrac{6}{7}-\dfrac{5}{7} = \dfrac{1}{7}.$

99. $\dfrac{x^2+y^2}{x^2-y^2}=\dfrac{\dfrac{x^2}{y^2}+1}{\dfrac{x^2}{y^2}-1}=\dfrac{\left(\dfrac{x}{y}\right)^2+1}{\left(\dfrac{x}{y}\right)^2-1}=\dfrac{\left(\dfrac{1}{3}\right)^2+1}{\left(\dfrac{1}{3}\right)^2-1}$

$=\dfrac{\left(\dfrac{1}{9}+1\right)}{\left(\dfrac{1}{9}-1\right)}=\dfrac{10}{9}\times\left(-\dfrac{9}{8}\right)=-\dfrac{5}{4}.$

100. $\dfrac{x}{2y}=\dfrac{6}{7}\Rightarrow\dfrac{x}{y}=\left(2\times\dfrac{6}{7}\right)=\dfrac{12}{7}.$

$\therefore\quad \dfrac{x-y}{x+y}+\dfrac{14}{19}=\dfrac{\dfrac{x}{y}-1}{\dfrac{x}{y}+1}+\dfrac{14}{19}=\dfrac{\dfrac{12}{7}-1}{\dfrac{12}{7}+1}+\dfrac{14}{19}=\dfrac{(5/7)}{(19/7)}+\dfrac{14}{19}$

$=\left(\dfrac{5}{7}\times\dfrac{7}{19}\right)+\dfrac{14}{19}=\dfrac{5}{19}+\dfrac{14}{19}=\dfrac{19}{19}=1.$

101. $\dfrac{a}{b}=\dfrac{4}{5}$ and $\dfrac{b}{c}=\dfrac{15}{16}\Rightarrow\left(\dfrac{a}{b}\times\dfrac{b}{c}\right)=\left(\dfrac{4}{5}\times\dfrac{15}{16}\right)\Rightarrow\dfrac{a}{c}=\dfrac{3}{4}.$

$\therefore\quad\dfrac{c^2-a^2}{c^2+a^2}=\dfrac{1-\left(\dfrac{a^2}{c^2}\right)}{1+\left(\dfrac{a^2}{c^2}\right)}=\dfrac{1-\left(\dfrac{a}{c}\right)^2}{1+\left(\dfrac{a}{c}\right)^2}=\dfrac{1-\dfrac{9}{16}}{1+\dfrac{9}{16}}=\dfrac{(7/16)}{(25/16)}=\dfrac{7}{25}.$

102. $x=y\Leftrightarrow 1-q=2q+1\Leftrightarrow 3q=0\Leftrightarrow q=0.$

103. $\dfrac{x}{5}-\dfrac{x}{6}=4\Leftrightarrow\dfrac{6x-5x}{30}=4\Leftrightarrow x=120.$

104. $\dfrac{3x}{2y}=\dfrac{21}{22}\Rightarrow\dfrac{x}{y}=\left(\dfrac{21}{22}\times\dfrac{2}{3}\right)=\dfrac{7}{11}\Rightarrow x=\dfrac{7}{11}y.$

$4x+5y=83\Rightarrow 4\times\dfrac{7}{11}y+5y=83\Rightarrow\dfrac{28}{11}y+5y=83$

$\Rightarrow 83y=83\times11\Rightarrow y=11.$

$\therefore\quad x=\dfrac{7}{11}y=\left(\dfrac{7}{11}\times11\right)=7.$

So, $y-x=11-7=4.$

105. $\dfrac{ab}{a+b}=\dfrac{\dfrac{x}{x+y}\cdot\dfrac{y}{x-y}}{\dfrac{x}{x+y}+\dfrac{y}{x-y}}=\dfrac{\dfrac{xy}{x^2-y^2}}{\dfrac{x(x-y)+y(x+y)}{x^2-y^2}}=\dfrac{xy}{x^2+y^2}.$

106. $\dfrac{a}{b}=\dfrac{1}{3}\Rightarrow b=3a;\ \dfrac{b}{c}=2\Rightarrow c=\dfrac{b}{2}=\dfrac{3a}{2};$

$\dfrac{c}{d}=\dfrac{1}{2}\Rightarrow d=2c=2\left(\dfrac{3a}{2}\right)=3a;$

$\dfrac{d}{e}=3\Rightarrow e=\dfrac{d}{3}=\left(\dfrac{3a}{3}\right)=a;\ \dfrac{e}{f}=\dfrac{1}{4}\Rightarrow f=4e=4a.$

$\therefore\quad\dfrac{abc}{def}=\dfrac{(a)(3a)\left(\dfrac{3a}{2}\right)}{(3a)(a)(4a)}=\dfrac{9}{2}a^3\times\dfrac{1}{12a^3}=\dfrac{3}{8}.$

107. $\dfrac{m}{n}=\dfrac{4}{3}$ and $\dfrac{r}{t}=\dfrac{9}{14}\Rightarrow\dfrac{mr}{nt}=\dfrac{4}{3}\times\dfrac{9}{14}=\dfrac{6}{7}.$

$\therefore\quad\dfrac{3mr-nt}{4nt-7mr}=\dfrac{3\dfrac{mr}{nt}-1}{4-7\dfrac{mr}{nt}}=\dfrac{3\times\dfrac{6}{7}-1}{4-7\times\dfrac{6}{7}}$

$=\dfrac{\dfrac{18}{7}-1}{4-6}=\dfrac{11}{7}\times\left(-\dfrac{1}{2}\right)=-\dfrac{11}{14}.$

108. $a+\dfrac{1}{b}=1\Rightarrow ab+1=b\Rightarrow ab-b=-1$

$\Rightarrow b(a-1)=-1\Rightarrow b=\dfrac{1}{(1-a)}.$

$b+\dfrac{1}{c}=1\Rightarrow bc+1=c\Rightarrow bc-c=-1$

$\Rightarrow c(b-1)=-1\Rightarrow c=\dfrac{1}{(1-b)}.$

$\therefore\quad c+\dfrac{1}{a}=\dfrac{1}{(1-b)}+\dfrac{1}{a}=\dfrac{1}{1-\left(\dfrac{1}{1-a}\right)}+\dfrac{1}{a}=\dfrac{1}{\dfrac{(1-a)-1}{(1-a)}}+\dfrac{1}{a}$

$=\dfrac{(1-a)}{-a}+\dfrac{1}{a}=\dfrac{(a-1)}{a}+\dfrac{1}{a}=\dfrac{a-1+1}{a}=\dfrac{a}{a}=1.$

109. $y+\dfrac{1}{z}=1\Rightarrow yz+1=z\Rightarrow yz-z=-1$

$\Rightarrow z(y-1)=-1\Rightarrow z=\dfrac{1}{(1-y)}.$

$x+\dfrac{1}{y}=1\Rightarrow xy+1=y\Rightarrow xy-y=-1$

$\Rightarrow y(x-1)=-1\Rightarrow y=\dfrac{1}{(1-x)}.$

$\therefore\quad xyz=x\left(\dfrac{1}{1-x}\right)\left(\dfrac{1}{1-y}\right)=x\left(\dfrac{1}{1-x}\right)\left(\dfrac{1}{1-\dfrac{1}{1-x}}\right)$

$=x\left(\dfrac{1}{1-x}\right)\left(\dfrac{1-x}{-x}\right)=-1.$

110. $\dfrac{x}{(2x+y+z)}=a\Rightarrow x=a(2x+y+z)$ ...(*i*)

$\dfrac{y}{(x+2y+z)}=a\Rightarrow y=a(x+2y+z)$ ...(*ii*)

$\dfrac{z}{(x+y+2z)}=a\Rightarrow z=a(x+y+2z)$ ...(*iii*)

Adding (*i*), (*ii*) and (*iii*), we get: $x+y+z$

$=a(4x+4y+4z)\Rightarrow a=\dfrac{x+y+z}{4(x+y+z)}=\dfrac{1}{4}.$

111. $\dfrac{a}{b+c}=K\Rightarrow a=K(b+c)$ ...(*i*)

$\dfrac{b}{c+a}=K\Rightarrow b=K(c+a)$ ...(*ii*)

$\dfrac{c}{a+b}=K\Rightarrow c=K(a+b)$ ...(*iii*)

Adding (i), (ii), and (iii), we get: $a + b + c$

$= K(2a + 2b + 2c) \Rightarrow K = \dfrac{a+b+c}{2(a+b+c)} = \dfrac{1}{2}.$

112. $a - 8 = b \Rightarrow a - b = 8$ and $b - a = -8$.

$\therefore\quad |a - b| - |b - a| = |8| - |-8| = 8 - 8 = 0.$

113. $x = \dfrac{a}{a-1} = 1 + \dfrac{1}{a-1} = 1 + y. \quad \therefore\ x > y.$

114. a is positive and $a < 1 \Rightarrow \dfrac{1}{a} > 1. \quad \therefore\ \left(a + \dfrac{1}{a}\right) > 2.$

115. $\dfrac{a}{x} + \dfrac{y}{b} = 1 \Rightarrow \dfrac{a}{x} = 1 - \dfrac{y}{b} = \dfrac{b-y}{b} \Rightarrow \dfrac{x}{a} = \dfrac{b}{b-y}.$

$\dfrac{b}{y} + \dfrac{z}{c} = 1 \Rightarrow \dfrac{z}{c} = 1 - \dfrac{b}{y} = \dfrac{y-b}{y} \Rightarrow \dfrac{c}{z} = \dfrac{y}{y-b} = \dfrac{-y}{(b-y)}.$

$\therefore\quad \dfrac{x}{a} + \dfrac{c}{z} = \dfrac{b}{(b-y)} - \dfrac{y}{(b-y)} = \dfrac{(b-y)}{(b-y)} = 1.$

116. $a^2 + b^2 = 45$ ...(i)

and $b^2 + c^2 = 40$ ...(ii)

Subtracting, we get: $a^2 - c^2 = 5 \Rightarrow (a + c)(a - c) = 5.$

$\therefore\quad (a + c) = 5$ and $(a - c) = 1.$

Solving, we get: $a = 3$, $c = 2$. Putting $c = 2$ in (ii), we get: $b = 6$.

117. $x + y = 15 \Rightarrow (x + y)^2 = (15)^2 = 225$

$\Rightarrow x^2 + y^2 + 2xy = 225$

$\Rightarrow x^2 + y^2 = 225 - 2xy = 225 - 2 \times 56$

$= 225 - 112 = 113.$

118. $(a - b) = 4 \Rightarrow (a - b)^2 = 4^2 = 16 \Rightarrow a^2 + b^2 - 2ab = 16$

$\Rightarrow a^2 + b^2 = 16 + 2ab = 16 + 2 \times 2$

$= 16 + 4 = 20.$

119. $a = bc$ and $c = a - b \Rightarrow a = b(a - b) \Rightarrow a = ab - b^2$

$\Rightarrow b^2 = ab - a = a(b-1) \Rightarrow a = \dfrac{b^2}{b-1}.$

120. $a + b + c = 0 \Rightarrow a = -(b + c) \Rightarrow a^2 = (b + c)^2.$

$\therefore\quad \dfrac{a^2}{(a^2 - bc)} + \dfrac{b^2}{(b^2 - ca)} + \dfrac{c^2}{(c^2 - ab)}$

$= \dfrac{(b+c)^2}{(b+c)^2 - bc} + \dfrac{b^2}{b^2 + c(b+c)} + \dfrac{c^2}{c^2 + b(b+c)}$

$= \dfrac{(b+c)^2}{b^2 + c^2 + bc} + \dfrac{b^2}{b^2 + c^2 + bc} + \dfrac{c^2}{b^2 + c^2 + bc}$

$= \dfrac{b^2 + c^2 + 2bc + b^2 + c^2}{b^2 + c^2 + bc} = \dfrac{2(b^2 + c^2 + bc)}{b^2 + c^2 + bc} = 2.$

121. $\dfrac{x^2 - y^2}{x^2 + y^2} = \dfrac{\left(\dfrac{x^2}{y^2}\right) - 1}{\left(\dfrac{x^2}{y^2}\right) + 1} = \dfrac{\left(\dfrac{x}{y}\right)^2 - 1}{\left(\dfrac{x}{y}\right)^2 + 1} = \dfrac{\left(\dfrac{a+2}{a-2}\right)^2 - 1}{\left(\dfrac{a+2}{a-2}\right)^2 + 1}$

$= \dfrac{(a+2)^2 - (a-2)^2}{(a+2)^2 + (a-2)^2} = \dfrac{4 \times a \times 2}{2(a^2 + 4)} = \dfrac{4a}{a^2 + 4}.$

122. $3x + 7 = 7x + 5 \Rightarrow 7x - 3x = 2 \Rightarrow 4x = 2 \Rightarrow x = \dfrac{1}{2}.$

Now, $3x + 7 = x^2 + P \Rightarrow \dfrac{3}{2} + 7 = \dfrac{1}{4} + P$

$\Rightarrow P = \dfrac{17}{2} - \dfrac{1}{4} = \dfrac{33}{4} = 8\dfrac{1}{4}.$

123. $\dfrac{2a + b}{a + 4b} = 3 \Rightarrow 2a + b = 3(a + 4b) \Rightarrow a = -11b.$

$\dfrac{a+b}{a+2b} = \dfrac{-11b + b}{-11b + 2b} = \dfrac{-10b}{-9b} = \dfrac{10}{9}.$

124. $(2a + 3b)(2c - 3d) = (2a - 3b)(2c + 3d)$

$\Rightarrow \dfrac{(2a + 3b)}{(2a - 3b)} = \dfrac{(2c + 3d)}{(2c - 3d)}$

$\Rightarrow \dfrac{2\left(\dfrac{a}{b}\right) + 3}{2\left(\dfrac{a}{b}\right) - 3} = \dfrac{2\left(\dfrac{c}{d}\right) + 3}{2\left(\dfrac{c}{d}\right) - 3} \Rightarrow \dfrac{a}{b} = \dfrac{c}{d}.$

125. $(a + b + 2c + 3d)(a - b - 2c + 3d)$

$= (a - b + 2c - 3d)(a + b - 2c - 3d)$

$\Rightarrow [(a + b) + (2c + 3d)]\,[(a - b) - (2c - 3d)]$

$= [(a - b) + (2c - 3d)]\,[(a + b) - (2c + 3d)]$

$\Rightarrow (a + b)(a - b) - (a + b)(2c - 3d) + (a - b)(2c + 3d) - (2c + 3d)(2c - 3d)$

$= (a - b)(a + b) - (a - b)(2c + 3d) + (a + b)(2c - 3d) - (2c + 3d)(2c - 3d)$

$\Rightarrow (a + b)(2c - 3d) = (a - b)(2c + 3d)$

$\Rightarrow 2ac - 3ad + 2bc - 3bd = 2ac + 3ad - 2bc - 3bd$

$\Rightarrow 4bc = 6ad \Rightarrow 2bc = 3ad.$

126. $\dfrac{x+y}{x-y} \div \dfrac{(x+y)^2}{x^2 - y^2} = \dfrac{x+y}{x-y} \times \dfrac{(x^2 - y^2)}{(x+y)^2}$

$= \dfrac{(x^2 - y^2)}{(x-y)(x+y)} = \dfrac{(x^2 - y^2)}{(x^2 - y^2)} = 1.$

127. $\dfrac{a^2 - b^2 - 2bc - c^2}{a^2 + b^2 + 2ab - c^2} = \dfrac{a^2 - (b^2 + 2bc + c^2)}{(a^2 + b^2 + 2ab) - c^2} = \dfrac{a^2 - (b+c)^2}{(a+b)^2 - c^2}$

$= \dfrac{(a+b+c)(a-b-c)}{(a+b+c)(a+b-c)} = \dfrac{a-b-c}{a+b-c}.$

128. $x + y + z = 0 \Rightarrow y = -(x + z).$

$\therefore\quad x^2 + xy + y^2 = x^2 + x(-x - z) + (x + z)^2$

$= x^2 - x^2 - xz + x^2 + z^2 + 2xz$

$= x^2 + z^2 + zx.$

129. $(s - a)^2 + (s - b)^2 + (s - c)^2 + s^2$

$= (s^2 + a^2 - 2sa) + (s^2 + b^2 - 2sb) + (s^2 + c^2 - 2sc) + s^2$

$= 4s^2 + (a^2 + b^2 + c^2) - 2s(a + b + c)$

$= (2s)^2 + (a^2 + b^2 + c^2) - (a + b + c)(a + b + c)$

$= (a + b + c)^2 + (a^2 + b^2 + c^2) - (a + b + c)^2$

$= a^2 + b^2 + c^2.$

130. $[(x + y)^2 - z^2] + [(y + z)^2 - x^2] + [(z + x)^2 - y^2]$

$= 4 + 9 + 36$

$\Rightarrow\quad (x + y + z)(x + y - z) + (x + y + z)$

$(y + z - x) + (x + y + z)(z + x - y) = 49$

$\Rightarrow\quad (x + y + z)\,[(x + y - z) + (y + z - x) + (z + x - y)] = 49$

$\Rightarrow\quad (x + y + z)(x + y + z) = 49 \Rightarrow (x + y + z)^2 = 49$

$\Rightarrow\quad (x + y + z) = \pm 7.$

131. $a + b = 2c \Rightarrow a = 2c - b.$

$$\therefore \frac{a}{a-c}+\frac{b}{b-c}=\frac{2c-b}{(2c-b)-c}+\frac{b}{(b-c)}=\frac{2c-b}{c-b}+\frac{b}{b-c}$$

$$=\frac{b-2c}{b-c}+\frac{b}{b-c}=\frac{b-2c+b}{b-c}=\frac{2(b-c)}{b-c}=2.$$

132. $$\frac{x}{x-1}+\frac{1}{x+1}+\frac{2x}{1-x^2}=\frac{x}{x-1}+\frac{1}{x+1}-\frac{2x}{x^2-1}$$

$$=\frac{x(x+1)+(x-1)-2x}{(x^2-1)}$$

$$=\frac{x^2+x+x-1-2x}{x^2-1}=\frac{x^2-1}{x^2-1}=1.$$

133. $$\frac{(a+b)^2}{(a^2-b^2)}=\frac{(a+b)(a+b)}{(a+b)(a-b)}=\frac{a+b}{a-b}.$$

134. $ab + bc + ca = 0 \Rightarrow ab = -bc - ca,\ bc = -ab - ca,$ $ca = -ab - bc.$

$$\therefore \frac{1}{a^2-bc}+\frac{1}{b^2-ca}+\frac{1}{c^2-ab}$$

$$=\frac{1}{a^2+ab+ac}+\frac{1}{b^2+ab+bc}+\frac{1}{c^2+bc+ca}$$

$$=\frac{1}{a(a+b+c)}+\frac{1}{b(a+b+c)}+\frac{1}{c(a+b+c)}$$

$$=\frac{bc+ca+ab}{abc(a+b+c)}=0.\ [\because ab+bc+ca=0]$$

135. Number of boxes required $=\frac{15\times1000}{250}=60.$

136. Bus fare for 1 person = ₹ 420.

Train fare for 1 person = ₹ $\left(\frac{3}{4}\times840\right)$ = ₹ 630.

$\therefore$ Total fare = ₹ (3 × 420 + 4 × 630)
= ₹ (1260 + 2520) = ₹ 3780.

137. Let the cost of one pen be ₹ x. Then, cost of 1 pencil = ₹ $\left(\frac{x}{3}\right)$.

$$\therefore\ 6x+3\times\frac{x}{3}=84\Rightarrow7x=84\Rightarrow x=12.$$

So, total cost of 4 pens and 5 pencils

= ₹ $\left(4x+\frac{5x}{3}\right)$ = ₹ $\left(\frac{17x}{3}\right)$ = ₹ $\left(\frac{17\times12}{3}\right)$ = ₹ 68.

138. Amount received by each person = ₹ $\left(\frac{436563}{69}\right)$ = ₹ 6327.

```
69)436563(6327
   414
   ---
    225
    207
    ---
     186
     138
     ---
      483
      483
      ---
       ×
```

139. Length of reel = (32 × 120 + 80) cm = 3920 cm = 39.20 m.

140. Number of bananas required daily $=\frac{798}{7}=114.$

$\therefore$ Required number = [114 × (31 + 29 + 31)] (Jan, Feb, Mar)
= (114 × 91) = 10374.

141. Suppose Mohan has ₹ x. Then, Ram has ₹ $(x + 6)$ and Sohan has ₹ $(x - 3)$.

$\therefore\ x + (x + 6) + (x - 3) = 33 \Leftrightarrow 3x = 30 \Leftrightarrow x = 10.$

So, Ram's share = ₹ (10 + 6) = ₹ 16.

142. 4 gal = (4 × 4) qt = 16 qt = (16 × 2) pt = 32 pt.

$\therefore$ Number of bottles $=\frac{32}{\left(\frac{1}{2}\right)}=64.$

143. $$\frac{1}{2}A=\frac{5}{6}B\Rightarrow A=\left(2\times\frac{5}{6}\right)B=\frac{5}{3}B.$$

$$\therefore\ A+B=80\Rightarrow\frac{5}{3}B+B=80\Rightarrow\frac{8}{3}B=80$$

$$\Rightarrow B=\left(\frac{80\times3}{8}\right)=30\text{ kg}.$$

144. $a = b + 2 \Rightarrow b = a - 2$

And, $b = c + 10 \Rightarrow c = b - 10 = (a - 2) - 10 = a - 12.$

$a + b + c = 130 \Rightarrow a + (a - 2) + (a - 12) = 130$
$\Rightarrow 3a = 144 \Rightarrow a = 48.$

$\therefore\ (b + c) - a = [(a - 2) + (a - 12)] - a$
$= (2a - 14) - a = (a - 14) = 48 - 14 = 34.$

145. Let the given condition be fulfilled n years after 2002.

Then, price of item X after n years = ₹ $(420 + 40n)$.

price of item Y after n years = ₹ $(630 + 15n)$.

$\therefore\ 420 + 40n = (630 + 15n) + 40$

$\Rightarrow\ 420 + 40n = 670 + 15n \Rightarrow 25n = 250 \Rightarrow n = 10.$

So, the required year is 10 years after 2002 i.e., 2012.

146. Number of pieces $=\left(\frac{42.5\times100}{85}\right)=\frac{4250}{85}=50.$

147. Total number of children = (30 × 16) = 480.

$\therefore$ Number of columns of 24 children each $=\left(\frac{480}{24}\right)=20.$

148. Original number of sections = (16 – 3) = 13.

Original number of students = (24 × 13) = 312.

Present number of students = (21 × 16) = 336.

Number of new students admitted = (336 – 312) = 24.

149. Money earned in 2 days = ₹ (20 – 15) = ₹ 5.

Money earned in 16 days = ₹ $\left(\frac{5}{2}\times16\right)$ = ₹ 40.

On 17th day, money in hand = ₹ (40 + 20) = ₹ 60.

150. Let the number of cars sold on the first day be x.

Then, $x + (x + 6) + (x + 12) + (x + 18) + (x + 24) + (x + 30) = 150$

$\Leftrightarrow 6x + 90 = 150 \Leftrightarrow 6x = 60 \Leftrightarrow x = 10.$

$\therefore$ Number of cars sold on 6th day = (10 + 30) = 40.

151. Let the number of captains in the group be x.

Then, number of soldiers = $15x$.

$\therefore\ x + 15x = 1200 \Leftrightarrow 16x = 1200 \Leftrightarrow x = 75.$

152. Required cost = ₹ $[1000 \times x + (z - 1000) \times y]$
= ₹ $(1000x + zy - 1000y)$
= ₹ $[1000(x - y) + yz]$.

153. Let the monthly salary of a man be ₹ x.
Then, monthly salary of a woman = ₹ $(x + 500)$.
$\therefore \quad 4x + 2(x + 500) = 46000 \Leftrightarrow 6x = 45000 \Leftrightarrow x = 7500.$
Monthly salary of a woman = $x + 500$ = ₹ 8000.

154. Let the number of pineapples and watermelons be x and y respectively.
Then, $7x + 5y = 38$ or $5y = (38 - 7x)$ or $y = \dfrac{38 - 7x}{5}$.
Clearly, y is a whole number, only when $(38 - 7x)$ is divisible by 5. This happens when $x = 4$.

155. Let F and C denote the temperatures in Fahrenheit and Celsius respectively.
Then, $\dfrac{F - 32}{212 - 32} = \dfrac{C - 0}{100 - 0} \Leftrightarrow \dfrac{F - 32}{180} = \dfrac{C}{100}$.
If $C = 35$, then $F = \left(\dfrac{35}{100} \times 180\right) + 32 = 63 + 32 = 95.$

156. Let the two parts be x and $(74 - x)$.
Then, $5x + 11(74 - x) = 454 \Leftrightarrow 6x = 360 \Leftrightarrow x = 60.$
So, the two parts are 60 and 14.

157. Let the quantity of water drained away be x litres.
Then, $12 - x = x - 6 \Rightarrow 2x = 18 \Rightarrow x = 9.$

158. Let the number of boys in the family be x.
Then each boy has $(x - 1)$ brothers and $(x - 1)$ sisters.
So, number of girls = $(x - 1)$.
Thus each girl has x brothers and $(x - 2)$ sisters.
$\therefore \quad x = 2(x - 2) \Leftrightarrow x = 2x - 4 \Leftrightarrow x = 4.$
So, there are 4 boys and 3 girls i.e., 4 brothers and 3 sisters in the family.

159. 5000 INR = 100 USD = $\left(100 \times \dfrac{1}{0.01}\right)$ Japanese Yen
= 10000 Japanese Yen
$\Rightarrow$ 1 INR = 2 Japanese Yen
$\Rightarrow$ 100 INR = 200 Japanese Yen.

160. Capacity of the tank = (13.5×12) litres = 162 litres.
$\therefore$ Required number of buckets = $\left(\dfrac{162}{9}\right) = 18.$

161. Given exp. $= \left[1 + \dfrac{1}{1 + \dfrac{1}{(4/3)}}\right] \div \dfrac{11}{7} = \left[1 + \dfrac{1}{1 + \dfrac{3}{4}}\right] \div \dfrac{11}{7}$

$= \left[1 + \dfrac{1}{(7/4)}\right] \div \dfrac{11}{7} = \left(1 + \dfrac{4}{7}\right) \div \dfrac{11}{7} = \dfrac{11}{7} \div \dfrac{11}{7} = 1.$

162. (a) $\dfrac{1}{3 + \dfrac{1}{1 + \dfrac{1}{16}}} = \dfrac{1}{3 + \dfrac{1}{(17/16)}} = \dfrac{1}{3 + \dfrac{16}{17}} = \dfrac{1}{(67/17)} = \dfrac{17}{67}.$

(b) $\dfrac{1}{2 + \dfrac{1}{1 + \dfrac{1}{8}}} = \dfrac{1}{2 + \dfrac{1}{(9/8)}} = \dfrac{1}{2 + \dfrac{8}{9}} = \dfrac{1}{(26/9)} = \dfrac{9}{26}.$

(c) $\dfrac{1}{3 + \dfrac{1}{1 + \dfrac{1}{1 + \dfrac{1}{8}}}} = \dfrac{1}{3 + \dfrac{1}{1 + \dfrac{1}{(9/8)}}} = \dfrac{1}{3 + \dfrac{1}{1 + \dfrac{8}{9}}}$

$= \dfrac{1}{3 + \dfrac{1}{(17/9)}} = \dfrac{1}{3 + \dfrac{9}{17}} = \dfrac{1}{\left(\dfrac{60}{17}\right)} = \dfrac{17}{60}.$

(d) $\dfrac{1}{3 + \dfrac{1}{1 + \dfrac{1}{2 + \dfrac{1}{4}}}} = \dfrac{1}{3 + \dfrac{1}{1 + \dfrac{1}{(9/4)}}} = \dfrac{1}{3 + \dfrac{1}{1 + \dfrac{4}{9}}}$

$= \dfrac{1}{3 + \dfrac{1}{(13/9)}} = \dfrac{1}{3 + \dfrac{9}{13}} = \dfrac{1}{(48/13)} = \dfrac{13}{48}.$

163. Given exp. $= \dfrac{1}{1 + \dfrac{1}{3 - \dfrac{4}{2 + \dfrac{1}{(5/2)}}}} + \dfrac{3}{3 - \dfrac{4}{3 + \dfrac{1}{(3/2)}}}$

$= \dfrac{1}{1 + \dfrac{1}{3 - \dfrac{4}{2 + \dfrac{2}{5}}}} + \dfrac{3}{3 - \dfrac{4}{3 + \dfrac{2}{3}}}$

$= \dfrac{1}{1 + \dfrac{1}{3 - \dfrac{4}{(12/5)}}} + \dfrac{3}{3 - \dfrac{4}{(11/3)}}$

$= \dfrac{1}{1 + \dfrac{1}{3 - \dfrac{20}{12}}} + \dfrac{3}{3 - \dfrac{12}{11}} = \dfrac{1}{1 + \dfrac{1}{3 - \dfrac{5}{3}}} + \dfrac{3}{(21/11)}$

$= \dfrac{1}{1 + \dfrac{1}{(4/3)}} + \dfrac{33}{21}$

$= \dfrac{1}{1 + \dfrac{3}{4}} + \dfrac{11}{7} = \dfrac{1}{(7/4)} + \dfrac{11}{7} = \dfrac{4}{7} + \dfrac{11}{7} = \dfrac{15}{7}.$

164. $x = 2 - \dfrac{1}{1 + \dfrac{1}{(13/4)}} = 2 - \dfrac{1}{1 + \dfrac{4}{13}} = 2 - \dfrac{1}{(17/13)} = 2 - \dfrac{13}{17} = \dfrac{21}{17}.$

165. $x = \dfrac{2 + \dfrac{1}{(19/5)}}{2 + \dfrac{1}{3 + \dfrac{1}{(5/4)}}} = \dfrac{2 + \dfrac{5}{19}}{2 + \dfrac{1}{3 + \dfrac{4}{5}}} = \dfrac{2 + \dfrac{5}{19}}{2 + \dfrac{1}{(19/5)}} = \dfrac{2 + \dfrac{5}{19}}{2 + \dfrac{5}{19}} = 1.$

166. Given exp. $= 8 - 8 \times \dfrac{\dfrac{11}{5} - \dfrac{9}{7}}{2 - \dfrac{1}{(35/6)}}$

$= 8 - 8 \times \dfrac{\dfrac{32}{35}}{2 - \dfrac{6}{35}} = 8 - 8 \times \dfrac{32}{35} \times \dfrac{35}{64} = 8 - 4 = 4.$

167. Given exp. $= \dfrac{2}{2 + \dfrac{2}{3 + \dfrac{2}{(11/3)}} \times 0.39} = \dfrac{2}{2 + \dfrac{2}{3 + \dfrac{6}{11}} \times 0.39}$

$$= \frac{2}{2 + \frac{2}{(39/11)} \times 0.39}$$

$$= \frac{2}{2 + \frac{22}{39} \times \frac{39}{100}} = \frac{2}{2 + \frac{22}{100}}$$

$$= \frac{2}{2 + \frac{11}{50}} = \frac{2}{(111/50)} = \frac{100}{111}.$$

168. Given exp. $= \dfrac{1}{1 + \dfrac{\frac{2}{3}}{\dfrac{8}{\frac{5}{3} + \frac{9}{(1/3)}}}} = \dfrac{1}{1 + \dfrac{2/3}{\frac{5}{3} + \frac{8}{9} \times 3}}$

$$= \frac{1}{1 + \frac{2/3}{(13/3)}} = \frac{1}{1 + \frac{2}{13}} = \frac{13}{15}.$$

169. $\dfrac{2}{2 + \dfrac{2}{2 + \frac{2}{x}}} = 3 \Leftrightarrow \dfrac{2}{2 + \dfrac{2}{\left(\frac{2x+2}{x}\right)}} = 3$

$$\Leftrightarrow \frac{2}{2 + \frac{2x}{2x+2}} = 3 \Leftrightarrow \frac{2}{\frac{2(2x+2) + 2x}{2x+2}} = 3$$

$$\Leftrightarrow \frac{2(2x+2)}{2(3x+2)} = 3$$

$$\Leftrightarrow \frac{(2x+2)}{(3x+2)} = 3 \Leftrightarrow 2x + 2 = 9x + 6$$

$$\Leftrightarrow 7x = -4 \Leftrightarrow x = -\frac{4}{7}.$$

170. $2 + \dfrac{1}{x + \dfrac{1}{y + \frac{1}{z}}} = \dfrac{37}{13} = 2\dfrac{11}{13} = 2 + \dfrac{11}{13} \Rightarrow \dfrac{1}{x + \dfrac{1}{y + \frac{1}{z}}}$

$$= \frac{11}{13} \Rightarrow x + \frac{1}{y + \frac{1}{z}} = \frac{13}{11}$$

$$\Rightarrow \quad x + \frac{1}{y + \frac{1}{z}} = 1 + \frac{2}{11}$$

$$\Rightarrow \quad x = 1, y + \frac{1}{z} = \frac{11}{2} = 5\frac{1}{2} = 5 + \frac{1}{2}$$

$\Rightarrow$ $x = 1$, $y = 5$, $z = 2$.

171. Clearly, we have: $x = 1 + \dfrac{1}{x} = \dfrac{x+1}{x}$.

$\Rightarrow \quad x^2 = x + 1 \quad \Rightarrow \quad x^2 - x - 1 = 0.$

172. Let $x = \dfrac{1}{3 + \dfrac{1}{4 + \dots}}$.

$$\dots$$

$$+ \frac{1}{1008}$$

Then, $P = \dfrac{1}{1 + \dfrac{1}{1+x}} = \dfrac{1+x}{2+x}$, $Q = \dfrac{1}{2+x}$.

$$\therefore \; P + Q = \frac{1+x}{2+x} + \frac{1}{2+x} = \frac{2+x}{2+x} = 1.$$

173. Given exp. $= \dfrac{a^2 - b^2}{a + b}$, where $a = \left(1 + \dfrac{1}{10 + \frac{1}{10}}\right)$ and

$$b = \left(1 - \frac{1}{10 + \frac{1}{10}}\right)$$

$$= (a - b) = \left(1 + \frac{1}{10 + \frac{1}{10}}\right) - \left(1 - \frac{1}{10 + \frac{1}{10}}\right)$$

$$= 2 \times \frac{1}{(101/10)} = \frac{20}{101}.$$

174. $3x + y = 19$ ...(i) and $x - y = 9$ ...(ii)

Adding (i) and (ii), we get: $4x = 28$ or $x = 7$.

Putting $x = 7$ in (i), we get: $y = -2$.

175. $4x = p(x + 3) + q(x - 1) \Rightarrow 4x = px + 3p + qx - q$

$\Rightarrow 4x = (p + q)\,x + (3p - q)$

$\Rightarrow p + q = 4$ and $3p - q = 0$

$\Rightarrow p + q = 4$ and $p = \dfrac{q}{3}$

$\Rightarrow \dfrac{q}{3} + q = 4 \Rightarrow \dfrac{4q}{3} = 4 \Rightarrow q = 3.$

$p + q = 4$ and $q = 3 \Rightarrow p = 1$.

176. $xyz = 256 \Rightarrow (2z)\,(2z)\,z = 256 \Rightarrow 4z^3$

$= 256 \Rightarrow z^3 = 64 \Rightarrow z = 4.$

$\therefore \quad x = 2z = (2 \times 4) = 8.$

177. $\dfrac{28x}{13y} = \dfrac{140}{39} \Rightarrow \dfrac{x}{y} = \left(\dfrac{140}{39} \times \dfrac{13}{28}\right) = \dfrac{5}{3} \Rightarrow x = \dfrac{5}{3}y.$

$3y + 9x = 54 \Rightarrow y + 3x = 18$

$\Rightarrow y + 3 \times \dfrac{5}{3}y = 18 \Rightarrow 6y = 18 \Rightarrow y = 3.$

$\therefore \quad x = \left(\dfrac{5}{3} \times 3\right) = 5.$

So, $y - x = (3 - 5) = -2$.

178. $3x + 7y = 75$ ...(i)

$5x - 5y = 25 \Rightarrow x - y = 5 \Rightarrow 7x - 7y = 35$ ...(ii)

Adding (i) and (ii), we get: $10x = 110$ or $x = 11$.

Putting $x = 11$ in (i), we get: $7y = 42$ or $y = 6$.

$\therefore \quad x + y = (11 + 6) = 17.$

179. $a + b = 5$ ...(i) and $3a + 2b = 20$ ...(ii)

Multiplying (i) by 2 and subtracting from (ii), we get: $a = 10$.

Putting $a = 10$ in (i), we get: $b = -5$.

$\therefore \quad (3a + b) = 3 \times 10 + (-5) = 30 - 5 = 25.$

180. $(2p + 3q) + (2p - q) = 18 + 2 \Rightarrow 4p + 2q = 20$

$\Rightarrow 2(2p + q) = 20 \Rightarrow 2p + q = 10.$

181. $2x + y = 5$ ...(i) and $3x - 4y = 2$ ...(ii)
Multiplying (i) by 4 and adding (ii) to it, we get:
$11x = 22$ or $x = 2$.
Putting $x = 2$ in (i), we get: $y = 1$.
So, $2xy = 2 \times 2 \times 1 = 4$.

182. $3x - 5y = 5$ ...(i) and $\frac{x}{x+y} = \frac{5}{7} \Rightarrow 7x = 5x + 5y$
$\Rightarrow 2x - 5y = 0$ ...(ii)
Subtracting (ii) from (i), we get: $x = 5$.
Putting $x = 5$ in (i), we get: $y = 2$. So, $x - y = 5 - 2 = 3$.

183. $4x + 3y = 18xy$ ...(i) and $2x - 5y = -4xy$ ...(ii)
Dividing (i) and (ii) by xy, we get:
$\frac{3}{x} + \frac{4}{y} = 18$ ...(iii) and $\frac{5}{x} - \frac{2}{y} = 4$ ...(iv)
Multiplying (iv) by 2 and adding (iii) to it, we get:
$\frac{13}{x} = 26$ or $x = \frac{1}{2}$.
Putting $x = \frac{1}{2}$ in (iii), we get : $y = \frac{1}{3}$.

184. $2x + y = 17$ ...(i)
$y + 2z = 15$ ...(ii)
and $x + y = 9$ ...(iii)
Subtracting (iii) from (i), we get: $x = 8$.
Putting $x = 8$ in (i), we get: $y = 1$. Putting $y = 1$ in (ii), we get: $2z = 14$ or $z = 7$.
$\therefore 4x + 3y + z = 4 \times 8 + 3 \times 1 + 7 = 42$.

185. $3x - 4y + z = 7$ ...(i)
$2x + 3y - z = 19$ ...(ii)
and $x + 2y + 2z = 24$ ...(iii)
Adding (i) and (ii), we get: $5x - y = 26$ ...(iv)
Subtracting (i) from (ii) and adding to (iii), we get:
$9y = 36$ or $y = 4$.
Putting $y = 4$ in (iv), we get: $5x = 30$ or $x = 6$.
Putting $x = 6$, $y = 4$ in (iii), we get: $2z = 10$ or $z = 5$.

186. $2x + y = 15$ ...(i)
$2y + z = 25$ ...(ii)
and $2z + x = 26$ ...(iii)
Adding (i), (ii) and (iii), we get: $3(x + y + z) = 66$ or $x + y + z = 22$ ...(iv)
From (ii), we have: $y = \frac{25 - z}{2}$. From (iii), we have: $x = 26 - 2z$.
$\therefore (26 - 2z) + \left(\frac{25 - z}{2}\right) + z = 22 \Leftrightarrow 77 - 3z = 44$
$\Leftrightarrow 3z = 33 \Leftrightarrow z = 11$.

187. $2x + 3y = 31$ ...(i)
$y - z = 4$ ...(ii)
and $x + 2z = 11$ ...(iii)
Multiplying (iii) by 2 and subtracting from (i), we get:
$3y - 4z = 9$ ...(iv)
Solving (ii) and (iv), we get: $y = 7$, $z = 3$.
Putting $y = 7$ in (i), we get: $x = 5$.
$\therefore x + y + z = (5 + 7 + 3) = 15$.

188. Let the cost of a chair and that of a table be ₹ x and ₹ y respectively.
Then, $10x = 4y$ or $y = \frac{5}{2}x$.
$\therefore 15x + 2y = 4000 \Leftrightarrow 15x + 2 \times \frac{5}{2}x = 4000 \Leftrightarrow 20x = 4000 \Leftrightarrow x = 200$.
So, $y = \left(\frac{5}{2} \times 200\right) = 500$.
$\therefore$ Cost of 12 chairs and 3 tables $= 12x + 3y$
= ₹ $(12 \times 200 + 3 \times 500)$ = ₹ $(2400 + 1500)$
= ₹ 3900.

189. Let the price of a jean be ₹ x and that of a shirt be ₹ y.
Then, $2x + 3y = 4000$ ...(i) and $3x + 2y = 3500$ ...(ii)
Adding (i) and (ii),
we get: $5x + 5y = 7500$ or $x + y = 1500$ ...(iii)
Subtracting (ii) from (i), we get: $-x + y = 500$ ...(iv)
Adding (iii) and (iv), we get: $2y = 2000$ or $y = 1000$.
Putting $y = 1000$ in (iii), we get: $x = 500$.
Hence, cost of a jean = ₹ 500.

190. Let the cost of one pen be ₹ x and that of one pencil be ₹ y.
Then, $8x + 4y = 176$ or $2x + y = 44$ ...(i)
And, $2x + 2y = 48$ or $x + y = 24$ ...(ii)
Subtracting (ii) from (i), we get: $x = 20$.
Hence, cost of 1 pen = ₹ 20.

191. Let the cost of 1 dozen apples be ₹ x and that of 1 dozen bananas be ₹ y. Then,
$2x + 3y = 136$ ...(i) and, $x + 5y = 110$ or $2x + 10y = 220$ ...(ii)
Subtracting (i) from (ii), we get: $7y = 84$ or $y = 12$.

192. Let the cost of 1 pencil, 1 pen and 1 eraser be ₹ x, ₹ y and ₹ z respectively.
Then, $x + 2y + 4z = 22$ ...(i)
and $5x + 4y + 2z = 32$ ...(ii)
Adding (i) and (ii), we get:
$6(x + y + z) = 54$ or $x + y + z = 9$.
$\therefore$ Cost of 3 pencils, 3 pens and 3 erasers
$= 3(x + y + z)$ = ₹ (3×9) = ₹ 27.

193. Let the number of cows and horses bought be x and y respectively.
Then, number of chicken bought $= 100 - (x + y)$.
$1000x + 300y + 50\,[100 - (x + y)] = 10000$
$\Rightarrow 1000x + 300y + 5000 - 50(x + y) = 10000$
$\Rightarrow 950x + 250y = 5000 \Rightarrow 50(19x + 5y) = 5000$
$\Rightarrow 19x + 5y = 100 \Rightarrow 5y = 100 - 19x \Rightarrow y = \frac{100 - 19x}{5}$.
Clearly, for y to be a whole number, $(100 - 19x)$ must be divisible by 5 and this is possible only when $x = 5$.
When $x = 5$, $y = \frac{100 - 19 \times 5}{5} = \frac{5}{5} = 1$.
$\therefore$ Number of chicken $= [100 - (5 + 1)] = 94$.

194. Let 1 man's daily earning be ₹ x and 1 boy's daily earning be ₹ y.

Then, $3x + 4y = \frac{756}{7} = 108$ ...(i)

And, $11x + 13y = \frac{3008}{8} = 376$ ...(ii)

Multiplying (i) by 11 and (ii) by 3, we get:

$33x + 44y = 1188$ ...(iii)

$33x + 39y = 1128$ ...(iv)

Subtracting (iv) from (iii), we get: $5y = 60$ or $y = 12$.

Putting $y = 12$ in (i), we get: $3x = 60$ or $x = 20$.

∴ Required time

$$= \frac{2480}{7x+9y} = \frac{2480}{7\times20+9\times12} = \frac{2480}{248} = 10 \text{ days.}$$

195. Let the price of 1 burger, 1 shake and 1 fries be ₹ x, ₹ y and ₹ z respectively. Then,

$3x + 7y + z = 120$ ...(i)

$4x + 10y + z = 164.50$ ...(ii)

Subtracting (i) from (ii), we get: $x + 3y = 44.50$

or $2x + 6y = 89$ ...(iii)

Subtracting (iii) from (i), we get: $x + y + z = (120 - 89) = 31$.

∴ Cost of 1 burger, 1 shake and 1 fries = ₹ 31.

196. $2x^2 + 12x + 18 = 0 \Leftrightarrow x^2 + 6x + 9 = 0$

$\Leftrightarrow x^2 + 3x + 3x + 9 = 0$

$\Leftrightarrow x(x + 3) + 3(x + 3) = 0$

$\Leftrightarrow (x + 3)^2 = 0 \Leftrightarrow x = -3.$

197. $x^2 - 7x = -12 \Leftrightarrow x^2 - 7x + 12 = 0$

$\Leftrightarrow x^2 - 3x - 4x + 12 = 0$

$\Leftrightarrow x(x - 3) - 4(x - 3) = 0$

$\Leftrightarrow (x - 3)(x - 4) = 0$

$\Leftrightarrow x = 3$ or $x = 4$.

198. $2x^2 - 11x + 15 = 0 \Leftrightarrow 2x^2 - 6x - 5x + 15 = 0$

$\Leftrightarrow 2x(x - 3) - 5(x - 3) = 0$

$\Leftrightarrow (x - 3)(2x - 5) = 0$

$\Leftrightarrow x = 3$ or $x = \frac{5}{2}$.

199. Given exp. $= \frac{1}{2}\times\frac{2}{3}\times\frac{3}{4}\times.....\times\frac{m-1}{m} = \frac{1}{m}$.

200. Given exp. $= \frac{4}{3}\times\frac{5}{4}\times\frac{6}{5}\times.....\times\frac{n+1}{n} = \frac{n+1}{3}$.

201. Given exp. $= \frac{5}{3}\times\frac{7}{5}\times\frac{9}{7}\times.....\times\frac{1001}{999} = \frac{1001}{3}$.

202. Given exp. $= \frac{3}{4}\times\frac{4}{3}\times\frac{5}{3}\times\frac{3}{5}\times\frac{13}{7}\times\frac{1}{13} = \frac{1}{7}$.

203. Given exp.

$$= \left(\frac{3^2-1}{3^2}\right)\left(\frac{4^2-1}{4^2}\right)\left(\frac{5^2-1}{5^2}\right).....\left(\frac{11^2-1}{11^2}\right)\left(\frac{12^2-1}{12^2}\right)$$

$$= \left[\frac{(3+1)(3-1)}{(2+1)(4-1)}\right]\left[\frac{(4+1)(4-1)}{(3+1)(5-1)}\right]\left[\frac{(5+1)(5-1)}{(4+1)(6-1)}\right] .....\left[\frac{(11+1)(11-1)}{(10+1)(12-1)}\right]\left[\frac{(12+1)(12-1)}{(11+1)(13-1)}\right]$$

$$= \frac{(3-1)}{(2+1)}\times\frac{(12+1)}{(13-1)} = \frac{2}{3}\times\frac{13}{12} = \frac{13}{18}.$$

204. Given exp. $= \frac{1}{(2-1)(2+1)} + \frac{1}{(4-1)(4+1)} + \frac{1}{(6-1)(6+1)} + ... + \frac{1}{(20-1)(20+1)}$

$$= \frac{1}{1\times3} + \frac{1}{3\times5} + \frac{1}{5\times7} + ... + \frac{1}{19\times21}$$

$$= \frac{1}{2}\left(1-\frac{1}{3}\right) + \frac{1}{2}\left(\frac{1}{3}-\frac{1}{5}\right) + \frac{1}{2}\left(\frac{1}{5}-\frac{1}{7}\right) + ... + \frac{1}{2}\left(\frac{1}{19}-\frac{1}{21}\right)$$

$$= \frac{1}{2}\left(1-\frac{1}{21}\right) = \frac{1}{2}\times\frac{20}{21} = \frac{10}{21}.$$

205. Given exp. $= \left(1-\frac{1}{2}\right) + \left(\frac{1}{2}-\frac{1}{3}\right) + \left(\frac{1}{3}-\frac{1}{4}\right) + \left(\frac{1}{4}-\frac{1}{5}\right) + ... + \left(\frac{1}{11}-\frac{1}{12}\right) = \left(1-\frac{1}{12}\right) = \frac{11}{12}.$

206. Clearly, sum of first 6 terms is zero. So, sum of first 30 terms = 0.

∴ Required sum $= \left(\frac{1}{2}+\frac{1}{3}-\frac{1}{4}-\frac{1}{2}-\frac{1}{3}\right) = -\frac{1}{4}.$

207. Given exp. $= (1+11+111+1111) + \left(\frac{1}{2}\times4\right)$

$= 1234 + 2 = 1236.$

208. Given exp. $= \left(1000 - \frac{1}{1000}\right)\times7 = \left(7000 - \frac{7}{1000}\right)$

$= 6999\frac{993}{1000}.$

209. Given exp. $= \left(1000 - \frac{4}{999}\right)\times999 = 999000 - 4 = 998996.$

210. Given exp. $= \left(1000-\frac{6}{7}\right) + \left(1000-\frac{5}{7}\right) + \left(1000-\frac{4}{7}\right) + \left(1000-\frac{3}{7}\right) + \left(1000-\frac{2}{7}\right) + \left(1000-\frac{1}{7}\right)$

$$= 6000 - \left(\frac{6}{7}+\frac{5}{7}+\frac{4}{7}+\frac{3}{7}+\frac{2}{7}+\frac{1}{7}\right)$$

$$= 6000 - \frac{21}{7} = 6000 - 3 = 5997.$$

Another Method:

Given exp. $= (999\times6) + \left(\frac{1}{7}+\frac{2}{7}+\frac{3}{7}+\frac{4}{7}+\frac{5}{7}+\frac{6}{7}\right)$

$= 5994 + \frac{21}{7} = 5994 + 3 = 5997.$

211. Given exp. $= (998\times5) + \left(\frac{2}{17}+\frac{3}{17}+\frac{5}{17}+\frac{8}{17}+\frac{16}{17}\right)$

$= 4990 + \frac{34}{17} = 4990 + 2 = 4992.$

212. Given exp. $= \left(1-\frac{1}{2}\right) + \left(\frac{1}{2}-\frac{1}{3}\right) + \left(\frac{1}{3}-\frac{1}{4}\right) + ... + \left(\frac{1}{9}-\frac{1}{10}\right)$

$= \left(1-\frac{1}{10}\right) = \frac{9}{10}.$

213. Given exp. $= \frac{1}{3}\left(1-\frac{1}{4}\right)+\frac{1}{3}\left(\frac{1}{4}-\frac{1}{7}\right)+\frac{1}{3}\left(\frac{1}{7}-\frac{1}{10}\right)$

$+\frac{1}{3}\left(\frac{1}{10}-\frac{1}{13}\right)+\frac{1}{3}\left(\frac{1}{13}-\frac{1}{16}\right)$

$= \frac{1}{3}\left[\left(1-\frac{1}{4}\right)+\left(\frac{1}{4}-\frac{1}{7}\right)+\left(\frac{1}{7}-\frac{1}{10}\right)+\left(\frac{1}{10}-\frac{1}{13}\right)+\left(\frac{1}{13}-\frac{1}{16}\right)\right]$

$= \frac{1}{3}\left(1-\frac{1}{16}\right) = \frac{1}{3}\times\frac{15}{16} = \frac{5}{16}.$

214. Given exp. $= \left(1-\frac{1}{2}\right)+\left(\frac{1}{2}-\frac{1}{3}\right)+\left(\frac{1}{3}-\frac{1}{4}\right)+\left(\frac{1}{4}-\frac{1}{5}\right)$

$+ \ldots + \left(\frac{1}{n}-\frac{1}{n+1}\right)$

$= \left(1-\frac{1}{n+1}\right) = \frac{n}{n+1}.$

215. Given exp. $= \frac{4\times3^3+3^2+3+1}{4\times3^3} = \frac{108+9+3+1}{108} = \frac{121}{108}.$

216. Given exp. $= \frac{4\cdot5\cdot6+5\cdot6+2\cdot6+2\cdot3}{1\cdot2\cdot3\cdot4\cdot5\cdot6} = \frac{120+30+12+6}{720}$

$= \frac{168}{720} = \frac{7}{30}.$

217. Given exp. $= \left(\frac{1}{1^2}-\frac{1}{2^2}\right)+\left(\frac{1}{2^2}-\frac{1}{3^2}\right)+\left(\frac{1}{3^2}-\frac{1}{4^2}\right)$

$+\left(\frac{1}{4^2}-\frac{1}{5^2}\right)+\ldots+\left(\frac{1}{9^2}-\frac{1}{10^2}\right)$

$= \left(\frac{1}{1^2}-\frac{1}{10^2}\right) = \left(1-\frac{1}{100}\right) = \frac{99}{100}.$

218. Given exp. $= \frac{4-1}{4\times1}+\frac{9-4}{9\times4}+\frac{16-9}{16\times9}+\ldots$

$= \left(1-\frac{1}{4}\right)+\left(\frac{1}{4}-\frac{1}{9}\right)+\left(\frac{1}{9}-\frac{1}{16}\right)+\ldots$

$= \left(\frac{1}{1^2}-\frac{1}{2^2}\right)+\left(\frac{1}{2^2}-\frac{1}{3^2}\right)+\left(\frac{1}{3^2}-\frac{1}{4^2}\right)+\ldots$

$\therefore$ 99th term of the series $= \left(\frac{1}{99^2}-\frac{1}{100^2}\right).$

$\therefore$ Given exp. $= \left(\frac{1}{1^2}-\frac{1}{2^2}\right)+\left(\frac{1}{2^2}-\frac{1}{3^2}\right)+\left(\frac{1}{3^2}-\frac{1}{4^2}\right)$

$+\ldots+\left(\frac{1}{98^2}-\frac{1}{99^2}\right)+\left(\frac{1}{99^2}-\frac{1}{100^2}\right)$

$= \left(1-\frac{1}{100^2}\right) = \left(1-\frac{1}{10000}\right) = \frac{9999}{10000}.$

219. Suppose Mayank, Mirza and Little paid ₹ x, ₹ y and ₹ z respectively.

Then, $x = \frac{1}{2}(60000-x),\ y = \frac{1}{3}(60000-y),\ z = \frac{1}{4}(60000-z).$

$\Rightarrow$ $2x = 60000 - x$, $3y = 60000 - y$, $4z = 60000 - z$

$\Rightarrow$ $3x = 60000$, $4y = 60000$, $5z = 60000$

$\Rightarrow$ $x = 20000$, $y = 15000$, $z = 12000$.

Amount paid by Jaspal

= ₹ [60000 – (20000 + 15000 + 12000)] = ₹ 13000

220. Income after 1 year = ₹ (4×2^1) lakhs.

Income after 2 years = ₹ $(4 \times 2 \times 2)$ lakhs

= ₹ (4×2^2) lakhs

$\therefore$ Income after 5 years = ₹ (4×2^5) lakhs = ₹ 128 lakhs

= ₹ 1.28 crores.

221. Since the population doubles every day, so it was half-full on 27/2/2007 and quarter-full on 26/2/2007.

222. Since the number doubles every minute, so the basket was $\frac{1}{2^n}$ full in $(60 - n)$ minutes.

Thus, it was $\frac{1}{32}\left(=\frac{1}{2^5}\right)$ full in (60 – 5) i.e., 55 minutes.

223. Total amount received by the man in 2010

= ₹ $[(5000 \times 2^4) + (5000 \times 2^3) + (5000 \times 2^2) + (5000 \times 2)]$

= ₹ (80000 + 40000 + 20000 + 10000) = ₹ 150000.

224. True length of the rope = 120 m + (3 × 120) cm

= 120 m + 360 cm

= 120 m + 3 m 60 cm = 123 m 60 cm.

225. Let the number be x. Then, $63x - 36x = 3834$

$\Leftrightarrow 27x = 3834$

$\Leftrightarrow x = 142.$

226. Among the given numbers, only 60489 is a multiple of 423.

227. Let the given number be x.

Then, $\frac{7}{8}x - \frac{7}{18}x = 770 \Leftrightarrow \frac{63x-28x}{72} = 770 \Leftrightarrow \frac{35x}{72} = 770$

$\Leftrightarrow x = \left(\frac{770\times72}{35}\right) = 1584.$

228. Let the number be x.

Then, $\frac{17}{8}x - \frac{8}{17}x = 225 \Leftrightarrow \frac{289x-64x}{136} = 225$

$\Leftrightarrow \frac{225}{136}x = 225 \Leftrightarrow x = 136.$

$\therefore$ Expected answer $= 136 \div \frac{17}{8} = \left(136\times\frac{8}{17}\right) = 64.$

229. Let the number be $2x$.

Then, $\left(\frac{x}{6}+\frac{x}{4}\right)-\frac{2x}{5} = 4 \Leftrightarrow \frac{10x+15x-24x}{60} = 4 \Leftrightarrow x = 240.$

Hence, required number = $2x$ = 480.

230. Final answer $= \left(9\frac{1}{9}-3\frac{2}{3}\right)\times450 = \left(\frac{82}{9}-\frac{11}{3}\right)\times450$

$= \left(\frac{49}{9}\times450\right) = 2450.$

231. $\frac{7}{8}$ of $1008 - \frac{3}{4}$ of $968 = \left(\frac{7}{8}\times1008\right)-\left(\frac{3}{4}\times968\right)$

$= 882 - 726 = 156.$

232. $x = y - \frac{y}{10} \Rightarrow x = \frac{9y}{10} \Rightarrow x = \frac{9}{10}\times y \Rightarrow x \propto y.$

Thus, as y increases, x also increases.

233. Let the number be x. Then,

$$\frac{3}{4} \text{ of } \frac{4}{5} \text{ of } x - \frac{1}{6} \text{ of } \frac{2}{5} \text{ of } x = 648$$

$$\Rightarrow \frac{3x}{5} - \frac{x}{15} = 648 \Rightarrow \frac{8x}{15} = 648 \Rightarrow x = \frac{648 \times 15}{8} = 1215.$$

234. Let the required number be x.

Then, $x + 1\frac{1}{2} = x \times 1\frac{1}{2} \Rightarrow x + \frac{3}{2} = \frac{3}{2}x \Rightarrow \frac{x}{2} = \frac{3}{2} \Rightarrow x = 3.$

235. Let the required sum be ₹ x.

Then, $\frac{5}{12} \text{ of } x = 3\frac{3}{4} \text{ of } 100 \Leftrightarrow \frac{5x}{12} = \left(\frac{15}{4} \times 100\right) = 375$

$$\Leftrightarrow x = \left(\frac{375 \times 12}{5}\right) = 900.$$

236. Let x of $\frac{1}{12} = \frac{3}{8}$. Then, $\frac{x}{12} = \frac{3}{8} \Leftrightarrow x = \left(\frac{3}{8} \times 12\right) = \frac{9}{2}.$

237. Sum of given fractions $= \frac{7}{4} + \frac{5}{2} + \frac{67}{12} + \frac{10}{3} + \frac{9}{4}$

$$= \left(\frac{21 + 30 + 67 + 40 + 27}{12}\right) = \frac{185}{12}.$$

The whole number just less than $\frac{185}{12}$ is 15.

Let $\frac{185}{12} - x = 15$. Then, $x = \left(\frac{185}{12} - 15\right) = \frac{5}{12}.$

238. Sum of given fractions $= 5\frac{3}{4} + 4\frac{4}{5} + 7\frac{3}{8} = \frac{23}{4} + \frac{24}{5} + \frac{59}{8}$

$$= \frac{230 + 192 + 295}{40} = \frac{717}{40} = 17\frac{37}{40}.$$

$\therefore$ Required fraction $= \left(18 - 17\frac{37}{40}\right) = \frac{3}{40}.$

239. Clearly, $\frac{x+1}{x}$ is the only fraction in which the numerator is greater than the denominator. So, it is the greatest fraction.

240. $\frac{6}{7/8} - \frac{6/7}{8} = 6 \times \frac{8}{7} - \frac{6}{7} \times \frac{1}{8} = \frac{48}{7} - \frac{6}{56}$

$$= \frac{384 - 6}{56} = \frac{378}{56} = \frac{27}{4} = 6\frac{3}{4}.$$

241. Let the value of the estate be ₹ x.

Then, $\frac{4}{5} \text{ of } x = 16800 \Leftrightarrow x = \left(\frac{16800 \times 5}{4}\right) = 21000$

$$\Leftrightarrow \frac{3}{7}x = \left(\frac{3}{7} \times 21000\right) = 9000.$$

242. Let the number be x. Then,

$\frac{2}{5} \text{ of } \frac{1}{4} \text{ of } \frac{3}{7} \text{ of } x = 15 \Leftrightarrow x = \left(15 \times \frac{7}{3} \times 4 \times \frac{5}{2}\right) = 350$

$$\Leftrightarrow \frac{1}{2}x = 175.$$

243. Required fraction $= \frac{1 \text{ sec.}}{1 \text{ hr.}} = \frac{1 \text{ sec.}}{(1 \times 60 \times 60) \text{ sec.}} = \frac{1}{3600}.$

244. Height at the third bounce $= \left[32 \times \left(\frac{3}{4}\right)^3\right] \text{m} = \left(32 \times \frac{27}{64}\right) \text{m}$

$$= \frac{27}{2} \text{ m} = 13\frac{1}{2} \text{ m}.$$

245. Suppose Sanket earns ₹ x in each of the other eleven months.

Then, Sanket's earning in March = ₹ $(2x)$.

Sanket's annual earning = ₹ $(11x + 2x)$ = ₹ $(13x)$.

$\therefore$ Required fraction $= \frac{2x}{13x} = \frac{2}{13}.$

246. Let the capacity of the tank be x litres.

Then, $\frac{1}{3}x = 80 \Leftrightarrow x = 240 \Leftrightarrow \frac{1}{2}x = 120.$

247. Distance travelled on foot $= \left[\frac{7}{2} - \left(\frac{5}{3} + \frac{7}{6}\right)\right]$ km

$$= \left(\frac{7}{2} - \frac{17}{6}\right) \text{km} = \frac{2}{3} \text{ km}.$$

$\therefore$ Required fraction $= \frac{(2/3)}{(7/2)} = \left(\frac{2}{3} \times \frac{2}{7}\right) = \frac{4}{21}.$

248. Let the required fraction be x. Then,

$\frac{4}{7}x + \frac{4}{7} = \frac{15}{14} \Leftrightarrow \frac{4}{7}x = \left(\frac{15}{14} - \frac{4}{7}\right) = \frac{7}{14} = \frac{1}{2}$

$$\Leftrightarrow x = \left(\frac{1}{2} \times \frac{7}{4}\right) = \frac{7}{8}.$$

249. Required fraction $= \frac{\frac{2}{3} \text{ of } \frac{1}{4} \text{ of ₹ } 25.20}{\frac{3}{2} \text{ of ₹ } 36} = \frac{\text{₹ } 4.20}{\text{₹ } 54} = \frac{42}{540} = \frac{7}{90}.$

250. Let the length of longer piece be x cm.

Then, length of shorter piece $= \left(\frac{2}{5}x\right)$ cm.

$\therefore \quad x + \frac{2}{5}x = 70 \Leftrightarrow \frac{7x}{5} = 70 \Leftrightarrow x = \left(\frac{70 \times 5}{7}\right) = 50.$

Hence, length of shorter piece $= \frac{2}{5}x = \left(\frac{2}{5} \times 50\right)$ cm = 20 cm.

251. Let the whole amount be ₹ x. Then,

A's share = ₹ $\left(\frac{3}{16}x\right)$; B's share = ₹ $\left(\frac{x}{4}\right)$;

and C's share = ₹ $\left[x - \left(\frac{3x}{16} + \frac{x}{4}\right)\right]$ = ₹ $\left(\frac{9x}{16}\right)$.

$\therefore \quad \frac{9x}{16} = 81 \Leftrightarrow x = \left(\frac{81 \times 16}{9}\right) = 144.$

Hence, B's share = ₹ $\left(\frac{144}{4}\right)$ = ₹ 36.

252. Green portion $= \left[1 - \left(\frac{1}{10} + \frac{1}{20} + \frac{1}{30} + \frac{1}{40} + \frac{1}{50} + \frac{1}{60}\right)\right]$

$$= \left[1 - \frac{1}{10}\left(1 + \frac{1}{2} + \frac{1}{3} + \frac{1}{4} + \frac{1}{5} + \frac{1}{6}\right)\right]$$

$= 1 - \frac{1}{10} \times \frac{147}{60} = 1 - \frac{147}{600} = \frac{453}{600}.$

Let the length of the pole be x metres.

Then, $\frac{453}{600} x = 12.08 \Leftrightarrow x = \left(\frac{12.08 \times 600}{453}\right) = 16.$

253. Let the fraction be $\frac{a}{b}$. Then,

$\left(\frac{a}{b} \times \frac{a}{b}\right) \div \frac{b}{a} = \frac{512}{27} \Leftrightarrow \frac{a}{b} \times \frac{a}{b} \times \frac{a}{b} = \frac{512}{27}$

$\Leftrightarrow \left(\frac{a}{b}\right)^3 = \left(\frac{8}{3}\right)^3 \Leftrightarrow \frac{a}{b} = \frac{8}{3} = 2\frac{2}{3}.$

254. Maximum internal assessment score $= \left(\frac{47}{50} \times 10\right) = 9.4.$

Minimum internal assessment score $= \left(\frac{14}{50} \times 10\right) = 2.8.$

$\therefore$ Required difference $= (9.4 - 2.8) = 6.6.$

255. Let savings in N.S.C. and P.P.F. be ₹ x and ₹ $(150000 - x)$ respectively. Then,

$\frac{1}{3} x = \frac{1}{2}(150000 - x) \Leftrightarrow \frac{x}{3} + \frac{x}{2} = 75000$

$\Leftrightarrow \frac{5x}{6} = 75000$

$\Leftrightarrow x = \left(\frac{75000 \times 6}{5}\right) = 90000.$

$\therefore$ Savings in Public Provident Fund = ₹ (150000 – 90000) = ₹ 60000.

256. Let there be $(x + 1)$ members. Then,

Father's share $= \frac{1}{4}$, share of each other member $= \frac{3}{4x}$.

$\therefore \quad 3\left(\frac{3}{4x}\right) = \frac{1}{4} \Leftrightarrow 4x = 36 \Leftrightarrow x = 9.$

Hence, total number of family members = 10.

257. Let salary = ₹ x. Then, tips = ₹ $\left(\frac{5}{4} x\right)$.

Total income = ₹ $\left(x + \frac{5}{4} x\right)$ = ₹ $\left(\frac{9x}{4}\right)$.

$\therefore$ Required fraction $= \left(\frac{5x}{4} \times \frac{4}{9x}\right) = \frac{5}{9}.$

258. Let C's share = ₹ x. Then, B's share = ₹ $\left(\frac{x}{4}\right)$, A's share

= ₹ $\left(\frac{2}{3} \times \frac{x}{4}\right)$ = ₹ $\frac{x}{6}$.

$\therefore \quad \frac{x}{6} + \frac{x}{4} + x = 1360 \Leftrightarrow \frac{17x}{12} = 1360$

$\Leftrightarrow x = \left(\frac{1360 \times 12}{17}\right)$ = ₹ 960.

Hence, B's share = ₹ $\left(\frac{960}{4}\right)$ = ₹ 240.

259. Let Tanya's share = ₹ x. Then, Veena's share

= ₹ $\left(\frac{x}{2}\right)$, Amita's share = ₹ $\left(\frac{2}{3} \times \frac{x}{2}\right)$ = ₹ $\left(\frac{x}{3}\right)$.

Total bill = ₹ $\left(x + \frac{x}{2} + \frac{x}{3}\right)$ = ₹ $\left(\frac{11x}{6}\right)$.

$\therefore$ Required fraction $= \left(\frac{x}{2} \times \frac{6}{11x}\right) = \frac{3}{11}.$

260. Let the capacity of the tank be x litres.

Then, $\frac{1}{4} x = 135 \Leftrightarrow x = 135 \times 4 = 540.$

$\therefore$ Required fraction $= \left(\frac{180}{540}\right) = \frac{1}{3}.$

261. Let the capacity of the tank be x litres.

Then, $\frac{6}{7} x - \frac{2}{5} x = 16$

$\Leftrightarrow 30x - 14x = 16 \times 35$

$\Leftrightarrow 16x = 560$

$\Leftrightarrow x = 35.$

262. Let the capacity of the drum be x litres.

Then, $\frac{3}{4} x - \frac{7}{12} x = 30$

$\Leftrightarrow 9x - 7x = 12 \times 30$

$\Leftrightarrow 2x = 360$

$\Leftrightarrow x = 180.$

263. Let x be the number of bottles of oil that the tin can contain.

Then, $\frac{5}{8} x - \frac{3}{5} x = 10 - 8 \Leftrightarrow 25x - 24x = 2 \times 40 \Leftrightarrow x = 80.$

264. R.F. $= \frac{10 \text{ cm}}{1 \text{ m}} = \frac{10 \text{ cm}}{100 \text{ cm}} = \frac{1}{10}.$

265. An area of 49 sq. km is represented by an area of 100 sq. cm on the map.

So, a distance of 7 km is represented by a length of 10 cm on the map.

$\therefore$ R.F. $= \frac{10 \text{ cm}}{7 \text{ km}} = \frac{10 \text{ cm}}{7 \times 10^5 \text{ cm}} = \frac{1}{70000}.$

266. Let the capacity of the bucket be x litres. Then,

Capacity of 1 large bottle $= \frac{x}{4}$; Capacity of 1 small bottle $= \frac{x}{7}$.

Fluid left in large bottle $= \left(\frac{x}{4} - \frac{x}{7}\right) = \frac{3x}{28}.$

$\therefore$ Required fraction $= \left(\frac{3x/28}{x/4}\right) = \left(\frac{3x}{28} \times \frac{4}{x}\right) = \frac{3}{7}.$

267. Let the capacity of 1 bucket = x.

Then, capacity of tank = $25x$.

New capacity of bucket $= \frac{2}{5} x.$

$\therefore$ Required number of buckets $= \frac{25x}{(2x/5)}$

$= \left(25x \times \frac{5}{2x}\right) = \frac{125}{2} = 62\frac{1}{2}.$

268. Clearly, more fuel, the longer will the engine run.

$\therefore \frac{4}{5}:\frac{1}{3}::12:x$ or $\frac{4}{5}x=\frac{1}{3}\times 12=4$ or $x=4\times\frac{5}{4}=5.$

269. Suppose the taller tree grows x feet in 1 year.

Then, the shorter tree grows $\frac{3x}{5}$ ft in 1 year.

$$\therefore \quad 4x+4\times\frac{3}{5}x=8 \Leftrightarrow 4x+\frac{12}{5}x=8 \Leftrightarrow \frac{32}{5}x=8$$

$$\Leftrightarrow x=\frac{8\times 5}{32}=\frac{5}{4}.$$

Growth of shorter tree in 2 years $=\left(2\times\frac{3x}{5}\right)$ ft

$$=\left(2\times\frac{3}{5}\times\frac{5}{4}\right)\text{ft}=\frac{3}{2}\text{ ft}=1\frac{1}{2}\text{ ft}.$$

270. Let the amount of fuel consumed while coming back be x gallons.

Then, amount of fuel consumed while going

$$=\left(x+\frac{x}{4}\right)\text{gallons}=\frac{5x}{4}\text{ gallons}.$$

$$\therefore \quad x+\frac{5x}{4}=4\frac{1}{2} \Leftrightarrow \frac{9x}{4}=\frac{9}{2} \Leftrightarrow x=\frac{9}{2}\times\frac{4}{9}=2.$$

271. Let the highest temperature be x degrees.

Then, lowest temperature $=\left[\left(1+\frac{1}{3}\right)\frac{x}{2}\right]$ degrees

$$=\left(\frac{4}{3}\times\frac{x}{2}\right)\text{degrees}=\frac{2x}{3}\text{ degrees}.$$

$$\therefore \quad x+\frac{2x}{3}=100 \Leftrightarrow \frac{5x}{3}=100 \Leftrightarrow x=\frac{100\times 3}{5}=60.$$

So, lowest temperature $=\left(\frac{2}{3}\times 60\right)$ degrees $=40$ degrees.

272. Let the total number of students in the class be x.

Then, number of boys $=\frac{2x}{3}$; number of girls $=\frac{x}{3}$.

Number of boys who are over 160 cm tall $=\left(\frac{3}{4}\times\frac{2x}{3}\right)=\frac{x}{2}$.

So, $\frac{x}{2}=18$ or $x=36$.

$\therefore$ Number of girls $=\frac{36}{3}=12$.

273. Suppose initially Peter had ₹ x. Then,

Amount received by Michael = ₹$\left(\frac{x}{4}\right)$. Amount remaining with Peter = ₹$\left(x-\frac{x}{4}\right)$ = ₹$\left(\frac{3x}{4}\right)$.

Amount received by Sam = ₹$\left(\frac{1}{2}\times\frac{x}{4}\right)$ = ₹$\left(\frac{x}{8}\right)$.

$$\therefore \quad \frac{3x}{4}-\frac{x}{8}=500 \Leftrightarrow 5x=4000 \Leftrightarrow x=800.$$

Hence, amount received by Michael = $(x/4)$ = ₹ 200.

274. A's share $=\frac{1}{3}$. Remainder $=\left(1-\frac{1}{3}\right)=\frac{2}{3}$.

B's share $=\frac{2}{5}$ of $\frac{2}{3}=\frac{4}{15}$. Rest $=\left(\frac{2}{3}-\frac{4}{15}\right)=\frac{6}{15}=\frac{2}{5}$.

C's share = D's share $=\frac{1}{2}$ of $\frac{2}{5}=\frac{1}{5}$.

275. Let the total length of the journey be x km.

Then, $\frac{2}{5}x=1200 \Leftrightarrow x=\frac{1200\times 5}{2}=3000.$

Distance travelled by car $=\left(\frac{1}{3}\times 3000\right)$km $=1000$ km.

$\therefore$ Distance travelled by train = [3000 − (1200 + 1000)] km = 800 km.

276. Let the total income be ₹ x.

Then, remaining money

$$= ₹\left[x-\left(\frac{x}{4}+\frac{x}{5}\right)\right] = ₹\left(x-\frac{9x}{20}\right) = ₹\,\frac{11x}{20}.$$

So, $\frac{11x}{20}=231 \Leftrightarrow x=\frac{231\times 20}{11}=420.$

277. Part read on first day $=\frac{3}{8}$. Remaining part $=\left(1-\frac{3}{8}\right)=\frac{5}{8}$.

Part read on second day $=\frac{4}{5}$ of $\frac{5}{8}=\frac{1}{2}$.

Unread part $=\left[1-\left(\frac{3}{8}+\frac{1}{2}\right)\right]=\frac{1}{8}$.

Let the number of pages be x.

Then, $\frac{1}{8}x=30$ or $x=30\times 8=240$.

278. Out of 5 girls, 1 took part in fete. Out of 8 boys, 1 took part in fete.

$\therefore$ Out of 13 students, 2 took part in fete.

Hence, $\frac{2}{13}$ of the total number took part in fete.

279. French men $=\frac{1}{5}$; French women $=\left(\frac{1}{5}+\frac{2}{3}\times\frac{1}{5}\right)=\frac{5}{15}=\frac{1}{3}$.

French people $=\left(\frac{1}{5}+\frac{1}{3}\right)=\frac{8}{15}$.

$\therefore$ Not French $=\left(1-\frac{8}{15}\right)=\frac{7}{15}$.

280. Girls $=\frac{3}{5}$; Boys $=\left(1-\frac{3}{5}\right)=\frac{2}{5}$.

Fraction of students absent $=\frac{2}{9}$ of $\frac{3}{5}+\frac{1}{4}$ of $\frac{2}{5}$

$$=\frac{6}{45}+\frac{1}{10}=\frac{21}{90}=\frac{7}{30}.$$

$\therefore$ Fraction of students present $=\left(1-\frac{7}{30}\right)=\frac{23}{30}$.

281. Number of boys who participate = 100.

$\therefore \frac{1}{3}$ of boys = 100 or total number of boys = 300.

Number of girls who participate = 200.

$\therefore \quad \frac{1}{2}$ of girls = 200 or total number of girls = 400.

Hence, total number of students = (300 + 400) = 700.

282. Let the number of votes cast be x. Then, number of votes required $= \frac{3x}{4}$.

Counted votes $= \frac{2x}{3}$. Uncounted votes $= \left(x - \frac{2x}{3}\right) = \frac{x}{3}$.

Votes won by the candidate $= \frac{5}{6}$ of $\frac{3x}{4} = \frac{5x}{8}$.

Remaining votes required $= \left(\frac{3x}{4} - \frac{5x}{8}\right) = \frac{x}{8}$.

$\therefore \quad$ Required fraction $= \frac{(x/8)}{(x/3)} = \left(\frac{x}{8} \times \frac{3}{x}\right) = \frac{3}{8}$.

283. Let the total number of shots be x. Then,

Shots fired by A $= \frac{5}{8}x$; Shots fired by B $= \frac{3}{8}x$.

Killing shots by A $= \frac{1}{3}$ of $\frac{5}{8}x = \frac{5x}{24}$;

Shots missed by B $= \frac{1}{2}$ of $\frac{3}{8}x = \frac{3}{16}x$.

$\therefore \quad \frac{3x}{16} = 27$ or $x = \left(\frac{27 \times 16}{3}\right) = 144$.

Birds killed by A $= \frac{5x}{24} = \left(\frac{5}{24} \times 144\right) = 30$.

284. Number of alterations required in 1 shirt $= \left(\frac{2}{3} + \frac{3}{4} + \frac{4}{5}\right)$

$= \frac{133}{60}$.

$\therefore$ Number of alterations required in 60 shirts $= \left(\frac{133}{60} \times 60\right)$

= 133.

285. Let the largest fraction be x and the smallest be y.

Then, $\frac{x}{y} = \frac{7}{6}$ or $y = \frac{6}{7}x$.

Let the middle one be z.

Then, $x + \frac{6}{7}x + z = \frac{59}{24}$ or $z = \left(\frac{59}{24} - \frac{13x}{7}\right)$

$\therefore \quad \frac{59}{24} - \frac{13x}{7} + \frac{1}{3} = \frac{7}{6} \Leftrightarrow \frac{13x}{7} = \frac{59}{24} + \frac{1}{3} - \frac{7}{6} = \frac{39}{24}$

$\Leftrightarrow x = \left(\frac{39}{24} \times \frac{7}{13}\right) = \frac{7}{8}$.

So, $x = \frac{7}{8}, y = \frac{6}{7} \times \frac{7}{8} = \frac{3}{4}$ and $z = \frac{59}{24} - \frac{13}{7} \times \frac{7}{8} = \frac{20}{24} = \frac{5}{6}$.

Hence, the fractions are $\frac{7}{8}, \frac{5}{6}$ and $\frac{3}{4}$.

286. Let the number of hats purchased be x. Then, number of brown hats $= \frac{x}{4}$.

Number of hats sold $= \frac{2x}{3}$. Number of hats left unsold $= \left(x - \frac{2x}{3}\right) = \frac{x}{3}$.

Number of brown hats sold $= \frac{4}{5}$ of $\frac{x}{4} = \frac{x}{5}$. Number of brown hats left unsold $= \left(\frac{x}{4} - \frac{x}{5}\right) = \frac{x}{20}$.

$\therefore \quad$ Required fraction $= \frac{\left(\frac{x}{20}\right)}{\left(\frac{x}{3}\right)} = \frac{x}{20} \times \frac{3}{x} = \frac{3}{20}$.

287. Let the capacities of the bigger and smaller jars be x litres and y litres respectively.

Then, $\frac{x}{4} = \frac{y}{3} \Rightarrow y = \frac{3}{4}x$.

Quantity of water in bigger jar $= \left(\frac{x}{4} + \frac{y}{3}\right)$ litres

$= \left(\frac{x}{4} + \frac{1}{3} \times \frac{3}{4}x\right)$ litres $= \frac{x}{2}$ litres.

Hence, $\frac{1}{2}$ of the larger jar is filled with water.

288. Let Mr. X's total income be ₹ x. Then, expenditure on food = ₹ $\frac{x}{4}$.

Expenditure on education = ₹ $\left[\left(1 - \frac{1}{3}\right)\frac{x}{4}\right]$

= ₹ $\left(\frac{2}{3} \times \frac{x}{4}\right)$ = ₹ $\frac{x}{6}$.

$\therefore \quad$ Required fraction $= \frac{\left(\frac{x}{4} + \frac{x}{6}\right)}{x} = \frac{5x}{12} \times \frac{1}{x} = \frac{5}{12}$.

289. Let the number of men in the 1st, 2nd, 3rd and 4th battalions be x, y, z and t respectively.

Then, $\frac{1}{2}x = \frac{2}{3}y = \frac{3}{4}z = \frac{4}{5}t \Rightarrow x = \frac{4}{3}y, z = \frac{8}{9}y, t = \frac{5}{6}y$.

Now, $x + y + z + t = 7300$

$\Rightarrow \quad \frac{4}{3}y + y + \frac{8}{9}y + \frac{5}{6}y = 7300$

$\Rightarrow \quad \frac{24y + 18y + 16y + 15y}{18} = 7300$

$\Rightarrow \quad 73y = 7300 \times 18 \Rightarrow y = 1800$.

290. Required fraction = Fraction of work left after Tuesday

$= 1 - \left(\frac{3}{5} + \frac{1}{3} \text{ of } \frac{2}{5}\right) = 1 - \left(\frac{3}{5} + \frac{2}{15}\right)$

$= 1 - \frac{11}{15} = \frac{4}{15}$.

291. Let the total score be x. Then, highest score $= \frac{3x}{11}$.

Remainder $= \left(x - \frac{3x}{11}\right) = \frac{8x}{11}$. Next highest score

$= \frac{3}{11}$ of $\frac{8x}{11} = \frac{24x}{121}$.

$\therefore \quad \frac{3x}{11} - \frac{24x}{121} = 9 \Leftrightarrow 33x - 24x = 9 \times 121$

$\Leftrightarrow 9x = 9 \times 121 \Leftrightarrow x = 121.$

292. Let the hourly wage of each sales person be ₹ x.
Then, hourly wage of each mechanic = ₹ $(2x)$.

Hourly wage of each custodial worker = ₹$\left(\frac{2x}{3}\right)$.

$\therefore$ Required fraction = $\frac{x}{\left(\frac{2x}{3}\right)} = \frac{3}{2}$.

293. Sukhvinder's monthly income = ₹$\left(\frac{234000}{12}\right)$ = ₹ 19500.

Jassi's monthly income = ₹$\left(\frac{3}{2} \times 19500\right)$ = ₹ 29250.

$\therefore$ Ganeshi's monthly income = ₹ (2 × 29250) = ₹ 58500.

294. Cost per kg of rice last year = ₹$\left(\frac{1044}{36}\right)$ = ₹ 29.

Cost per kg of rice this year = ₹$\left(\frac{768}{24}\right)$ = ₹ 32.

$\therefore$ Required difference = ₹ (32 – 29) = ₹ 3.

295. $12B + 30W = 8940 \Rightarrow \frac{1}{3}(12B + 30W) = \frac{1}{3} \times 8940$

$\Rightarrow 4B + 10W = 2980.$

296. $5P + 8C = 145785 \Rightarrow 3(5P + 8C) = 3 \times 145785$

$\Rightarrow 15P + 24C = 437355.$

297. $21T + 35C = 41825 \Rightarrow \frac{3}{7}(21T + 35C) = \frac{3}{7} \times 41825$

$\Rightarrow 9T + 15C = 17925.$

298. Cost of 1 kg of sugar = ₹$\left(\frac{195}{13}\right)$ = ₹ 15.

Cost of 1 kg of rice = ₹$\left(\frac{544}{17}\right)$ = ₹ 32.

Cost of 1 kg of wheat = ₹$\left(\frac{336}{21}\right)$ = ₹ 16.

$\therefore$ Required cost = ₹ (15 × 21 + 32 × 26 + 16 × 19)
= ₹ (315 + 832 + 304) = ₹ 1451.

299. (*a*) Price per kg = ₹$\left(\frac{160}{10}\right)$ = ₹ 16;

(*b*) Price per kg = ₹$\left(\frac{30}{2}\right)$ = ₹ 15;

(*c*) Price per kg = ₹$\left(\frac{70}{4}\right)$ = ₹ 17.50;

(*d*) Price per kg = ₹$\left(\frac{340}{20}\right)$ = ₹ 17;

(*e*) Price per kg = ₹$\left(\frac{130}{8}\right)$ = ₹ 16.25.

Clearly, the most economical price is 2 kilo for ₹ 30.

300. Let the time spent on each Maths problem be $(2x)$ minutes and that spent on each other question be x minutes.
Then, $50 \times 2x + 150x = 3 \times 60 \Leftrightarrow 250x = 180$

$\Leftrightarrow x = \frac{180}{250} = \frac{18}{25}$.

$\therefore$ Total time spent on Mathematics problems

$= \left(50 \times 2 \times \frac{18}{25}\right)$ min = 72 min.

301. Duration from 4.56 P.M. to 5.32 P.M. = 36 min.

$= \left(\frac{36}{60}\right)$ hour $= \frac{3}{5}$ hour.

302. 72 hr 6 min = (72 × 60 + 6) min = 4326 min.

$\therefore$ 72 hr 6 min ÷ 14 = 4326 min ÷ 14
= 309 min
= 5 hr 9 min.

```
    309
14)4326
   42
    126
    126
     ×
```

303. Time between 10 a.m. and 13.27 hours = 3 hrs. 27 min. = 207 min.
Total duration of free time = (5 × 3) min = 15 min.
Remaining time = (207 – 15) min. = 192 min.
$\therefore$ Duration of each of the 4 periods

$= \left(\frac{192}{4}\right)$ min. = 48 min.

304.

	Hrs.	Min.	Sec.
	3	17	49
(–)	1	54	50
	1	22	59

Total time = (1 × 60 + 22) min. + 59 sec.
= (82 × 60 + 59) sec.
= 4979 sec.

$\therefore$ Number of times the light is seen $= \left(\frac{4979}{13} + 1\right) = 384.$

305. The woman works from Sunday to Saturday and rests for the first time on Sunday. She then works from Monday to Sunday and rests for the second time on Monday. Likewise, she rests for the third time on Tuesday. Thus, starting from Sunday, for the 10th time she would rest on Tuesday. (as the cycle repeats after every 7 days).

306. $9 * 11 = 9^2 + (11)^2 - 9 \times 11 = 81 + 121 - 99 = 103.$

307. $(3 * -1) = \frac{3 \times (-1)}{3 + (-1)} = \frac{-3}{2}$. So, $3 * (3 * -1)$

$= 3 * \left(\frac{-3}{2}\right) = \frac{3 \times \left(\frac{-3}{2}\right)}{3 + \left(\frac{-3}{2}\right)} = \frac{-9}{2} \times \frac{2}{3} = -3.$

308. $3 * 5 + 5 * 3 = (2 \times 3 - 3 \times 5 + 3 \times 5) + (2 \times 5 - 3 \times 3 + 5 \times 3)$

$= (6 + 10 - 9 + 15) = 22.$

309. $4 \oplus (3 \oplus p) = 4 \oplus (3^2 + 2p) = 4 \oplus (9 + 2p) = 4^2 + 2(9 + 2p) = 34 + 4p.$

$\therefore \quad 34 + 4p = 50 \Rightarrow 4p = 50 - 34 = 16 \Rightarrow p = 4.$

310. $(a * b * c) * a * b = \left(\frac{a+b}{c}\right) * a * b = \frac{\left(\frac{a+b}{c}\right) + a}{b} = \frac{a + b + ac}{bc}.$

311. **Step I:** $6 \times 3 + 6^2 = 18 + 36 = 54$.
Step II: $(54 \div 5) + 6 = 10.8 + 6 = 16.8$.
Step III: $(16.8 \div 3)^2 = (5.6)^2 = 31.36$.

312. **Step I:** $2.5 \times 3 + (2.5)^2 = 7.5 + 6.25 = 13.75$.
Step II: $(13.75 \div 5) + 6 = 2.75 + 6 = 8.75$.
Step III: $(8.75 \div 3)^2 = (2.917)^2 = 8.508 \approx 8.51$.

313. **Step I:** $5 \times 3 + 5^2 = 15 + 25 = 40$.
Step II: $(40 \div 5) + 6 = 8 + 6 = 14$.
Step III: $(14 \div 3)^2 = (4.67)^2 \approx 21.80$.

314. $2 \wedge a = a \wedge 3 \Rightarrow 2 \times 2 + a = 2 \times a + 3$
$\Rightarrow 4 + a = 2a + 3 \Rightarrow a = 1$.

315. $$\left[\frac{(5 \oplus 7) + (4 \oplus 4)}{3(5 \oplus 5) - (15 \oplus 11) - 3}\right] = \left[\frac{(5+7)+4^2}{3\times 5^2 - 2\times 15 - 3}\right]$$
$$= \left[\frac{12+16}{75-30-3}\right] = \frac{28}{42} = \frac{2}{3}.$$

316. Thickness of snow at 3 p.m. $= \left[2\frac{1}{4} + \left(3 \times 1\frac{1}{4}\right)\right]$ inches
$= \left(\frac{9}{4} + 3 \times \frac{5}{4}\right)$ inches
$= \left(\frac{9}{4} + \frac{15}{4}\right)$ inches
$= \left(\frac{24}{4}\right)$ inches $= 6$ inches.

317. In 2 min, the squirrel climbs $(6 - 4)$ m $= 2$ m.
In (2×57), i.e., 114 min, the squirrel climbs (2×57) m $= 114$ m.
In 115 min, the squirrel climbs $(114 + 6)$ m $= 120$ m to reach the top.

318. For the money to grow 3 times, Ram needs to deposit ₹ (3000 – 1000) = ₹ 2000.
A net amount of ₹ (750 – 500) = ₹ 250 is deposited in 1 month.
So, a net amount of ₹ 2000 will be deposited in $\left(\frac{2000}{250}\right) = 8$ months.

319. In 11 days, the height of the plant increases by $(11 - 6)$ cm i.e., 5 cm.
In (11×18) i.e., 198 days, the height of the plant increases by (5×18) i.e., 90 cm.
In the next 10 days, the height of the plant increases by another 10 cm.
So, in 208 days, the height of the plant will increase by $(90 + 10) = 100$ cm or 1 m and become 2 m.

320. Number of steps $= \left(10 \div \frac{1}{2}\right) = 20$.

To reach the top, the ant covers the height of 20 steps and the width of 19 steps because the moment it ascends the height of 20th step, it reaches the top.
∴ Distance travelled by the ant
$= \left[\left(\frac{1}{2} \times 20\right) + (1 \times 19)\right]$ ft $= (10 + 19)$ ft $= 29$ ft.

321. Required sum $= \frac{1}{2} + \left(\frac{1}{3} + \frac{2}{3}\right) + \left(\frac{1}{4} + \frac{2}{4} + \frac{3}{4}\right) + \left(\frac{1}{5} + \frac{2}{5} + \frac{3}{5} + \frac{4}{5}\right) + \ldots + \left(\frac{1}{100} + \frac{2}{100} + \frac{3}{100} + \ldots + \frac{99}{100}\right)$
$= \frac{1}{2} + \frac{2}{2} + \frac{3}{2} + \frac{4}{2} + \ldots\ldots + \frac{99}{2}$
$= \frac{1}{2} \times (1 + 2 + 3 + \ldots.. + 99)$
$= \frac{1}{2} \times \frac{99 \times 100}{2} = 2475.$

322. Given exp. $= \frac{(1-x^2)(1+x^2)}{(1+x)} \times \frac{x}{1+x^2} \times \frac{1}{x(1-x)}$
$= \frac{(1-x)(1+x)(1+x^2)\,x}{(1+x)(1+x^2)\,x\,(1-x)} = 1.$

323. Given exp. $= \left(\frac{17}{15}\right)^2 + \left(\frac{2}{15}\right)^2 - 2 \times \frac{17}{15} \times \frac{2}{15} = \left(\frac{17}{15} - \frac{2}{15}\right)^2 = 1.$

324. Given exp. $= \left(13\frac{3}{4}\right)^2 + \left(5\frac{1}{4}\right)^2 + 2 \times 13\frac{3}{4} \times 5\frac{1}{4}$
$= \left(13\frac{3}{4} + 5\frac{1}{4}\right)^2 = \left(\frac{55}{4} + \frac{21}{4}\right)^2 = \left(\frac{76}{4}\right)^2 = (19)^2 = 361.$

325. Given exp. $= \frac{(75983)^2 - (45983)^2}{75983 - 45983}$
$= \frac{(75983 - 45983)(75983 + 45983)}{(75983 - 45983)}$
$= 75983 + 45983 = 121966.$

326. Given exp. $= \frac{a^2 - b^2}{a - b}$, $\left(\text{where } a = 13\frac{4}{7}, b = 8\frac{3}{7}\right)$
$= a + b = 13\frac{4}{7} + 8\frac{3}{7} = \frac{95}{7} + \frac{59}{7} = \frac{154}{7} = 22.$

327. $\frac{(a-b)^2 - (a+b)^2}{-4a} = \frac{x}{y} \Leftrightarrow \frac{(a^2 + b^2 - 2ab) - (a^2 + b^2 + 2ab)}{-4a} = \frac{x}{y}$
$\Leftrightarrow \frac{-4ab}{-4a} = \frac{x}{y} \Leftrightarrow b = \frac{x}{y} \Leftrightarrow x = yb.$

328. Given exp. $= \frac{\left(\frac{7}{8} + \frac{5}{6}\right)^2}{\left(\frac{7}{8}\right)^2 - \left(\frac{5}{6}\right)^2} = \frac{\left(\frac{7}{8} + \frac{5}{6}\right)^2}{\left(\frac{7}{8} + \frac{5}{6}\right)\left(\frac{7}{8} - \frac{5}{6}\right)}$
$= \frac{\left(\frac{7}{8} + \frac{5}{6}\right)}{\left(\frac{7}{8} - \frac{5}{6}\right)} = \left(\frac{41}{24} \times 24\right) = 41.$

329. Given exp. $= (1998 + 1997)(1998 - 1997) + (1996 + 1995)(1996 - 1995) + (1994 + 1993)(1994 - 1993)$
$= 1998 + 1997 + 1996 + 1995 + 1994 + 1993 = 11973.$

330. Given exp. $= \frac{(a+b)^2 + (a-b)^2}{a^2+b^2}$ (where $a = 856, b = 167$)

$= \frac{2(a^2+b^2)}{(a^2+b^2)} = 2.$

331. Given exp. $= \frac{(a+b)^2 - (a-b)^2}{ab} = \frac{4ab}{ab}$

$= 4$ (where $a = 469, b = 174$).

332. $2ab = (a^2 + b^2) - (a - b)^2 = 29 - 9 = 20 \Rightarrow ab = 10.$

333. $\frac{x^2-1}{x+1} = 4 \Leftrightarrow \frac{(x+1)(x-1)}{x+1} = 4 \Leftrightarrow x - 1 = 4 \Leftrightarrow x = 5.$

334. If $a = 3\frac{2}{3}, b = 2\frac{1}{2}, c = 4\frac{3}{4}, d = 3\frac{1}{3}$, then

Given exp. $= \frac{(a^2-b^2)}{(c^2-d^2)} \div \frac{(a-b)}{(c-d)} = \frac{(a^2-b^2)}{(c^2-d^2)} \times \frac{(c-d)}{(a-b)}$

$= \frac{(a+b)}{(c+d)} = \frac{3\frac{2}{3} + 2\frac{1}{2}}{4\frac{3}{4} + 3\frac{1}{3}} = \frac{\frac{11}{3} + \frac{5}{2}}{\frac{19}{4} + \frac{10}{3}}$

$= \frac{37}{6} \times \frac{12}{97} = \frac{74}{97}.$

335. Given exp. $= \frac{a^2-b^2}{a+b} = a - b$

$= \left(1 + \frac{1}{1 + \frac{1}{100}}\right) - \left(1 - \frac{1}{1 + \frac{1}{100}}\right)$

$= 2 \times \frac{1}{(101/100)} = 2 \times \frac{100}{101} = \frac{200}{101}.$

336. Given exp. $= \frac{769435 \times 770001 - (770001 - 769435)}{769435 + 770001 \times (769435 - 1)}$

$= \frac{769435 \times 770001 - 770001 + 769435}{769435 + 770001 \times 769435 - 770001} = 1.$

337. $a - b = 1 \Rightarrow (a - b)^3 = 1^3 = 1 \Rightarrow a^3 - b^3 - 3ab\,(a - b) = 1$

$\Rightarrow a^3 - b^3 - 3ab = 1$ [$\because a - b = 1$]

338. $x - y = 1 \Rightarrow (x - y)^2 = 1 \Rightarrow x^2 + y^2 - 2xy = 1$

$\Rightarrow 41 - 2xy = 1 \Rightarrow 2xy = 40.$

$\therefore \quad (x + y)^2 = x^2 + y^2 + 2xy = 41 + 40 = 81$

$\Rightarrow (x + y) = \pm 9.$

339. $x + y = 1 \Rightarrow (x + y)^2 = 1^2 = 1 \Rightarrow x^2 + y^2 + 2xy = 1$

$\Rightarrow x^2 + y^2 = 1 - 2xy$

$\Rightarrow (x^2 + y^2)^2 = (1 - 2xy)^2$

$\Rightarrow x^4 + y^4 + 2x^2y^2 = 1 + 4x^2y^2 - 4xy$

$\Rightarrow 2x^2y^2 - 4xy = 17 - 1 = 16$ [$\because x^4 + y^4 = 17$]

$\Rightarrow x^2y^2 - 2xy = 8.$

340. $\frac{x^2 + y^2 + z^2 - yz - zx - xy}{a^2 + b^2 + c^2 - ab - bc - ca}$

$= \frac{(a+m)^2 + (b+m)^2 + (c+m)^2 - (b+m)(c+m) - (c+m)(a+m) - (a+m)(b+m)}{a^2 + b^2 + c^2 - ab - bc - ca}$

$= \frac{a^2 + m^2 + 2am + b^2 + m^2 + 2bm + c^2 + m^2 + 2cm - bc - bm - cm - m^2 - ca - cm - am - m^2 - ab - am - bm - m^2}{a^2 + b^2 + c^2 - ab - bc - ca}$

$= \frac{a^2 + b^2 + c^2 - ab - bc - ca}{a^2 + b^2 + c^2 - ab - bc - ca} = 1.$

341. $(a + b + c)^2 = a^2 + b^2 + c^2 + 2(ab + bc + ca)$

$\Rightarrow \quad 2(ab + bc + ca) = (a + b + c)^2 - (a^2 + b^2 + c^2)$

$= 169 - 69 = 100$

$\Rightarrow \quad ab + bc + ca = 50.$

342. Given: $x^2 + y^2 + z^2 - 64 = -2(xy - yz - zx)$ ...(*i*)

Now, $[x + y + (-z)]^2 = x^2 + y^2 + z^2 + 2(xy - yz - zx)$

$\Rightarrow \quad (3z - z)^2 = x^2 + y^2 + z^2 + 2(xy - yz - zx)$

$\Rightarrow \quad -2(xy - yz - zx) = (x^2 + y^2 + z^2) - (2z)^2$ ...(*ii*)

From (*i*) and (*ii*), we get: $(2z)^2 = 64 \Leftrightarrow 4z^2 = 64$

$\Leftrightarrow z^2 = 16$

$\Leftrightarrow z = 4.$

343. Given exp. $= \left(\frac{a^3 + b^3}{a^2 + b^2 - ab}\right) = (a + b)$ (where $a = 785, b = 435$)

$= (785 + 435) = 1220.$

344. Given exp. $= \left(\frac{a^2 + ab + b^2}{a^3 - b^3}\right) = \left(\frac{1}{a - b}\right)$

(where $a = 147, b = 143$) $= \left(\frac{1}{147 - 143}\right) = \frac{1}{4}.$

345. Let $\frac{13^3 + 7^3}{13^2 + 7^2 - x} = 20.$

Then, $\frac{13^3 + 7^3}{13 + 7} = 13^2 + 7^2 - x$

$\Leftrightarrow 13^2 + 7^2 - 13 \times 7 = 13^2 + 7^2 - x$

$\Leftrightarrow x = 13 \times 7 = 91.$

346. Given exp. $= \frac{a^3 - b^3}{a^2 - b^2} = \frac{(a-b)(a^2 + ab + b^2)}{(a-b)(a+b)} = \frac{(a^2 + ab + b^2)}{(a+b)}$

$= \frac{\left(\frac{3}{5}\right)^2 + \left(\frac{3}{5} \times \frac{2}{5}\right) + \left(\frac{2}{5}\right)^2}{\left(\frac{3}{5} + \frac{2}{5}\right)}$

$= \frac{9}{25} + \frac{6}{25} + \frac{4}{25} = \frac{19}{25}.$

347. Given exp. $= \frac{a^3 + b^3 + c^3 - 3abc}{a^2 + b^2 + c^2 - ab - bc - ca}$

$= a + b + c = (38 + 34 + 28) = 100.$

348. Since $(x - y) + (y - z) + (z - x) = 0$,

so $(x - y)^3 + (y - z)^3 + (z - x)^3 = 3(x - y)(y - z)(z - x).$

$\therefore \quad$ Given exp. $= \frac{3(x-y)(y-z)(z-x)}{9(x-y)(y-z)(z-x)} = \frac{1}{3}.$

349. $\dfrac{x^3-y^3}{x^2-y^2}-\dfrac{3xy}{x+y}=\dfrac{(x-y)(x^2+y^2+xy)}{(x-y)(x+y)}-\dfrac{3xy}{(x+y)}$

$=\dfrac{(x^2+y^2+xy)-3xy}{(x+y)}=\dfrac{(x^2+y^2-2xy)}{(x+y)}$

$=\dfrac{(x-y)^2}{(x+y)}=\dfrac{(5-3)^2}{(5+3)}=\dfrac{4}{8}=\dfrac{1}{2}.$

350. $(a+b+c)=11 \Rightarrow (a+b+c)^2=(11)^2=121$

$\Rightarrow a^2+b^2+c^2+2(ab+bc+ca)=121$

$\Rightarrow a^2+b^2+c^2+2\times 20=121$

$\Rightarrow a^2+b^2+c^2=121-40=81.$

$\therefore \quad a^3+b^3+c^3-3abc=(a+b+c)(a^2+b^2+c^2-ab-bc-ca)$

$=11\,(81-20)=11\times 61=671.$

351. Since $(x-y)+(y-z)+(z-x)=0$,
so $(x-y)^3+(y-z)^3+(z-x)^3=3(x-y)(y-z)(z-x)$.
Since $(x^2-y^2)+(y^2-z^2)+(z^2-x^2)=0$,
so $(x^2-y^2)^3+(y^2-z^2)^3+(z^2-x^2)^3=3(x^2-y^2)(y^2-z^2)(z^2-x^2)$.

$\therefore$ Given exp. $=\dfrac{3(x-y)(y-z)(z-x)}{3(x^2-y^2)(y^2-z^2)(z^2-x^2)}$

$=\dfrac{1}{(x+y)(y+z)(z+x)}$

$=[(x+y)(y+z)(z+x)]^{-1}.$

352. $\dfrac{a^2}{bc}+\dfrac{b^2}{ca}+\dfrac{c^2}{ab}=\dfrac{a^3+b^3+c^3}{abc}=\dfrac{3abc}{abc}=3.$

$[\because a+b+c=0 \Rightarrow a^3+b^3+c^3=3abc]$

353. $a^3+b^3+c^3-3abc=(a+b+c)(a^2+b^2+c^2-ab-bc-ca)$

$=(29+24+27)[(29)^2+(24)^2+(27)^2-29\times 24-24\times 27-27\times 29]$

$=80\,(841+576+729-696-648-783)=80\times 19=1520.$

354. $\dfrac{x^2-1}{x}=4 \Rightarrow \left(\dfrac{x^2-1}{x}\right)^3=4^3=64$

$\Rightarrow \dfrac{x^6-1-3x^2(x^2-1)}{x^3}=64$

$\Rightarrow \dfrac{x^6-1-3x^2\cdot 4x}{x^3}=64$

$\Rightarrow x^6-1-12x^3=64x^3$

$\Rightarrow x^6-1=76x^3 \Rightarrow \dfrac{x^6-1}{x^3}=76.$

355. Let $a=32$, $b=79$, $c=-111$. Then, $a+b+c=0$.
So, $a^3+b^3+c^3=3abc \Rightarrow (32)^3+(79)^3-(111)^3$
$=3\times 32\times 79\times(-111)$

$\therefore$ Given exp. $=-(3\times 32\times 79\times 111)+3\times 32\times 79\times 111=0.$

356. $(x+y)=3 \Rightarrow (x+y)^2=9$

$\Rightarrow x^2+y^2+2xy=9$

$\Rightarrow x^2+y^2=9-2xy=9-4=5.$

$\therefore x^3+y^3=(x+y)(x^2+y^2-xy)=3\,(5-2)$

$=3\times 3=9.\ [\because x+y=3,\ x^2+y^2=5,\ xy=2]$

357. Given expression $=\dfrac{(x+y-z)(x-y+z)}{(x+z+y)(x+z-y)}+\dfrac{(y+x-z)(y-x+z)}{(x+y+z)(x+y-z)}+\dfrac{(z+x-y)(z-x+y)}{(y+z+x)(y+z-x)}$

$=\dfrac{(x+y-z)}{(x+y+z)}+\dfrac{(y-x+z)}{(x+y+z)}+\dfrac{(x-y+z)}{(x+y+z)}$

$=\dfrac{(x+y-z)+(y-x+z)+(x-y+z)}{(x+y+z)}$

$=\dfrac{x+y+z}{x+y+z}=1.$

358. $\dfrac{a}{p}+\dfrac{b}{q}+\dfrac{c}{r}=0 \Rightarrow aqr+bpr+cpq=0$ ...(i)

$\dfrac{p}{a}+\dfrac{q}{b}+\dfrac{r}{c}=1 \Rightarrow \left(\dfrac{p}{a}+\dfrac{q}{b}+\dfrac{r}{c}\right)^2=1$

$\Rightarrow \dfrac{p^2}{a^2}+\dfrac{q^2}{b^2}+\dfrac{r^2}{c^2}+2\left(\dfrac{pq}{ab}+\dfrac{pr}{ac}+\dfrac{qr}{bc}\right)=1$

$\Rightarrow \dfrac{p^2}{a^2}+\dfrac{q^2}{b^2}+\dfrac{r^2}{c^2}+\dfrac{2(pqc+prb+qra)}{abc}=1$

$\Rightarrow \dfrac{p^2}{a^2}+\dfrac{q^2}{b^2}+\dfrac{r^2}{c^2}=1$ [Using (i)]

359. $x^4-y^4=15 \Rightarrow (x^2-y^2)(x^2+y^2)=15=1\times 15$ or 3×5

$\Rightarrow (x^2-y^2)=3$ and $(x^2+y^2)=5$

[$\because$ x and y are natural numbers]

$\Rightarrow 2x^2=8 \Rightarrow x^2=4 \Rightarrow x=2.$

[Adding above two equations]

Putting $x=2$ in $x^2+y^2=5$, we get: $y=1$.

$\therefore \quad (x^4+y^4)=(2^4+1^4)=(16+1)=17.$

360. 26 trees have 25 gaps between them. Hence, required distance $=\left(\dfrac{225}{25}\right)\text{m}=9\text{ m}.$

361. Each row contains 12 plants.
12 plants have 11 gaps between them. So, total length of gaps = (11 × 2) metres and 1 metre is left on each side.
$\therefore$ Length = (22 + 2) m = 24 m.

362. Let the length of the side be x metres.
Then, number of posts required when placed 6 m apart $=\left(\dfrac{x}{6}+1\right)$.

And, number of posts required when placed 8 m apart $=\left(\dfrac{x}{8}+1\right)$.

$\therefore \left(\dfrac{x}{6}+1\right)-5=\left(\dfrac{x}{8}+1\right) \Leftrightarrow \dfrac{x}{6}-\dfrac{x}{8}=5 \Leftrightarrow \dfrac{x}{24}=5 \Leftrightarrow x=120\text{ m}.$

So, number of posts bought $=\left(\dfrac{120}{8}+1\right)=16.$

363. Gap between 2 consecutive trees $=\left(\dfrac{2000}{200}\right)\text{m}=10\text{ m}.$

[$\because$ 201 trees have 200 gaps between them]

$\therefore$ Required number of trees $=\left(\dfrac{50\times 1000}{10}+1\right)$

$==(5000+1)=5001.$

364. Total number of students = 54 × 30.

$\therefore$ Required number of rows = $\left(\frac{54 \times 30}{45}\right) = 36.$

365. Clearly, we have:

$x + 1 = y \Leftrightarrow x - y = -1$ ...(i)

And, $2(x - 1) = y \Leftrightarrow 2x - y = 2$ ...(ii)

Subtracting (i) from (ii), we get: $x = 3$. Putting $x = 3$ in (i), we get: $y = 4$.

366. Let the number of benches in the class be x.

Then, $6(x + 1) = 7x - 5 \Leftrightarrow x = 11$.

Hence, number of students in the class

$= 6(x + 1) = 6 \times 12 = 72.$

367. Let the number of benches in the class be x.

Then, $4(x - 3) = 3x + 3 \Leftrightarrow x = 15$.

$\therefore$ Total number of students = 3 × 15 + 3 = 48.

368. Let the number of students in a row be x and the total number of rows be y. Then,

total number of students in the class = xy.

$\therefore (x + 4)(y - 2) = xy \Rightarrow xy - 2x + 4y - 8 = xy$

$\Rightarrow 2x - 4y = -8 \Rightarrow x - 2y = -4$ ...(i)

And, $(x - 4)(y + 4) = xy \Rightarrow xy + 4x - 4y - 16 = xy$

$\Rightarrow 4x - 4y = 16 \Rightarrow x - y = 4$ ...(ii)

Subtracting (i) from (ii), we get: $y = 8$.

Putting $y = 8$ in (ii), we get: $x = 12$.

Hence, total number of students in the class = xy = (12 × 8) = 96.

369. Let Shyam's share be ₹ x. Then, Ram's share

$= ₹\left(x + \frac{3}{4}x\right) = ₹\frac{7x}{4}.$

$\therefore x + \frac{7x}{4} = 275 \Leftrightarrow \frac{11x}{4} = 275 \Leftrightarrow x = \frac{275 \times 4}{11} = 100.$

So, Ram's share = ₹$\left(\frac{7 \times 100}{4}\right)$ = ₹ 175.

370. Total number of sweets = (64 × 7 + 15) = 448 + 15 = 463.

371. Let the whole property be worth ₹ x. Then,

wife's share = ₹$\frac{x}{2}$; Son's share = ₹$\left(\frac{1}{2} \text{ of } \frac{x}{2}\right)$ = ₹$\frac{x}{4}$.

Remaining share = ₹$\left[x - \left(\frac{x}{2} + \frac{x}{4}\right)\right]$ = ₹$\frac{x}{4}$.

$\therefore$ Share of each daughter = ₹$\left(\frac{1}{2} \text{ of } \frac{x}{4}\right)$ = ₹$\frac{x}{8}$.

372. Let the number of children be x. Then, $10x + 3 = 11x - 4$

$\Rightarrow x = 7$.

$\therefore$ Number of sweets = (10 × 7 + 3) = 73.

373. Let the number of boys be x. Then, number of girls $= (70 - x)$.

$\therefore 2x + 3(70 - x) = 180 \Leftrightarrow x = 30.$

374. Let the total number of cows in the herd be x.

Then, share of fourth son = $x - \left(\frac{x}{2} + \frac{x}{4} + \frac{x}{5}\right) = x - \frac{19x}{20} = \frac{x}{20}.$

$\therefore \frac{x}{20} = 7$ or $x = 140.$

375. Let the total property be worth ₹ x.

Then, elder son's share = ₹$\left(\frac{5x}{11}\right)$. Balance = ₹$\left(x - \frac{5x}{11}\right)$

= ₹$\frac{6x}{11}$.

Younger son's share = ₹$\left(\frac{5}{11} \text{ of } \frac{6x}{11}\right)$ = ₹$\left(\frac{30x}{121}\right)$

$\therefore$ Widow's share = ₹$\left[x - \left(\frac{5x}{11} + \frac{30x}{121}\right)\right]$

= ₹$\left(x - \frac{85x}{121}\right)$ = ₹$\left(\frac{36x}{121}\right)$

$\frac{36x}{121} = 3600 \Leftrightarrow x = \frac{3600 \times 121}{36} = 12100.$

So, elder son's share = ₹$\left(\frac{5}{11} \times 12100\right)$ = ₹ 5500;

Younger son's share = ₹$\left(\frac{30}{121} \times 12100\right)$ = ₹ 3000.

376. Suppose each boy gets ₹ x. Then, each woman gets ₹ $2x$ and each man gets ₹ $(x + 2x)$ i.e., ₹ $3x$.

So, $10 \times 3x + 12 \times 2x + 20x = 370 \Leftrightarrow 30x + 24x + 20x = 370 \Leftrightarrow 74x = 370 \Leftrightarrow x = 5.$

$\therefore$ Amount received by 10 men = $30x$ = ₹ (30 × 5) = ₹ 150.

377. Let D's share = ₹ x. Then, C's share = ₹ x.

B's share = ₹ $(x + 125)$. A's share = ₹ $(x + x + 125)$ = ₹ $(2x + 125)$.

$\therefore (2x + 125) + (x + 125) + x + x = 750$

$\Leftrightarrow 5x = 500$

$\Leftrightarrow x = 100.$

Hence, A's share = $2x + 125$ = ₹ (2 × 100 + 125) = ₹ 325.

378. Let Gagan's share = ₹ x.

Then, Sachin's share = ₹$\left(\frac{x}{5}\right)$ and Rohit's share = ₹$\left(\frac{2x}{5}\right)$.

$\therefore \frac{2x}{5} + \frac{x}{5} + x = 1000 \Leftrightarrow 8x = 5000 \Leftrightarrow x = 625.$

379. If the second boy takes one-third of a certain number of marbles, the third boy is left with two-thirds of that number, which is twice the number with the second boy, regardless of the total number of marbles. Hence, the total number of marbles cannot be determined.

380. Wife's share = $\frac{1}{2}$. Remaining part = $\left(1 - \frac{1}{2}\right) = \frac{1}{2}$.

Share of 3 sons = $\left(\frac{2}{3} \text{ of } \frac{1}{2}\right) = \frac{1}{3}$. Remaining part

$= \left(\frac{1}{2} - \frac{1}{3}\right) = \frac{1}{6}.$

Each daughter's share = $\frac{1}{4} \times \frac{1}{6} = \frac{1}{24}$.

Let the total money be ₹ x. Then, $\frac{1}{24}x = 20000$

$\Leftrightarrow x = 20000 \times 24 = 480000.$

$\therefore$ Each son's share = ₹$\left[\frac{1}{3} \times \left(\frac{1}{3} \times 480000\right)\right]$ = ₹ 53,333.33.

381. $A + B + C + D = 47$ ...(i)
$A + B = 27$ ...(ii)
$A + C = 25$ ...(iii)
$A + D = 23$ ...(iv)
Adding (ii), (iii) and (iv), we get:
$2A + (A + B + C + D) = 75 \Leftrightarrow 2A + 47 = 75 \Leftrightarrow 2A = 28 \Leftrightarrow A = 14$.
Putting $A = 14$ in (ii), we get: $B = 13$.

382. Let the sum be ₹ x.
Then, $\frac{x}{12} - \frac{x}{16} = 400 \Leftrightarrow \frac{x}{48} = 400 \Leftrightarrow x = 400 \times 48 = 19200$.

383. Let the total number of sweets be $(25x + 8)$.
Then, $(25x + 8) - 22$ is divisible by 28
$\Leftrightarrow$ $(25x - 14)$ is divisible by 28
$\Leftrightarrow$ $28x - (3x + 14)$ is divisible by 28
$\Leftrightarrow$ $(3x + 14)$ is divisible by 28 $\Leftrightarrow x = 14$.
$\therefore$ Total number of sweets $= (25 \times 14 + 8) = 358$.

384. Let the total number of sweets be x. Then,
$\frac{x}{80} - \frac{x}{112} = 6 \Leftrightarrow \frac{7x - 5x}{560} = 6 \Leftrightarrow \frac{x}{280} = 6 \Leftrightarrow x = 1680$.
$\therefore$ Number of sweets each child was originally supposed to get $= \left(\frac{1680}{112}\right) = 15$.

385. Let the total number of children be n and the amount received by each child be ₹ x.
Then, total sum distributed = ₹ (nx).
So, $(n + 16)(x - 2) = nx$
$\Leftrightarrow nx - 2n + 16x - 32 = nx$
$\Leftrightarrow 16x - 2n = 32$ ...(i)
And, $(n - 16)(x + 3) = nx$
$\Leftrightarrow nx + 3n - 16x - 48 = nx$
$\Leftrightarrow 16x - 3n = -48$ ...(ii)
Subtracting (ii) from (i), we get: $n = 80$.
Putting $n = 80$ in (i), we get: $16x = 192$ or $x = 12$.
Hence, total sum distributed $= nx =$ ₹ $(80 \times 12) =$ ₹ 960.

386. Suppose, Sanya and Vidushi donate money to x and $(x + 5)$ people respectively.
Then, $\frac{100}{x} - \frac{100}{x+5} = 1 \Leftrightarrow 100(x + 5) - 100x = x(x + 5)$
$\Leftrightarrow x^2 + 5x - 500 = 0$
$\Leftrightarrow (x - 20)(x + 25) = 0 \Leftrightarrow x = 20$.
$\therefore$ Total number of recipients of charity $= x + (x + 5) = (2x + 5) = 45$.

387. Let the number of girls be x. Then, number of boys $= 3x$.
Total number of students $= x + 3x = 4x$.
Clearly, the total number of students must be a multiple of 4.

388. Let the number of boys be x. Then, number of girls $= (x - 2)$.
$\therefore$ $x^2 - (x - 2)^2 = 28$
$\Leftrightarrow$ $x^2 - (x^2 + 4 - 4x) = 28$
$\Leftrightarrow$ $4x - 4 = 28$
$\Leftrightarrow$ $4x = 32$
$\Leftrightarrow$ $x = 8$.
So, number of boys = 8; number of girls = 6.
$\therefore$ Total number of boys and girls $= 8 + 6 = 14$.

389. Let number of boys $= x$. Then, number of girls $= x$.
Now, $2(x - 8) = x$ or $x = 16$.
$\therefore$ Total number of students $= 2x = (2 \times 16) = 32$.

390. Given exp. $= (1 + x)(1 - x)(1 + x^2)(1 + x^4)(1 + x^8)$
$= (1 - x^2)(1 + x^2)(1 + x^4)(1 + x^8) = (1 - x^4)(1 + x^4)(1 + x^8)$
$= (1 - x^8)(1 + x^8) = (1 - x^{16})$.

391. Given exp. $= \left(\frac{1}{x-1} - \frac{1}{x+1}\right) - \frac{2}{x^2+1} - \frac{4}{x^4+1}$
$= \left[\frac{(x+1)-(x-1)}{(x-1)(x+1)}\right] - \frac{2}{x^2+1} - \frac{4}{x^4+1}$
$= \left(\frac{2}{x^2-1} - \frac{2}{x^2+1}\right) - \frac{4}{x^4+1}$
$= \left[\frac{2(x^2+1) - 2(x^2-1)}{(x^2-1)(x^2+1)}\right] - \frac{4}{x^4+1}$
$= \frac{4}{x^4-1} - \frac{4}{x^4+1} = \frac{4(x^4+1) - 4(x^4-1)}{(x^4-1)(x^4+1)}$
$= \frac{8}{(x^8-1)}$.

392. Given exp. $=$
$\left[\left(x+\frac{1}{x}\right)\left(x^2+\frac{1}{x^2}-x\cdot\frac{1}{x}\right)\right]\left[\left(x-\frac{1}{x}\right)\left(x^2+\frac{1}{x^2}+x\cdot\frac{1}{x}\right)\right]$
$= \left(x^3+\frac{1}{x^3}\right)\left(x^3-\frac{1}{x^3}\right) = \left(x^6-\frac{1}{x^6}\right)$.

393. $x + \frac{1}{x} = 3 \Rightarrow \left(x+\frac{1}{x}\right)^2 = 3^2 \Rightarrow x^2 + \frac{1}{x^2} + 2\cdot x\cdot\frac{1}{x} = 9$
$\Rightarrow x^2 + \frac{1}{x^2} = 9 - 2 = 7$.

394. $a - \frac{1}{a} = p \Rightarrow \left(a - \frac{1}{a}\right)^2 = p^2 \Rightarrow a^2 + \frac{1}{a^2} - 2\cdot a\cdot\frac{1}{a} = p^2$
$\Rightarrow a^2 + \frac{1}{a^2} = p^2 + 2$.

395. $\frac{x-1}{x} = 3 \Rightarrow 1 - \frac{1}{x} = 3 \Rightarrow \left(1 - \frac{1}{x}\right)^2 = 9$
$\Rightarrow 1 + \frac{1}{x^2} - \frac{2}{x} = 9$
$\Rightarrow 1 + \frac{1}{x^2} = 9 + \frac{2}{x} = 9 + \frac{2}{\left(-\frac{1}{2}\right)} = 9 - 4 = 5$.
$\left[\because \frac{x-1}{x} = 3 \Rightarrow 3x = x - 1 \Rightarrow 2x = -1 \Rightarrow x = -\frac{1}{2}\right]$

396. $x^2 + \frac{1}{x^2} = 34 \Rightarrow x^2 + \frac{1}{x^2} + 2\cdot x^2\cdot\frac{1}{x^2} = 34 + 2 = 36$
$\Rightarrow \left(x + \frac{1}{x}\right)^2 = 36 \Rightarrow \left(x + \frac{1}{x}\right) = 6$.

397. $\left(x+\frac{1}{x}\right)=2 \Rightarrow \left(x+\frac{1}{x}\right)^2=2^2$

$\Rightarrow x^2+\frac{1}{x^2}+2=4 \Rightarrow x^2+\frac{1}{x^2}=2$

$\Rightarrow x^2+\frac{1}{x^2}-2\cdot x\cdot\frac{1}{x}=2-2=0$

$\Rightarrow \left(x-\frac{1}{x}\right)^2=0 \Rightarrow x-\frac{1}{x}=0.$

398. $\left(a+\frac{1}{a}\right)=6 \Rightarrow \left(a+\frac{1}{a}\right)^2=6^2=36$

$\Rightarrow a^2+\frac{1}{a^2}+2=36 \Rightarrow \left(a^2+\frac{1}{a^2}\right)=34$

$\Rightarrow \left(a^2+\frac{1}{a^2}\right)^2=(34)^2$

$\Rightarrow a^4+\frac{1}{a^4}+2=1156 \Rightarrow \left(a^4+\frac{1}{a^4}\right)=1154.$

399. $\left(x-\frac{1}{x}\right)=2 \Rightarrow \left(x-\frac{1}{x}\right)^2=2^2=4$

$\Rightarrow x^2+\frac{1}{x^2}-2=4 \Rightarrow x^2+\frac{1}{x^2}=6$

$\Rightarrow \left(x^2+\frac{1}{x^2}\right)^2=6^2=36$

$\Rightarrow x^4+\frac{1}{x^4}+2=36 \Rightarrow x^4+\frac{1}{x^4}=34.$

400. $\left(x-\frac{1}{x}\right)=\sqrt{21} \Rightarrow \left(x-\frac{1}{x}\right)^2=(\sqrt{21})^2=21$

$\Rightarrow x^2+\frac{1}{x^2}-2=21 \Rightarrow x^2+\frac{1}{x^2}=23$

$\Rightarrow x^2+\frac{1}{x^2}+2=25$

$\Rightarrow \left(x+\frac{1}{x}\right)^2=5^2 \Rightarrow x+\frac{1}{x}5.$

$\therefore \quad \left(x^2+\frac{1}{x^2}\right)\left(x+\frac{1}{x}\right)=23\times 5=115.$

401. $x^4+\frac{1}{x^4}=322 \Rightarrow x^4+\frac{1}{x^4}+2=324$

$\Rightarrow \left(x^2+\frac{1}{x^2}\right)^2=(18)^2 \Rightarrow x^2+\frac{1}{x^2}=18$

$\Rightarrow x^2+\frac{1}{x^2}-2=16$

$\Rightarrow \left(x-\frac{1}{x}\right)^2=16 \Rightarrow \left(x-\frac{1}{x}\right)=4.$

402. $\left(x+\frac{1}{x}\right)=p \Rightarrow \left(x+\frac{1}{x}\right)^3=p^3$

$\Rightarrow x^3+\frac{1}{x^3}+3\cdot x\cdot\frac{1}{x}\left(x+\frac{1}{x}\right)=p^3$

$\Rightarrow x^3+\frac{1}{x^3}+3p=p^3 \Rightarrow x^3+\frac{1}{x^3}=p^3-3p.$

403. $\left(x-\frac{1}{x}\right)=1 \Rightarrow \left(x-\frac{1}{x}\right)^3=1$

$\Rightarrow x^3-\frac{1}{x^3}-3\cdot x\cdot\frac{1}{x}\left(x-\frac{1}{x}\right)=1$

$\Rightarrow x^3-\frac{1}{x^3}-3=1 \Rightarrow x^3-\frac{1}{x^3}=1+3=4.$

404. $\left(a^4+\frac{1}{a^4}\right)=1154 \Rightarrow a^4+\frac{1}{a^4}+2=1156$

$\Rightarrow \left(a^2+\frac{1}{a^2}\right)^2=1156 \Rightarrow \left(a^2+\frac{1}{a^2}\right)=34$

$\Rightarrow a^2+\frac{1}{a^2}+2=36$

$\Rightarrow \left(a+\frac{1}{a}\right)^2=36 \Rightarrow a+\frac{1}{a}=6$

$\Rightarrow \left(a+\frac{1}{a}\right)^3=6^3=216$

$\Rightarrow a^3+\frac{1}{a^3}+3\cdot a\cdot\frac{1}{a}\left(a+\frac{1}{a}\right)=216$

$\Rightarrow a^3+\frac{1}{a^3}+3\times 6=216$

$\Rightarrow a^3+\frac{1}{a^3}=216-18=198.$

405. $x+\frac{1}{x}=3 \Rightarrow \left(x+\frac{1}{x}\right)^3=3^3=27$

$\Rightarrow x^3+\frac{1}{x^3}+3\cdot x\cdot\frac{1}{x}\left(x+\frac{1}{x}\right)=27$

$\Rightarrow x^3+\frac{1}{x^3}+3\times 3=27 \Rightarrow x^3+\frac{1}{x^3}=18$

$\Rightarrow \left(x^3+\frac{1}{x^3}\right)^2=(18)^2=324$

$\Rightarrow x^6+\frac{1}{x^6}+2=324 \Rightarrow x^6+\frac{1}{x^6}=322.$

406. $x+\frac{1}{x}=\sqrt{13} \Rightarrow \left(x+\frac{1}{x}\right)^2-4=(\sqrt{13})^2-4=13-4=9$

$\Rightarrow \left(x-\frac{1}{x}\right)^2=9$

$\Rightarrow \left(x-\frac{1}{x}\right)=3$

$\Rightarrow \left(x-\frac{1}{x}\right)^3=3^3=27$

$\Rightarrow x^3-\frac{1}{x^3}-3\cdot x\cdot\frac{1}{x}\left(x-\frac{1}{x}\right)=27$

$\Rightarrow x^3\,\frac{1}{x^3}-3\times 3=27 \Rightarrow x^3-\frac{1}{x^3}=27+9=36.$

407. $\left(4b^2 + \frac{1}{b^2}\right) = 2 \Rightarrow \left(2b + \frac{1}{b}\right)^2 - 4 = 2$

$\Rightarrow \left(2b + \frac{1}{b}\right)^2 = 6 \Rightarrow \left(2b + \frac{1}{b}\right) = \sqrt{6}$

$\Rightarrow \left(2b + \frac{1}{b}\right)^3 = (\sqrt{6})^3 = 6\sqrt{6}$

$\Rightarrow 8b^3 + \frac{1}{b^3} + 3 \times 2b \times \frac{1}{b} \cdot \left(2b + \frac{1}{b}\right) = 6\sqrt{6}$

$\Rightarrow \left(8b^3 + \frac{1}{b^3}\right) + 6\sqrt{6} = 6\sqrt{6}$

$\Rightarrow \left(8b^3 + \frac{1}{b^3}\right) = 0.$

408. $\left(2p + \frac{1}{p}\right) = 4 \Rightarrow \frac{1}{2}\left(2p + \frac{1}{p}\right) = \frac{1}{2} \times 4 \Rightarrow \left(p + \frac{1}{2p}\right) = 2$

$\Rightarrow \left(p + \frac{1}{2p}\right)^3 = 2^3 = 8$

$\Rightarrow p^3 + \frac{1}{8p^3} + 3p \cdot \frac{1}{2p}\left(p + \frac{1}{2p}\right) = 8$

$\Rightarrow p^3 + \frac{1}{8p^3} + 3 \times \frac{1}{2} \times 2 = 8$

$\Rightarrow p^3 + \frac{1}{8p^3} = 8 - 3 = 5.$

409. Let the number of cows in the herd be x.
Then, number of legs = $4x$; number of heads = x.
$\therefore$ $4x - 2x = 14$ or $2x = 14$ or $x = 7$.

410. Let the number of buffaloes be x and the number of ducks be y.
Then, $4x + 2y = 2(x + y) + 24 \Leftrightarrow 2x = 24 \Leftrightarrow x = 12$.

411. Let the number of hens be x and the number of cows be y.
Then, $x + y = 59$ ...(*i*)
and $2x + 4y = 190$ or $x + 2y = 95$ ...(*ii*)
Subtracting (*i*) from (*ii*), we get: $y = 36$.

412. Let the number of parrots be x and the number of tigers be y.
Then, $x + y = 858$ ...(*i*)
and $2x + 4y = 1846$ or $x + 2y = 923$ ...(*ii*)
Subtracting (*i*) from (*ii*), we get: $y = 65$.
Putting $y = 65$ in (*i*), we get: $x = 858 - 65 = 793$.

413. Let the number of horses be x. Then, number of men = x.
$\therefore$ $4x + \frac{x}{2} \times 2 = 70 \Leftrightarrow 5x = 70 \Leftrightarrow x = 14.$

414. Let the full fare be ₹ x and the reservation charge be ₹ y per ticket.
Then, $x + y = 216$ ...(*i*)
and $\frac{3}{2}x + 2y = 327$ or $3x + 4y = 654$ ...(*ii*)
Multiplying (*i*) by 3 and subtracting from (*ii*), we get: $y = 6$.
Putting $y = 6$ in (*i*), we get: $x = 210$.

415. Let the distance travelled by taxi be x km.
Then, distance travelled by own car = $(90 - x)$ km.
$\therefore$ $7x + 6(90 - x) = 675 \Leftrightarrow x = 675 - 540 = 135$ km.

416. Clearly, first man shakes hand with all other 14 men; second man shakes hand with 13 men (other than first man); third shakes hand with 12 men and so on.
$\therefore$ Total number of hand-shakes = (14 + 13 + 12 + ... + 1)
$= \frac{14 \times 15}{2} = 105.$

417. Let there be n children in the group.
Then, first child exchanges gifts with other $(n - 1)$ children; second child exchanges gifts with other $(n - 2)$ children; and so on.
So, number of gifts = 2 [1 + 2 + ... + $(n - 1)$]
$= 2 \times \frac{n(n-1)}{2} = n(n-1).$
$\therefore$ $n(n - 1) = 132 \Leftrightarrow n^2 - n - 132 = 0$
$\Leftrightarrow n^2 - 12n + 11n - 132 = 0$
$\Leftrightarrow (n - 12)(n + 11) = 0 \Leftrightarrow n = 12.$

418. 1044 candles produce 1044 butts, from which $\frac{1044}{9} = 116$ candles can be formed.
The resultant 116 butts give $\frac{116}{9}$ i.e., 12 candles and 8 butts.
12 resultant butts plus 8 remaining butts = 20 butts from which $\frac{20}{9}$ i.e., 2 candles and 2 butts will be obtained.
In the end, 4 butts will be left behind.
$\therefore$ Total number of candles formed
= (116 + 12 + 2) = 130.

419. Number of lines printed in 1 hour = $\frac{176400}{7} = 25200.$
Number of lines printed per minute = $\frac{25200}{60} = 420.$

420. Number of pages typed by 1 man in 1 hour = $\frac{60}{8} = 7.5.$
$\therefore$ Number of men required = $\frac{1710}{7.5} = 228.$

421. Number of pages read by Ashu from 2: 30 to 3: 20 i.e., in 50 min or $\frac{5}{6}$ hr $= \left(\frac{5}{6} \times 30\right) = 25.$
Let the two read the same page x hours after 3: 20.
Then, pages read by Ashu = $(25 + 30x)$. And, pages read by Neeru = $40x$.
$\therefore$ $25 + 30x = 40x \Rightarrow x = \frac{5}{2} = 2\frac{1}{2}.$
Hence, the two read the same page $2\frac{1}{2}$ hours after 3: 20 i.e., at 5: 50.

422. $\frac{336}{x} = \frac{192}{400} \Rightarrow x = \frac{336 \times 400}{192} = 700.$

423. Maximum internal assessment score $= \left(\frac{47}{50} \times 10\right) = 9.4.$

Minimum internal assessment score $= \left(\frac{14}{50} \times 10\right) = 2.8.$

$\therefore$ Required difference = (9.4 – 2.8) = 6.6.

424. Let the number of questions answered correctly be x. Then, number of wrong answers = $(200 - x)$.

$\therefore \quad 4x - (200 - x) = 200 \Rightarrow 5x = 400 \Rightarrow x = 80.$

425. Let the number of correct answers be x. Then, number of wrong answers = $(26 - x)$.

$\therefore \quad 8x - 5(26 - x) = 0 \Rightarrow 13x = 130 \Rightarrow x = 10.$

426. Suppose the student attempted x questions of 2 marks correctly.

Then, number of 4 marks questions attempted correctly $= (15 - x)$.

$\therefore \quad 2x + 4(15 - x) = 40 \Leftrightarrow 2x + 60 - 4x = 40$

$\Leftrightarrow 2x = 20 \Leftrightarrow x = 10.$

427. Let the number of correct answers be x. Then, number of incorrect answers = $(30 - x)$.

$\therefore \quad x - 0.25\,(30 - x) = 13.75$

$\Leftrightarrow x - 7.5 + 0.25x = 13.75$

$\Leftrightarrow 1.25x = 21.25 \Leftrightarrow x = \frac{2125}{125} = 17.$

So, number of incorrect answers = 30 – 17 = 13.

428. Suppose he hits the target x times.

Then, he misses it $(100 - x)$ times.

$\therefore \quad x - (100 - x) = 30 \Rightarrow 2x = 130 \Rightarrow x = 65.$

So, number of times he misses the target = 100 – 65 = 35.

429. Let the number of cows be x. Then, number of bulls = $2x$.

Number of caretakers $= \frac{x + 2x + 45}{15} = \frac{3x + 45}{15} = \frac{x + 15}{5}.$

Number of heads $= x + 2x + 45 + \frac{x + 15}{5} = \frac{16x + 240}{5}.$

Number of feet $= 4x + 4 \times 2x + 2 \times 45 + 2\left(\frac{x + 15}{5}\right)$

$= 4x + 8x + 90 + \left(\frac{2x + 30}{5}\right) = \frac{62x + 480}{5}.$

$\therefore \quad \frac{62x + 480}{5} - \frac{16x + 240}{5} = 186 \Rightarrow 46x + 240 = 930$

$\Rightarrow 46x = 690 \Rightarrow x = 15.$

Hence, number of caretakers $= \frac{x + 15}{5} = \frac{30}{5} = 6.$

430. Man's basic pay per hour = ₹$\left(\frac{200}{40}\right)$ = ₹ 5.

Overtime charges per hour = 125% of ₹ 5 = ₹ 6.25.

Suppose the man worked overtime for x hours.

Then, $200 + 6.25x = 300 \Rightarrow 6.25x = 100 \Rightarrow x = 16.$

$\therefore$ Total number of working hours = (40 + 16) = 56.

431. Suppose the man works overtime for x hours.

Now, working hours in 4 weeks = (5 × 8 × 4) = 160.

$\therefore \quad 160 \times 24 + x \times 32 = 4320 \Rightarrow 32x = 480 \Rightarrow x = 15.$

Hence, total hours of work = (160 + 15) = 175.

432. Suppose their paths cross after x minutes.

Then, $11 + 57x = 51 - 63x \Leftrightarrow 120x = 40 \Leftrightarrow x = \frac{1}{3}.$

Number of floors covered by David in

$\frac{1}{3}$ min $= \left(\frac{1}{3} \times 57\right) = 19.$

So, their paths cross at (11 + 19) i.e., 30th floor.

433. Let the total number of steps be n.

Then, $\frac{30}{n - 26} = \frac{18}{n - 34} \Leftrightarrow 30(n - 34) = 18(n - 26)$

$\Leftrightarrow 30n - 18n = 552 \Leftrightarrow 12n = 552 \Leftrightarrow n = 46.$

434. Let the price of the uniform be ₹ x.

Then, servant's pay per day = ₹$\left(\frac{200 + x}{10}\right)$.

$\therefore \quad 5\left(\frac{200 + x}{10}\right) = 20 + x \Leftrightarrow 200 + x = 40 + 2x$

$\Leftrightarrow x = 160.$

435. Suppose he remained absent for x days.

Then, number of days on which he was present = $(20 - x)$.

$\therefore \quad 60(20 - x) - 5x = 745 \Leftrightarrow 65x = 455 \Rightarrow x = 7.$

436. Let the fixed charge be ₹ x and variable charge be ₹ y per km.

Then, $x + 16y = 156$ ...(*i*) and $x + 24y = 204$ ...(*ii*)

Subtracting (*i*) from (*ii*), we get: $8y = 48$ or $y = 6$.

Putting $y = 6$ in (*i*), we get: $x = 60$.

$\therefore$ Cost of travelling 30 km = ₹ (60 + 30 × 6) = ₹ 240.

437. Original contribution = ₹$\left(\frac{D}{M}\right)$.

New contribution = ₹$\left(\frac{D}{M - 3}\right)$.

$\therefore$ Required contribution = ₹$\left[\frac{D}{(M - 3)} - \frac{D}{M}\right]$

= ₹ $\frac{DM - D(M - 3)}{M(M - 3)}$

= ₹$\left(\frac{3D}{M^2 - 3M}\right)$.

438. $N \times 50 = (325000 - 300000) = 25000 \Rightarrow N = 500.$

439. Let number of boys = x. Then, number of girls = $(60 - x)$.

$\therefore \quad x(60 - x) + (60 - x)\,x = 1600$

$\Leftrightarrow 2x^2 - 120x + 1600 = 0$

$\Leftrightarrow x^2 - 60x + 800 = 0$

$\Leftrightarrow (x - 40)(x - 20) = 0$

$\Leftrightarrow x = 40$ or $x = 20.$

So, we are not definite, Hence, data is inadequate.

440. Original share of 1 person $= \frac{1}{8}$. New share $= \frac{1}{7}$.

Increase $= \left(\frac{1}{7} - \frac{1}{8}\right) = \frac{1}{56}.$

$\therefore$ Required fraction $= \frac{(1/56)}{(1/8)} = \left(\frac{1}{56} \times 8\right) = \frac{1}{7}.$

441. Let the original duration of the tour be n days.

Then, $\frac{360}{n} - \frac{360}{n+4} = 3 \Leftrightarrow 360\left[\frac{n+4-n}{n(n+4)}\right] = 3$

$\Leftrightarrow n(n + 4) = 120 \times 4 = 480$

$\Leftrightarrow n^2 + 4n - 480 = 0 \Leftrightarrow (n + 24)(n - 20) = 0 \Leftrightarrow n = 20.$

442. Let the original number of students be x.

Then, $\frac{500}{x-5} - \frac{500}{x} = 5 \Leftrightarrow \frac{1}{x-5} - \frac{1}{x} = \frac{1}{100} \Leftrightarrow x(x-5) = 500$

$\Leftrightarrow x^2 - 5x - 500 = 0$

$\Leftrightarrow (x - 25)(x + 20) = 0 \Leftrightarrow x = 25.$

Hence, number of students who attended the picnic $= (25 - 5) = 20.$

443. Let the original cost per student be ₹ x.

Then, $\frac{720}{x} - \frac{720}{x+9} = 4 \Leftrightarrow 720\left[\frac{x+9-x}{x(x+9)}\right] = 4$

$\Leftrightarrow x(x + 9) = 1620$

$\Leftrightarrow x^2 + 9x - 1620 = 0$

$\Leftrightarrow (x + 45)(x - 36) = 0 \Leftrightarrow x = 36.$

444. Let the total price of the CDs be ₹ x and the number of boys be n.

Then, $\frac{x}{n-2} - \frac{x}{n} = 1 \Leftrightarrow \frac{nx - x(n-2)}{n(n-2)} = 1$

$\Leftrightarrow 2x = n^2 - 2n \Leftrightarrow x = \frac{n^2 - 2n}{2}.$

Since x is a whole number, so n must be even.

For $n = 20$, we have: $x = 180 < 200.$

For $n = 22$, we have: $x = 220.$

For $n = 24$, we have: $x = 264 > 250.$

So, $n = 22$, $x =$ ₹ 220.

445. $X + 3X \times 0.50 + 14 \times 0.10 + 4X \times 0.05 = 50$

$\therefore \quad X + 1.5X + 1.40 + 0.2X = 50 \Leftrightarrow 2.7X = 48.60$

$\Leftrightarrow X = 18.$

446. Let the number of 20-paise coins be x. Then, number of 25-paise coins $= (324 - x)$.

$\therefore \quad 0.20 \times x + 0.25(324 - x) = 71$

$\Leftrightarrow 20x + 25(324 - x) = 7100$

$\Leftrightarrow 5x = 1000 \Leftrightarrow x = 200.$

Hence, number of 25-paise coins $= (324 - x) = 124.$

447. Let number of notes of each denomination be x.

Then, $x + 5x + 10x = 480 \Leftrightarrow 16x = 480 \Leftrightarrow x = 30.$

Hence, total number of notes $= 3x = 90.$

448. Let the number of coins of each denomination be x.

Then, $x + 0.5x + 0.25x + 0.10x + 0.05x = 380$

$\Rightarrow 1.9x = 380 \Rightarrow x = \frac{380}{1.9} = 200.$

Hence, number of one-rupee coins = 200.

449. Let the number of 50 p-coins and 25 p-coins be x and y respectively.

Then, number of 1 rupee coins $= 175 - (x + y).$

$\therefore \quad 0.5x = 0.25y$ or $2x = y.$

So, number of 50 p-coins $= x$, number of 25 p-coins $= 2x$, number of 1 rupee coins $= (175 - 3x).$

$\therefore \quad 175 - 3x = 0.5x \Leftrightarrow 3.5x = 175 \Leftrightarrow x = \frac{175}{3.5} = 50.$

Hence, total amount $= (175 - 3x) + 0.5x + 0.25 \times 2x$

$= 175 - 3x + 0.5x + 0.5x = 175 - 3x + x$

$= 175 - 2x =$ ₹ $(175 - 2 \times 50) =$ ₹ 75.

450. Total value of one 2-rupee coin, two 50-p coins and two 25-p coins

$=$ ₹ $(2 + 2 \times 0.50 + 2 \times 0.25) =$ ₹ 3.50.

Remaining amount $=$ ₹ $(25 - 3.50) =$ ₹ 21.50.

For the minimum number of coins, we must have maximum amount in denominations of 2-rupee and 50-p which shall be ten 2-rupee and three 50-p coins i.e., 13 more coins.

$\therefore$ Required number of coins $= (1 + 2 + 2) + 13 = 18.$

Questions 451 and 452

Let the circles M, R and F represent the number of children who took ride on merry-go-round, roller coaster and Ferris wheel only.

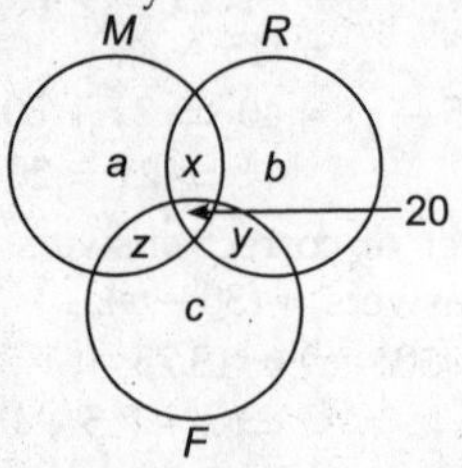

Let a = number of children who took ride on merry-go-round only;

b = number of children who took ride on roller coaster only;

c = number of children who took ride on Ferris wheel only;

x = number of children who took ride on both merry-go-round and roller coaster;

y = number of children who took ride on both roller-coaster and Ferris wheel;

z = number of children who took ride on both merry-go-round and Ferris wheel.

Then, number of children who took exactly one ride $= a + b + c$;

number of children who took exactly two rides $= x + y + z$;

number of children who took all three rides = 20;

number of children who took at least 2 rides $= x + y + z + 20.$

$\therefore$ We have: $x + y + z + 20 = 55 \Leftrightarrow x + y + z = 35$

Total receipt $=$ ₹ $[a + b + c + 2(x + y + z) + 3 \times 20]$

$=$ ₹ $(a + b + c + 2 \times 35 + 60)$

$=$ ₹ $(a + b + c + 130).$

$\therefore a + b + c + 130 = 145$ or $a + b + c = 15.$

451. Number of children who took exactly one ride $= a + b + c = 15.$

452. Number of children who did not try any ride

$= 85 - (a + b + c + x + y + z + 20)$

$= 85 - (15 + 35 + 20) = 15.$

453. Number of students who took any one or both the languages

B H

$= 50 - 12 = 38.$

$n(B) = 25, n(H) = 16, n(B \cup H) = 38.$

$\therefore$ Number of students who take both Bengali and Hindi

$= n(B \cap H) = n(B) + n(H) - n(B \cup H)$

$= (25 + 16) - 38 = (41 - 38) = 3.$

454. $n(T) = 60, n(C) = 40, n(T \cap C) = 25.$

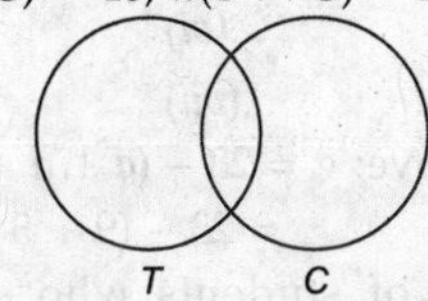

$\therefore$ Number of students who take either tea or coffee or both

$= n(T \cup C) = n(T) + n(C) - n(T \cap C)$

$= 60 + 40 - 25 = 100 - 25 = 75.$

$\therefore$ Required number of students $= (100 - 75) = 25.$

455. $n(M \cup B) = 25, n(M) = 12, n(M - B) = 8.$

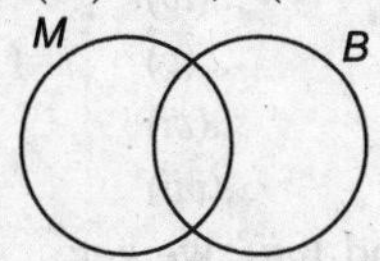

Number students who have taken both Mathematics and Biology $= n(M \cap B) = n(M) - n(M - B) = 12 - 8 = 4.$

456. $n(T \cup C) = 52, n(T - C) = 16, n(T) = 33.$

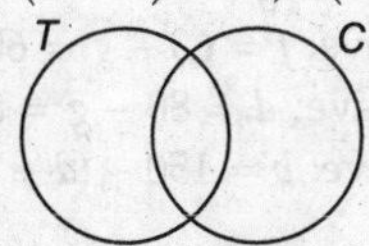

Number of persons who drink coffee but not tea

$= n(C - T) = n(T \cup C) - n(T) = 52 - 33 = 19.$

457. $n(E) = 3000, n(M) = 2000, n(E \cap M) = 1500.$

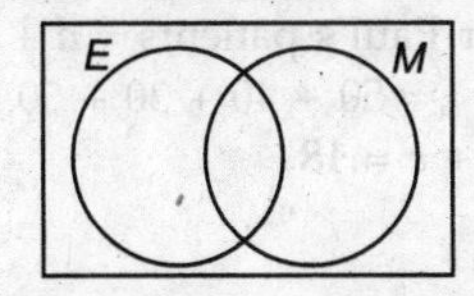

$n(E \cup M) = n(E) + n(M) - n(E \cap M) = 3000 + 2000 - 1500$

$= 3500.$

Number of pure vegetarians $= 4000 - n(E \cup M)$

$= 4000 - 3500 = 500.$

458. $n(E \cup H) = 50; n(E \cap H) = 10; n(E) = 21.$

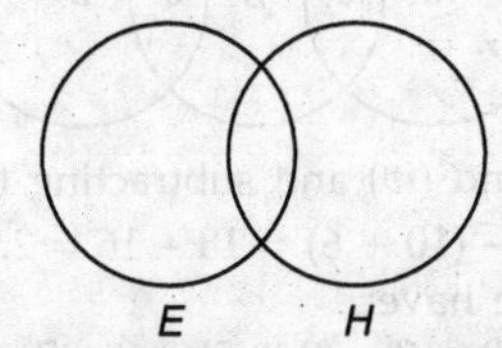

Number of students who can speak Hindi $= n(H)$

$= n(E \cap H) + n(E \cup H) - n(E) = 10 + 50 - 21 = 39.$

Number of students who can speak only Hindi

$= n(H - E) = n(H) - n(E \cap H) = 39 - 10 = 29.$

Number of students who can speak only English

$= n(E - H) = n(E) - n(E \cap H) = 21 - 10 = 11.$

459. Let the total number of staff members be x.

Then, the number who can type or take shorthand

$$= \left(x - \frac{3x}{4}\right) = \frac{x}{4}.$$

Let A and B represent the sets of persons who can type and take shorthand respectively.

Then, $n(A \cup B) = \frac{x}{4}, n(A) = \frac{x}{5}$ and $n(B) = \frac{x}{3}.$

$$n(A \cap B) = n(A) + n(B) - n(A \cup B)$$

$$= \left(\frac{x}{5} + \frac{x}{3} - \frac{x}{4}\right) = \left(\frac{12x + 20x - 15x}{60}\right) = \frac{17x}{60}.$$

460. Let circles B, H and C represent the number of players who play basketball, hockey and cricket respectively.

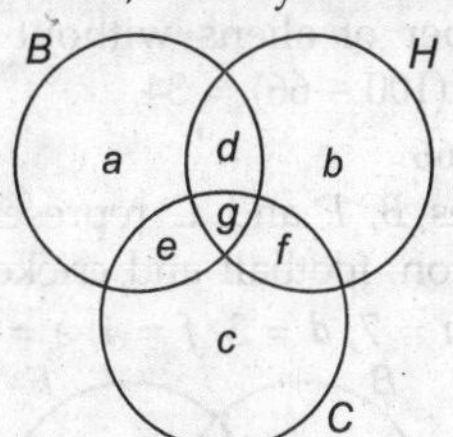

Then,
$a + d + e + g = 20$ ...(i)
$b + d + f + g = 24$ ...(ii)
$c + e + f + g = 27$ ...(iii)
$d + g = 12$ ...(iv)
$e + g = 10$ ...(v)
$f + g = 14$ ...(vi)
$g = 7$ ...(vii)

From (iv), (v), (vi) and (vii), we have:

$d = 12 - g = 12 - 7 = 5;$

$e = 10 - g = 10 - 7 = 3;$

$f = 14 - g = 14 - 7 = 7.$

From (iii), we have: $c = 27 - (e + f + g)$

$= 27 - (3 + 7 + 7) = 10.$

From (ii), we have: $b = 24 - (d + f + g)$

$= 24 - (5 + 7 + 7) = 5.$

From (i), we have: $a = 20 - (d + e + g)$

$= 20 - (5 + 3 + 7) = 5.$

Hence, total number of players $= a + b + c + d + e + f + g$

$= (5 + 5 + 10 + 5 + 3 + 7 + 7)$

$= 42.$

461. Let the circles A, B and C represent the aliens having two noses, three legs and four ears respectively.

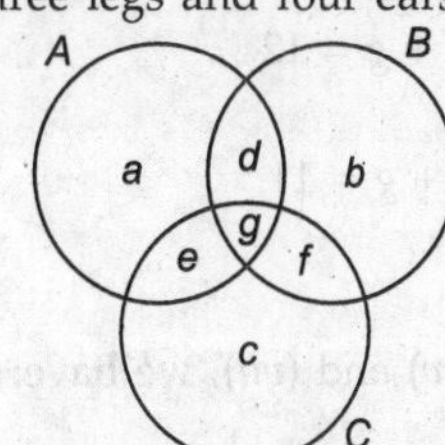

Then,
$a + d + e + g = 40$ ...(i)
$b + d + f + g = 30$ ...(ii)
$c + e + f + g = 20$ ...(iii)
$d + g = 10$ ...(iv)
$f + g = 12$ ...(v)
$e + g = 5$ ...(vi)
$g = 3$ ...(vii)

From (iv), (v), (vi) and (vii), we have:

$d = 10 - g = 10 - 3 = 7;$

$e = 5 - g = 5 - 3 = 2;$

$f = 12 - g = 12 - 3 = 9.$

From (*iii*), we have: $c = 20 - (e + f + g)$
$= 20 - (2 + 9 + 3) = 20 - 14 = 6.$

From (*ii*), we have: $b = 30 - (d + f + g)$
$= 30 - (7 + 9 + 3) = 30 - 19 = 11.$

From (*i*), we have: $a = 40 - (d + e + g)$
$= 40 - (7 + 2 + 3) = 40 - 12 = 28.$

∴ Number of aliens who had one or more of the three unusual features
$= a + b + c + d + e + f + g$
$= (28 + 11 + 6 + 7 + 2 + 9 + 3) = 66.$

Hence, number of aliens without any of the unusual features = (100 − 66) = 34.

Questions 462 to 466

Let the circles *B*, *F* and *C* represent the children who play badminton, football and cricket respectively. Then, $c = 5, b = 8, a = 7, d = 3, f = 4, e = 4, g = 2.$

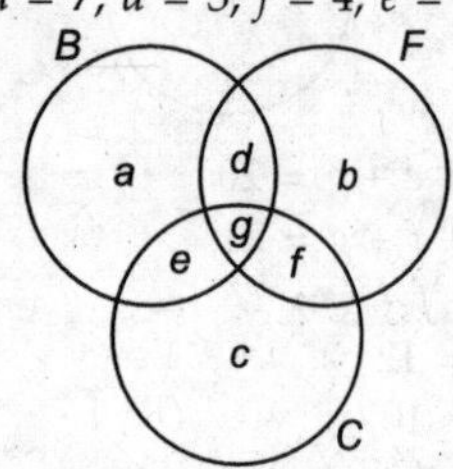

462. Required number $= f + g = 4 + 2 = 6.$

463. Required number $= a + d + e + g = 7 + 3 + 4 + 2 = 16.$

464. Required number $= b + d + f + g = 8 + 3 + 4 + 2 = 17.$

465. Required number $= e + g = 4 + 2 = 6.$

466. Required number $= a + b + c + d + e + f + g$
$= 7 + 8 + 5 + 3 + 4 + 4 + 2 = 33.$

467.

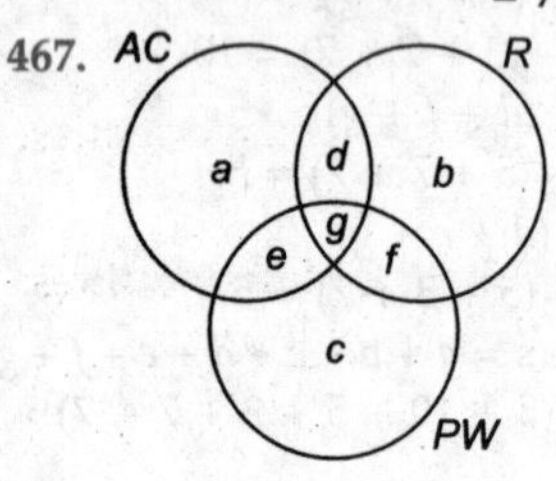

$a + d + e + g = 15$ ...(*i*)
$e = 2$ ...(*ii*)
$b + d + f + g = 12$ ...(*iii*)
$d = 6$ ...(*iv*)
$c + e + f + g = 11$ ...(*v*)
$f + g = 4$ ...(*vi*)
$g = 3$ ...(*vii*)

From (*i*), (*ii*), (*iv*) and (*vii*), we have: $a = 15 - (d + e + g)$
$= 15 - (6 + 2 + 3)$
$= 15 - 11 = 4.$

From (*vi*), we have: $f = 4 - g = 4 - 3 = 1.$

From (*iii*), we have: $b = 12 - (d + f + g)$
$= 12 - (6 + 1 + 3) = 2.$

From (*v*), we have: $c = 11 - (e + f + g)$
$= 11 - (2 + 1 + 3) = 5.$

∴ Number of cars which had at least one option
$= a + b + c + d + e + f + g$
$= 4 + 2 + 5 + 6 + 2 + 1 + 3 = 23.$

So, number of cars that had none of the options
$= 25 - 23 = 2.$

468. $a + d + e + g = 23$ ...(*i*)
$b + d + f + g = 15$ ...(*ii*)
$c + e + f + g = 18$ ...(*iii*)
$d = 3$ ...(*iv*)
$f = 6$ ...(*v*)
$e = 6$ ...(*vi*)
$a = 9$ ...(*vii*)

From (*i*), we have: $g = 23 - (a + d + e)$
$= 23 - (9 + 3 + 6) = 5.$

∴ Number of students who speak all the three languages $= g = 5.$

469. $a + d + e + g = 200$ ...(*i*)
$b + d + f + g = 150$ ...(*ii*)
$c + e + f + g = 150$ ...(*iii*)
$d + g = 80$ ...(*iv*)
$f + g = 60$ ...(*v*)
$e + g = 70$ ...(*vi*)
$a = 80$ ...(*vii*)

From (*i*), (*iv*) and (*vii*), we get:
$a + e = 200 - (d + g) = 200 - 80 = 120.$
$\Rightarrow \quad e = 120 - a = 120 - 80 = 40.$

From (*vi*), we have: $g = 70 - e = 70 - 40 = 30.$

From (*v*), we have: $f = 60 - g = 60 - 30 = 30.$

From (*iv*), we have: $d = 80 - g = 80 - 30 = 50.$

From (*ii*), we have: $b = 150 - (d + f + g) = 150 - (50 + 30 + 30) = 40.$

From (*iii*), we have: $c = 150 - (e + f + g)$
$= 150 - (40 + 30 + 30) = 50.$

Number of Dr Hormis' patients $= b = 40.$

Number of Dr Gerard's patients $= c = 50.$

Number of Dr Paul's patients $= d + e + f + g$
$= 50 + 40 + 30 + 30 = 150.$

470. $a + b + c + d + e = 18$ ...(*i*)
$a + d = 10$ ...(*ii*)
$b + d + e = 8$ ...(*iii*)
$c + e = 6$ ...(*iv*)
$d = 5$ ...(*v*)

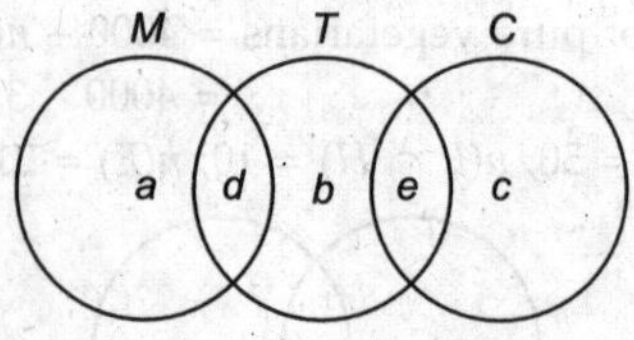

Adding (*ii*) and (*iv*) and subtracting from (*i*), we get:
$b = 18 - (10 + 6) = 18 - 16 = 2.$

From (*iii*), we have:
$e = 8 - (b + d) = 8 - (2 + 5) = 8 - 7 = 1.$

∴ Number of members who take tea as well as coffee $= e = 1.$

Questions 471 to 475

We have: $a = 650, b = 550,$
$c = 450, g = 100, d + g = 200,$
$f + g = 400, e + g = 300.$

So,
$e = 300 - g = 300 - 100 = 200; f = 400 - g = 400 - 100 = 300;$
$d = 200 - g = 200 - 100 = 100.$

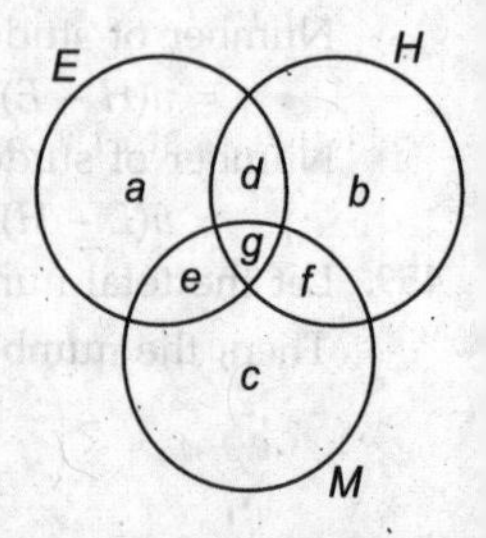

471. Number of members reading Hindi newspaper
$= b + d + f + g = 550 + 100 + 300 + 100 = 1050.$

472. Number of members who read only one newspaper
$= a + b + c = 650 + 550 + 450 = 1650.$

473. Number of members reading no newspaper
$= 2800 - (a + b + c + d + e + f + g)$
$= 2800 - (650 + 550 + 450 + 100 + 200 + 300 + 100)$
$= 2800 - 2350 = 450.$

474. Number of members who read at least 2 newspapers
$= d + e + f + g = 100 + 200 + 300 + 100 = 700.$

475. Required difference $= (e + g) - (d + g) = e - d$
$= 200 - 100 = 100.$

476. Let the consumption of ration be x kg per day. Then,
$75(x + 12) = 90(x + 8)$
$\Leftrightarrow 75x + 900 = 90x + 720$
$\Leftrightarrow 15x = 180 \Leftrightarrow x = 12.$

$\therefore$ Total quantity of ration $= 75(x + 12)$
$= (75 \times 24)$ kg $= 1800$ kg.

Hence, it would last for $\left(\frac{1800}{12}\right)$ days i.e., 150 days.

477. Let l be the length of each candle and x be the number of hours before 4 P.M. when the candles should be lighted.

Length of first candle burnt $= \frac{l}{3} \times x$. Length of second candle burnt $= \frac{l}{4} \times x$.

Remaining length of first candle $= l - \frac{xl}{3}$

Remaining length of second candle $= l - \frac{xl}{4}$.

$\therefore \; l - \frac{xl}{4} = 2\left(l - \frac{xl}{3}\right) \Leftrightarrow l\left(1 - \frac{x}{4}\right) = 2l\left(1 - \frac{x}{3}\right)$

$\Leftrightarrow 1 - \frac{x}{4} = 2\left(1 - \frac{x}{3}\right) \Leftrightarrow \frac{2x}{3} - \frac{x}{4} = 1$

$\Leftrightarrow \frac{5x}{12} = 1 \Leftrightarrow x = \frac{12}{5} = 2\frac{2}{5}$

So, the candles should be lighted $2\frac{2}{5}$ hrs i.e., 2 hr 24 min before 4 P.M. i.e., at 1: 36 P.M.

478. Suppose the man bought x apples. Then, number of oranges bought $= (40 - x)$.

Let the cost of each apple be ₹ a and that of each orange be ₹ b.

Then, $ax + b(40 - x) = 17 \Leftrightarrow ax - bx = 17 - 40b$ ...(*i*)

And, $a(40 - x) + bx = 15 \Leftrightarrow ax - bx = 40a - 15$ ...(*ii*)

From (*i*) and (*ii*), we get:

$40a - 15 = 17 - 40b \Leftrightarrow 40a + 40b$
$= 32 \Leftrightarrow 40(a + b) = 32 \Leftrightarrow a + b = \frac{4}{5}.$

Hence, cost of 1 apple and 1 orange

$= ₹ \frac{4}{5} = \left(\frac{4}{5} \times 100\right) p = 80 \; p.$

479. Suppose she purchased n books for ₹ 720. Then, cost of each book = ₹ $\left(\frac{720}{n}\right)$.

$\therefore \; \frac{720}{n} - \frac{720}{n+4} = 2 \Rightarrow \frac{(n+4) - n}{n(n+4)}$

$= \frac{1}{360} \Rightarrow n^2 + 4n - 1440 = 0$

$\Rightarrow (n + 40)(n - 36) = 0 \Rightarrow n = 36.$

480. Let the number of pineapple, mango and black-forest pastries be x, y and z respectively.

Then, cost of each pineapple pastry = ₹ x; cost of each mango pastry = ₹ y;

cost of each black-forest pastry = ₹ z.

Thus, $x + y + z = 23$. And, $x^2 + y^2 + z^2 = 211$.

So, we have to find 3 numbers whose sum is 23 and the sum of whose squares is 211. Such a triplet is (11, 9, 3).

481. Suppose each tube contains x grams initially. Then,

$4\left[\frac{1}{3}(x + 20)\right] = (x - 20) + \frac{2}{3}(x + 20)$

$\Leftrightarrow \frac{2}{3}(x + 20) = (x - 20)$

$\Leftrightarrow \frac{2}{3}x + \frac{40}{3} = x - 20$

$\Leftrightarrow \frac{x}{3} = \frac{40}{3} + 20 = \frac{100}{3} \Leftrightarrow x = 100.$

482. Let the capacity of the first bottle be x litres.

Then, capacity of the second bottle $= 2x$ litres.

And, capacity of the third bottle $= (x + 2x)$ litres
$= 3x$ litres.

Quantity of milk in the first bottle $= \frac{x}{2}$ litres.

Quantity of milk in the second bottle $= \left(\frac{2x}{4}\right)$ litres $= \frac{x}{2}$ litres.

Quantity of milk in the third bottle $= \left(\frac{x}{2} + \frac{x}{2}\right)$ litres $= x$ litres.

$\therefore$ Required fraction $= \left(\frac{x}{3x}\right) = \frac{1}{3}.$

483. Number of passengers after the first stop

$= \left[540 - \left(\frac{1}{9} \text{ of } 540\right) + 24\right] = 504.$

Number of passengers after the second stop

$= \left[504 - \left(\frac{1}{8} \text{ of } 504\right) + 9\right] = 450.$

484. Let the number of passengers at the start be x.

Then, number of passengers after the first stop

$= \left(\frac{x}{2} + 125\right).$

Number of passengers after the second stop

$= \frac{1}{2}\left(\frac{x}{2} + 125\right) + 100 = \left(\frac{x}{4} + \frac{325}{2}\right).$

$\therefore \; \frac{x}{4} + \frac{325}{2} = 250 \Rightarrow \frac{x}{4} = 250 - \frac{325}{2} = \frac{175}{2}$

$\Rightarrow x = \left(\frac{175}{2} \times 4\right) = 350.$

485. Total number of digits =
(No. of digits in 1-digit page nos. + No. of digits in 2-digit page nos. + No. of digits in 3-digit page nos.)
$= (1 \times 9 + 2 \times 90 + 3 \times 267)$
$= (9 + 180 + 801) = 990.$

486. No. of digits in 1-digit page nos. $= 1 \times 9 = 9$.
No. of digits in 2-digit page nos. $= 2 \times 90 = 180$.
No. of digits in 3-digit page nos. $= 3 \times 900 = 2700$.
No. of digits in 4-digit page nos. $= 3189 - (9 + 180 + 2700) = 3189 - 2889 = 300$.

$\therefore$ No. of pages with 4-digit page nos. $= \left(\frac{300}{4}\right) = 75$.

Hence, total number of pages $= (999 + 75) = 1074$.

487. Let the number of students in sections A and B be x and y respectively. Then,
$x + 10 = 3(y - 10) \Rightarrow 3y - x = 40$ ...(*i*)
And, $x - 10 = y + 10 \Rightarrow x - y = 20$ ...(*ii*)
Adding (*i*) and (*ii*), we get: $2y = 60$ or $y = 30$.
Putting $y = 30$ in (*ii*), we get: $x = 50$.

488. Clearly, the boy lost 7 chocolates, regained the 7 lost chocolates and won 20 more.
$\therefore$ Number of games played $= (7 + 7 + 20) = 34$.

489. Clearly, we have:
$J - 40 = \frac{1}{2}A$ ...(*i*)
$A - 40 = J$ ...(*ii*)
$A - 40 = R + 40$ ...(*iii*)
Solving (*i*) and (*ii*), we get: $J = 120$ and $A = 160$.
Putting $A = 160$ in (*iii*), we get: $R = 80$.
$\therefore$ Total money $= R + J + A =$ ₹ $(80 + 120 + 160) =$ ₹ 360.

490. We have:
$B + 8 = C$ ...(*i*)
$A - 8 = C - 3$ ...(*ii*)
$A + 6 = 2D$ ...(*iii*)
$B + D = 50$ ...(*iv*)
Putting $C = A - 5$ from (*ii*) into (*i*), we have:
$B + 8 = A - 5$ or $A - B = 13$ ...(*v*)
Putting $D = 50 - B$ from (*iv*) into (*iii*), we have:
$A + 6 = 100 - 2B$ or $A + 2B = 94$ ...(*vi*)
Solving (*v*) and (*vi*), we get: $B = 27$, $A = 40$.

491. We have:
$B - 3 = E$ ...(*i*)
$B + 3 = D$ ...(*ii*)
$A + B = D + E + 10$ ...(*iii*)
$B = C + 2$ ...(*iv*)
$A + B + C + D + E = 133$ ...(*v*)
From (*i*) and (*ii*), we have: $2B = D + E$ ...(*vi*)
Using (*iii*), (*iv*) and (*vi*) in (*v*), we get:
$(B + 10) + B + (B - 2) + 2B = 133$
$\Leftrightarrow$ $5B = 125$
$\Leftrightarrow$ $B = 25$.

492. Since A and B each has ₹ 16 in the end, so C gave each of them ₹ 8. So, before third transaction, C had ₹ (16 + 8 × 2) = ₹ 32 while A and B each had ₹ 8. Thus, in second transaction, B gave ₹ 4 to A and ₹ 16 to C. So, before second transaction, A had ₹ 4, B had ₹ (8 + 4 + 16) = ₹ 28 and C had ₹ 16. Thus, in first transaction, A gave ₹ 14 to B and ₹ 8 to C. So, before first transaction, A had ₹ (4 + 14 + 8) = ₹ 26, B had ₹ 14 and C had ₹ 8.

493. Suppose Iqbal has x cards and Mushtaq has y cards.
Let the number of cards given be z.
Then, $x + z = 4(y - z) \Rightarrow x - 4y = -5z$ ...(*i*)
And, $x - z = 3(y + z) \Rightarrow x - 3y = 4z$ ...(*ii*)
Subtracting (*i*) from (*ii*), we get: $y = 9z$. Putting $y = 9z$ in (*i*), we get: $x = 31z$.
Clearly, since a pack of playing cards has 52 cards, z cannot be greater than 1.
So, $x = 31$ and $y = 9$ [$\because z = 1$]
Hence, Iqbal had 31 cards.

494. Let the original number of boys be x. Then, number of apples first picked $= 3x$.
Final number of boys $= x + 3$. Final number of apples $= 3x + 1$.
$\therefore$ $\frac{3x+1}{x+3} = 2 \Leftrightarrow 3x + 1 = 2x + 6 \Leftrightarrow x = 5$.
Hence, required number of apples $= 3 \times 5 + 1 = 16$.

495. Let there be n students in the classroom.
Total number of friendship bands bought $= n(n - 1)$.
If two students were absent, number of bands utilized $= (n - 2)(n - 3)$.
$\therefore$ $n(n - 1) - (n - 2)(n - 3)$
$= 122 \Leftrightarrow n^2 - n - n^2 + 5n - 6$
$= 122 \Leftrightarrow 4n = 128 \Leftrightarrow n = 32$.
So, number of bands finally unutilized
$= 32 \times 31 - 31 \times 30 = 992 - 930 = 62$.

496. Let the total number of chocolates she bought be x and the total number of her friends be y.
Then, $3(y - 1) + 2 = x \Leftrightarrow x - 3y = -1$ ...(*i*)
And, $2y + 15 = x \Leftrightarrow x - 2y = 15$ ...(*ii*)
Subtracting (*i*) from (*ii*), we get: $y = 16$. Putting $y = 16$ in (*ii*), we get: $x = 47$.

497. Clearly, each committee has two members which are common to all three committees. In addition, it has a third member common to the second committee and a fourth one common to the third committee.

498. $2n + 5m = 50 \Leftrightarrow 2n = 50 - 5m \Leftrightarrow n = \frac{50 - 5m}{2}$.
Since n is a natural number, so $(50 - 5m)$ must be even and so, m must be even
i.e., $m = 2, 4, 6$ or 8
[$\because m < 10$, as for $m = 10$, $n = 0$]
If $m = 2$, $n = 20$;
If $m = 4$, $n = 15$;
If $m = 6$, $n = 10$;
If $m = 8$, $n = 5$.
$\therefore$ Least possible difference $= 8 - 5 = 3$.

499. Let the number of chairs with arms bought be x and those without arms be y.
Then, $x + y \geq 15$ or $y \geq 15 - x$
And, $160x + 100y \leq 2000$
$\Rightarrow$ $160x + 100(15 - x) \leq 2000$
[$\because$ For maximum value of x, y has to be minimum]
$\Rightarrow$ $160x + 1500 - 100x \leq 2000 \Rightarrow 60x \leq 500 \Rightarrow x \leq 8$.
Hence, maximum value of x is 8.

500. Let the number of cats be x. Then, number of dogs = $55 - x$.

Clearly, x is a multiple of 5 i.e., $x = 5n$ where $n \le 10$.

And, $(55 - x)$ is a multiple of 4 $\Rightarrow 55 - 5n = 4m$

$$\Rightarrow m = \frac{55 - 5n}{4}.$$

Since m is a natural number, $(55 - 5n)$ must be a multiple of 4 which happens for $n = 3$ or 7.

Case I. If $n = 3$, $m = 10$.

Number of cats = 15, Number of dogs = 40.

Number of pets adopted $= \left(\frac{1}{5} \times 15 + \frac{1}{4} \times 40\right) = 13.$

Case II. If $n = 7$, $m = 5$.

Number of cats = 35, Number of dogs = 20.

Number of pets adopted $= \left(\frac{1}{5} \times 35 + \frac{1}{4} \times 20\right) = 12.$

$\therefore$ Required number = 13.

501. The team has played a total of $(17 + 3) = 20$ matches. This constitutes $\frac{2}{3}$ of the matches. Hence, total number of matches played = 30. To win $\frac{3}{4}$ of them, a team has to win at least 23 of them. The team has thus to win a minimum of 6 matches out of remaining 10. So, it can lose a maximum of 4 of them.

502. Let M represent the number of mornings when they swam.

Then, total number of mornings in the vacation

$= 32 + M.$

Let E represent the number of evenings when they played tennis.

Then, total number of evenings in the vacation = $18 + E$.

$\therefore \quad 32 + M = 18 + E \Rightarrow E - M = 14.$ ...(*i*)

Total number of days when they swam or played $= E + M.$

$\therefore \quad E + M = 28$ ...(*ii*)

Adding (*i*) and (*ii*), we get: $2E = 42$ or $E = 21$.

Hence, duration of vacations = $18 + E = 18 + 21 = 39$.

503. Note: $10 \times 15 \ne 20 \times 10$. So, this is not a question of Chain Rule and the original quantity of grass and its growth rate are to be considered.

Let g be the total units of grass in the field originally, r be the units of grass grown per day and c be the units of grass each cow eats per day.

Then, $g + 15r = (10 \times 15)\, c = 150c$ ...(*i*)

$g + 10r = (20 \times 10)\, c = 200c$ ...(*ii*)

Subtracting (*ii*) from (*i*), we get: $5r = -50c$ or $r = -10c$.

Putting $r = -10c$ in (*i*), we get: $g = 300c$.

Let the required number of days be x.

Then, $g + xr = 30xc \Rightarrow 300c - 10xc = 30xc \Rightarrow 40xc = 300c$

$\Rightarrow 40x = 300 \Rightarrow x = 7\frac{1}{2}.$

504. Let g be the total units of grass in the field originally, r be the units of grass grown per day and c be the units of grass each cow eats per day.

Then, units of grass consumed by 70 cows in 24 days

$= (70 \times 24 \times c) = 1680c.$

Units of grass consumed by 30 cows in 60 days

$= (30 \times 60 \times c) = 1800c.$

We have: $g + 24r = 1680c$ ...(*i*)

$g + 60r = 1800c$ ...(*ii*)

Subtracting (*i*) from (*ii*), we get: $36r = 120c \Rightarrow r = \frac{10}{3}c.$

Putting $r = \frac{10}{3}c$ in (*i*), we get: $g = 1600c$.

Let the required number of cows be x.

Then, $g + 96r = x \times 96 \times c \Rightarrow 1600c + \frac{96 \times 10}{3}c = 96xc$

$\Rightarrow 1920c = 96xc \Rightarrow 96x = 1920 \Rightarrow x = 20.$

Questions 505 and 506

Let the total number of pilgrims in the group be x.

Then, total number of visits to shrines

= Number of shrines × Number of pilgrims visiting each shrine = $10 \times 4 = 40$.

So, $5x = 40$ or $x = 8$.

Let the number of lakes be n.

Then, total number of visits to lakes

= Number of lakes × Number of pilgrims visiting each lake = $6n$.

$\therefore \quad 6n = 8 \times 3 = 24$ or $n = 4$.

505. Number of lakes in the city = 4.

506. Number of pilgrims in the group = 8.

507. Let the total number of apples be x. Then,

Apples sold to 1st customer $= \left(\frac{x}{2} + 1\right)$. Remaining apples

$= x - \left(\frac{x}{2} + 1\right) = \left(\frac{x}{2} - 1\right).$

Apples sold to 2nd customer $= \frac{1}{3}\left(\frac{x}{2} - 1\right) + 1$

$= \frac{x}{6} - \frac{1}{3} + 1 = \left(\frac{x}{6} + \frac{2}{3}\right).$

Remaining apples $= \left(\frac{x}{2} - 1\right) - \left(\frac{x}{6} + \frac{2}{3}\right)$

$= \left(\frac{x}{2} - \frac{x}{6}\right) - \left(1 + \frac{2}{3}\right) = \left(\frac{x}{3} - \frac{5}{3}\right).$

Apples sold to 3rd customer $= \frac{1}{5}\left(\frac{x}{3} - \frac{5}{3}\right) + 1 = \left(\frac{x}{15} + \frac{2}{3}\right).$

Remaining apples $= \left(\frac{x}{3} - \frac{5}{3}\right) - \left(\frac{x}{15} + \frac{2}{3}\right)$

$= \left(\frac{x}{3} - \frac{x}{15}\right) - \left(\frac{5}{3} + \frac{2}{3}\right) = \left(\frac{4x}{15} - \frac{7}{3}\right).$

$\therefore \quad \frac{4x}{15} - \frac{7}{3} = 3 \Leftrightarrow \frac{4x}{15} = \frac{16}{3} \Leftrightarrow x = \left(\frac{16}{3} \times \frac{15}{4}\right) = 20.$

508. Let the time taken to read one page of Engineering Mathematics be M units and that taken to read one page of Engineering Drawing be D units.

Then, $80\,M + 100\,D = 50\,M + 250\,D \Rightarrow 30\,M = 150\,D \Rightarrow D = \frac{M}{5}.$

$\therefore \quad 80\,M + 100\,D = 80\,M + 100 \times \dfrac{M}{5}$

$= 80\,M + 20\,M = 100\,M.$

So, Ravi can read 100 pages of Engineering Mathematics.

509. Since Rohan paid ₹ 20 and because of lack of change, the clerk gave him stamps worth ₹ 3, it can be concluded that the total value of the stamps that he wanted to buy is ₹ 17. Since he ordered initially a minimum of 2 stamps of each denomination, if he bought exactly 2 stamps each, his total value is ₹ [2(5 + 2 + 1)] = ₹ 16. To make it ₹ 17, he must have bought 1 one-rupee stamp more.
So, total number of stamps ordered = (2 + 2 + 3) = 7.
Since the clerk gave him 3 more, so total number of stamps bought = (7 + 3) = 10.

510. Suppose Aditya bought x gel pens and y fountain pens. Then.

$300x + 400y = 3600 \Rightarrow 3x + 4y = 36$ ...(i)

Also, $(300x + 400y) - (400x + 300y) = 150$ or 200

$\Rightarrow \quad 100y - 100x = 150$ or 200

$\Rightarrow \quad y - x = 1.5$ or $y - x = 2$.

If $y - x = 1.5$, we don't get integral values for x and y.

$\therefore \quad y - x = 2$ ...(ii)

Solving (i) and (ii), we get: $x = 4$, $y = 6$.
Hence, total number of pens bought = 4 + 6 = 10.

Questions 511 to 513

Flowers left after first place of worship = $2x - y$.
Flowers left after second place of worship = $2(2x - y) - y = 4x - 3y$.
Flowers left after third place of worship = $2(4x - 3y) - y = 8x - 7y$.
Flowers left after fourth place of worship = $2(8x - 7y) - y = 16x - 15y$.

$\therefore \quad 16x - 15y = 0 \Rightarrow 16x = 15y.$

511. If $x = 30$, then $y = \dfrac{16 \times 30}{15} = 32.$

512. For minimum y, we find the L.C.M. of 16 and 15 which is 240.

$\therefore \quad 16x = 15y = 240 \Rightarrow x = 15,\ y = 16.$

513. Clearly, required number = minimum value of x = 15.

514. Suppose the thief stole x diamonds.

Diamonds given to first watchman = $\dfrac{x}{2} + 2 = \dfrac{x+4}{2}.$

Remaining diamonds = $x - \left(\dfrac{x+4}{2}\right) = \dfrac{x-4}{2}.$

Diamonds given to second watchman = $\dfrac{x-4}{4} + 2 = \dfrac{x+4}{4}.$

Remaining diamonds = $\left(\dfrac{x-4}{2}\right) - \left(\dfrac{x+4}{4}\right) = \dfrac{x-12}{4}.$

Diamonds given to third watchman = $\dfrac{x-12}{8} + 2 = \dfrac{x+4}{8}.$

Remaining diamonds = $\left(\dfrac{x-12}{4}\right) - \left(\dfrac{x+4}{8}\right) = \dfrac{x-28}{8}.$

$\therefore \quad \dfrac{x-28}{8} = 1$ or $x - 28 = 8$ or $x = 36.$

Another Method: The thief escaped with 1 diamond.
Before third watchman, he had (1 + 2) × 2 = 6 diamonds
Before second watchman, he had (6 + 2) × 2 = 16 diamonds
Before first watchman, he had (16 + 2) × 2 = 36 diamonds
Thus, he stole 36 diamonds originally.

515. Let there be x mints in the bowl originally.
Then, mints left after Divya had taken from the bowl

$= \left(\dfrac{2}{3}x + 4\right).$

Mints left after Reema had taken from the bowl

$= \dfrac{3}{4}\left(\dfrac{2}{3}x + 4\right) + 3 = \left(\dfrac{x}{2} + 6\right).$

Mints left after Shweta had taken from the bowl

$= \dfrac{1}{2}\left(\dfrac{x}{2} + 6\right) + 2 = \left(\dfrac{x}{4} + 5\right).$

$\therefore \quad \dfrac{x}{4} + 5 = 17 \Rightarrow \dfrac{x}{4} = 12 \Rightarrow x = 48.$

516. Let the cost of one gel-pen, one ball-point pen and one marker pen be ₹ x, ₹ y and ₹ z respectively.
Then, $4x + 8y + z = 185$ ...(i)
$7x + 15y + z = 315$ ...(ii)
Subtracting (i) from (ii), we get: $3x + 7y = 130$ ...(iii)
Multiplying (iii) by 2 and subtracting from (ii), we get
$x + y + z = 55$
Hence, required cost = ₹ 55.

517. Let the number of byes, wides and runs be x, y and z respectively.
Then, $x + y + z = 232$. Also, $z = 26y$ and $x = y + 8$. ...(i)

$\therefore \quad (y + 8) + y + 26y = 232 \Leftrightarrow 28y = 224$

$\Leftrightarrow \quad y = 8$. So, $z = 26y = 208$.

Let the number of runs scored by Ram and Shyam be $6a$ and $7a$ respectively.
Then, $6a + 7a = 208 \Leftrightarrow 13a = 208 \Leftrightarrow a = 16$.
Hence, runs scored by Ram = $6a = 6 \times 16 = 96$.

518. Let there be n rows of balls in the equilateral triangle.

So, total number of balls = $1 + 2 + \ldots + n = n = \dfrac{n(n+1)}{2}$

Since each row in the square has 8 balls less than that in the equilateral triangle, so the square has $(n - 8)$ rows with $(n - 8)$ balls in each row.
So, total number of balls = $(n - 8)^2$.

$\therefore \quad \dfrac{n(n+1)}{2} + 669 = (n - 8)^2$

$\Rightarrow \quad n^2 + n + 1338 = 2(n^2 + 64 - 16n)$

$\Rightarrow \quad n^2 - 33n - 1210 = 0$

$\Rightarrow \quad n^2 - 55n + 22n - 1210 = 0$

$\Rightarrow \quad (n - 55)(n + 22) = 0 \Rightarrow n = 55 \quad [\because n \neq -22]$

So, initial number of balls

$= \dfrac{n(n+1)}{2} = \dfrac{55 \times 56}{2} = 55 \times 28 = 1540.$

Questions 519 and 520

Let the number of men in the beginning be m.
Suppose each man shifts c crates on the first day. Then
$mc + (m + 6)(c - 5) + (m + 12)(c - 10) + (m + 18)(c - 15) + (m + 24)(c - 20) = 545$

$\Rightarrow$ $mc + mc - 5m + 6c - 30 + mc - 10m + 12c - 120 + mc - 15m + 18c - 270 + mc - 20m + 24c - 480 = 545$

$\Rightarrow$ $5mc - 50m + 60c = 1445$

$\Rightarrow$ $mc - 10m + 12c = 289$

$\Rightarrow$ $mc - 10m = 289 - 12c$

$\Rightarrow m = \frac{289-12c}{c-10}$.

Clearly, $c > 20$

[$\because$ if $c < 20$, then number of crates shifted on 5th day i.e., $(c - 20) < 0$ which is not possible]

Thus, we have to find $c > 20$ such that m is an integer. This is not so for $c = 21$ and $c = 22$.

For $c = 23$, we have: $m = \frac{289-276}{13} = \frac{13}{13} = 1.$

519. Number of crates shifted on third day $= (m + 12)(c - 10)$
$= (1 + 12)(23 - 10)$
$= 13 \times 13 = 169.$

520. Number of men on 5th day $= m + 24 = 25.$

521. Let the missing number be x.

Given $\frac{20+8\times0.5}{20-x} = 12$

$\Rightarrow \frac{20+4}{20-x} = 12 \Rightarrow \frac{24}{20-x} = 12$

$\Rightarrow 20 - x = \frac{24}{12} = 2$

$\Rightarrow x = 20 - 2 = 18$

Hence, the number is 18.

522. Given $\frac{a}{b} + \frac{b}{a} = 2$

$\Rightarrow \frac{a^2+b^2}{ab} = 2$

$\Rightarrow a^2 + b^2 = 2ab$

$\Rightarrow a^2 + b^2 - 2ab = 0$

$\Rightarrow (a-b)^2 = 0$

$\Rightarrow a - b = 0$

523. Given $(24.96)^2 \div (34.11 \div 20.05) + 67.96 - 89.11$

$(25)^2 \div (34 \div 20) + 68 - 89$

$\approx (25)^2 \div \left(\frac{34}{20}\right) + 68 - 89$

$\approx 625 \div 1.7 + 68 - 89$

$\approx 367.6 + 68 - 89$

$\approx 367 + 68 - 89 \approx 346$

524. $\frac{x+1}{x-1} = \frac{a}{b}$

By componendo and dividendo

$\frac{x+1+x-1}{x+1-x+1} = \frac{a+b}{a-b}$

$\Rightarrow \frac{2x}{2} = \frac{a+b}{a-b}$

$\Rightarrow x = \frac{a+b}{a-b}$ ...(i)

Again, $\frac{1-y}{1+y} = \frac{b}{a}$

$\Rightarrow \frac{1+y}{1-y} = \frac{a}{b}$

$\Rightarrow \frac{1+y+1-y}{1+y-1+y} = \frac{a+b}{a-b}$

$\Rightarrow \frac{2}{2y} = \frac{a+b}{a-b}$

$\Rightarrow \frac{1}{y} = \frac{a+b}{a-b}$

$\Rightarrow y = \frac{a-b}{a+b}$ ...(ii)

Subtracting equation (ii) from (i) we get

$\therefore x - y = \frac{a+b}{a-b} - \frac{a-b}{a+b}$

$\left\{\because (a+b)^2 - (a-b)^2 = 4ab \text{ and } a^2 - b^2 = (a-b)(a+b)\right\}$

$= \frac{(a+b)^2 - (a-b)^2}{(a+b)(a-b)} = \frac{4ab}{a^2-b^2}$

Multiply equation (i) and (ii) we get

$xy = \frac{a+b}{a-b} \times \frac{a-b}{a+b} = 1$

$\therefore$ Expression

$= \frac{x-y}{1+xy} = \frac{\frac{4ab}{a^2-b^2}}{1+1}$

$= \frac{4ab}{2(a^2-b^2)} = \frac{2ab}{a^2-b^2}$

525. Given $200 \div 25 \times 4 + 12 - 3$

$= \frac{200}{25} \times 4 + 12 - 3$

$= 8 \times 4 + 12 - 3$

$= 32 + 12 - 3 = 44 - 3 = 41$

526. Let the number be a.

Given $14 \times 627 \div \sqrt{1089} = (a)^3 + 141$

$14 \times 627 \div \sqrt{1089} = a^3 + 141$

$\Rightarrow 14 \times 627 \div 33 = a^3 + 141$

$\Rightarrow 14 \times 19 = a^3 + 141$

$\Rightarrow 266 = a^3 + 141$

$\Rightarrow a^3 = 125$

$\Rightarrow a = \sqrt[3]{125}$

$\Rightarrow a = 5$

527. Let the number be x.

Given $(923 - 347)/x = 32$

$\Rightarrow x = \frac{576}{32} = 18$

$\Rightarrow x = 18$

528. Let the number be a.

Given $1559.95 - 7.99 \times 24.96 - a^2 = 1154$

$\Rightarrow 1560 - 8 \times 25 - a^2 = 1154$

$\Rightarrow 1360 - 200 - a^2 = 1154$

$\Rightarrow a^2 = 1360 - 1154 = 206$

$\Rightarrow a \approx \sqrt{206} \approx 14$

529. Given $1\frac{4}{5} + 20 - 280 \div 25$

$= 1\frac{4}{5} + 20 - \frac{280}{25}$

$= \frac{9}{5} + 20 - \frac{56}{5}$

$= \frac{9 + 100 - 56}{5}$

$= \frac{53}{5} = 10\frac{3}{5}$

530. $= \{(64 - 38) \times 4\} \div 13$

$= \frac{26 \times 4}{13} = 8$

531. Given $x + y = 2a$

$\therefore \quad \frac{a}{x - a} + \frac{a}{y - a} = \frac{a(y - a) + a(x - a)}{(x - a)(y - a)}$

$= \frac{ay - a^2 + ax - a^2}{(x - a)(y - a)}$

$= \frac{a(x + y) - 2a^2}{(x - a)(y - a)}$

$= \frac{a \cdot 2a - 2a^2}{(x - a)(y - a)}$

$= \frac{2a^2 - 2a^2}{(x - a)(y - a)} = 0$

532. Let the number be x.

Given $421 \div 35 \times 299.97 \div 25.05 = x^2$

$(x)^2 \approx 420 \div 35 \times 300 \div 25$

$= 12 \times 300 \div 25 = 12 \times 12$

$\Rightarrow x^2 = 12 \times 12$

$\therefore \; x = \sqrt{12 \times 12} = 12$

Hence, the number is 12.

533. Given

$= 19.99 \times 15.98 + 224.98 + 125.02$

$\approx 20 \times 16 + 225 + 125 = 320 + 225 + 125 = 670$

534. Given $3625 \times ? = 1450$

$? = \frac{1450}{3625} = \frac{725 \times 2}{725 \times 5} = \frac{2}{5}$

535. Given: $128.43 + 30.21 + ? = 173$

$? = 173 - 128.43 - 30.21$

$= 173 - 158.64 = 14.36$

536. Given expression

$= 123 \times 999 + 123$

$= 123 \times (999 + 1)$

$= 123 \times 1000$

$= 123000$

537. Given expression $\frac{(359 + 256)^2 + (359 - 256)^2}{359 \times 359 + 256 \times 256}$

$= \frac{(359 + 256)^2 + (359 - 256)^2}{(359)^2 + (256)^2}$

Let, $a = 359$ and $b = 256$

$\therefore$ expression $= \frac{(a + b)^2 + (a - b)^2}{a^2 + b^2}$

$= \frac{2(a^2 + b^2)}{a^2 + b^2} = 2$

538. $84368 + 65466 - 72009 - 13964$

$= 149834 - 85973 = 63861$

539. Let the number be x.

$4376 + 3209 - 1784 + 97 = 3125 + x$

$\Rightarrow 7682 - 1784 = 3125 + x$

or, $x = 7682 - 1784 - 3125$

$\Rightarrow x = 2773$

Hence, the number is 2773.

540. Let the missing number is a.

Given $14 \times 627 \div \sqrt{(1089)} = (a)^3 + 141$

$\frac{14 \times 627}{\sqrt{1089}} = (a)^3 + 141$

$\frac{14 \times 627}{33} = a^3 + 141$

$266 = a^3 + 141$

$a^3 = 266 - 141$

$a^3 = 125$

$a = \sqrt[3]{125} = 5$

541. Given $\left(x + \frac{1}{x}\right) = 3$

On squaring both sides, we get

$\left(x + \frac{1}{x}\right)^2 = 3^2$

$\Rightarrow \left(x + \frac{1}{x}\right)^2 = 9$

$\Rightarrow x^2 + \frac{1}{x^2} + 2 = 9$

$\Rightarrow x^2 + \frac{1}{x^2} = 7$

542. As we know

$a^3 + b^3 + c^3 - 3abc = (a^2 + b^2 + c^2 - ab - bc - ca)(a + b + c)$

When $a + b + c = 0$

Then $a^3 + b^3 + c^3 - 3abc = 0$

When $x + y + z = 0$

$\Rightarrow x^3 + y^3 + z^3 = 3xyz$

$\Rightarrow x^3 + y^3 + z^3 + 3xyz = 3xyz + 3xyz = 6xyz$

543. Unit digit of $4^1 = 4$

Unit digit of $4^2 = 1\underline{6}$

Unit digit of $4^3 = 6\underline{4}$

Unit digit $4^{96} = 4^{2\times48} = 4^2 = 16$

$\because$ each unit digit of 4 repeats itself after two places

$\therefore$ 16 ÷ 6

$\therefore$ Remainder = 4

544. 67 × 119 + 17 – 27 ÷ 259

= 67 + 119 ÷ 17 × 27 – 259

= 67 + 7 × 27 – 259

= 67 + 189 – 259

= 256 – 259 = –3

545. Given $= \dfrac{(0.73)^3 + (0.27)^3}{(0.73)^2 + (0.27)^2 - 0.73\times0.27}$

Let $a = 0.73$ and $b = 0.27$

$$= \frac{(0.73+0.27)\left[(0.73)^2 + (0.27)^2 - 0.73\times0.27\right]}{(0.73)^2 + (0.27)^2 - 0.73\times0.27}$$

$$\left[\because a^3 + b^3 = (a+b)\left(a^2 + b^2 - ab\right)\right]$$

= 0.73 + 0.27 = 1

5 Square Roots and Cube Roots

IMPORTANT FACTS AND FORMULAE

I. Square Root: If $x^2 = y$, we say that the square root of y is x and we write, $\sqrt{y} = x$.

Thus, $\sqrt{4} = 2, \sqrt{9} = 3, \sqrt{196} = 14$.

II. Cube Root: The cube root of a given number x is the number whose cube is x. We denote the cube root of x by $\sqrt[3]{x}$.

Thus, $\sqrt[3]{8} = \sqrt[3]{2\times2\times2} = 2, \sqrt[3]{343} = \sqrt[3]{7\times7\times7} = 7$ etc.

Note:

1. $\sqrt{xy} = \sqrt{x}\times\sqrt{y}$
2. $\sqrt{\frac{x}{y}} = \frac{\sqrt{x}}{\sqrt{y}} = \frac{\sqrt{x}}{\sqrt{y}}\times\frac{\sqrt{y}}{\sqrt{y}} = \frac{\sqrt{xy}}{y}$.

SOLVED EXAMPLES

Ex. 1. ***Evaluate $\sqrt{6084}$ by factorization method.***

2	6084
2	3042
3	1521
3	507
13	169
	13

Sol. Method: Express the given number as the product of prime factors. Now, take the product of these prime factors choosing one out of every pair of the same primes. This product gives the square root of the given number.

Thus, resolving 6084 into prime factors, we get:

$6084 = 2^2 \times 3^2 \times 13^2$

$\therefore \quad \sqrt{6084} = (2 \times 3 \times 13) = 78.$

Ex. 2. ***Find the square root of 1471369.***

```
   1   | 1471369 (1213
       | 1
       |-------
  22   |  47
       |  44
       |-------
 241   |   313
       |   241
       |-------
2423   |    7269
       |    7269
       |-------
       |       ×
```

Sol. Method: In the given number, mark off the digits in pairs starting from the unit's digit. Each pair and the remaining one digit is called a period.

Now, $1^2 = 1$. On subtracting, we get 0 as remainder.

Now, bring down the next period i.e., 47.

Now, trial divisor is $1 \times 2 = 2$ and trial dividend is 47.

So, we take 22 as divisor and put 2 as quotient.

The remainder is 3.

Next, we bring down the next period which is 13.

Now, trial divisor is $12 \times 2 = 24$ and trial dividend is 313. So, we take 241 as dividend and 1 as quotient.

The remainder is 72.

Bring down the next period i.e., 69.

Now, the trial divisor is $121 \times 2 = 242$ and the trial dividend is 7269. So, we take 3 as quotient and 2423 as divisor. The remainder is then zero.

Hence, $\sqrt{1471369} = 1213$.

Ex. 3. ***Evaluate:*** $\sqrt{248+\sqrt{52+\sqrt{144}}}$. **(P.C.S., 2009)**

Sol. Given expression $= \sqrt{248+\sqrt{52+12}} = \sqrt{248+\sqrt{64}} = \sqrt{248+8} = \sqrt{256} = 16.$

Ex. 4. ***Simplify :*** $\dfrac{112}{\sqrt{196}} \times \dfrac{\sqrt{576}}{12} \times \dfrac{\sqrt{256}}{8}$.

Sol. Given expression = $\dfrac{112}{14} \times \dfrac{24}{12} \times \dfrac{16}{8} = 8 \times 2 \times 2 = 32.$

Ex. 5. ***If*** $a * b * c = \dfrac{\sqrt{(a+2)(b+3)}}{c+1}$, ***then find the value of*** $6 * 15 * 3$.

Sol. $6 * 15 * 3 = \dfrac{\sqrt{(6+2)(15+3)}}{3+1} = \dfrac{\sqrt{8 \times 18}}{4} = \dfrac{\sqrt{144}}{4} = \dfrac{12}{4} = 3.$

Ex. 6. ***Find the value of*** $\sqrt{1\dfrac{9}{16}}$.

Sol. $\sqrt{1\dfrac{9}{16}} = \sqrt{\dfrac{25}{16}} = \dfrac{\sqrt{25}}{\sqrt{16}} = \dfrac{5}{4} = 1\dfrac{1}{4}.$

Ex. 7. ***What is the square root of 0.0009?***

Sol. $\sqrt{0.0009} = \sqrt{\dfrac{9}{10000}} = \dfrac{\sqrt{9}}{\sqrt{10000}} = \dfrac{3}{100} = 0.03.$

Ex. 8. ***Evaluate*** $\sqrt{175.2976}$.

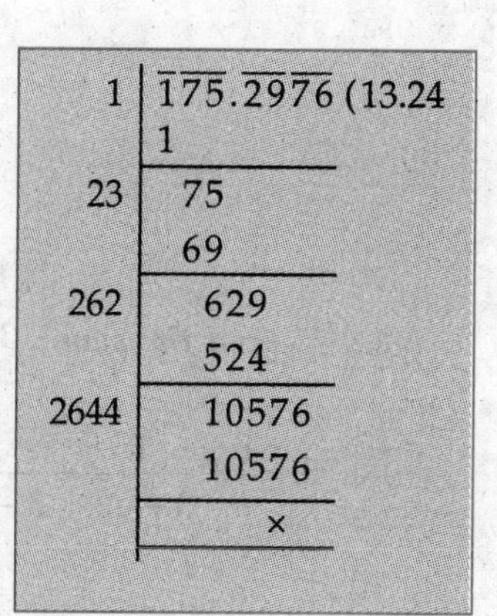

1 | 175.2976 (13.24
1
23 | 75
69
262 | 629
524
2644 | 10576
10576
×

Sol. Method: We make even number of decimal places by affixing a zero, if necessary. Now, we mark off periods and extract the square root as shown.

$\therefore \quad \sqrt{175.2976} = 13.24.$

Ex. 9. ***What will come in place of question mark in each of the following questions?***

(i) $\sqrt{\dfrac{32.4}{?}} = 2$ (ii) $\sqrt{86.49} + \sqrt{5 + (?)^2} = 12.3$

Sol. (i) Let $\sqrt{\dfrac{32.4}{x}} = 2$. Then, $\dfrac{32.4}{x} = 4 \Leftrightarrow 4x = 32.4 \Leftrightarrow x = 8.1.$

(ii) Let $\sqrt{86.49} + \sqrt{5 + x^2} = 12.3.$

Then, $9.3 + \sqrt{5 + x^2} = 12.3 \Leftrightarrow \sqrt{5 + x^2} = 12.3 - 9.3 = 3$

$\Leftrightarrow 5 + x^2 = 9 \Leftrightarrow x^2 = 9 - 5 = 4 \Leftrightarrow x = \sqrt{4} = 2.$

Ex. 10. ***Find the value of*** $\sqrt{\dfrac{0.289}{0.00121}}$. **(IGNOU, 2003)**

Sol. $\sqrt{\dfrac{0.289}{0.00121}} = \sqrt{\dfrac{0.28900}{0.00121}} = \sqrt{\dfrac{28900}{121}} = \dfrac{170}{11}.$

Ex. 11. ***If*** $\sqrt{841} = 29$, ***then find the value of*** $\sqrt{841} + \sqrt{8.41} + \sqrt{0.0841} + \sqrt{0.000841}$. **(M.B.A., 2006)**

Sol. Given expression = $\sqrt{841} + \sqrt{\dfrac{841}{10^2}} + \sqrt{\dfrac{841}{10^4}} + \sqrt{\dfrac{841}{10^6}} = \sqrt{841} + \dfrac{\sqrt{841}}{10} + \dfrac{\sqrt{841}}{10^2} + \dfrac{\sqrt{841}}{10^3}$

$= 29 + \dfrac{29}{10} + \dfrac{29}{100} + \dfrac{29}{1000} = 29 + 2.9 + 0.29 + 0.029 = 32.219.$

Ex. 12. ***If*** $\sqrt{1 + \dfrac{x}{144}} = \dfrac{13}{12}$, ***then find the value of x.***

Sol. $\sqrt{1+\frac{x}{144}}=\frac{13}{12} \Rightarrow \left(1+\frac{x}{144}\right)=\left(\frac{13}{12}\right)^2=\frac{169}{144} \Rightarrow \frac{x}{144}=\frac{169}{144}-1$

$\Rightarrow \frac{x}{144}=\frac{25}{144} \Rightarrow x = 25.$

Ex. 13. ***Simplify :*** $\frac{1}{\sqrt{100}-\sqrt{99}}-\frac{1}{\sqrt{99}-\sqrt{98}}+\frac{1}{\sqrt{98}-\sqrt{97}}-\frac{1}{\sqrt{97}-\sqrt{96}}+...+\frac{1}{\sqrt{2}-\sqrt{1}}.$ **(Section Officers', 2005)**

Sol. Given expression

$$=\frac{1}{\sqrt{100}-\sqrt{99}}\times\frac{\sqrt{100}+\sqrt{99}}{\sqrt{100}+\sqrt{99}}-\frac{1}{\sqrt{99}-\sqrt{98}}\times\frac{\sqrt{99}+\sqrt{98}}{\sqrt{99}+\sqrt{98}}+\frac{1}{\sqrt{98}-\sqrt{97}}\times\frac{\sqrt{98}+\sqrt{97}}{\sqrt{98}+\sqrt{97}}$$

$$-\frac{1}{\sqrt{97}-\sqrt{96}}\times\frac{\sqrt{97}+\sqrt{96}}{\sqrt{97}+\sqrt{96}}+...+\frac{1}{\sqrt{2}-\sqrt{1}}\times\frac{\sqrt{2}+\sqrt{1}}{\sqrt{2}+\sqrt{1}}$$

$$=\frac{\sqrt{100}+\sqrt{99}}{(100-99)}-\frac{\sqrt{99}+\sqrt{98}}{(99-98)}+\frac{\sqrt{98}+\sqrt{97}}{(98-97)}-\frac{\sqrt{97}+\sqrt{96}}{(97-96)}+...+\frac{\sqrt{2}+\sqrt{1}}{(2-1)}$$

$$=(\sqrt{100}+\sqrt{99})-(\sqrt{99}+\sqrt{98})+(\sqrt{98}+\sqrt{97})-(\sqrt{97}+\sqrt{96})+...+(\sqrt{2}+\sqrt{1})$$

$$=\sqrt{100}+\sqrt{1}=10+1=11.$$

Ex. 14. ***Find the sum :*** $3+\frac{1}{\sqrt{3}}+\frac{1}{3+\sqrt{3}}+\frac{1}{\sqrt{3}-3}.$ **(S.S.C., 2007)**

Sol. $3+\frac{1}{3}+\frac{1}{3+\sqrt{3}}-\frac{1}{3-\sqrt{3}}=3+\frac{1}{\sqrt{3}}\times\frac{\sqrt{3}}{\sqrt{3}}+\frac{1}{3+\sqrt{3}}\times\frac{3-\sqrt{3}}{3-\sqrt{3}}-\frac{1}{3-\sqrt{3}}\times\frac{3+\sqrt{3}}{3+\sqrt{3}}$

$$=3+\frac{\sqrt{3}}{3}+\frac{3-\sqrt{3}}{(9-3)}-\frac{3+\sqrt{3}}{(9-3)}=3+\frac{\sqrt{3}}{3}+\frac{3-\sqrt{3}}{6}-\frac{3+\sqrt{3}}{6}$$

$$=\frac{18+2\sqrt{3}+3-\sqrt{3}-3-\sqrt{3}}{6}=\frac{18}{6}=3.$$

Ex. 15. ***Find the value of $\sqrt{3}$ upto three places of decimal.***

Sol.

```
   1 | 3.000000 ( 1.732
     | 1
     |-------
  27 | 200
     | 189
     |-------
 343 |  1100
     |  1029
     |-------
3462 |    7100
     |    6924
```

$\therefore \sqrt{3} = 1.732.$

Ex. 16. ***If $\sqrt{3}$ = 1.732, find the value of*** $\sqrt{192}-\frac{1}{2}\sqrt{48}-\sqrt{75}$ ***correct to 3 places of decimal.*** **(S.S.C., 2004)**

Sol. $\sqrt{192}-\frac{1}{2}\sqrt{48}-\sqrt{75}=\sqrt{64\times3}-\frac{1}{2}\sqrt{16\times3}-\sqrt{25\times3}=8\sqrt{3}-\frac{1}{2}\times4\sqrt{3}-5\sqrt{3}$

$$=3\sqrt{3}-2\sqrt{3}=\sqrt{3}=1.732.$$

Ex. 17. ***If*** $\sqrt{0.05\times0.5\times a}=0.5\times0.05\times\sqrt{b}$, ***then find the value of*** $\frac{a}{b}$. **(M.B.A., 2006)**

Sol. Clearly, we have: $\frac{\sqrt{a}}{\sqrt{b}}=\frac{0.5\times0.05}{\sqrt{0.05\times0.5}}\Rightarrow\frac{a}{b}=\frac{0.5\times0.05\times0.5\times0.05}{0.05\times0.5}=0.5\times0.05=0.025.$

Ex. 18. ***Evaluate :*** $\sqrt{\dfrac{9.5 \times .0085 \times 18.9}{.0017 \times 1.9 \times 0.021}}$.

Sol. Given exp. $= \sqrt{\dfrac{9.5 \times .0085 \times 18.900}{.0017 \times 1.9 \times 0.021}}$.

Now, since the sum of decimal places in the numerator and denominator under the radical sign is the same, we remove the decimal.

$\therefore$ Given exp. $= \sqrt{\dfrac{95 \times 85 \times 18900}{17 \times 19 \times 21}} = \sqrt{5 \times 5 \times 900} = 5 \times 30 = 150.$

Ex. 19. ***Simplify :*** $\sqrt{[(12.1)^2 - (8.1)^2] \div [(0.25)^2 + (0.25)(19.95)]}$. **(C.B.I., 2003)**

Sol. Given exp. $= \sqrt{\dfrac{(12.1 + 8.1)(12.1 - 8.1)}{(0.25)(0.25 + 19.95)}} = \sqrt{\dfrac{20.2 \times 4}{0.25 \times 20.2}} = \sqrt{\dfrac{4}{0.25}} = \sqrt{\dfrac{400}{25}} = \sqrt{16} = 4.$

Ex. 20. ***If*** $x = 1 + \sqrt{2}$ ***and*** $y = 1 - \sqrt{2}$, ***find the value of*** $(x^2 + y^2)$.

Sol. $x^2 + y^2 = (1 + \sqrt{2})^2 + (1 - \sqrt{2})^2 = 2[(1)^2 + (\sqrt{2})^2] = 2 \times 3 = 6.$

Ex. 21. ***Evaluate*** $\sqrt{0.9}$ ***upto 3 places of decimal.***

Sol.

```
   9  | 0.900000 (0.948
      |   81
      |---------
 184  |   900
      |   736
      |---------
1888  |   16400
      |   15104
```

$\therefore \sqrt{0.9} = 0.948.$

Ex. 22. ***Find the square root of*** $0.\dot{1}$.

Sol. $\sqrt{0.\dot{1}} = \sqrt{\dfrac{1}{9}} = \dfrac{1}{3} = 0.333 \cdots = 0.\bar{3}.$

Ex. 23. ***If*** $\sqrt{15} = 3.88$, ***find the value of*** $\sqrt{\dfrac{5}{3}}$.

Sol. $\sqrt{\dfrac{5}{3}} = \sqrt{\dfrac{5 \times 3}{3 \times 3}} = \dfrac{\sqrt{15}}{3} = \dfrac{3.88}{3} = 1.2933..... = 1.29\bar{3}.$

Ex. 24. ***Find the least square number which is exactly divisible by 10, 12, 15 and 18.***

Sol. L.C.M. of 10, 12, 15, 18 = 180. Now, $180 = 2 \times 2 \times 3 \times 3 \times 5 = 2^2 \times 3^2 \times 5$.

To make it a perfect square, it must be multiplied by 5.

$\therefore$ Required number $= (2^2 \times 3^2 \times 5^2) = 900$.

Ex. 25. ***Find the greatest number of five digits which is a perfect square.***

Sol. Greatest number of 5 digits is 99999.

```
  3  | 99999 (316
     |  9
     |--------
 61  |  99
     |  61
     |--------
626  |  3899
     |  3756
     |--------
     |   143
```

$\therefore$ Required number $= (99999 - 143) = 99856$.

Ex. 26. ***Find the smallest number that must be added to 1780 to make it a perfect square.***

Sol.

```
 4 | 1780 (42
   | 16
---|-----
82 |  180
   |  164
   |  ---
   |   16
```

$\therefore$ Number to be added $= (43)^2 - 1780 = 1849 - 1780 = 69.$

Ex. 27. ***If*** $\sqrt{2} = 1.4142$, ***find the value of*** $\frac{\sqrt{2}}{(2+\sqrt{2})}$.

Sol. $\frac{\sqrt{2}}{(2+\sqrt{2})} = \frac{\sqrt{2}}{(2+\sqrt{2})} \times \frac{(2-\sqrt{2})}{(2-\sqrt{2})} = \frac{2\sqrt{2}-2}{(4-2)} = \frac{2(\sqrt{2}-1)}{2} = (\sqrt{2}-1) = (1.4142 - 1)$

$= 0.4142.$

Ex. 28. ***If*** $x = \left(\frac{\sqrt{5}+\sqrt{3}}{\sqrt{5}-\sqrt{3}}\right)$ ***and*** $y = \left(\frac{\sqrt{5}-\sqrt{3}}{\sqrt{5}+\sqrt{3}}\right)$, ***find the value of*** $(x^2 + y^2)$.

Sol. $x = \frac{(\sqrt{5}+\sqrt{3})}{(\sqrt{5}-\sqrt{3})} \times \frac{(\sqrt{5}+\sqrt{3})}{(\sqrt{5}+\sqrt{3})} = \frac{(\sqrt{5}+\sqrt{3})^2}{(5-3)} = \frac{5+3+2\sqrt{15}}{2} = 4+\sqrt{15}.$

$y = \frac{(\sqrt{5}-\sqrt{3})}{(\sqrt{5}+\sqrt{3})} \times \frac{(\sqrt{5}-\sqrt{3})}{(\sqrt{5}-\sqrt{3})} = \frac{(\sqrt{5}-\sqrt{3})^2}{(5-3)} = \frac{5+3-2\sqrt{15}}{2} = 4-\sqrt{15}.$

$\therefore x^2 + y^2 = (4+\sqrt{15})^2 + (4-\sqrt{15})^2 = 2[(4)^2 + (\sqrt{15})^2] = 2 \times 31 = 62.$

Ex. 29. ***Find the value of:*** $\sqrt{6+\sqrt{6+\sqrt{6+....}}}$ **(S.S.C., 2006)**

Sol. Let $\sqrt{6+\sqrt{6+\sqrt{6+\cdots}}} = x$.

Then, $\sqrt{6+x} = x \Leftrightarrow 6 + x = x^2 \Rightarrow x^2 - x - 6 = 0 \Leftrightarrow x^2 - 3x + 2x - 6 = 0$

$\Leftrightarrow x(x-3) + 2(x-3) = 0 \Leftrightarrow (x-3)(x+2) = 0 \Leftrightarrow x = 3.$ $[\because x \neq -2]$

Hence, $\sqrt{6+\sqrt{6+\sqrt{6+\cdots}}} = 3.$

Ex. 30. ***Find the cube root of 2744.***

Sol. Method : Resolve the given number as the product of prime factors and take the product of prime factors, choosing one out of three of the same prime factors.

Resolving 2744 as the product of prime factors, we get :

2	2744
2	1372
2	686
7	343
7	49
	7

$2744 = 2^3 \times 7^3.$

$\therefore \sqrt[3]{2744} = 2 \times 7 = 14.$

Ex. 31. ***By what least number 4320 be multiplied to obtain a number which is a perfect cube?***

Sol. Clearly, $4320 = 2^3 \times 3^3 \times 2^2 \times 5.$

To make it a perfect cube, it must be multiplied by 2×5^2 *i.e.,* 50.

EXERCISE
(OBJECTIVE TYPE QUESTIONS)

Directions: ***Mark (✓) against the correct answer:***

1. $\sqrt{53824} = ?$
(a) 202 (b) 232
(c) 242 (d) 332

2. The square root of 41209 is equal to **(L.I.C.A.D.O., 2008)**
(a) 103 (b) 203
(c) 303 (d) 403

3. The square root of 123454321 is **(P.C.S., 2008)**
(a) 111111 (b) 12341
(c) 11111 (d) 11211

4. The number of digits in the square root of 625685746009 is **(S.S.C., 2007)**
(a) 4 (b) 5
(c) 6 (d) 7

5. $\sqrt{\sqrt{17956} + \sqrt{24025}} = ?$ **(Bank P.O., 2008)**
(a) 19 (b) 155
(c) 256 (d) 289
(e) None of these

6. $\sqrt{\sqrt{44944} + \sqrt{52441}} = ?$ **(Bank P.O., 2008)**
(a) 17 (b) 312
(c) 441 (d) 485
(e) None of these

7. One-fourth of the sum of prime numbers, greater than 4 but less than 16, is the square of **(P.C.S., 2009)**
(a) 3 (b) 4
(c) 5 (d) 7

8. The value of $\sqrt{10 + \sqrt{25 + \sqrt{108 + \sqrt{154 + \sqrt{225}}}}}$ is
(a) 4 (b) 6
(c) 8 (d) 10

9. Evaluate $\sqrt{41 - \sqrt{21 + \sqrt{19 - \sqrt{9}}}}$.
(a) 3 (b) 5
(c) 6 (d) 6.4

10. $\sqrt{176 + \sqrt{2401}}$ is equal to
(a) 14 (b) 15
(c) 18 (d) 24

11. $\frac{\sqrt{196}}{7} \times \frac{\sqrt{441}}{7} \times \frac{120}{\sqrt{225}} = ?$ **(R.R.B., 2008)**
(a) 48 (b) 54
(c) 58 (d) 84

12. $\left(\sqrt{\frac{225}{729}} - \sqrt{\frac{25}{144}}\right) \div \sqrt{\frac{16}{81}} = ?$
(a) $\frac{1}{48}$ (b) $\frac{5}{48}$
(c) $\frac{5}{16}$ (d) None of these

13. $(15)^2 + (18)^2 - 20 = \sqrt{?}$ **(Bank P.O., 2006)**
(a) 22 (b) 23
(c) 529 (d) 279841
(e) None of these

14. $\sqrt{?} \times \sqrt{484} = 1034$ **(L.I.C.A.D.O., 2007)**
(a) 2025 (b) 2209
(c) 2304 (d) 2401
(e) None of these

15. $\sqrt{11881} \times \sqrt{?} = 10137$ **(Bank Recruitment, 2008)**
(a) 8281 (b) 8649
(c) 9216 (d) 9409
(e) None of these

16. In the equation $\frac{4050}{\sqrt{x}} = 450$, the value of x is **(L.I.C.A.D.O., 2008)**
(a) 9 (b) 49
(c) 81 (d) 100

17. $\sqrt{\frac{16}{25}} \times \sqrt{\frac{?}{25}} \times \frac{16}{25} = \frac{256}{625}$ **(R.R.B. 2008)**
(a) 5 (b) 8
(c) 16 (d) None of these

18. The square root of $(272^2 - 128^2)$ is
(a) 144 (b) 200
(c) 240 (d) 256

19. If $x * y = x + y + \sqrt{xy}$, the value of $6 * 24$ is
(a) 41 (b) 42
(c) 43 (d) 44

20. If $y = 5$, then what is the value of $10y\sqrt{y^3 - y^2}$?
(a) $50\sqrt{2}$ (b) 100
(c) $200\sqrt{5}$ (d) 500

21. $\sqrt{110\frac{1}{4}} = ?$
(a) 10.25 (b) 10.5
(c) 11.5 (d) 19.5

22. $\sqrt{\frac{25}{81} - \frac{1}{9}} = ?$ (Hotel Management, 2002)

(*a*) $\frac{2}{3}$ (*b*) $\frac{4}{9}$

(*c*) $\frac{16}{81}$ (*d*) $\frac{25}{81}$

23. $[(\sqrt{81})^2]^2 = (?)^2$ (Specialist Officers, 2006)

(*a*) 8 (*b*) 9

(*c*) 4096 (*d*) 6561

(*e*) None of these

24. The digit in the unit's place in the square root of 15876 is

(*a*) 2 (*b*) 4

(*c*) 6 (*d*) 8

25. Which of the following is closest to $\sqrt{3}$?

(S.S.C., 2005)

(*a*) 1.69 (*b*) $\frac{173}{100}$

(*c*) 1.75 (*d*) $\frac{9}{5}$

26. How many two-digit numbers satisfy this property: The last digit (unit's digit) of the square of the two-digit number is 8?

(*a*) 1 (*b*) 2

(*c*) 3 (*d*) None of these

27. What percentage of the numbers from 1 to 50 have squares that end in the digit 1? (M.B.A., 2006)

(*a*) 1 (*b*) 5

(*c*) 10 (*d*) 11

(*e*) 20

28. While solving a mathematical problem, Samidha squared a number and then subtracted 25 from it rather than the required i.e., first subtracting 25 from the number and then squaring it. But she got the right answer. What was the given number?

(Bank P.O., 2006)

(*a*) 13 (*b*) 38

(*c*) 48

(*d*) Cannot be determined (*e*) None of these

29. How many perfect squares lie between 120 and 300? (S.S.C., 2010)

(*a*) 5 (*b*) 6

(*c*) 7 (*d*) 8

30. The number of perfect square numbers between 50 and 1000 is

(*a*) 21 (*b*) 22

(*c*) 23 (*d*) 24

(Section Officers', 2003)

31. A man born in the first half of the nineteenth century was x years old in the year x^2. He was born in

(M.B.A., 2011)

(*a*) 1806 (*b*) 1812

(*c*) 1825 (*d*) 1836

32. R is a positive number. It is multiplied by 8 and then squared. The square is now divided by 4 and the square root is taken. The result of the square root is Q. What is the value of Q? (SNAP, 2010)

(*a*) $3R$ (*b*) $4R$

(*c*) $7R$ (*d*) $9R$

33. The smallest natural number which is a perfect square and which ends in 3 identical digits lies between

(*a*) 1000 and 2000 (*b*) 2000 and 3000

(*c*) 3000 and 4000 (*d*) 4000 and 5000

34. $\left(\sqrt{2} + \frac{1}{\sqrt{2}}\right)^2$ is equal to (S.S.C., 2005)

(*a*) $2\frac{1}{2}$ (*b*) $3\frac{1}{2}$

(*c*) $4\frac{1}{2}$ (*d*) $5\frac{1}{2}$

35. If the product of four consecutive natural numbers increased by a natural number p, is a perfect square, then the value of p is (C.P.O., 2006)

(*a*) 1 (*b*) 2

(*c*) 4 (*d*) 8

36. What is the square root of 0.16?

(*a*) 0.004 (*b*) 0.04

(*c*) 0.4 (*d*) 4

37. The value of $\sqrt{0.000441}$ is (S.S.C., 2002)

(*a*) 0.00021 (*b*) 0.0021

(*c*) 0.021 (*d*) 0.21

38. $\sqrt{0.00004761}$ equals (C.B.I., 2003)

(*a*) 0.00069 (*b*) 0.0069

(*c*) 0.0609 (*d*) 0.069

39. $1.5^2 \times \sqrt{0.0225} = ?$ (Bank P.O., 2002)

(*a*) 0.0375 (*b*) 0.3375

(*c*) 3.275 (*d*) 32.75

40. $\sqrt{0.01 + \sqrt{0.0064}} = ?$

(*a*) 0.03 (*b*) 0.3

(*c*) 0.42 (*d*) None of these

41. The value of $\sqrt{0.01} + \sqrt{0.81} + \sqrt{1.21} + \sqrt{0.0009}$ is

(S.S.C., 2002)

(*a*) 2.03 (*b*) 2.1

(*c*) 2.11 (*d*) 2.13

42. $\sqrt{.0025} \times \sqrt{2.25} \times \sqrt{.0001} = ?$

(a) .000075 (b) .0075
(c) .075 (d) None of these

43. $\sqrt{1.5625} = ?$ (S.B.I.P.O., 2003)

(a) 1.05 (b) 1.25
(c) 1.45 (d) 1.55

44. If $\sqrt{.00000676} = .0026$, the square root of 67,60,000 is:

(a) $\frac{1}{26}$ (b) 26
(c) 260 (d) 2600

45. If $\sqrt{18225} = 135$, then the value of $(\sqrt{182.25} + \sqrt{1.8225} + \sqrt{0.018225} + \sqrt{0.00018225})$ is

(a) 1.49985 (b) 14.9985
(c) 149.985 (d) 1499.85

46. If $\sqrt{4096} = 64$, then the value of $\sqrt{40.96} + \sqrt{0.4096} + \sqrt{0.004096} + \sqrt{0.00004096}$ up to two places of decimals is (S.S.C., 2005)

(a) 7.09 (b) 7.10
(c) 7.11 (d) 7.12

47. Given that $\sqrt{13} = 3.605$ and $\sqrt{130} = 11.40$, find the value of $\sqrt{1.3} + \sqrt{1300} + \sqrt{0.013}$.

(a) 36.164 (b) 36.304
(c) 37.164 (d) 37.304

48. If $\frac{52}{x} = \sqrt{\frac{169}{289}}$, the value of x is

(a) 52 (b) 58
(c) 62 (d) 68

49. For what value of * the statement $\left(\frac{*}{15}\right)\left(\frac{*}{135}\right) = 1$ is true? (S.S.C., 2002)

(a) 15 (b) 25
(c) 35 (d) 45

50. Which number should replace both the question marks in the following equation? (Bank P.O., 2008)

$\frac{?}{1776} = \frac{111}{?}$

(a) 343 (b) 414
(c) 644 (d) 543
(e) None of these

51. Which number can replace both the question marks in the equation $\frac{4\frac{1}{2}}{?} = \frac{?}{32}$.

(a) 1 (b) 7
(c) $7\frac{1}{2}$ (d) None of these

52. What should come in place of both the question marks in the equation $\frac{?}{\sqrt{128}} = \frac{\sqrt{162}}{?}$.

(a) 12 (b) 14
(c) 144 (d) 196

53. If $\sqrt{x + \frac{x}{y}} = x\sqrt{\frac{x}{y}}$, where x and y are positive real numbers, then y is equal to (Hotel Mgmt, 2010)

(a) $x + 1$ (b) $x - 1$
(c) $x^2 + 1$ (d) $x^2 - 1$

54. The number $25^{64} \times 64^{25}$ is the square of a natural number n. The sum of the digits of n is (A.A.O. Exam., 2010)

(a) 7 (b) 14
(c) 21 (d) 28

55. If $0.13 \div p^2 = 13$, then p equals

(a) 0.01 (b) 0.1
(c) 10 (d) 100

56. What number should be divided by $\sqrt{0.25}$ to give the result as 25? (C.B.I., 2003)

(a) 12.5 (b) 25
(c) 50 (d) 125

57. If $\sqrt{3^n} = 729$, then the value of n is (Section Officers, 2003)

(a) 6 (b) 8
(c) 10 (d) 12

58. If $\sqrt{18 \times 14 \times x} = 84$, then x equals

(a) 22 (b) 24
(c) 28 (d) 32

59. $28\sqrt{?} + 1426 = \frac{3}{4}$ of 2872

(a) 576 (b) 676
(c) 1296 (d) 1444

60. $\sqrt{\frac{?}{169}} = \frac{54}{39}$

(a) 108 (b) 324
(c) 2916 (d) 4800

61. If $\sqrt{x} \div \sqrt{441} = 0.02$, then the value of x is

(a) 0.1764 (b) 1.764
(c) 1.64 (d) 2.64

62. $\sqrt{\frac{.0196}{?}} = 0.2$

(a) 0.49 (b) 0.7
(c) 4.9 (d) None of these

63. $\sqrt{0.0169 \times ?} = 1.3$ (Hotel Management, 2001)

(a) 10 (b) 100
(c) 1000 (d) None of these

64. If $\sqrt{1369} + \sqrt{.0615 + x} = 37.25$, then x is equal to
(a) 10^{-1} (b) 10^{-2}
(c) 10^{-3} (d) None of these

65. If $\sqrt{(x-1)(y+2)} = 7$, x and y being positive whole numbers, then the values of x and y respectively are
(a) 8, 5 (b) 15, 12
(c) 22, 19 (d) None of these

66. If $\sqrt{.04 \times .4 \times a} = .004 \times .4 \times \sqrt{b}$, then $\frac{a}{b}$ is
(a) 16×10^{-3} (b) 16×10^{-4}
(c) 16×10^{-5} (d) None of these

67. Three-fifth of the square of a certain number is 126.15. What is the number?
(a) 14.5 (b) 75.69
(c) 145 (d) 210.25

68. $\sqrt{\frac{0.361}{0.00169}} = ?$
(a) $\frac{1.9}{13}$ (b) $\frac{19}{13}$
(c) $\frac{1.9}{130}$ (d) $\frac{190}{13}$

69. $\sqrt{\frac{48.4}{0.289}}$ is equal to (S.S.C., 2004)
(a) $1\frac{5}{17}$ (b) $12\frac{1}{17}$
(c) $12\frac{16}{17}$ (d) $129\frac{7}{17}$

70. If $\sqrt{1 + \frac{x}{169}} = \frac{14}{13}$, then x is equal to
(a) 1 (b) 13
(c) 27 (d) None of these

71. $\sqrt{1 + \frac{55}{729}} = 1 + \frac{x}{27}$, then the value of x is (C.D.S., 2003)
(a) 1 (b) 3
(c) 5 (d) 7

72. $\sqrt{\frac{4}{3}} - \sqrt{\frac{3}{4}} = ?$ (R.R.B., 2005)
(a) $\frac{4\sqrt{3}}{6}$ (b) $\frac{1}{2\sqrt{3}}$
(c) 1 (d) $-\frac{1}{2\sqrt{3}}$

73. The value of $\sqrt{2}$ upto three places of decimal is
(a) 1.410 (b) 1.412
(c) 1.413 (d) 1.414

74. $(2\sqrt{27} - \sqrt{75} + \sqrt{12})$ is equal to
(a) $\sqrt{3}$ (b) $2\sqrt{3}$
(c) $3\sqrt{3}$ (d) $4\sqrt{3}$

75. By how much does $\sqrt{12} + \sqrt{18}$ exceed $\sqrt{3} + \sqrt{2}$?
(a) $\sqrt{2} - 4\sqrt{3}$ (b) $\sqrt{3} + 2\sqrt{2}$
(c) $2(\sqrt{3} - \sqrt{2})$ (d) $3(\sqrt{3} - \sqrt{2})$

76. $\frac{\sqrt{24} + \sqrt{216}}{\sqrt{96}} = ?$
(a) $2\sqrt{6}$ (b) 2
(c) $6\sqrt{2}$ (d) $\frac{2}{\sqrt{6}}$

77. The value of $\frac{\sqrt{80} - \sqrt{112}}{\sqrt{45} - \sqrt{63}}$ is
(a) $\frac{3}{4}$ (b) $1\frac{1}{3}$
(c) $1\frac{7}{9}$ (d) $1\frac{3}{4}$

78. If $3\sqrt{5} + \sqrt{125} = 17.88$, then what will be the value of $\sqrt{80} + 6\sqrt{5}$?
(a) 13.41 (b) 20.46
(c) 21.66 (d) 22.35

79. $\sqrt{50} \times \sqrt{98}$ is equal to
(a) 63.75 (b) 65.95
(c) 70 (d) 70.25

80. Given $\sqrt{2} = 1.414$. The value of $\sqrt{8} + 2\sqrt{32} - 3\sqrt{128} + 4\sqrt{50}$ is: (S.S.C., 2003)
(a) 8.426 (b) 8.484
(c) 8.526 (d) 8.876

81. The approximate value of $\frac{3\sqrt{12}}{2\sqrt{28}} \div \frac{2\sqrt{21}}{\sqrt{98}}$ is (Section Officers, 2003)
(a) 1.0605 (b) 1.0727
(c) 1.6007 (d) 1.6026

82. $\sqrt{110.25} \times \sqrt{0.01} \div \sqrt{0.0025} - \sqrt{420.25}$ equals (SNAP, 2010)
(a) 0.50 (b) 0.64
(c) 0.73 (d) 0.75

83. $\sqrt{\frac{.081 \times .484}{.0064 \times 6.25}}$ is equal to
(a) 0.9 (b) 0.99
(c) 9 (d) 99

84. $\sqrt{\dfrac{0.204 \times 42}{0.07 \times 3.4}}$ is equal to

(a) $\dfrac{1}{6}$ (b) 0.06
(c) 0.6 (d) 6

85. $\sqrt{\dfrac{0.081 \times 0.324 \times 4.624}{1.5625 \times 0.0289 \times 72.9 \times 64}}$ is equal to

(a) 0.024 (b) 0.24
(c) 2.4 (d) 24

86. $\sqrt{\dfrac{9.5 \times .085}{.0017 \times .19}}$ equals

(a) .05 (b) 5
(c) 50 (d) 500

87. The value of $\sqrt{\dfrac{(0.03)^2 + (0.21)^2 + (0.065)^2}{(0.003)^2 + (0.021)^2 + (0.0065)^2}}$ is (S.S.C., 2002)

(a) 0.1 (b) 10
(c) 10^2 (d) 10^3

88. The square root of $(7 + 3\sqrt{5})(7 - 3\sqrt{5})$ is (S.S.C., 2004)

(a) $\sqrt{5}$ (b) 2
(c) 4 (d) $3\sqrt{5}$

89. $\left(\sqrt{3} - \dfrac{1}{\sqrt{3}}\right)^2$ simplifies to

(a) $\dfrac{3}{4}$ (b) $\dfrac{4}{\sqrt{3}}$
(c) $\dfrac{4}{3}$ (d) None of these

90. If $a = 0.1039$, then the value of $\sqrt{4a^2 - 4a + 1} + 3a$ is (C.B.I., 2003)

(a) 0.1039 (b) 0.2078
(c) 1.1039 (d) 2.1039

91. The square root of $\dfrac{(0.75)^3}{1 - 0.75} + [0.75 + (0.75)^2 + 1]$ is

(a) 1 (b) 2
(c) 3 (d) 4

92. If $3a = 4b = 6c$ and $a + b + c = 27\sqrt{29}$, then $\sqrt{a^2 + b^2 + c^2}$ is

(a) $3\sqrt{29}$ (b) 81
(c) 87 (d) None of these

93. The square root of $0.\bar{4}$ is (S.S.C., 2004)

(a) $0.\bar{6}$ (b) $0.\bar{7}$
(c) $0.\bar{8}$ (d) $0.\bar{9}$

94. Which one of the following numbers has rational square root?

(a) 0.4 (b) 0.09
(c) 0.9 (d) 0.025

95. The value of $\sqrt{0.4}$ is

(a) 0.02 (b) 0.2
(c) 0.51 (d) 0.63

96. $\sqrt{0.2} = ?$ (R.R.B., 2007)

(a) 0.02 (b) 0.2
(c) 0.447 (d) 0.632

97. The value of $\sqrt{0.121}$ is

(a) 0.011 (b) 0.11
(c) 0.347 (d) 1.1

98. The value of $\sqrt{0.064}$ is

(a) 0.008 (b) 0.08
(c) 0.252 (d) 0.8

99. The value of $\sqrt{\dfrac{0.16}{0.4}}$ is (IGNOU, 2003)

(a) 0.02 (b) 0.2
(c) 0.63 (d) None of these

100. The value of $\dfrac{1 + \sqrt{0.01}}{1 - \sqrt{0.1}}$ is close to

(a) 0.6 (b) 1.1
(c) 1.6 (d) 1.7

101. The square root of 535.9225 is (R.R.B., 2006)

(a) 23.15 (b) 23.45
(c) 24.15 (d) 28.25

102. If $\sqrt{5} = 2.236$, then the value of $\dfrac{1}{\sqrt{5}}$ is

(a) .367 (b) .447
(c) .745 (d) None of these

103. If $\sqrt{24} = 4.899$, the value of $\sqrt{\dfrac{8}{3}}$ is

(a) 0.544 (b) 1.333
(c) 1.633 (d) 2.666

104. If $\sqrt{6} = 2.449$, then the value of $\dfrac{3\sqrt{2}}{2\sqrt{3}}$ is

(a) 0.6122 (b) 0.8163
(c) 1.223 (d) 1.2245

105. If $\sqrt{5} = 2.236$, then the value of $\dfrac{\sqrt{5}}{2} - \dfrac{10}{\sqrt{5}} + \sqrt{125}$ is equal to

(a) 5.59 (b) 7.826
(c) 8.944 (d) 10.062

106. If 2 * 3 = $\sqrt{13}$ and 3 * 4 = 5, then the value of 5 * 12 is
(a) $\sqrt{17}$ (b) $\sqrt{29}$
(c) 12 (d) 13

107. If 1537* is a perfect square, then the digit which replaces * is (Hotel Management, 2007)
(a) 2 (b) 4
(c) 5 (d) 6

108. The smallest perfect square that is divisible by 7! is (I.I.F.T., 2010)
(a) 19600 (b) 44100
(c) 176400 (d) 705600

109. The least perfect square number divisible by 3, 4, 5, 6 and 8 is
(a) 900 (b) 1200
(c) 2500 (d) 3600

110. The least perfect square, which is divisible by each of 21, 36 and 66, is
(a) 213444 (b) 214344
(c) 214434 (d) 231444

111. The least number by which 294 must be multiplied to make it a perfect square, is
(a) 2 (b) 3
(c) 6 (d) 24

112. Find the smallest number by which 5808 should be multiplied so that the product becomes a perfect square.
(a) 2 (b) 3
(c) 7 (d) 11

113. The least number by which 1470 must be divided to get a number which is a perfect square, is
(a) 5 (b) 6
(c) 15 (d) 30

114. What is the smallest number to be subtracted from 549162 in order to make it a perfect square?
(a) 28 (b) 36
(c) 62 (d) 81

115. What is the least number which should be subtracted from 0.000326 to make it a perfect square?
(a) 0.000002 (b) 0.000004
(c) 0.02 (d) 0.04

116. What is the least number to be added to 7700 to make it a perfect square?
(a) 77 (b) 98
(c) 131 (d) 221
(e) None of these (Bank Recruitment, 2008)

117. The smallest number to be added to 680621 to make the sum a perfect square is (S.S.C., 2005)
(a) 4 (b) 5
(c) 6 (d) 8

118. The greatest four-digit perfect square number is
(a) 9000 (b) 9801
(c) 9900 (d) 9981

119. The least number of 4 digits which is a perfect square is
(a) 1000 (b) 1016
(c) 1024 (d) 1036

120. The sum of 18 consecutive natural numbers is a perfect square. What is the smallest possible value of this sum? (A.A.O. Exam, 2009)
(a) 169 (b) 225
(c) 289 (d) 441

121. $\sqrt{2+\sqrt{3}}\cdot\sqrt{2+\sqrt{2+\sqrt{3}}}\cdot\sqrt{2+\sqrt{2+\sqrt{2+\sqrt{3}}}}\cdot\sqrt{2-\sqrt{2+\sqrt{2+\sqrt{3}}}}$ is equal to
(a) 1 (b) 2
(c) 4 (d) $\sqrt{6}$

122. Given $\sqrt{5}=2.2361$, $\sqrt{3}=1.7321$, then $\frac{1}{\sqrt{5}-\sqrt{3}}$ is equal to
(a) 1.98 (b) 1.984
(c) 1.9841 (d) 2

123. $\frac{1}{(\sqrt{9}-\sqrt{8})}-\frac{1}{(\sqrt{8}-\sqrt{7})}+\frac{1}{(\sqrt{7}-\sqrt{6})}-\frac{1}{(\sqrt{6}-\sqrt{5})}+\frac{1}{(\sqrt{5}-\sqrt{4})}$ is equal to (M.B.A., 2007)
(a) 0 (b) $\frac{1}{3}$
(c) 1 (d) 5

124. Determine the value of
$$\frac{1}{\sqrt{1}+\sqrt{2}}+\frac{1}{\sqrt{2}+\sqrt{3}}+\frac{1}{\sqrt{3}+\sqrt{4}}+\dots+\frac{1}{\sqrt{120}+\sqrt{121}}.$$
(M.A.T., 2005)
(a) 8 (b) 10
(c) $\sqrt{120}$ (d) $12\sqrt{2}$

125. The expression $1-\frac{1}{1+\sqrt{3}}+\frac{1}{1-\sqrt{3}}$ equals (M.B.A., 2011)
(a) $1-\sqrt{3}$ (b) 1
(c) $-\sqrt{3}$ (d) $\sqrt{3}$

126. $\left(2+\sqrt{2}+\frac{1}{2+\sqrt{2}}+\frac{1}{\sqrt{2}-2}\right)$ simplifies to (M.B.A., 2007)
(a) $2-\sqrt{2}$ (b) 2
(c) $2+\sqrt{2}$ (d) $2\sqrt{2}$

127. What is the value of $\frac{1}{\sqrt{5}+\sqrt{3}}+\frac{2}{3+\sqrt{5}}-\frac{3}{3+\sqrt{3}}$? (I.I.F.T., 2005)

(a) $-\frac{1}{2}$ (b) 0
(c) $\frac{1}{2}$ (d) 1

128. If $\sqrt{2}$ = 1.4142, the value of $\frac{7}{(3+\sqrt{2})}$ is (R.R.B., 2005)

(a) 1.5858 (b) 3.4852
(c) 3.5858 (d) 4.4142

129. $\left[\frac{3\sqrt{2}}{\sqrt{6}-\sqrt{3}}-\frac{4\sqrt{3}}{\sqrt{6}-\sqrt{2}}-\frac{6}{\sqrt{8}-\sqrt{12}}\right]=?$ (Teachers' Exam, 2010)

(a) $\sqrt{3}-\sqrt{2}$ (b) $\sqrt{3}+\sqrt{2}$
(c) $5\sqrt{3}$ (d) 1

130. $\frac{\sqrt{7}+\sqrt{5}}{\sqrt{7}-\sqrt{5}}$ is equal to

(a) 1 (b) 2
(c) $6-\sqrt{35}$ (d) $6+\sqrt{35}$

131. If $\frac{5+2\sqrt{3}}{7+4\sqrt{3}}=a+b\sqrt{3}$, then (R.R.B., 2010)

(a) $a=-11, b=-6$ (b) $a=-11, b=6$
(c) $a=11, b=-6$ (d) $a=6, b=11$

132. If $\sqrt{2}$ = 1.414, the square root of $\frac{\sqrt{2}-1}{\sqrt{2}+1}$ is nearest to

(a) 0.172 (b) 0.414
(c) 0.586 (d) 1.414

133. Given that $\sqrt{3}$ = 1.732, the value of $\frac{3+\sqrt{6}}{5\sqrt{3}-2\sqrt{12}-\sqrt{32}+\sqrt{50}}$ is (S.S.C., 2007)

(a) 1.414 (b) 1.732
(c) 2.551 (d) 4.899

134. $\left(\frac{2+\sqrt{3}}{2-\sqrt{3}}+\frac{2-\sqrt{3}}{2+\sqrt{3}}+\frac{\sqrt{3}-1}{\sqrt{3}+1}\right)$ simplifies to (S.S.C., 2008)

(a) $16-\sqrt{3}$ (b) $4-\sqrt{3}$
(c) $2-\sqrt{3}$ (d) $2+\sqrt{3}$

135. If $x=\frac{\sqrt{5}+\sqrt{3}}{\sqrt{5}-\sqrt{3}}$ and $y=\frac{\sqrt{5}-\sqrt{3}}{\sqrt{5}+\sqrt{3}}$, then $(x+y)$ equals (S.S.C., 2005)

(a) $2(\sqrt{5}+\sqrt{3})$ (b) $2\sqrt{15}$
(c) 8 (d) 16

136. $\frac{\sqrt{2}(2+\sqrt{3})}{\sqrt{3}(\sqrt{3}+1)}\times\frac{\sqrt{2}(2-\sqrt{3})}{\sqrt{3}(\sqrt{3}-1)}$ is equal to (C.P.O., 2006)

(a) $3\sqrt{2}$ (b) $\frac{\sqrt{2}}{3}$
(c) $\frac{2}{3}$ (d) $\frac{1}{3}$

137. $\frac{12}{3+\sqrt{5}+2\sqrt{2}}$ is equal to (S.S.C., 2007)

(a) $1-\sqrt{5}+\sqrt{2}+\sqrt{10}$
(b) $1+\sqrt{5}+\sqrt{2}-\sqrt{10}$
(c) $1+\sqrt{5}-\sqrt{2}+\sqrt{10}$
(d) $1-\sqrt{5}-\sqrt{2}+\sqrt{10}$

138. $\left[\frac{1}{\sqrt{2}+\sqrt{3}-\sqrt{5}}+\frac{1}{\sqrt{2}-\sqrt{3}-\sqrt{5}}\right]$ in simplified form equals (S.S.C., 2005)

(a) 0 (b) $\frac{1}{\sqrt{2}}$
(c) 1 (d) $\sqrt{2}$

139. If $x=(7-4\sqrt{3})$, then the value of $\left(x+\frac{1}{x}\right)$ is

(a) $3\sqrt{3}$ (b) $8\sqrt{3}$
(c) 14 (d) $14+8\sqrt{3}$

140. If $x=3+\sqrt{8}$, then $x^2+\frac{1}{x^2}$ is equal to (S.S.C., 2007)

(a) 30 (b) 34
(c) 36 (d) 38

141. If $a=\frac{\sqrt{3}+\sqrt{2}}{\sqrt{3}-\sqrt{2}}, b=\frac{\sqrt{3}-\sqrt{2}}{\sqrt{3}+\sqrt{2}}$, then the value of a^2+b^2 would be (M.B.A., 2008)

(a) 10 (b) 98
(c) 99 (d) 100

142. If $a=\frac{\sqrt{5}+1}{\sqrt{5}-1}$ and $b=\frac{\sqrt{5}-1}{\sqrt{5}+1}$, the value of $\left(\frac{a^2+ab+b^2}{a^2-ab+b^2}\right)$ is

(a) $\frac{3}{4}$ (b) $\frac{4}{3}$
(c) $\frac{3}{5}$ (d) $\frac{5}{3}$

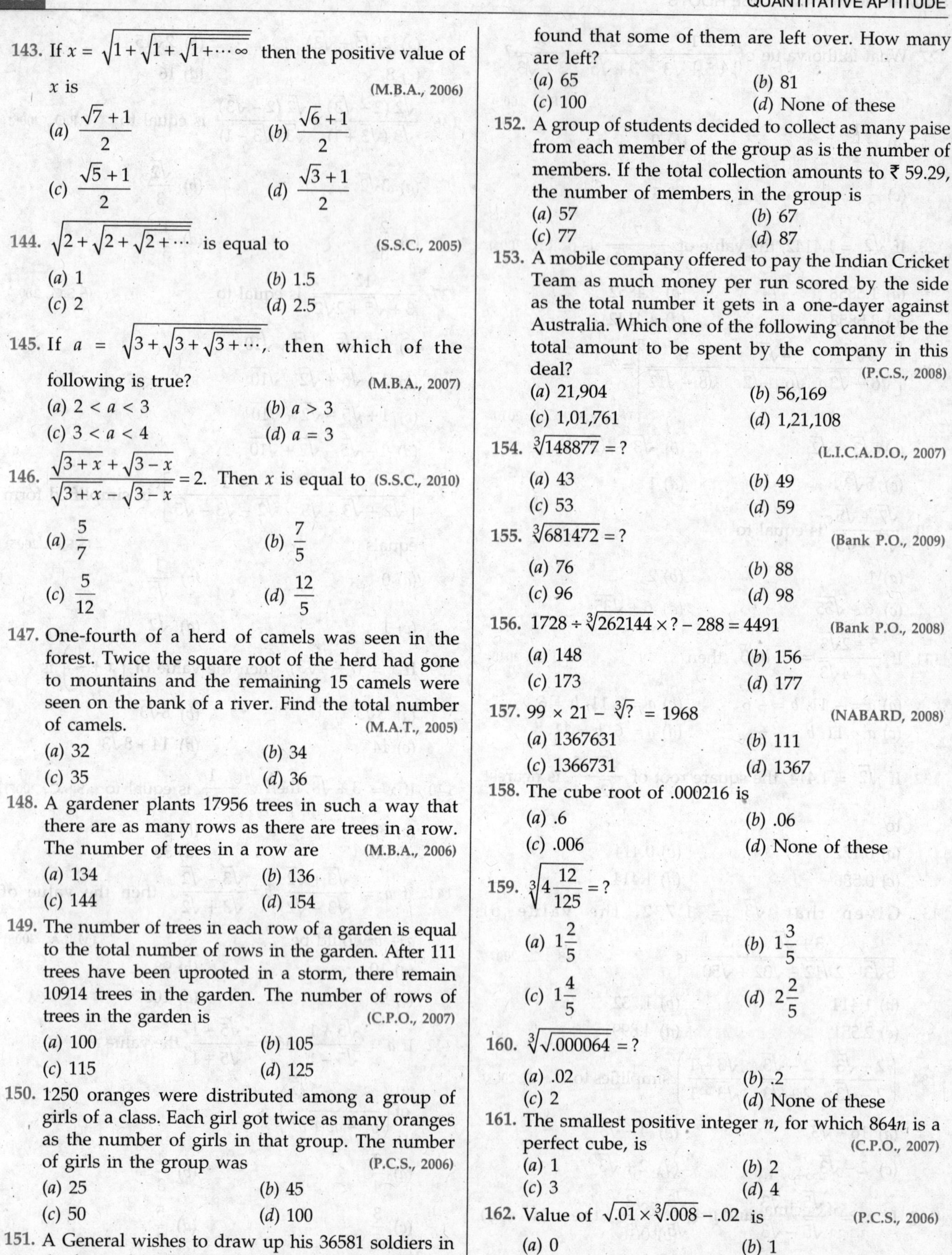

143. If $x = \sqrt{1+\sqrt{1+\sqrt{1+\cdots\infty}}}$ then the positive value of x is **(M.B.A., 2006)**

(a) $\frac{\sqrt{7}+1}{2}$ (b) $\frac{\sqrt{6}+1}{2}$

(c) $\frac{\sqrt{5}+1}{2}$ (d) $\frac{\sqrt{3}+1}{2}$

144. $\sqrt{2+\sqrt{2+\sqrt{2+\cdots}}}$ is equal to **(S.S.C., 2005)**

(a) 1 (b) 1.5

(c) 2 (d) 2.5

145. If $a = \sqrt{3+\sqrt{3+\sqrt{3+\cdots}}}$, then which of the following is true? **(M.B.A., 2007)**

(a) $2 < a < 3$ (b) $a > 3$

(c) $3 < a < 4$ (d) $a = 3$

146. $\frac{\sqrt{3+x}+\sqrt{3-x}}{\sqrt{3+x}-\sqrt{3-x}} = 2$. Then x is equal to **(S.S.C., 2010)**

(a) $\frac{5}{7}$ (b) $\frac{7}{5}$

(c) $\frac{5}{12}$ (d) $\frac{12}{5}$

147. One-fourth of a herd of camels was seen in the forest. Twice the square root of the herd had gone to mountains and the remaining 15 camels were seen on the bank of a river. Find the total number of camels. **(M.A.T., 2005)**

(a) 32 (b) 34

(c) 35 (d) 36

148. A gardener plants 17956 trees in such a way that there are as many rows as there are trees in a row. The number of trees in a row are **(M.B.A., 2006)**

(a) 134 (b) 136

(c) 144 (d) 154

149. The number of trees in each row of a garden is equal to the total number of rows in the garden. After 111 trees have been uprooted in a storm, there remain 10914 trees in the garden. The number of rows of trees in the garden is **(C.P.O., 2007)**

(a) 100 (b) 105

(c) 115 (d) 125

150. 1250 oranges were distributed among a group of girls of a class. Each girl got twice as many oranges as the number of girls in that group. The number of girls in the group was **(P.C.S., 2006)**

(a) 25 (b) 45

(c) 50 (d) 100

151. A General wishes to draw up his 36581 soldiers in the form of a solid square. After arranging them, he found that some of them are left over. How many are left?

(a) 65 (b) 81

(c) 100 (d) None of these

152. A group of students decided to collect as many paise from each member of the group as is the number of members. If the total collection amounts to ₹ 59.29, the number of members in the group is

(a) 57 (b) 67

(c) 77 (d) 87

153. A mobile company offered to pay the Indian Cricket Team as much money per run scored by the side as the total number it gets in a one-dayer against Australia. Which one of the following cannot be the total amount to be spent by the company in this deal? **(P.C.S., 2008)**

(a) 21,904 (b) 56,169

(c) 1,01,761 (d) 1,21,108

154. $\sqrt[3]{148877} = ?$ **(L.I.C.A.D.O., 2007)**

(a) 43 (b) 49

(c) 53 (d) 59

155. $\sqrt[3]{681472} = ?$ **(Bank P.O., 2009)**

(a) 76 (b) 88

(c) 96 (d) 98

156. $1728 \div \sqrt[3]{262144} \times ? - 288 = 4491$ **(Bank P.O., 2008)**

(a) 148 (b) 156

(c) 173 (d) 177

157. $99 \times 21 - \sqrt[3]{?} = 1968$ **(NABARD, 2008)**

(a) 1367631 (b) 111

(c) 1366731 (d) 1367

158. The cube root of .000216 is

(a) .6 (b) .06

(c) .006 (d) None of these

159. $\sqrt[3]{4\frac{12}{125}} = ?$

(a) $1\frac{2}{5}$ (b) $1\frac{3}{5}$

(c) $1\frac{4}{5}$ (d) $2\frac{2}{5}$

160. $\sqrt[3]{\sqrt{.000064}} = ?$

(a) .02 (b) .2

(c) 2 (d) None of these

161. The smallest positive integer n, for which $864n$ is a perfect cube, is **(C.P.O., 2007)**

(a) 1 (b) 2

(c) 3 (d) 4

162. Value of $\sqrt{.01} \times \sqrt[3]{.008} - .02$ is **(P.C.S., 2006)**

(a) 0 (b) 1

(c) 2 (d) 3

163. The value of 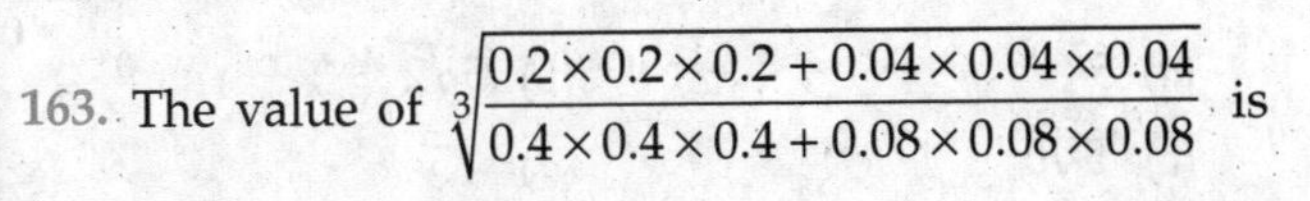 $\sqrt[3]{\dfrac{0.2\times0.2\times0.2+0.04\times0.04\times0.04}{0.4\times0.4\times0.4+0.08\times0.08\times0.08}}$ is (S.S.C., 2005)

(a) 0.125 (b) 0.25
(c) 0.5 (d) 0.75

164. A rationalising factor of $(\sqrt[3]{9}-\sqrt[3]{3}+1)$ is (S.S.C., 2007)

(a) $\sqrt[3]{3}-1$ (b) $\sqrt[3]{3}+1$
(c) $\sqrt[3]{9}-1$ (d) $\sqrt[3]{9}+1$

165. The largest four-digit number which is a perfect cube is

(a) 8000 (b) 9261
(c) 9999 (d) None of these

166. By what least number must 21600 be multiplied so as to make it a perfect cube? (M.A.T., 2002)

(a) 6 (b) 10
(c) 20 (d) 30

167. What is the smallest number by which 3600 be divided to make it a perfect cube?

(a) 9 (b) 50
(c) 300 (d) 450

168. Which smallest number must be added to 710 so that the sum is a perfect cube? (S.S.C., 2005)

(a) 11 (b) 19
(c) 21 (d) 29

169. Solve $\sqrt{7921}=?$ [Indian Railway Gr. 'D' Exam, 2014]

(a) 89 (b) 87
(c) 37 (d) 47

170. Solve $\sqrt[4]{(625)^3}=?$ [Indian Railway Gr. 'D' Exam, 2014]

(a) $\sqrt[3]{1875}$ (b) 25
(c) 125 (d) None of these

171. If $\sqrt{y}=4x$, then $\dfrac{x^2}{y}$ is [SSC—CHSL (10+2) Exam, 2015]

(a) 2 (b) $\dfrac{1}{16}$
(c) $\dfrac{1}{4}$ (d) 4

Direction (Q. No. 172): What approximate value will come in place of question mark(?) in the given question? (You are not expected to calculate the exact value)

172. $\sqrt{2025.11}\times\sqrt{256.04}+\sqrt{399.95}\times\sqrt{?}=33.98\times40.11$

[IBPS—Bank Spl. Officer (IT) Exam, 2015]

(a) 1682 (b) 1024
(c) 1582 (d) 678

173. If $\sqrt{7}$ = 2.645, then the value of $\dfrac{1}{\sqrt{28}}$ up to three places of decimal is [SSC—CHSL (10+2) Exam, 2015]

(a) 0.183 (b) 0.185
(c) 0.187 (d) 0.189

174. Solve: $\left(\sqrt{\dfrac{25}{9}}-\sqrt{\dfrac{64}{81}}\right)\div\sqrt{\dfrac{16}{324}}=?$

(a) 4.5 (b) 2.5
(c) 1.5 (d) 3.5

[United India Insurance Co. Ltd. (UIICL) Assistant (Online) Exam, 2015]

175. Solve $1728\div\sqrt[3]{262144}\times?-288=4491$

(a) 148 (b) 156
(c) 173 (d) 177
(e) 185

[United India Insurance Co. Ltd. (UIICL) Assistant (Online) Exam, 2015]

176. Solve: $\left(\sqrt{7}+11\right)^2=(?)^{\frac{1}{3}}+2\sqrt{847}+122$

(a) $36+44\sqrt{7}$ (b) 6
(c) 216 (d) 36

[IDBI Bank Executive Officers Exam, 2015]

Directions (Q. No. 177 & 178): What will come in place of question mark in these questions?

177. $?-\sqrt{(784)}=6\times\sqrt{(324)}$ (NICL—AAO Exam, 2015]

(a) 128 (b) 160
(c) 236 (d) 136

178. $\sqrt{(2116)}-\sqrt{1600}=\sqrt{(?)}$ [NICL—AAO Exam, 2015]

(a) 20 (b) 64
(c) 81 (d) 36

179. Solve $\sqrt{(27\div5\times?)+15}=5.4\div6+0.3$

[IBPS—RRB Office Assistant (Online) Exam, 2015]

(a) 2 (b) 6
(c) 10 (d) 4

180. $\sqrt{24\div0.5+1}+\sqrt{18\div0.6+6}=?$

(a) 19 (b) 13
(c) 12 (d) 15

[IBPS—RRB Office Assistant (Online) Exam, 2015]

181. $\left(\sqrt{63}+\sqrt{252}\right)\times\left(\sqrt{175}+\sqrt{28}\right)=?$

[IBPS—RRB Office Assistant (Online) Exam, 2015]

(a) $16\sqrt{7}$ (b) 441
(c) 16 (d) $7\sqrt{7}$

182. $9x^2+25-30x$ can be expressed as the square of

[SSC—CHSL (10+2) Exam, 2015]

(a) $3x^2-25$ (b) $3x-5$
(c) $-3x-5$ (d) $3x-5$

183. If $\sqrt{33}=5.745$, then which of the following values is approximately $\sqrt{\dfrac{3}{11}}$? [SSC—CHSL (10+2) Exam, 2015]

(a) 1 (b) 6.32
(c) 0.5223 (d) 2.035

184. $\sqrt{?}+14=\sqrt{2601}$ [SBI Jr. Associates (Pre.) Exam, 2016]

(*a*) 1521 (*b*) 1369
(*c*) 1225 (*d*) 961

185. If $a=\frac{\sqrt{3}}{2}$, then $\sqrt{1+a}+\sqrt{1-a}=?$

[DMRC—Train Operator (Station Controller) Exam, 2016]

(*a*) $\left(2-\sqrt{3}\right)$ (*b*) $\left(2+\sqrt{3}\right)$
(*c*) $\left(\frac{\sqrt{3}}{2}\right)$ (*d*) $\sqrt{3}$

186. What is $\frac{5+\sqrt{10}}{5\sqrt{5}-2\sqrt{20}-\sqrt{32}+\sqrt{50}}$ equal to? [CDS 2016]

(*a*) 5 (*b*) $5\sqrt{2}$
(*c*) $5\sqrt{5}$ (*d*) $\sqrt{5}$

187. The square root of $\frac{(0.75)^3}{1-0.75}+\left[0.75+(0.75)^2+1\right]$ is

(*a*) 1 (*b*) 2 [CDS 2016]
(*c*) 3 (*d*) 4

188. $\sqrt{10+2\sqrt{6}+2\sqrt{10}+2\sqrt{15}}$ is equal to

(*a*) $\left(\sqrt{2}+\sqrt{3}+\sqrt{5}\right)$ (*b*) $\left(\sqrt{2}+\sqrt{3}-\sqrt{5}\right)$
(*c*) $\left(\sqrt{2}+\sqrt{5}-\sqrt{3}\right)$ (*d*) None of these

[DMRC—Customer Relationship Assistant (CRA) Exam, 2016]

ANSWERS

1. (*b*)	2. (*b*)	3. (*c*)	4. (*c*)	5. (*e*)	6. (*e*)	7. (*a*)	8. (*a*)	9. (*c*)	10. (*b*)
11. (*a*)	12. (*c*)	13. (*d*)	14. (*b*)	15. (*b*)	16. (*c*)	17. (*c*)	18. (*c*)	19. (*b*)	20. (*d*)
21. (*b*)	22. (*b*)	23. (*e*)	24. (*c*)	25. (*b*)	26. (*d*)	27. (*e*)	28. (*a*)	29. (*c*)	30. (*d*)
31. (*a*)	32. (*b*)	33. (*a*)	34. (*c*)	35. (*a*)	36. (*c*)	37. (*c*)	38. (*b*)	39. (*b*)	40. (*b*)
41. (*d*)	42. (*d*)	43. (*b*)	44. (*d*)	45. (*b*)	46. (*c*)	47. (*d*)	48. (*d*)	49. (*d*)	50. (*e*)
51. (*d*)	52. (*a*)	53. (*d*)	54. (*b*)	55. (*b*)	56. (*a*)	57. (*d*)	58. (*c*)	59. (*b*)	60. (*b*)
61. (*a*)	62. (*a*)	63. (*b*)	64. (*c*)	65. (*a*)	66. (*c*)	67. (*a*)	68. (*d*)	69. (*c*)	70. (*c*)
71. (*a*)	72. (*b*)	73. (*d*)	74. (*c*)	75. (*b*)	76. (*b*)	77. (*b*)	78. (*d*)	79. (*c*)	80. (*b*)
81. (*a*)	82. (*a*)	83. (*b*)	84. (*d*)	85. (*a*)	86. (*c*)	87. (*b*)	88. (*b*)	89. (*c*)	90. (*c*)
91. (*b*)	92. (*c*)	93. (*a*)	94. (*b*)	95. (*d*)	96. (*c*)	97. (*c*)	98. (*c*)	99. (*c*)	100. (*c*)
101. (*a*)	102. (*b*)	103. (*c*)	104. (*d*)	105. (*b*)	106. (*d*)	107. (*d*)	108. (*c*)	109. (*d*)	110. (*a*)
111. (*c*)	112. (*b*)	113. (*d*)	114. (*d*)	115. (*a*)	116. (*e*)	117. (*a*)	118. (*b*)	119. (*c*)	120. (*b*)
121. (*a*)	122. (*c*)	123. (*d*)	124. (*b*)	125. (*a*)	126. (*b*)	127. (*b*)	128. (*a*)	129. (*c*)	130. (*d*)
131. (*c*)	132. (*b*)	133. (*b*)	134. (*a*)	135. (*c*)	136. (*d*)	137. (*b*)	138. (*b*)	139. (*c*)	140. (*b*)
141. (*b*)	142. (*b*)	143. (*c*)	144. (*c*)	145. (*a*)	146. (*d*)	147. (*d*)	148. (*a*)	149. (*b*)	150. (*a*)
151. (*c*)	152. (*c*)	153. (*d*)	154. (*c*)	155. (*b*)	156. (*d*)	157. (*a*)	158. (*b*)	159. (*b*)	160. (*b*)
161. (*b*)	162. (*a*)	163. (*c*)	164. (*b*)	165. (*b*)	166. (*b*)	167. (*d*)	168. (*b*)	169. (*a*)	170. (*c*)
171. (*b*)	172. (*b*)	173. (*d*)	174. (*d*)	175. (*d*)	176. (*c*)	177. (*d*)	178. (*d*)	179. (*d*)	180. (*b*)
181. (*b*)	182. (*d*)	183. (*c*)	184. (*b*)	185. (*d*)	186. (*d*)	187. (*b*)	188. (*a*)		

SOLUTIONS

1.

```
   2 | 5 38 24 (232
     | 4
     |--------
  43 | 1 38
     | 1 29
     |--------
 462 |   9 24
     |   9 24
     |--------
     |    ×
```

$\therefore \sqrt{53824}=232.$

2.

```
   2 | 4 12 09 (203
     | 4
     |--------
  40 |   12
     |    0
     |--------
 403 |   12 09
     |   12 09
     |--------
     |     ×
```

$\therefore \sqrt{41209}=203.$

3.

```
     1 | 1 23 45 43 21 (11111
       | 1
       |------------
    21 |   23
       |   21
       |------------
   221 |    2 45
       |    2 21
       |------------
  2221 |     24 43
       |     22 21
       |------------
 22221 |     222 21
       |     222 21
       |------------
       |        ×
```

$\therefore \sqrt{123454321}=11111.$

4. The number of digits in the square root of a perfect square number of n digits is

(i) $\frac{n}{2}$, if n is even

(ii) $\frac{n+1}{2}$, if n is odd

Here, $n = 12$. So, required number of digits $= \frac{n}{2} = \frac{12}{2} = 6$.

5. $\sqrt{\sqrt{17956} + \sqrt{24025}} = \sqrt{134 + 155} = \sqrt{289} = 17$.

6. $\sqrt{\sqrt{44944} + \sqrt{52441}} = \sqrt{212 + 229} = \sqrt{441} = 21$.

7. Sum of prime numbers greater than 4 but less than 16 = $(5 + 7 + 11 + 13) = 36$.

$\therefore \quad \frac{1}{4} \times 36 = 9 = 3^2$.

8. Given exp. $= \sqrt{10 + \sqrt{25 + \sqrt{108 + \sqrt{154 + 15}}}}$

$= \sqrt{10 + \sqrt{25 + \sqrt{108 + \sqrt{169}}}}$

$= \sqrt{10 + \sqrt{25 + \sqrt{108 + 13}}}$

$= \sqrt{10 + \sqrt{25 + \sqrt{121}}}$

$= \sqrt{10 + \sqrt{25 + 11}} = \sqrt{10 + \sqrt{36}}$

$= \sqrt{10 + 6} = \sqrt{16} = 4$.

9. Given exp. $= \sqrt{41 - \sqrt{21 + \sqrt{19 - 3}}}$

$= \sqrt{41 - \sqrt{21 + \sqrt{16}}} = \sqrt{41 - \sqrt{21 + 4}}$

$= \sqrt{41 - \sqrt{25}} = \sqrt{41 - 5} = \sqrt{36} = 6$.

10. Given exp. $= \sqrt{176 + 49} = \sqrt{225} = 15$.

11. Given exp. $= \frac{14}{7} \times \frac{21}{7} \times \frac{120}{15} = 2 \times 3 \times 8 = 48$.

12. Given exp. $= \left(\frac{\sqrt{225}}{\sqrt{729}} - \frac{\sqrt{25}}{\sqrt{144}}\right) \div \frac{\sqrt{16}}{\sqrt{81}}$

$= \left(\frac{15}{27} - \frac{5}{12}\right) \div \frac{4}{9} = \left(\frac{15}{108} \times \frac{9}{4}\right) = \frac{5}{16}$.

13. Let $(15)^2 + (18)^2 - 20 = \sqrt{x}$.

Then, $\sqrt{x} = 225 + 324 - 20 = 529$

$\Leftrightarrow x = (529)^2 = 279841$.

14. Let $\sqrt{x} \times \sqrt{484} = 1034$. Then, $\sqrt{x} \times 22 = 1034$

$\Leftrightarrow \sqrt{x} = \frac{1034}{22} = 47$

$\Leftrightarrow x = (47)^2 = 2209$.

15. Let $\sqrt{11881} \times \sqrt{x} = 10137$. Then, $109 \times \sqrt{x} = 10137$

$\Leftrightarrow \quad \sqrt{x} = \frac{10137}{109} = 93$

$\Leftrightarrow \quad x = (93)^2 = 8649$.

16. $\frac{4050}{\sqrt{x}} = 450 \Leftrightarrow \sqrt{x} = \frac{4050}{450} = 9$

$\Leftrightarrow x = 9^2 = 81$.

17. Let $\sqrt{\frac{16}{25}} \times \sqrt{\frac{x}{25}} \times \frac{16}{25} = \frac{256}{625}$.

Then, $\frac{4}{5} \times \frac{\sqrt{x}}{2} \times \frac{16}{25} = \frac{256}{625}$

$\Leftrightarrow \quad \frac{64\sqrt{x}}{625} = \frac{256}{625}$

$\Leftrightarrow \quad \sqrt{x} = \frac{256}{625} \times \frac{625}{64}$

$\Leftrightarrow x = 4^2 = 16$.

18. $\sqrt{(272)^2 - (128)^2} = \sqrt{(272 + 128)(272 - 128)}$

$= \sqrt{400 \times 144} = \sqrt{57600} = 240$.

19. $6 * 24 = 6 + 24 + \sqrt{6 \times 24} = 30 + \sqrt{144}$

$= 30 + 12 = 42$.

20. $10y\sqrt{y^3 - y^2} = 10 \times 5\sqrt{5^3 - 5^2}$

$= 50 \times \sqrt{125 - 25} = 50 \times \sqrt{100}$

$= 50 \times 10 = 500$.

21. $\sqrt{110\frac{1}{4}} = \sqrt{\frac{441}{4}} = \frac{\sqrt{441}}{\sqrt{4}} = \frac{21}{2} = 10.5$.

22. $\sqrt{\frac{25}{81} - \frac{1}{9}} = \sqrt{\frac{25 - 9}{81}} = \sqrt{\frac{16}{81}} = \frac{\sqrt{16}}{\sqrt{81}} = \frac{4}{9}$.

23. Let $[(\sqrt{81})^2]^2 = x^2$. Then, $x^2 = (81)^2$ or $x = 81$.

24.

```
  1 | 1 58 76 (126
    | 1
    |------
 22 |   58
    |   44
    |------
246 |   14 76
    |   14 76
    |---------
    |      ×
```

$\therefore \sqrt{15876} = 126$.

25.

```
   1 | 3.00 00 00 (1.732
     | 1
     |------
  27 | 2 00
     | 1 89
     |------
 343 |   11 00
     |   10 29
     |---------
3492 |      71 00
     |      69 84
     |---------
     |       1 16
```

$\therefore \sqrt{3} = 1.73 = \frac{173}{100}$.

26. A number ending in 8 can never be a perfect square.

27. The squares of numbers having 1 and 9 as the unit's digit end in the digit 1.

Such numbers are: 1, 9, 11, 19, 21, 29, 31, 39, 41, 49 i.e., there are 10 such numbers.

$\therefore$ Required percentage $= \left(\frac{10}{50} \times 100\right)\% = 20\%$.

28. Let the given number be x.
Then, $x^2 - 25 = (x - 25)^2 \Leftrightarrow x^2 - 25 = x^2 + 625 - 50x \Leftrightarrow 50x = 650 \Leftrightarrow x = 13$.

29. $(11)^2 = 121$ and $(17)^2 = 289$.
So, the perfect squares between 120 and 300 are the squares of numbers from 11 to 17. Clearly, these are 7 in number.

30. The first perfect square number after 50 is 64 ($= 8^2$) and the last perfect square number before 1000 is 961 [$= (31)^2$].
So, the perfect squares between 50 and 1000 are the squares of numbers from 8 to 31. Clearly, these are 24 in number.

31. Clearly, the man was born between 1800 and 1850.
The only perfect square number between 1800 and 1850 is 1849. And, $1849 = (43)^2$.
So, the man was 43 years old in 1849. Thus, he was born in $(1849 - 43) = 1806$.

32. $Q = \sqrt{\frac{(8R)^2}{4}} = \frac{\sqrt{(8R)^2}}{\sqrt{4}} = \frac{8R}{2} = 4R$.

33. The smallest such number is 1444[$= (38)^2$]. It lies between 1000 and 2000.

34. $\left(\sqrt{2} + \frac{1}{\sqrt{2}}\right)^2 = (\sqrt{2})^2 + \left(\frac{1}{\sqrt{2}}\right)^2 + 2 \times \sqrt{2} \times \frac{1}{\sqrt{2}}$
$= 2 + \frac{1}{2} + 2 = 4\frac{1}{2}$.

35. We have:
$1 \times 2 \times 3 \times 4 = 24$ and $24 + 1 = 25$ [$= 5^2$].
$2 \times 3 \times 4 \times 5 = 120$ and $120 + 1 = 121$ [$= 11^2$]
$3 \times 4 \times 5 \times 6 = 360$ and $360 + 1 = 361$ [$= 19^2$]
$4 \times 5 \times 6 \times 7 = 840$ and $840 + 1 = 841$ [$= 29^2$].
$\therefore p = 1$.

36. $\sqrt{0.16} = \sqrt{\frac{16}{100}} = \frac{\sqrt{16}}{\sqrt{100}} = \frac{4}{10} = 0.4$.

37. $\sqrt{0.000441} = \sqrt{\frac{441}{10^6}} = \frac{\sqrt{441}}{\sqrt{10^6}} = \frac{21}{10^3} = \frac{21}{1000} = 0.021$.

38. $\sqrt{0.00004761} = \sqrt{\frac{4761}{10^8}} = \frac{\sqrt{4761}}{\sqrt{10^8}} = \frac{69}{10^4} = \frac{69}{10000} = 0.0069$.

39. $1.5^2 \times \sqrt{0.0225} = 1.5^2 \times \sqrt{\frac{225}{10000}} = 2.25 \times \frac{15}{100}$
$= 2.25 \times 0.15 = 0.3375$.

40. $\sqrt{0.01 + \sqrt{0.0064}} = \sqrt{0.01 + \sqrt{\frac{64}{10000}}}$
$= \sqrt{0.01 + \frac{8}{100}} = \sqrt{0.01 + 0.08} = \sqrt{0.09} = 0.3$.

41. Given exp. $= \sqrt{\frac{1}{100}} + \sqrt{\frac{81}{100}} + \sqrt{\frac{121}{100}} + \sqrt{\frac{9}{10000}}$
$= \frac{1}{10} + \frac{9}{10} + \frac{11}{10} + \frac{3}{100}$
$= 0.1 + 0.9 + 1.1 + 0.03 = 2.13$.

42. Given exp. $= \sqrt{\frac{25}{10000}} \times \sqrt{\frac{225}{100}} \times \sqrt{\frac{1}{10000}}$
$= \frac{5}{100} \times \frac{15}{10} \times \frac{1}{100} = \frac{75}{100000} = 0.00075$.

43.

1	$1.\overline{56}\ \overline{25}$ (1.25
	1
22	56
	44
245	12 25
	12 25
	×

$\therefore \sqrt{1.5625} = 1.25$.

44. $\sqrt{6760000} = \sqrt{0.00000676 \times 10^{12}} = \sqrt{0.00000676} \times \sqrt{10^{12}}$
$= .0026 \times 10^6 = 2600$.

45. Given exp. $= \sqrt{\frac{18225}{10^2}} + \sqrt{\frac{18225}{10^4}} + \sqrt{\frac{18225}{10^6}} + \sqrt{\frac{18225}{10^8}}$
$= \frac{\sqrt{18225}}{10} + \frac{\sqrt{18225}}{10^2} + \frac{\sqrt{18225}}{10^3} + \frac{\sqrt{18225}}{10^4}$
$= \frac{135}{10} + \frac{135}{100} + \frac{135}{1000} + \frac{135}{10000}$
$= 13.5 + 1.35 + 0.135 + 0.0135 = 14.9985$.

46. Given exp. $= \sqrt{\frac{4096}{10^2}} + \sqrt{\frac{4096}{10^4}} + \sqrt{\frac{4096}{10^6}} + \sqrt{\frac{4096}{10^8}}$
$= \frac{\sqrt{4096}}{10} + \frac{\sqrt{4096}}{10^2} + \frac{\sqrt{4096}}{10^3} + \frac{\sqrt{4096}}{10^4}$
$= \frac{64}{10} + \frac{64}{100} + \frac{64}{1000} + \frac{64}{10000}$
$= 6.4 + 0.64 + 0.064 + 0.0064$
$= 7.1104 \approx 7.11$.

47. Given exp. $= \sqrt{1.30} + \sqrt{1300} + \sqrt{0.0130}$
$= \sqrt{\frac{130}{100}} + \sqrt{13 \times 100} + \sqrt{\frac{130}{10000}}$
$= \frac{\sqrt{130}}{10} + \sqrt{13} \times 10 + \frac{\sqrt{130}}{100}$
$= \frac{11.40}{10} + 3.605 \times 10 + \frac{11.40}{100}$
$= 1.14 + 36.05 + 0.114 = 37.304$.

48. $\frac{52}{x} = \sqrt{\frac{169}{289}}$
$\Leftrightarrow \frac{52}{x} = \frac{13}{17}$
$\Leftrightarrow x = \left(\frac{52 \times 17}{13}\right) = 68$.

49. Let the missing number be x.
Then, $x^2 = 15 \times 135 \Leftrightarrow x = \sqrt{15 \times 135}$
$= \sqrt{15^2 \times 3^2} = 15 \times 3 = 45$.

50. Let $\frac{x}{1776}=\frac{111}{x}$. Then, x^2

$= 111 \times 1776 = 111 \times 111 \times 16$

$\Rightarrow x = \sqrt{(111)^2 \times (4)^2} = 111 \times 4 = 444.$

51. Let $\frac{4\frac{1}{2}}{x}=\frac{x}{32}$. Then, $x^2 = 32 \times \frac{9}{2} = 144 \Leftrightarrow x = \sqrt{144} = 12.$

52. Let $\frac{x}{\sqrt{128}}=\frac{\sqrt{162}}{x}$. Then, $x^2 = \sqrt{128 \times 162} = \sqrt{64 \times 2 \times 18 \times 9}$

$= \sqrt{8^2 \times 6^2 \times 3^2} = 8 \times 6 \times 3 = 144.$

$\therefore \quad x = \sqrt{144} = 12.$

53. $\sqrt{x+\frac{x}{y}} = x\sqrt{\frac{x}{y}} \Rightarrow x + \frac{x}{y} = x^2 \cdot \frac{x}{y} \Rightarrow \frac{xy+x}{y} = \frac{x^3}{y}$

$\Rightarrow \quad xy + x = x^3$

$\Rightarrow \quad y + 1 = x^2$

$\Rightarrow \quad y = x^2 - 1.$

54. $n^2 = (25)^{64} \times (64)^{25} = (5^2)^{64} \times (2^6)^{25}$

$= 5^{128} \times 2^{150} = 5^{128} \times 2^{128} \times 2^{22}$

$\Rightarrow n = 5^{64} \times 2^{64} \times 2^{11} = (5 \times 2)^{64} \times 2^{11} = 10^{64} \times 2048.$

$\therefore$ Sum of digits of $n = 2 + 0 + 4 + 8 = 14.$

55. $\frac{0.13}{p^2} = 13$

$\Leftrightarrow p^2 = \frac{0.13}{13} = \frac{1}{100}$

$\Leftrightarrow p = \sqrt{\frac{1}{100}} = \frac{1}{10} = 0.1.$

56. Let the required number be x. Then, $\frac{x}{\sqrt{0.25}} = 25$

$\Leftrightarrow \frac{x}{0.5} = 25$

$\Leftrightarrow x = 25 \times 0.5 = 12.5.$

57. $\sqrt{3^n} = 729 = 3^6 \Leftrightarrow (\sqrt{3^n})^2 = (3^6)^2 \Leftrightarrow 3^n = 3^{12} \Leftrightarrow n = 12.$

58. $\sqrt{18 \times 14 \times x} = 84 \Leftrightarrow 18 \times 14 \times x = 84 \times 84$

$\Leftrightarrow x = \frac{84 \times 84}{18 \times 14} = 28.$

59. Let $28\sqrt{x} + 1426 = 3 \times 718.$

Then, $28\sqrt{x} = 2154 - 1426 \Leftrightarrow 28\sqrt{x} = 728 \Leftrightarrow \sqrt{x} = 26$

$\Leftrightarrow x = (26)^2 = 676.$

60. Let $\sqrt{\frac{x}{169}} = \frac{54}{39}$. Then, $\frac{\sqrt{x}}{13} = \frac{54}{39} \Leftrightarrow \sqrt{x} = \left(\frac{54}{39} \times 13\right) = 18$

$\Leftrightarrow \quad x = (18)^2 = 324.$

61. $\frac{\sqrt{x}}{\sqrt{441}} = 0.02 \Leftrightarrow \frac{\sqrt{x}}{21} = 0.02$

$\Leftrightarrow \sqrt{x} = 0.02 \times 21 = 0.42 \Leftrightarrow x$

$= (0.42)^2 = 0.1764.$

62. Let $\sqrt{\frac{.0196}{x}} = 0.2$. Then, $\frac{.0196}{x} = 0.04$

$\Leftrightarrow \quad x = \frac{.0196}{.04} = \frac{1.96}{4} = .49.$

63. Let $\sqrt{0.0169 \times x} = 1.3$. Then, $0.0169x = (1.3)^2 = 1.69$

$\Rightarrow x = \frac{1.69}{0.0169} = 100.$

64. $37 + \sqrt{.0615 + x} = 37.25 \Leftrightarrow \sqrt{.0615 + x} = 0.25$

$\Leftrightarrow .0615 + x = (0.25)^2 = 0.0625$

$\Leftrightarrow x = .001 = \frac{1}{10^3} = 10^{-3}.$

65. $\sqrt{(x-1)(y+2)} = 7 \Rightarrow (x-1)(y+2) = (7)^2 \Rightarrow (x-1) = 7$ and $(y+2) = 7 \Rightarrow x = 8$ and $y = 5.$

66. $\frac{\sqrt{a}}{\sqrt{b}} = \frac{.004 \times .4}{\sqrt{.04 \times .4}} \Rightarrow \frac{a}{b} = \frac{.004 \times .4 \times .004 \times .4}{.04 \times .4} = \frac{.0000064}{.04}$

$\Rightarrow \frac{a}{b} = \frac{.00064}{4} = .00016 = \frac{16}{10^5} = 16 \times 10^{-5}.$

67. Let the number be x. Then,

$\frac{3}{5}x^2 = 126.15 \Leftrightarrow x^2 = \left(126.15 \times \frac{5}{3}\right) = 210.25$

$\Leftrightarrow x = \sqrt{210.25} = 14.5.$

68. $\sqrt{\frac{0.361}{0.00169}} = \sqrt{\frac{0.36100}{0.00169}} = \sqrt{\frac{36100}{169}} = \frac{190}{13}.$

69. $\sqrt{\frac{48.4}{0.289}} = \sqrt{\frac{48.400}{0.289}} = \sqrt{\frac{48400}{289}} = \frac{220}{17} = 12\frac{16}{17}.$

70. $\sqrt{1 + \frac{x}{169}} = \frac{14}{13} \Rightarrow 1 + \frac{x}{169} = \frac{196}{169}$

$\Rightarrow \frac{x}{169} = \left(\frac{196}{169} - 1\right) = \frac{27}{169} \Rightarrow x = 27.$

71. $\sqrt{1 + \frac{55}{729}} = 1 + \frac{x}{27} \Rightarrow \sqrt{\frac{784}{729}} = \frac{27+x}{27}$

$\Rightarrow \frac{28}{27} = \frac{27+x}{27} \Rightarrow 27 + x = 28 \Rightarrow x = 1.$

72. $\sqrt{\frac{4}{3}} - \sqrt{\frac{3}{4}} = \frac{\sqrt{4}}{\sqrt{3}} - \frac{\sqrt{3}}{\sqrt{4}} = \frac{\sqrt{4} \times \sqrt{4} - \sqrt{3} \times \sqrt{3}}{\sqrt{12}} = \frac{4-3}{2\sqrt{3}} = \frac{1}{2\sqrt{3}}.$

73.

```
     1 | 2.00 00 00 (1.414
       | 1
   ----+-----------
    24 | 100
       |  96
   ----+-----------
   281 |  400
       |  281
   ----+-----------
  2824 |  11900
       |  11296
       +-----------
```

$\therefore \sqrt{2} = 1.414$

74. $2\sqrt{27} - \sqrt{75} + \sqrt{12} = 2\sqrt{9 \times 3} - \sqrt{25 \times 3} + \sqrt{4 \times 3}$

$= 6\sqrt{3} - 5\sqrt{3} + 2\sqrt{3} = 3\sqrt{3}.$

75. $(\sqrt{12}+\sqrt{18})-(\sqrt{3}+\sqrt{2})=(\sqrt{4\times3}+\sqrt{9\times2})-(\sqrt{3}+\sqrt{2})$

$=(2\sqrt{3}+3\sqrt{2})-(\sqrt{3}+\sqrt{2})$

$=(2\sqrt{3}-\sqrt{3})+(3\sqrt{2}-\sqrt{2})=\sqrt{3}+2\sqrt{2}.$

76. $\frac{\sqrt{24}+\sqrt{216}}{\sqrt{96}}=\frac{\sqrt{4\times6}+\sqrt{36\times6}}{\sqrt{16\times6}}=\frac{2\sqrt{6}+6\sqrt{6}}{4\sqrt{6}}=\frac{8\sqrt{6}}{4\sqrt{6}}=2.$

77. $\frac{\sqrt{80}-\sqrt{112}}{\sqrt{45}-\sqrt{63}}=\frac{\sqrt{16\times5}-\sqrt{16\times7}}{\sqrt{9\times5}-\sqrt{9\times7}}$

$=\frac{4\sqrt{5}-4\sqrt{7}}{3\sqrt{5}-3\sqrt{7}}=\frac{4(\sqrt{5}-\sqrt{7})}{3(\sqrt{5}-\sqrt{7})}=\frac{4}{3}=1\frac{1}{3}.$

78. $3\sqrt{5}+\sqrt{125}=17.88\Rightarrow 3\sqrt{5}+\sqrt{25\times5}=17.88$

$\Rightarrow 3\sqrt{5}+5\sqrt{5}=17.88 \Rightarrow 8\sqrt{5}=17.88\Rightarrow \sqrt{5}=2.235.$

$\therefore \sqrt{80}+6\sqrt{5}=\sqrt{16\times5}+6\sqrt{5}=4\sqrt{5}+6\sqrt{5}$

$=10\sqrt{5}=(10\times2.235)=22.35.$

79. $\sqrt{50}\times\sqrt{98}=\sqrt{50\times98}=\sqrt{4900}=70.$

80. Given exp. $=\sqrt{4\times2}+2\sqrt{16\times2}-3\sqrt{64\times2}+4\sqrt{25\times2}$

$=2\sqrt{2}+8\sqrt{2}-24\sqrt{2}+20\sqrt{2}=6\sqrt{2}=6\times1.414=8.484.$

81. Given exp. $=\frac{3\sqrt{12}}{2\sqrt{28}}\times\frac{\sqrt{98}}{2\sqrt{21}}=\frac{3\sqrt{4\times3}}{2\sqrt{4\times7}}\times\frac{\sqrt{49\times2}}{2\sqrt{21}}$

$=\frac{6\sqrt{3}}{4\sqrt{7}}\times\frac{7\sqrt{2}}{2\sqrt{21}}=\frac{21\sqrt{6}}{4\sqrt{7\times21}}=\frac{21\sqrt{6}}{28\sqrt{3}}$

$=\frac{3}{4}\sqrt{2}=\frac{3}{4}\times1.414=3\times0.3535=1.0605.$

82. Given exp. $=\sqrt{\frac{11025}{100}}\times\sqrt{\frac{1}{100}}\div\sqrt{\frac{25}{10000}}-\sqrt{\frac{42025}{100}}$

$=\frac{105}{10}\times\frac{1}{10}\div\frac{5}{100}-\frac{205}{10}$

$=\frac{105}{100}\times\frac{100}{5}-\frac{205}{10}$

$=21-\frac{205}{10}=\frac{5}{10}=\frac{1}{2}=0.50.$

83. Sum of decimal places in the numerator and denominator under the radical sign being the same, we remove the decimal.

$\therefore$ Given exp. $=\sqrt{\frac{81\times484}{64\times625}}=\frac{9\times22}{8\times25}=0.99.$

84. Given exp. $=\sqrt{\frac{204\times42}{7\times34}}=\sqrt{36}=6.$

85. Given exp. $=\sqrt{\frac{81\times324\times4624}{15625\times289\times729\times64}}$

$=\frac{9\times18\times68}{125\times17\times27\times8}=\frac{3}{125}=0.024.$

86. Given exp. $=\sqrt{\frac{9.5\times.08500}{.19\times.0017}}=\sqrt{\frac{95\times8500}{19\times17}}$

$=\sqrt{5\times500}=\sqrt{2500}=50.$

87. Given exp. $=\sqrt{\frac{(0.03)^2+(0.21)^2+(0.065)^2}{\left(\frac{0.03}{10}\right)^2+\left(\frac{0.21}{10}\right)^2+\left(\frac{0.065}{10}\right)^2}}$

$=\sqrt{\frac{100\,[(0.03)^2+(0.21)^2+(0.065)^2]}{(0.03)^2+(0.21)^2+(0.065)^2}}=\sqrt{100}=10.$

88. $\sqrt{(7+3\sqrt{5})(7-3\sqrt{5})}=\sqrt{(7)^2-(3\sqrt{5})^2}$

$=\sqrt{49-45}=\sqrt{4}=2.$

89. $\left(\sqrt{3}-\frac{1}{\sqrt{3}}\right)^2=(\sqrt{3})^2+\left(\frac{1}{\sqrt{3}}\right)^2-2\times\sqrt{3}\times\frac{1}{\sqrt{3}}$

$=3+\frac{1}{3}-2=1+\frac{1}{3}=\frac{4}{3}.$

90. $\sqrt{4a^2-4a+1}+3a$

$=\sqrt{(1)^2+(2a)^2-2\times1\times2a}+3a=\sqrt{(1-2a)^2}+3a$

$=(1-2a)+3a=(1+a)=(1+0.1039)=1.1039.$

91. $\sqrt{\frac{(0.75)^3}{(1-0.75)}+[0.75+(0.75)^2+1]}$

$=\sqrt{\frac{(0.75)^3+(1-0.75)[(1)^2+(0.75)^2+1\times0.75]}{1-0.75}}$

$=\sqrt{\frac{(0.75)^3+[(1)^3-(0.75)^3]}{1-0.75}}$

$=\sqrt{\frac{1}{0.25}}=\sqrt{\frac{100}{25}}=\sqrt{4}=2.$

92. $a+b+c=27\sqrt{29} \Rightarrow 2c+\frac{3}{2}c+c=27\sqrt{29}$

$\Rightarrow\frac{9}{2}c=27\sqrt{29} \Rightarrow c=6\sqrt{29}.$

$\sqrt{a^2+b^2+c^2}=\sqrt{(a+b+c)^2-2(ab+bc+ca)}$

$=\sqrt{(27\sqrt{29})^2-2\left(2c\times\frac{3}{2}c+\frac{3}{2}c\times c+c\times2c\right)}$

$=\sqrt{(729\times29)-2\left(3c^2+\frac{3}{2}c^2+2c^2\right)}$

$=\sqrt{(729\times29)-2\times\frac{13}{2}c^2}$

$=\sqrt{(729\times29)-13\times(6\sqrt{29})^2}=\sqrt{29(729-468)}$

$=\sqrt{29\times261}=\sqrt{29\times29\times9}=29\times3=87.$

93. $\sqrt{0.\bar{4}}=\sqrt{\frac{4}{9}}=\frac{2}{3}=0.666.....=0.\bar{6}.$

94. $\sqrt{0.09}=\sqrt{\frac{9}{100}}=\frac{3}{10}=0.3$, which is rational.

95.

```
    6 | 0.40 00 00 (.63
      |   36
      |----------
  123 |    4 00
      |    3 69
      |----------
```

$\therefore \sqrt{0.4} = 0.63$

96.

```
    4 | 0.20 00 00 (.447
      |   16
      |----------
   84 |    4 00
      |    3 36
      |----------
  887 |      64 00
      |      62 09
      |----------
```

$\therefore \sqrt{0.2} = 0.447$

97.

```
    3 | 0.12 10 00 (.347
      |    9
      |----------
   64 |    3 10
      |    2 56
      |----------
  687 |      54 00
      |      48 00
      |----------
```

$\therefore \sqrt{0.121} = 0.347$

98.

```
    2 | 0.06 40 00 (.252
      |    4
      |----------
   45 |    2 40
      |    2 25
      |----------
  502 |      1500
      |      1004
      |----------
```

$\therefore \sqrt{0.064} = 0.252$

99. $\sqrt{\dfrac{0.16}{0.4}} = \sqrt{\dfrac{0.16}{0.40}} = \sqrt{\dfrac{16}{40}} = \sqrt{\dfrac{4}{10}} = \sqrt{0.4} = 0.63.$

100. $\dfrac{1+\sqrt{0.01}}{1-\sqrt{0.1}} = \dfrac{1+0.1}{1-0.316} = \dfrac{1.1}{0.684} = \dfrac{1100}{684} = 1.6.$

```
    3 | 0.10 00 00 (0.316
      |    9
      |----------
   61 |    1 00
      |      61
      |----------
  626 |      39 00
      |      37 56
      |----------
```

101. $\sqrt{535.9225} = \sqrt{\dfrac{5359225}{10000}} = \dfrac{2315}{100} = 23.15.$

```
     2 | 5 35 92 25 (2315
       | 4
       |----------
    43 | 1 35
       | 1 29
       |----------
   461 |   6 92
       |   4 61
       |----------
  4625 |   231 25
       |   231 25
       |----------
       |      ×
```

102. $\dfrac{1}{\sqrt{5}} = \dfrac{1}{\sqrt{5}} \times \dfrac{\sqrt{5}}{\sqrt{5}} = \dfrac{\sqrt{5}}{5} = \dfrac{2.236}{5} = 0.447.$

103. $\sqrt{\dfrac{8}{3}} = \sqrt{\dfrac{8\times 3}{3\times 3}} = \dfrac{\sqrt{24}}{3} = \dfrac{4.899}{3} = 1.633.$

104. $\dfrac{3\sqrt{2}}{2\sqrt{3}} = \dfrac{3\sqrt{2}}{2\sqrt{3}} \times \dfrac{\sqrt{3}}{\sqrt{3}} = \dfrac{3\sqrt{6}}{2\times 3} = \dfrac{\sqrt{6}}{2} = \dfrac{2.449}{2} = 1.2245.$

105. $\dfrac{\sqrt{5}}{2} - \dfrac{10}{\sqrt{5}} + \sqrt{125} = \dfrac{(\sqrt{5})^2 - 20 + 2\sqrt{5}\times 5\sqrt{5}}{2\sqrt{5}}$

$= \dfrac{5-20+50}{2\sqrt{5}} = \dfrac{35}{2\sqrt{5}} \times \dfrac{\sqrt{5}}{\sqrt{5}} = \dfrac{35\sqrt{5}}{10} = \dfrac{7}{2} \times 2.236$

$= 7 \times 1.118 = 7.826.$

106. Clearly, $a * b = \sqrt{a^2 + b^2}$. $\therefore$ $5 * 12$

$= \sqrt{5^2 + 12^2} = \sqrt{25+144} = \sqrt{169} = 13.$

107. Let the missing digit be x.

```
     1 | 1 53 7x (124
       | 1
       |----------
    22 |   53
       |   44
       |----------
   244 |   9 7x
       |   9 76
       |----------
       |     ×
```

Then, $x = 6$.

108. $7! = 7 \times 6 \times 5 \times 4 \times 3 \times 2 \times 1$

$= 7 \times 2 \times 3 \times 5 \times 2^2 \times 3 \times 2$

$= 2^4 \times 3^2 \times 5 \times 7.$

Thus, the smallest perfect square number which is divisible by 7! is

$(2^4 \times 3^2 \times 5 \times 7) \times (5 \times 7)$

$= 5040 \times 35 = 176400.$

109. L.C.M. of 3, 4, 5, 6, 8 is 120. Now, 120

$= 2 \times 2 \times 2 \times 3 \times 5.$

To make it a perfect square, it must be multiplied by $2 \times 3 \times 5$.

So, required number $= 2^2 \times 2^2 \times 3^2 \times 5^2 = 3600.$

110. L.C.M. of 21, 36, 66

$= 2772$. Now, 2772

$= 2 \times 2 \times 3 \times 3 \times 7 \times 11.$

To make it a perfect square, it must be multiplied by 7×11.

So, required number $= 2^2 \times 3^2 \times 7^2 \times 11^2 = 213444.$

111. $294 = 7 \times 7 \times 2 \times 3.$

To make it a perfect square, it must be multiplied by 2×3 *i.e.*, 6.

$\therefore$ Required number = 6.

112. $5808 = 2 \times 2 \times 2 \times 2 \times 3 \times 11 \times 11 = 2^2 \times 2^2 \times 3 \times 11^2.$

To make it a perfect square, it must be multiplied by 3.

113. $1470 = 7 \times 7 \times 5 \times 6$. To make it a perfect square, it must be divided by 5×6, *i.e.*, 30.

114.

```
     7 | 54 91 62 (741
       | 49
   144 |  5 91
       |  5 76
  1481 |    15 62
       |    14 81
       |       81
```

$\therefore$ Required number to be subtracted = 81.

115. $0.000326 = \dfrac{326}{10^6}$

```
   1 | 3 26 (18
     | 1
  28 | 2 26
     | 2 24
     |    2
```

$\therefore$ Required number to be subtracted $= \dfrac{2}{10^6} = 0.000002.$

116.

```
    8 | 77 00 (87
      | 64
  167 | 13 00
      | 11 69
      |  1 31
```

$\therefore$ Number to be added

$= (88)^2 - 7700 = 7744 - 7700 = 44.$

117.

```
     8 | 68 06 21 (824
       | 64
   162 |  4 06
       |  3 24
  1644 |    82 21
       |    65 76
       |    16 45
```

$\therefore$ Number to be added $= (825)^2 - 680621$

$= 680625 - 680621 = 4.$

118. Greatest number of four digits is 9999.

```
    9 | 99 99 (99
      | 81
  189 | 18 99
      | 17 01
      |  1 98
```

$\therefore$ Reqd. number = (9999 – 198) = 9801.

119. Least number of 4 digits is 1000.

```
   3 | 10 00 (31
     |  9
  61 |  1 00
     |    61
     |    39
```

$\therefore (31)^2 < 1000 < (32)^2.$

Hence, required number $= (32)^2 = 1024.$

120. Let the 18 consecutive natural numbers be x, $(x + 1)$ $(x + 2)$, $(x + 3)$, ..., $(x + 17)$. Then, $x + (x + 1) + (x + 2) + ... + (x + 17) = 18x + (1 + 2 + 3 + ... + 17) = 18x + 153.$

Putting $x = 1, 2, 3, 4$, ... we find that the smallest value of x for which $(18x + 153)$ becomes a perfect square is $x = 4$.

$\therefore$ Required value $= 18 \times 4 + 153 = 72 + 153 = 225.$

121. Given expression

$$= \sqrt{2+\sqrt{3}} \cdot \sqrt{2+\sqrt{2+\sqrt{3}}} \cdot \sqrt{2^2 - \left(\sqrt{2+\sqrt{2+\sqrt{3}}}\right)^2}$$

$$= \sqrt{2+\sqrt{3}} \cdot \sqrt{2+\sqrt{2+\sqrt{3}}} \cdot \sqrt{4-(2+\sqrt{2+\sqrt{3}})}$$

$$= \sqrt{2+\sqrt{3}} \cdot \sqrt{2+\sqrt{2+\sqrt{3}}} \cdot \sqrt{2-\sqrt{2+\sqrt{3}}}$$

$$= \sqrt{2+\sqrt{3}} \cdot \sqrt{2^2 - \left(\sqrt{2+\sqrt{3}}\right)^2} = \sqrt{2+\sqrt{3}} \cdot \sqrt{2-\sqrt{3}}$$

$$= \sqrt{2^2 - (\sqrt{3})^2} = \sqrt{4-3} = \sqrt{1} = 1.$$

122. $$\frac{1}{(\sqrt{5}-\sqrt{3})} = \frac{1}{(\sqrt{5}-\sqrt{3})} \times \frac{(\sqrt{5}+\sqrt{3})}{(\sqrt{5}+\sqrt{3})} = \frac{(\sqrt{5}+\sqrt{3})}{(5-3)}$$

$$= \frac{(2.2361+1.7321)}{2} = \frac{3.9682}{2} = 1.9841.$$

123. Given expression $$= \frac{1}{(\sqrt{9}-\sqrt{8})} \times \frac{(\sqrt{9}+\sqrt{8})}{(\sqrt{9}+\sqrt{8})} - \frac{1}{(\sqrt{8}-\sqrt{7})} \times \frac{(\sqrt{8}+\sqrt{7})}{(\sqrt{8}+\sqrt{7})} + \frac{1}{(\sqrt{7}-\sqrt{6})} \times \frac{(\sqrt{7}+\sqrt{6})}{(\sqrt{7}+\sqrt{6})}$$

$$- \frac{1}{(\sqrt{6}-\sqrt{5})} \times \frac{(\sqrt{6}+\sqrt{5})}{(\sqrt{6}+\sqrt{5})} + \frac{1}{(\sqrt{5}-\sqrt{4})} \times \frac{(\sqrt{5}+\sqrt{4})}{(\sqrt{5}+\sqrt{4})}$$

$$= \frac{(\sqrt{9}+\sqrt{8})}{(9-8)} - \frac{(\sqrt{8}+\sqrt{7})}{(8-7)} + \frac{(\sqrt{7}+\sqrt{6})}{(7-6)} - \frac{(\sqrt{6}+\sqrt{5})}{(6-5)} + \frac{(\sqrt{5}+\sqrt{4})}{(5-4)}$$

$$= (\sqrt{9}+\sqrt{8}) - (\sqrt{8}+\sqrt{7}) + (\sqrt{7}+\sqrt{6}) - (\sqrt{6}+\sqrt{5}) + (\sqrt{5}+\sqrt{4}) = (\sqrt{9}+\sqrt{4}) = 3+2 = 5.$$

124. Given exp. $$= \frac{1}{\sqrt{2}+\sqrt{1}} + \frac{1}{\sqrt{3}+\sqrt{2}} + \frac{1}{\sqrt{4}+\sqrt{3}} + \dots + \frac{1}{\sqrt{121}+\sqrt{120}}$$

$$= \frac{1}{\sqrt{2}+\sqrt{1}} \times \frac{\sqrt{2}-\sqrt{1}}{\sqrt{2}-\sqrt{1}} + \frac{1}{\sqrt{3}+\sqrt{2}} \times \frac{\sqrt{3}-\sqrt{2}}{\sqrt{3}-\sqrt{2}} + \frac{1}{\sqrt{4}+\sqrt{3}} \times \frac{\sqrt{4}-\sqrt{3}}{\sqrt{4}-\sqrt{3}} + \dots + \frac{1}{\sqrt{121}+\sqrt{120}} \times \frac{\sqrt{121}-\sqrt{120}}{\sqrt{121}-\sqrt{120}}$$

$$= \frac{\sqrt{2}-\sqrt{1}}{2-1} + \frac{\sqrt{3}-\sqrt{2}}{3-2} + \frac{\sqrt{4}-\sqrt{3}}{4-3} + \dots + \frac{\sqrt{121}-\sqrt{120}}{121-120}$$

$$= \sqrt{2}-\sqrt{1}+\sqrt{3}-\sqrt{2}+\sqrt{4}-\sqrt{3}+\dots+\sqrt{121}-\sqrt{120}$$

$$= -1+\sqrt{121} = -1+11 = 10.$$

125. Given exp. $= \dfrac{(1+\sqrt{3})(1-\sqrt{3})-(1-\sqrt{3})+(1+\sqrt{3})}{(1+\sqrt{3})(1-\sqrt{3})}$

$= \dfrac{1-(\sqrt{3})^2-1+\sqrt{3}+1+\sqrt{3}}{1^2-(\sqrt{3})^2}$

$= \dfrac{2\sqrt{3}-2}{1-3} = \dfrac{2(\sqrt{3}-1)}{(-2)} = 1-\sqrt{3}.$

126. Given exp. $= (2+\sqrt{2}) + \dfrac{1}{(2+\sqrt{2})} \times \dfrac{(2-\sqrt{2})}{(2-\sqrt{2})}$

$- \dfrac{1}{(2-\sqrt{2})} \times \dfrac{(2+\sqrt{2})}{(2+\sqrt{2})}$

$= (2+\sqrt{2}) + \dfrac{(2-\sqrt{2})}{(4-2)} - \dfrac{(2+\sqrt{2})}{(4-2)}$

$= (2+\sqrt{2}) + \dfrac{1}{2}(2-\sqrt{2}) - \dfrac{1}{2}(2+\sqrt{2}) = 2.$

127. Given exp. $= \dfrac{1}{(\sqrt{5}+\sqrt{3})} \times \dfrac{(\sqrt{5}-\sqrt{3})}{(\sqrt{5}-\sqrt{3})} + \dfrac{2}{(3+\sqrt{5})}$

$\times \dfrac{(3-\sqrt{5})}{(3-\sqrt{5})} - \dfrac{3}{(3+\sqrt{3})} \times \dfrac{(3-\sqrt{3})}{(3-\sqrt{3})}$

$= \dfrac{(\sqrt{5}-\sqrt{3})}{(5-3)} + \dfrac{2(3-\sqrt{5})}{(9-5)} - \dfrac{3(3-\sqrt{3})}{(9-3)}$

$= \dfrac{\sqrt{5}-\sqrt{3}}{2} + \dfrac{2(3-\sqrt{5})}{4} - \dfrac{3(3-\sqrt{3})}{6}$

$= \dfrac{6(\sqrt{5}-\sqrt{3})+6(3-\sqrt{5})-6(3-\sqrt{3})}{12} = 0.$

128. $\dfrac{7}{(3+\sqrt{2})} = \dfrac{7}{(3+\sqrt{2})} \times \dfrac{(3-\sqrt{2})}{(3-\sqrt{2})} = \dfrac{7(3-\sqrt{2})}{(9-2)}$

$= (3-\sqrt{2}) = (3-1.4142) = 1.5858.$

129. Given exp. $= \dfrac{3\sqrt{2}}{(\sqrt{6}-\sqrt{3})} \times \dfrac{(\sqrt{6}+\sqrt{3})}{(\sqrt{6}+\sqrt{3})} - \dfrac{4\sqrt{3}}{(\sqrt{6}-\sqrt{2})}$

$\times \dfrac{(\sqrt{6}+\sqrt{2})}{(\sqrt{6}+\sqrt{2})} - \dfrac{6}{2(\sqrt{2}-\sqrt{3})}$

$= \dfrac{3\sqrt{2}(\sqrt{6}+\sqrt{3})}{(6-3)} - \dfrac{4\sqrt{3}(\sqrt{6}+\sqrt{2})}{(6-2)}$

$+ \dfrac{3}{(\sqrt{3}-\sqrt{2})} \times \dfrac{(\sqrt{3}+\sqrt{2})}{(\sqrt{3}+\sqrt{2})}$

$= \sqrt{2}(\sqrt{6}+\sqrt{3}) - \sqrt{3}(\sqrt{6}+\sqrt{2}) + 3(\sqrt{3}+\sqrt{2})$

$= \sqrt{12}+\sqrt{6}-\sqrt{18}-\sqrt{6}+3\sqrt{3}+3\sqrt{2}$

$= 2\sqrt{3}-3\sqrt{2}+3\sqrt{3}+3\sqrt{2} = 5\sqrt{3}$

130. $\dfrac{\sqrt{7}+\sqrt{5}}{\sqrt{7}-\sqrt{5}} = \dfrac{(\sqrt{7}+\sqrt{5})}{(\sqrt{7}-\sqrt{5})} \times \dfrac{(\sqrt{7}+\sqrt{5})}{(\sqrt{7}+\sqrt{5})} = \dfrac{(\sqrt{7}+\sqrt{5})^2}{(7-5)}$

$= \dfrac{7+5+2\sqrt{35}}{2} = \dfrac{12+2\sqrt{35}}{2} = 6+\sqrt{35}.$

131. $a+b\sqrt{3} = \dfrac{(5+2\sqrt{3})}{(7+4\sqrt{3})} \times \dfrac{(7-4\sqrt{3})}{(7-4\sqrt{3})} = \dfrac{35-20\sqrt{3}+14\sqrt{3}-24}{(7)^2-(4\sqrt{3})^2}$

$= \dfrac{11-6\sqrt{3}}{49-48} = 11-6\sqrt{3}.$ $\quad\therefore a = 11, b = -6.$

132. $\dfrac{\sqrt{2}-1}{\sqrt{2}+1} = \dfrac{(\sqrt{2}-1)}{(\sqrt{2}+1)} \times \dfrac{(\sqrt{2}-1)}{(\sqrt{2}-1)} = (\sqrt{2}-1)^2.$

$\therefore \sqrt{\dfrac{\sqrt{2}-1}{\sqrt{2}+1}} = (\sqrt{2}-1) = (1.414-1) = 0.414.$

133. Given exp. $= \dfrac{3+\sqrt{6}}{5\sqrt{3}-4\sqrt{3}-4\sqrt{2}+5\sqrt{2}} = \dfrac{(3+\sqrt{6})}{(\sqrt{3}+\sqrt{2})}$

$= \dfrac{(3+\sqrt{6})}{(\sqrt{3}+\sqrt{2})} \times \dfrac{(\sqrt{3}-\sqrt{2})}{(\sqrt{3}-\sqrt{2})}$

$= \dfrac{3\sqrt{3}-3\sqrt{2}+3\sqrt{2}-2\sqrt{3}}{(3-2)} = \sqrt{3} = 1.732.$

134. Given exp. $= \dfrac{(2+\sqrt{3})}{(2-\sqrt{3})} \times \dfrac{(2+\sqrt{3})}{(2+\sqrt{3})} + \dfrac{(2-\sqrt{3})}{(2+\sqrt{3})} \times \dfrac{(2-\sqrt{3})}{(2-\sqrt{3})}$

$+ \dfrac{(\sqrt{3}-1)}{(\sqrt{3}+1)} \times \dfrac{(\sqrt{3}-1)}{(\sqrt{3}-1)}$

$= \dfrac{(2+\sqrt{3})^2}{(4-3)} + \dfrac{(2-\sqrt{3})^2}{(4-3)} + \dfrac{(\sqrt{3}-1)^2}{(3-1)}$

$= [(2+\sqrt{3})^2 + (2-\sqrt{3})^2] + \dfrac{4-2\sqrt{3}}{2}$

$= 2(4+3)+2-\sqrt{3} = 16-\sqrt{3}.$

135. $x+y = \dfrac{\sqrt{5}+\sqrt{3}}{\sqrt{5}-\sqrt{3}} + \dfrac{\sqrt{5}+\sqrt{3}}{\sqrt{5}+\sqrt{3}} = \dfrac{(\sqrt{5}+\sqrt{3})}{(\sqrt{5}-\sqrt{3})} \times \dfrac{(\sqrt{5}+\sqrt{3})}{(\sqrt{5}+\sqrt{3})}$

$+ \dfrac{(\sqrt{5}-\sqrt{3})}{(\sqrt{5}+\sqrt{3})} \times \dfrac{(\sqrt{5}-\sqrt{3})}{(\sqrt{5}-\sqrt{3})}$

$= \dfrac{(\sqrt{5}+\sqrt{3})^2}{(\sqrt{5})^2-(\sqrt{3})^2} + \dfrac{(\sqrt{5}-\sqrt{3})^2}{(\sqrt{5})^2-(\sqrt{3})^2}$

$= \dfrac{(\sqrt{5}+\sqrt{3})^2+(\sqrt{5}-\sqrt{3})^2}{5-3}$

$= \dfrac{2\left[(\sqrt{5})^2+(\sqrt{3})^2\right]}{2} = 5+3 = 8.$

136. Given exp. $= \dfrac{(\sqrt{2})^2}{(\sqrt{3})^2} \cdot \dfrac{(2+\sqrt{3})(2-\sqrt{3})}{(\sqrt{3}+1)(\sqrt{3}-1)} = \dfrac{2}{3}\left[\dfrac{2^2-(\sqrt{3})^2}{(\sqrt{3})^2-1^2}\right]$

$= \dfrac{2}{3}\left(\dfrac{4-3}{3-1}\right) = \dfrac{2}{3} \times \dfrac{1}{2} = \dfrac{1}{3}.$

137. Given exp. $= \dfrac{12}{3+(\sqrt{5}+2\sqrt{2})} \times \dfrac{3-(\sqrt{5}+2\sqrt{2})}{3-(\sqrt{5}+2\sqrt{2})}$

$= \dfrac{12(3-\sqrt{5}-2\sqrt{2})}{3^2-(\sqrt{5}+2\sqrt{2})^2} = \dfrac{12(3-\sqrt{5}-2\sqrt{2})}{9-(5+8+4\sqrt{10})}$

$= \dfrac{12(3-\sqrt{5}-2\sqrt{2})}{(-4-4\sqrt{10})} = \dfrac{3(\sqrt{5}+2\sqrt{2}-3)}{\sqrt{10}+1}$

$= \dfrac{3(\sqrt{5}+2\sqrt{2}-3)}{\sqrt{10}+1} \times \dfrac{\sqrt{10}-1}{\sqrt{10}-1}$

$$= \frac{3\sqrt{50} - 3\sqrt{5} + 6\sqrt{20} - 6\sqrt{2} - 9\sqrt{10} + 9}{10 - 1}$$

$$= \frac{15\sqrt{2} - 3\sqrt{5} + 12\sqrt{5} - 6\sqrt{2} - 9\sqrt{10} + 9}{9}$$

$$= \frac{9\sqrt{2} + 9\sqrt{5} - 9\sqrt{10} + 9}{9} = 1 + \sqrt{2} + \sqrt{5} - \sqrt{10}.$$

138. Given exp. $= \frac{1}{(\sqrt{2} - \sqrt{5}) + \sqrt{3}} + \frac{1}{(\sqrt{2} - \sqrt{5}) - \sqrt{3}}$

$$= \frac{[(\sqrt{2} - \sqrt{5}) - \sqrt{3}] + [(\sqrt{2} - \sqrt{5}) + \sqrt{3}]}{[(\sqrt{2} - \sqrt{5}) + \sqrt{3}][(\sqrt{2} - \sqrt{5}) - \sqrt{3}]}$$

$$= \frac{2(\sqrt{2} - \sqrt{5})}{(\sqrt{2} - \sqrt{5})^2 - (\sqrt{3})^2} = \frac{2(\sqrt{2} - \sqrt{5})}{(2 + 5 - 2\sqrt{10}) - 3}$$

$$= \frac{2(\sqrt{2} - \sqrt{5})}{4 - 2\sqrt{10}} = \frac{\sqrt{2} - \sqrt{5}}{2 - \sqrt{10}}$$

$$= \frac{\sqrt{2} - \sqrt{5}}{\sqrt{2}(\sqrt{2} - \sqrt{5})} = \frac{1}{\sqrt{2}}.$$

139. $x + \frac{1}{x} = (7 - 4\sqrt{3}) + \frac{1}{(7 - 4\sqrt{3})} \times \frac{(7 + 4\sqrt{3})}{(7 + 4\sqrt{3})}$

$$= (7 - 4\sqrt{3}) + \frac{(7 + 4\sqrt{3})}{(49 - 48)}$$

$$= (7 - 4\sqrt{3}) + (7 + 4\sqrt{3}) = 14.$$

140. $x = 3 + \sqrt{8} \Rightarrow x^2 = (3 + \sqrt{8})^2 = 3^2 + (\sqrt{8})^2 + 2 \times 3 \times \sqrt{8}$

$$= 9 + 8 + 6\sqrt{8} = 17 + 12\sqrt{2}.$$

$$x^2 + \frac{1}{x^2} = (17 + 12\sqrt{2}) + \frac{1}{(17 + 12\sqrt{2})} \times \frac{(17 - 12\sqrt{2})}{(17 - 12\sqrt{2})}$$

$$= (17 + 12\sqrt{2}) + \frac{(17 - 12\sqrt{2})}{289 - 288}.$$

$$= (17 + 12\sqrt{2}) + (17 - 12\sqrt{2}) = 34.$$

141. $a = \frac{\sqrt{3} + \sqrt{2}}{\sqrt{3} - \sqrt{2}} = \frac{\sqrt{3} + \sqrt{2}}{\sqrt{3} - \sqrt{2}} \times \frac{\sqrt{3} + \sqrt{2}}{\sqrt{3} + \sqrt{2}}$

$$= \frac{(\sqrt{3} + \sqrt{2})^2}{(\sqrt{3})^2 - (\sqrt{2})^2} = \frac{3 + 2 + 2\sqrt{6}}{3 - 2} = 5 + 2\sqrt{6}.$$

$$b = \frac{\sqrt{3} - \sqrt{2}}{\sqrt{3} + \sqrt{2}} = \frac{\sqrt{3} - \sqrt{2}}{\sqrt{3} + \sqrt{2}} \times \frac{\sqrt{3} - \sqrt{2}}{\sqrt{3} - \sqrt{2}}$$

$$= \frac{(\sqrt{3} - \sqrt{2})^2}{(\sqrt{3})^2 - (\sqrt{2})^2} = \frac{3 + 2 - 2\sqrt{6}}{3 - 2} = 5 - 2\sqrt{6}.$$

$$a^2 + b^2 = (5 + 2\sqrt{6})^2 + (5 - 2\sqrt{6})^2 = 2[(5)^2 + (2\sqrt{6})^2]$$

$$= 2(25 + 24) = 2 \times 49 = 98.$$

142. $a = \frac{(\sqrt{5} + 1)}{(\sqrt{5} - 1)} \times \frac{(\sqrt{5} + 1)}{(\sqrt{5} + 1)}$

$$= \frac{(\sqrt{5} + 1)^2}{(5 - 1)} = \frac{5 + 1 + 2\sqrt{5}}{4} = \left(\frac{3 + \sqrt{5}}{2}\right).$$

$$b = \frac{(\sqrt{5} - 1)}{(\sqrt{5} + 1)} \times \frac{(\sqrt{5} - 1)}{(\sqrt{5} - 1)} = \frac{(\sqrt{5} - 1)^2}{(5 - 1)}$$

$$= \frac{5 + 1 - 2\sqrt{5}}{4} = \left(\frac{3 - \sqrt{5}}{2}\right).$$

$$\therefore a^2 + b^2 = \frac{(3 + \sqrt{5})^2}{4} + \frac{(3 - \sqrt{5})^2}{4}$$

$$= \frac{(3 + \sqrt{5})^2 + (3 - \sqrt{5})^2}{4} = \frac{2(9 + 5)}{4} = 7.$$

Also, $ab = \frac{(3 + \sqrt{5})}{2} \cdot \frac{(3 - \sqrt{5})}{2} = \frac{(9 - 5)}{4} = 1.$

$$\therefore \frac{a^2 + ab + b^2}{a^2 - ab + b^2} = \frac{(a^2 + b^2) + ab}{(a^2 + b^2) - ab} = \frac{7 + 1}{7 - 1} = \frac{8}{6} = \frac{4}{3}.$$

143. $x = \sqrt{1 + \sqrt{1 + \sqrt{1 + \cdots \infty}}} \Leftrightarrow x = \sqrt{1 + x}$

$\Leftrightarrow x^2 = 1 + x \Leftrightarrow x^2 - x - 1 = 0$

$$\Leftrightarrow x = \frac{1 \pm \sqrt{(-1^2) - 4 \times 1 \times (-1)}}{2}$$

$$\Leftrightarrow x = \frac{1 \pm \sqrt{1 + 4}}{2} = \frac{1 \pm \sqrt{5}}{2}.$$

Hence, positive value of x is $\frac{1 + \sqrt{5}}{2}$.

144. Let $x = \sqrt{2 + \sqrt{2 + \sqrt{2 + \cdots}}}$.

Then, $x = \sqrt{2 + x} \Leftrightarrow x^2 = 2 + x \Leftrightarrow x^2 - x - 2 = 0$

$\Leftrightarrow x^2 - 2x + x - 2 = 0$

$\Leftrightarrow x(x - 2) + (x - 2) = 0 \Leftrightarrow (x - 2)(x + 1) = 0$

$\Leftrightarrow x = 2.$ $[\because x \neq -1]$

145. $a = \sqrt{3 + \sqrt{3 + \sqrt{3 + \cdots}}} \Leftrightarrow a = \sqrt{3 + a} \Leftrightarrow a^2 = 3 + a$

$\Leftrightarrow a^2 - a - 3 = 0$

$$\Leftrightarrow a = \frac{1 \pm \sqrt{(-1)^2 - 4 \times 1 \times (-3)}}{2}$$

$$\Leftrightarrow a = \frac{1 \pm \sqrt{1 + 12}}{2} = \frac{1 \pm \sqrt{13}}{2} \Leftrightarrow a = \frac{1 + \sqrt{13}}{2} \quad [\because a > 0]$$

$$\Leftrightarrow a = \frac{1 + 3.6}{2} = \frac{4.6}{2} = 2.3.$$

$\therefore 2 < a < 3.$

146. $\frac{\sqrt{3 + x} + \sqrt{3 - x}}{\sqrt{3 + x} - \sqrt{3 - x}} = 2$

$$\Leftrightarrow \frac{\sqrt{3 + x} + \sqrt{3 - x}}{\sqrt{3 + x} - \sqrt{3 - x}} \times \frac{\sqrt{3 + x} + \sqrt{3 - x}}{\sqrt{3 + x} + \sqrt{3 - x}} = 2$$

$$\Leftrightarrow \frac{(\sqrt{3 + x} + \sqrt{3 - x})^2}{(\sqrt{3 + x})^2 - (\sqrt{3 - x})^2} = 2$$

$$\Leftrightarrow \frac{(3 + x) + (3 - x) + 2\sqrt{(3 + x)(3 - x)}}{(3 + x) - (3 - x)} = 2$$

$$\Leftrightarrow 6 + 2\sqrt{9 - x^2} = 4x \Leftrightarrow 2\sqrt{9 - x^2} = 4x - 6$$

$\Leftrightarrow \sqrt{9-x^2} = 2x - 3$

$\Leftrightarrow 9 - x^2 = (2x - 3)^2 = 4x^2 + 9 - 12x$

$\Leftrightarrow 5x^2 - 12x = 0 \Leftrightarrow 5x^2 = 12x$

$\Leftrightarrow x = \frac{12}{5}.$

147. Let the total number of camels be x.

Then, $x - \left(\frac{x}{4} + 2\sqrt{x}\right) = 15 \Leftrightarrow \frac{3x}{4} - 2\sqrt{x} = 15$

$\Leftrightarrow 3x - 8\sqrt{x} = 60 \Leftrightarrow 8\sqrt{x} = 3x - 60$

$\Leftrightarrow 64x = (3x - 60)^2 \Leftrightarrow 64x = 9x^2 + 3600 - 360x$

$\Leftrightarrow 9x^2 - 424x + 3600 = 0 \Leftrightarrow 9x^2 - 324x - 100x + 3600 = 0$

$\Leftrightarrow 9x(x - 36) - 100(x - 36) = 0 \Leftrightarrow (x - 36)(9x - 100) = 0$

$\Leftrightarrow x = 36.$ $\left[\because x \neq \frac{100}{9}\right]$

148.

```
  1 | 1 79 56 (134
    | 1
    |--------
 23 | 79
    | 69
    |--------
264 | 10 56
    | 10 56
    |--------
    |   ×
```

$\therefore$ Number of rows = 134.

149.

```
  1 | 1 10 25 (105
    | 1
    |--------
 20 | 10
    |  0
    |--------
205 | 10 25
    | 10 25
    |--------
    |   ×
```

Number of rows = $\sqrt{10914 + 111} = \sqrt{11025} = 105.$

150. Let the number of girls in the group be x.

Then, number of oranges given to each girl = $2x$.

$\therefore x \times 2x = 1250 \Leftrightarrow 2x^2 = 1250 \Leftrightarrow x^2 = 625 \Leftrightarrow x = \sqrt{625} = 25.$

151.

```
  1 | 3 65 81 (191
    | 1
    |--------
 29 | 2 65
    | 2 61
    |--------
381 |   4 81
    |   3 81
    |--------
    |   1 00
```

$\therefore$ Number of men left = 100.

152. Money collected = (59.29 × 100) paise = 5929 paise.

$\therefore$ Number of members = $\sqrt{5929} = 77.$

153. Clearly, the required number must be a perfect square. Since a number having 8 as the unit's digit cannot be a perfect square, so 1,21,108 is not a perfect square.

154. $148877 = 53 \times 53 \times 53$

$\therefore \sqrt[3]{148877} = 53.$

53	148877
53	2809
	53

155. $681472 = 8 \times 8 \times 8 \times 11 \times 11 \times 11 = 8^3 \times (11)^3.$

8	681472
8	85184
8	10648
11	1331
11	121
	11

$\sqrt[3]{681472} = 8 \times 11 = 88.$

156. $262144 = 8 \times 8 \times 8 \times 8 \times 8 \times 8 = 8^6.$

$\therefore \sqrt[3]{262144} = 8^2 = 64.$

Let $1728 \div \sqrt[3]{262144} \times x - 288 = 4491.$

Then, $1728 \div 64 \times x - 288 = 4491$

$\Leftrightarrow 27x = 4779$

$\Leftrightarrow x = \frac{4779}{27} = 177.$

8	262144
8	32768
8	4096
8	512
8	64
	8

157. Let $99 \times 21 - \sqrt[3]{x} = 1968.$

Then, $2079 - \sqrt[3]{x} = 1968 \Leftrightarrow \sqrt[3]{x} = 2079 - 1968 = 111$

$\Leftrightarrow x = (111)^3 = 1367631.$

158. $(.000216)^{1/3} = \left(\frac{216}{10^6}\right)^{1/3}$

$= \left(\frac{6 \times 6 \times 6}{10^2 \times 10^2 \times 10^2}\right)^{1/3} = \frac{6}{10^2} = \frac{6}{100} = .06.$

159. $\sqrt[3]{4\frac{12}{125}} = \sqrt[3]{\frac{512}{125}} = \left(\frac{8 \times 8 \times 8}{5 \times 5 \times 5}\right)^{1/3} = \frac{8}{5} = 1\frac{3}{5}.$

160. $\sqrt{.000064} = \sqrt{\frac{64}{10^6}} = \frac{8}{10^3} = \frac{8}{1000} = .008.$

$\therefore \sqrt[3]{\sqrt{.000064}} = \sqrt[3]{.008} = \sqrt[3]{\frac{8}{1000}} = \frac{2}{10} = 0.2.$

161. $864 = 3 \times 3 \times 3 \times 4 \times 4 \times 2.$

Clearly, 864 when multipled by 2 will become a perfect cube.

Hence, $n = 2$.

4	864
4	216
3	54
3	18
3	18
3	6
	2

162. $\sqrt{.01}\times\sqrt[3]{.008}-.02=\sqrt{(.1)^2}\times\sqrt[3]{(.2)^3}-.02$

$= .1 \times .2 - .02 = .02 - .02 = 0.$

163. Given exp. $=\sqrt[3]{\frac{0.008+0.000064}{0.064+0.000512}}=\sqrt[3]{\frac{0.008064}{0.064512}}$

$=\sqrt[3]{\frac{8064}{64512}}=\sqrt[3]{\frac{1}{8}}=\frac{1}{2}=0.5.$

164. Let $\sqrt[3]{3}=x$.

Then, $(\sqrt[3]{9}-\sqrt[3]{3}+1)=(x^2-x+1)=\frac{x^3+1}{x+1}=\frac{(\sqrt[3]{3})^3+1}{(\sqrt[3]{3}+1)}$.

$\Rightarrow(\sqrt[3]{9}-\sqrt[3]{3}+1)(\sqrt[3]{3}+1)=(\sqrt[3]{3})^3+1$

$= 3 + 1 = 4$, which is rational.

165. Clearly, $(21)^3 = 9261$ and $(22)^3 = 10648$.

So, 9261 is the largest four-digit number which is a perfect cube.

166. $21600 = 2^5 \times 3^3 \times 5^2$.

To make it a perfect cube, it must be multiplied by (2×5), i.e., 10.

167. $3600 = 2^3 \times 5^2 \times 3^2 \times 2$.

To make it a perfect cube, it must be divided by $5^2 \times 3^2 \times 2$, i.e. 450.

168. Required number to be added

$= 9^3 - 710 = 729 - 710 = 19.$

169.

8	$\overline{79}\ \overline{21}$	89
8	64	
169	1521	
9	1521	
	×	

$\Rightarrow\sqrt{7921}=89$

170. Given $?=\sqrt[4]{(625)^3}$

$=(625)^{\frac{3}{4}}=(5\times5\times5\times5)^{\frac{3}{4}}$

$=(5^4)^{\frac{3}{4}}=5^3=125$

171. Given $\sqrt{y}=4x$

$\Rightarrow y=(4x)^2=16x^2$

$\Rightarrow y=16x^2$

$\therefore \frac{x^2}{y}=\frac{1}{16}$

172. Let the number be x.

Given: $\sqrt{2025.11}\times\sqrt{256.04}+\sqrt{399.95}\times\sqrt{?}=33.98\times40$

$\sqrt{2025}\times\sqrt{256}+\sqrt{400}\times\sqrt{?}=34\times40$

$45\times16+20\times\sqrt{?}=1360$

$20\times\sqrt{?}=1360-720=640$

$\sqrt{?}=\frac{640}{20}=32$

$\Rightarrow ? = (32)^2$

$\therefore ? = 32 \times 32 = 1024$

Hence, the number is 1024.

173. $\frac{1}{\sqrt{28}}=\frac{1}{\sqrt{2\times2\times7}}=\frac{1}{2\sqrt{7}}$

$=\frac{\sqrt{7}}{2\sqrt{7}\times\sqrt{7}}=\frac{\sqrt{7}}{14}$

$=\frac{2.645}{14}=0.189$

174. $=\left(\sqrt{\frac{25}{9}}-\sqrt{\frac{64}{81}}\right)\div\sqrt{\frac{16}{324}}$

$=\left(\frac{5}{3}-\frac{8}{9}\right)\div\frac{4}{18}$

LCM of 3 and 9 is 9.

$=\left(\frac{15-8}{9}\right)\div\frac{2}{9}=\frac{7}{9}\div\frac{2}{9}$

$=\frac{7}{9}\times\frac{9}{2}=\frac{7}{2}=3.5$

175. Given: $1728\div\sqrt[3]{262144}\times?-288=4491$

$\Rightarrow 1728\div\sqrt[3]{64\times64\times64}\times?$

$= 4491 + 288$

$\Rightarrow \frac{1728}{64}\times?=4779$

$\Rightarrow 27 \times ? = 4779$

$\Rightarrow ?=\frac{4779}{27}=177$

176. Let the number be a.

$(\sqrt{7}+11)^2$

$=a^{\frac{1}{3}}+2\sqrt{847}+122$

$\Rightarrow 7+121+22\sqrt{7}$

$=a^{\frac{1}{3}}+22\sqrt{7}+122$

$\Rightarrow 128-122=a^{\frac{1}{3}}$

$\Rightarrow a^{\frac{1}{3}}=6$

$\Rightarrow a=(6)^3=216$

Hence, the number is 216.

177. Let the number be x.

$x-\sqrt{784}=6\times\sqrt{324}$

$x - 28 = 6 \times 18$

$x - 28 = 108$

$x = 108 + 28 = 136$

178. Let the number be x.

Given $\sqrt{2116}-\sqrt{1600}=\sqrt{(x)}$

$46 - 40 = \sqrt{(x)}$

$\Rightarrow 6=\sqrt{x}$

$\Rightarrow x=(6)^2=36$

Hence, the number is 36.

179. Let the number be x.

$\sqrt{(27 \div 5 \times x) \div 15} = 5.4 \div 6 + 0.3$

$\Rightarrow \sqrt{\frac{(27 \div 5 \times x)}{15}} = \frac{5.4}{6} + 0.3$

$\Rightarrow \sqrt{\frac{27 \times x}{5 \times 15}} = \frac{5.4}{6} + 0.3$

$\Rightarrow \sqrt{\frac{9 \times x}{5 \times 5}} = 0.9 + 0.3$

$\Rightarrow \frac{3}{5}\sqrt{x} = 1.2$

$\Rightarrow \sqrt{x} = \frac{1.2 \times 5}{3} = 2 \Rightarrow x = (2)^2$

$\Rightarrow x = 2 \times 2 = 4^2$

180. Given $\sqrt{24 \div 0.5 + 1} + \sqrt{18 \div 0.6 + 6}$

$= \sqrt{24 \times \frac{1}{0.5} + 1} + \sqrt{18 \times \frac{1}{0.6} + 6}$

$= \sqrt{24 \times \frac{10}{5} + 1} + \sqrt{\frac{18 \times 10}{6} + 6}$

$= \sqrt{48 + 1} + \sqrt{30 + 6}$

$\sqrt{49} + \sqrt{36} = 7 + 6 = 13$

181. Given $(\sqrt{63} + \sqrt{252}) \times (\sqrt{175} + \sqrt{28})$

$= (\sqrt{63} + \sqrt{4 \times 63}) \times (\sqrt{25 \times 7} + \sqrt{4 \times 7})$

$= (\sqrt{7 \times 9} + \sqrt{4 \times 9 \times 7}) \times (\sqrt{5 \times 5 \times 7} + \sqrt{2 \times 2 \times 7})$

$= (3\sqrt{7} + 6\sqrt{7}) \times (5\sqrt{7} + 2\sqrt{7})$

$= 9\sqrt{7} \times 7\sqrt{7} = 441$

182. Given $9x^2 + 25 - 30x$

We have to find $\sqrt{9x^2 + 25 - 30x}$

$= \sqrt{(3x)^2 - 2.3x \cdot 5 + (-5)^2}$ $\{\because a^2 - 2ab + b^2 = (a-b)^2\}$

$= \sqrt{(3x-5)^2} = 3x - 5$

183. $\sqrt{\frac{3}{11}} = \sqrt{\frac{3 \times 11}{11 \times 11}} = \frac{\sqrt{33}}{11}$

$= \frac{5.745}{11} = 0.5223$

184. Let the number be x.

Given $\sqrt{x} + 14 = \sqrt{2601}$

or, $\sqrt{x} = 51 - 14 = 37$

or $x = 37^2 = 1369$

185. $a = \frac{\sqrt{3}}{2}$ (given)

$\therefore \sqrt{1+a} + \sqrt{1-a}$

$= \sqrt{1 + \frac{\sqrt{3}}{2}} + \sqrt{1 - \frac{\sqrt{3}}{2}}$

$= \sqrt{\frac{2+\sqrt{3}}{2}} + \sqrt{\frac{2-\sqrt{3}}{2}}$

$= \sqrt{\frac{2(2+\sqrt{3})}{4}} + \sqrt{\frac{2(2-\sqrt{3})}{4}}$

$= \sqrt{\frac{4+2\sqrt{3}}{4}} + \sqrt{\frac{4-2\sqrt{3}}{4}}$

$= \sqrt{\frac{3+1+2\times\sqrt{3}\times 1}{2}} + \sqrt{\frac{3+1-2\times\sqrt{3}\times 1}{2}}$

$$\because \left\{\begin{array}{l} \sqrt{3}^2 + (1)^2 - 2\times\sqrt{3}\times 1 = (\sqrt{3}-1)^2 \\ (\sqrt{3})^2 + (1)^2 + 2\times\sqrt{3}\times 1 = (\sqrt{3}+1)^2 \\ a^2 + b^2 + 2ab = (a+b)^2 \\ a^2 + b^2 - 2ab = (a-b)^2 \end{array}\right\}$$

$= \frac{\sqrt{(\sqrt{3}+1)^2}}{2} + \frac{\sqrt{(\sqrt{3}-1)^2}}{2}$

$= \frac{\sqrt{3}+1+\sqrt{3}-1}{2}$

$= \frac{2\sqrt{3}}{2} = \sqrt{3}$

186. Given $\frac{5+\sqrt{10}}{5\sqrt{5} - 2\sqrt{20} - \sqrt{32} + \sqrt{50}}$

$= \frac{5+\sqrt{10}}{5\sqrt{5} - 2\times 2\sqrt{5} - 2\times 2\sqrt{2} + 5\sqrt{2}}$

$= \frac{5+\sqrt{10}}{5\sqrt{5} - 4\sqrt{5} - 4\sqrt{2} + 5\sqrt{2}}$

$= \frac{5+\sqrt{10}}{\sqrt{5}+\sqrt{2}} = \frac{\sqrt{5}(\sqrt{5}+\sqrt{2})}{\sqrt{5}+\sqrt{2}} = \sqrt{5}$

187. Given: $\frac{(0.75)^3}{1-0.75} + [0.75 + (0.75)^2 + 1]$

$= \frac{(0.75)^2 \times 0.75}{0.25} + [0.75 + 0.5625 + 1]$

$= 0.5625 \times 3 + [0.75 + 0.5625 + 1]$

$= 1.6875 + 2.3125 = 4$

Square root of 4 = 2

188. Given $\sqrt{10 + 2\sqrt{6} + 2\sqrt{10} + 2\sqrt{15}}$

$= \sqrt{10 + 2\times\sqrt{3}\times\sqrt{2} + 2\times\sqrt{2}\times\sqrt{5} + 2\times\sqrt{3}\times\sqrt{5}}$

$= \sqrt{2+3+5+2\times\sqrt{2}\times\sqrt{3} + 2\times\sqrt{5}\times\sqrt{2} + 2\times\sqrt{5}\times\sqrt{3}}$

$= \sqrt{(\sqrt{2})^2 + (\sqrt{3})^2 + (\sqrt{5})^2 + 2\times\sqrt{2}\times\sqrt{3} + 2\times\sqrt{5}\times\sqrt{2} + 2\times\sqrt{5}\times\sqrt{3}}$

$\{\because a^2 + b^2 + c^2 + 2ab + 2bc + 2ca = (a+b+c)^2\}$

$= \sqrt{(\sqrt{2}+\sqrt{3}+\sqrt{5})^2}$

$= (\sqrt{2}+\sqrt{3}+\sqrt{5})$

6 Average

IMPORTANT FACTS AND FORMULAE

I. Average $= \left(\frac{\text{Sum of observations}}{\text{Number of observations}}\right)$

II. Suppose a man covers a certain distance at x kmph and an equal distance at y kmph. Then, the average speed during the whole journey is $\left(\frac{2xy}{x+y}\right)$ kmph.

SOLVED EXAMPLES

Ex. 1. ***Find the average of the following set of numbers: 354, 281, 623, 518, 447, 702, 876.*** (Bank Recruitment, 2009)

Sol. Average of given numbers $= \left(\frac{354+281+623+518+447+702+876}{7}\right) = \frac{3801}{7} = 543.$

Ex. 2. ***The body weight of six boys is recorded as 54 kg, 64 kg, 75 kg, 67 kg, 45 kg and 91 kg. What is the average body weight of all six boys?*** (Bank Recruitment, 2010)

Sol. Average body weight $= \left(\frac{54+64+75+67+45+91}{6}\right)$ kg $= \left(\frac{396}{6}\right)$ kg $= 66$ kg.

Ex. 3. ***There are six numbers 30, 72, 53, 68, x and 87, out of which x is unknown. The average of the numbers is 60. What is the value of x?*** (Bank Recruitment, 2010)

Sol. Average of given numbers $= \left(\frac{30+72+53+68+x+87}{6}\right) = \left(\frac{310+x}{6}\right)$.

$\therefore \quad \frac{310+x}{6} = 60 \Rightarrow 310 + x = 360 \Rightarrow x = 50.$

Hence, $x = 50$.

Ex. 4. ***Find the average of all prime numbers between 30 and 50.***

Sol. There are five prime numbers between 30 and 50.

They are 31, 37, 41, 43 and 47.

$\therefore$ Required average $= \left(\frac{31+37+41+43+47}{5}\right) = \frac{199}{5} = 39.8.$

Ex. 5. ***Find the average of first 40 natural numbers.***

Sol. Sum of first n natural numbers $= \frac{n(n+1)}{2}$.

So, sum of first 40 natural numbers $= \frac{40 \times 41}{2} = 820.$

$\therefore$ Required average $= \frac{820}{40} = 20.5.$

Ex. 6. ***Find the average of first 20 multiples of 7.***

Sol. Required average $= \frac{7(1+2+3+.....+20)}{20} = \left(\frac{7 \times 20 \times 21}{20 \times 2}\right) = \left(\frac{147}{2}\right) = 73.5.$

Ex. 7. ***A man bought 5 shirts at ₹ 450 each, 4 trousers at ₹ 750 each and 12 pairs of shoes at ₹ 750 each. What is the average expenditure per article?*** (R.R.B., 2006)

Sol. Total expenditure = ₹ $(5 \times 450 + 4 \times 750 + 12 \times 750)$ = ₹ $(2250 + 3000 + 9000)$ = ₹ 14250.

Number of articles = (5 + 4 + 12) = 21.

$\therefore$ Average expenditure = ₹$\left(\frac{14250}{21}\right)$ = ₹$\frac{4750}{7}$ = ₹ 678.57.

Ex. 8. ***13 chairs and 5 tables were bought for ₹ 8280. If the average cost of a table be ₹ 1227, what is the average cost of a chair?*** **(S.S.C., 2005)**

Sol. Total cost of 5 tables = ₹ (1227 × 5) = ₹ 6135.

Total cost of 13 chairs = ₹ (8280 – 6135) = ₹ 2145.

$\therefore$ Average cost of a chair = ₹$\left(\frac{2145}{13}\right)$ = ₹ 165.

Ex. 9. ***The average of five consecutive numbers A, B, C, D and E is 48. What is the product of A and E?*** **(Bank Recruitment, 2008)**

Sol. Let the numbers A, B, C, D and E be x, $(x + 1)$, $(x + 2)$, $(x + 3)$ and $(x + 4)$ respectively. Then,

$$\frac{x+(x+1)+(x+2)+(x+3)+(x+4)}{5} = 48 \Rightarrow 5x + 10 = 240 \Rightarrow 5x = 230 \Rightarrow x = 46.$$

So, A = x = 46 and E = $(x + 4)$ = 50.

$\therefore$ Required product = 46 × 50 = 2300.

Ex. 10. ***The average monthly expenditure of a family was ₹ 2200 during the first 3 months; ₹ 2250 during the next 4 months and ₹ 3120 during the last 5 months of a year. If the total savings during the year were ₹ 1260, find the average monthly income of the family.*** **(M.A.T., 2006)**

Sol. Total yearly expenditure = ₹ (2200 × 3 + 2250 × 4 + 3120 × 5)

= ₹ (6600 + 9000 + 15600) = ₹ 31200.

Total yearly savings = ₹ 1260.

Total yearly income = ₹ (31200 + 1260) = ₹ 32460.

$\therefore$ Average monthly income = ₹$\left(\frac{32460}{12}\right)$ = ₹ 2705.

Ex. 11. ***Six persons went to a hotel for taking their meals. Five of them spent ₹ 32 each on their meals while the sixth person spent ₹ 80 more than the average expenditure of all the six. What was the total money spent by all the persons?*** **(C.P.O., 2006)**

Sol. Let the average expenditure of all the six be ₹ x.

Then, $32 \times 5 + (x + 80) = 6x \Rightarrow 240 + x = 6x \Rightarrow 5x = 240 \Rightarrow x = 48$.

$\therefore$ Total money spent = $6x$ = ₹ (6 × 48) = ₹ 288.

Ex. 12. ***The average age of a man and his son is 40 years. The ratio of their ages is 11 : 5 respectively. What is the son's age?*** **(Bank Recruitment, 2009)**

Sol. Let the ages of the man and his son be $11x$ and $5x$ years respectively.

Then, average age = $\left(\frac{11x+5x}{2}\right)$ years = $8x$ years. $\therefore 8x = 40 \Rightarrow x = 5$.

Hence, son's age = $5x$ = 25 years.

Ex. 13. ***Of the three numbers, second is twice the first and is also thrice the third. If the average of three numbers is 44, what is the largest number?*** **(M.B.A., 2007)**

Sol. Let the third number be x. Then, second number = $3x$.

First number = $\frac{3x}{2}$.

$$\therefore\ x + 3x + \frac{3x}{2} = 44 \times 3 \Rightarrow \frac{11x}{2} = 132 \Rightarrow x = \left(\frac{132 \times 2}{11}\right) = 24.$$

Hence, largest number = $3x$ = (3 × 24) = 72.

Ex. 14. ***The average of five numbers is 58. The average of the first two numbers is 48.5 and the average of last two numbers is 53.5. What is the third number?*** (Bank P.O., 2009)

Sol. Third number = (Sum of 5 numbers) – (Sum of 4 numbers)

= (58 × 5) – [(48.5 × 2) + (53.5 × 2)]

= 290 – (97 + 107) = 290 – 204 = 86.

Ex. 15. ***The average of marks of 13 papers is 40. The average of marks of the first 7 papers is 42 and that of the last 7 papers is 35. What are the marks of the seventh paper?*** (C.P.F., 2007)

Sol. Marks in the seventh paper = (42 × 7 + 35 × 7 – 40 × 13)

= (294 + 245 – 520) = 539 – 520 = 19.

Ex. 16. ***The average age of A and B is 20 years. If A is replaced by C, the average age becomes 19 years and if B is replaced by C, the average age becomes 21 years. Find the ages of A, B and C.*** (S.S.C., 2006)

Sol. Clearly, average age of A and B = 20 years;

average age of *B* and *C* = 19 years;

average age of *A* and *C* = 21 years.

Sum of ages of *A* and *B* = (20 × 2) years = 40 years ...(*i*)

Sum of ages of *B* and *C* = (19 × 2) years = 38 years ...(*ii*)

Sum of ages of *A* and *C* = (21 × 2) years = 42 years ...(*iii*)

Adding (*i*), (*ii*) and (*iii*), we get:

2 (Sum of ages of *A*, *B* and *C*) = 120 years

⇒ (Sum of ages of *A*, *B* and *C*) = 60 years ...(*iv*)

Subtracting (*i*) from (*iv*), we get: C's age = (60 – 40) yrs = 20 years

Subtracting (*ii*) from (*iv*), we get: A's age = (60 – 38) yrs = 22 years

Subtracting (*iii*) from (*iv*), we get: B's age = (60 – 42) yrs = 18 years

Ex. 17. ***In a class there are 50 students. Their average weight is 45 kg. When a student leaves the class, the average is reduced by 100 g. Find the weight of the student who left the class.*** (R.R.B., 2006)

Sol. Total weight of 50 students = (45 × 50) kg = 2250 kg.

Average weight of 49 students = (45 kg – 100 g) = 44.9 kg.

Total weight of 49 students = (44.9 × 49) kg = 2200.1 kg.

∴ Weight of the student who left the class = (2250 – 2200.1) kg = 49.9 kg.

Ex. 18. ***The average age of a class of 39 students is 15 years. If the age of the teacher be included, then the average increases by 3 months. Find the age of the teacher.***

Sol. Total age of 39 persons = (39 × 15) years = 585 years.

Average age of 40 persons = 15 years 3 months = $\frac{61}{4}$ years.

Total age of 40 persons = $\left(\frac{61}{4} \times 40\right)$ years = 610 years.

∴ Age of the teacher = (610 – 585) years = 25 years.

Ex. 19. ***The average of 11 players of a cricket team is increased by 2 months when two of them aged 18 years and 20 years are replaced by two new players. Find the average age of the new players.*** (S.S.C., 2007)

Sol. Total age increased = (2 × 11) months = 22 months = 1 years 10 months.

Sum of ages of two new players = (18 years + 20 years + 1 years 10 months)

= 39 yrs 10 months.

∴ Required average = $\left(\frac{\text{39 years 10 months}}{2}\right)$ = 19 years 11 months.

Ex. 20. ***The average age of a class was 15 years. When 5 boys whose average age was 12 years 6 months were admitted in the class, the average was reduced by 6 months. How many students were there in the class originally?*** (P.C.S., 2008)

Sol. Let the original number of students in the class be *x*. Then,

$15x + 12\frac{1}{2} \times 5 = 14\frac{1}{2}(x+5) \Rightarrow 15x + \frac{25}{2} \times 5 = \frac{29}{2}x + \frac{29}{2} \times 5 \Rightarrow \frac{x}{2} = 10 \Rightarrow x = 20.$

Hence, required number of students = 20.

Ex. 21. ***A batsman makes a score of 87 runs in the 17th inning and thus increases his average by 3. Find his average after 17th inning.***

Sol. Let the average after 17th inning = x.

Then, average after 16th inning = $(x - 3)$.

$\therefore$ $16(x - 3) + 87 = 17x$ or $x = (87 - 48) = 39$.

Ex. 22. ***The batting average for 40 innings of a cricket player is 50 runs. His highest score in an innings exceeds his lowest score by 172 runs. If these two innings are excluded, the average score of the remaining 38 innings is 48 runs. Find his highest score in an innings.*** **(S.S.C., 2006)**

Sol. Let the highest score be x. Then, lowest score = $(x - 172)$.

$\therefore$ $x + (x - 172) = 50 \times 40 - 48 \times 38 \Rightarrow 2x - 172 = 2000 - 1824 = 176$

$\Rightarrow 2x = 348 \Rightarrow x = 174$.

Hence, highest score in an innings = 174.

Ex. 23. ***10 years ago, the average age of a family of 4 members was 24 years. Since then, two children having been born, still the average age of the family is the same today. If the two children differ in age by 2 years, find the present age of the younger child.*** **(S.S.C., 2007)**

Sol. Total age of 4 members, 10 years ago = (24×4) years = 96 years.

Total age of 4 members now = $(96 + 10 \times 4)$ years = 136 years.

Total age of 6 members now = (24×6) years = 144 years.

Sum of the ages of 2 children = $(144 - 136)$ years = 8 years.

Let the age of the younger child be x years.

Then, age of the elder child = $(x + 2)$ years.

So, $x + x + 2 = 8 \Rightarrow 2x = 6 \Rightarrow x = 3$.

$\therefore$ Age of the younger child = 3 years.

Ex. 24. ***Distance between two stations A and B is 778 km. A train covers the journey from A to B at 84 km per hour and returns back to A with a uniform speed of 56 km per hour. Find the average speed of the train during the whole journey.***

Sol. Required average speed $= \left(\frac{2xy}{x+y}\right)$ km/hr $= \frac{2 \times 84 \times 56}{(84+56)}$ km/hr

$= \left(\frac{2 \times 84 \times 56}{140}\right)$ km/hr = 67.2 km/hr.

Ex. 25. ***The average salary of workers of a factory is ₹ 6000, while the average salary of 150 technicians is ₹ 12000 and that of non-technicians is ₹ 3750. Find the total number of workers in the factory.***

Sol. Let the total number of workers be x. Then,

$6000x = (12000 \times 150) + 3750(x - 150) \Rightarrow 2250x = 1237500 \Rightarrow x = 550$.

Hence, total number of workers in the factory = 550.

Ex. 26. ***The average score of girls in class X examination in a school is 73 and that of boys is 71. The average score in class X of that school is 71.8. Find the percentage of the number of girls and boys in class X of the school.*** **(Campus Recruitment, 2006, 2009; M.A.T., 2003, 06; S.S.C., 2008)**

Sol. Let the number of boys in the class be x and the number of girls be y.

Then, $71x + 73y = 71.8(x + y) \Rightarrow 0.8x = 1.2y \Rightarrow x = \frac{3}{2}y$.

Percentage of boys $= \left[\frac{x}{(x+y)} \times 100\right]\% = \left[\frac{\frac{3}{2}y}{\left(\frac{3}{2}y + y\right)} \times 100\right]\%$

$= \left(\frac{3y}{2} \times \frac{2}{5y} \times 100\right)\% = 60\%$.

Percentage of girls = $(100 - 60)\% = 40\%$.

EXERCISE

(OBJECTIVE TYPE QUESTIONS)

Directions: ***Mark (✓) against the correct answer:***

1. The body weight of seven students of a class is recorded as 54 kg, 78 kg, 43 kg, 82 kg, 67 kg, 42 kg and 75 kg. What is the average body weight of all the seven students? **(Bank Recruitment, 2010)**
   (*a*) 63 kg (*b*) 69 kg
   (*c*) 71 kg (*d*) 73 kg
   (*e*) None of these
2. Find the average of the following sets of scores:
   385, 441, 876, 221, 536, 46, 291, 428 **(Bank Recruitment, 2009)**
   (*a*) 221 (*b*) 403
   (*c*) 428 (*d*) 536
   (*e*) None of these
3. The monthly incomes of five persons are ₹ 1132, ₹ 1140, ₹ 1144, ₹ 1136 and ₹ 1148 respectively. What is their arithmetic mean? **(P.C.S., 2009)**
   (*a*) ₹ 1100 (*b*) ₹ 1120
   (*c*) ₹ 1132 (*d*) ₹ 1140
4. Among five people with monthly income (in ₹) 15000, 26000, 16000, 19000 and 50000, how many will have income less than the mean income of five people? **(P.C.S., 2006)**
   (*a*) 1 (*b*) 2
   (*c*) 3 (*d*) 4
5. The arithmetic mean of 15 numbers is 41.4. Then the sum of these numbers is **(P.C.S., 2010)**
   (*a*) 414 (*b*) 420
   (*c*) 620 (*d*) 621
6. If $25a + 25b = 115$, what is the average of a and b? **(Bank P.O., 2009)**
   (*a*) 2.5 (*b*) 3.4
   (*c*) 4.5 (*d*) 4.6
   (*e*) None of these
7. The following table shows the number of working hours and the number of employees employed in a small scale industry.

No. of working hours	No. of employees
3 – 5	7
5 – 7	10
7 – 9	18
9 – 11	57
11 – 13	14
13 – 15	8

   The average number of working hours of an employee is
   (*a*) 8.5 (*b*) 9.5
   (*c*) 10.5 (*d*) None of these
8. If the arithmetic mean of 0, 5, 4, 3 is a, that of – 1, 0, 1, 5, 4, 3 is b and that of 5, 4, 3 is c, then the relation between a, b and c is **(Hotel Management, 2007)**
   (*a*) $a = b = c$ (*b*) $a : b : c = 3 : 2 : 4$
   (*c*) $4a = 5b = c$ (*d*) $a + b + c = 12$
9. Kunal bought 65 books for ₹ 1050 from one shop and 50 books for ₹ 1020 from another. What is the average price he paid per book? **(Bank P.O., 2008)**
   (*a*) ₹ 18 (*b*) ₹ 18.20
   (*c*) ₹ 24 (*d*) ₹ 36.40
   (*e*) None of these
10. The average of the reciprocals of x and y is **(Campus Recruitment, 2010)**
    (*a*) $\frac{(x+y)}{(x-y)}$ (*b*) $\frac{(x+y)}{2xy}$
    (*c*) $\frac{2(x+y)}{xy}$ (*d*) $\frac{2xy}{(x+y)}$
11. The average of two numbers is XY. If one number is X, the other is **(R.R.B., 2006)**
    (*a*) $\frac{Y}{2}$ (*b*) Y
    (*c*) $2XY - X$ (*d*) $X(Y - 1)$
12. There are five boxes in a cargo hold. The weight of the first box is 200 kg and the weight of the second box is 20% more than the weight of the third box, whose weight is 25% more than the first box's weight. The fourth box at 350 kg is 30% lighter than the fifth box. The difference in the average weight of the four heaviest boxes and the four lightest boxes is **(M.A.T., 2005)**
    (*a*) 37.5 kg (*b*) 51.5 kg
    (*c*) 75 kg (*d*) 112.5 kg
13. In Arun's opinion, his weight is greater than 65 kg but less than 72 kg. His brother does not agree with Arun and he thinks that Arun's weight is greater than 60 kg but less than 70 kg. His mother's view is that his weight cannot be greater than 68 kg. If all of them are correct in their estimation, what is the average of different probable weights of Arun?
    (*a*) 67 kg (*b*) 68 kg
    (*c*) 69 kg (*d*) Data inadequate
    (*e*) None of these
14. The average of 20 numbers is zero. Of them, at the most, how many may be greater than zero ? **(Hotel Management, 2002)**
    (*a*) 0 (*b*) 1
    (*c*) 10 (*d*) 19

15. The mean of the first ten even natural numbers is **(Hotel Management, 2010)**
(*a*) 9 (*b*) 10
(*c*) 11 (*d*) 12

16. The arithmetic mean of first 11 natural numbers is **(P.C.S. 2009)**
(*a*) 5 (*b*) 5.5
(*c*) 6.0 (*d*) 6.5

17. Find the average of all the numbers between 6 and 34 which are divisible by 5.
(*a*) 18 (*b*) 20
(*c*) 24 (*d*) 30

18. The average of the first five multiples of 3 is
(*a*) 3 (*b*) 9
(*c*) 12 (*d*) 15

19. The average of the first nine prime numbers is
(*a*) 9 (*b*) 11
(*c*) $11\frac{1}{9}$ (*d*) $11\frac{2}{9}$

20. A student was asked to find the arithmetic mean of the numbers 3, 11, 7, 9, 15, 13, 8, 19, 17, 21, 14 and *x*. He found the mean to be 12. What should be the number in place of *x*?
(*a*) 3 (*b*) 7
(*c*) 17 (*d*) 31

21. The average of 2, 7, 6 and *x* is 5 and the average of 18, 1, 6, *x* and *y* is 10. What is the value of *y* ?
(*a*) 5 (*b*) 10
(*c*) 20 (*d*) 30

22. The total marks obtained by a student in Physics, Chemistry and Mathematics together is 120 more than the marks obtained by him in Chemistry. What is the average marks obtained by him in Physics and Mathematics together? **(Bank P.O., 2010)**
(*a*) 40 (*b*) 60
(*c*) 120 (*d*) Cannot be determined
(*e*) None of these

23. The average of the first 100 positive integers is **(S.S.C., 2010)**
(*a*) 49.5 (*b*) 50.5
(*c*) 51 (*d*) 100

24. The average of odd numbers up to 100 is **(S.S.C., 2010)**
(*a*) 49 (*b*) 49.5
(*c*) 50 (*d*) 50.5

25. In a family, the average age of a father and a mother is 35 years. The average age of the father, mother and their only son is 27 years. What is the age of the son? **(S.S.C., 2010)**
(*a*) 10 years (*b*) 10.5 years
(*c*) 11 years (*d*) 12 years

26. The average of X_1, X_2 and X_3 is 14. Twice the sum of X_2 and X_3 is 30. What is the value of X_1?
(*a*) 12 (*b*) 16
(*c*) 20 (*d*) 27

27. The average of x_1, x_2, x_3 and x_4 is 16. Half the sum of x_2, x_3, x_4 is 23. What is the value of x_1? **(R.R.B., 2006)**
(*a*) 17 (*b*) 18
(*c*) 19 (*d*) 20

28. If the mean of 5 observations x, $x + 2$, $x + 4$, $x + 6$ and $x + 8$ is 11, then the mean of the last three observations is
(*a*) 11 (*b*) 13
(*c*) 15 (*d*) 17

29. If the mean of a, b, c is M and $ab + bc + ca = 0$, then the mean of a^2, b^2, c^2 is
(*a*) M^2 (*b*) $3M^2$
(*c*) $6M^2$ (*d*) $9M^2$

30. The average of the two-digit numbers, which remain the same when the digits interchange their positions, is
(*a*) 33 (*b*) 44
(*c*) 55 (*d*) 66

31. Company C sells a line of 25 products with an average retail price of ₹ 1200. If none of these products sells for less than ₹ 420 and exactly 10 of the products sell for less than ₹ 1000, then what is the greatest possible selling price of the most expensive product? **(M.A.T., 2006)**
(*a*) ₹ 2600 (*b*) ₹ 3900
(*c*) ₹ 7800 (*d*) ₹ 11800

32. The average sale of a car dealership was 15 cars per week. After a promotional scheme the average sale increased to 21 cars per week. The percentage increase in the sale of cars was **(M.A.T., 2010)**
(*a*) 39.33% (*b*) 40%
(*c*) $42\frac{6}{7}$% (*d*) 140%

33. The mean of 1^2, 2^2, 3^2, 4^2, 5^2, 6^2, 7^2 is
(*a*) 10 (*b*) 20
(*c*) 30 (*d*) 40

34. If *a*, *b*, *c*, *d*, *e* are five consecutive odd numbers, their average is
(*a*) $5(a + 4)$ (*b*) $\frac{abcde}{5}$
(*c*) $5(a + b + c + d + e)$ (*d*) None of these

35. The average of a non-zero number and its square is 5 times the number. The number is
(*a*) 9 (*b*) 17
(*c*) 29 (*d*) 295

36. Total of Arun's marks in Sanskrit and Mathematics together are 80 more than his marks in Science. His average marks in the three subjects are 100. What are his marks in Science?

(a) 80 (b) 110
(c) 120 (d) Data inadequate
(e) None of these

37. The arithmetic mean of the series 1, 2, 4, 8, 16,..., 2^n is

(a) $\frac{2^n - 1}{n+1}$ (b) $\frac{2^n + 1}{n}$
(c) $\frac{2^n - 1}{n}$ (d) $\frac{2^{n+1} - 1}{n+1}$

38. The average of two numbers is 6.5 and square root of their product is 6. What are the numbers? (S.S.C., 2006)

(a) 11 and 2 (b) 8 and 5
(c) 9 and 4 (d) 10 and 3

39. Of four numbers whose average is 60, the first is one-fourth of the sum of the last three. The first number is (S.S.C., 2006)

(a) 15 (b) 42
(c) 45 (d) 48

40. The average of 4 positive integers is 59. The highest integer is 83 and the lowest integer is 29. The difference between the remaining two integers is 28. Which of the following integers is higher of the remaining two integers? (Bank Recruitment, 2008)

(a) 39 (b) 48
(c) 76 (d) Cannot be determined
(e) None of these

41. The average of 7 consecutive numbers is 20. The largest of these numbers is

(a) 20 (b) 22
(c) 23 (d) 24

42. The average of five consecutive odd numbers is 95. What is the fourth number in the descending order? (Bank Recruitment, 2009)

(a) 91 (b) 95
(c) 97 (d) 99
(e) None of these

43. A, B, C and D are four consecutive even numbers respectively and their average is 65. What is the product of A and D? (Bank P.O., 2007)

(a) 3968 (b) 4092
(c) 4216 (d) 4352
(e) None of these

44. The sum of the three consecutive even numbers is 44 more than the average of these numbers. Which of the following is the third largest of these numbers? (Bank P.O., 2008)

(a) 16 (b) 18
(c) 24 (d) Cannot be determined
(e) None of these

45. The average marks of a student in 4 subjects is 75. If the student obtained 80 marks in the fifth subject, then the new average is (P.C.S., 2008)

(a) 72.5 (b) 76
(c) 77 (d) 77.5

46. The average age of the boys in a class is 16 years and that of the girls is 15 years. The average age for the whole class is

(a) 15 years
(b) 15.5 years
(c) 16 years
(d) Cannot be computed with the given information

47. The average annual income (in ₹) of certain agricultural workers is S and that of other workers is T. The number of agricultural workers is 11 times that of other workers. Then the average monthly income (in ₹) of all the workers is (S.S.C. 2004)

(a) $\frac{S+T}{2}$ (b) $\frac{S+11T}{2}$
(c) $\frac{1}{11S}+T$ (d) $\frac{11S+T}{12}$

48. A family consists of grandparents, parents and three grandchildren. The average age of the grandparents is 67 years, that of the parents is 35 years and that of the grandchildren is 6 years. What is the average age of the family?

(a) $28\frac{4}{7}$ years (b) $31\frac{5}{7}$ years
(c) $32\frac{1}{7}$ years (d) None of these

49. A library has an average of 510 visitors on Sundays and 240 on other days. The average number of visitors per day in a month of 30 days beginning with a Sunday is

(a) 250 (b) 276
(c) 280 (d) 285

50. In a class there are 32 boys and 28 girls. The average age of the boys in the class is 14 years and the average age of the girls in the class is 13 years. What is the average age of the whole class (rounded to two digits after decimal)? (NABARD, 2009)

(a) 12.51 (b) 13.42
(c) 13.50 (d) 13.53
(e) None of these

51. The average weight of 16 boys in a class is 50.25 kgs and that of the remaining 8 boys is 45.15 kgs. Find the average weight of all the boys in the class.

(*a*) 47.55 kgs (*b*) 48 kgs
(*c*) 48.55 kgs (*d*) 49.25 kgs

52. The mean of 5 observations is 60, the mean of 10 observations is 30 and the mean of 15 observations is 20. The mean of all the 30 observations is **(P.C.S., 2009)**

(*a*) 20 (*b*) 25
(*c*) 30 (*d*) 40

53. The average expenditure of a man for the first five months of a year is ₹ 5000 and for the next seven months it is ₹ 5400. He saves ₹ 2300 during the year. His average monthly income is **(C.P.O., 2007)**

(*a*) ₹ 5425 (*b*) ₹ 5446
(*c*) ₹ 5500 (*d*) ₹ 5600

54. A school has 4 sections of Chemistry in Class X having 40, 35, 45 and 42 students. The mean marks obtained in Chemistry test are 50, 60, 55 and 45 respectively for the 4 sections. Determine the overall average of marks per student. **(M.A.T., 2006)**

(*a*) 50.25 (*b*) 51.25
(*c*) 52.25 (*d*) 53.25

55. If the average of m numbers is n^2 and that of n numbers is m^2, then the average of $(m + n)$ numbers is **(S.S.C., 2008)**

(*a*) $m - n$ (*b*) mn
(*c*) $m + n$ (*d*) $\frac{m}{n}$

56. The average of five consecutive numbers is x. If the next two numbers are also included, how shall the average vary? **(M.A.T., 2005, C.P.O., 2006, C.P.F. 2008)**

(*a*) It shall increase by 1
(*b*) It shall remain the same
(*c*) It shall increase by 1.4
(*d*) It shall increase by 2

57. A person purchases 1 kg of tomatoes from each of the 4 places at the rate of 1 kg, 2 kg, 3 kg, 4 kg per rupee respectively. On an average, he has purchased x kg of tomatoes per rupee. Then the value of x is **(M.A.T., 2006)**

(*a*) 1.92 (*b*) 2
(*c*) 2.5 (*d*) None of these

58. In a certain factory there are five workers A, B, C, D and *E*. *A* can complete a work in 4 minutes, *B* in 5 minutes, *C* in 6 minutes, *D* in 10 minutes and *E* in 12 minutes. The average number of units of work completed per worker per minute will be **(P.C.S., 2009)**

(*a*) 0.16 (*b*) 0.172
(*c*) 0.80 (*d*) 0.87

59. A car owner buys petrol at ₹ 17, ₹ 19 and ₹ 20 per litre for three consecutive years. Compute the average cost per litre, if he spends ₹ 6460 per year.

(*a*) ₹ 18.49 (*b*) ₹ 18.58
(*c*) ₹ 19.2 (*d*) ₹ 21.66

60. The average of six numbers is x and the average of three of these is y. If the average of the remaining three is z, then

(*a*) $x = y + z$ (*b*) $2x = y + z$
(*c*) $x = 2y + 2z$ (*d*) None of these

61. Out of 9 persons, 8 persons spent ₹ 30 each for their meals. The ninth one spent ₹ 20 more than the average expenditure of all the nine. The total money spent by all of them was

(*a*) ₹ 260 (*b*) ₹ 290
(*c*) ₹ 292.50 (*d*) ₹ 400.50

62. There were 35 students in a hostel. If the number of the students is increased by 7, then the expenses of the mess increase by ₹ 42 per day, while the average expenditure per head diminishes by ₹ 1. The original expenditure of the mess per day was **(S.S.C., 2005)**

(*a*) ₹ 400 (*b*) ₹ 420
(*c*) ₹ 432 (*d*) ₹ 442

63. The average price of three items of furniture is ₹ 15000. If their prices are in the ratio 3 : 5 : 7, the price of the cheapest item is

(*a*) ₹ 9000 (*b*) ₹ 15000
(*c*) ₹ 18000 (*d*) ₹ 21000

64. Of the four numbers, the first is twice the second, the second is one-third of the third and the third is 5 times the fourth. The average of the numbers is 24.75. The largest of these numbers is

(*a*) 9 (*b*) 25
(*c*) 30 (*d*) None of these

65. Out of three numbers, the first is twice the second and is half of the third. If the average of the three numbers is 56, then difference of first and third numbers is **(S.S.C., 2005)**

(*a*) 12 (*b*) 20
(*c*) 24 (*d*) 48

66. Of the three numbers, the first is twice the second and the second is twice the third. The average of the reciprocal of the numbers is $\frac{7}{72}$. The numbers are :

(*a*) 16, 8, 4 (*b*) 20, 10, 5
(*c*) 24, 12, 6 (*d*) 36, 18, 9

67. Of the three numbers, the average of the first and the second is greater than the average of the second and the third by 15. What is the difference between the first and the third of the three numbers?

(*a*) 15 (*b*) 45
(*c*) 60 (*d*) Data inadequate
(*e*) None of these

68. The average of 50 numbers is 38. If the numbers 45 and 55 are discarded, then the average of the remaining numbers is (Hotel Management, 2008)
(a) 36.5 (b) 37
(c) 37.5 (d) 37.52

69. The mean of 5 numbers is 18. If one number is excluded, their mean is 16. Find the excluded number.
(a) 25 (b) 26
(c) 27 (d) 28

70. The average of 6 observations is 45.5. If one new observation is added to the previous observations, then the new average becomes 47. The new observation is (S.S.C., 2007)
(a) 46 (b) 50
(c) 56 (d) 58

71. The average age of 30 students in a class is 15 years. If 6 students of this class have the average age of 16 years, then the average age of the remaining 24 students would be
(a) 14 years (b) 14 years 3 months
(c) 14 years 6 months (d) 14 years 9 months

72. If the average temperature of first four days of the week was 39°C and the average temperature of the week was 40°C, then what was the average temperature of the last three days of the week? (R.R.B., 2006)
(a) 39.9°C (b) 40.9°C
(c) 41.3°C (d) 42.1°C

73. The average of 80 boys in a class is 15. The average age of a group of 15 boys in the class is 16 and the average age of another 25 boys in the class is 14. What is the average age of the remaining boys in the class? (Bank P.O., 2010)
(a) 14 (b) 14.75
(c) 15.25 (d) Cannot be determined
(e) None of these

74. The mean monthly salary paid to 75 workers in a factory is ₹ 5680. The mean salary of 25 of them is ₹ 5400 and that of 30 others is ₹ 5700. The mean salary of the remaining workers is (M.A.T., 2008)
(a) ₹ 5000 (b) ₹ 6000
(c) ₹ 7000 (d) ₹ 8000

75. 16 children are to be divided into two groups A and B of 10 and 6 children. The average percent marks obtained by the children of group A is 75 and the average percent marks of all the 16 children is 76. What is the average percent marks of children of group B ? (B.S.R.B., 2003)
(a) $77\frac{1}{3}$ (b) $77\frac{2}{3}$
(c) $78\frac{1}{3}$ (d) $78\frac{2}{3}$

76. The average marks of a student in 8 subjects is 87. Of these, the highest marks are 2 more than the one next in value. If these two subjects are eliminated, the average marks of the remaining subjects is 85. What are the highest marks now obtained by him? (M.A.T., 2008)
(a) 89 (b) 91
(c) 94 (d) 96

77. The batting average for 40 innings of a cricket player is 50 runs. His highest score exceeds his lowest score by 172 runs. If these two innings are excluded, the average of the remaining 38 innings is 48 runs. The highest score of the player is
(a) 165 runs (b) 170 runs
(c) 172 runs (d) 174 runs

78. In a cricket eleven, the average age of eleven players is 28 years. Out of these, the average ages of three groups of three players each are 25 years, 28 years and 30 years respectively. If in these groups the captain and the youngest player are not included and the captain is eleven years older than the youngest player, what is the age of the captain? (M.B.A., 2007)
(a) 33 years (b) 34 years
(c) 35 years (d) 36 years

79. The average price of 10 books is ₹ 12 while the average price of 8 of these books is ₹ 11.75. Of the remaining two books, if the price of one book is 60% more than the price of the other, what is the price of each of these two books ?
(a) ₹5, ₹7.50 (b) ₹8, ₹12
(c) ₹10, ₹16 (d) ₹12, ₹14

80. If the average of 5 numbers is 10, the number which should be added to make the average 12 is (P.C.S., 2009)
(a) 12 (b) 18
(c) 22 (d) 24

81. The average of runs of a cricket player of 10 innings was 32. How many runs must he make in his next innings so as to increase his average of runs by 4? (S.S.C., 2004)
(a) 2 (b) 4
(c) 70 (d) 76

82. A grocer has a sale of ₹ 6435, ₹ 6927, ₹ 6855, ₹ 7230 and ₹ 6562 for 5 consecutive months. How much sale must he have in the sixth month so that he gets an average sale of ₹ 6500?
(a) ₹ 4991 (b) ₹ 5991
(c) ₹ 6001 (d) ₹ 6991

83. A company produces on an average 4000 items per month for the first 3 months. How many items it must produce on an average per month over the next 9 months, to average 4375 items per month over the whole?
(a) 4500 (b) 4600
(c) 4680 (d) 4710

84. In the first 10 overs of a cricket game, the run rate was only 3.2. What should be the run rate in the remaining 40 overs to reach the target of 282 runs?

(a) 6.25 (b) 6.5
(c) 6.75 (d) 7

85. In a one-day cricket match the captain of one of the teams scored 30 runs more than the average runs scored by the remaining six batsmen of that team who batted in the match. If the total runs scored by all the batsmen of that team were 310, how many runs did the captain score?

(a) 50 (b) 60
(c) 70 (d) Cannot be determined
(e) None of these

86. In a group of 120 people, one-fifth are men, one-fourth are women and the rest children. The average age of women is five-sixth of the average age of men. Average age of children is one-fourth of the average age of men. If average age of men is 60 years, what is the average age of the group?

(a) 32.75 (b) 38.45
(c) 45.25 (d) 50.5

87. Visitors to a show were charged ₹ 15 each on the first day, ₹ 7.50 each on the second day and ₹ 2.50 each on the third day. The attendance on the three days was in the ratio 2 : 5 : 13. The average charge per person for the whole show was

(a) ₹ 5 (b) ₹ 6.33
(c) ₹ 7.50 (d) ₹ 9

88. In an examination, a pupil's average marks was 63 per paper. If he had obtained 20 more marks for his Geography paper and 2 more marks for his History paper, his average per paper would have been 65. How many papers were there in the examination? **(M.A.T., 2007)**

(a) 8 (b) 9
(c) 10 (d) 11

89. The average age of all the students of a class is 18 years. The average age of boys of the class is 20 years and that of the girls is 15 years. If the number of girls in the class is 20, then find the number of boys in the class. **(M.A.T., 2008)**

(a) 15 (b) 30
(c) 45 (d) 50

90. There are 3 groups of students, each containing 25, 50 and 25 students respectively. The mean marks obtained by the first two groups are 60 and 55. The combined mean of all the three groups is 58. What is the mean of the marks scored by the third group?

(a) 52 (b) 57
(c) 58 (d) 60
(e) 62

91. A student obtained 60, 75 and 85 marks respectively in three monthly examinations in Physics and 95 marks in the final examination. The three monthly examinations are of equal weightage whereas the final examination is weighted twice as much as a monthly examination. His average marks in Physics are

(a) 78.75 (b) 79
(c) 82 (d) 85

92. A student obtained the following marks in percentages in his semester examination English 50, Maths 65, Statistics 70, Economics 58 and Accountancy 63. The weights of these subjects are 2, 2, 1, 1 and 1 respectively. What is the weighted arithmetic mean?

(a) 60 (b) 61
(c) 62 (d) 63

93. The average of 8 numbers is 20. The average of first two numbers is $15\frac{1}{2}$ and that of the next three is $21\frac{1}{3}$. If the sixth number be less than the seventh and eighth numbers by 4 and 7 respectively, then the eighth number is: **(S.S.C. 2004)**

(a) 18 (b) 22
(c) 25 (d) 27

94. If the arithmetic mean of seventy-five numbers is calculated, it is 35. If each number is increased by 5, then mean of new numbers is :

(a) 30 (b) 40
(c) 70 (d) 90

95. The average of ten numbers is 7. If each number is multiplied by 12, then the average of the new set of numbers is :

(a) 7 (b) 19
(c) 82 (d) 84

96. Average of ten positive numbers is $\overline{x}$. If each number is increased by 10%, then $\overline{x}$

(a) remains unchanged (b) may decrease
(c) may increase (d) is increased by 10%

97. The average height of 35 girls in a class was calculated as 160 cm. It was later found that the height of one of the girls in the class was wrongly written as 144 cm, whereas her actual height was 104 cm. What is the actual average height of the girls in the class? (rounded off to 2 digits after decimal) **(Bank P.O., 2010)**

(a) 158.54 cm (b) 158.74 cm
(c) 159.56 cm (d) 159.86 cm
(e) None of these

98. The mean of 25 observations was found to be 78.4. But later on it was found that 96 was misread as 69. The correct mean is **(M.A.T., 2007)**

(*a*) 76.54 (*b*) 78.4
(*c*) 79.48 (*d*) 81.32

99. The average marks in Science subject of a class of 20 students is 68. If the marks of two students were misread as 48 and 65 instead of the actual marks 72 and 61 respectively, what would be the correct average? **(Bank P.O., 2009)**

(*a*) 66 (*b*) 68.5
(*c*) 69 (*d*) 69.5
(*e*) 70

100. The average of 10 numbers is 40.2. Later it is found that two numbers have been wrongly added. The first is 18 greater than the actual number and the second number added is 13 instead of 33. Find the correct average.

(*a*) 40.2 (*b*) 40.4
(*c*) 40.6 (*d*) 40.8

101. A pupil's marks were wrongly entered as 83 instead of 63. Due to that the average marks for the class got increased by half. The number of pupils in the class is

(*a*) 10 (*b*) 20
(*c*) 40 (*d*) 73

102. While calculating the average of a batsman as 36 in 100 matches that he played, one of the scores 90 was incorrectly noted as 40. The percentage error is **(M.A.T., 2010)**

(*a*) 0.5% (*b*) 1.21%
(*c*) 1.34% (*d*) 1.36%

103. The average age of seven boys sitting in a row facing North is 26 years. If the average age of the first three boys is 19 years and the average age of the last three boys is 32 years, what is the age of the boy who is sitting in the middle of the row? **(Bank P.O., 2010)**

(*a*) 24 years (*b*) 28 years
(*c*) 29 years (*d*) 31 years
(*e*) None of these

104. The average of five numbers is 306.4. The average of the first two numbers is 431 and the average of the last two numbers is 214.5. What is the third number? **(Bank P.O., 2008)**

(*a*) 52 (*b*) 108
(*c*) 321 (*d*) Cannot be determined
(*e*) None of these

105. The average marks obtained by 22 candidates in an examination are 45. The average marks of the first ten are 55 and that of the last eleven are 40. The number of marks obtained by the 11th candidate is **(S.S.C., 2006)**

(*a*) 0 (*b*) 45
(*c*) 47.5 (*d*) 50

106. The average of 11 numbers is 10.9. If the average of the first six numbers is 10.5 and that of the last six numbers is 11.4, then the middle number is :

(*a*) 11 (*b*) 11.3
(*c*) 11.4 (*d*) 11.5

107. The average temperature for the first four days of a week is 40.2° C and that of the last four days is 41.3° C. If the average temperature for the whole week is 40.6° C, then the temperature on the fourth day is **(M.A.T. 2005)**

(*a*) 40.8°C (*b*) 41.3°C
(*c*) 41.8°C (*d*) 38.5°C

108. The average weight of three boys *A*, *B* and *C* is $54\frac{1}{3}$ kg, while the average weight of three boys *B*, *D* and *E* is 53 kg. What is the average weight of *A*, *B*, *C*, *D* and *E* ?

(*a*) 52.4 kg (*b*) 53.2 kg
(*c*) 53.8 kg (*d*) Data inadequate
(*e*) None of these

109. The average of the ages of Sumit, Krishna and Rishabh is 43 and the average of the ages of Sumit, Rishabh and Rohit is 49. If Rohit is 54 years old, what is Krishna's age? **(S.B.I.P.O., 2008)**

(*a*) 24 years (*b*) 36 years
(*c*) 45 years (*d*) Cannot be determined
(*e*) None of these

110. The mean temperature of Monday to Wednesday was 37°C and of Tuesday to Thursday was 34°C. If the temperature on Thursday was $\frac{4}{5}$ that of Monday, the temperature on Thursday was

(M.B.A. 2006, L.I.C.A.A.O. 2007, P.C.S., 2008)

(*a*) 34°C (*b*) 35.5°C
(*c*) 36°C (*d*) 36.5°C

111. The average temperature of the town in the first four days of a month was 58 degrees. The average for the second, third, fourth and fifth days was 60 degrees. If the temperatures of the first and fifth days were in the ratio 7 : 8, then what is the temperature on the fifth day? **(N.M.A.T., 2003)**

(*a*) 64 degrees (*b*) 62 degrees
(*c*) 56 degrees (*d*) None of these

112. The average weight of *A*, *B* and *C* is 45 kg. If the average weight of *A* and *B* be 40 kg and that of *B* and *C* be 43 kg, then the weight of B is: **(S.S.C., 2004)**

(*a*) 17 kg (*b*) 20 kg
(*c*) 26 kg (*d*) 31 kg

113. The average monthly income of P and Q is ₹ 5050. The average monthly income of Q and R is ₹ 6250 and the average monthly income of P and R is ₹ 5200. The monthly income of P is (R.R.B., 2004)
(a) ₹ 3500 (b) ₹ 4000
(c) ₹ 4050 (d) ₹ 5000

114. Average age of ten persons learning yoga is 32 years. When the age of their instructor is added, the average age becomes 34 years. The age of their instructor is (CLAT, 2010)
(a) 46 years (b) 52 years
(c) 54 years (d) 56 years

115. The average monthly income of a family of four earning members was ₹ 15130. One of the daughters in the family got married and left home, so the average monthly income of the family came down to ₹ 14660. What is the monthly income of the married daughter? (Bank P.O., 2009)
(a) ₹ 12000 (b) ₹ 15350
(c) ₹ 16540 (d) Cannot be determined
(e) None of these

116. The average weight of a class of 24 students is 35 kg. If the weight of the teacher be included, the average rises by 400 g. The weight of the teacher is
(a) 45 kg (b) 50 kg
(c) 53 kg (d) 55 kg

117. The average age of the mother and her six children is 12 years which is reduced by 5 years if the age of the mother is excluded. How old is the mother?
(a) 40 years (b) 42 years
(c) 48 years (d) 50 years

118. The average weight of 8 men is increased by 1.5 kg when one of the men, who weighs 65 kg is replaced by a new man. The weight of the new man is (R.R.B. 2006)
(a) 70 kg (b) 74 kg
(c) 76 kg (d) 77 kg

119. There were 24 students in a class. One of them, who was 18 years old, left the class and his place was filled up by a newcomer. If the average of the class thereby, was lowered by one month, the age of the newcomer is (S.S.C. 2007)
(a) 14 years (b) 15 years
(c) 16 years (d) 17 years

120. The average weight of 45 students in a class is 52 kg. Five of them whose average weight is 48 kg leave the class and other 5 students whose average weight is 54 kg join the class. What is the new average weight (in kg) of the class?
(a) $52\frac{1}{3}$ (b) $52\frac{1}{2}$
(c) $52\frac{2}{3}$ (d) None of these

121. The average height of 25 boys is 1.4 m. When 5 boys leave the group, then the average height increases by 0.15 m. What is the average height of the 5 boys who leave ?
(a) 0.8 m (b) 0.9 m
(c) 0.95 m (d) 1.05 m

122. The average of 11 players of a cricket team is decreased by 2 months when two of them aged 17 years and 20 years are replaced by two new players. The average age of the new players is (S.S.C. 2005)
(a) 17 years 1 month (b) 17 years 7 months
(c) 17 years 11 months (d) 18 years 3 months

123. The average age of an adult class is 40 years. 12 new students with an average age of 32 years join the class, thereby decreasing the average by 4 years. The original strength of the class was
(Campus Rec. 2011; M.B.A. 2006; M.A.T. 2007)
(a) 10 (b) 11
(c) 12 (d) 15

124. In a class with a certain number of students, if one student weighing 50 kg is added then the average weight of the class increases by 1 kg. If one more student weighing 50 kg is added, then the average weight of the class increases by 1.5 kg over the original average. What is the original average weight (in kg) of the class?
(a) 2 (b) 4
(c) 46 (d) 47

125. When 15 is included in a list of natural numbers, their mean is increased by 2. When 1 is included in this new list, the mean of the numbers in the new list is decreased by 1. How many numbers were there in the original list? (A.A.O. Exam, 2010)
(a) 4 (b) 5
(c) 6 (d) 8

126. The captain of a cricket team of 11 members is 26 years old and the wicket keeper is 3 years older. If the ages of these two are excluded, the average age of the remaining players is one year less than the average age of the whole team. What is the average age of the team?
(a) 23 years (b) 24 years
(c) 25 years (d) None of these

127. A batsman makes a score of 84 runs in the 21st inning and thus increases his average by 2 runs. His average after 21st inning is (P.C.S., 2009)
(a) 24 (b) 34
(c) 44 (d) 54

128. A cricketer whose bowling average is 12.4 runs per wicket takes 5 wickets for 26 runs and thereby decreases his average by 0.4. The number of wickets taken by him till the last match was
(a) 64 (b) 72
(c) 80 (d) 85

129. A team of 8 persons joins in a shooting competition. The best marksman scored 85 points. If he had scored 92 points, the average score for the team would have been 84. The number of points, the team scored was

(a) 588 (b) 645
(c) 665 (d) 672

130. A motorist travels to a place 150 km away at an average speed of 50 km / hr and returns at 30 km / hr. His average speed for the whole journey in km / hr is (L.I.C.A.D.O., 2008)

(a) 35 (b) 37
(c) 37.5 (d) 40

131. The average weight of 3 men A, B and C is 84 kg. Another man D joins the group and the average now becomes 80 kg. If another man E, whose weight is 3 kg more than that of D, replaces A, then the average weight of B, C, D and E becomes 79 kg. The weight of A is

(a) 70 kg (b) 72 kg
(c) 75 kg (d) 80 kg

132. The average age of a husband and his wife was 23 years at the time of their marriage. After five years they have a one-year old child. The average age of the family now is

(a) 19 years (b) 23 years
(c) 28.5 years (d) 29.3 years

133. Four years ago, the average age of A and B was 18 years. At present the average age of A, B and C is 24 years. What would be the age of C after 8 years? (R.R.B., 2006)

(a) 25 years (b) 28 years
(c) 32 years (d) 36 years

134. Five years ago the average age of A, B, C, D was 45 years. By including X the present average of all the five is 49 years. Then the present age of X is (P.C.S., 2009)

(a) 40 years (b) 45 years
(c) 48 years (d) 64 years

135. The average age of husband, wife and their child 3 years ago was 27 years and that of wife and the child 5 years ago was 20 years. The present age of the husband is

(a) 35 years (b) 40 years
(c) 50 years (d) None of these

136. The average age of a husband and wife at the time of their marriage was 25 years. A son was born to them two years after their marriage. The present average age of all three of them is 24 years. How many years is it since the couple got married?

(a) 5 years (b) 6 years
(c) 8 years (d) 9 years

137. When the average age of a couple and their son was 42 years, the son married and got a child after one year. When the child was 5 years old, the average age of the family became 36 years. What was the age of daughter-in-law at the time of their marriage? (S.S.C., 2006)

(a) 23 years (b) 24 years
(c) 25 years (d) 26 years

138. Four years ago, the average age of a family of four persons was 18 years. During this period, a baby was born. Today if the average age of the family is still 18 years, the age of the baby is (P.C.S., 2009)

(a) 1.2 years (b) 2 years
(c) 2.5 years (d) 3 years

139. After replacing an old member by a new member, it was found that the average age of five members of a club is the same as it was 3 years ago. What is the difference between the ages of the replaced and the new member?

(a) 2 years (b) 4 years
(c) 8 years (d) 15 years

140. The average age of 3 children in a family is 20% of the average age of the father and the eldest child. The total age of the mother and the youngest child is 39 years. If the father's age is 26 years, what is the age of the second child? (M.A.T., 2009)

(a) 15 years (b) 18 years
(c) 20 years (d) Cannot be determined

141. The average age of a group of persons going for picnic is 16 years. Twenty new persons with an average age of 15 years join the group on the spot due to which their average age becomes 15.5 years. The number of persons initially going for picnic is

(a) 5 (b) 10
(c) 20 (d) 30

142. Ten years ago, the ages of the members of a joint family of eight people added up to 231 years. Three years later, one member died at the age of 60 years and a child was born during the same year. After another three years, one more member died, again at 60, and a child was born during the same year. The current average of this eight-member joint family is nearest to (C.A.T., 2007)

(a) 21 years (b) 22 years
(c) 23 years (d) 24 years
(e) 25 years

143. Mr. Joe's family consists of six people–himself, his wife and their four children. It is known that the average age of the family immediately after the birth of the first, second, third and fourth child was 16, 15, 16 and 15 years respectively. Find the age of Mr. Joe's eldest son if the present average age of the entire family is 16 years.

(*a*) 8 years (*b*) 12 years
(*c*) 15 years (*d*) 16 years

144. Total expenses of a boarding house are partly fixed and partly varying linearly with the number of boarders. The average expense per boarder is ₹ 700 when there are 25 boarders and ₹ 600 when there are 50 boarders. What is the average expense per boarder when there are 100 boarders?

(*a*) ₹ 540 (*b*) ₹ 550
(*c*) ₹ 570 (*d*) ₹ 580

145. A certain factory employed 600 men and 400 women and the average wage was ₹ 25.50 per day. If a woman got ₹ 5 less than a man, then what are their daily wages?

(*a*) Man : ₹ 25; Woman : ₹ 20
(*b*) Man : ₹ 27.50, Woman : ₹ 22.50
(*c*) Man : ₹ 30, Woman : ₹ 25
(*d*) Man : ₹ 32.50, Woman : ₹ 27.50

146. The arithmetic mean of the scores of a group of students in a test was 52. The brightest 20% of them secured a mean score of 80 and the dullest 25% a mean score of 31. The mean score of remaining 55% is

(*a*) 45 (*b*) 50
(*c*) 51.4 approx. (*d*) 54.6 approx.

147. A coaching institute has students in 3 batches - X, Y and Z. In a certain examination, the average marks obtained by these batches are 72, 60 and 50 respectively. The average marks of batches X and Y taken together is 69. If the ratio of the number of students in batches Y and Z is 6 : 7, what is the average score of all the three batches put together?

(*a*) 59 (*b*) 61.6
(*c*) 63.5 (*d*) 64.7
(*e*) 65

148. The average salary of all the workers in a workshop is ₹ 8000. The average salary of 7 technicians is ₹ 12000 and the average salary of the rest is ₹ 6000. The total number of workers in the workshop is (M.A.T., 2005)

(*a*) 20 (*b*) 21
(*c*) 22 (*d*) 23

149. In a school with 600 students, the average age of the boys is 12 years and that of the girls is 11 years. If the average age of the school is 11 years 9 months, then the number of girls in the school is:

(*a*) 150 (*b*) 250
(*c*) 350 (*d*) 450

150. The average score of a class of boys and girls in an examination is *A*. The ratio of boys and girls in the class is 3 : 1. If the average score of the boys is $A + 1$, the average score of the girls is (S.S.C., 2006)

(*a*) $A - 1$ (*b*) $A - 3$
(*c*) $A + 1$ (*d*) $A + 3$

151. In an engineering college the average salary of all engineering graduates from Mechanical trade is ₹ 2.45 lacs per annum and that of the engineering graduates from Electronics trade is ₹ 3.56 lacs per annum. The average salary of all Mechanical and Electronics graduates is ₹ 3.12 lacs per annum. Find the least number of Electronics graduates passing out from this institute. (M.A.T., 2007)

(*a*) 43 (*b*) 59
(*c*) 67 (*d*) Cannot be determined

152. The average age of students of a class is 15.8 years. The average age of boys in the class is 16.4 years and that of the girls is 15.4 years. The ratio of the number of boys to the number of girls in the class is (M.A.T., 2007; M.B.A., 2010)

(*a*) 1 : 2 (*b*) 2 : 3
(*c*) 3 : 4 (*d*) 3 : 5

153. The mean monthly salary paid to graduating MBA class of a management institute is ₹ 16000. The mean monthly salary paid to students with work experience is ₹ 18000. The corresponding figure for the students without any work experience is ₹ 12000. Determine the percentage of students with work experience and those without any work experience in the class. (JMET, 2008)

(*a*) 66.67%, 33.33% (*b*) 33.33%, 66.67%
(*c*) 75%, 25% (*d*) 25%, 75%

154. My Scooty gives an average of 40 kmpl of petrol. But after recent filling at the new petrol pump, its average dropped to 38 kmpl. I investigated and found out that it was due to adulterated petrol. Petrol pumps add kerosene, which is $\frac{2}{3}$ cheaper than petrol, to increase their profits. Kerosene generates excessive smoke and knocking and gives an average of 18 km per 900 ml. If I paid ₹ 30 for a litre of petrol, what was the additional amount the pump-owner was making? (M.A.T., 2007)

(*a*) ₹ 1.75 (*b*) ₹ 1.80
(*c*) ₹ 2 (*d*) ₹ 2.30

155. Average score of a class of 60 students, in an exam, was 43. Average score of the students who had passed is 52 and the average score of students who had failed is 16. How many failed the exam?

[IBPS—RRB Officer's Gr. 'B' Exam, 2015]

(*a*) 25 (*b*) 20
(*c*) 15 (*d*) 18

156. The average of 11 results is 60. If the average of first six results is 58 and that of last six is 63, find the 6th result. **[Indian Railway Gr. 'D' Exam, 2014]**

(*a*) 66 (*b*) 55
(*c*) 64 (*d*) 68

157. The average weight of 21 boys was recorded as 64 *kg*. If the weight of the teacher was added, the average increased by 1 *kg*. What was the teacher's weight? **[Indian Railway Gr. 'D' Exam, 2014]**

(*a*) 86 kg (*b*) 64 kg
(*c*) 72 kg (*d*) 84 kg

158. The average of 12 numbers is 15 and the average of the first two is 14. What is the average of the rest?

[SSC—CHSL (10+2) Exam, 2015]

(*a*) 15 (*b*) $15\frac{1}{5}$
(*c*) 14 (*d*) $14\frac{1}{5}$

159. The average expenditure of a man for the first five months is ₹ 1200 and for the next seven months is ₹ 1300. If he saves ₹ 2900 in that year, his monthly average income is **[SSC—CHSL (10+2) Exam, 2015]**

(*a*) ₹ 1500 (*b*) ₹ 1600
(*c*) ₹ 1700 (*d*) ₹ 1400

160. In a primary school the average weight of male students is 65.9 kg and the average weight of female students is 57 kg. If the average weight of all the students (both male and female) is 60.3 kg and the number of male students in the school is 66, what is the number of female students in the school?

[IBPS—Bank Spl. Officers (IT) Exam, 2015]

(*a*) 162 (*b*) 168
(*c*) 180 (*d*) 112

161. Out of 10 teachers of a school, one teacher retires and in place of him a new teacher 25 years old joins. As a result of it average age of the teachers reduces by 3 years. Age of the retired teacher (in years) is:

[SSC—CHSL (10+2) Exam, 2015]

(*a*) 55 (*b*) 60
(*c*) 58 (*d*) 56

162. Six numbers are arranged in decreasing order. The average of the first five numbers is 30 and the average of the last five numbers is 25. The difference of the first and the last numbers is

[SSC—CHSL (10+2) Exam, 2015]

(*a*) 20 (*b*) 25
(*c*) 5 (*d*) 30

163. The average weight of A, B and C is 40 kgs. Weight of C is 24 kgs more than A's weight and 3 *kgs* less than B's weight. What will be the average weight of A, B, C and D, if D weights 15 kgs less than C?

[United India Insurance (UIICL) Assistant (Online) Exam, 2015]

(*a*) 42 kgs (*b*) 40 kgs
(*c*) 36 kgs (*d*) 38 kgs

Direction (*Question No. 164–165*): Each of the questions below consists of a question-statement and two statements I and II are given below it. You have to decide whether the data provided in the statements are sufficient to answer the question. Give answer.

(A) The data in statement I alone was sufficient to answer the question while II alone are not sufficient to answer the question.
(B) Data in statement II alone are sufficient to answer the question while data in statement I alone are not sufficient to answer the question.
(C) The data in statement I alone or in statement II alone are sufficient to answer the question.
(D) The data in both Statement I and II are not sufficient to answer the question.
(E) The data in both Statements I and II are sufficient to answer the question.

164. Whose body weight is second highest among the five boys Arun, Vinay, Suraj, Raju and Pratap?

[IDBI Bank Executive Officers Exam, 2015]

I. Average weight of Arun, Suraj and Vinay is 68 kg and average weight of Raju and Pratap is 72 kg. Also Suraj is 78 kg, Raju is 68 kg and Vinay is 46 kg.

II. Average weight of Arun, Suraj, Vinay and Raju is 68 kg and also Suraj is 78 kg, Raju is 68 kg and Vinay is 46 kg all of them have different weights.

165. What will be the total marks of Subodh in physics?

[IDBI Bank Executive Officers Exam, 2015]

I. The average marks of Subodh in History, Geography and Chemistry are 75.

II. His average marks in History, Geography and Physics are 78.

166. There are three positive numbers. One third of the average of all the three numbers is 8 less than the value of the highest number. The average of the lowest and the second lowest number is 8. What is the highest number? [IBPS—RRB Officer Exam, 2015]

(a) 11 (b) 14
(c) 10 (d) 9

167. A shop of electronic goods is closed on Monday. The average daily sales for remaining six days of a week is ₹ 15,640/- and the average sale of Tuesday to Saturday is ₹ 14,124/-. The sales on Sunday is

[SSC—CHSL (10+2) Exam, 2015]

(a) ₹ 20,188/- (b) Data inadequate
(c) ₹ 23,220/- (d) ₹ 21,704/-

168. The mean high temperature of the first four days of a week is 25°C whereas the mean of the last four days is 25.5°C. If the mean of the whole week is 25.2°C, then the temperature of the 4th day is

[SSC—CHSL (10 + 2) Exam, 2015]

(a) 25.2°C (b) 25.5°C
(c) 25.6°C (d) 25°C

169. Find the average of 205, 302, 108, 403 and 202

[ESIC—UDC Exam, 2016]

(a) 450 (b) 1225
(c) 244 (d) 1220

170. The average monthly income of P and Q is ₹ 6,000; that of Q and R is ₹ 5,250; and, that P and R is ₹ 5,500. What is P's monthly income?

[ESIC—UDC Exam, 2016]

(a) ₹ 3,500 (b) ₹ 4,500
(c) ₹ 6,250 (d) ₹ 4,800

171. The average of 6 numbers is 7. The average of three numbers of them is 5. What will be the average of remaining numbers? [ESIC—UDC Exam, 2016]

(a) 15 (b) 30
(c) 9 (d) 42

172. The average weight of boys in a class is 30 kg and the average weight of girls in the same class is 20 kg. If the average weight of the whole class is 23.25 kg, what could be the possible strength of boys and girls respectively in the same class?

[SBI Jr. Associates (Pre.) Exam, 2016]

(a) 14 and 26 (b) 13 and 27
(c) 17 and 27 (d) None of these

173. Average of a, b, and c is 11; average of c, d and e is 17; average of e and f is 22 and average of e and c is 17. Find out the average of a, b, c, d, e, and f.

[DMRC—Train Operator (Station Controller) Exam, 2016]

(a) $15\frac{2}{3}$ (b) $18\frac{1}{2}$
(c) $16\frac{1}{2}$ (d) None of these

174. There are 4 consecutive odd numbers (x_1, x_2, x_3 and x_4) and three consecutive even numbers (y_1, y_2 and y_3). The average of the odd numbers is 6 less than the average of the even numbers. If the sum of the three even numbers is 16 less than the sum of the four odd numbers, what is the average of x_1, x_2, x_3 and x_4 ? [CET—Maharashtra (MBA) Exam, 2016]

(a) 30 (b) 38
(c) 32 (d) 34

175. A library has an average of 510 visitors on Sundays and 240 on other days. What is the average number of visitors per day in the month of June beginning with a Sunday? [CLAT, 2016]

(a) 276 (b) 280
(c) 285 (d) 250

176. The marks of six boys in a group are 48, 59, 87, 37, 78 and 57. What are the average marks of all six boys?

[DMRC—Customer Relationship Assistant (CRA) Exam, 2014]

(a) 61 (b) 65
(c) 69 (d) None of these

177. The average weight of a group of 75 girls was calculated as 47 kgs. It was later discovered that the weight of one of the girls was read as 45 kgs. Whereas her actual weight was 25 kgs. What is the actual average weight of the group of 75 girls? (Rounded off to two digits after decimal)

[DMRC—Customer Relationship Assistant (CRA) Exam, 2014]

(a) 34 (b) 36
(c) 30 (d) None of these

ANSWERS

1. (a)	2. (b)	3. (d)	4. (c)	5. (d)	6. (e)	7. (b)	8. (b)	9. (a)	10. (b)
11. (c)	12. (c)	13. (a)	14. (d)	15. (c)	16. (c)	17. (b)	18. (b)	19. (c)	20. (b)
21. (c)	22. (b)	23. (b)	24. (c)	25. (c)	26. (d)	27. (b)	28. (b)	29. (b)	30. (c)
31. (d)	32. (b)	33. (b)	34. (d)	35. (a)	36. (b)	37. (d)	38. (c)	39. (d)	40. (c)
41. (c)	42. (e)	43. (c)	44. (c)	45. (b)	46. (d)	47. (d)	48. (b)	49. (d)	50. (d)
51. (c)	52. (c)	53. (a)	54. (c)	55. (b)	56. (a)	57. (a)	58. (a)	59. (b)	60. (b)
61. (c)	62. (b)	63. (a)	64. (d)	65. (d)	66. (c)	67. (e)	68. (c)	69. (b)	70. (c)
71. (d)	72. (c)	73. (c)	74. (b)	75. (b)	76. (c)	77. (d)	78. (c)	79. (c)	80. (c)
81. (d)	82. (a)	83. (a)	84. (a)	85. (c)	86. (a)	87. (a)	88. (d)	89. (b)	90. (e)
91. (c)	92. (a)	93. (c)	94. (b)	95. (d)	96. (d)	97. (e)	98. (c)	99. (c)	100. (b)
101. (c)	102. (d)	103. (c)	104. (e)	105. (a)	106. (d)	107. (c)	108. (d)	109. (b)	110. (c)
111. (a)	112. (d)	113. (b)	114. (c)	115. (c)	116. (a)	117. (b)	118. (d)	119. (c)	120. (c)
121. (a)	122. (b)	123. (c)	124. (d)	125. (a)	126. (a)	127. (c)	128. (d)	129. (c)	130. (c)
131. (c)	132. (a)	133. (d)	134. (b)	135. (b)	136. (c)	137. (c)	138. (b)	139. (d)	140. (d)
141. (c)	142. (d)	143. (b)	144. (b)	145. (b)	146. (c)	147. (d)	148. (b)	149. (a)	150. (b)
151. (c)	152. (b)	153. (a)	154. (c)	155. (c)	156. (a)	157. (a)	158. (b)	159. (a)	160. (d)
161. (a)	162. (b)	163. (d)	164.	165.	166. (a)	167. (c)	168. (c)	169. (c)	170. (c)
171. (c)	172. (b)	173. (a)	174. (d)	175. (c)	176. (a)	177. (d)			

SOLUTIONS

1. Average body weight

$$= \left(\frac{54+78+43+82+67+42+75}{7}\right) \text{kg}$$

$$= \left(\frac{441}{7}\right) \text{kg} = 63 \text{ kg}.$$

2. Average $= \left(\frac{385+441+876+221+536+46+291+428}{8}\right)$

$$= \left(\frac{3224}{8}\right) = 403.$$

3. Arithmetic mean $= ₹\left(\frac{1132+1140+1144+1136+1148}{5}\right)$

$$= ₹\left(\frac{5700}{5}\right) = ₹\,1140.$$

4. Mean income $= ₹\left(\frac{15000+26000+16000+19000+50000}{5}\right)$

$$= ₹\left(\frac{126000}{5}\right) = ₹\,25200.$$

Clearly, three people have monthly incomes below the mean income.

5. Sum of numbers = $(41.4 \times 15) = 621$.

6. $25a + 25b = 115 \Rightarrow 25(a+b) = 115$

$$\Rightarrow a + b = \frac{115}{25} = \frac{23}{5}.$$

$\therefore$ Average of a and b $= \frac{a+b}{2} = \frac{23}{5} \times \frac{1}{2} = \frac{23}{10} = 2.3.$

7. We have:

Mean working hours	4	6	8	10	12	14
No. of employees	7	10	18	57	14	8

Sum of working hours of all the employees

$= (4 \times 7 + 6 \times 10 + 8 \times 18 + 10 \times 57 + 12 \times 14 + 14 \times 8)$

$= (28 + 60 + 144 + 570 + 168 + 112) = 1082.$

Total number of employees

$= (7 + 10 + 18 + 57 + 14 + 8) = 114.$

$\therefore$ Average number of working hours

$$= \left(\frac{1082}{114}\right) = 9.49 \approx 9.5.$$

8. We have: $a = \frac{0+5+4+3}{4} = 3;\ b = \frac{-1+0+1+5+4+3}{6} = 2;$

$$c = \frac{5+4+3}{3} = 4.$$

$\therefore a : b : c = 3 : 2 : 4.$

9. Total money paid for 115 books = ₹ (1050 + 1020) = ₹ 2070.

$\therefore$ Average price paid per book $= ₹\left(\frac{2070}{115}\right) = ₹\,18.$

10. Required average $= \frac{\left(\frac{1}{x}+\frac{1}{y}\right)}{2} = \frac{x+y}{2xy}.$

11. Sum of numbers = $2XY$.

$\therefore$ Other number = $2XY - X$.

12. Weight of first box = 200 kg.
Weight of third box = 125% of 200 kg = 250 kg.
Weight of second box = 120% of 250 kg = 300 kg.
Weight of fourth box = 350 kg.
Let the weight of fifth box be x kg.
Then, 70% of x = 350 kg $\Rightarrow x = \left(\frac{350 \times 100}{70}\right) = 500$ kg.
Average weight of four heaviest boxes
$= \left(\frac{500 + 350 + 300 + 250}{4}\right)$ kg = 350 kg.
Average weight of four lightest boxes
$= \left(\frac{200 + 250 + 300 + 350}{4}\right)$ kg = 275 kg.
$\therefore$ Required difference = (350 − 275) kg = 75 kg.

13. Let Arun's weight be X kg.
According to Arun, $65 < X < 72$.
According to Arun's brother, $60 < X < 70$.
According to Arun's mother, $X \not> 68$ i.e. $X \le 68$.
The values satisfying all the above conditions are 66, 67 and 68.
$\therefore$ Required average $= \left(\frac{66 + 67 + 68}{3}\right)$ kg $= \left(\frac{201}{3}\right)$ kg = 67 kg.

14. Average of 20 numbers = 0.
$\therefore$ Sum of 20 numbers = (0 × 20) = 0.
It is quite possible that 19 of these numbers may be positive and if their sum is a, then 20th number is $(-a)$.

15. Required mean $= \left(\frac{2 + 4 + 6 + \cdots + 20}{10}\right) = \frac{2(1 + 2 + \cdots + 10)}{10}$
$= \left(\frac{1}{5} \times \frac{10 \times 11}{2}\right) = 11.$
$\left[\because 1 + 2 + 3 + \cdots + n = \frac{n(n+1)}{2}\right]$

16. Required mean $= \left(\frac{1 + 2 + \cdots + 11}{11}\right) = \left(\frac{1}{11} \times \frac{11 \times 12}{2}\right) = 6.$
$\left[\because 1 + 2 + \cdots + n = \frac{n(n+1)}{2}\right]$

17. Average $= \left(\frac{10 + 15 + 20 + 25 + 30}{5}\right) = \frac{100}{5} = 20.$

18. Average $= \frac{3(1 + 2 + 3 + 4 + 5)}{5} = \frac{45}{5} = 9.$

19. Average $= \left(\frac{2 + 3 + 5 + 7 + 11 + 13 + 17 + 19 + 23}{9}\right)$
$= \frac{100}{9} = 11\frac{1}{9}.$

20. Clearly, we have
$\left(\frac{3 + 11 + 7 + 9 + 15 + 13 + 8 + 19 + 17 + 21 + 14 + x}{12}\right) = 12$
or $137 + x = 144$ or $x = 144 - 137 = 7$.

21. We have : $\left(\frac{2 + 7 + 6 + x}{4}\right) = 5$ or $15 + x = 20$ or $x = 5$.
Also, $\left(\frac{18 + 1 + 6 + x + y}{5}\right) = 10$ or $25 + 5 + y = 50$ or $y = 20$.

22. $P + C + M = C + 120 \Rightarrow P + M = 120$.
$\therefore$ Required average $= \frac{P + M}{2} = \frac{120}{2} = 60.$

23. Required average $= \left(\frac{1 + 2 + 3 + \cdots + 100}{100}\right)$
$= \frac{1}{100} \times \frac{100 \times 101}{2} = 50.5.$

24. Sum of odd numbers upto 100 = 1 + 3 + 5 + ... + 99
$= \frac{50}{2}[2 + (50 - 1) \times 2] = 2500.$
$\left[\because \text{Sum of } n \text{ terms of an A.P. with first term } a \text{ and common diff. } d = \frac{n}{2}[2a + (n-1)d]\right]$
$\therefore$ Required average $= \frac{2500}{50} = 50.$

25. Sum of ages of father and mother = (35 × 2) years = 70 years.
Sum of ages of father, mother and son = (27 × 3) years = 81 years.
$\therefore$ Son's age = (81 − 70) years = 11 years.

26. $X_1 + X_2 + X_3 = (14 \times 3) = 42.$
$2(X_2 + X_3) = 30 \Rightarrow X_2 + X_3 = 15.$
$\therefore \quad X_1 = (42 - 15) = 27.$

27. $x_1 + x_2 + x_3 + x_4 = 16 \times 4 = 64.$
$\frac{1}{2}(x_2 + x_3 + x_4) = 23 \Rightarrow x_2 + x_3 + x_4 = 46.$
$\therefore x_1 = 64 - 46 = 18.$

28. We have : $\left[\frac{x + (x + 2) + (x + 4) + (x + 6) + (x + 8)}{5}\right] = 11$ or
$5x + 20 = 55$ or $x = 7$.
So, the numbers are 7, 9, 11, 13, 15.
$\therefore$ Required mean $= \left(\frac{11 + 13 + 15}{3}\right) = \frac{39}{3} = 13.$

29. We have : $\left(\frac{a + b + c}{3}\right) = M$ or $(a + b + c) = 3M$.
Now, $(a + b + c)^2 = (3M)^2 = 9M^2$
$\Leftrightarrow a^2 + b^2 + c^2 + 2(ab + bc + ca) = 9M^2$
$\Leftrightarrow a^2 + b^2 + c^2 = 9M^2$. $[\because (ab + bc + ca) = 0]$
$\therefore$ Required mean $= \left(\frac{a^2 + b^2 + c^2}{3}\right) = \frac{9M^2}{3} = 3M^2.$

30. Average $= \left(\frac{11 + 22 + 33 + 44 + 55 + 66 + 77 + 88 + 99}{9}\right)$
$= \left[\frac{(11 + 99) + (22 + 88) + (33 + 77) + (44 + 66) + 55}{9}\right]$
$= \left(\frac{4 \times 110 + 55}{9}\right) = \frac{495}{9} = 55.$

31. To find the greatest possible S.P. of the most expensive product, we need to consider the minimum S.P. of the remaining 24 products which is ₹420 each for 10 products and ₹ 1000 each for other 14 products.

Minimum S.P. of 24 products = ₹ (420 × 10 + 1000 × 14) = ₹ (4200 + 14000) = ₹ 18200.

Total S.P. of 25 products = ₹ (1200 × 25) = ₹ 30000.

∴ Greatest possible S.P. of the most expensive product = ₹ (30000 – 18200) = ₹ 11800.

32. Number of cars sold per week originally = 15 × 7 = 105.

Number of cars sold per week under scheme = 21 × 7 = 147.

Increase in sale = 147 – 105 = 42.

∴ Percentage increase = $\left(\frac{42}{105} \times 100\right)\% = 40\%$.

33. $1^2 + 2^2 + 3^2 + \ldots + n^2 = \frac{n(n+1)(2n+1)}{6}$.

∴ $1^2 + 2^2 + 3^2 + \ldots + 7^2 = \left(\frac{7 \times 8 \times 15}{6}\right) = 140.$

So, required average = $\left(\frac{140}{7}\right) = 20.$

34. Clearly, $b = a + 2$, $c = a + 4$, $d = a + 6$ and $e = a + 8$.

∴ Average = $\frac{a + (a+2) + (a+4) + (a+6) + (a+8)}{5}$

$= \left(\frac{5a + 20}{5}\right) = (a + 4).$

35. Let the number be x. Then,

$\frac{x + x^2}{2} = 5x \Leftrightarrow x^2 - 9x = 0$

$\Leftrightarrow x(x - 9) = 0$

$\Leftrightarrow x = 0$ or $x = 9$.

So, the number is 9.

36. $S + M + Sc = 100 \times 3 = 300$ and $S + M = Sc + 80$

$\Rightarrow Sc + 80 + Sc = 300 \Rightarrow 2Sc = 220 \Rightarrow Sc = 110.$

37. The given series is a G.P. with first term, $a = 1$ and common ratio, $r = 2$. It has $(n + 1)$ terms.

∴ Sum of the terms of the series = $\frac{(2^{n+1} - 1)}{(2 - 1)} = 2^{n+1} - 1.$

Arithmetic mean = $\frac{2^{n+1} - 1}{n + 1}$.

38. Let the two numbers be x and y.

Then, $x + y = 6.5 \times 2 = 13$ and $\sqrt{xy} = 6$ or $xy = 36$.

$(x - y)^2 = (x + y)^2 - 4xy = (13)^2 - 4 \times 36 = 169 - 144 = 25$

$\Rightarrow (x - y) = 5.$

Solving $x + y = 13$ and $x - y = 5$, we get: $x = 9$, $y = 4$.

39. Let the four numbers be a, b, c and d respectively.

Then, $a = \frac{1}{4}(b + c + d) \Rightarrow b + c + d = 4a.$

Also, $a + b + c + d = 60 \times 4 = 240$

$\Rightarrow a + 4a = 240 \Rightarrow 5a = 240 \Rightarrow a = 48.$

Hence, first number = 48.

40. Sum of four integers = 59 × 4 = 236.

Let the required integers be x and $x - 28$.

Then, $x + (x - 28) = 236 - (83 + 29) = 124$

$\Rightarrow 2x = 152 \Rightarrow x = 76.$

Hence, required integer = 76.

41. Let the numbers be x, $x + 1$, $x + 2$, $x + 3$, $x + 4$, $x + 5$ an[d] $x + 6$.

Then,

$\frac{x + (x+1) + (x+2) + (x+3) + (x+4) + (x+5) + (x+6)}{7} = 2$[0]

or $7x + 21 = 140$ or $7x = 119$ or $x = 17$.

∴ Largest number = $x + 6 = 23$.

42. Let the numbers be x, $x + 2$, $x + 4$, $x + 6$ and $x + 8$.

Then, $\frac{x + (x+2) + (x+4) + (x+6) + (x+8)}{5} = 95$ or $5x + 2$[0]

$= 475$ or $5x = 455$ or $x = 91$.

So, the numbers are 91, 93, 95, 97 and 99.

Clearly, the fourth number in the descending order is 93

43. Let x, $x + 2$, $x + 4$ and $x + 6$ represent numbers A, B, C and D respectively.

Then, $\frac{x + (x+2) + (x+4) + (x+6)}{4} = 65$

$\Rightarrow 4x + 12 = 260$

$\Rightarrow 4x = 248 \Rightarrow x = 62.$

So, $A = 62$, $B = 64$, $C = 66$, $D = 68$.

∴ $A \times D = 62 \times 68 = 4216.$

44. Let the numbers be x, $x + 2$ and $x + 4$.

Then, $(x + x + 2 + x + 4) - \frac{(x + x + 2 + x + 4)}{3} = 44$

$\Rightarrow (3x + 6) - \frac{(3x + 6)}{3} = 44$

$\Rightarrow 2(3x + 6) = 132$

$\Rightarrow 6x = 120 \Rightarrow x = 20.$

∴ Largest number = $x + 4 = 24$.

45. Sum of marks in 4 subjects = 75 × 4 = 300.

Sum of marks in 5 subjects = 300 + 80 = 380.

∴ New average = $\frac{380}{5} = 76.$

46. Clearly, to find the average, we ought to know the numbe[r] of boys, girls or students in the class, neither of whic[h] has been given.

So, the data provided is inadequate.

47. Let the number of other workers be x. Then, number o[f] agricultural workers = $11x$.

Total number of workers = $12x$.

∴ Average monthly income = $\frac{S \times 11x + T \times x}{12x} = \frac{11S + T}{12}$

48. Required average = $\left(\frac{67 \times 2 + 35 \times 2 + 6 \times 3}{2 + 2 + 3}\right)$

$= \left(\frac{134 + 70 + 18}{7}\right) = \frac{222}{7} = 31\frac{5}{7}$ years.

49. Since the month begins with a Sunday, so there will be five Sundays in the month.

$\therefore$ Required average $= \left(\dfrac{510 \times 5 + 240 \times 25}{30}\right) = \dfrac{8550}{30} = 285.$

50. Required average $= \left(\dfrac{32 \times 14 + 28 \times 13}{32 + 28}\right) = \left(\dfrac{448 + 364}{60}\right) = \dfrac{812}{60}$

$= 13.53.$

51. Required average $= \left(\dfrac{50.25 \times 16 + 45.15 \times 8}{16 + 8}\right)$

$= \left(\dfrac{804 + 361.20}{24}\right) = \dfrac{1165.20}{24} = 48.55.$

52. Required mean $= \left(\dfrac{60 \times 5 + 30 \times 10 + 20 \times 15}{5 + 10 + 15}\right)$

$= \left(\dfrac{300 + 300 + 300}{30}\right) = \dfrac{900}{30} = 30.$

53. Total yearly income = ₹ (5000 × 5 + 5400 × 7 + 2300)
= ₹(25000 + 37800 + 2300) = ₹ 65100.

$\therefore$ Average monthly income = ₹$\left(\dfrac{65100}{12}\right)$ = ₹ 5425.

54. Average marks $= \left(\dfrac{50 \times 40 + 60 \times 35 + 55 \times 45 + 45 \times 42}{40 + 35 + 45 + 42}\right)$

$= \left(\dfrac{2000 + 2100 + 2475 + 1890}{162}\right)$

$= \left(\dfrac{8465}{162}\right) = 52.25.$

55. Sum of m numbers $= mn^2$. Sum of n numbers $= nm^2$.
Sum of $(m + n)$ numbers $= mn^2 + nm^2 = mn\,(m + n)$.

$\therefore$ Average of $(m + n)$ numbers $= \dfrac{mn\,(m+n)}{(m+n)} = mn.$

56. Let the five consecutive numbers be z, $z + 1$, $z + 2$, $z + 3$ and $z + 4$. Then,

$\dfrac{z + (z+1) + (z+2) + (z+3) + (z+4)}{5} = x$

$\Rightarrow$ $5z + 10 = 5x$

$\Rightarrow$ $z = \dfrac{5x - 10}{5} = x - 2.$

So, the numbers are $x - 2$, $x - 1$, x, $x + 1$, $x + 2$.

$\therefore$ Required mean

$= \dfrac{(x-2) + (x-1) + x + (x+1) + (x+2) + (x+3) + (x+4)}{7}$

$= \dfrac{7x + 7}{7} = x + 1.$

57. Total quantity purchased = 4 kg.

Total money paid = ₹$\left(1 + \dfrac{1}{2} + \dfrac{1}{3} + \dfrac{1}{4}\right)$ = ₹$\dfrac{25}{12}$.

$\therefore$ Required average $= \left(4 \times \dfrac{12}{25}\right)$ kg/rupee

$= \left(\dfrac{48}{25}\right)$ kg/rupee = 1.92 kg/rupee.

58. Number of units of work completed by the five workers in 1 minute:

$A \to \dfrac{1}{4}, B \to \dfrac{1}{5}, C \to \dfrac{1}{6}, D \to \dfrac{1}{10}, E \to \dfrac{1}{12}.$

$\therefore$ Required average $= \dfrac{\left(\dfrac{1}{4} + \dfrac{1}{5} + \dfrac{1}{6} + \dfrac{1}{10} + \dfrac{1}{12}\right)}{5} = \left(\dfrac{4}{5} \times \dfrac{1}{5}\right) = \dfrac{4}{25}$

$= 0.16.$

59. Total quantity of petrol consumed in 3 years

$= \left(\dfrac{6460}{17} + \dfrac{6460}{19} + \dfrac{6460}{20}\right)$ litres

= (380 + 340 + 323) litres = 1043 litres.

Total amount spent = ₹ (3 × 6460) = ₹ 19380.

$\therefore$ Average cost = ₹$\left(\dfrac{19380}{1043}\right)$ = ₹ 18.58.

60. Clearly, we have: $x = \left(\dfrac{3y + 3z}{6}\right)$ or $2x = y + z$.

61. Let the average expenditure be ₹ x. Then,
$9x = 8 \times 30 + (x + 20)$ or $9x = x + 260$ or $8x = 260$
or $x = 32.50$.

$\therefore$ Total money spent = $9x$ = ₹ (9 × 32.50) = ₹ 292.50.

62. Let the original expenditure of the mess per day be ₹ x.
Then, new expenditure = ₹ $(x + 42)$.

$\therefore$ $\dfrac{x}{35} - \dfrac{(x+42)}{42} = 1$

$\Rightarrow$ $6x - 5\,(x + 42) = 210$

$\Rightarrow$ $x - 210 = 210$

$\Rightarrow$ $x = 420$.

63. Let their prices be $3x$, $5x$ and $7x$ respectively.
Then, $3x + 5x + 7x = 15000 \times 3$

$\Rightarrow$ $15x = 45000$

$\Rightarrow$ $x = 3000$.

$\therefore$ Cost of cheapest item = ₹ (3000 × 3) = ₹ 9000.

64. Let the fourth number be x.

Then, third number $= 5x$, second number $= \dfrac{5x}{3}$ and first number $= \dfrac{10x}{3}$.

$x + 5x + \dfrac{5x}{3} + \dfrac{10x}{3} = (24.75 \times 4)$ or $11x = 99$ or $x = 9$.

So, the numbers are 9, 45, 15 and 30.

$\therefore$ Largest number = 45.

65. Let the second number be x. Then, first number $= 2x$, third number $= 4x$.

$\therefore$ $2x + x + 4x = 56 \times 3 \Rightarrow 7x = 168 \Rightarrow x = 24$.

$\therefore$ Required difference $= 4x - 2x = 2x = 48$.

66. Let the third number be x. Then, second number $= 2x$.
First number $= 4x$.

$\therefore$ $\dfrac{1}{x} + \dfrac{1}{2x} + \dfrac{1}{4x} = \left(\dfrac{7}{72} \times 3\right)$ or $\dfrac{7}{4x} = \dfrac{7}{24}$ or $4x = 24$ or $x = 6$.

So, the numbers are 24, 12 and 6.

67. Let the numbers be x, y and z.

Then, $\left(\frac{x+y}{2}\right)-\left(\frac{y+z}{2}\right)=15$ or $(x+y)-(y+z)=30$

or $x-z=30$.

68. Sum of 50 numbers = 38 × 50 = 1900.

Sum of remaining 48 numbers = 1900 − (45 + 55) = 1800.

∴ Required average = $\left(\frac{1800}{48}\right)=37.5$.

69. Excluded number = (18 × 5) − (16 × 4) = 90 − 64 = 26.

70. New observation = (47 × 7) − (45.5 × 6) = 329 − 273 = 56.

71. Sum of the ages of 24 students = (15 × 30) − (16 × 6) = 450 − 96 = 354.

∴ Required average = $\left(\frac{354}{24}\right)=14\frac{3}{4}$ yrs = 14 yrs 9 mths.

72. Required average = $\left[\frac{(40\times7)-(39\times4)}{3}\right]^{\circ}C$

$=\left(\frac{124}{3}\right)^{\circ}C=41.3^{\circ}C$.

73. Required average = $\frac{(15\times80)-[(16\times15)+(14\times25)]}{80-(15+25)}$

$=\frac{1200-(240+350)}{40}=\frac{610}{40}=15.25$.

74. Required average = ₹ $\left[\frac{(5680\times75)-\{(5400\times25)+(5700\times30)\}}{75-(25+30)}\right]$

= ₹ $\left[\frac{426000-(135000+171000)}{20}\right]$

= ₹ $\left(\frac{120000}{20}\right)$ = ₹ 6000.

75. Required average = $\frac{(76\times16)-(75\times10)}{6}=\left(\frac{1216-750}{6}\right)$

$=\frac{466}{6}=\frac{233}{3}=77\frac{2}{3}$.

76. Let the highest marks obtained by the student be x.

Then, second highest marks = $x-2$.

Sum of marks of these 2 subjects = (87 × 8) − (85 × 6) = 696 − 510 = 186.

∴ $x+(x-2)=186 \Rightarrow 2x=188 \Rightarrow x=94$.

77. Let the highest score be x. Then, lowest score = $(x-172)$.

Then, $(50\times40)-[x+(x-172)]=38\times48$

$\Leftrightarrow 2x=2000+172-1824$

$\Leftrightarrow 2x=348$

$\Leftrightarrow x=174$.

78. Sum of ages of the captain and the youngest player

= [(28 × 11) − {(25 × 3) + (28 × 3) + (30 × 3)] years

= (308 − 249) years = 59 years.

Let the age of the youngest player be x years. Then, age of the captain = $(x+11)$ years.

∴ $x+(x+11)=59 \Rightarrow 2x=48 \Rightarrow x=24$.

79. Total price of the two books = ₹ [(12 × 10) − (11.75 × 8

= ₹ (120 − 94) = ₹ 26.

Let the price of one book be ₹ x.

Then, the price of other book = ₹ $(x+60\%$ of $x)$

= ₹ $\left(x+\frac{3}{5}x\right)$ = ₹ $\left(\frac{8x}{5}\right)$.

So, $x+\frac{8x}{5}=26 \Leftrightarrow 13x=130 \Leftrightarrow x=10$.

∴ The prices of the two books are ₹ 10 and ₹ 16.

80. Required number = (12 × 6) − (10 × 5) = 72 − 50 = 22.

81. Average after 11 innings = 36.

∴ Required number of runs = (36 × 11) − (32 × 10) = 396 − 320 = 76.

82. Total sale for 5 months = ₹ (6435 + 6927 + 6855 + 7230 + 656

= ₹ 34009.

∴ Required sale = ₹ [(6500 × 6) − 34009]

= ₹ (39000 − 34009) = ₹ 4991.

83. Required average = $\frac{(4375\times12)-(4000\times3)}{9}$

$=\frac{52500-12000}{9}=\frac{40500}{9}=4500$.

84. Required run rate = $\frac{282-(3.2\times10)}{40}=\frac{250}{40}=6.25$.

85. Let the average score of the remaining 6 batsmen b x runs.

Then, sum of their scores = $6x$; captain's score = $(x+30$

∴ $6x+(x+30)=310 \Rightarrow 7x=280 \Rightarrow x=40$.

Hence, captain's score = $x+30=70$.

86. Number of men = $\left(\frac{1}{5}\times120\right)=24$.

Number of women = $\left(\frac{1}{4}\times120\right)=30$.

Number of children = 120 − (24 + 30) = 66.

Average age of men = 60 years.

Average age of children = $\left(\frac{1}{4}\times60\right)$ years = 15 years.

Average age of women = $\left(\frac{5}{6}\times60\right)$ years = 50 years.

∴ Average age of the group

= $\left(\frac{60\times24+50\times30+15\times66}{120}\right)$ years

= $\left(\frac{3930}{120}\right)$ years = 32.75 years.

87. Let the attendance on the three days be $2x$, $5x$ and 1 respectively.

Then, total charges

= ₹ $(15\times2x+7.50\times5x+2.50\times13x)$

= ₹ $(30x+37.5x+32.5x)$

= ₹ $100x$.

∴ Average charge per person = ₹ $\left(\frac{100x}{2x+5x+13x}\right)$ = ₹ 5

88. Let the number of papers be x. Then, pupil's total score $= 63x$.

$\therefore \dfrac{63x + 20 + 2}{x} = 65 \Rightarrow 2x = 22 \Rightarrow x = 11.$

89. Let the number of boys in the class be x.

Then, $18(x + 20) = 20x + 15 \times 20$

$\Rightarrow 18x + 360 = 20x + 300$

$\Rightarrow 2x = 60 \Rightarrow x = 30.$

90. Let the mean marks of the third group be x. Then,

$\dfrac{25 \times 60 + 50 \times 55 + 25 \times x}{25 + 50 + 25} = 58$

$\Rightarrow 1500 + 2750 + 25x = 5800$

$\Rightarrow 25x = 1550 \Rightarrow x = 62.$

91. Average marks in Physics $= \dfrac{60 \times 1 + 75 \times 1 + 85 \times 1 + 95 \times 2}{1 + 1 + 1 + 2}$

$= \dfrac{60 + 75 + 85 + 190}{5} = \dfrac{410}{5} = 82.$

92. Weighted arithmetic mean

$= \dfrac{50 \times 2 + 65 \times 2 + 70 \times 1 + 58 \times 1 + 63 \times 1}{2 + 2 + 1 + 1 + 1}$

$= \dfrac{100 + 130 + 70 + 58 + 63}{7} = \dfrac{421}{7} = 60.14 \approx 60.$

93. Let the eighth number be x. Then, sixth number $= (x - 7)$.

Seventh number $= (x - 7) + 4 = (x - 3)$.

So, $\left(2 \times 15\frac{1}{2}\right) + \left(3 \times 21\frac{1}{3}\right) + (x - 7) + (x - 3) + x = 8 \times 20$

$\Leftrightarrow 31 + 64 + (3x - 10) = 160 \Leftrightarrow 3x = 75 \Leftrightarrow x = 25.$

94. A.M. of 75 numbers = 35. Sum of 75 numbers

$= (75 \times 35) = 2625.$

Total increase $= (75 \times 5) = 375$. Increased sum

$= (2625 + 375) = 3000.$

Increased average $= \dfrac{3000}{75} = 40.$

95. Average of 10 numbers = 7.

Sum of these 10 numbers $= (10 \times 7) = 70$.

$\therefore x_1 + x_2 + \ldots.. + x_{10} = 70$

$\Rightarrow 12x_1 + 12x_2 + \ldots.. + 12x_{10} = 840$

$\Rightarrow \dfrac{12x_1 + 12x_2 + \ldots.. + 12x_{10}}{10} = 84$

$\Rightarrow$ Average of new numbers is 84.

96. $\dfrac{x_1 + x_2 + \ldots.. + x_{10}}{10} = \overline{x}$

$\Rightarrow x_1 + x_2 + \ldots + x_{10} = 10\overline{x}$

$\Rightarrow \dfrac{110}{100}x_1 + \dfrac{110}{100}x_2 + \ldots.. + \dfrac{110}{100}x_{10} = \dfrac{110}{100} \times 10\overline{x}$

$\Rightarrow \dfrac{\dfrac{110}{100}x_1 + \dfrac{110}{100}x_2 + \ldots.. + \dfrac{110}{100}x_{10}}{10} = \dfrac{11}{10}\overline{x}$

$\Rightarrow$ Average is increased by 10%.

97. Correct sum $= (160 \times 35 + 104 - 144)$ cm $= 5560$ cm.

$\therefore$ Actual average height $= \left(\dfrac{5560}{35}\right)$ cm

$= 158.857$ cm ≈ 158.86 cm.

98. Correct sum $= (78.4 \times 25 + 96 - 69) = 1987$.

$\therefore$ Correct mean $= \dfrac{1987}{25} = 79.48.$

99. Correct sum $= (68 \times 20 + 72 + 61 - 48 - 65) = 1380$.

$\therefore$ Correct average $= \left(\dfrac{1380}{20}\right) = 69.$

100. Correct sum $= (40.2 \times 10 - 18 + 33 - 13) = 404$.

$\therefore$ Correct average $= \left(\dfrac{404}{10}\right) = 40.4.$

101. Let there be x pupils in the class.

Total increase in marks $= \left(x \times \dfrac{1}{2}\right) = \dfrac{x}{2}.$

$\therefore \dfrac{x}{2} = (83 - 63) \Rightarrow \dfrac{x}{2} = 20 \Rightarrow x = 40.$

102. Correct sum $= 36 \times 100 + 90 - 40 = 3650$.

Correct average $= \dfrac{3650}{100} = 36.5$. Error $= (36.5 - 36) = 0.5$.

$\therefore$ Error% $= \left(\dfrac{0.5}{36.5} \times 100\right)\% = \dfrac{100}{73}\% = 1.36\%.$

103. Age of the boy sitting in the middle

$= [26 \times 7 - (19 \times 3 + 32 \times 3)] = (182 - 153)$ years

$= 29$ years.

104. Third number $= [306.4 \times 5 - (431 \times 2 + 214.5 \times 2)]$

$= (1532 - 1291) = 241.$

105. Marks obtained by the 11th candidate

$= [(45 \times 22) - (55 \times 10 + 40 \times 11)]$

$= (990 - 990) = 0.$

106. Middle number $= [(10.5 \times 6 + 11.4 \times 6) - 10.9 \times 11]$

$= (131.4 - 119.9) = 11.5.$

107. Temperature on the fourth day $= [(40.2 \times 4 + 41.3 \times 4) - (40.6 \times 7)]$°C $= 41.8$ °C.

108. Total weight of $(A + B + C) = \left(54\frac{1}{3} \times 3\right)$ kg $= 163$ kg.

Total weight of $(B + D + E) = (53 \times 3)$ kg $= 159$ kg.

Adding both, we get : $A + 2B + C + D + E = (163 + 159)$ kg $= 322$ kg.

So, to find the average weight of A, B, C, D and E, we ought to know B's weight, which is not given. So, the data is inadequate.

109. Sumit + Krishna + Rishabh $= 43 \times 3 = 129$. ...(*i*)

Sumit + Rishabh + Rohit $= 49 \times 3 = 147$ ...(*ii*)

Subtracting (*i*) from (*ii*), we get: Rohit − Krishna = 18

$\Rightarrow$ Krishna $= 54 - 18 = 36$.

110. $M + T + W = (37 \times 3)$°C $= 111$° C ...(*i*)

$T + W + Th = (34 \times 3)$° C $= 102$° C ...(*ii*)

Subtracting (*ii*) from (*i*), we get:

$M - Th = 9° \text{ C} \Rightarrow M - \dfrac{4}{5}M = 9 \Rightarrow \dfrac{1}{5}M = 9 \Rightarrow M = 45.$

$\therefore$ Temperature on Thursday $= \left(\dfrac{4}{5} \times 45\right)$°C $= 36$° C.

111. Sum of temperatures on 1st, 2nd, 3rd and 4th days
$= (58 \times 4) = 232$ degrees ...(i)
Sum of temperatures on 2nd, 3rd, 4th and 5th days
$= (60 \times 4) = 240$ degrees ...(ii)
Subtracting (i) from (ii), we get:
Temperature on 5th day – Temp. on 1st day = 8 degrees.
Let the temperatures on 1st and 5th days be $7x$ and $8x$ degrees respectively.
Then, $8x - 7x = 8$ or $x = 8$.
$\therefore$ Temperature on the 5th day $= 8x = 64$ degrees.

112. Let A, B, C represent their respective weights. Then, we have:
$A + B + C = (45 \times 3) = 135$ ...(i)
$A + B = (40 \times 2) = 80$ ...(ii)
$B + C = (43 \times 2) = 86$ ...(iii)
Adding (ii) and (iii), we get: $A + 2B + C = 166$ ...(iv)
Subtracting (i) from (iv), we get: B = 31.
$\therefore$ B's weight = 31 kg.

113. Let P, Q and R represent their respective monthly incomes. Then, we have
$P + Q = (5050 \times 2) = 10100$ ...(i)
$Q + R = (6250 \times 2) = 12500$ ...(ii)
$P + R = (5200 \times 2) = 10400$ ...(iii)
Adding (i), (ii) and (iii), we get $2(P + Q + R) = 33000$ or $P + Q + R = 16500$ ...(iv)
Subtracting (ii) from (iv), we get $P = 4000$.
$\therefore$ P's monthly income = ₹ 4000.

114. Age of the instructor $= (34 \times 11 - 32 \times 10)$ years
$= (374 - 320)$ years $= 54$ years.

115. Monthly income of the married daughter
$=$ ₹ $(15130 \times 4 - 14660 \times 3)$
$=$ ₹ $(60520 - 43980) =$ ₹ 16540.

116. Weight of the teacher $= (35.4 \times 25 - 35 \times 24)$ kg $= 45$ kg.

117. Age of the mother $= (12 \times 7 - 7 \times 6)$ years $= 42$ years.

118. Total weight increased $= (8 \times 1.5)$ kg $= 12$ kg.
Weight of the new man $= (65 + 12)$ kg $= 77$ kg.

119. Total age decreased $= (24 \times 1)$ months $= 24$ months
$= 2$ years.
$\therefore$ Age of the newcomer $= (18 - 2)$ years $= 16$ years.

120. Sum of the weights of the students after replacement
$= [(52 \times 45) - (48 \times 5) + (54 \times 5)]$ kg $= 2370$ kg.
$\therefore$ New average $= \left(\frac{2370}{45}\right)$ kg $= 52\frac{2}{3}$ kg.

121. Sum of heights of the 5 boys $= (25 \times 1.4 - 20 \times 1.55)$ m
$= 4$ m.
$\therefore$ Required average $= \left(\frac{4}{5}\right)$ m $= 0.8$ m.

122. Total age decreased $= (11 \times 2)$ months $= 22$ months
$= 1$ year 10 months.
$\therefore$ Average age of two new players $= \left(\frac{35 \text{ years } 2 \text{ months}}{2}\right)$
$= 17$ years 7 months.

123. Let the original strength of the class be x.
Sum of ages of the whole class $= (40x)$ years.
Sum of ages of 12 new students $= (12 \times 32)$ years
$= 384$ years.
$\therefore \frac{40x + 384}{x + 12} = 36$
$\Rightarrow 40x + 384 = 36x + 432$
$\Rightarrow 4x = 48$
$\Rightarrow x = 12$.
Hence, the original strength of the class = 12.

124. Let the original average weight of the class be x kg and let there be n students.
Then, sum of weights of n students $= (nx)$ kg.
$\therefore \frac{nx + 50}{n + 1} = x + 1$
$\Rightarrow nx + 50 = (n + 1)(x + 1)$
$\Rightarrow nx + 50 = nx + x + n + 1$
$\Rightarrow x + n = 49 \Rightarrow 2x + 2n = 98$ ...(i)
And, $\frac{nx + 100}{n + 2} = x + 1.5$
$\Rightarrow nx + 100 = (n + 2)(x + 1.5)$
$\Rightarrow nx + 100 = nx + 1.5n + 2x + 3$
$\Rightarrow 2x + 1.5n = 97$ ...(ii)
Subtracting (ii) from (i), we get: $0.5n = 1$ or $n = 2$.
Putting $n = 2$ in (i), we get: $x = 47$.

125. Let there be n numbers in the original list and let their mean be x.
Then, sum of n numbers $= nx$.
$\therefore \frac{nx + 15}{n + 1} = x + 2$
$\Rightarrow nx + 15 = (n + 1)(x + 2)$
$\Rightarrow nx + 15 = nx + 2n + x + 2$
$\Rightarrow 2n + x = 13$ ...(i)
And, $\frac{nx + 16}{n + 2} = (x + 2) - 1$
$\Rightarrow nx + 16 = (n + 2)(x + 1)$
$\Rightarrow nx + 16 = nx + n + 2x + 2$
$\Rightarrow n + 2x = 14$ ...(ii)
Solving (i) and (ii), we get: $n = 4, x = 5$.

126. Let the average age of the whole team be x years.
$\therefore 11x - (26 + 29) = 9(x - 1)$
$\Leftrightarrow 11x - 9x = 46$
$\Leftrightarrow 2x = 46 \Leftrightarrow x = 23$.
So, the average age of the team is 23 years.

127. Let the average for 20 innings be x. Then,
$\frac{20x + 84}{21} = x + 2$
$\Rightarrow 20x + 84 = 21x + 42$
$\Rightarrow x = 42$.
$\therefore$ Average after 21st inning $= 42 + 2 = 44$.

128. Let the number of wickets taken till the last match be x. Then,

$$\frac{12.4x + 26}{x+5} = 12 \Rightarrow 12.4x + 26 = 12x + 60$$

$$\Rightarrow 0.4x = 34 \Rightarrow x = \frac{34}{0.4} = \frac{340}{4} = 85.$$

129. Let the total score be x.

$\therefore \frac{x + 92 - 85}{8} = 84 \Rightarrow x + 7 = 672 \Rightarrow x = 665.$

130. Average speed $= \frac{2xy}{x+y} = \left(\frac{2 \times 50 \times 30}{50 + 30}\right)$ km/hr $= 37.5$ km/hr.

131. Let A, B, C, D and E represent their respective weights. Then,

$A + B + C = (84 \times 3) = 252$ kg, $A + B + C + D = (80 \times 4) = 320$ kg.

$\therefore$ $D = (320 - 252)$ kg $= 68$ kg, $E = (68 + 3)$ kg $= 71$ kg.

$B + C + D + E = (79 \times 4) = 316$ kg.

Now, $(A + B + C + D) - (B + C + D + E) = (320 - 316)$ kg $= 4$ kg.

$\therefore$ $A - E = 4 \Rightarrow A = (4 + E) = 75$ kg.

132. Sum of the present ages of husband, wife and child $= (23 \times 2 + 5 \times 2) + 1 = 57$ years.

$\therefore$ Required average $= \left(\frac{57}{3}\right) = 19$ years.

133. Sum of the present ages of A and B $= (18 \times 2 + 4 \times 2)$ years $= 44$ years.

Sum of the present ages of A, B and C $= (24 \times 3)$ years $= 72$ years.

C's present age $= (72 - 44)$ years $= 28$ years.

$\therefore$ C's age after 8 years $= (28 + 8)$ years $= 36$ years.

134. Sum of the present ages of A, B, C and D $= (45 \times 4 + 5 \times 4)$ years $= 200$ years.

Sum of the present ages of A, B, C, D and X $= (49 \times 5)$ years $= 245$ years.

$\therefore$ X's present age $= (245 - 200)$ years $= 45$ years.

135. Sum of the present ages of husband, wife and child $= (27 \times 3 + 3 \times 3)$ years $= 90$ years.

Sum of the present ages of wife and child $= (20 \times 2 + 5 \times 2)$ years $= 50$ years.

$\therefore$ Husband's present age $= (90 - 50)$ years $= 40$ years.

136. Sum of the ages of husband and wife at the time of their marriage $= (25 \times 2)$ yrs $= 50$ yrs.

Sum of the ages of husband and wife when their son was born $= (50 + 2 \times 2)$ yrs. $= 54$ yrs.

Sum of the ages of husband, wife and son at present $= (24 \times 3)$ years $= 72$ years.

$\therefore$ Age of son $= \frac{(72 - 54)}{3} = \frac{18}{3} = 6$ years.

Hence, the couple got married $(6 + 2) = 8$ years ago.

137. Sum of the ages of father, mother and son at the time of son's marriage $= (42 \times 3)$ years $= 126$ years.

Sum of the present ages of father, mother and son $= (126 + 3 \times 6)$ years $= 144$ years.

Sum of the present ages of father, mother, son and grandson $= (144 + 5)$ years $= 149$ years.

Sum of the present ages of father, mother, son, daughter-in-law and grandson $= (36 \times 5)$ years $= 180$ years.

Daughter-in-law's present age $= (180 - 149)$ years $= 31$ years.

$\therefore$ Age of daughter-in-law at the time of marriage $= (31 - 6)$ years $= 25$ years.

138. Sum of the ages of 4 members, 4 years ago $= (18 \times 4)$ years $= 72$ years.

Sum of the ages of 4 members now $= (72 + 4 \times 4)$ years $= 88$ years.

Sum of the ages of 5 members now $= (18 \times 5)$ years $= 90$ years.

$\therefore$ Age of the baby $= (90 - 88)$ years $= 2$ years.

139. Age decreased $= (5 \times 3)$ years $= 15$ years.

So, the required difference $= 15$ years.

140. Since the total or average age of all the family members is not given, the given data is inadequate. So, the age of second child cannot be determined.

141. Let the initial number of persons be x. Then,

$16x + 20 \times 15 = 15.5 (x + 20) \Leftrightarrow 0.5x = 10 \Leftrightarrow x = 20.$

142. Sum of the ages of all 8 members, 10 years ago $= 231$ years.

Sum of the ages of all members, 7 years ago $= (231 + 8 \times 3 - 60)$ years $= 195$ years.

Sum of the ages of all members, 4 years ago $= (195 + 8 \times 3 - 60)$ years $= 159$ years.

Sum of the present ages of all 8 members $= (159 + 8 \times 4)$ years $= 191$ years.

$\therefore$ Current average age $= \left(\frac{191}{8}\right)$ years $= 23.8$ years ≈ 24 years.

143. When the first child was born, the total age of all the family members $= (16 \times 3)$ years $= 48$ years.

When the second child was born, the total age of all the family members $= (15 \times 4)$ years $= 60$ years.

By the time the second child was born, each one of the 3 family members had grown by

$$\left(\frac{60 - 48}{3}\right) = \frac{12}{3} = 4 \text{ years.}$$

Hence, the age of eldest son when the second child was born $= 4$ years.

When the third child was born, the total age of all the family members $= (16 \times 5)$ years $= 80$ years.

By the time, the third child was born, each one of the four family members had grown by $\left(\frac{80 - 60}{4}\right) = 5$ years.

So, the age of the eldest son when the third child was born = (4 + 5) years = 9 years.

When the fourth child was born, the total age of all the family members = (15 × 6) years

= 90 years.

By the time, the fourth child was born, each of the five family members had grown by $\left(\frac{90-80}{5}\right) = 2$ years.

So, the age of the eldest son when the fourth child was born = (9 + 2) years = 11 years.

At present, the total age of all the 6 family members

= (16 × 6) years = 96 years.

By now, each one of the 6 members have grown by $\left(\frac{96-90}{6}\right) = 1$ year.

Hence, the present age of the eldest son

= (11 + 1) years = 12 years.

144. Let the fixed cost be ₹ x and the variable cost be ₹ y per boarder.

Then, $x + 25y = 700 \times 25 \Rightarrow x + 25y = 17500$ ...(i)

$x + 50y = 600 \times 50 \Rightarrow x + 50y = 30000$ ...(ii)

Subtracting (i) from (ii), we get: $25y = 12500$ or $y = 500$.

Putting $y = 500$ in (i), we get: $x = 5000$.

∴ Total expenses of 100 boarders = ₹ (5000 + 500 × 100)

= ₹ 55000.

Hence, average expense = ₹ $\left(\frac{55000}{100}\right)$ = ₹ 550.

145. Let the daily wage of a man be ₹ x. Then, daily wage of a woman = ₹ $(x - 5)$.

Now, $600x + 400(x - 5) = 25.50 \times (600 + 400)$

$\Leftrightarrow 1000x = 27500$

$\Leftrightarrow x = 27.50$.

∴ Man's daily wages = ₹ 27.50; Woman's daily wages = $(x - 5)$ = ₹ 22.50.

146. Let the required mean score be x. Then,

$20 \times 80 + 25 \times 31 + 55 \times x = 52 \times 100$

$\Leftrightarrow 1600 + 775 + 55x = 5200$

$\Leftrightarrow 55x = 2825 \Leftrightarrow x = \frac{565}{11} \approx 51.4$.

147. Let the number of students in batches Y and Z be $6x$ and $7x$ respectively, and the number of students in batch X be y.

Then, $72y + 60 \times 6x = 69(6x + y)$

$\Rightarrow 72y + 360x = 414x + 69y$

$\Rightarrow 3y = 54x \Rightarrow y = 18x$.

∴ Required average $= \frac{72 \times 18x + 60 \times 6x + 50 \times 7x}{18x + 6x + 7x}$

$= \frac{1296 + 360 + 350}{31} = \frac{2006}{31} = 64.7$.

148. Let the total number of workers be x. Then,

$8000x = (12000 \times 7) + 6000(x - 7)$

$\Leftrightarrow 2000x = 42000$

$\Leftrightarrow x = 21$.

149. Let the number of girls be x. Then, number of boys = $(600 - x)$.

Then, $\left(11\frac{3}{4} \times 600\right) = 11x + 12(600 - x)$

$\Leftrightarrow x = 7200 - 7050$

$\Leftrightarrow x = 150$.

150. Let the number of boys and girls in the class be $3x$ and x respectively. Let the average score of the girls be y.

Then, $3x(A + 1) + xy = (3x + x)A$

$\Rightarrow 3(A + 1) + y = 4A$

$\Rightarrow y = A - 3$.

151. Let the number of Mechanical Engineering graduates be M and the number of Electronics Engineering graduates be E.

Then, $2.45M + 3.56E = 3.12(M + E)$

$\Rightarrow 2.45M + 3.56E = 3.12M + 3.12E$

$\Rightarrow 0.44E = 0.67M$

$\Rightarrow \frac{M}{E} = \frac{0.44}{0.67} = \frac{44}{67}$.

Since the ratio 44 : 67 is in its simplest form, so least number of Electronics graduates = 67.

152. Let the ratio be $k : 1$. Then,

$k \times 16.4 + 1 \times 15.4 = (k + 1) \times 15.8$

$\Leftrightarrow (16.4 - 15.8)k = (15.8 - 15.4)$

$\Leftrightarrow k = \frac{0.4}{0.6} = \frac{2}{3}$.

∴ Required ratio $= \frac{2}{3} : 1 = 2 : 3$.

153. Let the number of students with work experience be x and those without work experience be y.

Then, $18000x + 12000y = 16000(x + y)$

$\Rightarrow 2000x = 4000y$

$\Rightarrow \frac{x}{y} = \frac{2}{1}$.

∴ Percentage of students with work experience

$= \left(\frac{2}{3} \times 100\right)\% = 66.67\%$.

Percentage of students without work experience

= (100 − 66.67)% = 33.33%.

154. Let x ml of kerosene be there in 1 litre mixture.

Then, quantity of petrol in 1 litre mixture = $(1000 - x)$ ml

∴ $\frac{40}{1000}(1000 - x) + \frac{18}{900}x = 38$

$\Rightarrow \frac{x}{25} - \frac{x}{50} = 2 \Rightarrow \frac{x}{50} = 2$

$\Rightarrow x = 100$.

So, 1 litre mixture has 900 ml petrol and 100 ml kerosene.

Cost of 1 litre petrol = ₹ 30.

Cost of 1 litre kerosene = ₹ $\left[\left(1 - \frac{2}{3}\right) \times 30\right]$ = ₹ 10.

Cost of 1 litre mixture = ₹ $\left(\frac{30}{1000} \times 900 + \frac{10}{1000} \times 100\right)$ = ₹ 28

∴ Additional amount earned by pump-owner

= ₹ (30 − 28) = ₹ 2.

155. Total number of students in class = 60
Average score of passed students = 52
Average score of failed students = 16
By applying the rule of alligation,

Average score of passed students — Average score of failed studnets

52 — 16

43 →

43–16 = 27 — 52 – 43 = 9

⇒ 3 — 1

∴ Number of students who failed in exam = $\frac{1}{4}\times 60 = 15$

156. The average of 11 results = 60
The total of 11 results = 60 × 11 = 660
Average of first six results = 58
Average of last six results = 63
Total of first six results = 58 × 6 = 348
Total of last six results = 63 × 6 = 378
∴ sixth results = total of first and last six results − total of 11 results
= (348 + 378) − 660
= 726 − 660 = 66

157. Average weights of 21 boys = 64 kg
Total weights of 21 boys = 64 × 21 = 1344kg
The weight of the teacher was added then average increase by 1kg
⇒ total weight of teachers and 21 boys = 65 × 21 = 1430 kg
Weight of teacher = 1430 − 1344 = 86kg

158. Average of 12 number = 15
Total of 12 number = 15 × 12 = 180
Average of first two number = 14
Total of first two number = 14 × 2 = 28
Total of remaining ten numbers = 180 − 28 = 152
Required average of remaining ten number = $\frac{152}{10} = \frac{76}{5} = 15\frac{1}{5}$

159. Average expenditure of a man for the first five month = ₹ 1200
Average expenditure of a man for the next seven month = ₹ 1300
Total annual expenditure of man
= ₹ (5 × 1200 + 7 × 1300)
= ₹ (6000 + 9100)
= ₹ 15100
Man saves = ₹ 2900
His total annual income
= ₹ (15100 + 2900)
= ₹ 18000
∴ Average monthly income = $\frac{18000}{12}$ = ₹ 1500

160. Let the number of female students be x
Let weight of female students = $57x$
Number of male students = 66
Total weight of male students = 65.9 × 66
Average weight of all the students 60.3 kg
Total weigh of all the students = 60.3 $(66 + x)$
According to given information
Then, 60.3 $(66 + x)$ = 66 × 65.9 + $57x$
60.3 × 66 + $60.3x$ = 66 × 65.9 + $57x$
$60.3x - 57x = 66(65.9 - 60.3)$
or, $3.3x = 66(65.9 - 60.3)$
or, $3.3x = 66 \times 5.6$
$\therefore\ x = \frac{66\times 5.6}{3.3} = 2\times 56 = 112$

161. Total number of teachers = 10
Age of new teacher = 25 years
Age of the retired teacher
= (25 + 3 × 10) years
= 55 years

162. Numbers are
$x > y > z > p > q > r$
According to the question,
Average of first five numbers = 30
Sum of first five number
$= a + y + z + p + q = 5\times 30 = 150$ ....(i)
Average of last five number = 25
Sum of last five numbers
$= y + z + p + q + r = 5\times 25 = 125$ ....(ii)
By equation (i) and (ii) $a - r = 150 - 125 = 25$

163. Average weight of A, B and C = 40 kgs
Total weights of A, B and C = 40 × 3 = 120 kgs
Weight of C = (A + 24)kg and C = (B − 3) kg
∴ A + 24 = B − 3
⇒ B = A + 27
Now A + B + C = 120
⇒ A + A + 27 + A + 24 = 120
⇒ 3A + 51 = 120
⇒ A = $\frac{69}{3}$ = 23 kg
B = A + 27 = 23 + 27 = 50 kg
C = 120 − 23 − 50 = 47 kg
D = 47 − 15 = 32 kg
∴ Required average weight of A, B, C and D
$= \frac{23 + 50 + 47 + 32}{4}$
$= \frac{152}{4} = 38$ kg

164. Total weight of Arun + Suraj + Vinay = 68 × 3 = 204 ..(i)
Total weight of Raju + Pratap = 72 × 2 = 144. ...(ii)
Weight of Suraj = 78 kg

Weight of Raju = 68 kg
Weight of Vinay = 46 kg
Then, from (ii)
Weight of Pratap = 144 – 68 = 76 kg
And from (i)
Weight of Arun = 204 – 124 = 80 kg
Arun > Suraj > Pratap > Raju > Vinay
Second highest weight gainer = Suraj
Total weight of (Arun + Suraj + Vinay + Raju)
= (68 × 4) = 272 kg

Weight of Suraj = 78 kg
Weight of Raju = 68 kg
Weight of Vinay = 46 kg
Weight of Pratap is not known.
Only statement I alone was sufficient to answer the question.

165. Average marks of Subodh in History Geography and Chemistry = 75
Total marks of H + G + C = 75 × 3 = 225 ...(i)
H + G + P = 78 × 3 = 234 ...(ii)
From (i) and (ii)
Marks of Subodh in Physics = 234 – 225 = 9

166. Let the three positive numbers in increasing order be a, b and c and the average of these numbers be A.

Then, $\frac{a+b+c}{3} = A$ ...(i)

Given $c - \frac{A}{3} = 8$

or, $c - \frac{a+b+c}{9} = 8$ ...(ii)

Also, given $\frac{b+a}{2} = 8$ ...(iii)

$\Rightarrow a + b = 16$

Putting the value of $(a + b)$ in equation (ii), we get

$c - \left(\frac{16+c}{9}\right) = 8$

or, $9c - 16 - c = 72$

or, $8c = 72 + 16 = 88$

or, $8z = 88$

$\therefore c = 11$

∴ Highest number = 11

167. Average sales per day for six days of the week = ₹ 15,640/-
Total sales of six days of the week = 15640 × 6 = ₹ 93,840/-
Average sales of Tuesday to Saturday = ₹ 14,124/-
Total sales from Tuesday to Saturday = 14,124 × 5
= ₹ 70,620/-

∴ Sales on Sunday = (₹ 93,840 – 70,620) = ₹ 23,220/-

168. Average temperature of first four days = 25°C
Total temperature of first four days = 25° × 4 = 100°C
Average temperature last four days = 25.5°
Total temperature of four days = 25.5° × 4 = 102°C
Total temperature of whole week = 25.2 × 7 = 176.4°C
∴ Temperature of the 4th day = 100° + 102° – 176.4° = 25.6°C

169. Sum of numbers = 205 + 302 + 108 + 403 + 202 = 1220

Required average $= \frac{1220}{5} = 244$

170. Average monthly income of P and Q = ₹ 6,000/-
Average monthly income of Q and R = ₹ 5,250/-
Average monthly income of P and R = ₹ 5,500/-
Total income of P + Q = 2 × 6,000 = ₹ 12,000/- ...(i)
Total income of Q + R = 2 × 5,250 = ₹ 10,500/- ...(ii)
Total income of R + P = 2 × 5,500 = ₹ 11,000/- ...(iii)
On adding equation (i) (ii) and (iii), we get
2(P + Q + R) = 12,000 + 10,500 + 11,000

$\Rightarrow$ P + Q + R = $\frac{33500}{2}$

= ₹ 16,750/- ....(iv)
By equation (iv) – (ii)
P's monthly income
= ₹ (16,750 – 10,500) = ₹ 6,250/-

171. Average of 6 numbers = 7
Sum of 6 numbers = 6 × 7 = 42
Average of three numbers = 5
Sum of three numbers = 5 × 3 = 15
∴ Sum of the remaining three numbers
= 42 – 15 = 27

∴ Required average = $\frac{27}{3} = 9$

172. Let the number of boys and girls in the class are x and y
According to given information

$30x + 20y = 23.25(x + y)$

$30x + 20y = 23.25x + 23.25y$

$30x - 23.25x = 23.25y - 20y$

$6.75x = 3.25y$

or, $\frac{x}{y} = \frac{3.25}{6.75} = \frac{13}{27}$

Hence, possible number of boys and girls 13 and 27 respectively.

173. Average of a, b and c = 11
Total of a, b and c = 33 ...(i)
Similarly, Average of c, d, and e = 17
Sum of $c + d + e = 3 \times 17 = 51$ (ii)
Average of e and f is 22
Sum of $e + f = 2 \times 22 = 44$ ...(iii)
Average of e and c is 17
Sum of $e + c = 2 \times 17 = 34$ ....(iv)
By equations (i) + (ii) + (iii) – (iv)
$a + b + c + c + d + e + e + f - e - c$

= 33 + 51 + 44 – 34
= 128 – 34 = 94

∴ Required average = $\frac{94}{6}$

$= \frac{47}{3} = 15\frac{2}{3}$

174. According to given information average of odd numbers = Average of even numbers – 6

$\Rightarrow \frac{x_1+x_2+x_3+x_4}{4}$

$= \frac{y_1+y_2+y_3}{3} - 6$

$\Rightarrow \frac{x_1+x_2+x_3+x_4}{4} = \frac{y_1+y_2+y_3-18}{3}$

$\Rightarrow 3(x_1+x_2+x_3+x_4)$

$= 4(y_1+y_2+y_3)-72$

Also, $y_1+y_2+y_3 = x_1+x_2+x_3+x_4-16$

$\Rightarrow x_1+x_2+x_3+x_4 = y_1+y_2+y_3+16$ ...(i)

So, we have

$3(y_1+y_2+y_3+16)$

$= 4(y_1+y_2+y_3)-72$

$\Rightarrow 3y_1+3y_2+3y_3+48$

$\Rightarrow = 4y_1+4y_2+4y_3-72$

$\Rightarrow 4y_1+4y_2+4y_3-3y_1-3y_2-3y_3 = 48+72$

$\Rightarrow y_1+y_2+y_3 = 120$

$\Rightarrow x_1+x_2+x_3+x_4 = 120+16 = 136$ [From (i)]

∴ Average of four odd numbers

$= \frac{x_1+x_2+x_3+x_4}{4} = \frac{136}{4} = 34$

175. If a month beings with Sunday then there are 5 Sundays in that month.

Total number of visitors come on Sunday
= 510 × 5 = 2550

Total number of visitors come on other days
= 240 × 25 = 6000

∴ Average number of visitors per day

$= \frac{2550+6000}{30} = \frac{8550}{30} = 285$

176. Total marks of six boys = 48 + 59 + 87 + 37 + 78 + 57 = 366

Required average $= \frac{366}{6} = 61$

177. Average weight of 75 girls = 47 kgs
Total weight of 75 girls = 47 × 75 = 3525 kg
Actual weight of 75 girls = x
Correct weight of 75 girls
3525 – 45 + 25 = 3525 – 20 = 3505 kg

∴ Required average weight = $x = \frac{3505}{75} = 46.73$ kg

EXERCISE

(DATA SUFFICIENCY TYPE QUESTIONS)

Directions (*Questions 1 to 28*): *Each of the questions given below consists of a statement and/or a question and two statements numbered I and II given below it. You have to decide whether the data provided in the statement(s) is/are sufficient to answer the given question. Read both the statements and*

Give answer (a) if the data in Statement I alone are sufficient to answer the question, while the data in Statement II alone are not sufficient to answer the question;

Give answer (b) if the data in Statement II alone are sufficient to answer the question, while the data in Statement I alone are not sufficient to answer the question;

Give answer (c) if the data either in Statement I or in Statement II alone are sufficient to answer the question;

Give answer (d) if the data even in both Statements I and II together are not sufficient to answer the question;

Give answer (e) if the data in both Statements I and II together are necessary to answer the question.

1. Sachin's monthly salary is ₹ 4,000. What is Rajan's monthly salary? **(Bank P.O., 2010)**
   I. Rajan gets ₹ 500 more than the average salary of his and Sachin's.
   II. Average of Sachin's and Rajan's salary is ₹ 4500.

2. Is r equal to the average of x, y and z?
   I. $x + y + z = 3r$ II. $\frac{x+y+z}{6} = \frac{r}{2}$

3. What marks have been obtained by Arun?
   I. Arun's marks are the average of marks of Nitin and Manick.
   II. Nitin obtained 80 marks and this is 25% more than the marks obtained by Manick.

4. Which of the four numbers w, x, y and z is the largest?
   I. The average of w, x, y and z is 25.
   II. The numbers w, x and y are each less than 24.

5. What is the average weight of the three new members who are recently included into the team?
   I. The average weight of the team increases by 20 kg.
   II. The three new men substitute earlier members whose weights are 64 kg, 75 kg and 66 kg.

6. The total of the present ages of A, B, C and D is 96 years. What is B's present age? **(SNAP, 2005)**
   I. The average age of A, B and D is 20 years.
   II. The average age of C and D is 25 years.

7. What is the average age of children in the class? **(N.M.A.T., 2006)**

I. Age of the teacher is as many years as the number of children.
II. Average age increased by 1 year if the teacher's age is also included.

8. If there is an average of 250 words on each page, how many pages can Michael read in an hour? **(M.A.T., 2006)**
I. There is an average of 25 ten-word lines on each page.
II. Michael can read 30 ten-word lines per minute.

9. John had an average score of 85 in three tests. What was John's lowest score?
I. John's highest score was 95. **(M.B.A., 2007)**
II. Average of John's two highest scores was 92.

10. The average age of P, Q, R and S is 30 years. How old is R? **(R.B.I., 2003)**
I. The sum of ages of P and R is 60 years.
II. S is 10 years younger than R.

11. How old will C be after 10 years ?
I. Five years ago, the average age of A and B was 15 years.
II. Average age of A, B and C today is 20 years.

12. What is the salary of R, in a group of P, Q, R, S and T whose average salary is ₹ 45980? **(Bank P.O., 2008)**
I. Total of the salary of P and T is ₹ 90670.
II. Total of the salary of Q and S is ₹ 76540.

13. The average of three quotations for a particular item is ₹ 120. Is the highest quotation less than or equal to ₹ 139? **(M.B.A., 2008)**
I. The lowest quotation is of ₹ 90.
II. One of the quotations is ₹ 125.

14. During a five day period, Monday through Friday, the average high temperature was 86 degrees Fahrenheit. What was the high temperature on Friday?
I. The average high temperature for Monday through Thursday was 87 degrees Fahrenheit.
II. The high temperature on Friday reduced the average high temperature by 1 degree Fahrenheit.

15. Find out the value of the eleventh number in a set of eleven numbers.
I. The average of the first ten numbers in the set is x. **(J.M.E.T., 2007)**
II. The average of all the eleven numbers is y.

16. Find the average score for all the juniors and seniors combined.
I. The average of the scores was 85 for juniors and 89 for seniors.
II. The groups are of equal size.

17. What is the average monthly income per family member? **(Bank P.O., 2011)**
I. Each male earns ₹ 1250 a month and each female earns ₹ 1050 a month.
II. Ratio of males to females in the family is 2 : 1.

18. How many children are there in the group?
I. Average age of the children in this group is 15 years. The total age of all the children in this group is 240 years.
II. The total age of all the children in the group and the teacher is 264 years. The age of the teacher is 9 years more than the average age of the children.

19. Deepak's marks in Hindi are 15 more than the average marks obtained by him in Hindi, Economics, Sociology and Philosophy. What are his marks in Philosophy? **(S.N.A.P., 2005)**
I. The total marks obtained by him in Hindi and Philosophy together is 120.
II. The difference between the marks obtained by him in Sociology and Economics is 120.

20. How many candidates were interviewed everyday by the panel A out of the three panels A, B and C? **(Campus Recruitment, 2008)**
I. The three panels on an average interview 15 candidates everyday.
II. Out of a total of 45 candidates interviewed everyday by the three panels, the number of candidates interviewed by panel A is more by 2 than the candidates interviewed by panel C and is more by 1 than the candidates interviewed by panel B.

21. P, Q, R and S are four consecutive even numbers. What is the value of the largest integer among these?
I. The average of the four numbers is the first prime number greater than 10.
II. The ratio between the largest and the smallest of the numbers is less than 10.

22. Is 500 the average score on the GMAT? **(C.A.T., 2002)**
I. Half of the people, who take the GMAT, score above 500 and half of the people score below 500.
II. The highest GMAT score is 800 and the lowest score is 200.

23. What is the average of the best and worst score out of 8 tests taken by a student?
I. The average of all 8 tests is 84%.
II. After dropping the best and worst grade, the average of remaining 6 tests is 86%.

24. Sapna's marks in Geography are 16 more than the average marks obtained by her in Mathematics, Science, English and Hindi. What are her marks in Geography? **(N.M.A.T. 2005)**
I. The maximum marks in each subject were 100.

II. The total marks obtained by her in Mathematics, Science, English and Hindi were 250.

25. What was the combined average attendance per game at the Jawaharlal Nehru stadium for the months of June and July?

I. The total attendance for the month of June was 23100 and the total attendance for the month of July was 25200.

II. There were 20 games played in June and 22 games played in July.

26. The average age of teacher and students in a class is 3 years more than the average age of students. What is the age of the class teacher?

I. There are 11 students in the class.

II. The average age of teacher and students is 14 years.

27. What will be the average weight of the remaining class? (N.M.A.T., 2005)

I. Average weight of 30 children out of total 46 in the class is 22.5 kg and that of the remaining children is 29.125 kg. A child having weight more than 40 kg is excluded.

II. Average weight of a class of 46 children is 23.5 kg. A child weighing 46 kg is dropped out.

28. How long did the secretary's speech last?

I. He spoke at an average of 50 words per minute.

II. He would have spoken for 10 minutes extra, had his speech rate been 4 words less per minute.

Directions (*Questions 29 to 36*) : *Each of the questions given below consists of a question followed by three statements. You have to study the question and the statements and decide which of the statement(s) is/are necessary to answer the question.*

29. How many marks did Tarun secure in English?

I. The average marks obtained by Tarun in four subjects including English is 60.

II. The total marks obtained by him in English and Mathematics together is 170.

III. The total marks obtained by him in Mathematics and Science together is 180.

(*a*) I and II only (*b*) II and III only
(*c*) I and III only (*d*) All I, II and III
(*e*) None of these

30. What is the average weight of girls in the class? (S.B.I.P.O., 2005)

I. Average weight of all the 60 students is 42 kg.

II. Average weight of boys is 43 kg.

III. Total weight of all girls together is 1144 kg.

(*a*) I and II only
(*b*) II and III only
(*c*) All I, II and III
(*d*) Any two of the three
(*e*) Question cannot be answered even with information in all three statements

31. What is the average age of 45 students studying in a class? (Bank P.O., 2008)

I. The average age of boys is 15.4 years while the average age of girls is 14.6 years.

II. Boys and girls are respectively in the ratio 4 : 5.

III. The number of boys is less than that of girls by 5.

(*a*) Only I and II (*b*) Only I and III
(*c*) All I, II and III (*d*) I and either II or III
(*e*) None of these

32. What is the average of the six members *A*, *B*, *C*, *D*, *E* and *F* in the family?

I. Total age of *D* and *E* is 14 years.

II. Average age of *A*, *B*, *C* and *F* is 50 years.

III. Average age of *A*, *B*, *D* and *E* is 40 years. (Bank P.O., 2009)

(*a*) Only I and II (*b*) Only I and III
(*c*) Only II and III (*d*) All I, II and III
(*e*) None of these

33. Find three positive consecutive even numbers. (M.A.T., 2006)

I. The average of four consecutive even numbers starting from the last of the given numbers is 17.

II. The difference of the highest and the lowest numbers is 4.

III. The sum of the squares of the three numbers is 440.

(*a*) I only (*b*) III only
(*c*) I and II only (*d*) Either I or III only
(*e*) None of these

34. Is the average of the largest and the smallest of four given numbers greater than the average of the four numbers? (M.A.T., 2006)

I. The difference between the largest and the second largest numbers is less than the difference between the second largest and the second smallest numbers.

II. The difference between the largest and the second largest numbers is greater than the difference between the second smallest and the smallest numbers.

III. The difference between the largest and the second smallest numbers is greater than the difference between the second largest and the smallest numbers.

(*a*) I only (*b*) Either II or III
(*c*) I and either II or III (*d*) Any two of them

35. The mean temperature of Monday to Wednesday was 37°C and of Tuesday to Thursday was 34°C. What was the temperature on Thursday ?

I. The temperature on Thursday was $\frac{4}{5}$th that of Monday.

II. The mean temperature of Monday and Thursday was 40.5°C.

III. The difference between the temperature on Monday and that on Thursday was 9°C.

(*a*) I and II only (*b*) II and III only
(*c*) Either I or II (*d*) Either I, II or III
(*e*) Any two of the three

36. In a cricket eleven, the average age of eleven players is 28 years. What is the age of the captain ?

I. The captain is eleven years older than the youngest player.

II. The average age of 10 players, other than the captain is 27.3 years.

III. Leaving aside the captain and the youngest player, the average ages of three groups of three players each are 25 years, 28 years and 30 years respectively.

(*a*) Any two of the three
(*b*) All I, II and III
(*c*) II only or I and III only
(*d*) II and III only
(*e*) None of these

Directions (*Question* 37): ***The given question is followed by three statements labelled I, II and III. You have to study the question and all the three statements given to decide whether any information provided in the statement(s) is / are redundant and can be dispensed with while answering the given question.***

37. What is the average salary of 15 employees?

I. Average salary of 7 clerical cadre (out of the 15 employees) is ₹ 8500.

II. Average salary of 5 officer cadre (out of the 15 employees) is ₹ 10000.

III. Average salary of the 3 sub-staff employees (out of the 15 employees) is ₹ 2500.

(*a*) None (*b*) Only I
(*c*) Only II (*d*) Only III
(*e*) Question cannot be answered even with information in all the three statements.

ANSWERS

1. (*c*)	2. (*c*)	3. (*e*)	4. (*e*)	5. (*d*)	6. (*d*)	7. (*d*)	8. (*b*)	9. (*b*)	10. (*d*)
11. (*e*)	12. (*e*)	13. (*e*)	14. (*c*)	15. (*e*)	16. (*e*)	17. (*e*)	18. (*a*)	19. (*d*)	20. (*b*)
21. (*a*)	22. (*d*)	23. (*e*)	24. (*a*)	25. (*e*)	26. (*e*)	27. (*b*)	28. (*e*)	29. (*e*)	30. (*c*)
31. (*d*)	32. (*a*)	33. (*d*)	34. (*b*)	35. (*c*)	36. (*c*)	37. (*a*)			

SOLUTIONS

1. I. Let their average salary be ₹ x. Then, Rajan's salary = ₹ $(x + 500)$.

$\therefore \frac{4000 + (x + 500)}{2} = x \Rightarrow 4500 + x = 2x \Rightarrow x = 4500.$

Sum of Rajan's and Sachin's salaries = ₹ (4500 × 2) = ₹ 9000.

∴ Rajan's salary = ₹ (9000 – 4000) = ₹ 5000.

So, I alone gives the answer.

II. Rajan's salary can be calculated from the given data as shown above.

So, II alone also gives the answer.

∴ Correct answer is (*c*).

2. From each one of I and II, we have: $r = \frac{x + y + z}{3}$.

i.e., r = average of x, y and z.

So, either I alone or II alone gives the answer.

∴ Correct answer is (*c*).

3. II. Let the marks obtained by Manick be x.

Then, 125% of $x = 80 \Rightarrow x = \left(\frac{80 \times 100}{125}\right) = 64.$

I. Average of marks of Nitin and Manick $= \frac{80 + 64}{2} = 72.$

∴ Arun's marks = 72.

So, both I and II together give the answer.

∴ Correct answer is (*e*).

4. I. $w + x + y + z = 25 \times 4 = 100.$ ...(*i*)

II. $w < 24, x < 24, y < 24$

$\Rightarrow w + x + y < (24 \times 3)$

$\Rightarrow w + x + y < 72$ ...(*ii*)

From (*i*) and (*ii*), we have: $z > 28$. So, z is the largest number.

Thus, both I and II together are needed.

∴ Correct answer is (*e*).

5. Let the number of team members be n.

I. Total increase in weight on replacement = $(20n)$ kg.

II. Total weight of new members = $[(64 + 75 + 66) + 20n]$ kg $= (205 + 20n)$ kg.

$\therefore$ Required average = $\frac{(205+20n)}{3}$ kg and we need n to get the answer.

$\therefore$ Correct answer is (d).

6. $A + B + C + D = 96$ ...(i)

I. gives, $A + B + D = (3 \times 20) \Rightarrow A + B + D = 60$ ...(ii)

II. gives, $C + D = (2 \times 25) \Rightarrow C + D = 50$. ...(iii)

From (i), (ii) and (iii) also, we cannot find B.

$\therefore$ Correct answer is (d).

7. Let there be x children.

I. gives, age of teacher = x years.

II. gives, average age of $(x + 1)$ persons = $(x + 1)$ years.

$\therefore$ Teacher's age $= (x + 1)(x + 1) - x^2$
$= (x^2 + 1 + 2x) - x^2 = (1 + 2x)$.

Thus, teacher's age cannot be obtained.

$\therefore$ Correct answer is (d).

8. I. gives, total number of words on each page $= (25 \times 10) = 250$

which is the same as given in the question.

II. gives, number of words Michael reads in 1 hour $= (30 \times 10 \times 60) = 18000$.

$\therefore$ Number of pages read by Michael in 1 hour $= \frac{18000}{250} = 72$.

So, II alone gives the answer while I alone does not.

$\therefore$ Correct answer is (b).

9. II. gives, John's lowest score $= (85 \times 3) - (92 \times 2)$
$= 255 - 184 = 71$.

So, II alone gives the answer while I alone does not.

$\therefore$ Correct answer is (b)

10. $P + Q + R + S = (30 \times 4) \Rightarrow P + Q + R + S = 120$ ...(i)

I. $P + R = 60$ ...(ii)

II. $S = (R - 10)$ ...(iii)

From (i), (ii) and (iii), we cannot find R.

$\therefore$ Correct answer is (d).

11. I. $A + B = (15 \times 2) + (5 \times 2)$
$\Rightarrow A + B = 40$ ...(i)

II. $A + B + C = (20 \times 3)$
$\Rightarrow A + B + C = 60$ ...(ii)

From (i) and (ii), we get $C = 20$.

C's age after 10 years $= (20 + 10)$ years $= 30$ years.

$\therefore$ Correct answer is (e).

12. $P + Q + R + S + T = 45980 \times 5 = 229900$ ...(i)

I. $P + T = 90670$ ...(ii)

II. $Q + S = 76540$ ...(iii)

Adding (ii) and (iii) and subtracting from (i), we get:

$R = 229900 - (90670 + 76540) = 229900 - 167210 = 62690$.

Thus, both I and II together give the answer.

$\therefore$ Correct answer is (e).

13. I and II give:

Highest quotation $= (120 \times 3) - (90 + 125) = 360 - 215$
$= 145 > 139$.

So, both I and II together give the answer.

$\therefore$ Correct answer is (e).

14. $M + T + W + Th + F = (86 \times 5) = 430$. ...(i)

I. gives: $M + T + W + Th = (87 \times 4) = 348$. ...(ii)

II. gives: $M + T + W + Th = (87 \times 4) = 348$. ...(iii)

Thus, from (i) and (ii), as well as from (i) and (iii), we have: $F = (430 - 348) = 82°F$.

Thus, either I alone or II alone gives the answer.

$\therefore$ Correct answer is (c).

15. I. gives, sum of first 10 numbers $= 10x$. ...(i)

II. gives, sum of all the 11 numbers $= 11y$. ...(ii)

From (i) and (ii), we have 11th number $= 11y - 10x$.

So, both I and II together are needed.

$\therefore$ Correct answer is (e).

16. From both I and II, we have:

Let each group have x students.

Then, the average score for all $= \left(\frac{85x + 89x}{2x}\right) = \frac{174}{2} = 87$.

So, both I and II together give the answer.

$\therefore$ Correct answer is (e).

17. From both I and II, we have:

Let the number of males and females in the family be $2x$ and x respectively.

Then, the average monthly income per member

$= ₹\left(\frac{1250 \times 2x + 1050 \times x}{2x + x}\right) = ₹\left(\frac{3550}{3}\right) = ₹\,1183.33$.

So, both I and II together are needed.

$\therefore$ Correct answer is (e).

18. Let there be x children in the group.

I. Average age = 15 years. $\therefore$ Total age $= 15x$ years.

$\therefore 15x = 240 \Leftrightarrow x = \frac{240}{15} \Leftrightarrow x = 16$.

So, there are 16 children in the group.

II. Total age of x children and 1 teacher is 264 years.

Age of teacher $= (15 + 9)$ years $= 24$ years.

Total age of x children $= (264 - 24)$ years $= 240$ years.

This does not give the answer.

$\therefore$ Correct answer is (a).

19. $H = \frac{(H+E+S+P)}{4} + 15$

$\Rightarrow 4(H - 15) = H + E + S + P$

$\Rightarrow 3H - 60 = E + S + P$ ...(i)

I. $H + P = 120$ ...(ii)

II. $S - E = 120$ ...(iii)

From (i), (ii) and (iii), we cannot find P.

$\therefore$ Correct answer is (d).

20. I. Total candidates interviewed by 3 panels $= (15 \times 3) = 45$.

This is already given in II.

II. Let x candidates be interviewed by C.
Number of candidates interviewed by $A = (x + 2)$.
Number of candidates interviewed by $B = (x + 1)$.
$\therefore x + (x + 2) + (x + 1) = 45 \Leftrightarrow 3x = 42 \Leftrightarrow x = 14$.
So, the number of candidates interviewed by panel A is 14.
Thus, II alone is sufficient. Hence, the correct answer is (*b*).

21. Let $P = x$, $Q = x + 2$, $R = x + 4$ and $S = x + 6$.

I gives, $\dfrac{x+(x+2)+(x+4)+(x+6)}{4} = 11$

$\Rightarrow 4x + 12 = 44$

$\Rightarrow 4x = 32 \Rightarrow x = 8$.

$\therefore$ Largest integer $= x + 6 = 14$.

So, I alone gives the answer.

II gives, $\dfrac{x+6}{x} < 10 \Rightarrow x + 6 < 10x \Rightarrow 9x > 6 \Rightarrow x > \dfrac{2}{3}$.

Thus, II alone does not give the answer.

$\therefore$ Correct answer is (*a*).

22. The average score depends on all the individual scores and the range of scores as given in I and II, is insufficient to calculate it.
So, both I and II together are insufficient.
$\therefore$ Correct answer is (*d*).

23. I gives, sum of all 8 scores $= (84 \times 8) = 672$. ...(*i*)
II gives, sum of remaining 6 scores $= (86 \times 6) = 516$. ...(*ii*)
From (*i*) and (*ii*), we have:
Sum of best and worst scores $= 672 - 516 = 156$.

$\therefore$ Average of best and worst scores $= \dfrac{156}{2} = 78\%$.

Thus, both I and II together give the answer. $\therefore$ Correct answer is (*e*).

24. II gives, Average of marks in Mathematics, Science, English and Hindi $= \dfrac{250}{4} = 62.5$.

$\therefore$ Marks in Geography $= (62.5 + 16) = 78.5$.
So, II alone gives the answer while I alone is insufficient.
$\therefore$ Correct answer is (*b*).

25. To calculate the average attendance per game, we need to know the total attendance and the number of games played.
I and II give:
Combined average attendance per game

$$= \left(\frac{23100 + 25200}{20 + 22}\right) = \frac{48300}{42} = 1150.$$

So, both I and II together are needed.
$\therefore$ Correct answer is (*e*).

26. Average age of 11 students and 1 teacher = 14 years
$\Rightarrow$ Total age of (11 students and 1 teacher) $= (14 \times 12)$ years = 168 years.
Average age of (11 students and 1 teacher) = (Average age of 11 students) + 3
$\Rightarrow$ Average age of 11 students $= (14 - 3)$ years = 11 years
$\Rightarrow$ Total age of 11 students $= (11 \times 11)$ years = 121 years.
$\therefore$ Age of the teacher $= (168 - 121)$ years = 47 years.
Thus, both I and II are needed to get the answer.
$\therefore$ Correct answer is (*e*).

27. I. Total weight of 46 children $= [(22.5 \times 30) + (29.125 \times 16)]$ kg = 1141 kg.
Weight excluded is not exact. So, average of remaining class cannot be obtained.

II. Total weight of 45 children $= [(23.5 \times 46) - 46]$ kg $= 1035$ kg.

Average weight of 45 children $= \dfrac{1035}{45}$ kg $= 23$ kg.

$\therefore$ Data in II is sufficient to answer the question, while the data in I is not sufficient.
$\therefore$ Correct answer is (*b*).

28. Suppose the secretary's speech lasted for x minutes.
I gives, number of words in the speech $= 50x$.
II gives, number of words in the speech $= 46 (x + 10)$.
$\therefore 50x = 46 (x + 10) \Rightarrow 4x = 460 \Rightarrow x = 115$.
So, the secretary's speech lasted for 115 min *i.e.*, 1 hr 55 min.
Thus, both I and II are needed to find the answer.
$\therefore$ Correct answer is (*e*).

29. I gives, total marks in 4 subjects $= (60 \times 4) = 240$. ...(*i*)
II gives, E + M = 170. ...(*ii*)
III gives, M + S = 180.
Thus, none of (*a*), (*b*), (*c*), (*d*) it true.
$\therefore$ Correct answer is (*e*).

30. I gives, sum of weights of 60 students $= (42 \times 60)$ kg $= 2520$ kg. ...(*i*)
II gives, if there be x boys in the class, sum of weights of x boys $= (43x)$ kg. ...(*ii*)
III gives, sum of weights of all the girls = 1144 kg. ...(*iii*)
From (*i*), (*ii*), and (*iii*), we have:
$43x + 1144 = 2520 \Rightarrow 43x = 1376 \Rightarrow x = 32$.
So, number of boys = 32, number of girls $= (60 - 32) = 28$.

$\therefore$ Average weight of girls $= \left(\dfrac{1144}{28}\right)$ kg $= 40.86$ kg.

Thus, all I, II and III are needed to find the answer.
$\therefore$ Correct answer is (*c*).

31. From I and II, we have:
Let the number of boys and girls be $4x$ and $5x$ respectively.
Then, $4x + 5x = 45 \Rightarrow 9x = 45$ or $x = 5$.
So, number of boys = 20; number of girls = 25.

$\therefore$ Average age of 45 students $= \left(\dfrac{15.4 \times 20 + 14.6 \times 25}{45}\right)$ yrs

$= \left(\dfrac{673}{45}\right)$ years $= 14.96$ years.

Thus, I and II together give the answer.
From I and III, we have
Let number of girls be x. Then, number of boys $= x - 5$.

Then, $x + x - 5 = 45 \Rightarrow 2x = 50 \Rightarrow x = 25$.

So, number of girls = 25, number of boys = 20.

As calculated above, required average = 14.96 years.

Thus, I and III together also give the answer.

$\therefore$ Correct answer is (*d*).

32. I gives: $D + E = 14$ ...(*i*)

II gives: $A + B + C + F = 50 \times 4 = 200$ ...(*ii*)

III gives: $A + B + D + E = 40 \times 4 = 160$ ...(*iii*)

Adding (*i*) and (*ii*), we have: $A + B + C + D + E + F = 214$.

$\therefore$ Required average = $\left(\frac{214}{6}\right)$ years = 35.67 years.

Thus, only I and II together give the answer

$\therefore$ Correct answer is (*a*).

33. Let the three consecutive even numbers be x, $x + 2$ and $x + 4$.

I gives, $\frac{(x+4)+(x+6)+(x+8)+(x+10)}{4} = 17$

$\Rightarrow x + 7 = 17 \Rightarrow x = 10$.

So, the required numbers are 10, 12 and 14.

Thus, I alone gives the answer.

II gives, Difference between highest and lowest numbers $= (x + 4) - x = 4$.

This does not help to find the value of x.

So, II alone is insufficient.

III gives, $x^2 + (x + 2)^2 + (x + 4)^2 = 440$

$\Rightarrow x^2 + (x^2 + 4 + 4x) + (x^2 + 16 + 8x) = 440$

$\Rightarrow 3x^2 + 12x - 420 = 0$

$\Rightarrow x^2 + 4x - 140 = 0$

$\Rightarrow x^2 + 14x - 10x - 140 = 0$

$\Rightarrow (x + 14)(x - 10) = 0 \Rightarrow x = 10$.

So, the required numbers are 10, 12 and 14.

Thus, III alone also gives the answer.

$\therefore$ Correct answer is (*d*).

34. Let the four numbers in decreasing order be x, y, z and w. Then, we have to find whether the following statement is true or false:

$\frac{x+w}{2} > \frac{x+y+z+w}{4}$

I gives, $x - y < y - z$

II gives, $x - y > z - w$

$\Rightarrow x + w > y + z$

$\Rightarrow 2(x + w) > x + y + z + w$

7 Problems on Numbers

In this chapter, questions involving a set of numbers are put in the form of a puzzle. You have to analyse the given conditions, assume the unknown numbers and form equations accordingly, which on solving yield the unknown numbers.

SOLVED EXAMPLES

Ex. 1. ***A number is as much greater than 36 as is less than 86. Find the number.***

Sol. Let the number be x. Then, $x - 36 = 86 - x \Rightarrow 2x = 86 + 36 = 122 \Rightarrow x = 61$.

Hence, the required number is 61.

Ex. 2. ***Find a number such that when 15 is subtracted from 7 times the number, the result is 10 more than twice the number.*** **(Hotel Management, 2002)**

Sol. Let the number be x. Then, $7x - 15 = 2x + 10 \Rightarrow 5x = 25 \Rightarrow x = 5$.

Hence, the required number is 5.

Ex. 3. ***The sum of a rational number and its reciprocal is $\frac{13}{6}$. Find the number.***

Sol. Let the number be x. Then,

$$x + \frac{1}{x} = \frac{13}{6} \Rightarrow \frac{x^2+1}{x} = \frac{13}{6} \Rightarrow 6x^2 - 13x + 6 = 0 \Rightarrow 6x^2 - 9x - 4x + 6 = 0$$

$$\Rightarrow (3x-2)(2x-3) = 0 \Rightarrow x = \frac{2}{3} \text{ or } x = \frac{3}{2}.$$

Hence, the required number is $\frac{2}{3}$ or $\frac{3}{2}$.

Ex. 4. ***The sum of two numbers is 184. If one-third of the one exceeds one-seventh of the other by 8, find the smaller number.*** **(Bank Recruitment, 2011)**

Sol. Let the numbers be x and $(184 - x)$. Then,

$$\frac{x}{3} - \frac{(184-x)}{7} = 8 \Rightarrow 7x - 3(184 - x) = 168 \Rightarrow 10x = 720 \Rightarrow x = 72.$$

So, the numbers are 72 and 112. Hence, smaller number = 72.

Ex. 5. ***The difference of two numbers is 11 and one-fifth of their sum is 9. Find the numbers.***

Sol. Let the numbers be x and y. Then

$$x - y = 11 \quad \ldots(i)$$

and $$\frac{1}{5}(x + y) = 9 \Rightarrow x + y = 45 \quad \ldots(ii)$$

Adding (*i*) and (*ii*), we get : $2x = 56$ or $x = 28$.

Putting $x = 28$ in (*i*), we get : $y = 17$.

Hence, the numbers are 28 and 17.

Ex. 6. ***If the sum of two numbers is 42 and their product is 437, then find the absolute difference between the numbers.*** **(S.S.C., 2003; B.Ed., 2010)**

Sol. Let the numbers be x and y. Then, $x + y = 42$ and $xy = 437$.

$$x - y = \sqrt{(x+y)^2 - 4xy} = \sqrt{(42)^2 - 4 \times 437} = \sqrt{1764 - 1748} = \sqrt{16} = 4.$$

$\therefore$ Required difference = 4.

Ex. 7. ***If the sum of two numbers is 10 and the sum of their reciprocals is $\frac{5}{12}$, find the numbers.*** **(P.C.S., 2006)**

Sol. Let the numbers be x and y.

Then, $x + y = 10$ ...(*i*)

And, $\frac{1}{x}+\frac{1}{y}=\frac{5}{12} \Rightarrow \frac{x+y}{xy} = \frac{5}{12} \Rightarrow xy = \frac{10\times12}{5} = 24$ ...(*ii*)

$\therefore\ x - y = \sqrt{(x+y)^2 - 4xy} = \sqrt{(10)^2 - 4\times24} = \sqrt{100-96} = \sqrt{4} = 2 \Rightarrow x - y = 2$ ...(*iii*)

Adding (*i*) and (*iii*), we get: $2x = 12$ or $x = 6$.

Putting $x = 6$ in (*i*), we get: $y = 4$.

Hence, the required numbers are 6 and 4.

Ex. 8. ***Three numbers are in the ratio 3 : 2 : 5. The sum of their squares is 1862. Find the numbers.*** **(R.R.B., 2007)**

Sol. Let the numbers be $3x$, $2x$ and $5x$.

Then, $(3x)^2 + (2x)^2 + (5x)^2 = 1862 \Rightarrow 9x^2 + 4x^2 + 25x^2 = 1862$

$\Rightarrow 38x^2 = 1862 \Rightarrow x^2 = \frac{1862}{38} = 49 \Rightarrow x = \sqrt{49} = 7.$

Hence, the numbers are 21, 14 and 35.

Ex. 9. ***The sum of seven consecutive natural numbers is 1617. How many of these numbers are prime?*** **(S.S.C., 2006)**

Sol. Let the seven consecutive numbers be x, $(x + 1)$, $(x + 2)$, $(x + 3)$, $(x + 4)$, $(x + 5)$ and $(x + 6)$.

Then, $x + (x + 1) + (x + 2) + (x + 3) + (x + 4) + (x + 5) + (x + 6) = 1617$

$\Rightarrow 7x + 21 = 1617 \Rightarrow 7x = 1596 \Rightarrow x = 228.$

Thus, the numbers are 228, 229, 230, 231, 232, 233 and 234.

Of these numbers, only two numbers i.e. 229 and 233, are prime.

Ex. 10. ***The product of two consecutive numbers is 4032. Find the numbers.*** **(Bank P.O., 2008)**

Sol. Let the numbers be x and $(x + 1)$.

Then, $x(x + 1) = 4032 \Rightarrow x^2 + x - 4032 = 0 \Rightarrow x^2 + 64x - 63x - 4032 = 0$

$\Rightarrow x(x + 64) - 63(x + 64) = 0 \Rightarrow (x + 64)(x - 63) = 0$

$\Rightarrow x = 63.$ $[\because x \neq -64]$

Hence, the required numbers are 63 and 64.

Ex. 11. ***The sum of two numbers is 15 and the sum of their squares is 113. Find the numbers.*** **(R.R.B., 2006)**

Sol. Let the numbers be x and $(15 - x)$.

Then, $x^2 + (15 - x)^2 = 113 \Rightarrow x^2 + 225 + x^2 - 30x = 113$

$\Rightarrow 2x^2 - 30x + 112 = 0 \Rightarrow x^2 - 15x + 56 = 0$

$\Rightarrow (x - 7)(x - 8) = 0 \Rightarrow x = 7$ or $x = 8$.

So, the numbers are 7 and 8.

Ex. 12. ***The average of four consecutive even numbers is 27. Find the largest of these numbers.***

Sol. Let the four consecutive even numbers be x, $x + 2$, $x + 4$ and $x + 6$.

Then, sum of these numbers = $(27 \times 4) = 108$.

So, $x + (x + 2) + (x + 4) + (x + 6) = 108$ or $4x = 96$ or $x = 24$.

$\therefore$ Largest number = $(x + 6) = 30$.

Ex. 13. ***The sum of the squares of three consecutive odd numbers is 2531. Find the numbers.*** **(R.R.B., 2010)**

Sol. Let the numbers be x, $x + 2$ and $x + 4$.

Then, $x^2 + (x + 2)^2 + (x + 4)^2 = 2531 \Rightarrow 3x^2 + 12x - 2511 = 0 \Rightarrow x^2 + 4x - 837 = 0$

$\Rightarrow (x - 27)(x + 31) = 0 \Rightarrow x = 27.$

Hence, the required numbers are 27, 29 and 31.

Ex. 14. ***Of two numbers, 4 times the smaller one is less than 3 times the larger one by 5. If the sum of the numbers is larger than 6 times their difference by 6, find the two numbers.***

Sol. Let the numbers be x and y, such that $x > y$.

Then, $3x - 4y = 5$ ...(*i*)

and $(x + y) - 6(x - y) = 6 \Rightarrow -5x + 7y = 6$ ...(*ii*)

Solving (*i*) and (*ii*), we get : $x = 59$ and $y = 43$.

Hence, the required numbers are 59 and 43.

Ex. 15. ***The ratio between a two-digit number and the sum of the digits of that number is 4 : 1. If the digit in the unit's place is 3 more than the digit in the ten's place, what is the number?*** **(S.B.I.P.O., 2005)**

Sol. Let the ten's digit be x. Then, unit's digit $= (x + 3)$.

Sum of the digits $= x + (x + 3) = 2x + 3$. Number $= 10x + (x + 3) = 11x + 3$.

$\therefore \frac{11x+3}{2x+3} = \frac{4}{1} \Leftrightarrow 11x + 3 = 4(2x + 3) \Leftrightarrow 3x = 9 \Leftrightarrow x = 3.$

Hence, required number $= 11x + 3 = 36$.

Ex. 16. ***A number consists of two digits. The sum of the digits is 9. If 63 is subtracted from the number, its digits are interchanged. Find the number.***

Sol. Let the ten's digit be x. Then, unit's digit $= (9 - x)$.

Number $= 10x + (9 - x) = 9x + 9$.

Number obtained by reversing the digits $= 10(9 - x) + x = 90 - 9x$.

$\therefore (9x + 9) - 63 = 90 - 9x \Leftrightarrow 18x = 144 \Leftrightarrow x = 8.$

So, ten's digit = 8 and unit's digit = 1.

Hence, the required number is 81.

Ex. 17. ***In a three-digit number, the digit in the units place is four times the digit in the hundreds place. If the digits in the units place and the tens place are interchanged, the new number so formed is 18 more than the original number. If the digit in the hundreds place is one-third of the digit in the tens place, what is the original number?*** **(L.I.C., 2005)**

Sol. Let the digit in the hundreds place be x.

Then, digit in the units place $= 4x$. And, digit in the tens place $= 3x$.

Original number $= 100x + 10 \times 3x + 4x = 100x + 30x + 4x = 134x$.

Number formed on interchanging the unit's and ten's digits

$= 100x + 10 \times 4x + 3x = 143x$.

$\therefore 143x - 134x = 18 \Leftrightarrow 9x = 18 \Leftrightarrow x = 2.$

Hence, original number $= 134x = (134 \times 2) = 268$.

Ex. 18. ***If the digits of a two-digit number are interchanged, the number formed is greater than the original number by 45. If the difference between the digits is 5, what is the original number?*** **(Bank P.O., 2009)**

Sol. Since the number formed by interchanging the digits is greater so the ten's digit of the original number is smaller than the unit's digit.

Let the ten's digit be x. Then, unit's digit $= x + 5$.

Original number $= 10x + (x + 5) = 11x + 5$.

Number formed on interchanging the digits $= 10(x + 5) + x = 11x + 50$.

$\therefore (11x + 50) - (11x + 5) = 45 \Rightarrow 45 = 45$, which is independent of x.

Hence, the number cannot be determined from the given data.

Ex. 19. ***A fraction becomes $\frac{2}{3}$ when 1 is added to both its numerator and denominator. And, it becomes $\frac{1}{2}$ when 1 is subtracted from both the numerator and denominator. Find the fraction.***

Sol. Let the required fraction be $\frac{x}{y}$. Then,

$\frac{x+1}{y+1} = \frac{2}{3} \Rightarrow 3x - 2y = -1$ ...(*i*) and $\frac{x-1}{y-1} = \frac{1}{2} \Rightarrow 2x - y = 1$ ... (i)

Solving (*i*) and (*ii*), we get : $x = 3, y = 5$.

$\therefore$ Required fraction $= \frac{3}{5}$.

Ex. 20. ***50 is divided into two parts such that the sum of their reciprocals is $\frac{1}{12}$. Find the two parts.***

Sol. Let the two parts be x and $(50 - x)$.

Then, $\frac{1}{x} + \frac{1}{50 - x} = \frac{1}{12} \Rightarrow \frac{50 - x + x}{x(50 - x)} = \frac{1}{12} \Rightarrow x^2 - 50x + 600 = 0$

$\Rightarrow (x - 30)(x - 20) = 0 \Rightarrow x = 30$ or $x = 20$.

So, the parts are 30 and 20.

Ex. 21. ***If three numbers are added in pairs, the sums equal 10, 19 and 21. Find the numbers.***

Sol. Let the numbers be x, y and z. Then,

$x + y = 10$ ...(i)

$y + z = 19$ ...(ii)

$x + z = 21$ ...(iii)

Adding (i), (ii) and (iii), we get : $2(x + y + z) = 50$ or $(x + y + z) = 25$.

Thus, $x = (25 - 19) = 6$; $y = (25 - 21) = 4$; $z = (25 - 10) = 15$.

Hence, the required numbers are 6, 4 and 15.

EXERCISE

(OBJECTIVE TYPE QUESTIONS)

Directions : *Mark (✓) against the correct answer:*

1. By how much is $\frac{3}{4}$th of 568 lesser than $\frac{7}{8}$th of 1008? **(Bank P.O., 2008)**
(a) 444 (b) 448
(c) 452 (d) 456
(e) None of these

2. The difference between a number and its three-fifths is 50. What is the number?
(a) 75 (b) 100
(c) 125 (d) None of these

3. If a number is added to two-fifths of itself, the value so obtained is 455. What is the number? **(Bank Recruitment, 2010)**
(a) 325 (b) 350
(c) 400 (d) 420
(e) None of these

4. If a number is multiplied by two-thirds of itself the value so obtained is 864. What is the number? **(Bank Recruitment, 2010)**
(a) 34 (b) 36
(c) 38 (d) 44
(e) 46

5. If a number is decreased by 4 and divided by 6, the result is 8. What would be the result if 2 is subtracted from the number and then it is divided by 5?
(a) $9\frac{2}{3}$ (b) 10
(c) $10\frac{1}{5}$ (d) $11\frac{1}{5}$
(e) None of these

6. A number when multiplied by 13 is increased by 180. The number is **(P.C.S., 2004)**
(a) 5 (b) 12
(c) 15 (d) 45

7. The sum of twice a number and three times of 42 is 238. What is the sum of thrice the number and two times of 42? **(Bank P.O., 2010)**
(a) 245 (b) 250
(c) 252 (d) 264
(e) None of these

8. If one-third of one-fourth of a number is 15, then three-tenths of that number is
(a) 35 (b) 36
(c) 45 (d) 54

9. The difference between $\frac{3}{5}$th of $\frac{2}{3}$rd of a number and $\frac{2}{5}$th of $\frac{1}{4}$th of the same number is 288. What is the number? **(Bank P.O., 2006)**
(a) 850 (b) 895
(c) 955 (d) 960

10. A number is doubled and 9 is added. If the resultant is trebled, it becomes 75. What is that number?
(a) 3.5 (b) 6
(c) 8 (d) None of these

11. Three-fourth of a number is 60 more than its one-third. The number is
(a) 84 (b) 108
(c) 144 (d) None of these

12. A number whose fifth part increased by 4 is equal to its fourth part diminished by 10, is **(SNAP, 2010)**
(a) 240 (b) 260
(c) 270 (d) 280

13. When 24 is subtracted from a number, it reduces to its four-seventh. What is the sum of the digits of that number?
(*a*) 1 (*b*) 9
(*c*) 11 (*d*) Data inadequate
(*e*) None of these

14. Find the number which when multiplied by 15 is increased by 196. **(L.I.C., 2003)**
(*a*) 14 (*b*) 20
(*c*) 26 (*d*) 28

15. If a number, when divided by 4, is reduced by 21, the number is
(*a*) 18 (*b*) 20
(*c*) 28 (*d*) 38

16. A number whose fifth part increased by 4 is equal to its fourth part diminished by 10, is
(*a*) 240 (*b*) 260
(*c*) 270 (*d*) 280

17. The difference of two numbers is 20% of the larger number. If the smaller number is 12, the larger one is
(*a*) 15 (*b*) 16
(*c*) 18 (*d*) 20

18. If one-seventh of a number exceeds its eleventh part by 100, then the number is
(*a*) 770 (*b*) 1100
(*c*) 1825 (*d*) 1925

19. If the sum of one-half and one-fifth of a number exceeds one-third of that number by $7\frac{1}{3}$, the number is
(*a*) 15 (*b*) 18
(*c*) 20 (*d*) 30

20. If doubling a number and adding 20 to the result gives the same answer as multiplying the number by 8 and taking away 4 from the product, the number is
(*a*) 2 (*b*) 3
(*c*) 4 (*d*) 6

21. If 50 is subtracted from two-third of a number, the result is equal to sum of 40 and one-fourth of that number. What is the number? **(R.R.B., 2002)**
(*a*) 174 (*b*) 216
(*c*) 246 (*d*) 336

22. A student was asked to divide the half of a certain number by 6 and the other half by 4 and then to add the two quantities so obtained. Instead of doing so the student divided the number by 5 and the result fell short by 4. The given number was **(P.C.S., 2009)**
(*a*) 240 (*b*) 288
(*c*) 384 (*d*) 480

23. One-third of a two-digit number exceeds one-fourth of its successive number by 1. The number is
(*a*) 12 (*b*) 15
(*c*) 18 (*d*) 21

24. If the sum of a number and its square is 182, what is the number?
(*a*) 15 (*b*) 26
(*c*) 28 (*d*) 91
(*e*) None of these

25. If $(73)^2$ is subtracted from the square of a number, the answer so obtained is 5075. What is the number? **(L.I.C.A.D.O., 2007)**
(*a*) 96 (*b*) 98
(*c*) 102 (*d*) 106

26. Twenty times a positive integer is less than its square by 96. What is the integer?
(*a*) 20
(*b*) 24
(*c*) 30
(*d*) Cannot be determined
(*e*) None of these

27. Thrice the square of a natural number decreased by 4 times the number is equal to 50 more than the number. The number is **(S.S.C., 2003)**
(*a*) 4 (*b*) 5
(*c*) 6 (*d*) 10

28. The sum of a number and its reciprocal is one-eighth of 34. What is the product of the number and its square root?
(*a*) 8 (*b*) 27
(*c*) 32 (*d*) None of these

29. Two-third of a positive number and $\frac{25}{216}$ of its reciprocal are equal. The number is
(*a*) $\frac{5}{12}$ (*b*) $\frac{12}{5}$
(*c*) $\frac{25}{144}$ (*d*) $\frac{144}{25}$

30. Find the whole number which when increased by 20 is equal to 69 times the reciprocal of the number. **(M.A.T., 2007)**
(*a*) 2.5 (*b*) 3
(*c*) 5 (*d*) 7

31. A positive number when decreased by 4 is equal to 21 times the reciprocal of the number. The number is
(*a*) 3 (*b*) 5
(*c*) 7 (*d*) 9

32. The sum and product of two numbers are 12 and 35 respectively. The sum of their reciprocals will be **(S.S.C., 2007)**

(a) $\frac{12}{35}$ (b) $\frac{1}{35}$

(c) $\frac{35}{8}$ (d) $\frac{7}{32}$

33. The sum of a positive number and its reciprocal is thrice the difference of the number and its reciprocal. The number is

(a) $\sqrt{2}$ (b) $\frac{1}{\sqrt{2}}$

(c) $\sqrt{3}$ (d) $\frac{1}{\sqrt{3}}$

34. The product of two whole numbers is 37. The square root of the difference of the numbers is **(C.P.O., 2007)**

(a) 4.5 (b) 6

(c) 7.5 (d) 8

35. The product of two natural numbers is 17. Then, the sum of the reciprocals of their squares is

(a) $\frac{1}{289}$ (b) $\frac{289}{290}$

(c) $\frac{290}{289}$ (d) 289

36. If $2\frac{1}{2}$ is added to a number and the sum multiplied by $4\frac{1}{2}$ and 3 is added to the product and the sum is divided by $1\frac{1}{5}$, the quotient becomes 25. What is the number?

(a) $2\frac{1}{2}$ (b) $3\frac{1}{2}$

(c) $4\frac{1}{2}$ (d) $5\frac{1}{2}$

37. Three numbers are in the ratio 4 : 5 : 6 and their average is 25. The largest number is

(a) 30 (b) 32

(c) 36 (d) 42

38. Three numbers are in the ratio of 3 : 4 : 6 and their product is 1944. The largest of these numbers is **(M.B.A., 2006)**

(a) 6 (b) 12

(c) 18 (d) None of these

39. The ratio between a two-digit number and the sum of the digits of that number is 4 : 1. If the digit in the unit's place is 3 more than the digit in the ten's place, then the number is **(M.B.A., 2004)**

(a) 24 (b) 36

(c) 63 (d) 96

40. Two numbers are such that the square of one is 224 less than 8 times the square of the other. If the numbers be in the ratio of 3 : 4, the numbers are

(a) 6, 8 (b) 9, 12

(c) 12, 16 (d) None of these

41. Two numbers are such that the ratio between them is 4 : 7. If each is increased by 4, the ratio becomes 3 : 5. The larger number is

(a) 36 (b) 48

(c) 56 (d) 64

42. The sum of three numbers is 264. If the first number be twice the second and third number be one-third of the first, then the second number is: **(R.R.B., 2004)**

(a) 48 (b) 54

(c) 72 (d) 84

43. The sum of two numbers is 22. Five times one number is equal to 6 times the other. The bigger of the two numbers is

(a) 10 (b) 12

(c) 15 (d) 16

44. One-fifth of a number is equal to $\frac{5}{8}$ of another number. If 35 is added to the first number, it becomes four times of the second number. The second number is

(a) 25 (b) 40

(c) 70 (d) 125

45. The sum of two numbers is 25 and their difference is 13. Find their product.

(a) 104 (b) 114

(c) 315 (d) 325

46. If the sum of two numbers is 33 and their difference is 15, the smaller number is

(a) 9 (b) 12

(c) 15 (d) 18

47. The sum of two numbers is 40 and their difference is 4. The ratio of the numbers is

(a) 11 : 9 (b) 11 : 18

(c) 21 : 19 (d) 22 : 9

48. The product of two numbers is 192 and the sum of these two numbers is 28. What is the smaller of these two numbers?

(a) 12 (b) 14

(c) 16 (d) 18

(e) None of these

49. There are two numbers such that the sum of twice the first number and thrice the second number is 100 and the sum of thrice the first number and twice the second number is 120. Which is the larger number? **(Bank P.O., 2010)**

(a) 12 (b) 14
(c) 32 (d) 35
(e) None of these

50. What is the greater of the two numbers whose product is 1092 and the sum of the two numbers exceeds their difference by 42? **(S.B.I.P.O., 2008)**

(a) 44 (b) 48
(c) 52 (d) 54
(e) None of these

51. The difference between two integers is 5. Their product is 500. Find the numbers. **(Hotel Management, 2003)**

(a) 15, 20 (b) 20, 25
(c) 30, 25 (d) 21, 26

52. Two numbers differ by 5. If their product is 336, then the sum of the two numbers is

(a) 21 (b) 28
(c) 37 (d) 51

53. Two different natural numbers are such that their product is less than their sum. One of the numbers must be

(a) 1 (b) 2
(c) 3 (d) None of these

54. The product of two numbers is 9375 and the quotient, when the larger one is divided by the smaller, is 15. The sum of the numbers is. **(S.S.C., 2004)**

(a) 380 (b) 395
(c) 400 (d) 425

55. The difference between two numbers is 1365. When the larger number is divided by the smaller one, the quotient is 6 and the remainder is 15. The smaller number is

(a) 240 (b) 270
(c) 295 (d) 360

56. The difference between two numbers is 16. If one-third of the smaller number is greater than one-seventh of the larger number by 4, then the two numbers are

(a) 9 and 25 (b) 12 and 28
(c) 33 and 49 (d) 56 and 72

57. The sum of two numbers is 40 and their product is 375. What will be the sum of their reciprocals?

(a) $\frac{1}{40}$ (b) $\frac{8}{75}$
(c) $\frac{75}{4}$ (d) $\frac{75}{8}$

58. The sum of two positive integers multiplied by the bigger number is 204, and their difference multiplied by the smaller number is 35. The numbers are

(a) 12, 5 (b) 13, 4
(c) 14, 3 (d) 24, 10

59. If the sum and difference of two numbers are 20 and 8 respectively, then the difference of their squares is

(a) 12 (b) 28
(c) 160 (d) 180

60. Two numbers are such that their difference, their sum and their product are to one another as 1 : 7 : 24. The product of the two numbers is **(M.B.A., 2010)**

(a) 6 (b) 12
(c) 24 (d) 48

61. The product of two numbers is 120 and the sum of their squares is 289. The sum of the numbers is **(R.R.B., 2004)**

(a) 20 (b) 23
(c) 169 (d) None of these

62. The product of two numbers is 45 and the sum of their squares is 106. The numbers are **(R.R.B., 2002)**

(a) 3 and 5 (b) 5 and 9
(c) 5 and 19 (d) 45 and 1

63. The sum of the squares of two numbers is 3341 and the difference of their squares is 891. The numbers are **(M.B.A., 2006)**

(a) 25, 36 (b) 25, 46
(c) 35, 46 (d) None of these

64. The difference between two positive integers is 3. If the sum of their squares is 369, then the sum of the numbers is **(S.S.C., 2003)**

(a) 25 (b) 27
(c) 33 (d) 81

65. If the sum of two numbers is 22 and the sum of their squares is 404, then the product of the numbers is

(a) 40 (b) 44
(c) 80 (d) 88

66. The difference between the squares of two numbers is 256000 and the sum of the numbers is 1000. The numbers are

(a) 600, 400 (b) 628, 372
(c) 640, 360 (d) None of these

67. The difference between two numbers is 3 and the difference between their squares is 63. Which is the larger number? **(Bank P.O., 2009)**

(a) 9
(b) 12
(c) 15
(d) Cannot be determined
(e) None of these

68. A, B, C, D and E are five consecutive odd numbers. The sum of A and C is 146. What is the value of E? **(Bank P.O., 2009)**

(*a*) 71 (*b*) 75
(*c*) 79 (*d*) 81
(*e*) None of these

69. Out of six consecutive natural numbers if the sum of first three is 27, what is the sum of the other three? **(S.S.C., 2010)**

(*a*) 24 (*b*) 25
(*c*) 35 (*d*) 36

70. The sum of seven consecutive numbers is 175. What is the difference between twice the largest number and thrice the smallest number? **(Bank Recruitment, 2010)**

(*a*) 7 (*b*) 8
(*c*) 10 (*d*) 12
(*e*) None of these

71. The sum of five consecutive odd numbers is 575. What is the sum of the next set of five consecutive odd numbers? **(NABARD, 2009)**

(*a*) 595
(*b*) 615
(*c*) 635
(*d*) Cannot be determined
(*e*) None of these

72. The sum of three consecutive odd numbers and three consecutive even numbers together is 231. Also, the smallest odd number is 11 less than the smallest even number. What is the sum of the largest odd number and the largest even number? **(Bank P.O., 2010)**

(*a*) 74
(*b*) 82
(*c*) 83
(*d*) Cannot be determined
(*e*) None of these

73. Three times the first of three consecutive odd integers is 3 more than twice the third. The third integer is **(M.B.A., 1998)**

(*a*) 9 (*b*) 11
(*c*) 13 (*d*) 15

74. The sum of four consecutive even integers is 1284. The greatest of them is

(*a*) 320 (*b*) 322
(*c*) 324 (*d*) 326

75. The sum of three consecutive odd numbers is 20 more than the first of these numbers. What is the middle number?

(*a*) 7 (*b*) 9
(*c*) 11 (*d*) Data inadequate
(*e*) None of these

76. The product of three consecutive even numbers when divided by 8 is 720. The product of their square roots is **(Hotel Management, 2006)**

(*a*) $12\sqrt{10}$ (*b*) $24\sqrt{10}$
(*c*) 120 (*d*) None of these

77. The sum of three consecutive multiples of 3 is 72. What is the largest number?

(*a*) 21 (*b*) 24
(*c*) 27 (*d*) 36

78. What is the sum of two consecutive even numbers, the difference of whose squares is 84? **(S.S.C., 2003)**

(*a*) 34 (*b*) 38
(*c*) 42 (*d*) 46

79. The sum of the squares of three consecutive natural numbers is 2030. What is the middle number?

(*a*) 25 (*b*) 26
(*c*) 27 (*d*) 28

80. If the product of three consecutive integers is 120, then the sum of the integers is **(M.B.A., 2006)**

(*a*) 9 (*b*) 12
(*c*) 14 (*d*) 15
(*e*) 18

81. There are two numbers such that the sum of twice the first and thrice the second is 39, while the sum of thrice the first and twice the second is 36. The larger of the two is

(*a*) 6 (*b*) 8
(*c*) 9 (*d*) 12

82. In a two-digit number, the digit in the unit's place is four times the digit in ten's place and sum of the digits is equal to 10. What is the number?

(*a*) 14 (*b*) 41
(*c*) 82 (*d*) Data inadequate
(*e*) None of these

83. A number of two digits has 3 for its unit's digit, and the sum of digits is $\frac{1}{7}$ of the number itself. The number is **(L.I.C., 2003)**

(*a*) 43 (*b*) 53
(*c*) 63 (*d*) 73

84. If a number of two digits is k times the sum of its digits, then the number formed by interchanging the digits is the sum of the digits multiplied by **(M.B.A., 2005)**

(*a*) $k - 1$ (*b*) $11 - k$
(*c*) $9 + k$ (*d*) $10 - k$

85. A two-digit number exceeds the sum of the digits of that number by 18. If the digit at the unit's place is double the digit in the ten's place, what is the number?
(*a*) 24 (*b*) 42
(*c*) 48 (*d*) Data inadequate

86. The sum of the digits of a two-digit number is 15 and the difference between the digits is 3. What is the two-digit number?
(*a*) 69
(*b*) 78
(*c*) 96
(*d*) Cannot be determined
(*e*) None of these

87. A two-digit number is 7 times the sum of its two digits. The number that is formed by reversing its digits is 18 less than the original number. What is the number? **(R.R.B., 2006)**
(*a*) 42 (*b*) 52
(*c*) 62 (*d*) 72

88. If the digit in the unit's place of a two-digit number is halved and the digit in the ten's place is doubled, the number thus obtained is equal to the number obtained by interchanging the digits. Which of the following is definitely true? **(NMAT, 2005)**
(*a*) Sum of the digits is a two-digit number.
(*b*) Digit in the unit's place is half of the digit in the ten's place.
(*c*) Digit in the unit's place and the ten's place are equal.
(*d*) Digit in the unit's place is twice the digit in the ten's place.

89. In a two-digit number, if it is known that its unit's digit exceeds its ten's digit by 2 and that the product of the given number and the sum of its digits is equal to 144, then the number is **(C.B.I., 2003)**
(*a*) 24 (*b*) 26
(*c*) 42 (*d*) 46

90. A number consists of two digits. If the digits interchange places and the new number is added to the original number, then the resulting number will be divisible by **(S.S.C., 2003)**
(*a*) 3 (*b*) 5
(*c*) 9 (*d*) 11

91. The sum of the digits of a two-digit number is 9 less than the number. Which of the following digits is at unit's place of the number?
(*a*) 1 (*b*) 2
(*c*) 4 (*d*) Data inadequate

92. The difference between a two-digit number and the number obtained by interchanging the positions of its digits is 36. What is the difference between the two digits of that number? **(Bank P.O., 2003)**
(*a*) 3 (*b*) 4
(*c*) 9 (*d*) Cannot be determined
(*e*) None of these

93. The difference between a two-digit number and the number obtained by interchanging the two digits is 63. Which is the smaller of the two numbers? **(Bank P.O., 2003)**
(*a*) 29
(*b*) 70
(*c*) 92
(*d*) Cannot be determined
(*e*) None of these

94. The sum of the digits of a two-digit number is $\frac{1}{5}$ of the difference between the number and the number obtained by interchanging the positions of the digits. What is definitely the difference between the digits of that number?
(*a*) 5 (*b*) 7
(*c*) 9 (*d*) Data inadequate
(*e*) None of these

95. The number obtained by interchanging the two digits of a two-digit number is lesser than the original number by 54. If the sum of the two digit of the number is 12, then what is the original number? **(Bank P.O., 2009)**
(*a*) 28
(*b*) 39
(*c*) 82
(*d*) Cannot be determined
(*e*) None of these

96. The difference between a two-digit number and the number obtained by interchanging the digits is 36. What is the difference between the sum and the difference of the digits of the number if the ratio between the digits of the number is 1 : 2?
(*a*) 4 (*b*) 8
(*c*) 16 (*d*) None of these

97. In a two-digit positive number, the digit in the unit's place is equal to the square of the digit in ten's place, and the difference between the number and the number obtained by interchanging the digits is 54. What is 40% of the original number? **(Bank P.O., 2008)**
(*a*) 15.6 (*b*) 24
(*c*) 37.2 (*d*) 39
(*e*) None of these

98. A number consists of 3 digits whose sum is 10. The middle digit is equal to the sum of the other two and the number will be increased by 99 if its digits are reversed. The number is **(Hotel Management, 2003)**

(*a*) 145 (*b*) 253
(*c*) 370 (*d*) 352

99. A two-digit number becomes five-sixth of itself when its digits are reversed. The two digits differ by one. The number is

(*a*) 45 (*b*) 54
(*c*) 56 (*d*) 65

100. If the square of a two-digit number is reduced by the square of the number formed by reversing the digits of the number, the final result is **(N.M.A.T., 2008)**

(*a*) divisible by 11 (*b*) divisible by 9
(*c*) necessarily irrational (*d*) Both (*a*) and (*b*)

101. A number consists of two digits such that the digit in the ten's place is less by 2 than the digit in the unit's place. Three times the number added to $\frac{6}{7}$ times the number obtained by reversing the digits equals 108. The sum of the digits in the number is **(S.S.C., 2003)**

(*a*) 6 (*b*) 7
(*c*) 8 (*d*) 9

102. The digit in the unit's place of a number is equal to the digit in the ten's place of half of that number and the digit in the ten's place of that number is less than the digit in unit's place of half of the number by 1. If the sum of the digits of the number is 7, then what is the number? **(S.B.I.P.O., 2001)**

(*a*) 34 (*b*) 52
(*c*) 162 (*d*) Data inadequate
(*e*) None of these

103. In a two-digit number, the digit in the unit's place is more than twice the digit in ten's place by 1. If the digits in the unit's place and the ten's place are interchanged, difference between the newly formed number and the original number is less than the original number by 1. What is the original number?

(*a*) 25 (*b*) 37
(*c*) 49 (*d*) 52
(*e*) 73

104. A certain number of two digits is three times the sum of its digits and if 45 be added to it, the digits are reversed. The number is **(N.M.A.T. 2006; L.I.C.A.A.O., 2003)**

(*a*) 23 (*b*) 27
(*c*) 32 (*d*) 72

105. A two-digit number is such that the product of the digits is 8. When 18 is added to the number, then the digits are reversed. The number is **(M.B.A., 2003)**

(*a*) 18 (*b*) 24
(*c*) 42 (*d*) 81

106. In a number of three digits, the digits in the unit's place and in the hundred's place are equal and the sum of all the digits is 8. The number of such numbers is

(*a*) 3 (*b*) 4
(*c*) 5 (*d*) 6

107. In a three-digit number, the digit in the unit's place is 75% of the digit in the ten's place. The digit in the ten's place is greater than the digit in the hundred's place by 1. If the sum of the digits in the ten's place and the hundred's place is 15, what is the number? **(Bank P.O., 2006)**

(*a*) 687
(*b*) 786
(*c*) 795
(*d*) Cannot be determined
(*e*) None of these

108. The product of two fractions is $\frac{14}{15}$ and their quotient is $\frac{35}{24}$. The greater fraction is **(S.S.C., 2005)**

(*a*) $\frac{4}{5}$ (*b*) $\frac{7}{6}$
(*c*) $\frac{7}{4}$ (*d*) $\frac{7}{3}$

109. In a pair of fractions, fraction A is twice the fraction B and the product of two fractions is $\frac{2}{25}$. What is the value of fraction A?

(*a*) $\frac{1}{5}$ (*b*) $\frac{1}{25}$
(*c*) $\frac{2}{5}$ (*d*) Data inadequate

110. If the difference between the reciprocal of a positive proper fraction and the fraction itself be $\frac{9}{20}$, then the fraction is **(C.P.O., 2006)**

(*a*) $\frac{3}{5}$ (*b*) $\frac{4}{5}$
(*c*) $\frac{5}{4}$ (*d*) $\frac{3}{10}$

111. The sum of the numerator and denominator of a fraction is 11. If 1 is added to the numerator and 2 is subtracted from the denominator, it becomes $\frac{2}{3}$. The fraction is

(*a*) $\frac{5}{6}$ (*b*) $\frac{6}{5}$
(*c*) $\frac{3}{8}$ (*d*) $\frac{8}{3}$

112. The denominator of a fraction is 3 more than the numerator. If the numerator as well as the denominator is increased by 4, the fraction becomes $\frac{4}{5}$. What was the original fraction?

(a) $\frac{8}{11}$ (b) $\frac{5}{8}$

(c) $\frac{10}{13}$ (d) $\frac{7}{10}$

113. The difference between the numerator and the denominator of a fraction is 5. If 5 is added to its denominator, the fraction is decreased by $1\frac{1}{4}$. Find the value of the fraction.

(a) $\frac{1}{6}$ (b) $2\frac{1}{4}$

(c) $3\frac{1}{4}$ (d) 6

114. The numerator and denominator of a fraction are in the ratio of 2 : 3. If 6 is subtracted from the numerator, the result is a fraction that has a value $\frac{2}{3}$ of the original fraction. The numerator of the original fraction is

(a) 6 (b) 18

(c) 27 (d) 36

115. If 1 is added to the denominator of a fraction, the fraction becomes $\frac{1}{2}$. If 1 is added to the numerator of the fraction, the fraction becomes 1. The fraction is

(a) $\frac{1}{3}$ (b) $\frac{2}{3}$

(c) $\frac{3}{4}$ (d) $\frac{3}{2}$

116. If the numerator of a fraction is increased by 2 and the denominator is increased by 3, the fraction becomes $\frac{7}{9}$ and if both the numerator as well as the denominator are decreased by 1, the fraction becomes $\frac{4}{5}$. What is the original fraction?

(a) $\frac{5}{6}$ (b) $\frac{9}{11}$

(c) $\frac{13}{16}$ (d) $\frac{17}{21}$

117. If the numerator of a fraction is increased by $\frac{1}{4}$ and the denominator is decreased by $\frac{1}{3}$, the new fraction obtained is $\frac{33}{64}$. What was the original fraction?

(Bank P.O., 2008)

(a) $\frac{3}{7}$ (b) $\frac{5}{7}$

(c) $\frac{7}{9}$ (d) Cannot be determined

(e) None of these

118. If the numerator of a fraction is increased by 200% and the denominator is increased by 300%, the resultant fraction is $\frac{15}{26}$. What was the original fraction?

(S.B.I.P.O., 2008)

(a) $\frac{8}{11}$ (b) $\frac{10}{11}$

(c) $\frac{9}{13}$ (d) $\frac{10}{13}$

(e) None of these

119. When the numerator of a fraction increases by 4, the fraction increases by $\frac{2}{3}$. The denominator of the fraction is

(a) 2 (b) 3

(c) 4 (d) 6

120. A fraction is such that if the double of the numerator and the triple of the denominator is changed by + 10 percent and –30 percent respectively, then we get 11 percent of $\frac{16}{21}$. Find the fraction.

(A.T.M.A., 2004)

(a) $\frac{2}{25}$ (b) $\frac{3}{25}$

(c) $\frac{4}{25}$ (d) None of these

121. 54 is to be divided into two parts such that the sum of 10 times the first and 22 times the second is 780. The bigger part is

(a) 24 (b) 34

(c) 30 (d) 32

122. 243 has been divided into three parts such that half of the first part, one-third of the second part and one-fourth of the third part are equal. The largest part is

(a) 74 (b) 86

(c) 92 (d) 108

123. The sum of four numbers is 64. If you add 3 to the first number, 3 is subtracted from the second number, the third is multiplied by 3 and the fourth is divided by 3, then all the results are equal. What is the difference between the largest and the smallest of the original numbers?

(*a*) 21 (*b*) 27
(*c*) 32 (*d*) Cannot be determined
(*e*) None of these

124. The sum of the squares of three numbers is 138, while the sum of their products taken two at a time is 131. Their sum is **(Hotel Management, 1999)**

(*a*) 20 (*b*) 30
(*c*) 40 (*d*) None of these

125. The sum of three numbers is 136. If the ratio between first and second be 2 : 3 and that between second and third is 5 : 3, then the second number is

(*a*) 40 (*b*) 48
(*c*) 60 (*d*) 72

126. Of the three numbers, the sum of the first two is 73; the sum of the second and the third is 77 and the sum of the third and thrice the first is 104. The third number is **(NABARD, 2008)**

(*a*) 25 (*b*) 39
(*c*) 48 (*d*) Cannot be determined
(*e*) None of these

127. If the product of two numbers is 5 and one of the number is $\frac{3}{2}$, then the sum of two numbers is **[Indian Railways—Gr. 'D' Exam, 2014]**

(a) $4\frac{1}{3}$ (b) $4\frac{2}{3}$
(c) $4\frac{5}{6}$ (d) $5\frac{1}{6}$

128. The sum of the squares of two positive integers is 100 and the difference of their squares is 28. The sum of the numbers is **[Indian Railways—Gr. 'D' Exam, 2014]**

(a) 12 (b) 13
(c) 14 (d) 15

129. The sum of two number is 37 and the difference of their squares is 185, then the difference between the two numbers is: **[SSC—CHSL (10 +2) Exam, 2015]**

(a) 10 (b) 4
(c) 5 (d) 3

130. A man bought some eggs of which 10% are rotten. He gives 80% of the remainder to his neighbors. Now he is left out with 36 eggs. How many eggs he bought? **[SSC—CHSL (10 +2) Exam, 2015]**

(a) 40 (b) 100
(c) 200 (d) 72

131. The sum of two numbers is 75 and their difference is 25. The product of the two numbers is: **[SSC—CHSL (10 +2) Exam, 2015]**

(a) 1350 (b) 1250
(c) 125 (d) 1000

132. In a Mathematics examination the number scored by 5 candidates are 5 successive odd integers. If their total marks are 185, the highest score is **[NICL—AAO Exam, 2015]**

(a) 39 (b) 43
(c) 41 (d) 47

133. The difference between two numbers is 10 and one-fifth of their sum is equal to 8. Find the smaller number **[ESIC—UDC Exam, 2016]**

(a) 28 (b) 45
(c) 35 (d) 15

ANSWERS

1. (*d*)	2. (*c*)	3. (*a*)	4. (*b*)	5. (*b*)	6. (*c*)	7. (*c*)	8. (*d*)	9. (*d*)	10. (*c*)
11. (*c*)	12. (*d*)	13. (*c*)	14. (*a*)	15. (*c*)	16. (*d*)	17. (*a*)	18. (*d*)	19. (*c*)	20. (*c*)
21. (*b*)	22. (*d*)	23. (*b*)	24. (*e*)	25. (*c*)	26. (*b*)	27. (*b*)	28. (*a*)	29. (*a*)	30. (*b*)
31. (*c*)	32. (*a*)	33. (*a*)	34. (*b*)	35. (*c*)	36. (*b*)	37. (*a*)	38. (*c*)	39. (*b*)	40. (*a*)
41. (*c*)	42. (*c*)	43. (*b*)	44. (*b*)	45. (*b*)	46. (*a*)	47. (*a*)	48. (*a*)	49. (*c*)	50. (*c*)
51. (*b*)	52. (*c*)	53. (*a*)	54. (*c*)	55. (*b*)	56. (*c*)	57. (*b*)	58. (*a*)	59. (*c*)	60. (*d*)
61. (*b*)	62. (*b*)	63. (*c*)	64. (*b*)	65. (*a*)	66. (*b*)	67. (*b*)	68. (*c*)	69. (*d*)	70. (*e*)
71. (*e*)	72. (*e*)	73. (*d*)	74. (*c*)	75. (*b*)	76. (*b*)	77. (*c*)	78. (*c*)	79. (*b*)	80. (*d*)
81. (*c*)	82. (*e*)	83. (*c*)	84. (*b*)	85. (*a*)	86. (*d*)	87. (*a*)	88. (*d*)	89. (*a*)	90. (*d*)
91. (*d*)	92. (*b*)	93. (*d*)	94. (*d*)	95. (*e*)	96. (*b*)	97. (*a*)	98. (*b*)	99. (*b*)	100. (*d*)
101. (*a*)	102. (*b*)	103. (*b*)	104. (*b*)	105. (*b*)	106. (*b*)	107. (*b*)	108. (*b*)	109. (*c*)	110. (*b*)
111. (*c*)	112. (*a*)	113. (*b*)	114. (*b*)	115. (*b*)	116. (*a*)	117. (*d*)	118. (*d*)	119. (*d*)	120. (*a*)
121. (*b*)	122. (*d*)	123. (*c*)	124. (*a*)	125. (*c*)	126. (*e*)	127. (*c*)	128. (*c*)	129. (*c*)	130. (*c*)
131. (*b*)	132. (*c*)	133. (*d*)							

SOLUTIONS

1. $\frac{7}{8}$ of 1008 − $\frac{3}{4}$ of 568 = $\left(1008\times\frac{7}{8}\right)-\left(568\times\frac{3}{4}\right)$
$= 882 - 426 = 456.$

2. Let the number be x.
Then, $x - \frac{3}{5}x = 50 \Leftrightarrow \frac{2}{5}x = 50$
$\Leftrightarrow x = \left(\frac{50\times5}{2}\right) = 125.$

3. Let the number be x.
Then, $x + \frac{2}{5}x = 455 \Leftrightarrow \frac{7}{5}x = 455 \Leftrightarrow x = \left(\frac{455\times5}{7}\right) = 325.$

4. Let the number be x. Then, $x \times \frac{2}{3}x = 864$
$\Leftrightarrow \frac{2}{3}x^2 = 864$
$\Leftrightarrow x^2 = \left(\frac{864\times3}{2}\right) = 1296 \Leftrightarrow x = \sqrt{1296} = 36.$

5. Let the number be x. Then, $\frac{x-4}{6} = 8$
$\Leftrightarrow x - 4 = 48$
$\Leftrightarrow x = 52.$
$\therefore \frac{x-2}{5} = \frac{52-2}{5} = \frac{50}{5} = 10.$

6. Let the number be x.
Then, $13x = x + 180 \Leftrightarrow 12x = 180$
$\Leftrightarrow x = \frac{180}{12} = 15.$

7. Let the number be x.
Then, $2x + 3 \times 42 = 238 \Leftrightarrow 2x + 126 = 238$
$\Leftrightarrow 2x = 112 \Leftrightarrow x = 56.$
$\therefore$ Required sum $= 3x + 2 \times 42 = 3 \times 56 + 2 \times 42$
$= 168 + 84 = 252.$

8. Let the number be x. Then, $\frac{1}{3}$ of $\frac{1}{4}$ of $x = 15$
$\Leftrightarrow x = 15 \times 12 = 180.$
So, required number $= \left(\frac{3}{10}\times180\right) = 54.$

9. Let the number be x.
Then, $\frac{3}{5}$ of $\frac{2}{3}$ of $x - \frac{2}{5}$ of $\frac{1}{4}$ of $x = 288$
$\Leftrightarrow \left(x\times\frac{3}{5}\times\frac{2}{3}\right)-\left(x\times\frac{2}{5}\times\frac{1}{4}\right)=288$
$\Leftrightarrow \frac{2}{5}x - \frac{1}{10}x = 288$
$\Leftrightarrow \frac{3x}{10} = 288 \Leftrightarrow x = \left(\frac{288\times10}{3}\right) = 960.$

10. Let the number be x.
Then, $3(2x + 9) = 75 \Leftrightarrow 2x + 9 = 25$
$\Leftrightarrow 2x = 16 \Leftrightarrow x = 8.$

11. Let the number be x.
Then, $\frac{3}{4}x - \frac{1}{3}x = 60$
$\Leftrightarrow \frac{5x}{12} = 60$
$\Leftrightarrow x = \left(\frac{60\times12}{5}\right) = 144.$

12. Let the number be x.
Then, $\frac{x}{5} + 4 = \frac{x}{4} - 10 \Leftrightarrow \frac{x}{4} - \frac{x}{5} = 14$
$\Leftrightarrow \frac{x}{20} = 14 \Leftrightarrow x = 14 \times 20 = 280.$

13. Let the number be x.
Then, $x - 24 = \frac{4}{7}x \Leftrightarrow x - \frac{4}{7}x = 24$
$\Leftrightarrow \frac{3}{7}x = 24 \Leftrightarrow x = \left(\frac{24\times7}{3}\right) = 56.$
$\therefore$ Sum of the digits $= (5 + 6) = 11.$

14. Let the number be x.
Then, $15x - x = 196$
$\Leftrightarrow 14x = 196$
$\Leftrightarrow x = 14.$

15. Let the number be x.
Then, $\frac{x}{4} = x - 21 \Leftrightarrow x = 4x - 84$
$\Leftrightarrow 3x = 84 \Leftrightarrow x = 28.$

16. Let the number be x.
Then, $\left(\frac{1}{5}x+4\right)=\left(\frac{1}{4}x-10\right)$
$\Leftrightarrow \frac{x}{20} = 14 \Leftrightarrow x = 14\times20 = 280.$

17. Let the number be x.
Then, $x - 12 = 20\%$ of $x \Leftrightarrow x - \frac{x}{5} = 12$
$\Leftrightarrow \frac{4x}{5} = 12 \Leftrightarrow x = \left(\frac{12\times5}{4}\right) = 15.$

18. Let the number be x.
Then, $\frac{1}{7}x - \frac{1}{11}x = 100 \Leftrightarrow \frac{4x}{77}$
$= 100 \Leftrightarrow x = \frac{7700}{4} = 1925.$

19. Let the number be x.
Then, $\left(\frac{1}{2}x+\frac{1}{5}x\right)-\frac{1}{3}x = \frac{22}{3} \Leftrightarrow \frac{11x}{30}$
$= \frac{22}{3} \Leftrightarrow x = \left(\frac{22\times30}{3\times11}\right) = 20.$

20. Let the number be x.
Then, $2x + 20 = 8x - 4 \Leftrightarrow 6x = 24$
$\Leftrightarrow x = 4.$

21. Let the number be x.

Then, $\frac{2}{3}x - 50 = \frac{1}{4}x + 40 \Leftrightarrow \frac{2}{3}x - \frac{1}{4}x = 90$

$\Leftrightarrow \frac{5x}{12} = 90 \Leftrightarrow x = \left(\frac{90 \times 12}{5}\right) = 216.$

22. Let the number be x.

Then, $\left[\frac{(x/2)}{6} + \frac{(x/2)}{4}\right] - \frac{x}{5} = 4 \Leftrightarrow \frac{x}{12} + \frac{x}{8} - \frac{x}{5} = 4$

$\Leftrightarrow \frac{10x + 15x - 24x}{120} = 4$

$\Leftrightarrow x = 4 \times 120 = 480.$

23. Let the number be x.

Then, $\frac{x}{3} - \frac{(x+1)}{4} = 1 \Leftrightarrow 4x - 3(x + 1) = 12 \Leftrightarrow x = 15.$

24. Let the number be x.

Then, $x + x^2 = 182 \Leftrightarrow x^2 + x - 182 = 0$

$\Leftrightarrow (x + 14)(x - 13) = 0 \Leftrightarrow x = 13.$

25. Let the number be x.

Then, $x^2 - (73)^2 = 5075 \Leftrightarrow x^2 - 5329 = 5075$

$\Leftrightarrow x^2 = 5075 + 5329 = 10404$

$\Leftrightarrow x = \sqrt{10404} = 102.$

26. Let the integer be x.

Then, $x^2 - 20x = 96$

$\Leftrightarrow x^2 - 20x - 96 = 0$

$\Leftrightarrow (x + 4)(x - 24) = 0$

$\Leftrightarrow x = 24.$

27. Let the number be x.

Then, $3x^2 - 4x = x + 50$

$\Leftrightarrow 3x^2 - 5x - 50 = 0$

$\Leftrightarrow (3x + 10)(x - 5) = 0$

$\Leftrightarrow x = 5.$

28. Let the number be x.

Then, $x + \frac{1}{x} = \frac{34}{8} \Leftrightarrow \frac{x^2 + 1}{x} = \frac{34}{8}$

$\Leftrightarrow 8x^2 - 34x + 8 = 0$

$\Leftrightarrow 4x^2 - 17x + 4 = 0$

$\Leftrightarrow (4x - 1)(x - 4) = 0$

$\Leftrightarrow x = 4.$

[neglecting $x = \frac{1}{4}$, as x is a natural no.]

$\therefore$ Required number $= 4 \times \sqrt{4} = 4 \times 2 = 8.$

29. Let the number be x.

Then, $\frac{2}{3}x = \frac{25}{216} \times \frac{1}{x} \Leftrightarrow x^2 = \frac{25}{216} \times \frac{3}{2}$

$= \frac{25}{144} \Leftrightarrow x = \sqrt{\frac{25}{144}} = \frac{5}{12}.$

30. Let the required number be x.

Then, $x + 20 = \frac{69}{x} \Leftrightarrow x^2 + 20x - 69 = 0$

$\Leftrightarrow x^2 + 23x - 3x - 69 = 0$

$\Leftrightarrow x(x + 23) - 3(x + 23) = 0$

$\Leftrightarrow (x + 23)(x - 3) = 0$

$\Leftrightarrow x = 3$ $\quad [\because x \neq -23]$

31. Let the number be x.

Then, $x - 4 = \frac{21}{x} \Leftrightarrow x^2 - 4x - 21 = 0$

$\Leftrightarrow (x - 7)(x + 3) = 0 \Leftrightarrow x = 7.$

32. Let the numbers be x and y.

Then, $x + y = 12$ and $xy = 35$.

$\therefore \frac{1}{x} + \frac{1}{y} = \frac{x + y}{xy} = \frac{12}{35}.$

33. Let the number be x.

Then, $x + \frac{1}{x} = 3\left(x - \frac{1}{x}\right)$

$\Leftrightarrow \frac{x^2 + 1}{x} = 3\left(\frac{x^2 - 1}{x}\right)$

$\Leftrightarrow x^2 + 1 = 3x^2 - 3$

$\Leftrightarrow 2x^2 = 4$

$\Leftrightarrow x^2 = 2$

$\Leftrightarrow x = \sqrt{2}.$

34. Let the numbers be a and b.

Then, $ab = 37 \Rightarrow a = 1$ and $b = 37$.

So, $\sqrt{b - a} = \sqrt{37 - 1} = \sqrt{36} = 6.$

35. Let the numbers be a and b.

Then, $ab = 17 \Rightarrow a = 1$ and $b = 17$.

So, $\frac{1}{a^2} + \frac{1}{b^2} = \frac{a^2 + b^2}{a^2 b^2} = \frac{1^2 + (17)^2}{(1 \times 17)^2} = \frac{290}{289}.$

36. Let the number be x. Then,

$\frac{4\frac{1}{2}\left(x + 2\frac{1}{2}\right) + 3}{1\frac{1}{5}} = 25 \Leftrightarrow \frac{\frac{9}{2}\left(x + \frac{5}{2}\right) + 3}{\frac{6}{5}} = 25$

$\Leftrightarrow \frac{9x}{2} + \frac{45}{4} + 3 = 25 \times \frac{6}{5} = 30$

$\Leftrightarrow \frac{9x}{2} = 30 - \frac{57}{4} \Leftrightarrow \frac{9x}{2} = \frac{63}{4}$

$\Leftrightarrow x = \left(\frac{63}{4} \times \frac{2}{9}\right) = \frac{7}{2} = 3\frac{1}{2}.$

37. Let the numbers be $4x$, $5x$ and $6x$.

Then, $\frac{4x + 5x + 6x}{3} = 25 \Leftrightarrow 5x = 25 \Leftrightarrow x = 5.$

$\therefore$ Largest number $= 6x = 30.$

38. Let the numbers be $3x$, $4x$ and $6x$.

Then, $3x \times 4x \times 6x = 1944$

$\Leftrightarrow 72x^3 = 1944 \Leftrightarrow x^3 = 27$

$\Leftrightarrow x = 3.$

$\therefore$ Largest number $= 6x = 18.$

39. Let the ten's digit be x. Then, unit's digit = $x + 3$.

Number = $10x + (x + 3) = 11x + 3$.

Sum of digits = $x + (x + 3) = 2x + 3$.

$\therefore \quad \frac{11x+3}{2x+3} = \frac{4}{1} \Leftrightarrow 11x + 3 = 8x + 12$

$\Leftrightarrow 3x = 9 \Leftrightarrow x = 3.$

Hence, required number = $11x + 3 = 11 \times 3 + 3 = 36$.

40. Let the numbers be $3x$ and $4x$.

Then, $(4x)^2 = 8 \times (3x)^2 - 224$

$\Leftrightarrow 16x^2 = 72x^2 - 224$

$\Leftrightarrow 56x^2 = 224 \Leftrightarrow x^2 = 4$

$\Leftrightarrow x = 2.$

So, the numbers are 6 and 8.

41. Let the numbers be $4x$ and $7x$.

Then, $\frac{4x+4}{7x+4} = \frac{3}{5} \Leftrightarrow 5(4x+4) = 3(7x+4) \Leftrightarrow x = 8.$

$\therefore$ Larger number = $7x = 56$.

42. Let the second number be x. Then, first number = $2x$ and third number = $\frac{2x}{3}$.

$\therefore \quad 2x + x + \frac{2x}{3} = 264 \Leftrightarrow \frac{11x}{3} = 264$

$\Leftrightarrow x = \left(\frac{264 \times 3}{11}\right) = 72.$

43. Let the numbers be x and $(22 - x)$. Then, $5x = 6(22 - x)$

$\Leftrightarrow 11x = 132 \Leftrightarrow x = 12.$

So, the numbers are 12 and 10.

44. Let the numbers be x and y. Then, $\frac{1}{5}x = \frac{5}{8}y \Leftrightarrow y = \frac{8}{25}x.$

Now, $x + 35 = 4y \Leftrightarrow x + 35 = \frac{32}{25}x$

$\Leftrightarrow \frac{7}{25}x = 35 \Leftrightarrow x = \left(\frac{35 \times 25}{7}\right) = 125.$

$\therefore$ Second number = $y = \frac{8}{25}x = \left(\frac{8}{25} \times 125\right) = 40.$

45. Let the numbers be x and y.

Then, $x + y = 25$ and $x - y = 13$.

$4xy = (x + y)^2 - (x - y)^2 = (25)^2 - (13)^2$

$= 625 - 169 = 456 \Rightarrow xy = 114.$

46. Let the numbers be x and y. Then,

$x + y = 33$ ...(i)

and $x - y = 15$ ...(ii)

Solving (i) and (ii), we get : $x = 24$, $y = 9$.

$\therefore$ Smaller number = 9.

47. Let the numbers be x and y.

Then, $\frac{x+y}{x-y} = \frac{40}{4} = 10 \Leftrightarrow (x + y) = 10(x - y)$

$\Leftrightarrow 9x = 11y \Leftrightarrow \frac{x}{y} = \frac{11}{9}.$

48. Let the numbers be x and $(28 - x)$.

Then, $x(28 - x) = 192 \Leftrightarrow x^2 - 28x + 192 = 0$

$\Leftrightarrow (x - 16)(x - 12) = 0$

$\Leftrightarrow x = 16$ or $x = 12$.

So, the numbers are 16 and 12.

49. Let the numbers be x and y. Then,

$2x + 3y = 100$ ...(i)

and $3x + 2y = 120$ ...(ii)

Adding (i) and (ii), we get : $5x + 5y = 220$

or $x + y = 44$ ...(iii)

Subtracting (i) from (ii); we get : $x - y = 20$ ...(iv)

Adding (iii) and (iv), we get: $2x = 64$ or $x = 32$.

Putting $x = 32$ in (iii), we get : $y = 12$.

Hence, larger number = 32.

50. Let the numbers be x and y. Then,

$xy = 1092$ ...(i)

And, $(x + y) - (x - y) = 42$

$\Leftrightarrow 2y = 42$

$\Leftrightarrow y = 21.$

Putting $y = 21$ in (i), we get : $x = \frac{1092}{21} = 52.$

Hence, greater number = 52.

51. Let the integers be x and $(x + 5)$. Then,

$x(x + 5) = 500 \Leftrightarrow x^2 + 5x - 500 = 0$

$\Leftrightarrow (x + 25)(x - 20) = 0$

$\Leftrightarrow x = 20.$

So, the numbers are 20 and 25.

52. Let the numbers be x and y.

Then, $x - y = 5$ and $xy = 336$.

$(x + y)^2 = (x - y)^2 + 4xy = 25 + 4 \times 336 = 1369$

$\Rightarrow x + y = \sqrt{1369} = 37.$

53. Since $1 . x < 1 + x$, so one of the numbers is 1.

54. Let the numbers be x and y.

Then, $xy = 9375$ and $\frac{x}{y} = 15$.

$\frac{xy}{(x/y)} = \frac{9375}{15} \Leftrightarrow y^2 = 625 \Leftrightarrow y = 25$

$\Rightarrow x = 15y = (15 \times 25) = 375.$

$\therefore$ Sum of the numbers = $375 + 25 = 400$.

55. Let the numbers be x and $(x + 1365)$.

Then, $x + 1365 = 6x + 15 \Leftrightarrow 5x = 1350 \Leftrightarrow x = 270.$

56. Let the numbers be x and $(x + 16)$.

Then, $\frac{x}{3} - \frac{(x+16)}{7} = 4 \Leftrightarrow 7x - 3(x + 16)$

$= 84 \Leftrightarrow 4x = 84 + 48$

$= 132 \Leftrightarrow x = 33.$

Hence, the numbers are 33 and 49.

57. Let the numbers be x and y.

Then, $x + y = 40$ and $xy = 375$.

$\therefore \quad \frac{1}{x} + \frac{1}{y} = \frac{x+y}{xy} = \frac{40}{375} = \frac{8}{75}.$

58. Let the numbers be x and y such that $x > y$.

Then, $x(x + y) = 204 \Rightarrow x^2 + xy = 204$ ...(i)

and $y(x - y) = 35 \Rightarrow xy - y^2 = 35$ ...(ii)

Subtracting (ii) from (i), we get : $x^2 + y^2 = 169$.

The only triplet satisfying this condition is (12, 5, 13). Thus, $x = 12$, $y = 5$.

59. Let the numbers be x and y.

Then, $x + y = 20$ and $x - y = 8$.

$\therefore \quad x^2 - y^2 = (x + y)(x - y) = 20 \times 8 = 160$.

60. Let the numbers be x and y.

Let $a - b = k$ ...(i)

$a + b = 7k$ ...(ii)

$ab = 24k$ ...(iii)

Adding (i) and (ii), we get : $2a = 8k$ or $a = 4k$.

Putting $a = 4k$ in (i), we get : $b = 3k$.

Putting $a = 4k$ and $b = 3k$ in (iii), we get : $4k \times 3k$

$= 24k \Leftrightarrow 12k^2 = 24k \Leftrightarrow k = 2$.

Hence, product of numbers $= 24k = 24 \times 2 = 48$.

61. Let the numbers be x and y.

Then, $xy = 120$ and $x^2 + y^2 = 289$.

$\therefore \quad (x + y)^2 = x^2 + y^2 + 2xy = 289 + 240 = 529$.

$\therefore \quad x + y = \sqrt{529} = 23$.

62. Let the numbers be x and y.

Then, $xy = 45$ and $x^2 + y^2 = 106$.

$$(x + y) = \sqrt{(x^2 + y^2) + 2xy}$$

$$= \sqrt{106 + 90} = \sqrt{196} \Rightarrow x + y = 14 \quad ...(i)$$

$$(x - y) = \sqrt{(x^2 + y^2) - 2xy}$$

$$= \sqrt{106 - 90} = \sqrt{16} \Rightarrow x - y = 4 \quad ...(ii)$$

Solving (i) and (ii), we get : $x = 9$ and $y = 5$.

63. Let the numbers be x and y. Then,

$x^2 + y^2 = 3341$ ...(i)

and $x^2 - y^2 = 891$ ...(ii)

Adding (i) and (ii), we get :

$2x^2 = 4232$ or $x^2 = 2116$ or $x = 46$.

Subtracting (ii) from (i), we get :

$2y^2 = 2450$ or $y^2 = 1225$ or $y = 35$.

So, the numbers are 35 and 46.

64. Let the numbers be x and $(x + 3)$. Then,

$x^2 + (x + 3)^2 = 369$

$\Leftrightarrow \quad x^2 + x^2 + 9 + 6x = 369$

$\Leftrightarrow \quad 2x^2 + 6x - 360 = 0$

$\Leftrightarrow \quad x^2 + 3x - 180 = 0$

$\Leftrightarrow \quad (x + 15)(x - 12) = 0$

$\Leftrightarrow \quad x = 12$.

So, the numbers are 12 and 15.

$\therefore \quad$ Required sum $= (12 + 15) = 27$.

65. Let the numbers be x and y.

Then, $(x + y) = 22$ and $x^2 + y^2 = 404$.

Now, $2xy = (x + y)^2 - (x^2 + y^2) = (22)^2 - 404$

$= 484 - 404 = 80 \Rightarrow xy = 40$.

66. Let the numbers be x and y.

Then, $x^2 - y^2 = 256000$ and $x + y = 1000$.

On dividing, we get : $x - y = 256$.

Solving $x + y = 1000$ and $x - y = 256$,

we get : $x = 628$ and $y = 372$.

67. Let the numbers be x and y.

Then, $x^2 - y^2 = 63$ and $x - y = 3$.

On dividing, we get : $x + y = 21$.

Solving $x + y = 21$ and $x - y = 3$,

we get : $x = 12$ and $y = 9$.

$\therefore \quad$ Larger number $= 12$.

68. Let $A = x$, $B = x + 2$, $C = x + 4$,

$D = x + 6$ and $E = x + 8$.

Then, $A + C = 146 \Rightarrow x + (x + 4) = 146$

$\Rightarrow \quad 2x = 142 \Rightarrow x = 71$.

$\therefore \quad E = x + 8 = 71 + 8 = 79$.

69. Let the six numbers be x, $x + 1$, $x + 2$, $x + 3$, $x + 4$ and $x + 5$.

Then, $x + (x + 1) + (x + 2) = 27 \Rightarrow 3x + 3 = 27$.

Required sum $= (x + 3) + (x + 4) + (x + 5)$

$= 3x + 12 = (3x + 3) + 9 = 27 + 9 = 36$.

70. Let the seven numbers be x, $x + 1$, $x + 2$, $x + 3$, $x + 4$, $x + 5$ and $x + 6$.

Then, $x + (x + 1) + (x + 2) + (x + 3) + (x + 4) + (x + 5) + (x + 6) = 175$

$\Leftrightarrow \quad 7x + 21 = 175 \Leftrightarrow 7x = 154$

$\Leftrightarrow \quad x = 22$.

Required difference $= 2(x + 6) - 3x = 12 - x$

$= 12 - 22 = -10$.

71. Let the five numbers be x, $x + 2$, $x + 4$, $x + 6$ and $x + 8$.

Then, $x + (x + 2) + (x + 4) + (x + 6) + (x + 8) = 575$

$\Leftrightarrow \quad 5x + 20 = 575 \Leftrightarrow 5x = 555 \Leftrightarrow x = 111$.

$\therefore \quad$ Required sum $= (x + 10) + (x + 12) + (x + 14) + (x + 16) + (x + 18)$

$= 5x + 70 = 5 \times 111 + 70 = 555 + 70 = 625$.

72. Let the three odd numbers be x, $x + 2$, $x + 4$ and the three even numbers be $x + 11$, $x + 13$ and $x + 15$.

Then, $x + (x + 2) + (x + 4) + (x + 11) + (x + 13) + (x + 15) = 231$

$\Leftrightarrow \quad 6x + 45 = 231 \Leftrightarrow 6x = 186 \Leftrightarrow x = 31$.

$\therefore$ Required sum $= (x + 4) + (x + 15) = 2x + 19 = 2 \times 31 + 19 = 62 + 19 = 81$.

73. Let the three integers be x, $x + 2$ and $x + 4$.

Then, $3x = 2(x + 4) + 3 \Leftrightarrow x = 11$.

$\therefore \quad$ Third integer $= x + 4 = 15$.

74. Let the four integers be x, $x + 2$, $x + 4$ and $x + 6$.

Then, $x + (x + 2) + (x + 4) + (x + 6) = 1284$

$\Leftrightarrow 4x = 1272 \Leftrightarrow x = 318$.

$\therefore \quad$ Greatest integer $= x + 6 = 324$.

75. Let the numbers be x, $x + 2$ and $x + 4$.
Then, $x + (x + 2) + (x + 4) = x + 20$
$\Leftrightarrow 2x = 14 \Leftrightarrow x = 7$.
$\therefore$ Middle number $= x + 2 = 9$.

76. Let the numbers be x, $x + 2$ and $x + 4$.
Then, $\frac{x(x+2)(x+4)}{8} = 720$
$\Rightarrow x(x+2)(x+4) = 5760$.
$\therefore \sqrt{x} \times \sqrt{(x+2)} \times \sqrt{(x+4)}$
$= \sqrt{x(x+2)(x+4)} = \sqrt{5760} = 24\sqrt{10}$.

77. Let the numbers be $3x$, $3x + 3$ and $3x + 6$.
Then, $3x + (3x + 3) + (3x + 6) = 72$
$\Leftrightarrow 9x = 63$
$\Leftrightarrow x = 7$.
$\therefore$ Largest number $= 3x + 6 = 27$.

78. Let the numbers be x and $x + 2$.
Then, $(x + 2)^2 - x^2 = 84$
$\Leftrightarrow 4x + 4 = 84$
$\Leftrightarrow 4x = 80$
$\Leftrightarrow x = 20$.
$\therefore$ Required sum $= x + (x + 2) = 2x + 2 = 42$.

79. Let the numbers be x, $x + 1$ and $x + 2$.
Then, $x^2 + (x + 1)^2 + (x + 2)^2 = 2030$
$\Leftrightarrow 3x^2 + 6x - 2025 = 0$
$\Leftrightarrow x^2 + 2x - 675 = 0$
$\Leftrightarrow (x + 27)(x - 25) = 0$
$\Leftrightarrow x = 25$.
$\therefore$ Middle number $= (x + 1) = 26$.

80. $120 = 2 \times 2 \times 2 \times 3 \times 5 = (2 \times 2) \times 5 \times (2 \times 3) = 4 \times 5 \times 6$.
Clearly, the three consecutive integers whose product is 120 are 4, 5 and 6.
Required sum $= 4 + 5 + 6 = 15$.

81. Let the numbers be x and y.
Then, $2x + 3y = 39$ ...(*i*)
and $3x + 2y = 36$ ...(*ii*)
On solving (*i*) and (*ii*), we get : $x = 6$ and $y = 9$.
$\therefore$ Larger number = 9.

82. Let the ten's digit be x. Then, unit's digit $= 4x$.
$\therefore x + 4x = 10 \Leftrightarrow 5x = 10 \Leftrightarrow x = 2$.
So, ten's digit = 2, unit's digit = 8.
Hence, the required number is 28.

83. Let the ten's digit be x.
Then, number $= 10x + 3$ and sum of digits $= (x + 3)$.
So, $(x+3) = \frac{1}{7}(10x+3) \Leftrightarrow 7x+21$
$= 10x+3 \Leftrightarrow 3x = 18 \Leftrightarrow x = 6$.
Hence, the number is 63.

84. Let the ten's digit be x and the unit's digit be y.
Then, number $= 10x + y$.
$\therefore 10x + y = k(x + y) \Rightarrow k = \frac{10x+y}{x+y}$.
Number formed by interchanging the digits $= 10y + x$.
Let $10y + x = h(x + y)$.
Then, $h = \frac{10y+x}{x+y} = \frac{11(x+y)-(10x+y)}{x+y}$
$= 11 - \frac{10x+y}{x+y} = 11 - k$.

85. Let the ten's digit be x.
Then, unit's digit $= 2x$.
Number $= 10x + 2x = 12x$; Sum of digits $= x + 2x = 3x$.
$\therefore 12x - 3x = 18 \Leftrightarrow 9x = 18 \Leftrightarrow x = 2$.
Hence, required number $= 12x = 24$.

86. Let the ten's digit be x and unit's digit be y.
Then, $x + y = 15$ and $x - y = 3$ or $y - x = 3$.
Solving $x + y = 15$ and $x - y = 3$, we get : $x = 9$, $y = 6$.
Solving $x + y = 15$ and $y - x = 3$, we get : $x = 6$, $y = 9$.
So, the number is either 96 or 69. Hence, the number cannot be determined.

87. Let the ten's digit be x and the unit's digit be y.
Then, number $= 10x + y$.
$\therefore 10x + y = 7(x + y) \Leftrightarrow 3x = 6y \Leftrightarrow x = 2y$.
Number formed by reversing the digits $= 10y + x$.
$\therefore (10x + y) - (10y + x) = 18 \Leftrightarrow 9x - 9y = 18 \Leftrightarrow x - y = 2 \Leftrightarrow 2y - y = 2 \Leftrightarrow y = 2$.
So, $x = 2y = 4$.
Hence, required number $= 10x + y = 40 + 2 = 42$.

88. Let the ten's digit be x and the unit's digit be y. Then, number $= 10x + y$.
New number $= 10 \times 2x + \frac{y}{2} = 20x + \frac{y}{2}$.
$\therefore 20x + \frac{y}{2} = 10y + x \Rightarrow 40x + y = 20y + 2x$
$\Rightarrow 38x = 19y \Rightarrow y = 2x$.
So, the unit's digit is twice the ten's digit.

89. Let the ten's digit be x. Then, unit's digit $= x + 2$.
Number $= 10x + (x + 2) = 11x + 2$; Sum of digits $= x + (x + 2) = 2x + 2$.
$\therefore (11x + 2)(2x + 2) = 144$
$\Leftrightarrow 22x^2 + 26x - 140 = 0$
$\Leftrightarrow 11x^2 + 13x - 70 = 0$
$\Leftrightarrow (x - 2)(11x + 35) = 0$
$\Leftrightarrow x = 2$.
Hence, required number $= 11x + 2 = 24$.

90. Let the ten's digit be x and unit's digit be y.
Then, number $= 10x + y$.
Number obtained by interchanging the digits $= 10y + x$.
$\therefore (10x + y) + (10y + x)$
$= 11(x + y)$, which is divisible by 11.

91. Let the ten's digit be x and unit's digit be y.
Then, $(10x + y) - (x + y) = 9$ or $x = 1$.
From this data, we cannot find y, the unit's digit.
So, the data is inadequate.

92. Let the ten's digit be x and unit's digit be y.
Then, $(10x + y) - (10y + x) = 36$
$\Leftrightarrow 9(x - y) = 36 \Leftrightarrow x - y = 4.$

93. Let the ten's digit be x and unit's digit be y.
Then, $(10x + y) - (10y + x) = 63$
$\Leftrightarrow 9(x - y) = 63 \Leftrightarrow x - y = 7.$
Thus, none of the numbers can be determined.

94. Let the ten's digit be x and unit's digit be y.
Then, $x + y = \frac{1}{5}[(10x + y) - (10y + x)]$
$\Leftrightarrow 5x + 5y = 9x - 9y \Leftrightarrow 4x = 14y.$
Thus, the value of $(x - y)$ cannot be determined from the given data.

95. Let ten's digit $= x$. Then, unit's digit $= (12 - x)$.
$\therefore [10x + (12 - x)] - [10(12 - x) + x]$
$= 54 \Leftrightarrow 18x - 108 = 54 \Leftrightarrow 18x = 162 \Leftrightarrow x = 9.$
So, ten's digit = 9 and unit's digit = 3. Hence, original number = 93.

96. Since the number is greater than the number obtained on reversing the digits, so the ten's digit is greater than the unit's digit.
Let the ten's and unit's digits be $2x$ and x respectively.
Then, $(10 \times 2x + x) - (10x + 2x) = 36 \Leftrightarrow 9x = 36 \Leftrightarrow x = 4.$
$\therefore$ Required difference $= (2x + x) - (2x - x) = 2x = 8.$

97. Let ten's digit $= x$. Then, unit's digit $= x^2$. Then, number $= 10x + x^2$.
Clearly, since $x^2 > x$, so the number formed by interchanging the digits is greater than the original number.
$\therefore (10x^2 + x) - (10x + x^2)$
$= 54 \Leftrightarrow 9x^2 - 9x = 54 \Leftrightarrow x^2 - x$
$= 6 \Leftrightarrow x^2 - x - 6 = 0$
$\Leftrightarrow x^2 - 3x + 2x - 6 = 0$
$\Leftrightarrow x(x - 3) + 2(x - 3) = 0$
$\Leftrightarrow (x - 3)(x + 2) = 0$
$\Leftrightarrow x = 3.$
So, ten's digit = 3, unit's digit $= 3^2 = 9$.
$\therefore$ Original number = 39.
Required result = 40% of 39 = 15.6.

98. Let the middle digit be x.
Then, $2x = 10$ or $x = 5$.
So, the number is either 253 or 352.
Since the number increases on reversing the digits, so the hundred's digit is smaller than the unit's digit. Hence, required number = 253.

99. Since the number reduces on reversing the digits, so ten's digit is greater than the unit's digit.
Let the unit's digit be x.
Then, ten's digit $= (x + 1)$.
$\therefore 10x + (x+1) = \frac{5}{6}[10(x+1) + x] \Leftrightarrow 66x + 6$
$= 55x + 50 \Leftrightarrow 11x = 44 \Leftrightarrow x = 4.$
Hence, required number = 54.

100. Let the two-digit number be $10x + y$.
Then, number formed by reversing the digits $= 10y + x$.
Difference of squares of the numbers
$= (10x + y)^2 - (10y + x)^2$
$= (100x^2 + y^2 + 20xy) - (100y^2 + x^2 + 20xy)$
$= 99(x^2 - y^2)$, which is divisible by both 9 and 11

101. Let the unit's digit be x. Then, ten's digit $= (x - 2)$.
$\therefore 3[10(x-2) + x] + \frac{6}{7}[10x + (x-2)] = 108$
$\Leftrightarrow 231x - 420 + 66x - 12 = 756$
$\Leftrightarrow 297x = 1188$
$\Leftrightarrow x = 4.$
Hence, sum of the digits $= x + (x - 2) = 2x - 2 = 6.$

102. Let the ten's digit be x and unit's digit be y.
Then, $\frac{10x + y}{2} = 10y + (x + 1)$
$\Leftrightarrow 10x + y = 20y + 2x + 2$
$\Leftrightarrow 8x - 19y = 2$ ...(*i*)
and $x + y = 7$ ...(*ii*)
Solving (*i*) and (*ii*), we get : $x = 5, y = 2$. Hence, required number = 52.

103. Let the ten's digit be x.
Then, unit's digit $= 2x + 1$.
$[10x + (2x + 1)] - [\{10(2x + 1) + x\} - \{10x + (2x + 1)\}] = 1$
$\Leftrightarrow (12x + 1) - (9x + 9) = 1 \Leftrightarrow 3x = 9 \Leftrightarrow x = 3.$
So, ten's digit = 3 and unit's digit = 7. Hence, original number = 37.

104. Let the ten's digit be x and unit's digit be y.
Then, $10x + y = 3(x + y) \Rightarrow 7x - 2y = 0$ ...(*i*)
$10x + y + 45 = 10y + x \Rightarrow y - x = 5$ ...(*ii*)
Solving (*i*) and (*ii*), we get : $x = 2$ and $y = 7$.
$\therefore$ Required number = 27.

105. Let the ten's and unit's digits be x and $\frac{8}{x}$ respectively.
Then, $\left(10x + \frac{8}{x}\right) + 18 = 10 \times \frac{8}{x} + x$
$\Leftrightarrow 10x^2 + 8 + 18x = 80 + x^2$
$\Leftrightarrow 9x^2 + 18x - 72 = 0$
$\Leftrightarrow x^2 + 2x - 8 = 0$
$\Leftrightarrow (x + 4)(x - 2) = 0$
$\Leftrightarrow x = 2.$
So, ten's digit = 2 and unit's digit = 4. Hence, required number = 24.

106. Clearly, there are 4 such numbers: 161, 242, 323 and 404.

107. Let hundred's digit $= x$.
Then, ten's digit $= (x + 1)$.
Unit's digit = 75% of $(x + 1) = \frac{3}{4}(x + 1)$.
$\therefore (x + 1) + x = 15 \Leftrightarrow 2x = 14 \Leftrightarrow x = 7.$
So, hundreds' digit = 7; ten's digit = 8; unit's digit $= \frac{3}{4}(7 + 1) = \frac{3}{4} \times 8 = 6.$
Hence, required number = 786.

108. Let the two fractions be a and b. Then, $ab = \frac{14}{15}$ and $\frac{a}{b} = \frac{35}{24}$.

$$\frac{ab}{(a/b)} = \left(\frac{14}{15} \times \frac{24}{35}\right) \Leftrightarrow b^2 = \frac{16}{25} \Leftrightarrow b = \frac{4}{5};$$

$$ab = \frac{14}{15} \Rightarrow a = \left(\frac{14}{15} \times \frac{5}{4}\right) = \frac{7}{6}.$$

Since $a > b$, so greater fraction is $\frac{7}{6}$.

109. $A = 2B \Rightarrow B = \frac{1}{2}A$. So, $AB = \frac{2}{25}$

$$\Rightarrow \frac{1}{2}A^2 = \frac{2}{25} \Rightarrow A^2 = \frac{4}{25} \Rightarrow A = \frac{2}{5}.$$

110. Let the fraction be $\frac{a}{1}$.

Then, $\frac{1}{a} - a = \frac{9}{20} \Leftrightarrow \frac{1-a^2}{a} = \frac{9}{20}$

$\Leftrightarrow 20 - 20a^2 = 9a$

$\Leftrightarrow 20a^2 + 9a - 20 = 0$

$\Leftrightarrow 20a^2 + 25a - 16a - 20 = 0$

$\Leftrightarrow 5a(4a + 5) - 4(4a + 5) = 0$

$\Leftrightarrow (4a + 5)(5a - 4) = 0 \Leftrightarrow a = \frac{4}{5}$. $\left[\because a \neq -\frac{5}{4}\right]$

111. Let the fraction be $\frac{x}{y}$.

Then, $x + y = 11$ ...(i)

$\frac{x+1}{y-2} = \frac{2}{3} \Rightarrow 3(x+1)$

$= 2(y-2) \Rightarrow 3x - 2y = -7$ ...(ii)

Solving (i) and (ii), we get: $x = 3$ and $y = 8$.

So, the fraction is $\frac{3}{8}$.

112. Let the numerator be x. Then, denominator $= x + 3$.

Now, $\frac{x+4}{(x+3)+4} = \frac{4}{5} \Leftrightarrow 5(x+4)$

$= 4(x+7) \Leftrightarrow x = 8$.

So, the fraction is $\frac{8}{11}$.

113. Let the denominator be x.

Then, numerator $= x + 5$.

Now, $\frac{x+5}{x} - \frac{x+5}{x+5} = \frac{5}{4} \Leftrightarrow \frac{x+5}{x} = \frac{5}{4} + 1 = \frac{9}{4} = 2\frac{1}{4}$.

So, the fraction is $2\frac{1}{4}$.

114. Let the fraction be $\frac{2x}{3x}$.

Then, $\frac{2x-6}{3x} = \frac{2}{3} \times \frac{2x}{3x} \Leftrightarrow \frac{2x-6}{3x}$

$= \frac{4x}{9x} \Leftrightarrow 18x^2 - 54x = 12x^2$

$\Leftrightarrow 6x^2 = 54x \Leftrightarrow x = 9$.

Hence, numerator of the original fraction $= 2x = 18$.

115. Let the fraction be $\frac{x}{y}$. Then,

$\frac{x}{y+1} = \frac{1}{2} \Leftrightarrow 2x - y = 1$ ...(i)

and, $\frac{x+1}{y} = 1 \Leftrightarrow x - y = -1$ ...(ii)

Solving (i) and (ii), we get : $x = 2$, $y = 3$.

Hence, the required fraction is $\frac{2}{3}$.

116. Let the fraction be $\frac{x}{y}$. Then,

$\frac{x+2}{y+3} = \frac{7}{9} \Leftrightarrow 9x - 7y = 3$ ...(i)

and $\frac{x-1}{y-1} = \frac{4}{5} \Leftrightarrow 5x - 4y = 1$ ...(ii)

Solving (i) and (ii), we get : $x = 5$, $y = 6$.

Hence, the original fraction is $\frac{5}{6}$.

117. Let the fraction be $\frac{x}{y}$. Then,

$$\frac{x+\frac{1}{4}}{y-\frac{1}{3}} = \frac{33}{64} \Leftrightarrow \frac{3(4x+1)}{4(3y-1)} = \frac{33}{64} \Leftrightarrow \frac{4x+1}{3y-1} = \frac{33}{64} \times \frac{4}{3} = \frac{11}{16}$$

$\Leftrightarrow 16(4x + 1) = 11(3y - 1)$

$\Leftrightarrow 64x + 16 = 33y - 11$

$\Leftrightarrow 64x - 33y = -27$, which cannot be solved to find $\frac{x}{y}$.

Hence, the original fraction cannot be determined from the given data.

118. Let the fraction be $\frac{x}{y}$.

Then, $\frac{x + 200\% \text{ of } x}{y + 300\% \text{ of } y} = \frac{15}{26} \Leftrightarrow \frac{3x}{4y} = \frac{15}{26} \Leftrightarrow \frac{x}{y} = \frac{15}{26} \times \frac{4}{3} = \frac{10}{13}$.

119. Let the fraction be $\frac{x}{y}$.

Then, $\frac{x+4}{y} - \frac{x}{y} = \frac{2}{3} \Leftrightarrow \frac{4}{y} = \frac{2}{3} \Leftrightarrow y = \left(\frac{4 \times 3}{2}\right) = 6$.

$\therefore$ Denominator $= 6$.

120. Let the fraction be $\frac{x}{y}$.

Then, $\frac{110\% \text{ of } 2x}{70\% \text{ of } 3y} = 11\% \text{ of } \frac{16}{21} \Leftrightarrow \frac{22x}{21y} = \frac{11}{100} \times \frac{16}{21}$

$\Leftrightarrow \frac{x}{y} = \left(\frac{11}{100} \times \frac{16}{21} \times \frac{21}{22}\right) = \frac{2}{25}$

121. Let the two parts be $(54 - x)$ and x.

Then, $10(54-x)+22x=780 \Leftrightarrow 12x=240 \Leftrightarrow x=20$.

$\therefore$ Bigger part $=(54-x)=34$.

122. Let the three parts be A, B and C.

Let $\frac{A}{2}=\frac{B}{3}=\frac{C}{4}=x$.

Then, $A=2x$, $B=3x$ and $C=4x$.

So, $A:B:C=2:3:4$.

$\therefore$ Largest part $=\left(243\times\frac{4}{9}\right)=108$.

123. Let the four numbers be A, B, C and D.

Let $A+3=B-3=3C=\frac{D}{3}=x$.

Then, $A=x-3$, $B=x+3$, $C=\frac{x}{3}$ and $D=3x$.

$A+B+C+D=64 \Rightarrow (x-3)+(x+3)+\frac{x}{3}+3x=64$

$\Rightarrow 5x+\frac{x}{3}=64 \Rightarrow 16x=192 \Rightarrow x=12$.

Thus, the numbers are 9, 15, 4 and 36.

$\therefore$ Required difference $=(36-4)=32$.

124. Let the numbers be a, b and c. Then, $a^2+b^2+c^2=138$ and $(ab+bc+ca)=131$.

$(a+b+c)^2=a^2+b^2+c^2+2(ab+bc+ca)=138+2\times131=400$

$\Rightarrow (a+b+c)=\sqrt{400}=20$.

125. $A:B=2:3$ and $B:C=5:3=\frac{3}{5}\times5:\frac{3}{5}\times3=3:\frac{9}{5}$.

So, $A:B:C=2:3:\frac{9}{5}=10:15:9$.

$\therefore$ Second number $=\left(136\times\frac{15}{34}\right)=60$.

126. Let the numbers be x, y and z.

Then, $x+y=73$, $y+z=77$ and $3x+z=104$.

$\therefore$ $y=73-x$, $z=77-y=77-(73-x)=4+x$.

$\therefore$ $3x+4+x=104 \Leftrightarrow 4x=100 \Leftrightarrow x=25$.

$y=(73-25)=48$ and $z=(4+25)=29$.

$\therefore$ Third number $=29$.

127. Let two numbers be a and b

Given $ab=5$ and $a=\frac{3}{2}$

$\Rightarrow b=\frac{5}{a}$

$b=\frac{5}{\frac{3}{2}}=\frac{5\times2}{3}=\frac{10}{3}$

$\therefore$ Required sum of $a+b=\frac{3}{2}+\frac{10}{3}$

LCM of 2 and 3 = 6

$=\frac{9+20}{6}=\frac{29}{6}=4\frac{5}{6}$

128. Let the positive integers be a and b where $a>b$.

According to the question,

$a^2+b^2=100$ ....(i)

$a^2-b^2=28$ ....(ii)

By adding (i) and (ii), we get

$\therefore a^2+b^2+a^2-b^2=100+28$

$\Rightarrow 2a^2=128$

$\Rightarrow a^2=\frac{128}{2}=64$

$\therefore a=\sqrt{64}=8$

From equation (i).

$8^2+b^2=100$

$\Rightarrow b^2=100-64=36$

$\Rightarrow b=\sqrt{36}=6$

$\therefore a+b=8+6=14$

129. Let the numbers be a and b where $a>b$.

According to the question,

$a+b=37$ and $a^2-b^2=185$

$\Rightarrow (a+b)(a-b)=185$

$\Rightarrow 37(a-b)=185$

$\Rightarrow a-b=\frac{185}{37}=5$

130. Let the total number of eggs bought be a.

10% of eggs are rotten.

$\therefore$ Remaining eggs

$=a-10\%$ of $a=a-\frac{10a}{100}=\frac{100a-10a}{100}=\frac{90a}{100}=\frac{9a}{10}$

Man gives 80% of $\frac{9a}{100}$ eggs to his neighbour

$=\frac{80}{100}\times\frac{9a}{10}=\frac{72a}{100}$

Remaining eggs $=\frac{9a}{10}-\frac{72a}{100}=\frac{90a-72a}{100}=\frac{18a}{100}=\frac{9a}{50}$

According to the question.

$\frac{9a}{50}=36 \Rightarrow 9a=36\times50$

$\Rightarrow a=\frac{36\times50}{9}=200$

Hence the total number of eggs. bought be 200.

131. Let the numbers be a and b.

According to the question.

$a+b=75$

$a-b=25$

$\because (a+b)^2-(a-b)^2=4ab$

$\Rightarrow 75^2-25^2=4ab$

$4ab=(75+25)(75-25)$

$\left[\because a^2-b^2=(a+b)(a-b)\right]$

$\Rightarrow 4ab=100\times50$

$\Rightarrow ab=\frac{100\times50}{4}=1250$

132. Let the five successive odd number be,

$x, x+2, x+4, x+6, x+8$

Then, according to given information

$185 = x + x + 2 + x + 4 + x + 6 + x + 8$

$\Rightarrow 185 = 5x + 20$

$\Rightarrow 5x = 185 - 20 = 165$

$\Rightarrow x = 33$

Highest number = 33 + 8 = 41

133. Let the numbers be a and b where $a > b$.

According to the questions,

$a - b = 10$ .....(i)

And $\frac{a+b}{5} = 8$

By cross multiplying, we get

$\Rightarrow a + b = 40$ ...(ii)

By subtracting equation (ii) from (i) we get

$2b = 40 - 10 = 30$

$\Rightarrow b = \frac{30}{2} = 15$

And from (i)

$a = 10 + 15 = 25$

$\Rightarrow a = 23$

EXERCISE

(DATA SUFFICIENCY TYPE QUESTIONS)

Directions (Questions 1 to 15): Each of the questions given below consists of a statement and/or a question and two statements numbered I and II given below it. You have to decide whether the data provided in the statement(s) is/are sufficient to answer the question. Read both the statements and

Give answer (a) if the data in Statement I alone are sufficient to answer the question, while the data in Statement II alone are not sufficient to answer the question;

Give answer (b) if the data in Statement II alone are sufficient to answer the question, while the data in Statement I alone are not sufficient to answer the question;

Give answer (c) if the data either in Statement I or in Statement II alone are sufficient to answer the question;

Give answer (d) if the data even in both Statements I and II together are not sufficient to answer the question;

Give answer (e) if the data in both Statements I and II together are necessary to answer the question.

1. What is the two-digit number? (Bank P.O., 2008)
   I. The difference between the two digits is 9.
   II. The sum of the digits is equal to the difference between the two digits.
2. What is the value of the two-digit number ab?
   I. The difference between its digits is 2.
   II. The sum of its digits is 4. (M.A.T., 2005)
3. What is the two-digit number where the digit at the unit's place is smaller?
   I. The difference between the two digits is 5. (Bank P.O., 2006)
   II. The sum of the two digits is 7.
4. How much is four-fifths of the number? (Bank P.O., 2009)
   I. Three-fourths of the number is 2.5 less than its four-fifths.
   II. Half of the number added to it is 75.
5. What is the smaller of the two numbers?
   I. The difference between these two numbers is one-third of the greater number.
   II. The sum of these two numbers is 30.
6. What is the two-digit number? (Bank P.O., 2009)
   I. Sum of the digits is 6.
   II. Digit in the ten's place is double the digit in the unit's place.
7. What is the difference between the digits of a two-digit number? (M.A.T., 2007)
   I. The sum of the digits of that number is 8.
   II. One-fifth of that number is 15 less than half of 44.
8. What is the three-digit number? (Bank P.O., 2008)
   I. Two-fifth of that number is less than half of that number by 20.
   II. One-fourth of that number is 25% of that number.
9. What is the difference between two two-digit numbers? (Bank. P.O., 2010)
   I. The square of the first number is 9 times the second number.
   II. The ratio of the first number to the second number is 3 : 4.
10. What is the third number of 8 consecutive real numbers? (M.A.T., 2001)
    I. Product of the numbers is 34,459,425.
    II. Sum of numbers is 84.
11. What is the ratio between the two numbers?
    I. The sum of two numbers is twice their difference.
    II. The smaller number is 6.
12. What is the two-digit number whose first digit is a and the second digit is b? The number is greater than 9. (M.A.T., 2000)
    I. The number is a multiple of 51.
    II. The sum of the digits a and b is 6.
13. What is the two-digit number? (SIDBI, 2006)
    I. The sum of the two digits of the number is 13.
    II. The number obtained by interchanging the two digits of the number is smaller than the original number by 45.
14. What is the original number? (M.B.A., 2007)
    I. Sum of the two digits of a number is 10. The ratio between the two digits is 1 : 4.

II. Product of two digits of a number is 16 and quotient of two digits is 4.

15. What is the value of the two-digit number? (Bank P.O., 2009)

I. The product of the digits is 72 and the difference between the digits is 1.

II. The digit at the unit place is greater than the other.

Directions (Questions 16 to 22): Each of the questions given below consists of a question followed by three statements. You have to study the question and the statements and decide which of the statement(s) is/are necessary to answer the given question.

16. What is the two-digit number? (M.B.A., 2002)

I. Sum of the digits is 7.

II. Difference between the number and the number obtained by interchanging the digits is 9.

III. Digit in the ten's place is bigger than the digit in the unit's place by 1.

(*a*) I and II only (*b*) II and III only
(*c*) I and III only (*d*) All I, II and III
(*e*) None of these

17. What is the sum of the digits of the two-digit number?

I. The ratio between the ten's digit and unit's digit of the number is 3 : 2.

II. The number obtained on revering the order of its digits is 18 less than the original number.

III. The product of the digits is 24.

(*a*) Any two of the three (*b*) I only or II and III only
(*c*) All I, II and III (*d*) I and II only
(*e*) None of these

18. What will be the sum of two numbers?

I. Among the two numbers, the bigger number is greater than the smaller number by 6.

II. 40% of the smaller number is equal to 30% of the bigger number.

III. The ratio between half of the bigger number and one-third of the smaller number is 2 : 1.

(*a*) I and II only (*b*) II and III only
(*c*) All I, II and III (*d*) Any two of the three
(*e*) None of these

19. What is the two-digit number? (M.A.T., 2005)

I. The difference between the two-digit number and the number formed by interchanging the digits is 27.

II. The difference between the two digits is 3.

III. The digit at unit's place is less than that at ten's place by 3.

(*a*) I and II only (*b*) I and III only
(*c*) All I, II and III (*d*) I, and either II or III
(*e*) Even with all I, II and III, answer cannot be given.

20. What is the two-digit number? (Bank P.O., 2004)

I. Digit in the ten's place is cube of the digit in unit's place.

II. Digit in the ten's place is four times the digit in the unit's place.

III. The two digits are not equal.

(*a*) I and II only (*b*) I and III only
(*c*) Any two of the three (*d*) I and either II or III only
(*e*) None of these

21. Find three positive consecutive even numbers. (M.A.T., 2006)

I. The average of four consecutive even numbers starting from the last of the given numbers is 17.

II. The difference of the highest and the lowest numbers is 4.

III. The sum of the squares of the three numbers is 440.

(*a*) I only (*b*) I and II only
(*c*) III only (*d*) Either I or III

22. What is the two-digit number? (Bank P.O., 2006)

I. The number obtained by interchanging the digits of the number is greater than the original number by 18.

II. Sum of the digits of the number is 14.

III. Difference between the two digits of the number is 2.

(*a*) Any two of the three (*b*) Only I and III
(*c*) II and either I or III (*d*) III and either I or II
(*e*) All of these

ANSWERS

1. (*a*)	2. (*d*)	3. (*e*)	4. (*c*)	5. (*e*)	6. (*e*)	7. (*b*)	8. (*a*)	9. (*e*)	10. (*b*)
11. (*a*)	12. (*a*)	13. (*e*)	14. (*b*)	15. (*e*)	16. (*e*)	17. (*a*)	18. (*e*)	19. (*e*)	20. (*a*)
21. (*d*)	22. (*c*)								

SOLUTIONS

1. I. Two digits with difference 9 are 9 and 0. And, the two-digit number formed using 9 and 0 is 90.

II. Let the ten's and unit's digits be x and y respectively.
Then, $x - y = x + y \Leftrightarrow 2y = 0 \Leftrightarrow y = 0$.
So, the ten's digit cannot be determined.
Thus, I only gives the answer, while II does not.
$\therefore$ The correct answer is (*a*).

2. I. gives, $a - b = 2$ ...(*i*)
or $b - a = 2$ ...(*ii*)

II. gives, $a + b = 4$ ...(*iii*)
Solving (*i*) and (*iii*), we get : $a = 3$ and $b = 1$.
Solving (*ii*) and (*iii*), we get : $a = 1$ and $b = 3$.
So, the required number is either 13 or 31.
Thus, even both I and II together do not give the answer.
$\therefore$ The correct answer is (*d*).

3. Let the ten's and unit's digits be x and y respectively, where $x > y$.
I. gives, $x - y = 5$ ...(i)
II. gives, $x + y = 7$ ...(ii)
Solving (i) and (ii), we get : $x = 6$ and $y = 1$. So, the required number is 61.
Thus, both I and II together give the answer.
∴ The correct answer is (e).

4. Let the required number be x.
I. $\frac{4}{5}x - \frac{3}{4}x = 2.5 \Leftrightarrow \frac{x}{20} = 2.5 \Leftrightarrow x = 50$.
So, $\frac{4}{5}x = \left(\frac{4}{5} \times 50\right) = 40$.
II. $x + \frac{x}{2} = 75 \Leftrightarrow \frac{3x}{2} = 75 \Leftrightarrow x = \left(\frac{75 \times 2}{3}\right) = 50$.
So, $\frac{4}{5}x = \left(\frac{4}{5} \times 50\right) = 40$.
Thus, either I or II alone gives the answer.
∴ The correct answer is (c).

5. II. Let the greater number be x. Then, smaller number $= (30 - x)$.
I. $x - (30 - x) = \frac{x}{3} \Leftrightarrow 2x - 30 = \frac{x}{3} \Leftrightarrow 6x - 90 = x$
$\Leftrightarrow 5x = 90 \Leftrightarrow x = 18$.
So, smaller number $= 30 - 18 = 12$.
Thus, both I and II together give the answer.
∴ The correct answer is (e).

6. Let the ten's and unit's digits be x and y respectively.
I. $x + y = 6$ ...(i)
II. $x = 2y$ ...(ii)
Solving (i) and (ii), we get : $x = 4$, $y = 2$. So, the required number is 42.
Thus, both I and II together give the answer.
∴ The correct answer is (e).

7. I. Let the ten's and unit's digits of the number be a and b respectively.
Then, $a + b = 8$.
II. Let the required number be x.
Then, $\frac{x}{5} = \left(\frac{1}{2} \text{ of } 44\right) - 15 = 7 \Leftrightarrow x = 35$.
So, the required number is 35.
Thus, II alone gives the answer.
∴ The correct answer is (b).

8. Let the required number be x.
I. $\frac{x}{2} - \frac{2x}{5} = 20 \Leftrightarrow \frac{5x - 4x}{10} = 20 \Leftrightarrow \frac{x}{10} = 20 \Leftrightarrow x = 200$.
II. $\frac{x}{4} = 25\%$ of $x \Leftrightarrow \frac{x}{4} = \frac{x}{4}$.
Thus, I alone gives the answer.
∴ The correct answer is (a).

9. II. Let the two numbers be $3x$ and $4x$.
I. $(3x)^2 = 9 \times 4x \Leftrightarrow 9x^2 = 36x \Leftrightarrow x = 4$.
So, the numbers are 12 and 16.
∴ Required difference $= 16 - 12 = 4$.
Thus, both I and II together give the answer.
∴ The correct answer is (e).

10. Let the 8 consecutive real numbers be x, $(x + 1)$, $(x + 2)$, $(x + 3)$, $(x + 4)$, $(x + 5)$, $(x + 6)$ and $(x + 7)$.
I. gives, $x(x + 1)(x + 2)(x + 3)(x + 4)(x + 5)(x + 6)(x + 7) = 34459425$.
This equation cannot be solved for x.
II. gives, $x + (x + 1) + (x + 2) + (x + 3) + (x + 4) + (x + 5) + (x + 6) + (x + 7) = 84$
$\Leftrightarrow 8x + 28 = 84 \Leftrightarrow 8x = 56 \Leftrightarrow x = 7$.
∴ Third number $= x + 2 = 7 + 2 = 9$.
Thus, II alone gives the answer.
∴ The correct answer is (b).

11. Let the two numbers be x and y.
I. gives, $x + y = 2(x - y) \Leftrightarrow x = 3y$
$\Leftrightarrow \frac{x}{y} = \frac{3}{1} \Leftrightarrow x : y = 3 : 1$.
Thus, I only gives the answer.
II. does not give the answer.
∴ Correct answer is (a).

12. The only two-digit number which is a multiple of 51, is 51. So, I alone gives the answer while II alone does not.
∴ The correct answer is (a).

13. Let the ten's digit be x and the unit's digit be y. Then, number $= 10x + y$.
I. $x + y = 13 \Leftrightarrow y = (13 - x)$.
So, number $= 10x + (13 - x)$.
II. $[10x + (13 - x)] - [10(13 - x) + x] = 45$
$\Leftrightarrow (9x + 13) - (130 - 9x) = 45$
$\Leftrightarrow 18x = 162 \Leftrightarrow x = 9$.
$y = 13 - x = 13 - 9 = 4$.
So, required number $= 94$.
Thus, both I and II together give the answer.
∴ The correct answer is (e).

14. Let the ten's and unit's digits be x and y respectively. Then,
I. $x + y = 10$ and $\frac{x}{y} = \frac{1}{4}$.
II. $xy = 16$ and $\frac{x}{y} = \frac{4}{1}$.
∴ II gives, $x^2 = 64 \Leftrightarrow x = 8$.
So, $4y = 8 \Leftrightarrow y = 2$.
Thus, II alone gives the answer while I alone does not.
∴ The correct answer is (b).

15. Let the ten's digit be x and the unit's digit be y.
II. $y > x$.
I. $xy = 72$ and $y - x = 1$ or $y = x + 1$
$\Leftrightarrow x(x + 1) = 72 \Leftrightarrow x^2 + x - 72 = 0$
$\Leftrightarrow x^2 + 9x - 8x - 72 = 0$
$\Leftrightarrow x(x + 9) - 8(x + 9) = 0$
$\Leftrightarrow (x + 9)(x - 8) = 0 \Leftrightarrow x = 8$.
So, $y = x + 1 = 9$
∴ Required number $= 89$.
Thus, both I and II together give the answer.
∴ The correct answer is (e).

16. Let the ten's and unit's digit be x and y respectively.
I. $x + y = 7$.

II. $(10x + y) - (10y + x) = 9 \Rightarrow x - y = 1$.

III. $x - y = 1$.

Thus, I and II as well as I and III give the answer.

$\therefore$ Correct answer is (*e*).

17. I. Let the ten's and unit's digit be $3x$ and $2x$ respectively.

II. $(30x + 2x) - (20x + 3x) = 18 \Leftrightarrow x = 2$.

III. $3x \times 2x = 24 \Leftrightarrow x^2 = 4 \Leftrightarrow x = 2$.

Thus, any two of the three will give the answer.

$\therefore$ Correct answer is (*a*).

18. Let the required numbers be x and y, where $x > y$.

I. $x - y = 6$ ...(*i*)

II. $\frac{30}{100}x = \frac{40}{100}y \Leftrightarrow 3x - 4y = 0$ ...(*ii*)

III. $\frac{\frac{1}{2}x}{\frac{1}{3}y} = \frac{2}{1} \Leftrightarrow \frac{3x}{2y} = \frac{2}{1} \Leftrightarrow \frac{x}{y} = \frac{4}{3} \Leftrightarrow 3x - 4y = 0$ ...(*iii*)

So, we may solve (*i*) and (*ii*) or (*i*) and (*iii*) together to find x and y.

Thus, I, and either II or III together give the answer.

$\therefore$ Correct answer is (*e*).

19. Let the ten's and unit's digit be x and y respectively.

I. $(10x + y) - (10y + x) = 27 \Leftrightarrow x - y = 3$.

II. $x - y = 3$.

III. $x - y = 3$.

Thus, even all the given three statements together do not give the answer.

$\therefore$ Correct answer is (*e*).

20. Let the ten's digit be x and the unit's digit be y.

I. $x = y^3$ ...(*i*)

II. $x = 4y$ ...(*ii*)

III. $x \neq y$ ...(*iii*)

From (*i*) and (*ii*), we have : $y^3 = 4y \Leftrightarrow y^3 - 4y = 0$

$\Leftrightarrow y(y^2 - 4) = 0$

$\Leftrightarrow y^2 - 4 = 0$ $[\because y \neq 0]$

$\Leftrightarrow y^2 = 4 \Leftrightarrow y = 2$.

So, $x = y^3 = 2^3 = 8$.

$\therefore$ The required number is 82.

Thus, I and II together give the answer.

$\therefore$ Correct answer is (*a*).

21. Let the three consecutive even numbers be x, $(x + 2)$ and $(x + 4)$.

I. $\frac{(x+4)+(x+6)+(x+8)+(x+10)}{4} = 17$

$\Leftrightarrow 4x + 28 = 68 \Leftrightarrow 4x = 40 \Leftrightarrow x = 10$.

So, the required numbers are 10, 12 and 14.

II. $(x + 4) - x = 4 \Leftrightarrow 4 = 4$.

So, the value of x cannot be determined.

III. $x^2 + (x + 2)^2 + (x + 4)^2 = 440$

$\Leftrightarrow x^2 + x^2 + 4 + 4x + x^2 + 16 + 8x = 440$

$\Leftrightarrow 3x^2 + 12x - 420 = 0$

$\Leftrightarrow x^2 + 4x - 140 = 0$

$\Leftrightarrow x^2 + 14x - 10x - 140$

$\Leftrightarrow x(x + 14) - 10(x + 14) = 0$

$\Leftrightarrow (x + 14)(x - 10) = 0$

$\Leftrightarrow x = 10$.

So, the required numbers are 10, 12 and 14.

Thus, I alone or III alone gives the answer.

$\therefore$ Correct answer is (*d*).

22. Let the ten's digit be x and unit's digit be y.

(I and II). $x + y = 14$ or $y = (14 - x)$ ...(*i*)

And, $[10(14 - x) + x] - [10x + (14 - x)]$

$= 18 \Leftrightarrow (140 - 9x) - (9x + 14) = 18$

$\Leftrightarrow 18x = 108 \Leftrightarrow x = 6$.

So, $y = 14 - 6 = 8$.

$\therefore$ Required number = 68.

(II and III). $x + y = 14$ ...(*ii*)

and $x - y = \pm 2$ ...(*iii*)

Solving (*ii*) and (*iii*), we get : $x = 6$ or 8.

If $x = 6$, $y = 8$ & If $x = 8$, $y = 6$.

$\therefore$ Required number is either 68 or 86.

(I and III). Since the number obtained by interchanging the digits is greater, the ten's digit is smaller than the unit's digit.

$x + y = 14$ ...(*iv*)

And, $y - x = 2$ ...(*v*)

Solving (*iv*) and (*v*), we get : $y = 8$.

So, $x = 14 - y = 6$.

$\therefore$ Required number = 68.

Thus, II and either I or III gives the answer.

$\therefore$ Correct answer is (*c*).

8 Problems on Ages

SOLVED EXAMPLES

Ex. 1. ***The ratio of the ages of Tina and Rakesh is 9 : 10 respectively. Ten years ago, the ratio of their ages was 4 : 5 respectively. What is the present age of Rakesh?*** **(Bank P.O., 2010)**

Sol. Let Tina's age be $9x$ years. Then, Rakesh's age = $10x$ years.

$\therefore \frac{9x-10}{10x-10} = \frac{4}{5} \Rightarrow 5(9x-10) = 4(10x-10) \Rightarrow 45x - 40x = 50 - 40 \Rightarrow 5x = 10 \Rightarrow x = 2.$

$\therefore$ Present age of Rakesh = (10×2) years = 20 years.

Ex.2. ***Samir's age is one-fourth of his father's age and two-third of his sister Reema's age. What is the ratio of the ages of Samir, Reema and their father respectively?*** **(Bank P.O., 2009)**

Sol. Samir's age = $\frac{1}{4} \times$ Father's age = $\frac{2}{3} \times$ Reema's age = x years (say).

Then, Samir's age = x years, Reema's age = $\frac{3}{2}x$ years and Father's age = $4x$ years.

Ratio of the ages of Samir, Reema and father = $x : \frac{3}{2}x : 4x = 2 : 3 : 8.$

Ex.3. ***The age of father 10 years ago was thrice the age of his son. 10 years hence father's age will be twice that of his son. Find the ratio of their present ages.*** **(L.I.C., 2003)**

Sol. Let son's age 10 years ago be x years. Then, father's age 10 years ago = $3x$ years.

Son's age 10 years hence = $(x + 20)$ years.

Father's age 10 years hence = $(3x + 20)$ years.

$\therefore \quad 3x + 20 = 2(x + 20) \Rightarrow x = (40 - 20) = 20.$

Ratio of father's age and son's age at present = $(3x + 10) : (x + 10)$

$= (3 \times 20 + 10) : (20 + 10) = 70 : 30 = 7 : 3.$

Ex. 4. ***A man's present age is two-fifths of the age of his mother. After 8 years, he will be one-half of the age of his mother. How old is the mother at present?*** **(M.A.T., 2009)**

Sol. Let mother's age be x years. Then, man's age = $\frac{2x}{5}$ years.

$\frac{2x}{5} + 8 = \frac{1}{2}(x+8) \Rightarrow \frac{2x}{5} + 8 = \frac{1}{2}x + 4 \Rightarrow \frac{1}{2}x - \frac{2x}{5} = 4 \Rightarrow 5x - 4x = 40 \Rightarrow x = 40.$

$\therefore$ Mother's age = 40 years.

Ex. 5. ***The ages of two persons differ by 16 years. If 6 years ago, the elder one be three times as old as the younger one, find their present ages.*** **(L.I.C., 2009)**

Sol. Let their ages be x years and $(x - 16)$ years. Then,

$(x - 6) = 3\{(x - 16) - 6\} \Rightarrow x - 6 = 3(x - 22) \Rightarrow 3x - x = 66 - 6 \Rightarrow 2x = 60 \Rightarrow x = 30.$

So, their ages are 30 years and $(30 - 16)$ = 14 years.

Ex. 6. ***The product of the ages of Ankit and Nikita is 240. If twice the age of Nikita is more than Ankit's age by 4 years, then find Nikita's age.***

Sol. Let Ankit's age be x years. Then, Nikita's age = $\frac{240}{x}$ years. $2 \times \frac{240}{x} - x = 4 \Rightarrow \frac{480}{x} - x = 4 \Rightarrow 480 - x^2 = 4x$

$\Rightarrow x^2 + 4x - 480 = 0$

$\Rightarrow x^2 + 24x - 20x - 480 = 0 \Rightarrow x(x + 24) - 20(x + 24) = 0$

$\Rightarrow (x + 24)(x - 20) = 0 \Rightarrow x = 20$ $[\because x \neq -24]$

$\therefore$ Nikita's age $= \frac{240}{20}$ years = 12 years.

Ex. 7. ***Reenu's age after 6 years will be three–sevenths of her father's age. 10 years ago, the ratio of their ages was 1 : 5. What is Reenu's father's age at present?***

Sol. Let Reenu's age 10 years ago be x years.

Then, her father's age 10 years ago = $5x$ years.

$(x + 10) + 6 = \frac{3}{7} \times [(5x + 10) + 6] \Rightarrow x + 16 = \frac{3}{7}(5x + 16) \Rightarrow 7x + 112 = 15x + 48 \Rightarrow 8x = 64 \Rightarrow x = 8.$

$\therefore$ Reenu's father's present age = $(5x + 10) = (5 \times 8 + 10)$ years = 50 years.

EXERCISE–A

(OBJECTIVE TYPE QUESTIONS)

Directions: Mark (√) against the correct answer.

1. The ratio of the present ages of a mother and her daughter is 7 : 1. Four years ago, the ratio of their ages was 19 : 1. What will be the mother's age four years from now? (S.B.I. P.O., 2010)

(*a*) 42 years (*b*) 38 years
(*c*) 46 years (*d*) 36 years
(*e*) None of these

2. The ages of Nishi and Vinnee are in the ratio 6 : 5 respectively. After 9 years, the ratio of their ages will be 9 : 8. What is the difference in their ages now ? (Bank P.O., 2008)

(*a*) 3 years (*b*) 5 years
(*c*) 7 years (*d*) 9 years
(*e*) None of these

3. The present ages of Amit and his father are in the ratio 2 : 5 respectively. Four years hence, the ratio of their ages becomes 5 : 11 respectively. What was the father's age five years ago? (Bank P.O., 2009)

(*a*) 30 years (*b*) 35 years
(*c*) 40 years (*d*) 45 years
(*e*) None of these

4. The ratio of the ages of a father and his son is 17 : 7 respectively. Six years ago, the ratio of their ages was 3 : 1 respectively. What is the father's present age ? (Bank P.O., 2009)

(*a*) 64 years (*b*) 51 years
(*c*) 48 years (*d*) Cannot be determined
(*e*) None of these

5. The ages of Shakti and Kanti are in the ratio of 8 : 7 respectively. After 10 years, the ratio of their ages will be 13 : 12. What is the difference between their ages ? (Bank P.O., 2008)

(*a*) 2 years (*b*) 4 years
(*c*) 8 years (*d*) 6 years
(*e*) None of these

6. The ages of A and B are in the ratio 6 : 5 and the sum of their ages is 44 years. What will be the ratio of their ages after 8 years? (P.C.S., 2008)

(*a*) 7 : 6 (*b*) 8 : 7
(*c*) 9 : 8 (*d*) 3 : 4

7. Farah got married 8 years ago. Today her age is $1\frac{2}{7}$ times her age at the time of her marriage. At present her daughter's age is one-sixth of her age. What was her daughter's age 3 years ago? (Bank P.O., 2009)

(*a*) 4 years (*b*) 3 years
(*c*) 6 years (*d*) Cannot be determined
(*e*) None of these

8. The age of a mother today is thrice that of her daughter. After 12 years, the age of the mother will be twice that of her daughter. The present age of the daughter is: (S.S.C., 2006)

(*a*) 12 years (*b*) 14 years
(*c*) 16 years (*d*) 18 years

9. The present age of Mr. Sanyal is three times the age of his son. Six years hence, the ratio of their ages will be 5 : 2. What is the present age of Mr. Sanyal? (L.I.C., 2007)

(*a*) 48 years (*b*) 50 years
(*c*) 54 years (*d*) 60 years
(*e*) None of these

10. The average of the ages of a man and his daughter is 34 years. If the respective ratio of their ages four years from now is 14 : 5, what is daughter's present age? (Bank P.O., 2008)

(*a*) 10 years (*b*) 12 years
(*c*) 18 years (*d*) Cannot be determined
(*e*) None of these

11. Ratio of Rani's and Komal's ages is 3 : 5 respectively. Ratio of Komal's and Pooja's ages is 2 : 3 respectively.

If Rani is two-fifth of Pooja's age, what is Rani's age? **(Bank P.O., 2009)**

(*a*) 10 years (*b*) 15 years
(*c*) 14 years (*d*) Cannot be determined
(*e*) None of these

12. The age of a father 10 years ago was thrice the age of his son. 10 years hence, the father's age will be twice that of his son. The ratio of their present ages is **(P.C.S., 2009)**

(*a*) 8 : 5 (*b*) 7 : 3
(*c*) 9 : 5 (*d*) 5 : 2

13. The ratio between the ages of Ram and Mohan is 4 : 5 and that between the ages of Ram and Anil is 5 : 6. If the sum of the ages of the three is 69 years, what is Mohan's age? **(Railways, 2008)**

(*a*) 20 years (*b*) 24 years
(*c*) 25 years (*d*) 30 years

14. At present, Suresh's age is twice the age of his daughter. After 6 years from now, the ratio of the ages of Suresh and his daughter will be 23 : 13. What is the present age of Suresh? **(Bank P.O., 2008)**

(*a*) 36 years (*b*) 40 years
(*c*) 46 years (*d*) Cannot be determined
(*e*) None of these

15. The difference between the present ages of Arun and Deepak is 14 years. Seven years ago, the ratio of their ages was 5 : 7 respectively. What is Deepak's present age? **(Bank P.O., 2008)**

(*a*) 35 years (*b*) 42 years
(*c*) 49 years (*d*) 56 years
(*e*) None of these

16. Ten years ago, a man was seven times as old as his son. Two years hence, twice his age will be equal to five times the age of his son. What is the present age of the son? **(Railways, 2006)**

(*a*) 12 years (*b*) 13 years
(*c*) 14 years (*d*) 15 years

17. The ages of Samina and Suhana are in the ratio of 7 : 3 respectively. After 6 years, the ratio of their ages will be 5 : 3. What is the difference in their ages? **(Bank P.O., 2008)**

(*a*) 6 years (*b*) 8 years
(*c*) 10 years (*d*) 12 years
(*e*) None of these

18. The ages of Sulekha and Arunima are in the ratio of 9 : 8 respectively. After 5 years, the ratio of their ages will be 10 : 9. What is the difference in their ages? **(Bank P.O., 2008)**

(*a*) 4 years (*b*) 5 years
(*c*) 6 years (*d*) 7 years
(*e*) None of these

19. The ages of A and B are presently in the ratio of 5 : 6 respectively. Six years hence, this ratio will become 6 : 7 respectively. What was B's age 5 years ago? **(Bank P.O., 2009)**

(*a*) 25 years (*b*) 30 years
(*c*) 31 years (*d*) 36 years
(*e*) None of these

20. The age of the mother today is thrice that of her daughter. After 12 years, the age of the mother will be twice that of her daughter. The age of the daughter today is **(S.S.C., 2006)**

(*a*) 12 years (*b*) 14 years
(*c*) 16 years (*d*) 18 years

21. The sum of the ages of a daughter and her mother is 56 years. After four years, the age of the mother will be three times that of the daughter. At present their ages are **(S.S.C., 2006)**

(*a*) 10 years, 46 years (*b*) 12 years, 44 years
(*c*) 11 years, 45 years (*d*) 13 years, 43 years

22. The present age of son is half of the present age of his mother. Ten years ago, his mother's age was thrice the age of her son. What is the present age of the son? **(Railways, 2006)**

(*a*) 20 years (*b*) 25 years
(*c*) 30 years (*d*) 40 years

23. Ram's son's age is $\frac{1}{3}$ of Ram's wife's age. Ram's wife's age is $\frac{4}{5}$ of Ram's age and Ram's age is $\frac{3}{5}$ of Ram's father's age. Find the age of Ram's son, if Ram's father is 50 years old. **(Railways, 2005)**

(*a*) 6 years (*b*) 8 years
(*c*) 10 years (*d*) 12 years

24. Ratio between the ages of Subhash, Prasad and Amar is 3 : 6 : 7. If the difference between the ages of Prasad and Amar is 10 years, then what is the difference between the ages of Subhash and Prasad? **(Railways, 2006)**

(*a*) 5 years (*b*) 10 years
(*c*) 20 years (*d*) 30 years

25. Rajan got married 8 years ago. His present age is $\frac{6}{5}$ times his age at the time of his marriage. Rajan's sister was 10 years younger to him at the time of his marriage. The age of Rajan's sister is **(M.A.T., 2005)**

(*a*) 32 years (*b*) 36 years
(*c*) 38 years (*d*) 40 years

26. The ages of two persons differ by 20 years. If 5 years ago, the older one be 5 times as old as the younger one, then their present ages are **(M.A.T., 2004)**

(*a*) 25 years, 5 years (*b*) 30 years, 10 years
(*c*) 35 years, 15 years (*d*) 50 years, 30 years

27. A couple has a son and a daughter. The age of the father is four times that of the son and the age of the daughter is one-third of that of her mother. The wife is 6 years younger to her husband and the sister is 3 years older than her brother. The mother's age is **(P.C.S., 2008)**

(*a*) 42 years (*b*) 48 years
(*c*) 54 years (*d*) 63 years

28. The present ages of three persons are in the proportion 4 : 7 : 9. Eight years ago, the sum of their ages was 56 years. The present age of the eldest person is

(*a*) 28 years (*b*) 36 years
(*c*) 45 years (*d*) None of these

29. In 10 years, A will be twice as old as B was 10 years ago. If A is now 9 years older than B, the present age of B is

(*a*) 19 years (*b*) 29 years
(*c*) 39 years (*d*) 49 years
(*e*) None of these

30. Reenu's father was 38 years of age when she was born while her mother was 36 years old when her brother 4 years younger to her was born. What is the difference between the ages of her parents?

(*a*) 2 years (*b*) 4 years
(*c*) 6 years (*d*) 8 years
(*e*) None of these

31. The sum of the ages of 5 children born at the intervals of 3 years each is 50 years. What is the age of the youngest child?

(*a*) 4 years (*b*) 6 years
(*c*) 8 years (*d*) 10 years
(*e*) None of these

32. A man was asked to state his age in years. His reply was, "Take my age 3 years hence, multiply it by 3 and then subtract 3 times my age 3 years ago and you will know how old I am." What is the age of the man? **(S.S.C., 2004)**

(*a*) 18 years (*b*) 20 years
(*c*) 24 years (*d*) 32 years

33. The sum of the ages of Jayant, Prem and Paras is 93 years. Ten years ago, the ratio of their ages was 2 : 3 : 4. What is the present age of Paras?

(*a*) 24 years (*b*) 28 years
(*c*) 32 years (*d*) 34 years
(*e*) 38 years

34. The sum of the ages of a man and his son is 45 years. Five years ago, the product of their ages was 34. The man's age is

(*a*) 40 years (*b*) 45 years
(*c*) 50 years (*d*) 55 years
(*e*) None of these

35. The ratio of a man's age and his son's age is 7 : 3 and the product of their ages is 756. The ratio of their ages after 6 years will be

(*a*) 5 : 2 (*b*) 2 : 1
(*c*) 11 : 7 (*d*) 13 : 9
(*e*) None of these

36. Sonal is 40 years old and Nitya is 60 years old. How many years ago was the ratio of their ages 3 : 5?

(*a*) 5 years (*b*) 10 years
(*c*) 20 years (*d*) 37 years
(*e*) None of these

37. The ratio between the present ages of A and B is 5 : 3 respectively. The ratio between A's age 4 years ago and B's age 4 years hence is 1 : 1. What is the ratio between A's age 4 years hence and B's age 4 years ago?

(*a*) 1 : 3 (*b*) 3 : 1
(*c*) 2 : 1 (*d*) 4 : 1
(*e*) None of these

38. The ratio of the ages of a man and his wife is 4 : 3. After 4 years, this ratio will be 9 : 7. If at the time of their marriage, the ratio of their ages was 5 : 3, then how many years ago were they married?

(*a*) 8 years (*b*) 10 years
(*c*) 12 years (*d*) 15 years
(*e*) None of these

39. The ratio between the ages of Neelam and Shiny is 5 : 6 respectively. If the ratio between the one-third age of Neelam and half of Shiny's age is 5 : 9, then what is Shiny's age? **(Bank P.O., 2002)**

(*a*) 25 years (*b*) 30 years
(*c*) 36 years (*d*) Cannot be determined
(*e*) None of these

40. 18 years ago, a man was three times as old as his son. Now, the man is twice as old as his son. The sum of the present ages of the man and his son is **(S.S.C., 2003)**

(*a*) 54 years (*b*) 72 years
(*c*) 105 years (*d*) 108 years

41. A man is aged three times more than his son Ronit. After 8 years, he would be two and a half times of Ronit's age. After further 8 years, how many times would he be of Ronit's age?

(*a*) 2 times (*b*) $2\frac{1}{2}$ times

(c) $2\frac{3}{4}$ times (d) 3 times

42. One year ago, Promila was four times as old as her daughter Sakshi. Six years hence, Promila's age will exceed her daughter's age by 9 years. The ratio of the present ages of Promila and her daughter is

(a) 9 : 2 (b) 11 : 3
(c) 12 : 5 (d) 13 : 4
(e) None of these

43. The age of a man 10 years ago was thrice the age of his son. 10 years hence, the man's age will be twice the age of his son. The ratio of their present ages is **(L.I.C., 2003)**

(a) 5 : 2 (b) 7 : 3
(c) 9 : 2 (d) 13 : 4

44. Tanya's grandfather was 8 times older to her 16 years ago. He would be 3 times of her age 8 years from now. 8 years ago, what was the ratio of Tanya's age to that of her grandfather? **(S.S.C., 2003)**

(a) 1 : 2 (b) 1 : 5
(c) 3 : 8 (d) None of these

45. The difference between the ages of two men is 10 years. 15 years ago, the elder one was twice as old as the younger one. The present age of the elder man is

(a) 25 years (b) 35 years
(c) 45 years (d) 52 years
(e) 55 years

46. 6 years ago, the ratio of the ages of Kunal and Sagar was 6 : 5. Four years hence, the ratio of their ages will be 11 : 10. What is Sagar's age at present? **(Bank P.O., 2009)**

(a) 16 years (b) 18 years
(c) 20 years (d) Cannot be determined
(e) None of these

47. Sneh's age is $\frac{1}{6}$th of her father's age. Sneh's father's age will be twice of Vimal's age after 10 years. If Vimal's 8th birthday was celebrated 2 years ago, then what is Sneh's present age?

(a) $6\frac{2}{3}$ years (b) 10 years
(c) 12 years (d) 15 years
(e) None of these

48. The ages of Samina and Suhana are in the ratio of 7 : 3 respectively. After 6 years, the ratio of their ages will be 5 : 3. What is the difference in their ages? **(Bank P.O., 2008)**

(a) 6 years (b) 8 years
(c) 10 years (d) 12 years
(e) None of these

49. The ages of Sulekha and Arunima are in the ratio 9 : 8 respectively. After 5 years, the ratio of their ages will be 10 : 9. What is the difference in their ages? **(Bank P.O., 2008)**

(a) 4 years (b) 5 years (c) 6 years
(d) 7 years (e) None of these

50. Three years ago, the ratio of the ages of Amisha and Nimisha was 8 : 9 respectively. 3 years hence, the ratio of their ages will be 11 : 12 respectively. What is the present age of Amisha? **(Bank P.O., 2009)**

(a) 16 years (b) 19 years
(c) 21 years (d) Cannot be determined
(e) None of these

51. If 10 years are subtracted from the present age of Mr. Roy and the remainder divided by 14, then you would get the present age of his grandson Sachin. If Sachin is 9 years younger to Saloni whose age is 14 years, then what is the present age of Mr. Roy?

(a) 60 years (b) 70 years
(c) 74 years (d) 80 years
(e) None of these

52. X's age 3 years ago was three times the present age of Y. At present, Z's age is twice the age of Y. Also Z is 12 years younger than X. What is the present age of Z?

[IBPS—RRB Officer's Gr. 'B' Exam, 2015]

(a) 15 year (b) 24 year
(c) 12 year (d) 18 year
(e) 6 year

53. Eight year ago, Poorvi's age was equal to the sum of the present ages of her one son and one daughter. Five years hence, the respective ratio between the ages of her daughter and her son that time will be 7 : 6. If Poorvi's husband is 7 years elder to her and his present age is three times the present age of their son, what is the present age of the daughter? (in years) **[RBI Gr. 'B' (Phase I) Exam, 2015]**

(a) 15 years (b) 23 years
(c) 19 years (d) 27 years
(e) 13 years

54. The sum of present ages of a father and his son is 8 years more than the present age of the mother. The mother is 22 years older than the son. What will be the age of the father after 4 years?

[United India Insurance Co. Ltd., (UIICL) Assistant (Online) Exam, 2015]

(a) 34 years (b) 36 years
(c) 40 years (d) 38 years
(e) 28 years

55. Rahul is as much younger than Sagar as he is older than Purav. If the sum of the ages of Purav and Sagar is 66 years, and Sagar's age is 48 years, then what is Purav's age? (in years)
[NICL—AAO Exam, 2015]
(a) 18 (b) cannot be determined
(c) 16 (d) 20
(e) 12

56. 4 years ago, the ratio of 1/2 of A's age at that time and four times of B's age at the time was 5 : 12. Eight years hence, 1/2 of A's age at that time will be less than B's age at that time by 2 years. What is B's present age?
[IBPS—RRB Officers Exam, 2015]
(a) 10 years (b) 14 years
(c) 12 years (d) 5 years
(e) 8 years

57. Ten years hence, the respective ratio between Simmi's age and Niti's age will be 7 : 9. Two years ago, the respective ratio between Simmi's age and Niti's age was 1 : 3. If Abhay is 4 years older to his sister Niti, what is Abhay's present age? (in years)
[CET—Maharashtra (MBA) Exam, 2016]
(a) 8 (b) 4
(c) 16 (d) 12
(e) 20

ANSWERS

1. (c)	2. (a)	3. (b)	4. (b)	5. (a)	6. (b)	7. (b)	8. (a)	9. (c)	10. (e)
11. (d)	12. (b)	13. (c)	14. (b)	15. (d)	16. (c)	17. (b)	18. (b)	19. (c)	20. (a)
21. (b)	22. (a)	23. (b)	24. (d)	25. (c)	26. (b)	27. (c)	28. (b)	29. (c)	30. (c)
31. (a)	32. (a)	33. (e)	34. (e)	35. (b)	36. (b)	37. (b)	38. (c)	39. (d)	40. (d)
41. (a)	42. (d)	43. (b)	44. (d)	45. (b)	46. (a)	47. (a)	48. (b)	49. (b)	50. (b)
51. (d)	52. (d)	53. (b)	54. (a)	55. (a)	56. (a)	57. (d)			

SOLUTIONS

1. Let mother's age be $7x$ years. Then, daughter's age = x years. $\frac{7x-4}{x-4} = \frac{19}{1}$
$\Rightarrow 7x - 4 = 19(x - 4)$
$\Rightarrow 19x - 7x = 76 - 4$
$\Rightarrow 12x = 72$
$\Rightarrow x = 6.$
Mother's age after 4 years = $(7x + 4)$
$= (7 \times 6 + 4)$ years = 46 years.

2. Let Nishi's age be $6x$ years. Then, Vinnee's age = $5x$ years.
$\therefore \frac{6x+9}{5x+9} = \frac{9}{8} \Rightarrow 8(6x + 9) = 9(5x + 9)$
$\Rightarrow 48x - 45x = 81 - 72$
$\Rightarrow 3x = 9$
$\Rightarrow x = 3.$
Difference in their ages = $(6x - 5x) = x$ years = 3 years.

3. Let Amit's age be $2x$ years. Then, his father's age = $5x$ years.
$\therefore \frac{2x+4}{5x+4} = \frac{5}{11} \Rightarrow 11(2x + 4) = 5(5x + 4)$
$\Rightarrow 22x + 44 = 25x + 20$
$\Rightarrow 3x = 24$
$\Rightarrow x = 8.$
Father's age 5 years ago = $(5x - 5)$ years
$= (5 \times 8 - 5)$ years = 35 years.

4. Let father's age be $17x$ years. Then, son's age = $7x$ years.
$\frac{17x-6}{7x-6} = \frac{3}{1} \Rightarrow 3(7x - 6) = 17x - 6$
$\Rightarrow 21x - 18 = 17x - 6$
$\Rightarrow 4x = 12$
$\Rightarrow x = 3.$
$\therefore$ Father's present age = $17x$ years
$= (17 \times 3)$ years = 51 years.

5. Let Shakti's age be $8x$ years. Then, Kanti's age = $7x$ years.
$\therefore \frac{8x+10}{7x+10} = \frac{13}{12} \Rightarrow 12(8x + 10) = 13(7x + 10)$
$\Rightarrow 96x + 120 = 91x + 130$
$\Rightarrow 5x = 10$
$\Rightarrow x = 2.$
Difference between their ages = $(8x - 7x)$ years
$= x$ years = 2 years.

6. A's age = $\left(44 \times \frac{6}{11}\right)$ years = 24 years and B's age
= (44 – 24) years = 20 years.
Ratio of their ages after 8 years = $\frac{(24+8)}{(20+8)} = \frac{32}{28} = \frac{8}{7} = 8:7.$

7. Let Farah's age 8 years ago be x years. Then, her present age = $(x + 8)$ years.

$\therefore\ x + 8 = \frac{9}{7}x \Rightarrow 7x + 56 = 9x$

$\Rightarrow 2x = 56$

$\Rightarrow x = 28.$

$\therefore$ Farah's age now = $(x + 8)$ years = $(28 + 8)$ years = 36 years.

Her daughter's age now = $\left(\frac{1}{6} \times 36\right)$ years = 6 years.

Her daughter's age 3 years ago = $(6 - 3)$ years = 3 years.

8. Let the daughter's age be x years. Then, mother's age = $3x$ years.

$3x + 12 = 2(x + 12)$

$\Rightarrow 3x + 12 = 2x + 24$

$\Rightarrow x = 12.$

Present age of daughter = 12 years.

9. Let the son's age be x years. Then, Mr. Sanyal's age = $3x$ years.

$\therefore\ \frac{3x+6}{x+6} = \frac{5}{2} \Rightarrow 2(3x + 6) = 5(x + 6)$

$\Rightarrow 6x + 12 = 5x + 30$

$\Rightarrow x = 18.$

$\therefore$ Present age of Mr. Sanyal = $3x$ years = (3×18) years = 54 years.

10. Average age of man and his daughter = 34 years.

Their total age = (34×2) years = 68 years.

Let man's age be x years. Then, daughter's age = $(68 - x)$ years.

$\therefore\ \frac{x+4}{68-x+4} = \frac{14}{5} \Rightarrow 5(x + 4) = 14(72 - x)$

$\Rightarrow 5x + 20 = 1008 - 14x$

$\Rightarrow 19x = 988$

$\Rightarrow x = 52.$

$\therefore$ Daughter's present age = $(68 - 52)$ years = 16 years.

11. Rani's age : Komal's age = $3 : 5 = \frac{3}{5} : 1.$

Komal's age : Pooja's age = $2 : 3 = 1 : \frac{3}{2}.$

Rani's age : Komal's age : Pooja's age = $\frac{3}{5} : 1 : \frac{3}{2} = 6 : 10 : 15.$

Let Rani's age be $6x$ years. Then, Komal's age = $10x$ years and Pooja's age = $15x$ years.

Rani's age = $\frac{2}{5}$ of Pooja's age $\Rightarrow 6x = \frac{2}{5} \times 15x.$

Thus, we can not find the value of x and therefore of $6x$.

So, the answer cannot be determined.

12. Let son's age 10 years ago be x years.

Then, father's age 10 years ago = $3x$ years.

Son's age now = $(x + 10)$ years, Father's age now = $(3x + 10)$ years.

$(3x + 10) + 10 = 2[(x + 10) + 10]$

$\Rightarrow 3x + 20 = 2(x + 20)$

$\Rightarrow 3x + 20 = 2x + 40$

$\Rightarrow x = 20.$

Ratio of present ages of father and son

$= \frac{3x+10}{x+10} = \frac{3 \times 20 + 10}{20 + 10} = \frac{70}{30} = \frac{7}{3} = 7 : 3.$

13. Ram's age : Mohan's age = $4 : 5 = 1 : \frac{5}{4}.$

Ram's age : Anil's age = $5 : 6 = 1 : \frac{6}{5}.$

Let Ram's age be x years. Then, Mohan's age = $\frac{5x}{4}$ years.

And, Anil's age = $\frac{6x}{5}$ years.

$\therefore\ x + \frac{5x}{4} + \frac{6x}{5} = 69$

$\Rightarrow 20x + 25x + 24x = 1380$

$\Rightarrow 69x = 1380$

$\Rightarrow x = 20.$

Mohan's age = $\frac{5x}{4}$ years = $\frac{5 \times 20}{4}$ years = 25 years.

14. Let daughter's age be x years. Suresh's age = $2x$ years.

$\therefore\ \frac{2x+6}{x+6} = \frac{23}{13} \Rightarrow 13(2x + 6) = 23(x + 6)$

$\Rightarrow 26x + 78 = 23x + 138$

$\Rightarrow 3x = 60$

$\Rightarrow x = 20.$

Present age of Suresh = $2x$ years = (2×20) years = 40 years.

15. Let the ages of Arun and Deepak 7 years ago be $5x$ years and $7x$ years respectively. Then,

Arun's present age = $(5x + 7)$ years, Deepak's present age = $(7x + 7)$ years.

$\therefore\ (7x + 7) - (5x + 7) = 14$

$\Rightarrow 2x = 14$

$\Rightarrow x = 7.$

Deepak's present age = $(7 \times 7 + 7)$ years = 56 years.

16. Let son's age 10 years ago be x years. Then, man's age 10 years ago = $7x$ years.

Son's present age = $(x + 10)$ years, Man's present age = $(7x + 10)$ years.

$\therefore\ 2[(7x + 10) + 2] = 5[(x + 10) + 2]$

$\Rightarrow 2(7x + 12) = 5(x + 12)$

$\Rightarrow 14x + 24 = 5x + 60$

$\Rightarrow 9x = 36$

$\Rightarrow x = 4.$

$\therefore$ Son's present age = $(x + 10)$ years = $(4 + 10)$ years = 14 years.

17. Let Samina's age be $7x$ years. Then, Suhana's age = $3x$ years.

$\therefore\ \frac{7x+6}{3x+6} = \frac{5}{3} \Rightarrow 3(7x + 6) = 5(3x + 6)$

$\Rightarrow 21x + 18 = 15x + 30$

$\Rightarrow 6x = 12$

$\Rightarrow x = 2.$

Difference in their ages = $(7x - 3x)$ years

= $4x$ years= (4×2) years = 8 years.

18. Let Sulekha's age be $9x$ years. Then, Arunima's age = $8x$ years.

$\therefore \frac{9x+5}{8x+5} = \frac{10}{9} \Rightarrow 9(9x+5) = 10(8x+5)$

$\Rightarrow 81x + 45 = 80x + 50$

$\Rightarrow x = 5.$

Difference in their ages = $(9x - 8x)$ years

= x years = 5 years.

19. Let A's age be $5x$ years. Then, B's age = $6x$ years.

$\therefore \frac{5x+6}{6x+6} = \frac{6}{7} \Rightarrow 7(5x+6) = 6(6x+6)$

$\Rightarrow 35x + 42 = 36x + 36$

$\Rightarrow x = 6.$

B's age 5 years ago = $(6x - 5)$ years

= $(6 \times 6 - 5)$ years = 31 years.

20. Let daughter's age be x years. Then, mother's age = $3x$ years.

$(3x + 12) = 2(x + 12)$

$\Rightarrow 3x + 12 = 2x + 24$

$\Rightarrow x = 12.$

$\therefore$ Daughter's age today = 12 years.

21. Let daughter's age be x years. Then, mother's age = $(56 - x)$ years.

$(56 - x) + 4 = 3(x + 4)$

$\Rightarrow 60 - x = 3x + 12$

$\Rightarrow 4x = 48$

$\Rightarrow x = 12.$

$\therefore$ Daughter's age = 12 years, Mother's age = 44 years.

22. Let mother's age be $2x$ years. Then, son's age = x years.

$(2x - 10) = 3(x - 10)$

$\Rightarrow 2x - 10 = 3x - 30$

$\Rightarrow x = 20.$

Son's age = 20 years.

23. Ram's father's age = 50 years, Ram's age

$= \left(\frac{3}{5} \times 50\right)$ years = 30 years.

Ram's wife's age = $\left(\frac{4}{5} \times 30\right)$ years = 24 years.

Ram's son's age = $\left(\frac{1}{3} \times 24\right)$ years = 8 years.

24. Let Subhash's age be $3x$ years. Then, Prasad's age = $6x$ years and Amar's age = $7x$ years.

$\therefore \quad 7x - 6x = 10$

$\Rightarrow x = 10.$

Required difference = $(6x - 3x)$ years

= $3x$ years = (3×10) years = 30 years.

25. Let Rajan's age 8 years ago be x years. His present age = $(x + 8)$ years.

$\therefore \quad x + 8 = \frac{6}{5}x \Rightarrow 5x + 40 = 6x \Rightarrow x = 40.$

Rajan's sister's age 8 years ago = $(40 - 10)$ years = 30 years.

His sister's age now = $(30 + 8)$ years = 38 years.

26. Let their present ages be x years and $(x - 20)$ years.

$(x - 5) = 5[(x - 20) - 5]$

$\Rightarrow (x - 5) = 5(x - 25)$

$\Rightarrow (x - 5) = 5x - 125$

$\Rightarrow 4x = 120$

$\Rightarrow x = 30.$

$\therefore$ Their present ages are 30 years and 10 years.

27. M–Mother, F–Father, S–Son and D–Daughter.

$F = 4S,\ D = \frac{1}{3}M,\ M = F - 6 \text{ and } S = D - 3$

$\therefore \quad M = 3D = 3(S + 3)$

$= 3S + 9 = \frac{3}{4}F + 9 = \frac{3}{4}(M + 6) + 9$

$= \frac{3}{4}M + \frac{3}{4} \times 6 + 9$

$\Rightarrow \quad \left(M - \frac{3}{4}M\right) = \left(\frac{9}{2} + 9\right) \Rightarrow \frac{1}{4}M = \frac{27}{2}$

$\Rightarrow M = \left(\frac{27}{2} \times 4\right) = 54$ years.

$\therefore$ The mother is 54 years old.

28. A : B : C = 4 : 7 : 9 and (A + B + C)

= 56 + (8 + 8 + 8) = 80.

$\therefore$ C's age = $\left(80 \times \frac{9}{20}\right)$ years = 36 years.

29. Let B's age be x years. Then, A's age = $(x + 9)$ years.

$(x + 9) + 10 = 2(x - 10)$

$\Rightarrow x + 19 = 2x - 20$

$\Rightarrow x = 39.$

B's age = 39 years.

30. Mother's age when Reenu's brother was born = 36 years.

Father's age when Reenu's brother was born = (38 + 4) years = 42 years.

Required difference = (42 – 36) years = 6 years.

31. Let the ages of children be x, $(x + 3)$, $(x + 6)$, $(x + 9)$ and $(x + 12)$ years.

Then, $x + x + 3 + x + 6 + x + 9 + x + 12 = 50$

$\Rightarrow 5x = 20 \Rightarrow x = 4.$

$\therefore$ Age of youngest child = 4 years.

32. Let the present age of the man be x years. Then

$3(x + 3) - 3(x - 3) = x$

$\Rightarrow (3x + 9) - (3x - 9) = x$

$\Rightarrow x = 18.$

$\therefore$ The present age of the man is 18 years.

33. Let their ages 10 years ago be $2x$ years, $3x$ years and $4x$ years respectively.

Then, $(2x + 10) + (3x + 10) + (4x + 10) = 93$

$\Rightarrow 9x + 30 = 93$

$\Rightarrow 9x = 63 \Rightarrow x = 7.$

Present age of Paras = $(4 \times 7 + 10)$ years = 38 years.

34. Let the man's age be x years.

Then, son's age = $(45 - x)$ years.

$(x - 5)(45 - x - 5) = 34$

$\Rightarrow (x - 5)(40 - x) = 34$

$\therefore \quad 40x - x^2 - 200 + 5x = 34$

$\Rightarrow x^2 - 45x + 234 = 0$

$\Rightarrow \quad x^2 - 39x - 6x + 234 = 0$

$\Rightarrow x(x - 39) - 6(x - 39) = 0$

$\Rightarrow \quad (x - 39)(x - 6) = 0$

$\Rightarrow x = 39$ or $x = 6$.

$\therefore$ Man's age = 39 years.

35. Let the man's age be $7x$ years. Then, son's age = $3x$ years.

$\therefore \quad 7x \times 3x = 756$

$\Rightarrow 21x^2 = 756$

$\Rightarrow x^2 = 36 = 6^2$

$\Rightarrow x = 6.$

The ratio of their ages after 6 years = $(7x + 6) : (3x + 6)$

$= (7 \times 6 + 6) : (3 \times 6 + 6)$

$= 48 : 24 = 2 : 1.$

36. Let x years ago the ratio of their ages be 3 : 5.

Then, $\frac{40 - x}{60 - x} = \frac{3}{5} \Rightarrow 3(60 - x) = 5(40 - x)$

$\Rightarrow 180 - 3x = 200 - 5x$

$\Rightarrow 2x = 20$

$\Rightarrow x = 10.$

$\therefore$ 10 years ago, their ages were in the ratio 3 : 5.

37. Let A' s age be $5x$ years. Then, B's age = $3x$ years.

$\frac{5x - 4}{3x + 4} = \frac{1}{1} \Rightarrow 5x - 4 = 3x + 4 \Rightarrow 2x = 8 \Rightarrow x = 4.$

$\therefore \quad \frac{\text{A's age 4 years hence}}{\text{B's age 4 years ago}} = \frac{5x + 4}{3x - 4}$

$= \frac{5 \times 4 + 4}{3 \times 4 - 4} = \frac{24}{8} = \frac{3}{1} = 3:1.$

38. Let the man's age be $4x$ years. Then, his wife's age = $3x$ years.

Then, $\frac{4x + 4}{3x + 4} = \frac{9}{7} \Rightarrow 7(4x + 4) = 9(3x + 4)$

$\Rightarrow 28x + 28 = 27x + 36 \Rightarrow x = 8.$

Man's age = (4×8) years

= 32 years, Wife's age

= (3×8) years = 24 years.

Let they be married y years ago. Then,

$\frac{32 - y}{24 - y} = \frac{5}{3} \Rightarrow 3(32 - y) = 5(24 - y$

$\Rightarrow 96 - 3y = 120 - 5y$

$\Rightarrow 2y = (120 - 96) = 24$

$\Rightarrow y = 12.$

So, they were married 12 years ago.

39. Let Neelam's age be $5x$ years and Shiny's age be $6x$ years.

$\left(\frac{1}{3} \times 5x\right) : \left(\frac{1}{2} \times 6x\right) = 5:9 \Rightarrow \frac{5x}{3 \times 3x} = \frac{5}{9}.$

Thus, Shiny's age cannot be determined.

40. Let the son's age 18 years ago be x years. Then, man's age 18 years ago = $3x$ years.

$(3x + 18) = 2(x + 18)$

$\Rightarrow 3x + 18 = 2x + 36$

$\Rightarrow x = 18.$

Sum of their present ages = $(3x + 18 + x + 18)$ years

= $(4x + 36)$ years

= $(4 \times 18 + 36)$ years = 108 years.

41. Let Ronit's present age be x years.

Then, the man's age = $(x + 3x)$ years = $4x$ years.

$4x + 8 = \frac{5}{2}(x + 8) \Rightarrow 8x + 16 = 5x + 40 \Rightarrow 3x = 24 \Rightarrow x = 8.$

$\therefore \quad \text{Required ratio} = \frac{(4x + 16)}{(x + 16)} = \frac{(4 \times 8 + 16)}{(8 + 16)} = \frac{48}{24} = 2$ times.

42. Let Sakshi's age 1 year ago be x years. Then, Promila's age 1 year ago = $4x$ years.

$\therefore$ Sakshi's age now = $(x + 1)$ years, Promila's age now = $(4x + 1)$ years.

$(4x + 1) + 6 = (x + 1 + 6) + 9$

$\Rightarrow 4x + 7 = x + 16$

$\Rightarrow 3x = 9$

$\Rightarrow x = 3.$

Ratio of Promila's age and Sakshi's age now

$= \frac{(4x + 1)}{(x + 1)} = \frac{13}{4} = 13:4.$

43. Let son's age 10 years ago be x years. Then, man's age 10 years ago = $3x$ years.

Son's present age = $(x + 10)$ years, Man's present age = $(3x + 10)$ years.

$(3x + 10) + 10 = 2(x + 10 + 10)$

$\Rightarrow 3x + 20 = 2(x + 20)$

$\Rightarrow 3x + 20 = 2x + 40$

$\Rightarrow x = 20.$

Ratio of present ages of man and the son

$= \frac{3x + 10}{x + 10} = \frac{3 \times 20 + 10}{20 + 10} = \frac{70}{30} = 7:3.$

44. 16 years ago, let $T = x$ years and $G = 8x$ years.

After 8 years from now, $T = (x + 16 + 8)$ years and $G = (8x + 16 + 8)$ years.

$\therefore \quad 8x + 24 = 3(x + 24)$

$\Rightarrow 8x - 3x = 72 - 24$

$\Rightarrow 5x = 48.$

8 years ago, $\frac{T}{G} = \frac{x + 8}{8x + 8} = \frac{\frac{48}{5} + 8}{8 \times \frac{48}{5} + 8} = \frac{48 + 40}{384 + 40} = \frac{88}{424} = \frac{11}{53}.$

45. Let their ages be x years and $(x + 10)$ years.

Then $(x + 10 - 15) = 2(x - 15)$

$\Rightarrow x - 5 = 2x - 30$

$\Rightarrow x = 25.$

Present age of the elder man = $(x + 10)$ years = $(25 + 10)$ years = 35 years.

46. Let the ages of Kunal and Sagar 6 years ago be $6x$ and $5x$ years.

Then, $\frac{(6x+6)+4}{(5x+6)+4} = \frac{11}{10} \Rightarrow \frac{6x+10}{5x+10} = \frac{11}{10}$

$\Rightarrow 10(6x + 10) = 11(5x + 10)$

$\Rightarrow 60x + 100 = 55x + 110$

$\Rightarrow 5x = 10$

$\Rightarrow x = 2.$

Sagar's present age = $(5x + 6)$ years = $(5 \times 2 + 6)$ years = 16 years.

47. Vimal's present age = $(8 + 2)$ years = 10 years.

Sneh's father's age = $2(10 + 10)$ years = 40 years.

Sneh's age = $\left(\frac{1}{6} \times 40\right)$ years $= \frac{20}{3}$ years $= 6\frac{2}{3}$ years.

48. Let Samina's age be $7x$ years. Then, Suhana's age = $3x$ years.

$\therefore \frac{7x+6}{3x+6} = \frac{5}{3} \Rightarrow 3(7x + 6) = 5(3x + 6)$

$\Rightarrow 21x + 18 = 15x + 30$

$\Rightarrow 6x = 12$

$\Rightarrow x = 2.$

Difference in their ages = $(7x - 3x)$ years = $4x$ years = (4×2) years = 8 years.

49. Let Sulekha's age be $9x$ years. Then, Arunima's age = $8x$ years.

$\frac{9x+5}{8x+5} = \frac{10}{9} \Rightarrow 9(9x + 5) = 10(8x + 5)$

$\Rightarrow 81x + 45 = 80x + 50$

$\Rightarrow x = 5.$

Difference in their ages = $(9x - 8x)$ years = x years = 5 years.

50. Let Amisha's age 3 years ago be $8x$ years. Then, Nimisha's age 3 years ago = $9x$ years.

Present age of Amisha = $(8x + 3)$ years.

Present age of Nimisha = $(9x + 3)$ years.

$\frac{(8x+3)+3}{(9x+3)+3} = \frac{11}{12} \Rightarrow \frac{8x+6}{9x+6} = \frac{11}{12}$

$\Rightarrow 12(8x + 6) = 11(9x + 6)$

$\Rightarrow 96x + 72 = 99x + 66$

$\Rightarrow 3x = 6$

$\Rightarrow x = 2.$

Amisha's present age = $(8 \times 2 + 3)$ years = 19 years.

51. Saloni's age = 14 years $\Rightarrow$ Sachin's age = $(14 - 9)$ years = 5 years.

Let the present age of Mr. Roy be x years.

$\frac{x-10}{14} = 5 \Rightarrow x - 10 = 70 \Rightarrow x = 80$ years.

52. Let the present age of Y be a years.

Three years ago X's age = $3a$ years

Then, present age of X is $(3a + 3)$

Z's present age = $2a$

According to the given information

Now, $(3a + 3) - 2a = 12 \Rightarrow a = 9$ year

$\therefore$ Present age of Z = $2a = 2 \times 9 = 18$ years

53. Let the age of the son and the daughter of Poorvi be $6a$ years and $7a$ years respectively. 5 years hence, present age of son = $6a - 5$ and present age of daughter = $7a - 5$

According to the question,

Eight years ago, the age of Poorvi $= 6a - 5 + 7a - 5$
$= 13a - 10$

So, present age of Poorvi = $13a - 10 + 8 = 13a - 2$.

Since, present age of Poorvi husband = $3(6a - 5)$

The difference of present age of Poorvi husband and Poorvi = 7, (given)

$3(6a-5)-(13a-2)=7, \Rightarrow 18a - 15 - 13a + 2 = 7$

$\Rightarrow 5a = 20 \Rightarrow a = 4$

The present age of daughter = $(7a - 5) = 7 \times 4 - 5 = 23$ years

54. Let present age of father, mother and son be x, y and z respectively

Sum of present ages of father and son = (Mother's present age + 8 years)

$\Rightarrow x + z = y + 8$ years ...(i)

Mother's present age = (Son's present age + 22)

$\Rightarrow y = z + 22$ ...(ii)

Put the value of y in equation (i) we get

$x + z = z + 22 + 8$

$\Rightarrow x + z = z + 30$

$\Rightarrow x = 30$ years

$\therefore$ Father's present age = 30 years

Age of father after four years = 30 + 4 = 34 years

$\therefore$ Required age of father = 34 years

55. Let the age of Rahul, Sagar and Purav be x, y and z respectively

According to the given information

Age of Sagar − Age of Rahul = Age of Rahul − Age of Purav

$\Rightarrow y - x = x - z$

$\Rightarrow 2x = y + z$ ...(i)

Also $y + z = 66$ years

From (i) $x = 33$ years

Also as per Eq (i) we have Purav's age + Sagar's age = 66 years.

By going through option (a) given Purav = 18, and Rahul = 33 years, Sagar = 48 years

Difference between Rahul's and Purav's age = 18 years

56. Let the present age of A be a years and that of B be b years.

Then, 4 years ago,

A's age = $(a - 4)$ years

B's age = $(b - 4)$ years

Now, according to the given information in question,

$$\frac{\frac{a-4}{2}}{4(b-4)}=\frac{5}{12} \text{ or } \frac{a-4}{2(4b-16)}=\frac{5}{12} \text{ or } \frac{a-4}{4b-16}=\frac{5}{6}$$

By cross multiplying we get

or, $6a - 24 = 20b - 80$

or, $6a - 20b = -56$

or $10b - 3a = 28$

After 8 years,

$\frac{a+8}{2}+2=b+8$

or, $\frac{a}{2}+4+2=b+8$

or, $b-\frac{a}{2}=-2$

or, $2b-a=-4$ ...(i)

or, $a=2b+4$ ....(ii)

Putting the value of a in equation (i), we get

$10b-3(2b+4)=28$

Or, $10b - 6b - 12 = 28$

Or, $4b = 40$

$\therefore b = 10$

Hence, the present age of B is 10 years.

57. Let present ages of Simmi and Niti be a and b year respectively.

Ten years hence, the ratio between Simmi's age and Niti age = 7 : 9

According to the question, $\frac{a+10}{b+10}=\frac{7}{9}$

By cross multiplying we get

$\Rightarrow 9a+90=7b+70$

$\Rightarrow 7b-9a=20$ .....(i)

Also, $\frac{a-2}{b-2}=\frac{1}{3}$

By cross multiplying we get

$3a-6=b-2$

$\Rightarrow 3a-b=4$ ...(ii)

Multiplying equation (ii) by 3

$9a - 3b = 12$ ...(iii)

Adding equation (ii) and (iii) we get

$-9a+7b=20$

$4b = 32 \Rightarrow b = 8$year

From equation (ii) we get

$a=\frac{4+b}{3}=\frac{4+8}{3}=\frac{12}{3}=4$ years

Since, Abhay is 4 years older to Niti.

So, Abhay present age = 8 + 4 = 12 years

EXERCISE–B

(DATA SUFFICIENCY TYPE QUESTIONS)

Directions (*Questions 1 to 8*)**:** ***Each of the questions given below consists of a statement and/or a question and two statements numbered I and II given below it. You have to decide whether the data provided in the statement(s) is/are sufficient to answer the question. Read both the statements and***

Give answer (a) if the data in Statement I alone are sufficient to answer the question, while the data in Statement II alone are not sufficient to answer the question;

Give answer (b) if the data in Statement II alone are sufficient to answer the question, while the data in Statement I alone are not sufficient to answer the question;

Give answer (c) if the data either in Statement I or in Statement II alone are sufficient to answer the question;

Give answer (d) if the data even in both Statements I and II together are not sufficient to answer the question;

Give answer (e) if the data in both Statements I and II together are necessary to answer the question.

1. The sum of the ages of P, Q and R is 96 years. What is the age of Q ?
   I. P is 6 years older than R.
   II. The total of the ages of Q and R is 56 years.

2. What is Sonia's present age ?
   I. Sonia's present age is five times Deepak's present age.
   II. Five years ago her age was twenty-five time Deepak's age at that time.

3. How old is C now ?
   I. Three years ago, the average of A and B wa 18 years.
   II. With C joining them now, the average becom 22 years.

4. What is Reena's present age ?
   I. Reena's present age is five times her son's prese age.
   II. Reena's age two years hence will be three time her daughter's age at that time.

5. What is the average age of A and B ?
   (Bank P.O., 200

   I. The ratio between one-fifth of A's age and on fourth of B's age is 1 : 2.
   II. The product of their ages is 20 times B's age.

6. Average age of employees working in a departme is 30 years. In the next year, ten workers will retir What will be the average age in the next year ?
   I. Retirement age is 60 years.
   II. There are 50 employees in the department.

7. What is the ratio between the ages of the father and the son ?
   I. The sum of their ages is 50 years.
   II. 3 times the sum of their ages is equal to 5 times the father's age.
8. Divya is twice as old as Shruti. What is the difference in their ages ?
   I. Five years hence, the ratio of their ages would be 9 : 5.
   II. Ten years back, the ratio of their ages was 3 : 1.

Directions (*Questions 9 to 13*): *Each of the questions given below consists of a question followed by three statements. You have to study the question and the statements and decide which of the statements is/are necessary to answer the question.*

9. What is the present age of A ?
   I. The sum of the ages of A and B is 21 years.
   II. The difference of the ages of A and B is 5 years.
   III. The product of the ages of A and B is 104 years.
   (*a*) I and II only (*b*) II and III only
   (*c*) I and III only
   (*d*) Any two of the three (*e*) None of these
10. What is the present age of Tanya ? **(Bank P.O., 2008)**
   I. The ratio between the present ages of Tanya and her brother Rahul is 3 : 4 respectively.
   II. After 5 years the ratio between the ages of Tanya and Rahul will be 4 : 5.
   III. Rahul is 5 years older than Tanya.
   (*a*) I and II only (*b*) II and III only
   (*c*) I and III only (*d*) All I, II and III
   (*e*) Any two of the three
11. What is the difference between the ages of Y and X?
   I. The ratio between the ages of X and Y is 2 : 3.
   II. Y's age is 50% more than X's age.
   III. One-fourth of X's age is equal to one-sixth of Y's age.
   (*a*) All I, II and III (*b*) Any two of the three
   (*c*) III, and either I or II (*d*) Only I and II
   (*e*) Question cannot be answered even with information in all three statements
12. What is Arun's present age ?
   I. Five years ago, Arun's age was double that of his son's age at that time.
   II. Present ages of Arun and his son are in the ratio of 11 : 6 respectively.
   III. Five years hence, the respective ratio of Arun's age and his son's age will become 12 : 7.
   (*a*) Only I and II (*b*) Only II and III
   (*c*) Only I and III (*d*) Any two of the three
   (*e*) None of these
13. What is Ravi's present age ?
   I. The present age of Ravi is half of that of his father.
   II. After 5 years, the ratio of Ravi's age to that of his father's age will be 6 : 11.
   III. Ravi is 5 years younger than his brother.
   (*a*) I and II only (*b*) II and III only
   (*c*) I and III only (*d*) All I, II and III
   (*e*) Even with all the three statements answer cannot be given.

Directions (*Questions 14 to 16*): *Each of these questions is followed by three statements. You have to study the question and all the three statements given to decide whether any information provided in the statement(s) is redundant and can be dispensed with while answering the given question.*

14. What is the ratio of the present ages of Anna and her mother ?
   I. The sum of the ages of Anna, her mother and her father is 62.
   II. Five years ago, Anna's age was one-fifth of her father's age.
   III. Two years ago, the sum of the ages of Anna and her father was 36.
   (*a*) I or II only (*b*) II or III only
   (*c*) III only (*d*) I or III only
   (*e*) All I, II and III are required.
15. What will be the ratio between the ages of Sam and Albert after 5 years ?
   I. Sam's present age is more than Albert's present age by 4 years.
   II. Albert's present age is 20 years.
   III. The ratio of Albert's present age to Sam's present age is 5 : 6.
   (*a*) I or II or III only (*b*) II only
   (*c*) III only (*d*) I or III only
   (*e*) II or III only.
16. What is the difference between the present ages of Ayush and Deepak ?
   I. The ratio between Ayush's present age and his age after 8 years is 4 : 5.
   II. The ratio between the present ages of Ayush and Deepak is 4 : 3.
   III. The ratio between Deepak's present age and his age four years ago is 6 : 5.
   (*a*) Any two of I, II and III
   (*b*) I or III only
   (*c*) Any one of the three
   (*d*) All I, II and III are required
   (*e*) Even with all I, II and III, the answer cannot be obtained.

ANSWERS

1. (e)	2. (e)	3. (e)	4. (d)	5. (e)	6. (e)	7. (b)	8. (c)	9. (d)	10. (e)
11. (e)	12. (d)	13. (a)	14. (e)	15. (a)	16. (c)				

SOLUTIONS

1. Given : $P + Q + R = 96$ ...(*i*)

I. $P = R + 6$ ...(*ii*)

II. $Q + R = 56$ ...(*iii*)

On subtracting (*iii*) from (*i*), we get $P = 40$.

Putting $P = 40$ in (*ii*), we get $R = 34$. Putting $R = 34$ in (*iii*), we get $Q = 22$.

Thus, I and II both together give the answer. So, correct answer is (*e*).

2. **I.** $S = 5D \Rightarrow D = \frac{S}{5}$ ...(*i*)

II. $S - 5 = 25(D - 5) \Leftrightarrow S = 25D - 120$ ...(*ii*)

Using (*i*) in (*ii*), we get

$S = \left(25 \times \frac{S}{5}\right) - 120 \Leftrightarrow 4S = 120 \Leftrightarrow S = 30.$

Thus, I and II both together give the answer. So, correct answer is (*e*).

3. **I.** 3 years ago, $\frac{1}{2}(A + B) = 18$

$\Rightarrow$ 3 years ago, $(A + B) = 36$

Now, $(A + B) = (36 + 3 + 3) = 42$

$\Rightarrow A + B = 42$ ...(*i*)

II. Now, $\frac{1}{3}(A + B + C) = 22$

$\Rightarrow A + B + C = 66$ ...(*ii*)

From (*i*) and (*ii*), we get $C = (66 - 42) = 24$.

Thus, I and II both together give the answer. So, correct answer is (*e*).

4. **I.** Reena's present age = 5 × (Her son's present age).

II. Reena's age 2 years hence = 3 times her daughter's age at that time.

Clearly, data even in I and II is not sufficient to get Reena's present age.

∴ Correct answer is (*d*).

5. **I.** $\frac{A}{5} : \frac{B}{4} = 1 : 2 \Leftrightarrow \frac{A}{5} \times \frac{4}{B} = \frac{1}{2}$

$\Leftrightarrow \frac{A}{B} = \left(\frac{1}{2} \times \frac{5}{4}\right) = \frac{5}{8} \Leftrightarrow A : B = 5 : 8.$

II. $20B = AB$.

Let A's age be $5x$ years. Then, B's age is $8x$ years.

∴ $20 \times 8x = 5x \times 8x \Leftrightarrow 40x = 160 \Leftrightarrow x = 4.$

∴ $A = 20$ and $B = 32$.

Thus, I and II together give the answer. So, correct answer is (*e*).

6. **I.** Retirement age is 60 years.

II. There are 50 employees in the department.

Average age of 50 employees = 30 years.

Total age of 50 employees = (50 × 30) years = 1500 years.

Number of employees next year = 40.

Total age of 40 employees next year

= (1500 + 50 – 60 × 10) = 940.

Average age next year = $\frac{940}{40}$ years = $23\frac{1}{2}$ years.

Thus, I and II together give the answer. So, correct answer is (*e*).

7. **I.** $F + S = 50$ ...(*i*)

II. $3(F + S) = 5F$ ...(*ii*)

From II, we get $2F = 3S \Leftrightarrow \frac{F}{S} = \frac{3}{2}$.

Thus, II alone gives the answer, but I alone does not give the answer.

∴ Correct answer is (*b*).

8. Let Divya's present age be D years and Shruti's present age be S years.

Then, $D = 2 \times S \Leftrightarrow D - 2S = 0$ ...(*i*)

I. $\frac{D+5}{S+5} = \frac{9}{5}$ ...(*ii*)

II. $\frac{D-10}{S-10} = \frac{3}{1}$ ...(*iii*)

From (*ii*), we get $5D + 25 = 9S + 45$

$\Leftrightarrow 5D - 9S = 20$ ...(*iv*)

From (*iii*), we get $D - 10 = 3S - 30$

$\Leftrightarrow D - 3S = -20$ ...(*v*)

Thus from (*i*) and (*iv*), we get the answer.

Also, from (*i*) and (*v*), we get the answer.

∴ I alone as well as II alone gives the answer. Hence, the correct answer is (*c*).

9. **I.** $A + B = 21$.

II. $A - B = 5$.

III. $AB = 104$.

Clearly, any two of three will give the answer. So, correct answer is (*d*).

10. **I.** Let the present ages of Tanya and Rahul be $3x$ years and $4x$ years respectively.

II. After 5 years, (Tanya's age) : (Rahul's age) = 4 : 5.

III. (Rahul's age) = (Tanya's age) + 5.

From I and II, we get $\frac{3x+5}{4x+5} = \frac{4}{5}$. This gives x.

∴ Tanya's age = $3x$ can be found. Thus, I and II give the answer.

From I and III, we get $4x = 3x + 5$. This gives x.

∴ Tanya's age = $3x$ can be found. Thus, I and III give the answer.

From III : Let Tanya's present age be t years.

Then, Rahul's present age = $(t + 5)$ years.

Thus, **from II and III,** we get : $\frac{t+5}{t+10} = \frac{4}{5}$. This gives t.

Thus, II and III give the answer.

$\therefore$ Correct answer is (*e*).

11. I. $X : Y = 2 : 3 \Rightarrow \frac{X}{Y} = \frac{2}{3} \Rightarrow 3X = 2Y$.

II. $Y = \frac{150}{100}X \Rightarrow Y = \frac{3X}{2} \Rightarrow 3X = 2Y$.

III. $\frac{1}{4}X = \frac{1}{6}Y \Rightarrow 6X = 4Y \Rightarrow 3X = 2Y$.

Thus, even I, II and III together do not give the answer.

$\therefore$ Correct answer is (*e*).

12. II. Let the present ages of Arun and his son be $11x$ and $6x$ years respectively.

I. 5 years ago, Arun's age = 2 × His son's age $\Rightarrow 11x - 5 = 2(6x - 5)$.

III. 5 years hence, $\frac{\text{Arun's age}}{\text{Son's age}} = \frac{12}{7}$.

Clearly, any two of the above will give Arun's present age.

$\therefore$ Correct answer is (*d*).

13. I. Let Ravi's present age be x years. Then, his father's present age = $2x$ years.

II. From I and II, we get $\frac{x+5}{2x+5} = \frac{6}{11}$. This gives x, the answer.

III. Ravi is younger than his brother.

From I and II, we get $\frac{x+5}{2x+5} = \frac{6}{11}$. This gives x, the answer.

Thus, I and II together give the answer. Clearly, III is redundant.

$\therefore$ Correct answer is (*a*).

14. I. $A + M + F = 62$.

II. $(A - 5) = \frac{1}{5}(F - 5)$.

III. $(A - 2) + (F - 2) = 36$.

From II and III, we may get A and F.

Putting these values in I, we get M.

Thus, all I, II and III are required to get the answer.

$\therefore$ Correct answer is (*e*).

15. Clearly, any two of the given statements will give the answer and in each case, the third is redundant.

$\therefore$ Correct answer is (*a*).

16. Clearly, any two of the given statements will give the answer and in each case, the third is redundant.

$\therefore$ Correct answer is (*c*).

9 Surds and Indices

IMPORTANT FACTS AND FORMULAE

I. Laws of Indices:

(i) $a^m \times a^n = a^{m+n}$ (ii) $\frac{a^m}{a^n} = a^{m-n}$ (iii) $(a^m)^n = a^{mn}$

(iv) $(ab)^n = a^n b^n$ (v) $\left(\frac{a}{b}\right)^n = \frac{a^n}{b^n}$ (vi) $a^0 = 1$

II. Surds: *Let a be a rational number and n be a positive integer such that* $a^{\frac{1}{n}} = \sqrt[n]{a}$ *is irrational. Then,* $\sqrt[n]{a}$ *is called a surd of order n.*

III. Laws of Surds:

(i) $\sqrt[n]{a} = a^{\frac{1}{n}}$ (ii) $\sqrt[n]{ab} = \sqrt[n]{a} \times \sqrt[n]{b}$ (iii) $\sqrt[n]{\frac{a}{b}} = \frac{\sqrt[n]{a}}{\sqrt[n]{b}}$

(iv) $(\sqrt[n]{a})^n = a$ (v) $\sqrt[m]{\sqrt[n]{a}} = \sqrt[mn]{a}$ (vi) $(\sqrt[n]{a})^m = \sqrt[n]{a^m}$

SOLVED EXAMPLES

Ex. 1. ***Simplify : (i)*** $(27)^{\frac{2}{3}}$ ***(ii)*** $(1024)^{-\frac{4}{5}}$ ***(iii)*** $\left(\frac{8}{125}\right)^{-\frac{4}{3}}$.

Sol. (i) $(27)^{\frac{2}{3}} = (3^3)^{\frac{2}{3}} = 3^{\left(3 \times \frac{2}{3}\right)} = 3^2 = 9.$

(ii) $(1024)^{-\frac{4}{5}} = (4^5)^{-\frac{4}{5}} = 4^{\left\{5 \times \frac{(-4)}{5}\right\}} = 4^{-4} = \frac{1}{4^4} = \frac{1}{256}.$

(iii) $\left(\frac{8}{125}\right)^{-\frac{4}{3}} = \left\{\left(\frac{2}{5}\right)^3\right\}^{-\frac{4}{3}} = \left(\frac{2}{5}\right)^{\left\{3 \times \frac{(-4)}{3}\right\}} = \left(\frac{2}{5}\right)^{-4} = \left(\frac{5}{2}\right)^4 = \frac{5^4}{2^4} = \frac{625}{16}.$

Ex. 2. ***What will come in place of both the question marks in the following question?*** (Bank Recruitment, 2010)

$$(?)^{\frac{1}{4}} = \frac{48}{(?)^{\frac{3}{4}}}$$

Sol. Let $x^{\frac{1}{4}} = \frac{48}{x^{\frac{3}{4}}}$. Then, $x^{\frac{1}{4}} . x^{\frac{3}{4}} = 48 \Leftrightarrow x^{\left(\frac{1}{4}+\frac{3}{4}\right)} = 48 \Leftrightarrow x = 48.$

Ex. 3. ***Evaluate : (i)*** $(.00032)^{\frac{3}{5}}$ ***(ii)*** $(256)^{0.16} \times (16)^{0.18}$.

Sol. (i) $(0.00032)^{\frac{3}{5}} = \left(\frac{32}{100000}\right)^{\frac{3}{5}} = \left(\frac{2^5}{10^5}\right)^{\frac{3}{5}} = \left\{\left(\frac{2}{10}\right)^5\right\}^{\frac{3}{5}} = \left(\frac{1}{5}\right)^{\left(5 \times \frac{3}{5}\right)} = \left(\frac{1}{5}\right)^3 = \frac{1}{125}.$]

(ii) $(256)^{0.16} \times (16)^{0.18} = \{(16)^2\}^{0.16} \times (16)^{0.18} = (16)^{(2 \times 0.16)} \times (16)^{0.18}$

$$= (16)^{0.32} \times (16)^{0.18} = (16)^{(0.32+0.18)} = (16)^{0.5} = (16)^{\frac{1}{2}} = 4.$$

Ex. 4. *Solve : $9^{8.6} \times 8^{3.9} \times 72^{4.4} \times 9^{3.9} \times 8^{8.6} = 72^?$.* (L.I.C., 2005)

Sol. Let $9^{8.6} \times 8^{3.9} \times 72^{4.4} \times 9^{3.9} \times 8^{8.6} = 72^x$.

Then, $9^{(8.6 + 3.9)} \times 8^{(3.9 + 8.6)} \times 72^{4.4} = 72^x$

$\Leftrightarrow \quad 9^{12.5} \times 8^{12.5} \times 72^{4.4} = 72^x \Leftrightarrow (9 \times 8)^{12.5} \times 72^{4.4} = 72^x$

$\Leftrightarrow \quad 72^{12.5} \times 72^{4.4} = 72^x \Leftrightarrow 72^{(12.5 + 4.4)} = 72^x \Leftrightarrow 72^{16.9} = 72^x \Leftrightarrow x = 16.9.$

Ex. 5. *Solve : $(0.064) \times (0.4)^7 = (0.4)^? \times (0.0256)^2$.* (Bank P.O., 2010)

Sol. Let $(0.064) \times (0.4)^7 = (0.4)^x \times (0.0256)^2$.

Then, $(0.4)^3 \times (0.4)^7 = (0.4)^x \times [(0.4)^4]^2$

$\Leftrightarrow \quad (0.4)^{(3 + 7)} = (0.4)^x \times (0.4)^8 \Leftrightarrow (0.4)^{10} = (0.4)^{x + 8} \Leftrightarrow x + 8 = 10 \Leftrightarrow x = 2.$

Ex. 6. *What is the quotient when $(x^{-1} - 1)$ is divided by $(x - 1)$?*

Sol. $\dfrac{x^{-1}-1}{x-1} = \dfrac{\frac{1}{x}-1}{x-1} = \dfrac{(1-x)}{x} \times \dfrac{1}{(x-1)} = -\dfrac{1}{x}.$

Hence, the required quotient is $-\dfrac{1}{x}$.

Ex. 7. *If $2^{x - 1} + 2^{x + 1} = 1280$, then find the value of x.*

Sol. $2^{x-1} + 2^{x+1} = 1280 \Leftrightarrow 2^{x-1}(1 + 2^2) = 1280$

$$\Leftrightarrow \quad 2^{x-1} = \frac{1280}{5} = 256 = 2^8 \quad \Leftrightarrow \quad x - 1 = 8 \quad \Leftrightarrow \quad x = 9.$$

Hence, $x = 9$.

Ex. 8. *Find the value of $\left[5\left(8^{\frac{1}{3}} + 27^{\frac{1}{3}}\right)^3\right]^{\frac{1}{4}}$.*

Sol. $\left[5\left(8^{\frac{1}{3}} + 27^{\frac{1}{3}}\right)^3\right]^{\frac{1}{4}} = \left[5\left\{(2^3)^{\frac{1}{3}} + (3^3)^{\frac{1}{3}}\right\}^3\right]^{\frac{1}{4}} = \left[5\left\{2^{\left(3\times\frac{1}{3}\right)} + 3^{\left(3\times\frac{1}{3}\right)}\right\}^3\right]^{\frac{1}{4}}$

$$= \{5\,(2+3)^3\}^{\frac{1}{4}} = (5 \times 5^3)^{\frac{1}{4}} = (5^4)^{\frac{1}{4}} = 5^{\left(4\times\frac{1}{4}\right)} = 5^1 = 5.$$

Ex. 9. *Find the value of $\left\{(16)^{\frac{3}{2}} + (16)^{-\frac{3}{2}}\right\}$.*

Sol. $\left[(16)^{\frac{3}{2}} + (16)^{-\frac{3}{2}}\right] = \left[(4^2)^{\frac{3}{2}} + (4^2)^{-\frac{3}{2}}\right] = 4^{\left(2\times\frac{3}{2}\right)} + 4^{\left\{2\times\frac{(-3)}{2}\right\}}$

$$= 4^3 + 4^{-3} = 4^3 + \frac{1}{4^3} = \left(64 + \frac{1}{64}\right) = \frac{4097}{64}.$$

Ex. 10. *If $\left(\frac{1}{5}\right)^{3y} = 0.008$, then find the value of $(0.25)^y$.*

Sol. $\left(\dfrac{1}{5}\right)^{3y} = 0.008 = \dfrac{8}{1000} = \dfrac{1}{125} = \left(\dfrac{1}{5}\right)^3 \Leftrightarrow 3y = 3 \Leftrightarrow y = 1.$

$\therefore \; (0.25)^y = (0.25)^1 = 0.25.$

Ex. 11. ***Simplify :*** $\dfrac{(6.25)^{\frac{1}{2}} \times (0.0144)^{\frac{1}{2}} + 1}{(0.027)^{\frac{1}{3}} \times (81)^{\frac{1}{4}}}$. (S.S.C., 200

Sol. Given expression $= \dfrac{\{(2.5)^2\}^{\frac{1}{2}} \times \{(0.12)^2\}^{\frac{1}{2}} + 1}{\{(0.3)^3\}^{\frac{1}{3}} \times (3^4)^{\frac{1}{4}}} = \dfrac{(2.5)^{\left(2\times\frac{1}{2}\right)} \times (0.12)^{\left(2\times\frac{1}{2}\right)} + 1}{(0.3)^{\left(3\times\frac{1}{3}\right)} \times 3^{\left(4\times\frac{1}{4}\right)}}$

$= \dfrac{2.5 \times 0.12 + 1}{0.3 \times 3} = \dfrac{0.3 + 1}{0.9} = \dfrac{1.3}{0.9} = \dfrac{13}{9} = 1.444 \ldots = 1.\bar{4}.$

Ex. 12. ***Find the value of*** $\dfrac{(243)^{\frac{n}{5}} \cdot 3^{2n+1}}{9^n \times 3^{n-1}}$.

Sol. $\dfrac{(243)^{\frac{n}{5}} \cdot 3^{2n+1}}{9^n \times 3^{n-1}} = \dfrac{(3^5)^{\frac{n}{5}} \times 3^{2n+1}}{(3^2)^n \times 3^{n-1}} = \dfrac{3^{\left(5\times\frac{n}{5}\right)} \times 3^{2n+1}}{3^{2n} \times 3^{n-1}} = \dfrac{3^n \times 3^{2n+1}}{3^{2n} \times 3^{n-1}}$

$= \dfrac{3^{n+(2n+1)}}{3^{2n+n-1}} = \dfrac{3^{(3n+1)}}{3^{(3n-1)}} = 3^{(3n+1)-(3n-1)} = 3^2 = 9.$

Ex. 13. ***Find the value of*** $\left(2^{\frac{1}{4}} - 1\right)\left(2^{\frac{3}{4}} + 2^{\frac{1}{2}} + 2^{\frac{1}{4}} + 1\right)$. (N.I.F.T., 200

Sol. Putting $2^{\frac{1}{4}} = x$, we get :

$\left(2^{\frac{1}{4}} - 1\right)\left(2^{\frac{3}{4}} + 2^{\frac{1}{2}} + 2^{\frac{1}{4}} + 1\right) = (x-1)(x^3 + x^2 + x + 1)$

$= (x - 1)\,[x^2\,(x + 1) + (x + 1)]$

$= (x - 1)\,(x + 1)\,(x^2 + 1) = (x^2 - 1)\,(x^2 + 1)$

$= (x^4 - 1) = \left[\left(2^{\frac{1}{4}}\right)^4 - 1\right] = \left[2^{\left(\frac{1}{4}\times 4\right)} - 1\right] = (2 - 1) = 1.$

Ex. 14. ***Find the value of*** $\dfrac{6^{\frac{2}{3}} \times \sqrt[3]{6^7}}{\sqrt[3]{6^6}}$.

Sol. $\dfrac{6^{\frac{2}{3}} \times \sqrt[3]{6^7}}{\sqrt[3]{6^6}} = \dfrac{6^{\frac{2}{3}} \times (6^7)^{\frac{1}{3}}}{(6^6)^{\frac{1}{3}}} = \dfrac{6^{\frac{2}{3}} \times 6^{\left(7\times\frac{1}{3}\right)}}{6^{\left(6\times\frac{1}{3}\right)}} = \dfrac{6^{\frac{2}{3}} \times 6^{\left(\frac{7}{3}\right)}}{6^2}$

$= 6^{\frac{2}{3}} \times 6^{\left(\frac{7}{3}-2\right)} = 6^{\frac{2}{3}} \times 6^{\frac{1}{3}} = 6^{\left(\frac{2}{3}+\frac{1}{3}\right)} = 6^1 = 6.$

Ex. 15. ***If*** $\left(\dfrac{p}{q}\right)^{rx-s} = \left(\dfrac{q}{p}\right)^{px-q}$, ***then find the value of x.***

Sol. $\left(\dfrac{p}{q}\right)^{rx-s} = \left(\dfrac{q}{p}\right)^{px-q} \Leftrightarrow \left(\dfrac{p}{q}\right)^{rx-s} = \left(\dfrac{p}{q}\right)^{-(px-q)}$

$\Leftrightarrow rx - s = -\,(px - q) \Leftrightarrow rx - s = -\,px + q$

$\Leftrightarrow rx + px = q + s \Leftrightarrow x\,(p + r) = q + s$

$\Leftrightarrow x = \dfrac{q+s}{p+r}.$

Ex. 16. ***If $x = y^a$, $y = z^b$ and $z = x^c$, then find the value of abc.***

Sol. $z^1 = x^c = (y^a)^c$ $\quad [\because x = y^a]$

$= y^{(ac)} = (z^b)^{ac}$ $\quad [\because y = z^b]$

$= z^{b(ac)} = z^{abc}$

$\therefore abc = 1.$

Ex. 17. ***Simplify :*** $\left(\dfrac{x^a}{x^b}\right)^{(a^2+b^2+ab)} \times \left(\dfrac{x^b}{x^c}\right)^{(b^2+c^2+bc)} \times \left(\dfrac{x^c}{x^a}\right)^{(c^2+a^2+ca)}.$

Sol. Given Expression $= \{x^{(a-b)}\}^{(a^2+b^2+ab)} \cdot \{x^{(b-c)}\}^{(b^2+c^2+bc)} \cdot \{x^{(c-a)}\}^{(c^2+a^2+ca)}$

$= x^{(a-b)(a^2+b^2+ab)} \cdot x^{(b-c)(b^2+c^2+bc)} \cdot x^{(c-a)(c^2+a^2+ca)}$

$= x^{(a^3-b^3)} \cdot x^{(b^3-c^3)} \cdot x^{(c^3-a^3)} = x^{(a^3-b^3+b^3-c^3+c^3-a^3)} = x^0 = 1.$

Ex. 18. ***If $8^x \cdot 2^y = 512$ and $3^{3x+2y} = 9^6$, then what is the value of x and y?*** **(M.A.T., 2004)**

Sol. $8^x 2^y = 512 \Leftrightarrow (2^3)^x \cdot 2^y = 2^9 \Leftrightarrow 2^{3x+y} = 2^9 \Leftrightarrow 3x + y = 9$ ...(*i*)

And, $3^{3x+2y} = 9^6 \Leftrightarrow 3^{3x+2y} = (3^2)^6 = 3^{12} \Leftrightarrow 3x + 2y = 12$ ...(*ii*)

Subtracting (*i*) from (*ii*), we get: $y = 3$.

Putting $y = 3$ in (*i*), we get: $3x = 6$ or $x = 2$.

Hence, $x = 2$ and $y = 3$.

Ex. 19. ***Find the largest from among $\sqrt[4]{6}$, $\sqrt{2}$ and $\sqrt[3]{4}$.***

Sol. Given surds are of order 4, 2 and 3 respectively. Their L.C.M. is 12.

Changing each to a surd of order 12, we get :

$\sqrt[4]{6} = 6^{\frac{1}{4}} = 6^{\left(\frac{1}{4}\times\frac{3}{3}\right)} = \left(6^{\frac{3}{12}}\right) = (6^3)^{\frac{1}{12}} = (216)^{\frac{1}{12}}.$

$\sqrt{2} = 2^{\frac{1}{2}} = 2^{\left(\frac{1}{2}\times\frac{6}{6}\right)} = \left(2^{\frac{6}{12}}\right) = (2^6)^{\frac{1}{12}} = (64)^{\frac{1}{12}}.$

$\sqrt[3]{4} = 4^{\frac{1}{3}} = 4^{\left(\frac{1}{3}\times\frac{4}{4}\right)} = \left(4^{\frac{4}{12}}\right) = (4^4)^{\frac{1}{12}} = (256)^{\frac{1}{12}}.$

Clearly, $(256)^{\frac{1}{12}} > (216)^{\frac{1}{12}} > (64)^{\frac{1}{12}}$.

$\therefore$ Largest one is $(256)^{\frac{1}{12}}$ *i.e.,* $\sqrt[3]{4}$.

Ex. 20. ***Find the square root of $(3 + \sqrt{5})$.*** **(L.I.C.A.A.O., 2007)**

Sol. $\sqrt{3+\sqrt{5}} = \sqrt{3 + 2\sqrt{\dfrac{5}{4}}} = \sqrt{\dfrac{5}{2} + \dfrac{1}{2} + 2\sqrt{\dfrac{5}{2}\times\dfrac{1}{2}}} = \sqrt{\left(\sqrt{\dfrac{5}{2}}\right)^2 + \left(\sqrt{\dfrac{1}{2}}\right)^2 + 2\sqrt{\dfrac{5}{2}}\sqrt{\dfrac{1}{2}}}$

$= \sqrt{\left(\sqrt{\dfrac{5}{2}} + \sqrt{\dfrac{1}{2}}\right)^2} = \left(\sqrt{\dfrac{5}{2}} + \sqrt{\dfrac{1}{2}}\right).$

Ex. 21. ***If $x = 3 + 2\sqrt{2}$, find the value of $\left(\sqrt{x} - \dfrac{1}{\sqrt{x}}\right)$.***

Sol. $\left(\sqrt{x} - \dfrac{1}{\sqrt{x}}\right)^2 = x + \dfrac{1}{x} - 2 = (3 + 2\sqrt{2}) + \dfrac{1}{(3 + 2\sqrt{2})} - 2$

$= (3 + 2\sqrt{2}) + \dfrac{1}{(3 + 2\sqrt{2})} \times \dfrac{(3 - 2\sqrt{2})}{(3 - 2\sqrt{2})} - 2 = (3 + 2\sqrt{2}) + (3 - 2\sqrt{2}) - 2 = 4.$

$\therefore \left(\sqrt{x} - \dfrac{1}{\sqrt{x}}\right) = 2.$

Ex. 22. *If* $2^x = 3^y = 6^{-z}$, *find the value of* $\left(\frac{1}{x}+\frac{1}{y}+\frac{1}{z}\right)$.

Sol. Let $2^x = 3^y = 6^{-z} = k$. Then, $2 = k^{\frac{1}{x}}, 3 = k^{\frac{1}{y}}$ and $6 = k^{-\frac{1}{z}}$.

Now, $2 \times 3 = 6 \Leftrightarrow k^{\frac{1}{x}} \times k^{\frac{1}{y}} = k^{-\frac{1}{z}} \Leftrightarrow k^{\left(\frac{1}{x}+\frac{1}{y}\right)} = k^{-\frac{1}{z}}$

$\Leftrightarrow \frac{1}{x}+\frac{1}{y} = -\frac{1}{z} \Leftrightarrow \frac{1}{x}+\frac{1}{y}+\frac{1}{z} = 0.$

Ex. 23. *Given* $t = 2+\sqrt[3]{4}+\sqrt[3]{2}$, *determine the value of* $t^3 - 6t^2 + 6t - 2$. (M.A.T., 2005)

Sol. $t = 2+\sqrt[3]{4}+\sqrt[3]{2} \Rightarrow t-2 = \sqrt[3]{4}+\sqrt[3]{2} \Rightarrow (t-2)^3 = (\sqrt[3]{4}+\sqrt[3]{2})^3$

$\Rightarrow t^3 - 8 - 6t\,(t-2) = 4 + 2 + 3\,\sqrt[3]{8}\,(\sqrt[3]{4}+\sqrt[3]{2})$

$\Rightarrow t^3 - 8 - 6t^2 + 12t = 6 + 3 \times 2\,(t-2)$

$\Rightarrow t^3 - 6t^2 + 12t - 8 = 6 + 6t - 12 \Rightarrow t^3 - 6t^2 + 6t - 2 = 0.$

EXERCISE

(OBJECTIVE TYPE QUESTIONS)

Directions: *Mark (✓) against the correct answer:*

1. $\sqrt[3]{5}$ is a surd of the order (R.R.B., 2008)
(a) $\frac{1}{3}$ (b) 1
(c) 2 (d) 3

2. $5^0 \times 8$ =? (R.R.B., 2006)
(a) 0 (b) 8
(c) 40 (d) 200

3. Which of the following are equal in value?
I. 4^1 II. 1^4
III. 4^0 IV. 0^4
(a) I and II (b) II and III
(c) III and IV (d) I and IV

4. If $289 = 17^{\frac{1}{5}x}$, then x =? (Bank P.O., 2009)
(a) $\frac{2}{5}$ (b) 8
(c) 16 (d) 32
(e) None of these

5. $(81)^4 \div (9)^5$ =? (Agriculture Officers', 2009)
(a) 9 (b) 81
(c) 729 (d) 6561
(e) None of these

6. The value of $\left(\frac{9^2 \times 18^4}{3^{16}}\right)$ is (R.R.B., 2006)
(a) $\frac{3}{2}$ (b) $\frac{4}{9}$
(c) $\frac{16}{81}$ (d) $\frac{32}{243}$

7. $[4^3 \times 5^4] \div 4^5$ =? (Bank Recruitment, 2008)
(a) 29.0825 (b) 30.0925
(c) 35.6015 (d) 39.0625
(e) None of these

8. $9^3 \times 6^2 \div 3^3$ =? (L.I.C.A.D.O., 2007)
(a) 948 (b) 972
(c) 984 (d) 1012
(e) None of these

9. $(19)^{12} \times (19)^8 \div (19)^4 = (19)^?$ (Bank Recruitment, 2008)
(a) 6 (b) 8
(c) 12 (d) 24
(e) None of these

10. $(64)^4 \div (8)^5$ =? (Agriculture Officer's, 2008)
(a) $(8)^8$ (b) $(8)^2$
(c) $(8)^{12}$ (d) $(8)^4$
(e) None of these

11. $(1000)^{12} \div (10)^{30}$ =? (Bank P.O., 2008)
(a) $(1000)^2$ (b) 10
(c) 100 (d) $(100)^2$
(e) None of these

12. $(3)^8 \times (3)^4$ =? (Bank P.O., 2009)
(a) $(27)^3$ (b) $(27)^5$
(c) $(729)^2$ (d) $(729)^3$
(e) None of these

13. $\frac{343 \times 49}{216 \times 16 \times 81}$ =? (Bank P.O., 2010)
(a) $\frac{7^5}{6^7}$ (b) $\frac{7^5}{6^8}$
(c) $\frac{7^6}{6^7}$ (d) $\frac{7^4}{6^8}$
(e) None of these

14. $\frac{16 \times 32}{9 \times 27 \times 81} = ?$ (Bank P.O., 2009)

(a) $\left(\frac{2}{3}\right)^9$ (b) $\left(\frac{2}{3}\right)^{11}$

(c) $\left(\frac{2}{3}\right)^{12}$ (d) $\left(\frac{2}{3}\right)^{13}$

(e) None of these

15. $9^3 \times (81)^2 \div (27)^3 = (3)^?$ (Bank P.O., 2010)

(a) 3 (b) 4

(c) 5 (d) 6

(e) None of these

16. $(6)^4 \div (36)^3 \times 216 = 6^{(? - 5)}$ (Bank Recruitment, 2010)

(a) 1 (b) 4

(c) 6 (d) 7

(e) None of these

17. $(0.2)^2, \frac{1}{100}, (0.01)^{\frac{1}{2}}, (0.008)^{\frac{1}{3}}$. Of these, which one is the greatest? (P.C.S., 2004)

(a) $(0.008)^{\frac{1}{3}}$ (b) $(0.01)^{\frac{1}{2}}$

(c) $(0.2)^2$ (d) $\frac{1}{100}$

18. Which of the following expressions has the greatest value?

(a) $[(2^{-1})^0]^2$ (b) $\left[(4^0)^{-\frac{1}{2}}\right]^2$

(c) $[(2^{-2})^{-1}]^2$ (d) $[(2^{-1})^2]^2$

19. $(10)^{24} \times (10)^{-21} = ?$ (Bank Recruitment, 2008)

(a) 3 (b) 10

(c) 100 (d) 1000

(e) None of these

20. The value of $(256)^{\frac{5}{4}}$ is

(a) 512 (b) 984

(c) 1024 (d) 1032

21. The value of $(\sqrt{8})^{\frac{1}{3}}$ is

(a) 2 (b) 4

(c) $\sqrt{2}$ (d) 8

22. The value of $\left(\frac{32}{243}\right)^{-\frac{4}{5}}$ is

(a) $\frac{4}{9}$ (b) $\frac{9}{4}$

(c) $\frac{16}{81}$ (d) $\frac{81}{16}$

23. The value of $\left(-\frac{1}{216}\right)^{-\frac{2}{3}}$ is

(a) 36 (b) – 36

(c) $\frac{1}{36}$ (d) $-\frac{1}{36}$

24. The value of $27^{-\frac{2}{3}}$ lies between (C.D.S., 2002)

(a) 0 and 1 (b) 1 and 2

(c) 2 and 3 (d) 3 and 4

25. The value of $\sqrt[3]{2^4\sqrt{2^{-5}\sqrt{2^6}}}$ is (S.S.C., 2005)

(a) 1 (b) 2

(c) $2^{\frac{5}{3}}$ (d) 2^5

26. $\sqrt{2\sqrt{2\sqrt{2\sqrt{2\sqrt{2}}}}} = ?$ (R.R.B., 2007)

(a) $2^{\frac{29}{31}}$ (b) $2^{\frac{31}{32}}$

(c) $2^{\frac{9}{2}}$ (d) $2^{\frac{11}{2}}$

27. The value of $(0.03125)^{-\frac{2}{5}}$ is (R.R.B., 2006)

(a) 4 (b) 9

(c) 12 (d) 31.25

28. $\left(\frac{1}{2}\right)^{-\frac{1}{2}}$ is equal to (Section Officer's, 2005)

(a) $\frac{1}{\sqrt{2}}$ (b) $2\sqrt{2}$

(c) $-\sqrt{2}$ (d) $\sqrt{2}$

29. Simplified form of $\left[\left(\sqrt[5]{x^{-\frac{3}{5}}}\right)^{-\frac{5}{3}}\right]^5$ is (S.S.C., 2010)

(a) $\frac{1}{x}$ (b) x

(c) x^{-5} (d) x^5

30. What will come in place of both the question marks in the following question? (Bank Recruitment, 2010)

$$\frac{(?)^{\frac{2}{3}}}{42} = \frac{5}{(?)^{\frac{1}{3}}}$$

(a) 10 (b) $10\sqrt{2}$

(c) $\sqrt{20}$ (d) 20

(e) 210

31. The value of $5^{\frac{1}{4}} \times (125)^{0.25}$ is :

(a) $\sqrt{5}$ (b) 5

(c) $5\sqrt{5}$ (d) 25

32. The value of $\frac{1}{(216)^{-\frac{2}{3}}} + \frac{1}{(256)^{-\frac{3}{4}}} + \frac{1}{(32)^{-\frac{1}{5}}}$ is (M.B.A., 2003)

(a) 102 (b) 105
(c) 107 (d) 109

33. $(2.4 \times 10^3) \div (8 \times 10^{-2}) = ?$

(a) 3×10^{-5} (b) 3×10^4
(c) 3×10^5 (d) 30

34. $\left(\frac{1}{216}\right)^{-\frac{2}{3}} \div \left(\frac{1}{27}\right)^{-\frac{4}{3}} = ?$

(a) $\frac{3}{4}$ (b) $\frac{2}{3}$
(c) $\frac{4}{9}$ (d) $\frac{1}{8}$

35. $(48)^{-\frac{2}{7}} \times (16)^{-\frac{5}{7}} \times (3)^{-\frac{5}{7}} = ?$ (P.C.S., 2008)

(a) $\frac{1}{3}$ (b) $\frac{1}{48}$
(c) 1 (d) 48

36. If $10^x = \frac{1}{2}$, then $10^{-8x} = ?$ (P.C.S., 2008)

(a) $\frac{1}{256}$ (b) 16
(c) 80 (d) 256

37. If $\left(\frac{3}{5}\right)^3 \left(\frac{3}{5}\right)^{-6} = \left(\frac{3}{5}\right)^{2x-1}$, then x is equal to (S.S.C., 2010)

(a) – 2 (b) – 1
(c) 1 (d) 2

38. $49 \times 49 \times 49 \times 49 = 7^?$

(a) 4 (b) 7
(c) 8 (d) 16

39. The value of $(8^{-25} - 8^{-26})$ is

(a) 7×8^{-25} (b) 7×8^{-26}
(c) 8×8^{-26} (d) None of these

40. $(64)^{-\frac{1}{2}} - (-32)^{-\frac{4}{5}} = ?$

(a) $\frac{1}{8}$ (b) $\frac{3}{8}$
(c) $\frac{1}{16}$ (d) $\frac{3}{16}$
(e) None of these

41. If $\left(\frac{a}{b}\right)^{x-1} = \left(\frac{b}{a}\right)^{x-3}$, then the value of x is (P.C.S., 2009)

(a) $\frac{1}{2}$ (b) 1
(c) 2 (d) $\frac{7}{2}$

42. If $2^{2n-1} = \frac{1}{8^{n-3}}$, then the value of n is

(a) – 2 (b) 0
(c) 2 (d) 3

43. If $5^a = 3125$, then the value of $5^{(a-3)}$ is

(a) 25 (b) 125
(c) 625 (d) 1625

44. If $5\sqrt{5} \times 5^3 \div 5^{-\frac{3}{2}} = 5^{a+2}$, then the value of a is (M.B.A., 2006)

(a) 4 (b) 5
(c) 6 (d) 8

45. If $\sqrt{2^n} = 64$, then the value of n is

(a) 2 (b) 4
(c) 6 (d) 12

46. If $(\sqrt{3})^5 \times 9^2 = 3^n \times 3\sqrt{3}$, then the value of n is

(a) 2 (b) 3
(c) 4 (d) 5

47. If $\frac{9^n \times 3^5 \times (27)^3}{3 \times (81)^4} = 27$, then the value of n is

(a) 0 (b) 2
(c) 3 (d) 4

48. If $\left(\frac{9}{4}\right)^x \cdot \left(\frac{8}{27}\right)^{x-1} = \frac{2}{3}$, then the value of x is

(a) 1 (b) 2
(c) 3 (d) 4

49. If $2^x = \sqrt[3]{32}$, then x is equal to

(a) 5 (b) 3
(c) $\frac{3}{5}$ (d) $\frac{5}{3}$

50. If $2^x \times 8^{\frac{1}{5}} = 2^{\frac{1}{5}}$, then x is equal to

(a) $\frac{1}{5}$ (b) $-\frac{1}{5}$
(c) $\frac{2}{5}$ (d) $-\frac{2}{5}$

51. If $5^{(x+3)} = 25^{(3x-4)}$, then the value of x is

(a) $\frac{5}{11}$ (b) $\frac{11}{5}$
(c) $\frac{11}{3}$ (d) $\frac{13}{5}$

52. $\frac{2^{n+4} - 2(2^n)}{2(2^{n+3})}$ when simplified is (M.B.A., 2011)

(a) $2^{n+1} - \frac{1}{8}$ (b) -2^{n+1}
(c) $1 - 2^n$ (d) $\frac{7}{8}$

53. Simplify $\left[\sqrt[3]{\sqrt[6]{a^9}}\right]^4\left[\sqrt[6]{\sqrt[3]{a^9}}\right]^4$; the result is (M.B.A., 2011)

(a) a^4 (b) a^8
(c) a^{12} (d) a^{16}

54. $(256)^{0.16} \times (256)^{0.09} = ?$ (S.S.C., 2004)

(a) 4 (b) 16
(c) 64 (d) 256.25

55. $(0.04)^{-1.5} = ?$ (Bank P.O., 2003)

(a) 25 (b) 125
(c) 250 (d) 625

56. $(17)^{3.5} \times (17)^? = 17^8$ (Bank P.O., 2003)

(a) 2.29 (b) 2.75
(c) 4.25 (d) 4.5

57. $6^{1.2} \times 36^? \times 30^{2.4} \times 25^{1.3} = 30^5$ (Specialist Officers', 2006)

(a) 0.1 (b) 0.7
(c) 1.4 (d) 2.6
(e) None of these

58. $2^{3.6} \times 4^{3.6} \times 4^{3.6} \times (32)^{2.3} = (32)^?$ (Specialist Officers', 2007)

(a) 5.9 (b) 7.7
(c) 9.5 (d) 13.1
(e) None of these

59. $3^{3.5} \times 21^2 \times 42^{2.5} \div 2^{2.5} \times 7^{3.5} = 21^?$ (Bank P.O., 2006)

(a) 6.5 (b) 8
(c) 10 (d) 12.5
(e) None of these

60. $8^{0.4} \times 4^{1.6} \times 2^{1.6} = ?$ (Agriculture Officers', 2009)

(a) 48 (b) 52
(c) 64 (d) 76
(e) None of these

61. $8^7 \times 2^6 \div 8^{2.4} = 8^?$ (Bank P.O., 2009)

(a) 6.6 (b) 8.6
(c) 9.6 (d) 10.6
(e) None of these

62. $25^{2.7} \times 5^{4.2} \div 5^{5.4} = 25^?$ (Bank Recruitment, 2010)

(a) 1.6 (b) 1.7
(c) 3.2 (d) 3.6
(e) None of these

63. $8^{2.4} \times 2^{3.7} - (16)^{1.3} = 2^?$ (Bank Recruitment, 2010)

(a) 4.8 (b) 5.7
(c) 5.8 (d) 7.1
(e) None of these

64. $(0.04)^2 \div (0.008) \times (0.2)^6 = (0.2)^?$ (Bank Recruitment, 2010)

(a) 5 (b) 6
(c) 8 (d) 9
(e) None of these

65. $(18)^{3.5} \div (27)^{3.5} \times 6^{3.5} = 2^?$ (Bank P.O., 2003)

(a) 3.5 (b) 4.5
(c) 6 (d) 7
(e) None of these

66. $(25)^{7.5} \times (5)^{2.5} \div (125)^{1.5} = 5^?$ (Bank P.O., 2003)

(a) 8.5 (b) 13
(c) 16 (d) 17.5
(e) None of these

67. The value of $\dfrac{(243)^{0.13} \times (243)^{0.07}}{(7)^{0.25} \times (49)^{0.075} \times (343)^{0.2}}$ is (C.B.I., 2003)

(a) $\dfrac{3}{7}$ (b) $\dfrac{7}{3}$
(c) $1\dfrac{3}{7}$ (d) $2\dfrac{2}{7}$

68. $(64x^3 \div 27\,a^{-3})^{-\frac{2}{3}} = ?$ (R.R.B., 2006)

(a) $\dfrac{9ax}{16}$ (b) $\dfrac{9}{16ax}$
(c) $\dfrac{9}{16x^2\,a^2}$ (d) $\dfrac{3}{4}x^{-2}\,a^{-2}$

69. If $2^{n+4} - 2^{n+2} = 3$, then n is equal to

(a) 0 (b) 2
(c) – 1 (d) – 2

70. If $2^{n-1} + 2^{n+1} = 320$, then n is equal to

(a) 6 (b) 8
(c) 5 (d) 7

71. If $3^x - 3^{x-1} = 18$, then the value of x^x is

(a) 3 (b) 8
(c) 27 (d) 216

72. $\dfrac{2^{n+4} - 2 \times 2^n}{2 \times 2^{(n+3)}} + 2^{-3}$ is equal to

(a) 2^{n+1} (b) $\left(\dfrac{9}{8} - 2^n\right)$
(c) $\left(-2^{n+1} + \dfrac{1}{8}\right)$ (d) 1

73. The value of $\dfrac{2^{3x+4} + 8^{x+1}}{8^{x+1} - 2^{3x+2}}$ is

(a) 3 (b) 4
(c) 5 (d) 6

74. The value of $\dfrac{2^{n-1} - 2^n}{2^{n+4} + 2^{n+1}}$ is

(a) $-\dfrac{1}{36}$ (b) $\dfrac{2}{3}$
(c) $\dfrac{1}{13}$ (d) $\dfrac{5}{13}$

75. If $x = 5+2\sqrt{6}$, then $\sqrt{x} - \frac{1}{\sqrt{x}}$ is (A.A.O. Exam, 2009)

(a) $2\sqrt{2}$ (b) $2\sqrt{3}$
(c) $\sqrt{3}+\sqrt{2}$ (d) $\sqrt{3}-\sqrt{2}$

76. $(4+\sqrt{7})$, expressed as a perfect square, is equal to (Section Officers', 2005)

(a) $(2+\sqrt{7})^2$ (b) $\left(\frac{\sqrt{7}}{2}+\frac{1}{2}\right)^2$
(c) $\left\{\frac{1}{2}(\sqrt{7}+1)^2\right\}$ (d) $(\sqrt{3}+\sqrt{4})^2$

77. $\sqrt{8-2\sqrt{15}}$ is equal to (C.P.O., 2007)

(a) $3-\sqrt{5}$ (b) $\sqrt{5}-\sqrt{3}$
(c) $5-\sqrt{3}$ (d) $\sqrt{5}+\sqrt{3}$

78. $\sqrt{6-4\sqrt{3}+\sqrt{16-8\sqrt{3}}}$ is equal to (A.A.O. Exam, 2010)

(a) $1-\sqrt{3}$ (b) $\sqrt{3}-1$
(c) $2(2-\sqrt{3})$ (d) $2(2+\sqrt{3})$

79. The value of $\frac{1}{\sqrt{12-\sqrt{140}}} - \frac{1}{\sqrt{8-\sqrt{60}}} - \frac{2}{\sqrt{10+\sqrt{84}}}$ is (S.S.C., 2005)

(a) 0 (b) 1
(c) 2 (d) 3

80. The value of the expression
$\sqrt{4+\sqrt{15}}+\sqrt{4-\sqrt{15}}-\sqrt{12-4\sqrt{5}}$ is

(a) an irrational number
(b) a negative integer
(c) a natural number
(d) a non-integer rational number

81. If $N = \frac{\sqrt{\sqrt{5}+2}+\sqrt{\sqrt{5}-2}}{\sqrt{\sqrt{5}+1}} - \sqrt{3-2\sqrt{2}}$, then the value of N is (A.A.O. Exam., 2009)

(a) $2\sqrt{2}-1$ (b) 3
(c) 1 (d) 2

82. Given that $10^{0.48} = x$, $10^{0.70} = y$ and $x^z = y^2$, then the value of z is close to

(a) 1.45 (b) 1.88
(c) 2.9 (d) 3.7

83. If m and n are whole numbers suchthat $m^n = 121$, then the value of $(m-1)^{n+1}$ is (S.S.C., 2001)

(a) 1 (b) 10
(c) 121 (d) 1000

84. Number of prime factors in $(216)^{\frac{3}{5}} \times (2500)^{\frac{2}{5}} \times (300)^{\frac{1}{5}}$ is

(a) 6 (b) 7
(c) 8 (d) None of these

85. Number of prime factors in $\frac{6^{12} \times (35)^{28} \times (15)^{16}}{(14)^{12} \times (21)^{11}}$ is

(a) 56 (b) 66
(c) 112 (d) None of these

86. $1 + (3+1)(3^2+1)(3^4+1)(3^8+1)(3^{16}+1)(3^{32}+1)$ is equal to (Section Officers', 2005)

(a) $\frac{3^{64}-1}{2}$ (b) $\frac{3^{64}+1}{2}$
(c) $3^{64}-1$ (d) $3^{64}+1$

87. $\frac{1}{1+a^{(n-m)}} + \frac{1}{1+a^{(m-n)}} = ?$ (M.B.A., 2003; NMAT, 2006)

(a) 0 (b) $\frac{1}{2}$
(c) 1 (d) a^{m+n}

88. If $a + b + c = 0$, then the value of $(x^a)^{a^2-bc} . (x^b)^{b^2-ca} . (x^c)^{c^2-ab}$ is equal to

(a) − 2 (b) − 1
(c) 0 (d) 1

89. $\frac{1}{1+x^{(b-a)}+x^{(c-a)}} + \frac{1}{1+x^{(a-b)}+x^{(c-b)}} + \frac{1}{1+x^{(b-c)}+x^{(a-c)}} = ?$ (M.B.A., 2003)

(a) 0 (b) 1
(c) x^{a-b-c} (d) None of these

90. $\left(\frac{x^b}{x^c}\right)^{(b+c-a)} \cdot \left(\frac{x^c}{x^a}\right)^{(c+a-b)} \cdot \left(\frac{x^a}{x^b}\right)^{(a+b-c)} = ?$ (NMAT, 2005; L.I.C., 2003)

(a) x^{abc} (b) 1
(c) $x^{ab+bc+ca}$ (d) x^{a+b+c}

91. $\left(\frac{x^a}{x^b}\right)^{(a+b)} \cdot \left(\frac{x^b}{x^c}\right)^{(b+c)} \cdot \left(\frac{x^c}{x^a}\right)^{(c+a)} = ?$ (M.B.A., 2006)

(a) 0 (b) x^{abc}
(c) x^{a+b+c} (d) 1

92. $\left(\frac{x^a}{x^b}\right)^{\frac{1}{ab}} \cdot \left(\frac{x^b}{x^c}\right)^{\frac{1}{bc}} \cdot \left(\frac{x^c}{x^a}\right)^{\frac{1}{ca}} = ?$

(a) 1 (b) $x^{\frac{1}{abc}}$
(c) $x^{\frac{1}{(ab+bc+ca)}}$ (d) None of these

93. The expression $\dfrac{\left(x+\frac{1}{y}\right)^a \cdot \left(x-\frac{1}{y}\right)^b}{\left(y+\frac{1}{x}\right)^a \cdot \left(y-\frac{1}{x}\right)^b}$ reduces to

(a) $\left(\frac{x}{y}\right)^{a-b}$ (b) $\left(\frac{y}{x}\right)^{a-b}$
(c) $\left(\frac{x}{y}\right)^{a+b}$ (d) $\left(\frac{y}{x}\right)^{a+b}$

94. The value of $\left(x^{\frac{b+c}{c-a}}\right)^{\frac{1}{a-b}} \cdot \left(x^{\frac{c+a}{a-b}}\right)^{\frac{1}{b-c}} \cdot \left(x^{\frac{a+b}{b-c}}\right)^{\frac{1}{c-a}}$ is

(a) 1 (b) a
(c) b (d) c

95. If $x^{\frac{1}{p}} = y^{\frac{1}{q}} = z^{\frac{1}{r}}$ and $xyz = 1$, then the value of $p + q + r$ would be (M.B.A. 2008)

(a) 0 (b) 1
(c) 2 (d) a rational number

96. If $a^x = b^y = c^z$ and $b^2 = ac$, then y equals

(a) $\frac{xz}{x+z}$ (b) $\frac{xz}{2(x-z)}$
(c) $\frac{xz}{2(z-x)}$ (d) $\frac{2xz}{(x+z)}$

97. If $a^x = b$, $b^y = c$ and $c^z = a$, then the value of xyz is (M.B.A., 2005; R.R.B., 2008)

(a) 0 (b) 1
(c) $\frac{1}{abc}$ (d) abc

98. If $2^x = 4^y = 8^z$ and $\left(\frac{1}{2x}+\frac{1}{4y}+\frac{1}{6z}\right) = \frac{24}{7}$, then the value of z is

(a) $\frac{7}{16}$ (b) $\frac{7}{32}$
(c) $\frac{7}{48}$ (d) $\frac{7}{64}$

99. Suppose $4^a = 5$, $5^b = 6$, $6^c = 7$, $7^d = 8$, then the value of $abcd$ is (A.A.O. Exam, 2009)

(a) 1 (b) $\frac{3}{2}$
(c) 2 (d) $\frac{5}{2}$

100. If $abc = 1$, then $\left(\frac{1}{1+a+b^{-1}} + \frac{1}{1+b+c^{-1}} + \frac{1}{1+c+a^{-1}}\right) = ?$ (C.D.S. 2004)

(a) 0 (b) 1
(c) $\frac{1}{ab}$ (d) ab

101. If a, b, c are real numbers, then the value of $\sqrt{a^{-1}b} \cdot \sqrt{b^{-1}c} \cdot \sqrt{c^{-1}a}$ is

(a) abc (b) $\sqrt{abc}$
(c) $\frac{1}{abc}$ (d) 1

102. If $3^{(x-y)} = 27$ and $3^{(x+y)} = 243$, then x is equal to (R.R.B., 2003)

(a) 0 (b) 2
(c) 4 (d) 6

103. If $x^y = y^x$, then $\left(\frac{x}{y}\right)^{\frac{x}{y}}$ is equal to (M.C.A., 2005)

(a) $x^{\frac{y}{x}}$ (b) $x^{\frac{x}{y}-1}$
(c) 1 (d) $x^{\frac{x}{y}}$

104. If $4^{x+y} = 1$ and $4^{x-y} = 4$, then the values of x and y respectively are

(a) $-\frac{1}{2}$ and $\frac{1}{2}$ (b) $-\frac{1}{2}$ and $-\frac{1}{2}$
(c) $\frac{1}{2}$ and $-\frac{1}{2}$ (d) $\frac{1}{2}$ and $\frac{1}{2}$

105. If $2^{2x-1} + 4^x = 2^{x-\frac{1}{2}} + 2^{x+\frac{1}{2}}$, then x equals

(a) $\frac{1}{2}$ (b) $\frac{2}{3}$
(c) $\frac{3}{2}$ (d) 1

106. If $3^{2x-y} = 3^{x+y} = \sqrt{27}$, the value of y is (R.R.B., 2005)

(a) $\frac{1}{2}$ (b) $\frac{1}{4}$
(c) $\frac{3}{2}$ (d) $\frac{3}{4}$

107. If $3^x = 5^y = 45^z$, then (C.D.S., 2002)

(a) $\frac{2}{z} = \frac{1}{y} - \frac{1}{x}$ (b) $\frac{2}{y} = \frac{1}{x} - \frac{1}{z}$
(c) $\frac{2}{x} = \frac{1}{z} - \frac{1}{y}$ (d) $x + y + z = 0$

108. Given $2^x = 8^{y+1}$ and $9^y = 3^{x-9}$, the value of $x + y$ is (M.B.A., 2010)

(a) 18 (b) 21
(c) 24 (d) 27

109. What are the values of x and y that satisfy the equation $2^{0.7x} \cdot 3^{-1.25y} = \frac{8\sqrt{6}}{27}$? (C.A.T., 2006)

(a) $x = 2.5, y = 6$ (b) $x = 3, y = 5$
(c) $x = 3, y = 4$ (d) $x = 5, y = 2$

110. Let r be the result of doubling both thebase and the exponent of a^b, $b \neq 0$. If r equals the product of a^b by x^b, then x equals (M.B.A., 2010)
(a) 2 (b) 4
(c) 2a (d) 4a

111. Which of the following is the greatest? (Section Officers', 2005)
(a) $\sqrt{2}$ (b) $\sqrt[3]{3}$
(c) $\sqrt[4]{4}$ (d) $\sqrt[6]{6}$

112. The greatest of $\sqrt{2}, \sqrt[6]{3}, \sqrt[3]{4}, \sqrt[4]{5}$ is (S.S.C., 2005)
(a) $\sqrt{2}$ (b) $\sqrt[3]{4}$
(c) $\sqrt[4]{5}$ (d) $\sqrt[6]{3}$

113. The largest number in the sequence $1, 2^{\frac{1}{2}}, 3^{\frac{1}{3}}, 4^{\frac{1}{4}}, ..., n^{\frac{1}{n}}$ is (I.I.F.T., 2005)
(a) $2^{\frac{1}{2}}$ (b) $3^{\frac{1}{3}}$
(c) $5^{\frac{1}{5}}$ (d) $6^{\frac{1}{6}}$

114. If $x = 5 + 2\sqrt{6}$, then $\frac{(x-1)}{\sqrt{x}}$ is equal to
(a) $\sqrt{2}$ (b) $2\sqrt{2}$
(c) $\sqrt{3}$ (d) $2\sqrt{3}$

115. If $x^{\frac{1}{3}} + y^{\frac{1}{3}} = z^{\frac{1}{3}}$, then $\{(x + y - z)^3 + 27xyz\}$ equals
(a) – 1 (b) 0
(c) 1 (d) 27

116. If $x = 2 + 2^{\frac{2}{3}} + 2^{\frac{1}{3}}$, then the value of $x^3 - 6x^2 + 6x$ is (R.R.B., 2008)
(a) 1 (b) 2
(c) 3 (d) None of these

117. Find the value of $(-2)^5 \times (2)^{-5} \times (3)^3$. [ESIC—UDC Exam, 2016]
(a) –108 (b) 27
(c) $(2)^{25} \times (3)^3$ (d) –27

118. The quotient when 10^{100} is divided by 5^{75} is [SSC—CHSL (10+2) Exam, 2015]
(a) $2^{25} \times 10^{75}$ (b) 10^{25}
(c) 2^{75} (d) $2^{75} \times 10^{25}$

119. The exponential form of $\sqrt{\sqrt{2} \times \sqrt{3}}$ is [SSC—CHSL (10+2) Exam, 2015]
(a) 6 (b) $6^{\frac{1}{2}}$
(c) $6^{\frac{1}{3}}$ (d) $6^{\frac{1}{4}}$

120. $21^? \times 21^{6.5} = 21^{12.4}$ [United India Insurance Co. Ltd., UIICL—Assistant (Online) Exam, 2015]
(a) 18.9 (b) 4.4
(c) 5.9 (d) 13.4

121. $\frac{5.4 \div 3 \times 16 + 2}{18 \div 5 \times 6 \div 3}$ [United India Insurance Co. Ltd., UIICL—Assistant (Online) Exam, 2015]
(a) 2 (b) 4
(c) 6 (d) 8

122. $\left(32 \times 10^{-5}\right)^{-2} \times 64 \div \left(2^{16} \times 10^{-4}\right) = 10^?$ [IBPS—RRB Office Assistant (Online) Exam, 2015]
(a) 6 (b) 10
(c) –8 (d) –6

ANSWERS

1. (d)	2. (b)	3. (b)	4. (e)	5. (c)	6. (c)	7. (d)	8. (b)	9. (e)	10. (e)
11. (a)	12. (c)	13. (a)	14. (a)	15. (c)	16. (c)	17. (a)	18. (c)	19. (d)	20. (c)
21. (c)	22. (d)	23. (a)	24. (a)	25. (b)	26. (b)	27. (a)	28. (d)	29. (b)	30. (e)
31. (b)	32. (a)	33. (b)	34. (c)	35. (b)	36. (d)	37. (b)	38. (c)	39. (b)	40. (c)
41. (c)	42. (c)	43. (a)	44. (a)	45. (d)	46. (d)	47. (c)	48. (d)	49. (d)	50. (d)
51. (b)	52. (d)	53. (a)	54. (a)	55. (b)	56. (d)	57. (b)	58. (a)	59. (b)	60. (c)
61. (a)	62. (e)	63. (b)	64. (e)	65. (d)	66. (b)	67. (a)	68. (c)	69. (d)	70. (d)
71. (c)	72. (d)	73. (d)	74. (a)	75. (a)	76. (c)	77. (b)	78. (b)	79. (a)	80. (a)
81. (c)	82. (c)	83. (d)	84. (b)	85. (b)	86. (b)	87. (c)	88. (d)	89. (b)	90. (b)
91. (d)	92. (a)	93. (c)	94. (a)	95. (a)	96. (d)	97. (b)	98. (c)	99. (b)	100. (b)
101. (d)	102. (c)	103. (b)	104. (c)	105. (a)	106. (a)	107. (c)	108. (d)	109. (d)	110. (d)
111. (b)	112. (b)	113. (b)	114. (b)	115. (b)	116. (b)	117. (d)	118. (d)	119. (d)	120. (c)
121. (a)	122. (d)								

SOLUTIONS

1. $\sqrt[n]{a}$ is called a surd of order n.

2. $5^0 \times 8 = 1 \times 8 = 8$. $[\because 5^0 = 1]$

3. I. $4^1 = 4$ II. $1^4 = 1$
III. $4^0 = 1$ IV. $0^4 = 0$

4. $289 = 17^{\frac{1}{5}x} \Rightarrow 17^2 = 17^{\frac{1}{5}x} \Rightarrow \frac{1}{5}x = 2 \Rightarrow x = 2 \times 5 = 10.$

5. $(81)^4 \div (9)^5 = \frac{(9^2)^4}{(9^5)} = \frac{9^{(2\times4)}}{9^5} = \frac{9^8}{9^5} = 9^{(8-5)} = 9^3 = 729.$

6. $\left(\frac{9^2 \times 18^4}{3^{16}}\right) = \frac{9^2 \times (9\times2)^4}{3^{16}} = \frac{(3^2)^2 \times (3^2)^4 \times 2^4}{3^{16}}$

$= \frac{3^4 \times 3^8 \times 2^4}{3^{16}} = \frac{3^{(4+8)} \times 2^4}{3^{16}} = \frac{3^{12} \times 2^4}{3^{16}}$

$= \frac{2^4}{3^{(16-12)}} = \frac{2^4}{3^4} = \frac{16}{81}.$

7. $\frac{4^3 \times 5^4}{4^5} = \frac{5^4}{4^{(5-3)}} = \frac{5^4}{4^2} = \frac{625}{16} = 39.0625.$

8. $\frac{9^3 \times 6^2}{3^3} = \frac{(3^2)^3 \times (3\times2)^2}{3^3} = \frac{3^{(2\times3)} \times 3^2 \times 2^2}{3^3} = \frac{3^{(6+2)} \times 2^2}{3^3}$

$= 3^{(8-3)} \times 2^2 = 3^5 \times 2^2 = 243 \times 4 = 972.$

9. $\frac{(19)^{12} \times (19)^8}{(19)^4} = \frac{19^{(12+8)}}{(19)^4} = \frac{(19)^{20}}{(19)^4} = (19)^{(20-4)} = (19)^{16}.$

Hence, missing number = 16.

10. $(64)^4 \div (8)^5 = (8^2)^4 \div (8)^5 = (8)^{(2\times4)} \div 8^5 = \frac{8^8}{8^5} = 8^{(8-5)} = 8^3.$

11. $(1000)^{12} \div (10)^{30} = \frac{(10^3)^{12}}{(10)^{30}} = \frac{(10)^{(3\times12)}}{(10)^{30}} = \frac{(10)^{36}}{(10)^{30}} = (10)^{(36-30)}$

$= 10^6 = (10^3)^2 = (1000)^2.$

12. $3^8 \times 3^4 = 3^{(8+4)} = 3^{12} = (3^6)^2 = (729)^2.$

13. $\frac{343 \times 49}{216 \times 16 \times 81} = \frac{7^3 \times 7^2}{6^3 \times 2^4 \times 3^4} = \frac{7^{(3+2)}}{6^3 \times (2\times3)^4}$

$= \frac{7^5}{6^3 \times 6^4} = \frac{7^5}{6^{(3+4)}} = \frac{7^5}{6^7}.$

14. $\frac{16 \times 32}{9 \times 27 \times 81} = \frac{2^4 \times 2^5}{3^2 \times 3^3 \times 3^4} = \frac{2^{(4+5)}}{3^{(2+3+4)}} = \frac{2^9}{3^9} = \left(\frac{2}{3}\right)^9.$

15. Let $9^3 \times (81)^2 \div (27)^3 = 3^x$. Then,

$3^x = \frac{(3^2)^3 \times (3^4)^2}{(3^3)^3} = \frac{3^{(2\times3)} \times 3^{(4\times2)}}{3^{(3\times3)}} = \frac{3^6 \times 3^8}{3^9} = \frac{3^{(6+8)}}{3^9}$

$\Rightarrow 3^x = \frac{3^{14}}{3^9} = 3^{(14-9)} = 3^5 \Rightarrow x = 5.$

16. Let $6^4 \div (36)^3 \times 216 = 6^{(x-5)}$.
Then, $6^{(x-5)} = 6^4 \div (6^2)^3 \times 6^3$
$= 6^4 \div 6^{(2\times3)} \times 6^3 = 6^4 \div 6^6 \times 6^3 = 6^{(4-6+3)} = 6$
$\Rightarrow x - 5 = 1 \Rightarrow x = 6.$

17. $(0.2)^2 = 0.2 \times 0.2 = 0.04;$

$\frac{1}{100} = 0.01;$ $(0.01)^{\frac{1}{2}} = \left[(0.1)^2\right]^{\frac{1}{2}} = (0.1)^{\left(2\times\frac{1}{2}\right)} = 0.1;$

$(0.008)^{\frac{1}{3}} = [(0.2)^3]^{\frac{1}{3}} = (0.2)^{\left(3\times\frac{1}{3}\right)} = 0.2.$

Clearly, $0.2 > 0.1 > 0.04 > 0.01$.

So, $(0.008)^{\frac{1}{3}}$ is the greatest.

18. $[(2^{-1})^0]^2 = \left[\left(\frac{1}{2}\right)^0\right]^2 = (1)^2 = 1.$

$\left[(4^0)^{-\frac{1}{2}}\right]^2 = \left[(1)^{-\frac{1}{2}}\right]^2 = (1)^2 = 1.$

$\left[(2^{-2})^{-1}\right]^2 = \left[\left(\frac{1}{2^2}\right)^{-1}\right]^2 = \left[\left(\frac{1}{4}\right)^{-1}\right]^2 = (4)^2 = 16.$

$\left[(2^{-1})^2\right]^2 = \left[\left(\frac{1}{2}\right)^2\right]^2 = \left(\frac{1}{4}\right)^2 = \frac{1}{16}.$

19. $(10)^{24} \times (10)^{-21} = 10^{(24-21)} = 10^3 = 1000.$

20. $(256)^{\frac{5}{4}} = (4^4)^{\frac{5}{4}} = 4^{\left(4\times\frac{5}{4}\right)} = 4^5 = 1024.$

21. $(\sqrt{8})^{\frac{1}{3}} = \left(8^{\frac{1}{2}}\right)^{\frac{1}{3}} = 8^{\left(\frac{1}{2}\times\frac{1}{3}\right)}$

$= 8^{\frac{1}{6}} = (2^3)^{\frac{1}{6}} = 2^{\left(3\times\frac{1}{6}\right)} = 2^{\frac{1}{2}} = \sqrt{2}.$

22. $\left(\frac{32}{243}\right)^{-\frac{4}{5}} = \left\{\left(\frac{2}{3}\right)^5\right\}^{-\frac{4}{5}} = \left(\frac{2}{3}\right)^{5\times\frac{(-4)}{5}}$

$= \left(\frac{2}{3}\right)^{(-4)} = \left(\frac{3}{2}\right)^4 = \frac{3^4}{2^4} = \frac{81}{16}.$

23. $\left(-\frac{1}{216}\right)^{-\frac{2}{3}} = \left[\left(-\frac{1}{6}\right)^3\right]^{-\frac{2}{3}} = \left(-\frac{1}{6}\right)^{3\times\frac{(-2)}{3}}$

$= \left(-\frac{1}{6}\right)^{-2} = \frac{1}{\left(-\frac{1}{6}\right)^2} = \frac{1}{\left(\frac{1}{36}\right)} = 36.$

24. $(27)^{-\frac{2}{3}} = (3^3)^{-\frac{2}{3}} = 3^{\left[3\times\left(-\frac{2}{3}\right)\right]} = 3^{-2} = \frac{1}{3^2} = \frac{1}{9}.$

Clearly, $0 < \frac{1}{9} < 1$.

25. $\sqrt[3]{2^4\sqrt{2^{-5}\sqrt{2^6}}} = \sqrt[3]{2^4\sqrt{2^{-5}(2^6)^{\frac{1}{2}}}} = \sqrt[3]{2^4\sqrt{2^{-5}(2)^{\left(6\times\frac{1}{2}\right)}}}$

$= \sqrt[3]{2^4\sqrt{2^{-5}.2^3}} = \sqrt[3]{2^4\sqrt{2^{(-5+3)}}}$

$= \sqrt[3]{2^4\sqrt{2^{(-2)}}} = \sqrt[3]{2^4.(2^{-2})^{\frac{1}{2}}} = \sqrt[3]{2^4.2^{\left(-2\times\frac{1}{2}\right)}}$

$= \sqrt[3]{2^4 \cdot 2^{(-1)}} = \sqrt[3]{2^{(4-1)}} = \sqrt[3]{2^3} = (2^3)^{\frac{1}{3}}$

$= 2^{\left(3\times\frac{1}{3}\right)} = 2.$

26. $\sqrt{2\sqrt{2\sqrt{2\sqrt{2\sqrt{2}}}}} = \sqrt{2\sqrt{2\sqrt{2\sqrt{2 . 2^{\frac12}}}}} = \sqrt{2\sqrt{2\sqrt{2\sqrt{2^{\left(1+\frac12\right)}}}}}$

$= \sqrt{2\sqrt{2\sqrt{2\sqrt{2^{\frac32}}}}} = \sqrt{2\sqrt{2\sqrt{2 . \left(2^{\frac32}\right)^{\frac12}}}}$

$= \sqrt{2\sqrt{2\sqrt{2 . 2^{\left(\frac32\times\frac12\right)}}}} = \sqrt{2\sqrt{2\sqrt{2 . 2^{\frac34}}}}$

$= \sqrt{2\sqrt{2\sqrt{2^{\left(1+\frac34\right)}}}} = \sqrt{2\sqrt{2\sqrt{2^{\frac74}}}}$

$= \sqrt{2\sqrt{2 . \left(2^{\frac74}\right)^{\frac12}}} = \sqrt{2\sqrt{2 . 2^{\left(\frac74\times\frac12\right)}}}$

$= \sqrt{2\sqrt{2 . 2^{\frac78}}} = \sqrt{2\sqrt{2^{\left(1+\frac78\right)}}} = \sqrt{2\sqrt{2^{\frac{15}{8}}}}$

$= \sqrt{2\left(2^{\frac{15}{8}}\right)^{\frac12}} = \sqrt{2 . 2^{\frac{15}{16}}} = \sqrt{2^{\left(1+\frac{15}{16}\right)}}$

$= \sqrt{2^{\frac{31}{16}}} = \left(2^{\frac{31}{16}}\right)^{\frac12} = 2^{\left(\frac{31}{16}\times\frac12\right)} = 2^{\frac{31}{32}}.$

27. $(0.03125)^{-\frac25} = [(0.5)^5]^{-\frac25} = 0.5^{\left[5\times\left(-\frac25\right)\right]} = (0.5)^{-2}$

$= \frac{1}{(0.5)^2} = \frac{1}{0.25} = 4.$

28. $\left(\frac12\right)^{-\frac12} = (2)^{\frac12} = \sqrt2.$

29. $\left[\left(\sqrt[5]{x^{-\frac35}}\right)^{-\frac53}\right]^5 = \left[\left\{\left(x^{-\frac35}\right)^{\frac15}\right\}^{-\frac53}\right]^5 = \left[\left(x^{\left\{\left(-\frac35\right)\times\frac15\right\}}\right)^{-\frac53}\right]^5$

$= \left[\left(x^{-\frac{3}{25}}\right)^{-\frac53}\right]^5 = \left[x^{\left\{\left(-\frac{3}{25}\right)\times\left(-\frac53\right)\right\}}\right]^5$

$= \left(x^{\frac15}\right)^5 = x^{\left(\frac15\times5\right)} = x.$

30. Let $\frac{x^{\frac23}}{42} = \frac{5}{x^{\frac13}}$.

Then, $x^{\frac23} . x^{\frac13} = 42\times5 = 210 \Rightarrow x^{\left(\frac23+\frac13\right)} = 210 \Rightarrow x = 210.$

31. $5^{\frac14}\times(125)^{0.25} = 5^{0.25}\times(5^3)^{0.25} = 5^{0.25}\times5^{(3\times0.25)}$

$= 5^{0.25}\times5^{0.75} = 5^{(0.25+0.75)} = 5^1 = 5.$

32. $\frac{1}{(216)^{-\frac23}} + \frac{1}{(256)^{-\frac34}} + \frac{1}{(32)^{-\frac15}}$

$= \frac{1}{(6^3)^{-\frac23}} + \frac{1}{(4^4)^{\left(-\frac34\right)}} + \frac{1}{(2^5)^{-\frac15}}$

$= \frac{1}{6^{3\times\frac{(-2)}{3}}} + \frac{1}{4^{4\times\frac{(-3)}{4}}} + \frac{1}{2^{5\times\frac{(-1)}{5}}} = \frac{1}{6^{-2}} + \frac{1}{4^{-3}} + \frac{1}{2^{-1}}$

$= (6^2 + 4^3 + 2^1) = (36 + 64 + 2) = 102.$

33. $(2.4\times10^3)\div(8\times10^{-2}) = \frac{2.4\times10^3}{8\times10^{-2}} = \frac{24\times10^2}{8\times10^{-2}} = (3\times10^4).$

34. $\left(\frac{1}{216}\right)^{-\frac23}\div\left(\frac{1}{27}\right)^{-\frac43} = (216)^{\frac23}\div(27)^{\frac43} = \frac{(216)^{\frac23}}{(27)^{\frac43}} = \frac{(6^3)^{\frac23}}{(3^3)^{\frac43}}$

$= \frac{6^{\left(3\times\frac23\right)}}{3^{\left(3\times\frac43\right)}} = \frac{6^2}{3^4} = \frac{36}{81} = \frac49.$

35. $(48)^{-\frac27}\times(16)^{-\frac57}\times(3)^{-\frac57} = (16\times3)^{-\frac27}\times(16)^{-\frac57}\times(3)^{-\frac57}$

$= (16)^{-\frac27}\times(3)^{-\frac27}\times(16)^{-\frac57}\times(3)^{-\frac57}$

$= (16)^{\left(-\frac27-\frac57\right)}\times(3)^{\left(-\frac27-\frac57\right)}$

$= (16)^{\left(-\frac77\right)}\times(3)^{\left(-\frac77\right)} = (16)^{-1}\times(3)^{-1}$

$= \frac{1}{16}\times\frac13 = \frac{1}{48}.$

36. $10^{-8x} = (10^x)^{-8} = \left(\frac12\right)^{-8} = 2^8 = 256.$

37. $\left(\frac35\right)^3\left(\frac35\right)^{-6} = \left(\frac35\right)^{2x-1} \Rightarrow \left(\frac35\right)^{(3-6)} = \left(\frac35\right)^{2x-1}$

$\Rightarrow \left(\frac35\right)^{-3} = \left(\frac35\right)^{2x-1}$

$\Rightarrow 2x-1 = -3 \Rightarrow 2x = -2 \Rightarrow x = -1.$

38. $49\times49\times49\times49 = 7^2\times7^2\times7^2\times7^2 = 7^{(2+2+2+2)} = 7^8.$

∴ Required number = 8.

39. $8^{-25} - 8^{-26} = \left(\frac{1}{8^{25}} - \frac{1}{8^{26}}\right) = \frac{(8-1)}{8^{26}} = 7\times8^{-26}.$

40. $(64)^{-\frac12} - (-32)^{-\frac45} = (8^2)^{-\frac12} - [(-2)^5]^{-\frac45}$

$= 8^{\left[2\times\left(\frac{-1}{2}\right)\right]} - (-2)^{\left[5\times\left(\frac{-4}{5}\right)\right]}$

$= 8^{-1} - (-2)^{-4} = \frac18 - \frac{1}{(-2)^4}$

$= \left(\frac18 - \frac{1}{16}\right) = \frac{1}{16}.$

41. $\left(\frac{a}{b}\right)^{x-1} = \left(\frac{b}{a}\right)^{x-3} \Leftrightarrow \left(\frac{a}{b}\right)^{x-1} = \left(\frac{a}{b}\right)^{-(x-3)} = \left(\frac{a}{b}\right)^{(3-x)}$

$\Leftrightarrow x - 1 = 3 - x \Leftrightarrow 2x = 4 \Leftrightarrow x = 2.$

42. $2^{2n-1} = \frac{1}{8^{n-3}} \Leftrightarrow 2^{2n-1} = \frac{1}{(2^3)^{n-3}}$

$= \frac{1}{2^{3(n-3)}} = \frac{1}{2^{(3n-9)}} = 2^{(9-3n)}$

$\Leftrightarrow 2n - 1 = 9 - 3n \Leftrightarrow 5n = 10$

$\Leftrightarrow n = 2.$

43. $5^a = 3125 = 5^5 \Rightarrow a = 5. \Rightarrow 5^{(a-3)} = 5^{(5-3)} = 5^2 = 25.$

44. $5\sqrt{5} \times 5^3 \div 5^{-\frac{3}{2}} = 5^{a+2} \Leftrightarrow \frac{5 \times 5^{\frac{1}{2}} \times 5^3}{5^{-\frac{3}{2}}} = 5^{a+2}$

$\Leftrightarrow 5^{\left(1+\frac{1}{2}+3+\frac{3}{2}\right)} = 5^{a+2} \Leftrightarrow 5^6 = 5^{a+2}$

$\Leftrightarrow a + 2 = 6 \Leftrightarrow a = 4.$

45. $\sqrt{2^n} = 64 \Leftrightarrow (2^n)^{\frac{1}{2}} = 2^6 \Leftrightarrow 2^{\frac{n}{2}} = 2^6 \Leftrightarrow \frac{n}{2} = 6$

$\Leftrightarrow n = 12.$

46. $(\sqrt{3})^5 \times 9^2 = 3^n \times 3\sqrt{3} \Leftrightarrow \left(3^{\frac{1}{2}}\right)^5 \times (3^2)^2 = 3^n \times 3 \times 3^{\frac{1}{2}}$

$\Leftrightarrow 3^{\left(\frac{1}{2}\times 5\right)} \times 3^{(2\times 2)} = 3^{\left(n+1+\frac{1}{2}\right)}$

$\Leftrightarrow 3^{\left(\frac{5}{2}+4\right)} = 3^{\left(n+\frac{3}{2}\right)} \Leftrightarrow n + \frac{3}{2} = \frac{13}{2}$

$\Leftrightarrow n = \left(\frac{13}{2} - \frac{3}{2}\right) = \frac{10}{2} = 5.$

47. $\frac{9^n \times 3^5 \times (27)^3}{3 \times (81)^4} = 27 \Leftrightarrow \frac{(3^2)^n \times 3^5 \times (3^3)^3}{3 \times (3^4)^4} = 3^3$

$\Leftrightarrow \frac{3^{2n} \times 3^5 \times 3^{(3\times 3)}}{3 \times 3^{(4\times 4)}} = 3^3$

$\Leftrightarrow \frac{3^{2n+5+9}}{3 \times 3^{16}} = 3^3 \Leftrightarrow \frac{3^{2n+14}}{3^{17}} = 3^3$

$\Leftrightarrow 3^{(2n+14-17)} = 3^3$

$\Leftrightarrow 3^{2n-3} = 3^3 \Leftrightarrow 2n - 3 = 3 \Leftrightarrow 2n = 6 \Leftrightarrow n = 3.$

48. $\left(\frac{9}{4}\right)^x \cdot \left(\frac{8}{27}\right)^{x-1} = \frac{2}{3} \Leftrightarrow \frac{9^x}{4^x} \times \frac{8^{(x-1)}}{27^{(x-1)}} = \frac{2}{3}$

$\Leftrightarrow \frac{(3^2)^x}{(2^2)^x} \times \frac{(2^3)^{(x-1)}}{(3^3)^{(x-1)}} = \frac{2}{3} \Leftrightarrow \frac{3^{2x} \times 2^{3(x-1)}}{2^{2x} \times 3^{3(x-1)}} = \frac{2}{3}$

$\Leftrightarrow \frac{2^{(3x-3-2x)}}{3^{(3x-3-2x)}} = \frac{2}{3} \Leftrightarrow \frac{2^{(x-3)}}{3^{(x-3)}} = \frac{2}{3} \Leftrightarrow \left(\frac{2}{3}\right)^{(x-3)} = \left(\frac{2}{3}\right)^1$

$\Leftrightarrow x - 3 = 1 \Leftrightarrow x = 4.$

49. $2^x = \sqrt[3]{32} \Leftrightarrow 2^x = (32)^{\frac{1}{3}} = (2^5)^{\frac{1}{3}} = 2^{\frac{5}{3}} \Leftrightarrow x = \frac{5}{3}.$

50. $2^x \times 8^{\frac{1}{5}} = 2^{\frac{1}{5}} \Leftrightarrow 2^x \times (2^3)^{\frac{1}{5}} = 2^{\frac{1}{5}} \Leftrightarrow 2^x \times 2^{\frac{3}{5}} = 2^{\frac{1}{5}}$

$\Leftrightarrow 2^{\left(x+\frac{3}{5}\right)} = 2^{\frac{1}{5}}$

$\Leftrightarrow x + \frac{3}{5} = \frac{1}{5} \Leftrightarrow x = \left(\frac{1}{5} - \frac{3}{5}\right) = \frac{-2}{5}.$

51. $5^{(x+3)} = 25^{(3x-4)} \Leftrightarrow 5^{(x+3)} = (5^2)^{(3x-4)} \Leftrightarrow 5^{(x+3)}$

$= 5^{2(3x-4)} \Leftrightarrow 5^{(x+3)} = 5^{(6x-8)}$

$\Leftrightarrow x + 3 = 6x - 8 \Leftrightarrow 5x = 11$

$\Leftrightarrow x = \frac{11}{5}.$

52. $\frac{2^{n+4} - 2(2^n)}{2(2^{n+3})} = \frac{2^{n+4} - 2^{n+1}}{2^{n+4}} = \frac{2^{n+4}}{2^{n+4}} - \frac{2^{n+1}}{2^{n+4}}$

$= 1 - 2^{n+1-(n+4)} = 1 - 2^{-3} = 1 - \frac{1}{8} = \frac{7}{8}.$

53. $\left[\sqrt[3]{\sqrt[6]{a^9}}\right]^4 \left[\sqrt[6]{\sqrt[3]{a^9}}\right]^4 = \left[\left\{(a^9)^{\frac{1}{6}}\right\}^{\frac{1}{3}}\right]^4 . \left[\left\{(a^9)^{\frac{1}{3}}\right\}^{\frac{1}{6}}\right]^4$

$= a^{\left(9\times\frac{1}{6}\times\frac{1}{3}\times 4\right)} . a^{\left(9\times\frac{1}{3}\times\frac{1}{6}\times 4\right)}$

$= a^2 . a^2 = a^4.$

54. $(256)^{0.16} \times (256)^{0.09} = (256)^{(0.16+0.09)} = (256)^{0.25}$

$= (256)^{\left(\frac{25}{100}\right)}$

$= (256)^{\frac{1}{4}} = (4^4)^{\frac{1}{4}} = 4^{\left(4\times\frac{1}{4}\right)} = 4^1 = 4.$

55. $(0.04)^{-1.5} = \left(\frac{4}{100}\right)^{-1.5} = \left(\frac{1}{25}\right)^{-\frac{3}{2}} = (25)^{\frac{3}{2}} = (5^2)^{\frac{3}{2}}$

$= 5^{\left(2\times\frac{3}{2}\right)} = 5^3 = 125.$

56. Let $(17)^{3.5} \times (17)^x = 17^8$. Then, $(17)^{(3.5+x)} = (17)^8$.

$\therefore \quad 3.5 + x = 8 \Leftrightarrow x = (8 - 3.5)$

$\Leftrightarrow x = 4.5.$

57. Let $6^{1.2} \times 36^x \times 30^{2.4} \times 25^{1.3} = 30^5$.

Then, $6^{1.2} \times (6^2)^x \times (6 \times 5)^{2.4} \times (5^2)^{1.3} = 30^5$

$\Leftrightarrow 6^{1.2} \times 6^{2x} \times 6^{2.4} \times 5^{2.4} \times 5^{2.6} = (6 \times 5)^5$

$\Leftrightarrow 6^{(1.2+2x+2.4)} \times 5^{(2.4+2.6)} = 6^5 \times 5^5$

$\Leftrightarrow 6^{(3.6+2x)} \times 5^5 = 6^5 \times 5^5 \Leftrightarrow 3.6 + 2x = 5 \Leftrightarrow 2x = 1.4$

$\Leftrightarrow x = 0.7.$

58. Let $2^{3.6} \times 4^{3.6} \times 4^{3.6} \times 32^{2.3} = 32^x$.

Then, $2^{3.6} \times (2^2)^{3.6} \times (2^2)^{3.6} \times (2^5)^{2.3} = (2^5)^x$

$\Leftrightarrow 2^{3.6} \times 2^{(2\times 3.6)} \times 2^{(2\times 3.6)} \times (2^5)^{2.3} = (2^5)^x$

$\Leftrightarrow 2^{(3.6+7.2+7.2)} \times (2^5)^{2.3} = (2^5)^x \Leftrightarrow 2^{18} \times (2^5)^{2.3} = (2^5)^x$

$\Leftrightarrow (2^5)^{3.6} \times (2^5)^{2.3} = (2^5)^x \Leftrightarrow (2^5)^{(3.6+2.3)} = (2^5)^x$

$\Leftrightarrow (2^5)^{5.9} = (2^5)^x \Leftrightarrow x = 5.9.$

59. Let $3^{3.5} \times (21)^2 \times (42)^{2.5} \div 2^{2.5} \times 7^{3.5} = 21^x$.

Then, $3^{3.5} \times 7^{3.5} \times (21)^2 \times (21 \times 2)^{2.5} \div 2^{2.5} = 21^x$

$\Leftrightarrow (21)^x = (3 \times 7)^{3.5} \times (21)^2 \times (21)^{2.5} \times 2^{2.5} \div 2^{2.5}$

$\Leftrightarrow (21)^x = (21)^{3.5} \times (21)^{(2+2.5)} \Leftrightarrow (21)^x = (21)^{3.5} \times (21)^{(4.5)}$

$\Leftrightarrow (21)^x = (21)^{(3.5+4.5)} = (21)^8$

$\Leftrightarrow x = 8.$

60. $8^{0.4} \times 4^{1.6} \times 2^{1.6} = (2^3)^{0.4} \times (2^2)^{1.6} \times 2^{1.6}$

$= 2^{(3 \times 0.4)} \times 2^{(2 \times 1.6)} \times 2^{1.6}$

$= 2^{1.2} \times 2^{3.2} \times 2^{1.6} = 2^{(1.2+3.2+1.6)} = 2^6 = 64.$

61. Let $8^7 \times 2^6 \div 8^{2.4} = 8^x$.

Then, $8^7 \times (2^3)^2 \div 8^{2.4} = 8^x$

$\Leftrightarrow 8^7 \times 8^2 \div 8^{2.4} = 8^x$

$\Leftrightarrow 8^x = 8^{(7+2-2.4)} \Leftrightarrow 8^x = 8^{6.6} \Leftrightarrow x = 6.6.$

62. Let $25^{2.7} \times 5^{4.2} \div 5^{5.4} = 25^x$.

Then, $(25)^{2.7} \times 5^{(4.2-5.4)} = 25^x$

$\Leftrightarrow (25)^{2.7} \times 5^{(-1.2)} = 25^x \Leftrightarrow (25)^{2.7} \times \frac{1}{5^{1.2}} = 25^x$

$\Leftrightarrow \frac{(25)^{2.7}}{(5^2)^{0.6}} = 25^x \Leftrightarrow \frac{(25)^{2.7}}{(25)^{0.6}} = 25^x$

$\Leftrightarrow 25^x = 25^{(2.7-0.6)} = 25^{2.1} \Leftrightarrow x = 2.1$

63. Let $8^{2.4} \times 2^{3.7} \div (16)^{1.3} = 2^x$.

Then, $(2^3)^{2.4} \times 2^{3.7} \div (2^4)^{1.3} = 2^x$

$\Leftrightarrow 2^{(3 \times 2.4)} \times 2^{3.7} \div 2^{(4 \times 1.3)} = 2^x$

$\Leftrightarrow 2^{7.2} \times 2^{3.7} \div 2^{5.2} = 2^x$

$\Leftrightarrow 2^x = 2^{(7.2+3.7-5.2)} = 2^{5.7} \Leftrightarrow x = 5.7.$

64. Let $(0.04)^2 \div (0.008) \times (0.2)^6 = (0.2)^x$.

Then, $(0.2)^x = [(0.2)^2]^2 \div (0.2)^3 \times (0.2)^6$

$\Leftrightarrow (0.2)^x = (0.2)^{(2 \times 2)} \div (0.2)^3 \times (0.2)^6$

$\Leftrightarrow (0.2)^x = (0.2)^4 \div (0.2)^3 \times (0.2)^6 = (0.2)^{(4-3+6)} = (0.2)^7$

$\Leftrightarrow x = 7.$

65. $(18)^{3.5} \div (27)^{3.5} \times 6^{3.5} = 2^x$

$\Leftrightarrow (18)^{3.5} \times \frac{1}{(27)^{3.5}} \times 6^{3.5} = 2^x$

$\Leftrightarrow (3^2 \times 2)^{3.5} \times \frac{1}{(3^3)^{3.5}} \times (2 \times 3)^{3.5} = 2^x 11$

$\Leftrightarrow 3^{(2 \times 3.5)} \times 2^{3.5} \times \frac{1}{3^{(3 \times 3.5)}} \times 2^{3.5} \times 3^{3.5} = 2^x$

$\Leftrightarrow 3^7 \times 2^{3.5} \times \frac{1}{3^{10.5}} \times 2^{3.5} \times 3^{3.5} = 2^x$

$\Leftrightarrow \frac{3^{(7+3.5)}}{3^{10.5}} \times 2^{(3.5+3.5)} \Leftrightarrow 2^7 = 2^x \Leftrightarrow x = 7.$

66. Let $(25)^{7.5} \times (5)^{2.5} \div (125)^{1.5} = 5^x$.

Then, $\frac{(5^2)^{7.5} \times (5)^{2.5}}{(5^3)^{1.5}} = 5^x \Leftrightarrow \frac{5^{(2 \times 7.5)} \times 5^{2.5}}{5^{(3 \times 1.5)}} = 5^x$

$\Leftrightarrow 1\frac{5^{15} \times 5^{2.5}}{5^{4.5}} = 5^x$

$\Leftrightarrow 5^x = 5^{(15+2.5-4.5)} = 5^{13} \Leftrightarrow x = 13.$

67. $\frac{(243)^{0.13} \times (243)^{0.07}}{7^{0.25} \times (49)^{0.075} \times (343)^{0.2}} = \frac{(243)^{(0.13+0.07)}}{7^{0.25} \times (7^2)^{0.075} \times (7^3)^{0.2}}$

$= \frac{(243)^{0.2}}{7^{0.25} \times 7^{(2 \times 0.075)} \times 7^{(3 \times 0.2)}}$

$= \frac{(3^5)^{0.2}}{7^{0.25} \times 7^{0.15} \times 7^{0.6}} = \frac{3^{(5 \times 0.2)}}{7^{(0.25+0.15+0.6)}} = \frac{3^1}{7^1} = \frac{3}{7}.$

68. $(64x^3 \div 27a^{-3})^{-\frac{2}{3}} = \left(\frac{64x^3}{27a^{-3}}\right)^{-\frac{2}{3}} = \left(\frac{4^3 . x^3}{3^3 . a^{-3}}\right)^{-\frac{2}{3}}$

$= \left(\frac{4^3 . x^3 . a^3}{3^3}\right)^{-\frac{2}{3}}$

$= \frac{\{(4ax)^3\}^{-\frac{2}{3}}}{3^{3 \times \left(-\frac{2}{3}\right)}} = \frac{(4ax)^{3 \times \left(-\frac{2}{3}\right)}}{3^{-2}} = \frac{(4ax)^{-2}}{3^{-2}}$

$= \frac{3^2}{(4ax)^2} = \frac{9}{16a^2x^2}.$

69. $2^{n+4} - 2^{n+2} = 3 \Leftrightarrow 2^{n+2}(2^2 - 1) = 3$

$\Leftrightarrow 2^{n+2} = 1 = 2^0$

$\Leftrightarrow n + 2 = 0 \Leftrightarrow n = -2.$

70. $2^{n-1} + 2^{n+1} = 320 \Leftrightarrow 2^{n-1}(1 + 2^2) = 320$

$\Leftrightarrow 5 \times 2^{n-1} = 320$

$\Leftrightarrow 2^{n-1} = \frac{320}{5} = 64 = 2^6$

$\Leftrightarrow n - 1 = 6 \Leftrightarrow n = 7.$

71. $3^x - 3^{x-1} = 18 \Leftrightarrow 3^{x-1}(3 - 1) = 18$

$\Leftrightarrow 3^{x-1} = 9 = 3^2 \Leftrightarrow x - 1 = 2 \Leftrightarrow x = 3.$

$\therefore x^x = 3^3 = 27.$

72. $\frac{2^{n+4} - 2 \times 2^n}{2 \times 2^{n+3}} + 2^{-3} = \frac{2^{n+4} - 2^{n+1}}{2^{n+4}} + \frac{1}{2^3}$

$= \frac{2^{n+1}(2^3 - 1)}{2^{n+4}} + \frac{1}{2^3}$

$= \frac{2^{n+1} \times 7}{2^{n+1} \times 2^3} + \frac{1}{2^3} = \left(\frac{7}{8} + \frac{1}{8}\right) = \frac{8}{8} = 1.$

73. $\frac{2^{3x+4} + 8^{x+1}}{8^{x+1} - 2^{3x+2}} = \frac{2^{3x+4} + (2^3)^{x+1}}{(2^3)^{x+1} - 2^{3x+2}} = \frac{2^{3x+4} + 2^{3(x+1)}}{2^{3(x+1)} - 2^{3x+2}}$

$= \frac{2^{3x+4} + 2^{3x+3}}{2^{3x+3} - 2^{3x+2}} = \frac{2^{3x+3}(2+1)}{2^{3x+2}(2-1)}$

$= 3.2^{(3x+3)-(3x+2)} = 3.2^1$

$= 3 \times 2 = 6.$

74. $\frac{2^{n-1} - 2^n}{2^{n+4} + 2^{n+1}} = \frac{2^{n-1}(1-2)}{2^{n+1}(2^3+1)} = \left(-\frac{1}{9}\right).2^{(n-1)-(n+1)}$

$= \left(-\frac{1}{9}\right). 2^{-2} = \left(-\frac{1}{9}\right) \times \frac{1}{2^2} = \left(-\frac{1}{9}\right) \times \frac{1}{4}$

$= -\frac{1}{36}.$

75. $\left(\sqrt{x} - \frac{1}{\sqrt{x}}\right)^2 = x + \frac{1}{x} - 2 = (5 + 2\sqrt{6}) + \frac{1}{(5 + 2\sqrt{6})} - 2$

$= (5 + 2\sqrt{6}) + \frac{1}{(5 + 2\sqrt{6})} \times \frac{(5 - 2\sqrt{6})}{(5 - 2\sqrt{6})} - 2$

$= (5 + 2\sqrt{6}) + (5 - 2\sqrt{6}) - 2 = 8.$

$\therefore \quad \left(\sqrt{x}-\frac{1}{\sqrt{x}}\right)=\sqrt{8}=2\sqrt{2}.$

76. $4+\sqrt{7}=\frac{7}{2}+\frac{1}{2}+2\times\frac{\sqrt{7}}{\sqrt{2}}\times\frac{1}{\sqrt{2}}$

$=\left(\frac{\sqrt{7}}{\sqrt{2}}\right)^2+\left(\frac{1}{\sqrt{2}}\right)^2+2\times\frac{\sqrt{7}}{\sqrt{2}}\times\frac{1}{\sqrt{2}}$

$=\left(\frac{\sqrt{7}}{\sqrt{2}}+\frac{1}{\sqrt{2}}\right)^2=\frac{1}{2}(\sqrt{7}+1)^2.$

77. $\sqrt{8-2\sqrt{15}}=\sqrt{5+3-2\times\sqrt{5}\times\sqrt{3}}$

$=\sqrt{(\sqrt{5})^2+(\sqrt{3})^2-2\times\sqrt{5}\times\sqrt{3}}$

$=\sqrt{(\sqrt{5}-\sqrt{3})^2}=(\sqrt{5}-\sqrt{3}).$

78. $\sqrt{6-4\sqrt{3}+\sqrt{16-8\sqrt{3}}}=\sqrt{6-4\sqrt{3}+\sqrt{12+4-8\sqrt{3}}}$

$=\sqrt{6-4\sqrt{3}+\sqrt{(2\sqrt{3})^2+(2)^2-2\times2\sqrt{3}\times2}}$

$=\sqrt{6-4\sqrt{3}+\sqrt{(2\sqrt{3}-2)^2}}=\sqrt{6-4\sqrt{3}+2\sqrt{3}-2}$

$=\sqrt{(\sqrt{3})^2+(1)^2-2\times\sqrt{3}\times1}=\sqrt{(\sqrt{3}-1)^2}=\sqrt{3}-1.$

79. $\frac{1}{\sqrt{12-\sqrt{140}}}-\frac{1}{\sqrt{8-\sqrt{60}}}-\frac{2}{\sqrt{10+\sqrt{84}}}$

$=\frac{1}{\sqrt{12-\sqrt{4\times35}}}-\frac{1}{\sqrt{8-\sqrt{4\times15}}}-\frac{2}{\sqrt{10+\sqrt{4\times21}}}$

$=\frac{1}{\sqrt{12-2\sqrt{35}}}-\frac{1}{\sqrt{8-2\sqrt{15}}}-\frac{2}{\sqrt{10+2\sqrt{21}}}$

$=\frac{1}{\sqrt{7+5-2\sqrt{35}}}-\frac{1}{\sqrt{5+3-2\sqrt{15}}}-\frac{2}{\sqrt{7+3+2\sqrt{21}}}$

$=\frac{1}{\sqrt{(\sqrt{7})^2+(\sqrt{5})^2-2\times\sqrt{7}\times\sqrt{5}}}-\frac{1}{\sqrt{(\sqrt{5})^2+(\sqrt{3})^2-2\times\sqrt{5}\times\sqrt{3}}}-\frac{2}{\sqrt{(\sqrt{7})^2+(\sqrt{3})^2+2\times\sqrt{7}\times\sqrt{3}}}$

$=\frac{1}{\sqrt{(\sqrt{7}-\sqrt{5})^2}}-\frac{1}{\sqrt{(\sqrt{5}-\sqrt{3})^2}}-\frac{2}{\sqrt{(\sqrt{7}+\sqrt{3})^2}}$

$=\frac{1}{(\sqrt{7}-\sqrt{5})}-\frac{1}{(\sqrt{5}-\sqrt{3})}-\frac{2}{(\sqrt{7}+\sqrt{3})}$

$=\frac{1}{\sqrt{7}-\sqrt{5}}\times\frac{\sqrt{7}+\sqrt{5}}{\sqrt{7}+\sqrt{5}}-\frac{1}{\sqrt{5}-\sqrt{3}}\times\frac{\sqrt{5}+\sqrt{3}}{\sqrt{5}+\sqrt{3}}-\frac{2}{\sqrt{7}+\sqrt{3}}\times\frac{\sqrt{7}-\sqrt{3}}{\sqrt{7}-\sqrt{3}}$

$=\frac{\sqrt{7}+\sqrt{5}}{7-5}-\frac{\sqrt{5}+\sqrt{3}}{5-3}-\frac{2(\sqrt{7}-\sqrt{3})}{7-3}$

$=\frac{(\sqrt{7}+\sqrt{5})}{2}-\frac{(\sqrt{5}+\sqrt{3})}{2}-\frac{(\sqrt{7}-\sqrt{3})}{2}$

$=\frac{\sqrt{7}+\sqrt{5}-\sqrt{5}-\sqrt{3}-\sqrt{7}+\sqrt{3}}{2}=0.$

80. $\sqrt{4+\sqrt{15}}=\sqrt{\frac{5}{2}+\frac{3}{2}+2\times\frac{\sqrt{5}}{\sqrt{2}}\times\frac{\sqrt{3}}{\sqrt{2}}}$

$=\sqrt{\left(\frac{\sqrt{5}}{\sqrt{2}}\right)^2+\left(\frac{\sqrt{3}}{\sqrt{2}}\right)^2+2\times\frac{\sqrt{5}}{\sqrt{2}}\times\frac{\sqrt{3}}{\sqrt{2}}}$

$=\sqrt{\left(\frac{\sqrt{5}}{\sqrt{2}}+\frac{\sqrt{3}}{\sqrt{2}}\right)^2}=\frac{\sqrt{5}}{\sqrt{2}}+\frac{\sqrt{3}}{\sqrt{2}}.$

Similarly, $\sqrt{4-\sqrt{15}}=\frac{\sqrt{5}}{\sqrt{2}}-\frac{\sqrt{3}}{\sqrt{2}}.$

$\sqrt{12-4\sqrt{5}}=\sqrt{10+2-2\times\sqrt{10}\times\sqrt{2}}$

$=\sqrt{(\sqrt{10})^2+(\sqrt{2})^2-2\times\sqrt{10}\times\sqrt{2}}$

$=\sqrt{(\sqrt{10}-\sqrt{2})^2}=(\sqrt{10}-\sqrt{2}).$

$\therefore$ Given expression

$=\left(\frac{\sqrt{5}}{\sqrt{2}}+\frac{\sqrt{3}}{\sqrt{2}}\right)+\left(\frac{\sqrt{5}}{\sqrt{2}}-\frac{\sqrt{3}}{2}\right)-(\sqrt{10}-\sqrt{2})$

$=\frac{2\sqrt{5}}{\sqrt{2}}-\sqrt{10}+\sqrt{2}=\sqrt{10}-\sqrt{10}+\sqrt{2}=\sqrt{2},$

which is an irrational number.

81. Let $X=\frac{\sqrt{\sqrt{5}+2}+\sqrt{\sqrt{5}-2}}{\sqrt{\sqrt{5}+1}}.$

Then $X^2=\frac{(\sqrt{\sqrt{5}+2}+\sqrt{\sqrt{5}-2})^2}{(\sqrt{\sqrt{5}+1})^2}$

$=\frac{(\sqrt{5}+2)+(\sqrt{5}-2)+2\sqrt{(\sqrt{5}+2)(\sqrt{5}-2)}}{(\sqrt{5}+1)}$

$=\frac{2\sqrt{5}+2\sqrt{(\sqrt{5})^2-(2)^2}}{\sqrt{5}+1}=\frac{2\sqrt{5}+2}{\sqrt{5}+1}$

$=\frac{2(\sqrt{5}+1)}{(\sqrt{5}+1)}=2$

$\Rightarrow \quad X=\sqrt{2}.$

$\therefore \quad N=\sqrt{2}-\sqrt{3-2\sqrt{2}}=\sqrt{2}-\sqrt{(\sqrt{2})^2+1^2-2\times\sqrt{2}\times1}$

$=\sqrt{2}-\sqrt{(\sqrt{2}-1)^2}=\sqrt{2}-(\sqrt{2}-1)=1.$

82. $x^z=y^2 \Leftrightarrow (10^{0.48})^z=(10^{0.70})^2$

$\Leftrightarrow 10^{(0.48z)}=10^{(2\times0.70)}=10^{1.40}$

$\Leftrightarrow 0.48z=1.40$

$\Leftrightarrow z=\frac{140}{48}=\frac{35}{12}=2.9$ (approx.).

83. We know that $11^2=121$.

Putting $m=11$ and $n=2$, we get :

$(m-1)^{n+1}=(11-1)^{(2+1)}=10^3=1000.$

84. $(216)^{\frac{3}{5}} \times (2500)^{\frac{2}{5}} \times (300)^{\frac{1}{5}} = (3^3 \times 2^3)^{\frac{3}{5}} \times (5^4 \times 2^2)^{\frac{2}{5}} \times (5^2 \times 2^2 \times 3)^{\frac{1}{5}}$

$= 3^{\left(3\times\frac{3}{5}\right)} \times 2^{\left(3\times\frac{3}{5}\right)} \times 5^{\left(4\times\frac{2}{5}\right)} \times 2^{\left(2\times\frac{2}{5}\right)} \times 5^{\left(2\times\frac{1}{5}\right)} \times 2^{\left(2\times\frac{1}{5}\right)} \times 3^{\frac{1}{5}}$

$= 3^{\frac{9}{5}} \times 2^{\frac{9}{5}} \times 5^{\frac{8}{5}} \times 2^{\frac{4}{5}} \times 5^{\frac{2}{5}} \times 2^{\frac{2}{5}} \times 3^{\frac{1}{5}}$

$= 3^{\left(\frac{9}{5}+\frac{1}{5}\right)} \times 2^{\left(\frac{9}{5}+\frac{4}{5}+\frac{2}{5}\right)} \times 5^{\left(\frac{8}{5}+\frac{2}{5}\right)} = 3^2 \times 2^3 \times 5^2.$

Hence, the number of prime factors = (2 + 3 + 2) = 7.

85. $\dfrac{6^{12} \times (35)^{28} \times (15)^{16}}{(14)^{12} \times (21)^{11}} = \dfrac{(2\times3)^{12} \times (5\times7)^{28} \times (3\times5)^{16}}{(2\times7)^{12} \times (3\times7)^{11}}$

$= \dfrac{2^{12} \times 3^{12} \times 5^{28} \times 7^{28} \times 3^{16} \times 5^{16}}{2^{12} \times 7^{12} \times 3^{11} \times 7^{11}}$

$= 2^{(12-12)} \times 3^{(12+16-11)} \times 5^{(28+16)} \times 7^{(28-12-11)}$

$= 2^0 \times 3^{17} \times 5^{44} \times 7^5 = 3^{17} \times 5^{44} \times 7^5.$

Number of prime factors = 17 + 44 + 5 = 66.

86. $1 + (3+1)(3^2+1)(3^4+1)(3^8+1)(3^{16}+1)(3^{32}+1)$

$= 1 + \frac{1}{2}[(3-1)(3+1)(3^2+1)(3^4+1)(3^8+1)(3^{16}+1)(3^{32}+1)]$

$= 1 + \frac{1}{2}[(3^2-1)(3^2+1)(3^4+1)(3^8+1)(3^{16}+1)(3^{32}+1)]$

$= 1 + \frac{1}{2}[(3^4-1)(3^4+1)(3^8+1)(3^{16}+1)(3^{32}+1)]$

$= 1 + \frac{1}{2}[(3^8-1)(3^8+1)(3^{16}+1)(3^{32}+1)]$

$= 1 + \frac{1}{2}[(3^{16}-1)(3^{16}+1)(3^{32}+1)]$

$= 1 + \frac{1}{2}[(3^{32}-1)(3^{32}+1)]$

$= 1 + \frac{1}{2}(3^{64}-1) = \dfrac{2 + 3^{64} - 1}{2} = \dfrac{3^{64}+1}{2}.$

87. $\dfrac{1}{1+a^{(n-m)}} + \dfrac{1}{1+a^{(m-n)}} = \dfrac{1}{\left(1+\dfrac{a^n}{a^m}\right)} + \dfrac{1}{\left(1+\dfrac{a^m}{a^n}\right)}$

$= \dfrac{a^m}{(a^m+a^n)} + \dfrac{a^n}{(a^m+a^n)} = \dfrac{(a^m+a^n)}{(a^m+a^n)} = 1.$

88. $(x^a)^{a^2-bc} \cdot (x^b)^{b^2-ca} \cdot (x^c)^{c^2-ab}$

$= x^{[a(a^2-bc)]} \cdot x^{[b(b^2-ca)]} \cdot x^{[c(c^2-ab)]}$

$= x^{(a^3-abc)} \cdot x^{(b^3-abc)} \cdot x^{(c^3-abc)}$

$= x^{(a^3-abc+b^3-abc+c^3-abc)} = x^{(a^3+b^3+c^3-3abc)}$

$= x^{(3abc-3abc)} = x^0 = 1.$

[∴ If $a+b+c=0$, $a^3+b^3+c^3=3abc$]

89. Given Exp. $= \dfrac{1}{\left(1+\dfrac{x^b}{x^a}+\dfrac{x^c}{x^a}\right)} + \dfrac{1}{\left(1+\dfrac{x^a}{x^b}+\dfrac{x^c}{x^b}\right)} + \dfrac{1}{\left(1+\dfrac{x^b}{x^c}+\dfrac{x^a}{x^c}\right)}$

$= \dfrac{x^a}{(x^a+x^b+x^c)} + \dfrac{x^b}{(x^a+x^b+x^c)} + \dfrac{x^c}{(x^a+x^b+x^c)}$

$= \dfrac{(x^a+x^b+x^c)}{(x^a+x^b+x^c)} = 1.$

90. Given Exp.

$= x^{(b-c)(b+c-a)} \cdot x^{(c-a)(c+a-b)} \cdot x^{(a-b)(a+b-c)}$

$= x^{(b-c)(b+c)-a(b-c)} \cdot x^{(c-a)(c+a)-b(c-a)} \cdot x^{(a-b)(a+b)-c(a-b)}$

$= x^{(b^2-c^2+c^2-a^2+a^2-b^2)} \cdot x^{-a(b-c)-b(c-a)-c(a-b)}$

$= (x^0 \times x^0) = (1 \times 1) = 1.$

91. Given Exp. $= x^{(a-b)(a+b)} \cdot x^{(b-c)(b+c)} \cdot x^{(c-a)(c+a)}$

$= x^{(a^2-b^2)} \cdot x^{(b^2-c^2)} \cdot x^{(c^2-a^2)}$

$= x^{(a^2-b^2+b^2-c^2+c^2-a^2)} = x^0 = 1.$

92. Given Exp. $= \{x^{(a-b)}\}^{\frac{1}{ab}} \cdot \{x^{(b-c)}\}^{\frac{1}{bc}} \cdot \{x^{(c-a)}\}^{\frac{1}{ca}}$

$= x^{\frac{(a-b)}{ab}} \cdot x^{\frac{(b-c)}{bc}} \cdot x^{\frac{(c-a)}{ca}}$

$= x^{\left\{\frac{(a-b)}{ab}+\frac{(b-c)}{bc}+\frac{(c-a)}{ca}\right\}}$

$= x^{\left(\frac{1}{b}-\frac{1}{a}\right)+\left(\frac{1}{c}-\frac{1}{b}\right)+\left(\frac{1}{a}-\frac{1}{c}\right)} = x^0 = 1.$

93. Given Exp. $= \dfrac{\left(\dfrac{xy+1}{y}\right)^a \cdot \left(\dfrac{xy-1}{y}\right)^b}{\left(\dfrac{xy+1}{x}\right)^a \cdot \left(\dfrac{xy-1}{x}\right)^b}$

$= \dfrac{(xy+1)^a \cdot (xy-1)^b \cdot x^a \cdot x^b}{(xy+1)^a \cdot (xy-1)^b \cdot y^a \cdot y^b}$

$= \dfrac{x^{a+b}}{y^{a+b}} = \left(\dfrac{x}{y}\right)^{a+b}.$

94. Given Exp. $= x^{\frac{b+c}{(a-b)(c-a)}} \cdot x^{\frac{c+a}{(a-b)(b-c)}} \cdot x^{\frac{a+b}{(b-c)(c-a)}}$

$= x^{\frac{(b+c)(b-c)+(c+a)(c-a)+(a+b)(a-b)}{(a-b)(b-c)(c-a)}}$

$= x^{\frac{(b^2-c^2)+(c^2-a^2)+(a^2-b^2)}{(a-b)(b-c)(c-a)}} = x^0 = 1.$

95. Let $x^{\frac{1}{p}} = y^{\frac{1}{q}} = z^{\frac{1}{r}} = k.$ Then, $x = k^p$, $y = k^q$, $z = k^r$.

∴ $xyz = 1 \Rightarrow k^p \cdot k^q \cdot k^r = 1 = k^0$

$\Rightarrow k^{(p+q+r)} = k^0 \Rightarrow p+q+r = 0.$

96. Let $a^x = b^y = c^z = k$.

Then, $a = k^{\frac{1}{x}}, b = k^{\frac{1}{y}}$ and $c = k^{\frac{1}{z}}$.

$\therefore \quad b^2 = ac \Leftrightarrow \left(k^{\frac{1}{y}}\right)^2 = k^{\frac{1}{x}} \times k^{\frac{1}{z}} \Leftrightarrow k^{\left(\frac{2}{y}\right)} = k^{\left(\frac{1}{x}+\frac{1}{z}\right)}$

$\therefore \quad \frac{2}{y} = \frac{(x+z)}{xz} \Leftrightarrow \frac{y}{2} = \frac{xz}{(x+z)} \Leftrightarrow y = \frac{2xz}{(x+z)}$.

97. $a^1 = c^z = (b^y)^z = b^{yz} = (a^x)^{yz} = a^{xyz} \Rightarrow xyz = 1$.

98. $2^x = 4^y = 8^z \Leftrightarrow 2^x = 2^{2y} = 2^{3z} \Leftrightarrow x = 2y = 3z$.

$\therefore \quad \frac{1}{2x} + \frac{1}{4y} + \frac{1}{6z} = \frac{24}{7} \Leftrightarrow \frac{1}{6z} + \frac{1}{6z} + \frac{1}{6z} = \frac{24}{7}$

$\Leftrightarrow \frac{3}{6z} = \frac{24}{7} \Leftrightarrow z = \left(\frac{3}{6} \times \frac{7}{24}\right) = \frac{7}{48}$.

99. $8 = 7^d = (6^c)^d = 6^{cd} = (5^b)^{cd} = 5^{bcd} = (4^a)^{bcd} = 4^{abcd}$

$\Rightarrow \quad 4^{abcd} = 8 \Rightarrow (2^2)^{abcd} = 2^3 \Rightarrow 2abcd = 3$

$\Rightarrow \quad abcd = \frac{3}{2}$.

100. Given Exp. $= \frac{1}{1+a+b^{-1}} + \frac{1}{1+b+c^{-1}} + \frac{1}{1+c+a^{-1}}$

$= \frac{1}{1+a+b^{-1}} + \frac{b^{-1}}{b^{-1}+1+b^{-1}c^{-1}} + \frac{a}{a+ac+1}$

$= \frac{1}{1+a+b^{-1}} + \frac{b^{-1}}{1+b^{-1}+a} + \frac{a}{a+b^{-1}+1}$

$= \frac{1+a+b^{-1}}{1+a+b^{-1}} = 1$.

[$\because abc = 1 \Rightarrow (bc)^{-1} = a \Rightarrow b^{-1}c^{-1} = a$ and $ac = b^{-1}$]

101. $\sqrt{a^{-1}b} \cdot \sqrt{b^{-1}c} \cdot \sqrt{c^{-1}a} = (a^{-1})^{\frac{1}{2}} \cdot b^{\frac{1}{2}} \cdot (b^{-1})^{\frac{1}{2}} \cdot c^{\frac{1}{2}} \cdot (c^{-1})^{\frac{1}{2}} \cdot a^{\frac{1}{2}}$

$= (a^{-1}a)^{\frac{1}{2}} \cdot (b \cdot b^{-1})^{\frac{1}{2}} \cdot (c \cdot c^{-1})^{\frac{1}{2}}$

$= (1)^{\frac{1}{2}} \cdot (1)^{\frac{1}{2}} \cdot (1)^{\frac{1}{2}} = (1 \times 1 \times 1) = 1$.

102. $3^{x-y} = 27 = 3^3$

$\Leftrightarrow \quad x - y = 3 \quad \ldots (i)$

$3^{x+y} = 243 = 3^5$

$\Leftrightarrow \quad x + y = 5 \quad \ldots (ii)$

On solving (*i*) and (*ii*), we get $x = 4$.

103. Let $x^y = y^x = k$.

Then, $x = k^{\frac{1}{y}}$ and $y = k^{\frac{1}{x}}$.

$\therefore \quad \left(\frac{x}{y}\right)^{\frac{x}{y}} = \left(\frac{k^{\frac{1}{y}}}{k^{\frac{1}{x}}}\right)^{\frac{x}{y}} = k^{\left[\left(\frac{1}{y}-\frac{1}{x}\right)\frac{x}{y}\right]} = k^{\left(\frac{x-y}{xy}\right)\frac{x}{y}} = k^{\left(\frac{x-y}{y^2}\right)}$

$= (x^y)^{\left(\frac{x-y}{y^2}\right)} = x^{\left(\frac{x-y}{y}\right)} = x^{\left(\frac{x}{y}-1\right)}$.

104. $4^{x+y} = 1 = 4^0 \Leftrightarrow x + y = 0 \quad \ldots (i)$

$4^{x-y} = 4 = 4^1 \Rightarrow x - y = 1 \quad \ldots (ii)$

Adding (*i*) and (*ii*), we get : $2x = 1$ or $x = \frac{1}{2}$.

Putting $x = \frac{1}{2}$ in (*i*), we get : $y = -\frac{1}{2}$.

105. $2^{2x-1} + 4^x = 2^{x-\frac{1}{2}} + 2^{x+\frac{1}{2}} \Leftrightarrow 2^{2x-1} + 2^{2x} = 2^{x-\frac{1}{2}} + 2^{x+\frac{1}{2}}$

$\Leftrightarrow \quad 2^{(2x-1)}(1+2) = 2^{\left(x-\frac{1}{2}\right)}(1+2)$

$\Leftrightarrow \quad 2^{(2x-1)} = 2^{\left(x-\frac{1}{2}\right)} \Leftrightarrow 2x - 1 = x - \frac{1}{2} \Leftrightarrow x = \frac{1}{2}$.

106. $3^{2x-y} = 3^{x+y} = \sqrt{3^3} = 3^{\frac{3}{2}} \Leftrightarrow 2x - y = \frac{3}{2}$ and $x + y = \frac{3}{2}$

$\Leftrightarrow \quad 3x = \frac{3}{2} + \frac{3}{2} = 3 \Leftrightarrow x = 1$.

$\therefore \quad y = \left(\frac{3}{2} - 1\right) = \frac{1}{2}$.

107. Let $3^x = 5^y = 45^z = k$. Then, $3 = k^{\frac{1}{x}}, 5 = k^{\frac{1}{y}}, 45 = k^{\frac{1}{z}}$.

$45 = 3^2 \times 5$

$\Leftrightarrow \quad k^{\frac{1}{z}} = \left(k^{\frac{1}{x}}\right)^2 \cdot \left(k^{\frac{1}{y}}\right) = k^{\frac{2}{x}} \cdot k^{\frac{1}{y}} = k^{\left(\frac{2}{x}+\frac{1}{y}\right)}$

$\Leftrightarrow \quad \frac{1}{z} = \frac{2}{x} + \frac{1}{y} \Leftrightarrow \frac{2}{x} = \frac{1}{z} - \frac{1}{y}$.

108. $2^x = 8^{y+1} \Leftrightarrow 2^x = (2^3)^{y+1} = 2^{(3y+3)}$

$\Leftrightarrow x = 3y + 3 \Leftrightarrow x - 3y = 3 \quad \ldots (i)$

$9^y = 3^{x-9} \Leftrightarrow (3^2)^y = 3^{x-9}$

$\Leftrightarrow 2y = x - 9 \Leftrightarrow x - 2y = 9 \quad \ldots (ii)$

Subtracting (*i*) from (*ii*), we get: $y = 6$. Putting $y = 6$ (*i*), we get $x = 21$.

$\therefore \quad x + y = 21 + 6 = 27$.

109. $2^{0.7x} \cdot 3^{-1.25y} = \frac{8\sqrt{6}}{27}$

$\Leftrightarrow \quad \frac{2^{0.7x}}{3^{1.25y}} = \frac{2^3 \cdot 2^{\frac{1}{2}} \cdot 3^{\frac{1}{2}}}{3^3} = \frac{2^{\left(3+\frac{1}{2}\right)}}{3^{\left(3-\frac{1}{2}\right)}} = \frac{2^{\frac{7}{2}}}{3^{\frac{5}{2}}} = \frac{2^{3.5}}{3^{2.5}}$.

$\therefore \quad 0.7x = 3.5 \Rightarrow x = \frac{3.5}{0.7} = 5$ and $1.25y = 2.5$

$\Rightarrow \quad y = \frac{2.5}{1.25} = 2$.

110. $r = (2a)^{2b} = 2^{2b} \times a^{2b} = (2^2)^b \times (a^b)^2 = 4^b \times (a^b)^2$.

Also, $r = a^b \times x^b$.

$\therefore \quad a^b \times x^b = 4^b \times (a^b)^2 \Leftrightarrow x^b = 4^b \times a^b = (4a)^b \Leftrightarrow x = 4a$.

111. L.C.M. of 2, 3, 4, 6 is 12.

$\sqrt{2} = 2^{\frac{1}{2}} = 2^{\left(\frac{1}{2}\times\frac{6}{6}\right)} = 2^{\frac{6}{12}} = (2^6)^{\frac{1}{12}} = (64)^{\frac{1}{12}} = \sqrt[12]{64}$.

$\sqrt[3]{3} = 3^{\frac{1}{3}} = 3^{\left(\frac{1}{3}\times\frac{4}{4}\right)} = 3^{\frac{4}{12}} = (3^4)^{\frac{1}{12}} = (81)^{\frac{1}{12}} = \sqrt[12]{81}$.

$\sqrt[4]{4}=4^{\frac{1}{4}}=4^{\left(\frac{1}{4}\times\frac{3}{3}\right)}=4^{\frac{3}{12}}=(4^3)^{\frac{1}{12}}=(64)^{\frac{1}{12}}=\sqrt[12]{64}.$

$\sqrt[6]{6}=6^{\frac{1}{6}}=6^{\left(\frac{1}{6}\times\frac{2}{2}\right)}=6^{\frac{2}{12}}=(6^2)^{\frac{1}{12}}=(36)^{\frac{1}{12}}=\sqrt[12]{36}.$

Clearly, $\sqrt[12]{81}$ *i.e.*, $\sqrt[3]{3}$ is the greatest.

112. L.C.M of 2, 3, 4, 6 is 12.

$\sqrt{2}=2^{\frac{1}{2}}=2^{\left(\frac{1}{2}\times\frac{6}{6}\right)}=2^{\frac{6}{12}}=(2^6)^{\frac{1}{12}}=(64)^{\frac{1}{12}}=\sqrt[12]{64}.$

$\sqrt[6]{3}=3^{\frac{1}{6}}=3^{\left(\frac{1}{6}\times\frac{2}{2}\right)}=3^{\frac{2}{12}}=(3^2)^{\frac{1}{12}}=(9)^{\frac{1}{12}}=\sqrt[12]{9}.$

$\sqrt[3]{4}=4^{\frac{1}{3}}=4^{\left(\frac{1}{3}\times\frac{4}{4}\right)}=4^{\frac{4}{12}}=(4^4)^{\frac{1}{12}}=(256)^{\frac{1}{12}}=\sqrt[12]{256}.$

$\sqrt[4]{5}=5^{\frac{1}{4}}=5^{\left(\frac{1}{4}\times\frac{3}{3}\right)}=5^{\frac{3}{12}}=(5^3)^{\frac{1}{12}}=(125)^{\frac{1}{12}}=\sqrt[12]{125}.$

Clearly, $\sqrt[12]{256}$ *i.e.*, $\sqrt[3]{4}$ is the greatest.

113. ....

114. $x=5+2\sqrt{6}=3+2+2\sqrt{6}=(\sqrt{3})^2+(\sqrt{2})^2+2\times\sqrt{3}\times\sqrt{2}$

$=(\sqrt{3}+\sqrt{2})^2.$

Also, $(x-1)=4+2\sqrt{6}=2(2+\sqrt{6})=2\sqrt{2}(\sqrt{2}+\sqrt{3}).$

$\therefore\quad \frac{(x-1)}{\sqrt{x}}=\frac{2\sqrt{2}(\sqrt{3}+\sqrt{2})}{(\sqrt{3}+\sqrt{2})}=2\sqrt{2}.$

115. $x^{\frac{1}{3}}+y^{\frac{1}{3}}=z^{\frac{1}{3}}\Rightarrow\left(x^{\frac{1}{3}}+y^{\frac{1}{3}}\right)^3=\left(z^{\frac{1}{3}}\right)^3$

$\Rightarrow\quad x+y+3x^{\frac{1}{3}}y^{\frac{1}{3}}\left(x^{\frac{1}{3}}+y^{\frac{1}{3}}\right)=z.$

$\Rightarrow\quad x+y+3x^{\frac{1}{3}}y^{\frac{1}{3}}z^{\frac{1}{3}}=z$

$\Rightarrow\quad x+y-z=-3x^{\frac{1}{3}}y^{\frac{1}{3}}z^{\frac{1}{3}}$

$\Rightarrow\quad (x+y-z)^3=\left(-3x^{\frac{1}{3}}y^{\frac{1}{3}}z^{\frac{1}{3}}\right)^3$

$\Rightarrow\quad (x+y-z)^3=-27xyz\Rightarrow(x+y-z)^3+27xyz=0.$

116. $x=2+2^{\frac{2}{3}}+2^{\frac{1}{3}}\Rightarrow(x-2)=2^{\frac{2}{3}}+2^{\frac{1}{3}}$

$\Rightarrow\quad (x-2)^3=\left(2^{\frac{2}{3}}+2^{\frac{1}{3}}\right)^3$

$=2^2+2+3.2^{\frac{2}{3}}\cdot2^{\frac{1}{3}}\left(2^{\frac{2}{3}}+2^{\frac{1}{3}}\right)$

$\Rightarrow\quad (x-2)^3=6+6(x-2)=6+6x-12$

$\Rightarrow\quad (x-2)^3=6x-6\Rightarrow x^3-8-6x(x-2)=6x-6$

$\Rightarrow\quad x^3-8-6x^2+12x=6x-6\Rightarrow x^3-6x^2+6x=2.$

117. Given expression $(-2)^5\times(2)^{-5}\times(3)^3$

$\frac{(-2)^5}{2^5}\times(3)^3\qquad\left\{\because a^{-m}=\frac{1}{a^m}\right\}$

$\frac{(-1)^5(2)^5\times(3)^3}{(2^5)}=(-3)^3=-27$

118. Expression $=\frac{(10)^{100}}{(5)^{75}}$

$=\frac{(2\times5)^{100}}{(5)^{75}}=\frac{(2)^{100}\times(5)^{100}}{(5)^{75}}=2^{100}\times\frac{5^{100}}{5^{75}}=2^{100}\times5^{(100-75)}$

$\left\{\because\frac{a^m}{a^n}=a^{m-n}\right\}$

$=2^{100}\times5^{25}$

$=2^{25}\times5^{25}\times2^{75}\qquad\{\because a^m\times a^n=a^{m+n}\}$

$=(10)^{25}\times2^{75}\qquad\{\because a^m\times b^m=ab^m\}$

119. Expression $=\sqrt{\sqrt{2}\times\sqrt{3}}$

$=\left(\sqrt{2}\times\sqrt{3}\right)^{\frac{1}{2}}=\left(2^{\frac{1}{2}}\times3^{\frac{1}{2}}\right)^{\frac{1}{2}}\qquad\{\because a^m\times b^m=ab^m\}$

$=(6)^{\frac{1}{2}\times\frac{1}{2}}=(6)^{\frac{1}{4}}\qquad\left\{\because\left(a^m\right)^n=a^{mn}\right\}$

120. $21^?\times21^{6.5}=21^{12.4}\qquad\{\because a^m\times a^n=a^{m+n}\}$

$\Rightarrow 21^{?+6.5}=21^{12.4}$

$\Rightarrow ?+6.5=12.4$

$\Rightarrow ?=12.4-6.5=5.9$

121. $\frac{5.4\div3\times16\div2}{18\div5\times6\div3}$

$=\frac{\frac{5.4}{3}\times\frac{16}{2}}{\frac{18}{5}\times\frac{6}{3}}=\frac{1.8\times8}{3.6\times2}=2$

122. $\left(32\times10^{-5}\right)^2\times64\div\left(2^{16}\times10^{-4}\right)=10^?$

$\Rightarrow\left(2^5\times10^{-5}\right)^2\times2^6\div\left(2^{16}\times10^{-4}\right)=10^?\qquad\left\{\because\left(a^m\right)^n=a^{mn}\right\}$

$\Rightarrow\frac{2^{10}\times10^{-10}\times2^6}{2^{16}\times10^{-4}}=10^?\qquad\{\because a^m\times a^n=a^{m+n}\}$

$\Rightarrow\frac{2^{16}\times10^4}{2^{16}\times10^{10}}=10^?\qquad\left\{\because a^{-m}=\frac{1}{a^m}\right\}$

$\Rightarrow 10^{4-10}=10^?$

$\Rightarrow 10^{-6}=10^?$

$\Rightarrow ?=-6$

10 Logarithms

IMPORTANT FACTS AND FORMULAE

I. Logarithm: If a is a positive real number, other than 1 and $a^m = x$, then we write: $m = \log_a x$ and we say that the value of log x to the base a is m.

Example:

(*i*) $10^3 = 1000 \Rightarrow \log_{10} 1000 = 3$ (*ii*) $3^4 = 81 \Rightarrow \log_3 81 = 4$

(*ii*) $2^{-3} = \frac{1}{8} \Rightarrow \log_2 \frac{1}{8} = -3$ (*iv*) $(.1)^2 = .01 \Rightarrow \log_{(.1)} \cdot 01 = 2$

II. Properties of Logarithms:

1. $\log_a (xy) = \log_a x + \log_a y$
2. $\log_a \left(\frac{x}{y}\right) = \log_a x - \log_a y$
3. $\log_x x = 1$
4. $\log_a 1 = 0$
5. $\log_a (x^p) = p (\log_a x)$
6. $\log_a x = \frac{1}{\log_x a}$
7. $\log_a x = \frac{\log_b x}{\log_b a} = \frac{\log x}{\log a}$
8. $a^{\log_a x} = x$
9. $x^{\log_a y} = y^{\log_a x}$
10. $\log_{a^q} x^p = \frac{p}{q} \log_a x$

Remember: When base is not mentioned, it is taken as 10.

III. Common Logarithms: Logarithms to the base 10 are known as common logarithms.

IV. The logarithm of a number contains two parts, namely *characteristic* and *mantissa*.

Characteristic: The integral part of the logarithm of a number is called its ***characteristic.***

Case I : When the number is greater than 1.

In this case, the characteristic is one less than the number of digits to the left of the decimal point in the given number.

Case II : When the number is less than 1.

In this case, the characteristic is one more than the number of zeros between the decimal point and the first significant digit of the number and it is negative.

Instead of – 1, – 2, etc. we write, $\bar{1}$ (one bar), $\bar{2}$ (two bar), etc.

Example:

Number	*Characteristic*	*Number*	*Characteristic*
348.25	2	0.6173	$\bar{1}$
46.583	1	0.03125	$\bar{2}$
9.2193	0	0.00125	$\bar{3}$

Mantissa: The decimal part of the logarithm of a number is known as its ***mantissa.***

For mantissa, we look through log table.

SOLVED EXAMPLES

Ex. 1. ***Evaluate : (i)*** $\log_3 27$ ***(ii)*** $\log_7 \left(\frac{1}{343}\right)$ ***(iii)*** $\log_{100} (0.01)$ ***(iv)*** $\log_8 128$

Sol. (*i*) $\log_3 27 = \log_3 3^3 = 3 \log_3 3 = 3.$ $[\because \log_3 3 = 1]$

(ii) $\log_7\left(\frac{1}{343}\right) = \log_7\left(\frac{1}{7^3}\right) = \log_7 7^{-3} = -3\log_7 7 = -3.$

(iii) Let $\log_{100}(0.01) = \log_{100}\left(\frac{1}{100}\right) = \log_{100}(100)^{-1} = -1\log_{100}100 = -1.$

(iv) $\log_8 128 = \log_{2^3}(2^7) = \frac{7}{3}\log_2 2 = \frac{7}{3}.$

Ex. 2. ***Evaluate: (i) $\log_7 1 = 0$ (ii) $\log_{34} 34$ (iii) $36^{\log 6 4}$***

Sol. (i) We know that $\log_a 1 = 0$, so $\log_7 1 = 0$.

(ii) We know that $\log_a a = 1$, so $\log_{34} 34 = 1$.

(iii) We know that $a^{\log a\, x} = x$.

Now, $36^{\log 6 4} = 6^{2(\log 6\, 4)} = 6^{\log 6\,(4^2)} = 6^{\log 6 16} = 16.$

Ex. 3. ***If $\log_{\sqrt{8}} x = 3\frac{1}{3}$, find the value of x.***

Sol. $\log_{\sqrt{8}} x = \frac{10}{3} \Leftrightarrow x = (\sqrt{8})^{10/3} = (2^{3/2})^{10/3} = 2^{\left(\frac{3}{2}\times\frac{10}{3}\right)} = 2^5 = 32.$

Ex. 4. ***Evaluate: (i) $\log_5 3 \times \log_{27} 25$ (ii) $\log_9 27 - \log_{27} 9$***

Sol. (i) $\log_5 3 \times \log_{27} 25 = \frac{\log 3}{\log 5} \times \frac{\log 25}{\log 27} = \frac{\log 3}{\log 5} \times \frac{\log(5^2)}{\log(3^3)} = \frac{\log 3}{\log 5} \times \frac{2\log 5}{3\log 3} = \frac{2}{3}.$

(ii) Let $\log_9 27 = n$. Then, $9^n = 27 \Leftrightarrow 3^{2n} = 3^3 \Leftrightarrow 2n = 3 \Leftrightarrow n = \frac{3}{2}.$

Again, let $\log_{27} 9 = m$.

Then, $27^m = 9 \Leftrightarrow 3^{3m} = 3^2 \Leftrightarrow 3m = 2 \Leftrightarrow m = \frac{2}{3}.$

$\therefore \quad \log_9 27 - \log_{27} 9 = (n - m) = \left(\frac{3}{2} - \frac{2}{3}\right) = \frac{5}{6}.$

Ex. 5. ***Simplify: $\left(\log\frac{75}{16} - 2\log\frac{5}{9} + \log\frac{32}{243}\right)$***

Sol. $\log\frac{75}{16} - 2\log\frac{5}{9} + \log\frac{32}{243} = \log\frac{75}{16} - \log\left(\frac{5}{9}\right)^2 + \log\frac{32}{243}$

$= \log\frac{75}{16} - \log\frac{25}{81} + \log\frac{32}{243} = \log\left(\frac{75}{16}\times\frac{32}{243}\times\frac{81}{25}\right) = \log 2.$

Ex. 6. ***If $\log_2[\log_3(\log_2 x)] = 1$, find the value of x.*** **(M.B.A., 2005)**

Sol. $\log_2[\log_3(\log_2 x)] = 1 \Rightarrow \log_3(\log_2 x) = 2^1 = 2 \Rightarrow \log_2 x = 3^2 = 9.$

Ex. 7. ***If $\log_{10}(x^2 - 6x + 45) = 2$, find the value of x.*** **(R.R.B., 2006)**

Sol. $\log 10\,(x^2 - 6x + 45) = 2 \Rightarrow x^2 - 6x + 45 = 10^2 = 100$

$\Rightarrow x^2 - 6x - 55 = 0 \Rightarrow x^2 - 11x + 5x - 55 = 0$

$\Rightarrow x(x - 11) + 5(x - 11) = 0 \Rightarrow (x - 11)(x + 5) = 0$

$\Rightarrow x = 11$ or $x = -5$.

Ex. 8. ***Find the value of x which satisfies the relation $\log_{10} 3 + \log_{10}(4x + 1) = \log_{10}(x + 1) + 1$*** **(M.B.A., 2002)**

Sol. $\log_{10} 3 + \log_{10}(4x + 1) = \log_{10}(x + 1) + 1$

$\Leftrightarrow \log_{10} 3 + \log_{10}(4x + 1) = \log_{10}(x + 1) + \log_{10} 10$

$\Leftrightarrow \log_{10}[3(4x + 1)] = \log_{10}[10(x + 1)]$

$\Leftrightarrow 3(4x + 1) = 10(x + 1) \Leftrightarrow 12x + 3 = 10x + 10 \Leftrightarrow 2x = 7 \Leftrightarrow x = \frac{7}{2}.$

Ex. 9. ***Simplify: $\left[\frac{1}{\log_{xy}(xyz)} + \frac{1}{\log_{yz}(xyz)} + \frac{1}{\log_{zx}(xyz)}\right]$*** **(M.A.T., 2005)**

Sol. Given expression $= \log_{xyz}(xy) + \log_{xyz}(yz) + \log_{xyz}(zx)$

$= \log_{xyz}(xy \times yz \times zx) = \log_{xyz}(xyz)^2$

$= 2\log_{xyz}(xyz) = 2 \times 1 = 2$ $\left[\because \log_a x = \dfrac{1}{\log_x a}\right]$

Ex. 10. ***If*** $\log_a b = \dfrac{1}{2}, \log_b c = \dfrac{1}{3}$ ***and*** $\log_c a = \dfrac{k}{5}$, ***find the value of k.*** (M.A.T., 2006)

Sol. $\log_a b = \dfrac{1}{2}, \log_b c = \dfrac{1}{3}, \log_c a = \dfrac{k}{5} \Rightarrow \dfrac{\log b}{\log a} = \dfrac{1}{2}, \dfrac{\log c}{\log b} = \dfrac{1}{3}, \dfrac{\log a}{\log c} = \dfrac{k}{5}$

$\Rightarrow \dfrac{\log b}{\log a} \times \dfrac{\log c}{\log b} \times \dfrac{\log a}{\log c} = \dfrac{1}{2} \times \dfrac{1}{3} \times \dfrac{k}{5} \Rightarrow \dfrac{k}{30} = 1 \Rightarrow k = 30.$

Ex. 11. ***If*** $\log_{10} 2 = 0.30103$, ***find the value of*** $\log_{10} 50$.

Sol. $\log_{10} 50 = \log_{10}\left(\dfrac{100}{2}\right) = \log_{10} 100 - \log_{10} 2 = 2 - 0.30103 = 1.69897.$

Ex. 12. ***If*** $\log 2 = 0.3010$ ***and*** $\log 3 = 0.4771$, ***find the values of :***

(*i*) *log 25* (*ii*) *log 4.5*

Sol. (*i*) $\log 25 = \log\left(\dfrac{100}{4}\right) = \log 100 - \log 4 = 2 - 2\log 2 = (2 - 2 \times 0.3010) = 1.398.$

(*ii*) $\log 4.5 = \log\left(\dfrac{9}{2}\right) = \log 9 - \log 2 = 2\log 3 - \log 2$

$= (2 \times 0.4771 - 0.3010) = 0.6532$

Ex. 13. ***If*** $\log 2 = 0.30103$, ***find the number of digits in*** 2^{56}. (M.A.T. 2005)

Sol. $\log(2^{56}) = 56\log 2 = (56 \times 0.30103) = 16.85768.$

Its characteristic is 16. Hence, the number of digits in 2^{56} is 17.

EXERCISE

(OBJECTIVE TYPE QUESTIONS)

Directions: ***Mark (✓) against the correct answer:***

1. The value of $\log_2 16$ is
(*a*) $\dfrac{1}{8}$ (*b*) 4
(*c*) 8 (*d*) 16

2. The value of $\log_{343} 7$ is
(*a*) $\dfrac{1}{3}$ (*b*) -3
(*c*) $-\dfrac{1}{3}$ (*d*) 3

3. The value of $\log_5 \dfrac{(125)(625)}{25}$ is equal to (M.B.A., 2011)
(*a*) 725 (*b*) 5
(*c*) 3125 (*d*) 6

4. The value of $\log_{\sqrt{2}} 32$ is
(*a*) $\dfrac{5}{2}$ (*b*) 5
(*c*) 10 (*d*) $\dfrac{1}{10}$

5. Determine the value of $\log_{3\sqrt{2}}\left(\dfrac{1}{18}\right)$. (M.A.T., 2005)
(*a*) 2 (*b*) -2
(*c*) $\sqrt{2}$ (*d*) $\sqrt{3}$

6. The value of $\log_{10}(.0001)$ is
(*a*) $\dfrac{1}{4}$ (*b*) $-\dfrac{1}{4}$
(*c*) -4 (*d*) 4

7. The value of $\log_{.01}(1000)$ is
(*a*) $\dfrac{1}{3}$ (*b*) $-\dfrac{1}{3}$
(*c*) $\dfrac{3}{2}$ (*d*) $-\dfrac{3}{2}$

8. What is the value of $[\log_{10}(5\log_{10} 100)]^2$? (M.B.A., 2010)
(*a*) 1 (*b*) 2
(*c*) 10 (*d*) 25

9. The logarithm of 0.0625 to the base 2 is
(*a*) -4 (*b*) -2
(*c*) 0.25 (*d*) 0.5

10. The logarithm of 0.00001 to the base 0.01 is equal to
(*a*) $-\dfrac{5}{2}$ (*b*) $\dfrac{5}{2}$
(*c*) 3 (*d*) 5

11. If $\log_3 x = -2$, then x is equal to
(a) -9 (b) -6
(c) -8 (d) $\frac{1}{9}$

12. If $\log_8 x = \frac{2}{3}$, then the value of x is
(a) $\frac{3}{4}$ (b) $\frac{4}{3}$
(c) 3 (d) 4

13. If $\log_8 p = 25$ and $\log_2 q = 5$, then
(a) $p = q^{15}$ (b) $p^2 = q^3$
(c) $p = q^5$ (d) $p^3 = q$

14. If $\log_x \left(\frac{9}{16}\right) = -\frac{1}{2}$, then x is equal to
(a) $-\frac{3}{4}$ (b) $\frac{3}{4}$
(c) $\frac{81}{256}$ (d) $\frac{256}{81}$

15. If $\log_x 4 = 0.4$, then the value of x is
(a) 1 (b) 4
(c) 16 (d) 32

16. If $\log_{10000} x = -\frac{1}{4}$, then x is equal to (N.M.A.T., 2006)
(a) $\frac{1}{10}$ (b) $\frac{1}{100}$
(c) $\frac{1}{1000}$ (d) $\frac{1}{10000}$

17. If $\log_x 4 = \frac{1}{4}$, then x is equal to
(a) 16 (b) 64
(c) 128 (d) 256

18. If $\log_x (0.1) = -\frac{1}{3}$, then the value of x is
(a) 10 (b) 100
(c) 1000 (d) $\frac{1}{1000}$

19. If $\log_{32} x = 0.8$, then x is equal to
(a) 25.6 (b) 16
(c) 10 (d) 12.8

20. If $\log_x y = 100$ and $\log_2 x = 10$, then the value of y is
(a) 2^{10} (b) 2^{100}
(c) 2^{1000} (d) 2^{10000}

21. The value of $\log_{(-1/3)} 81$ is equal to
(a) -27 (b) -4
(c) 4 (d) 27

22. The value of $\log_{2\sqrt{3}} (1728)$ is
(a) 3 (b) 5
(c) 6 (d) 9

23. $\frac{\log \sqrt{8}}{\log 8}$ is equal to (M.B.A. 2004, I.A.F., 2002)
(a) $\frac{1}{\sqrt{8}}$ (b) $\frac{1}{4}$
(c) $\frac{1}{2}$ (d) $\frac{1}{8}$

24. Which of the following statements is not correct ? (M.B.A., 2003)
(a) $\log_{10} 10 = 1$
(b) $\log (2 + 3) = \log (2 \times 3)$
(c) $\log_{10} 1 = 0$
(d) $\log (1 + 2 + 3) = \log 1 + \log 2 + \log 3$

25. The value of $\frac{6 \log_{10} 1000}{3 \log_{10} 100}$ is equal to (C.D.S., 2002)
(a) 0 (b) 1
(c) 2 (d) 3

26. $\log_{10} (10 \times 10^2 \times 10^3 \times \ldots\ldots \times 10^9)$ is
(a) 10 (b) 20
(c) 45 (d) 55

27. The value of $\log_2 (\log_5 625)$ is :
(a) 2 (b) 5
(c) 10 (d) 15

28. If $\log_2 [\log_3 (\log_2 x)] = 1$, then x is equal to : (M.B.A., 2007)
(a) 0 (b) 12
(c) 128 (d) 512

29. $\log_{10} \log_{10} \log_{10} (10^{1010})$ is equal to
(a) 0 (b) 1
(c) 10 (d) 100

30. The value of $\log_2 \log_2 \log_3 \log_3 27^3$ is
(a) 0 (b) 1
(c) 2 (d) 3

31. The value of $\log_2 [\log_2 \{\log_4 (\log_4 256^4)\}]$ is
(a) 0 (b) 1
(c) 2 (d) 4

32. If $a^x = b^y$, then
(a) $\log \frac{a}{b} = \frac{x}{y}$ (b) $\frac{\log a}{\log b} = \frac{x}{y}$
(c) $\frac{\log a}{\log b} = \frac{y}{x}$ (d) None of these

33. log 360 is equal to
(a) 2 log 2 + 3 log 3
(b) 3 log 2 + 2 log 3
(c) 3 log 2 + 2 log 3 – log 5
(d) 3 log 2 + 2 log 3 + log 5

34. $\log_{10} \frac{26}{51} + \log_{10} \frac{119}{91} - \log_{10} \frac{13}{32} - \log_{10} \frac{64}{39}$ is equal to
(a) 0 (b) 1
(c) 2 (d) 3

35. The value of $\left(\frac{1}{3}\log_{10} 125 - 2\log_{10} 4 + \log_{10} 32\right)$ is

(a) 0 (b) $\frac{4}{5}$
(c) 1 (d) 2

36. The value of $\log_{10} 1\frac{1}{2} + \log_{10} 1\frac{1}{3} + \ldots$ up to 198 terms is equal to

(a) 0 (b) 2
(c) 10 (d) 100

37. What is the value of the following expression?

$\log\left(\frac{9}{14}\right) - \log\left(\frac{15}{16}\right) + \log\left(\frac{35}{24}\right)$ (I.I.F.T., 2005)

(a) 0 (b) 1
(c) 2 (d) 3

38. $2\log_{10} 5 + \log_{10} 8 - \frac{1}{2}\log_{10} 4 = ?$ (M.B.A., 2002)

(a) 2 (b) 4
(c) $2 + 2\log_{10} 2$ (d) $4 - 4\log_{10} 2$

39. The value of $\log_{10} 2 + 16\log_{10}\frac{16}{15} + 12\log_{10}\frac{25}{24} + 7\log_{10}\frac{81}{80}$ is

(a) 0 (b) 1
(c) 2 (d) 3

40. If $\log_a (ab) = x$, then $\log_b (ab)$ is (M.A.T., 2002)

(a) $\frac{1}{x}$ (b) $\frac{x}{x+1}$
(c) $\frac{x}{1-x}$ (d) $\frac{x}{x-1}$

41. If $\log_a m = x$, then $\log_{\frac{1}{a}}\left(\frac{1}{m}\right)$ equals

(a) $-\frac{1}{x}$ (b) $\frac{1}{x}$
(c) $-x$ (d) x

42. If $\log_{10} 2 = a$ and $\log_{10} 3 = b$, then $\log_5 12$ equals (M.B.A., 2010)

(a) $\frac{a+b}{1+a}$ (b) $\frac{2a+b}{1+a}$
(c) $\frac{a+2b}{1+a}$ (d) $\frac{2a+b}{1-a}$

43. If $\log 2 = x$, $\log 3 = y$ and $\log 7 = z$, then the value of $\log (4.\sqrt[3]{63})$ is

(a) $2x + \frac{2}{3}y - \frac{1}{3}z$ (b) $2x + \frac{2}{3}y + \frac{1}{3}z$
(c) $2x - \frac{2}{3}y + \frac{1}{3}z$ (d) $-2x + \frac{2}{3}y + \frac{1}{3}z$

44. If $\log_4 x + \log_2 x = 6$, then x is equal to

(a) 2 (b) 4
(c) 8 (d) 16

45. If $\log_{10} (x^2 - 6x + 10) = 0$, then the value of x is

(a) 1 (b) 2
(c) 3 (d) 4

46. If $\log_{10} x + \log_{10} y = 3$ and $\log_{10} x - \log_{10} y = 1$, then x and y are respectively

(a) 10 and 100 (b) 100 and 10
(c) 1000 and 100 (d) 100 and 1000

47. If $\log_{10} x + \log_{10} 5 = 2$, then x equals

(a) 15 (b) 20
(c) 25 (d) 100

48. If $\log_8 x + \log_8 \frac{1}{6} = \frac{1}{3}$, then the value of x is

(a) 12 (b) 16
(c) 18 (d) 24

49. If $\log_{10} 125 + \log_{10} 8 = x$, then x is equal to (M.B.A., 2005)

(a) $\frac{1}{3}$ (b) .064
(c) -3 (d) 3

50. The value of $(\log_9 27 + \log_8 32)$ is

(a) $\frac{7}{2}$ (b) $\frac{19}{6}$
(c) 4 (d) 7

51. $(\log_5 3) \times (\log_3 625)$ equals

(a) 1 (b) 2
(c) 3 (d) 4

52. $(\log_5 5)(\log_4 9)(\log_3 2)$ is equal to

(a) 1 (b) $\frac{3}{2}$
(c) 2 (d) 5

53. If $\log_{12} 27 = a$, then $\log_6 16$ is

(a) $\frac{3-a}{4(3+a)}$ (b) $\frac{3+a}{4(3-a)}$
(c) $\frac{4(3+a)}{(3-a)}$ (d) $\frac{4(3-a)}{(3+a)}$

54. If $\log_{10} 5 + \log_{10} (5x + 1) = \log_{10} (x + 5) + 1$, then x is equal to

(a) 1 (b) 3
(c) 5 (d) 10

55. If $\log_5 (x^2 + x) - \log_5 (x + 1) = 2$, then the value of x is (M.B.A., 2007)

(a) 5 (b) 10
(c) 25 (d) 32

56. $\frac{1}{2}(\log x + \log y)$ will equal $\log\left(\frac{x+y}{2}\right)$ if (R.R.B., 2005)

(a) $y = 0$ (b) $x = \sqrt{y}$

(c) $x = y$ (d) $x = \frac{y}{2}$

57. The value of $\left(\frac{1}{\log_3 60} + \frac{1}{\log_4 60} + \frac{1}{\log_5 60}\right)$ is

(a) 0 (b) 1

(c) 5 (d) 60

58. The value of $(\log_3 4)(\log_4 5)(\log_5 6)(\log_6 7)(\log_7 8)(\log_8 9)$ is

(a) 2 (b) 7

(c) 8 (d) 33

59. The value of $16^{\log_4 5}$ is

(a) $\frac{5}{64}$ (b) 5

(c) 16 (d) 25

60. If $\log x + \log y = \log (x + y)$, then

(a) $x = y$ (b) $xy = 1$

(c) $y = \frac{x-1}{x}$ (d) $y = \frac{x}{x-1}$

61. If $\log\frac{a}{b} + \log\frac{b}{a} = \log (a + b)$, then (M.B.A., 2007)

(a) $a + b = 1$ (b) $a - b = 1$

(c) $a = b$ (d) $a^2 - b^2 = 1$

62. $\left[\log\left(\frac{a^2}{bc}\right) + \log\left(\frac{b^2}{ac}\right) + \log\left(\frac{c^2}{ab}\right)\right]$ is equal to (M.B.A., 2006)

(a) 0 (b) 1

(c) 2 (d) abc

63. $\frac{1}{\log_a b} \times \frac{1}{\log_b c} \times \frac{1}{\log_c a}$ is equal to (Hotel Management, 2010)

(a) $a + b + c$ (b) abc

(c) 0 (d) 1

64. $\left[\frac{1}{(\log_a bc)+1} + \frac{1}{(\log_b ca)+1} + \frac{1}{(\log_c ab)+1}\right]$ is equal to (I.I.F.T., 2005)

(a) 1 (b) $\frac{3}{2}$

(c) 2 (d) 3

65. The value of $\left[\frac{1}{\log_{(p/q)} x} + \frac{1}{\log_{(q/r)} x} + \frac{1}{\log_{(r/p)} x}\right]$ is

(a) 0 (b) 1

(c) 2 (d) 3

66. If $\log_{10} 7 = a$, then $\log_{10}\left(\frac{1}{70}\right)$ is equal to (C.D.S., 2003)

(a) $-(1 + a)$ (b) $(1 + a)^{-1}$

(c) $\frac{a}{10}$ (d) $\frac{1}{10a}$

67. If $a = b^x$, $b = c^y$ and $c = a^z$, then the value of xyz is equal to

(a) -1 (b) 0

(c) 1 (d) abc

68. If $\log x - 5 \log 3 = -2$, then x equals (M.B.A., 2011)

(a) 0.8 (b) 0.81

(c) 1.25 (d) 2.43

69. If $a = b^2 = c^3 = d^4$, then the value of $\log_a (abcd)$ would be (M.B.A., 2008)

(a) $\log_a 1 + \log_a 2 + \log_a 3 + \log_a 4$ (b) $\log_a 24$

(c) $1 + \frac{1}{2} + \frac{1}{3} + \frac{1}{4}$ (d) $1 + \frac{1}{2!} + \frac{1}{3!} + \frac{1}{4!}$

70. If $\log_3 x + \log_9 x^2 + \log_{27} x^3 = 9$, then x equals (M.B.A., 2010)

(a) 3 (b) 9

(c) 27 (d) None of these

71. If $\log_7 \log_5 (\sqrt{x+5} + \sqrt{x}) = 0$, what is the value of x? (M.B.A., 2009)

(a) 2 (b) 3

(c) 4 (d) 5

72. If $a = \log_8 225$ and $b = \log_2 15$, then a in terms of b, is (M.B.A., 2010)

(a) $\frac{b}{2}$ (b) $\frac{2b}{3}$

(c) b (d) $\frac{3b}{2}$

73. If $\log 27 = 1.431$, then the value of $\log 9$ is

(a) 0.934 (b) 0.945

(c) 0.954 (d) 0.958

74. If $\log_{10} 2 = 0.3010$, then $\log_2 10$ is equal to

(a) $\frac{699}{301}$ (b) $\frac{1000}{301}$

(c) 0.3010 (d) 0.6990

75. If $\log_{10} 2 = 0.3010$, the value of $\log_{10} 5$ is

(a) 0.3241 (b) 0.6911

(c) 0.6990 (d) 0.7525

76. If $\log_{10} 2 = 0.3010$, the value of $\log_{10} 80$ is

(a) 1.6020 (b) 1.9030

(c) 3.9030 (d) None of these

77. If log 3 = 0.477 and $(1000)^x = 3$, then x equals
(a) 0.0159 (b) 0.0477
(c) 0.159 (d) 10

78. If $\log_{10} 2 = 0.3010$, the value of $\log_{10} 25$ is
(a) 0.6020 (b) 1.2040
(c) 1.3980 (d) 1.5050

79. If $\log_{10}20 = 1.3010$ and $\log_{10}30 = 1.4771$, then $\log_{10}$ (60000) is equal to
(a) 0.7781 (b) 1.7781
(c) 2.7781 (d) 4.7781

80. If log 2 = 0.3010 and log 3 = 0.4771, the value of $\log_5 512$ is (M.A.T., 2002)
(a) 2.870 (b) 2.967
(c) 3.876 (d) 3.912

81. If $\log_{10}3 = 0.4771$ and $\log_{10}7 = 0.8451$, then the value of $\log_{10}\left(23\frac{1}{3}\right)$ is equal to
(a) 0.368 (b) 1.356
(c) 1.368 (d) 1.477

82. If $\log_{10} 2 = 0.3010$ and $\log_{10} 3 = 0.4771$, then the value of $\log_{10} 1.5$ is
(a) 0.1761 (b) 0.7116
(c) 0.7161 (d) 0.7611

83. If $\log_{10} 2 = 0.3010$ and $\log_{10} 7 = 0.8451$, then the value of $\log_{10} 2.8$ is
(a) 0.4471 (b) 1.4471
(c) 2.4471 (d) None of these

84. If $\log (0.57) = \bar{1}.756$, then the value of $\log 57 + \log (0.57)^3 + \log \sqrt{0.57}$ is
(a) 0.902 (b) $\bar{2}.146$
(c) 1.902 (d) $\bar{1}.146$

85. If the logarithm of a number is – 3.153, what are characteristic and mantisa? (M.B.A., 2009)
(a) Characteristic = – 4, mantissa = 0.847
(b) Characteristic = – 3, mantissa = – 0.153
(c) Characteristic = 4, mantissa = – 0.847
(d) Characteristic = 3, mantissa = – 0.153

86. If log 2 = 0.30103, the number of digits in 2^{64} is
(a) 18 (b) 19
(c) 20 (d) 21

87. If log 2 = 0.30103, the number of digits in 4^{50} is (Hotel Management, 2009)
(a) 30 (b) 31
(c) 100 (d) 200

88. If log 2 = 0.30103, then the number of digits in 5^{20} is
(a) 14 (b) 16
(c) 18 (d) 25

89. If log 2 = 0.30103, log 3 = 0.47712, then the number of digits in 6^{20} is
(a) 15 (b) 16
(c) 17 (d) 18

90. The number of digits in $4^9 \times 5^{17}$, when expressed in usual form, is (A.A.O. Exam, 2009)
(a) 16 (b) 17
(c) 18 (d) 19

91. If log 3 log $(3^x - 2)$ and log $(3^x + 4)$ are in arithmetic progression, then x is equal to (IIFT, 2012)
(a) 8/3 (b) $\log 3^8$
(c) $\log 2^3$ (d) 8

92. If $\log_{10}a = p$ and $\log_{10}b = q$, then what is $\log_{10} (a^p b^q)$ equal to ? (CDS, 2012)
(a) $p^2 + q^2$ (b) $p^2 - q^2$
(c) p^2q^2 (d) $\frac{p^2}{q^2}$

ANSWERS

1. (b)	2. (a)	3. (b)	4. (c)	5. (b)	6. (c)	7. (d)	8. (a)	9. (a)	10. (b)
11. (d)	12. (d)	13. (a)	14. (d)	15. (d)	16. (a)	17. (d)	18. (c)	19. (b)	20. (c)
21. (b)	22. (c)	23. (c)	24. (b)	25. (d)	26. (c)	27. (a)	28. (d)	29. (b)	30. (a)
31. (a)	32. (c)	33. (d)	34. (a)	35. (c)	36. (b)	37. (a)	38. (a)	39. (b)	40. (d)
41. (d)	42. (d)	43. (b)	44. (d)	45. (c)	46. (b)	47. (b)	48. (a)	49. (d)	50. (b)
51. (d)	52. (a)	53. (d)	54. (b)	55. (c)	56. (c)	57. (b)	58. (a)	59. (d)	60. (d)
61. (a)	62. (a)	63. (d)	64. (a)	65. (a)	66. (a)	67. (c)	68. (d)	69. (c)	70. (c)
71. (c)	72. (b)	73. (c)	74. (b)	75. (c)	76. (b)	77. (c)	78. (c)	79. (d)	80. (c)
81. (c)	82. (a)	83. (a)	84. (a)	85. (a)	86. (c)	87. (b)	88. (a)	89. (b)	90. (c)
91. (c)	92. (a)								

SOLUTIONS

1. $\log_2 16 = \log_2 2^4 = 4 \log_2 2 = 4.$

2. $\log_{343} 7 = \log_{7^3} 7 = \frac{1}{3}\log_7 7 = \frac{1}{3}.$

3. $\log_5\left(\frac{125\times 625}{25}\right) = \log_5\left(\frac{5^3\times 5^4}{5^2}\right) = \log_5 5^5 = 5\log_5 5 = 5.$

4. $\log_{\sqrt{2}} 32 = \log_{2^{1/2}} 2^5 = \frac{5}{\left(\frac{1}{2}\right)}\log_2 2 = 5\times 2 = 10.$

5. $\log_{3\sqrt{2}}\left(\frac{1}{18}\right) = \log_{3\sqrt{2}}\left[\frac{1}{(3\sqrt{2})^2}\right] = \log_{3\sqrt{2}}(3\sqrt{2})^{-2}$

$= (-2)\log_{3\sqrt{2}} 3\sqrt{2} = -2.$

6. $\log_{10}(.0001) = \log_{10}\left(\frac{1}{10000}\right) = \log_{10}\left(\frac{1}{10^4}\right) = \log_{10} 10^{-4}$

$= -4\log_{10} 10 = -4.$

7. $\log_{.01}(1000) = \log_{10^{-2}}(10^3) = -\frac{3}{2}\log_{10} 10 = -\frac{3}{2}.$

8. $[\log_{10}(5\log_{10} 100)]^2 = [\log_{10}\{5\log_{10}(10)^2\}]^2 = [\log_{10}(5\times 2)]^2 = (\log_{10} 10)^2 = 1.$

9. $\log_2 0.0625 = \log_2\left(\frac{625}{10000}\right) = \log_2\left(\frac{1}{16}\right) = \log_2 2^{-4}$

$= (-4)\log_2 2 = -4.$

10. $\log_{0.01} 0.0001 = \log_{10^{-2}} 10^{-5} = \left(\frac{-5}{-2}\right)\log_{10} 10 = \frac{5}{2}.$

11. $\log_3 x = -2 \Rightarrow x = 3^{-2} = \frac{1}{3^2} = \frac{1}{9}.$

12. $\log_8 x = \frac{2}{3} \Rightarrow x = 8^{2/3} = (2^3)^{\frac{2}{3}} = 2^{\left(3\times\frac{2}{3}\right)} = 2^2 = 4.$

13. $\log_8 p = 25$ and $\log_2 q = 5 \Rightarrow p = 8^{25}$ and $q = 2^5$

$\Rightarrow p = (2^3)^{25}$ and $q = 2^5.$

$\Rightarrow p = 2^{75}$ and $q = 2^5$

$\Rightarrow p = (2^5)^{15}$ and $q = 2^5$

$\Rightarrow p = q^{15}.$

14. $\log_x\left(\frac{9}{16}\right) = -\frac{1}{2} \Leftrightarrow x^{-1/2} = \frac{9}{16} \Leftrightarrow \frac{1}{\sqrt{x}} = \frac{9}{16} \Leftrightarrow \sqrt{x} = \frac{16}{9}$

$\Leftrightarrow x = \left(\frac{16}{9}\right)^2 = \frac{256}{81}.$

15. $\log_x 4 = 0.4 \Leftrightarrow \log_x 4 = \frac{4}{10} = \frac{2}{5} \Leftrightarrow x^{2/5} = 4$

$\Leftrightarrow x = 4^{5/2} = (2^2)^{5/2}$

$\Leftrightarrow x = 2^{\left(2\times\frac{5}{2}\right)} = 2^5 \Leftrightarrow x = 32.$

16. Let $\log_{10000} x = -\frac{1}{4} \Leftrightarrow x = (10000)^{-\frac{1}{4}} = (10^4)^{-1/4}$

$= 10^{-1} = \frac{1}{10}.$

17. $\log_x 4 = \frac{1}{4} \Leftrightarrow x^{1/4} = 4 \Leftrightarrow x = 4^4 = 256.$

18. $\log_x(0.1) = -\frac{1}{3} \Leftrightarrow x^{-1/3} = 0.1 \Leftrightarrow \frac{1}{x^{1/3}} = 0.1$

$\Leftrightarrow x^{1/3} = \frac{1}{0.1} = 10 \Leftrightarrow x = (10)^3 = 1000.$

19. $\log_{32} x = 0.8 \Leftrightarrow x = (32)^{0.8} = (2^5)^{4/5} = 2^4 = 16.$

20. $\log_2 x = 10 \Rightarrow x = 2^{10}.$

$\therefore \log_x y = 100 \Rightarrow y = x^{100} = (2^{10})^{100} \Rightarrow y = 2^{1000}.$

21. Let $\log_{(-1/3)} 81 = x$. Then,

$\left(-\frac{1}{3}\right)^x = 81 = 3^4 = (-3^4) = \left(-\frac{1}{3}\right)^4$

$\therefore x = -4$ *i.e.*, $\log_{(-1/3)} 81 = -4.$

22. Let $\log_{2\sqrt{3}}(1728) = x$. Then,

$(2\sqrt{3})^x = 1728 = (12)^3 = [(2\sqrt{3})^2]^3 = (2\sqrt{3})^6.$

$\therefore x = 6$, *i.e.*, $\log_{2\sqrt{3}}(1728) = 6.$

23. $\frac{\log\sqrt{8}}{\log 8} = \frac{\log(8)^{1/2}}{\log 8} = \frac{\frac{1}{2}\log 8}{\log 8} = \frac{1}{2}.$

24. (*a*) Since $\log_a a = 1$, so $\log_{10} 10 = 1.$

(*b*) $\log(2+3) = 5$ and $\log(2\times 3) = \log 6 = \log 2 + \log 3.$

$\therefore \log(2+3) \neq \log(2\times 3).$

(*c*) Since $\log_a 1 = 0$, so $\log_{10} 1 = 0.$

(*d*) $\log(1+2+3) = \log 6 = \log(1\times 2\times 3) = \log 1 + \log 2 + \log 3.$

So, (*b*) is incorrect.

25. $\frac{6\log_{10} 1000}{3\log_{10} 100} = \frac{6\log_{10} 10^3}{3\log_{10} 10^2} = \frac{6\times 3\log_{10} 10}{3\times 2\log_{10} 10} = \frac{18}{6} = 3.$

26. $\log_{10}(10\times 10^2\times 10^3\times \ldots \times 10^9)$

$= \log_{10} 10^{(1+2+3+\ldots+9)} = \log_{10} 10^{45} = 45\log_{10} 10 = 45.$

27. $\log_2(\log_5 625) = \log_2(\log_5 5^4) = \log_2(4\log_5 5) = \log_2 4 = \log_2 2^2 = 2\log_2 2 = 2.$

28. $\log_2[\log_3(\log_2 x)] = 1 \Rightarrow \log_3(\log_2 x) = 2^1 = 2 \Rightarrow \log_2 x = 3^2 = 9 \Rightarrow x = 2^9 = 512.$

29. $\log_{10}\log_{10}\log_{10}(10^{10^{10}})$

$= \log_{10}\log_{10}(10^{10}\log_{10} 10) = \log_{10}\log_{10}(10^{10})$

$= \log_{10}(10\log_{10} 10) = \log_{10} 10 = 1.$

30. $\log_2\log_2\log_3(\log_3 27^3)$

$= \log_2\log_2\log_3[\log_3(3^3)^3] = \log_2\log_2\log_3[\log_3(3)^9]$

$= \log_2\log_2\log_3(9\log_3 3) = \log_2\log_2\log_3 9$ $[\because \log_3 3 = 1]$

$= \log_2\log_2[\log_3(3)^2] = \log_2\log_2(2\log_3 3)$

$= \log_2\log_2 2 = \log_2 1 = 0.$

31. $\log_2[\log_2\{\log_4(\log_4 256^4)\}] = \log_2\log_2[\log_4\{\log_4(4^4)^4\}] = \log_2\log_2[\log_4\{\log_4 4^{16}\}]$

$= \log_2\log_2[\log_4\{16\log_4 4\}] = \log_2\log_2\log_4 16 = \log_2\log_2\log_4(4^2) = \log_2\log_2(2\log_4 4)$

$= \log_2\log_2 2 = \log_2 1 = 0.$

32. $a^x = b^y \Rightarrow \log a^x = \log b^y$
$\Rightarrow x \log a = y \log b \Rightarrow \dfrac{\log a}{\log b} = \dfrac{y}{x}$.

33. $360 = (2 \times 2 \times 2) \times (3 \times 3) \times 5$.
So, $\log 360 = \log (2^3 \times 3^2 \times 5) = \log 2^3 + \log 3^2 + \log 5 = 3 \log 2 + 2 \log 3 + \log 5$.

34. $\log_{10}\dfrac{26}{51} + \log_{10}\dfrac{119}{91} - \log_{10}\dfrac{13}{32} - \log_{10}\dfrac{64}{39}$

$= \left(\log_{10}\dfrac{26}{51} + \log_{10}\dfrac{119}{91}\right) - \left(\log_{10}\dfrac{13}{32} + \log_{10}\dfrac{64}{39}\right)$

$= \log_{10}\left(\dfrac{26}{51}\times\dfrac{119}{91}\right) - \log_{10}\left(\dfrac{13}{32}\times\dfrac{64}{39}\right) = \log_{10}\dfrac{2}{3} - \log_{10}\dfrac{2}{3} = 0.$

35. $\dfrac{1}{3}\log_{10} 125 - 2\log_{10} 4 + \log_{10} 32 = \log_{10} (125)^{1/3} - \log_{10} (4)^2 + \log_{10} 32$

$= \log_{10} 5 - \log_{10} 16 + \log_{10} 32 = \log_{10}\left(\dfrac{5\times 32}{16}\right)$

$= \log_{10} 10 = 1.$

36. $\log_{10} 1\dfrac{1}{2} + \log_{10} 1\dfrac{1}{3} + \cdots$ upto 198 terms $= \log_{10}\left(1\dfrac{1}{2}\times 1\dfrac{1}{3}\times\cdots\times 1\dfrac{1}{199}\right)$

$= \log_{10}\left(\dfrac{3}{2}\times\dfrac{4}{3}\times\cdots\times\dfrac{200}{199}\right) = \log_{10}\left(\dfrac{200}{2}\right)$

$= \log_{10} 100 = \log_{10} 10^2 = 2\log_{10} 10 = 2.$

37. $\log\left(\dfrac{9}{14}\right) - \log\left(\dfrac{15}{16}\right) + \log\left(\dfrac{35}{24}\right)$

$= \log\left(\dfrac{9}{14}\div\dfrac{15}{16}\times\dfrac{35}{24}\right) = \log\left(\dfrac{9}{14}\times\dfrac{16}{15}\times\dfrac{35}{24}\right) = \log 1 = 0.$

38. $2\log_{10} 5 + \log_{10} 8 - \dfrac{1}{2}\log_{10} 4 = \log_{10} (5^2) + \log_{10} 8 - \log_{10} (4^{1/2})$

$= \log_{10} 25 + \log_{10} 8 - \log_{10} 2 = \log_{10}\left(\dfrac{25\times 8}{2}\right)$

$= \log_{10} 100 = 2.$

39. $\log_{10} 2 + 16\log_{10}\dfrac{16}{15} + 12\log_{10}\dfrac{25}{24} + 7\log_{10}\dfrac{81}{80}$

$= \log_{10} 2 + \log_{10}\left(\dfrac{16}{15}\right)^{16} + \log_{10}\left(\dfrac{25}{24}\right)^{12} + \log_{10}\left(\dfrac{81}{80}\right)^{7}$

$= \log_{10}\left[2\times\left(\dfrac{16}{15}\right)^{16}\times\left(\dfrac{25}{24}\right)^{12}\times\left(\dfrac{81}{80}\right)^{7}\right]$

$= \log_{10}\left[2\times\dfrac{(2^4)^{16}}{5^{16}\times 3^{16}}\times\dfrac{(5^2)^{12}}{(2^3)^{12}\times 3^{12}}\times\dfrac{(3^4)^7}{(2^4)^7\times 5^7}\right]$

$= \log_{10}\left[\dfrac{2\times 2^{64}\times 5^{24}\times 3^{28}}{5^{16}\times 3^{16}\times 2^{36}\times 3^{12}\times 2^{28}\times 5^7}\right]$

$= \log_{10} [2^{(1+64-36-28)}\times 5^{(24-16-7)}\times 3^{(28-16-12)}]$
$= \log_{10} (2^1\times 5^1\times 3^0) = \log_{10} 10 = 1.$

40. $\log_a (ab) = x \Leftrightarrow \dfrac{\log ab}{\log a} = x \Leftrightarrow \dfrac{\log a + \log b}{\log a} = x$

$\Leftrightarrow 1 + \dfrac{\log b}{\log a} = x \Leftrightarrow \dfrac{\log b}{\log a} = x - 1 \Leftrightarrow \dfrac{\log a}{\log b} = \dfrac{1}{x-1}$

$\Leftrightarrow 1 + \dfrac{\log a}{\log b} = 1 + \dfrac{1}{x-1} \Leftrightarrow \dfrac{\log b}{\log b} + \dfrac{\log a}{\log b} = \dfrac{x}{x-1}$

$\Leftrightarrow \dfrac{\log b + \log a}{\log b} = \dfrac{x}{x-1} \Leftrightarrow \dfrac{\log (ab)}{\log b} = \dfrac{x}{x-1}$

$\Leftrightarrow \log_b (ab) = \dfrac{x}{x-1}$.

41. $\log_{\frac{1}{a}}\left(\dfrac{1}{m}\right) = \log_{a^{-1}} m^{-1} = \dfrac{-1}{-1}\log_a m = \log_a m = x.$

42. $\log_5 12 = \log_5 (3\times 4) = \log_5 3 + \log_5 4 = \log_5 3 + 2\log_5 2$

$= \dfrac{\log_{10} 3}{\log_{10} 5} + \dfrac{2\log_{10} 2}{\log_{10} 5} = \dfrac{\log_{10} 3}{\log_{10} 10 - \log_{10} 2} + \dfrac{2\log_{10} 2}{\log_{10} 10 - \log_{10} 2}$

$= \dfrac{b}{1-a} + \dfrac{2a}{1-a} = \dfrac{2a+b}{1-a}$.

43. $\log (4\cdot\sqrt[3]{63}) = \log 4 + \log (\sqrt[3]{63}) = \log 4 + \log (63)^{1/3} = \log (2^2) + \log (7\times 3^2)^{1/3}$

$= 2\log 2 + \dfrac{1}{3}\log 7 + \dfrac{2}{3}\log 3 = 2x + \dfrac{1}{3}z + \dfrac{2}{3}y.$

44. $\log_4 x + \log_2 x = 6 \Leftrightarrow \dfrac{\log x}{\log 4} + \dfrac{\log x}{\log 2} = 6 \Leftrightarrow \dfrac{\log x}{2\log 2} + \dfrac{\log x}{\log 2} = 6$

$\Leftrightarrow 3\log x = 12\log 2 \Leftrightarrow \log x = 4\log 2$
$\Leftrightarrow \log x = \log (2^4) = \log 16 \Leftrightarrow x = 16.$

45. $\log_{10} (x^2 - 6x + 10) = 0 \Rightarrow (x^2 - 6x + 10) = 10^0 = 1$
$\Rightarrow x^2 - 6x + 9 = 0$
$\Rightarrow (x-3)^2 = 0 \Rightarrow x = 3.$

46. $\log_{10} x + \log_{10} y = 3$ ...(*i*)
$\log_{10} x - \log_{10} y = 1$ ...(*ii*)
Adding (*i*) and (*ii*), we get:
$2\log_{10} x = 4$ or $\log_{10} x = 2 \Rightarrow \therefore x = 10^2 = 100.$
Also, $\log_{10} y = 3 - \log_{10} x = 3 - 2 = 1 \Rightarrow y = 10^1 = 10.$
Hence, $x = 100$, $y = 10$.

Another method:

$\log_{10} x + \log_{10} y = 3 \Rightarrow \log_{10} (xy) = 3 \Rightarrow xy = 10^3 = 1000.$
$\log_{10} x - \log_{10} y = 1$
$\Rightarrow \log_{10}\left(\dfrac{x}{y}\right) = 1 \Rightarrow \dfrac{x}{y} = 10^1 = 10 \Rightarrow x = 10y \Rightarrow 10y.y = 1000$
$\Rightarrow 10y^2 = 1000 \Rightarrow y^2 = 100 \Rightarrow y = 10.$
$\therefore x = 10y = 10\times 10 = 100.$

47. $\log_{10} x + \log_{10} 5 = 2 \Rightarrow \log_{10} 5x = 2$
$\Rightarrow 5x = 10^2 = 100 \Rightarrow x = 20.$

48. $\log_8 x + \log_8\left(\dfrac{1}{6}\right) = \dfrac{1}{3}$

$\Leftrightarrow \dfrac{\log x}{\log 8} + \dfrac{\log\frac{1}{6}}{\log 8} = \dfrac{1}{3} \Leftrightarrow \log x + \log\dfrac{1}{6} = \dfrac{1}{3}\log 8$

$\Leftrightarrow \quad \log x + \log \frac{1}{6} = \log (8^{1/3}) = \log 2 \quad \Leftrightarrow \quad \log x = \log 2 - \log \frac{1}{6} = \log \left(2 \times \frac{6}{1}\right) = \log 12. \quad \therefore x = 12.$

49. $\log_{10} 125 + \log_{10} 8 = x \Rightarrow \log_{10} (125 \times 8) = x$
$\Rightarrow x = \log_{10} (1000) = \log_{10} (10)^3 = 3 \log_{10} 10 = 3.$

50. $\log_9 27 + \log_8 32 = \log_{3^2}(3^3) + \log_{2^3}(2^5)$
$= \frac{3}{2}\log_3 3 + \frac{5}{3}\log_2 2 = \frac{3}{2} + \frac{5}{3} = \frac{9+10}{6} = \frac{19}{6}.$

51. Given expression
$= \left(\frac{\log 3}{\log 5} \times \frac{\log 625}{\log 3}\right) = \frac{\log 625}{\log 5} = \frac{\log (5^4)}{\log 5} = \frac{4 \log 5}{\log 5} = 4.$

52. Given expression
$= \frac{\log 9}{\log 4} \times \frac{\log 2}{\log 3} = \frac{\log 3^2}{\log 2^2} \times \frac{\log 2}{\log 3} = \frac{2 \log 3}{2 \log 2} \times \frac{\log 2}{\log 3} = 1.$
$[\because \log_5 5 = 1]$

53. $\log_{12} 27 = a \Rightarrow \frac{\log 27}{\log 12} = a \Rightarrow \frac{\log 3^3}{\log (3 \times 2^2)} = a$

$\Rightarrow \frac{3 \log 3}{\log 3 + 2 \log 2} = a \Rightarrow \frac{\log 3 + 2 \log 2}{3 \log 3} = \frac{1}{a}$

$\Rightarrow \frac{\log 3}{3 \log 3} + \frac{2 \log 2}{3 \log 3} = \frac{1}{a} \Rightarrow \frac{2 \log 2}{3 \log 3} = \frac{1}{a} - \frac{1}{3} = \left(\frac{3-a}{3a}\right)$

$\Rightarrow \frac{\log 2}{\log 3} = \left(\frac{3-a}{2a}\right) \Rightarrow \log 3 = \left(\frac{2a}{3-a}\right) \log 2.$

$\log_6 16 = \frac{\log 16}{\log 6} = \frac{\log 2^4}{\log (2 \times 3)} = \frac{4 \log 2}{\log 2 + \log 3} = \frac{4 \log 2}{\log 2 \left[1 + \left(\frac{2a}{3-a}\right)\right]}$

$= \frac{4}{\left(\frac{3+a}{3-a}\right)} = \frac{4(3-a)}{(3+a)}.$

54. $\log_{10} 5 + \log_{10} (5x + 1) = \log_{10} (x + 5) + 1$
$\Rightarrow \quad \log_{10} 5 + \log_{10} (5x + 1) = \log_{10} (x + 5) + \log_{10} 10$
$\Rightarrow \quad \log_{10} [5 (5x + 1)] = \log_{10} [10 (x + 5)]$
$\Rightarrow \quad 5 (5x + 1) = 10 (x + 5)$
$\Rightarrow \quad 5x + 1 = 2x + 10 \Rightarrow 3x = 9 \Rightarrow x = 3.$

55. $\log_5 (x^2 + x) - \log_5 (x + 1) = 2$
$\Rightarrow \quad \log_5 \left(\frac{x^2 + x}{x + 1}\right) = 2 \Rightarrow \log_5 \left[\frac{x(x+1)}{x+1}\right] = 2$

$\Rightarrow \log_5 x = 2 \Rightarrow x = 5^2 = 25.$

56. $\frac{1}{2}(\log x + \log y) = \log \left(\frac{x+y}{2}\right) \Rightarrow \frac{1}{2}\log (xy) = \log \left(\frac{x+y}{2}\right)$

$\Rightarrow \log (xy)^{\frac{1}{2}} = \log \left(\frac{x+y}{2}\right) \Rightarrow (xy)^{\frac{1}{2}} = \left(\frac{x+y}{2}\right) \Rightarrow xy = \left(\frac{x+y}{2}\right)^2$
$\Rightarrow 4xy = x^2 + y^2 + 2xy$
$\Rightarrow x^2 + y^2 - 2xy = 0$
$\Rightarrow (x - y)^2 = 0 \Rightarrow x - y = 0 \Rightarrow x = y.$

57. Given expression
$= \log_{60} 3 + \log_{60} 4 + \log_{60} 5 = \log_{60} (3 \times 4 \times 5)$
$= \log_{60} 60 = 1.$

58. Given Expression
$= \left(\frac{\log 4}{\log 3} \times \frac{\log 5}{\log 4} \times \frac{\log 6}{\log 5} \times \frac{\log 7}{\log 6} \times \frac{\log 8}{\log 7} \times \frac{\log 9}{\log 8}\right)$

$= \frac{\log 9}{\log 3} = \frac{\log 3^2}{\log 3} = \frac{2 \log 3}{\log 3} = 2.$

59. We know that : $a^{\log_a x} = x.$
$\therefore 16^{\log_4 5} = (4^2)^{\log_4 5} = 4^{2 \log_4 5} = 4^{\log_4 (5^2)} = 4^{\log_4 25} = 25$

60. $\log x + \log y = \log (x + y)$
$\Rightarrow \log (x + y) = \log (xy)$
$\Rightarrow x + y = xy \Rightarrow y (x - 1) = x \Rightarrow y = \frac{x}{x-1}.$

61. $\log \frac{a}{b} + \log \frac{b}{a} = \log (a + b) \Rightarrow \log (a + b) = \log \left(\frac{a}{b} \times \frac{b}{a}\right) = \log 1$
So, $a + b = 1.$

62. Given expression $= \log \left(\frac{a^2}{bc} \times \frac{b^2}{ac} \times \frac{c^2}{ab}\right) = \log 1 = 0.$

63. Given expression $= \left(\frac{\log a}{\log b} \times \frac{\log b}{\log c} \times \frac{\log c}{\log a}\right) = 1.$

64. Given expression
$= \frac{1}{\log_a bc + \log_a a} + \frac{1}{\log_b ca + \log_b b} + \frac{1}{\log_c ab + \log_c c}$
$= \frac{1}{\log_a (abc)} + \frac{1}{\log_b (abc)} + \frac{1}{\log_c (abc)}$
$= \log_{abc} a + \log_{abc} b + \log_{abc} c$
$= \log_{abc} (abc) = 1.$

65. Given expression
$= \log_x \left(\frac{p}{q}\right) + \log_x \left(\frac{q}{r}\right) + \log_x \left(\frac{r}{p}\right)$

$= \log_x \left(\frac{p}{q} \times \frac{q}{r} \times \frac{r}{p}\right) = \log_x 1 = 0.$

66. $\log_{10} \left(\frac{1}{70}\right) = \log_{10} 1 - \log_{10} 70 = -\log_{10} (7 \times 10) = -(\log_{10} 7 + \log_{10} 10) = -(a + 1)$

67. $a = b^x, b = c^y, c = a^z \Rightarrow x = \log_b a, y = \log_c b, z = \log_a c$
$\Rightarrow \quad xyz = (\log_b a) \times (\log_c b) \times (\log_a c)$
$\Rightarrow xyz = \left(\frac{\log a}{\log b} \times \frac{\log b}{\log c} \times \frac{\log c}{\log a}\right) = 1.$

68. $\log x - 5 \log 3 = -2 \Rightarrow \log x - \log 3^5 = -2$
$\Rightarrow \log \left(\frac{x}{3^5}\right) = -2 \Rightarrow \frac{x}{243} = 10^{-2} = \frac{1}{100} \Rightarrow x = \frac{243}{100} = 2.43$

69. $a = b^2 = c^3 = d^4 \Rightarrow b = a^{\frac{1}{2}}, c = a^{\frac{1}{3}}, d = a^{\frac{1}{4}}.$

$\therefore \log_a (abcd) = \log_a \left(a \cdot a^{\frac{1}{2}} \cdot a^{\frac{1}{3}} \cdot a^{\frac{1}{4}}\right) = \log_a a^{\left(1 + \frac{1}{2} + \frac{1}{3} + \frac{1}{4}\right)}$

$= \left(1 + \frac{1}{2} + \frac{1}{3} + \frac{1}{4}\right) \log_a a = 1 + \frac{1}{2} + \frac{1}{3} + \frac{1}{4}.$

70. $\log_3 x + \log_a x^2 + \log_{27} x^3 = 9 \Rightarrow \log_3 x + \log_{3^2} x^2 + \log_{3^3} x^3 = 9$

$\Rightarrow \log_3 x + \frac{2}{2}\log_3 x + \frac{3}{3}\log_3 x = 9 \Rightarrow 3\log_3 x = 9 \Rightarrow \log_3 x = 3 \Rightarrow x = 3^3 = 27.$

71. $\log_7 \log_5 (\sqrt{x+5}+\sqrt{x}) = 0 \Rightarrow \log_5 (\sqrt{x+5}+\sqrt{x}) = 7^0 = 1$

$\Rightarrow \sqrt{x+5}+\sqrt{x} = 5^1 = 5 \Rightarrow (\sqrt{x+5}+\sqrt{x})^2 = 25$

$\Rightarrow (x+5)+x+2\sqrt{x+5}\sqrt{x} = 25 \Rightarrow 2x+2\sqrt{x}\sqrt{x+5} = 20$

$\Rightarrow \sqrt{x}\sqrt{x+5} = 10-x \Rightarrow x(x+5) = (10-x)^2$

$\Rightarrow x^2 + 5x = 100 + x^2 - 20x \Rightarrow 25x = 100 \Rightarrow x = 4.$

72. $a = \log_8 225 = \log_{2^3}(15^2) = \frac{2}{3}\log_2 15 = \frac{2b}{3}.$

73. $\log 27 = 1.431$

$\Rightarrow \log(3^3) = 1.431 \Rightarrow 3\log 3 = 1.431 \Rightarrow \log 3 = 0.477.$

$\therefore \log 9 = \log(3^2) = 2\log 3 = (2 \times 0.477) = 0.954.$

74. $\log_2 10 = \frac{1}{\log_{10} 2} = \frac{1}{0.3010} = \frac{10000}{3010} = \frac{1000}{301}.$

75. $\log_{10} 5 = \log_{10}\left(\frac{10}{2}\right) = \log_{10} 10 - \log_{10} 2 = 1 - \log_{10} 2$

$= (1 - 0.3010) = 0.6990.$

76. $\log_{10} 80 = \log_{10}(8 \times 10) = \log_{10} 8 + \log_{10} 10 = \log_{10}(2^3) + 1 = 3\log_{10} 2 + 1 = (3 \times 0.3010) + 1 = 1.9030.$

77. $(1000)^x = 3 \Rightarrow \log[(1000)^x] = \log 3 \Rightarrow x \log 1000 = \log 3$

$\Rightarrow x \log(10^3) = \log 3 \Rightarrow 3x \log 10 = \log 3$

$\Rightarrow 3x = \log 3$

$\Rightarrow x = \frac{0.477}{3} = 0.159.$

78. $\log_{10} 25 = \log_{10}\left(\frac{100}{4}\right) = \log_{10} 100 - \log_{10} 4$

$= 2 - 2\log_{10} 2 = (2 - 2 \times 0.3010)$

$= (2 - 0.6020) = 1.3980.$

79. $\log_{10}(60000) = \log_{10}(20 \times 30 \times 100) = \log_{10} 20 + \log_{10} 30 + \log_{10} 100$

$= 1.3010 + 1.4771 + 2 = 4.7781.$

80. $\log_5 512 = \frac{\log 512}{\log 5} = \frac{\log 2^9}{\log\left(\frac{10}{2}\right)} = \frac{9\log 2}{\log 10 - \log 2}$

$= \frac{(9 \times 0.3010)}{1 - 0.3010} = \frac{2.709}{0.699} = \frac{2709}{699} = 3.876.$

81. $\log_{10}\left(23\frac{1}{3}\right) = \log_{10}\left(\frac{70}{3}\right) = \log_{10} 70 - \log_{10} 3 = \log_{10}(7 \times 10) - \log_{10} 3$

$= \log_{10} 7 + \log_{10} 10 - \log_{10} 3 = 0.8451 + 1 - 0.4771 = 1.368.$

82. $\log_{10}(1.5) = \log_{10}\left(\frac{3}{2}\right) = \log_{10} 3 - \log_{10} 2 = (0.4771 - 0.3010) = 0.1761.$

83. $\log_{10}(2.8) = \log_{10}\left(\frac{28}{10}\right) = \log_{10} 28 - \log_{10} 10 = \log_{10}(7 \times 2^2) - 1 = \log_{10} 7 + 2\log_{10} 2 - 1$

$= 0.8451 + 2 \times 0.3010 - 1 = 0.8451 + 0.602 - 1 = 0.4471.$

84. $\log(0.57) = \bar{1}.756 \Rightarrow \log 57 = 1.756$

[$\because$ mantissa will remain the same]

$\therefore \quad \log 57 + \log(0.57)^3 + \log\sqrt{0.57}$

$= \log 57 + 3\log\left(\frac{57}{100}\right) + \log\left(\frac{57}{100}\right)^{1/2}$

$= \log 57 + 3\log 57 - 3\log 100 + \frac{1}{2}\log 57 - \frac{1}{2}\log 100$

$= \frac{9}{2}\log 57 - \frac{7}{2}\log 100 = \frac{9}{2} \times 1.756 - \frac{7}{2} \times 2 = 7.902 - 7$

$= 0.902.$

85. Let $\log x = -3.153$.

Then, $\log x = -3.153 = -3 + (-0.153)$

$= (-3 - 1) + (1 - 0.153) = -4 + 0.847 = \bar{4}.847.$

Hence, characteristic = – 4, mantissa = 0.847.

86. $\log(2^{64}) = 64 \times \log 2 = (64 \times 0.30103) = 19.26592.$

Its characteristic is 19. Hence, the number of digits in 2^{64} is 20.

87. $\log 4^{50} = 50\log 4 = 50\log 2^2 = (50 \times 2)\log 2 = 100 \times \log 2 = (100 \times 0.30103) = 30.103.$

$\therefore$ Characteristic = 30. Hence, the number of digits in $4^{50} = 31$.

88. $\log 5^{20} = 20\log 5 = 20 \times \left[\log\left(\frac{10}{2}\right)\right] = 20(\log 10 - \log 2)$

$= 20(1 - 0.3010) = 20 \times 0.6990 = 13.9800.$

$\therefore$ Characteristic = 13. Hence, the number of digits in 5^{20} is 14.

89. $\log 6^{20} = 20\log(2 \times 3) = 20(\log 2 + \log 3)$

$= 20(0.30103 + 0.47712)$

$= 20 \times 0.77815 = 15.563.$

$\therefore$ Characteristic = 15. Hence, the number of digits in $6^{20} = 16$.

90. $\log(4^9 \times 5^{17}) = \log(4^9) + \log(5^{17}) = \log(2^2)^9 + \log(5^{17})$

$= \log(2^{18}) + \log(5^{17})$

$= 18\log 2 + 17\log 5 = 18\log 2 + 17(\log 10 - \log 2)$

$= 18\log 2 + 17\log 10 - 17\log 2 = \log 2 + 17\log 10$

$= 0.3010 + 17 \times 1 = 17.3010.$

$\therefore$ Characteristic = 17. Hence, the number of digits in $(4^9 \times 5^{17}) = 18$.

91. In arithmetic progression common ratios are equal to

$\log(3^x - 2) - \log 3 = \log(3^x + 4) - \log(3^x - 2)$

$\frac{\log(3^x - 2)}{\log 3} = \frac{\log(3^x + 4)}{\log(3^x - 2)} \left(\because \log a - \log b = \log\frac{a}{b}\right)$

$\frac{\log 3^x}{\log 2 \log 3} = \frac{x \log 3 \log 4 \log 2}{x \log 3}$

$\frac{x \log 3}{\log 2 \log 3} = \frac{x \log 3 \log 4 \log 2}{x \log 2}$

$\frac{x}{\log 2} = \log 4 \log 2$

$x = \log 4 \log 2 \log 2$

$x = \log 8$

$x = \log 2^3$

92. Given $\log_{10} a = p$, $\log_{10} b = q$

$\log_{10}(a^p b^q) = \log_{10} a^p + \log_{10} b^q$

$= p\log_{10} a + q\log_{10} b = p^2 + q^2$

11 Percentage

IMPORTANT FACTS AND FORMULAE

I. **Concept of Percentage:** By a certain *percent*, we mean that many hundredths. Thus, x percent means x hundredths, written as $x\%$.

To express x% as a fraction: We have, $x\% = \frac{x}{100}$.

Thus, $20\% = \frac{20}{100} = \frac{1}{5}$; $48\% = \frac{48}{100} = \frac{12}{25}$, etc.

Thus, $\frac{1}{4} = \left(\frac{1}{4} \times 100\right)\% = 25\%$; $0.6 = \frac{6}{10} = \frac{3}{5} = \left(\frac{3}{5} \times 100\right)\% = 60\%$.

II. If a certain value p increases by $x\%$, then increased value $= (100 + x)\%$ of p.
If a certain value p decreases by $x\%$, then decreased value $= (100 - x)\%$ of p.

III. If the price of a commodity increases by R%, then the reduction in consumption so as not to increase the expenditure is

$$\left[\frac{R}{(100 + R)} \times 100\right]\%$$

If the price of a commodity decreases by R%, then the increase in consumption so as not to decrease the expenditure is

$$\left[\frac{R}{(100 - R)} \times 100\right]\%$$

IV. **Results on Population:** Let the population of a town be P now and suppose it increases at the rate of R% per annum, then:

1. Population after n years $= P\left(1 + \frac{R}{100}\right)^n$.

2. Population n years ago $= \frac{P}{\left(1 + \frac{R}{100}\right)^n}$.

V. **Results on Depreciation:** Let the present value of a machine be P. Suppose it depreciates at the rate of R% per annum. Then:

1. Value of the machine after n years $= P\left(1 - \frac{R}{100}\right)^n$.

2. Value of the machine n years ago $= \frac{P}{\left(1 - \frac{R}{100}\right)^n}$.

VI. If A is R% more than B, then B is less than A by $\left[\frac{R}{(100 + R)} \times 100\right]\%$.

If A is R% less than B, then B is more than A by $\left[\frac{R}{(100 - R)} \times 100\right]\%$.

SOLVED EXAMPLES

Ex. 1. *Express each of the following as a fraction:*

***(i)* 56%** ***(ii)* 4%** ***(iii)* 0.6%** ***(iv)* 0.08%**

Sol. *(i)* $56\% = \frac{56}{100} = \frac{14}{25}$. *(ii)* $4\% = \frac{4}{100} = \frac{1}{25}$.

(iii) $0.6\% = \frac{0.6}{100} = \frac{6}{1000} = \frac{3}{500}$. *(iv)* $0.08\% = \frac{0.08}{100} = \frac{8}{10000} = \frac{1}{1250}$.

Ex. 2. *Express each of the following as a decimal:* **(R.R.B., 2006)**

***(i)* 6%** ***(ii)* 28%** ***(iii)* 0.2%** ***(iv)* 0.04%** ***(v)* $\frac{1}{2}\%$**

Sol. *(i)* $6\% = \frac{6}{100} = 0.06$. *(ii)* $28\% = \frac{28}{100} = 0.28$.

(iii) $0.2\% = \frac{0.2}{100} = 0.002$. *(iv)* $0.04\% = \frac{0.04}{100} = 0.0004$.

(v) $\frac{1}{2}\% = \frac{1}{2} \times \frac{1}{100} = \frac{1}{200} = 0.005$.

Ex. 3. *Express each of the following as rate percent:*

***(i)* $\frac{23}{36}$** ***(ii)* 0.004** ***(iii)* $6\frac{3}{4}$**

Sol. *(i)* $\frac{23}{36} = \left(\frac{23}{36} \times 100\right)\% = \left(\frac{575}{9}\right)\% = 63\frac{8}{9}\%$.

(ii) $0.004 = \frac{4}{1000} = \left(\frac{4}{1000} \times 100\right)\% = 0.4\%$.

(iii) $6\frac{3}{4} = \frac{27}{4} = \left(\frac{27}{4} \times 100\right)\% = 675\%$.

Ex. 4. *Evaluate:* **(Bank P.O., 2009)**

***(i)* 70% of 320 + 45% of 240** ***(ii)* $16\frac{2}{3}\%$ of 600 gm – $33\frac{1}{3}\%$ of 180 gm**

Sol. *(i)* 70% of 320 + 45% of 240 $= \left(\frac{70}{100} \times 320 + \frac{45}{100} \times 240\right) = 224 + 108 = 332$.

(ii) $16\frac{2}{3}\%$ of 600 gm – $33\frac{1}{3}\%$ of 180 gm

$= \left[\left(\frac{50}{3} \times \frac{1}{100} \times 600\right) - \left(\frac{100}{3} \times \frac{1}{100} \times 180\right)\right]$ gm = (100 – 60) gm = 40 gm.

Ex. 5. *(i)* 2 *is what percent of 50?*

***(ii)* $\frac{1}{2}$ *is what percent of* $\frac{1}{3}$?**

***(iii)* What percent of 7 is 84?**

***(iv)* What percent of 2 metric tonnes is 40 quintals?**

***(v)* What percent of 6.5 litres is 130 ml?**

***(vi)* What percent is 1 minute 10 seconds of half an hour?** **(P.C.S., 2009)**

Sol. *(i)* Required percentage $= \left(\frac{2}{50} \times 100\right)\% = 4\%$.

(ii) Required percentage $= \left(\frac{1}{2} \times \frac{3}{1} \times 100\right)\% = 150\%$.

(*iii*) Required percentage $= \left(\frac{84}{7} \times 100\right)\% = 1200\%.$

(*iv*) 1 metric tonne = 10 quintals.

$\therefore$ Required percentage $= \left(\frac{40}{2 \times 10} \times 100\right)\% = 200\%.$

(*v*) Required percentage $= \left(\frac{130}{6.5 \times 1000} \times 100\right)\% = 2\%.$

(*vi*) 1 minute 10 seconds $= 1\frac{10}{60}$ min $= 1\frac{1}{6}$ min $= \frac{7}{6}$ min.

Half an hour = 30 min.

$\therefore$ Required percentage $= \left(\frac{7}{6} \times \frac{1}{30} \times 100\right)\% = \left(\frac{35}{9}\right)\% = 3.89\%.$

Ex. 6. ***Find the missing figures:***
(i)?% of 25 = 2.125 ***(ii) 9% of? = 63*** ***(iii) 0.25% of? = 0.04***

Sol. (*i*) Let x% of 25 = 2.125. Then, $\frac{x}{100} \times 25 = 2.125 \Leftrightarrow x = (2.125 \times 4) = 8.5.$

(*ii*) Let 9% of x = 6.3. Then, $\frac{9}{100}x = 6.3 \Leftrightarrow x = \left(\frac{6.3 \times 100}{9}\right) = 70.$

(*iii*) Let 0.25% of x = 0.04. Then, $\frac{0.25}{100}x = 0.04 \Leftrightarrow x = \left(\frac{0.04 \times 100}{0.25}\right) = 16.$

Ex. 7. ***Which is greatest in $16\frac{2}{3}\%, \frac{2}{15}$ and 0.17?***

Sol. $16\frac{2}{3}\% = \left(\frac{50}{3} \times \frac{1}{100}\right) = \frac{1}{6} = 0.166, \frac{2}{15} = 0.133.$ Clearly, 0.17 is the greatest.

Ex. 8. ***Saroj invests ₹ 72318, which is 17% of her annual income, in mutual funds. What is her monthly income?*** **(Bank Recruitment, 2009)**

Sol. Let the annual income be ₹ x.

Then, 17% of x = 72318 $\Rightarrow \frac{17}{100}x = 72318 \Rightarrow x = \left(\frac{72318 \times 100}{17}\right) = 425400.$

$\therefore$ Saroj's monthly income = ₹ $\left(\frac{425400}{12}\right)$ = ₹ 35450.

Ex. 9. ***An inspector rejects 0.08% of the meters as defective. How many will he examine to reject 2?***

Sol. Let the number of meters to be examined be x.

Then, 0.08% of $x = 2 \Leftrightarrow \left(\frac{8}{100} \times \frac{1}{100} \times x\right) = 2 \Leftrightarrow x = \left(\frac{2 \times 100 \times 100}{8}\right) = 2500.$

Ex. 10. ***The price of a TV set inclusive of sales tax of 9% is ₹ 13407. Find its marked price.*** **(R.R.B., 2008)**

Sol. Let the M.P. of T.V. set be ₹ x.

Then, x + 9% of $x = 13407 \Rightarrow x + \frac{9x}{100} = 13407 \Rightarrow \frac{109x}{100} = 13407 \Rightarrow x = \left(\frac{13407 \times 100}{109}\right) = 12300.$

Hence, marked price = ₹ 12300.

Ex. 11. ***The difference between 31% of a number and 13% of the same number is 576. What is 17% of that number?*** **(Bank Recruitment, 2010)**

Sol. Let the number be x.

Then, 31% of x – 13% of x = 576 $\Rightarrow$ (31 – 13)% of x = 576 $\Rightarrow$ 18% of x = 576

$\Rightarrow \frac{18}{100}x = 576 \Rightarrow x = \left(\frac{576 \times 100}{18}\right) = 3200.$

$\therefore$ 17% of the number = 17% of 3200 $= \left(\frac{17}{100} \times 3200\right) = 544.$

Ex. 12. ***Sixty-five percent of a number is 21 less than four-fifths of that number. What is the number?***

Sol. Let the number be x.

Then, $\frac{4}{5}x - (65\% \text{ of } x) = 21 \Leftrightarrow \frac{4}{5}x - \frac{65}{100}x = 21 \Leftrightarrow 15x = 2100 \Leftrightarrow x = 140.$

Ex. 13. ***If the sales tax be reduced from $3\frac{1}{2}\%$ to $3\frac{1}{3}\%$, then what difference does it make to a person who purchases an article with marked price of ₹ 8400?***

Sol. Required difference $= \left(3\frac{1}{2}\% \text{ of ₹ } 8400\right) - \left(3\frac{1}{3}\% \text{ of ₹ } 8400\right)$

$= \left(\frac{7}{2} - \frac{10}{3}\right)\% \text{ of ₹ } 8400 = \frac{1}{6}\% \text{ of ₹ } 8400 = ₹\left(\frac{1}{6} \times \frac{1}{100} \times 8400\right) = ₹\ 14.$

Ex. 14. ***Difference of two numbers is 1660. If 7.5% of one number is 12.5% of the other number, find the two numbers.***

Sol. Let the numbers be x and y. Then, 7.5% of x = 12.5% of y $\Leftrightarrow$ $x = \frac{125}{75}y = \frac{5}{3}y.$

Now, $x - y = 1660 \Rightarrow \frac{5}{3}y - y = 1660 \Rightarrow \frac{2}{3}y = 1660 \Rightarrow y = \left(\frac{1660 \times 3}{2}\right) = 2490.$

$\therefore$ One number = 2490, Second number = $\frac{5}{3}y = 4150.$

Ex. 15. ***The difference between the value of a number increased by 25% and the value of the original number decreased by 30% is 22. What is the original number?*** **(SNAP, 2010)**

Sol. Let the number be x. Then,

125% of x – 70% of x = 22 $\Rightarrow$ 55% of x = 22 $\Rightarrow \frac{55}{100}x = 22 \Rightarrow x = \left(\frac{22 \times 100}{55}\right) = 40.$

Hence, required number = 40.

Ex. 16. ***Mrs. Roy spent ₹ 44620 on Deepawali shopping, ₹ 32764 on buying laptop and the remaining 32% of the total amount she had as cash with her. What was the total amount?*** **(S.B.I.,P.O., 2008)**

Sol. Let the total amount be ₹ x. Then,

$(100 - 32)\%$ of x = 44620 + 32764 $\Rightarrow$ 68% of x = 77384 $\Rightarrow x = \left(\frac{77384 \times 100}{68}\right) = 113800.$

Hence, total amount = ₹ 113800.

Ex. 17. ***In expressing a length 81.472 km as nearly as possible with three significant digits, find the percentage error.***

Sol. Error = (81.5 – 81.472) km = 0.028 km.

$\therefore$ Required percentage $= \left(\frac{0.028}{81.472} \times 100\right)\% = 0.034\%.$

Ex. 18. ***The monthly income of a person was ₹ 13500 and his monthly expenditure was ₹ 9000. Next year, his income increased by 14% and his expenditure by 7%. Find the percentage increase in his savings.*** **(S.S.C., 2006)**

Sol. Increased income = 114% of ₹ 13500 = ₹ $\left(\frac{114}{100} \times 13500\right)$ = ₹ 15390.

Increased expenditure = 107% of ₹ 9000 = ₹ $\left(\frac{107}{100} \times 9000\right)$ = ₹ 9630.

Increased saving = ₹ (15390 – 9630) = ₹ 5760.

Original savings = ₹ (13500 – 9000) = ₹ 4500.

Increase = ₹ (5760 – 4500) = ₹ 1260.

$\therefore$ Increase % in savings $= \left(\frac{1260}{4500} \times 100\right)\% = 28\%.$

Ex. 19. ***Salesperson A's compensation for any week is ₹ 360 plus 6 percent of the portion of A's total sales above ₹ 1000 for that week. Salesperson B's compensation for any week is 8 percent of B's total sales for that week. For what amount of total weekly sales would both salespersons earn the same compensation?*** (M.B.A., 2006)

Sol. Let the required weekly sales be ₹ x.

Then, A's compensation = ₹ [360 + 6% of $(x - 1000)$]

B's compensation = 8% of ₹ x.

$\therefore$ 360 + 6% of $(x - 1000)$ = 8% of $x \Rightarrow 360 + \frac{6}{100}(x - 1000) = \frac{8}{100}x$

$$\Rightarrow 360 + \frac{3}{50}x - 60 = \frac{2}{25}x \Rightarrow \frac{x}{50} = 300 \Rightarrow x = 15000.$$

Hence, required weekly sales = ₹ 15000.

Ex. 20. ***A man buys a house for ₹ 5 lakh and rents it. He puts $12\frac{1}{2}\%$ of each month's rent aside for repairs, pays ₹ 1660 as annual taxes and realizes 10% on his investment thereafter. Find the monthly rent of the house.*** (M.A.T., 2009)

Sol. Let the annual rent of the house be ₹ x. Then,

$$x - \left(12\frac{1}{2}\% \text{ of } x + 1660\right) = 10\% \text{ of } 500000$$

$$\Rightarrow x - \left(\frac{25}{2} \times \frac{1}{100} \times x + 1660\right) = 50000$$

$$\Rightarrow \frac{7x}{8} - 1660 = 50000 \Rightarrow \frac{7x}{8} = 51660 \Rightarrow x = \left(\frac{51660 \times 8}{7}\right) = 59040.$$

Hence, monthly rent = ₹ $\left(\frac{59040}{12}\right)$ = ₹ 4920.

Ex. 21. ***The present population of a village is 5500. If the number of males increases by 11% and the number of females increases by 20%, then the population will become 6330. What is the present population of females in the village?***

Sol. Let the number of males be x. Then, number of females = $(5500 - x)$.

$\therefore$ 111% of x + 120% of $(5500 - x)$ = 6330

$$\Rightarrow \frac{111}{100}x + \frac{120}{100}(5500 - x) = 6330$$

$\Rightarrow 111x + 660000 - 120x = 633000 \Rightarrow 9x = 27000 \Rightarrow x = 3000.$

Hence, present population of females = 5500 – 3000 = 2500.

Ex. 22. ***In an election between two candidates, 75% of the voters cast their votes, out of which 2% of the votes were declared invalid. A candidate got 9261 votes which were 75% of the total valid votes. Find the total number of votes enrolled in that election.***

Sol. Let the total number of votes enrolled be x. Then,

Number of votes cast = 75% of x. Valid votes = 98% of (75% of x).

$\therefore$ 75% of [98% of (75% of x)] = 9261

$$\Leftrightarrow \left(\frac{75}{100} \times \frac{98}{100} \times \frac{75}{100} \times x\right) = 9261 \Leftrightarrow x = \left(\frac{9261 \times 100 \times 100 \times 100}{75 \times 98 \times 75}\right) = 16800.$$

Ex. 23. ***Shobha's Mathematics Test had 75 problems i.e., 10 arithmetic, 30 algebra and 35 geometry problems. Although she answered 70% of the arithmetic, 40% of the algebra and 60% of the geometry problems correctly, she did not pass the test because she got less than 60% of the problems right. How many more questions she would have needed to answer correctly to earn a 60% passing grade?***

Sol. Number of questions attempted correctly = (70% of 10 + 40% of 30 + 60% of 35)

= (7 + 12 + 21) = 40.

Questions to be answered correctly for 60% grade = 60% of 75 = 45.

$\therefore$ Required number of questions = (45 – 40) = 5.

Ex. 24. ***If 50% of (x – y) = 30% of (x + y), then what percent of x is y?***

Sol. 50% of $(x - y)$ = 30% of $(x + y)$ $\Leftrightarrow \frac{50}{100}(x-y) = \frac{30}{100}(x+y)$

$\Leftrightarrow 5(x-y) = 3(x+y) \Leftrightarrow 2x = 8y \Leftrightarrow x = 4y.$

$\therefore$ Required percentage $= \left(\frac{y}{x} \times 100\right)\% = \left(\frac{y}{4y} \times 100\right)\% = 25\%.$

Ex. 25. ***Mr. Jones gave 40% of the money he had, to his wife. He also gave 20% of the remaining amount to each of his three sons. Half of the amount now left was spent on miscellaneous items and the remaining amount of ₹ 12,000 was deposited in the bank. How much money did Mr. Jones have initially?***

Sol. Let the initial amount with Mr. Jones be ₹ x. Then,

Money given to wife = ₹ $\frac{40}{100}x$ = ₹ $\frac{2x}{5}$. Balance = ₹ $\left(x - \frac{2x}{5}\right)$ = ₹ $\frac{3x}{5}$.

Money given to 3 sons = ₹ $\left[3 \times \left(\frac{20}{100} \times \frac{3x}{5}\right)\right]$ = ₹ $\frac{9x}{25}$.

Balance = ₹ $\left(\frac{3x}{5} - \frac{9x}{25}\right)$ = ₹ $\frac{6x}{25}$.

Amount deposited in bank = ₹ $\left(\frac{1}{2} \times \frac{6x}{25}\right)$ = ₹ $\frac{3x}{25}$.

$\therefore \frac{3x}{25} = 12000 \Leftrightarrow x = \left(\frac{12000 \times 25}{3}\right) = 100000.$

So, Mr. Jones initially had ₹ 1,00,000 with him.

Short-cut Method: Let the initial amount with Mr. Jones be ₹ x. Then,

$\frac{1}{2}$ of $[100 - (3 \times 20)]\%$ of $(100 - 40)\%$ of $x = 12000.$

$\Leftrightarrow \frac{1}{2} \times \frac{40}{100} \times \frac{60}{100} \times x = 12000 \Leftrightarrow \frac{3}{25}x = 12000 \Leftrightarrow x = \left(\frac{12000 \times 25}{3}\right) = 100000.$

Ex. 26. ***Peter got 30% of the maximum marks in an examination and failed by 10 marks. However, Paul who took the same examination got 40% of the total marks and got 15 marks more than the passing marks. What were the passing marks in the examination?*** **(M.B.A., 2007)**

Sol. Let the maximum marks be x. Then,

(30% of x) + 10 = (40% of x) – 15 $\Rightarrow \frac{30}{100}x + 10 = \frac{40}{100}x - 15 \Rightarrow \frac{10x}{100} = 25 \Rightarrow x = 250.$

$\therefore$ Passing marks = (30% of 250) + 10 = $\left(\frac{30}{100} \times 250\right) + 10 = 85.$

Ex. 27. ***10% of the inhabitants of a village having died of cholera, a panic set in, during which 25% of the remaining inhabitants left the village. The population is then reduced to 4050. Find the number of original inhabitants.***

Sol. Let the total number of original inhabitants be x.

Then, (100 – 25)% of (100 – 10)% of x = 4050

$\Leftrightarrow \left(\frac{75}{100} \times \frac{90}{100} \times x\right) = 4050 \Leftrightarrow \frac{27}{40}x = 4050 \Leftrightarrow x = \left(\frac{4050 \times 40}{27}\right) = 6000.$

$\therefore$ Number of original inhabitants = 6000.

Ex. 28. ***If*** $z = \frac{x^2}{y}$ ***and x, y are both increased in value by 10%, find the percentage change in the value of z.*** **(M.B.A., 2007)**

Sol. Let X, Y and Z represent the changed values of x, y and z respectively.

Then, X = 110% of $x = \frac{11x}{10}$; Y = 110% *of* $y = \frac{11y}{10}$.

$\therefore Z = \frac{X^2}{Y} = \frac{\left(\frac{11x}{10}\right)^2}{\left(\frac{11y}{10}\right)} = \frac{11}{10} \cdot \frac{x^2}{y} = \frac{11}{10} Z.$

Increase in the value of $z = \left(\frac{11z}{10} - z\right) = \frac{z}{10}$.

$\therefore$ Increase % $= \left(\frac{z}{10} \times \frac{1}{z} \times 100\right)\% = 10\%.$

Ex. 29. ***An investor earns 3% return on $\frac{1}{4}$ of his capital, 5% on $\frac{2}{3}$ and 11% on the remainder. What is the average rate of return he earns on his total capital?*** **(M.A.T., 2008)**

Sol. Let the investor's total capital be ₹ x.

Then, total return = ₹ $\left[3\% \text{ of } \frac{x}{4} + 5\% \text{ of } \frac{2x}{3} + 11\% \text{ of } \left\{x - \left(\frac{x}{4} + \frac{2x}{3}\right)\right\}\right]$

$= ₹ \left(\frac{3x}{400} + \frac{10x}{300} + \frac{11x}{1200}\right) = ₹ \frac{x}{20}$.

$\therefore$ Average rate of return $= \left(\frac{x}{20} \times \frac{1}{x} \times 100\right)\% = 5\%.$

Ex. 30. ***In a tournament, a player has a record of 40% wins, out of the number of games he has played so far which in turn is $\frac{2}{5}$ of the total number of games he plays. What is the maximum percentage of the remaining games that the player can lose and still win 50% of all the games played?***

Sol. Let the total number of games played be x.

Number of games already played $= \frac{2x}{5}$.

Games already lost = 60% of $\frac{2x}{5} = \frac{6x}{25}$.

Number of games that the player can lose = 50% of $x = \frac{x}{2}$.

$\therefore$ Number of games that the player can still lose $= \left(\frac{x}{2} - \frac{6x}{25}\right) = \frac{13x}{50}$.

Remaining games to be played $= \left(x - \frac{2x}{5}\right) = \frac{3x}{5}$.

$\therefore$ Required percentage $= \left(\frac{13x}{50} \times \frac{5}{3x} \times 100\right)\% = 43.3\%.$

Ex. 31. ***A man's wage was reduced by 50%. Again the reduced wage was increased by 50%. Find his loss in terms of percentage.*** **(R.R.B., 2008)**

Sol. Let original wage = ₹ 100.

New final wage = 150% of (50% of ₹ 100) = ₹ $\left(\frac{150}{100} \times \frac{50}{100} \times 100\right)$ = ₹ 75.

$\therefore$ Loss = 25%.

Ex. 32. ***A man's working hours a day were increased by 20% and his wages per hour were increased by 15%. By how much percent was his daily earning increased?*** **(R.R.B., 2008)**

Sol. Let the original number of working hours a day be x and original wages per hour be ₹ y.

Then, original daily earning = ₹ (xy). Increased working hours = 120% of $x = \frac{6x}{5}$.

Increased wages per hour = 115% of ₹ y = ₹ $\frac{23y}{20}$.

New daily earning = ₹ $\left(\frac{6x}{5} \times \frac{23y}{20}\right)$ = ₹ $\left(\frac{69xy}{50}\right)$.

Increase in daily earning = ₹ $\left(\frac{69\,xy}{50} - xy\right)$ = ₹ $\left(\frac{19\,xy}{50}\right)$.

$\therefore$ Increase % = $\left(\frac{19\,xy}{50} \times \frac{1}{xy} \times 100\right)\% = 38\%$.

Ex. 33. ***The salary of a person was reduced by 10%. By what percent should his reduced salary be raised so as to bring it at par with his original salary?*** **(S.S.C., 2005, 2007)**

Sol. Let the original salary be ₹ 100. New salary = ₹ 90.

Increase on 90 = 10. Increase on 100 = $\left(\frac{10}{90} \times 100\right)\% = 11\frac{1}{9}\%$.

Ex. 34. ***When the price of a product was decreased by 10%, the number sold increased by 30%. What was the effect on the total revenue?***

Sol. Let the price of the product be ₹ 100 and let original sale be 100 pieces.

Then, Total Revenue = ₹ (100 × 100) = ₹ 10000.

New revenue = ₹ (90 × 130) = ₹ 11700.

$\therefore$ Increase in revenue = $\left(\frac{1700}{10000} \times 100\right)\% = 17\%$.

Ex. 35. ***If the numerator of a fraction be increased by 15% and its denominator be diminished by 8%, the value of the fraction is*** $\frac{15}{16}$. ***Find the original fraction.***

Sol. Let the original fraction be $\frac{x}{y}$.

Then, $\frac{115\% \text{ of } x}{92\% \text{ of } y} = \frac{15}{16} \Rightarrow \frac{115x}{92y} = \frac{15}{16} \Rightarrow \frac{x}{y} = \left(\frac{15}{16} \times \frac{92}{115}\right) = \frac{3}{4}$.

Ex. 36. ***The price of petrol is increased by 25%. How much percent must a car owner reduce his consumption of petrol so as not to increase his expenditure on petrol?*** **(S.S.C., 2005, 2007)**

Sol. Reduction in consumption = $\left[\frac{R}{(100+R)} \times 100\right]\% = \left(\frac{25}{125} \times 100\right)\% = 20\%$.

Ex. 37. ***The population of a town is 1,76,400. If it increases at the rate of 5% per annum, what will be its population 2 years hence? What was it 2 years ago?***

Sol. Population after 2 years $= 176400 \times \left(1 + \frac{5}{100}\right)^2 = \left(176400 \times \frac{21}{20} \times \frac{21}{20}\right) = 194481$.

Population 2 years ago $= \frac{176400}{\left(1 + \frac{5}{100}\right)^2} = \left(176400 \times \frac{20}{21} \times \frac{20}{21}\right) = 160000$.

Ex. 38. ***The value of a machine depreciates at the rate of 10% per annum. If its present value is ₹ 1,62,000, what will be its worth after 2 years? What was the value of the machine 2 years ago?***

Sol. Value of the machine after 2 years

= ₹ $\left[162000 \times \left(1 - \frac{10}{100}\right)^2\right]$ = ₹ $\left(162000 \times \frac{9}{10} \times \frac{9}{10}\right)$ = ₹ 131220.

Value of the machine 2 years ago

= ₹ $\left[\frac{162000}{\left(1 - \frac{10}{100}\right)^2}\right]$ = ₹ $\left(162000 \times \frac{10}{9} \times \frac{10}{9}\right)$ = ₹ 200000.

Ex. 39. ***During one year, the population of a town increased by 5% and during the next year, the population decreased by 5%. If the total population is 9975 at the end of the second year, then what was the population size in the beginning of the first year?***

Sol. Population in the beginning of the first year

$$= \frac{9975}{\left(1+\frac{5}{100}\right)\left(1-\frac{5}{100}\right)} = \left(9975 \times \frac{20}{21} \times \frac{20}{19}\right) = 10000.$$

Ex. 40. ***If A earns $33\frac{1}{3}\%$ more than B, how much percent does B earn less than A?*** **(B.Ed Entrance, 2009)**

Sol. Required percentage $= \left[\frac{\left(\frac{100}{3}\right)}{\left(100+\frac{100}{3}\right)} \times 100\right]\% = \left(\frac{100}{400} \times 100\right)\% = 25\%.$

Ex. 41. ***If A's salary is 30% less than that of B, then how much percent is B's salary more than that of A?*** **(R.R.B., 2008)**

Sol. Required percentage $= \left[\frac{30}{(100-30)} \times 100\right]\% = \frac{300}{7}\% = 42\frac{6}{7}\%.$

Ex. 42. ***How many kg of pure salt must be added to 30 kg of 2% solution of salt and water to increase it to a 10% solution?*** **(M.A.T., 2004)**

Sol. Amount of salt in 30 kg solution $= \left(\frac{2}{100} \times 30\right)$ kg $= 0.6$ kg.

Let x kg of pure salt be added.

Then, $\frac{0.6+x}{30+x} = \frac{10}{100} \Leftrightarrow 60 + 100x = 300 + 10x \Leftrightarrow 90x = 240 \Leftrightarrow x = \frac{8}{3} = 2\frac{2}{3}.$

Ex. 43. ***After 25 kg of water had been evaporated from a solution of salt and water, which had 20% salt, the remaining solution had 30% salt. Find the weight of the original solution.*** **(S.S.C., 2007)**

Sol. Let the weight of the original solution be x kg.

Then, weight of salt in x kg solution $=$ 20% of x kg $= \frac{x}{5}$ kg.

Weight of water in x kg solution $= \left(x - \frac{x}{5}\right)$ kg $= \frac{4x}{5}$ kg.

Weight of solution after evaporation $= (x - 25)$ kg.

$\therefore \frac{x}{5(x-25)} = \frac{30}{100} \Leftrightarrow 150\,(x-25) = 100x \Leftrightarrow 50\,x = 3750 \Leftrightarrow x = 75.$

Hence, weight of the original solution = 75 kg.

Ex. 44. ***Due to a reduction of $6\frac{1}{4}\%$ in the price of sugar, a man is able to buy 1 kg more for ₹ 120. Find the original and reduced rate of sugar.***

Sol. Let original rate be ₹ x per kg.

Reduced rate = ₹ $\left[\left(100 - \frac{25}{4}\right) \times \frac{1}{100} \times x\right]$ = ₹ $\frac{15x}{16}$ per kg.

$\therefore \frac{120}{\frac{15x}{16}} - \frac{120}{x} = 1 \Leftrightarrow \frac{128}{x} - \frac{120}{x} = 1 \Leftrightarrow x = 8.$

So, original rate = ₹ 8 per kg.

Reduced rate = ₹ $\left(\frac{15}{16} \times 8\right)$ per kg = ₹ 7.50 per kg.

Ex. 45. ***In an examination, 35% of total students failed in Hindi, 45% failed in English and 20% in both. Find the percentage of those who passed in both the subjects.***

Sol. Let A and B be the sets of students who failed in Hindi and English respectively.

Then, $n(A) = 35$, $n(B) = 45$, $n(A \cap B) = 20$.

So, $n(A \cup B) = n(A) + n(B) - n(A \cap B) = (35 + 45 - 20) = 60$.

$\therefore$ Percentage failed in Hindi or English or both = 60%.

Hence, percentage passed = (100 – 60)% = 40%.

Ex. 46. ***In an examination, 80% of the students passed in English, 85% in Mathematics and 75% in both English and Mathematics. If 40 students failed in both the subjects, find the total number of students.***

Sol. Let the total number of students be x.

Let A and B represent the sets of students who passed in English and Mathematics respectively.

Then, number of students passed in one or both the subjects

$= n(A \cup B) = n(A) + n(B) - n(A \cap B) = 80\%$ of $x + 85\%$ of $x - 75\%$ of x

$$= \left(\frac{80}{100}x + \frac{85}{100}x - \frac{75}{100}x\right) = \frac{90}{100}x = \frac{9}{10}x.$$

$\therefore$ Students who failed in both the subjects $= \left(x - \frac{9x}{10}\right) = \frac{x}{10}$.

So, $\frac{x}{10} = 40$ or $x = 400$. Hence, total number of students = 400.

Ex. 47. ***Ajay ordered 4 pairs of black socks and some additional pairs of blue socks. The price of the black socks per pair was twice that of the blue ones. When the order was filled, it was found that the number of pairs of the two colours had been interchanged. This increased the bill by 50%. Find the ratio of the number of pairs of black socks to the number of pairs of blue socks in the original order.*** **(M.B.A., 2011)**

Sol. Suppose he ordered n pairs of blue socks.

Let the price of each pair of blue socks be ₹ x.

Then, price of each pair of black socks = ₹ $2x$.

Actual bill = ₹ $(4 \times 2x + nx)$ = ₹ $(8x + nx)$.

Bill made on interchange = ₹ $(2nx + 4x)$.

$\therefore$ $2nx + 4x = 150\%$ of $(8x + nx) \Rightarrow 2nx + 4x = \frac{3}{2}(8x + nx)$

$\Rightarrow 2(2nx + 4x) = 3(8x + nx)$

$\Rightarrow 4nx + 8x = 24x + 3nx \Rightarrow nx = 16x \Rightarrow n = 16$.

Hence, required ratio = 4: 16 = 1: 4.

EXERCISE

(OBJECTIVE TYPE QUESTIONS)

Directions: ***Mark (✓) against the correct answer:***

1. How is $\frac{3}{4}$ expressed as percentage? **(R.R.B., 2006)**
   (*a*) 0.75% (*b*) 7.5%
   (*c*) 75% (*d*) 60%

2. The ratio 5: 4 expressed as a percent equals
   (*a*) 12.5% (*b*) 40%
   (*c*) 80% (*d*) 125%

3. 3.5 can be expressed in terms of percentage as
   (*a*) 0.35% (*b*) 3.5%
   (*c*) 35% (*d*) 350%

4. When expressed as a fraction 64% would mean
   (*a*) $\frac{16}{25}$ (*b*) $\frac{9}{64}$
   (*c*) $\frac{8}{81}$ (*d*) $\frac{12}{121}$

5. Half of 1 percent written as a decimal is **(L.I.C.A.D.O., 2008)**
   (*a*) 0.005 (*b*) 0.05
   (*c*) 0.02 (*d*) 0.2

6. 12% of 5000 =? **(CLAT, 2010)**
   (*a*) 600 (*b*) 620
   (*c*) 680 (*d*) 720

7. 38% of 341 =? (Bank Recruitment, 2009)
(a) 120.68 (b) 129.58
(c) 135.78 (d) 136.28
(e) None of these

8. (550% of 250) ÷ 275 =? (Bank P.O., 2009)
(a) 15 (b) 0.5
(c) 1.5 (d) 25
(e) None of these

9. 280% of 3940 =? (L.I.C.A.D.O., 2007)
(a) 10132 (b) 11032
(c) 11230 (d) 11320
(e) None of these

10. 92.5% of 550 =? (Bank Recruitment, 2008)
(a) 506.45 (b) 508.75
(c) 518.55 (d) 521.65
(e) None of these

11. 2% of 2 =?
(a) 0.04 (b) 0.4
(c) 0.02 (d) 0.004

12. 10% of 5 and 5% of 10 add up to (P.C.S., 2008)
(a) 0.10 (b) 0.25
(c) 1.0 (d) 2.5

13. 36% of 245 – 40% of 210 = 10 –? (Bank P.O., 2010)
(a) 4.2 (b) 4.9
(c) 5.6 (d) 6.8
(e) None of these

14. 45% of 300 + $\sqrt{?}$ = 56% of 750 – 10% of 250 (R.R.B., 2009)
(a) 60 (b) 130
(c) 260 (d) 67600

15. 15% of 578 + 22.5% of 644 =? (Bank P.O., 2010)
(a) 231.4 (b) 231.6
(c) 231.8 (d) 233.6
(e) None of these

16. 140% of 56 + 56% of 140 =? (Bank P.O., 2009)
(a) 78.4 (b) 87.4
(c) 156.6 (d) 158.6
(e) None of these

17. (7.9% of 134) – (3.4% of 79) =? (Bank P.O., 2009)
(a) 7.3 (b) 7.8
(c) 8.1 (d) 8.6
(e) None of these

18. (23.6% of 1254) – (16.6% of 834) =? (S.B.I.P.O., 2008)
(a) 153.5 (b) 155.5
(c) 157.5 (d) 159.5
(e) None of these

19. (0.85% of 405) + (2.25% of 550) =? (Bank P.O., 2007)
(a) 13.8175 (b) 14.7125
(c) 15.7150 (d) 16.7175
(e) None of these

20. What is 45% of 25% of $\frac{4}{5}$th of 850? (Bank P.O., 2009)
(a) 67.5 (b) 69.5
(c) 76.5 (d) 83.5
(e) None of these

21. What is 28% of 36% of $\frac{5}{7}$th of 5000? (Bank P.O., 2008)
(a) 360 (b) 375
(c) 420 (d) 480
(e) None of these

22. (0.56% of 225) × (3.25% of 430) =? (Bank P.O., 2006)
(a) 15.3195 (b) 15.6175
(c) 17.3075 (d) 17.6085
(e) None of these

23. An agent sells goods of value of ₹ 15000. The commission which he receives at the rate of $12\frac{1}{2}$% is (SNAP, 2010)
(a) ₹ 1875 (b) ₹ 2000
(c) ₹ 2125 (d) ₹ 2700

24. One-eighth of a number is 41.5. What will 69% of that number be?
(a) 219.12 (b) 225.76
(c) 229.08 (d) 232.4
(e) None of these

25. Ten percent of twenty plus twenty percent of ten equals
(a) 10 percent of 20 (b) 20 percent of 10
(c) 1 percent of 200 (d) 2 percent of 200

26. 60% of 264 is the same as
(a) 10% of 44 (b) 15% of 1056
(c) 30% of 132 (d) None of these

27. 270 candidates appeared for an examination, of which 252 passed. The pass percentage is:
(a) 80% (b) $83\frac{1}{2}$%
(c) $90\frac{1}{3}$% (d) $93\frac{1}{3}$%

28. 5 out of 2250 parts of earth is sulphur. What is the percentage of sulphur in earth?
(a) $\frac{11}{50}$ (b) $\frac{2}{9}$
(c) $\frac{1}{45}$ (d) $\frac{2}{45}$

29. In an examination Sumit scores a total of 626 marks out of 850. What is his approximate percentage in the examination? **(Bank Recruitment, 2009)**

(*a*) 64 (*b*) 67
(*c*) 74 (*d*) 79
(*e*) 83

30. The marks obtained by a student are given below. What is his total percentage in all the subjects?

Subjects	Total Marks	Marks Obtained
Mathematics	100	100
Science	100	84
Social Studies	100	67
English	50	25
Hindi	50	24

(*a*) 56% (*b*) 68%
(*c*) 75% (*d*) 80%

31. The following table gives the marks obtained by a student in the first and second semester examinations in four subjects in a given year.

Subjects	1st Semester	2nd Semester	Maximum Marks
Physics	35	30	50
Chemistry	30	25	50
Mathematics	65	45	100
Social Science	80	85	100

The aggregate percentage of marks obtained by the student in the given year is nearly

(*a*) 56 (*b*) 61
(*c*) 64 (*d*) 66

32. I paid ₹ 27.20 as sales tax on a watch worth ₹ 340. Find the rate of sales tax.

(*a*) 8% (*b*) 9%
(*c*) 10% (*d*) 12%

33. What percent of 88 is 33?

(*a*) 34.5% (*b*) 35.5%
(*c*) 36.5% (*d*) 37.5%

34. 0.01 is what percent of 0.1? **(S.S.C., 2005)**

(*a*) $\frac{1}{100}$ (*b*) $\frac{1}{10}$
(*c*) 10 (*d*) 100

35. What percent is 1 minute and 12 seconds of an hour?

(*a*) 2% (*b*) 10%
(*c*) 12% (*d*) 20%

36. The enrolment of students in a school increases from 560 to 581. What is the percent increase in the enrolment?

(*a*) 2.75% (*b*) 3.25%
(*c*) 3.72% (*d*) 3.75%

37. What percent of 7.2 kg is 18 gms?

(*a*) .025% (*b*) .25%
(*c*) 2.5% (*d*) 25%

38. What percent of ₹ 2650 is ₹ 1987.50?

(*a*) 60% (*b*) 75%
(*c*) 80% (*d*) 90%

39. What percent of a day is 3 hours?

(*a*) $12\frac{1}{2}\%$ (*b*) $16\frac{2}{3}\%$
(*c*) $18\frac{2}{3}\%$ (*d*) $22\frac{1}{2}\%$

40. The price for a pair of cuff links is ₹ 1.00. The price for a 5-pair package of cuff links is ₹ 3.40. The 5-pair package is what percent cheaper per pair than 5 pairs purchased separately? **(M.A.T., 2004)**

(*a*) 32% (*b*) 47%
(*c*) 62% (*d*) 63%

41. A bakery opened with its daily supply of 40 dozen rolls. Half of the rolls were sold by noon and 60% of the remaining rolls were sold between noon and closing time. How many dozen rolls were left unsold? **(SNAP, 2010)**

(*a*) 6 (*b*) 8
(*c*) 10 (*d*) 12

42. 5 kg of metal A and 20 kg of metal B are mixed to form an alloy. The percentage of metal A in the alloy is

(*a*) 20% (*b*) 25%
(*c*) 40% (*d*) None of these

43. 30% apples out of 450 are rotten. How many apples are in good condition? **(R.R.B., 2006)**

(*a*) 125 (*b*) 180
(*c*) 240 (*d*) 315

44. A company pays rent of ₹ 25000 per month for office space to its owner. But if the company pays the annual rent at the beginning of the year the owner gives a discount of 5% on the total annual rent. What is the annual amount the company pays to the owner after the discount? **(Bank Recruitment, 2008)**

(*a*) ₹ 2,75,000 (*b*) ₹ 2,85,000
(*c*) ₹ 2,95,000 (*d*) ₹ 3,00,000
(*e*) None of these

45. An interval of 3 hours 40 minutes is wrongly estimated as 3 hours 45.5 minutes. The error percentage is **(S.S.C., 2006)**

(*a*) 2.5 (*b*) 5
(*c*) 5.2 (*d*) 5.5

46. The following table gives the income distribution of 200 households of a village:

Monthly Income (in ₹)	Number of Households
< 1000	25
< 2000	80
< 5000	170
< 10000	200

What is the percentage of households whose monthly income is above ₹ 2000 but below ₹ 5000? (P.C.S., 2006)

(*a*) 32.5 (*b*) 45
(*c*) 85 (*d*) 90

47. In two successive years 100 and 75 students of a school appeared at the final examination. Respectively 75% and 60% of them passed. The average rate of pass is

(*a*) $68\frac{4}{7}\%$ (*b*) 78%
(*c*) 80% (*d*) $80\frac{1}{2}\%$

48. A toy merchant announces 25% rebate in prices of balls. If one needs to have a rebate of ₹ 40, then how many balls each costing ₹ 32, he should purchase? (M.B.A., 2007)

(*a*) 5 (*b*) 6
(*c*) 7 (*d*) 10

49. 1.14 expressed as a percent of 1.9 is (S.S.C., 2010)

(*a*) 6% (*b*) 10%
(*c*) 60% (*d*) 90%

50. Kamal has 160 toffees. He gave 5% toffees to Ravi, 15% toffees to Anita and one-fourth of the toffees to Gagan. How many toffees are left with Kamal after the distribution? (Bank Recruitment, 2010)

(*a*) 78 (*b*) 69
(*c*) 88 (*d*) 79
(*e*) None of these

51. A shopkeeper sells note-books at the rate of ₹ 45 each and earns a commission of 4%. He also sells pencil boxes at the rate of ₹ 80 each and earns a commission of 20%. How much amount of commission will he earn in two weeks if he sells 10 note-books and 6 pencil boxes a day?

(*a*) ₹ 1496 (*b*) ₹ 1586
(*c*) ₹ 1596 (*d*) ₹ 1956
(*e*) None of these

52. It costs ₹ 1 to photocopy a sheet of paper. However, 2% discount is allowed on all photocopies done after first 1000 sheets. How much will it cost to copy 5000 sheets of paper? (IGNOU, 2003)

(*a*) ₹ 3920 (*b*) ₹ 3980
(*c*) ₹ 4900 (*d*) ₹ 4920

53. A housewife saved ₹ 2.50 in buying an item on sale. If she spent ₹ 25 for the item, approximately how much percent she saved in the transaction? (Section Officers', 2003)

(*a*) 8% (*b*) 9%
(*c*) 10% (*d*) 11%

54. How many litres of pure acid are there in 8 litres of a 20% solution?

(*a*) 1.4 (*b*) 1.5
(*c*) 1.6 (*d*) 2.4

55. Rajeev buys goods worth ₹ 6650. He gets a rebate of 6% on it. After getting the rebate, he pays sales tax @ 10%. Find the amount he will have to pay for the goods. (M.A.T., 2002)

(*a*) ₹ 6876.10 (*b*) ₹ 6999.20
(*c*) ₹ 6654 (*d*) ₹ 7000

56. Which one of the following shows the best percentage?

(*a*) $\frac{384}{540}$ (*b*) $\frac{425}{500}$
(*c*) $\frac{570}{700}$ (*d*) $\frac{480}{660}$

57. In a class of 65 students and 4 teachers, each student got sweets that are 20% of the total number of students and each teacher got sweets that are 40% of the total number of students. How many sweets are there? (Bank P.O., 2009)

(*a*) 104 (*b*) 845
(*c*) 949 (*d*) 897
(*e*) None of these

58. A student scores 55% marks in 8 papers of 100 marks each. He scores 15% of his total marks in English. How much does he score in English? (Bank Recruitment, 2008)

(*a*) 44 (*b*) 45
(*c*) 66 (*d*) 77
(*e*) None of these

59. A, B, C and D have ₹ 40, 50, 60 and 70 respectively when they go to visit a fair. A spends ₹ 18, B spends ₹ 21, C spends ₹ 24 and D spends ₹ 27. Who has done the highest expenditure proportionate to his resources?

(*a*) A (*b*) B
(*c*) C (*d*) D

60. A country follows a progressive taxation system under which the income tax rate applicable varies for different slabs of income. Total tax is computed by calculating the tax for each slab and adding them up. The rates applicable are as follows: (M.A.T., 2005, 2006)

Annual Income Slab (in ₹)	Tax Rate Applicable
0 – 50,000	0%
50,001 – 60,000	10%
60,001 – 1,50,000	20%
> 1,50,000	30%

If my annual income is ₹ 1,70,000, then what is the tax payable by me?

(*a*) ₹ 17000 (*b*) ₹ 25000
(*c*) ₹ 34000 (*d*) ₹ 51000

61. 40% of 60% of $\frac{3}{5}$th of a number is 504. What is 25% of $\frac{2}{5}$th of that number? **(NABARD, 2009)**

(*a*) 175 (*b*) 180
(*c*) 350 (*d*) 360
(*e*) None of these

62. 125% of 3060 – 85% of? = 408 **(Bank P.O., 2010)**

(*a*) 3890 (*b*) 3940
(*c*) 4015 (*d*) 4020
(*e*) None of these

63. 40% of 265 + 35% of 180 = 50% of? **(Bank P.O., 2010)**

(*a*) 84.5 (*b*) 169
(*c*) 253.5 (*d*) 338
(*e*) None of these

64. ? % of 450 + 46% of 285 = 257.1 **(Bank P.O., 2009)**

(*a*) 21 (*b*) 28
(*c*) 32 (*d*) 34
(*e*) None of these

65. 36% of 365 +? % of 56.2 = 156.69 **(Bank P.O., 2010)**

(*a*) 30 (*b*) 35
(*c*) 40 (*d*) 45
(*e*) None of these

66. 35568 ÷? % of 650 = 456

(*a*) 12 (*b*) 14
(*c*) 16 (*d*) 18
(*e*) None of these

67. 23% of 8040 + 42% of 545 =? % of 3000 **(Bank P.O., 2006)**

(*a*) 56.17 (*b*) 63.54
(*c*) 69.27 (*d*) 71.04
(*e*) None of these

68. 3.2% of 500 × 2.4% of? = 288 **(S.B.I.P.O., 2008)**

(*a*) 600 (*b*) 650
(*c*) 700 (*d*) 750

69. 85% of 485.5 = 50% of? **(Bank P.O., 2006)**

(*a*) 675.75 (*b*) 735.65
(*c*) 825.35 (*d*) 915.5
(*e*) None of these

70. 40% of 4.5 +? % of $\frac{2}{3}$ = 20% of 10

(*a*) 20 (*b*) 25
(*c*) 30 (*d*) 35
(*e*) None of these

71. 30% of 28% of 480 is the same as

(*a*) 15% of 56% of 240 (*b*) 60% of 28% of 240
(*c*) 60% of 56% of 240 (*d*) None of these

72. What is 25% of 25% equal to?

(*a*) 0.00625 (*b*) 0.0625
(*c*) 0.625 (*d*) 6.25

73. What percent is 3% of 5%?

(*a*) 15% (*b*) 30%
(*c*) 50% (*d*) 60%

74. 64% of a number is 2592. What is 88% of that number? **(Bank Recruitment, 2009)**

(*a*) 3202 (*b*) 3458
(*c*) 3564 (*d*) 3826
(*e*) None of these

75. 42% of a number is 892.5. What is 73% of that number? **(Bank Recruitment, 2009)**

(*a*) 1466.25 (*b*) 1508.75
(*c*) 1551.25 (*d*) 1636.25
(*e*) None of these

76. 15% of 45% of a number is 105.3. What is 24% of that number? **(Bank P.O., 2009)**

(*a*) 374.4 (*b*) 375
(*c*) 385.5 (*d*) 390
(*e*) None of these

77. If 0.03 is X% of 0.3, then the value of X is **(I.A.M., 2007)**

(*a*) 3 (*b*) 10
(*c*) 30 (*d*) Cannot be determined

78. 40% of 60% of 32% of an amount is ₹ 432. What is the amount? **(Bank Recruitment, 2007)**

(*a*) ₹ 5000 (*b*) ₹ 5600
(*c*) ₹ 6400 (*d*) None of these

79. Find the greatest possible number for which 30% of that number is less than 100.

(*a*) 325 (*b*) 328
(*c*) 331 (*d*) 333
(*e*) 335

80. If ₹ 2800 is $\frac{2}{7}$ percent of the value of a house, the worth of the house (in ₹) is

(*a*) 8,00,000 (*b*) 9,80,000
(*c*) 10,00,000 (*d*) 12,00,000

81. 15% of? % of 582 = 17.46

(*a*) 2 (*b*) 10
(*c*) 20 (*d*) None of these

82. In a year, a man manages to sell only 65% of the chicken he owns. How many chicken should the man own to sell 47775 chicken in a year? **(M.B.A., 2005)**

(*a*) 55000 (*b*) 68500
(*c*) 73000 (*d*) 82500
(*e*) None of these

83. If 35% of a number is 175, then what percent of 175 is that number?

(*a*) 35% (*b*) 65%
(*c*) 280% (*d*) None of these

84. If an electricity bill is paid before due date, one gets a reduction of 4% on the amount of the bill. By paying the bill before due date a person got a reduction of ₹ 13. The amount of his electricity bill was **(S.S.C., 2010)**

(*a*) ₹ 125 (*b*) ₹ 225
(*c*) ₹ 325 (*d*) ₹ 425

85. In an examination X secures 58% marks and Y secures 105 marks less than X. If the maximum marks were 700, then what percent of marks did Y secure?

(*a*) 42 percent (*b*) 43 percent
(*c*) 52 percent (*d*) None of these

86. Ms. Pooja invests 13% of her monthly salary, i.e. ₹ 8554 in Mediclaim Policies. Later she invests 23% of her monthly salary on Child Education Policies ; also she invests another 8% of her monthly salary on Mutual Funds. What is the total annual amount invested by Ms. Pooja? **(S.B.I.P.O., 2008)**

(*a*) ₹ 28952 (*b*) ₹ 43428
(*c*) ₹ 173712 (*d*) ₹ 347424
(*e*) None of these

87. Nupur invests ₹ 89856, which is 26% of her annual income, in mutual funds. What is her monthly income? **(Bank Recruitment, 2008)**

(*a*) ₹ 23980.50 (*b*) ₹ 28800
(*c*) ₹ 28990 (*d*) ₹ 33606.25
(*e*) None of these

88. David and his wife each receives an 8 percent annual rise. If David receives a raise of ₹ 800 and his wife receives a raise of ₹ 840, what is the difference between their annual incomes after their raises? **(Campus Recruitment, 2008)**

(*a*) ₹ 40 (*b*) ₹ 460
(*c*) ₹ 500 (*d*) ₹ 540

89. If the average of a number, its 75% and its 25% is 240, then the number is **(P.C.S., 2006)**

(*a*) 280 (*b*) 320
(*c*) 360 (*d*) 400

90. A company bought a total of 60 computers and 2[...] printers to modernise billing operations. If the pric[e] of each computer was three times the price of eac[h] printer, what percent of the total cost of the purchas[e] was the total cost of the printers?

(*a*) 10% (*b*) 11%
(*c*) 15% (*d*) 20%

91. An individual pays 30% income tax. On this ta[x] he has to pay a surcharge of 10%. Thus the net ta[x] rate, he has to pay, is

(*a*) 27% (*b*) 33%
(*c*) 40% (*d*) 45%

92. Anand has drawn an angle of measure 45° 2[...] when he was asked to draw an angle of 45°. Th[e] percentage error in his drawing is

(*a*) 0.5 (*b*) 1.0
(*c*) 1.5 (*d*) 2.0

93. The value of which of the following fractions is les[s] than twenty percent? **(Bank P.O., 201[...])**

(*a*) $\frac{5}{6}$ (*b*) $\frac{2}{3}$
(*c*) $\frac{2}{5}$ (*d*) $\frac{1}{4}$
(*e*) $\frac{2}{11}$

94. The difference between 54% of a number and 26[%] of the same number is 22526. What is 66% of tha[t] number? **(Bank Recruitment, 2009)**

(*a*) 48372 (*b*) 49124
(*c*) 51218 (*d*) 53097
(*e*) None of these

95. The difference between 38% of a number and 24[%] of the same number is ₹ 135.10. What is 40% of tha[t] number? **(M.A.T., 2009)**

(*a*) 370 (*b*) 378
(*c*) 386 (*d*) 394

96. 76% of the students in a school are boys. If th[e] number of girls is 204, then the total number [of] students is **(R.R.B., 201[...])**

(*a*) 760 (*b*) 800
(*c*) 850 (*d*) 900

97. In an examination, 65% of the total examinees passe[d]. If the number of failures is 420, the total number [of] examinees is

(*a*) 1000 (*b*) 1200
(*c*) 1500 (*d*) 1625

98. There are 340 vacancies for a particular post in an organisation. Experience shows that 15% of the candidates interviewed get rejected. How many candidates should be interviewed to fill all the vacancies?

(*a*) 226 (*b*) 391
(*c*) 400 (*d*) 420
(*e*) None of these

99. Rajan got 76 percent marks and Sonia got 480 marks in a test. The maximum marks of the test is equal to the marks obtained by Rajan and Sonia together. How many marks did Rajan score in the test? **(Bank P.O., 2010)**

(*a*) 1450 (*b*) 1520
(*c*) 1540 (*d*) 2000
(*e*) None of these

100. If a bucket is 80% full, then it contains 2 litres more water than when it is $66\frac{2}{3}\%$ full. What is the capacity of the bucket? **(S.S.C., 2005)**

(*a*) 10 litres (*b*) 15 litres
(*c*) $16\frac{2}{3}$ litres (*d*) 20 litres

101. Vinay decided to donate 5% of his salary. On the day of donation he changed his mind and donated ₹ 1687.50, which was 75% of what he had decided earlier. How much is Vinay's salary? **(Bank P.O., 2008)**

(*a*) ₹ 33750 (*b*) ₹ 37500
(*c*) ₹ 45000 (*d*) Cannot be determined
(*e*) None of these

102. One-fourth of sixty percent of a number is equal to two-fifths of twenty percent of another number. What is the respective ratio of the first number to the second number? **(Bank P.O., 2008)**

(*a*) 4: 7 (*b*) 5: 9
(*c*) 8: 13 (*d*) Cannot be determined
(*e*) None of these

103. The sum of two numbers is 2490. If 6.5% of one number is equal to 8.5% of the other, the greater number is **(R.R.B., 2006)**

(*a*) 1079 (*b*) 1250
(*c*) 1380 (*d*) 1411

104. The number of students who opted for IT courses decreased by 23%. If the number is 1540 now, then the original number of students opting for IT courses was

(*a*) 1600 (*b*) 1800
(*c*) 2000 (*d*) 2200

105. If the monthly salary of an employee is increased by $2\frac{2}{3}\%$, he gets ₹ 72 more. His monthly salary (in ₹) is

(*a*) 2000 (*b*) 2700
(*c*) 3600 (*d*) 7200

106. A store raised the price of an item by exactly 10 percent. Which of the following could not be the resulting price of the item?

(*a*) ₹ 5.50 (*b*) ₹ 7.60
(*c*) ₹ 11.00 (*d*) ₹ 12.10

107. A number increased by $37\frac{1}{2}\%$ gives 33. The number is **(Hotel Management, 2005)**

(*a*) 22 (*b*) 24
(*c*) 25 (*d*) 27

108. Three-fourths of a number is equal to 60% of another number and the difference between these two numbers is 20. What is the sum of these two numbers?

(*a*) 170 (*b*) 180
(*c*) 220 (*d*) Cannot be determined
(*e*) None of these

109. The number which exceeds 16% of it by 42 is

(*a*) 50 (*b*) 52
(*c*) 58 (*d*) 60

110. What percentage of numbers from 1 to 70 have squares that end in the digit 1?

(*a*) 1 (*b*) 14
(*c*) 20 (*d*) 21

111. By how much percent is four-fifths of 70 lesser than five-sevenths of 112? **(G.B.O., 2007)**

(*a*) 24% (*b*) 30%
(*c*) 36% (*d*) 42%

112. If a number x is 10% less than another number y and y is 10% more than 125, then x is equal to

(*a*) 123.75 (*b*) 140.55
(*c*) 143 (*d*) 150

113. If 75% of a number is added to 75, then the result is the number itself. The number is **(P.C.S., 2008)**

(*a*) 50 (*b*) 60
(*c*) 300 (*d*) 400

114. When 125 is subtracted from a number, it reduces to its 37.5 percent. What is 25 percent of that number? **(Bank P.O., 2011)**

(*a*) 50 (*b*) 75
(*c*) 125 (*d*) 175
(*e*) None of these

115. Which of the following multipliers will cause a number to be increased by 29.7%?

(*a*) 1.297 (*b*) 12.97
(*c*) 129.7 (*d*) 1297

116. The sum of two numbers is $\frac{28}{25}$ of the first number. The second number is what percent of the first?

(*a*) 12% (*b*) 14%
(*c*) 16% (*d*) 18%

117. A number reduced by 25% becomes 225. What percent should it be increased so that it becomes 390? **(R.R.B., 2010)**

(*a*) 25% (*b*) 30%
(*c*) 35% (*d*) 45%

118. If 25% of a number is subtracted from a second number, the second number reduces to its five-sixths. What is the ratio of the first number to the second number?

(*a*) 1: 3 (*b*) 2: 3
(*c*) 3: 2 (*d*) Data inadequate

119. The difference of two numbers is 20% of the larger number. If the smaller number is 20, then the larger number is: **(Bank P.O., 2010)**

(*a*) 25 (*b*) 45
(*c*) 50 (*d*) 80

120. When any number is divided by 12, then dividend becomes $\frac{1}{4}$th of the other number. By how much percent first number is greater than the second number?

(*a*) 150 (*b*) 200
(*c*) 300 (*d*) Data inadequate

121. If one number is 80% of the other and 4 times the sum of their squares is 656, then the numbers are

(*a*) 4, 5 (*b*) 8, 10
(*c*) 16, 20 (*d*) None of these

122. Two numbers A and B are such that the sum of 5% of A and 4% of B is two-thirds of the sum of 6% of A and 8% of B. Find the ratio of A:B. **(M.A.T., 2009)**

(*a*) 2: 3 (*b*) 1: 1
(*c*) 3: 4 (*d*) 4: 3

123. Three candidates contested an election and received 1136, 7636 and 11628 votes respectively. What percentage of the total votes did the winning candidate get?

(*a*) 57% (*b*) 60%
(*c*) 65% (*d*) 90%

124. The population of a town increased from 1,75,000 to 2,62,500 in a decade. The average percent increase of population per year is

(*a*) 4.37% (*b*) 5%
(*c*) 6% (*d*) 8.75%

125. A student multiplied a number by $\frac{3}{5}$ instead of $\frac{5}{3}$. What is the percentage error in the calculation?

(*a*) 34% (*b*) 44%
(*c*) 54% (*d*) 64%

126. A tempo is insured to the extent of $\frac{4}{5}$ of its original value. If the premium on it at the rate of 1.3 percent amounts to ₹ 910, the original value of the tempo is

(*a*) ₹ 78,500 (*b*) ₹ 80,000
(*c*) ₹ 82,500 (*d*) ₹ 87,500

127. When 15% is lost in grinding wheat, a country can export 30 lakh tons of wheat. On the other hand, if 10% is lost in grinding, it can export 40 lakh tons of wheat. The production of wheat in the country is:

(*a*) 20 lakh tons (*b*) 80 lakh tons
(*c*) 200 lakh tons (*d*) 800 lakh tons

128. In a competitive examination in State A, 6% candidates got selected from the total appeared candidates. State B had an equal number of candidates appeared and 7% candidates got selected with 80 more candidates got selected than A. What was the number of candidates appeared from each State?

(*a*) 7600 (*b*) 8000
(*c*) 8400 (*d*) Data inadequate

129. The price of a car is ₹ 3,25,000. It was insured to 85% of its price. The car was damaged completely in an accident and the insurance company paid 90% of the insurance. What was the difference between the price of the car and the amount received? **(B.Ed Entrance, 2010)**

(*a*) ₹ 32,500 (*b*) ₹ 48,750
(*c*) ₹ 76,375 (*d*) ₹ 81,250

130. Gauri went to the stationers and bought things worth ₹ 25, out of which 30 paise went on sales tax on taxable purchases. If the tax rate was 6%, then what was the cost of the tax free items?

(*a*) ₹ 15 (*b*) ₹ 15.70
(*c*) ₹ 19.70 (*d*) ₹ 20

131. A batsman scored 110 runs which included 3 boundaries and 8 sixes. What percent of his total score did he make by running between the wickets? **(S.S.C., 2004)**

(*a*) 45% (*b*) $45\frac{5}{11}\%$
(*c*) $54\frac{6}{11}\%$ (*d*) 55%

132. After deducting a commission of 5%, a T.V. set costs ₹ 9595. Its marked price is:
(a) ₹ 10,000 (b) ₹ 10,075
(c) ₹ 10,100 (d) ₹ 10,500

133. A person who spends $66\frac{2}{3}\%$ of his income is able to save ₹ 1200 per month. His monthly expenses (in ₹) are
(a) ₹ 1200 (b) ₹ 2400
(c) ₹ 3000 (d) ₹ 3200

134. Twenty-five percent of Reena's yearly income is equal to seventy-five percent of Anubhav's monthly income. If Anubhav's yearly income is ₹ 240000, what is Reena's monthly income? (Bank Recruitment, 2010)
(a) ₹ 60000 (b) ₹ 12000
(c) ₹ 5200 (d) Cannot be determined
(e) None of these

135. Twelve percent of Kaushal's monthly salary is equal to sixteen percent of Nandini's monthly salary. Sonal's monthly salary is half that of Nandini's. If Sonal's annual salary is ₹ 1.08 lacs, what is Kaushal's monthly salary? (Bank P.O., 2010)
(a) ₹ 18000 (b) ₹ 20000
(c) ₹ 24000 (d) ₹ 26000
(e) None of these

136. Aman's expense is 30% more than Vimal's and Vimal's expense is 10% less than Raman's. If the sum of their expenses is ₹ 6447, then what would be Aman's expense? (Bank P.O., 2009)
(a) ₹ 1890 (b) ₹ 2100
(c) ₹ 2200 (d) ₹ 2457
(e) None of these

137. Two tailors X and Y are paid a total of ₹ 550 per week by their employer. If X is paid 20 percent more than the sum paid to Y, how much is Y paid per week?
(a) ₹ 200 (b) ₹ 250
(c) ₹ 300 (d) None of these

138. Prithvi spent ₹ 89745 on his college fees, ₹ 51291 on Personality Development Classes and the remaining 27% of the total amount he had as cash with him. What was the total amount? (Bank P.O., 2008)
(a) ₹ 185400 (b) ₹ 189600
(c) ₹ 191800 (d) ₹ 193200
(e) None of these

139. If a number is reduced by 40% it becomes two-thirds of another number. What is the ratio of the first number to the second number?
(a) 8: 9 (b) 9: 8
(c) 10: 9 (d) 9: 10
(e) None of these

140. To meet a government requirement, a bottler must test 5 percent of its spring water and 10 percent of its sparkling water for purity. If a customer ordered 120 cases of spring water and 80 cases of sparkling water, then what percent of all the cases must the bottler test before he can send it out? (M.A.T., 2006)
(a) 6.5% (b) 7.0%
(c) 7.5% (d) 8.0%

141. When income tax is 3 paise in a rupee, a person's net income is ₹ 237650. What will it be when the income tax is raised to 7 paise? (M.B.A., 2007)
(a) ₹ 233000 (b) ₹ 231650
(c) ₹ 227850 (d) None of these

142. A monthly return railway ticket costs 25 percent more than a single ticket. A week's extension can be had for the former by paying 5 percent of the monthly ticket's cost. If the money paid for the monthly ticket (with extension) is ₹ 84, the price of the single ticket is (M.A.T., 2007)
(a) ₹ 48 (b) ₹ 64
(c) ₹ 72 (d) ₹ 80

143. In limestone, 40% is calcium and the rest is carbon and oxygen. If in 20 kg of limestone, there is 9.4 kg of oxygen, then what is the percentage of carbon in it?
(a) 12% (b) 13%
(c) 14% (d) 15%

144. In a class of 72 children, children are seated in rows and columns in such a way that the number of children in each row is 12.5% more than the number of children in each column. How many children are there in each row?
(a) 8 (b) 9
(c) 12 (d) 18
(e) None of these

145. The owner of a boutique decides to calculate the percentage of customers who purchase hats. If 40 percent of the store's customers decide to purchase items, and of those customers 15 percent purchase hats, what percent of the store's customers purchase hats?
(a) 4% (b) 6%
(c) 15% (d) 24%

146. In a market research project, 20% opted for Nirma detergent whereas 60% opted for Surf Blue detergent. The remaining individuals were not certain. If the difference between those who opted for Surf Blue and those who were uncertain was 720, how many respondents were covered in the survey? (M.B.A., 2007)
(a) 1440 (b) 1800
(c) 3600 (d) Data inadequate

147. In an examination it is required to get 36% of the aggregate marks to pass. A student gets 198 marks and is declared failed by 36 marks. What is the maximum aggregate marks a student can get? **(L.I.C.A.D.O., 2007)**

(*a*) 480 (*b*) 550
(*c*) 650 (*d*) Cannot be determined
(*e*) None of these

148. In a test, minimum passing percentage for girls and boys is 35% and 40% respectively. A boy scored 483 marks and failed by 117 marks. What is the minimum passing marks for girls? **(Bank P.O., 2010)**

(*a*) 425 (*b*) 500
(*c*) 520 (*d*) 625
(*e*) None of these

149. In an examination it is required to get 40% of the aggregate marks to pass. A student get 261 marks and is declared failed by 4% marks. What are the maximum aggregate marks a student can get? **(Bank Recruitment, 2008)**

(*a*) 700 (*b*) 730
(*c*) 745 (*d*) 765
(*e*) None of these

150. A candidate has to obtain minimum 33% of the total marks to pass. He got 25% of the total marks and failed by 40 marks. The maximum marks are

(*a*) 300 (*b*) 400
(*c*) 500 (*d*) 600

151. In an examination it is required to get 296 of the total maximum aggregate marks to pass. A student gets 259 marks and is decided failed. The difference of marks obtained by the student and that required to pass is 5%. What are the maximum aggregate marks a student can get? **(M.A.T., 2009)**

(*a*) 690 (*b*) 740
(*c*) 780 (*d*) Cannot be determined

152. Two candidates fought an election. One of them got 62% of the total votes and won by 432 votes. What is the total number of votes polled? **(Bank Recruitment, 2009)**

(*a*) 1500 (*b*) 1600
(*c*) 1800 (*d*) Cannot be determined
(*e*) None of these

153. In a college election between two candidates, one candidate got 55% of the total valid votes, 15% of the votes were invalid. If the total votes were 15200, what is the number of valid votes the other candidate got? **(Bank P.O., 2009)**

(*a*) 5814 (*b*) 6840
(*c*) 7106 (*d*) 8360
(*e*) None of these

154. At an election involving two candidates, 68 votes were declared invalid. The winning candidate secures 52% and wins by 98 votes. The total number of votes polled is

(*a*) 2382 (*b*) 2450
(*c*) 2518 (*d*) None of these

155. In a certain assembly constituency election, 80% of voters exercised their voting right and the winning candidate got elected with 65% of votes polled. What percent of total votes did he poll?

(*a*) 35 (*b*) 52
(*c*) 55 (*d*) 57

156. In an election, a total of 5,00,000 voters participated. A candidate got 2,55,000 votes which was 60% of the total valid votes. What was the percentage of invalid votes?

(*a*) 10% (*b*) 12%
(*c*) 15% (*d*) $\frac{300}{17}\%$

157. 10% of the voters did not cast their vote in an election between two candidates. 10% of the votes polled were found invalid. The successful candidate got 54% of the valid votes and won by a majority of 1620 votes. The number of voters enrolled on the voters' list was

(*a*) 25000 (*b*) 33000
(*c*) 35000 (*d*) 40000

158. 8% of the people eligible to vote are between 18 and 21 years of age. In an election, 85% of those eligible to vote, who were between 18 and 21, actually voted. In that election, the number of persons between 18 and 21, who actually voted, was what percent of those eligible to vote?

(*a*) 4.2 (*b*) 6.4
(*c*) 6.8 (*d*) 8

159. In an election, 30% of the voters voted for candidate A whereas 60% of the remaining voted for candidate B. The remaining voters did not vote. If the difference between those who voted for candidate A and those who did not vote was 1200, how many individuals were eligible for casting vote in that election?

(*a*) 10,000 (*b*) 45,000
(*c*) 60,000 (*d*) 72,000

160. While purchasing one item costing ₹ 400, I had to pay the sales tax at 7% and on another costing ₹ 6400, the sales tax was 9%. What percent of the sales tax I had to pay, taking the two items together on an average?

(*a*) 8% (*b*) $8\frac{13}{17}\%$
(*c*) $8\frac{15}{17}\%$ (*d*) $8\frac{1}{2}\%$

1. A student secures 90%, 60% and 54% marks in test papers with 100, 150 and 200 respectively as maximum marks. The percentage of his aggregate is

(*a*) 64 (*b*) 68
(*c*) 70 (*d*) None of these

2. 1100 boys and 700 girls are examined in a test; 42% of the boys and 30% of the girls pass. The percentage of the total who failed is

(*a*) 58% (*b*) $62\frac{2}{3}\%$
(*c*) 64% (*d*) 78%

3. In a certain school, 20% of students are below 8 years of age. The number of students above 8 years of age is $\frac{2}{3}$ of the number of students of 8 years age which is 48. What is the total number of students in the school?

(*a*) 72 (*b*) 80
(*c*) 120 (*d*) 150
(*e*) None of these

4. In an examination, 5% of the applicants were found ineligible and 85% of the eligible candidates belonged to the general category. If 4275 eligible candidates belonged to other categories, then how many candidates applied for the examination?

(*a*) 30,000 (*b*) 35,000
(*c*) 37,000 (*d*) None of these

5. Two students appeared at an examination. One of them secured 9 marks more than the other and his marks was 56% of the sum of their marks. The marks obtained by them are:

(*a*) 39, 30 (*b*) 41, 32
(*c*) 42, 33 (*d*) 43, 34

6. At a special sale, 5 tickets can be purchased for the price of 3 tickets. If 5 tickets are purchased at the sale, the amount saved will be what percent of the original price of the 5 tickets? (Campus Recruitment, 2010)

(*a*) 20% (*b*) $33\frac{1}{3}\%$
(*c*) 40% (*d*) 60%

7. In September 2009, the sales of a product were $\frac{2}{3}$rd of that in July 2009. In November 2009, the sales of the product were higher by 5% as compared to September 2009. How much is the percentage of increase in sales in November 2009 with respect to the base figure in July 2009? (SNAP, 2010)

(*a*) – 20% (*b*) 25%
(*c*) – 30% (*d*) + 40%

168. If earth's rotational motion increases by 12%, then the relation between a day and hours will be (I.A.M., 2007)

(*a*) 12 hours = 1 day (*b*) $20\frac{5}{7}$ hours = 1 day
(*c*) $21\frac{3}{7}$ hours = 1 day (*d*) None of these

169. A and B are two fixed points 5 cm apart and C is a point on AB such that AC is 3 cm. If the length of AC is increased by 6%, the length of CB is decreased by (S.S.C., 2007)

(*a*) 6% (*b*) 7%
(*c*) 8% (*d*) 9%

170.

On time	$x\%$
Up to 15 minutes delayed	43%
15-30 minutes delayed	17%
30-60 minutes delayed	12%
More than 60 minutes delayed	3%

The chart above describes departures from a certain airport on a certain day. If 1200 flights were delayed, how many flights departed on time? (N.M.A.T., 2005)

(*a*) 250 (*b*) 300
(*c*) 350 (*d*) 400

171. A shopkeeper has a certain number of eggs of which 5% are found to be broken. He sells 93% of the remainder and still has 266 eggs left. How many eggs did he originally have?

(*a*) 3800 (*b*) 4000
(*c*) 4200 (*d*) None of these

172. Ganpat went to fruit market with a certain amount of money. With this money he can buy either 50 oranges or 40 mangoes. He retains 10% of the money for taxi fare. If he buys 20 mangoes, the number of oranges he can buy is

(*a*) 6 (*b*) 18
(*c*) 20 (*d*) 25

173. A 14.4 kg gas cylinder runs for 104 hours when the smaller burner on the gas stove is fully opened while it runs for 80 hours when the larger burner on the gas stove is fully opened. Which of these values is the closest to the percentage difference in the usage of gas per hour, of the smaller burner over the larger burner? (SNAP, 2008)

(*a*) 23.07% (*b*) 26.23%
(*c*) 30% (*d*) 32.23%

Directions (*Questions 174 to 178*): ***A survey of magazine reading habits of the people living in five cities P, Q, R, S and T is summarised in a table given below. The Column I in the table gives percentage of magazine-readers in each city who read only one magazine a week. The Column II gives the total number of magazine-readers***

who read two or more magazines a week. Read the table and then answer these questions:

City	I	II
P	75	6000
Q	80	3500
R	60	3000
S	55	2700
T	25	4200

174. The city with the lowest number of magazine-readers is
(*a*) Q (*b*) R
(*c*) S (*d*) T

175. Which city has the highest number of magazine-readers who read only one magazine a week?
(*a*) P (*b*) Q
(*c*) R (*d*) S

176. The highest number of magazine-readers in any given city is
(*a*) 17500 (*b*) 18000
(*c*) 24000 (*d*) 30000

177. How many magazine-readers in city Q read only one magazine a week?
(*a*) 14000 (*b*) 18000
(*c*) 12500 (*d*) 16500

178. The total number of all the magazine-readers in the five cities who read only one magazine a week is
(*a*) 19400 (*b*) 24000
(*c*) 41200 (*d*) 42000

179. If X is 90% of Y, then what percent of X is Y?
(*a*) 90% (*b*) $101\frac{1}{9}\%$
(*c*) $111\frac{1}{9}\%$ (*d*) 190%

180. $x\%$ of y is $y\%$ of
(*a*) x (*b*) $100x$
(*c*) $\frac{x}{100}$ (*d*) $\frac{y}{100}$

181. If 20% of $a = b$, then $b\%$ of 20 is the same as
(*a*) 4% of a (*b*) 5% of a
(*c*) 20% of a (*d*) None of these

182. If $x\%$ of y is the same as $\frac{4}{5}$ of 80, then the value of xy is
(*a*) 320 (*b*) 400
(*c*) 640 (*d*) None of these

183. If $x\%$ of y is 100 and $y\%$ of z is 200, find a relatic between x and z.
(*a*) $z = \frac{x}{2}$ (*b*) $z = 2x$
(*c*) $z = \frac{x}{4}$ (*d*) $z = 4x$

184. If $x\%$ of 500 = $y\%$ of 300 and $x\%$ of $y\%$ of 200 = 6 then x =? **(Bank P.O., 200**
(*a*) $10\sqrt{2}$ (*b*) $20\sqrt{2}$
(*c*) $15\sqrt{2}$ (*d*) $30\sqrt{2}$
(*e*) None of these

185. If x, y, z are three positive integers such that x greater than y and y is greater than z, then whi of the following is definitely true? **(Campus Recruitment, 20**
(*a*) $x\%$ of y is greater than $y\%$ of z
(*b*) $y\%$ of x is greater than $z\%$ of y
(*c*) $z\%$ of x is greater than $y\%$ of z
(*d*) All of these

186. If 20% of A = 50% of B, what percentage of A B?
(*a*) 20 (*b*) 30
(*c*) 40 (*d*) 50

187. If $p\%$ of p is 36, then p is equal to
(*a*) 15 (*b*) 60
(*c*) 600 (*d*) 3600

188. If $x\%$ of y is equal to z, what percent of z is x?
(*a*) $\frac{y^2}{100}$ (*b*) $\frac{y}{100^2}$
(*c*) $\frac{100}{y}$ (*d*) $\frac{100^2}{y}$

189. If x is 80% of y, then what percent of $2x$ is y?
(*a*) 40% (*b*) $62\frac{1}{2}\%$
(*c*) $66\frac{2}{3}\%$ (*d*) 80%

190. Subtracting 6% of x from x is equivalent multiplying x by how much?
(*a*) 0.094 (*b*) 0.94
(*c*) 9.4 (*d*) 94

191. ($x\%$ of y + $y\%$ of x) =? **(M.B.A., 20**
(*a*) $x\%$ of y (*b*) $y\%$ of x
(*c*) 2% of xy (*d*) $xy\%$ of 3

192. $x\%$ of x is the same as 10% of **(M.B.A., 20**
(*a*) $\frac{x}{10}$ (*b*) $\frac{x^2}{10}$
(*c*) $\frac{x^3}{10}$ (*d*) None of these

193. If a exceeds b by x%, then which one of the following equations is correct? **(M.B.A., 2007)**

(a) $a - b = \frac{x}{100}$ (b) $b = a + 100x$

(c) $a = \frac{bx}{100 + x}$ (d) $a = b + \frac{bx}{100}$

194. If A is 150 percent of B, then B is what percent of (A + B)?

(a) $33\frac{1}{3}$% (b) 40%

(c) $66\frac{2}{3}$% (d) 75%

195. If 8% of x = 4% of y, then 20% of x is

(a) 10% of y (b) 16% of y

(c) 80% of y (d) None of these

196. If 20% of A = B and 40% of B = C, then 60% of (A + B) is

(a) 30% of C (b) 60% of C

(c) 75% of C (d) None of these

197. If x% of a is the same as y% of b, then z% of b is **(Campus Recruitment, 2010)**

(a) $\frac{xy}{z}$% of a (b) $\frac{yz}{x}$% of a

(c) $\frac{xz}{y}$% of a (d) None of these

198. If $A = x\%$ of y and $B = y\%$ of x, then which of the following is true?

(a) A is smaller than B.

(b) A is greater than B.

(c) Relationship between A and B cannot be determined.

(d) If x is smaller than y, then A is greater than B.

(e) None of these

199. If 50% of $(x - y)$ = 30% of $(x + y)$, then what percent of x is y?

(a) 25% (b) $33\frac{1}{3}$%

(c) 40% (d) 400%

200. If a is 60% of b, then what percent of $4a$ is $5b$?

(a) $\frac{25}{12}$% (b) 148%

(c) $\frac{625}{3}$% (d) 240%

201. If x = 63% of y, then y^2 is approximately what percent of x^2? **(M.C.A., 2005)**

(a) 125 (b) 200

(c) 250 (d) 350

202. If $a = b \times \frac{d}{c}$; b, c and d are each increased by 10%, then by how much does a increase?

(a) 10% (b) 11%

(c) 20% (d) 21%

203. If a% of x is equal to b% of y, then c% of y is what % of x?

(a) abc% (b) $\frac{bc}{a}$%

(c) $\frac{ac}{b}$% (d) c%

204. The firm uses the following function to calculate the production output (PO): PO = $5.3 C^2 L^{15}$, where C = capital invested and L = labour employed. If the capital invested (C) increases by 20 percent, the change in PO will be **(JMET, 2008)**

(a) 20% decrease (b) 32% increase

(c) 44% increase (d) 56% increase

205. A company received two shipments of ball bearings. In the first shipment, 1 percent of the ball bearings were defective. In the second shipment, which was twice as large as the first, 4.5 percent of the ball bearings were defective. If the company received a total of 100 defective ball bearings, how many ball bearings were in the first shipment?

(a) 990 (b) 1000

(c) 2000 (d) 3000

206. In a graduate class of 200, 40% are women and $\frac{1}{5}$ become lecturers. If the number of men who become lecturers is twice that of women, calculate approximate percentage of men who became lecturers. **(SNAP, 2004)**

(a) 16% (b) 18%

(c) 20% (d) 27%

207. The contents of a certain box consist of 14 apples and 23 oranges. How many oranges must be removed from the box so that 70% of the pieces of fruit in the box will be apples? **(M.A.T., 2005)**

(a) 6 (b) 12

(c) 17 (d) 36

208. The weight of an empty bucket is 25% of the weight of the bucket when filled with some liquid. Some of the liquid has been removed. Then, the bucket, along with the remaining liquid, weighed three-fifths of the original weight. What percentage of the liquid has been removed? **(N.M.A.T., 2008)**

(a) 40% (b) $62\frac{1}{2}$%

(c) $56\frac{2}{3}$% (d) $53\frac{1}{3}$%

209. A part of ₹ 9600 is invested at a 5% annual return, while the remainder is invested at a 3% annual return. If the annual income from both portions is the same, what is the total income from the two investments? (M.B.A., 2011)
(a) ₹ 320 (b) ₹ 380
(c) ₹ 410 (d) ₹ 440
(e) None of these

210. A salesman's commission is 5% on all sales up to ₹ 10000 and 4% of all sales exceeding this amount. He remits ₹ 31100 to the parent company after deducting his commission. His sales were worth (M.B.A., 2008)
(a) ₹ 32500 (b) ₹ 35000
(c) ₹ 35100 (d) ₹ 36100

211. In a co-educational school there are 15 more girls than boys. If the number of girls is increased by 10% and the number of boys is also increased by 16%, there would be nine more girls than boys. What is the number of students in the school?
(a) 125 (b) 140
(c) 255 (d) 265

212. 5 kg of tea and 8 kg of sugar together cost ₹ 172. The price of tea has risen by 20% and that of sugar by 10%. Hence the same quantities of tea and sugar now cost ₹ 199.20. What is the original price of tea per kg? (R.R.B., 2005)
(a) ₹ 16 (b) ₹ 18
(c) ₹ 19 (d) ₹ 20

213. 605 sweets were distributed equally among children in such a way that the number of sweets received by each child is 20% of the total number of children. How many sweets did each child receive? (Bank P.O., 2006)
(a) 11 (b) 24
(c) 45 (d) Cannot be determined
(e) None of these

214. In a certain organisation, 40% employees are matriculates, 50% of the remaining are graduates and the remaining 180 are post-graduates. What is the number of graduate employees? (R.R.B., 2007)
(a) 180 (b) 240
(c) 300 (d) 360

215. Gaurav spends 30% of his monthly income on food articles, 40% of the remaining on conveyance and clothes and saves 50% of the remaining. If his monthly salary is ₹ 18,400, how much money does he save every month?
(a) ₹ 3624 (b) ₹ 3864
(c) ₹ 4264 (d) ₹ 5888

216. A spider climbed $62\frac{1}{2}\%$ of the height of the pole in one hour and in the next hour it covered $12\frac{1}{2}\%$ of the remaining height. If the height of the pole is 192 m, then distance climbed in second hour is
(a) 3 m (b) 5 m
(c) 7 m (d) 9 m

217. A man spends 35% of his income on food, 25% on children's education and 80% of the remaining on house rent. What percent of his income he is left with?
(a) 8% (b) 10%
(c) 12% (d) 14%

218. Mr. More spent 20% of his monthly income on food and 15% on children's education. 40% of the remaining he spent on entertainment and transport together and 30% on medical. He is left with an amount of ₹ 8775 after all these expenditures. What is Mr. More's monthly income? (Bank P.O., 2009)
(a) ₹ 35000 (b) ₹ 38000
(c) ₹ 40000 (d) ₹ 42000
(e) None of these

219. From the salary of an officer, 10% is deducted as house rent, 20% of the rest, he spends on conveyance, 20% of the rest he pays as income tax and 10% of the balance, he spends on clothes. Then, he is left with ₹ 15,552. Find his total salary. (M.A.T., 2007)
(a) ₹ 25,000 (b) ₹ 30,000
(c) ₹ 35,000 (d) ₹ 40,000

220. Aman gave 40% of the amount he had to Rohan. Rohan in turn gave one-fourth of what he received from Aman to Sahil. After paying ₹ 200 to the taxi driver out of the amount he got from Rohan, Sahil now has ₹ 600 left with him. How much amount did Aman have?
(a) ₹ 4000 (b) ₹ 8000
(c) ₹ 12,000 (d) Data inadequate

221. On a test consisting of 250 questions, Jassi answered 40% of the first 125 questions correctly. What percent of the other 125 questions does she need to answer correctly for her grade on the entire exam to be 60%? (Bank P.O., 2009)
(a) 60 (b) 75
(c) 80 (d) Cannot be determined
(e) None of these

222. In a certain month a baseball team that played 60 games had won 30% of its games played. After a phenomenal winning streak this team raised its average to 50%. How many games must the team have won in a row to attain this average? (Campus Recruitment, 2009)
(a) 12 (b) 20
(c) 24 (d) 30

223. The sum of the number of boys and girls in a school is 150. If the number of boys is x, then the number of girls becomes x% of the total number of students. The number of boys is
(a) 40 (b) 50
(c) 60 (d) 90

224. In an examination of n questions, a student replied 15 out of the first 20 questions correctly. Of the remaining questions, he answered one-third correctly. All the questions have the same credit. If the student gets 50% marks, the value of n is
(a) 20 (b) 40
(c) 50 (d) 100

225. The salaries of A and B together amount to ₹ 2000. A spends 95% of his salary and B, 85% of his. If now, their savings are the same, what is A's salary?
(a) ₹ 750 (b) ₹ 1250
(c) ₹ 1500 (d) ₹ 1600

226. A's marks in Biology are 20 less than 25% of the total marks obtained by him in Biology, Maths and Drawing. If his marks in Drawing be 50, what are his marks in Maths?
(a) 40 (b) 45
(c) 50 (d) Cannot be determined

227. In an examination, there are three papers and a candidate has to get 35% of the total to pass. In one paper, he gets 62 out of 150 and in the second 35 out of 150. How much must he get, out of 180, in the third paper to just qualify for a pass?
(a) 60.5 (b) 68
(c) 70 (d) 71

228. In a History examination, the average for the entire class was 80 marks. If 10% of the students scored 95 marks and 20% scored 90 marks, what was the average marks of the remaining students of the class?
(a) 65.5 (b) 72.5
(c) 75 (d) 85

229. A scored 30% marks and failed by 15 marks. B scored 40% marks and obtained 35 marks more than those required to pass. The pass percentage is
(a) 33% (b) 38%
(c) 43% (d) 46%

230. In an area, of the total people 40% were women and 45% coffee drinkers. One-third of the males are coffee drinkers. Suppose the total number of persons in the area is 100, then the number of female non-coffee drinkers is (P.C.S., 2009)
(a) 15 (b) 20
(c) 25 (d) None of these

231. A city has a population of 3,00,000 out of which 1,80,000 are males. 50% of the population is literate. If 70% of the males are literate, then the percentage of females who are literate is (P.C.S., 2009)
(a) 20% (b) 25%
(c) 35% (d) 45%

232. In a company there are 75% skilled workers and the remaining are unskilled. 80% of skilled workers and 20% of unskilled workers are permanent. If the number of temporary workers is 126, then what is the total number of workers? (M.A.T., 2006)
(a) 360 (b) 377
(c) 480 (d) 510

233. A clothing supplier stores 800 coats in a warehouse, of which 15 percent are full-length coats. If 500 of the short-length coats are removed form the warehouse, then what percent of the remaining coats are full length? (M.A.T., 2006)
(a) 5.62% (b) 9.37%
(c) 35% (d) 40%

234. At the college entrance examination, each candidate is admitted or rejected according to whether he has passed or failed the tests. Of the candidates who are really capable, 80% pass the tests and of the incapable, 25% pass the test. Given that 40% of the candidates are really capable, the proportion of capable college students is about (M.A.T., 2007)
(a) 68% (b) 70%
(c) 73% (d) 75%

235. In a public school, $\frac{1}{5}$th of girls and $\frac{1}{4}$th of boys are under 12 years of age. If the number of girls is $\frac{2}{5}$th of the total, what part of the total strength of the school is accounted for by those who are 12 years or more of age? (M.B.A., 2008)
(a) 23% (b) 45%
(c) 55% (d) 77%

236. In a city, 35% of the population is composed of migrants, 20% of whom are from rural areas. Of the local population, 48% is female while this figure for rural and urban migrants is 30% and 40% respectively. What percent of the total population comprises of females? (N.M.A.T., 2005)
(a) 42.75% (b) 44.5%
(c) 48% (d) None of these

237. In a recent survey, 40% houses contained two or more people. Of those houses containing only one person, 25% were having only a male. What is the percentage of all houses, which contain exactly one female and no males?
(a) 15 (b) 40
(c) 75 (d) Cannot be determined
(e) None of these

238. $37\frac{1}{2}\%$ of the candidates in an examination were girls, 75% of the boys and $62\frac{1}{2}\%$ of the girls passed and 342 girls failed. The number of boys failed was:

(a) 350 (b) 360
(c) 370 (d) 380

239. $\frac{5}{9}$ part of the population in a village are males. If 30% of the males are married, the percentage of unmarried females in the total population is

(a) 20% (b) $27\frac{7}{9}\%$
(c) 40% (d) 70%

240. The boys and girls in a college are in the ratio 3: 2. If 20% of the boys and 25% of the girls are adults, the percentage of students who are not adults is

(a) 58% (b) 67.5%
(c) 78% (d) 82.5%

241. A debtor can pay 87 paise in the rupee, but if his creditors would take 20% of his debts, he could pay them and have ₹ 42 left. His debts and assets respectively are:

(a) ₹ 400, ₹ 520 (b) ₹ 500, ₹ 521
(c) ₹ 600, ₹ 522 (d) ₹ 1000, ₹ 525

242. Of the 50 researchers in a workgroup, 40% will be assigned to Team A and the remaining 60% to Team B. However, 70% of the researchers prefer Team A and 30% prefer Team B. What is the least possible number of researchers who will not be assigned to the team they prefer? (M.A.T., 2005)

(a) 15 (b) 20
(c) 30 (d) 35

243. A train starts from station A with some passengers. At station B 10% of the passengers get down and 100 passengers get in. At station C 50% get down and 25 get in. At station D 50% get down and 50 get in making the total number of passengers 200. The number of passengers who boarded the train at station A was (P.C.S., 2008)

(a) 400 (b) 500
(c) 600 (d) 700

244. The charges for a five-day trip by a tourist bus for one full ticket and a half-ticket are ₹ 1440 inclusive of boarding charges which are same for a full ticket and a half-ticket. The charges for the same trip for 2 full tickets and one half-ticket inclusive of boarding charges are ₹ 2220. The fare for a half-ticket is 75% of the full ticket. Find the fare and the boarding charges separately for one full ticket.

(a) ₹ 580, ₹ 400 (b) ₹ 280, ₹ 200
(c) ₹ 480, ₹ 300 (d) ₹ 380, ₹ 400

245. Asha's monthly income is 60% of Deepak's monthly income and 120% of Maya's monthly income. What is Maya's monthly income if Deepak's monthly income is ₹ 78000? (NABARD, 2009)

(a) ₹ 36000 (b) ₹ 39000
(c) ₹ 42000 (d) Cannot be determined
(e) None of these

246. Raju's monthly salary is 20 percent more than Anuj's monthly salary. Ravi's monthly salary is ₹ 1500 more than Anuj's salary. The sum of Raju's, Ravi's and Anuj's yearly salaries is ₹ 325200. What is the sum of the monthly salaries of Raju and Anuj together? (Bank P.O., 2010)

(a) ₹ 16600 (b) ₹ 17500 (c) ₹ 17600
(d) ₹ 17680 (e) None of these

247. A sum of ₹ 2236 is divided among A, B and C in such a way that A receives 25% more than C and C receives 25% less than B. What is A's share in the amount? (Bank P.O., 2009)

(a) ₹ 460 (b) ₹ 780
(c) ₹ 890 (d) ₹ 1280
(e) None of these

248. A sum of ₹ 6100 was divided among 8 men, 10 women and 12 children in such a way that each man received 25% more than a woman and each woman received 25% more than a child. How much did each woman receive? (R.R.B., 2006)

(a) ₹ 201.68 (b) ₹ 203.68
(c) ₹ 206.08 (d) ₹ 206.68

249. In an examination in which full marks were 800, A gets 20% more than B, B gets 20% more than C, and C gets 15% less than D. If A got 576, what percentage of full marks did D get (approximately)?

(a) 45.7 (b) 51.2
(c) 58.8 (d) 61.7

250. In an examination, the percentage of students qualified to the number of students appeared from school A is 70%. In school B, the number of students appeared is 20% more than the students appeared from school A and the number of students qualified from school B is 50% more than the students qualified from school A. What is the percentage of students qualified to the number of students appeared from school B?

(a) 30% (b) 70%
(c) 78.5% (d) 87.5%

251. If the price of a book is first decreased by 25% and then increased by 20%, then the net change in the price will be

(a) No change (b) 5% increase
(c) 5% decrease (d) 10% decrease

252. The price of a shirt is increased by 15% and then reduced by 15%. The final price of the shirt is
(*a*) does not change (*b*) increases by 2.25%
(*c*) decreases by 2.25% (*d*) None of these

253. A number is first decreased by 10% and then increased by 10%. The number so obtained is 50 less than the original number. The original number is (S.S.C., 2005)
(*a*) 5000 (*b*) 5050
(*c*) 5500 (*d*) 5900

254. A shopkeeper first increased the price of an article by 25% and then by 20%. What is the total percent increase? (P.C.S., 2008)
(*a*) 40% (*b*) 45%
(*c*) 50% (*d*) 55%

255. Two successive price increases of 10% each on an article are equivalent to a single price increase of (S.S.C., 2010)
(*a*) 19% (*b*) 20%
(*c*) 21% (*d*) 22%

256. The price of an article was first increased by 10% and then again by 20%. If the last increased price be ₹ 33, the original price was (S.S.C., 2010)
(*a*) ₹ 25 (*b*) ₹ 26.50
(*c*) ₹ 27.50 (*d*) ₹ 30

257. The price of an article was increased by r%. Later the new price was decreased by r%. If the latest price was ₹ 1, then the original price was
(*a*) ₹ 1 (*b*) ₹ $\left(\frac{1-r^2}{100}\right)$
(*c*) ₹ $\frac{\sqrt{1-r^2}}{100}$ (*d*) ₹ $\left(\frac{10000}{10000-r^2}\right)$

258. In a factory, producing parts for an automobile, the parts manufactured on the shop floor are required to go through three quality checks, each conducted after a specific part of the processing on the raw material is completed. Only parts that are not rejected at one stage are put through the subsequent stages of production and testing. If average rejection rates at these testing machines during a month are 10%, 5% and 2% respectively, then what is the effective rejection rate for the whole plant? (M.A.T., 2005)
(*a*) 15.20% (*b*) 16.21%
(*c*) 16.48% (*d*) 17%

259. Peter could save 10% of his income. But two years later when his income is increased by 20%, he could save the same amount only as before. By how much percent has his expenditure increased?
(*a*) 22% (*b*) $22\frac{2}{9}$%
(*c*) $23\frac{1}{3}$% (*d*) 24%

260. A man spends 80% of his income. With an increase in the cost of living, his expenditure increases by $37\frac{1}{2}$% and his income increases by $16\frac{2}{3}$%. His present percent savings are (A.A.O. Exam, 2010)
(*a*) $5\frac{3}{7}$% (*b*) $5\frac{5}{7}$%
(*c*) $6\frac{1}{3}$% (*d*) $6\frac{2}{3}$%

261. A person spends 75% of his income. If his income increases by 20% and expenses increase by 15%, his saving will increase by (R.R.B., 2008)
(*a*) $17\frac{1}{2}$% (*b*) 20%
(*c*) $33\frac{1}{2}$% (*d*) 35%

262. Madan pays income tax at the rate of 10%. If his income increased by 10% and his tax rate increases to 15%, his net income would increase by ₹ 350. What is Madan's income?
(*a*) ₹ 8000 (*b*) ₹ 10,000
(*c*) ₹ 12,000 (*d*) ₹ 14,000

263. Mr. X, a businessman had the income in the year 2010, such that he earned a profit of 20% on his investment in the business. In the year 2011, his investment was less by ₹ 5000 but still had the same income (Income = Investment + Profit) as that in 2010. Thus, the percent profit earned in 2011 increased by 6%. What was his investment in 2010?
(*a*) ₹ 1,02,000 (*b*) ₹ 1,05,000
(*c*) ₹ 1,50,500 (*d*) Data inadequate
(*e*) None of these

264. In the expression xy^2, the values of both variables x and y are decreased by 20%. By this, the value of the expression is decreased by (C.P.O., 2007)
(*a*) 40% (*b*) 48.8%
(*c*) 51.2% (*d*) 80%

265. When water is changed into ice, its volume increases by 9%. If ice changes into water, the percentage decrease in volume is (R.R.B., 2006)
(*a*) $8\frac{28}{109}$% (*b*) 9%
(*c*) 10% (*d*) 18%

266. If the price of a commodity is decreased by 20% and its consumption is increased by 20%, what will be the increase or decrease in the expenditure on the commodity? (S.S.C., 2007)
(*a*) 4% increase (*b*) 4% decrease
(*c*) 8% increase (*d*) 8% decrease

267. Income tax is raised from 4 paise to 5 paise in a rupee but the revenue is increa-sed by 10% only. Find the decrease percent in the amount taxed. **(M.B.A., 2007)**

(*a*) 12 (*b*) 14
(*c*) 16 (*d*) None of these

268. The ticket for admission to an exhibition was ₹ 5 and it was later reduced by 20%. As a result, the sale proceeds of tickets increased by 44%. What was the percentage increase in number of visitors?

(*a*) 25% (*b*) 50%
(*c*) 75% (*d*) 80%

269. The income of a broker remains unchanged though the rate of commission is increased from 4% to 5%. The percentage of slump in business is

(*a*) 1% (*b*) 8%
(*c*) 20% (*d*) 80%

270. By how much percent must a motorist increase his speed in order to reduce by 20%, the time taken to cover a certain distance? **(R.R.B., 2006)**

(*a*) 20 (*b*) 25
(*c*) 30 (*d*) 35

271. What percent decrease in salaries would exactly cancel out the 20 percent increase?

(*a*) $16\frac{2}{3}$ (*b*) 18
(*c*) 20 (*d*) $33\frac{1}{3}$

272. The price of an article is reduced by 25%. In order to retain the original price, the present price has to be increased by **(P.C.S., 2007)**

(*a*) 20% (*b*) 25%
(*c*) $33\frac{1}{3}\%$ (*d*) 50%

273. A number is increased by 20% and then again by 20%. By what percent should the increased number be reduced so as to get back the original number?

(*a*) $19\frac{11}{31}\%$ (*b*) $30\frac{5}{9}\%$
(*c*) 40% (*d*) 44%

274. A person's salary is decreased by steps of 20%, 15% and 10%. Approximately by what percent should the reduced salary be increased so as to get back the original salary? **(Campus Recruitment, 2009)**

(*a*) 39% (*b*) 44%
(*c*) 56% (*d*) 63%

275. In a fraction, if numerator is increased by 40% and denominator is increased by 80%, then what fraction of the original is the new fraction?

(*a*) $\frac{1}{2}$ (*b*) $\frac{7}{9}$
(*c*) $\frac{7}{18}$ (*d*) Data inadequate

276. If the numerator of a fraction is increased by 240% and the denominator of the fraction is decreased by 50%, the resultant fraction is $2\frac{5}{6}$. What is the original fraction? **(NABARD, 2009)**

(*a*) $\frac{1}{4}$ (*b*) $\frac{2}{3}$
(*c*) $\frac{5}{12}$ (*d*) $\frac{4}{11}$
(*e*) None of these

277. The price of a certain item is increased by 15%. If a consumer wants to keep his expenditure on the item same as before, how much percent must he reduce his consumption of that item? **(S.S.C., 2007)**

(*a*) $10\frac{20}{23}\%$ (*b*) $13\frac{1}{23}\%$
(*c*) $16\frac{2}{3}\%$ (*d*) 15%

278. If the price of oil is increased by 30%, then by how much percent a family should reduce its consumption so that the expenditure would remain the same? **(R.R.B., 2005)**

(*a*) $15\frac{1}{23}\%$ (*b*) $15\frac{3}{14}\%$
(*c*) $23\frac{1}{13}\%$ (*d*) $76\frac{12}{13}\%$

279. The price of wheat falls by 16%. By what percentage a person can increase the consumption of wheat so that his overall budget does not change?

(*a*) 16% (*b*) 18%
(*c*) 18.5% (*d*) 19%

280. The price of oil is increased by 25%. If the expenditure is not allowed to increase, the ratio between the reduction in consumption and the original consumption is

(*a*) 1: 3 (*b*) 1: 4
(*c*) 1: 5 (*d*) 1: 6

281. The price of sugar per kg increased from ₹ 16 to ₹ 20. The percentage reduction in the use of sugar so that the expenditure does not increase, should be **(P.C.S., 2008)**

(*a*) 15% (*b*) 20%
(*c*) 25% (*d*) 40%

282. The price of sugar increases by 32%. A family reduces its consumption so that the expenditure of the sugar is up only by 10%. If the total consumption of the sugar before the price rise was 10 kg per month, then the consumption of sugar per month at present (in kg) is **(Campus Recruitment, 2011)**

(*a*) $8\frac{1}{3}$ (*b*) $8\frac{1}{2}$
(*c*) $8\frac{3}{4}$ (*d*) 9

283. Prices register an increase of 10% on foodgrains and 15% on other items of expenditure. If the ratio of an employee's expenditure on foodgrains and other items be 2: 5, by how much should his salary be increased in order that he may maintain the same level of consumption as before, his present salary being ₹ 2590?

(a) ₹ 323.75 (b) ₹ 350
(c) ₹ 360.50 (d) None of these

284. In the year 2010, 5000 students were admitted in a college. It is found that the number of students admitted is constantly increasing by 24 percent per year. How many students will be admitted in the college in the year 2012? (Bank P.O., 2010)

(a) 7400 (b) 7480
(c) 7688 (d) 7868

285. The salary of an employee increases consistently by 50% every year. If his salary today is ₹ 10000, what will be the salary after another 4 years? (S.B.I. P.O., 2005)

(a) ₹ 26500 (b) ₹ 33750
(c) ₹ 50625 (d) ₹ 62500
(e) None of these

286. A district has 64000 inhabitants. If the population increases at the rate of $2\frac{1}{2}\%$ per annum, then the number of inhabitants at the end of 3 years will be

(a) 68911 (b) 68921
(c) 69200 (d) 70000

287. If inflation increases at a rate of 8% p.a., what will a ₹ 20 article cost at the end of two years?

(a) Between ₹ 20 and ₹ 21
(b) Between ₹ 21 and ₹ 22
(c) Between ₹ 22 and ₹ 23
(d) Between ₹ 23 and ₹ 24

288. The population of a town is 4.2×10^6. If the population increases by 75 per 1000 per annum, then what will be the population after 2 years? (R.R.B., 2006)

(a) 4633628 (b) 4853625
(c) 5253495 (d) 5853615

289. The population of a town is 8500. It increases by 20% in the first year and by another 25% in the second year. What would be the population of the town after 2 years? (Bank P.O., 2008)

(a) 10950 (b) 11950
(c) 12550 (d) 12750
(e) None of these

290. The population of a town was 1,60,000 three years ago. If it increased by 3%, 2.5% and 5% respectively in the last three years, then the present population is

(a) 1,77,000 (b) 1,77,366
(c) 1,77,461 (d) 1,77,596

291. The population of a town 2 years ago was 62,500. Due to migration to big cities, it decreases every year at the rate of 4%. The present population of the town is

(a) 56,700 (b) 57,600
(c) 58,800 (d) 60,000

292. Depreciation applicable to an equipment is 20%. The value of the equipment 3 years from now will be less by (M.B.A., 2009)

(a) 45% (b) 48.8%
(c) 51.2% (d) 60%

293. A papaya tree was planted 2 years ago. It grows at the rate of 20% every year. If at present, the height of the tree is 540 cm, what was it when the tree was planted? (M.A.T., 2007)

(a) 324 cm (b) 375 cm
(c) 400 cm (d) 432 cm

294. A merchant invests a certain sum and his annual gain percent is 25. If at the end of the third year, his capital is ₹ 10000, then the amount invested by him is equal to

(a) ₹ 5120 (b) ₹ 5210
(c) ₹ 5500 (d) ₹ $5714\frac{2}{7}$

295. The population of a town is 1771561. If it had been increasing at 10% per annum, its population 6 years ago was (P.C.S., 2008)

(a) 1000000 (b) 1100000
(c) 1210000 (d) 1331000

296. The value of a machine depreciates at the rate of 12 percent per annum. It was purchased three years ago. Its present value is ₹ 29644.032. What was the purchase price of the machine? (S.B.I.P.O., 2008)

(a) ₹ 38900 (b) ₹ 39000
(c) ₹ 43500 (d) ₹ 48700
(e) None of these

297. The value of a fixed asset depreciates at the rate of 10% of the value at the beginning of each year. If the value of the asset, two years ago, was ₹ 12000 more than the value of the asset one year ago, then find the present value of the asset, given that the asset was bought two years ago.

(a) ₹ 14520 (b) ₹ 17520
(c) ₹ 96000 (d) ₹ 97200

298. A tree increases annually by $\frac{1}{8}$ of its height. By how much will it increase after $2\frac{1}{2}$ years if it stands today 8 m high? (R.R.B., 2006)

(a) 10.75 m (b) 11.85 m
(c) 12.25 m (d) 15.60 m

299. The population of a town is 189000. It decreases by 8% in the first year and increases by 5% in the second year. What is the population of the town at the end of 2 years? **(Bank Recruitment, 2008)**

(a) 182574 (b) 185472
(c) 191394 (d) 193914
(e) None of these

300. Ashish started a business with an initial investment of ₹ 500000. In the first year, he incurred a loss of 4%. However, during the second year, he earned a profit of 5% which in the third year rose to 10%. Calculate his net profit for the entire period of three years.

(a) ₹ 48800 (b) ₹ 54400
(c) ₹ 55000 (d) None of these

301. The present value of an optical instrument is ₹ 20000. If its value will depreciate 5% in the first year, 4% in the second year and 2% in the third year, what will be its value after 3 years? **(M.B.A., 2009)**

(a) ₹ 16534.5 (b) ₹ 16756.5
(c) ₹ 17556.8 (d) ₹ 17875.2

302. The population of a variety of tiny bush in an experimental field increased by 10% in the first year, increased by 8% in the second year but decreased by 10% in the third year. If the present number of bushes in the experimental field is 26730, then the number of bushes in the beginning was **(M.A.T., 2002)**

(a) 25000 (b) 27000
(c) 28000 (d) 24600

303. The production of a company has ups and downs every year. The production increases for two consecutive years consistently by 15% and in the third year it decreases by 10%. Again in the next two years it increases by 15% each year and decreases by 10% in the third year. If we start counting from the year 2008, approximately what will be the effect on production of the company in 2012?

(a) 27% increase (b) 32% increase
(c) 37% increase (d) 42% increase
(e) 52% increase

304. The present population of a country estimated to be 10 crores is expected to increase to 13.31 crores during the next three years. The uniform rate of growth is

(a) 8% (b) 10%
(c) 12.7% (d) 15%

305. The price of a commodity which was ₹ 250 three years ago is ₹ 2000 now. The annual rate of increase in the price is **(P.C.S., 2009)**

(a) 100% (b) 200%
(c) $266\frac{2}{3}\%$ (d) None of these

306. Raju's factory kept increasing its output by the same percentage every year. Find the percentage if it is known that his output is doubled after two years. **(M.A.T., 2010)**

(a) $100\sqrt{2}\%$ (b) $100(\sqrt{2}+1)\%$
(c) $100(\sqrt{2}-1)\%$ (d) $50(\sqrt{3}-1)\%$

307. The population of a colony was 3600 three years back. It is 4800 right now. What will be the population three years down the line, if the rate of growth of population has been co stant over the years and has been compounding annually? **(M.A.T., 2010)**

(a) 6000 (b) 6400
(c) 7200 (d) 9600

308. The value of a flat worth ₹ 500000 is depreciating at the rate of 10% p.a. In how many years will its value be reduced to ₹ 364500?

(a) 3 years (b) 4 years
(c) 5 years (d) 6 years

309. A building worth ₹ 1,33,100 is constructed on land worth ₹ 72,900. After how many years will the value of both be the same if land appreciates at 10% p.a. and building depreciates at 10% p.a.? **(G.B.O., 2007)**

(a) $1\frac{1}{2}$ (b) 2
(c) $2\frac{1}{2}$ (d) 3

310. Given that carbon-14 decays at a constant rate in such a way that it reduces to 50% in 5568 years, find the age of an old wooden piece in which the carbon is only 12.5% of the original.

(a) 15836 years (b) 16668 years
(c) 16704 years (d) 17552 years

311. The population of a town increases 4% annually but is decreased by emigration annually to the extent of (1/2)%. What will be the increase percent in 3 years?

(a) 9.8 (b) 10
(c) 10.5 (d) 10.8

312. The current birth rate per thousand is 32, whereas the corresponding death rate is 11 per thousand. The net growth rate in terms of population increase in percent is given by

(a) 0.0021% (b) 0.021%
(c) 2.1% (d) 21%

313. Mr. Jones' total annual gross salary, which was ₹ 10 lakhs per year in 2007, was reduced by 10% in 2008. In 2007 his family expenditure for food items was 40% of the total annual gross salary. The prices of average food items increased by 5% between 2007 and 2008. Assuming that the family consumed the same amount of food in 2008, the percentage expenditure on food items, calculated on total annual gross salary in 2008, is (J.M.E.T., 2009)

(a) 43% (b) 45%
(c) 47% (d) 49%

314. A man's income is increased by ₹ 1200 and at the same time, the rate of tax to be paid is reduced from 12% to 10%. He now pays the same amount of tax as before. What is his increased income if 20% of his income is exempted from tax in both cases? (M.A.T., 2010)

(a) ₹ 4500 (b) ₹ 6300
(c) ₹ 6500 (d) ₹ 7200

315. If A's income is 10% more than B's, how much percentage is B's income less than A's? (P.C.S., 2009, 2008; S.S.C., 2007; C.P.O., 2006)

(a) 9% (b) $9\frac{1}{2}\%$
(c) $9\frac{1}{11}\%$ (d) 10%

316. A's income is 25% more than B's income. B's income in terms of A's income is (M.B.A., 2006)

(a) 75% (b) 80%
(c) 90% (d) 96%

317. If A's wage with respect to B's wage is 20% more, then how much percent is B's wage less with respect to A's wage? (Bank P.O., 2010)

(a) $16\frac{2}{3}\%$ (b) 17%
(c) 18% (d) None of these

318. If A's income is 50% less than that of B, then B's income is what percent more than that of A? (S.S.C., 2010)

(a) 50 (b) 75
(c) 100 (d) 125

319. If x is 25% less than y, then what percent is y more than x? (M.B.A., 2007)

(a) $16\frac{1}{2}\%$ (b) 29%
(c) $33\frac{1}{3}\%$ (d) None of these

320. p is six times as large as q. The percent that q is less than p, is

(a) $16\frac{2}{3}$ (b) 60
(c) $83\frac{1}{3}$ (d) 90

321. Two numbers are respectively 20% and 25% lower than a third number. By how much percentage is the second number lower than the first? (R.R.B., 2006)

(a) 5% (b) $6\frac{1}{4}\%$
(c) $8\frac{1}{2}\%$ (d) 10%

322. Two numbers are respectively $12\frac{1}{2}\%$ and 25% more than a third number. The first number as a percentage of the second number is (Bank P.O., 2008)

(a) 50 (b) 60
(c) 75 (d) 90

323. A's salary is 40% of B's salary which is 25% of C's salary. What percentage of C's salary is A's salary?

(a) 5% (b) 10%
(c) 15% (d) 20%

324. Peter earned 40% more money than Albert. Albert earned 20% less than Michael. Peter earned more than Michael by

(a) 10% (b) 12%
(c) 20% (d) 25%

325. Fresh fruit contains 68% water and dry fruit contains 20% water. How much dry fruit can be obtained from 100 kg of fresh fruits?

(a) 32 kg (b) 40 kg
(c) 52 kg (d) 80 kg

326. A large watermelon weighs 20 kg with 96% of its weight being water. It is allowed to stand in the sun and some of the water evaporates so that only 95% of its weight is water. Its reduced weight will be

(a) 16 kg (b) 16.5 kg
(c) 17 kg (d) 18 kg

327. Fresh grapes contain 80 percent water while dry grapes contain 10 percent water. If the weight of dry grapes is 250 kg what was its total weight when it was fresh? (M.A.T., 2007)

(a) 1000 kg (b) 1100 kg
(c) 1125 kg (d) 1225 kg

328. An alloy of gold and silver weighs 50 g. It contains 80% gold. How much gold should be added to the alloy so that percentage of gold is increased to 90? (SNAP, 2010)

(a) 30 g (b) 40 g
(c) 50 g (d) 60 g

329. In a mixture of milk and water, the proportion of water by weight was 75%. If in the 60 gms mixture 15 gm of water was added, what would be the percentage of water? (Bank P.O., 2009)

(a) 75% (b) 88%
(c) 90% (d) 100%
(e) None of these

330. One litre of water is evaporated from a 6 litre solution containing 4% sugar. The percentage of sugar in the remaining solution is (R.R.B., 2006)

(a) $3\frac{1}{3}\%$ (b) 4%
(c) $4\frac{4}{5}\%$ (d) 5%

331. The quantity of water (in ml) needed to reduce 9 ml shaving lotion containing 50% alcohol to a lotion containing 30% alcohol, is

(a) 4 (b) 5
(c) 6 (d) 7

332. 1 litre of water is added to 5 litres of alcohol-water solution containing 40% alcohol strength. The strength of alcohol in the new solution will be (S.S.C., 2007)

(a) 30% (b) $33\frac{1}{3}\%$
(c) $33\frac{2}{3}\%$ (d) 33%

333. To strengthen 400 ml of 15% alcohol solution to 32% alcohol solution, a pharmacist would need additional pure alcohol amounting to

(a) 50 ml (b) 75 ml
(c) 100 ml (d) 125 ml

334. 6 c.c. of a 20% solution of alcohol in water is mixed with 4 c.c. of a 60% solution of alcohol in water. The alcoholic strength of the mixture is (M.C.A., 2005)

(a) 20% (b) 26%
(c) 36% (d) 40%

335. One type of liquid contains 20% water and the second type of liquid contains 35% of water. A glass is filled with 10 parts of first liquid and 4 parts of second liquid. The percentage of water in the new mixture in the glass is

(a) 20% (b) $24\frac{2}{7}\%$
(c) 37% (d) 40%

336. In some quantity of ghee, 60% is pure ghee and 40% is vanaspati. If 10 kg of pure ghee is added, then the strength of vanaspati ghee becomes 20%. The original quantity was (Hotel Management, 2003)

(a) 10 kg (b) 15 kg
(c) 20 kg (d) 25 kg

337. From 5 litres of a 20% solution of alcohol in water, 2 litres of solution is taken out and 2 litres of water is added to it. Find the strength of alcohol in the new solution. (S.S.C., 2008)

(a) 10% (b) 12%
(c) 15% (d) 18%

338. After 30 kg of water had been evaporated from a solution of salt and water, which had 15% salt, the remaining solution had 20% salt. The weight of the original solution was (S.S.C., 2008)

(a) 80 kg (b) 90 kg
(c) 120 kg (d) 135 kg

339. 85% and 92% alcoholic solutions are mixed to get 35 litres of an 89% alcoholic solution. How many litres of each solution are there in the new mixture?

(a) 10 of the first and 25 of the second
(b) 20 of the first and 15 of the second
(c) 15 of the first and 20 of the second
(d) 12 of the first and 23 of the second

340. How many litres of a 30% alcohol solution should be added to 40 litres of a 60% alcohol solution to prepare a 50% solution? (SNAP, 2010)

(a) 20 (b) 24
(c) 30 (d) 32

341. A 27 quartz capacity car radiator is filled with 18% alcohol solution. How many quartz be drained and then be replaced by a 90% alcohol solution for resulting solution to contain 42% alcohol? (SNAP, 2004)

(a) 7 quartz (b) 9 quartz
(c) 11 quartz (d) 14 quartz

342. Two vessels contain equal quantities of 40% alcohol. Sachin changed the concentration of the first vessel to 50% by adding extra quantity of pure alcohol. Vivek changed the concentration of the second vessel to 50% replacing a certain quantity of the solution with pure alcohol. By what percentage is the quantity of alcohol added by Sachin more/less than that replaced by Vivek?

(a) $11\frac{1}{9}\%$ less (b) $11\frac{1}{9}\%$ more
(c) $16\frac{2}{3}\%$ less (d) 20% more

343. From a container having pure milk, 20% is replaced by water and the process is repeated thrice. At the end of the third operation, the milk is

(a) 40% pure (b) 50% pure
(c) 51.2% pure (d) 58.8% pure

344. An empty fuel tank of a car was filled with A type petrol. When the tank was half-empty, it was filled with B type petrol. Again when the tank was half-empty, it was filled with A type petrol. When the tank was half-empty again, it was filled with B type petrol. What is the percentage of A type petrol at present in the tank?

(a) 33.5% (b) 37.5%
(c) 40% (d) 50%

345. A bag contains 600 coins of 25 p denomination and 1200 coins of 50 p denomination. If 12% of 25 p coins and 24% of 50 p coins are removed, the percentage of money removed from the bag is nearly
(*a*) 15.6% (*b*) 17.8%
(*c*) 21.6% (*d*) 30%

346. The price of rice is reduced by 2%. How many kilograms of rice can now be bought for the money which was sufficient to buy 49 kg of rice earlier?
(*a*) 48 kg (*b*) 49 kg
(*c*) 50 kg (*d*) 51 kg

347. If the price of erasers goes down by 25%, a man can buy 2 more erasers for a rupee. How many erasers are available for a rupee? **(S.S.C., 2005)**
(*a*) 2 (*b*) 4
(*c*) 6 (*d*) 8

348. A reduction of 21% in the price of wheat enables a person to buy 10.5 kg more for ₹ 100. What is the reduced price per kg?
(*a*) ₹ 2 (*b*) ₹ 2.25
(*c*) ₹ 2.30 (*d*) ₹ 2.50

349. Due to an increase of 30% in the price of eggs, 3 eggs less are available for ₹ 7.80. The present rate of eggs per dozen is
(*a*) ₹ 8.64 (*b*) ₹ 8.88
(*c*) ₹ 9.36 (*d*) ₹ 10.40

350. The price of sugar having gone down by 10%, Sharad can buy 6.2 kg more for ₹ 279. The difference between the original and the reduced price (per kg) is
(*a*) ₹ 0.50 (*b*) ₹ 1
(*c*) ₹ 1.50 (*d*) ₹ 4.50

351. If the price of sugar falls by $2\frac{1}{2}$%, a person can buy 9 kg more of sugar for ₹ 1260 than before. If the price had risen by $12\frac{1}{2}$%, how much sugar would he have bought for the same sum?
(*a*) 288 kg (*b*) 312 kg
(*c*) 328 kg (*d*) 336 kg

352. In a survey of a city, it was found that 90 percent of the people in the city own a refrigerator and 15 percent own a washing machine. If everybody owns at least one appliance, what percentage owns both?
(*a*) 5 percent (*b*) 8 percent
(*c*) 10 percent (*d*) None of these

353. In an examination, 34% of the students failed in Mathematics and 42% failed in English. If 20% of the students failed in both the subjects, then the percentage of students who passed in both the subjects was
(*a*) 44 (*b*) 50
(*c*) 54 (*d*) 56

354. 40% of the people read newspaper X, 50% read newspaper Y and 10% read both the papers. What percentage of the people read neither newspaper?
(*a*) 10% (*b*) 15%
(*c*) 20% (*d*) 25%

355. Out of 450 students of a school, 325 play football, 175 play cricket and 50 neither play football nor cricket. How many students play both football and cricket?
(*a*) 50 (*b*) 75
(*c*) 100 (*d*) 225

356. In a hotel, 60% had vegetarian lunch while 30% had non-vegetarian lunch and 15% had both types of lunch. If 96 people were present, how many did not eat either type of lunch?
(*a*) 20 (*b*) 24
(*c*) 26 (*d*) 28

357. There are 600 boys in a hostel. Each plays either hockey or football or both. If 75% play hockey and 45% play football, how many play both?
(*a*) 48 (*b*) 60
(*c*) 80 (*d*) 120

358. In a certain office, 72% of the workers prefer tea and 44% prefer coffee. If each of them prefers tea or coffee and 40 like both, the total number of workers in the office is
(*a*) 200 (*b*) 240
(*c*) 250 (*d*) 320

359. In an examination, 30% and 35% students respectively failed in History and Geography while 27% students failed in both the subjects. If the number of students passing the examination is 248, find the total number of students who appeared in the examination. **(M.A.T., 2010)**
(*a*) 380 (*b*) 400
(*c*) 425 (*d*) 725

360. In an examination, 35% candidates failed in one subject and 42% failed in another subject while 15% failed in both the subjects. If 2500 candidates appeared at the examination, how many passed in either subject but not in both?
(*a*) 325 (*b*) 1175
(*c*) 2125 (*d*) None of these

361. Arnav ordered 4 pairs of black socks and some additional pairs of blue socks. The price of the black socks per pair was twice that of the blue socks. When the order was filled, it was found that the number of pairs of the two colours had been interchanged. This increased the bill by 50%. The ratio of the number of pairs of black socks to the number of pairs of blue socks in the original order was **(M.B.A., 2011)**
(*a*) 1: 2 (*b*) 1: 4
(*c*) 2: 1 (*d*) 4: 1

362. A man ordered a length of rope by telephone from his nearest hardware shop. But when a worker in the shop brought the rope, he found that the man on the telephone had miswritten the order by interchanging feet and inches. As a result of this, the length of rope received was only 30% of the length he had ordered. The length of the rope which the man ordered was between

(*a*) 6 ft and $7\frac{1}{2}$ ft (*b*) $7\frac{1}{2}$ ft and 9 ft

(*c*) 9 ft and $10\frac{1}{2}$ ft (*d*) $10\frac{1}{2}$ ft and 12 ft

363. A gardener has supply of fertilizer A which consists of 10% nitrogen and 6% phosphoric acid and fertilizer B which consists of 5% nitrogen and 10% phosphoric acid. After testing the soil conditions, he finds that he needs at least 14 kg of nitrogen and 14 kg of phosphoric acid for his crop. If fertilizer A costs ₹ 10.60 per kg and fertilizer B costs ₹ 8.40 per kg, what is the minimum cost at which the farmer can meet the nutrient requirement by using a combination of both types of fertilizers?

(*a*) ₹ 1488 (*b*) ₹ 1576

(*c*) ₹ 1648 (*d*) ₹ 1732

364. I bought 5 pens, 7 pencils and 4 erasers. Rajan bought 6 pens, 8 erasers and 14 pencils for an amount which was half more than that I had paid. What percent of the total amount paid by me was paid for the pen?

(*a*) 37.5% (*b*) 50%

(*c*) 62.5% (*d*) None of these

365. The majority against a certain motion is equal to 8% of the total number of voting. If 14 of those who voted against it had voted for it, the motion would have been carried by 4 votes. Find the number of votes for and against the motion.

(*a*) 112, 126 (*b*) 138, 162

(*c*) 128, 144 (*d*) 148, 172

366. The number of votes not cast for the Praja Party increased by 25% in the National General Election over those not cast for it in the previous Assembly polls and the Praja Party lost by a majority twice as large as that by which it had won the previous Assembly polls. If a total 2,60,000 people voted each time how many voted for the Praja Party in the previous Assembly polls?

(*a*) 110000 (*b*) 120000

(*c*) 140000 (*d*) 150000

367. Solve $[180\% \text{ of } (?)] \div 2 = 504$

[Indian Railway Gr. 'D' Exam, 2014]

(*a*) 400 (*b*) 480

(*c*) 560 (*d*) 600

368. What will come in the place of (?) in the expression below:

$x\%$ of y is $y\%$ of (?) [Indian Railway Gr. 'D' Exam, 2014]

(*a*) x (*b*) $100x$

(*c*) $\frac{x}{100}$ (*d*) $\frac{y}{100}$

369. How much $66\frac{2}{3}\%$ of ₹ 312 exceeds ₹ 200?

[SSC—CHSL (10+2) Exam, 2015]

(*a*) ₹ 96 (*b*) ₹ 4

(*c*) ₹ 8 (*d*) ₹ 104

370. Solve:

105.27% of 1200.11 + 11.80% of 2360.85 = 21.99% of (?) + 140.29 [IBPS—Bank Spl. Officers (IT) Exam, 2015]

(*a*) 500 (*b*) 240

(*c*) 310 (*d*) 550

371. State Electricity Board gives 15% discount on electric bills if it is paid before due date. One person gets ₹ 54 as discount. The amount of actual bill was:

(*a*) ₹ 362 (*b*) ₹ 359

(*c*) ₹ 360 (*d*) ₹ 361

[SSC—CHSL (10+2) Exam, 2015]

372. Solve (550% of 250) ÷ 275 = (?)

[United India Insurance (UIICL) Assistant (Online) Exam, 2015]

(*a*) 15 (*b*) 1.5

(*c*) 0.5 (*d*) None of these

Direction: In the question below consists of question-statement and two statements I and II are given below it. You have to decide whether the data provided in the statement are sufficient to answer the question. Give answer.

(*a*) The data in statement I alone are sufficient to answer the question while II alone are not sufficient to answer the question.

(*b*) Data in statement II alone are sufficient to answer the question while data in statement I alone are not sufficient to answer the question.

(*c*) The data in statement I alone or in statement II alone are sufficient to answer the question.

(*d*) The data in both Statements I and II are not sufficient to answer the question.

(*e*) The data in both Statements I and II are sufficient to answer the question.

373. What is the minimum passing percentage in a test?

[IDBI Bank Executive Officers Examination, 2015]

I. Raman scored 25% marks in the test and Sunil scored 288 marks which is 128 more than Raman.

II. Raman scored 64 marks less than the minimum passing marks.

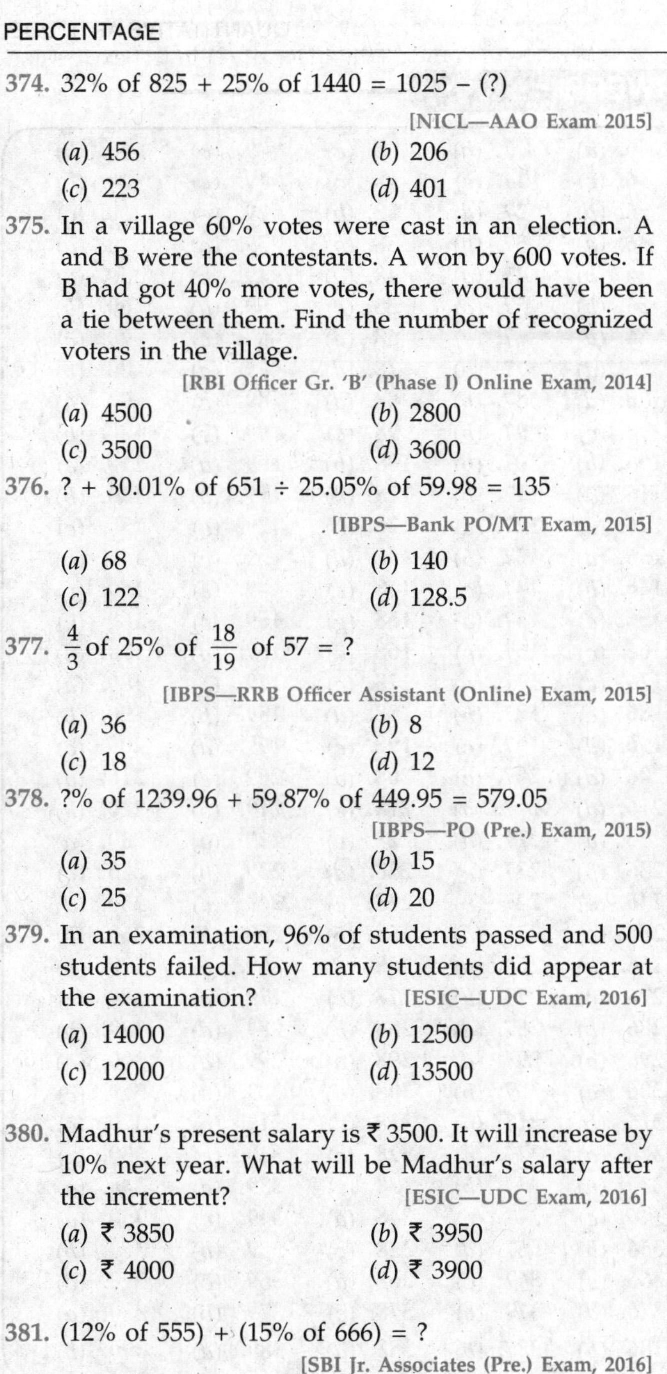

374. 32% of 825 + 25% of 1440 = 1025 – (?)

[NICL—AAO Exam 2015]

(*a*) 456 (*b*) 206
(*c*) 223 (*d*) 401

375. In a village 60% votes were cast in an election. A and B were the contestants. A won by 600 votes. If B had got 40% more votes, there would have been a tie between them. Find the number of recognized voters in the village.

[RBI Officer Gr. 'B' (Phase I) Online Exam, 2014]

(*a*) 4500 (*b*) 2800
(*c*) 3500 (*d*) 3600

376. ? + 30.01% of 651 ÷ 25.05% of 59.98 = 135

[IBPS—Bank PO/MT Exam, 2015]

(*a*) 68 (*b*) 140
(*c*) 122 (*d*) 128.5

377. $\frac{4}{3}$ of 25% of $\frac{18}{19}$ of 57 = ?

[IBPS—RRB Officer Assistant (Online) Exam, 2015]

(*a*) 36 (*b*) 8
(*c*) 18 (*d*) 12

378. ?% of 1239.96 + 59.87% of 449.95 = 579.05

[IBPS—PO (Pre.) Exam, 2015)

(*a*) 35 (*b*) 15
(*c*) 25 (*d*) 20

379. In an examination, 96% of students passed and 500 students failed. How many students did appear at the examination? [ESIC—UDC Exam, 2016]

(*a*) 14000 (*b*) 12500
(*c*) 12000 (*d*) 13500

380. Madhur's present salary is ₹ 3500. It will increase by 10% next year. What will be Madhur's salary after the increment? [ESIC—UDC Exam, 2016]

(*a*) ₹ 3850 (*b*) ₹ 3950
(*c*) ₹ 4000 (*d*) ₹ 3900

381. (12% of 555) + (15% of 666) = ?

[SBI Jr. Associates (Pre.) Exam, 2016]

(*a*) 166.5 (*b*) 167.5
(*c*) 168.5 (*d*) None of these

382. 85% of 420 + ?% of 1080 = 735

[SBI Jr. Associates (Pre.) Exam, 2016]

(*a*) 25 (*b*) 30
(*c*) 35 (*d*) 40

383. 30% of 1225 – 64% of 555 = ?

[SBI Jr. Associates (Pre.) Exam, 2016]

(*a*) 10.7 (*b*) 12.3
(*c*) 13.4 (*d*) None of these

384. Nagaraj could save 10% of his income. But 2 years later, when his income increased by 20%, he could save the same amount only as before. By how much percentage has his expenditure increased?

[CDS, 2016]

(*a*) $22\frac{2}{9}$% (*b*) $23\frac{1}{3}$%
(*c*) $24\frac{2}{9}$% (*d*) $25\frac{2}{9}$%

385. 14% of 14 + 28% of 28 + 92% of 96 – 15% of 85 = ?

[DMRC—Customer Relations Assistant (CRA) Exam, 2016]

(*a*) 8.37 (*b*) 85.37
(*c*) 89.37 (*d*) None of these

386. The marked price of an article is ₹ 2400. The shopkeeper gives successive discounts of x% and 15% to the customer. If the customer pays ₹ 1876.8 for the article, find the value of x.

[DMRC—Customer Relation Assistant (CRA) Exam, 2016]

(*a*) 9% (*b*) 8%
(*c*) 12% (*d*) 11%

387. Out of a total of 85 children playing Badminton or Table Tennis or both, total number of girls in the group is 70% of the total number of boys in the group, the number of boys playing only Badminton is 50% of the number of boys and total number of boys playing Badminton is 60% of the total number of boys. Number of children only playing table Tennis is 40% of the total number of children and a total of 12 children play both Badminton and Table Tennis. What is the number of girls playing only Badminton?

[DMRC—Customer Relations Assistant (CRA) Exam, 2016]

(*a*) 16 (*b*) 14
(*c*) 17 (*d*) None of these

388. Nandini Basu bought an article for ₹ 5844. She gave ₹ 156 to a mechanic to remove its defect. She then sold it for ₹ 5700. What was her loss per cent?

[ESI—UDC Exam, 2016]

(*a*) 5% (*b*) 5.5%
(*c*) 2.5% (*d*) 2.46%

389. A wrist watch of cost price ₹ 1250 was sold by Sharel for ₹ 1500. What was the profit percent?

[ESIC—UDC Exam, 2016]

(*a*) 21% (*b*) 24%
(*c*) 25% (*d*) 20%

390. In a village three people contested for the post of village Pradhan. Due to their own interest, all the voters voted and no one vote was invalid. The losing candidate got 30% votes. What could be the minimum absolute margin of votes by which the winning candidate led by the nearest rival, if each candidate got an integral per cent of votes?

[SBI Jr. Associates (Pre.) Exam, 2016]

(*a*) 4 (*b*) 2
(*c*) 1 (*d*) None of these

ANSWERS

1. (c)	2. (d)	3. (d)	4. (a)	5. (a)	6. (a)	7. (b)	8. (e)	9. (b)	10. (b)
11. (a)	12. (c)	13. (e)	14. (d)	15. (b)	16. (e)	17. (e)	18. (c)	19. (e)	20. (c)
21. (a)	22. (d)	23. (a)	24. (c)	25. (d)	26. (b)	27. (d)	28. (b)	29. (c)	30. (c)
31. (d)	32. (a)	33. (d)	34. (c)	35. (a)	36. (d)	37. (b)	38. (b)	39. (a)	40. (a)
41. (b)	42. (a)	43. (d)	44. (b)	45. (a)	46. (b)	47. (a)	48. (a)	49. (c)	50. (c)
51. (c)	52. (d)	53. (b)	54. (c)	55. (a)	56. (b)	57. (c)	58. (c)	59. (a)	60. (b)
61. (c)	62. (d)	63. (d)	64. (b)	65. (d)	66. (a)	67. (c)	68. (d)	69. (c)	70. (c)
71. (b)	72. (b)	73. (d)	74. (c)	75. (c)	76. (a)	77. (b)	78. (d)	79. (d)	80. (b)
81. (c)	82. (e)	83. (d)	84. (c)	85. (b)	86. (d)	87. (b)	88. (d)	89. (c)	90. (a)
91. (b)	92. (b)	93. (e)	94. (d)	95. (c)	96. (c)	97. (b)	98. (c)	99. (b)	100. (b)
101. (c)	102. (e)	103. (d)	104. (c)	105. (b)	106. (b)	107. (b)	108. (b)	109. (a)	110. (c)
111. (b)	112. (a)	113. (c)	114. (a)	115. (a)	116. (a)	117. (b)	118. (b)	119. (a)	120. (b)
121. (b)	122. (d)	123. (a)	124. (b)	125. (d)	126. (d)	127. (c)	128. (b)	129. (c)	130. (c)
131. (b)	132. (c)	133. (b)	134. (e)	135. (c)	136. (d)	137. (b)	138. (d)	139. (c)	140. (b)
141. (c)	142. (b)	143. (b)	144. (b)	145. (b)	146. (b)	147. (c)	148. (e)	149. (e)	150. (c)
151. (b)	152. (c)	153. (a)	154. (c)	155. (b)	156. (c)	157. (a)	158. (c)	159. (c)	160. (c)
161. (a)	162. (b)	163. (e)	164. (a)	165. (c)	166. (c)	167. (c)	168. (c)	169. (d)	170. (d)
171. (b)	172. (c)	173. (a)	174. (d)	175. (a)	176. (c)	177. (a)	178. (c)	179. (c)	180. (a)
181. (a)	182. (d)	183. (b)	184. (d)	185. (d)	186. (c)	187. (b)	188. (d)	189. (b)	190. (b)
191. (c)	192. (b)	193. (d)	194. (b)	195. (a)	196. (d)	197. (c)	198. (e)	199. (a)	200. (c)
201. (c)	202. (a)	203. (c)	204. (c)	205. (b)	206. (d)	207. (c)	208. (d)	209. (e)	210. (a)
211. (d)	212. (d)	213. (a)	214. (a)	215. (b)	216. (d)	217. (a)	218. (e)	219. (b)	220. (b)
221. (c)	222. (c)	223. (c)	224. (c)	225. (c)	226. (d)	227. (d)	228. (c)	229. (a)	230. (a)
231. (a)	232. (a)	233. (d)	234. (a)	235. (d)	236. (b)	237. (e)	238. (d)	239. (b)	240. (c)
241. (c)	242. (a)	243. (b)	244. (c)	245. (b)	246. (c)	247. (b)	248. (c)	249. (c)	250. (d)
251. (d)	252. (c)	253. (a)	254. (c)	255. (c)	256. (a)	257. (d)	258. (b)	259. (b)	260. (b)
261. (d)	262. (b)	263. (b)	264. (b)	265. (a)	266. (b)	267. (a)	268. (d)	269. (c)	270. (b)
271. (a)	272. (c)	273. (b)	274. (d)	275. (b)	276. (c)	277. (b)	278. (c)	279. (d)	280. (c)
281. (b)	282. (a)	283. (d)	284. (c)	285. (c)	286. (b)	287. (d)	288. (b)	289. (d)	290. (b)
291. (b)	292. (b)	293. (b)	294. (a)	295. (a)	296. (c)	297. (d)	298. (a)	299. (a)	300. (b)
301. (d)	302. (a)	303. (c)	304. (b)	305. (a)	306. (c)	307. (b)	308. (a)	309. (d)	310. (c)
311. (d)	312. (c)	313. (c)	314. (d)	315. (c)	316. (b)	317. (a)	318. (c)	319. (c)	320. (c)
321. (b)	322. (d)	323. (b)	324. (b)	325. (b)	326. (a)	327. (c)	328. (c)	329. (e)	330. (c)
331. (c)	332. (b)	333. (c)	334. (c)	335. (b)	336. (a)	337. (b)	338. (c)	339. (c)	340. (a)
341. (b)	342. (d)	343. (c)	344. (b)	345. (c)	346. (c)	347. (c)	348. (a)	349. (c)	350. (a)
351. (b)	352. (a)	353. (a)	354. (c)	355. (c)	356. (b)	357. (d)	358. (c)	359. (b)	360. (b)
361. (b)	362. (c)	363. (d)	364. (c)	365. (b)	366. (c)	367. (c)	368. (a)	369. (c)	370. (d)
371. (c)	372. (e)	373. (e)	374. (d)	375. (c)	376. (d)	377. (c)	378. (c)	379. (b)	380. (a)
381. (a)	382. (c)	383. (b)	384. (a)	385. (b)	386. (b)	387. (b)	388. (a)	389. (d)	390. (b)

SOLUTIONS

1. $\frac{3}{4} = \left(\frac{3}{4} \times 100\right)\% = 75\%.$

2. $5 : 4 = \frac{5}{4} = \left(\frac{5}{4} \times 100\right)\% = 125\%.$

3. $3.5 = \left(\frac{35}{10} \times 100\right)\% = 350\%.$

4. $64\% = \frac{64}{100} = \frac{16}{25}.$

5. $\frac{1}{2}\% = \left(\frac{1}{2} \times \frac{1}{100}\right) = \frac{0.5}{100} = 0.005.$

6. $12\% \text{ of } 5000 = \left(\frac{12}{100} \times 5000\right) = 600.$

7. $38\% \text{ of } 341 = \left(\frac{38}{100} \times 341\right) = \frac{12958}{100} = 129.58.$

8. $(550\% \text{ of } 250) \div 275 = \left(\frac{550}{100} \times 250\right) \div 275 = \frac{55 \times 25}{275} = 5.$

9. $280\% \text{ of } 3940 = \left(\frac{280}{100} \times 3940\right) = 11032.$

10. $92.5\% \text{ of } 550 = \left(\frac{925}{10} \times \frac{1}{100} \times 550\right) = 508.75.$

11. 2% of 2 = $\left(\frac{2}{100}\times 2\right)=\frac{4}{100}=0.04.$

12. $10\% \text{ of } 5+5\% \text{ of } 10=\left(\frac{10}{100}\times 5\right)+\left(\frac{5}{100}\times 10\right)=0.5+0.5=1.0.$

13. Let 36% of 245 − 40% of 210 = 10 − x.

Then, $\left(\frac{36}{100}\times 245\right)-\left(\frac{40}{100}\times 210\right)=10-x \Rightarrow$

$88.20 - 84 = 10 - x \Rightarrow 10 - x = 4.20 \Rightarrow x = 5.8.$

14. Let 45% of 300 + $\sqrt{x}$ = 56% of 750 − 10% of 250.

Then, $\left(\frac{45}{100}\times 300\right)+\sqrt{x}=\left(\frac{56}{100}\times 750\right)-\left(\frac{10}{100}\times 250\right)$

$\Rightarrow\ 135 + \sqrt{x} = 420 - 25 \Rightarrow \sqrt{x} = 260$

$\Rightarrow\ x = (260)^2 = 67600.$

15. $15\% \text{ of } 578+22.5\% \text{ of } 644=\left(\frac{15}{100}\times 578\right)+\left(\frac{225}{10}\times\frac{1}{100}\times 644\right)$

$= 86.7 + 144.9 = 231.6.$

16. 140% of 56 + 56% of 140 = $\left(\frac{140}{100}\times 56\right)+\left(\frac{56}{100}\times 140\right)$

$= 78.4 + 78.4 = 156.8.$

17. (7.9% of 134) − (3.4% of 79)

$=\left(\frac{79}{10}\times\frac{1}{100}\times 134\right)-\left(\frac{34}{10}\times\frac{1}{100}\times 79\right)$

$=\frac{79}{1000}\times(134-34)=\frac{79}{1000}\times 100=\frac{79}{10}=7.9.$

18. (23.6% of 1254) − (16.6% of 834)

$=\left(\frac{236}{10}\times\frac{1}{100}\times 1254\right)-\left(\frac{166}{10}\times\frac{1}{100}\times 834\right)$

$=\frac{1}{1000}(236\times 1254-166\times 834)$

$=\frac{12}{1000}(24662-11537)=\left(\frac{12\times 13125}{1000}\right)=157.5.$

19. (0.85% of 405) + (2.25% of 550)

$=\left(\frac{85}{100}\times\frac{1}{100}\times 405\right)+\left(\frac{225}{100}\times\frac{1}{100}\times 550\right)$

$=\frac{225}{10000}(153+550)=\left(\frac{225\times 703}{10000}\right)=15.8175.$

20. Given expression = $\left(\frac{45}{100}\times\frac{25}{100}\times\frac{4}{5}\times 850\right)=\frac{153}{2}=76.5.$

21. Given expression = $\left(\frac{28}{100}\times\frac{36}{100}\times\frac{5}{7}\times 5000\right)=360.$

22. (0.56% of 225) × (3.25% of 430)

$=\left(\frac{56}{100}\times\frac{1}{100}\times 225\right)\times\left(\frac{325}{100}\times\frac{1}{100}\times 430\right)$

$=\left(\frac{126}{100}\times\frac{13975}{1000}\right)=1.26\times 13.975=17.6085.$

23. Commission = $12\frac{1}{2}$% of ₹ 15000

$=₹\left(\frac{25}{2}\times\frac{1}{100}\times 15000\right)=₹\ 1875.$

24. Let the number be x.

Then, $\frac{1}{8}x=41.5 \Rightarrow x=41.5\times 8=332.$

$\therefore$ 69% of 332 = $\left(\frac{69}{100}\times 332\right)=229.08.$

25. 10% of 20 + 20% of 10 = $\left(\frac{10}{100}\times 20\right)+\left(\frac{20}{100}\times 10\right)$

$=\frac{2}{100}(100+100)=\frac{2}{100}$ of 200

= 2% of 200.

26. 60% of 264 = $\left(\frac{60}{100}\times 264\right)$

$= 158.40;$ 10% of 44 = $\left(\frac{10}{100}\times 44\right)=4.40;$

15% of 1056 = $\left(\frac{15}{100}\times 1056\right)$

$= 158.40;$ 30% of 132 = $\left(\frac{30}{100}\times 132\right)=39.60.$

$\therefore$ 60% of 264 = 15% of 1056.

27. Pass percentage = $\left(\frac{252}{270}\times 100\right)\%=\frac{280}{3}\%=93\frac{1}{3}\%.$

28. Required percentage = $\left(\frac{5}{2250}\times 100\right)\%=\frac{2}{9}\%.$

29. Required percentage = $\left(\frac{626}{850}\times 100\right)\%$

$=\frac{1252}{17}\%=73.65\%\approx 74\%.$

30. Required percentage = $\left(\frac{100+84+67+25+24}{100+100+100+50+50}\times 100\right)\%$

$=\left(\frac{300}{400}\times 100\right)\%=75\%.$

31. Total marks obtained = (35 + 30 + 30 + 25 + 65 + 45 + 80 + 85) = 395.

Maximum marks = (50 × 2 + 50 × 2 + 100 × 2 + 100 × 2) = 600.

$\therefore$ Percentage of marks = $\left(\frac{395}{600}\times 100\right)\%=65.8\%\approx 66\%.$

32. Rate of sales tax = $\left(\frac{27.20}{340}\times 100\right)\%=8\%.$

33. Required percentage = $\left(\frac{33}{88}\times 100\right)\%=\frac{75}{2}\%=37.5\%.$

34. Required percentage = $\left(\frac{0.01}{0.1}\times 100\right)\%=\left(\frac{1}{10}\times 100\right)\%=10\%.$

35. 1 min 12 sec = $1\frac{12}{60}$ min = $1\frac{1}{5}$ min = $\frac{6}{5}$ min.

1 hour = 60 min.

$\therefore$ Required percentage = $\left(\frac{6}{5}\times\frac{1}{60}\times 100\right)\%=2\%.$

36. Percentage increase = $\left(\frac{21}{560}\times 100\right)\%=\frac{15}{4}\%=3.75\%.$

37. Required percentage $= \left(\frac{18}{7200} \times 100\right)\% = \frac{1}{4}\% = 0.25\%.$

38. Required percentage $= \left(\frac{1987.50}{2650} \times 100\right)\%$

$= \left(\frac{19875}{265} \times \frac{1}{100} \times 100\right)\% = 75\%.$

39. Required percentage $= \left(\frac{3}{24} \times 100\right)\% = \frac{25}{2}\% = 12\frac{1}{2}\%.$

40. Price of 5 pairs when purchased separately = ₹ 5.
Price of 5 pair package = ₹ 3.40.
Difference in price = ₹ (5 − 3.40) = ₹ 1.60.

∴ Required percentage $= \left(\frac{1.6}{5} \times 100\right)\% = 32\%.$

41. Number of rolls sold by noon $= \frac{1}{2}$ of 40 dozen = 20 dozen.

Number of rolls sold between noon and closing time

$= 60\%$ of 20 dozen $= \left(\frac{60}{100} \times 20\right)$ dozen = 12 dozen.

Number of rolls left unsold = [40 − (20 + 12)] dozen = 8 dozen.

42. Weight of metal A = 5 kg.
Total weight of the alloy = (5 + 20) kg = 25 kg.

∴ Required percentage $= \left(\frac{5}{25} \times 100\right)\% = 20\%.$

43. Number of rotten apples = 30% of 450 $= \left(\frac{30}{100} \times 450\right) = 135.$

∴ Number of good apples = (450 − 135) = 315.

44. Total annual rent = ₹ (25000 × 12) = ₹ 300000.

Discount = 5% of ₹ 300000 = ₹ $\left(\frac{5}{100} \times 300000\right)$ = ₹ 15000.

∴ Annual rent paid after discount = ₹ (300000 − 15000) = ₹ 285000.

45. Correct time = 3 hrs 40 min = (3 × 60 + 40) min = 220 min.
Error = 5.5 min.

∴ Error % $= \left(\frac{5.5}{220} \times 100\right)\% = \frac{5}{2}\% = 2.5\%.$

46. Total number of households = 200.
Number of households whose monthly income is above ₹ 2000 but below ₹ 5000 = (170 − 80) = 90.

∴ Required percentage $= \left(\frac{90}{200} \times 100\right)\% = 45\%.$

47. Total number of students = (100 + 75) = 175.
Number of students passed = 75% of 100 + 60% of 75 = 75 + 45 = 120.

∴ Pass percentage $= \left(\frac{120}{175} \times 100\right)\% = \left(\frac{480}{7}\right)\% = 68\frac{4}{7}\%.$

48. Rebate on one ball = 25% of ₹ 32 = ₹ $\left(\frac{25}{100} \times 32\right)$ = ₹ 8.

∴ Required number of balls $= \frac{40}{8} = 5.$

49. Required percentage $= \left(\frac{1.14}{1.9} \times 100\right)\%$

$= \left(\frac{114}{190} \times 100\right)\% = 60\%.$

50. Number of toffees distributed

= 5% of 160 + 15% of 160 + $\frac{1}{4}$ of 160

$= \left(\frac{5}{100} \times 160\right) + \left(\frac{15}{100} \times 160\right) + \left(160 \times \frac{1}{4}\right)$

= 8 + 24 + 40 = 72.

∴ Number of toffees left behind = 160 − 72 = 88.

51. Revenue obtained from sale of notebooks in 2 weeks = ₹ (45 × 10 × 14) = ₹ 6300.

Revenue obtained from sale of pencil boxes in 2 weeks = ₹ (80 × 6 × 14) = ₹ 6720.

∴ Total commission earned
= 4% of ₹ 6300 + 20% of ₹ 6720
= 252 + 1344 = 1596.

52. Total cost = ₹ [1 × 1000 + (100 − 2)% of 1 × 4000]
= ₹ (1000 + 0.98 × 4000)
= ₹ (1000 + 3920) = ₹ 4920.

53. Actual price = ₹ (25 + 2.50) = ₹ 27.50.

∴ Saving $= \left(\frac{2.50}{27.50} \times 100\right)\% = \frac{100}{11}\% = 9\frac{1}{11}\% \approx 9\%.$

54. Quantity of pure acid = 20% of 8 litres $= \left(\frac{20}{100} \times 8\right)$ litres = 1.6 litres.

55. Rebate = 6% of ₹ 6650 = ₹ $\left(\frac{6}{100} \times 6650\right)$ = ₹ 399.

Sales tax = 10% of ₹ (6650 − 399) = ₹ $\left(\frac{10}{100} \times 6251\right)$ = ₹ 625.10.

∴ Final amount = ₹ (6251 + 625.10) = ₹ 6876.10.

56. $\frac{384}{540} = \left(\frac{384}{540} \times 100\right)\% = 71\frac{1}{9}\%;\ \frac{425}{500} = \left(\frac{425}{500} \times 100\right)\% = 85\%;$

$\frac{570}{700} = \left(\frac{570}{700} \times 100\right)\% = 81\frac{3}{7}\%;\ \frac{480}{660}$

$= \left(\frac{480}{660} \times 100\right)\% = 72\frac{8}{11}\%.$

∴ $\frac{425}{500}$ shows the best percentage.

57. Number of sweets obtained by each student = 20% of 65 = 13.
Number of sweets obtained by each teacher = 40% of 65 = 26.
∴ Total number of sweets
= 65 × 13 + 4 × 26 = 845 + 104 = 949.

58. Total marks obtained by the student = 55% of 800

$= \left(\frac{55}{100} \times 800\right) = 440.$

∴ Marks scored in English

$= 15\%$ of $440 = \left(\frac{15}{100} \times 440\right) = 66.$

59. Percentage of A's expenditure = $\left(\frac{18}{40}\times 100\right)\% = 45\%$.

Percentage of B's expenditure = $\left(\frac{21}{50}\times 100\right)\% = 42\%$.

Percentage of C's expenditure = $\left(\frac{24}{60}\times 100\right)\% = 40\%$.

Percentage of D's expenditure = $\left(\frac{27}{70}\times 100\right)\% = 38\frac{4}{7}\%$.

Clearly, A has done the highest expenditure.

60. Tax on first ₹ 50000 = Nil.

Tax on next ₹ 10000 = 10% of ₹ 10000 = ₹ 1000.

Tax on next ₹ 90000 = 20% of ₹ 90000 = ₹ 18000.

Tax on next ₹ 20000 = 30% of ₹ 20000 = ₹ 6000.

∴ Tax payable = ₹ (1000 + 18000 + 6000) = ₹ 25000.

61. Let the number be x.

Then, 40% of 60% of $\frac{3}{5}$ of x = 504

$\Rightarrow \left(\frac{40}{100}\times\frac{60}{100}\times\frac{3}{5}\times x\right) = 504$

$\Rightarrow \frac{18}{125}x = 504 \Rightarrow x = \frac{504\times 125}{18} = 3500.$

$\therefore$ 25% of $\frac{2}{5}$ of 3500 = $\left(\frac{25}{100}\times\frac{2}{5}\times 3500\right) = 350.$

62. Let 125% of 3060 – 85% of x = 408. Then,

85% of $x = \left(\frac{125}{100}\times 3060\right) - 408$

$\Rightarrow \frac{85}{100}x = 3825 - 408$

$\Rightarrow \frac{17x}{20} = 3417$

$\Rightarrow x = \left(\frac{3417\times 20}{17}\right) = 4020.$

63. Let 40% of 265 + 35% of 180 = 50% of x.

Then, $\left(\frac{40}{100}\times 265\right) + \left(\frac{35}{100}\times 180\right) = \left(\frac{50}{100}\times x\right)$

$\Rightarrow 106 + 63 = \frac{x}{2}$

$\Rightarrow x = 169 \times 2 = 338.$

64. Let x% of 450 + 46% of 285 = 257.1. Then,

$\left(\frac{x}{100}\times 450\right) + \left(\frac{46}{100}\times 285\right) = 257.1$

$\Rightarrow \frac{9x}{2} = 257.1 - 131.1 = 126$

$\Rightarrow x = \frac{126\times 2}{9} = 28.$

65. Let 36% of 365 + x% of 56.2 = 156.69.

Then, $\left(\frac{36}{100}\times 365\right) + \left(\frac{x}{100}\times 56.2\right) = 156.69$

$\Rightarrow \frac{281}{500}x = 156.69 - 131.4 = 25.29$

$\Rightarrow x = \frac{25.29\times 500}{281} = 45.$

66. Let 35568 ÷ x% of 650 = 456. Then,

$35568 \div \left(\frac{x}{100}\times 650\right) = 456$

$\Rightarrow \frac{13x}{2}\times 456 = 35568$

$\Rightarrow 2964x = 35568$

$\Rightarrow x = \frac{35568}{2964} = 12.$

67. Let 23% of 8040 + 42% of 545 = x% of 3000. Then,

$\left(\frac{23}{100}\times 8040\right) + \left(\frac{42}{100}\times 545\right) = \left(\frac{x}{100}\times 3000\right)$

$\Rightarrow 30x = 1849.2 + 228.9 = 2078.1$

$\Rightarrow x = \frac{2078.1}{30} = 69.27.$

68. Let 3.2% of 500 × 2.4% of x = 288.

Then, $\left(\frac{32}{10}\times\frac{1}{100}\times 500\right)\times\left(\frac{24}{10}\times\frac{1}{100}\times x\right) = 288$

$\Rightarrow 16\times\frac{3x}{125} = 288 \Rightarrow x = \frac{288\times 125}{16\times 3} = 750.$

69. Let 85% of 485.5 = 50% of x.

Then, $\left(\frac{85}{100}\times 485.5\right) = \frac{50x}{100} \Rightarrow \frac{x}{2} = 412.675$

$\Rightarrow x = 825.35.$

70. Let 40% of 4.5 + x% of $\frac{2}{3}$ = 20% of 10.

Then, $\left(\frac{40}{100}\times 4.5\right) + \left(\frac{x}{100}\times\frac{2}{3}\right) = \left(\frac{20}{100}\times 10\right)$

$\Rightarrow \frac{x}{150} = 2 - 1.8 = 0.2$

$\Rightarrow x = 0.2 \times 150 = 30.$

71. Clearly, 60% of 28% of 240 = $\left(\frac{60}{100}\times\frac{28}{100}\times 240\right)$

$= \left(\frac{30}{100}\times\frac{28}{100}\times 2\times 240\right)$

$= \left(\frac{30}{100}\times\frac{28}{100}\times 480\right)$

= 30% of 28% of 480.

72. 25% of 25% = $\frac{25}{100}\times\frac{25}{100} = \frac{1}{16} = 0.0625.$

73. Required percentage = $\left(\frac{3\%}{5\%}\times 100\right)\%$

$= \left[\frac{(3/100)}{(5/100)}\times 100\right]\% = 60\%.$

74. Let the number be x.

Then, 64% of x = 2592 $\Rightarrow \frac{64x}{100} = 2592$

$\Rightarrow x = \left(\frac{2592\times 100}{64}\right) = 4050.$

$\therefore$ 88% of 4050 = $\left(\frac{88}{100} \times 4050\right) = 3564.$

75. Let the number be x.

Then, 42% of x = 892.50 $\Rightarrow \frac{42x}{100} = 892.50$

$\Rightarrow x = \left(\frac{892.5 \times 100}{42}\right) = 2125.$

$\therefore$ 73% of 2125 = $\left(\frac{73}{100} \times 2125\right) = 1551.25.$

76. Let the number be x. Then, 15% of 45% of x = 105.3

$\Rightarrow \left(\frac{15}{100} \times \frac{45}{100} \times x\right) = 105.3$

$\Rightarrow \frac{27x}{400} = 105.3$

$\Rightarrow x = \left(\frac{105.3 \times 400}{27}\right) = 1560.$

$\therefore$ 24% of 1560 = $\left(\frac{24}{100} \times 1560\right) = 374.4.$

77. X% of 0.3 = 0.03 $\Rightarrow \frac{X}{100} \times 0.3 = 0.03$

$\Rightarrow X = \left(\frac{0.03 \times 100}{0.3}\right) = 10.$

78. Let the required amount be ₹ x.

Then, 40% of 60% of 32% of x = 432

$\Rightarrow \frac{40}{100} \times \frac{60}{100} \times \frac{32}{100} \times x = 432$

$\Rightarrow x = \frac{432 \times 100 \times 100 \times 100}{40 \times 60 \times 32} = 5625.$

79. Let the required number be x.

Then, 30% of x

$< 100 \Rightarrow \frac{30}{100} x < 100 \Rightarrow x < \frac{1000}{3} \Rightarrow x < 333.33.$

Hence, greatest possible value of x = 333.

80. Let the worth of the house be ₹ x.

Then, $\frac{2}{7}$% of x = 28000 $\Leftrightarrow \left(\frac{2}{7} \times \frac{1}{100} \times x\right) = 2800$

$\Leftrightarrow x = \left(\frac{2800 \times 100 \times 7}{2}\right) = 9,80,000.$

81. Let 15% of x% of 582 = 17.46.

Then, $\frac{15}{100} \times \frac{x}{100} \times 582 = \frac{1746}{100} \Leftrightarrow x = \left(\frac{1746}{100} \times \frac{100 \times 100}{15 \times 582}\right)$

$= 20.$

82. Let the required number of chicken be x.

Then, 65% of x = 47775

$\Rightarrow \frac{65}{100} x = 47775$

$\Rightarrow x = \frac{47775 \times 100}{65} = 73500.$

83. Let the number be x.

Then, 35% of x = 175

$\Leftrightarrow \left(\frac{35}{100} \times x\right) = 175 \Leftrightarrow x = \left(\frac{175 \times 100}{35}\right) = 500.$

Now, let y% of 175 = 500.

Then, $\left(\frac{y}{100} \times 175\right) = 500 \Leftrightarrow y = \left(\frac{500 \times 100}{175}\right) = \frac{2000}{7} = 285\frac{5}{7}.$

84. Let the amount of the bill be ₹ x.

Then, 4% of x = 13 $\Rightarrow \frac{4}{100} x = 13 \Rightarrow x = \frac{13 \times 100}{4} = 325.$

85. Marks secured by X = 58% of 700 = $\left(\frac{58}{100} \times 700\right) = 406.$

Marks secured by Y = (406 – 105) = 301.

$\therefore$ Required percentage = $\left(\frac{301}{700} \times 100\right)\% = 43\%.$

86. Let Pooja's monthly salary be ₹ x.

Then, 13% of x = 8554 $\Rightarrow \frac{13x}{100} = 8554$

$\Rightarrow x = \frac{8554 \times 100}{13} = 65800.$

Total percentage of salary invested = (13 + 23 + 8)%
= 44%.

$\therefore$ Total amount invested monthly = 44% of ₹ 65800

= ₹ $\left(\frac{44}{100} \times 65800\right)$ = ₹ 28952

87. Let Nupur's annual salary be ₹ x.

Then, 26% of x = 89856 $\Rightarrow \frac{26x}{100} = 89856$

$\Rightarrow x = \left(\frac{89856 \times 100}{26}\right) = 345600.$

$\therefore$ Nupur's monthly income = ₹ $\left(\frac{345600}{12}\right)$ = ₹ 28800.

88. Let David's annual income be ₹ x and his wife's annual income be ₹ y.

Then, 8% of x = 800 $\Rightarrow \frac{8}{100} x = 800$

$\Rightarrow x = \left(\frac{800 \times 100}{8}\right) = 10000.$

And, 8% of y = 840 $\Rightarrow \frac{8}{100} y = 840$

$\Rightarrow y = \left(\frac{840 \times 100}{8}\right) = 10500.$

$\therefore$ Required difference = ₹ [(10500 + 840) – (10000 + 800)]
= ₹ (11340 – 10800) = ₹ 540.

89. Let the number be x.

Then, $\frac{x + 75\% \text{ of } x + 25\% \text{ of } x}{3} = 240$

$\Rightarrow x + \frac{75}{100} x + \frac{25}{100} x = 240 \times 3 = 720$

$\Rightarrow \quad x + \frac{3}{4}x + \frac{1}{4}x = 720$

$\Rightarrow \quad 2x = 720 \Rightarrow x = 360.$

90. Let the price of each printer be ₹ x. Then, price of each computer = ₹ $(3x)$.

Total cost of printers = ₹ $(20x)$.

Total cost of purchase = ₹ $(60 \times 3x + 20x)$ = ₹ $(200x)$.

$\therefore$ Required percentage = $\left(\frac{20x}{200x} \times 100\right)\% = 10\%.$

91. Let his taxable income be ₹ 100.

Then, income tax
= 30% of ₹ 100 = ₹ 30.

Surcharge = 10% of ₹ 30 = ₹ 3.

Total tax paid = ₹ (30 + 3) = ₹ 33.

$\therefore$ Net tax rate = $\left(\frac{33}{100} \times 100\right)\% = 33\%.$

92. Error = $(45°27' - 45°) = 27'$.

Accurate measure = $45° = (45 \times 60)' = 2700'$.

$\therefore$ Percentage error = $\left(\frac{27}{2700} \times 100\right)\% = 1\%.$

93. $\frac{5}{6} = \left(\frac{5}{6} \times 100\right)\% = 83\frac{1}{3}\%$

$\frac{2}{3} = \left(\frac{2}{3} \times 100\right)\% = 66\frac{2}{3}\%$; $\frac{2}{5} = \left(\frac{2}{5} \times 100\right)\% = 40\%$;

$\frac{1}{4} = \left(\frac{1}{4} \times 100\right)\% = 25\%$; $\frac{2}{11} = \left(\frac{2}{11} \times 100\right)\% = 18\frac{2}{11}\% < 20\%.$

94. Let the number be x.

Then,

54% of x – 26% of x = 22526

$\Rightarrow \frac{54}{100}x - \frac{26}{100}x = 22526 \Rightarrow \frac{28}{100}x = 22526$

$\Rightarrow x = \left(\frac{22526 \times 100}{28}\right) = 80450.$

$\therefore$ 66% of 80450 = $\left(\frac{66}{100} \times 80450\right) = 53097.$

95. Let the number be x.

Then,

38% of x – 24% of x = 135.10

$\Rightarrow \frac{38}{100}x - \frac{24}{100}x = 135.10 \Rightarrow \frac{14}{100}x = 135.10$

$\Rightarrow x = \left(\frac{135.10 \times 100}{14}\right) = 965.$

$\therefore$ 40% of 965 = $\left(\frac{40}{100} \times 965\right) = 386.$

96. Let the total number of students be x.

Then, (100 – 76)% of x = 204

$\Rightarrow$ 24% of x = 204

$\Rightarrow \frac{24}{100}x = 204 \Rightarrow x = \left(\frac{204 \times 100}{24}\right) = 850.$

97. Let the total number of examinees be x.

Then, (100 – 65)% of x

= 420 $\Rightarrow$ 35% of x = 420 $\Rightarrow \frac{35}{100}x$

$= 420 \Rightarrow x = \left(\frac{420 \times 100}{35}\right) = 1200.$

98. Let the total number of candidates be x.

Then, (100 – 15)% of x = 340 $\Rightarrow$ 85% of x = 340

$\Rightarrow \frac{85}{100}x = 340$

$\Rightarrow x = \left(\frac{340 \times 100}{85}\right) = 400.$

99. Let the maximum marks be x.

Then, 76% of x + 480

= $x \Rightarrow x$ – 76% of x = 480 $\Rightarrow$ 24% of x = 480

$\Rightarrow \frac{24x}{100} = 480 \Rightarrow x = \left(\frac{480 \times 100}{24}\right) = 2000.$

$\therefore$ Marks scored by Rajan = 76% of 2000

$= \left(\frac{76}{100} \times 2000\right) = 1520.$

100. Let the capacity of the bucket be x litres.

Then, 80% of x – $66\frac{2}{3}\%$ of x = 2

$\Rightarrow \left(80 - 66\frac{2}{3}\right)\%$ of $x = 2 \Rightarrow 13\frac{1}{3}\%$ of $x = 2$

$\Rightarrow \frac{40}{3} \times \frac{1}{100} \times x = 2 \Rightarrow x = \left(\frac{2 \times 100 \times 3}{40}\right) = 15.$

101. Let Vinay's salary be ₹ x. Then,

75% of 5% of x = 1687.50

$\Rightarrow \frac{75}{100} \times \frac{5}{100} \times x = 1687.50$

$\Rightarrow x = \left(\frac{1687.50 \times 100 \times 100}{75 \times 5}\right) = 45000.$

102. Let the first number be x and the second number be y.

Then,

$\frac{1}{4}$ of 60% of $x = \frac{2}{5}$ of 20% of y

$\Rightarrow \frac{1}{4} \times \frac{60}{100} \times x = \frac{2}{5} \times \frac{20}{100} \times y \Rightarrow \frac{3x}{20} = \frac{2y}{25}$

$\Rightarrow \frac{x}{y} = \frac{2}{25} \times \frac{20}{3} = \frac{8}{15}.$

103. Let the numbers be x and $(2490 - x)$. Then,

6.5% of x = 8.5% of $(2490 - x)$

$\Rightarrow \frac{65}{10} \times \frac{1}{100} \times x = \frac{85}{10} \times \frac{1}{100} \times (2490 - x)$

$\Rightarrow 13x = 17(2490 - x) \Rightarrow 30x = 2490 \times 17$

$\Rightarrow x = \left(\frac{2490 \times 17}{30}\right) = 1411.$

Hence, the numbers are 1411 and 1079.

104. Let the original number of students opting for IT courses be x.

Then, (100 – 23)% of x = 1540

$\Rightarrow$ 77% of x = 1540

$\Rightarrow \frac{77}{100}x = 1540 \Rightarrow x = \left(\frac{1540 \times 100}{77}\right) = 2000.$

105. Let the monthly salary be ₹ x.

Then, $2\frac{2}{3}\%$ of x = 72

$\Rightarrow \frac{8}{3} \times \frac{1}{100} \times x = 72 \Rightarrow x = \left(\frac{72 \times 3 \times 100}{8}\right) = 2700.$

106. Let the original price be ₹ x and increased price be ₹ y.

Then, 110% of $x = y \Rightarrow x = \frac{100y}{110} = \frac{10}{11}y.$

(*a*) Original price = ₹ $\left(\frac{10}{11} \times 5.50\right)$ = ₹ 5.

(*b*) Original price = ₹ $\left(\frac{10}{11} \times 7.60\right)$ = ₹ $\left(\frac{76}{11}\right)$ = ₹ 6.9090 .....

which is not possible.

(*c*) Original price = ₹ $\left(\frac{10}{11} \times 11\right)$ = ₹ 10.

(*d*) Original price = ₹ $\left(\frac{10}{11} \times 12.10\right)$ = ₹ 11.

107. Let the number be x.

Then, $\left(100 + 37\frac{1}{2}\right)\%$ of x = 33

$\Rightarrow 137\frac{1}{2}\%$ of $x = 33 \Rightarrow \frac{275}{2} \times \frac{1}{100} \times x = 33$

$\Rightarrow x = \left(\frac{33 \times 2 \times 100}{275}\right) = 24.$

108. Let the numbers be x and x + 20. Then,

$\frac{3}{4}x$ = 60% of (x + 20)

$\Rightarrow \frac{3}{4}x = \frac{60}{100}(x + 20) \Rightarrow \frac{5}{4}x = x + 20$

$\Rightarrow \frac{x}{4} = 20 \Rightarrow x = 20 \times 4 = 80.$

$\therefore$ Required sum = $x + x + 20 = 2x + 20 = 2 \times 80 + 20$ = 180.

109. Let the number be x. Then, x – 16% of x = 42

$\Leftrightarrow x - \frac{16}{100}x = 42 \Leftrightarrow x - \frac{4}{25}x = 42$

$\Leftrightarrow \frac{21}{25}x = 42 \Leftrightarrow x = \left(\frac{42 \times 25}{21}\right) = 50.$

110. Clearly, the numbers which have 1 or 9 in the unit's digit, have squares that end in the digit 1. Such numbers from 1 to 70 are 1, 9, 11, 19, 21, 29, 31, 39, 41, 49, 51, 59, 61, 69.

Number of such numbers = 14.

$\therefore$ Required percentage = $\left(\frac{14}{70} \times 100\right)\% = 20\%.$

111. $\frac{4}{5} \times 70 = 56$ and $\frac{5}{7} \times 112 = 80.$

$\therefore$ Required percentage = $\left(\frac{80 - 56}{80} \times 100\right)\%$

$= \left(\frac{24}{80} \times 100\right)\% = 30\%.$

112. y = 125 + 10% of 125 = 125 + 12.50 = 137.50.

$\therefore$ x = 137.50 – 10% of 137.50 = 137.50 – 13.75 = 123.75.

113. Let the number be x. Then,

75% of $x + 75 = x \Leftrightarrow x - \frac{75}{100}x = 75 \Leftrightarrow x - \frac{3}{4}x = 75$

$\Leftrightarrow \frac{x}{4} = 75 \Leftrightarrow x = 300.$

114. Let the number be x.

Then, $x - 125 = 37\frac{1}{2}\%$ of $x \Rightarrow x - 125 = \frac{75}{2} \times \frac{1}{100} \times x = \frac{3x}{8}$

$\Rightarrow x - \frac{3x}{8} = 125 \Rightarrow \frac{5x}{8} = 125$

$\Rightarrow x = \left(\frac{125 \times 8}{5}\right) = 200.$

$\therefore$ 25% of 200 = $\left(\frac{25}{100} \times 200\right) = 50.$

115. Let the number be 100 and required multiplier be y.

Then, $100y = 129.7$ or $y = \frac{129.7}{100} = 1.297.$

116. Let the numbers be x and y. Then,

$x + y = \frac{28}{25}x \Leftrightarrow y = \frac{28}{25}x - x$

$\Leftrightarrow y = \frac{3}{25}x \Leftrightarrow \frac{y}{x} = \left(\frac{3}{25} \times 100\right)\% = 12\%.$

117. Let the number be x.

Then, $x - 25\%$ of $x = 225 \Rightarrow x - \frac{25}{100}x = 225 \Rightarrow \frac{75x}{100} = 225$

$\Rightarrow x = \left(\frac{225 \times 100}{75}\right) = 300.$

Required increase = (390 – 300) = 90.

$\therefore$ Increase % = $\left(\frac{90}{300} \times 100\right)\% = 30\%.$

118. Let the numbers be x and y.

Then, $y - 25\%$ of $x = \frac{5}{6}y \Leftrightarrow y - \frac{5}{6}y = \frac{25}{100}x \Leftrightarrow \frac{y}{6} = \frac{x}{4} \Leftrightarrow \frac{x}{y} = \frac{4}{6} = \frac{2}{3}.$

119. Let the larger number be x.

Then, $x - 20 = \frac{20}{100}x \Leftrightarrow x - \frac{1}{5}x = 20$

$\Leftrightarrow \frac{4}{5}x = 20 \Leftrightarrow x = \left(20 \times \frac{5}{4}\right) = 25.$

120. Let the numbers be x and y. Then, $\frac{x}{12} = \frac{y}{4} \Leftrightarrow x = 3y.$

$\therefore$ Required percentage = $\left(\frac{x - y}{y} \times 100\right)\%$

$= \left(\frac{2y}{y} \times 100\right)\% = 200\%.$

121. Let one number = x. Then, other number = 80% of $x = \frac{4x}{5}$.

$\therefore 4\left[x^2+\left(\frac{4}{5}x\right)^2\right]=656 \Leftrightarrow x^2+\frac{16}{25}x^2=164 \Leftrightarrow \frac{41}{25}x^2=164$

$\Leftrightarrow x^2=\left(\frac{164\times 25}{41}\right)=100 \Leftrightarrow x=10.$

So, the numbers are 10 and 8.

122. 5% of A + 4% of $B = \frac{2}{3}$ (6% of A + 8% of B)

$\Leftrightarrow \frac{5}{100}A+\frac{4}{100}B=\frac{2}{3}\left(\frac{6}{100}A+\frac{8}{100}B\right)$

$\Leftrightarrow \frac{1}{20}A+\frac{1}{25}B=\frac{1}{25}A+\frac{4}{75}B$

$\Leftrightarrow \left(\frac{1}{20}-\frac{1}{25}\right)A=\left(\frac{4}{75}-\frac{1}{25}\right)B$

$\Leftrightarrow \frac{1}{100}A=\frac{1}{75}B \Leftrightarrow \frac{A}{B}=\frac{100}{75}=\frac{4}{3}.$

123. Total number of votes polled = (1136 + 7636 + 11628) = 20400.

$\therefore$ Required percentage $=\left(\frac{11628}{20400}\times 100\right)\%=57\%.$

124. Increase in 10 years = (262500 − 175000) = 87500.

Increase% $=\left(\frac{87500}{175000}\times 100\right)\%=50\%.$

$\therefore$ Required average $=\left(\frac{50}{10}\right)\%=5\%.$

125. Let the number be x. Then, error $=\frac{5}{3}x-\frac{3}{5}x=\frac{16}{15}x.$

Error % $=\left(\frac{16x}{15}\times\frac{3}{5x}\times 100\right)\%=64\%.$

126. Let the original value of the tempo be ₹ x. Then,

1.3% of $\frac{4}{5}$ of $x = 910 \Leftrightarrow \frac{13}{10}\times\frac{1}{100}\times\frac{4}{5}\times x=910$

$\Leftrightarrow x=\left(\frac{910\times 10\times 100\times 5}{13\times 4}\right)=87500.$

127. Let the total production be x lakh tons. Then, 15% of x − 10% of x = (40 − 30) lakh tons

$\Leftrightarrow$ 5% of x = 10 lakh tons

$\Leftrightarrow x=\left(\frac{10\times 100}{5}\right)=200$ lakh tons.

128. Let the number of candidates appeared from each state be x.

Then, 7% of x − 6% of x = 80

$\Leftrightarrow$ 1% of x = 80

$\Leftrightarrow x = 80 \times 100 = 8000.$

129. Amount paid to car owner = 90% of 85% of ₹ 3,25,000

= ₹ $\left(\frac{90}{100}\times\frac{85}{100}\times 325000\right)$ = ₹ 2,48,625.

$\therefore$ Required difference = ₹ (325000 − 248625) = ₹ 76,375.

130. Let the amount of taxable purchases be ₹ x.

Then, 6% of $x=\frac{30}{100} \Leftrightarrow x=\left(\frac{30}{100}\times\frac{100}{6}\right)=5.$

$\therefore$ Cost of tax free items = ₹ [25 − (5 + 0.30)] = ₹ 19.70.

131. Number of runs made by running = 110 − (3 × 4 + 8 × 6) = 50.

$\therefore$ Required percentage $=\left(\frac{50}{110}\times 100\right)\%=45\frac{5}{11}\%.$

132. Let the marked price be ₹ x.

Then, x − 5% of x = 9595 $\Leftrightarrow$ 95% of x = 9595

$\Leftrightarrow x=\left(\frac{9595\times 100}{95}\right)=10100.$

133. Let the monthly income be ₹ x. Then,

$\left(100-66\frac{2}{3}\right)\%$ of $x = 1200$

$\Leftrightarrow 33\frac{1}{3}\%$ of $x = 1200$

$\Leftrightarrow \frac{100}{3}\times\frac{1}{100}\times x=1200$

$\Leftrightarrow x = 1200 \times 3 = 3600.$

$\therefore$ Monthly expenses = ₹ (3600 − 1200) = ₹ 2400.

134. Let Reena's yearly income be ₹ x.

Anubhav's monthly income = ₹ $\left(\frac{240000}{12}\right)$ = ₹ 20000.

Then, 25% of x = 75% of 20000

$\Rightarrow \frac{25}{100}x=\frac{75}{100}\times 20000$

$\Rightarrow \frac{x}{4}=15000 \Rightarrow x=60000.$

$\therefore$ Reena's monthly income = ₹ $\left(\frac{60000}{12}\right)$ = ₹ 5000.

135. Sonal's annual salary = ₹ 108000. Sonal's monthly salary = ₹ $\left(\frac{108000}{12}\right)$ = ₹ 9000.

Nandini's monthly salary = ₹ (9000 × 2) = ₹ 18000.

Let Kaushal's monthly salary be ₹ x. Then,

12% of x = 16% of 18000

$\Rightarrow \frac{12}{100}x=\left(\frac{16}{100}\times 18000\right)=2880$

$\Rightarrow x=\left(\frac{2880\times 100}{12}\right)=24000.$

136. Let Raman's expense be ₹ x. Then, Vimal's expense = 90% of ₹ x = ₹ $\left(\frac{90}{100}\times x\right)$ = ₹ $\frac{9}{10}x$.

Aman's expense = 130% of ₹ $\left(\frac{9x}{10}\right)$ = ₹ $\left(\frac{130}{100}\times\frac{9x}{10}\right)$ = ₹ $\frac{117x}{100}$.

$\therefore \frac{117x}{100}+\frac{9x}{10}+x=6447 \Rightarrow \frac{117x+90x+100x}{100}=6447$

$\Rightarrow 307x = 644700$

$\Rightarrow x=\frac{644700}{307}=2100.$

Hence, Aman's expense = ₹ $\left(\frac{117\times 2100}{100}\right)$ = ₹ 2457.

137. Let the sum paid to Y per week be ₹ x.

Then, sum paid to X per week

$= 120\%$ of ₹ x = ₹ $\left(\frac{120}{100} \times x\right) =$ ₹ $\frac{6}{5}x$.

$\therefore x + \frac{6x}{5} = 550 \Rightarrow \frac{11x}{5} = 550 \Rightarrow x = \frac{550 \times 5}{11} = 250.$

138. Let the total amount be ₹ x. Then, $(100 - 27)\%$ of x = 89745 + 51291

$\Rightarrow 73\%$ of $x = 141036$

$\Rightarrow \frac{73}{100}x = 141036$

$\Rightarrow x = \left(\frac{141036 \times 100}{73}\right) = 193200.$

139. Let the numbers be x and y respectively.

Then, 60% of $x = \frac{2}{3}y \Rightarrow \frac{60}{100}x = \frac{2}{3}y \Rightarrow \frac{3}{5}x = \frac{2}{3}y$

$\Rightarrow \frac{x}{y} = \frac{2}{3} \times \frac{5}{3} = \frac{10}{9}.$

140. Number of cases required to be tested

$= 5\%$ of 120 + 10% of 80

$= \left(\frac{5}{100} \times 120\right) + \left(\frac{10}{100} \times 80\right) = 6 + 8 = 14.$

$\therefore$ Required percentage

$= \left(\frac{14}{120 + 80} \times 100\right)\% = \left(\frac{14}{200} \times 100\right)\% = 7\%.$

141. Let the person's gross income be ₹ x. Then, $(100 - 3)\%$ of $x = 237650 \Rightarrow 97\%$ of $x = 237650$

$\Rightarrow \frac{97}{100}x = 237650$

$\Rightarrow x = \left(\frac{237650 \times 100}{97}\right) = 245000.$

$\therefore$ When income tax is raised to 7%, we have:

Net income

$= (100 - 7)\%$ of ₹ 245000 = 93% of ₹ 245000

= ₹ $\left(\frac{93}{100} \times 245000\right)$ = ₹ 227850.

142. Let the cost of a single ticket be ₹ x.

Then, cost of monthly return ticket

$= 125\%$ of ₹ x = ₹ $\left(\frac{125}{100}x\right)$ = ₹ $\frac{5x}{4}$

Cost of monthly return ticket with extension

$= 105\%$ of ₹ $\frac{5x}{4}$ = ₹ $\left(\frac{105}{100} \times \frac{5x}{4}\right)$ = ₹ $\frac{21x}{16}$.

$\therefore \frac{21x}{16} = 84 \Rightarrow x = \left(\frac{84 \times 16}{21}\right) = 64.$

143. Percentage of oxygen $= \left(\frac{9.4}{20} \times 100\right)\% = 47\%.$

$\therefore$ Percentage of carbon $= [100 - (40 + 47)]\% = 13\%.$

144. Let the number of children in each column be x.

Then, number of children in each row $= 112\frac{1}{2}\%$ of x

$= \frac{225}{2} \times \frac{1}{100} \times x = \frac{9x}{8}$

$\therefore x \times \frac{9x}{8} = 72 \Rightarrow x^2 = \frac{72 \times 8}{9} = 64 \Rightarrow x = 8.$

So, number of children in each row $= \frac{9x}{8} = 9.$

145. Let the total number of customers be x.

Then, number of customers who purchase hats = 15% of 40% of $x = \left(\frac{15}{100} \times \frac{40}{100} \times x\right) = \frac{6x}{100}$

$= 6\%$ of x.

$\therefore$ Required percentage = 6%.

146. Let the total number of respondents be x.

Percentage of uncertain individuals

$= [100 - (20 + 60)]\% = 20\%.$

$\therefore$ 60% of x − 20% of x = 720 ⇒ 40% of x = 720

$\Rightarrow \frac{40}{100}x = 720 \Leftrightarrow x = \left(\frac{720 \times 100}{40}\right) = 1800.$

147. Let the maximum marks be x.

Then, 36% of $x = 198 + 36 \Rightarrow \frac{36x}{100} = 234 \Rightarrow x = \left(\frac{234 \times 100}{36}\right)$

$= 650.$

148. Let the maximum marks be x.

Then, 40% of x = 483 + 117

$\Rightarrow \frac{40x}{100} = 600 \Rightarrow x = \left(\frac{600 \times 100}{40}\right) = 1500.$

$\therefore$ Minimum passing marks for girls = 35% of 1500

$= \left(\frac{35}{100} \times 1500\right) = 525.$

149. Let the maximum marks be x.

Then, $(40 - 4)\%$ of $x = 261 \Rightarrow 36\%$ of $x = 261$

$\Rightarrow \frac{36}{100}x = 261 \Rightarrow x = \left(\frac{261 \times 100}{36}\right) = 725.$

150. Let the maximum marks be x.

Then, 33% of x − 25% of x = 40

$\Rightarrow$ 8% of $x = 40 \Rightarrow \frac{8x}{100} = 40$

$\Rightarrow x = \left(\frac{40 \times 100}{8}\right) = 500.$

151. Let the maximum marks be x.

Then, 5% of $x = 296 - 259 \Rightarrow \frac{5x}{100} = 37$

$\Rightarrow x = \left(\frac{37 \times 100}{5}\right) = 740.$

152. Let the total number of votes polled be x.

Then, votes polled by other candidate $= (100 - 62)\%$ of x = 38% of x.

$\therefore$ 62% of x − 38% of x = 432

$\Rightarrow \frac{24x}{100} = 432 \Rightarrow x = \left(\frac{432 \times 100}{24}\right) = 1800.$

153. Number of valid votes

$= (100 - 15)\%$ of 15200 = 85% of 15200

$= \left(\frac{85}{100} \times 15200\right) = 12920.$

Valid votes polled by other candidate

$= (100 - 55)\%$ of $12920 = \left(\frac{45}{100} \times 12920\right) = 5814.$

154. Let the number of valid votes be x. Then, 52% of x – 48% of $x = 98$

$\Leftrightarrow$ 4% of $x = 98 \Leftrightarrow \frac{4}{100}x = 98$

$\Leftrightarrow x = 98 \times 25 = 2450.$

$\therefore$ Total number of votes polled = (2450 + 68) = 2518.

155. Let the total number of votes be x.

Then, number of votes polled by wining candidate = 65% of 80% of x

$= \left(\frac{65}{100} \times \frac{80}{100} \times x\right) = \frac{52x}{100} = 52\%$ of x.

$\therefore$ Required percentage = 52%.

156. Let the number of valid votes be x.

Then, 60% of $x = 255000 \Rightarrow x = \left(\frac{255000 \times 100}{60}\right) = 425000.$

Number of invalid votes = (500000 – 425000) = 75000.

$\therefore$ Required percentage $= \left(\frac{75000}{500000} \times 100\right)\% = 15\%.$

157. Let the total number of voters be x. Then, votes polled = 90% of x.

Valid votes = 90% of (90% of x).

$\therefore$ 54% of [90% of (90% of x)] – 46% of [90% of (90% of x)] = 1620

$\Leftrightarrow$ 8% of [90% of (90% of x)] = 1620

$\Leftrightarrow \frac{8}{100} \times \frac{90}{100} \times \frac{90}{100} \times x = 1620$

$\Leftrightarrow x = \left(\frac{1620 \times 100 \times 100 \times 100}{8 \times 90 \times 90}\right) = 25000.$

158. Let the number of persons eligible to vote be x. Then, Number of eligible persons between 18 and 21 = 8% of x. Number of persons between 18 and 21, who voted = 85% of (8% of x) $= \left(\frac{85}{100} \times \frac{8}{100} \times x\right) = \frac{68}{1000}x.$

$\therefore$ Required percentage $= \left(\frac{68x}{1000} \times \frac{1}{x} \times 100\right)\% = 6.8\%.$

159. Let the number of persons eligible to vote be x.

Then, voters who voted for A = 30% of x.

Voters who voted for B = 60% of (70% of x)

$= \left(\frac{60}{100} \times \frac{70}{100} \times 100\right)\%$ of $x = 42\%$ of x.

Voters who did not vote = [100 – (30 + 42)]% of x = 28% of x.

$\therefore$ 30% of x – 28% of x = 1200

$\Leftrightarrow$ 2% of $x = 1200 \Leftrightarrow x = \left(\frac{1200 \times 100}{2}\right) = 60000.$

160. Total sales tax paid = 7% of ₹ 400 + 9% of ₹ 6400

$=$ ₹ $\left(\frac{7}{100} \times 400 + \frac{9}{100} \times 6400\right)$ = ₹ (28 + 576) = ₹ 604.

Total cost of the items = ₹ (400 + 6400) = ₹ 6800.

$\therefore$ Required percentage $= \left(\frac{604}{6800} \times 100\right)\% = 8\frac{15}{17}\%.$

161. Total marks secured = (90% of 100 + 60% of 150 + 54% of 200)

$= \left(\frac{90}{100} \times 100 + \frac{60}{100} \times 150 + \frac{54}{100} \times 200\right)$

= (90 + 90 + 108) = 288.

Total maximum marks = (100 + 150 + 200) = 450.

$\therefore$ Aggregate percentage $= \left(\frac{288}{450} \times 100\right)\% = 64\%.$

162. Total number of students = 1100 + 700 = 1800.

Number of students passed = (42% of 1100 + 30% of 700) = (462 + 210) = 672.

Number of failures = 1800 – 672 = 1128.

$\therefore$ Percentage failure $= \left(\frac{1128}{1800} \times 100\right)\% = 62\frac{2}{3}\%.$

163. Let the number of students be x. Then,

Number of students of or above 8 years = (100 – 20)% of x = 80% of x.

$\therefore$ 80% of $x = 48 + \frac{2}{3}$ of $48 \Leftrightarrow \frac{80}{100}x = 80 \Leftrightarrow x = 100.$

164. Let the total number of applicants be x. Number of eligible candidates = 95% of x.

Eligible candidates of other categories = 15% of (95% of x)

$= \left(\frac{15}{100} \times \frac{95}{100} \times x\right) = \frac{57}{400}x.$

$\therefore \frac{57}{400}x = 4275 \Leftrightarrow x = \left(\frac{4275 \times 400}{57}\right) = 30000.$

165. Let their marks be $(x + 9)$ and x.

Then, $x + 9 = \frac{56}{100}(x + 9 + x)$

$\Leftrightarrow 25(x + 9) = 14(2x + 9) \Leftrightarrow 3x = 99 \Leftrightarrow x = 33.$

So, their marks are 42 and 33.

166. Let the original price of each ticket be ₹ 100.

Then, original price of 5 tickets = ₹ 500.

Sale price of 5 tickets = ₹ 300.

Amount saved = ₹ (500 – 300) = ₹ 200.

$\therefore$ Required percentage $= \left(\frac{200}{500} \times 100\right)\% = 40\%.$

167. Let the total sales in July 2009 be ₹ x. Then, sales in September 2009 = ₹ $\frac{2x}{3}$.

Sales in November 2009 = 105% of ₹ $\frac{2x}{3}$

$=$ ₹ $\left(\frac{105}{100} \times \frac{2x}{3}\right) =$ ₹ $\frac{7x}{10}.$

Decrease in sales = ₹ $\left(x - \frac{7x}{10}\right) =$ ₹ $\frac{3x}{10}$

$\therefore$ Decrease % $= \left(\frac{3x}{10} \times \frac{1}{x} \times 100\right)\% = 30\%.$

168. Earth takes 1 day or 24 hours to complete one rotation. Let the time taken to complete one rotation with increased speed be x hours.

Since time taken is inversely proportional to speed, we have:

100: 112:: x: 24 or $112x = 2400$ or $x = \frac{2400}{112} = \frac{150}{7} = 21\frac{3}{7}$.

$\therefore$ 1 day = $21\frac{3}{7}$ hours.

169. A ——3 cm—— C ——2 cm—— B

Original length of AB = 5 cm.
Original length of AC = 3 cm.
Original length of CB = (5 – 3) cm = 2 cm.

New length of AC = 106% of 3 cm = $\left(\frac{106}{100} \times 3\right)$ cm = 3.18 cm.

New length of CB = (5 – 3.18) cm = 1.82 cm.
Decrease in length of CB = (2 – 1.82) cm = 0.18 cm.

$\therefore$ Decrease % = $\left(\frac{0.18}{2} \times 100\right)\% = 9\%$.

170. Percentage of delayed flights = (43 + 17 + 12 + 3)% = 75%.
Percentage of on-time flights = (100 – 75)% = 25%.
Let the total number of flights be x.

Then, 75% of $x = 1200 \Rightarrow x = \left(\frac{1200 \times 100}{75}\right) = 1600$.

$\therefore$ Number of on-time flights = 25% of 1600 = 400.

171. Let the total number of eggs originally be x.
Then, number of eggs which are intact = (100 – 5)% of x

$= \frac{95x}{100} = \frac{19x}{20}$.

Number of eggs left unsold = (100 – 93)% of $\frac{19x}{20}$

$= \left(\frac{7}{100} \times \frac{19x}{20}\right)$.

$\therefore \frac{7}{100} \times \frac{19x}{20} = 266 \Rightarrow x = \left(\frac{266 \times 100 \times 20}{7 \times 19}\right) = 4000$.

172. Suppose Ganpat has ₹ x.

Then, cost of 1 orange = ₹ $\left(\frac{x}{50}\right)$; cost of 1 mango = ₹ $\left(\frac{x}{40}\right)$.

Money left after paying taxi fare = 90% of ₹ x = ₹ $\frac{9x}{10}$.

Money spent in buying 20 mangoes = ₹ $\left(\frac{x}{40} \times 20\right)$ = ₹ $\frac{x}{2}$.

Money left = ₹ $\left(\frac{9x}{10} - \frac{x}{2}\right)$ = ₹ $\frac{4x}{10}$ = ₹ $\frac{2x}{5}$.

$\therefore$ Number of oranges that can be bought

$= \left(\frac{2x}{5} \times \frac{50}{x}\right) = 20$.

173. Consumption of gas in the smaller burner in 1 hour

$= \left(\frac{14.4}{104}\right)$ kg $= \frac{9}{65}$ kg.

Consumption of gas in the larger burner in 1 hour

$= \left(\frac{14.4}{80}\right)$ kg $= \frac{9}{50}$ kg.

Difference in consumption = $\left(\frac{9}{50} - \frac{9}{65}\right)$ kg $= \frac{27}{650}$ kg.

Required percentage difference

$= \left(\frac{27}{650} \times \frac{50}{9} \times 100\right)\% = \left(\frac{300}{13}\right)\% = 23.07\%$.

Questions 174 to 178

Let the number of magazine-readers in city P be x.
Then, (100 – 75)% of x = 6000

$\Leftrightarrow \frac{25}{100}x = 6000 \Leftrightarrow x = \left(\frac{6000 \times 100}{25}\right) = 24000$.

Number of readers in P, reading only one magazine a week = (24000 – 6000) = 18000.

Similarly, we can find these values in other cases. Thus, we have the following table:

City	No. of magazine-readers	No. of readers reading only one magazine a week
P	24000	18000
Q	17500	14000
R	7500	4500
S	6000	3300
T	5600	1400

174. The lowest number of magazine-readers is 5600 and this is in the case of city T.

175. The highest number of magazine-readers who read only one magazine a week is 18000 and this is in the case of city P.

176. The highest number of magazine-readers is 24000.

177. Number of magazine-readers in city Q reading only one magazine a week = 14000.

178. Total number of magazine-readers reading only one magazine a week

= (18000 + 14000 + 4500 + 3300 + 1400) = 41200.

179. $X = \frac{90}{100}Y \Rightarrow X = \frac{9}{10}Y \Rightarrow Y = \frac{10}{9}X \Rightarrow \frac{Y}{X} = \frac{10}{9}$.

$\therefore$ Required percentage

$= \left(\frac{Y}{X} \times 100\right)\% = \left(\frac{10}{9} \times 100\right)\% = 111\frac{1}{9}\%$.

180. $x\%$ of $y = \left(\frac{x}{100} \times y\right) = \left(\frac{y}{100} \times x\right) = y\%$ of x.

181. 20% of $a = b \Rightarrow \frac{20}{100}a = b$.

$\therefore b\%$ of $20 = \left(\frac{b}{100} \times 20\right) = \left(\frac{20}{100}a \times \frac{1}{100} \times 20\right)$

$= \frac{4}{100}a = 4\%$ of a.

182. $\frac{x}{100} \times y = \frac{4}{5} \times 80 \Rightarrow xy = 64 \times 100 = 6400$.

183. Clearly, $y\%$ of $z = 2$ ($x\%$ of y) $\Rightarrow \frac{yz}{100} = \frac{2xy}{100} \Rightarrow z = 2x$.

184. $x\%$ of $500 = y\%$ of 300

$\Rightarrow \frac{x}{100}\times 500 = \frac{y}{100}\times 300 \Rightarrow 5x = 3y \Rightarrow y = \frac{5}{3}x.$

$x\%$ of $y\%$ of $200 = 60 \Rightarrow \frac{x}{100}\times\frac{y}{100}\times 200 = 60$

$\Rightarrow xy = 3000 \Rightarrow x\times\frac{5}{3}x = 3000$

$\Rightarrow x^2 = 3000\times\frac{3}{5} = 1800 \Rightarrow x = 30\sqrt{2}.$

185. (a) $x\%$ of $y = \frac{xy}{100}$ and $y\%$ of $z = \frac{yz}{100}.$

$x > y, y > z \Rightarrow xy > yz \Rightarrow \frac{xy}{100} > \frac{yz}{100} \Rightarrow x\%$ of $y > y\%$ of $z.$

(b) $y\%$ of $x = \frac{xy}{100}$ and $z\%$ of $y = \frac{yz}{100}.$

As proved above, $y\%$ of $x > z\%$ of $y.$

(c) $z\%$ of $x = \frac{xz}{100}$ and $y\%$ of $z = \frac{yz}{100}.$

$x > y \Rightarrow xz > yz \Rightarrow \frac{xz}{100} > \frac{yz}{100} \Rightarrow z\%$ of $x > y\%$ of $z.$

186. 20% of $A = 50\%$ of $B \Rightarrow \frac{20}{100}\times A = \frac{50}{100}\times B$

$\Rightarrow \frac{A}{5} = \frac{B}{2} \Rightarrow B = \frac{2A}{5}.$

Required percentage $= \left(\frac{B}{A}\times 100\right)\%$

$= \left(\frac{2A}{5}\times\frac{1}{A}\times 100\right)\% = 40\%.$

187. $p\%$ of $p = 36 \Leftrightarrow \left(\frac{p}{100}\times p\right) = 36 \Leftrightarrow p^2 = 3600 \Leftrightarrow p = 60.$

188. $x\%$ of $y = z \Rightarrow \frac{x}{100}y = z \Rightarrow \frac{x}{z} = \frac{100}{y}.$

$\therefore$ Required percentage $= \left(\frac{x}{z}\times 100\right)\%$

$= \left(\frac{100}{y}\times 100\right)\% = \left(\frac{100^2}{y}\right)\%.$

189. $x = 80\%$ of $y \Rightarrow x = \frac{80}{100}y \Leftrightarrow \frac{y}{x} = \frac{5}{4} \Leftrightarrow \frac{y}{2x} = \frac{5}{8}.$

$\therefore$ Required percentage $= \left(\frac{y}{2x}\times 100\right)\%$

$= \left(\frac{5}{8}\times 100\right)\% = 62\frac{1}{2}\%.$

190. Let $x - 6\%$ of $x = xz.$

Then, 94% of $x = xz \Leftrightarrow \frac{94}{100}x\times\frac{1}{x} = z \Leftrightarrow z = 0.94.$

191. $x\%$ of $y + y\%$ of $x = \frac{x}{100}y + \frac{y}{100}x = \frac{2xy}{100} = 2\%$ of $xy.$

192. Let $x\%$ of $x = 10\%$ of $y.$

Then, $\frac{x}{100}\times x = \frac{10}{100}\times y \Rightarrow y = \frac{x^2}{100}\times 10 = \frac{x^2}{10}.$

193. A exceeds b by $x\% \Rightarrow a = b + x\%$ of $b \Rightarrow a = b + \frac{bx}{100}.$

194. $A = 150\%$ of $B \Rightarrow A = \frac{150}{100}B \Rightarrow \frac{A}{B} = \frac{3}{2} \Rightarrow \frac{A}{B}+1 = \frac{3}{2}+1$

$\Rightarrow \frac{A+B}{B} = \frac{5}{2} \Rightarrow \frac{B}{A+B} = \frac{2}{5}.$

$\therefore$ Required percentage $= \left(\frac{B}{A+B}\times 100\right)\%$

$= \left(\frac{2}{5}\times 100\right)\% = 40\%.$

195. 8% of $x = 4\%$ of $y \Rightarrow \frac{8}{100}x = \frac{4}{100}y \Rightarrow x = \frac{1}{2}y.$

$\therefore 20\%$ of $x = 20\%$ of $\frac{1}{2}y = 10\%$ of $y.$

196. $\frac{20}{100}A = B$ and $\frac{40}{100}B = C \Rightarrow \frac{1}{5}A = B$ and $\frac{2}{5}B = C$

$\Rightarrow A = 5B$ and $B = \frac{5}{2}C \Rightarrow A = \frac{25}{2}C$ and $B = \frac{5}{2}C.$

$\therefore 60\%$ of $(A+B) = \frac{60}{100}\left(\frac{25}{2}C + \frac{5}{2}C\right)$

$= \frac{60\times 15}{100}C = \frac{900}{100}C = 900\%$ of $C.$

197. $x\%$ of $a = y\%$ of $b \Rightarrow \frac{x}{100}a = \frac{y}{100}b \Rightarrow b = \left(\frac{x}{y}\right)a.$

$\therefore z\%$ of $b = \left(z\%\text{ of }\frac{x}{y}\right)a = \left(\frac{xz}{y\times 100}\right)a = \left(\frac{xz}{y}\right)\%$ of $a.$

198. $x\%$ of $y = \left(\frac{x}{100}\times y\right) = \left(\frac{y}{100}\times x\right) = y\%$ of $x \Rightarrow A = B.$

199. 50% of $(x-y) = 30\%$ of $(x+y)$

$\Rightarrow 5(x-y) = 3(x+y)$

$\Rightarrow 5x - 5y = 3x + 3y \Rightarrow 2x = 8y \Rightarrow y = \frac{x}{4}.$

$\therefore$ Required percentage $= \left(\frac{y}{x}\times 100\right)\%$

$= \left(\frac{x}{4}\times\frac{1}{x}\times 100\right)\% = 25\%.$

200. $a = 60\%$ of $b \Rightarrow a = \frac{60}{100}b \Rightarrow b = \frac{5}{3}a.$

$\therefore$ Required percentage $= \left(\frac{5b}{4a}\times 100\right)\%$

$= \left(5\times\frac{5}{3}a\times\frac{1}{4a}\times 100\right)\%$

$= \left(\frac{625}{3}\right)\%.$

201. $x = 63\%$ of $y \Rightarrow x = \frac{63}{100}y \Rightarrow y = \frac{100x}{63}.$

$\therefore$ Required percentage $= \left(\frac{y^2}{x^2}\times 100\right)\%$

$$= \left[\left(\frac{100x}{63}\right)^2 \times \frac{1}{x^2} \times 100\right]\%$$

$$= \left(\frac{10000}{3969} \times 100\right)\% = 251.96\% \approx 250\%.$$

202. Let $B = 110\%$ of $b = \frac{11b}{10}$; $C = 110\%$ of $c = \frac{11c}{10}$;

$D = 110\%$ of $d = \frac{11d}{10}$.

Then, $A = B \times \frac{D}{C} = \frac{11b}{10} \times \frac{11d}{10} \times \frac{10}{11c} = \frac{11bd}{10c}$

$= \frac{11}{10}a = \frac{110}{100}a = 110\%$ of a.

$\therefore$ Increase % = 10%.

203. $a\%$ of $x = b\%$ of $y \Rightarrow \frac{ax}{100} = \frac{by}{100} \Rightarrow y = \frac{ax}{100} \times \frac{100}{b} = \frac{ax}{b}$.

$\therefore$ Required percentage $= \left[\frac{c\% \text{ of } y}{x} \times 100\right]\%$

$= \left(\frac{c}{100} \times \frac{ax}{b} \times \frac{1}{x} \times 100\right)\% = \frac{ac}{b}\%.$

204. $PO_{initial} = 5.3\ C^2\ L^{15}$

$PO_{new} = 5.3\ (1.2C)^2\ L^{15} = 1.44\ (5.3\ C^2\ L^{15}) = 1.44\ PO_{initial}$

Increase in PO $= 0.44\ PO_{initial}$

$\therefore$ Increase% $= (0.44 \times 100)\% = 44\%$.

205. Let the total number of ball bearings in the first shipment be x.

Then, total number of ball bearings in the second shipment $= 2x$.

$\therefore$ 1% of x + 4.5% of $2x = 100 \Rightarrow \frac{x}{100} + \frac{9x}{100} = 100$

$\Rightarrow 10x = 10000$

$\Rightarrow x = 1000.$

206. Number of women = 40% of 200 = 80.

Number of men = 200 – 80 = 120.

Number of women lecturers $= \frac{1}{5}$ of 80 = 16.

Number of men lecturers = 16 × 2 = 32.

$\therefore$ Required percentage $= \left(\frac{32}{120} \times 100\right)\% = \frac{80}{3}\%$

$= 26\frac{2}{3}\% \approx 27\%.$

207. Total number of fruits = (14 + 23) = 37.

Let x oranges be removed.

Then, 70% of $(37 - x) = 14$

$\Rightarrow 7(37 - x) = 140$

$\Rightarrow 37 - x = 20 \Rightarrow x = 17.$

208. Let the weight of the bucket when it is full, be 1 kg.

Then, weight of empty bucket = 25% of 1 kg $= \frac{1}{4}$kg.

Weight of liquid in the bucket $= \left(1 - \frac{1}{4}\right)$ kg $= \frac{3}{4}$ kg.

On removing the liquid,

Weight of (bucket + liquid) $= \frac{3}{5}$ kg.

Weight of liquid in the bucket $= \left(\frac{3}{5} - \frac{1}{4}\right)$ kg $= \frac{7}{20}$ kg.

Weigh of liquid removed $= \left(\frac{3}{4} - \frac{7}{20}\right)$ kg $= \frac{8}{20}$ kg $= \frac{2}{5}$ kg.

Hence, required percentage $= \left(\frac{2}{5} \times \frac{4}{3} \times 100\right)\%$

$= \frac{160}{3}\% = 53\frac{1}{3}\%.$

209. Let the sum invested at 5% be ₹ x and that invested at 3% be ₹ $(9600 - x)$.

Then, 5% of x = 3% of $(9600 - x)$

$\Rightarrow 5x = 3(9600 - x)$

$\Rightarrow 8x = 28800 \Rightarrow x = 3600.$

Hence, total income = 5% of x + 3% of $(9600 - x)$

= ₹ (5% of 3600 + 3% of 6000)

= ₹ (180 + 180) = ₹ 360.

210. Let his total sales be ₹ x. Now, Total sales – Commission = ₹ 31100.

$\therefore x - [5\%$ of $10000 + 4\%$ of $(x - 10000)] = 31100$

$\Leftrightarrow x - \left[\frac{5}{100} \times 10000 + \frac{4}{100}(x - 10000)\right] = 31100$

$\Leftrightarrow x - 500 - \left(\frac{x - 10000}{25}\right) = 31100$

$\Leftrightarrow x - \frac{x}{25} = 31200 \Leftrightarrow \frac{24x}{25} = 31200$

$\Leftrightarrow x = \left(\frac{31200 \times 25}{24}\right) = 32500.$

211. Let the number of boys be x. Then, number of girls $= x + 15$.

$\therefore$ 110% of $(x + 15)$ – 116% of $x = 9$

$\Rightarrow \frac{110}{100}(x + 15) - \frac{116}{100}x = 9 \Rightarrow 110x + 1650 - 116x = 900$

$\Rightarrow 6x = 750 \Rightarrow x = 125.$

Hence, number of students in the school

$= x + (x + 15) = (2x + 15) = 2 \times 125 + 15 = 265.$

212. Let the original price of tea be ₹ x per kg and that of sugar be ₹ y per kg.

Then, $5x + 8y = 172 \Rightarrow 15x + 24y = 516$ ...(i)

And, 120% of $5x$ + 110% of $8y = 199.20$

$\Rightarrow 600x + 880y = 19920 \Rightarrow 15x + 22y = 498$ ...(ii)

Subtracting (ii) from (i), we get: $2y = 18$ or $y = 9$.

Putting $y = 9$ in (i), we get: $x = 20$.

213. Let the total number of children be x.

Then, $x \times$ (20% of x) = 605

$\Rightarrow \frac{1}{5}x^2 = 605 \Rightarrow x^2 = 3025 \Rightarrow x = 55.$

$\therefore$ Number of sweets received by each child
$= 20\%$ of $55 = 11$.

214. Let the total number of employees be x.
Then, $(100 - 50)\%$ of $(100 - 40)\%$ of $x = 180 \Rightarrow 50\%$ of 60% of $x = 180$

$\Rightarrow \left(\frac{50}{100} \times \frac{60}{100} \times x\right) = 180 \Rightarrow x = \left(\frac{180 \times 10}{3}\right) = 600.$

$\therefore$ Number of graduate employees $= 50\%$ of 60% of x
$= \left(\frac{50}{100} \times \frac{60}{100} \times 600\right) = 180.$

215. Saving $= 50\%$ of $(100 - 40)\%$ of $(100 - 30)\%$ of ₹ 18,400
$= ₹\left(\frac{50}{100} \times \frac{60}{100} \times \frac{70}{100} \times 18400\right) = ₹\ 3864.$

216. Height climbed in second hour
$= 12\frac{1}{2}\%$ of $\left(100 - 62\frac{1}{2}\right)\%$ of 192 m
$= \left(\frac{25}{2} \times \frac{1}{100} \times \frac{75}{2} \times \frac{1}{100} \times 192\right)$ m $= 9$ m.

217. Let the total income be x.
Then, income left $= (100 - 80)\%$ of $[100 - (35 + 25)]\%$ of $x = 20\%$ of 40% of x.
$= \left(\frac{20}{100} \times \frac{40}{100} \times 100\right)\%$ of $x = 8\%$ of x.

218. Let Mr. More's monthly income be ₹ x.
Then, $[100 - (40 + 30)]\%$ of $[100 - (20 + 15)]\%$ of $x = 8775$
$\Rightarrow$ 30% of 65% of $x = 8775$
$\Rightarrow \left(\frac{30}{100} \times \frac{65}{100} \times x\right) = 8775$
$\Rightarrow \frac{39}{200}x = 8775 \Rightarrow x = \left(\frac{8775 \times 200}{39}\right) = 45000.$

219. Let the total salary be ₹ x.
Then, $(100 - 10)\%$ of $(100 - 20)\%$ of $(100 - 20)\%$ of $(100 - 10)\%$ of $x = 15552$
$\Leftrightarrow \left(\frac{90}{100} \times \frac{80}{100} \times \frac{80}{100} \times \frac{90}{100} \times x\right) = 15552$
$\Leftrightarrow x = \left(\frac{15552 \times 10000}{64 \times 81}\right) = 30000.$

220. Let the amount with Aman be ₹ x.
Then, amount received by Sahil $= \frac{1}{4}$ of 40% of ₹ $x = 10\%$ of ₹ x.
$\therefore$ 10% of $x = 600 + 200$
$\Rightarrow \frac{10}{100}x = 800 \Rightarrow x = 800 \times 10 = 8000.$

221. Number of questions answered correctly $= 40\%$ of $125 = 50$.
For 60% grade, number of questions to be answered correctly $= 60\%$ of $250 = 150$.
Remaining number of questions to be answered correctly $= 150 - 50 = 100$.
$\therefore$ Required percentage $= \left(\frac{100}{125} \times 100\right)\% = 80\%.$

222. Number of games already won $= 30\%$ of $60 = 18$.
Let the required number of games be x.
Then, $\frac{18 + x}{60 + x} \times 100 = 50 \Rightarrow \frac{18 + x}{60 + x} = \frac{1}{2}$
$\Rightarrow 36 + 2x = 60 + x \Rightarrow x = 24.$

223. We have: $x + x\%$ of $150 = 150$
$\Leftrightarrow x + \frac{x}{100} \times 150 = 150 \Leftrightarrow \frac{5}{2}x = 150 \Leftrightarrow x = \left(\frac{150 \times 2}{5}\right) = 60.$

224. $15 + \frac{1}{3}(n - 20) = 50\%$ of $n = \frac{50}{100}n = \frac{n}{2}$
$\Leftrightarrow 90 + 2n - 40 = 3n \Leftrightarrow n = 50.$

225. Let A's salary = ₹ x. Then, B's salary = ₹ $(2000 - x)$.
$(100 - 95)\%$ of A $= (100 - 85)\%$ of B
$\Rightarrow \frac{5}{100}x = \frac{15}{100}(2000 - x) \Leftrightarrow x = 1500.$

226. Let B + M + D = x. Then, B = 25% of $x - 20$
$= \left(\frac{25}{100}x - 20\right) = \left(\frac{x}{4} - 20\right)$ and D = 50.
$\therefore \frac{x}{4} - 20 + M + 50 = x$ or $M = \left(\frac{3x}{4} - 30\right)$.
So, marks in Maths cannot be determined.

227. Let the marks required be x. Then, $(62 + 35 + x) = 35\%$ of $(150 + 150 + 180)$
$\Leftrightarrow 97 + x = \frac{35}{100} \times 480 \Leftrightarrow x = 168 - 97 = 71.$

228. Let the number of students in the class be 100 and let the required average be x.
Then, $(10 \times 95) + (20 \times 90) + (70 \times x) = (100 \times 80)$
$\Rightarrow 70x = 8000 - (950 + 1800) = 5250 \Leftrightarrow x = 75.$

229. Let total marks $= x$. Then, (30% of x) + 15 = (40% of x) $- 35$
$\Leftrightarrow \frac{30}{100}x + 15 = \frac{40}{100}x - 35 \Leftrightarrow \frac{1}{10}x = 50 \Leftrightarrow x = 500.$
So, passing marks = (30% of 500) + 15
$= \left(\frac{30}{100} \times 500 + 15\right) = 165.$
$\therefore$ Pass percentage $= \left(\frac{165}{500} \times 100\right)\% = 33\%.$

230. Number of women $= 40\%$ of $100 = 40$.
Number of men $= (100 - 40) = 60$.
Number of coffee-drinkers $= 45\%$ of $100 = 45$.
Number of male coffee-drinkers $= \frac{1}{3}$ of $60 = 20$.
Number of female coffee-drinkers $= (45 - 20) = 25$.
$\therefore$ Number of female non-coffee drinkers $= (40 - 25) = 15$.

231. Number of males = 180000. Number of females
$= (300000 - 180000) = 120000$.
Number of literates $= 50\%$ of $300000 = 150000$.
Number of literate males $= 70\%$ of $180000 = 126000$.
Number of literate females $= (150000 - 126000) = 24000$.
$\therefore$ Required percentage $= \left(\frac{24000}{120000} \times 100\right)\% = 20\%.$

232. Let the total number of workers be x. Then, number of skilled workers = 75% of $x = \frac{3x}{4}$.

Number of unskilled workers = $\left(x - \frac{3x}{4}\right) = \frac{x}{4}$.

Number of temporary workers

$= (100 - 80)\%$ of $\frac{3x}{4} + (100 - 20)\%$ of $\frac{x}{4}$

$= 20\%$ of $\frac{3x}{4} + 80\%$ of $\frac{x}{4} = \left(\frac{20}{100} \times \frac{3x}{4} + \frac{80}{100} \times \frac{x}{4}\right) = \frac{7x}{20}$.

$\therefore \frac{7x}{20} = 126 \Rightarrow x = \left(\frac{126 \times 20}{7}\right) = 360.$

233. Number of short-length coats before removal

$= (100 - 15)\%$ of 800 = 85% of 800 = $\left(\frac{85}{100} \times 800\right) = 680.$

Number of short-length coats after removal = (680 – 500) = 180.

Total number of coats after removal = (800 – 500) = 300.

Number of full-length coats after removal = (300 – 180) = 120.

$\therefore$ Required percentage = $\left(\frac{120}{300} \times 100\right)\% = 40\%.$

234. Let the total number of candidates be x.

Number of capable candidates who got admitted to college = 80% of 40% of $x = \left(\frac{80}{100} \times \frac{40}{100} \times x\right) = \frac{8x}{25}$.

Number of incapable college students = 25% of $(100 - 40)\%$ of $x = \left(\frac{25}{100} \times \frac{60}{100} \times x\right) = \frac{3x}{20}$.

Total number of candidates who got admitted to college $= \frac{8x}{25} + \frac{3x}{20} = \frac{47x}{100}$.

$\therefore$ Required percentage = $\left(\frac{8x}{25} \times \frac{100}{47x} \times 100\right)\%$

$= \left(\frac{3200}{47}\right)\% = 68.09\% \approx 68\%.$

235. Let the total strength of the school be x.

Number of girls = $\frac{2x}{5}$; Number of boys = $\left(x - \frac{2x}{5}\right) = \frac{3x}{5}$.

Number of students who are 12 years or more of age

$= \left(1 - \frac{1}{5}\right)$ of $\frac{2x}{5} + \left(1 - \frac{1}{4}\right)$ of $\frac{3x}{5}$

$= \left(\frac{4}{5} \times \frac{2x}{5}\right) + \left(\frac{3}{4} \times \frac{3x}{5}\right) = \frac{8x}{25} + \frac{9x}{20} = \frac{77x}{100}$

$\therefore$ Required percentage = $\left(\frac{77x}{100} \times \frac{1}{x} \times 100\right)\% = 77\%.$

236. Let the total population be x.

Then, migrant population = 35% of $x = \left(\frac{35}{100} \times x\right) = \frac{7x}{20}$.

Local population = $\left(x - \frac{7x}{20}\right) = \frac{13x}{20}$.

Number of rural migrants = 20% of $\frac{7x}{20} = \left(\frac{20}{100} \times \frac{7x}{20}\right) = \frac{7x}{100}$.

Number of urban migrants = $\left(\frac{7x}{20} - \frac{7x}{100}\right) = \frac{28x}{100} = \frac{7x}{25}$.

Female population = 48% of $\frac{13x}{20}$ + 30% of $\frac{7x}{100}$ + 40% of $\frac{7x}{25}$

$= \left(\frac{48}{100} \times \frac{13x}{20}\right) + \left(\frac{30}{100} \times \frac{7x}{100}\right) + \left(\frac{40}{100} \times \frac{7x}{25}\right)$

$= \frac{39x}{125} + \frac{21x}{1000} + \frac{14x}{125} = \frac{445x}{1000}$.

$\therefore$ Required percentage = $\left(\frac{445x}{1000} \times \frac{1}{x} \times 100\right)\% = 44.5\%.$

237. Let the total number of houses be x. Then,

Number of houses having one female only = $(100 - 25)\%$ of $(100 - 40)\%$ of $x = \left(\frac{75}{100} \times \frac{60}{100} \times x\right) = \frac{9}{20}x$.

$\therefore$ Required percentage = $\left(\frac{9x}{20} \times \frac{1}{x} \times 100\right)\% = 45\%.$

238. Let the total number of candidates be x.

Then, $\left(100 - 62\frac{1}{2}\right)\%$ of $37\frac{1}{2}\%$ of $x = 342$

$\Leftrightarrow \frac{75}{2} \times \frac{1}{100} \times \frac{75}{2} \times \frac{1}{100} \times x = 342$

$\Leftrightarrow \frac{9x}{64} = 342 \Leftrightarrow x = \left(\frac{342 \times 64}{9}\right) = 2432.$

Number of boys failed = $(100 - 75)\%$ of $\left(100 - 37\frac{1}{2}\right)\%$ of 2432 $= \left(\frac{25}{100} \times \frac{125}{2} \times \frac{1}{100} \times 2432\right) = 380.$

239. Let total population = x. Then, number of males = $\frac{5}{9}x$.

Married males = 30% of $\frac{5}{9}x = \left(\frac{30}{100} \times \frac{5}{9}x\right) = \frac{x}{6}$.

Married females = $\frac{x}{6}$;

Number of females = $\left(x - \frac{5}{9}x\right) = \frac{4x}{9}$.

Unmarried females = $\left(\frac{4x}{9} - \frac{x}{6}\right) = \frac{5x}{18}$.

$\therefore$ Required percentage = $\left(\frac{5x}{18} \times \frac{1}{x} \times 100\right)\% = 27\frac{7}{9}\%.$

240. Let the number of boys and girls be $3x$ and $2x$ respectively. Then,

No. of students who are not adults = $\left(\frac{80}{100} \times 3x\right) + \left(\frac{75}{100} \times 2x\right)$

$= \left(\frac{12x}{5} + \frac{3x}{2}\right) = \frac{39x}{10}$.

$\therefore$ Required percentage = $\left(\frac{39x}{10} \times \frac{1}{5x} \times 100\right)\% = 78\%.$

241. Let total debt = x. Asset = $\frac{87}{100}x$.

After paying 20% of the debt, he is left with 80% of the debt plus ₹ 42.

$\therefore$ 80% of $x + 42 = \frac{87}{100}x \Leftrightarrow \frac{87}{100}x - \frac{80}{100}x = 42 \Leftrightarrow x = 600.$

So, debt = ₹ 600 and assets = ₹ $\left(\frac{87}{100}\times 600\right)$ = ₹ 522.

242. Number of researchers who prefer Team A = 70% of 50 = 35.
Number of researchers who prefer Team B = (50 – 35) = 15.
Number of researchers assigned to Team A = 40% of 50 = 20.
Number of researchers assigned to Team B = (50 – 20) = 30.
To find the least possible number of researchers who will not be assigned to the team they prefer, we assume that the maximum number of researchers get the team they prefer.
So, number of researchers who are assigned to the team they prefer
= 20 (Team A) + 15 (Team B) = 35.
$\therefore$ Required number = (50 – 35) = 15.

243. Let the number of passengers who boarded the train at station A be x. Then,
Number of passengers after the train left station B
= (100 – 10)% of x + 100 = 90% of x + 100 = $\left(\frac{9x}{10}+100\right)$.

Number of passengers after the train left station C
= (100 – 50)% of $\left(\frac{9x}{10}+100\right)+25=\frac{50}{100}\left(\frac{9x}{10}+100\right)+25$
$=\left(\frac{9x}{20}+75\right)$.

Number of passengers after the train left station D
= (100 – 50)% of $\left(\frac{9x}{20}+75\right)+50$
$=\frac{50}{100}\left(\frac{9x}{20}+75\right)+50=\left(\frac{9x}{40}+\frac{175}{2}\right)$.

$\therefore \frac{9x}{40}+\frac{175}{2}=200 \Rightarrow \frac{9x}{40}=200-\frac{175}{2}=\frac{225}{2}$

$\Rightarrow x=\left(\frac{225}{2}\times\frac{40}{9}\right)=500.$

244. Let the fare for a full ticket be ₹ x and the boarding charges be ₹ y per ticket.

Then, fare for a half-ticket = 75% of ₹ x = ₹ $\frac{3x}{4}$.

$\therefore (x+y)+\left(\frac{3}{4}x+y\right)=1440 \Rightarrow \frac{7x}{4}+2y=1440$

$\Rightarrow 7x + 8y = 5760$ ...(i)

And, $2(x+y)+\left(\frac{3}{4}x+y\right)=2220$

$\Rightarrow \frac{11x}{4}+3y=2220$

$\Rightarrow 11x + 12y = 8880$ ...(ii)

Solving (i) and (ii), we have: x = 480, y = 300.

245. Asha's monthly income = 60% of ₹ 78000
= ₹ $\left(\frac{60}{100}\times 78000\right)$ = ₹ 46800.

Let Maya's monthly income be ₹ x.

Then, 120% of $x = 46800 \Rightarrow x=\left(\frac{46800\times100}{120}\right)=39000.$

246. Let Anuj's monthly salary be ₹ x. Then, Raju's monthly salary = 120% of ₹ x = ₹ $\frac{6x}{5}$.

Ravi's monthly salary = ₹ $(x + 1500)$.

$\therefore \frac{6x}{5}+(x+1500)+x=\frac{325200}{12}=27100$

$\Rightarrow 16x + 7500 = 135500$

$\Rightarrow 16x = 128000 \Rightarrow x = 8000.$

Hence, sum of Raju's and Anuj's monthly salaries
= ₹ $\left(\frac{6x}{5}+x\right)$ = ₹ $\frac{11x}{5}$ = ₹ $\left(\frac{11\times8000}{5}\right)$ = ₹ 17600.

247. Let the amount received by B be ₹ x.

Then, amount received by C = 75% of ₹ x = ₹ $\frac{3x}{4}$.

And, amount received by A = 125% of ₹ $\frac{3x}{4}$ = ₹ $\frac{15x}{16}$.

$\therefore \frac{15x}{16}+x+\frac{3x}{4}=2236 \Rightarrow \frac{43x}{16}=2236$

$\Rightarrow x=\left(\frac{2236\times16}{43}\right)=832.$

Hence, A's share = ₹ $\left(\frac{15}{16}\times 832\right)$ = ₹ 780.

248. Let the amount received by each child be ₹ x.
Then, amount received by each woman = 125% of ₹ x
= ₹ $\frac{5x}{4}$.

Amount received by each man = 125% of ₹ $\frac{5x}{4}$ = ₹ $\frac{25x}{16}$.

$\therefore 8\times\frac{25x}{16}+10\times\frac{5x}{4}+12x$

$=6100 \Rightarrow \frac{25x}{2}+\frac{25x}{2}+12x=6100 \Rightarrow 74x = 6100 \times 2$

$\Rightarrow x=\left(\frac{6100\times2}{74}\right).$

Hence, amount received by each woman
= ₹ $\left(\frac{5}{4}\times\frac{6100\times2}{74}\right)$ = ₹ $\frac{7625}{37}$ = ₹ 206.08.

249. $A=\frac{120}{100}B, B=\frac{120}{100}C$ and $C=\frac{85}{100}D.$

$\therefore B=\frac{5}{6}A, C=\frac{5}{6}B$ and $D=\frac{20}{17}C.$

$B=\frac{5}{6}\times576=480; C=\frac{5}{6}\times480=400; D=\frac{20}{17}\times400=\frac{8000}{17}.$

So, required percentage $= \left(\frac{8000}{17} \times \frac{1}{800} \times 100\right)\% = 58.82\%$.

250. Let number of students appeared from school $A = 100$.
Then, number of students qualified from school $A = 70$.
Number of students appeared from school $B = 120$.
Number of students qualified from school B

$= \left(\frac{150}{100} \times 70\right) = 105.$

$\therefore$ Required percentage $= \left(\frac{105}{120} \times 100\right)\% = 87.5\%$.

251. Let the original price be ₹ 100.
New final price = 120% of (75% of ₹ 100)

$= ₹\left(\frac{120}{100} \times \frac{75}{100} \times 100\right) = ₹\,90.$

$\therefore$ Decrease = 10%.

252. Let the original price be ₹ 100.
New final price = 85% of (115% of ₹ 100)

$= ₹\left(\frac{85}{100} \times \frac{115}{100} \times 100\right) = ₹\,97.75.$

$\therefore$ Decrease = (100 – 97.75)% = 2.25%.

253. Let the original number be x.
Final number obtained = 110% of (90% of x)

$= \left(\frac{110}{100} \times \frac{90}{100} \times x\right) = \frac{99}{100}x.$

$\therefore x - \frac{99}{100}x = 50 \Leftrightarrow \frac{1}{100}x = 50 \Leftrightarrow x = 50 \times 100 = 5000.$

254. Let the original price be ₹ 100.
New final price = 120% of (125% of ₹ 100)

$= ₹\left(\frac{120}{100} \times \frac{125}{100} \times 100\right) = ₹\,150.$

$\therefore$ Increase = (150 – 100)% = 50%.

255. Let the original price be ₹ 100.
New final price = 110% of (110% of ₹ 100)

$= ₹\left(\frac{110}{100} \times \frac{110}{100} \times 100\right) = ₹\,121.$

$\therefore$ Total increase = (121 – 100)% = 21%.

256. Let the original price be ₹ x.
New final price = 120% of (110% of ₹ x)

$= ₹\left(\frac{120}{100} \times \frac{110}{100} \times x\right) = ₹\,\frac{132x}{100}.$

$\therefore \frac{132x}{100} = 33 \Rightarrow x = \left(\frac{33 \times 100}{132}\right) = 25.$

257. Let the original price be ₹ x.

$\therefore$ $(100 - r)\%$ of $(100 + r)\%$ of $x = 1$

$\Rightarrow \frac{(100 - r)}{100} \times \frac{(100 + r)}{100} \times x = 1$

$\Rightarrow x = \frac{100 \times 100}{(100 - r)(100 + r)} = \frac{10000}{(10000 - r^2)}.$

258. Let the number of parts before the quality checks be 100.
Then, number of parts passed after quality checks

= (100 – 2)% of (100 – 5)% of (100 – 10)% of 100
= 98% of 95% of 90% of 100

$= \left(\frac{98}{100} \times \frac{95}{100} \times \frac{90}{100} \times 100\right) = \left(\frac{8379}{100}\right) = 83.79.$

$\therefore$ Effective rejection rate = (100 – 83.79)% = 16.21%.

259. Let original income = ₹ 100. Then, saving = ₹ 10 and expenditure = ₹ 90.
New income = ₹ 120, New saving = ₹ 10. New expenditure = ₹ (120 – 10) = ₹ 110.
Increase in expenditure = ₹ (110 – 90) = ₹ 20.

$\therefore$ Increase % $= \left(\frac{20}{90} \times 100\right)\% = 22\frac{2}{9}\%.$

260. Let original income = ₹ 100. Then, saving = ₹ 20 and expenditure = ₹ 80.

New income $= ₹\,116\frac{2}{3} = ₹\left(\frac{350}{3}\right).$

New expenditure $= 137\frac{1}{2}\%$ of ₹ 80

$= ₹\left(\frac{275}{2} \times \frac{1}{100} \times 80\right) = ₹\,110.$

New saving $= ₹\left(\frac{350}{3} - 110\right) = ₹\,\frac{20}{3}.$

$\therefore$ Required percentage $= \left(\frac{20}{3} \times \frac{3}{350} \times 100\right)\%$

$= \frac{40}{7}\% = 5\frac{5}{7}\%.$

261. Let original income = ₹ 100. Then, saving = ₹ 25 and expenditure = ₹ 75.
New income = ₹ 120.

New expenditure = 115% of ₹ 75 $= ₹\left(\frac{115}{100} \times 75\right) = ₹\,\frac{345}{4}.$

New saving $= ₹\left(120 - \frac{345}{4}\right) = ₹\,\frac{135}{4}.$

Increase in saving $= ₹\left(\frac{135}{4} - 25\right) = ₹\,\frac{35}{4}.$

$\therefore$ Percentage increase $= \left(\frac{35}{4} \times \frac{1}{25} \times 100\right)\% = 35\%.$

262. Let Madan's income be ₹ x.

Then, Net income = (100 – 10)% of ₹ x = 90% of ₹ $x = ₹\,\frac{9x}{10}.$

New net income = 85% of 110% of ₹ x

$= ₹\left(\frac{85}{100} \times \frac{110}{100} \times x\right) = ₹\,\frac{187}{200}x.$

$\therefore \frac{187}{200} - \frac{9x}{10} = 350 \Leftrightarrow \frac{7x}{200} = 350$

$\Leftrightarrow x = \left(\frac{350 \times 200}{7}\right) = 10000.$

263. Let his investment in the year 2000 be ₹ x.

Then, income in 2010 = ₹ [x + 20% of x] $= ₹\,\frac{120}{100}x.$

Income in 2011 = ₹ $\left[\frac{126}{100}(x-5000)\right]$.

$\therefore \frac{120}{100}x = \frac{126}{100}(x-5000) \Leftrightarrow 120x = 126(x-5000)$

$\Leftrightarrow 6x = 630000 \Leftrightarrow x = 105000.$

264. Let X and Y denote the new values of x and y respectively.

Then, X = 80% of $x = \frac{4x}{5}$; Y = 80% of $y = \frac{4y}{5}$.

$\therefore XY^2 = \frac{4x}{5} \times \left(\frac{4y}{5}\right)^2 = \frac{4x}{5} \times \frac{16y^2}{25} = \frac{64}{125}xy^2.$

Decrease in the value $= \left(xy^2 - \frac{64}{125}xy^2\right) = \frac{61}{125}xy^2.$

$\therefore$ Decrease % $= \left(\frac{61xy^2}{125} \times \frac{1}{xy^2} \times 100\right)\% = 48.8\%.$

265. Let V denote the volume of 1 c.c. of water.

Then, volume of ice formed from it = 109% of V = $\frac{109}{100}$ V.

When this ice changes into water, decrease in volume

$= \left(\frac{109}{100}V - V\right) = \frac{9}{100}V.$

$\therefore$ Decrease% $= \left(\frac{9V}{100} \times \frac{100}{109\,V} \times 100\right)\% = \frac{900}{109}\% = 8\frac{28}{109}\%.$

266. Let original consumption = 100 units and original price = ₹ 100 per unit.

Original expenditure = ₹ (100 × 100) = ₹ 10000.

New expenditure = ₹ (120 × 80) = ₹ 9600.

$\therefore$ Decrease in expenditure $= \left(\frac{400}{10000} \times 100\right)\% = 4\%.$

267. Let the original taxed amount be ₹ x and new taxed amount be ₹ y.

Let original revenue be ₹ 100.

Then, 4% of x = 100 or $x = \left(\frac{100 \times 100}{4}\right)$ = ₹ 2500.

New revenue = 110% of ₹ 100 = ₹ 110.

Then, 5% of y = 110 or $y = \left(\frac{110 \times 100}{5}\right)$ = ₹ 2200.

Decrease in taxed amount = ₹ (2500 – 2200) = ₹ 300.

$\therefore$ Decrease % $= \left(\frac{300}{2500} \times 100\right)\% = 12\%.$

268. Let the total original sale be ₹ 100. Then, original number of visitors $= \frac{100}{5} = 20.$

Reduced price of ticket = 80% of ₹ 5 = ₹ 4. New sale = 144% of ₹ 100 = ₹ 144.

New number of visitors $= \frac{144}{4} = 36.$

$\therefore$ Increase % $= \left(\frac{16}{20} \times 100\right)\% = 80\%.$

269. Suppose the business value changes from x to y.

4% of x = 5% of $y \Rightarrow \frac{4}{100}x = \frac{5}{100}y \Rightarrow y = \frac{4}{5}x.$

$\therefore$ Change in business $= \left(x - \frac{4}{5}x\right) = \frac{x}{5}.$

Percentage slump $= \left(\frac{x}{5} \times \frac{1}{x} \times \frac{1}{100}\right)\% = 20\%.$

270. Let the distance be x km and the original time taken be y hours. Then,

Original speed $= \left(\frac{x}{y}\right)$ km/hr.

New speed $= \left(\frac{x}{80\% \text{ of } y}\right)$ km/hr $= \left(\frac{5}{4} \cdot \frac{x}{y}\right)$ km/hr.

Increase in speed $= \left(\frac{5x}{4y} - \frac{x}{y}\right) = \frac{x}{4y}.$

$\therefore$ Increase% $= \left(\frac{x}{4y} \times \frac{y}{x} \times 100\right)\% = 25\%.$

271. Let original salary = ₹ 100. New salary = ₹ 120.

Decrease on 120 = 20.

Decrease on 100 $= \left(\frac{20}{120} \times 100\right)\% = 16\frac{2}{3}\%.$

272. Let original price = ₹ 100. New price = ₹ 75.

Increase on 75 = 25. Increase on 100

$= \left(\frac{25}{75} \times 100\right)\% = \frac{100}{3}\% = 33\frac{1}{3}\%.$

273. Let original number = 100.

New number = 120% of 120% of 100

$= \left(\frac{120}{100} \times \frac{120}{100} \times 100\right) = 144.$

Decrease on 144 = 44. Decrease on 100

$= \left(\frac{44}{144} \times 100\right)\% = 30\frac{5}{9}\%.$

274. Let original salary = ₹ 100.

New salary = 90% of 85% of 80% of ₹ 100

= ₹ $\left(\frac{90}{100} \times \frac{85}{100} \times \frac{80}{100} \times 100\right)$ = ₹ $\frac{306}{5}$.

Increase on $\frac{306}{5} = \left(100 - \frac{306}{5}\right) = \frac{194}{5}.$

Increase on 100 $= \left(\frac{194}{5} \times \frac{5}{306} \times 100\right)\% = \frac{9700}{153}\%$

= 63.39% ≈ 63%.

275. Let the original fraction be $\frac{x}{y}$. Then, new fraction

$= \frac{140\% \text{ of } x}{180\% \text{ of } y} = \frac{140x}{180y} = \frac{7x}{9y}.$

$\therefore \frac{\text{New fraction}}{\text{Original fraction}} = \left(\frac{7x}{9y} \times \frac{y}{x}\right) = \frac{7}{9}.$

276. Let the original fraction be $\frac{x}{y}$.

Then, new fraction $= \frac{(100+240)\% \text{ of } x}{(100-50)\% \text{ of } y} = \frac{340\% \text{ of } x}{50\% \text{ of } y}$

$= \frac{34x}{5y}$.

$\therefore \frac{34x}{5y} = 2\frac{5}{6} = \frac{17}{6} \Rightarrow \frac{x}{y} = \frac{17}{6} \times \frac{5}{34} = \frac{5}{12}$.

277. Reduction in consumption $= \left[\frac{R}{(100+R)} \times 100\right]\%$

$= \left(\frac{15}{115} \times 100\right)\%$

$= \frac{300}{23}\% = 13\frac{1}{23}\%$.

278. Decrease in consumption $= \left[\frac{R}{(100+R)} \times 100\right]\%$

$= \left(\frac{30}{130} \times 100\right)\% = 23\frac{1}{13}\%$.

279. Increase in consumption $= \left[\frac{R}{(100-R)} \times 100\right]\%$

$= \left(\frac{16}{84} \times 100\right)\%$

$= \frac{400}{21}\% = 19.04\% \approx 19\%$.

280. Let original consumption be 1 unit costing ₹ 100.

New cost = ₹ 125. New consumption $= \left(\frac{1}{125} \times 100\right) = \frac{4}{5}$ unit.

$\therefore \frac{\text{Reduction in consumption}}{\text{Original consumption}} = \frac{\left(1 - \frac{4}{5}\right)}{1} = \frac{1}{5}$, *i.e.*, 1 : 5.

281. Let original consumption = 100 kg and new consumption = x kg.

So, $100 \times 16 = x \times 20 \Leftrightarrow x = 80$.

$\therefore$ Reduction in consumption = 20%.

282. Let the original price of sugar be ₹ 10 per kg.

Then, original expenditure = ₹ (10 × 10) = ₹ 100.

New expenditure = 110% of ₹ 100 = ₹ 110.

New price of sugar = 132% of ₹ 10 = ₹ 13.20.

New consumption $= \left(\frac{110}{13.20}\right)$ kg $= \frac{25}{3}$ kg $= 8\frac{1}{3}$ kg.

283. Let expenditures on food and other items be ₹ $2x$ and ₹ $5x$.

Then, $2x + 5x = 2590$ or $x = 370$.

So, expenditure on food = ₹ (2 × 370) = ₹ 740.

Expenditure on other items = ₹ (5 × 370) = ₹ 1850.

New expenditure = 110% of ₹ 740 + 115% of ₹ 1850

= ₹ $\left(\frac{110}{100} \times 740 + \frac{115}{100} \times 1850\right)$

= ₹ (814 + 2127.50) = ₹ 2941.50.

$\therefore$ Desired increase = ₹ (2941.50 − 2590) = ₹ 351.50.

284. Number of students admitted in 2012

$= 5000\left(1 + \frac{24}{100}\right)^2 = \left(5000 \times \frac{31}{25} \times \frac{31}{25}\right) = 7688$.

285. Salary after 4 years = ₹ $\left[10000\left(1 + \frac{50}{100}\right)^4\right]$

= ₹ $\left(10000 \times \frac{3}{2} \times \frac{3}{2} \times \frac{3}{2} \times \frac{3}{2}\right)$ = ₹ 50625

286. Population after 3 years $= 64000 \times \left(1 + \frac{5}{2 \times 100}\right)^3$

$= \left(64000 \times \frac{41}{40} \times \frac{41}{40} \times \frac{41}{40}\right) = 68921$.

287. Cost after 2 years = ₹ $\left[20 \times \left(1 + \frac{8}{100}\right)^2\right]$

= ₹ $\left(20 \times \frac{27}{25} \times \frac{27}{25}\right)$ = ₹ 23.33.

288. Percentage annual increase $= \left(\frac{75}{1000} \times 100\right)\% = 7\frac{1}{2}\% = \frac{15}{2}\%$.

Population after 2 years $= 4200000\left(1 + \frac{15}{2 \times 100}\right)^2$

$= \left(4200000 \times \frac{43}{40} \times \frac{43}{40}\right) = 4853625$.

289. Population after 2 years $= 8500\left(1 + \frac{20}{100}\right)\left(1 + \frac{25}{100}\right)$

$= \left(8500 \times \frac{6}{5} \times \frac{5}{4}\right) = 12750$.

290. Present population

$= 160000 \times \left(1 + \frac{3}{100}\right)\left(1 + \frac{5}{2 \times 100}\right)\left(1 + \frac{5}{100}\right)$

$= \left(160000 \times \frac{103}{100} \times \frac{41}{40} \times \frac{21}{20}\right) = 177366$.

291. Present population

$= 62500 \times \left(1 - \frac{4}{100}\right)^2 = \left(62500 \times \frac{24}{25} \times \frac{24}{25}\right) = 57600$.

292. Let the present value be ₹ 100.

Value after 3 years = ₹ $\left[100 \times \left(1 - \frac{20}{100}\right)^3\right]$

= ₹ $\left(100 \times \frac{4}{5} \times \frac{4}{5} \times \frac{4}{5}\right)$ = ₹ 51.20.

$\therefore$ Reduction in value = (100 − 51.20)% = 48.8%.

293. Height of the tree 2 years ago $= \frac{540}{\left(1 + \frac{20}{100}\right)^2}$ cm

$= \left(540 \times \frac{5}{6} \times \frac{5}{6}\right)$ cm = 375 cm.

294. Amount invested = ₹ $\left[\frac{10000}{\left(1 + \frac{25}{100}\right)^3}\right]$ = ₹ $\left(10000 \times \frac{4}{5} \times \frac{4}{5} \times \frac{4}{5}\right)$

= ₹ 5120.

295. Population 6 years ago $= \left[\frac{1771561}{\left(1 + \frac{10}{100}\right)^6}\right]$

$= 1771561 \times \left(\frac{10}{11}\right)^6 = \frac{1771561 \times 1000000}{1771561}$

$= 1000000.$

296. Purchase price $= ₹\left[\frac{29644.032}{\left(1-\frac{12}{100}\right)^3}\right]$

$= ₹\left(29644.032 \times \frac{25}{22} \times \frac{25}{22} \times \frac{25}{22}\right) = ₹\,43500.$

297. Let the present value of the asset be ₹ x. Then,

$\frac{x}{\left(1-\frac{10}{100}\right)^2} - \frac{x}{\left(1-\frac{10}{100}\right)} = 12000 \Rightarrow \frac{x - x\left(1-\frac{10}{100}\right)}{\left(1-\frac{10}{100}\right)^2} = 12000$

$\Rightarrow \frac{x}{10} = 12000 \times \frac{9}{10} \times \frac{9}{10} \Rightarrow x = 97200.$

298. Percentage annual increase $= \left(\frac{1}{8} \times 100\right)\% = \frac{25}{2}\%.$

Height after $2\frac{1}{2}$ years

$= \left[8\left(1+\frac{25}{2 \times 100}\right)^2\left(1+\frac{25}{4 \times 100}\right)\right]$ m

$= \left(8 \times \frac{9}{8} \times \frac{9}{8} \times \frac{17}{16}\right)$ m $= \left(\frac{1377}{128}\right)$ m $= 10.75$ m.

299. Population at the end of 2 years

$= 189000\left(1-\frac{8}{100}\right)\left(1+\frac{5}{100}\right) = \left(189000 \times \frac{23}{25} \times \frac{21}{20}\right)$

$= 182574.$

300. Final value $= ₹\left[500000\left(1-\frac{4}{100}\right)\left(1+\frac{5}{100}\right)\left(1+\frac{10}{100}\right)\right]$

$= ₹\left[500000 \times \frac{24}{25} \times \frac{21}{20} \times \frac{11}{10}\right] = ₹\,554400.$

$\therefore$ Net profit = ₹ (554400 – 500000) = ₹ 54400.

301. Value after 3 years $= ₹\left[20000\left(1-\frac{5}{100}\right)\left(1-\frac{4}{100}\right)\left(1-\frac{2}{100}\right)\right]$

$= ₹\left(20000 \times \frac{95}{100} \times \frac{96}{100} \times \frac{98}{100}\right) = ₹\,17875.2.$

302. Number of bushes in the beginning

$= \frac{26730}{\left(1+\frac{10}{100}\right)\left(1+\frac{8}{100}\right)\left(1-\frac{10}{100}\right)}$

$= \left(26730 \times \frac{10}{11} \times \frac{25}{27} \times \frac{10}{9}\right) = 25000.$

303. Let the production in 2008 be 100 units. Then,

Production in 2012 $= 100 \times \left(1+\frac{15}{100}\right)^2\left(1-\frac{10}{100}\right)\left(1+\frac{15}{100}\right)$

$= \left(100 \times \frac{23}{20} \times \frac{23}{20} \times \frac{9}{10} \times \frac{23}{20}\right) = 136.88.$

$\therefore$ Increase in production $= (136.88 - 100)\% = 36.88\% \approx 37\%.$

304. $10 \text{ crores} \times \left(1+\frac{R}{100}\right)^3 = 13.31 \text{ crores}.$

$\therefore \left(1+\frac{R}{100}\right)^3 = \frac{13.31 \text{ crores}}{10 \text{ crores}} = \frac{13.31}{10} = \frac{1331}{1000} = \left(\frac{11}{10}\right)^3.$

So, $\left(1+\frac{R}{100}\right) = \frac{11}{10} \Leftrightarrow \left(1+\frac{R}{100}\right) = \left(1+\frac{1}{10}\right) \Leftrightarrow \frac{R}{100} = \frac{1}{10} \Leftrightarrow R = 10.$

305. $250\left(1+\frac{R}{100}\right)^3 = 2000 \Rightarrow \left(1+\frac{R}{100}\right)^3 = \frac{2000}{250} = 8 = (2)^3$

$\Rightarrow \left(1+\frac{R}{100}\right) = 2 \Rightarrow \frac{R}{100} = 1 \Rightarrow R = 100.$

306. Let the initial output be x and let the rate of increase be R% per year.

Then, $x\left(1+\frac{R}{100}\right)^2 = 2x \Rightarrow \left(1+\frac{R}{100}\right)^2 = 2 = (\sqrt{2})^2$

$\Rightarrow \left(1+\frac{R}{100}\right) = \sqrt{2} \Rightarrow R = 100(\sqrt{2}-1).$

307. Let the rate of growth be R% per annum.

Then, $3600\left(1+\frac{R}{100}\right)^3 = 4800 \Rightarrow \left(1+\frac{R}{100}\right)^3 = \frac{4}{3}.$

$\therefore$ Population after 3 years $= 4800\left(1+\frac{R}{100}\right)^3$

$= 4800 \times \frac{4}{3} = 6400.$

308. Let the required time be n years.

Then, $500000\left(1-\frac{10}{100}\right)^n = 364500$

$\Rightarrow \left(\frac{9}{10}\right)^n = \frac{364500}{500000} = \frac{729}{1000}$

$\Rightarrow \left(\frac{9}{10}\right)^n = \left(\frac{9}{10}\right)^3 \Rightarrow n = 3.$

309. Let the required time be n years. Then,

$72900 \times \left(1+\frac{10}{100}\right)^n = 133100 \times \left(1-\frac{10}{100}\right)^n \Leftrightarrow \left(\frac{11}{10}\right)^n \times \left(\frac{10}{9}\right)^n$

$= \frac{133100}{72900} \Leftrightarrow \left(\frac{11}{9}\right)^n = \frac{1331}{729} = \left(\frac{11}{9}\right)^3 \Leftrightarrow n = 3.$

310. Let T denote the required number of 5568 year-intervals.

Then, $x\left(1-\frac{50}{100}\right)^T = 12.5\%$ of $x \Rightarrow \left(1-\frac{50}{100}\right)^T$

$= \frac{x}{8} \times \frac{1}{x} = \frac{1}{8} \Rightarrow \left(\frac{1}{2}\right)^T = \left(\frac{1}{2}\right)^3 \Rightarrow T = 3.$

311. Let original population = 100.

Population after 3 years

$= 100 \times \left(1+\frac{3\frac{1}{2}}{100}\right)^3 = 100 \times \frac{207}{200} \times \frac{207}{200} \times \frac{207}{200} = 110.87.$

$\therefore$ Increase $= (110.87 - 100)\% = 10.87\% \approx 10.8\%.$

312. Net growth on 1000 = (32 – 11) = 21. Net growth on 100 $= \left(\frac{21}{1000} \times 100\right)\% = 2.1\%$.

313. Annual gross salary in 2007 = ₹ 1000000.

Expenditure on food items in 2007 = 40% of ₹ 1000000 = ₹ 400000.

Annual gross salary in 2008 = 90% of ₹ 1000000 = ₹ 900000.

Expenditure on food items in 2008 = 105% of ₹ 400000 = ₹ 420000.

$\therefore$ Required percentage $= \left(\frac{420000}{900000} \times 100\right)\% = \frac{140}{3}\%$ $= 46.6\% \approx 47\%$.

314. Let the man's original income be ₹ x.

Then, original tax paid = ₹ [12% of (80% of x)]

$= ₹ \left(\frac{12}{100} \times \frac{80}{100} \times x\right) = ₹ \frac{12x}{125}$.

New income = ₹ (x + 1200).

New tax paid = ₹ [10% of {80% of (x + 1200)}]

$= ₹ \left[\frac{10}{100} \times \frac{80}{100} \times (x+1200)\right]$

$= ₹ \left[\frac{2}{25}(x+1200)\right] = ₹ \left(\frac{2x}{25} + 96\right)$.

$\therefore \frac{12x}{125} = \frac{2x}{25} + 96 \Rightarrow \frac{2x}{125} = 96 \Rightarrow x = \frac{96 \times 125}{2} = 6000$.

Hence, increased income = ₹ (6000 + 1200) = ₹ 7200.

315. B's income is less than A's by $\left[\frac{10}{(100+10)} \times 100\right]\%$, i.e. $\frac{100}{11}\% = 9\frac{1}{11}\%$.

316. A = 125% of B

$\Rightarrow A = \frac{125}{100} B \Rightarrow B = \frac{100}{125} A = \left(\frac{4}{5} \times 100\right)\%$ of A = 80% of A.

317. B's wage is less than A's by $\left[\frac{20}{(100+20)} \times 100\right]\%$ *i.e.* $\frac{50}{3}\% = 16\frac{2}{3}\%$.

318. B's income is more than A's by $\left[\frac{50}{(100-50)} \times 100\right]\%$, i.e. 100%.

319. y is more than x by $\left[\frac{25}{(100-25)} \times 100\right]\%$, i.e. $\frac{100}{3}\% = 33\frac{1}{3}\%$.

320. $p = 6q$. So, q is less than p by $5q$.

$\therefore$ Required percentage

$= \left(\frac{5q}{p} \times 100\right)\% = \left(\frac{5q}{6q} \times 100\right)\% = 83\frac{1}{3}\%$.

321. Let the third number be x.

Then, first number = 80% of x = $\left(\frac{80}{100} \times x\right) = \frac{4x}{5}$.

Second number = 75% of x = $\left(\frac{75}{100} \times x\right) = \frac{3x}{4}$.

Difference $= \left(\frac{4x}{5} - \frac{3x}{4}\right) = \frac{x}{20}$.

$\therefore$ Required percentage $= \left(\frac{x}{20} \times \frac{5}{4x} \times 100\right)\% = \frac{25}{4}\% = 6\frac{1}{4}\%$

322. Let third number be x.

Then, first number = $112\frac{1}{2}\%$ of x = $\frac{9x}{8}$;

Second number = 125% of x = $\frac{5}{4}x$.

$\therefore$ Required percentage $= \left(\frac{9x}{8} \times \frac{4}{5x} \times 100\right)\% = 90\%$.

323. A = 40% of B = 40% of (25% of C) $= \left(\frac{40}{100} \times \frac{25}{100} \times 100\right)\%$ of C = 10% of C.

324. $P = \frac{140}{100} A = \frac{140}{100}\left(\frac{80}{100} M\right)$

$= \left(\frac{140}{100} \times \frac{80}{100} \times 100\right)\%$ of M = 112% of M.

$\therefore$ Peter earned 12% more than Michael

325. Quantity of pulp in 100 kg of fresh fruits = (100 – 68)% of 100 kg = 32 kg.

Let the quantity of dry fruit obtained be x kg.

Then, (100 – 20)% of x = 32

$\Leftrightarrow \frac{80}{100}x = 32 \Leftrightarrow x = \left(\frac{32 \times 100}{80}\right) = 40$.

326. Let the reduced weight be x kg.

Clearly, the quantity of pulp remains the same in both the cases.

So, (100 – 96)% of 20 kg = (100 – 95)% of x kg

$\Leftrightarrow$ 4% of 20 kg = 5% of x kg $\Rightarrow x = \left(\frac{4}{5} \times 20\right)$ kg = 16 kg.

327. Quantity of pulp in fresh grapes = Quantity of pulp in dry grapes

= (100 – 10)% of 250 kg = 90% of 250 kg = 225 kg.

Let the total weight of fresh grapes be x kg.

Then, (100 – 80)% of x

= 225 $\Rightarrow$ 20% of x = 225 $\Rightarrow \frac{x}{5} = 225$

$\Rightarrow x = 225 \times 5 = 1125$.

Hence, total weight of fresh grapes = 1125 kg.

328. Quantity of gold in the alloy = 80% of 50 g

$= \left(\frac{80}{100} \times 50\right)$ g = 40 g.

Let x g of gold be added.

Then, $\frac{40+x}{50+x} = \frac{90}{100} = \frac{9}{10} \Rightarrow 400 + 10x = 450 + 9x \Rightarrow x = 50$.

329. Weight of water in 60 gms mixture = 75% of 60 gm

$= \left(\frac{75}{100} \times 60\right)$ gm = 45 gm.

Weight of water in 75 gms mixture = (45 + 15) gm = 60 gm.

$\therefore$ Required percentage $= \left(\frac{60}{75} \times 100\right)\% = 80\%$.

330. Quantity of sugar $= \left(\frac{4}{100} \times 6\right)$ kg $= 0.24$ kg.

$\therefore$ New percentage $= \left(\frac{0.24}{5} \times 100\right)\% = 4\frac{4}{5}\%$.

331. Quantity of alcohol in 9 ml lotion $= \left(\frac{50}{100} \times 9\right)$ ml $= 4.5$ ml.

Let the water to be added be x ml.

Then, $\frac{4.5}{9+x} = \frac{30}{100} \Leftrightarrow 270 + 30x = 450 \Leftrightarrow x = 6$ ml.

332. Quantity of alcohol $= \left(\frac{40}{100} \times 5\right)$ litres $= 2$ litres.

$\therefore$ New strength $= \left(\frac{2}{6} \times 100\right)\% = 33\frac{1}{3}\%$.

333. Quantity of alcohol in 400 ml solution = 15% of 400 ml = 60 ml.

Let x ml of alcohol be added.

Then, $\frac{60+x}{400+x} = \frac{32}{100} \Rightarrow 6000 + 100x = 12800 + 32x$

$\Rightarrow 68x = 6800 \Rightarrow x = 100$.

334. Quantity of alcohol in 10 c.c. solution

$= (20\% \text{ of } 6 + 60\% \text{ of } 4)$ c.c. $= \left(\frac{20}{100} \times 6 + \frac{60}{100} \times 4\right)$ c.c.

$= (1.2 + 2.4)$ c.c. $= 3.6$ c.c.

$\therefore$ Required strength $= \left(\frac{3.6}{10} \times 100\right)\% = 36\%$.

335. Required percentage $= \left(\frac{20\% \text{ of } 10 + 35\% \text{ of } 4}{10+4} \times 100\right)\%$

$= \left(\frac{3.4}{14} \times 100\right)\% = 24\frac{2}{7}\%$.

336. Let the original quantity be x kg. Vanaspati ghee in x kg

$= \left(\frac{40}{100}x\right)$ kg $= \left(\frac{2x}{5}\right)$ kg.

Now, $\frac{\frac{2x}{5}}{x+10} = \frac{20}{100} \Leftrightarrow \frac{2x}{5x+50} = \frac{1}{5} \Leftrightarrow 5x = 50 \Leftrightarrow x = 10$.

337. Quantity of alcohol in 5 litres solution = 20% of 5 litres = 1 litres.

Quantity of alcohol removed = 20% of 2 litres = 400 ml.

Quantity of alcohol in new solution = (1000 – 400) ml = 600 ml.

$\therefore$ Strength of alcohol in new solution

$= \left(\frac{600}{5000} \times 100\right)\% = 12\%$.

338. Let the weight of the original solution be x kg.

Weight of salt in x kg of solution = 15% of x kg $= \frac{3x}{20}$ kg.

$\therefore \frac{\frac{3x}{20}}{(x-30)} = \frac{20}{100} \Rightarrow \frac{3x}{20(x-30)} = \frac{1}{5}$

$\Rightarrow 15x = 20(x - 30) \Rightarrow 15x = 20x - 600$

$\Rightarrow 5x = 600 \Rightarrow x = 120$.

339. Let x litres of the first and $(35 - x)$ litres of the second solution be mixed together.

Then, 85% of x + 92% of $(35 - x)$ = 89% of 35

$\Rightarrow 85x + 92(35 - x) = 89 \times 35$

$\Rightarrow 85x + 3220 - 92x = 3115 \Rightarrow 7x = 105 \Rightarrow x = 15$.

Hence, quantity of first solution = 15 litres ; quantity of second solution = 20 litres.

340. Let x litres of 30% alcohol solution be added.

Then, 30% of x + 60% of 40 = 50% of $(x + 40)$

$\Rightarrow 30x + 60 \times 40 = 50(x + 40)$

$\Rightarrow 30x + 2400 = 50x + 2000$

$\Rightarrow 20x = 400$

$\Rightarrow x = 20$.

341. Let x quartz of the first solution be drained and replaced by x quartz of the second solution.

Then, 18% of $(27 - x)$ + 90% of x = 42% of 27

$\Rightarrow 18(27 - x) + 90x = 42 \times 27$

$\Rightarrow 486 - 18x + 90x = 1134$

$\Rightarrow 72x = 648$

$\Rightarrow x = 9$.

342. Let each vessel contain 100 litres of 40% alcohol.

Suppose Sachin added x litres of pure alcohol.

Then, $\frac{40+x}{100+x} = \frac{50}{100} = \frac{1}{2} \Rightarrow 80 + 2x = 100 + x \Rightarrow x = 20$.

Suppose Vivek replaced y litres.

Then, alcohol in y litres = 40% of $y = \frac{2y}{5}$ litres.

$\therefore \frac{40 - \frac{2y}{5} + y}{100} = \frac{50}{100} = \frac{1}{2} \Rightarrow 80 + \frac{6y}{5} = 100$

$\Rightarrow y = \frac{20 \times 5}{6} = \frac{50}{3}$.

Required percentage $= \left[\frac{\left(20 - \frac{50}{3}\right)}{\left(\frac{50}{3}\right)} \times 100\right]\%$

$= \left(\frac{10}{3} \times \frac{3}{50} \times 100\right)\% = 20\%$.

343. Let total quantity of original milk = 1000 gm.

Milk after first operation = 80% of 1000 = 800 gm.

Milk after second operation = 80% of 800 = 640 gm.

Milk after third operation = 80% of 640 = 512 gm.

$\therefore$ Strength of final mixture = 51.2%.

344. Let the capacity of the tank be 100 litres. Then,

Initially: A type petrol = 100 litres.

After first operation:

A type petrol $= \left(\frac{100}{2}\right) = 50$ litres ; B type petrol = 50 litres.

After second operation:

A type petrol $= \left(\frac{50}{2} + 50\right) = 75$ litres ;

B type petrol $= \left(\frac{50}{2}\right) = 25$ litres.

After third operation:

A type petrol $= \left(\frac{75}{2}\right) = 37.5$ litres ;

B type petrol $= \left(\frac{25}{2} + 50\right) = 62.5$ litres.

$\therefore$ Required percentage = 37.5%.

345. Total money $= ₹\left(600 \times \frac{25}{100} + 1200 \times \frac{50}{100}\right) = ₹750.$

25 paise coins removed $= \left(\frac{12}{100} \times 600\right) = 72.$ 50 paise coins removed $= \left(\frac{24}{100} \times 1200\right) = 288.$

Money removed $= ₹\left(72 \times \frac{25}{100} + 288 \times \frac{50}{100}\right) = ₹162.$

$\therefore$ Required percentage $= \left(\frac{162}{750} \times 100\right)\% = 21.6\%.$

346. Let the original price be ₹ 100 per kg.
Money required to buy 49 kg of rice = ₹ (100 × 49) = ₹ 4900.
New price = ₹ 98 per kg.

$\therefore$ Quantity of rice bought $= \left(\frac{4900}{98}\right)$ kg = 50 kg.

347. Let the original price of an eraser be ₹ x.
Reduced price = 75% of ₹ x = ₹ $\frac{3x}{4}$.

$$\therefore \frac{1}{\left(\frac{3x}{4}\right)} - \frac{1}{x} = 2$$

$$\Rightarrow \frac{4}{3x} - \frac{1}{x} = 2 \Rightarrow \frac{1}{3x} = 2 \Rightarrow 6x = 1 \Rightarrow x = \frac{1}{6}.$$

Hence, number of erasers available for a rupee = 6.

348. Let original price = ₹ x per kg. Reduced price = ₹ $\left(\frac{79x}{100}\right)$ per kg.

$$\therefore \frac{100}{\frac{79x}{1000}} - \frac{100}{x} = 10.5 \Leftrightarrow \frac{10000}{79x} - \frac{100}{x} = 10.5$$

$$\Leftrightarrow 10000 - 7900 = 10.5 \times 79x \Leftrightarrow x = \frac{2100}{10.5 \times 79}.$$

$\therefore$ Reduced price $= ₹\left(\frac{79}{100} \times \frac{2100}{10.5 \times 79}\right)$ per kg = ₹ 2 per kg.

349. Let the original price per egg be ₹ x. Then, increased price $= ₹\left(\frac{130}{100}x\right)$.

$$\therefore \frac{7.80}{x} - \frac{7.80}{\frac{130}{100}x} = 3 \Leftrightarrow \frac{7.80}{x} - \frac{780}{130x} = 3$$

$$\Leftrightarrow 1014 - 780 = 3 \times 130x \Rightarrow 390x = 234 \Leftrightarrow x = 0.6.$$

So, present price per dozen $= ₹\left(12 \times \frac{130}{100} \times 0.6\right) = ₹9.36.$

350. Let original price = ₹ x per kg. Reduced price $= ₹\left(\frac{90x}{100}\right)$ per kg.

$$\therefore \frac{279}{\left(\frac{90x}{100}\right)} - \frac{279}{x} = 6.2 \Leftrightarrow \frac{27900}{90x} - \frac{279}{x} = 6.2$$

$$\Leftrightarrow 27900 - 25110 = 6.2 \times 90x$$

$$\Leftrightarrow 558x = 2790 \Leftrightarrow x = 5.$$

$\therefore$ Required difference = 10% of ₹ 5 = ₹ 0.50.

351. Let the original price of sugar be ₹ x per kg.

Then, reduced price $= 97\frac{1}{2}\%$ of ₹ x

$$= ₹\left(\frac{195}{2} \times \frac{1}{100} \times x\right) = ₹\frac{39x}{40}$$

$$\therefore \frac{1260}{\left(\frac{39x}{40}\right)} - \frac{1260}{x} = 9 \Rightarrow \frac{16800}{13x} - \frac{1260}{x} = 9$$

$$\Leftrightarrow 13x = \frac{420}{9} \Rightarrow x = \frac{140}{39}.$$

Increased price $= 112\frac{1}{2}\%$ of ₹ $\frac{140}{39}$

$$= ₹\left(\frac{225}{2} \times \frac{1}{100} \times \frac{140}{39}\right) = ₹\frac{105}{26}.$$

$\therefore$ Quantity of sugar bought for ₹ 1260 $= \left(1260 \times \frac{26}{105}\right)$ kg = 312 kg.

352. $n(A) = 90,\ n(B) = 15,\ n(A \cup B) = 100.$
So, $n(A \cap B) = n(A) + n(B) - n(A \cup B) = 90 + 15 - 100 = 5.$
$\therefore$ Percentage of people who own both = 5%.

353. $n(A) = 34,\ n(B) = 42,\ n(A \cap B) = 20.$
So, $n(A \cup B) = n(A) + n(B) - n(A \cap B) = 34 + 42 - 20 = 56.$
$\therefore$ Percentage failed in either or both the subjects = 56.
Hence, percentage passed = (100 – 56)% = 44%.

354. $n(A) = 40,\ n(B) = 50,\ n(A \cap B) = 10.$
$n(A \cup B) = n(A) + n(B) - n(A \cap B) = 40 + 50 - 10 = 80.$
$\therefore$ Percentage reading either or both newspapers = 80%.
Hence, percentage reading neither newspaper = (100 – 80)% = 20%.

355. $n(A) = 325,\ n(B) = 175,\ n(A \cup B) = 450 - 50 = 400.$
Required number $= n(A \cap B) = n(A) + n(B) - n(A \cup B) = 325 + 175 - 400 = 100.$

356. $n(A) = \left(\frac{60}{100} \times 96\right) = \frac{288}{5},\ n(B) = \left(\frac{30}{100} \times 96\right) = \frac{144}{5},\ n(A \cap B) = \left(\frac{15}{100} \times 96\right) = \frac{72}{5}.$

$\therefore n(A \cup B) = n(A) + n(B) - n(A \cap B)$

$= \frac{288}{5} + \frac{144}{5} - \frac{72}{5} = \frac{360}{5} = 72.$

So, people who had either or both types of lunch = 72.
Hence, people who had neither type of lunch = (96 – 72) = 24.

357. $n(A) = \left(\frac{75}{100} \times 600\right) = 450, n(B) = \left(\frac{45}{100} \times 600\right) = 270,$

$n(A \cup B) - 600.$

$\therefore \quad n(A \cap B) = n(A) + n(B) - n(A \cup B)$
$= (450 + 270 - 600) = 120.$

358. Let total number be x. Then,

$n(A) = \frac{72}{100}x = \frac{18x}{25}, n(B) = \frac{44}{100}x = \frac{11x}{25}$ and $n(A \cap B) = 40.$

$n(A \cup B) = n(A) + n(B) - n(A \cap B)$

$\Rightarrow \quad x = \frac{18x}{25} + \frac{11x}{25} - 40 \Rightarrow \frac{29x}{25} - x = 40$

$\Rightarrow \quad \frac{4x}{25} = 40 \Rightarrow x = 250.$

359. Percentage of failed candidates = (30 + 35 – 27)% = 38%.
Percentage of passed candidates = (100 – 38)% = 62%.
Let the total number of students appeared be x.

Then, 62% of $x = 248 \Rightarrow x = \frac{248 \times 100}{62} = 400.$

360. Failed in 1st subject = $\left(\frac{35}{100} \times 2500\right) = 875.$

Failed in 2nd subject = $\left(\frac{42}{100} \times 2500\right) = 1050.$

Failed in both = $\left(\frac{15}{100} \times 2500\right) = 375.$

Failed in 1st subject only = (875 – 375) = 500.
Failed in 2nd subject only = (1050 – 375) = 675.
$\therefore$ Passed in 2nd only + Passed in 1st only
= (675 + 500) = 1175.

361. Suppose he ordered n pairs of blue socks.
Let the price of each pair of blue socks be ₹ x.
Then, price of each pair of black socks = ₹ $2x$.
Actual bill = ₹ $(4 \times 2x + nx)$ = ₹ $(8x + nx)$.
Bill made on interchange = ₹ $(2nx + 4x)$.

$\therefore \quad 2nx + 4x = 150\%$ of $(8x + nx)$

$\Rightarrow \quad 2nx + 4x = \frac{3}{2}(8x + nx)$

$\Rightarrow \quad 2(2nx + 4x) = 3(8x + nx)$

$\Rightarrow \quad nx = 16x \Rightarrow n = 16.$

Hence, required ratio = 4: 16 = 1: 4.

362. Suppose the man ordered x feet y inches of the rope. Since x and y represent inches in the miswritten and actual order respectively, so each one of x and y is less than 12.

[$\because$ 1 feet = 12 inches]

Actual order = x feet y inches = $(12x + y)$ inches.
Miswritten order = y feet x inches = $(12y + x)$ inches.

$\therefore \quad (12y + x) = 30\%$ of $(12x + y) = \frac{3}{10}(12x + y)$

$\Rightarrow \quad 10(12y + x) = 3(12x + y)$

$\Rightarrow \quad 26x = 117y \Rightarrow x = \frac{117}{26} = \frac{9}{2}.$

Since $x < 12$, $y < 12$, so $x = 9$, $y = 2$.
Hence the man ordered 9 feet 2 inches of rope.

363. Let the quantity of fertilizer A required be x kg and that of fertilizer B be y kg. Then,

10% of x + 5% of y = 14 $\Rightarrow 0.1x + 0.05y = 14$ ...(i)
6% of x + 10% of y = 14 $\Rightarrow 0.06x + 0.1y = 14$ ...(ii)

Subtracting (ii) from (i), we get: $0.04x - 0.05y = 0$

$\Rightarrow \quad x = \frac{5}{4}y.$

Substituting $x = \frac{5}{4}y$ in (i), we get: $0.5y + 0.2y = 56$

$\Rightarrow \quad 0.7y = 56 \Rightarrow y = 80.$

Putting $y = 80$ in (ii), we get: $x = 100$.

$\therefore$ Required cost = ₹ (100 × 10.60 + 80 × 8.40) = ₹ 1732.

364. Let the individual cost of 1 pen, 1 pencil and 1 eraser be ₹ x, ₹ y and ₹ z respectively.

Then, $5x + 7y + 4z = p$ (say) ...(i)
And, $6x + 14y + 8z = 1.5p$ ...(ii)

Multiplying (i) by 2 and subtracting (ii) from it, we get: $4x = 0.5p$ or $x = 0.125p$.

$\therefore$ Required percentage = $\left(\frac{0.625p}{p} \times 100\right)\% = 62.5\%.$

365. Let the number of votes for the motion be F and those against the motion be A.
Let the total number of votes be x.
Then, (F + 14) – (A – 14) = 4 $\Rightarrow$ A – F = 24.

$\therefore$ 8% of $x = 24 \Rightarrow x = \frac{24 \times 100}{8} = 300.$

So, F + A = 300 $\Rightarrow$ F + (F + 24) = 300
$\Rightarrow$ 2F = 276 $\Rightarrow$ F = 138.

$\therefore$ A = (300 – 138) = 162.

366. Let x be the number of votes not cast for the Praja Party in the previous polls.
So, number of votes not cast for the party this year = $1.25x$.
Then, number of votes cast for Praja party in the previous polls = $(260000 - x)$.
Number of votes cast for the party this year = $(260000 - 1.25x)$.
Margin of victory in previous polls = (Votes cast in favour) – (Votes not cast in favour)
$= (260000 - x) - x = (260000 - 2x).$
Margin of loss in this year's polls = (Votes not cast in favour) – (Votes cast in favour)
$= 1.25x - (260000 - 1.25x) = 2.5x - 260000.$

$\therefore \quad 2.5x - 260000$
$= 2(260000 - 2x) \Rightarrow 6.5x = 780000 \Rightarrow x = 120000.$

Hence, number of people who voted for Praja Party in previous polls = 260000 – 120000 = 140000.

367. Given (180 % of ?) ÷ 2 = 504

$\Rightarrow \left(? \times \frac{180}{100}\right) \div 2 = 504$

$\Rightarrow ? \times \frac{180}{100} = 504 \times 2$

$\Rightarrow ? \times \frac{180}{100} = 1008$

$= ? = \frac{1008 \times 100}{180} = 560$

368. x % of y = $\frac{xy}{100}$ ...(i)

and y% of x = $\frac{xy}{100}$ ... (ii)

from *(i)* & *(ii)*

x% of y = y % of x

369. $66\frac{2}{3}$% of ₹ 312/- exceeds ₹ 200 by ₹ x

According to the question, required difference

$= ₹ \left(312 \times \frac{200}{3}\% - 200\right) = \left(312 \times \frac{200}{3 \times 100} - 200\right)$

$= ₹ \left(312 \times \frac{200}{300} - 200\right)$

$\Rightarrow$ ₹ x = ₹ (208 – 200) = ₹ 8/-

370. 105.27% of 1200.11 + 11.80% of 2360.85 = 21.99% of (?) + 1420.99

105 % of 1200 + 12% of 2360 = 22 % of (?) + 1421

$\frac{105 \times 1200}{100} + \frac{12 \times 2360}{100} = \frac{22 \times ?}{100} + 1421$

or, $\frac{22 \times (?)}{100} = 1260 + 283.20 - 1421$

$\Rightarrow \frac{22 \times (?)}{100} = 1543 - 1421 \Rightarrow \frac{22 \times (?)}{100} = 121$

$\therefore ? = \frac{122 \times 100}{22} = \frac{122 \times 50}{11} = \frac{6100}{11} = 554.5 \approx 550$

371. Let the amount of actual bill be ₹ x.

According to the question, 15% of x = ₹ 54

$= \frac{x \times 15}{100} = 54$

$x = \frac{54 \times 100}{15}$ = ₹ 360

372. Given (550 % of 250) ÷ 275 = (?)

$(?) = \frac{550 \times 250}{100} \div 275$

$\Rightarrow$ (?) = (55 × 25) ÷ 275

$\Rightarrow (?) = \frac{55 \times 25}{275} = 5$

373. Statement I

Let maximum marks for test be x

Raman scored marks = 288 – 128 = 160 marks

According to question 25% of x = 160

$\Rightarrow x = \frac{160 \times 100}{25} = 640$

Statement II : let minimum passing percentage be y marks

Marks score by Raman = 460

Minimum passing marks = 160 + 64 = 224

According to question y% of 640 = 224

$y = \frac{224 \times 100}{640} = 35\%$

Both Statement I and II together are necessary to answer the question

Hence option (*e*) is correct

374. Given 32% of 825 + 25% of 1440 = 1025 – (?)

(?) = [1025 – (32% of 825) – (25% of 1440)]

$\Rightarrow 1025 - \left(\frac{32 \times 825}{100}\right) - \left(\frac{25 \times 1440}{100}\right)$

= (1025 – 264 – 360)

= 401

375. Let the number of recognized voters in the village be x.

A won election by votes = 600

B got 40% more votes

For candidate B

∵ 40% = 300

$\therefore 100\% = \frac{300}{40} \times 100 = 750$

Votes got by B = 750

∴ Votes got by A = 750 + 600 = 1350

According to the question,

Number of votes cost in election 60% of

x = 1350 + 750 = 2100

$\Rightarrow \frac{60x}{100} = 2100$

$\Rightarrow x = \frac{2100 \times 100}{60} = 3500$

376. Given (?) + (30.01% of 651) ÷ (25.05% of 59.98) = 135

$\Rightarrow$ (?) + (30% of 650) ÷ (25% of 60) = 135

$\Rightarrow (?) + \left(\frac{30 \times 650}{100}\right) \div \left(\frac{25 \times 60}{100}\right) = 135$

$\Rightarrow$ (?) + (195 ÷ 15) = 135

$\Rightarrow$ (?) + 13 = 135

$\Rightarrow$ (?) = (135 – 13) = 122

377. Given

$\frac{4}{3}$ of 25% of $\frac{18}{19}$ of 57 = ?

$? = \left[\left(\frac{25}{100} \times \frac{4}{3}\right) \times \left(\frac{18}{19} \times 57\right)\right]$

$= \left(\frac{1}{4} \times \frac{4}{3}\right) \times \left(\frac{18}{19} \times 57\right)$

= 18

378. Given

[(?) % of 1239.96] + [59.87% of 449.95] = 579.05

$\Rightarrow$ [(?) % of 1240] + [60% of 450] = 580

$\Rightarrow \left(\frac{(?) \times 1240}{100}\right) + \left(\frac{60 \times 450}{100}\right) = 580$

$\Rightarrow \left(\frac{(?)\times 1240}{100}\right)+270=580$

$\Rightarrow \left(\frac{(?)\times 1240}{100}\right)=(580-270)$

$\Rightarrow \left(\frac{(?)\times 1240}{100}\right)=310$

$\Rightarrow$ (?) = $\left(\frac{310\times 100}{1240}\right)$

$\Rightarrow$ (?) = 25%

379. Let number of students who appeared at the examination be x

Passed percentage = 96%

Failed percentage = 4%

According to given information we get

Unsuccessful students $\Rightarrow$ 4%

$\therefore$ 4% of x = 500

$\Rightarrow \left(\frac{x\times 4}{100}\right)=500$

$\Rightarrow x=\left(\frac{500\times 100}{4}\right)=12500$

380. $\because$ Krishna's present Salary = ₹ 3500

Salary Increase by 10%

Increased salary of Krishna

$=\left(\frac{3500\times 110}{100}\right)=$ ₹ 3,850

381. Given 12% of 555 + 15% of 666

$\Rightarrow$ (?) = $\left(\frac{12}{100}\times 555\right)+\left(\frac{15}{100}\times 666\right)$

= (66.6 + 99.9)

= 166.5

382. Given

(85% of 420) + (?% of 1080) = 735

$\Rightarrow \left(\frac{85\times 420}{100}\right)+\left(\frac{(?)\times 1080}{100}\right)=735$

$\Rightarrow 357+\left(\frac{(?)+1080}{100}\right)=735$

$\Rightarrow \left(\frac{(?)\times 1080}{100}\right)=(735-357)=378$

$\Rightarrow (?)=\frac{378\times 100}{1080}=35$

383. Given 30% of 1225 – 64% of 555 = (?)

$\left(\frac{30}{100}\times 1225\right)-\left(\frac{64}{100}\times 555\right)$

= (367.5 – 355.2)

= 12.3

384. Let, his income be ₹ 100

Saving = ₹ 10

Expenditure = ₹ 90

Increased income = ₹ 120

Increased expenditure = ₹ 110

Increased in expenditure

$=\frac{110-90}{90}\times 100$

$=\frac{200}{9}=22\frac{2}{9}\%$

385. It is given that,

(14% of 14) + (28% of 28) + (92% of 96) – (15% of 85) = (?)

$(?)=\left(\frac{14\times 14}{100}\right)+\left(\frac{28\times 28}{100}\right)+\left(\frac{92\times 96}{100}\right)-\left(\frac{15\times 85}{100}\right)$

= (1.96 + 7.84 + 88.32 – 12.75)

= (98.12 – 12.75)

= 85.37

386. Marked price of an article = ₹ 2400

According to given information

2400 × (100 – x)% of 85% = 1876.80

$\Rightarrow 2400\times \frac{100-x}{100}\times \frac{85}{100}$

= 1876.80

$\Rightarrow$ (100 – x)

$=\frac{1876.80\times 100\times 100}{2400\times 85}$

$=(100-x)=\frac{18768000}{204000}$

$\Rightarrow$ (100 – x) = 92

$\Rightarrow x$ = 100 – 92 = 8%

387. Boys: Girls – 10 : 7

$\therefore$ Boys $=\frac{10}{17}\times 85=50$

Girls = (85 – 50) = 35

Boys who play only badminton 50 % of 50 = $\frac{50\times 50}{100}=25$

Boys who play badminton

$=\frac{60\times 50}{100}=30$

Children who play only table

Tennis = $\frac{85\times 40}{100}=34$

Children who play badminton and table tennis = 12

Boys who play only table tennis = 50 – 30 = 20

$\therefore$ Girls who play only table tennis = 34 – 20 = 14

Girls who play badminton and table tennis

= 12 – (30 – 25) = 12 – 30 + 25 = 37 – 30 = 7

$\therefore$ Girls who play only badminton

= 35 – 14 – 7 = 35 – 21 = 14

388. Actual Cost price of an article

= ₹ (5844 + 156)

= ₹ 6000

S.P. = ₹ 5700

Loss = ₹ (6000 – 5700) = ₹ 300

Loss per cent

$=\frac{300}{6000}\times 100=5\%$

389. Cost price of wrist watch = ₹ 1250
Sale price of wrist watch = ₹ 1500
Profit percent

$= \left(\frac{1500-1250}{1250}\right)\times 100$

$= \frac{250}{1250}\times 100$

$= \frac{25000}{1250} = 20\%$

390. Let total votes in village = 100
Losing candidate got votes = 30% of 100 = 30 votes
Winner's and nearer rival's votes

$= 100 - \frac{30}{100}\times 100 = 70$

∴ If both get equal votes then, it should be, 35.
∴ Minimum difference between winner and nearer riva
= (36 – 34) = 2

EXERCISE

(DATA–SUFFICIENCY TYPE QUESTIONS)

Directions (*Questions 1 to 18*): ***Each of the questions given below consists of a statement and/or a question and two statements numbered I and II given below it. You have to decide whether the data provided in the statement(s) is/are sufficient to answer the question. Read both the statements and***

Give answer (a) if the data in statement I alone are sufficient to answer the question while the data in statement II alone are not sufficient to answer the question;

Give answer (b) if the data in statement II alone are sufficient to answer the question while the data in statement I alone are not sufficient to answer the question ;

Give answer (c) if the data either in statement I or in statement II alone are sufficient to answer the question ;

Give answer (d) if the data even in both statements I and II together are not sufficient to answer the question ;

Give answer (e) if the data in both statements I and II together are necessary to answer the question.

1. What percentage of families in the city have telephones?
   I. 50% of the families of the city possess television.
   II. 30% of the television owners of the city have telephones.
2. If a certain factory has filled 120 orders, then what percent of the total number of orders has been filled?
   I. The total number of orders on file is 300.
   II. The number of orders that the factory has already filled represents two-fifths of the total number of orders.
3. By what percent is the salary of the elder son more than that of the younger son?
   I. The father's salary is less than that of the elder son by 37%.
   II. His salary is less than that of the younger son by 30%.
4. 55% of all teachers in a school are females. If 8% of the female teachers in that school teach 5 classes a day, what is the number of female teachers who d not teach 5 classes a day? (N.I.F.T., 2007)
   I. There are 135 male teachers in the school.
   II. There are 27 male teachers in the school wh do not teach 5 classes a day.
5. What are the pass marks in an examination?
   I. A student secures 30% marks but fails by 10 mark
   II. The total marks is 200.
6. How much minimum marks will be required t pass an examination? (M.A.T., 2005
   I. Student A secured 32% marks in that examinatio and he failed by 1 mark. Student B secured 36 marks in the same examination and his mark were 1 more than the minimum pass marks.
   II. Student A secured 30% of full marks in the ex amination and he failed by 2 marks. If he ha secured 5 more marks his percentage of mark would have been 40%.
7. Are at least 20% of the people in City X who ar 30 years old or older bilingual? (M.A.T., 200
   I. In City X, 30% of the population is at least 3 years old.
   II. In City X, of the population 30 years old or olde 18 percent of the women and 17 percent of th men are bilingual.
8. What is the net effect on gross receipts?
   I. Prices are reduced by 25%.
   II. Sales increase by 20%.
9. What was Altaf's income in 2010?
   I. His income for 2008, 2009 and 2010 wa ₹ 3,00,000.
   II. He earned 20% more in 2009 than what he di in 2008.
10. For a Lata Mangeshkar show, a total of 10000 ticke were sold in VIP area, sitting and standing categorie How many VIP area tickets were sold?
    I. The number of sitting category tickets was ha the number of tickets sold in standing categor

II. The total of sitting and standing category tickets were 150% greater than the number of tickets sold in the VIP area category.

11. How many chocolates can Sheetal buy if she has to spend 20% of her budget on vegetables and 30% on groceries?
I. Sheetal has ₹ 50 with her.
II. Each chocolate costs 25 paise.

12. What is the value of 20 percent of x? (M.B.A., 2002)
I. One-fourth of 20 percent of x is 5.
II. $4x = S$, $5y = S$ and $y = 80$.

13. What is the ratio of two numbers x and y? (Bank P.O., 2010)
I. 40% of x is 20% of 50.
II. 30% of y is 25% of 72.

14. What is the ratio of the total number of girls to the total number of boys in the school? (SIDBI, 2006)
I. There are 680 students in the school out of which 45% are girls.
II. 55% of the total number of students are boys.

15. What is the population of State A? (Bank P.O., 2005)
I. Population of State B is 80% of the population of State A.
II. Average population of States A and B is 18 lakhs.

16. What is Mr. Roy's annual income for the year April 2011 to March 2012?
I. Annual income of Mr. Roy is 70% of his boss' annual income.
II. Mr. Roy's income for April 2011 was ₹ 12000 and his income increased every month by 10%.

17. How many students are there in the class?
I. There are 40 girls in the class.
II. The boys are 80% of the total number of students in the class.

18. Is (60% of a) + (40% of b) greater than 50% of $(a + b)$?
I. $a > b$ II. $b > 0$

Directions (*Questions 19 to 25*): *Each of the following questions consists of a question followed by three statements I, II and III. You have to study the question and the statements and decide which of the statement(s) is/are necessary to answer the question.*

19. What is Ritu's present salary?
I. The salary increases every year by 15%.
II. Her salary at the time of joining was ₹ 10000.
III. She had joined exactly 5 years ago.
(*a*) I and II only (*b*) II and III only
(*c*) I and III only (*d*) All I, II and III
(*e*) None of these

20. A, B and C secured 45%, 50% and 60% marks respectively in Biology. D's marks in Biology are 10 more than A's marks and 20 less than C's marks. Find out the total marks of the four students. (M.A.T., 2006)
I. Maximum marks for Biology are 200.
II. Total of D's and A's marks is 190.
III. C has obtained 120 marks.
(*a*) I and II
(*b*) III only
(*c*) Either I and II together or III alone
(*d*) Any one of the three
(*e*) All the three together

21. What is the overall percentage of marks obtained by Sangeeta in all five subjects? (S.B.I.P.O., 2005)
I. Sangeeta scored 75% marks in Maths and Science together.
II. Her aggregate marks in History and Science are 72%.
III. She has scored 85% marks in Sanskrit.
(*a*) Any two of the three
(*b*) All I, II and III
(*c*) I and either II or III
(*d*) III and either I or II
(*e*) Question cannot be answered even with the information in all three statements

22. How many children are there in the class?
I. 20% children in the class can speak only Hindi.
II. 44 children can speak languages other than Hindi.
III. There are 30 boys in the class.
(*a*) I and II only (*b*) II and either I or III
(*c*) All I, II and III (*d*) Any two of the three
(*e*) None of these

23. How much profit did the company earn in the year 2011?
I. The company earned 40% more profit in the year 2012 than that in the year 2010.
II. The company earned a total profit of ₹ 20 crores in the years 2010 and 2011 taken together.
III. In the year 2012, the company earned 80 percent profit of that in 2011.
(*a*) I and II or III
(*b*) Any two of the three
(*c*) Either I and II or II and III
(*d*) All I, II and III
(*e*) Question cannot be answered even with all I, II and III

24. What was the total number of candidates appeared at the examination?
I. 30% of appeared candidates succeeded in the examination.
II. The number of unsuccessful candidates was 1000 more than the successful candidates.
III. 1750 candidates were unsuccessful.
(*a*) Any two of the three
(*b*) Only I and II
(*c*) Only I and either II or III

(*d*) All I, II and III
(*e*) Even with all the three statements answer cannot be given.

25. What is Sumit's present salary?
I. The salary increases every year by 12%.
II. His salary at the time of joining was ₹ 3500.
III. He had joined exactly 7 years ago.
(*a*) I and II only (*b*) II and III only
(*c*) I and III only (*d*) All I, II and III
(*e*) None of these

Directions (*Questions 26-27*): *Each of these questions is followed by three statements. You have to study the question and all the three statements given and decide whether any information provided in the statement(s) is/are redundant and can be dispensed with while answering the questions.*

26. A 25 m long wire is cut into 3 pieces. How long is the longest piece? **(S.B.I.P.O., 2005)**
I. Two pieces are each 1 m shorter that the longest piece.
II. Two pieces of the wire are of the same length
III. The longest piece of the wire is 12.5% more than the smallest piece.
(*a*) I only
(*b*) Either I alone or II alone or II and III together
(*c*) Only II and III together
(*d*) II and either I or III

27. What is the monthly income of Mr. X? **(R.B.I., 2009)**
I. Mr. X spends 85% of his income on various items and the remaining amount is saved.
II. The monthly savings of Mr. X are ₹ 4500.
III. Out of the total money spent by Mr. X in a month, one-fifth is spent on food and an amount of ₹ 20400 on other items.
(*a*) Only II
(*b*) Only III
(*c*) Only either II or III
(*d*) Question cannot be answered even with the information in all the three statements
(*e*) None of these

ANSWERS

1. (*e*)	2. (*c*)	3. (*e*)	4. (*a*)	5. (*e*)	6. (*c*)	7. (*b*)	8. (*e*)	9. (*d*)	10. (*b*)
11. (*e*)	12. (*c*)	13. (*e*)	14. (*c*)	15. (*e*)	16. (*b*)	17. (*e*)	18. (*a*)	19. (*d*)	20. (*d*)
21. (*e*)	22. (*a*)	23. (*d*)	24. (*a*)	25. (*d*)	26. (*b*)	27. (*e*)			

SOLUTIONS

1. Let the total number of families be x.
Then, from I and II, we have
Number of families which have telephones

$= 30\%$ of 50% of $x = \left(\frac{30}{100} \times \frac{50}{100} \times x\right)$

$= \frac{15}{100} x = 15\%$ of x.

$\therefore$ Required percentage = 15%.
So, both I and II are required to answer the question.
$\therefore$ Correct answer is (*e*).

2. From I, we have

Required percentage $= \left(\frac{120}{300} \times 100\right)\% = 40\%.$

Thus, I alone gives the answer.
From II, we have: Required percentage

$= \left(\frac{2}{5} x \times \frac{1}{x} \times 100\right)\% = 40\%.$

So, I alone as well as II alone gives the answer.
$\therefore$ Correct answer is (*c*).

3. Let the father's salary be ₹ x.
From I, we have: $x = (100 - 37)\%$ of elder son's salary

$\Rightarrow$ elder son's salary = ₹ $\left(\frac{100x}{63}\right)$.

From II, we have: $x = (100 - 30)\%$ of younger son's salary

$\Rightarrow$ younger son's salary = ₹ $\left(\frac{100x}{70}\right)$ = ₹ $\left(\frac{10x}{7}\right)$.

Difference = ₹ $\left(\frac{100x}{63} - \frac{10x}{7}\right)$ = ₹ $\left(\frac{10x}{63}\right)$.

$\therefore$ Required percentage $= \left(\frac{10x}{63} \times \frac{7}{10x} \times 100\right)\% = 11\frac{1}{9}\%.$

So, both I and II together give the answer.
$\therefore$ Correct answer is (*e*).

4. Let the total number of teachers in the school be x.
From I, we have

$(100 - 55)\%$ of $x = 135 \Rightarrow x = \frac{135 \times 100}{45} = 300.$

$\therefore$ Reqd. number of teachers $= (100 - 8)\%$ of 55% of $300 = \left(\frac{92}{100} \times \frac{55}{100} \times 300\right)$.

So, I alone gives the answer while II alone is insufficient.
$\therefore$ Correct answer is (*a*).

5. From both I and II, we have
Pass marks = 30% of 200 + 10 = 60 + 10 = 70.
So, both I and II together are needed to get the answer.
$\therefore$ Correct answer is (*e*).

6. Let the maximum marks be x.

From I, we have: 32% of x + 1 = 36% of x – 1

$\Rightarrow \frac{4}{100} x = 2 \Rightarrow x = 50.$

$\therefore$ Pass marks = 32% of 50 + 1 = 17.

From II, we have: 30% of x + 2 = 40% x – 3

$\Rightarrow \frac{10}{100} x = 5 \Rightarrow x = 50.$

$\therefore$ Pass marks = 30% of 50 + 2 = 17.

So, I alone as well as II alone gives the answer.

$\therefore$ Correct answer is (*c*).

7. From II, it is clear that less than 20 percent of the population of age 30 years or more is bilingual.

So, II alone gives the answer while I alone does not.

$\therefore$ Correct answer is (*b*).

8. Clearly, gross receipts are affected by change in both price and sale of products.

So, from I and II, we have:

Let the original price be ₹ 100 per unit and original sale be 100 units.

Original gross receipts = ₹ (100 × 100) = ₹ 10000.

New price = ₹ 75, New sale = 120 units.

New gross receipts = ₹ (75 × 120) = ₹ 9000.

$\therefore$ Net decrease $= \left(\frac{1000}{10000} \times 100\right)\% = 10\%.$

Thus, both I and II together are needed to get the answer.

$\therefore$ Correct answer is (*e*).

9. From both I and II, we have

Let Altaf's income in 2008 be ₹ x.

Then, his income in 2009 = 120% of ₹ x = ₹ $\frac{6x}{5}$.

$\therefore$ Income in 2010 = ₹ $\left[300000 - \left(x + \frac{6x}{5}\right)\right]$

= ₹ $\left(300000 - \frac{11x}{5}\right)$ which cannot be determined.

So, even I and II together cannot give the answer.

$\therefore$ Correct answer is (*d*).

10. From II, we have:

Let the number of tickets in VIP area category be x.

Then, total number of tickets in standing and sitting categories

= (100 + 150)% of x = 250% of x = $\frac{5x}{2}$.

$\therefore x + \frac{5x}{2} = 10000 \Rightarrow \frac{7x}{2} = 10000 \Rightarrow x = \frac{10000 \times 2}{7}.$

So, II alone gives the answer while I alone is insufficient.

$\therefore$ Correct answer is (*b*).

11. To find the number of chocolates that Sheetal can buy, we need to know the total amount available with her for chocolates and the cost of each chocolate.

From I, we have

Amount available with Sheetal for chocolates

= [100 – (20 + 30)]% of ₹ 50 = ₹ 25.

From II, we have

Required number of chocolates = ₹ $\left(\frac{25}{0.25}\right) = 100.$

So, both I and II together are needed to get the answer.

$\therefore$ Correct answer is (*e*).

12. From I, we have 20% of x = 5 × 4 = 20.

From II, we have: $4x = S = 5y$ = 5 × 80 = 400 or x = 100.

So, 20% of x = 20.

Thus, either I alone or II alone gives the answer.

$\therefore$ Correct answer is (*c*).

13. From I, we have 40% of x = 20% of 50 = 10

or $x = \frac{10 \times 100}{40} = 25$ ...(*i*)

From II, we have 30% of y = 25% of 72 = 18

or $y = \frac{18 \times 100}{30} = 60.$ ...(*ii*)

From (*i*) and (*ii*), we have: x: y = 25: 60 = 5: 12.

Thus, both I and II together are needed together the answer.

$\therefore$ Correct answer is (*e*).

14. From I, we have

Number of girls = 45% of 680 = 306.

Number of boys = (680 – 306) = 374.

$\therefore$ Required ratio = 306: 374 = 9: 11.

From II, we have

Required ratio = (100 – 55)% of x: 55% of x = 45: 55

= 9: 11.

Thus, either I alone or II alone gives the answer.

$\therefore$ Correct answer is (*c*).

15. From I we have

Let population of State A be x.

Then, population of State B = 80% of x = $\frac{4x}{5}$.

From II, we have

Sum of population of States A and B = (18 × 2) lakhs = 3600000.

From I and II, we have:

$x + \frac{4x}{5} = 3600000 \Rightarrow \frac{9x}{5} = 3600000$

$\Rightarrow x = \frac{3600000 \times 5}{9} = 2000000.$

$\therefore$ Population of State A = 2000000.

Thus, both I and II together are needed to get the answer.

$\therefore$ Correct answer is (*e*).

16. From II, we may calculate Mr. Roy's income for each month by calculating a 10% increase on previous month's income. The monthly incomes may then be added to get the annual income.

So, II alone gives the answer while I alone is insufficient.

$\therefore$ Correct answer is (*b*).

17. Let the total number of students in the class be x.

From II, we have: Percentage of girls = (100 – 80)%

= 20%.

So, from I and II, we have: 20% of $x = 40$

$\Rightarrow x = \frac{40 \times 100}{20} = 200.$

Thus, both I and II together are needed to get the answer.

$\therefore$ Correct answer is (*e*).

18. We have

(60% of a) + (40% of b) = 50% of ($a + b$), when $a = b$.

(60% of a) + (40% of b) > 50% of ($a + b$), when $a > b$.

(60% of a) + (40% of b) < 50% of ($a + b$), when $a < b$.

So, I alone gives the answer while II alone does not.

$\therefore$ Correct answer is (*a*).

19. From I, II and III, we have

Ritu's present salary = ₹ $\left[10000\left(1+\frac{15}{100}\right)^5\right]$.

So, all I, II and III are needed to get the answer.

$\therefore$ Correct answer is (*d*).

20. I. A's marks = 45% of 200 = 90 ; B's marks = 50% of 200 = 100;

C's marks = 60% of 200 = 120 ; D's marks = 90 + 10 = 100.

II. Let maximum marks = x.

Then, (45% of x) + (45% of x + 10) = 190

$\Rightarrow \frac{90}{100}x = 180 \Rightarrow x = \frac{180 \times 100}{90} = 200.$

We may calculate the marks of each student as above.

III. Let maximum marks = x.

Then, 60% of $x = 120 \Rightarrow x = \frac{120 \times 100}{60} = 200.$

We may again calculate the marks of each student as above.

Thus, any one of I, II and III alone is sufficient.

$\therefore$ Correct answer is (*d*).

21. Let maximum marks in each subject be 100.

I. M + Sc = 75% of 200 $\Rightarrow$ M + Sc = 150 ...(*i*)

II. H + Sc = 72% of 200 $\Rightarrow$ H + Sc = 144 ...(*ii*)

III. S = 85% of 100 $\Rightarrow$ S = 85 ...(*iii*)

Adding (*i*), (*ii*) and (*iii*), we get: M + H + 2Sc + S = 379.

Since marks in Science are not known, the total score of all the subjects cannot be calculated. Thus the question cannot be answered even with the information in all the three statements.

$\therefore$ Correct answer is (*e*).

22. Let the total number of children in the class be x.

I. Percentage of children speaking Hindi = 20%.

II. (100 – 20)% of $x = 44 \Rightarrow$ 80% of $x = 44$

$\Rightarrow x = \frac{44 \times 100}{80} = 55.$

Thus, both I and II together give the answer.

$\therefore$ Correct answer is (*a*).

23. Let the profit earned in 2012 be ₹ x.

I. 140% of (profit in 2010) = $x \Rightarrow$ Profit in 2010 $= \frac{x \times 100}{140} = \frac{5x}{7}$.

II. 80% of (profit in 2011) = $x \Rightarrow$ Profit in 2011 $= \frac{x \times 100}{80} = \frac{5x}{4}$.

III. $\frac{5x}{7} + \frac{5x}{4} = 20$ crore $\Rightarrow \frac{55x}{28} = 20$ crore

$\Rightarrow x = \left(\frac{20 \times 28}{55}\right)$ crore.

$\therefore$ Profit earned in 2011 = ₹ $\left(\frac{5}{4} \times \frac{20 \times 28}{55}\right)$ crore.

Thus, all the three statements together are needed.

$\therefore$ Correct answer is (*d*).

24. Let the total number of candidates be x.

I and II. We have: 70% of x – 30% of x = 1000

$\Rightarrow$ 40% of $x = 1000 \Rightarrow x = \left(\frac{1000 \times 100}{40}\right) = 2500.$

II and III. Number of unsuccessful candidates = 1750.

Number of successful candidates = 1750 – 1000 = 750.

$\therefore$ Total number of candidates = 1750 + 750 = 2500.

I and III. Percentage of unsuccessful candidates = (100 – 30)% = 70%.

So, 70% of $x = 1750 \Rightarrow x = \left(\frac{1750 \times 100}{70}\right) = 2500.$

Thus, any two of the three is sufficient to answer the question.

$\therefore$ Correct answer is (*a*).

25. Sumit's present salary = ₹ $\left[3500\left(1+\frac{12}{100}\right)^7\right]$.

Thus, all the three statements are needed to answer the question.

$\therefore$ Correct answer is (*d*).

26. I. Let the length of the longest piece be x metres and that of each shorter piece be (x – 1) metres.

Then, $2(x - 1) + x = 25 \Rightarrow 3x = 27 \Rightarrow x = 9$.

So, length of the longest piece = 9 m.

II and III. Let the length of each of the two smaller pieces be l metres.

Then, length of the longest piece = $112\frac{1}{2}\%$ of $l = \frac{9l}{8}$ m.

$\therefore 2l + \frac{9l}{8} = 25 \Rightarrow 25l = 25 \times 8 \Rightarrow l = 8.$

So, length of the longest piece = $\left(\frac{9 \times 8}{8}\right)$ m = 9 m.

I and III. Let the length of each of the two smaller pieces be l metres.

Then, $12\frac{1}{2}\%$ of $l = 1 \Rightarrow l = 8$.

So, length of the longest piece = (8 + 1) m = 9 m.

Thus, (I alone) or (II and III together) or (I and III together) are needed to answer the question *i.e.*, either (II or II together) or (I alone) or (II alone) is redundant.

$\therefore$ Correct answer is (*b*).

27. **I and II.** Let the monthly income of Mr. X be ₹ p.

Then, $(100 - 85)\%$ of $p = 4500$

$\Rightarrow$ 15% of $p = 4500$

$$\Rightarrow p = \left(\frac{4500 \times 100}{15}\right) = 30000.$$

II and III. Let the monthly expenditure be ₹ x.

$$\text{Then, } x = \frac{x}{5} + 20400 \Rightarrow \frac{4x}{5} = 20400$$

$$\Rightarrow x = \frac{20400 \times 5}{5} = 25500$$

So, monthly income of Mr. X = ₹ (25500 + 4500) = ₹ 30000.

I and III. Let the monthly income of Mr X be ₹ p.

$$\text{Then, } \left(1 - \frac{1}{5}\right) \text{ of } 85\% \text{ of } p = 20400$$

$$\Rightarrow \frac{4}{5} \times \frac{85}{100} \times p = 20400$$

$$\Rightarrow p = \left(\frac{20400 \times 5 \times 100}{4 \times 85}\right) = 30000.$$

Thus, any one of the three is redundant.

$\therefore$ Correct answer is (*e*).

12 Profit and Loss

IMPORTANT FACTS AND FORMULAE

Cost Price: The price at which an article is purchased, is called its ***cost price***, abbreviated as ***C.P.***

Selling Price: The price at which an article is sold, is called its ***selling price***, abbreviated as ***S.P.***

Profit or Gain: If S.P. is greater than C.P., the seller is said to have a ***profit*** or ***gain***.

Loss: If S.P. is less than C.P., the seller is said to have incurred a ***loss***.

I. Gain = (S.P.) – (C.P.)

II. Loss = (C.P.) – (S.P.)

III. Loss or gain is always reckoned on C.P.

IV. $\text{Gain\%} = \left(\frac{\text{Gain} \times 100}{\text{C.P.}}\right)$

V. $\text{Loss\%} = \left(\frac{\text{Loss} \times 100}{\text{C.P.}}\right)$

VI. $\text{S.P.} = \frac{(100 + \text{Gain\%})}{100} \times \text{C.P.}$

VII. $\text{S.P.} = \frac{(100 - \text{Loss\%})}{100} \times \text{C.P.}$

VIII. $\text{C.P.} = \frac{100}{(100 + \text{Gain\%})} \times \text{S.P.}$

IX. $\text{C.P.} = \frac{100}{(100 - \text{Loss\%})} \times \text{S.P.}$

X. If an article is sold at a gain of say, 35%, then S.P. = 135% of C.P.

XI. If an article is sold at a loss of say, 35%, then S.P. = 65% of C.P.

XII. When a person sells two similar items, one at a gain of say, x%, and the other at a loss of x%, then the seller always incurs a loss given by:

$$\text{Loss\%} = \left(\frac{\text{Common Loss and Gain\%}}{10}\right)^2 = \left(\frac{x}{10}\right)^2.$$

XIII. If a trader professes to sell his goods at cost price, but uses false weights, then

$$\text{Gain\%} = \left[\frac{\text{Error}}{(\text{True Value}) - (\text{Error})} \times 100\right]\%.$$

XIV. If a trader professes to sell his goods at a profit of x% but uses false weight which is y% less than the actual weight, then

$$\text{Gain \%} = \left\{\left(\frac{x + y}{100 - y}\right) \times 100\right\}\%$$

XV. If a trader professes to sell his goods at a loss of x% but uses false weight which is y% less than the actual weight, then

$$\text{Gain or Loss \%} = \left\{\left(\frac{y - x}{100 - y}\right) \times 100\right\}\%$$

according as the sign is + ve or – ve.

SOLVED EXAMPLES

Ex. 1. ***Mansi purchased a car for ₹ 2,50,000 and sold it for ₹ 3,48,000. What is the percent profit she made on the car?*** **(Bank P.O., 2010)**

Sol. C.P. = ₹ 250000 ; S.P. = ₹ 348000.

Profit = ₹ (348000 – 250000) = ₹ 98000.

$\therefore$ Profit % = $\left(\frac{98000}{250000} \times 100\right)\% = 39.2\%$.

Ex. 2. ***If C.P. is ₹ 2516 and S.P. is ₹ 2272, find the percentage loss.*** **(R.R.B., 2006)**

Sol. C.P. = ₹ 2516, S.P. = ₹ 2272. Loss = ₹ (2516 – 2272) = ₹ 244.

$\therefore$ Loss% = $\left(\frac{244}{2516} \times 100\right)\% = 9.69\%$.

Ex. 3. ***Find S.P., when***

(i) C.P. = ₹ 56.25, Gain = 20% ***(ii) C.P. = ₹ 80.40, Loss = 15%***

Sol. (*i*) S.P. = 120% of ₹ 56.25 = ₹ $\left(\frac{120}{100} \times 56.25\right)$ = ₹ 67.50.

(*ii*) S.P. = 85% of ₹ 80.40 = ₹ $\left(\frac{85}{100} \times 80.40\right)$ = ₹ 68.34.

Ex. 4. ***A gold bracelet is sold for ₹ 14500 at a loss of 20%. What is the cost price of the gold bracelet?*** **(Bank Recruitment, 2008)**

Sol. C.P. = ₹ $\left(\frac{100}{80} \times 14500\right)$ = ₹ 18125.

Ex. 5. ***The owner of a cell phone charges his customer 23% more than the cost price. If a customer paid ₹ 7011 for a cell phone, then what was the cost price of the cell phone?*** **(Bank Recruitment, 2008)**

Sol. C.P. = ₹ $\left(\frac{100}{123} \times 7011\right)$ = ₹ 5700.

Ex. 6. ***Shaloo sold a mobile phone at the cost of ₹ 1950 at a loss of 25%. At what cost will she have to sell it to get a profit of 30%?*** **(Bank Recruitment, 2010)**

Sol. Case I. S.P. = 1950, Loss = 25%.

$\therefore$ C.P. = ₹ $\left(\frac{100}{75} \times 1950\right)$ = ₹ 2600.

Case II. C.P. = ₹ 2600, Profit = 30%.

$\therefore$ S.P. = ₹ $\left(\frac{130}{100} \times 2600\right)$ = ₹ 3380.

Another Method:

Let the new S.P. be ₹ x. Then,

(100 – loss%) : (1st S.P.) = (100 + gain%) : (2nd S.P.)

$\Rightarrow (100 - 25) : 1950 = (100 + 30) : x$

$\Rightarrow 75 : 1950 = 130 : x \Rightarrow x = \left(\frac{1950 \times 130}{75}\right) = 3380$.

Ex. 7. ***A television manufacturer earns 20% profit by selling each T.V. set for ₹ 14400. If the production cost is increased by 15%, what should be the new selling price of a set so as to gain 15%?*** **(S.S.C., 2006)**

Sol. S.P. = ₹ 14400, Profit = 20%.

$\therefore$ C.P. = ₹ $\left(\frac{100}{120} \times 14400\right)$ = ₹ 12000.

New C.P. = ₹ $\left(\frac{115}{100} \times 12000\right)$ = ₹ 13800 ; Gain = 15%.

$\therefore$ Required S.P. = ₹ $\left(\frac{115}{100} \times 13800\right)$ = ₹ 15870.

Ex. 8. ***A book was sold for ₹ 27.50 with a profit of 10%. If it were sold for ₹ 25.75, then what would have be the percentage of profit or loss?***

Sol. S.P. = ₹ 27.50, Profit = 10%.

So, C.P. = ₹ $\left(\frac{100}{110} \times 27.50\right)$ = ₹ 25.

When S.P. = ₹ 25.75, profit = ₹ (25.75 – 25) = ₹ 0.75.

$\therefore$ Profit% = $\left(\frac{0.75}{25} \times 100\right)\% = 3\%$.

Ex. 9. ***If the cost price is 96% of the selling price, then what is the profit percent?***

Sol. Let S.P. = ₹ 100. Then, C.P. = ₹ 96; Profit = ₹ 4.

$\therefore$ Profit% = $\left(\frac{4}{96} \times 100\right)\% = \frac{25}{6}\% = 4.17\%$.

Ex. 10. ***A manufacturer makes 800 articles at a cost of ₹ 1.50 per article. He fixes the selling price such that if on 600 articles are sold, he would make a profit of 30% on his outlay. However, he sold 620 articles at th price. Find his actual profit percent of the total outlay, assuming that the unsold articles are useless.***

(P.C.S., 20

Sol. C.P. of 800 articles = ₹ (1.50 × 800) = ₹ 1200.

S.P. of 600 articles = ₹ $\left(\frac{130}{100} \times 1200\right)$ = ₹ 1560.

S.P. of 620 articles = ₹ $\left(\frac{1560}{600} \times 620\right)$ = ₹ 1612.

Profit = ₹ (1612 – 1200) = ₹ 412.

$\therefore$ Profit % = $\left(\frac{412}{1200} \times 100\right)\% = 34\frac{1}{3}\%$.

Ex. 11. ***The selling price of 30 items is equal to the purchase price of 25 items. What is the profit or loss percen***

(Bank Recruitment, 20

Sol. Let C.P. of each article be ₹ 1.

Then, C.P. of 30 items = ₹ 30, S.P. of 30 items = ₹ 25.

Loss = ₹ (30 – 25) = ₹ 5.

$\therefore$ Loss% = $\left(\frac{5}{30} \times 100\right)\% = 16\frac{2}{3}\%$.

Ex. 12. ***By selling 33 metres of cloth, one gains the selling price of 11 metres. Find the gain percent.***

Sol. (S.P. of 33 m) – (C.P. of 33 m) = Gain = S.P. of 11 m.

$\therefore$ S.P. of 22 m = C.P. of 33 m.

Let C.P. of each metre be ₹ 1. Then, C.P. of 22 m = ₹ 22, S.P. of 22 m = ₹ 33.

$\therefore$ Gain% = $\left(\frac{11}{22} \times 100\right)\% = 50\%$.

Ex. 13. ***A vendor bought bananas at 6 for ₹ 10 and sold them at 4 for ₹ 6. Find his gain or loss percent.***

Sol. Suppose, number of bananas bought = L.C.M. of 6 and 4 = 12.

$\therefore$ C.P. = ₹ $\left(\frac{10}{6} \times 12\right)$ = ₹ 20; S.P. = ₹ $\left(\frac{6}{4} \times 12\right)$ = ₹ 18.

$\therefore$ Loss% = $\left(\frac{2}{20} \times 100\right)\% = 10\%$.

Ex. 14. A ***vendor sells 10 clips for a rupee gaining thereby 40%. How many clips did he buy for a rupee?***

Sol. S.P. of 10 clips = ₹ 1, Gain = 40%. C.P. of 10 clips = ₹ $\left(\frac{100}{140} \times 1\right)$ = ₹ $\frac{5}{7}$.

For ₹ $\frac{5}{7}$, clips bought = 10. For ₹ 1, clips bought = $\left(10 \times \frac{7}{5}\right) = 14$.

Ex. 15. ***A vendor bought buttons at 6 for a rupee. How many for a rupee must he sell to gain 20%?***

Sol. C.P. of 6 buttons = ₹ 1, Gain = 20%. S.P. of 6 buttons = ₹ $\left(\frac{120}{100} \times 1\right) = ₹ \frac{6}{5}$.

For ₹ $\frac{6}{5}$, buttons sold = 6. For ₹ 1, buttons sold = $\left(6 \times \frac{5}{6}\right) = 5$.

Ex. 16. ***A grocer purchased 80 kg of sugar at ₹ 13.50 per kg and mixed it with 120 kg sugar at ₹ 16 per kg. At what rate should he sell the mixture to gain 16%?***

Sol. C.P. of 200 kg of mixture = ₹ (80 × 13.50 + 120 × 16) = ₹ 3000.

S.P. = 116% of ₹ 3000 = ₹ $\left(\frac{116}{100} \times 3000\right)$ = ₹ 3480.

∴ Rate of S.P. of the mixture = ₹ $\left(\frac{3480}{200}\right)$ per kg = ₹ 17.40 per kg.

Ex. 17. ***Pure ghee costs ₹ 100 per kg. After adulterating it with vegetable oil costing ₹ 50 per kg, a shopkeeper sells the mixture at the rate of ₹ 96 per kg, thereby making a profit of 20%. In what ratio does he mix the two?***

Sol. Mean cost price = ₹ $\left(\frac{100}{120} \times 96\right)$ = ₹ 80 per kg.

By the rule of alligation:

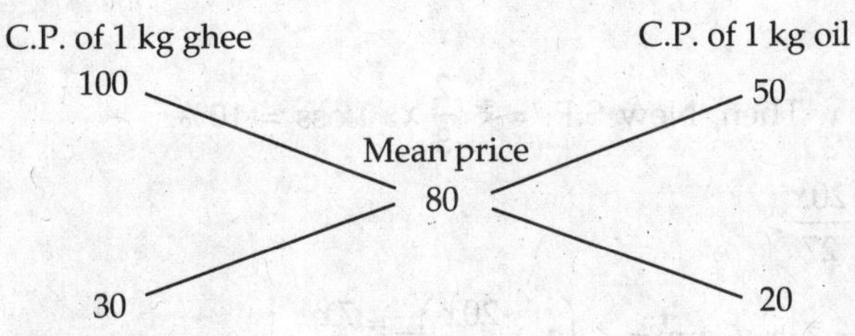

∴ Required ratio = 30 : 20 = 3 : 2.

Ex. 18. ***A dishonest dealer professes to sell his goods at cost price but uses a weight of 960 gms for a kg. weight. Find his gain percent.***

Sol. Gain % = $\left[\frac{\text{Error}}{(\text{True Value}) - (\text{Error})} \times 100\right]\% = \left(\frac{40}{960} \times 100\right)\% = 4\frac{1}{6}\%$.

Ex. 19. ***A shopkeeper advertises for selling cloth at 4% loss. However, by using a false metre scale he actually gains 25%. What is the actual length of the scale?*** **(R.R.B., 2008)**

Sol. Let C.P. of 1 m of cloth be ₹ 1.

Professed S.P. of 1 m cloth = ₹ $\left(\frac{96}{100}\right)$ = ₹ 0.96. Gain = 25%.

Actual C.P. of the cloth sold for ₹ 0.96 = ₹ $\left(\frac{100}{125} \times 0.96\right)$ = ₹ 0.768.

Actual length of the scale = Length bought for ₹ 0.768 = 76.8 cm.

Ex. 20. ***A dishonest dealer sells the goods at $6\frac{1}{4}\%$ loss on cost price but uses $12\frac{1}{2}\%$ less weight. What is his percentage profit or loss?***

Sol. Let the C.P. of 1 kg goods be ₹ 1.

Then, S.P. of $\left[\left(100 - 12\frac{1}{2}\right)\% \text{ of } 1 \text{ kg}\right]$ *i.e.*, 875 g goods = ₹ 0.9375.

S.P. of 1 kg goods = ₹ $\left(\frac{0.9375}{875} \times 1000\right)$ = ₹ $1\frac{1}{14}$.

∴ Profit % = $\left(\frac{1}{14} \times 100\right)\% = 7\frac{1}{7}\%$.

Ex. 21. ***If the manufacturer gains 10%, the wholesale dealer 15% and the retailer 25%, then find the cost of production of a table, the retail price of which is ₹ 1265?*** **(G.B.O., 2007)**

Sol. Let the cost of production of the table be ₹ x.

Then, 125% of 115% of 110% of x = 1265

$$\Rightarrow \frac{125}{100} \times \frac{115}{100} \times \frac{110}{100} \times x = 1265 \Rightarrow \frac{253}{160} x = 1265 \Rightarrow x = \left(\frac{1265 \times 160}{253}\right) = ₹\, 800.$$

Ex. 22. ***Monika purchased a pressure cooker at $\frac{9}{10}$th of its selling price and sold it at 8% more than its S.P. Find her gain percent.***

Sol. Let the S.P. be ₹ x. Then, C.P. = ₹ $\frac{9x}{10}$, Receipt = 108% of ₹ x = ₹ $\frac{27x}{25}$.

$$\text{Gain} = ₹\left(\frac{27x}{25} - \frac{9x}{10}\right) = ₹\left(\frac{108x - 90x}{100}\right) = ₹\, \frac{18x}{100}.$$

$$\therefore \quad \text{Gain\%} = \left(\frac{18x}{100} \times \frac{10}{9x} \times 100\right)\% = 20\%.$$

Ex. 23. ***An article is sold at a certain price. By selling it at $\frac{2}{3}$ of that price one loses 10%. Find the gain percent at original price.***

Sol. Let the original S.P. be ₹ x. Then, New S.P. = ₹ $\frac{2}{3}x$, Loss = 10%.

$$\text{So, C.P.} = ₹\left(\frac{100}{90} \times \frac{2}{3}x\right) = \frac{20x}{27}.$$

$$\text{Now, C.P.} = ₹\, \frac{20x}{27}, \text{ S.P.} = ₹\, x. \text{ Gain} = ₹\left(x - \frac{20x}{27}\right) = ₹\, \frac{7x}{27}.$$

$$\therefore \quad \text{Gain\%} = \left(\frac{7x}{27} \times \frac{27}{20x} \times 100\right)\% = 35\%.$$

Ex. 24. ***A tradesman sold an article at a loss of 20%. If the selling price had been increased by ₹ 100, there would have been a gain of 5%. What was the cost price of the article?*** **(S.S.C., 2004)**

Sol. Let C.P. be ₹ x. Then, (105% of x) – (80% of x) = 100 or 25% of x = 100

$$\therefore \quad \frac{x}{4} = 100 \text{ or } x = 400.$$

So, C.P. = ₹ 400.

Ex. 25. ***A man sells an article at a profit of 25%. If he had bought it at 20% less and sold it for ₹ 10.50 less, he would have gained 30%. Find the cost price of the article.***

Sol. Let the C.P. be ₹ x.

$$\text{1st S.P.} = 125\% \text{ of } x = \frac{125}{100} x = \frac{5x}{4}; \text{ 2nd C.P.} = 80\% \text{ of } x = \frac{80}{100} x = \frac{4x}{5}.$$

$$\text{2nd S.P.} = 130\% \text{ of } \frac{4x}{5} = \left(\frac{130}{100} \times \frac{4x}{5}\right) = \frac{26x}{25}.$$

$$\therefore \quad \frac{5x}{4} - \frac{26x}{25} = 10.50 \Leftrightarrow \frac{21x}{100} = 10.50 \Leftrightarrow x = \left(\frac{10.50 \times 100}{21}\right) = 50.$$

Hence, C.P. = ₹ 50.

Ex. 26. ***The price of a jewel, passing through three hands, rises on the whole by 65%. If the first and the second sellers earned 20% and 25% profit respectively, find the percentage profit earned by the third seller.***

Sol. Let the original price of the jewel be ₹ P and let the profit earned by the third seller be x%.

Then, $(100 + x)$% of 125% of 120% of P = 165% of P

$$\Rightarrow \left[\frac{(100 + x)}{100} \times \frac{125}{100} \times \frac{120}{100} \times P\right] = \left(\frac{165}{100} \times P\right) \Rightarrow (100 + x) = \left(\frac{165 \times 100 \times 100}{125 \times 120}\right) = 110 \Rightarrow x = 10\%.$$

Ex. 27. ***A man sold two flats for ₹ 6,75,958 each. On one he gains 16% while on the other he loses 16%. How much does he gain or lose in the whole transaction?***

Sol. Remember: In such a case, there is always a loss. The selling price is immaterial.

$$\therefore \quad \text{Loss\%} = \left(\frac{\text{Common Loss and Gain\%}}{10}\right)^2 = \left(\frac{16}{10}\right)^2 \% = \left(\frac{64}{25}\right)\% = 2.56\%.$$

Ex. 28. ***Two-thirds of a consignment was sold at a profit of 5% and the remainder at a loss of 2%. If the total profit was ₹ 400, find the value of the consignment.*** **(M.A.T., 2009)**

Sol. Let the value of the consignment be ₹ x.

C.P. of $\frac{2}{3}$rd = ₹ $\frac{2x}{3}$; C.P. of $\frac{1}{3}$rd = ₹ $\frac{x}{3}$.

$$\text{Total S.P.} = ₹\left[\left(105\% \text{ of } \frac{2x}{3}\right) + \left(98\% \text{ of } \frac{x}{3}\right)\right] = ₹\left(\frac{7x}{10} + \frac{49x}{150}\right) = ₹\left(\frac{154x}{150}\right) = ₹\left(\frac{77x}{75}\right).$$

$$\text{Gain} = ₹\left(\frac{77x}{75} - x\right) = ₹\frac{2x}{75}.$$

$$\therefore \quad \frac{2x}{75} = 400 \Rightarrow x = \left(\frac{400 \times 75}{2}\right) = 15000.$$

Hence, value of the consignment = ₹ 15000.

Ex. 29. ***A man bought a horse and a carriage for ₹ 3000. He sold the horse at a gain of 20% and the carriage at a loss of 10%, thereby gaining 2% on the whole. Find the cost of the horse.***

Sol. Let the C.P. of the horse be ₹ x. Then, C.P. of the carriage = ₹ $(3000 - x)$.

$\therefore$ 20% of x – 10% of $(3000 - x)$ = 2% of 3000

$$\Rightarrow \quad \frac{x}{5} - \frac{(3000 - x)}{10} = 60 \Rightarrow 2x - 3000 + x = 600 \Rightarrow 3x = 3600 \Rightarrow x = 1200.$$

Hence, C.P. of the horse = ₹ 1200.

Ex. 30. ***Find the single discount equivalent to a series discount of 10%, 20% and 30%.*** **(S.S.C., 2010)**

Sol. Let marked price be ₹ 100.

Then, Net S.P. = (100 – 30)% of (100 – 20)% of (100 – 10)% of ₹ 100

= 70% of 80% of 90% of ₹ 100

$$= ₹\left(\frac{70}{100} \times \frac{80}{100} \times \frac{90}{100} \times 100\right) = ₹\ 50.40.$$

$\therefore$ Required discount = (100 – 50.40)% = 49.6%.

Ex. 31. ***After getting two successive discounts, a shirt with a list price of ₹ 150 is available at ₹ 105. If the second discount is 12.5%, find the first discount.***

Sol. Let the first discount be x%.

Then, 87.5% of $(100 - x)$% of 150 = 105

$$\Rightarrow \quad \frac{87.5}{100} \times \frac{(100 - x)}{100} \times 150 = 105 \Rightarrow 100 - x = \left(\frac{105 \times 100 \times 100}{150 \times 87.5}\right) = 80$$

$\Rightarrow$ x = (100 – 80) = 20.

$\therefore$ First discount = 20%.

Ex. 32. ***An uneducated retailer marks all his goods at 50% above the cost price and thinking that he will still make 25% profit, offers a discount of 25% on the marked price. What is his actual profit on the sales?***

Sol. Let C.P. = ₹ 100. Then, marked price = ₹ 150.

S.P. = 75% of ₹ 150 = ₹ 112.50.

$\therefore$ Gain% = 12.50%.

Ex. 33. ***A retailer buys 40 pens at the marked price of 36 pens from a wholesaler. If he sells these pens giving a discount of 1%, what is the profit percent?***

Sol. Let the marked price of each pen be ₹ 1.

Then, C.P. of 40 pens = ₹ 36. S.P. of 40 pens = 99% of ₹ 40 = ₹ 39.60.

$\therefore$ Profit % = $\left(\frac{3.60}{36} \times 100\right)\% = 10\%$.

Ex. 34. ***By how much above the cost should the goods be marked for sale so that after allowing a trade discount of 20% and a cash discount of $6\frac{1}{4}\%$, a net gain of 20% on the cost is made?*** **(A.A.O., 2009)**

Sol. Let C.P. = ₹ 100. Then, S.P. = ₹ 120.

Let M.P. be ₹ x.

Then, $\left(100 - 6\frac{1}{4}\right)\%$ of $(100 - 20)\%$ of $x = 120$

$\Rightarrow$ $93\frac{3}{4}\%$ of 80% of $x = 120$

$\Rightarrow$ $\left(\frac{375}{4} \times \frac{1}{100} \times \frac{80}{100} x\right) = 120 \Rightarrow \frac{3}{4}x = 120 \Rightarrow x = \left(\frac{120 \times 4}{3}\right) = 160.$

$\therefore$ Marked price = 60% above C.P.

Ex. 35. ***When a producer allows 36% commission on the retail price of his product, he earns a profit of 8.8%. What would be his profit percent if the commission is reduced by 24%?***

Sol. Let retail price = ₹ 100. Then, commission = ₹ 36.

$\therefore$ S.P. = ₹ (100 − 36) = ₹ 64. But, profit = 8.8%.

$\therefore$ C.P. = ₹ $\left(\frac{100}{108.8} \times 64\right) = ₹ \frac{1000}{17}$.

New commission = ₹ 12. New S.P. = ₹ (100 − 12) = ₹ 88.

Gain = ₹ $\left(88 - \frac{1000}{17}\right) = ₹ \frac{496}{17}$.

$\therefore$ Gain % = $\left(\frac{496}{17} \times \frac{17}{1000} \times 100\right)\% = 49.6\%$.

EXERCISE

(OBJECTIVE TYPE QUESTIONS)

Directions: ***Mark* (✓) *against the correct answer:***

1. Mr Kashyap purchased an airconditioner for ₹ 12000 and sold it for ₹ 15000. What was the profit percentage? **(Bank Recruitment, 2010)**
   (*a*) 15 (*b*) 20
   (*c*) 25 (*d*) 35
   (*e*) None of these

2. In terms of percentage profit, which is the best transaction?

	C.P. (in ₹)	**Profit (in ₹)**
(*a*)	36	17
(*b*)	50	24
(*c*)	40	19
(*d*)	60	29

3. If books bought at prices ranging from ₹ 200 to ₹ 350 are sold at prices ranging from ₹ 300 to ₹ 425, what is the greatest possible profit that might be made in selling eight books?
   (*a*) ₹ 400 (*b*) ₹ 600
   (*c*) Cannot be determined (*d*) None of these

4. A shopkeeper bought an article for ₹ 2090.42. Approximately, what will be the percentage profit if he sold that article for ₹ 2602.58?
   (*a*) 15% (*b*) 20%
   (*c*) 25% (*d*) 30%

5. The cost price of an article is ₹ 7840. What should be the selling price of the article so that there is a profit of 7%? **(R.R.B., 2008)**
   (*a*) ₹ 8000 (*b*) ₹ 8300
   (*c*) ₹ 8388.80 (*d*) ₹ 8500.50

6. Rakesh purchased a mobile phone for ₹ 5400 and a refrigerator for ₹ 9600. He sold the mobile phone at three-fourths of its cost price and the refrigerator at $1\frac{1}{3}$ of its cost price. What was the profit/loss? **(Bank Recruitment, 2010)**

(*a*) ₹ 1580 (*b*) ₹ 1750
(*c*) ₹ 1850 (*d*) ₹ 1870
(*e*) None of these

7. Rajni purchased a mobile phone and a refrigerator for ₹ 12000 and ₹ 10000 respectively. She sold the refrigerator at a loss of 12 percent and the mobile phone at a profit of 8 percent. What is her overall loss/profit? **(Bank P.O., 2010)**

(*a*) Loss of ₹ 280 (*b*) Loss of ₹ 240
(*c*) Profit of ₹ 2060 (*d*) Profit of ₹ 2160
(*e*) None of these

8. Mohanlal purchased a TV set for ₹ 12500 and spent ₹ 300 on transportation and ₹ 800 on installation. At what price should he sell it so as to earn an overall profit of 15%? **(Specialist Officers, 2009)**

(*a*) ₹ 14375 (*b*) ₹ 14560
(*c*) ₹ 15375 (*d*) ₹ 15460
(*e*) None of these

9. Harshad bought 15 pieces of DVD players @ ₹ 4500 each and sold all of them at the total price of ₹ 81000. What is the percent profit earned in the deal? **(Bank P.O., 2009)**

(*a*) $16\frac{2}{3}$ (*b*) 20
(*c*) $20\frac{1}{2}$ (*d*) 25
(*e*) None of these

10. Alfred buys an old scooter for ₹ 4700 and spends ₹ 800 on its repairs. If he sells the scooter for ₹ 5800, his gain percent is

(*a*) $4\frac{4}{7}\%$ (*b*) $5\frac{5}{11}\%$
(*c*) 10% (*d*) 12%

11. A shopkeeper purchased 70 kg of potatoes for ₹ 420 and sold the whole lot at the rate of ₹ 6.50 per kg. What will be his gain percent? **(S.S.C., 2007)**

(*a*) $4\frac{1}{6}\%$ (*b*) $6\frac{1}{4}\%$
(*c*) $8\frac{1}{3}\%$ (*d*) 20%

12. Sam purchased 20 dozens of toys at the rate of ₹ 375 per dozen. He sold each one of them at the rate of ₹ 33. What was his percentage profit?

(*a*) 3.5 (*b*) 4.5
(*c*) 5.6 (*d*) 6.5
(*e*) None of these

13. 100 oranges are bought at the rate of ₹ 350 and sold at the rate of ₹ 48 per dozen. The percentage of profit or loss is **(B.Ed Entrance, 2008)**

(*a*) $14\frac{2}{7}\%$ gain (*b*) 15% gain
(*c*) $14\frac{2}{7}\%$ loss (*d*) 15% loss

14. A sells an article which costs him ₹ 400 to B at a profit of 20%. B then sells it to C, making a profit of 10% on the price he paid to A. How much does C pay B?

(*a*) ₹ 472 (*b*) ₹ 476
(*c*) ₹ 528 (*d*) ₹ 532

15. By selling an article for ₹ 100, a man gains ₹ 15. Then, his gain % is **(R.R.B., 2010)**

(*a*) 15% (*b*) $12\frac{2}{3}\%$
(*c*) $17\frac{11}{17}\%$ (*d*) $17\frac{1}{4}\%$

16. A trader buys some goods for ₹ 150. If the overhead expenses be 12% of cost price, then at what price should it be sold to earn 10%? **(R.R.B., 2007)**

(*a*) ₹ 184.80 (*b*) ₹ 185.80
(*c*) ₹ 187.80 (*d*) ₹ 188.80

17. A man buys 10 articles for ₹ 8 and sells them at the rate of ₹ 1.25 per article. His profit is

(*a*) $19\frac{1}{2}\%$ (*b*) 20%
(*c*) 50% (*d*) $56\frac{1}{4}\%$

18. If an article is sold at 200 percent profit, then the ratio of its cost price to its selling price will be **(S.S.C., 2010)**

(*a*) 1 : 2 (*b*) 2 : 1
(*c*) 1 : 3 (*d*) 3 : 1

19. If the ratio of cost price and selling price of an article be 10 : 11, the percentage of profit is **(S.S.C., 2010)**

(*a*) 8 (*b*) 10
(*c*) 11 (*d*) 15

20. A trader sells an article and loses $12\frac{1}{2}\%$. The ratio of cost price to the selling price is **(Hotel Management, 2007)**

(*a*) 7 : 8 (*b*) 9 : 8
(*c*) 8 : 7 (*d*) 8 : 9

21. A person buys an article for ₹ p and sells it for ₹ q thereby gaining r%. The selling price in terms of cost price may be written as **(R.R.B., 2005)**

(*a*) $\frac{pr}{100}$ (*b*) $\frac{r(100+p)}{100}$
(*c*) $\frac{p(100+r)}{100}$ (*d*) $\frac{p(100-r)}{100}$

22. The owner of a furniture shop charges his customer 28% more than the cost price. If a customer paid ₹ 23680 for a dining table set, then what was the original price of the dining set? **(Bank Recruitment, 2009)**
(*a*) ₹ 15700 (*b*) ₹ 16250
(*c*) ₹ 17500 (*d*) ₹ 18500
(*e*) None of these

23. A gold bracelet is sold for ₹ 14500 at a loss of 20%. What is the cost price of the gold bracelet? **(Bank Recruitment, 2007)**
(*a*) ₹ 15225 (*b*) ₹ 16800
(*c*) ₹ 17400 (*d*) ₹ 18125
(*e*) None of these

24. A shopkeeper expects a gain of $22\frac{1}{2}\%$ on his cost price. If in a week, his sale was of ₹ 392, what was his profit?
(*a*) ₹ 18.20 (*b*) ₹ 70
(*c*) ₹ 72 (*d*) ₹ 88.25

25. The sale price of an article including the sales tax is ₹ 616. The rate of sales tax is 10%. If the shopkeeper has made a profit of 12%, then the cost price of the article is
(*a*) ₹ 500 (*b*) ₹ 515
(*c*) ₹ 550 (*d*) ₹ 600

26. A shopkeeper buys 144 eggs at 90 paise each. On the way 20 eggs were broken. He sold the remaining eggs at ₹ 1.20 each. The percentage gain or loss is **(R.R.B., 2006)**
(*a*) 4.8% loss (*b*) 8.5% loss
(*c*) 12.9% gain (*d*) 14.8% gain

27. Abhishek purchased 140 shirts and 250 trousers @ ₹ 450 and @ ₹ 550 respectively. What should be the overall average selling price of shirts and trousers so that 40% profit is earned? (rounded off to next integer) **(Specialist Officers', 2009)**
(*a*) ₹ 700 (*b*) ₹ 710
(*c*) ₹ 720 (*d*) ₹ 725
(*e*) None of these

28. A person purchased 10 dozen pens at the rate of ₹ 4 per dozen. On checking, he found that 20 pens were not working. In order to earn 25% profit, he should sell the remaining pens each at **(P.C.S., 2008)**
(*a*) 40 paise (*b*) 44 paise
(*c*) 50 paise (*d*) 55 paise

29. Saransh purchased 120 reams of paper at ₹ 80 per ream. He spent ₹ 280 on transportation, paid octroi at the rate of 40 paise per ream and paid ₹ 72 to the coolie. If he wants to have a gain of 8%, what must be the selling price per ream?
(*a*) ₹ 86 (*b*) ₹ 87.48
(*c*) ₹ 89 (*d*) ₹ 90

30. A person bought 20 litres of milk at the rate of ₹ 8 per litre. He got it churned after spending ₹ 10 and 5 kg of cream and 20 litres of toned milk were obtained. If he sold the cream at ₹ 30 per kg and toned milk at ₹ 4 per litre, his profit in the transaction is
(*a*) 25% (*b*) 35.3%
(*c*) 37.5% (*d*) 42.5%

31. Jacob bought a scooter for a certain sum of money. He spent 10% of the cost on repairs and sold the scooter for a profit of ₹ 1100. How much did he spend on repairs if he made a profit of 20%?
(*a*) ₹ 400 (*b*) ₹ 440
(*c*) ₹ 500 (*d*) ₹ 550

32. A manufacturer undertakes to supply 2000 pieces of a particular component at ₹ 25 per piece. According to his estimates, even if 5% fail to pass the quality tests, then he will make a profit of 25%. However, as it turned out, 50% of the components were rejected. What is the loss to the manufacturer? **(M.A.T., 2003)**
(*a*) ₹ 12,000 (*b*) ₹ 13,000
(*c*) ₹ 14,000 (*d*) ₹ 15,000

33. Ronit and Vinit purchased a scooter for ₹ 25000 and sold the same for ₹ 26250. If at the time of purchase Ronit paid $1\frac{1}{2}$ times as much as Vinit, how much did Vinit receive out of profit? **(P.C.S., 2004)**
(*a*) ₹ 400 (*b*) ₹ 500
(*c*) ₹ 600 (*d*) ₹ 700

34. A trader buys a chair for ₹ 600 and sells it for ₹ 765 at a credit of 4 months. Reckoning money worth 6% p.a., his gain percent is
(*a*) 20% (*b*) $22\frac{1}{2}\%$
(*c*) 25% (*d*) $27\frac{1}{2}\%$

35. By selling a bicycle for ₹ 2850, a shopkeeper gains 14%. If the profit is reduced to 8% then the selling price will be **(S.S.C., 2010)**
(*a*) ₹ 2600 (*b*) ₹ 2700
(*c*) ₹ 2800 (*d*) ₹ 3000

36. When a plot is sold for ₹ 18,700, the owner loses 15%. At what price must the plot be sold in order to gain 15%? **(A.A.O. Exam, 2003)**
(*a*) ₹ 21,000 (*b*) ₹ 22,500
(*c*) ₹ 25,300 (*d*) ₹ 25,800

37. A fruitseller sells mangoes at the rate of ₹ 9 per kg and thereby loses 20%. At what price per kg, he should have sold them to make a profit of 5%?
(*a*) ₹ 11.81 (*b*) ₹ 12
(*c*) ₹ 12.25 (*d*) ₹ 12.31

38. Raju purchased an item for ₹ 8200 and sold it at a gain of 25%. From that amount he purchased another item and sold it at a loss of 20%. What is his overall gain/loss? **(Bank Recruitment, 2010)**

(*a*) Loss of ₹ 120 (*b*) Gain of ₹ 120
(*c*) Loss of ₹ 140 (*d*) Neither loss nor gain

39. A property dealer sells a house for ₹ 6,30,000 and in the bargain makes a profit of 5%. Had he sold it for ₹ 5,00,000, then what percentage of loss or gain he would have made?

(*a*) $2\frac{1}{4}\%$ gain (*b*) 10% loss
(*c*) $12\frac{1}{2}\%$ loss (*d*) $16\frac{2}{3}\%$ loss

40. A shopkeeper sells one transistor for ₹ 840 at a gain of 20% and another for ₹ 960 at a loss of 4%. His total gain or loss percent is

(*a*) $5\frac{15}{17}\%$ loss (*b*) $5\frac{15}{17}\%$ gain
(*c*) $6\frac{2}{3}\%$ gain (*d*) None of these

41. If selling price of an article is $\frac{4}{3}$ of its cost price, the profit in the transaction is **(M.B.A., 2006)**

(*a*) $16\frac{2}{3}\%$ (*b*) $20\frac{1}{2}\%$
(*c*) $25\frac{1}{2}\%$ (*d*) $33\frac{1}{3}\%$

42. The ratio between the sale price and the cost price of an article is 7 : 5. What is the ratio between the profit and the cost price of that article?

(*a*) 2 : 7 (*b*) 5 : 2
(*c*) 7 : 2 (*d*) Data inadequate
(*e*) None of these

43. If an article is sold for ₹ x, there is a loss of 15%. If the same article is sold for ₹ y, there is a profit of 15%. The ratio of $(y - x)$ to $(y + x)$ is **(Hotel Mgmt, 2010)**

(*a*) 3 : 20 (*b*) 20 : 3
(*c*) 17 : 23 (*d*) 20 : 23

44. By selling an article at some price, a man gains 10%. If the article is sold at twice of the price, the gain percent will be **(R.R.B., 2006)**

(*a*) 20% (*b*) 60%
(*c*) 100% (*d*) 120%

45. If selling price is doubled, the profit triples. Find the profit percent.

(*a*) $66\frac{2}{3}$ (*b*) 100
(*c*) $105\frac{1}{3}$ (*d*) 120

46. At what profit percent must an article be sold so that by selling at half that price, there may be a loss of 30%?

(*a*) 25% (*b*) 36%
(*c*) 40% (*d*) 42%

47. The C.P. of an article is 40% of the S.P. The percent that the S.P. is of C.P. is

(*a*) 250 (*b*) 240
(*c*) 60 (*d*) 40

48. By selling a pen for ₹ 15, a man loses one-sixteenth of what it costs him. The cost price of the pen is

(*a*) ₹ 16 (*b*) ₹ 18
(*c*) ₹ 20 (*d*) ₹ 21

49. By selling an article, Michael earned a profit equal to one-fourth of the price he bought it. If he sold it for ₹ 375, what was the cost price?

(*a*) ₹ 281.75 (*b*) ₹ 300
(*c*) ₹ 312.50 (*d*) ₹ 350

50. 10% loss on selling price is what percent loss on the cost price?

(*a*) $9\frac{1}{11}\%$ (*b*) $9\frac{2}{11}\%$
(*c*) 10% (*d*) 11%

51. If loss is $\frac{1}{3}$ of S.P., the loss percentage is

(*a*) $16\frac{2}{3}\%$ (*b*) 20%
(*c*) 25% (*d*) $33\frac{1}{3}\%$

52. In a certain store, the profit is 320% of the cost. If the cost increases by 25% but the selling price remains constant, approximately what percentage of the selling price is the profit?

(*a*) 30% (*b*) 70%
(*c*) 100% (*d*) 250%

53. Ashok buys a car at 20% discount of the price and sells it at 20% higher price. His percentage gain is **(R.R.B., 2006)**

(*a*) 20% (*b*) 40%
(*c*) 50% (*d*) $66\frac{2}{3}\%$

54. The profit earned after selling an article for ₹ 1754 is the same as loss incurred after selling the article for ₹ 1492. What is the cost price of the article? **(Bank P.O., 2009)**

(*a*) ₹ 1523 (*b*) ₹ 1589
(*c*) ₹ 1623 (*d*) ₹ 1689
(*e*) None of these

55. The profit earned by selling an article for ₹ 832 is equal to the loss incurred when the same article is sold for ₹ 448. What should be the sale price for making 50% profit?
(a) ₹ 920 (b) ₹ 960
(c) ₹ 1060 (d) ₹ 1200
(e) None of these

56. The profit earned by selling an article for ₹ 900 is double the loss incurred when the same article is sold for ₹ 450. At what price should the article be sold to make 25% profit?
(a) ₹ 600 (b) ₹ 750
(c) ₹ 800 (d) Data inadequate

57. The percentage profit earned by selling an article for ₹ 1920 is equal to the percentage loss incurred by selling the same article for ₹ 1280. At what price should the article be sold to make 25% profit?
(a) ₹ 2000 (b) ₹ 2200
(c) ₹ 2400 (d) Data inadequate
(e) None of these

58. Profit earned by selling an article for ₹ 1060 is 20% more than the loss incurred by selling the article for ₹ 950. At what price should the article be sold to earn 20% profit?
(a) ₹ 980 (b) ₹ 1080
(c) ₹ 1800 (d) None of these

59. When an article is sold for ₹ 116, the profit percent is thrice as much as when it is sold for ₹ 92. The cost price of the article is (S.S.C., 2005)
(a) ₹ 68 (b) ₹ 72
(c) ₹ 78 (d) ₹ 80

60. If the cost price of 15 books is equal to the selling price of 20 books, the loss percent is (S.S.C., 2010)
(a) 16 (b) 20
(c) 24 (d) 25

61. If the cost price of 10 articles is equal to the selling price of 7 articles, then the gain or loss percent is (C.P.O., 2005)
(a) 35% loss (b) $42\frac{6}{7}$% loss
(c) $42\frac{6}{7}$% gain (d) 51% gain

62. A wholeseller buys 20 pens at the marked price of 16 pens to a retailer. The retailer in turn sells them at the marked price. Determine the gain or loss percent to the retailer.
(a) 20% (b) 23%
(c) 25% (d) 30%

63. A farmer bought 749 sheep. He sold 700 of them for the price paid for the 749 sheep. The remaining 49 sheep were sold at the same price per head as the other 700. Based on the cost, the percent gain on the entire transaction is (M.B.A., 2010)
(a) 6.5 (b) 6.75
(c) 7.0 (d) 7.5

64. If by selling 110 mangoes, the C.P. of 120 mangoes is realised, the gain percent is
(a) $9\frac{1}{11}$% (b) $9\frac{1}{9}$%
(c) $10\frac{10}{11}$% (d) $11\frac{1}{9}$%

65. The cost price of 20 articles is the same as the selling price of x articles. If the profit is 25%, then the value of x is (M.A.T., 2004)
(a) 15 (b) 16
(c) 18 (d) 25

66. On an order of 5 dozen boxes of a consumer product, a retailer receives an extra dozen free. This is equivalent to allowing him a discount of
(a) 15% (b) $16\frac{1}{6}$%
(c) $16\frac{2}{3}$% (d) 20%

67. A man sold 18 cots for ₹ 16,800, gaining thereby the cost price of 3 cots. The cost price of a cot is
(a) ₹ 650 (b) ₹ 700
(c) ₹ 750 (d) ₹ 800

68. Mohan bought 20 dining tables for ₹ 12000 and sold them at a profit equal to the selling price of 4 dining tables. The selling price of 1 dining table is (R.R.B., 2006)
(a) ₹ 700 (b) ₹ 725
(c) ₹ 750 (d) ₹ 775

69. By selling 100 pencils, a shopkeeper gains the selling price of 20 pencils. His gain percent is (S.S.C., 2007)
(a) 12 (b) 15
(c) 20 (d) 25

70. On selling 17 balls at ₹ 720, there is a loss equal to the cost price of 5 balls. The cost price of a ball is (S.S.C., 2004)
(a) ₹ 45 (b) ₹ 50
(c) ₹ 55 (d) ₹ 60

71. A vendor loses the selling price of 4 oranges on selling 36 oranges. His loss percent is
(a) 10% (b) 11%
(c) $12\frac{1}{2}$% (d) None of these

72. A man buys 2 dozen bananas at ₹ 16 per dozen. After selling 18 bananas at the rate of ₹ 12 per dozen, the shopkeeper reduced the rate to ₹ 4 per dozen. The percent loss is
(a) 25.2% (b) 32.4%
(c) 36.5% (d) 37.5%

73. A man bought apples at the rate of 8 for ₹ 34 and sold them at the rate of 12 for ₹ 57. How many apples should be sold to earn a net profit of ₹ 45?
(*a*) 90 (*b*) 100
(*c*) 135 (*d*) 150

74. Vinod makes a profit of ₹ 110 if he sells a certain number of pencils he has at the price of ₹ 2.50 per pencil and incurs a loss of ₹ 55 if he sells the same number of pencils for ₹ 1.75 per pencil. How many pencils does Vinod have? **(Bank P.O., 2010)**
(*a*) 200 (*b*) 220
(*c*) 240 (*d*) Cannot be determined
(*e*) None of these

75. Ram bought 1600 eggs at ₹ 3.75 a dozen. He sold 900 of them at 2 for ₹ 1 and the remaining at 5 for ₹ 2. His percent gain or loss is **(R.R.B., 2006)**
(*a*) 40% (*b*) 42%
(*c*) 45% (*d*) 46%

76. A shopkeeper purchases 11 knives in ₹ 10 and sells them at the rate of 10 knives for ₹ 11. He earns a profit of **(R.R.B., 2008)**
(*a*) 11% (*b*) 15%
(*c*) 20% (*d*) 21%

77. Oranges are bought at 5 for ₹ 10 and sold at 6 for ₹ 15. The profit or loss as percentage is **(R.R.B., 2009)**
(*a*) 25% (*b*) 35%
(*c*) 40% (*d*) 50%

78. A fruit seller buys lemons at 2 for a rupee and sells them at 5 for three rupees. His profit percent is **(S.S.C., 2007)**
(*a*) 10 (*b*) 15
(*c*) 20 (*d*) 25

79. A man bought pencils at the rate of 6 for ₹ 4 and sold them at the rate of 4 for ₹ 6. His gain in the transaction is **(S.S.C., 2005)**
(*a*) 75% (*b*) 80%
(*c*) 100% (*d*) 125%

80. A man purchased a box full of pencils at the rate of 7 for ₹ 9 and sold all of them at the rate of 8 for ₹ 11. In this transaction, he gained ₹ 10. How many pencils did the box contain?
(*a*) 100 (*b*) 112
(*c*) 114 (*d*) 115

81. A man bought a number of clips at 3 for a rupee and an equal number at 2 for a rupee. At what price per dozen should he sell them to make a profit of 20%?
(*a*) ₹ 4 (*b*) ₹ 5
(*c*) ₹ 6 (*d*) ₹ 7

82. A man buys eggs at 2 for ₹ 1 and an equal number at 3 for ₹ 2 and sells the whole at 5 for ₹ 3. His gain or loss percent is
(*a*) $2\frac{2}{7}$% loss (*b*) $3\frac{6}{7}$% gain
(*c*) $3\frac{2}{7}$% loss (*d*) $2\frac{6}{7}$% gain

83. A person buys certain number of marbles at 20 per rupee and an equal number at 30 per rupee. He mixes them and sells them at 25 per rupee. His gain or loss in the transaction is **(S.S.C., 2005)**
(*a*) 2% loss (*b*) 2% gain
(*c*) 4% loss (*d*) 4% gain

84. A man bought some oranges at ₹ 10 per dozen and bought the same number of oranges at ₹ 8 per dozen. He sold these oranges at ₹ 11 per dozen and gained ₹ 120. The total number of oranges bought by him was
(*a*) 30 dozens (*b*) 40 dozens
(*c*) 50 dozens (*d*) 60 dozens

85. A person bought some articles at the rate of 5 per rupee and the same number at the rate of 4 per rupee. He mixed both the types and sold at the rate of 9 for 2 rupees. In this business he suffered a loss of ₹ 3. The total number of articles bought by him was **(C.P.O., 2006)**
(*a*) 540 (*b*) 545
(*c*) 1080 (*d*) 1090

86. A grocer purchases three qualities of lemons at different rates. The first quality was purchased at 2 for ₹ 1, the second at 3 for ₹ 2 and the third at 4 for ₹ 3. He sold all the lemons at 5 for ₹ 4. If the ratio of the number of lemons of the three qualities is 1 : 2 : 3, then what is the approximate gain or loss percentage incurred by the grocer?
(*a*) 2.65% loss (*b*) 17.56% loss
(*c*) 17.56% gain (*d*) 18.65% gain
(*e*) None of these

87. A vendor bought toffees at 6 for a rupee. How many for a rupee must he sell to gain 20%?
(*a*) 3 (*b*) 4
(*c*) 5 (*d*) 6

88. Reynolds Superink pens are bought at the rate of 8 for ₹ 100. To make a profit of 60 per cent, these must be sold at
(*a*) 5 for ₹ 100 (*b*) 6 for ₹ 100
(*c*) 9 for ₹ 200 (*d*) None of these

89. By selling 12 toffees for a rupee, a man loses 20%. How many for a rupee should he sell to get a gain of 20%?
(*a*) 5 (*b*) 8
(*c*) 10 (*d*) 15

90. By selling 45 lemons for ₹ 40, a man loses 20%. How many should he sell for ₹ 24 to gain 20% in the transaction?

(a) 16 (b) 18
(c) 20 (d) 22

91. By selling 90 ball pens for ₹ 160, a person loses 20%. How many ball pens should be sold for ₹ 96 so as to have a profit of 20%? **(B.B.A., 2005)**

(a) 24 (b) 36
(c) 39 (d) 42

Directions (*Questions 92 to 96*): *Read the following information carefully and answer the questions that follow :*

A train journey from P to D by an X-express has 4 classes of fares

3 tier	₹ 300	72 berths per bogie	Train has 8 bogies
AC-3 tier	₹ 898	64 berths per bogie	Train has 2 bogies
AC-2 tier	₹ 1388	45 berths per bogie	Train has 2 bogies
AC-first class	₹ 2691	26 berths per bogie	Train has 1 bogie

The distance between P and D is 1100 km. Assume that the train does not stop at any station unless otherwise indicated.

The running cost per kilometre:

AC - bogie – ₹ 25, non-AC-bogie – ₹ 10

92. What is the approximate profit for the railways if the X-expressway runs at full occupancy on a particular day?

(a) ₹ 2,50,000 (b) ₹ 2,75,000
(c) ₹ 3,00,000 (d) Cannot be determined

93. Assuming full occupancy, a bogie of which class exhibits the highest profit margin?

(a) 3 tier (b) AC-3 tier
(c) AC-2 tier (d) AC-first class

94. The highest revenue for a journey from P to D will always be generated by

(a) AC- 2 tier (b) 3 tier
(c) AC-3 tier (d) Cannot be determined

95. Assuming full occupancy in all the classes, for a journey between P and D, the profit margin (as a percentage of running costs) of the class showing the lowest profit is approximately

(a) 109% (b) 116%
(c) 127% (d) None of these

96. For Q. 92, the percentage of the total profit that comes out of AC bogie is approximately

(a) 50% (b) 60%
(c) 70% (d) 80%

97. A shopkeeper bought three varieties A, B and C of rice in different amounts at the rates of ₹ 34.50, ₹ 28.60 and ₹ 32.40 per kg respectively. In which of the following transactions will he gain maximum? **(S.B.I.P.O., 2005)**

(a) He bought 25 kg of rice of variety C and sold at ₹ 42 per kg and he bought 30 kg of variety A and sold at ₹ 38 per kg.

(b) He bought 40 kg of rice of variety B and sold at ₹ 37 per kg and he bought 20 kg of variety A and sold at ₹ 40 per kg.

(c) He bought 20 kg of rice of varieties A and C each and sold at ₹ 38 and ₹ 36 per kg respectively.

(d) He bought 30 kg of rice of variety A and sold at ₹ 37 per kg and he bought 20 kg of variety B and sold at ₹ 33 per kg.

(e) He bought 20 kg of rice of variety B and sold at ₹ 40 per kg and he bought 40 kg of variety C and sold at ₹ 38 per kg.

98. Nikita bought 30 kg of wheat at the rate of ₹ 9.50 per kg and 40 kg of wheat at the rate of ₹ 8.50 per kg and mixed them. She sold the mixture at the rate of ₹ 8.90 per kg. Her total profit or loss in the transaction was **(S.S.C., 2005)**

(a) ₹ 2 loss (b) ₹ 2 profit
(c) ₹ 7 loss (d) ₹ 7 profit

99. Manish purchased 25 kg of rice @ ₹ 32 per kg and 15 kg of rice @ ₹ 36 per kg. He mixed the two varieties of rice and sold it @ ₹ 40.20 per kg. What is the percent profit earned? **(Bank P.O., 2009)**

(a) 20 (b) 25
(c) 30 (d) 40
(e) None of these

100. One variety of sugar is sold for ₹ 3.20 per kg at a loss of 20% and another variety is sold for ₹ 6 per kg at a gain of 20%. If equal quantities of the two are mixed together and the mixture is sold at ₹ 5.40 per kg, what is the loss or gain percentage? **(R.R.B., 2005)**

(a) Gain 20% (b) Loss 20%
(c) No profit, no loss (d) None of these

101. Arun purchased 30 kg of wheat at the rate of ₹ 11.50 per kg and 20 kg of wheat at the rate of ₹ 14.25 per kg. He mixed the two and sold the mixture. Approximately what price per kg should he sell the mixture to make 30% profit? **(Bank P.O., 2011)**

(a) ₹ 14.80 (b) ₹ 15.40
(c) ₹ 15.60 (d) ₹ 16.30
(e) ₹ 18.20

102. Padam purchased 30 kg of rice at the rate of ₹ 17.50 per kg and another 30 kg rice at a certain rate. He mixed the two and sold the entire quantity at the rate of ₹ 18.60 per kg and made 20% overall profit. At what price per kg did he purchase the lot of another 30 kg rice? (N.M.A.T., 2006)

(a) ₹ 12.50 (b) ₹ 13.50
(c) ₹ 14.50 (d) ₹ 15.50
(e) None of these

103. A person blends two varieties of tea–one costing ₹ 160 per kg and the other costing ₹ 200 per kg in the ratio 5 : 4. He sells the blended variety at ₹ 192 per kg. His profit percent is (C.P.O., 2007)

(a) 8 (b) 9
(c) 10 (d) 12

104. A trader mixes three varieties of groundnuts costing ₹ 50, ₹ 20 and ₹ 30 per kg in the ratio 2 : 4 : 3 in terms of weight, and sells the mixture at ₹ 33 per kg. What percentage of profit does he make?

(a) 8% (b) 9%
(c) 10% (d) None of these

105. A shopkeeper bought 30 kg of wheat at the rate of ₹ 45 per kg. He sold forty percent of the total quantity at the rate of ₹ 50 per kg. Approximately at what price per kg should he sell the remaining quantity to make 25 percent overall profit? (Bank P.O., 2010)

(a) ₹ 50 (b) ₹ 52
(c) ₹ 54 (d) ₹ 56
(e) ₹ 60

106. A dealer buys dry fruit at the rate of ₹ 100, ₹ 80 and ₹ 60 per kg. He bought them in the ratio 12 : 15 : 20 by weight. He in total gets 20% profit by selling the first two and at last he finds he has no gain no loss in selling the whole quantity which he had. What was the percentage loss he suffered for the third quantity? (M.A.T., 2007)

(a) 20% (b) 30%
(c) 40% (d) 50%

107. A dairyman pays ₹ 6.40 per litre of milk. He adds water and sells the mixture at ₹ 8 per litre, thereby making 37.5% profit. The proportion of water to milk received by the customers is

(a) 1 : 10 (b) 1 : 12
(c) 1 : 15 (d) 1 : 20

108. Five litres of water is added to a certain quantity of pure milk costing ₹ 3 per litre. If by selling the mixture at the same price as before, a profit of 20% is made, then what is the amount of pure milk in the mixture? (M.A.T., 2006)

(a) 20 litres (b) 25 litres
(c) 30 litres (d) 35 litres

109. By mixing two brands of tea and selling the mixture at the rate of ₹ 177 per kg, a shopkeeper makes a profit of 18%. If to every 2 kg of one brand costing ₹ 200 per kg, 3 kg of the other brand is added, then how much per kg does the other brand cost?

(a) ₹ 110 (b) ₹ 120
(c) ₹ 140 (d) None of these

110. The manufacturer of a certain item can sell all he can produce at the selling price of ₹ 60 each. It costs him ₹ 40 in materials and labour to produce each item and he has overhead expenses of ₹ 3000 per week in order to operate the plant. The number of units he should produce and sell in order to make a profit of at least ₹ 1000 per week, is

(a) 200 (b) 250
(c) 300 (d) 400

111. A milkman cheats his customer in two ways. He mixes 10% water in pure milk and increases the price of milk by 10%. He purchases 20 kg pure milk at a rate of ₹ 15 per kg. His total profit by selling it is (Hotel Management, 2007)

(a) ₹ 40 (b) ₹ 63
(c) ₹ 80 (d) ₹ 100

112. A dishonest dealer uses a scale of 90 cm instead of a metre scale and claims to sell at cost price. His profit is

(a) 9% (b) 10%
(c) 12% (d) None of these

113. A dealer professes to sell his goods at cost price but he uses a false weight of 950 grams for a kilogram. The gain percent of the dealer is (R.R.B., 2008)

(a) $4\frac{5}{19}\%$ (b) 5%
(c) $5\frac{5}{19}\%$ (d) $19\frac{1}{5}\%$

114. A fruit seller professes to sell his fruits at cost price, but still gains 25% on his outlay. What weight does he substitute for a kilogram? (P.C.S., 2009)

(a) 800 gm (b) 850 gm
(c) 890 gm (d) 900 gm

115. A dishonest dealer professes to sell his goods at cost price. But he uses a false weight and thus gains $6\frac{18}{47}\%$. For a kg, he uses a weight of

(a) 940 gms (b) 947 gms
(c) 953 gms (d) 960 gms

116. A shopkeeper cheats to the extent of 10% while buying as well as selling, by using false weights. His total gain is (S.S.C., 2006)

(a) 10% (b) 11%
(c) 20% (d) 21%
(e) $22\frac{2}{9}\%$

117. Left pan of a faulty balance weighs 100 grams more than its right pan. A shopkeeper keeps the weight measure in the left pan while buying goods but keeps it in the right pan while selling his goods. He uses only 1 kg weight measure. If he sells his goods at the listed cost price, what is his gain? **(Civil Services, 2005; Hotel Mgmt, 2007)**

(*a*) $\frac{100}{11}\%$ (*b*) $\frac{200}{11}\%$

(*c*) $\frac{100}{9}\%$ (*d*) $\frac{200}{9}\%$

118. A grocer sells rice at a profit of 10% and uses weights which are 20% less than the market weight. The total gain earned by him will be

(*a*) 30% (*b*) 35%

(*c*) 37.5% (*d*) None of these

119. A dishonest dealer sells the goods at 20% loss on cost price but uses 15% less weight. What is his percentage profit or loss?

(*a*) $5\frac{11}{17}\%$ loss (*b*) $5\frac{15}{17}\%$ loss

(*c*) $5\frac{15}{17}\%$ gain (*d*) $5\frac{11}{17}\%$ gain

120. A merchant professes to lose 4% on a certain tea but he uses a weight equal to 840g instead of 1 kg. Find his real loss or gain percent.

(*a*) $14\frac{2}{7}\%$ loss (*b*) $14\frac{2}{7}\%$ gain

(*c*) $16\frac{2}{7}\%$ loss (*d*) $16\frac{2}{7}\%$ gain

121. A shopkeeper advertises for selling cloth at 4% loss. However, by using a false metre scale he actually gains 20%. What is the actual length of the scale? **(R.R.B., 2006)**

(*a*) 70 cm (*b*) 75 cm

(*c*) 80 cm (*d*) 90 cm

122. Instead of a metre scale, a cloth merchant uses a 120 cm scale while buying but uses an 80 cm scale while selling the same cloth. If he offers a discount of 20% on cash payment what is his overall profit percentage?

(*a*) 15% (*b*) 20%

(*c*) 25% (*d*) 40%

123. A trader professes to sell his goods at a nominal gain percentage but actually earns $37\frac{1}{2}\%$ profit by using false weight. If for a kg he uses a weight of 800 gm, what is the nominal gain percentage at which he claims to be selling his goods?

(*a*) 8% (*b*) 10%

(*c*) 15% (*d*) 20%

124. A dry fruit merchant professes to sell 2 kg almond packs at a loss of 20%. However, he uses two false weights each of which is marked 1 kg and thus gains $6\frac{2}{3}\%$ on selling every 2 kg of almonds. If it is given that one of the weights weighs only 850 gm, then how much does the other weight weigh?

(*a*) 650 gm (*b*) 700 gm

(*c*) 725 gm (*d*) 750 gm

125. A stockist wants to make some profit by selling sugar. He contemplates about various methods. Which of the following would maximize his profit?

(*a*) Sell sugar at 10% profit

(*b*) Use 900 g of weight instead of 1 kg

(*c*) Mix 10% impurities in sugar and sell sugar at cost price

(*d*) Increase the price by 5% and reduce the weight by 5%

126. A fair price shopkeeper takes 10% profit on his goods. He lost 20% goods during theft. His loss percent is

(*a*) 8 (*b*) 10

(*c*) 11 (*d*) 12

127. Prateek sold a music system to Kartik at 20% gain and Kartik sold it to Swastik at 40% gain. If Swastik paid ₹ 10500 for the music system, what amount did Prateek pay for the same? **(Bank P.O., 2009)**

(*a*) ₹ 6250 (*b*) ₹ 7500

(*c*) ₹ 8240 (*d*) Cannot be determined

(*e*) None of these

128. A manufacturer sells an article to a wholesale dealer at a profit of 20% and the wholesale dealer sells it to a retail merchant at a loss of 5%. Find the resultant loss or profit. **(R.R.B., 2006)**

(*a*) 12% loss (*b*) 12% gain

(*c*) 14% loss (*d*) 14% gain

129. A bought a radio set and spent ₹ 110 on its repairs. He then sold it to B at 20% profit, B sold it to C at a loss of 10% and C sold it for ₹ 1188 at a profit of 10%. What is the amount for which A bought the radio set?

(*a*) ₹ 850 (*b*) ₹ 890

(*c*) ₹ 930 (*d*) ₹ 950

130. A car worth ₹ 1,50,000 was sold by X to Y at 5% profit. Y sold the car back to X at 2% loss. In the entire transaction **(C.P.O., 2007)**

(*a*) X gained ₹ 4350 (*b*) X lost ₹ 4350

(*c*) X gained ₹ 3150 (*d*) X lost ₹ 3150

131. A manufacturer sold a machine to a wholesale dealer at a profit of 10%. The wholesale dealer sold it to a retailer at a profit of 20%. While transporting some defect occurred in the machine and hence the retailer sold it at a loss of 5%. The customer paid ₹ 627. Find the cost of the machine for the manufacturer. **(M.A.T., 2010)**

(*a*) ₹ 500 (*b*) ₹ 534
(*c*) ₹ 600 (*d*) ₹ 672

132. Goods pass successively through the hands of three traders and each of them sells his goods at a profit of 25% of his cost price. If the last trader sold the goods for ₹ 250, then how much did the first trader pay for them? **(S.S.C., 2005)**

(*a*) ₹ 128 (*b*) ₹ 150
(*c*) ₹ 192 (*d*) ₹ 200

133. An article passing through two hands is sold at a profit of 38% at the original cost price. If the first dealer makes a profit of 20%, then the profit percent made by the second is **(C.P.O., 2006)**

(*a*) 5 (*b*) 10
(*c*) 12 (*d*) 15

134. A merchant buys an article for ₹ 27 and sells it at a profit of 10 percent of the selling price. The selling price of the article is **(C.P.O., 2005)**

(*a*) ₹ 29.70 (*b*) ₹ 30
(*c*) ₹ 32 (*d*) ₹ 37

135. By selling an article, a man makes a profit of 25% of its selling price. His profit percent is **(S.S.C., 2010)**

(*a*) $16\frac{2}{3}$ (*b*) 20
(*c*) 25 (*d*) $33\frac{1}{3}$

136. If there is a profit of 20% on the cost price of an article, the percentage of profit calculated on its selling price will be **(S.S.C., 2010)**

(*a*) $8\frac{1}{3}$ (*b*) $16\frac{2}{3}$
(*c*) 20 (*d*) 24

137. Vineet calculates his profit percentage on the selling price whereas Roshan calculates his profit on the cost price. They find that the difference of their profits is ₹ 275. If the selling price of both of them are the same and Vineet gets 25% profit whereas Roshan gets 15% profit, find their selling price. **(N.M.A.T., 2005)**

(*a*) ₹ 2100 (*b*) ₹ 2250
(*c*) ₹ 2300 (*d*) ₹ 2350

138. A clock was sold for ₹ 144. If the percentage of profit was numerically equal to the cost price, the cost of the clock was **(S.S.C., 2005; R.R.B., 2009; P.C.S., 2009)**

(*a*) ₹ 72 (*b*) ₹ 80
(*c*) ₹ 90 (*d*) ₹ 100

139. By selling an article at $\frac{2}{3}$ of the marked price, there is a loss of 10%. The profit percent, when the article is sold at the marked price, is **(C.P.O., 2006)**

(*a*) 20% (*b*) 30%
(*c*) 35% (*d*) 40%

140. Raghavan purchase a scooter at $\frac{13}{15}$ of its selling price and sold it at 12% more than its selling price. His gain is **(S.S.C., 2005)**

(*a*) 20% (*b*) $29\frac{3}{13}$%
(*c*) 30% (*d*) $38\frac{1}{13}$%

141. A man buys an article for 10% less than its value and sells it for 10% more than its value. His gain or loss percent is

(*a*) no profit, no loss (*b*) 20% profit
(*c*) less than 20% profit (*d*) more than 20% profit

142. Samant bought a microwave oven and paid 10% less than the original price. He sold it with 30% profit on the price he had paid. What percentage of profit did Samant earn on the original price?

(*a*) 17% (*b*) 20%
(*c*) 27% (*d*) 32%
(*e*) None of these

143. If 5% more is gained by selling an article for ₹ 350 than by selling it for ₹ 340, the cost of the article is

(*a*) ₹ 50 (*b*) ₹ 160
(*c*) ₹ 200 (*d*) ₹ 225

144. If a man reduces the selling price of a fan from ₹ 400 to ₹ 380, his loss increases by 2%. The cost price of the fan is

(*a*) ₹ 480 (*b*) ₹ 500
(*c*) ₹ 600 (*d*) None of these

145. An increase of ₹ 3 in the selling price of an article turns a loss of $7\frac{1}{2}$% into a gain of $7\frac{1}{2}$%. The cost price (in ₹) of the article is **(C.P.O., 2007)**

(*a*) 10 (*b*) 15
(*c*) 20 (*d*) 25

146. A shopkeeper sells an article at $12\frac{1}{2}$% loss. If he sells it for ₹ 92.50 more then he gains 6%. What is the cost price of the article? **(M.A.T., 2008)**

(*a*) ₹ 500 (*b*) ₹ 510
(*c*) ₹ 575 (*d*) ₹ 600

147. A dealer sold an article at a loss of $2\frac{1}{2}$%. Had he sold it for ₹ 100 more, he would have gained $7\frac{1}{2}$%. To gain $12\frac{1}{2}$%, he should sell it for

(a) ₹ 850 (b) ₹ 925
(c) ₹ 1080 (d) ₹ 1125

148. A man sells a book at a profit of 20%. If he had bought it at 20% less and sold it for ₹ 18 less, he would have gained 25%. The cost price of the book is (M.A.T., 2009)

(a) ₹ 60 (b) ₹ 70
(c) ₹ 80 (d) ₹ 90

149. A bookseller sells a book at a profit of 10%. If he had bought it at 4% less and sold it for ₹ 6 more, he would have gained $18\frac{3}{4}$%. The cost price of the book is (S.S.C., 2007)

(a) ₹ 130 (b) ₹ 140
(c) ₹ 150 (d) ₹ 160

150. A watch is sold at a profit of 20%. If both the cost price and the selling price of the watch are decreased by ₹ 100, the profit would be 5% more. Original cost price of the watch is (A.A.O. Exam, 2010)

(a) ₹ 450 (b) ₹ 500
(c) ₹ 550 (d) ₹ 600

151. An article is sold at a profit of 20%. If the cost price is increased by 10% and the sale price by ₹ 26, then the percentage of profit reduces by 5%. Determine the cost price. (M.C.A., 2005)

(a) ₹ 300 (b) ₹ 400
(c) ₹ 500 (d) ₹ 600

152. The difference between the cost price and sale price of an article is ₹ 240. If the profit is 20%, the selling price is

(a) ₹ 1240 (b) ₹ 1400
(c) ₹ 1600 (d) None of these

153. The cash difference between the selling prices of an article at a profit of 4% and 6% is ₹ 3. The ratio of the two selling prices is (C.B.I., 2003)

(a) 51 : 52 (b) 52 : 53
(c) 51 : 53 (d) 52 : 55

154. Shailja earns 15 percent on an investment but loses 10 percent on another investment. If the ratio of the two investments is 3 : 5, then the combined loss percent is (S.S.C., 2006)

(a) $\frac{5}{8}$ (b) $\frac{8}{5}$
(c) $\frac{4}{5}$ (d) $\frac{5}{4}$

155. A shopkeeper bought three watches w_1, w_2 and w_3 from a dealer and sold them to three different customers. The ratio of the selling prices of the watches w_1, w_2 and w_3 was 2 : 3 : 4. The shopkeeper gains 30% and 20% on the watches w_1 and w_2 respectively but loses 40% on the watch w_3. What was the shopkeeper's approximate percent gain or loss in the whole transaction?

(a) 16% profit (b) 16% loss
(c) 15% loss (d) Data inadequate

156. A man sells two articles for ₹ 240 each. On one he gains 20% and on the other he loses 20%. What is the gain or loss percent in the entire transaction? (S.S.C., 2005)

(a) 1% gain (b) 2% loss
(c) 4% gain (d) 4% loss

157. A shopkeeper sells two watches for ₹ 308 each. On one he gets 12% profit and on the other 12% loss. His profit or loss in the entire transaction was (R.R.B., 2006; S.S.C., 2007)

(a) Neither profit, nor loss (b) $1\frac{11}{25}$% loss
(c) $1\frac{11}{25}$% profit (d) $3\frac{2}{25}$% loss

158. A man sells two flats at the rate of ₹ 1.995 lakhs each. On one he gains 5% and on the other, he loses 5%. His gain or loss percent in the whole transaction is

(a) 0.25% loss (b) 0.25% gain
(c) 2.5% loss (d) 25% loss

159. A man sells two commodities for ₹ 4000 each, neither losing nor gaining in the deal. If he sold one commodity at a gain of 25%, the other commodity is sold at a loss of:

(a) $16\frac{2}{3}$% (b) $18\frac{2}{9}$%
(c) 25% (d) None of these

160. A house and a shop were sold for ₹ 1 lakh each. In this transaction, the house sale resulted into 20% loss whereas the shop sale resulted into 20% profit. The entire transaction resulted in

(a) no loss, no gain (b) loss of ₹ $\frac{1}{12}$ lakh
(c) loss of ₹ $\frac{1}{18}$ lakh (d) gain of ₹ $\frac{1}{24}$ lakh

161. A man sells two articles at ₹ 99 each. He gains 10% on one and loses 10% on the other. Then on overall basis he (P.C.S., 2006)

(a) gains ₹ 2 (b) neither gains nor loses
(c) loses ₹ 2 (d) loses ₹ 1

162. A man sold two steel chairs for ₹ 500 each. On one, he gains 20% and on the other, he loses 12%. How much does he gain or lose in the whole transaction? **(M.A.T., 2006)**

(*a*) 1.5% gain (*b*) 1.5% loss
(*c*) 2% gain (*d*) 2% loss

163. Ranjan purchased 120 tables at a price of ₹ 110 per table. He sold 30 tables at a profit of ₹ 12 per table and 75 tables at a profit of ₹ 14 per table. The remaining tables were sold at a loss of ₹ 7 per table. What is the average profit per table?

(*a*) ₹ 10.04 (*b*) ₹ 10.875
(*c*) ₹ 12.80 (*d*) ₹ 12.875

164. Hemant sold 10 sarees for a total profit of ₹ 460 and 12 sarees for a total profit of ₹ 144. At what profit per saree should he sell the remaining 20 sarees so that he gets an average profit of ₹ 18 per saree?

(*a*) ₹ 7.40 (*b*) ₹ 7.60
(*c*) ₹ 7.80 (*d*) ₹ 8

165. Sanket purchased 20 dozen notebooks at ₹ 48 per dozen. He sold 8 dozen at 10% profit and the remaining 12 dozen with 20% profit. What is his profit percentage in the transaction?

(*a*) 7.68 (*b*) 15
(*c*) 16 (*d*) 19.2

166. In a shop, 80% of the articles are sold at a profit of 10% and the remaining at a loss of 40%. What is the overall profit/loss? **(Campus Recruitment, 2009)**

(*a*) 10% profit (*b*) 10% loss
(*c*) 5% loss (*d*) No profit no loss

167. If a person makes a profit of 10% on one-fourth of the quantity sold and a loss of 20% on the rest, then what is the average percent profit or loss? **(J.M.E.T., 2004)**

(*a*) 11.25% loss (*b*) 11.75% profit
(*c*) 12.5% profit (*d*) 12.5% loss

168. I purchased 120 exercise books at the rate of ₹ 3 each and sold $\frac{1}{3}$ of them at the rate of ₹ 4 each, $\frac{1}{2}$ of them at the rate of ₹ 5 each and the rest at the cost price. My profit percent is **(C.P.O., 2006)**

(*a*) 44% (*b*) $44\frac{2}{3}\%$
(*c*) $44\frac{4}{9}\%$ (*d*) 45%

169. A departmental store receives a shipment of 1000 pens, for which it pays ₹ 9000. The store sells the pens at a price 80 percent above cost for one month, after which it reduces the price of the pens to 20 percent above cost. The store sells 75 percent of the pens during the first month and 50 percent of the remaining pens afterwards. How much gross income did the sales of the pens generate?

(*a*) ₹ 10000 (*b*) ₹ 10800
(*c*) ₹ 12150 (*d*) ₹ 13500

170. If a shopkeeper sells $\frac{1}{3}$ of his goods at a profit of 14%, $\frac{3}{5}$ of the goods at a profit of 17.5% and the remaining at a profit of 20%, then his profit on the whole is equal to

(*a*) 15.5% (*b*) 16%
(*c*) 16.5% (*d*) 17%

171. A cloth merchant sold half of his cloth at 20% profit, half of the remaining at 20% loss and the rest was sold at the cost price. In the total transaction, his gain or loss will be

(*a*) Neither loss nor gain (*b*) 5% loss
(*c*) 5% gain (*d*) 10% gain

172. A person purchases 90 clocks and sells 40 clocks at a gain of 10% and 50 clocks at a gain of 20%. If he sold all of them at a uniform profit of 15%, then he would have got ₹ 40 less. The cost price of each clock is

(*a*) ₹ 50 (*b*) ₹ 60
(*c*) ₹ 80 (*d*) ₹ 90

173. A person earns 15% on an investment but loses 10% on another investment. If the ratio of the two investments be 3 : 5, what is the gain or loss on the two investments taken together?

(*a*) $6\frac{1}{4}\%$ loss (*b*) $13\frac{1}{8}\%$ gain
(*c*) $13\frac{1}{8}\%$ loss (*d*) None of these

174. A man bought goods worth ₹ 6000 and sold half of them at a gain of 10%. At what gain percent must he sell the remainder so as to get a gain of 25% on the whole?

(*a*) 25% (*b*) 30%
(*c*) 35% (*d*) 40%

175. A merchant has 1000 kg of sugar, part of which he sells at 8% profit and the rest at 18% profit. He gains 14% on the whole. The quantity (in kg) sold at 18% profit is **(L.I.C.A.A.O., 2007)**

(*a*) 400 (*b*) 560
(*c*) 600 (*d*) 640

176. A fruitseller has 24 kg of apples. He sells a part of these at a gain of 20% and the balance at a loss of 5%. If on the whole he earns a profit of 10%, the amount of apples sold at a loss is

(*a*) 4.6 kg (*b*) 6 kg
(*c*) 9.6 kg (*d*) 11.4 kg

177. A man sells two horses for ₹ 1475. The cost price of the first is equal to the selling price of the second. If the first is sold at 20% loss and the second at 25% gain, what is his total gain or loss (in rupees)?
(*a*) ₹ 60 loss (*b*) ₹ 80 gain
(*c*) ₹ 60 gain (*d*) Neither gain nor loss

178. Two-thirds of a consignment was sold at a profit of 6% and the rest at a loss of 3%. If however there was an overall profit of ₹ 540, the value of consignment was **(M.B.A., 2007)**
(*a*) ₹ 15000 (*b*) ₹ 16000
(*c*) ₹ 18000 (*d*) None of these

179. A trader purchases a watch and a wall clock for ₹ 390. He sells them making a profit of 10% on the watch and 15% on the wall clock. He earns a profit of ₹ 51.50. The difference between the original prices of the wall clock and the watch is equal to **(N.M.A.T., 2005)**
(*a*) ₹ 80 (*b*) ₹ 100
(*c*) ₹ 110 (*d*) ₹ 120

180. Albert buys 4 horses and 9 cows for ₹ 13,400. If he sells the horses at 10% profit and the cows at 20% profit, then he earns a total profit of ₹ 1880. The cost of a horse is
(*a*) ₹ 1000 (*b*) ₹ 2000
(*c*) ₹ 2500 (*d*) ₹ 3000

181. A man purchases two clocks A and B at a total cost of ₹ 650. He sells A with 20% profit and B at a loss of 25% and gets the same selling price for both the clocks. What are the purchasing prices of A and B respectively?
(*a*) ₹ 225, ₹ 425 (*b*) ₹ 250, ₹ 400
(*c*) ₹ 275, ₹ 375 (*d*) ₹ 300, ₹ 350

182. A farmer sold a cow and an ox for ₹ 800 and got a profit of 20% on the cow and 25% on the ox. If he sells the cow and the ox for ₹ 820 he gets a profit of 25% on the cow and 20% on the ox. The individual cost price of the cow and the ox is **(N.M.A.T., 2005)**
(*a*) ₹ 530.60, ₹ 130.60 (approx)
(*b*) ₹ 515.60, ₹ 115.60 (approx)
(*c*) ₹ 531.50, ₹ 135.50 (approx)
(*d*) Cannot be determined

183. The C.P. of two watches taken together is ₹ 840. If by selling one at a profit of 16% and the other at a loss of 12%, there is no loss or gain in the whole transaction, then the C.P. of the two watches are respectively
(*a*) ₹ 360, ₹ 480 (*b*) ₹ 480, ₹ 360
(*c*) ₹ 380, ₹ 460 (*d*) ₹ 400, ₹ 440

184. On selling a chair at 7% loss and a table at 17% gain, a man gains ₹ 296. If he sells the chair at 7% gain and the table at 12% gain, then he gains ₹ 400. The actual price of the table is
(*a*) ₹ 1600 (*b*) ₹ 1800
(*c*) ₹ 2200 (*d*) ₹ 2400

185. A space research company wants to sell its two products A and B. If the product A is sold at 20% loss and the product B at 30% gain, the company will not lose anything. If the product A is sold at 15% loss and the product B at 15% gain, the company will lose ₹ 6 million in the deal. What is the cost of product B? **(M.B.A., 2009)**
(*a*) ₹ 80 million (*b*) ₹ 100 million
(*c*) ₹ 120 million (*d*) ₹ 140 million

186. A small and medium enterprise imports two components A and B from Taiwan and China respectively and assembles them with other components to form a toy. Component A contributes to 10% of production cost while component B contributes to 20% of production cost. Usually the company sells this toy at 20% above the production cost. Due to increase in the raw material and labour cost in both the countries, component A became 20% costlier and component B became 40% costlier. Owing to these reasons the company increased its selling price by 15%. Considering that cost of other components does not change, what will be the profit percentage if the toy is sold at the new price? **(I.I.F.T., 2010)**
(*a*) 15.5% (*b*) 25.5%
(*c*) 35.5% (*d*) 40%

187. A firm of readymade garments makes both men's and women's shirts. Its average profit is 6% of the sales. Its profit in men's shirts average 8% of the sales and women's shirts comprise 60% of the output. The average profit per sales rupee in women's shirts is **(M.A.T., 2006)**
(*a*) 0.0166 (*b*) 0.0466
(*c*) 0.0666 (*d*) None of these

188. The cost of manufacturing an article rose by 18% as a result of the increase in the cost of raw material. A manufacturer revised the selling price of the article so as to maintain the same profit percentage as before. However, he found that he now got ₹ 9 more than the earlier profit by selling each article. What was the earlier profit per article?
(*a*) ₹ 36 (*b*) ₹ 45
(*c*) ₹ 50 (*d*) ₹ 54

189. The cost of raw materials of a product increases by 30%, the manufacturing cost increases by 20% and the selling price of the product increases by 60%. The raw material and the manufacturing cost originally formed 40% and 60% of the total cost respectively. If the original profit percentage was one-fourth the original manufacturing cost, find the approximate new profit percentage.
(*a*) 48.39% (*b*) 54.76%
(*c*) 63.85% (*d*) 66.72%

190. Previously, the manufacturing cost of a product was thrice the cost of raw material. Now the cost of raw material increases in the ratio 5 : 12 and manufacturing cost increases in the ratio of 3 : 5. The previous cost of the product was ₹ 8. What should be the present selling price so that 25% profit can be made? **(Hotel Management, 2007)**

(a) ₹ 13.70 (b) ₹ 14.80
(c) ₹ 18.50 (d) ₹ 19.50

191. A milk vendor mixes water with milk in the ratio 1 : 4. He then measures 800 ml instead of a litre and sells the milk at a nominal profit of 20% over the cost price. What is his actual profit percentage?

(a) 37.5% (b) 50%
(c) 62.5% (d) 87.5%

192. A shopkeeper offers 2.5% discount on cash purchases. What cash amount would Rohan pay for a cycle, the marked price of which is ₹ 650? **(IGNOU, 2003)**

(a) ₹ 633.25 (b) ₹ 633.75
(c) ₹ 634 (d) ₹ 635

193. If a company sells a car with a marked price of ₹ 2,72,000 and gives a discount of 4% on ₹ 2,00,000 and 2.5% on the remaining amount of ₹ 72,000, then the actual price charged by the company for the car is

(a) ₹ 2,50,000 (b) ₹ 2,55,000
(c) ₹ 2,60,100 (d) ₹ 2,62,200

194. Garima purchased a briefcase with an additional 10% discount on the reduced price after deducting 20% on the labelled price. If the labelled price was ₹ 1400, at what price did she purchase the briefcase?

(a) ₹ 980 (b) ₹ 1008
(c) ₹ 1056 (d) ₹ 1120
(e) None of these

195. A T-shirt bought for ₹ 50 is marked at 8 percent profit and then sold at a 10 percent sales discount on marked price. What is the selling price of the T-shirt?

(a) ₹ 48 (b) ₹ 50
(c) ₹ 52 (d) None of these

196. An umbrella marked at ₹ 80 is sold for ₹ 68. The rate of discount is **(P.C.S., 2008)**

(a) 15% (b) 17%
(c) 18.5% (d) 20%

197. A dress shop marked down all items as following:

Group	Regular price	Sale price
A	₹ 65	₹ 55
B	₹ 60	₹ 50
C	₹ 70	₹ 60
D	₹ 75	₹ 65

Which group of items was offered at the greatest rate of discount?

(a) A (b) B
(c) C (d) D

198. Vanita bought a watch with 25% discount on the selling price. If the watch cost her ₹ 780, what is the original selling price of the watch? **(M.A.T., 2009)**

(a) ₹ 950 (b) ₹ 1000
(c) ₹ 1040 (d) Cannot be determined

199. In a sale, perfume is available at a discount of 15% on the selling price. If the perfume's discounted selling price is ₹ 3675.40, what was the original selling price of the perfume? **(Bank P.O., 2009)**

(a) ₹ 4294 (b) ₹ 4324
(c) ₹ 4386 (d) ₹ 4400
(e) None of these

200. A pair of articles was bought for ₹ 37.40 at a discount of 15%. What must be the marked price of each of the articles?

(a) ₹ 11 (b) ₹ 22
(c) ₹ 33 (d) ₹ 44

201. A shopkeeper gives 12% additional discount on the discounted price, after giving an initial discount of 20% on the labelled price of a radio. If the final sale price of the radio is ₹ 704, then what is its labelled price?

(a) ₹ 844.80 (b) ₹ 929.28
(c) ₹ 1000 (d) ₹ 1044.80

202. A fan is listed at ₹ 1500 and a discount of 20% is offered on the list price. What additional discount must be offered to the customer to bring the net price to ₹ 1104?

(a) 8% (b) 10%
(c) 12% (d) 15%

203. A discount of 15% on one article is the same as a discount of 20% on another article. The costs of the two articles can be

(a) ₹ 40, ₹ 20 (b) ₹ 60, ₹ 40
(c) ₹ 80, ₹ 60 (d) ₹ 60, ₹ 40

204. If the S.P. of ₹ 24 results in a 20% discount on list price, what S.P. would result in a 30% discount on list price?

(a) ₹ 18 (b) ₹ 20
(c) ₹ 21 (d) ₹ 27

205. An article was sold for ₹ y after giving a discount of x%. Then, its list price is

(a) $\frac{100y}{100-x}$ (b) $\frac{100y}{1-x}$
(c) $\frac{100y}{1-(x/100)}$ (d) None of these

206. A seller allows a discount of 5% on a watch. If he allows a discount of 7% he earns ₹ 15 less in the profit. What is the marked price? (R.R.B., 2006)

(a) ₹ 697.50 (b) ₹ 712.50

(c) ₹ 750 (d) ₹ 817.50

207. Jatin bought a refrigerator with 20% discount on the labelled price. Had he bought it with 25% discount, he would have saved ₹ 500. At what price did he buy the refrigerator?

(a) ₹ 5000 (b) ₹ 10,000

(c) ₹ 12,500 (d) ₹ 15,000

208. A sells a scooter priced at ₹ 36000. He gives a discount of 8% on the first ₹ 20000 and 5% on the next ₹ 10000. How much discount can he afford on the remaining ₹ 6000 if he is to get as much as when 7% discount is allowed on the total?

(a) 5% (b) 6%

(c) 7% (d) 8%

209. Manoj sold an article for ₹ 15000. Had he offered a discount of 10% on the selling price he would have earned a profit of 8%. What is the cost price? (Bank P.O., 2009)

(a) ₹ 12250 (b) ₹ 12500

(c) ₹ 13250 (d) ₹ 13500

(e) None of these

210. A manufacturer offers a 20% rebate on the marked price of a product. The retailer offers another 30% rebate on the reduced price. The two reductions are equivalent to a single reduction of

(a) 40% (b) 44%

(c) 46% (d) 50%

211. Successive discounts of 10%, 12% and 15% amount to a single discount of (R.R.B., 2009; S.S.C., 2008)

(a) 32.68% (b) 35.28%

(c) 36.68% (d) None of these

212. A discount series of p% and q% on an invoice is the same as a single discount of (M.B.A., 2007)

(a) $\left[p+q+\frac{pq}{100}\right]\%$ (b) $\left[p-q+\frac{pq}{100}\right]\%$

(c) $100-\left[p+q+\frac{pq}{100}\right]\%$ (d) None of these

213. Three successive discounts of 20% on the marked price of a commodity are together equivalent to a single discount of

(a) 48.8% (b) 50.2%

(c) 55.8% (d) 60%

214. A shop gives 10% discount on the purchase of an item. If paid for in cash immediately, a further discount of 12% is given. If the original price of the item is ₹ 250, what is the price of the article if a cash purchase is made? (R.R.B., 2006)

(a) ₹ 190 (b) ₹ 195

(c) ₹ 198 (d) ₹ 200

215. Find the selling price of an article if a shopkeeper allows two successive discounts of 5% each on the marked price of ₹ 80. (C.B.I., 2003)

(a) ₹ 70.10 (b) ₹ 70.20

(c) ₹ 72 (d) ₹ 72.20

216. A dealer buys an article marked at ₹ 25000 with 20% and 5% off. He spends ₹ 1000 on its repairs and sells it for ₹ 25000. What is his gain or loss percent? (S.S.C., 2007)

(a) Loss of 25% (b) Gain of 25%

(c) Loss of 10% (d) Gain of 10%

217. If an article with marked price of ₹ 400 is sold at successive discounts of 10%, 25% and 15%, what is the approximate price the customer has to pay? (Campus Recruitment, 2009)

(a) ₹ 230 (b) ₹ 270

(c) ₹ 300 (d) ₹ 360

218. For the purchase of a motor car, a man has to pay ₹ 17000 when a single discount of 15% is allowed. How much will he have to pay for it if two successive discounts of 5% and 10% respectively are allowed? (S.S.C., 2005)

(a) ₹ 17000 (b) ₹ 17010

(c) ₹ 17100 (d) ₹ 18000

219. After successive discounts of 12% and 5% an article was sold for ₹ 209. What was the original price of the article?

(a) ₹ 226 (b) ₹ 250

(c) ₹ 252 (d) ₹ 269

220. Applied to a bill for ₹ 1,00,000, the difference between a discount of 40% and two successive discounts of 36% and 4% is

(a) Nil (b) ₹ 1440

(c) ₹ 2500 (d) ₹ 1960

221. Two stores A and B mark the price of an item identically. A allows 3 successive discounts of 10% each. B allows 10% discount on the list price and a subsequent discount of 19%. Under the circumstances, which of the following is true?

(a) The price of the article is cheaper at A.

(b) The price of the article is cheaper at B.

(c) The price of the article is same at A and B.

(d) The price cannot be determined.

222. If on a marked price, the difference of selling prices with a discount of 30% and two successive discounts of 20% and 10% is ₹ 72, then the marked price (in ₹) is (S.S.C., 2010)

(a) 2400 (b) 2500

(c) 3000 (d) 3600

223. An article is listed at ₹ 900 and two successive discounts of 8% and 8% are given on it. How much would the seller gain or lose, if he gives a single discount of 16%, instead of two discounts? (S.S.C., 2007)

(a) Gain of ₹ 4.76 (b) Loss of ₹ 5.76
(c) Loss of ₹ 4.76 (d) Gain of ₹ 5.76

224. Two shopkeepers announce the same price of ₹ 700 for a sewing machine. The first offers successive discounts of 30% and 6% while the second offers successive discounts of 20% and 16%. The shopkeeper that offers better discount, charges .... less than the other shopkeeper. (M.A.T., 2009)

(a) ₹ 9.80 (b) ₹ 16.80
(c) ₹ 22.40 (d) ₹ 36.40

225. A company offers three types of successive discounts (i) 25% and 15% ; (ii) 30% and 10% ; (iii) 35% and 5%.
Which offer is the best for a customer? (S.S.C., 2007)

(a) First offer
(b) Second offer
(c) Third offer
(d) Any one; all are equally good

226. On a ₹ 10000 payment order, a person has choice between 3 successive discounts of 10%, 10% and 30%, and 3 successive discounts of 40%, 5% and 5%. By choosing the better one he can save (in rupees) (L.I.C.A.A.O., 2007)

(a) 200 (b) 255
(c) 400 (d) 433

227. A shopkeeper gives 3 consecutive discounts of 10%, 15% and 15% after which he sells his goods at a percentage profit of 30.05 percent on the cost price. Find the value of the percentage profit that the shopkeeper would have earned if he had given discounts of 10% and 15% only. (M.B.A., 2008)

(a) 53% (b) 62.5%
(c) 68.6% (d) 72.5%

228. A shopkeeper gives two successive discounts on an article marked ₹ 450. The first discount given is 10%. If the customer pays ₹ 344.25 for the article, the second discount given is (S.S.C., 2006)

(a) 10% (b) 12%
(c) 14% (d) 15%

229. The marked price of a watch was ₹ 820. A man bought the same for ₹ 570.72 after getting two successive discounts of which the first was 20%. The rate of second discount was (S.S.C., 2008)

(a) 12% (b) 13%
(c) 15% (d) 18%

230. A shopkeeper purchased 150 identical pieces of calculators at the rate of ₹ 250 each. He spent an amount of ₹ 2500 on transport and packing. He fixed the labelled price of each calculator at ₹ 320. However, he decided to give a discount of 5% on the labelled price. What is the percentage profit earned by him?

(a) 14% (b) 15%
(c) 16% (d) 20%
(e) None of these

231. A person first increases the price of a commodity by 10% and then he announces a discount of 15%. The actual discount on the original price is (M.C.A., 2005; R.R.B., 2009)

(a) 5% (b) 6.5%
(c) 7.5% (d) 12.5%

232. Raman bought a camera and paid 20% less than its original price. He sold it at 40% profit on the price he had paid. The percentage of profit earned by Raman on the original price was (S.S.C., 2007)

(a) 12 (b) 15
(c) 22 (d) 32

233. A trader marked the price of a product in such a way that it is 20% more than the cost price. If he allows 10% discount on the marked price to the customer then his gain is (L.I.C.A.D.O., 2008; S.S.C., 2005, 06; C.P.O., 2007; Hotel Mgmt, 2007)

(a) 8% (b) 10%
(c) 15% (d) 20%

234. A trader marked the price of his commodity so as to include a profit of 25%. He allowed discount of 16% on the marked price. His actual profit was (S.S.C., 2004)

(a) 5% (b) 9%
(c) 16% (d) 25%

235. A tradesman marks his goods 30% above the C.P. If he allows a discount of $6\frac{1}{4}\%$, then his gain percent is

(a) $21\frac{7}{8}\%$ (b) 22%
(c) $23\frac{3}{4}\%$ (d) None of these

236. A shopkeeper earns a profit of 12% on selling a book at 10% discount on the printed price. The ratio of the cost price and the printed price of the book is (S.S.C., 2010; R.R.B., 2006)

(a) 45 : 56 (b) 50 : 61
(c) 99 : 125 (d) None of these

237. A showroom owner sells a leather jacket for ₹ X and claims to make a profit of 10%. He plans to have a stall in the trade fair and marks the same jacket at ₹ 2X. At the stall, he allows a discount of 20%. What will be the percentage profit that he will make at the trade fair? (M.B.A., 2006)

(a) 60% (b) 76%
(c) 80% (d) 86%

238. The price of an article is raised by 30% and then two successive discounts of 10% each are allowed. Ultimately, the price of the article is
(a) decreased by 5.3% (b) increased by 3%
(c) increased by 5.3% (d) increased by 10%

239. A retailer buys 30 articles from a wholesaler at the price of 27. If he sells them at their marked price, the gain percent in the transaction is
(a) $9\frac{1}{11}\%$ (b) 10%
(c) $11\frac{1}{9}\%$ (d) $16\frac{2}{3}\%$

240. By selling an umbrella for ₹ 300, a shopkeeper gains 20%. During a clearance sale, the shopkeeper allows a discount of 10% on the marked price. His gain percent during the sale is
(a) 7 (b) 7.5
(c) 8 (d) 9

241. The cost price of an article is 64% of the marked price. Calculate the gain percent after allowing a discount of 12%.
(a) 37.5% (b) 48%
(c) 50.5% (d) 52%

242. A shopkeeper allows a discount of 10% on the marked price of an item but charges a sales tax of 8% on the discounted price. If the customer pays ₹ 680.40 as the price including the sales tax, then what is the marked price of the item?
(a) ₹ 630 (b) ₹ 700
(c) ₹ 780 (d) None of these

243. At what percent above the cost price must a shopkeeper mark his goods so that he gains 20% even after giving a discount of 10% on the marked price? **(S.S.C., 2004; R.R.B., 2008)**
(a) 25% (b) 30%
(c) $33\frac{1}{3}\%$ (d) $37\frac{1}{2}\%$

244. A retailer allows a trade discount of 20% and a cash discount of $6\frac{1}{4}\%$ on the market price of the products and gets a net profit of 20% on the cost. By how much above the cost, should the products be labelled for sale? **(A.A.O., 2009; M.B.A., 2007)**
(a) 40% (b) 50%
(c) 60% (d) 70%

245. A shopkeeper marks his goods at such a price that after allowing a discount of 12.5% on the marked price, he still earns a profit of 10%. The marked price of an article which costs him ₹ 4900 is
(a) ₹ 5390 (b) ₹ 5490
(c) ₹ 6160 (d) ₹ 6260

246. By selling an article at $\frac{2}{5}$ of the marked price, there is a loss of 25%. The ratio of the marked price and the cost price of the article is
(a) 2 : 5 (b) 5 : 2
(c) 8 : 15 (d) 15 : 8

247. A video magazine distributor made 3500 copies of the March issue of the magazine at a cost of ₹ 350000. He gave 500 cassettes free to some key video libraries. He also allowed a 25% discount on the market price of the cassette and gave one extra cassette free with every 29 cassettes bought at a time. In this manner, he was able to sell all the 3500 cassettes that were produced. If the market price of a cassette was ₹ 150, then what is his gain or loss percent for the March issue of video magazine? **(M.A.T., 2005)**
(a) 10% gain (b) 25% loss
(c) 40% gain (d) 6.8% loss

248. A tradesman gives 4% discount on the marked price and gives 1 article free for buying every 15 articles and thus gains 35%. The marked price is above the cost price by
(a) 20% (b) 39%
(c) 40% (d) 50%

249. A trader marked the selling price of an article at 10% above the cost price. At the time of selling, he allows certain discount and suffers a loss of 1%. He allowed a discount of
(a) 9% (b) 10%
(c) 10.5% (d) 11%

250. A shopkeeper fixes the marked price of an item 35% above its cost price. The percentage of discount allowed to gain 8% is
(a) 20% (b) 27%
(c) 31% (d) 43%

251. A trader marked his goods at 20% above the cost price. He sold half the stock at the marked price, one quarter at a discount of 20% on the marked price and the rest at a discount of 40% on the marked price. His total gain is **(S.S.C., 2004)**
(a) 2% (b) 4.5%
(c) 13.5% (d) 15%

252. A product when sold with 10% rebate on the listed price gave a profit of ₹ 70. What was its cost price? **(Bank P.O., 2003)**
(a) ₹ 200
(b) ₹ 350
(c) ₹ 700
(d) Cannot be determined
(e) None of these

253. A manufacturer marked an article at ₹ 50 and sold it allowing 20% discount. If his profit was 25%, then the cost price of the article was (S.S.C., 2010)
(a) ₹ 30 (b) ₹ 32
(c) ₹ 35 (d) ₹ 40

254. The labelled price of a cupboard is ₹ 6500. The shopkeeper sold it by giving 5% discount on the labelled price and earned a profit of 15%. What approximately is the cost price of the cupboard? (Bank P.O., 2008)
(a) ₹ 5000 (b) ₹ 5350
(c) ₹ 5600 (d) ₹ 5800
(e) ₹ 6000

255. Kunal bought a suitcase with 15% discount on the labelled price. He sold the suitcase for ₹ 2880 with 20% profit on the labelled price. At what price did he buy the suitcase?
(a) ₹ 2040 (b) ₹ 2400
(c) ₹ 2604 (d) ₹ 2640
(e) None of these

256. A shopkeeper sells a badminton racket, whose marked price is ₹ 30, at a discount of 15% and gives a shuttle cock costing ₹ 1.50 free with each racket. Even then he makes a profit of 20%. His cost price per racket is
(a) ₹ 19.75 (b) ₹ 20
(c) ₹ 21 (d) ₹ 21.25

257. If a commission of 10% is given on the written price of an article, the gain is 20%. If the commission is increased to 20%, the gain is (R.R.B., 2008)
(a) $6\frac{2}{3}\%$ (b) $7\frac{1}{4}\%$
(c) $12\frac{1}{2}\%$ (d) $13\frac{1}{3}\%$

258. A shopkeeper offered a discount of 15% on the labelled price. By selling an article for ₹ 340 after giving discount he earned a profit of $13\frac{1}{3}\%$. What would have been the percent profit earned if no discount was offered? (Bank P.O., 2008)
(a) 27 (b) $28\frac{1}{3}$
(c) $30\frac{1}{3}$ (d) $33\frac{1}{3}$
(e) None of these

259. A shopkeeper sold an air-conditioner for ₹ 25935 with a discount of 9% and earned a profit of 3.74%. What would have been the percentage of profit if no discount were offered? (M.B.A., 2006)
(a) 12.3% (b) 15.6%
(c) 16% (d) None of these

260. A shopkeeper sells 25 articles at ₹ 45 per article after giving 10% discount and earns 50% profit. If the discount is not given, the profit gained is
(a) 60% (b) $60\frac{2}{3}\%$
(c) 66% (d) $66\frac{2}{3}\%$
(e) None of these

261. A shopkeeper sold sarees at ₹ 266 each after giving 5% discount on labelled price. Had he not given the discount, he would have earned a profit of 12% on the cost price. What was the cost price of each saree?
(a) ₹ 240 (b) ₹ 260
(c) ₹ 280 (d) Data inadequate
(e) None of these

262. The marked price of a shirt and trousers are in the ratio 1 : 2. The shopkeeper gives 40% discount on the shirt. If the total discount on the set of the shirt and trousers is 30%, the discount offered on the trousers is (S.S.C., 2007)
(a) 15% (b) 20%
(c) 25% (d) 30%

263. If the selling price of an article is five times the discount offered and if the percentage of discount is equal to the percentage profit, find the ratio of the discount offered to the cost price.
(a) 1 : 5 (b) 1 : 6
(c) 7 : 30 (d) 11 : 30

264. Even after reducing the marked price of a transistor by ₹ 32, a shopkeeper makes a profit of 15%. If the cost price be ₹ 320, what percentage of profit would he have made if he had sold the transistor at the marked price?
(a) 10% (b) 20%
(c) 25% (d) None of these

265. A shopkeeper sold an article offering a discount of 5% and earned a profit of 23.5%. What would have been the percentage of profit earned if no discount was offered?
(a) 24.5 (b) 28.5
(c) 30 (d) Data inadequate
(e) None of these

266. Komal buys an article at a discount of 25%. At what percentage above the cost price should he sell it to make a profit of 25% over the original list price?
(a) 25 (b) 30
(c) 40 (d) 66.67

267. Peter bought an item at 20% discount on its original price. He sold it with 40% increase on the price he bought it. The new sale price is by what percent more than the original price?

(*a*) 7.5 (*b*) 8
(*c*) 10 (*d*) 12
(*e*) None of these

268. Tarun got 30% concession on the labelled price of an article and sold it for ₹ 8750 with 25% profit on the price he bought. What was the labelled price?
(*a*) ₹ 10,000 (*b*) ₹ 12,000
(*c*) ₹ 16,000 (*d*) Data inadequate
(*e*) None of these

269. A merchant marks his goods at 25% above the cost price. Due to a slump in the market, his cost reduces by 5%. He thus offers a discount of 8% due to which the sales go up by 25%. Compute the change in the merchant's profit.
(*a*) 5% higher (*b*) $7\frac{1}{2}$% higher
(*c*) 8% lower (*d*) Unchanged

270. Aditya, a trader, sells an item to a retailer at 20% discount, but charges 10% on the discounted price, for delivery and packaging. The retailer sells it for ₹ 2046 more, thereby earning a profit of 25%. At what price had the trader marked the item?
[IBPS—RRB Officers Gr. 'B' Exam, 2015]
(*a*) ₹ 9400 (*b*) ₹ 9000
(*c*) ₹ 8000 (*d*) ₹ 9300

271. A box is bought of ₹ 75 and sold at a gain of 8%. Find its selling price
[Indian Railway Gr. 'D' Exam, 2014]
(*a*) 81 (*b*) 82
(*c*) 89 (*d*) 86

272. Oranges are bought at 5 for ₹ 10 and sold at 6 for ₹ 15. The gain percent is
[Indian Railway Gr. 'D' Exam, 2014]
(*a*) 50% (*b*) 40%
(*c*) 35% (*d*) 25%

273. Dhar bought two articles A and B at a total cost of ₹ 8000. He sold article A at 20% profit and article B at 12% loss. In the whole deal he made no gain and no loss. At what price should Dhar have sold article B to make an overall profit of 25%?
[RBI Gr. 'B' (Phase I) Exam, 2015]
(*a*) ₹ 5200 (*b*) ₹ 5800
(*c*) ₹ 6400 (*d*) ₹ 6200

274. A dealer marked the price of an item 40% above the cost price. He allowed two successive discounts of 20% and 25% to a particular customer. As a result he incurred a loss of ₹448. At what price did he sell the item to the said customer?
[IBPS—Bank Spl. Officer (IT) Exam, 2015]
(*a*) ₹ 2,416 (*b*) ₹ 2,352
(*c*) ₹ 2,268 (*d*) ₹ 2, 152

275. The marked price is 10% higher than the cost price. A discount of 10% is given on the marked price. In this kind of sale, the seller
[SSC—CHSL (10 + 2) Exam, 2015]
(*a*) gains 2% (*b*) bears no loss, no gain
(*c*) gains 1% (*d*) loses 1%

276. The profit earned by selling a article at ₹ 5520 is equal to the loss incurred on selling the same article at ₹ 4080. What will be percent profit, if the article is sold at ₹ 6000?
[United India Insurance (UIICL) Assistant (Online) Exam, 2015]
(*a*) 20 (*b*) 12
(*c*) 25 (*d*) 15

277. Rajlani sold a machine for ₹ 22, 000 with a discount of 8% on the labeled price and made a profit of $22\frac{2}{3}$%. What would have been the profit percent if the machine was sold without any discount on the labeled price?
[NICL—AAO Exam, 2015]
(*a*) 36 1/3 (*b*) 30 2/3
(*c*) 27 1/3 (*d*) 33 1/3

278. An item was bought for ₹ X and sold for ₹ Y, thereby earning a profit of 20%. Had the value of X been 15 less and the value of Y ₹ 76 less, a profit of 30% would have been earned. What was the value of 'X'? [IBPS—RRB Officers Gr. 'B' Exam, 2015]
(*a*) ₹ 640 (*b*) ₹ 400
(*c*) ₹ 600 (*d*) ₹ 800

279. A trader has 600 kgs of rice, a part of which he sells at 15% profit and the remaining quantity at 20% loss. On the whole, he incurs an overall loss of 6%. What is the quantity of rice he sold at 20% loss?
[IBPS—Bank PO/MT Exam, 2015]
(*a*) 250 kgs (*b*) 320 kgs
(*c*) 420 kgs (*d*) 360 kgs

280. When an article was sold for ₹ 696, percent profit earned was P%. When the same article was sold for ₹ 841, percent profit earned was (p + 25%). What is the value of P?
[IBPS—RRB Officer Assistant (Online) Exam, 2015]
(*a*) 10 (*b*) 25
(*c*) 15 (*d*) 20

281. Raza purchased a bicycle for ₹ 6810. He had paid a VAT of 13.5%. The list price of the bicycle was
[SSC—CHSL (10+2) Exam, 2015]
(*a*) ₹ 6696.50 (*b*) ₹ 6140
(*c*) ₹ 5970.50 (*d*) ₹ 6000

282. Srinivas sold an article for ₹ 6800 and incurred a loss. Had he sold the article for ₹ 7850, his gain would have been equal to half of the amount of loss that he incurred. At what price should he sell the article to have 20% profit?
[IBPS—Bank PO (Pre.) Exam, 2015]

(a) ₹ 7500 (b) ₹ 9000
(c) ₹ 10680 (d) ₹ 9600

283. Subroto sold an article for ₹ 528 after allowing a discount of 12% on its marked price. What was the marked price of the article?

[ESIC—UDC Exam, 2016]

(a) ₹ 600 (b) ₹ 700
(c) ₹ 650 (d) ₹ 590

284. Sanjay made a profit of 8% by selling a shirt after offering a discount of 12%. If the marked price of the shirt is ₹ 1080, find its cost price.

[SBI Jr. Associates (Pre.) Exam, 2016]

(a) 890 (b) 780
(c) 880 (d) 900

285. The sale price of an article including the sales tax is ₹ 1232. The rate of sales tax is 10%. If the shopkeeper has made a profit of 12%, then the cost price of the article is

[DMRC—Train Operator (Station Controller) Exam, 2016]

(a) ₹ 900 (b) ₹ 950
(c) ₹ 1000 (d) ₹ 1120

286. The value of a machine depreciates every year at the rate of 10% on its value at the beginning of that year. If the present value of the machine is ₹ 729, its worth three years ago was **[CLAT, 2016]**

(a) ₹ 947.70 (b) ₹ 1000
(c) ₹ 750.87 (d) ₹ 800

287. Meena Kumari goes to a shop and buys a saree, costing ₹ 5,225, including sales tax of 12%. The shopkeeper gives her a discount, so that the price is decreased by an amount equivalent to sales tax. The price is decreased by (nearest value).

[IBPS—Bank Specialist Officer (Marketing) Exam, 2016]

(a) ₹ 615 (b) ₹ 650
(c) ₹ 560 (d) ₹ 580

288. The profit earned by selling a chair for ₹ 752 is 1.2 times the loss incurred when the same chair was sold for ₹ 400. What is the cost price of the chair?

[DMRC—Customer Relations Assistant (CRA) Exam, 2016]

(a) ₹ 540 (b) ₹ 592
(c) ₹ 560 (d) None of these

289. A publisher sells copies of books to a retail dealer at ₹ 5 per copy but allows 24 copies to be counted as 24. If the retailer sells each of the 25 copies at ₹ 6, his profit per cent is

[DMRC—Jr. Engineer (Electronics) Exam, 2016]

(a) 20% (b) 24%
(c) 25% (d) 40%

290. Supriya sold a washing machine for ₹ 8500. She incurred a loss of 15% in this transaction. At what price had she bought the washing machine?

[ESIC—UDC Exam, 2016]

(a) ₹ 10000 (b) ₹ 1200
(c) ₹ 11000 (d) ₹ 10500

291. The price of a cycle is marked at ₹ 1150. A shopkeeper earns a profit of 15% after allowing a discount of 15% on the marked price. Find the cost price of the cycle. **[ESIC—UDC Exam, 2016]**

(a) ₹ 900 (b) ₹ 1000
(c) ₹ 850 (d) ₹ 950

292. The price of an article is first increased by 20% and later on decreased by 25% due to reduction in sales. Find the net percentage change in final price of the article.

[SBI Jr. Associates (Pre.) Exam, 2016]

(a) 20% (b) 18%
(c) 38% (d) None of these

ANSWERS

1. (c)	2. (d)	3. (d)	4. (c)	5. (c)	6. (c)	7. (b)	8. (e)	9. (b)	10. (b)
11. (c)	12. (c)	13. (a)	14. (c)	15. (c)	16. (a)	17. (d)	18. (c)	19. (b)	20. (c)
21. (c)	22. (d)	23. (d)	24. (c)	25. (a)	26. (d)	27. (c)	28. (c)	29. (d)	30. (b)
31. (c)	32. (b)	33. (b)	34. (c)	35. (b)	36. (c)	37. (a)	38. (d)	39. (d)	40. (b)
41. (d)	42. (e)	43. (a)	44. (d)	45. (b)	46. (c)	47. (a)	48. (a)	49. (b)	50. (a)
51. (c)	52. (b)	53. (c)	54. (c)	55. (b)	56. (b)	57. (a)	58. (d)	59. (d)	60. (d)
61. (c)	62. (c)	63. (c)	64. (a)	65. (b)	66. (c)	67. (d)	68. (c)	69. (d)	70. (d)
71. (a)	72. (d)	73. (a)	74. (b)	75. (d)	76. (d)	77. (a)	78. (c)	79. (d)	80. (b)
81. (c)	82. (d)	83. (c)	84. (d)	85. (c)	86. (c)	87. (c)	88. (a)	89. (b)	90. (b)
91. (b)	92. (a)	93. (a)	94. (b)	95. (d)	96. (c)	97. (e)	98. (a)	99. (a)	100. (a)
101. (d)	102. (b)	103. (a)	104. (c)	105. (e)	106. (c)	107. (a)	108. (b)	109. (d)	110. (a)
111. (b)	112. (d)	113. (c)	114. (a)	115. (a)	116. (d)	117. (d)	118. (c)	119. (b)	120. (b)
121. (c)	122. (b)	123. (b)	124. (a)	125. (b)	126. (d)	127. (a)	128. (d)	129. (b)	130. (c)
131. (a)	132. (a)	133. (d)	134. (b)	135. (d)	136. (b)	137. (c)	138. (b)	139. (c)	140. (b)

141. (*d*)	142. (*a*)	143. (*c*)	144. (*d*)	145. (*c*)	146. (*a*)	147. (*d*)	148. (*d*)	149. (*c*)	150. (*b*)
151. (*b*)	152. (*d*)	153. (*b*)	154. (*a*)	155. (*b*)	156. (*d*)	157. (*b*)	158. (*a*)	159. (*a*)	160. (*b*)
161. (*c*)	162. (*a*)	163. (*b*)	164. (*b*)	165. (*c*)	166. (*d*)	167. (*d*)	168. (*c*)	169. (*d*)	170. (*c*)
171. (*c*)	172. (*c*)	173. (*d*)	174. (*d*)	175. (*c*)	176. (*c*)	177. (*d*)	178. (*c*)	179. (*c*)	180. (*b*)
181. (*b*)	182. (*a*)	183. (*a*)	184. (*d*)	185. (*a*)	186. (*b*)	187. (*b*)	188. (*c*)	189. (*a*)	190. (*c*)
191. (*d*)	192. (*b*)	193. (*d*)	194. (*b*)	195. (*d*)	196. (*a*)	197. (*b*)	198. (*c*)	199. (*b*)	200. (*b*)
201. (*c*)	202. (*a*)	203. (*c*)	204. (*c*)	205. (*a*)	206. (*c*)	207. (*b*)	208. (*c*)	209. (*b*)	210. (*b*)
211. (*a*)	212. (*d*)	213. (*a*)	214. (*c*)	215. (*d*)	216. (*b*)	217. (*a*)	218. (*c*)	219. (*b*)	220. (*b*)
221. (*c*)	222. (*d*)	223. (*b*)	224. (*a*)	225. (*c*)	226. (*b*)	227. (*a*)	228. (*d*)	229. (*b*)	230. (*a*)
231. (*b*)	232. (*a*)	233. (*a*)	234. (*a*)	235. (*a*)	236. (*a*)	237. (*b*)	238. (*c*)	239. (*c*)	240. (*c*)
241. (*a*)	242. (*b*)	243. (*c*)	244. (*c*)	245. (*c*)	246. (*d*)	247. (*d*)	248. (*d*)	249. (*b*)	250. (*a*)
251. (*a*)	252. (*d*)	253. (*b*)	254. (*b*)	255. (*a*)	256. (*b*)	257. (*a*)	258. (*d*)	259. (*d*)	260. (*d*)
261. (*e*)	262. (*c*)	263. (*c*)	264. (*c*)	265. (*c*)	266. (*d*)	267. (*d*)	268. (*a*)	269. (*d*)	270. (*d*)
271. (*a*)	272. (*d*)	273. (*c*)	274. (*b*)	275. (*d*)	276. (*c*)	277. (*d*)	278. (*d*)	279. (*d*)	280. (*d*)
281. (*d*)	282. (*c*)	283. (*a*)	284. (*c*)	285. (*c*)	286. (*b*)	287. (*c*)	288. (*c*)	289. (*c*)	290. (*a*)
291. (*c*)	292. (*d*)								

SOLUTIONS

1. C.P. = ₹ 12000, S.P. = ₹ 15000. Profit = ₹ (15000 – 12000) = ₹ 3000.

$\therefore$ Profit % = $\left(\frac{3000}{12000}\times 100\right)\% = 25\%.$

2. (*a*) Profit % = $\left(\frac{17}{36}\times 100\right)\% = 47\frac{2}{9}\%.$

(*b*) Profit % = $\left(\frac{24}{50}\times 100\right)\% = 48\%.$

(*c*) Profit % = $\left(\frac{19}{40}\times 100\right)\% = 47\frac{1}{2}\%.$

(*d*) Profit % = $\left(\frac{29}{60}\times 100\right)\% = 48\frac{1}{3}\%.$

Clearly, (*d*) is the best transaction.

3. Least C.P. = ₹ (200 × 8) = ₹ 1600.

Greatest S.P. = ₹ (425 × 8) = ₹ 3400.

Required profit = ₹ (3400 – 1600) = ₹ 1800.

4. Profit = ₹ (2602.58 – 2090.42) = ₹ 512.16.

Profit % = $\left(\frac{512.16}{2090.42}\times 100\right)\% = \left(\frac{512160}{209042}\times 10\right)\%$

= 24.5% ≈ 25%.

5. C.P. = ₹ 7840, Profit = 7%.

$\therefore$ S.P. = ₹ $\left(\frac{107}{100}\times 7840\right)$ = ₹ 8388.80.

6. Total C.P. = ₹ (5400 + 9600) = ₹ 15000.

Total S.P. = ₹ $\left(\frac{3}{4}\text{ of } 5400 + \frac{4}{3}\text{ of } 9600\right)$

= ₹ $\left(5400\times\frac{3}{4} + 9600\times\frac{4}{3}\right)$ = ₹ (4050 + 12800)

= ₹ 16850.

Profit = ₹ (16850 – 15000) = ₹ 1850.

7. Total C.P. = ₹ (12000 + 10000) = ₹ 22000.

Total S.P. = ₹ $\left(\frac{108}{100}\times 12000 + \frac{88}{100}\times 10000\right)$

= ₹ (12960 + 8800) = ₹ 21760.

$\therefore$ Loss = ₹ (22000 – 21760) = ₹ 240.

8. Total C.P. = ₹ (12500 + 300 + 800) = ₹ 13600. Profit = 15%.

$\therefore$ S.P. = ₹ $\left(\frac{115}{100}\times 13600\right)$ = ₹ 15640.

9. Total C.P. = ₹ (4500 × 15) = ₹ 67500.

Total S.P. = ₹ 81000.

Profit = ₹ (81000 – 67500) = ₹ 13500.

$\therefore$ Profit % = $\left(\frac{13500}{67500}\times 100\right)\% = 20\%.$

10. C.P. = ₹ (4700 + 800) = ₹ 5500; S.P. = ₹ 5800.

Gain % = $\left(\frac{300}{5500}\times 100\right)\% = 5\frac{5}{11}\%.$

11. C.P. of 1 kg = ₹ $\left(\frac{420}{70}\right)$ = ₹ 6. S.P. of 1 kg = ₹ 6.50.

$\therefore$ Gain % = $\left(\frac{0.50}{6}\times 100\right)\% = \frac{25}{3}\% = 8\frac{1}{3}\%.$

12. C.P. of 1 toy = ₹ $\left(\frac{375}{12}\right)$ = ₹ 31.25. S.P. of 1 toy = ₹ 33.

$\therefore$ Profit % = $\left(\frac{1.75}{31.25}\times 100\right)\% = \frac{28}{5}\% = 5.6\%.$

13. C.P. of 1 orange = ₹ $\left(\frac{350}{100}\right)$ = ₹ 3.50. S.P. of 1 orange = ₹ $\left(\frac{48}{12}\right)$ = ₹ 4.

$\therefore$ Gain % = $\left(\frac{0.50}{3.50}\times 100\right)\% = \frac{100}{7}\% = 14\frac{2}{7}\%.$

14. C.P. for B = 120% of ₹ 400 = ₹ $\left(\frac{120}{100} \times 400\right)$ = ₹ 480.

C.P. for C = 110% of ₹ 480 = ₹ $\left(\frac{110}{100} \times 480\right)$ = ₹ 528.

15. S.P. = ₹ 100, Gain = ₹ 15.

∴ C.P. = ₹ (100 – 15) = ₹ 85.

Gain % = $\left(\frac{15}{85} \times 100\right)\% = \frac{300}{17}\% = 17\frac{11}{17}\%$.

16. Total C.P. = Cost + Overhead expenses = ₹ (150 + 12% of 150) = ₹ (150 + 18) = ₹ 168.

∴ S.P. = ₹ $\left(\frac{110}{100} \times 168\right)$ = ₹ 184.80.

17. C.P. of 10 articles = ₹ 8. S.P. of 10 articles = ₹ (1.25 × 10) = ₹ 12.5.

Profit = ₹ (12.5 – 8) = ₹ 4.50.

∴ Profit % = $\left(\frac{4.5}{8} \times 100\right)\% = 56\frac{1}{4}\%$.

18. Let C.P. = ₹ x. Profit = 200 %.

∴ S.P. = 300% of ₹ x = ₹ $3x$.

Required ratio = $x : 3x = 1 : 3$.

19. Let C.P. = ₹ $10x$ and S.P. = ₹ $11x$.

Profit = ₹ $(11x - 10x)$ = ₹ x.

∴ Profit % = $\left(\frac{x}{10x} \times 100\right)\% = 10\%$.

20. Let C.P. = ₹ x. Loss = $12\frac{1}{2}\%$.

S.P. = $87\frac{1}{2}\%$ of ₹ x = ₹ $\left(\frac{175}{2} \times \frac{1}{100} \times x\right)$ = ₹ $\frac{7x}{8}$.

∴ Required ratio = $x : \frac{7x}{8} = 8 : 7$.

21. C.P. = ₹ p. Gain = r%. ∴ S.P. = q

= $(100 + r)\%$ of ₹ p = $\frac{p(100+r)}{100}$.

22. S.P. = ₹ 23680. Profit = 28%.

∴ C.P. = ₹ $\left(\frac{100}{128} \times 23680\right)$ = ₹ 18500.

23. S.P. = ₹ 14500. Loss = 20%.

∴ C.P. = ₹ $\left(\frac{100}{80} \times 14500\right)$ = ₹ 18125.

24. C.P. = ₹ $\left(\frac{100}{122.50} \times 392\right)$ = ₹ $\left(\frac{1000}{1225} \times 392\right)$ = ₹ 320.

∴ Profit = ₹ (392 – 320) = ₹ 72.

25. 110% of S.P. = 616 ⇒ S.P. = ₹ $\left(\frac{616 \times 100}{110}\right)$ = ₹ 560.

∴ C.P. = ₹ $\left(\frac{100}{112} \times 560\right)$ = ₹ 500.

26. Total C.P. = ₹ (144 × 0.90) = ₹ 129.60.

Total S.P. = ₹ (124 × 1.20) = ₹ 148.80.

Gain = ₹ (148.80 – 129.60) = ₹ 19.20.

∴ Gain % = $\left(\frac{19.20}{129.60} \times 100\right)\% = 14.81\%$.

27. Total C.P. = ₹ (140 × 450 + 250 × 550)

= ₹ (63000 + 137500) = ₹ 200500.

Total S.P. = ₹ $\left(\frac{140}{100} \times 200500\right)$ = ₹ 280700.

∴ Average S.P. = ₹ $\left(\frac{280700}{140+250}\right)$ = ₹ $\left(\frac{280700}{390}\right)$

= ₹ 719.74 ≈ 720.

28. Total C.P. of (10 × 12) *i.e.*, 120 pens = ₹ (4 × 10) = ₹ 40.

Number of working pens = (120 – 20) = 100.

Total S.P. of 100 pens = ₹ $\left(\frac{125}{100} \times 40\right)$ = ₹ 50.

∴ S.P. of each pen = ₹ $\left(\frac{50}{100}\right)$ = 50 paise.

29. Total investment = ₹ $\left(120 \times 80 + 280 + \frac{40}{100} \times 120 + 72\right)$

= ₹ (9600 + 280 + 48 + 72)

= ₹ 10000.

S.P. of 120 reams = 108% of ₹ 10000 = ₹ 10800.

∴ S.P. per ream = ₹ $\left(\frac{10800}{120}\right)$ = ₹ 90.

30. Investment = ₹ (20 × 8 + 10) = ₹ 170.

Receipt = ₹ (30 × 5 + 20 × 4) = ₹ 230.

∴ Gain % = $\left(\frac{60}{170} \times 100\right)\%$ = 35.29% ≈ 35.3%.

31. Let the C.P. be ₹ x.

Then, 20% of x = 1100 ⇒ $\frac{20}{100} \times x = 1100 \Rightarrow x = 5500$.

C.P. = ₹ 5500, Expenditure on repairs = 10%.

Actual price = ₹ $\left(\frac{100}{110} \times 5500\right)$ = ₹ 5000.

∴ Expenditure on repairs = ₹ (5500 – 5000) = ₹ 500.

32. Total cost incurred = ₹ $\left[\frac{100}{125} \times 25 \times (95\% \text{ of } 2000)\right]$

= ₹ $\left(\frac{100}{125} \times 25 \times 1900\right)$ = ₹ 38000.

Loss to the manufacturer = ₹ [38000 – (25 × 1000)]

= ₹ 13000.

33. Ratio of profit = Ratio of investments = $\frac{3}{2} : 1 = 3 : 2$.

Profit = ₹ (26250 – 25000) = ₹ 1250.

∴ Vinit's share = ₹ $\left(\frac{2}{5} \times 1250\right)$ = ₹ 500.

34. C.P. = ₹ $\left(600 + \frac{600 \times 6 \times 4}{100 \times 12}\right)$ = ₹ 612.

Gain = ₹ (765 – 612) = ₹ 153.

∴ Gain % = $\left(\frac{153}{612} \times 100\right)\% = 25\%$.

35. Let the new S.P. be ₹ x.

Then, 114 : 2850 = 108 : x ⇒ $x = \left(\frac{2850 \times 108}{114}\right)$ = 2700.

36. Let the new S.P. be ₹ x.

Then, $85 : 18700 = 115 : x \Rightarrow x = \left(\frac{18700 \times 115}{85}\right) = 25300.$

37. Let the new S.P. be ₹ x.

Then, $80 : 9 = 105 : x \Rightarrow x = \left(\frac{9 \times 105}{80}\right) = 11.81.$

38. Initial investment = ₹ 8200.

S.P. of 1st item = ₹ $\left(\frac{125}{100} \times 8200\right)$ = ₹ 10250.

C.P. of 2nd item = ₹ 10250. Loss = 20%.

Final receipt = S.P. of 2nd item = ₹ $\left(\frac{80}{100} \times 10250\right)$

= ₹ 8200.

Since initial investment = final receipt, there was neither gain nor loss.

39. C.P. = ₹ $\left(\frac{100}{105} \times 630000\right)$ = ₹ 600000.

$\therefore$ Required loss% = $\left(\frac{100000}{600000} \times 100\right)\% = 16\frac{2}{3}\%.$

40. C.P. of 1st transistor = ₹ $\left(\frac{100}{120} \times 840\right)$ = ₹ 700.

C.P. of 2nd transistor = ₹ $\left(\frac{100}{96} \times 960\right)$ = ₹ 1000.

So, total C.P. = ₹ (700 + 1000) = 1700.

Total S.P. = ₹ (840 + 960) = ₹ 1800.

$\therefore$ Gain% = $\left(\frac{100}{1700} \times 100\right)\% = 5\frac{15}{17}\%.$

41. Let C.P. = ₹ x. Then, S.P. = ₹ $\frac{4x}{3}$.

Gain = ₹ $\left(\frac{4x}{3} - x\right)$ = ₹ $\frac{x}{3}$.

$\therefore$ Gain% = $\left(\frac{x}{3} \times \frac{1}{x} \times 100\right)\% = 33\frac{1}{3}\%.$

42. Let C.P. = ₹ $5x$ and S.P. = ₹ $7x$.

Then, Gain = ₹ $2x$.

$\therefore$ Required ratio = $2x : 5x = 2 : 5$.

43. Let C.P. of the article be ₹ p.

Then, x = 85% of ₹ p = ₹ $\frac{85}{100}p$.

And, y = 115% of ₹ p = ₹ $\frac{115}{100}p$.

$\therefore (y - x) : (y + x) = \left(\frac{115}{100}p - \frac{85}{100}p\right) : \left(\frac{115}{100}p + \frac{85}{100}p\right)$

$= \frac{30}{100}p : \frac{200}{100}p = \frac{3}{10} : 2 = 3 : 20.$

44. Let C.P. = ₹ x. Then, S.P. = 110% of ₹ x = ₹ $\frac{11x}{10}$.

New S.P. = ₹ $\left(2 \times \frac{11x}{10}\right)$ = ₹ $\frac{11x}{5}$. Gain = ₹ $\left(\frac{11x}{5} - x\right)$ = ₹ $\frac{6x}{5}$.

$\therefore$ Gain% = $\left(\frac{6x}{5} \times \frac{1}{x} \times 100\right)\% = 120\%.$

45. Let C.P. be ₹ x and S.P. be ₹ y.

Then, $3(y - x) = (2y - x) \Rightarrow y = 2x$.

Profit = ₹ $(y - x)$ = ₹ $(2x - x)$ = ₹ x.

$\therefore$ Profit % = $\left(\frac{x}{x} \times 100\right)\% = 100\%.$

46. Let S.P. = ₹ x. New S.P. = ₹ $\frac{x}{2}$, Loss = 30%.

So, C.P. = ₹ $\left(\frac{100}{70} \times \frac{x}{2}\right)$ = ₹ $\frac{5x}{7}$.

Profit = ₹ $\left(x - \frac{5x}{7}\right)$ = ₹ $\frac{2x}{7}$.

$\therefore$ Profit% = $\left(\frac{2x}{7} \times \frac{7}{5x} \times 100\right)\% = 40\%.$

47. C.P. = $\frac{40}{100}$ × S.P. ⇒ S.P. = $\frac{5}{2}$

C.P. = $\left(\frac{5}{2} \times 100\right)\%$ of C.P. = 250% of C.P.

48. Let the C.P. be ₹ x.

Then, $x - 15 = \frac{x}{16} \Rightarrow x - \frac{x}{16} = 15 \Rightarrow \frac{15x}{16} = 15 \Rightarrow x = 16.$

$\therefore$ C.P. = ₹ 16.

49. S.P. = C.P. + $\frac{1}{4}$C.P. = $\frac{5}{4}$C.P.

$\therefore \frac{5}{4}$C.P. = 375 ⇒ C.P. = ₹ $\left(375 \times \frac{4}{5}\right)$ = ₹ 300.

50. Let S.P. = ₹ 100. Then, Loss = ₹ 10, C.P. = ₹ (100 + 10) = ₹ 110.

$\therefore$ Loss% = $\left(\frac{10}{110} \times 100\right)\% = 9\frac{1}{11}\%.$

51. Let S.P. = ₹ x. Then, Loss = ₹ $\frac{x}{3}$.

C.P. = ₹ $\left(x + \frac{x}{3}\right)$ = ₹ $\frac{4x}{3}$.

$\therefore$ Loss% = $\left(\frac{x}{3} \times \frac{3}{4x} \times 100\right)\% = 25\%.$

52. Let C.P. = ₹ 100. Then, Profit = ₹ 320, S.P. = ₹ 420.

New C.P. = 125% of ₹ 100 = ₹ 125; New S.P. = ₹ 420.

Profit = ₹ (420 − 125) = ₹ 295.

$\therefore$ Required percentage = $\left(\frac{295}{420} \times 100\right)\% = \frac{1475}{21}\% \approx 70\%.$

53. Let the price of the car be ₹ 100.

Then, C.P. = 80% of ₹ 100 = ₹ 80.

S.P. = 120% of ₹ 100 = ₹ 120.

Gain = ₹ (120 − 80) = ₹ 40.

$\therefore$ Gain% = $\left(\frac{40}{80} \times 100\right)\% = 50\%.$

54. Let C.P. = ₹ x. Then, $1754 - x = x - 1492$

$\Rightarrow 2x = 3246 \Rightarrow x = 1623.$

55. Let C.P. = ₹ x. Then, $832 - x = x - 448$

$\Rightarrow 2x = 1280 \Rightarrow x = 640.$

$\therefore$ Required S.P. = 150% of ₹ 640 = ₹ $\left(\frac{150}{100} \times 640\right)$ = ₹ 960.

56. Let C.P. = ₹ x. Then, $900 - x = 2(x - 450)$
$\Rightarrow 3x = 1800 \Rightarrow x = 600$.
$\therefore$ Required S.P. = 125% of ₹ 600 = ₹ $\left(\frac{125}{100} \times 600\right)$ = ₹ 750.

57. Let C.P. be ₹ x.
Then, $\frac{1920 - x}{x} \times 100 = \frac{x - 1280}{x} \times 100 \Rightarrow 1920 - x = x - 1280$
$\Rightarrow 2x = 3200 \Rightarrow x = 1600$.
$\therefore$ Required S.P. = 125% of ₹ 1600
= ₹ $\left(\frac{125}{100} \times 1600\right)$ = ₹ 2000.

58. Let C.P. be ₹ x.
Then, $(1060 - x) = \frac{120}{100}(x - 950)$
$\Rightarrow 106000 - 100x = 120x - 120 \times 950$
$\Rightarrow 220x = 220000 \Rightarrow x = 1000$.
$\therefore$ Desired S.P. = ₹ $\left(\frac{120}{100} \times 1000\right)$ = ₹ 1200.

59. Let C.P. be ₹ x.
Then, $\frac{116 - x}{x} \times 100 = 3\left[\frac{92 - x}{x} \times 100\right] \Leftrightarrow x = 80$.

60. Let C.P. of each book be ₹ 1.
Then, C.P. of 20 books = ₹ 20; S.P. of 20 books = ₹ 15.
$\therefore$ Loss% = $\left(\frac{5}{20} \times 100\right)\% = 25\%$.

61. Let C.P. of each article be ₹ 1.
Then, C.P. of 7 articles = ₹ 7; S.P. of 7 articles = ₹ 10.
$\therefore$ Gain% = $\left(\frac{3}{7} \times 100\right)\% = 42\frac{6}{7}\%$.

62. Let M.P. of each pen be ₹ 1.
Then, C.P. of 20 pens = ₹ 16; S.P. of 20 pens = ₹ 20.
$\therefore$ Gain% = $\left(\frac{4}{16} \times 100\right)\% = 25\%$.

63. Let C.P. of each sheep be ₹ 1.
Then, C.P. of 700 sheep = ₹ 700; S.P. of 700 sheep = ₹ 749.
$\therefore$ Gain% = $\left(\frac{49}{700} \times 100\right)\% = 7\%$.

64. Let C.P. of each mango be ₹ 1.
C.P. of 110 mangoes = ₹ 110, S.P. of 110 mangoes = ₹ 120.
$\therefore$ Gain% = $\left(\frac{10}{110} \times 100\right)\% = 9\frac{1}{11}\%$.

65. Let C.P. of each article be ₹ 1. C.P. of x articles = ₹ x; S.P. of x articles = ₹ 20.
Profit = ₹ $(20 - x)$.
$\therefore \frac{20 - x}{x} \times 100 = 25 \Rightarrow 2000 - 100x = 25x$
$\Rightarrow 125x = 2000 \Rightarrow x = 16$.

66. Clearly, the retailer gets 1 dozen out of 6 dozens free.
$\therefore$ Equivalent discount = $\left(\frac{1}{6} \times 100\right)\% = 16\frac{2}{3}\%$.

67. (S.P. of 18 cots) – (C.P. of 18 cots) = (C.P. of 3 cots)
$\Rightarrow$ C.P. of 21 cots = S.P. of 18 cots = ₹ 16800
$\Rightarrow$ C.P. of 1 cot = ₹ $\left(\frac{16800}{21}\right)$ = ₹ 800.

68. (S.P. of 20 dining tables) – (C.P. of 20 dining tables)
= S.P. of 4 dining tables
$\Rightarrow$ C.P. of 20 dining tables = S.P. of 16 dining tables
= ₹ 12000
$\Rightarrow$ S.P. of 1 dining table = ₹ $\left(\frac{12000}{16}\right)$ = ₹ 750.

69. (S.P. of 100 pencils) – (C.P. of 100 pencils)
= S.P. of 20 pencils
$\Rightarrow$ C.P. of 100 pencils = S.P. of 80 pencils.
Let C.P. of each pencil be ₹ 1.
Then, C.P. of 80 pencils = ₹ 80; S.P. of 80 pencils = ₹ 100.
$\therefore$ Gain % = $\left(\frac{20}{80} \times 100\right)\% = 25\%$.

70. (C.P. of 17 balls) – (S.P. of 17 balls) = (C.P. of 5 balls)
$\Rightarrow$ C.P. of 12 balls = S.P. of 17 balls = ₹ 720
$\Rightarrow$ C.P. of 1 ball = ₹ $\left(\frac{720}{12}\right)$ = ₹ 60.

71. (C.P. of 36 mangoes) – (S.P. of 36 mangoes)
= Loss = (S.P. of 4 mangoes)
$\Rightarrow$ S.P. of 40 mangoes = C.P. of 36 mangoes.
Let C.P. of each mango be ₹ 1.
C.P. of 40 mangoes = ₹ 40; S.P. of 40 mangoes = ₹ 36.
$\therefore$ Loss% = $\left(\frac{4}{40} \times 100\right)\% = 10\%$.

72. C.P. = ₹ $(16 \times 2) = 32$. S.P. = ₹ $(12 \times 1.5 + 4 \times 0.5)$
= ₹ $(18 + 2)$ = ₹ 20.
$\therefore$ Loss% = $\left(\frac{12}{32} \times 100\right)\% = 37.5\%$.

73. C.P. of 1 apple = ₹ $\left(\frac{34}{8}\right)$ = ₹ 4.25. S.P. of 1 apple
= ₹ $\left(\frac{57}{12}\right)$ = ₹ 4.75.
Profit on each apple = ₹ 0.50.
$\therefore$ Number of apples required = $\left(\frac{45}{0.50}\right) = 90$.

74. Suppose Vinod has n pencils.
Then, $2.50\,n - 1.75\,n = 110 + 55$
$\Rightarrow 0.75\,n = 165 \Rightarrow n = \frac{165}{0.75} = 220$.

75. C.P. of 1600 eggs = ₹ $\left(\frac{3.75}{12} \times 1600\right)$ = ₹ 500.
S.P. of 1600 eggs = ₹ $\left(\frac{1}{2} \times 900 + \frac{2}{5} \times 700\right)$ = ₹ 730.
$\therefore$ Gain% = $\left(\frac{230}{500} \times 100\right)\% = 46\%$.

76. Suppose, number of knives bought = L.C.M. of 11 and 10 = 110.

C.P. of 110 knives = ₹ $\left(\frac{10}{11}\times 110\right)$ = ₹ 100.

S.P. of 110 knives = ₹ $\left(\frac{11}{10}\times 110\right)$ = ₹ 121.

∴ Profit% = $\left(\frac{21}{100}\times 100\right)\% = 21\%$.

77. Suppose, number of oranges bought = L.C.M. of 5 and 6 = 30.

C.P. of 30 oranges = ₹ $\left(\frac{10}{5}\times 30\right)$ = ₹ 60.

S.P. of 30 oranges = ₹ $\left(\frac{15}{6}\times 30\right)$ = ₹ 75.

∴ Profit% = $\left(\frac{15}{60}\times 100\right)\% = 25\%$.

78. Suppose number of lemons bought = L.C.M. of 2 and 5 = 10.

C.P. of 10 lemons = ₹ $\left(\frac{1}{2}\times 10\right)$ = ₹ 5.

S.P. of 10 lemons = ₹ $\left(\frac{3}{5}\times 10\right)$ = ₹ 6.

∴ Profit% = $\left(\frac{1}{5}\times 100\right)\% = 20\%$.

79. Suppose number of pencils bought = L.C.M. of 6 and 4 = 12.

C.P. of 12 pencils = ₹ $\left(\frac{4}{6}\times 12\right)$ = ₹ 8.

S.P. of 12 pencils = ₹ $\left(\frac{6}{4}\times 12\right)$ = ₹ 18.

∴ Gain% = $\left(\frac{10}{8}\times 100\right)\% = 125\%$.

80. Suppose, number of pencils bought = L.C.M. of 7 and 8 = 56.

C.P. of 56 pencils = ₹ $\left(\frac{9}{7}\times 56\right)$ = ₹ 72.

S.P. of 56 pencils = ₹ $\left(\frac{11}{8}\times 56\right)$ = ₹ 77.

Now, ₹ 5 are gained on 56 pencils.

So, ₹ 10 are gained on $\left(\frac{56}{5}\times 10\right) = 112$ pencils.

81. Suppose he bought 1 dozen clips of each kind.

C.P. of 2 dozens = ₹ $\left(\frac{1}{3}\times 12+\frac{1}{2}\times 12\right)$ = ₹ 10.

∴ S.P. of 2 dozens = 120% of ₹ 10 = ₹ $\left(\frac{120}{100}\times 10\right)$ = ₹ 12.

Hence, S.P. per dozen = ₹ 6.

82. Suppose he buys 6 eggs of each kind.

C.P. of 12 eggs = ₹ $\left(\frac{1}{2}\times 6+\frac{2}{3}\times 6\right)$

= ₹ 7. S.P. of 12 eggs = ₹ $\left(\frac{3}{5}\times 12\right)$ = ₹ 7.20.

∴ Gain = $\left(\frac{0.20}{7}\times 100\right)\% = 2\frac{6}{7}\%$.

83. Suppose number of marbles bought of each kind = L.C.M of 20, 30, 25 = 300.

C.P. of 600 marbles = ₹ $\left(\frac{1}{20}\times 300+\frac{1}{30}\times 300\right)$ = ₹ 25.

S.P. of 600 marbles = ₹ $\left(\frac{1}{25}\times 600\right)$ = ₹ 24.

∴ Loss% = $\left(\frac{1}{25}\times 100\right)\% = 4\%$.

84. C.P. of 2 dozen oranges = ₹ (10 + 8) = ₹ 18.

S.P. of 2 dozen oranges = ₹ 22.

If profit is ₹ 4, oranges bought = 2 dozen.

If profit is ₹ 120, oranges bought = $\left(\frac{2}{4}\times 120\right)$ dozens = 60 dozens.

85. Suppose number of articles bought of each kind = L.C.M. of 5, 4, 9 = 180.

C.P. of 360 articles = ₹ $\left(\frac{1}{5}\times 180+\frac{1}{4}\times 180\right)$ = ₹ 81.

S.P. of 360 articles = ₹ $\left(\frac{2}{9}\times 360\right)$ = ₹ 80.

If loss is ₹ 1, articles bought = 360.

If loss is ₹ 3 , articles bought = (360 × 3) = 1080.

86. L.C.M. of 2, 3, 4, 5 = 60.

Suppose the grocer purchased (60 × 1), (60 × 2), (60 × 3) lemons *i.e.,* 60, 120 and 180 lemons of first, second and third qualities respectively.

Then, C.P. of 60 lemons of first quality = ₹ $\left(\frac{1}{2}\times 60\right)$ = ₹ 30.

C.P. of 120 lemons of second quality = ₹ $\left(\frac{2}{3}\times 120\right)$ = ₹ 80.

C.P. of 180 lemons of third quality = ₹ $\left(\frac{3}{4}\times 180\right)$ = ₹ 135.

Total C.P. of (60 + 120 + 180) *i.e.,* 360 lemons = ₹ (30 + 80 + 135) = ₹ 245.

S.P. of 360 lemons = ₹ $\left(\frac{4}{5}\times 360\right)$ = ₹ 288.

Gain = ₹ (288 – 245) = ₹ 43.

∴ Gain% = $\left(\frac{43}{245}\times 100\right)\% = 17.56\%$.

87. C.P. of 6 toffees = ₹ 1. S.P. of 6 toffees = 120% of ₹ 1 = ₹ $\frac{6}{5}$.

For ₹ $\frac{6}{5}$, toffees sold = 6. For ₹ 1, toffees sold = $\left(6\times\frac{5}{6}\right) = 5$.

88. C.P. of 8 pens = ₹ 100. S.P. of 8 pens = 160% of ₹ 100 = ₹ 160.

For ₹ 160, pens sold = 8.

For ₹ 100, pens sold = $\left(\frac{8}{160}\times 100\right) = 5$.

89. Let S.P. of 12 toffees be ₹ x.

Then, 80 : 1 = 120 : x or $x = \left(\frac{120}{80}\right) = \frac{3}{2}$.

For ₹ $\frac{3}{2}$, toffees sold = 12.

For ₹ 1, toffees sold = $\left(12 \times \frac{2}{3}\right) = 8$.

90. Let S.P. of 45 lemons be ₹ x.

Then, 80 : 40 = 120 : x or $x = \left(\frac{120 \times 40}{80}\right) = 60$.

For ₹ 60, lemons sold = 45.

For ₹ 24, lemons sold = $\left(\frac{45}{60} \times 24\right) = 18$.

91. S.P. of 90 ball pens = ₹ 160, Loss = 20%.

C.P. of 90 ball pens = ₹ $\left(\frac{100}{80} \times 160\right)$ = ₹ 200.

∴ Desired S.P. of 90 ball pens = ₹ $\left(\frac{120}{100} \times 200\right)$ = ₹ 240.

For ₹ 240, ball pens sold = 90.

For ₹ 96, ball pens sold = $\left(\frac{90}{240} \times 96\right) = 36$.

92. Total fare collected at full occupancy
= ₹ (8 × 72 × 300 + 2 × 64 × 898 + 2 × 45 × 1388 + 1 × 26 × 2691)
= ₹ (172800 + 114944 + 124920 + 69966) = ₹ 482630.

Total running cost = ₹ (25 × 5 × 1100 + 10 × 8 × 1100)
= ₹ (137500 + 88000) = ₹ 225500.

∴ Profit = ₹ (482630 – 225500) = ₹ 257130 ≈ ₹ 250000.

93. Clearly, we have:
Profit margin = Total fare collected – Total running cost

Profit margin exhibited by 3 tier
= ₹ [(8 × 72 × 300) – (8 × 10 × 1100)]
= ₹ (172800 – 88000) = ₹ 84800.

Profit margin exhibited by AC – 3 tier
= ₹ [(2 × 64 × 898) – (2 × 25 × 1100)] = ₹ (114944 – 55000)
= ₹ 59944.

Profit margin exhibited by AC – 2 tier
= ₹ [(2 × 45 × 1388) – (2 × 25 × 1100)]
= ₹ (124920 – 55000) = ₹ 69920.

Profit margin exhibited by AC-first class
= ₹ [(1 × 26 × 2691) – (1 × 25 × 1100)]
= ₹ (69966 – 27500) = ₹ 42466.

Clearly, it is the highest for 3 tier.

94. Revenue generated by 3 tier = ₹ (8 × 72 × 300) = ₹ 172800.

Revenue generated by AC-3 tier = ₹ (2 × 64 × 898) = ₹ 114944.

Revenue generated by AC-2 tier = ₹ (2 × 45 × 1388) = ₹ 124920.

Revenue generated by AC-first class = ₹ (1 × 26 × 2691) = ₹ 69966.

Clearly, it is the highest for 3 tier.

95. The profit margin collected by AC-first class is the lowest.

∴ Required percentage = $\left(\frac{42466}{27500} \times 100\right)\% = 154.4\%$.

96. As calculated in Q. 92,
Total profit = ₹ 257130.
Profit from AC bogies = ₹ [(114944 + 124920 + 69966) – 137500] = ₹ (309830 – 137500) = ₹ 172330.

∴ Required percentage = $\left(\frac{172330}{257130} \times 100\right)\% = 67\% \approx 70\%$.

97. (*a*) Profit = ₹ [{(42 – 32.40) × 25} + {(38 – 34.50) × 30}]
= ₹ [(9.6 × 25) + (3.5 × 30)] = ₹ (240 + 105) = ₹ 345.

(*b*) Profit = ₹ [{(37 – 28.60) × 40} + {(40 – 34.50) × 20}]
= ₹ [(8.4 × 40) + (5.5 × 20)] = ₹ (336 + 110) = ₹ 446.

(*c*) Profit = ₹ [{(38 – 34.50) × 20} + {(36 – 32.40) × 20}]
= ₹ [(3.5 × 20) + (3.6 × 20)] = ₹ (70 + 72) = ₹ 142.

(*d*) Profit = ₹ [{(37 – 34.50) × 30} + {(33 – 28.60) × 20}]
= ₹ [(2.5 × 30) + (4.4 × 20)] = ₹ (75 + 88) = ₹ 163.

(*e*) Profit = ₹ [{(40 – 28.60) × 20} + {(38 – 32.40) × 40}]
= ₹ [(11.4 × 20) + (5.6 × 40)] = ₹ (228 + 224) = ₹ 452.

Clearly, the shopkeeper gains the maximum in transaction (*e*).

98. C.P. of 70 kg wheat
= ₹ (30 × 9.50 + 40 × 8.50) = ₹ (285 + 340) = ₹ 625.
S.P. of 70 kg wheat
= ₹ (70 × 8.90) = ₹ 623.
∴ Loss = ₹ (625 – 623) = ₹ 2.

99. C.P. of 40 kg rice
= ₹ (25 × 32 + 15 × 36) = ₹ (800 + 540) = ₹ 1340.
S.P. of 40 kg rice
= ₹ (40 × 40.20) = 1608.
Profit = ₹ (1608 – 1340) = 268.

∴ Profit % = $\left(\frac{268}{1340} \times 100\right)\% = 20\%$.

100. C.P. per kg of first variety = ₹ $\left(\frac{100}{80} \times 3.20\right)$ = ₹ 4.

C.P. per kg of second variety = ₹ $\left(\frac{100}{120} \times 6\right)$ = ₹ 5.

C.P. of 2 kg of sugar = ₹ (4 + 5) = ₹ 9.
S.P. of 2 kg of sugar = ₹ (2 × 5.40) = ₹ 10.80.
Gain = ₹ (10.80 – 9) = ₹ 1.80.

∴ Gain% = $\left(\frac{1.80}{9} \times 100\right)\% = 20\%$.

101. C.P. of 50 kg wheat = ₹ (30 × 11.50 + 20 × 14.25)
= ₹ (345 + 285) = ₹ 630.

S.P. of 50 kg wheat = 130% of ₹ 630 = ₹ $\left(\frac{130}{100} \times 630\right)$ = ₹ 819.

∴ S.P. per kg = ₹ $\left(\frac{819}{50}\right)$ = ₹ 16.38 ≈ ₹ 16.30.

102. Let the required price per kg be ₹ x. Then,
C.P. of 60 kg rice = ₹ (30 × 17.50 + 30 × x) = ₹ (525 + 30x).
S.P. of 60 kg rice = ₹ (60 × 18.60) = ₹ 1116.

$$\therefore \frac{1116 - (525 + 30x)}{525 + 30x} \times 100 = 20 \Leftrightarrow \frac{591 - 30x}{525 + 30x} = \frac{1}{5}$$

$\Leftrightarrow$ $2955 - 150x = 525 + 30x$

$\Leftrightarrow$ $180x = 2430$

$\Leftrightarrow$ $x = \left(\frac{2430}{180}\right) = \left(\frac{27}{2}\right) = 13.50.$

So, the C.P. of second lot is ₹ 13.50 per kg.

103. Suppose he bought 5 kg and 4 kg of the two varieties respectively.

C.P. of 9 kg = ₹ (5 × 160 + 4 × 200) = ₹ 1600.

S.P. of 9 kg = ₹ (9 × 192) = ₹ 1728.

$\therefore$ Profit % = $\left(\frac{128}{1600} \times 100\right)\% = 8\%.$

104. Suppose he bought 2 kg, 4 kg and 3 kg of the three varieties respectively.

C.P. of 9 kg = ₹ (2 × 50 + 4 × 20 + 3 × 30) = ₹ 270.

S.P. of 9 kg = ₹ (9 × 33) = ₹ 297.

$\therefore$ Profit% = $\left(\frac{27}{270} \times 100\right)\% = 10\%.$

105. C.P. of 30 kg wheat = ₹ (30 × 45) = ₹ 1350.

Quantity of wheat sold = 40% of 30 kg = 12 kg.

Quantity left = (30 – 12) kg = 18 kg.

For 25% profit, desired S.P. = ₹ $\left(\frac{125}{100} \times 1350\right)$ = ₹ 1687.50.

Money realised by selling 12 kg wheat = ₹ (12 × 50) = ₹ 600.

Balance required = ₹ (1687.50 – 600) = ₹ 1087.50.

$\therefore$ Required price = ₹ $\left(\frac{1087.50}{18}\right)$ per kg

= ₹ 60.41 per kg ≈ ₹ 60 per kg.

106. Suppose he bought 12 kg, 15 kg and 20 kg of the three varieties respectively.

Then, total C.P. = ₹ (12 × 100 + 15 × 80 + 20 × 60)

= ₹ (1200 + 1200 + 1200) = ₹ 3600.

Let the loss on the third quantity be x%.

Then, 120% of 2400 + (100 – x)% of 1200 = 3600

$\Rightarrow \left(\frac{6}{5} \times 24\right) + \left(\frac{100 - x}{100} \times 12\right) = 36$

$\Rightarrow \frac{100 - x}{100} \times 12 = 36 - \frac{144}{5} = \frac{36}{5}$

$\Rightarrow \frac{100 - x}{100} = \frac{36}{5} \times \frac{1}{12} = \frac{3}{5} \Rightarrow 500 - 5x = 300$

$\Rightarrow 5x = 200 \Rightarrow x = 40\%.$

107. Mean cost price = ₹ $\left(\frac{100}{137.5} \times 8\right)$ = ₹ $\frac{64}{11}$.

By the rule of alligation :

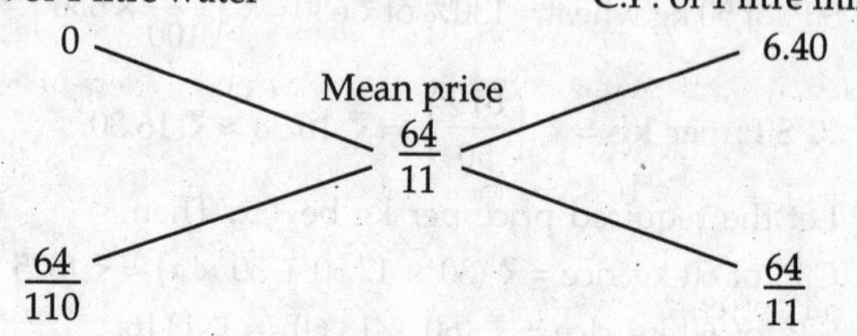

$\therefore$ Required ratio = $\frac{64}{110} : \frac{64}{11} = 1 : 10.$

108. Mean cost price = ₹ $\left(\frac{100}{120} \times 3\right)$ = ₹ $\frac{5}{2}$.

By the rule of alligation:

C.P. of 1 litre water — C.P. of 1 litre milk

0 — 3

Mean price $\frac{5}{2}$

$\frac{1}{2}$ — $\frac{5}{2}$

$\therefore$ Ratio of water and milk = $\frac{1}{2} : \frac{5}{2} = 1 : 5.$

So, required quantity of milk = (5 × 5) litres = 25 litres.

109. Let the cost of the other brand be ₹ x per kg.

C.P. of 5 kg = ₹ (2 × 200 + 3 × x) = ₹ (400 + 3x).

S.P. of 5 kg = ₹ (5 × 177) = ₹ 885.

$\therefore \frac{885 - (400 + 3x)}{400 + 3x} \times 100 = 18 \Leftrightarrow \frac{485 - 3x}{400 + 3x} = \frac{9}{50}$

$\Leftrightarrow 24250 - 150x = 3600 + 27x$

$\Leftrightarrow 177x = 20650 \Leftrightarrow x = \left(\frac{350}{3}\right) = 116\frac{2}{3}.$

So, cost of the other brand = ₹ 116.66.

110. Suppose, he must produce x items.

Then, C.P. = ₹ (40x + 3000), S.P. = 60x.

$\therefore$ $60x - (40x + 3000) = 1000$ or $20x = 4000$ or $x = 200$.

111. C.P. of 20 kg milk = ₹ (20 × 15) = ₹ 300.

Quantity of water added = 10% of 20 kg = 2 kg.

S.P. of 1 kg mixture = 110% of ₹ 15 = ₹ 16.50.

S.P. of 22 kg mixture = ₹ (22 × 16.50) = ₹ 363.

$\therefore$ Profit = ₹ (363 – 300) = ₹ 63.

112. Gain% = $\left(\frac{10}{90} \times 100\right)\% = 11\frac{1}{9}\%.$

113. Gain% = $\left(\frac{50}{950} \times 100\right)\% = 5\frac{5}{19}\%.$

114. Let error = x gms.

Then, $\frac{x}{1000 - x} \times 100 = 25 \Leftrightarrow \frac{100x}{1000 - x} = 25$

$\Leftrightarrow 100x = 25000 - 25x \Leftrightarrow 125x = 25000$

$\Leftrightarrow x = 200.$

$\therefore$ Weight used = (1000 – 200) gms = 800 gms.

115. Let error = x gms. Then,

$\frac{x}{1000 - x} \times 100 = 6\frac{18}{47} \Leftrightarrow \frac{100x}{1000 - x} = \frac{300}{47}$

$\Leftrightarrow 47x = 3(1000 - x) \Leftrightarrow 50x = 3000 \Leftrightarrow x = 60.$

$\therefore$ Weight used = (1000 – 60) = 940 gms.

116. **Rule:** Gain% = $\frac{(100 + \text{common gain }\%)^2}{100} - 100.$

$\therefore$ Gain% = $\left[\frac{(100 + 10)^2}{100} - 100\right]\%$

$= \left(\frac{12100 - 10000}{100}\right)\% = 21\%.$

117. Let the C.P. of 1 kg goods be ₹ 1.
Then, he buys 1100 g goods for ₹ 1 and sells 900 g goods for ₹ 1.
$\therefore$ C.P. of 1100 g goods = ₹ 1
$\Rightarrow$ C.P. of 900 g goods = ₹ $\left(\frac{1}{1100}\times 900\right) = ₹\frac{9}{11}$.
S.P. of 900 g goods = ₹ 1.
Gain = ₹ $\left(1-\frac{9}{11}\right) = ₹\frac{2}{11}$.
$\therefore$ Gain% = $\left(\frac{2}{11}\times\frac{11}{9}\times 100\right)\% = \frac{200}{9}\%$.

118. Let us consider a packet of rice marked 1 kg.
Its actual weight is 80% of 1000 gm = 800 gm.
Let C.P. of each gm be ₹ 1.
Then, C.P. of this packet = ₹ 800.
S.P. of this packet = 110% of
C.P. of 1 kg = ₹ $\left(\frac{110}{100}\times 1000\right) = ₹ 1100$.
$\therefore$ Gain% = $\left(\frac{300}{800}\times 100\right)\% = 37.5\%$.
Short cut Method: Using the formula, we have:
Gain% = $\left\{\left(\frac{x+y}{100-y}\right)\times 100\right\}\% = \left\{\left(\frac{10+20}{100-20}\right)\times 100\right\}\%$
$= \left(\frac{30}{80}\times 100\right)\% = 37.5\%$.

119. Gain/Loss% = $\left\{\left(\frac{y-x}{100-y}\right)\times 100\right\}\% = \left\{\left(\frac{15-20}{100-15}\right)\times 100\right\}\%$
$= \left(\frac{-5}{85}\times 100\right)\% = -\frac{100}{17}\%$
$= -5\frac{15}{17}\%$.
Since it is –ve, hence it is a loss.

120. Percentage deduction in weight = $\left(\frac{160}{1000}\times 100\right)\% = 16\%$.
$\therefore$ Gain/Loss% = $\left[\left(\frac{y-x}{100-y}\right)\times 100\right]\% = \left(\frac{16-4}{100-16}\times 100\right)\%$
$= \left(\frac{12}{84}\times 100\right)\% = \frac{100}{7}\% = 14\frac{2}{7}\%$.
Since it is +ve, hence it is a gain.

121. Let the percentage deduction in weight be y %.
Then, $\frac{y-4}{100-y}\times 100 = 20 \Rightarrow \frac{y-4}{100-y} = \frac{1}{5}$
$\Rightarrow 5y - 20 = 100 - y \Rightarrow 6y = 120 \Rightarrow y = 20$.
Hence, for a metre, length used = (100 – 20)% of 1 m = 80% of 100 cm = 80 cm.

122. Let the actual C.P. of 1 m cloth be ₹ 1.
Then, the merchant buys 120 cm cloth for ₹ 1 and sells 80 cm cloth at a discount of 20% on ₹ 1.
So, C.P. of 120 cm cloth = ₹ 1
$\Rightarrow$ C.P. of 80 cm cloth = ₹ $\left(\frac{1}{120}\times 80\right) = ₹\frac{2}{3}$.
S.P. of 80 cm cloth = 80% of ₹ 1 = ₹ $\frac{4}{5}$.
Profit = ₹ $\left(\frac{4}{5}-\frac{2}{3}\right) = ₹\frac{2}{15}$.
$\therefore$ Profit % = $\left(\frac{2}{15}\times\frac{3}{2}\times 100\right)\% = 20\%$.

123. Let the required gain be x%.
Percentage deduction in weight = $\left(\frac{200}{1000}\times 100\right)\% = 20\%$.
$\therefore \frac{20+x}{100-20}\times 100 = 37\frac{1}{2} \Rightarrow \frac{20+x}{80} = \frac{3}{8}$
$\Rightarrow 20 + x = 30 \Rightarrow x = 10$.
Hence, nominal gain percentage = 10%.

124. Let the C.P. of 1 kg of almonds be ₹ 100.
Then, S.P. realised by the merchant on selling a 2 kg pack = ₹ (2 × 80) = ₹ 160.
Profit = $6\frac{2}{3}\%$.
C.P. of each pack
= ₹ $\left(\frac{100}{106\frac{2}{3}}\times 160\right) = ₹\left(100\times\frac{3}{320}\times 160\right) = ₹ 150$.
Clearly, the 2 kg pack has 1 kg 500 gm of almonds.
So, other weight = (1 kg 500 gm – 850 gm) = 650 gm.

125. We find the net profit in each case :
(*a*) In this case, profit = 10%.
(*b*) Profit = $\left(\frac{100}{900}\times 100\right)\% = 11\frac{1}{9}\%$.
(*c*) Let C.P. of sugar be ₹ 1 per kg.
Then, he mixes 100 gm impurities and realizes the C.P. of 1.1 kg sugar by selling 1 kg of sugar. *i.e.*, S.P. of sugar = ₹ 1.10 per kg.
$\therefore$ Profit = $\left(\frac{0.1}{1}\times 100\right)\% = 10\%$.
(*d*) Let C.P. of sugar be ₹ 1 per kg.
Since he weighs 950 gm instead of a kg, his actual C.P. = ₹ 0.95.
S.P. = 105% of ₹ 1 = ₹ 1.05.
$\therefore$ Profit = $\left(\frac{0.10}{0.95}\times 100\right)\% = 10\frac{10}{19}\%$.
Clearly, the maximum profit is earned when he used a 900 gm weight for a kg.

126. Suppose he has 100 items. Let C.P. of each item be ₹ 1.
Total cost = ₹ 100. Number of items left after theft = 80.
S.P. of each item = ₹ 1.10.
$\therefore$ Total sale = ₹ (1.10 × 80) = ₹ 88.
Hence, Loss% = $\left(\frac{12}{100}\times 100\right)\% = 12\%$.

127. Let the price paid by Prateek be ₹ x.
Then, 140% of 120% of x = 10500

$$\Rightarrow \frac{140}{100}\times\frac{120}{100}\times x = 10500 \Rightarrow x = \left(10500\times\frac{25}{42}\right) = 6250.$$

128. Let the cost of the article be ₹ x.
Then, cost paid by retail merchant = 95% of 120% of ₹ x

$$= ₹\left(\frac{95}{100}\times\frac{120}{100}\times x\right) = ₹\left(\frac{114}{100}x\right) = 114\% \text{ of } ₹\ x$$

∴ Gain = 14%.

129. 110% of 90% of 120% of A = 1188

$$\Rightarrow \frac{110}{100}\times\frac{90}{100}\times\frac{120}{100}A = 1188 \Rightarrow \frac{1188}{1000}A = 1188 \Rightarrow A = 1000.$$

∴ A purchased it for ₹ (1000 – 110) = ₹ 890.

130. Money spent by X = ₹ 150000.
Money received by X = 105% of ₹ 150000 = ₹ 157500.
C.P. to X = 98% of ₹ 157500 = ₹ 154350.
∴ X gains ₹ (157500 – 154350) = ₹ 3150.

131. Let the C.P. for the manufacturer be ₹ x.
Then, 95% of 120% of 110% of x = 627

$$\Rightarrow \frac{95}{100}\times\frac{120}{100}\times\frac{110}{100}\times x = 627 \quad \Rightarrow \quad x = 500.$$

132. Let the cost paid by the first trader be ₹ x.
Then, 125% of 125% of 125% of x = 250

$$\Rightarrow \frac{125}{100}\times\frac{125}{100}\times\frac{125}{100}\times x = 250 \Rightarrow x = \left(250\times\frac{64}{125}\right) = 128.$$

133. Let the original cost of the article be ₹ P and the profit percent made by the second be x%.
Then, 120% of (100 + x)% of P = 138% of P

$$\Rightarrow \frac{120}{100}\times\frac{(100+x)}{100} = \frac{138}{100} \quad \Rightarrow \quad \frac{100+x}{100} = \frac{23}{20}$$

$\Rightarrow 100 + x = 115 \Rightarrow x = 15.$

134. Let the S.P. be ₹ x. Then,

$$x - 10\% \text{ of } x = 27 \Leftrightarrow 90\% \text{ of } x = 27 \Leftrightarrow x = \left(27\times\frac{10}{9}\right) = 30.$$

135. Let the S.P. be ₹ x. Profit = 25%

Then, C.P. = x – 25% of ₹ x = 75% of ₹ x = ₹ $\left(\frac{3}{4}x\right)$.

$$\text{Profit} = ₹\left(x - \frac{3}{4}x\right) = ₹\frac{x}{4}.$$

$$\therefore \text{Profit\%} = \left(\frac{x}{4}\times\frac{4}{3x}\times 100\right)\% = 33\frac{1}{3}\%.$$

136. Let C.P. be ₹ x. Then, profit = 20% of ₹ x = ₹ $\frac{x}{5}$.

$$\text{S.P.} = ₹\left(x + \frac{x}{5}\right) = ₹\frac{6x}{5}.$$

$$\therefore \text{Desired profit \%} = \left(\frac{x}{5}\times\frac{5}{6x}\times 100\right)\% = 16\frac{2}{3}\%.$$

137. Let Roshan's C.P. = ₹ p.

$$\text{Profit} = 15\% \text{ of } ₹\ p = ₹\left(\frac{3}{20}p\right).$$

$$\text{S.P.} = ₹\left(p + \frac{3}{20}p\right) = ₹\left(\frac{23}{20}p\right).$$

$$\text{Profit \% on S.P.} = \left(\frac{3p}{20}\times\frac{20}{23p}\times 100\right)\% = \left(\frac{300}{23}\right)\%.$$

Now, let S.P. of each be ₹ x.

Then, 25% of x – $\frac{300}{23}$% of x = 275

$$\Rightarrow \frac{275}{23}x = 27500 \Rightarrow x = \left(\frac{27500\times 23}{275}\right) = 2300.$$

138. Let C.P. = ₹ x, Profit% = x % and S.P. = ₹ 144.

$$\therefore x = \left[\frac{100}{(100+x)}\times 144\right] \Rightarrow x^2 + 100x = 14400$$

$\Rightarrow x^2 + 100x - 14400 = 0$

$\Rightarrow x^2 + 180x - 80x - 14400 = 0$

$\Rightarrow (x + 180)(x - 80) = 0 \Rightarrow x = 80.$

139. Let the M.P. be ₹ x.

Then, S.P. = ₹ $\frac{2}{3}x$, Loss = 10%.

$$\text{C.P.} = ₹\left(\frac{100}{90}\times\frac{2}{3}x\right) = ₹\frac{20}{27}x.$$

If an article is sold at M.P., then

$$\text{Profit} = ₹\left(x - \frac{20}{27}x\right) = ₹\frac{7x}{27}.$$

$$\therefore \text{Profit\%} = \left(\frac{7x}{27}\times\frac{27}{20x}\times 100\right)\% = 35\%.$$

140. Let S.P. be ₹ x. Then, C.P.

$= ₹\ \frac{13}{15}x$, Receipt = 112% of ₹ x = ₹ $\frac{28}{25}x$.

$$\text{Gain} = ₹\left(\frac{28x}{25} - \frac{13x}{15}\right) = ₹\frac{19x}{75}.$$

$$\therefore \text{Gain\%} = \left(\frac{19x}{75}\times\frac{15}{13x}\times 100\right)\% = \frac{380}{13}\% = 29\frac{3}{13}\%.$$

141. Let the article be worth ₹ x.

C.P. = 90% of ₹ x = ₹ $\frac{9x}{10}$;

S.P. = 110% of ₹ x = ₹ $\frac{11x}{10}$.

$$\text{Gain} = ₹\left(\frac{11x}{10} - \frac{9x}{10}\right) = ₹\frac{x}{5}.$$

$$\therefore \text{Gain\%} = \left(\frac{x}{5}\times\frac{10}{9x}\times 100\right)\% = 22\frac{2}{9}\% > 20\%.$$

142. Let original price = ₹ 100.

Then, C.P. = ₹ 90, S.P. = 130% of ₹ 90 = ₹ $\left(\frac{130}{100}\times 90\right)$ = ₹ 117.

∴ Required percentage = (117 – 100)% = 17%.

143. Let C.P. be ₹ x.

Then, 5% of x = (350 – 340) = 10 $\Rightarrow \frac{x}{20} = 10 \quad \Rightarrow \quad x = 200.$

144. Let C.P. be ₹ x. Then, 2% of x = (400 – 380) = 20

$\Rightarrow \frac{x}{50} = 20 \Rightarrow x = 1000.$

145. Let C.P. be ₹ x.

Then, $107\frac{1}{2}\%$ of $x - 92\frac{1}{2}\%$ of $x = 3$

$\Rightarrow \frac{215}{200}x - \frac{185}{200}x = 3 \Rightarrow \frac{30x}{200} = 3 \Rightarrow x = 20.$

146. Let C.P. be ₹ x. Then,

$(106\%\text{ of } x) - \left(87\frac{1}{2}\%\text{ of } x\right) = 92.50$

$\Rightarrow 18\frac{1}{2}\%\text{ of } x = 92.50 \Rightarrow x = \left(\frac{92.50 \times 100 \times 2}{37}\right) = 500.$

147. Let C.P. be ₹ x. Then, $\left(107\frac{1}{2}\%\text{ of } x\right) - \left(97\frac{1}{2}\%\text{ of } x\right) = 100$

$\Rightarrow 10\%\text{ of } x = 100 \Rightarrow x = 1000.$

$\therefore$ Desired S.P. = $112\frac{1}{2}\%$ of ₹ 1000

$= ₹\left(\frac{225}{2} \times \frac{1}{100} \times 1000\right) = ₹\,1125.$

148. Let the C.P. be ₹ 100. Then, profit = 20%. S.P. = ₹ 120.
New C.P. = 20% less = ₹ 80.

If gain is 25% then S.P. = $₹\left(\frac{125}{100} \times 80\right) = ₹\,100.$

Difference in S.P. = ₹ (120 – 100) = ₹ 20.
If difference in S.P. is ₹ 20, then C.P. = ₹ 100.

If difference in S.P. is ₹ 18, then C.P. = $₹\left(\frac{100}{20} \times 18\right) = ₹\,90.$

149. Let C.P. of the book be ₹ 100.
Profit = 10%. S.P. = ₹ 110.
New C.P. = 4% less = ₹ 96.

If gain is $18\frac{3}{4}\%$, then S.P. = $\left(118\frac{3}{4}\%\text{ of } ₹\,96\right)$

$= ₹\left(\frac{475}{4} \times \frac{1}{100} \times 96\right) = ₹\,114.$

Difference in S.P. = ₹ (114 – 110) = ₹ 4.
If difference in S.P. is ₹ 4, C.P. = ₹ 100.

If difference in S.P. is ₹ 6, C.P. = $₹\left(\frac{100}{4} \times 6\right) = ₹\,150.$

150. Let C.P. be ₹ x. Profit = 20%. S.P. = 120% of ₹ x = ₹ $\frac{6x}{5}$.

New C.P. = ₹ $(x - 100)$. New S.P. = $₹\left(\frac{6x}{5} - 100\right)$.

Profit = $₹\left[\left(\frac{6x}{5} - 100\right) - (x - 100)\right] = ₹\,\frac{x}{5}.$

$\therefore \frac{x}{5} \times \frac{1}{(x-100)} \times 100 = 25 \Rightarrow 20x = 25(x - 100)$

$\Rightarrow 5x = 2500 \Rightarrow x = 500.$

151. Let the C.P. be ₹ x. Profit = 20%.

S.P. = $₹\left(\frac{120}{100} \times x\right) = ₹\,\frac{6x}{5}.$

New C.P. = $₹\left(\frac{110}{100} \times x\right) = ₹\,\frac{11x}{10}.$

New S.P. = $₹\left(\frac{6x}{5} + 26\right).$

New profit = $₹\left[\left(\frac{6x}{5} + 26\right) - \frac{11x}{10}\right] = ₹\left(\frac{x}{10} + 26\right).$

$\therefore \left(\frac{x}{10} + 26\right) \times \frac{10}{11x} \times 100 = 15 \Rightarrow 100\,(x + 260) = 165x$

$\Rightarrow 65x = 26000 \Rightarrow x = 400.$

152. Let the C.P. be ₹ x.

Then, S.P. = 120% of ₹ x = $₹\left(x \times \frac{120}{100}\right) = ₹\,\frac{6x}{5}.$

$\therefore \frac{6x}{5} - x = 240 \Leftrightarrow x = 1200.$

$\therefore$ S.P. = $₹\left(\frac{6}{5} \times 1200\right) = ₹\,1440.$

153. Let C.P. of the article be ₹ x.

Then, Required ratio = $\frac{104\%\text{ of } x}{106\%\text{ of } x} = \frac{104}{106} = \frac{52}{53} = 52:53.$

154. Let the two investments be ₹ $3x$ and ₹ $5x$ respectively.
Then, total investment = ₹ $(3x + 5x)$ = ₹ $8x$.
Total output = ₹ (115% of $3x$ + 90% of $5x$)
= ₹ $(3.45x + 4.5x)$ = ₹ $7.95x$.
Loss = ₹ $(8x - 7.95x)$ = ₹ $0.05x$.

$\therefore$ Loss percent = $\left(\frac{0.05x}{8x} \times 100\right)\% = \frac{5}{8}\%.$

155. Let the S.P. of watches w_1, w_2 and w_3 be ₹ $2x$, ₹ $3x$ and ₹ $4x$ respectively.
Gain on watch w_1 = 30%.

C.P. of watch w_1 = $₹\left(\frac{100}{130} \times 2x\right) = ₹\,\frac{20x}{13}.$

Gain on watch w_2 = 20%.

C.P. of watch w_2 = $₹\left(\frac{100}{120} \times 3x\right) = ₹\,\frac{5x}{2}.$

Loss on watch w_3 = 40%.

C.P. of watch w_3 = $₹\left(\frac{100}{60} \times 4x\right) = ₹\,\frac{20x}{3}.$

Total C.P. of three watches = $₹\left(\frac{20x}{13} + \frac{5x}{2} + \frac{20x}{3}\right)$

$= ₹\left(\frac{120x + 195x + 520x}{78}\right) = ₹\,\frac{835x}{78}.$

Total S.P. of three watches = ₹ $(2x + 3x + 4x)$ = $9x$.

Loss = $₹\left(\frac{835x}{78} - 9x\right) = ₹\,\frac{133x}{78}.$

$\therefore$ Loss% = $\left(\frac{133x}{78} \times \frac{78}{835x} \times 100\right)\%$

$= \left(\frac{2660}{167}\right)\% = 15.93\% \approx 16\%.$

156. Loss% = $\left(\frac{\text{Common Gain \& Loss\%}}{10}\right)^2\% = \left(\frac{20}{10}\right)^2\% = 4\%.$

157. Loss% $= \left(\frac{\text{Common Loss and Gain\%}}{10}\right)^2 \%$

$= \left(\frac{12}{10}\right)^2 \% = \frac{36}{25}\% = 1\frac{11}{25}\%.$

158. Loss% $= \left(\frac{5}{10}\right)^2 \% = (0.5)^2\% = 0.25\%.$

159. Total S.P. = ₹ 8000 and Total C.P. = ₹ 8000.

S.P. of 1st commodity = ₹ 4000.

Gain on it = 25%.

∴ C.P. of 1st commodity

$= ₹ \left(\frac{100}{125} \times 4000\right) = ₹ 3200.$

C.P. of 2nd commodity

= ₹ (8000 − 3200) = ₹ 4800.

S.P. of 2nd commodity

= ₹ 4000.

∴ Loss on 2nd commodity

$= \left(\frac{800}{4800} \times 100\right)\% = 16\frac{2}{3}\%.$

160. Total S.P. = ₹ 2 lakh.

C.P. of house $= ₹ \left(\frac{100}{80} \times 1\right)$ lakh $= ₹ \frac{5}{4}$ lakh.

C.P. of shop $= ₹ \left(\frac{100}{120} \times 1\right)$ lakh $= ₹ \frac{5}{6}$ lakh.

Total C.P. $= ₹ \left(\frac{5}{4} + \frac{5}{6}\right)$ lakh $= ₹ \frac{25}{12}$ lakh.

∴ Loss $= ₹ \left(\frac{25}{12} - 2\right)$ lakh $= ₹ \frac{1}{12}$ lakh.

161. Total S.P. = ₹ (2 × 99) = ₹ 198.

C.P. of first article $= ₹ \left(\frac{100}{110} \times 99\right) = ₹ 90.$

C.P. of second article $= ₹ \left(\frac{100}{90} \times 99\right) = ₹ 110.$

Total C.P. = ₹ (90 + 110) = ₹ 200.

∴ Loss = ₹ (200 − 198) = ₹ 2.

162. Total S.P. = ₹ (2 × 500) = ₹ 1000.

C.P. of first chair $= ₹ \left(\frac{100}{120} \times 500\right) = ₹ \frac{1250}{3}.$

C.P. of second chair $= ₹ \left(\frac{100}{88} \times 500\right) = ₹ \frac{6250}{11}.$

Total C.P. $= ₹ \left(\frac{1250}{3} + \frac{6250}{11}\right) = ₹ \left(\frac{32500}{33}\right).$

Gain $= ₹ \left(1000 - \frac{32500}{33}\right) = ₹ \left(\frac{500}{33}\right).$

∴ Gain % $= \left(\frac{500}{33} \times \frac{33}{32500} \times 100\right)\% = 1.54\% \approx 1.5\%.$

163. Total C.P. = ₹ (120 × 110) = ₹ 13200.

Total S.P. = ₹ [(30 × 110 + 30 × 12) + (75 × 110 + 75 × 14) + (15 × 110 − 15 × 7)] = ₹ 14505.

Average profit $= ₹ \left(\frac{14505 - 13200}{120}\right) = ₹ \frac{1305}{120} = ₹ 10.875.$

164. Total profit required = ₹ (42 × 18) = ₹ 756.

Profit on 22 sarees = ₹ (460 + 144) = ₹ 604.

Profit on 20 sarees = ₹ (756 − 604) = ₹ 152.

Average profit on these sarees $= ₹ \left(\frac{152}{20}\right) = ₹ 7.60.$

165. C.P. of 20 dozen = ₹ (48 × 20) = ₹ 960.

C.P. of 8 dozen = ₹ (48 × 8) = ₹ 384.

C.P. of 12 dozen = ₹ (960 − 384) = ₹ 576.

Total S.P. $= ₹ \left(\frac{110}{100} \times 384 + \frac{120}{100} \times 576\right) = ₹ 1113.60.$

∴ Profit % $= \left(\frac{153.60}{960} \times 100\right)\% = 16\%.$

166. Let the total C.P. of all the articles be ₹ x.

Then, C.P. of 80% of the articles = 80% of ₹ $x = ₹ \frac{4x}{5}.$

C.P. of the remaining articles $= ₹ \left(x - \frac{4x}{5}\right) = ₹ \frac{x}{5}.$

Total S.P. $= ₹ \left(110\% \text{ of } \frac{4x}{5} + 60\% \text{ of } \frac{x}{5}\right) = ₹ \left(\frac{22x}{25} + \frac{3x}{25}\right) = ₹ x.$

Since C.P. = S.P., there is no profit, no loss.

167. Let the C.P. of the whole be ₹ x.

C.P. of $\frac{1}{4}$th $= ₹ \frac{x}{4}$, C.P. of $\frac{3}{4}$th $= ₹ \frac{3x}{4}.$

Total S.P. $= ₹ \left(110\% \text{ of } \frac{x}{4} + 80\% \text{ of } \frac{3x}{4}\right)$

$= ₹ \left(\frac{11x}{40} + \frac{3x}{5}\right) = ₹ \frac{7x}{8}.$

Loss $= ₹ \left(x - \frac{7x}{8}\right) = ₹ \frac{x}{8}.$

∴ Loss% $= \left(\frac{x}{8} \times \frac{1}{x} \times 100\right)\% = 12.5\%.$

168. Total C.P. = ₹ (120 × 3) = ₹ 360.

Total S.P. = ₹ (40 × 4 + 60 × 5 + 20 × 3) = ₹ 520.

Profit = ₹ (520 − 360) = ₹ 160.

∴ Profit% $= \left(\frac{160}{360} \times 100\right)\% = \left(\frac{400}{9}\right)\% = 44\frac{4}{9}\%.$

169. C.P. of each pen $= ₹ \left(\frac{9000}{1000}\right) = ₹ 9.$

Pens sold during first month = 75% of 1000 = 750.

S.P. of each pen sold during first month = 180% of ₹ 9

$= ₹ \frac{81}{5}.$

Pens sold afterwards = 50% of 250 = 125.

S.P. of each pen sold afterwards = 120% of ₹ 9 $= ₹ \frac{54}{5}.$

Total S.P. = ₹ $\left(750 \times \frac{81}{5} + 125 \times \frac{54}{5}\right)$

= ₹ (12150 + 1350) = ₹ 13500.

170. Let the C.P. of whole be ₹ x.

Then, C.P. of $\frac{1}{3}$rd goods = ₹ $\frac{x}{3}$,

C.P. of $\frac{3}{5}$th goods = ₹ $\frac{3x}{5}$.

C.P. of remaining goods = ₹ $\left[x - \left(\frac{x}{3} + \frac{3x}{5}\right)\right] = ₹ \frac{x}{15}$.

Total S.P. = ₹ $\left(114\% \text{ of } \frac{x}{3} + 117\frac{1}{2}\% \text{ of } \frac{3x}{5} + 120\% \text{ of } \frac{x}{15}\right)$

= ₹ $\left(\frac{38x}{100} + \frac{141x}{200} + \frac{8x}{100}\right) = ₹ \left(\frac{233x}{200}\right)$.

Profit = ₹ $\left(\frac{233x}{200} - x\right) = ₹ \frac{33x}{200}$.

$\therefore$ Profit % = $\left(\frac{33x}{200} \times \frac{1}{x} \times 100\right)\% = \frac{33}{2}\% = 16.5\%$.

171. Let C.P. of whole be ₹ x.

C.P. of $\frac{1}{2}$ stock = ₹ $\frac{x}{2}$, C.P. of $\frac{1}{4}$ stock = ₹ $\frac{x}{4}$.

Total S.P. = ₹ $\left[\left(120\% \text{ of } \frac{x}{2}\right) + \left(80\% \text{ of } \frac{x}{4}\right) + \frac{x}{4}\right]$

= ₹ $\left(\frac{3x}{5} + \frac{x}{5} + \frac{x}{4}\right) = ₹ \frac{21x}{20}$.

Gain = ₹ $\left(\frac{21x}{20} - x\right) = ₹ \frac{x}{20}$.

$\therefore$ Gain% = $\left(\frac{x}{20} \times \frac{1}{x} \times 100\right)\% = 5\%$.

172. Let C.P. of each clock be ₹ x.

Then, C.P. of 90 clocks = ₹ $90x$.

$\therefore$ [(110% of $40x$) + (120% of $50x$)] − (115% of $90x$) = 40

$\Rightarrow 44x + 60x - 103.5x = 40 \Rightarrow 0.5x = 40 \Rightarrow x = 80$.

173. Let the investments be $3x$ and $5x$.

Then, total investment = $8x$.

Total receipt = (115% of $3x$ + 90% of $5x$)

= ($3.45x + 4.5x$) = $7.95x$.

$\therefore$ Loss = $\left(\frac{0.05x}{8x} \times 100\right)\% = \frac{5}{8}\%$.

174. Let the required gain percent be x%.

Then, (110% of 3000) + [(100 + x)% of 3000]

= 125% of 6000

$\Rightarrow \left(\frac{110}{100} \times 3000\right) + \left[\frac{(100+x)}{100} \times 3000\right] = \frac{125}{100} \times 6000$

$\Rightarrow$ 30 (100 + x) = 4200 $\Rightarrow$ 100 + x = 140 $\Rightarrow x = 40\%$.

175. Let the quantity sold at 18% profit be x kg and let C.P. per kg be ₹ 1.

Then, quantity sold at 8% profit = (1000 − x) kg.

Total C.P. = ₹ 1000.

Total S.P. = ₹ [108% of (1000 − x) + 118% of x]

= ₹ $\left[\frac{27}{25}(1000 - x) + \frac{59x}{50}\right] = ₹ \left(1080 + \frac{x}{10}\right)$.

$\therefore 1080 + \frac{x}{10} = 114\% \text{ of } 1000 \Rightarrow 1080 + \frac{x}{10} = 1140$

$\Rightarrow \frac{x}{10} = 60 \Rightarrow x = 600$.

176. Let the quantity sold at a loss be x kg and let C.P. per kg be ₹ 1.

Total C.P. = ₹ 24.

Total S.P. = ₹ [120% of (24 − x) + 95% of x]

= ₹ $\left[\frac{6}{5}(24 - x) + \frac{19x}{20}\right] = ₹ \left(\frac{576 - 5x}{20}\right)$

$\therefore \frac{576 - 5x}{20} = 110\% \text{ of } 24 \Rightarrow \frac{576 - 5x}{20} = \frac{264}{10} \Rightarrow 576 - 5x = 528$

$\Rightarrow 5x = 48 \Rightarrow x = 9.6$ kg.

177. Let the S.P. of the first horse be ₹ x.

Then, S.P. of the second horse = ₹ (1475 − x).

C.P. of first horse = ₹ (1475 − x).

Loss on first horse = 20%.

$\therefore \frac{80}{100} \times (1475 - x) = x \Rightarrow 4(1475 - x) = 5x$

$\Rightarrow 9x = 5900 \Rightarrow x = \frac{5900}{9}$.

S.P. of second horse = ₹ $\left(1475 - \frac{5900}{9}\right) = ₹ \frac{7375}{9}$.

C.P. of second horse = ₹ $\left(\frac{100}{125} \times \frac{7375}{9}\right) = ₹ \frac{5900}{9}$.

$\therefore$ C.P. of 1st horse = S.P. of 2nd horse and C.P. of 2nd horse = S.P. of 1st horse.

So, Total C.P. = Total S.P.

Hence, there is neither gain nor loss.

178. Let the total value be ₹ x.

Value of $\frac{2}{3}$rd = ₹ $\frac{2x}{3}$, Value of $\frac{1}{3}$rd = ₹ $\frac{x}{3}$.

Total S.P. = ₹ $\left[\left(106\% \text{ of } \frac{2x}{3}\right) + \left(97\% \text{ of } \frac{x}{3}\right)\right]$

= ₹ $\left(\frac{53x}{75} + \frac{97x}{300}\right) = ₹ \left(\frac{309x}{300}\right)$.

$\therefore \frac{309x}{300} - x = 540 \Rightarrow \frac{9x}{300} = 540 \Rightarrow x = \left(\frac{540 \times 300}{9}\right) = 18000$.

179. Let C.P. of watch be ₹ x.

Then, C.P. of wall clock = ₹ (390 − x).

$\therefore$ (10% of x) + [15% of (390 − x)] = 51.50

$\Rightarrow \frac{10}{100} \times x + \frac{15}{100} \times (390 - x) = \frac{515}{10}$

$\Rightarrow 10x + 5850 - 15x = 5150 \Rightarrow 5x = 700 \Rightarrow x = 140$.

So, C.P. of watch = ₹ 140, C.P. of wall clock = ₹ 250.

$\therefore$ Difference = ₹ (250 − 140) = ₹ 110.

180. Let C.P. of each horse be ₹ x and C.P. of each cow be ₹ y.
Then, $4x + 9y = 13400$. ...(*i*)
And, 10% of $4x$ + 20% of $9y$ = 1880

$\Rightarrow \frac{2}{5}x + \frac{9}{5}y = 1880 \Rightarrow 2x + 9y = 9400$ ...(*ii*)

Solving (*i*) and (*ii*), we get : $x = 2000$ and $y = 600$.
$\therefore$ Cost price of each horse = ₹ 2000.

181. Let C.P. of clock A be ₹ x and that of clock B be ₹ $(650 - x)$. Then, 120% of x = 75% of $(650 - x)$

$\Rightarrow 650 - x = \frac{120}{75}x = \frac{8}{5}x$

$\Rightarrow \frac{13}{5}x = 650 \Rightarrow x = \left(\frac{650 \times 5}{13}\right) = 250.$

$\therefore$ C.P. of A = ₹ 250, C.P. of B = ₹ 400.

182. Let the C.P. of the cow be ₹ x and that of the ox be ₹ y.

Then, 120% of x + 125% of y = 800 $\Rightarrow \frac{6x}{5} + \frac{5y}{4} = 800$

$\Rightarrow 24x + 25y = 16000$ ...(*i*)

And, 125% of x + 120% of y = 820 $\Rightarrow \frac{5x}{4} + \frac{6y}{5} = 820$

$\Rightarrow 25x + 24y = 16400$ ...(*ii*)
Adding (*i*) and (*ii*), we get : $49x + 49y = 32400$

$\Rightarrow x + y = \frac{32400}{49}$ ...(*iii*)

Subtracting (*i*) from (*ii*), we get : $x - y = 400$ ...(*iv*)
Adding (*iii*) and (*iv*), we get :

$2x = \frac{32400}{49} + 400 = \frac{52000}{49} \Rightarrow x = \frac{26000}{49} \approx 530.60.$

Putting $x = \frac{26000}{49}$ in (*iii*), we get:

$y = \frac{32400}{49} - \frac{26000}{49} = \frac{6400}{49} \approx 130.60.$

183. Let the C.P. of the watches be ₹ x and ₹ $(840 - x)$.
$\therefore$ (116% of x) + [88% of $(840 - x)$] = 840
$\Rightarrow 116x + 73920 - 88x = 84000$
$\Rightarrow 28x = 10080 \Rightarrow x = 360.$
$\therefore$ Their cost prices are ₹ 360 and ₹ 480.

184. Let C.P. of the chair be ₹ x and that of the table be ₹ y.
Then, 17% of y − 7% of x = 296 $\Rightarrow 17y - 7x = 29600$...(*i*)
And, 12% of y + 7% of x = 400 $\Rightarrow 12y + 7x = 40000$...(*ii*)
Solving (*i*) and (*ii*), we get : $y = 2400$ and $x = 1600$.
$\therefore$ C.P. of table = ₹ 2400.

185. Let the cost of product A be ₹ x and that of product B be ₹ y.

Then, 20% of x = 30% of $y \Rightarrow \frac{x}{5} = \frac{3y}{10} \Rightarrow x = \frac{3y}{2}$ ...(*i*)

And, 15% of x − 15% of y = 6 $\Rightarrow \frac{15}{100}(x - y) = 6$

$\Rightarrow x - y = 40 \Rightarrow \frac{3y}{2} - y = 40$

$\Rightarrow \frac{y}{2} = 40 \Rightarrow y = 80.$

Hence, cost of product B = ₹ 80 million.

186. Let the original cost of the toy be ₹ 100.
Then, original cost of component A = 10% of ₹ 100 = ₹ 10.
Original cost of component B = 20% of ₹ 100 = ₹ 20.
Original S.P. of the toy = 120% of ₹ 100 = ₹ 120.
New cost of component A = 120% of ₹ 10 = ₹ 12.
New cost of component B = 140% of ₹ 20 = ₹ 28.
New price of the toy = ₹ [100 + (12 + 28) − (10 + 20)] = ₹ 110.
New S.P. of the toy = 115% of ₹ 120 = ₹ 138.
Profit = ₹ (138 − 110) = ₹ 28.

$\therefore$ Profit% = $\left(\frac{28}{110} \times 100\right)\% = 25.45\% \approx 25.5\%.$

187. Let the total sales be ₹ x and let the profit in women's shirts average y% of the sales.
Then, 8% of 40% of x + y% of 60% of x = 6% of x

$\Rightarrow \frac{8}{100} \times \frac{40}{100} \times x + \frac{y}{100} \times \frac{60}{100} \times x = \frac{6}{100} \times x$

$\Rightarrow \frac{32}{10} + \frac{6y}{10} = 6 \Rightarrow \frac{6y}{10} = \frac{28}{10} \Rightarrow y = \frac{28}{6} = 4.66.$

$\therefore$ Average profit per sales rupee in women's shirt

= 4.66% of ₹ 1 = ₹ $\left(\frac{4.66}{100}\right)$ = ₹ 0.0466.

188. Let original C.P. be ₹ 100 and original S.P. be ₹ x.
Profit = ₹ $(x - 100)$. Profit% = $(x - 100)$%.
New C.P. = ₹ 118.

New profit = $(x - 100)$% of ₹ 118 = ₹ $\left[\frac{59}{50}(x - 100)\right]$.

$\therefore \frac{59}{50}(x - 100) - (x - 100) = 9 \Rightarrow \frac{9}{50}(x - 100) = 9$

$\Rightarrow x - 100 = 50.$
Hence, earlier profit per article = ₹ 50.

189. Let the total initial cost of production be ₹ 100.
Then, manufacturing cost = ₹ 60, Cost of raw materials = ₹ 40.

Original S.P. = ₹ $\left(100 + \frac{60}{4}\right)$ = ₹ 115.

New cost of raw materials = 130% of ₹ 40 = ₹ 52.
New manufacturing cost = 120% of ₹ 60 = ₹ 72.
New cost of the product = ₹ (52 + 72) = ₹ 124.

New S.P. = 160% of ₹ 115 = ₹ $\left(\frac{160}{100} \times 115\right)$ = ₹ 184.

New profit = ₹ (184 − 124) = ₹ 60.

$\therefore$ New profit % = $\left(\frac{60}{124} \times 100\right)\% = 48.39\%.$

190. Original C.P. of the product = ₹ 8. Original manufacturing cost = ₹ $\left(\frac{3}{4} \times 8\right)$ = ₹ 6.

Original cost of raw material = ₹ (8 − 6) = ₹ 2.

New manufacturing cost = ₹ $\left(\frac{5}{3} \times 6\right)$ = ₹ 10.

New cost of raw material = ₹ $\left(\frac{12}{5} \times 2\right)$ = ₹ $\frac{24}{5}$.

New S.P. of the product $= ₹\left(10+\frac{24}{5}\right)=₹\frac{74}{5}$.

$\therefore$ Desired S.P. = 125% of ₹ $\frac{74}{5}$ = ₹$\left(\frac{125}{100}\times\frac{74}{5}\right)$ = ₹ 18.50.

91. Let C.P. of pure milk be ₹ 10 per litre.
In 1 litre of the mixture, there is 800 ml milk and 200 ml water.
But the milk vendor measures only 800 ml instead of a litre.
So, quantity of milk in 1 litre mixture that he sells
= (0.8 × 800) ml = 640 ml.
$\therefore$ Actual C.P. of 1 litre = ₹ 6.40.
S.P. of 1 litre = 120% of ₹ 10 = ₹ 12.
Profit = ₹ (12 – 6.40) = ₹ 5.60.

Profit% $=\left(\frac{5.60}{6.40}\times 100\right)\% = 87.5\%$.

92. S.P. $= 97\frac{1}{2}\%$ of ₹ 650 = ₹$\left(\frac{195}{2}\times\frac{1}{100}\times 650\right)$ = ₹ 633.75.

93. M.P. = ₹ 272000.
Discount = ₹ [(4% of 200000) + (2.5% of 72000)]
= ₹ (8000 + 1800) = ₹ 9800.
$\therefore$ Actual price = ₹ (272000 – 9800) = ₹ 262200.

94. C.P. = 90% of 80% of ₹ 1400 = ₹$\left(\frac{90}{100}\times\frac{80}{100}\times 1400\right)$ = ₹ 1008.

95. C.P. = ₹ 50. M.P. = 108% of ₹ 50 = ₹$\left(\frac{108}{100}\times 50\right)$ = ₹ 54.

Discount = 10% of ₹ 54 = ₹ 5.40.
$\therefore$ S.P. = ₹ (54 – 5.40) = ₹ 48.60.

96. Rate of discount $=\left(\frac{12}{80}\times 100\right)\% = 15\%$.

97. **Group A:** Rate of discount $=\left(\frac{10}{65}\times 100\right)\% = 15.38\%$.

Group B: Rate of discount $=\left(\frac{10}{60}\times 100\right)\% = 16.66\%$.

Group C: Rate of discount $=\left(\frac{10}{70}\times 100\right)\% = 14.29\%$.

Group D: Rate of discount $=\left(\frac{10}{75}\times 100\right)\% = 13.33\%$.

98. Let the original S.P. of the watch be ₹ x.

Then, 75% of $x = 780 \Rightarrow x = \left(\frac{780\times 100}{75}\right) = 1040$.

99. Let the original S.P. of the perfume be ₹ x.

Then, 85% of $x = 3675.40 \Rightarrow x = \left(\frac{3675.40\times 100}{85}\right) = 4324$.

00. S.P. of each article = ₹$\left(\frac{37.40}{2}\right)$ = ₹ 18.70.

Let M.P. be ₹ x.

Then, 85% of $x = 18.70 \Rightarrow x = \left(\frac{18.70\times 100}{85}\right) = 22$.

01. Let the labelled price be ₹ x.

88% of 80% of $x = 704 \Rightarrow x = \left(\frac{704\times 100\times 100}{88\times 80}\right) = 1000$.

202. S.P. after 1st discount = ₹$\left(\frac{80}{100}\times 1500\right)$ = ₹ 1200.

Net S.P. = ₹ 1104. Discount on ₹ 1200 = ₹ 96.

$\therefore$ Required discount $=\left(\frac{96}{1200}\times 100\right)\% = 8\%$.

203. Let the costs of the two articles be x and y.

Then, 15% of x = 20% of $y \Rightarrow \frac{x}{y}=\frac{20}{15}=\frac{4}{3}$.

So, x and y must be in the ratio of 4 : 3.

204. Let the list price be ₹ x.

Then, $\frac{80}{100}x = 24 \Rightarrow x = \frac{24\times 100}{80} = 30$.

$\therefore$ Required S.P. = 70% of ₹ 30 = ₹ 21.

205. Let the list price be ₹ z.

$\therefore$ $(100 - x)\%$ of $z = y \Rightarrow \left(\frac{100-x}{100}\right)\times z = y$

$\Rightarrow z = \left(\frac{100y}{100-x}\right)$.

206. Let the marked price be ₹ x.
Then, 7% of x – 5% of x = 15 ⇒ 2% of x = 15

$\Rightarrow x = \left(\frac{15\times 100}{2}\right) = 750$.

207. Let the labelled price be ₹ x. Then,
(80% of x) – (75% of x) = 500

$\Rightarrow$ 5% of $x = 500 \Rightarrow x = \left(\frac{500\times 100}{5}\right) = 10000$.

208. Let the discount on ₹ 6000 be x%.
Then, $(100 - x)\%$ of 6000
= 93% of 36000 – (92% of 20000 + 95% of 10000)
= 33480 – (18400 + 9500) = 5580.

$\Rightarrow (100 - x) = \frac{5580\times 100}{6000} = 93$

$\Rightarrow x = 7$.

209. When discount = 10%, S.P. = 90% of ₹ 15000 = ₹ 13500.
Profit = 8%.

$\therefore$ C.P. = ₹$\left(\frac{100}{108}\times 13500\right)$ = ₹ 12500.

210. Let marked price be ₹ 100.
Then, Final S.P. = 70% of 80% of ₹ 100

= ₹$\left(\frac{70}{100}\times\frac{80}{100}\times 100\right)$ = ₹ 56.

$\therefore$ Single discount = (100 – 56)% = 44%.

211. Let marked price be ₹ 100.
Then, S.P. = 85% of 88% of 90% of ₹ 100

= ₹$\left(\frac{85}{100}\times\frac{88}{100}\times\frac{90}{100}\times 100\right)$ = ₹ 67.32.

$\therefore$ Single discount = (100 – 67.32)% = 32.68%.

212. Let marked price be ₹ 100.
Then, S.P. = $(100 - q)\%$ of $(100 - p)\%$ of ₹ 100

$= ₹\left[\frac{100-q}{100}\times\frac{100-p}{100}\times 100\right] = ₹\left[\frac{(100-q)(100-p)}{100}\right]$

$\therefore$ Single discount $= \left\{100 - \left[\frac{(100-q)(100-p)}{100}\right]\right\}\%$

$= \left(p+q-\frac{pq}{100}\right)\%.$

213. Let marked price be ₹ 100.
Then, S.P. = 80% of 80% of 80% of ₹ 100

$= ₹\left(\frac{80}{100}\times\frac{80}{100}\times\frac{80}{100}\times 100\right) = ₹\,51.20.$

$\therefore$ Single discount = (100 − 51.20)% = 48.8%.

214. S.P. = 88% of 90% of ₹ 250 = $₹\left(\frac{88}{100}\times\frac{90}{100}\times 250\right) = ₹\,198.$

215. S.P. = 95% of 95% of ₹ 80 = $₹\left(\frac{95}{100}\times\frac{95}{100}\times 80\right) = ₹\,72.20.$

216. C.P. of the article = ₹ [(95% of 80% of 25000) + 1000]

$= ₹\left[\left(\frac{95}{100}\times\frac{80}{100}\times 25000\right) + 1000\right]$

= ₹ 20000.

S.P. of the article = ₹ 25000.

$\therefore$ Gain% $= \left(\frac{5000}{20000}\times 100\right)\% = 25\%.$

217. Price paid by the customer = 85% of 75% of 90% of ₹ 400

$= ₹\left(\frac{85}{100}\times\frac{75}{100}\times\frac{90}{100}\times 400\right) = ₹\,229.50 \approx ₹\,230.$

218. Let M.P. be ₹ x.

Then, 85% of x = 17000 $\Rightarrow x = \left(\frac{17000\times 100}{85}\right) = 20000.$

$\therefore$ Required S.P. = 90% of 95% of ₹ 20000

$= ₹\left(\frac{90}{100}\times\frac{95}{100}\times 20000\right) = ₹\,17100.$

219. Let the original price be ₹ x. Then,

95% of 88% of x = 209 $\Rightarrow x = \left(\frac{209\times 100\times 100}{95\times 88}\right) = 250.$

220. S.P. in 1st case = 60% of ₹ 100000 = ₹ 60000.
S.P. in 2nd case = 96% of 64% of ₹ 100000

$= ₹\left(\frac{96}{100}\times\frac{64}{100}\times 100000\right) = ₹\,61440.$

$\therefore$ Difference = ₹ (61440 − 60000) = ₹ 1440.

221. Let the M.P. of the item at each of the stores A and B be ₹ 100.
Final price at A = 90% of 90% of 90% of ₹ 100

$= ₹\left(\frac{90}{100}\times\frac{90}{100}\times\frac{90}{100}\times 100\right) = ₹\,72.90.$

Final price at B = 81% of 90% of ₹ 100

$= ₹\left(\frac{81}{100}\times\frac{90}{100}\times 100\right) = ₹\,72.90.$

Hence, the price of the article is same at A and B.

222. Let the M.P. be ₹ x.
Then, (90% of 80% of x) − (70% of x) = 72

$\Rightarrow \left(\frac{90}{100}\times\frac{80}{100}\times x\right) - \left(\frac{70}{100}\times x\right) = 72$

$\Rightarrow \frac{72}{100}x - \frac{70}{100}x = 72 \Rightarrow \frac{2}{100}x = 72$

$\Rightarrow x = \left(\frac{72\times 100}{2}\right) = 3600.$

223. Loss = ₹ [(92% of 92% of 900) − (84% of 900)]

$= ₹\left[\left(\frac{92}{100}\times\frac{92}{100}\times 900\right) - \left(\frac{84}{100}\times 900\right)\right]$

= ₹ (761.76 − 756) = ₹ 5.76.

224. S.P. in 1st case = 94% of 70% of ₹ 700

$= ₹\left(\frac{94}{100}\times\frac{70}{100}\times 700\right) = ₹\,460.60.$

S.P. in 2nd case = 84% of 80% of ₹ 700

$= ₹\left(\frac{84}{100}\times\frac{80}{100}\times 700\right) = ₹\,470.40.$

$\therefore$ Difference = ₹ (470.40 − 460.60) = ₹ 9.80.

225. Let the M.P. of an article be ₹ 100. We may calculate the final price of this article under each of the three offers:

(*i*) Final price = 85% of 75% of ₹ 100

$= ₹\left(\frac{85}{100}\times\frac{75}{100}\times 100\right) = ₹\,63.75$

(*ii*) Final price = 90% of 70% of ₹ 100

$= ₹\left(\frac{90}{100}\times\frac{70}{100}\times 100\right) = ₹\,63.$

(*iii*) Final price = 95% of 65% of ₹ 100

$= ₹\left(\frac{95}{100}\times\frac{65}{100}\times 100\right) = ₹\,61.75.$

The final price is lowest in (*iii*). So, it is the best offer.

226. Final price in 1st case
= 70% of 90% of 90% of ₹ 10000

$= ₹\left(\frac{70}{100}\times\frac{90}{100}\times\frac{90}{100}\times 10000\right) = ₹\,5670.$

Final price in 2nd case
= 95% of 95% of 60% of ₹ 10000

$= ₹\left(\frac{95}{100}\times\frac{95}{100}\times\frac{60}{100}\times 10000\right) = ₹\,5415.$

$\therefore$ Money saved by choosing the better offer
= ₹ (5670 − 5415) = ₹ 255.

227. Let M.P. be ₹ x.
S.P. in 1st case = 85% of 85% of 90% of ₹ x

$= ₹\left(\frac{85}{100}\times\frac{85}{100}\times\frac{90}{100}\times x\right) = ₹\left(\frac{65025}{100000}x\right).$

Profit = 30.05%.

$\therefore$ C.P. $= ₹\left(\frac{100}{130.05}\times\frac{65025}{100000}x\right) = ₹\,\frac{x}{2}.$

S.P. in 2nd case = 85% of 90% of ₹ x

$= ₹\left(\frac{85}{100}\times\frac{90}{100}\times x\right) = ₹\left(\frac{765x}{1000}\right).$

Profit = ₹ $\left(\frac{765x}{1000} - \frac{x}{2}\right) = ₹\left(\frac{265x}{1000}\right)$.

Profit% = $\left(\frac{265x}{1000} \times \frac{2}{x} \times 100\right)\% = 53\%$.

228. Let the second discount rate be x%.
Then, $(100 - x)\%$ of 90% of 450 = 344.25

$\Rightarrow \frac{100-x}{100} \times \frac{90}{100} \times 450 = 344.25$

$\Rightarrow (100 - x) = \left(\frac{34425}{9 \times 45}\right) = 85 \Rightarrow x = 15.$

∴ Second discount rate = 15%.

229. Let the second discount rate be x%.
Then, $(100 - x)\%$ of 80% of 820 = 570.72

$\Rightarrow \frac{(100-x)}{100} \times \frac{80}{100} \times 820 = 570.72$

$\Rightarrow (100 - x) = \left(\frac{57072}{8 \times 82}\right) = 87 \Rightarrow x = 13.$

∴ Second discount rate = 13%.

230. Cost of each calculator = ₹ $\left(250 + \frac{2500}{150}\right) = ₹\, 266\frac{2}{3}$.

S.P. of each calculator = ₹ $\left(\frac{95}{100} \times 320\right) = ₹\, 304.$

∴ Profit % = $\left(\frac{112}{3} \times \frac{3}{800} \times 100\right)\% = 14\%.$

231. Let the original price of the commodity be ₹ 100.
Increased price = ₹ 110.
Price after discount

= 85% of ₹ 110 = ₹ $\left(\frac{85}{100} \times 110\right) = ₹\, 93.50.$

∴ Discount on original price = (100 – 93.5)% = 6.5%.

232. Let the original price of the camera be ₹ 100.
Discounted price = ₹ 80. Profit = 40%.

∴ S.P. = 140% of ₹ 80 = ₹ $\left(\frac{140}{100} \times 80\right) = ₹\, 112.$

So, profit percentage on original price = (112 – 100)% = 12%.

233. Let C.P. = ₹ 100. Then, marked price = ₹ 120.

S.P. = 90% of ₹ 120 = ₹ $\left(\frac{90}{100} \times 120\right) = ₹\, 108.$

∴ Profit% = (108 – 100)% = 8%.

234. Let C.P. be ₹ 100. Then, marked price = ₹ 125.

S.P. = 84% of ₹ 125 = ₹ $\left(\frac{84}{100} \times 125\right) = ₹\, 105.$

∴ Profit% = (105 – 100)% = 5%.

235. Let C.P. be ₹ 100. Then, marked price = ₹ 130.

S.P. = $\left(100 - \frac{25}{4}\right)\%$ of ₹ 130 = ₹ $\left(\frac{375}{400} \times 130\right) = ₹\, 121.875.$

∴ Profit% = (121.875 – 100)% = 21.875% = $\frac{21875}{1000}\% = 21\frac{7}{8}\%.$

236. Let the printed price be ₹ 100.
S.P. = 90% of ₹ 100 = ₹ 90.

C.P. = ₹ $\left(\frac{100}{112} \times 90\right) = ₹\, \frac{4500}{56}.$

∴ C.P. : Printed price = $\frac{4500}{56} : 100 = 45 : 56.$

237. S.P. = ₹ X. Profit = 10%.

C.P. = ₹ $\left(\frac{100}{110} \times X\right) = ₹\, \frac{10X}{11}.$

M.P. = ₹ 2X, Discount = 20%.

S.P. at trade fair = 80% of ₹ 2X = ₹ $\left(\frac{80}{100} \times 2X\right) = ₹\, \frac{8X}{5}.$

Profit = ₹ $\left(\frac{8X}{5} - \frac{10X}{11}\right) = ₹\, \frac{38X}{55}.$

∴ Profit % = $\left(\frac{38X}{55} \times \frac{11}{10X} \times 100\right)\% = 76\%.$

238. Let the original price be ₹ 100.
Then, marked price = ₹ 130.
Final price = 90% of 90% of ₹ 130

= ₹ $\left(\frac{90}{100} \times \frac{90}{100} \times 130\right) = ₹\, 105.30.$

∴ Increase in price = (105.30 – 100)% = 5.3%.

239. Let the marked price of each article be ₹ 1.
Then, C.P. of 30 = ₹ 27, S.P. of 30 = ₹ 30.

∴ Gain% = $\left(\frac{3}{27} \times 100\right)\% = 11\frac{1}{9}\%.$

240. Marked price = ₹ 300. C.P. = ₹ $\left(\frac{100}{120} \times 300\right) = ₹\, 250.$

Sale price = 90% of ₹ 300 = ₹ 270.

∴ Required gain% = $\left(\frac{20}{250} \times 100\right)\% = 8\%.$

241. Let marked price = ₹ 100.
Then, C.P. = ₹ 64. S.P = ₹ 88.

∴ Gain% = $\left(\frac{24}{64} \times 100\right)\% = 37.5\%.$

242. Let the marked price be ₹ x.
Then, 108% of 90% of x = 680.40

$\Rightarrow \frac{108}{100} \times \frac{90}{100} x = 680.40 \Rightarrow x = \left(\frac{68040 \times 100}{108 \times 90}\right) = ₹\, 700.$

243. Let C.P. = ₹ 100. Then, S.P. = ₹ 120.
Let marked price be ₹ x.
Then, 90% of $x = 120 \Rightarrow x = \left(\frac{120 \times 100}{90}\right) = 133\frac{1}{3}.$

∴ Marked price = $33\frac{1}{3}\%$ above C.P.

244. Let C.P. = ₹ 100.
Then, S.P. = ₹ 120.
Let M.P. be ₹ x.
Then, $93\frac{3}{4}\%$ of 80% of $x = 120$

$\Rightarrow \frac{375}{4} \times \frac{1}{100} \times \frac{80}{100} \times x = 120$

$\Rightarrow \frac{3}{4}x = 120 \Rightarrow x = \left(\frac{120 \times 4}{3}\right) = 160.$

$\therefore$ Marked price = 60% above C.P.

245. C.P. = ₹ 4900. S.P. = 110% of ₹ 4900 = ₹ $\left(\frac{110}{100} \times 4900\right)$ = ₹ 5390.

Let marked price be ₹ x.

Then, $87\frac{1}{2}\%$ of $x = 5390 \Rightarrow \left(\frac{175}{2} \times \frac{1}{100} \times x\right) = 5390$

$\Rightarrow x = \left(\frac{5390 \times 8}{7}\right) = 6160.$

$\therefore$ Marked price = ₹ 6160.

246. Let cost price = ₹ 100. Then,

$\frac{2}{5}$ of Marked Price = 75

$\Rightarrow$ Marked Price = ₹ $\left(\frac{75 \times 5}{2}\right)$ = ₹ $\left(\frac{375}{2}\right)$.

$\therefore$ Required ratio = $\frac{375}{2} : 100 = 375 : 200 = 15 : 8.$

247. Clearly, the distributor sold (3500 – 500 *i.e.*, 3000 cassettes. Out of these, in every 30 cassettes, 1 was given free.

$\therefore$ Total number of cassettes given free

$= \left(\frac{3000}{30} + 500\right) = 600.$

Number of cassettes sold = (3500 – 600) = 2900.

S.P. of 1 cassette = 75% of ₹ 150 = ₹ $\left(\frac{75}{100} \times 150\right)$ = ₹ 112.50.

Money realised from sale of cassettes
= ₹ (112.50 × 2900) = ₹ 326250.

Total money invested = ₹ 350000.

Loss = ₹ (350000 – 326250) = ₹ 23750.

Loss% = $\left(\frac{23750}{350000} \times 100\right)\% = 6.78\% \approx 6.8\%.$

248. Let the C.P. of each article be ₹ 100.

Then, C.P. of 16 articles = ₹ (100 × 16) = ₹ 1600.

S.P. of 15 articles = ₹ $\left(1600 \times \frac{135}{100}\right)$ = ₹ 2160.

S.P. of each article = ₹ $\frac{2160}{15}$ = ₹ 144.

If S.P. is ₹ 96, marked price = ₹ 100.

If S.P. is ₹ 144, marked price = ₹ $\left(\frac{100}{96} \times 144\right)$ = ₹ 150.

$\therefore$ Marked price = 50% above C.P.

249. Let C.P. = ₹ 100.

Then, Marked Price = ₹ 110, S.P. = ₹ 99.

$\therefore$ Discount% = $\left(\frac{11}{110} \times 100\right)\% = 10\%.$

250. Let C.P. = ₹ 100.

Then, Marked Price = ₹ 135, S.P. = ₹ 108.

$\therefore$ Discount% = $\left(\frac{27}{135} \times 100\right)\% = 20\%.$

251. Let C.P. of whole stock = ₹ 100.

Then, Marked Price of whole stock = ₹ 120.

M.P. of $\frac{1}{2}$ stock = ₹ 60, M.P. of $\frac{1}{4}$ stock = ₹ 30.

$\therefore$ Total S.P. = ₹ [60 + (80% of 30) + (60% of 30)]
= ₹ (60 + 24 + 18) = ₹ 102.

Hence, gain% = (102 – 100)% = 2%.

252. Since the marked price is not given, so the cost price cannot be determined.

253. S.P. = 80% of ₹ 50 = ₹ $\left(\frac{80}{100} \times 50\right)$ = ₹ 40. Profit = 25%.

$\therefore$ C.P. = ₹ $\left(\frac{100}{125} \times 40\right)$ = ₹ 32.

254. S.P. = 95% of ₹ 6500 = ₹ $\left(\frac{95}{100} \times 6500\right)$ = ₹ 6175.

Profit = 15%.

$\therefore$ C.P. = ₹ $\left(\frac{100}{115} \times 6175\right)$ = ₹ 5369.56 ≈ ₹ 5350.

255. Let the labelled price be ₹ x.

Then, 120% of $x = 2880 \Rightarrow x = \left(\frac{2880 \times 100}{120}\right) = 2400.$

$\therefore$ C.P. = 85% of ₹ 2400 = ₹ $\left(\frac{85}{100} \times 2400\right)$ = ₹ 2040.

256. Marked price = ₹ 30.

S.P. = ₹ $\left[\left(\frac{85}{100} \times 30\right) - 1.50\right]$ = ₹ (25.50 – 1.50) = ₹ 24.

Let C.P. be ₹ x. Then, 120% of $x = 24 \Rightarrow x = \left(\frac{24 \times 100}{120}\right)$ = ₹ 20.

257. Let the marked price be ₹ 100.

Then, S.P. = ₹ $\left(\frac{90}{100} \times 100\right)$ = ₹ 90. Gain = 20%.

$\therefore$ C.P. = ₹ $\left(\frac{100}{120} \times 90\right)$ = ₹ 75.

New commission = ₹ 20; New S.P. = ₹ 80.

$\therefore$ New Profit = $\left(\frac{5}{75} \times 100\right)\% = 6\frac{2}{3}\%.$

258. S.P. = ₹ 340. Let marked price be ₹ x.

Then, 85% of $x = 340 \Rightarrow x = \left(\frac{340 \times 100}{85}\right) = 400.$

C.P. = ₹ $\left(100 \times \frac{3}{340} \times 340\right)$ = ₹ 300.

Now, C.P. = ₹ 300. S.P. = ₹ 400.

$\therefore$ Required profit % = $\left(\frac{100}{300} \times 100\right)\% = 33\frac{1}{3}\%.$

259. S.P. = ₹ 25935. Let marked price be ₹ x.

Then, 91% of $x = 25935 \Rightarrow x = \left(\frac{25935 \times 100}{91}\right) = 28500.$

C.P. = ₹$\left(\frac{100}{103.74}\times 25935\right)$ = ₹ 25000.

Now C.P. = ₹ 25000, S.P. = ₹ 28500.

Profit = ₹ (28500 − 25000) = ₹ 3500.

∴ Required profit% = $\left(\frac{3500}{25000}\times 100\right)\% = 14\%$.

260. S.P. of 1 article = ₹ 45. Let marked price of each article be ₹ x.

Then, $\frac{90}{100}x = 45 \Rightarrow x =$ ₹$\left(\frac{45\times 100}{90}\right)$ = ₹ 50.

C.P. = ₹$\left(\frac{100}{150}\times 45\right)$ = ₹ 30.

When no discount is given, C.P. = ₹ 30, S.P. = ₹ 50.

∴ Required profit% = $\left(\frac{20}{30}\times 100\right)\% = 66\frac{2}{3}\%$.

261. S.P. of 1 saree = ₹ 266.

Let the labelled price of each saree be ₹ x.

Then, $\frac{95}{100}x = 266 \Rightarrow x =$ ₹$\left(\frac{266\times 100}{95}\right)$ = ₹ 280.

Now, S.P. = ₹ 280, Profit = 12%.

∴ C.P. of 1 saree = ₹$\left(\frac{100}{112}\times 280\right)$ = ₹ 250.

262. Let the marked price of the shirt and trousers be ₹ x and ₹ $2x$ respectively.

Let the discount offered on trousers be y%.

Then, S.P. of shirt = 60% of ₹ x = ₹$\left(\frac{60}{100}\times x\right)$ = ₹$\frac{3x}{5}$.

S.P. of trousers = (100 − y)% of ₹ $2x$

= ₹$\left[\frac{(100-y)}{100}\times 2x\right]$ = ₹$\left[\frac{(100-y)x}{50}\right]$

Combined S.P. of shirt and trousers = 70% of ₹ (x + $2x$)

= ₹$\left(\frac{70}{100}\times 3x\right)$ = ₹$\frac{21x}{10}$

$\therefore \frac{3x}{5}+\frac{(100-y)x}{50}=\frac{21x}{10} \Rightarrow \frac{130-y}{50}=\frac{21}{10}$

$\Rightarrow 1300 - 10y = 1050 \Rightarrow y = 25$.

263. Let C.P. = ₹ 100 and Profit = x%.

Then, S.P. = ₹ (100 + x).

Now, discount = $\frac{1}{5}\times$S.P. So,

M.P. = (S.P. + discount) = $\frac{6}{5}$ S.P.

Discount% = Profit % $\Rightarrow \frac{\frac{1}{5}S.P.}{\frac{6}{5}S.P.}\times 100 = x \Rightarrow x = \frac{50}{3}$.

Discount = $\frac{1}{5}\times$S.P. = ₹$\left[\frac{1}{5}(100+x)\right]$ = ₹$\left[\frac{1}{5}\left(100+\frac{50}{3}\right)\right]$

= ₹$\left(\frac{1}{5}\times\frac{350}{3}\right)$ = ₹$\left(\frac{70}{3}\right)$

∴ Required ratio = $\frac{70}{3}:100 = \frac{7}{3}:10 = 7:30$.

264. C.P. = ₹ 320, Profit = 15%.

S.P. = ₹$\left(\frac{115}{100}\times 320\right)$ = ₹ 368.

Marked price = ₹ (368 + 32) = ₹ 400.

∴ Required profit% = $\left(\frac{80}{320}\times 100\right)\% = 25\%$.

265. Let C.P. be ₹ 100. Then, S.P. = ₹ 123.50.

Let marked price be ₹ x.

Then, $\frac{95}{100}x = 123.50 \Rightarrow x =$ ₹$\left(\frac{12350}{95}\right)$ = ₹ 130.

Now, S.P. = ₹ 130, C.P. = ₹ 100.

∴ Profit% = 30%.

266. Let original list price = ₹ 100.

Then, C.P. = ₹ 75. Desired S.P. = ₹ 125.

∴ Required percentage = $\left(\frac{50}{75}\times 100\right)\% = 66.67\%$.

267. Let the original price be ₹ 100.

Then, C.P. = ₹ 80.

S.P. = 140% of ₹ 80 = ₹$\left(\frac{140}{100}\times 80\right)$ = ₹ 112.

∴ Required percentage = (112 − 100)% = 12%.

268. C.P. = ₹$\left(\frac{100}{125}\times 8750\right)$ = ₹ 7000.

Let the labelled price be ₹ x.

Then $\frac{70}{100}x = 7000 \Rightarrow x =$ ₹$\left(\frac{7000\times 100}{70}\right)$ = ₹ 10000.

269. Let the C.P. of each article be ₹ 100 and the number of pieces sold be x.

Then, original S.P. = ₹ 125.

Original profit = ₹ [(125 − 100)x] = ₹ 25x.

New C.P. = ₹ 95.

New S.P. = 92% of ₹ 125 = ₹$\left(\frac{92}{100}\times 125\right)$ = ₹ 115.

Number of articles sold now = 1.25 x.

New profit = ₹ [1.25x (115 − 95)] = ₹ 25x.

Hence, the profit remains unchanged.

270. Let the marked price of the time be ₹ 100 x

Discount % = 20%

Changes for delivery and packaging

= 10% on discounted Price

Then, $100x \xrightarrow{-20\%} 80x \xrightarrow{+10\%} 88x$

$\therefore 88x + 88x\times\frac{25}{100} - 88x = 2046$

$\Rightarrow 110x - 88x = 2046 \Rightarrow 22x = 2046$

$\Rightarrow x = 93$

Hence, 100x = 93 × 100 = 9300

∴ Marked price = ₹ 9300

271. Cost price of box = Rs 75

Gain % = 8%

Now, required selling price or S.P.

$= (108\% \text{ of } ₹\ 75)$

$= ₹\left(\frac{75 \times 108}{100}\right)$

$= ₹\ 81$

272. Let, the (LCM of 5 and 6) = 30 oranges be bought.

∴ C.P. of 30 oranges

$= \frac{10}{5} \times 30 = ₹\ 60$

Their S.P. $= \frac{15}{6} \times 30 = ₹\ 75$

Profit = Rs (75 – 60) = Rs 15

∴ Profit percent

$= \left(\frac{15}{60}\right) \times 100 = 25\%$

273. Cost Price of two articles A and B = ₹ 8000

The cost price of B = $\frac{20}{32} \times 8000 = 5000$

The cost price of $A = \frac{12}{32} \times 8000 = 3000$

Since, he sold article A at 20% profit,

Hence, selling price of A = $\left(\text{CP} \times \frac{(100 + \text{gain}\%)}{100}\right)$

$= 3000 \times \frac{120}{100}$

$= ₹\ 3600$

Since article B sold at 12% loss,

Hence, selling price of article B

$= \left(\text{CP} \times \frac{(100 - \text{loss}\%)}{100}\right)$

$= \frac{5000 \times 88}{100}$

$= ₹\ 4400$

Dhar wants to make an overall profit of 25%

Total sale price of both article = 8000 + $\frac{8000 \times 25}{100} = 10000$

Sale price of article B = ₹ (10000 – 3600) = ₹ 6400

274. Let the cost price be ₹ 100.

CP	MP			SP
100	140	20% of discount $= \frac{20 \times 140}{100} = 28$ ₹ (140 – 28) = ₹ 112	25% of discount $= \frac{25 \times 112}{100} = 28$ ₹ (112 – 28) = ₹ 84	₹ 84

Loss = 100 – 84 = 16%

∵ If ₹ 16 loss, cost price ₹ 100.

∴ If ₹ 448 loss, cost price = $\frac{100}{16} \times 448$

= 28 × 100 = ₹ 2800

∴ Selling price = $\frac{2800 \times 84}{100} = ₹\ 2352$

275. Let CP of article be ₹ 100

∴ Marked price = ₹ 110

Discount % on marked Price = 10%

S.P. = $\frac{110 \times 90}{100} = ₹\ 99$ i.e., 1% loss

276. C.P. of article

$= ₹\left(\frac{5520 + 4080}{2}\right)$

$= ₹\ \frac{9600}{2} = ₹ 4800$

When S.P. = ₹ 6000 then

Profit = ₹ (6000 – 4800) = ₹ 1200

∴ Profit per cent = $\frac{1200}{4800} \times 100 = 25\%$

277. Marked Price of machine = ₹ 22000

Selling price = ₹ $\left(22000 - \frac{8 \times 22000}{100}\right) = ₹\ 20240$

Profit = $22\frac{2}{3}\% = \frac{68}{3}\%$

Let cost price of machine be ₹ x

$x + \frac{68}{3}\%$ of $x = ₹\ 20240$

$\Rightarrow x + \frac{68x}{300} = ₹ 20240$

$\Rightarrow \frac{368x}{300} = ₹ 20240$

$\Rightarrow x = ₹\left(\frac{20240 \times 300}{368}\right) = ₹\ 16500$

Profit % when machine was sold without discount

$= \frac{22000 - 16500}{16500} \times 100$

$= 33\frac{1}{3}\%$

278. The cost price of the item is ₹ X

And SP = ₹ Y.

Given, Y = ₹ 1.2X

If the cost price of the item is 15% less

Then, CP = 0.85 × X = ₹ 0.85 X

According to the questions,

$0.85X \times \frac{130}{100} = 1.2X - 76$

$\frac{85X}{100} \times \frac{130}{100} = \frac{12X}{10} - 76$

$\frac{11050}{10000} = \frac{12X}{10} - 76$

11.05X = 12X – 760

0.95X = 760

∴ X = $\frac{760}{0.95} = ₹\ 800$

∴ Cost price of the item ₹ 800

279. Let Quantity of rice sold at 20% loss be x kg

∴ Quantity of rice sold at 15% gain = (600 – x) kg

On the whole transaction he incurs an overall Loss of 6%

According to the question,

$(600 - x) \times \frac{115}{100} + \frac{x \times 80}{100}$

$= \frac{600 \times 94}{100}$

$\Rightarrow 115 \times 600 - 115x + 80x$

$= 600 \times 94$

$\Rightarrow 69000 - 35x = 56400$

$\Rightarrow 35x = 12600$

$\Rightarrow x = \frac{12600}{35}$

$= 360$ kg

280. Sale price of an article is ₹ 696 When profit = P%

Sale price of an article is ₹ 841 when Profit = P + 25%

Difference in sale price

= ₹ (841 – 696)

= ₹ 145

Difference of profit percentages = P + 25% – p = 25%

∴ Let the C.P of article be ₹ x, then,

25% of x = 145

$\Rightarrow x \times \frac{25}{100} = ₹ 145$

$\Rightarrow x = \frac{145 \times 100}{25} = ₹ 580$

∴ Profit = Sale price – Cost price = ₹ (696 – 580) = ₹ 116

Profit = p%

$\therefore 580 \times \frac{p}{100} = 116$

$\Rightarrow p = \frac{116 \times 100}{580} = 20\%$

281. VAT % = 13.5%

Cost price (including VAT) = ₹ 6810

$\therefore$ List price = $\frac{6810}{113.5} \times 100 =$ ₹ 6000

282. Let the cost price of a article be x.

Then, loss = $(6800 - x)$

Again, profit = $(7850 - x)$

According to given information we get

Now, $(7850 - x) = \frac{(6800 - x)}{2}$

$15700 - 2x = 6800 - x$

$x = 15700 - 6800 = 8900$

If profit % = 20% then

∴ Selling price = $\frac{8900 \times 120}{100}$ = ₹ 10680

283. Let marked price of article be ₹ x

According to the question, $\frac{x \times 88}{100} = 528$

$\Rightarrow x = \frac{528 \times 100}{88} = ₹ 600$

284. Marked price of shirt = ₹ 1080

Selling price of shirt = ₹ 1080 - $\frac{1080 \times 12}{100}$

= ₹ (1080 – 129.60) = ₹ 950.40

Let cost price of shirt is ₹ x.

$\therefore x + \frac{x \times 8}{100} = 950.40$

$\Rightarrow \frac{108x}{100} = 950.40$

$x = 950.40 \times \frac{100}{108} = ₹ 880$

285. Let the C.P. of article be ₹ x.

Profit = 12%

Rate of sales tax = 10%

Sale price of an article including sales tax = ₹ 1232

According to the question.

$\frac{112x}{100} + \frac{112x \times 10}{10000} = 1232$

$\Rightarrow \frac{1120x + 112x}{1000} = 1232$

$\Rightarrow 1232x = 1232 \times 1000$

$\Rightarrow x = ₹ 1000$

286. Given, Present value of machine = ₹ 729

Rate of depreciation = 10%

∴ Worth three years ago $= \frac{P}{(1-r)^3} = \frac{729}{\left(1 - \frac{10}{100}\right)^3} = \frac{729}{\left(\frac{9}{10}\right)^3}$

$= \frac{729 \times 10 \times 10 \times 10}{9 \times 9 \times 9} = ₹ 1000$

Hence three year ago, price of machine was ₹ 1000

287. Price of saree including sales tax = ₹ 5225

Cost price without sales tax

$= \frac{5,225}{112} \times 100 = 4,665$

The price is decreased

= ₹ (5,225 – 4,665) = 560

288. Let C.P. of chair be ₹ x

According to the question,

$752 - a = (a - 400) \times 1.2$

$\Rightarrow 752 - a = 1.2a - 480$

$\Rightarrow 1.2a + a = 752 + 480$

$\Rightarrow 2.2a = 1232$

$\Rightarrow a = \frac{1232}{2.2} = ₹ 560$

289. C.P. of each copy = ₹ 5

C.P. of 24 copies

= ₹ (24 × 5) = ₹ 120

S.P. of 25 copies = ₹ (25 × 6)

= ₹ 150

Profit = ₹ (150 – 120) = ₹ 30

Profit per cent = $\frac{30}{120} \times 100 = 25\%$

290. S.P. of washing machine = ₹ 8500

Loss% = 15%

C.P. of washing machine

$= ₹ \left(\frac{100}{85} \times 8500\right)$

$= ₹ 10000$

291. Marked price of cycle = ₹ 1150

Discount percent = 15%

Sale price $= 1150 - \frac{1150 \times 15}{100}$ = ₹(1150 – 172.5) = ₹ 977.5

Let CP of cycle be ₹ x

According to given information

x + 15% of x = ₹ 977.5

$\Rightarrow \frac{115x}{100} = 977.5$

$x = \frac{977.5 \times 100}{115}$

x = ₹ 850

292. Let price of article is ₹ 100.

First increase% = 20%

After increase, price of article

$= 100 \times \frac{120}{100} = ₹ 120$

Second decrease% = 25%

After decrease, price of article $= 120 - \frac{120 \times 25}{100} = ₹ 90$

Net change percent in price

$= \frac{100-90}{100} \times 100 = \frac{10}{100} \times 100 = 10\%$

EXERCISE

(DATA SUFFICIENCY TYPE QUESTIONS)

1. A shopkeeper sells some toys at ₹ 250 each. What percent profit does he make?

To find the answer, which of the following information given in Statements I and II is/are necessary?

I. Number of toys sold II. Cost price of each toy

(a) Only I is necessary.

(b) Only II is necessary.

(c) Both I and II are necessary.

(d) Either I or II is necessary.

(e) None of these

2. A shopkeeper sells some articles at the profit of 25% on the original price. What is the exact amount of profit?

To find the answer, which of the following information given in Statements I and II is/are necessary?

I. Sale price of the article II. Number of articles sold

(a) Only I is necessary.

(b) Only II is necessary.

(c) Either I or II is necessary.

(d) Both I and II are necessary.

(e) None of these

Directions (*Questions 3 to 20*): ***Each of the questions given below consists of a statement and/or a question and two statements numbered I and II given below it. You have to decide whether the data provided in the statement(s) is/are sufficient to answer the question. Read both the statements and***

Give answer (a) if the data in Statement I alone are sufficient to answer the question, while the data in Statement II alone are not sufficient to answer the question;

Give answer (b) if the data in Statement II alone are sufficient to answer the question, while the data in Statement I alone are not sufficient to answer the question;

Give answer (c) if the data either in Statement I or in Statement II alone are sufficient to answer the question;

Give answer (d) if the data even in both Statements I and II together are not sufficient to answer the question,

Give answer (e) if the data in both Statements I and II together are necessary to answer the question.

3. By selling a product with 20% profit, how much profit was earned?

I. The difference between cost and selling price is ₹ 40.

II. The selling price is 120 percent of the cost price.

4. What is the amount of profit earned? **(Bank P.O., 2006)**

I. 20% profit is earned by selling an article for ₹ 1740.

II. Cost price of the article is ₹ 1450.

5. What is the cost price of the article?

I. The profit earned on the article is one-third of the cost price.

II. The article is sold for ₹ 400.

6. What was the percent profit/loss made/incurred by selling an article for ₹ 24000?

I. The ratio of the selling price to the cost price of the article is 5 : 3.

II. The difference between the cost price and the selling price is ₹ 9600. **(Bank P.O., 2010)**

7. What would have been the selling price per kg of rice?

I. 50 kg of rice was purchased for ₹ 3350 and ₹ 150 were spent on transport.

II. Profit earned was 5%.

8. How much was the loss? (M.B.A., 2005)
I. The cost is ₹ 300.
II. The loss is 25% of the selling price.

9. What is the percentage profit on the cost price? (M.A.T., 2008)
I. The cost price is ₹ 368.35.
II. There is a 20% profit on the selling price.

10. A pair of skis originally cost \$160. After a discount of x%, the skis were discounted y%. Do the skis cost less than \$130 after the discounts? (M.B.A., 2006)
I. $x = 20$
II. $y = 15$

11. A man mixes two types of rice (X and Y) and sells the mixture at the rate of ₹ 17 per kg. Find his profit percentage.
I. The rate of X is ₹ 20 per kg.
II. The rate of Y is ₹ 13 per kg.

12. What is the percent profit earned by selling the product?
I. The profit earned was ₹ 50.
II. Had it been sold for ₹ 310, the profit would have been ₹ 70.

13. What is the cost price of the cassette?
I. The percent profit made when the cassette is sold for ₹ 78 is twice as much as when it is sold for ₹ 69.
II. If the price of the cassette is marked at 20% above the cost price and a discount of 10% is offered on the marked price, the seller gains 8%.

14. What was the cost price of the suitcase purchased by Richard? (SNAP, 2005)
I. Richard got 20% concession on the labelled price.
II. Richard sold the suitcase for ₹ 2000 with 25% profit on the labelled price.

15. What percent is the earned profit? (Bank P.O., 2003, 2005, 2007)
I. 10% discount is offered on the marked price.
II. If no discount is given, the profit will be 30%.

16. By selling a product for ₹ 200, how much profit was earned?
I. The profit was 25 percent of the cost price.
II. 12.5 percent profit would have been earned if the product had been sold for ₹ 180.
(S.I.D.B.I., 2006, M.A.T., 2006)

17. A trader sold two washing machines each for ₹ 7392. What was his total profit or loss on these two transactions?
I. On one transaction he got a profit of 12% on investment
II. On the other transaction he suffered a loss of 4% on investment.

18. What is the price of a banana?
I. A man can buy 14 bananas and 35 oranges for ₹ 84.
II. With 50% discount on the price of bananas, ₹ 12 would buy 4 bananas and 5 oranges.

19. How much profit did Anand make by selling a bed?
I. He bought the bed with 40% discount on labelled price.
II. He sold it with 20% profit on the labelled price.

20. What is the profit earned by selling a laptop for ₹ 26250? (Bank P.O., 2009)
I. The cost price of 5 such laptops is equal to selling price of 4 such laptops.
II. 25% profit is earned by selling each laptop.

Directions (*Questions 21–27*): ***Each of the following questions consists of a question followed by three statements I, II and III. You have to study the question and the statements and decide which of the statement(s) is/are necessary to answer the question.***

21. How many articles were sold? (Bank P.O., 2008)
I. Total profit earned was ₹ 1596.
II. Cost price per article was ₹ 632.
III. Selling price per article was ₹ 765.
(*a*) Any two of the three (*b*) I and II only
(*c*) II and III only (*d*) All I, II and III
(*e*) Question cannot be answered even with the information in all the three statements.

22. What was the amount of profit earned?
I. 10% discount was offered on the labelled price.
II. Had there been no discount, profit would have been 30%.
III. Selling price was more than the cost price by 20%.
(*a*) All I, II and III (*b*) Any two of the three
(*c*) III, and either I or II (*d*) I, and either II or III
(*e*) Question cannot be answered even with the information in all the three statements.

23. What was the cost price of the watch?
I. The shopkeeper labelled the price of the watch 20% above the cost price.
II. After allowing a discount of 15% on the labelled price, the shopkeeper charges ₹ 408 for the watch.
III. Had there been no discount, the shopkeeper would have earned 20% profit.
(*a*) I, and either II or III (*b*) II, and either I or III
(*c*) III, and either I or II (*d*) I and II only
(*e*) Any two of the three

24. How much profit did Manick earn on the cost price of an article by selling it?
I. He got 15% discount on the marked price at the time of purchase.

II. He sold it for ₹ 3060.

III. He earned 2% profit on the marked price.

(M.A.T., 2006)

(*a*) I and II only
(*b*) II and III only
(*c*) I only or II and III together
(*d*) All I, II and III
(*e*) Even I, II and III together are not sufficient to answer the question.

25. By selling an article what is the profit percent gained?

I. 5% discount is given on list price.

II. If discount is not given, 20% profit is gained.

III. The cost price of the article is ₹ 5000.

(*a*) Only I and II (*b*) Only II and III
(*c*) Only I and III (*d*) All I, II and III
(*e*) None of these

26. An item costing ₹ 3000 is sold at a certain discount. Find the rate of discount offered.

I. The profit earned after discount is 5%.

II. Had the discount rate been doubled, the seller incurs a loss of 15%.

III. The item is marked at a price 25% above the cost price.

(*a*) Only I and II (*b*) Only II and III
(*c*) Only I and III (*d*) All I, II and III
(*e*) Any two of the three

27. What was the percentage of discount given?

I. 23.5% profit was earned by selling an almirah for ₹ 12,350.

II. If there were no discount, the earned profit would have been 30%.

III. The cost price of the almirah was ₹ 10,000.

(*a*) Only I and II
(*b*) Only II and III
(*c*) Only I and III
(*d*) Any two of the three
(*e*) None of these

Directions (*Questions 28-29*): *Each of these questions is followed by three statements. You have to study the question and all the three statements given to decide whether any information provided in the statement(s) is / are redundant and can be dispensed with while answering the given question.*

28. What is the percent profit earned by the shopkeeper on selling the articles in his shop?

I. Labelled price of the articles sold was 130% of the cost price.

II. Cost price of each article was ₹ 550.

III. A discount of 10% on labelled price was offered.

(N.M.A.T., 2005)

(*a*) Only I
(*b*) Only II
(*c*) Only III
(*d*) All the three are required
(*e*) Question cannot be answered even with information in all the three statements.

29. What is the marked price of the suitcase?

I. When a discount of 15% is offered, the profit earned is 10.5%.

II. The cost price of the suitcase is ₹ 1500.

III. The marked price is 30% above the cost price.

(*a*) I only
(*b*) Either I or III
(*c*) Any one of the three
(*d*) All I, II and III are required
(*e*) None of these

ANSWERS

1. (*b*)	2. (*d*)	3. (*a*)	4. (*a*)	5. (*e*)	6. (*a*)	7. (*e*)	8. (*e*)	9. (*b*)	10. (*a*)
11. (*d*)	12. (*b*)	13. (*a*)	14. (*e*)	15. (*e*)	16. (*c*)	17. (*e*)	18. (*d*)	19. (*d*)	20. (*c*)
21. (*d*)	22. (*e*)	23. (*b*)	24. (*d*)	25. (*a*)	26. (*e*)	27. (*e*)	28. (*b*)	29. (*b*)	

SOLUTIONS

1. S.P. = ₹ 250 each. To find gain percent, we must know the C.P. of each.

∴ Correct answer is (*b*).

2. Gain = 25% of C.P.

In order to find gain, we must know the sale price of each article and the number of articles sold.

∴ Correct answer is (*d*).

3. Gain = 20%

I. Profit = (S.P.) – (C.P.) = ₹ 40.

Thus, I gives the answer.

But, II does not give the answer.

∴ Correct answer is (*a*).

4. I. S.P. = ₹ 1740.

Profit = 20%. C.P. = ₹ $\left(\frac{100}{120} \times 1740\right)$ = ₹ 1450.

$\therefore$ Profit = ₹ (1740 − 1450) = ₹ 290.

Thus, I alone gives the answer.

The information given in II can be deduced from I as shown and is insufficient.

$\therefore$ Correct answer is (*a*).

5. I. Gain = $\frac{1}{3}$ (C.P.).

II. S.P. = ₹ 400.

Gain = (S.P.) − (C.P.)

$\Rightarrow \frac{1}{3}$ (C.P.) = (₹ 400) − (C.P.)

$\Rightarrow \left(1+\frac{1}{3}\right)$ (C.P.) = ₹ 400

$\Rightarrow$ C.P. = ₹ $\left(400 \times \frac{3}{4}\right)$ = ₹ 300.

Thus, I and II both are needed to get the answer.

$\therefore$ Correct answer is (*e*).

6. I. Let C.P. = ₹ $3x$ and S.P. = ₹ $5x$.

Profit = ₹ $(5x - 3x)$ = ₹ $2x$.

$\therefore$ Profit% = $\left(\frac{2x}{3x} \times 100\right)\% = 66\frac{2}{3}\%$.

Thus, I alone gives the answer.

II. From the given information, it cannot be deduced whether it is a profit or loss.

Thus, II alone is insufficient.

$\therefore$ Correct answer is (*a*).

7. I. Total C.P. of 50 kg = ₹ (3350 + 150) = ₹ 3500.

$\therefore$ C.P. of 1 kg = ₹ $\left(\frac{3500}{50}\right)$ = ₹ 70.

II. Gain = 5%.

$\therefore$ S.P. of 1 kg = 105% of ₹ 70 = ₹ $\left(70 \times \frac{105}{100}\right)$ = ₹ 73.50.

Thus, both I and II are needed to get the answer.

$\therefore$ Correct answer is (*e*).

8. I. C.P. = ₹ 300.

II. Loss = 25% of S.P.

Let S.P. be ₹ x. Then, loss = 25% of ₹ x = ₹ $\frac{x}{4}$.

Loss = (C.P.) − (S.P.)

$\Rightarrow \frac{x}{4} = 300 - x \Rightarrow \left(x + \frac{x}{4}\right) = 300$

$\Rightarrow x = \left(300 \times \frac{4}{5}\right) = 240.$

$\therefore$ Loss = 25% of ₹ 240 = ₹ $\left(\frac{25}{100} \times 240\right)$ = ₹ 60.

Thus, I and II are required to get the answer. $\therefore$ Correct answer is (*e*).

9. II. Let. S.P. = ₹ x. Then, profit = 20% of ₹ x = ₹ $\frac{x}{5}$.

C.P. = ₹ $\left(x - \frac{x}{5}\right)$ = ₹ $\frac{4x}{5}$.

$\therefore$ Profit% = $\left(\frac{x}{5} \times \frac{5}{4x} \times 100\right)\% = 25\%$.

So, II alone gives the answer, while I alone does not.

$\therefore$ Correct answer is (*b*).

10. I. Price of skis after discount of 20%

= ₹ $\left(\frac{80}{100} \times 160\right)$ = ₹ 128 (< ₹ 130)

So, I alone gives the answer, while II alone does not.

$\therefore$ Correct answer is (*a*).

11. The ratio in which X and Y are mixed, is not given.

So, both I and II together cannot give the answer.

$\therefore$ Correct answer is (*d*).

12. II gives, S.P. = ₹ 310 and gain = ₹ 70.

$\therefore$ C.P = ₹ (310 − 70) = ₹ 240.

$\therefore$ Gain% = $\left(\frac{70}{240} \times 100\right)\%$.

Thus, II alone gives the answer.

Clearly, I alone does not give the answer.

$\therefore$ Correct answer is (*b*).

13. Let the C.P. be ₹ x. Then,

I. $\frac{(78 - x)}{x} \times 100 = 2 \times \frac{(69 - x)}{x} \times 100$

$\Leftrightarrow 78 - x = 138 - 2x \Leftrightarrow x = 60.$

Thus, I only gives the answer.

II. Let the C.P. be ₹ x. Then, M.P. = ₹ $\left(\frac{120}{100} \times x\right)$ = ₹ $\frac{6x}{5}$.

$\therefore$ S.P. = 90% of ₹ $\frac{6x}{5}$ = ₹ $\left(\frac{6x}{5} \times \frac{90}{100}\right)$ = ₹ $\frac{27x}{25}$.

Thus, 108% of $x = \frac{27x}{25}$. This does not give x.

$\therefore$ II does not give the answer.

$\therefore$ Correct answer is (*a*).

14. Let the labelled price be ₹ x.

I. C.P. = 80% of ₹ x = ₹ $\left(x \times \frac{80}{100}\right)$ = ₹ $\frac{4x}{5}$.

II. S.P. = ₹ 2000, S.P. = 125% of ₹ x = ₹ $\left(\frac{125}{100} \times x\right)$ = ₹ $\frac{5x}{4}$.

$\therefore \frac{5x}{4} = 2000 \Rightarrow x = \frac{2000 \times 4}{5} = 1600.$

$\therefore$ C.P. = ₹ $\frac{4x}{5}$ = ₹ $\left(\frac{4}{5} \times 1600\right)$ = ₹ 1280.

Thus, I and II together give the answer.

$\therefore$ Correct answer is (*e*).

15. II. Let C.P. = ₹ x. Then, M.P. = 130% of ₹ x = ₹ $\left(\frac{13x}{10}\right)$.

I. Discount = 10%.

S.P. = 90% of ₹ $\frac{13x}{10}$ = ₹ $\left(\frac{90}{100} \times \frac{13x}{10}\right)$ = ₹ $\left(\frac{117x}{100}\right)$.

Profit = ₹ $\left(\frac{117x}{100} - x\right)$ = ₹ $\frac{17x}{100}$.

$\therefore$ Profit% = $\left(\frac{17x}{100} \times \frac{1}{x} \times 100\right)\% = 17\%$.

Thus, I and II together give the answer.

$\therefore$ Correct answer is (e).

16. S.P. = ₹ 200.

I. C.P. = ₹ $\left(\frac{100}{125} \times 200\right)$ = ₹ 160.

$\therefore$ Profit = ₹ (200 – 160) = ₹ 40.

So, I alone gives the answer.

II. When S.P. = ₹ 180, Gain = 12.5%.

$\therefore$ C.P. = ₹ $\left(\frac{100}{112.5} \times 180\right)$ = ₹ 160.

Profit earned = ₹ (200 – 160) = ₹ 40.

Thus, II alone also gives the answer.

$\therefore$ Correct answer is (c).

17. I. S.P. = ₹ 7392. Profit = 12%.

C.P. of first machine = ₹ $\left(\frac{100}{112} \times 7392\right)$ = ₹ 6600.

II. S.P. = ₹ 7392. Loss = 4%.

C.P. of second machine = ₹ $\left(\frac{100}{96} \times 7392\right)$ = ₹ 7700.

Total C.P. = ₹ (6600 + 7700) = ₹ 14300.

Total S.P.= ₹ (7392 × 2) = ₹ 14784.

Profit = ₹ (14784 – 14300) = ₹ 484.

Thus, I and II together give the answer.

$\therefore$ Correct answer is (e).

18. Let the price of a banana be ₹ x and that of an orange ₹ y.

I. $14x + 35y = 84 \Rightarrow 2x + 5y = 12$ ...(i)

II. $4 \times \frac{x}{2} + 5y = 12 \Rightarrow 2x + 5y = 12$ ...(ii)

Thus, even I and II together do not give the answer.

$\therefore$ Correct answer is (d).

19. I. Let the labelled price be ₹ x.

C.P. = 60% of ₹ x = ₹ $\left(x \times \frac{60}{100}\right)$ = ₹ $\frac{3x}{5}$.

II. S.P. = 120% of ₹ x = ₹ $\left(x \times \frac{120}{100}\right)$ = ₹ $\frac{6x}{5}$.

Profit = ₹ $\left(\frac{6x}{5} - \frac{3x}{5}\right)$ = ₹ $\frac{3x}{5}$.

Thus, even I and II together do not give the answer.

$\therefore$ Correct answer is (d).

20. I. S.P. of 1 laptop = ₹ 26250.

C.P. of 5 laptops = S.P. of 4 laptops

= ₹ (26250 × 4) = ₹ 105000.

$\Rightarrow$ C.P. of 1 laptop = ₹ $\left(\frac{105000}{5}\right)$ = ₹ 21000.

Profit earned by selling a laptop

= ₹ (26250 – 21000) = ₹ 5250.

So, I alone gives the answer.

II. S.P. = ₹ 26250, Profit = 25%.

C.P. = ₹ $\left(\frac{100}{125} \times 26250\right)$ = ₹ 21000.

Profit = ₹ (26250 – 21000) = ₹ 5250.

So, II alone also gives the answer.

$\therefore$ Correct answer is (c).

21. I. Total gain = ₹ 1596.

II. C.P. of each article = ₹ 632.

III. S.P. of each article = ₹ 765.

Let the number of articles be x.

Then, $765x - 632x = 1596 \Rightarrow x = \frac{1596}{133} = 12$.

Thus, all I, II and III are needed to get the answer

$\therefore$ Correct answer is (d).

22. Let the M.P. be ₹ x.

I. S.P. = 90% of ₹ x = ₹ $\left(x \times \frac{90}{100}\right)$ = ₹ $\frac{9x}{10}$.

II. If S.P. = ₹ x, then gain = 30%.

$\therefore$ C.P. = ₹ $\left(\frac{100}{130} \times x\right)$ = ₹ $\frac{10x}{13}$.

III. Gain = 20%.

Thus, I, II, III do not give the answer.

$\therefore$ Correct answer is (e).

23. I. Let the C.P. be ₹ x.

Then, M.P. = 120% of ₹ x = ₹ $\left(\frac{120}{100} \times x\right)$ = ₹ $\frac{6x}{5}$.

II. S.P. = 85% of M.P. = ₹ $\left(\frac{6x}{5} \times \frac{85}{100}\right)$ = ₹ $\frac{51x}{50}$.

$\therefore$ $\frac{51x}{50} = 408 \Rightarrow x = \left(408 \times \frac{50}{51}\right) \Rightarrow x = 400$.

Thus, I and II give the answer.

III. When there is no discount, then S.P. = M.P. = ₹ $\frac{6x}{5}$

[From I]

Thus, II and III give the same answer.

$\therefore$ Correct answer is (b).

24. Let the M.P. be ₹ x.

I. C.P. = 85% of ₹ x = ₹ $\left(x \times \frac{85}{100}\right)$ = ₹ $\frac{17x}{20}$.

II. S.P. = ₹ 3060.

III. 102% of x = 3060 $\Rightarrow x = \left(3060 \times \frac{100}{102}\right) = 3000$.

$\therefore$ C.P. = ₹ $\frac{17x}{20}$ = ₹ $\left(\frac{17}{20} \times 3000\right)$ = ₹ 2550.

So, gain = ₹ (3060 – 2550) = ₹ 510.

Thus all I, II and III give the answer.

$\therefore$ Correct answer is (d).

25. I. Let the list price be ₹ x.

Then, S.P. = 95% of ₹ x = ₹ $\left(x \times \frac{95}{100}\right)$ = ₹ $\frac{19x}{20}$.

II. When S.P. = ₹ x and gain = 20%.

Then, C.P. = ₹ $\left(\frac{100}{120} \times x\right)$ = ₹ $\frac{5x}{6}$.

$\therefore$ Gain $= \left(\frac{19x}{20} - \frac{5x}{6}\right) = \left(\frac{57x - 50x}{60}\right) = \frac{7x}{60}$.

$\therefore$ Gain% $= \left(\frac{7x}{60} \times \frac{6}{5x} \times 100\right)\% = 14\%$.

Thus, I and II only give the answer.

$\therefore$ Correct answer is (*a*).

26. C.P. = ₹ 3000. Let the rate of discount be $x\%$.

I. S.P. = 105% of ₹ 3000 = ₹ 3150.

II. Let M.P. = ₹ x.

Then, $\frac{(x - 3150)}{(x - 85\% \text{ of } 3000)} = \frac{1}{2} \Rightarrow x = 3750$.

From I and II, discount = ₹ (3750 − 3150) = ₹ 600.

Discount% $= \left(\frac{600}{3750} \times 100\right)\% = 16\%$.

Thus, I and II give the answer.

III. M.P. = 125% of ₹ 3000 = ₹ 3750.

From I and III, discount = (M.P.) − (S.P.) = ₹ 600.

Thus, Discount% can be calculated.

Thus, I and III give the answer.

From II and III, we get :

discount $= ₹\left(\frac{3750 - 85\% \text{ of } 3000}{2}\right) = ₹\, 600$.

Thus, II and III give the answer.

$\therefore$ Correct answer is (*e*).

27. I. S.P. = ₹ 12350, Gain = 23.5%.

$\therefore$ C.P. $= ₹\left(\frac{100}{123.5} \times 12350\right) = ₹\, 10000$.

II. M.P. = 130% of C.P. = 130% of ₹ 10000 = ₹ 13000.

From I and II, discount = ₹ (13000 − 12350) = ₹ 650.

Discount% $= \left(\frac{650}{13000} \times 100\right)\% = 5\%$.

Thus, I and II give the answer.

III. gives C.P. = ₹ 10000.

So, II and III give the answer.

$\therefore$ Correct answer is (*e*).

28. I. Let C.P. be ₹ x.

Then, M.P. = 130% of x = ₹ $\frac{13x}{10}$.

III. S.P. = 90% of M.P.

Thus, I and III give, S.P. $= ₹\left(\frac{90}{100} \times \frac{13x}{10}\right) = ₹\, \frac{117x}{100}$.

Gain $= ₹\left(\frac{117x}{100} - x\right) = ₹\, \frac{17x}{100}$.

Thus, from I and III, gain% can be obtained.

Clearly, II is redundant.

$\therefore$ Correct answer is (*b*).

29. II. C.P. = ₹ 1500.

I. Gain = 10.5%.

$\therefore$ From I and II, we get : S.P. = 110.5% of C.P.

$= ₹\left(\frac{110.5}{100} \times 1500\right) = ₹\, 1657.50$.

Discount = 15%.

$\therefore$ M.P. $= ₹\left(\frac{100}{85} \times 1657.50\right) = ₹\, 1950$.

Thus, I and II give the answer and so III is redundant.

III. M.P. = 130% of C.P.

From II and III, we get: M.P. $= ₹\left(\frac{130}{100} \times 1500\right) = ₹\, 1950$.

$\therefore$ II and III give the answer and so I is redundant.

So, either I or III is redundant.

$\therefore$ Correct answer is (*b*).

13 Ratio and Proportion

IMPORTANT CONCEPTS

I. Ratio: The ratio of two quantities a and b in the same units, is the fraction $\frac{a}{b}$ and we write it as $a : b$.

In the ratio $a : b$, we call a as the first term or antecedent and b, the second term or consequent.

Ex. The ratio 5 : 9 represents $\frac{5}{9}$ with antecedent = 5, consequent = 9.

Rule: The multiplication or division of each term of a ratio by the same non-zero number does not affect the ratio.

Ex. 4 : 5 = 8 : 10 = 12 : 15 etc. Also, 4 : 6 = 2 : 3.

II. Proportion: *The equality of two ratios is called proportion.*

If $a : b = c : d$, we write, $a : b :: c : d$ and we say that a, b, c, d are in proportion.

Here a and d are called extremes, while b and c are called mean terms.

Product of means = Product of extremes.

Thus, $a : b :: c : d \Leftrightarrow (b \times c) = (a \times d)$.

III. (*i*) **Fourth Proportional:** If $a : b = c : d$, then d is called the fourth proportional to a, b, c.

(*ii*) **Third Proportional:** If $a : b = b : c$, then c is called the third proportional to a and b.

(*iii*) **Mean Proportional:** Mean proportional between a and b is $\sqrt{ab}$.

IV. (*i*) **Comparison of Ratios:** We say that $(a : b) > (c : d) \Leftrightarrow \frac{a}{b} > \frac{c}{d}$.

(*ii*) **Compounded Ratio:**

The compounded ratio of the ratios $(a : b)$, $(c : d)$, $(e : f)$ is $(ace : bdf)$.

V. (*i*) **Duplicate ratio** of $(a : b)$ is $(a^2 : b^2)$.

(*ii*) **Sub-duplicate ratio** of $(a : b)$ is $(\sqrt{a} : \sqrt{b})$.

(*iii*) **Triplicate ratio** of $(a : b)$ is $(a^3 : b^3)$.

(*iv*) **Sub-triplicate ratio** of $(a : b)$ is $\left(a^{\frac{1}{3}} : b^{\frac{1}{3}}\right)$.

(*v*) If $\frac{a}{b} = \frac{c}{d}$, then $\frac{a+b}{a-b} = \frac{c+d}{c-d}$. (componendo and dividendo)

VI. Variation:

(*i*) We say that x is directly proportional to y, if $x = ky$ for some constant k and we write, $x \propto y$.

(*ii*) We say that x is inversely proportional to y, if $xy = k$ for some constant k and we write, $x \propto \frac{1}{y}$.

VII. Suppose a container contains x units of liquid from which y units are taken out and replaced by water. After n operations, the quantity of pure liquid in the final mixture = $\left[x\left(1-\frac{y}{x}\right)^n\right]$ units.

class the ratio of female students to male students is 16 : 9. What percentage of the class is female? (M.B.A., 2006)

of every (16 + 9) i.e., 25 students, 16 are female.

quired percentage = $\left(\frac{16}{25}\times 100\right)\% = 64\%$.

xceeds B by 40%, B is less than C by 20%, then find A : C.

0% of C = $\frac{4}{5}C$;

40% of $\frac{4}{5}C = \left(\frac{140}{100}\times\frac{4}{5}C\right) = \frac{28}{25}C$.

$C = \frac{28}{25}C : C = \frac{28}{25}:1 = 28:25$.

e the number 455 in the ratio 4 : 3. (L.I.C.A.D.O., 2008)

art = $\left(455\times\frac{4}{7}\right) = 260$;

l part = $\left(455\times\frac{3}{7}\right) = 195$.

of ₹ 427 is to be divided among A, B and C is such a way that 3 times A's share, 4 times B's share times C's share are all equal. Find the share of each.

B = 7C = k (say)

$= \frac{k}{3}, B = \frac{k}{4}, C = \frac{k}{7} \Rightarrow A:B:C = \frac{k}{3}:\frac{k}{4}:\frac{k}{7} = \frac{1}{3}:\frac{1}{4}:\frac{1}{7} = 28:21:12$.

ratio terms = (28 + 21 + 12) = 61.

share = ₹ $\left(427\times\frac{28}{61}\right)$ = ₹ 196;

share = ₹ $\left(427\times\frac{21}{61}\right)$ = ₹ 147;

share = ₹ $\left(427\times\frac{12}{61}\right)$ = ₹ 84.

₹ 6450 among A, B, C and D such that when A gets ₹ 9, B gets ₹ 8; when B gets ₹ 6, C gets ₹ 5 and gets ₹ 4, D gets ₹ 3.

9 : 8, B : C = 6 : 5 = $\left(6\times\frac{4}{3}\right):\left(5\times\frac{4}{3}\right) = 8:\frac{20}{3}$,

4 : 3 = $\left(4\times\frac{5}{3}\right):\left(3\times\frac{5}{3}\right) = \frac{20}{3}:5$.

$B : C : D = 9 : 8 : \frac{20}{3} : 5$ = 27 : 24 : 20 : 15.

of ratio terms = (27 + 24 + 20 + 15) = 86.

share = ₹ $\left(6450\times\frac{27}{86}\right)$ = ₹ 2025; B's share = ₹ $\left(6450\times\frac{24}{86}\right)$ = ₹ 1800;

hare = ₹ $\left(6450\times\frac{20}{86}\right)$ = ₹ 1500; D's share = ₹ $\left(6450\times\frac{15}{86}\right)$ = ₹ 1125.

₹ 1290 is divided between A, B and C such that A's share is $1\frac{1}{2}$ times that of B and B's share is that of C. What is C's share?

SOLVED EXAMPLES

Ex. 1. ***If 10% of x is equal to 20% of y, then find x : y.***

Sol. 10% of x = 20% of $y \Rightarrow \frac{10}{100}x = \frac{20}{100}y \Rightarrow \frac{x}{10} = \frac{y}{5} \Rightarrow \frac{x}{y} = \frac{10}{5} = \frac{2}{1}$.

Hence, $x : y = 2 : 1$.

Ex. 2. ***A man spends ₹ 500 in buying 12 tables and chairs. The cost of one table is ₹ 50 and that of one chair is ₹ 40. What is the ratio of the numbers of the chairs and tables purchased?***

Sol. Let the number of tables purchased be x.

Then, number of chairs purchased = $(12 - x)$.

$\therefore$ $50x + 40(12 - x) = 500$

$\Leftrightarrow$ $50x - 40x = 500 - 480$

$\Leftrightarrow$ $10x = 20$

$\Leftrightarrow$ $x = 2$.

So, number of tables = 2 and number of chairs = 10.

Hence, required ratio = 10 : 2 = 5 : 1.

Ex. 3. ***If 7 : x = 17.5 : 22.5, then find the value of x.*** (Bank P.O., 2007)

Sol. $7 : x = 17.5 : 22.5$

$\Leftrightarrow 17.5x = 7 \times 22.5$

$\Leftrightarrow x = \frac{7\times 22.5}{17.5} = 9$.

Hence, $x = 9$.

Ex. 4. ***If 20% of (P + Q) = 50% of (P – Q), then find P : Q.***

Sol. 20% of $(P + Q)$ = 50% of $(P - Q)$

$\Rightarrow \frac{20}{100}(P+Q) = \frac{50}{100}(P-Q) \Rightarrow \frac{P+Q}{5} = \frac{P-Q}{2}$

$\Rightarrow 2(P + Q) = 5(P - Q) \Rightarrow 3P = 7Q \Rightarrow \frac{P}{Q} = \frac{7}{3} \Rightarrow P : Q = 7 : 3$.

Ex. 5. ***If 30% of A = 0.25 of B = $\frac{1}{5}$ of C, then find A : B : C.***

Sol. 30% of A = 0.25 of B = $\frac{1}{5}$ of C

$\Rightarrow \frac{30}{100}A = \frac{25}{100}B = \frac{1}{5}C \Rightarrow \frac{3A}{10} = \frac{B}{4} = \frac{C}{5} = k$ (say)

$\Rightarrow A = \frac{10k}{3}$, $B = 4k$, $C = 5k$

$\Rightarrow A : B : C = \frac{10k}{3} : 4k : 5k = \frac{10}{3} : 4 : 5 = 10 : 12 : 15$.

Ex. 6. ***If $2x^2 - 7xy + 3y^2 = 0$, then find the value of x : y.***

Sol. $2x^2 - 7xy + 3y^2 = 0 \Leftrightarrow 2x^2 - 6xy - xy + 3y^2 = 0$

$\Leftrightarrow 2x(x - 3y) - y(x - 3y) = 0$

$\Leftrightarrow (x - 3y)(2x - y) = 0 \Leftrightarrow x = 3y$ or $2x = y$

$\Leftrightarrow \frac{x}{y} = 3$ or $\frac{x}{y} = \frac{1}{2}$.

$\therefore$ $x : y = 3 : 1$ or $1 : 2$.

Ex. 7. ***If A, B, C, D are quantities of the same kind such that A : B = 3 : 4, B : C = 5 : 7 and C : D = 8 : 9, find***

(a) A : C ***(b) B : D*** ***(c) A : D*** ***(d) A : B : C : D***

Sol.(a) $A : C = \frac{A}{C} = \frac{A}{B} \times \frac{B}{C} = \frac{3}{4} \times \frac{5}{7} = \frac{15}{28} = 15 : 28.$

(b) $B : D = \frac{B}{D} = \frac{B}{C} \times \frac{C}{D} = \frac{5}{7} \times \frac{8}{9} = \frac{40}{63} = 40 : 63.$

(c) $A : D = \frac{A}{D} = \frac{A}{B} \times \frac{B}{C} \times \frac{C}{D} = \frac{3}{4} \times \frac{5}{7} \times \frac{8}{9} = \frac{10}{21} = 10 : 21.$

(d) $A : B = 3 : 4;\ B : C = 5 : 7 = \left(5 \times \frac{4}{5}\right) : \left(7 \times \frac{4}{5}\right) = 4 : \frac{28}{5};$

$C : D = 8 : 9 = \left(8 \times \frac{7}{10}\right) : \left(9 \times \frac{7}{10}\right) = \frac{28}{5} : \frac{63}{10}.$

$\therefore A : B : C : D = 3 : 4 : \frac{28}{5} : \frac{63}{10} = 30 : 40 : 56 : 63.$

Ex. 8. *If* $a : b = \frac{2}{9} : \frac{1}{3},\ b : c = \frac{2}{7} : \frac{5}{14}$ *and* $d : c = \frac{7}{10} : \frac{3}{5}$*, then find* $a : b : c : d$.

Sol. $a : b = \frac{2}{9} : \frac{1}{3} = 2 : 3,\ b : c = \frac{2}{7} : \frac{5}{14} = 4 : 5 = \left(4 \times \frac{3}{4}\right) : \left(5 \times \frac{3}{4}\right) = 3 : \frac{15}{4},$

$c : d = \frac{3}{5} : \frac{7}{10} = 6 : 7 = \left(6 \times \frac{5}{8}\right) : \left(7 \times \frac{5}{8}\right) = \frac{15}{4} : \frac{35}{8}.$

$\therefore a : b : c : d = 2 : 3 : \frac{15}{4} : \frac{35}{8} = 16 : 24 : 30 : 35.$

Ex. 9. *If* $m : n = 3 : 2$*, then find the ratio* $(4m + 5n) : (4m - 5n)$. (S.S.C., 2007, 2008)

Sol. $\frac{m}{n} = \frac{3}{2} \Rightarrow \frac{4m + 5n}{4m - 5n} = \frac{4\left(\frac{m}{n}\right) + 5}{4\left(\frac{m}{n}\right) - 5} = \frac{4 \times \frac{3}{2} + 5}{4 \times \frac{3}{2} - 5} = \frac{11}{1}.$

$\therefore (4m + 5n) : (4m - 5n) = 11 : 1.$

Ex. 10. *If* $(2x + 3y) : (3x + 5y) = 18 : 29$*, what is the value of* $x : y$? (B.Ed Entrance, 2010)

Sol. $\frac{2x + 3y}{3x + 5y} = \frac{18}{29} \Rightarrow 29\,(2x + 3y) = 18\,(3x + 5y)$

$\Rightarrow 58x + 87y = 54x + 90y$

$\Rightarrow 4x = 3y \Rightarrow \frac{x}{y} = \frac{3}{4}.$

Hence, $x : y = 3 : 4$.

Ex. 11. *If* $(x + y) : (x - y) = 7 : 3$*, then find the ratio* $(x^3 + y^3) : (x^3 - y^3)$.

Sol. $\frac{(x + y)}{(x - y)} = \frac{7}{3} \Rightarrow 3x + 3y = 7x - 7y$

$\Rightarrow 4x = 10y \Rightarrow \frac{x}{y} = \frac{10}{4} = \frac{5}{2}$

$\Rightarrow \frac{x^3 + y^3}{x^3 - y^3} = \frac{\left(\frac{x^3}{y^3}\right) + 1}{\left(\frac{x^3}{y^3}\right) - 1} = \frac{\left(\frac{x}{y}\right)^3 + 1}{\left(\frac{x}{y}\right)^3 - 1} = \frac{\frac{125}{8} + 1}{\frac{125}{8} - 1} = \frac{133}{8} \times \frac{8}{117} = \frac{133}{117}.$

Hence, $(x^3 + y^3) : (x^3 - y^3) = \frac{133}{117}.$

Ex. 12. *If* $a : 5 = b : 7 = c : 8$*, then* $\frac{a + b + c}{a} = ?$

Sol. Let $\frac{a}{5} = \frac{b}{7} = \frac{c}{8} = k$. Then, $a = 5k,\ b = 7k,\ c = 8k$.

$\therefore \frac{a + b + c}{a} = \frac{5k + 7k + 8k}{5k} = \frac{20k}{5k} = 4.$

Ex. 13. *If* $p : q = r : s = t : u = 2 : 3$*, then find* $(mp + nr + ot) : (mq + ns + ou)$.

Sol. $\frac{p}{q} = \frac{r}{s} = \frac{t}{u} = \frac{2}{3} \Rightarrow p = \frac{2q}{3},\ r = \frac{2s}{3},\ t = \frac{2u}{3}.$

$\therefore \frac{mp + nr + ot}{mq + ns + ou} = \frac{m \times \frac{2q}{3} + n \times \frac{2s}{3} + o \times \frac{2u}{3}}{mq + ns + ou} = \frac{\frac{2}{3}(mq + ns + ou)}{(mq + ns + ou)} = \frac{2}{3}.$

Ex. 14. *Find :* *(i) the fourth proportional to 4, 9, 12 ;*
(ii) the third proportional to 16 and 36 ;
(iii) the mean proportional between 0.08 and 0.18 ;
(iv) the mean proportional between $6 + 3\sqrt{3}$ *and* $8 - 4\sqrt{3}$.

Sol. (*i*) Let the fourth proportional to 4, 9, 12 be x.

Then, $4 : 9 :: 12 : x \Leftrightarrow 4 \times x = 9 \times 12 \Leftrightarrow x = \frac{9 \times 12}{4} = 27.$

$\therefore$ Fourth proportional to 4, 9, 12 is 27.

(*ii*) Let the third proportional to 16 and 36 be x.

Then, $16 : 36 :: 36 : x \Leftrightarrow 16 \times x = 36 \times 36 \Leftrightarrow x = \frac{36 \times 36}{16} = 81.$

$\therefore$ Third proportional to 16 and 36 is 81.

(*iii*) Mean proportional between 0.08 and 0.18

$= \sqrt{0.08 \times 0.18} = \sqrt{\frac{8}{100} \times \frac{18}{100}} = \sqrt{\frac{144}{100 \times 100}} = \frac{12}{100} = 0.12.$

(*iv*) Mean proportional between $6 + 3\sqrt{3}$ and $8 - 4\sqrt{3}$

$= \sqrt{(6 + 3\sqrt{3})(8 - 4\sqrt{3})} = \sqrt{48 - 36} = \sqrt{12} = 2\sqrt{3}.$

Ex. 15. *Find two numbers such that their mean proportional is 6 and third p*

Sol. Let the two numbers be x and y.

Then, $\sqrt{xy} = 6$ and $x : y :: y : 20.25$

$\Rightarrow xy = (6)^2 = 36$ and $y^2 = 20.25x$

$\Rightarrow x = \frac{36}{y}$ and $y^2 = 20.25 \times \frac{36}{y} = \frac{729}{y}$

$\Rightarrow y^3 = 729 = 9^3 \Rightarrow y = 9 \Rightarrow x = \frac{36}{9} = 4.$

Hence, the required numbers are 4 and 9.

Ex. 16. *When 20% of a number is added to another number the number in* *ratio between the first and the second numbers?*

Sol. Let the two numbers be x and y.

Then, y + 20% of x = 150% of $y \Rightarrow y + \frac{20}{100}x = \frac{150}{100}y \Rightarrow y + \frac{x}{5} = \frac{3}{2}$

Hence, required ratio = 5 : 2.

Ex. 17. *In a*
Sol. Out
∴ R
Ex. 18. *If A*
Sol. B =
A =
∴ A
Ex. 19. *Divic*
Sol. First
Secon
Ex. 20. *A sur*
and 7
Sol. 3A =
⇒
Sum c
∴ A
B'
C'
Ex. 21. *Divide*
when C
Sol. A : B =
C : D =
∴ A :
Sur
A's
C's
Ex. 22. *A sum o*
$1\frac{3}{4}$ *time*

Sol. Let C's share = ₹ x.

Then, B's share = ₹ $\left(1\frac{3}{4}x\right)$ = ₹ $\left(\frac{7x}{4}\right)$;

A's share = ₹ $\left(\frac{3}{2} \times \frac{7x}{4}\right)$ = ₹ $\left(\frac{21x}{8}\right)$.

$A : B : C = \frac{21x}{8} : \frac{7x}{4} : x = \frac{21}{8} : \frac{7}{4} : 1 = 21 : 14 : 8.$

Sum of ratio terms = (21 + 14 + 8) = 43.

$\therefore$ C's share = ₹ $\left(1290 \times \frac{8}{43}\right)$ = ₹ 240.

Ex. 23. ***Divide ₹ 1050 among A, B and C such that A receives $\frac{2}{5}$ as much as B and C together and B receives $\frac{3}{7}$ as much as A and C together.***

Sol. $A = \frac{2}{5}(B + C),\ B = \frac{3}{7}(A + C)$

$\Rightarrow A = \frac{2}{5}\left(\frac{3}{7}A + \frac{3}{7}C + C\right) = \frac{2}{5}\left(\frac{3}{7}A + \frac{10}{7}C\right) = \frac{6}{35}A + \frac{4}{7}C$

$\Rightarrow \frac{29}{35}A = \frac{4}{7}C \Rightarrow A = \left(\frac{4}{7} \times \frac{35}{29}\right)C = \frac{20}{29}C.$

$\therefore B = \frac{3}{7}\left(\frac{20}{29}C + C\right) = \frac{3}{7} \times \frac{49}{29}C = \frac{21}{29}C.$

$A : B : C = \frac{20}{29}C : \frac{21}{29}C : C = 20 : 21 : 29.$

Sum of ratio terms = (20 + 21 + 29) = 70.

A's share = ₹ $\left(1050 \times \frac{20}{70}\right)$ = ₹ 300; B's share = ₹ $\left(1050 \times \frac{21}{70}\right)$ = ₹ 315;

C's share = ₹ $\left(1050 \times \frac{29}{70}\right)$ = ₹ 435.

Ex. 24. ***The cost of an article depends on three items – material, labour and other expenses. The cost on these items is in the ratio 3 : 4 : 1 respectively. If the cost of material is ₹ 22.50, find the cost of the article.*** **(R.R.B., 2006)**

Sol. Let the cost of material, labour and other expenses be ₹ $3x$, $4x$ and x respectively.

Then, $3x = 22.50$ or $x = 7.50$.

$\therefore$ Cost of the article = $3x + 4x + x = 8x$ = ₹ (8 × 7.50) = ₹ 60.

Ex. 25. ***Three numbers are in the ratio $\frac{1}{2} : \frac{2}{3} : \frac{3}{4}$. The difference between the greatest and the smallest numbers is 36. Find the numbers.***

Sol. Ratio of numbers = $\frac{1}{2} : \frac{2}{3} : \frac{3}{4} = 6 : 8 : 9.$

Let the numbers be $6x$, $8x$ and $9x$.

Then, $9x - 6x = 36$ or $3x = 36$ or $x = 12$.

$\therefore$ The numbers are (6 × 12), (8 × 12) and (9 × 12) i.e., 72, 96 and 108.

Ex. 26. ***Find three numbers in the ratio of 3 : 2 : 5 such that the sum of their squares is equal to 1862.***

Sol. Let the numbers be $3x$, $2x$ and $5x$.

Then, $(3x)^2 + (2x)^2 + (5x)^2 = 1862 \Rightarrow 9x^2 + 4x^2 + 25x^2 = 1862 \Rightarrow 38x^2 = 1862 \Rightarrow x^2 = 49 \Rightarrow x = 7.$

Hence, the numbers are 21, 14 and 35.

Ex. 27. ***The ratio of incomes of A and B is 3 : 4. The ratio of their expenditures is 4 : 5. Find the ratio of their savings if the savings of A is one-fourth of his income.*** **(Campus Recruitment, 2008)**

Sol. Let the incomes of A and B be $3x$ and $4x$ and their expenditures be $4y$ and $5y$ respectively.

Then, A's savings = $3x - 4y$.

$\therefore \quad 3x - 4y = \frac{1}{4}$ of $3x \Rightarrow 12x - 16y = 3x \Rightarrow 9x = 16y \Rightarrow y = \frac{9}{16}x.$

So, ratio of savings $= \frac{A\text{'s savings}}{B\text{'s savings}} = \frac{3x - 4y}{4x - 5y} = \frac{3x - 4\times\frac{9}{16}x}{4x - 5\times\frac{9}{16}x}$

$= \frac{3x - \frac{9}{4}x}{4x - \frac{45}{16}x} = \left(\frac{3}{4}x \times \frac{16}{19x}\right) = 12 : 19.$

Ex. 2 . ***Weekly incomes of two persons are in the ratio of 7 : 3 and their weekly expenses are in the ratio of 5 : 2. If each of them saves ₹ 300 per week, find their weekly incomes.*** (SNAP, 2010)

Sol. Let the incomes of the two persons be ₹ $7x$ and ₹ $3x$ and their expenses be ₹ $5y$ and ₹ $2y$ respectively. Then,

$7x - 5y = 3x - 2y \Rightarrow 4x = 3y \Rightarrow y = \frac{4}{3}x.$

Now, $7x - 5y = 300 \Rightarrow 7x - 5 \times \frac{4}{3}x = 300$

$\Rightarrow 7x - \frac{20x}{3} = 300 \Rightarrow x = 900.$

$\therefore$ Weekly income of first person = ₹ (7×900) = ₹ 6300.

Weekly income of second person = ₹ (3×900) = ₹ 2700.

Ex. 29. ***The salary of A, B and C together amounts to ₹ 33300. If they spend 80%, 85% and 75% of their respective incomes, their savings are as 7 : 6 : 9. Find the salary of B.***

Sol. Since A, B and C spend 80%, 85% and 75% of their incomes, they save 20%, 15% and 25% of their incomes.

Let the salary of A, B and C be x, y and z respectively.

Then, 20% of x : 15% of y : 25% of z = $7 : 6 : 9 \Rightarrow \frac{x}{5} : \frac{3y}{20} : \frac{z}{4} = 7 : 6 : 9.$

$\frac{x}{5} : \frac{3y}{20} :: 7 : 6 \Rightarrow \frac{x}{5} \times 6 = \frac{3y}{20} \times 7 \Rightarrow \frac{x}{y} = \frac{3}{20} \times \frac{7}{6} \times 5 = \frac{7}{8}.$

$\frac{3y}{20} : \frac{z}{4} :: 6 : 9 \Rightarrow \frac{3y}{20} \times 9 = \frac{z}{4} \times 6 \Rightarrow \frac{y}{z} = \frac{1}{4} \times \frac{6}{9} \times \frac{20}{3} = \frac{10}{9}.$

So, $x : y = 7 : 8$ and $y : z = 10 : 9 = \left(10 \times \frac{4}{5}\right) : \left(9 \times \frac{4}{5}\right) = 8 : \frac{36}{5}.$

$x : y : z = 7 : 8 : \frac{36}{5} = 35 : 40 : 36.$

Let $x = 35k$, $y = 40k$ and $z = 36k$.

$\therefore 35k + 40k + 36k = 33300 \Rightarrow 111k = 33300 \Rightarrow k = 300.$

Hence, B's salary = ₹ (40×300) = ₹ 12000.

Ex. 30. ***What must be added to each term of the ratio 7 : 11 so as to make it equal to 3 : 4?*** (S.S.C., 2010)

Sol. Let the number to be added be x.

Then, $\frac{7 + x}{11 + x} = \frac{3}{4} \Rightarrow 4(7 + x) = 3(11 + x) \Rightarrow 28 + 4x = 33 + 3x \Rightarrow x = 5.$

Hence, required number = 5.

Ex. 31. ***What should be subtracted from 15, 28, 20 and 38 so that the remaining numbers may be proportional?***

(M.A.T., 2009)

Sol. Let the required number be x.

Then, $\frac{15-x}{28-x}=\frac{20-x}{38-x}$

$\Leftrightarrow (15-x)(38-x)=(20-x)(28-x)$

$\Leftrightarrow 570-53x+x^2=560-48x+x^2$

$\Leftrightarrow 5x=10 \Leftrightarrow x=2.$

Hence, required number = 2.

Ex. 32. ***The ratio of milk and water in 64 litres of a mixture is 5 : 3. What amount of water is added to make the ratio 3 : 5?*** (P.C.S., 2006)

Sol. Quantity of milk $=\left(64\times\frac{5}{8}\right)$ litres = 40 litres.

Quantity of water $=\left(64\times\frac{3}{8}\right)$ litres = 24 litres.

Let x litres of water be added.

Then, $\frac{40}{24+x}=\frac{3}{5} \Rightarrow 200=72+3x$

$\Rightarrow 3x=128$

$\Rightarrow x=\frac{128}{3}=42\frac{2}{3}$

Hence, required quantity $=42\frac{2}{3}$ litres.

Ex. 33. ***The dimensions of a rectangular room when increased by 4 metres, are in the ratio of 4 : 3 and when decreased by 4 metres, are in the ratio of 2 : 1. Find the dimensions of the room.***

Sol. Let the length and breadth of the room be x metres and y metres respectively.

Then, $\frac{x+4}{y+4}=\frac{4}{3} \Rightarrow 3x+12=4y+16$

$\Rightarrow 3x-4y=4$ ...(*i*)

And, $\frac{x-4}{y-4}=\frac{2}{1} \Rightarrow x-4=2y-8$

$\Rightarrow x-2y=-4$ ...(*ii*)

Multiplying (*ii*) by 3 and subtracting from (*i*), we get : $y=8$.

Putting $y=8$ in (*i*), we get : $x=12$.

Hence, the dimensions of the room are 12 m and 8 m.

Ex. 34. ***The ages of Chinmay and Maulik are in the ratio of 5 : 2 respectively. After 7 years, the ratio of their ages will be 4 : 3. What is the age of Chinmay?*** (M.A.T., 2007)

Sol. Let the present ages of Chinmay and Maulik be $5x$ and $2x$ years respectively.

Chinmay's age 7 years hence = $(5x+7)$ years.

Maulik's age 7 years hence = $(2x+7)$ years.

$\therefore \frac{5x+7}{2x+7}=\frac{4}{3} \Leftrightarrow 3(5x+7)=4(2x+7) \Leftrightarrow 15x+21=8x+28 \Leftrightarrow 7x=7$

$\Leftrightarrow x=1.$

Hence, Chinmay's age = 5 years.

Ex. 35. ***A bag contains one-rupee, 50-paise and 25-paise coins in the ratio 5 : 6 : 8. If the total amount of money in the bag is ₹ 210, find the number of coins of each kind.***

Sol. Let the number of one-rupee, 50-paise and 25-paise coins be $5x$, $6x$ and $8x$ respectively.

Then, sum of their values = ₹ $\left(5x+\frac{50\times 6x}{100}+\frac{25\times 8x}{100}\right)$ = ₹ $(5x+3x+2x)$ = ₹ $10x$.

$\therefore \quad 10x = 210 \Rightarrow x = 21.$

So, number of one-rupee coins $= 5 \times 21 = 105$;

number of 50-paise coins $= 6 \times 21 = 126$;

number of 25-paise coins $= 8 \times 21 = 168$.

Ex. 36. ***If m is proportional to n and m = 5 when n = 4, then what is the value of m when n = 18?***

Sol. $m \propto n \Rightarrow m = kn$ for some constant k.

When $m = 5$ and $n = 4$, $m = kn \Rightarrow 5 = 4k \Rightarrow k = \frac{5}{4}$.

When $n = 18$, we have : $m = \frac{5}{4}n = \frac{5}{4} \times 18 = \frac{45}{2} = 22.5$.

Ex. 37. ***x^2 varies directly as y^3 and when x = 6, y = 3. Deduce the relation between x and y.***

Sol. $x^2 \propto y^3 \Rightarrow x^2 = ky^3$ for some constant k.

When $x = 6$ and $y = 3$, we have :

$$x^2 = ky^3 \Rightarrow 6^2 = k \times 3^3 \Rightarrow 36 = 27k \Rightarrow k = \frac{36}{27} = \frac{4}{3}.$$

$$\therefore \quad x^2 = \frac{4}{3}y^3 \Rightarrow 3x^2 = 4y^3.$$

Ex. 38. ***The time of oscillation of a pendulum varies as the square root of its length. If a pendulum of length 40 cm oscillates once in a second, find the length of the pendulum oscillating once in 2.5 seconds.***

Sol. $T \propto \sqrt{l} \Rightarrow T = k\sqrt{l}$ for some constant k.

When $l = 40$ cm, $T = 1$ sec, $T = k\sqrt{l} \Rightarrow 1 = k\sqrt{40} \Rightarrow k = \frac{1}{\sqrt{40}}$.

Let the required length be x cm.

Then, $2.5 = \frac{1}{\sqrt{40}} . \sqrt{x} \Rightarrow \sqrt{x} = 2.5 \times \sqrt{40} \Rightarrow x = (2.5 \times \sqrt{40})^2 = 6.25 \times 40 = 250.$

Hence, required length = 250 cm.

Ex. 39. ***The ratio of the number of students studying in schools A, B and C is 6:8:7 respectively. If the number of students studying in each of the schools is increased by 20%, 15% and 20% respectively, what will be the new ratio of the number of students in schools A, B and C?*** **(NABARD, 2008)**

Sol. Let the number of students studying in schools A, B and C be $6x$, $8x$ and $7x$ respectively.

Then, new strength of school A = 120% of $6x = \frac{36x}{5}$;

new strength of school B = 115% of $8x = \frac{46x}{5}$;

new strength of school C = 120% of $7x = \frac{42x}{5}$.

$$\therefore \quad \text{Required ratio} = \frac{36x}{5} : \frac{46x}{5} : \frac{42x}{5} = 18 : 23 : 21.$$

Ex. 40. ***The cost of manufacturing a car is made up of three items : cost of materials, labour and overheads. In a year, the cost of these items were in the ratio 4 : 3 : 2. Next year the cost of materials rose by 10%, cost of labour increased by 8% but the overheads reduced by 5%. Find the increase percent in the price of the car.***

Sol. Let the cost of materials, labour and overheads in the first year be ₹ $4x$, ₹ $3x$ and ₹ $2x$ respectively.

Then, cost of materials in second year = 110% of ₹ $4x$ = ₹ $\left(\frac{110}{100} \times 4x\right)$ = ₹ $\frac{440x}{100}$.

Cost of labour in second year = 108% of ₹ $3x$ = ₹ $\left(\frac{108}{100} \times 3x\right)$ = ₹ $\frac{324x}{100}$.

Overheads in second year = 95% of ₹ 2x = ₹ $\left(\frac{95}{100} \times 2x\right)$ = ₹ $\left(\frac{190x}{100}\right)$.

Price of the car in first year = ₹ $(4x + 3x + 2x)$ = ₹ $9x$.

Price of the car in second year = ₹ $\left(\frac{440x}{100} + \frac{324x}{100} + \frac{190x}{100}\right)$ = ₹ $\left(\frac{954x}{100}\right)$.

Increase in price = ₹ $\left(\frac{954x}{100} - 9x\right)$ = ₹ $\frac{54x}{100}$.

$\therefore$ Increase % = $\left(\frac{54x}{100} \times \frac{1}{9x} \times 100\right)\% = 6\%$.

Ex. 41. ***Cost of a diamond varies directly as the square of its weight. A diamond broke into four pieces with their weights in the ratio 1 : 2 : 3 : 4. If the loss in the total value of the diamond was ₹ 70000, find the price of the original diamond.*** **(A.A.O. Exam, 2010)**

Sol. Let the weights of the four pieces be x, $2x$, $3x$ and $4x$.

Then, original weight of the diamond = $(x + 2x + 3x + 4x) = 10x$.

Original price of the diamond = $k \times (10x)^2 = 100kx^2$, where k is a constant.

Prices of the smaller pieces will be kx^2, $4kx^2$, $9kx^2$ and $16kx^2$.

Total price of the four pieces = $(kx^2 + 4kx^2 + 9kx^2 + 16kx^2) = 30kx^2$.

Loss in value = $(100kx^2 - 30kx^2) = 70kx^2$.

$\therefore$ $70kx^2 = 70000$ or $kx^2 = 1000$.

Hence, price of original diamond = ₹ (100×1000) = ₹ 100000.

Ex.42. ***In a mixture of three varieties of tea, the ratio of their weights is 4 : 5 : 8. If 5 kg tea of the first variety, 10 kg tea of the second variety and some quantity of tea of the third variety are added to the mixture, the ratio of the weights of three varieties of tea becomes 5 : 7 : 9. Find the quantity of the third variety of tea in the final mixture.*** **(P.C.S., 2006)**

Sol. Let the weights of 1st, 2nd and 3rd varieties of tea in the original mixture be $4x$, $5x$ and $8x$ kg respectively.

Then, $\frac{4x+5}{5x+10} = \frac{5}{7} \Leftrightarrow 7(4x + 5) = 5(5x + 10)$

$\Leftrightarrow 28x + 35 = 25x + 50$

$\Leftrightarrow 3x = 15 \Leftrightarrow x = 5$.

So, the weights of 1st, 2nd and 3rd varieties in the original mixture are 20 kg, 25 kg and 40 kg respectively.

Let y kg of third variety be added.

Then, $\frac{25+10}{40+y} = \frac{7}{9} \Leftrightarrow 7(40 + y) = 9 \times 35 \Leftrightarrow 40 + y = \frac{9 \times 35}{7} = 45 \Leftrightarrow y = 5$.

Hence, quantity of third variety in the final mixture = $(40 + 5)$ kg = 45 kg.

Ex. 43. ***A shopkeeper mixes two varieties of tea – one costing ₹ 75 per kg and the other costing ₹ 50 per kg in the ratio 3 : 2. If he sells the mixed variety at ₹ 62.40 per kg, find his gain or loss percent.*** **(S.S.C., 2008)**

Sol. Suppose the shopkeeper mixes $3x$ kg of first variety and $2x$ kg of second variety.

Then, C.P. of $(5x)$ kg of mixture = ₹ $(3x \times 75 + 2x \times 50)$ = ₹ $(325x)$.

S.P. of $(5x)$ kg of mixture = ₹ $(5x \times 62.40)$ = ₹ $(312x)$.

Loss = ₹ $(325x - 312x)$ = ₹ $(13x)$.

$\therefore$ Loss % = $\left(\frac{13x}{325x} \times 100\right)\% = 4\%$.

Ex. 44. ***Initially two cups of same volume are filled with milk upto $\frac{3}{5}$th and $\frac{4}{5}$th of their volumes. Water is then filled. Then two mixtures are mixed and poured into a jug. Find the ratio of water to milk in the mixture.*** **(Campus Recruitment, 2008)**

Sol. Let the volume of each of the two cups be x.

Then, volume of milk in the first cup $= \frac{3}{5}x$.

Volume of water in the first cup $= \frac{2}{5}x$.

Volume of milk in the second cup $= \frac{4}{5}x$.

Volume of water in the second cup $= \frac{x}{5}$.

$\therefore$ Ratio of water to milk in the jug $= \left(\frac{2}{5}x + \frac{x}{5}\right) : \left(\frac{3}{5}x + \frac{4}{5}x\right) = \frac{3}{5}x : \frac{7}{5}x = 3:7.$

Ex. 45. ***Three equal jugs are filled with a mixture of milk and water. The proportion of milk and water in each glass is in the ratio 1 : 2, 2 : 3 and 3 : 4. The contents of the three jugs are emptied into a single vessel. What is the proportion of milk and water in it?*** **(M.A.T., 2008)**

Sol. Let the volume of each jug be x litres. Then,

milk in 1st glass $= \frac{x}{3}$ litres; water in 1st glass $= \frac{2x}{3}$ litres;

milk in 2nd glass $= \frac{2x}{5}$ litres; water in 2nd glass $= \frac{3x}{5}$ litres;

milk in 3rd glass $= \frac{3x}{7}$ litres; water in 3rd glass $= \frac{4x}{7}$ litres.

Total milk in final mixture $= \left(\frac{x}{3} + \frac{2x}{5} + \frac{3x}{7}\right)$ litres $= \frac{122}{105}$ litres.

Total water in final mixture $= \left(\frac{2x}{3} + \frac{3x}{5} + \frac{4x}{7}\right)$ litres $= \frac{193}{105}$ litres.

$\therefore$ Required ratio of milk and water $= \frac{122}{105} : \frac{193}{105} = 122 : 193.$

Ex. 46. ***The resistance of a wire is directly proportional to its length and inversely proportional to the square of its radius. Two wires of the same material have the same resistance and their radii are in the ratio of 9 : 8. If the length of the first wire is 162 cm, find the length of the other wire.***

Sol. Clearly, we have : $R \propto l$ and $R \propto \frac{1}{r^2} \Rightarrow R \propto \frac{l}{r^2} \Rightarrow R = \frac{kl}{r^2}$, where k is a constant.

Let the radii of the two wires be $9x$ and $8x$ and their lengths be l_1 and l_2 respectively.

Then, $\frac{kl_1}{(9x)^2} = \frac{kl_2}{(8x)^2} \Rightarrow \frac{l_1}{81x^2} = \frac{l_2}{64x^2} \Rightarrow \frac{l_2}{64} = \frac{162}{81} = 2$

$\Rightarrow l_2 = (64 \times 2)$ cm $= 128$ cm

Hence, length of the other wire = 128 cm.

Ex.47. ***Visitors to a show were charged ₹ 12 each on the first day, ₹ 9.50 on the second, ₹ 4 on the third day and the total attendance on three days were in the ratio 3 : 6 : 11 respectively. Find the average charge per person for the whole show.***

Sol. Let the attendance on the three days be $3x$, $6x$ and $11x$ respectively.

Then, total charges collected = ₹ $(12 \times 3x + 9.5 \times 6x + 4 \times 11x)$

= ₹ $(36x + 57x + 44x)$ = ₹ $(137x)$.

Total attendance on 3 days $= (3x + 6x + 11x) = 20x$.

$\therefore$ Average charge per person = ₹ $\left(\frac{137x}{20x}\right)$ = ₹ 6.85.

Ex. 48. ***7 men, 5 women and 8 children were given an assignment of distributing 2000 books to students in a school over a period of three days. All of them distributed books on the first day. On the second day, 1 man, 3 women and 3 children remained absent and on the third day, 4 men and 5 children remained absent. If the ratio of the number of books distributed in a day by a man, a woman and a child was 5 : 4 : 2 respectively, a total of how many books were distributed on the second day?***

Sol. Let the number of books distributed in a day by a man, a woman and a child be $5x$, $4x$ and $2x$ respectively.

Then, number of books distributed on the first day

$$= (7 \times 5x + 5 \times 4x + 8 \times 2x) = 71x.$$

Number of books distributed on the second day

$$= (6 \times 5x + 2 \times 4x + 5 \times 2x) = 48x.$$

Number of books distributed on the third day

$$= (3 \times 5x + 5 \times 4x + 3 \times 2x) = 41x.$$

$$\therefore\ 71x + 48x + 41x = 2000 \Rightarrow 160x = 2000 \Rightarrow x = \frac{2000}{160} = \frac{25}{2}.$$

Hence, number of books distributed on the second day $= 48x = \left(48 \times \frac{25}{2}\right) = 600.$

Ex. 49. ***Ratio of the incomes of A, B and C last year was 3 : 4 : 5. The ratio of their individual incomes of the last year and this year are 4 : 5, 2 : 3 and 3 : 4 respectively. If the sum of their present incomes is ₹ 78800, then find the present individual incomes of A, B and C.***

Sol. Let the incomes of A, B and C last year be ₹ $3x$, ₹ $4x$ and ₹ $5x$ respectively.

Then, A's present income = ₹ $\left(\frac{5}{4} \times 3x\right)$ = ₹ $\left(\frac{15x}{4}\right)$.

B's present income = ₹ $\left(\frac{3}{2} \times 4x\right)$ = ₹ $6x$.

C's present income = ₹ $\left(\frac{4}{3} \times 5x\right)$ = ₹ $\left(\frac{20x}{3}\right)$.

$$\therefore\ \frac{15x}{4} + 6x + \frac{20x}{3} = 78800$$

$$\Rightarrow\ 45x + 72x + 80x = 78800 \times 12$$

$$\Rightarrow\ x = \frac{78800 \times 12}{197} = 4800.$$

Hence, A's present income = ₹ $\left(\frac{15}{4} \times 4800\right)$ = ₹ 18000.

B's present income = ₹ (6×4800) = ₹ 28800.

C's present income = ₹ $\left(\frac{20}{3} \times 4800\right)$ = ₹ 32000.

Ex. 50. ***Two identical vessels A and B contain mixtures of milk and water in the ratios 4 : 5 and 5 : 1 respectively. In what ratio should quantities of mixtures be taken from A and B to form a mixture in which milk to water is in the ratio 5 : 4?***

Sol. Milk in $A = \frac{4}{9}$ units; Milk in $B = \frac{5}{6}$ units;

Water in $A = \frac{5}{9}$ units; Water in $B = \frac{1}{6}$ units.

Let A and B be taken in the ratio $1 : y$.

Then, $\dfrac{\frac{4}{9} + \frac{5y}{6}}{\frac{5}{9} + \frac{y}{6}} = \frac{5}{4} \Rightarrow \frac{8 + 15y}{10 + 3y} = \frac{5}{4}$

$\Rightarrow 4\,(8 + 15y) = 5\,(10 + 3y)$

$\Rightarrow 32 + 60y = 50 + 15y$

$\Rightarrow 45y = 18 \Rightarrow y = \frac{2}{5}$

$\therefore$ Required ratio $= 1 : \frac{2}{5} = 5 : 2.$

Ex. 51. ***A pot contains 81 litres of pure milk.*** $\frac{1}{3}$ ***of the milk is replaced by the same amount of water. Again,*** $\frac{1}{3}$ ***of the mixture is replaced by that amount of water. Find the ratio of milk and water in the new mixture.***

Sol. If from x units of liquid in a container, y units are taken out and replaced by water n times, then quantity of pure liquid in the mixture $= \left[x\left(1-\frac{y}{x}\right)^n\right]$ units.

Quantity of milk replaced each time $= \frac{1}{3}$ of 81 litres = 27 litres.

So, $x = 81$ litres, $y = 27$ litres, $n = 2$.

Quantity of milk in the new mixture $= \left[81\left(1-\frac{27}{81}\right)^2\right]$ litres $= \left[81 \times \left(\frac{2}{3}\right)^2\right]$ litres

$= \left(81 \times \frac{4}{9}\right)$ litres = 36 litres.

Quantity of water in the new mixture = (81 – 36) litres = 45 litres.

$\therefore$ Required ratio = 36 : 45 = 4 : 5.

EXERCISE

(OBJECTIVE TYPE QUESTIONS)

Directions: ***Mark (✓) against the correct answer :***

1. The total number of students in a school is 2140. If the number of girls in the school is 1200, then what is the ratio of the total number of boys to the total number of girls in the school? **(Bank Recruitment, 2009)**
   (*a*) 18 : 13 (*b*) 26 : 25
   (*c*) 47 : 60 (*d*) 31 : 79
   (*e*) None of these

Directions (*Questions 2 to 6*) : ***These questions are based on the following table :***

Weight distribution in the average adult	
Organs	Weight (in grams)
Muscles	30000
Skeleton	10000
Blood	5000
Gastrointestinal tract	2000
Lungs	1000
Liver	1700
Brain	1500

2. The total body weight of the average adult is
   (*a*) 50000 grams (*b*) 70000 grams
   (*c*) less than 50 kg (*d*) more than 51 kg
   (*e*) None of these
3. If the weight of the skeleton is represented as *S*, then the weight of the liver can be represented as
   (*a*) 0.17*S* (*b*) 1.7*S*
   (*c*) 17*S* (*d*) 71*S*
   (*e*) None of these
4. The ratio expressed in decimals of the weight of the blood to the weight of the gastrointestinal tract is
   (*a*) 0.25 (*b*) 0.4
   (*c*) 2.5 (*d*) 4
   (*e*) None of these
5. The ratio expressed in decimals for weight of the brain to the weight of the muscles is
   (*a*) 0.05 (*b*) 0.15
   (*c*) 0.20 (*d*) 0.50
   (*e*) None of these
6. The ratio expressed in decimals of the weight of the brain to the weight of the lungs is
   (*a*) 0.15 (*b*) 1.5
   (*c*) 5.1 (*d*) 15
   (*e*) None of these
7. What is the ratio in ₹ 2.80 and 40 paise?
   (*a*) 1 : 7 (*b*) 2 : 7
   (*c*) 7 : 1 (*d*) 1 : 14

8. Which of the following is the ratio between a number and the number obtained by adding one-fifth of that number to it?
(a) 4 : 5 (b) 5 : 4
(c) 5 : 6 (d) 6 : 5

9. A person spends ₹ 8100 in buying some tables at ₹ 1200 each and some chairs at ₹ 300 each. The ratio of the number of chairs to that of tables when the maximum possible number of tables is purchased, is (S.S.C., 2005)
(a) 1 : 2 (b) 1 : 4
(c) 2 : 1 (d) 5 : 7

10. If 60% of $A = \frac{3}{4}$ of B, then A : B is (S.S.C., 2010)
(a) 4 : 5 (b) 5 : 4
(c) 9 : 20 (d) 20 : 9

11. If $\frac{2}{3}$ A = 75% of B, then A : B is
(a) 1 : 1 (b) 9 : 8
(c) 8 : 9 (d) 10 : 11

12. Which of the following represents $ab = 64$? (Bank P.O., 2010)
(a) $8 : a = 8 : b$ (b) $a : 16 = b : 4$
(c) $a : 8 = b : 8$ (d) $32 : a = b : 2$
(e) None of these

13. A jar contains black and white marbles. If there are ten marbles in the jar, then which of the following could not be the ratio of black to white marbles?
(a) 1 : 4 (b) 1 : 10
(c) 7 : 3 (d) 9 : 1

14. The ratio of boys and girls in a club is 3 : 2. Which of the following could be the actual number of members?
(a) 16 (b) 18
(c) 24 (d) 25

15. Which of the following is the lowest ratio? (R.R.B., 2005)
(a) 7 : 15 (b) 15 : 23
(c) 17 : 25 (d) 21 : 39

16. If 5 : a : : 20 : 28, then a is equal to
(a) 4 (b) 6
(c) 7 (d) 8

17. $\frac{3}{4}:\frac{1}{2}::27y:?$ (E.S.I.C., 2007)
(a) $12y$ (b) $18y$
(c) $21y$ (d) $24y$
(e) None of these

18. If $x : 7.5 = 7 : 17.5$, the value of x is
(a) 1 (b) 2.5
(c) 3 (d) 3.5

19. The value of x where $x:2\frac{1}{3}::21:50$ is
(a) $1\frac{1}{49}$ (b) $1\frac{1}{50}$
(c) $\frac{49}{50}$ (d) $\frac{27}{50}$

20. If $(x + 1) : 8 = 3.75 : 7$, then the value of x is
(a) $1\frac{2}{7}$ (b) $2\frac{2}{7}$
(c) $3\frac{2}{7}$ (d) $4\frac{2}{7}$

21. If $\sqrt{2}:(1+\sqrt{3})::\sqrt{6}:x$, then x is equal to
(a) $\sqrt{3}+3$ (b) $1-\sqrt{3}$
(c) $1+\sqrt{3}$ (d) $\sqrt{3}-3$

22. What will be the simplest form of the ratio 3 hours: 1 day? (R.R.B., 2006)
(a) 1 : 3 (b) 1 : 6
(c) 1 : 8 (d) 1 : 25

23. The simplest form of the ratio 1.5 : 2.5 is
(a) 3 : 5 (b) 6 : 10
(c) 15 : 25 (d) 0.75 : 1.25

24. $9^{3.04} : 9^{2.04}$ is equal to
(a) 1 : 9 (b) 3 : 2
(c) 9 : 1 (d) 76 : 51

25. The ratio $4^{3.5} : 2^5$ is the same as
(a) 2 : 1 (b) 4 : 1
(c) 7 : 5 (d) 7 : 10

26. In a proportion the product of 1st and 4th terms is 40 and that of 2nd and 3rd terms is $2.5x$. Then the value of x is (M.A.T., 2007)
(a) 16 (b) 26
(c) 75 (d) 90

27. If 20% of A = 30% of B = $\frac{1}{6}$ of C, then A : B : C is (S.S.C., 2007)
(a) 2 : 3 : 16 (b) 3 : 2 : 16
(c) 10 : 15 : 18 (d) 15 : 10 : 18

28. 25% of A's income is equal to 35% of B's income. The ratio of the incomes of A and B is
(a) 5 : 7 (b) 7 : 5
(c) 13 : 15 (d) 15 : 13

29. If $x=\frac{1}{3}y$ and $y=\frac{1}{2}z$, then $x : y : z$ is equal to
(a) 1 : 2 : 6 (b) 1 : 3 : 6
(c) 2 : 4 : 6 (d) 3 : 2 : 1

30. If $2A = 3B = 4C$, then A : B : C is equal to
(a) 2 : 3 : 4 (b) 3 : 4 : 6
(c) 4 : 3 : 2 (d) 6 : 4 : 3

31. If $x^2 + 4y^2 = 4xy$, then $x : y$ is
(a) 1 : 1 (b) 1 : 2
(c) 2 : 1 (d) 1 : 4

32. If $5x^2 - 13xy + 6y^2 = 0$, then $x : y$ is
(a) 2 : 1 only (b) 3 : 5 only
(c) 5 : 3 or 1 : 2 (d) 3 : 5 or 2 : 1

33. If $a : b = 7 : 9$ and $b : c = 15 : 7$, then what is $a : c$?
(a) 3 : 5 (b) 5 : 3
(c) 7 : 15 (d) 7 : 21

34. If the ratio between the ages of P and Q is 2 : 3 and that between the ages of Q and R is 4 : 5, then the ratio between the ages of P and R is
(a) 3 : 4 (b) 3 : 5
(c) 5 : 6 (d) 8 : 15

35. If $W_1 : W_2 = 2 : 3$ and $W_1 : W_3 = 1 : 2$, then $W_2 : W_3$ is **(S.S.C., 2010)**
(a) 3 : 4 (b) 4 : 3
(c) 2 : 3 (d) 4 : 5

36. If $A : B = 2 : 3$, $B : C = 2 : 4$ and $C : D = 2 : 5$, then $A : D$ is equal to **(C.P.O., 2007)**
(a) 1 : 5 (b) 2 : 5
(c) 3 : 5 (d) 2 : 15

37. If $3A = 5B$ and $4B = 6C$, then $A : C$ is equal to
(a) 2 : 5 (b) 3 : 5
(c) 4 : 5 (d) 5 : 2

38. If one star equals four circles and three circles equal four diamonds, then what is the ratio of star to diamond?
(a) 1 : 3 (b) 3 : 4
(c) 3 : 16 (d) 16 : 3

39. In a business, the ratio of the capitals of A and B is 2 : 1, that of B and C is 4 : 3 and that of D and C is 6 : 5. Then the ratio of the capitals of A and D is
(a) 9 : 20 (b) 3 : 5
(c) 5 : 3 (d) 20 : 9

40. If $A : B = 7 : 9$ and $B : C = 5 : 4$, then $A : B : C$ is
(a) 7 : 45 : 36 (b) 28 : 36 : 35
(c) 35 : 45 : 36 (d) None of these

41. If $A : B = 2 : 3$, $B : C = 4 : 5$ and $C : D = 6 : 7$, then $A : B : C : D$ is
(a) 16 : 22 : 30 : 35 (b) 16 : 24 : 15 : 35
(c) 16 : 24 : 30 : 35 (d) 18 : 24 : 30 : 35

42. If $A : B = \frac{1}{2} : \frac{1}{3}$ and $B : C = \frac{1}{2} : \frac{1}{3}$, then $A : B : C$ is equal to
(a) 1 : 2 : 6 (b) 2 : 3 : 3
(c) 3 : 2 : 6 (d) 9 : 6 : 4

43. If $A : B = \frac{1}{2} : \frac{3}{8}$, $B : C = \frac{1}{3} : \frac{5}{9}$ and $C : D = \frac{5}{6} : \frac{3}{4}$, then the ratio $A : B : C : D$ is
(a) 4 : 6 : 8 : 10 (b) 8 : 6 : 10 : 9
(c) 6 : 8 : 9 : 10 (d) 6 : 4 : 8 : 10

44. For each 200 rupees spent by the research department, sales department spends 20 rupees. For every 400 rupees spent by the sales department, the advertising department spends 150 rupees. The triple ratio of the money spent by the research department to the money spent by the sales department to the money spent by the advertising department can be expressed as
(a) 2 : 1 : 5 (b) 20 : 4 : 1
(c) 40 : 8 : 3 (d) 80 : 8 : 3

45. In a ratio which is equal to 7 : 8, if the antecedent is 35, what is the consequent?
(a) 35 (b) 40
(c) 56 (d) 64

46. If $8a = 9b$ then the ratio of $\frac{a}{9}$ to $\frac{b}{8}$ is **(Campus Recruitment, 2009)**
(a) 1 : 1 (b) 1 : 2
(c) 2 : 1 (d) 64 : 81
(e) 81 : 64

47. If $x : y = 3 : 4$, then $(2x + 3y) : (3y - 2x)$ would be equal to **(M.B.A., 2007)**
(a) 2 : 1 (b) 3 : 1
(c) 3 : 2 (d) 21 : 1

48. If $a : b = 2 : 5$, then the value of $(2a + 3b) : (7a + 5b)$ is
(a) 19 : 31 (b) 19 : 39
(c) 31 : 19 (d) 99 : 13

49. If $x : y = 3 : 2$, then the ratio $(2x^2 + 3y^2) : (3x^2 - 2y^2)$ is equal to
(a) 5 : 3 (b) 6 : 5
(c) 12 : 5 (d) 30 : 19

50. If $x : y = 3 : 1$, then $x^3 - y^3 : x^3 + y^3 = ?$
(a) 10 : 11 (b) 11 : 10
(c) 13 : 14 (d) 14 : 13

51. If $5a + 3b : 2a - 3b = 23 : 5$, then the value of $a : b$ is
(a) 1 : 2 (b) 1 : 4
(c) 2 : 1 (d) 4 : 1

52. If $x : y = 7 : 3$, then the value of $\frac{xy + y^2}{x^2 - y^2}$ is
(a) $\frac{3}{4}$ (b) $\frac{4}{3}$
(c) $\frac{3}{7}$ (d) $\frac{7}{3}$

53. If $\frac{a}{b}=\frac{4}{5}$ and $\frac{b}{c}=\frac{15}{16}$, then $\frac{c^2-a^2}{c^2+a^2}$ would be

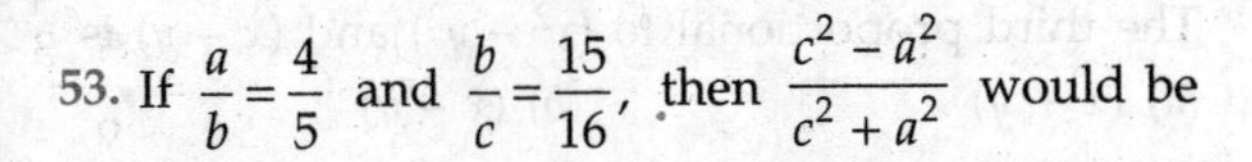

(a) $\frac{1}{7}$ (b) $\frac{3}{4}$
(c) $\frac{7}{25}$ (d) None of these

54. If $a : b = b : c$, then $a^4 : b^4$ would be equal to (M.B.A., 2007)
(a) $ac : b^2$ (b) $a^2 : c^2$
(c) $c^2 : a^2$ (d) $b^2 : ac$

55. If $(4x^2 - 3y^2) : (2x^2 + 5y^2) = 12 : 19$, then $x : y$ is
(a) 2 : 3 (b) 1 : 2
(c) 3 : 2 (d) 2 : 1

56. If $x : y = 3 : 4$ and $a : b = 1 : 2$, then the value of $\frac{2xa+yb}{3yb-4xa}$ is
(a) $\frac{5}{6}$ (b) $\frac{6}{5}$
(c) $\frac{6}{7}$ (d) $\frac{7}{6}$

57. If $a : b : c = 2 : 3 : 4$, then $\frac{1}{a}:\frac{1}{b}:\frac{1}{c}$ is equal to
(a) $\frac{1}{4}:\frac{1}{3}:\frac{1}{2}$ (b) 4 : 3 : 2
(c) 6 : 4 : 3 (d) None of these

58. If $\frac{1}{x}:\frac{1}{y}:\frac{1}{z} = 2 : 3 : 5$, then $x : y : z$ is equal to
(a) 2 : 3 : 5 (b) 15 : 10 : 6
(c) 5 : 3 : 2 (d) 6 : 10 : 15

59. If $(x + y) : (x - y) = 4 : 1$, then $(x^2 + y^2) : (x^2 - y^2)$ =?
(a) 8 : 17 (b) 17 : 8
(c) 16 : 1 (d) 25 : 9

60. If $a : (b + c) = 1 : 3$ and $c : (a + b) = 5 : 7$, then $b : (a + c)$ is equal to (S.S.C., 2006)
(a) 1 : 2 (b) 2 : 3
(c) 1 : 3 (d) 2 : 1

61. If $a : b = 3 : 4$, $b : c = 4 : 7$, then $\frac{a+b+c}{c}$ is equal to (Hotel Management, 2010)
(a) 1 (b) 2
(c) 3 (d) 7

62. If $A : B : C = 2 : 3 : 5$ and $A = x\%$ of $(B + C)$, then x is equal to (I.A.M. 2007)
(a) 20 (b) 24
(c) 25 (d) 28

63. x, y, z, u are real numbers such that $x : y = y : z = z : u$ and $x : u = 64 : 27$. The value of $x : z$ is (Campus Recruitment, 2010)
(a) 64 : 27 (b) 16 : 9
(c) 4 : 3 (d) 3 : 4

64. If $a : b : c = 2 : 3 : 4$ and $2a - 3b + 4c = 33$, then the value of c is (S.S.C., 2007)
(a) 6 (b) 9
(c) 12 (d) $\frac{66}{7}$

65. If $p : q : r = 1 : 2 : 4$, then $\sqrt{5p^2 + q^2 + r^2}$ is equal to (C.P.O., 2006)
(a) 5 (b) $2q$
(c) $5p$ (d) $4r$

66. If $A : B : C = 2 : 3 : 4$, then the ratio $\frac{A}{B}:\frac{B}{C}:\frac{C}{A}$ is equal to
(a) 4 : 9 : 16 (b) 8 : 9 : 24
(c) 8 : 9 : 12 (d) 8 : 9 : 16

67. If $a : b = 5 : 7$ and $c : d = 2a : 3b$, then $ac : bd$ is
(a) 10 : 21 (b) 20 : 38
(c) 50 : 147 (d) 50 : 151

68. If $\frac{a}{b}=\frac{b}{c}=\frac{c}{d}$, then $\frac{b^3+c^3+d^3}{a^3+b^3+c^3}$ will be equal to
(a) $\frac{a}{b}$ (b) $\frac{b}{c}$
(c) $\frac{c}{d}$ (d) $\frac{d}{a}$

69. If $p : q = 3 : 4$, $r : s = 8 : 5$ and $x : y = 10 : 6$, then $psx : qry$ is equal to
(a) $\frac{16}{25}$ (b) $\frac{25}{32}$
(c) 2 (d) $\frac{75}{32}$

70. If $\frac{x}{2}=\frac{y}{3}=\frac{z}{4}=\frac{2x-3y+5z}{k}$, then the value of k is
(a) 12 (b) 15
(c) 16 (d) 18

71. If $a : b = c : d$, then $\frac{ma+nc}{mb+nd}$ is equal to
(a) $m : n$ (b) $dm : cn$
(c) $an : mb$ (d) $a : b$

72. Let $\frac{a}{b}:\frac{b}{a} = x : y$. If $(x - y) = \left\{\frac{a}{b}+\frac{b}{a}\right\}$, then x is equal to
(a) $\frac{a-b}{a}$ (b) $\frac{a+b}{a}$
(c) $\frac{a+b}{b}$ (d) None of these

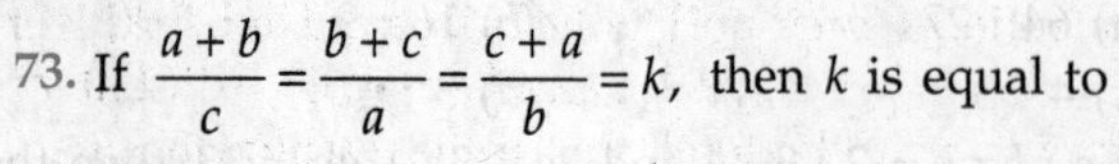

73. If $\frac{a+b}{c} = \frac{b+c}{a} = \frac{c+a}{b} = k$, then k is equal to

(a) 0 (b) 1
(c) 2 (d) $a + b + c$

74. If $a : b = 2 : 3$ and $b : c = 4 : 5$, then $(a + b) : (b + c)$ is equal to

(a) 6 : 8 (b) 8 : 6
(c) 20 : 27 (d) 27 : 20

75. If $a : b = c : d = e : f = 1 : 2$, then $(3a + 5c + 7e) : (3b + 5d + 7f)$ is equal to

(a) 1 : 2 (b) 1 : 4
(c) 2 : 1 (d) 8 : 7

Directions (*Questions 76 to 78*): *These questions are based on the following information:*

Given that $a : b = 5 : 3$ and $b : c = 2 : 5$.

76. Which of the following is true?

(a) $a < b < c$ (b) $b < a < c$
(c) $c > a > b$ (d) $b < a > c$

77. If $c = 50$, the value of $a + b + c$ will be

(a) more than 50 but less than 100
(b) more than 100 but less than 103
(c) more than 103 but less than 105
(d) more than 105

78. $(c - a)$ will be equal to

I. $10 (a + c)$
II. $10a + 25b$

(a) Only I is true (b) Only II is true
(c) Both I and II are true (d) Both I and II are false

79. If $a + b : b + c : c + a = 6 : 7 : 8$ and $a + b + c = 14$, then the value of c is

(a) 6 (b) 7
(c) 8 (d) 14

80. The fourth proportional to 5, 8, 15 is

(a) 18 (b) 20
(c) 21 (d) 24

81. The fourth proportional to 0.12, 0.21 and 8 is

(a) 8.9 (b) 14
(c) 17 (d) 56

82. Fourth proportional to $(a^2 - b^2)$, $(a^2 - ab)$, $(a^3 + b^3)$ is

(a) $(a - b)$ (b) $a^4 + b^4$
(c) $a(a^2 - ab + b^2)$ (d) $a^3 - a^2b^2 + b^2$

83. The third proportional to 38 and 15 is

(a) $\frac{15 \times 15}{38}$ (b) $\frac{38 \times 15}{2}$
(c) $\frac{38 \times 38}{15}$ (d) $\frac{15}{38 \times 38}$

84. The third proportional to $(x^2 - y^2)$ and $(x - y)$ is

(a) $(x + y)$ (b) $(x - y)$
(c) $\frac{x+y}{x-y}$ (d) $\frac{x-y}{x+y}$

85. The mean proportional between 234 and 104 is

(a) 12 (b) 39
(c) 54 (d) None of these

86. The mean proportional between 0.02 and 0.32 is

(a) 0.3 (b) 0.08
(c) 0.16 (d) 0.34

87. The mean proportional between $(3+\sqrt{2})$ and $(12-\sqrt{32})$ is

(a) $\sqrt{7}$ (b) $2\sqrt{7}$
(c) 6 (d) $\frac{15-3\sqrt{2}}{2}$

88. The ratio between the third proportional of 12 and 30 and mean proportional of 9 and 25 is

(a) 2 : 1 (b) 5 : 1
(c) 7 : 15 (d) 9 : 14

89. The product of the duplicate ratio of $2a : 6b$ and the reciprocal ratio of $4a^2 : 25b^2$ is

(a) 0 (b) 1
(c) $a : b$ (d) None of these

90. Find the two numbers whose mean proportion is 12 and the third proportional is 324. (R.R.B., 2006)

(a) 6 and 8 (b) 4 and 36
(c) 3 and 24 (d) None of these

91. The present ages of A, B and C are in the ratio of 8 : 14 : 22 respectively. The present ages of B, C and D are in the ratio of 21 : 33 : 44 respectively. Which of the following represents the ratio of the present ages of A, B, C and D respectively?

(a) 12 : 21 : 36 : 44 (b) 12 : 21 : 33 : 44
(c) 12 : 22 : 31 : 44
(d) Cannot be determined (e) None of these

92. When 30% of one number is subtracted from another number, the second number reduces to its four-fifths. What is the ratio of the first to the second number? (Bank P.O., 2010)

(a) 2 : 5 (b) 3 : 2
(c) 4 : 7 (d) Cannot be determined
(e) None of these

93. Rita invested 25% more than Sunil. Sunil invested 30% less than Abhinav, who invested ₹ 6000. What is the ratio of the amount that Rita invested to the total amount invested by all of them together? (Bank P.O., 2010)

(a) 35 : 104 (b) 13 : 29
(c) 101 : 36 (d) 35 : 103
(e) None of these

94. One-fourth of sixty percent of a number is equal to two-fifths of twenty percent of another number. What is the respective ratio of the first number to the second number? **(Bank P.O., 2008)**

(*a*) 4 : 7 (*b*) 5 : 9
(*c*) 8 : 13 (*d*) Cannot be determined
(*e*) None of these

95. The total number of boys in a school is 16% more than the total number of girls in the school. What is the respective ratio of the total number of boys to the total number of girls in the school? **(Bank Recruitment, 2008)**

(*a*) 25 : 21 (*b*) 29 : 35
(*c*) 25 : 29 (*d*) Cannot be determined
(*e*) None of these

96. The number of students in two sections *A* and *B* having different heights is shown in the table given below.

Height (in metres)	Number of students	
	Section A	Section B
1.55	3	2
1.60	7	6
1.62	12	14
1.65	15	14
1.68	8	9
1.71	6	5
1.75	3	4

The ratio of the number of students of a particular height in section *A* to that in section *B* is the maximum for the height of

(*a*) 1.55 m (*b*) 1.60 m
(*c*) 1.65 m (*d*) 1.71 m

97. Determine the ratio of the number of people having characteristic *X* to the number of people having characteristic *Y* in a population of 100 subjects from the following table :

Having *X* and *Y*	10
Having *X* but not *Y*	30
Having *Y* but not *X*	20
Having neither *X* nor *Y*	40

(*a*) 1 : 2 (*b*) 2 : 3
(*c*) 3 : 2 (*d*) 4 : 3

98. Five mangoes and four oranges cost as much as three mangoes and seven oranges. What is the ratio of the cost of one mango to the cost of one orange? **(Campus Recruitment, 2009)**

(*a*) 4 : 3 (*b*) 1 : 3
(*c*) 3 : 2 (*d*) 5 : 2

99. The ratio of urea and potash in a mixed fertilizer is 7 : 3. Express the quantity of urea present as percentage of the total amount of fertilizer. **(P.C.S., 2008)**

(*a*) 20% (*b*) 50%
(*c*) 60% (*d*) 70%

100. Profits of a business are divided among three partners *A*, *B* and *C* in such a way that 4 times the amount received by *A* is equal to 6 times the amount received by *B* and 11 times the amount received by *C*. The ratio in which the three received the amount is **(M.A.T. 2006, Bank P.O., 2008)**

(*a*) 4 : 6 : 11 (*b*) 11 : 6 : 4
(*c*) 33 : 22 : 12 (*d*) $\frac{1}{4}:\frac{1}{6}:\frac{1}{11}$

101. The bus fare and train fare of a place from Kolkata were ₹ 20 and ₹ 30 respectively. Train fare has been increased by 20% and the bus fare has been increased by 10%. The ratio of new train fare to new bus fare is **(S.S.C., 2007)**

(*a*) 3 : 5 (*b*) 5 : 3
(*c*) 11 : 18 (*d*) 18 : 11

102. The monthly incomes of two families *A* and *B* are shown by the following diagrams:

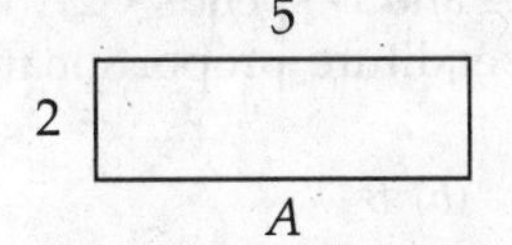

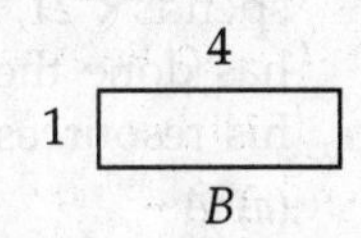

If the income of family *B* is ₹ 12000, then the income of family *A* would be **(P.C.S., 2006)**

(*a*) ₹ 15000 (*b*) ₹ 20000
(*c*) ₹ 25000 (*d*) ₹ 30000

103. In a class the number of girls is 20% more than that of the boys. The strength of the class is 66. If 4 more girls are admitted to the class, the ratio of the number of boys to that of the girls is

(*a*) 1 : 2 (*b*) 1 : 4
(*c*) 3 : 4 (*d*) 3 : 5

104. If the income of *A* is 10% more than that of *B* and the income of *B* is 20% less than that of *C*, then the incomes of *A*, *B* and *C* respectively are in the ratio

(*a*) 11 : 10 : 8 (*b*) 22 : 20 : 25
(*c*) 10 : 9 : 7 (*d*) 22 : 18 : 25

105. Two numbers are respectively 20 percent and 50 percent more than a third number. These two numbers are in the ratio

(*a*) 2 : 5 (*b*) 3 : 5
(*c*) 4 : 5 (*d*) 6 : 7

106. What is the ratio whose terms differ by 40 and the measure of which is $\frac{2}{7}$?

(a) 6 : 56 (b) 14 : 56
(c) 16 : 56 (d) 16 : 72

107. ₹ 16000 are to be distributed between B and A such that B gets ₹ 4000 less than A. The ratio of the amount received by A to that received by B is

(a) 1 : 3 (b) 3 : 5
(c) 5 : 3 (d) 6 : 1

108. Find the fraction which will bear the same ratio to $\frac{1}{27}$ that $\frac{3}{11}$ does to $\frac{5}{9}$.

(a) $\frac{1}{55}$ (b) $\frac{15}{99}$
(c) $\frac{40}{33}$ (d) 55

109. Given that 24 carat gold is pure gold ; 18 carat gold is $\frac{3}{4}$ gold and 20 carat gold is $\frac{5}{6}$ gold, the ratio of the pure gold in 18 carat gold to the pure gold in 20 carat gold is

(a) 5 : 8 (b) 8 : 5
(c) 9 : 10 (d) 15 : 22

110. A, B, C and D have ₹ 40, ₹ 50, ₹ 60 and ₹ 70 respectively when they go to visit a fair. A spends ₹ 18, B spends ₹ 21, C spends ₹ 24 and D spends ₹ 27. Who has done the highest expenditure proportionate to his resources?

(a) A (b) B
(c) C (d) D

111. The ratio of the arithmetic mean of two numbers to one of the numbers is 3 : 5. What is the ratio of the smaller number to the larger one?

(a) 1 : 2 (b) 1 : 3
(c) 1 : 4 (d) 1 : 5

112. Seema and Meena divide a sum of ₹ 25000 in the ratio of 3 : 2 respectively. If ₹ 5000 is added to each of their shares, what would be the new ratio formed? **(P.C.S., 2010)**

(a) 2 : 3 (b) 3 : 4
(c) 5 : 4 (d) 4 : 3

113. Of 132 examinees of a certain school, the ratio of successful to unsuccessful candidates is 9 : 2. If 4 more students passed, what would have been the ratio of successful to unsuccessful students?

(a) 25 : 4 (b) 4 : 25
(c) 28 : 5 (d) 3 : 28

114. A person divided ₹ 10800 among his three sons in the ratio 3 : 4 : 5. Second son kept ₹ 1000 for himself, gave ₹ 600 to his wife and divided the remaining money among his two daughters in the ratio 11 : 9. Then one of his daughters received

(a) ₹ 1000 (b) ₹ 1050
(c) ₹ 1100 (d) ₹ 1150

115. The sides of a triangle are in the ratio 3 : 4 : 5. The measure of the largest angle of the triangle is

(a) 60° (b) 75°
(c) 120° (d) 150°

116. The numbers x, y, z are proportional to 2, 3, 5. The sum of x, y, z is 100. If $y = px - 10$, then p is equal to **(M.B.A., 2011)**

(a) $\frac{3}{2}$ (b) 2
(c) $\frac{5}{2}$ (d) 3

117. A, B and C are boxes containing marbles in the ratio 1 : 2 : 3. Total number of marbles is 60. The above ratio can be changed to 3 : 4 : 5 by transferring

(a) 2 marbles from A to B and 1 from C to B
(b) 3 marbles from B to C
(c) 4 marbles from C to B
(d) 5 marbles from C to A

118. An amount of ₹ 53 is divided among A, B and C such that A gets ₹ 7 more than B and B gets ₹ 8 more than C. What is the ratio of their shares? **(R.R.B., 2009)**

(a) 15 : 8 : 30 (b) 16 : 9 : 18
(c) 18 : 25 : 10 (d) 25 : 18 : 10

119. A sum of money is shared in the ratio of 3 : 4 : 5. The smallest share is divided again in the ratio of 1 : 2. What fraction of the total sum of money is the larger of the two latter shares?

(a) $\frac{1}{3}$ (b) $\frac{1}{6}$
(c) $\frac{2}{3}$ (d) $\frac{1}{12}$

120. If an amount of ₹ 1,50,000 is shared among A, B and C in the ratio of 2 : 3 : 5, then A receives the same amount as he would receive if another sum of money is shared between A, B and C in the ratio of 5 : 3 : 2. The ratio of ₹ 1,50,000 to the second amount of money is

(a) 2 : 3 (b) 3 : 2
(c) 5 : 2 (d) 5 : 3

121. In an alloy, the ratio of copper and zinc is 5 : 2. If 1.250 kg of zinc is mixed in 17 kg 500 g of alloy, then the ratio of copper and zinc in the alloy will be

(a) 1 : 2 (b) 2 : 1
(c) 2 : 3 (d) 3 : 2

122. A sum of ₹ 650 is divided between A and B in such a manner that in every 100 rupees A gets 30 rupees more than B. How much does B get?

(a) ₹ 288 (b) ₹ 227.50
(c) ₹ 312.50 (d) ₹ 422.50

123. A sum of ₹ 731 is divided among A, B and C such that A receives 25% more than B and B receives 25% less than C. What is C's share in the amount? (Bank P.O., 2006)

(a) ₹ 172 (b) ₹ 200
(c) ₹ 258 (d) ₹ 262
(e) None of these

124. A sum of ₹ 6400 is divided among three workers in the ratio $\frac{3}{5}:2:\frac{5}{3}$. The share (in rupees) of the second worker is (S.S.C., 2007)

(a) 2560 (b) 3000
(c) 3200 (d) 3840

125. If ₹ x are divided between A and B in the ratio $\frac{a}{b}:\frac{c}{d}$, then A gets rupees

(a) $\frac{adx}{ab + cd}$ (b) $\frac{adx}{ad + bc}$
(c) $\frac{abx}{ad + bc}$ (d) $\frac{abx}{ac + bd}$

126. A man distributes ₹ 165000 among his daughter, wife and son in such a manner that $\frac{1}{2}$ of the daughter's share, $\frac{1}{4}$ of the wife's share and $\frac{1}{5}$ of the son's share are equal. Find the daughter's share.

(a) ₹ 15000 (b) ₹ 30000
(c) ₹ 45000 (d) ₹ 60000

127. A sum of ₹ 1250 is divided among A, B, C so that A gets $\frac{2}{9}$ of B's share and C gets $\frac{3}{4}$ of A's share. The share of C is

(a) ₹ 75 (b) ₹ 90
(c) ₹ 135 (d) ₹ 150

128. Instead of dividing ₹ 117 among P, Q, R in the ratio $\frac{1}{2}:\frac{1}{3}:\frac{1}{4}$, by mistake it was divided in the ratio 2 : 3 : 4. Who gained in the transaction?

(a) Only P (b) Only Q
(c) Only R (d) Both Q and R

129. ₹ 33630 are divided among A, B and C in such a manner that the ratio of the amount of A to that of B is 3 : 7 and the ratio of the amount of B to that of C is 6 : 5. The amount of money received by B is (S.S.C., 2007)

(a) ₹ 12390 (b) ₹ 13290
(c) ₹ 14868 (d) ₹ 16257

130. In an innings of a cricket match, three players A, B and C scored a total of 361 runs. If the ratio of the number of runs scored by A to that scored by B and also number of runs scored by B to that scored by C be 3 : 2, the number of runs scored by A was

(a) 161 (b) 171
(c) 181 (d) 185

131. ₹ 8400 are divided among A, B, C and D in such a way that the shares of A and B, B and C as well as C and D are in the ratios of 2 : 3, 4 : 5 and 6 : 7 respectively. The share of A is

(a) ₹ 1280 (b) ₹ 1320
(c) ₹ 8210 (d) ₹ 8400

132. A sum of ₹ 1300 is divided among P, Q, R and S such that

$$\frac{P\text{'s share}}{Q\text{'s share}} = \frac{Q\text{'s share}}{R\text{'s share}} = \frac{R\text{'s share}}{S\text{'s share}} = \frac{2}{3}.$$ How much is P's share?

(a) ₹ 140 (b) ₹ 160
(c) ₹ 240 (d) ₹ 320

133. The sum of three numbers is 116. The second number and the third number are in the ratio of 9 : 16 while the first number and the third number are in the ratio of 1 : 4. Find the second number.

(a) 8 (b) 16
(c) 64 (d) Cannot be determined
(e) None of these

134. ₹ 2010 are to be divided among A, B, C in such a way that if A gets ₹ 5, then B must get ₹ 12 and if B gets ₹ 4, then C must get ₹ 5.50. The share of C will exceed that of B by (C.P.O., 2007)

(a) ₹ 270 (b) ₹ 360
(c) ₹ 430 (d) ₹ 620

135. ₹ 600 are divided among A, B, C so that ₹ 40 more than $\frac{2}{5}$ of A's share, ₹ 20 more than $\frac{2}{7}$ of B's share and ₹ 10 more than $\frac{9}{17}$ of C's share may all be equal. What is A's share? (L.I.C.A.A.O., 2007)

(a) ₹ 150 (b) ₹ 170
(c) ₹ 200 (d) ₹ 280

136. ₹ 1050 are divided among P, Q and R. The share of P is $\frac{2}{5}$ of the combined share of Q and R. P gets

(a) ₹ 200 (b) ₹ 300
(c) ₹ 320 (d) ₹ 420

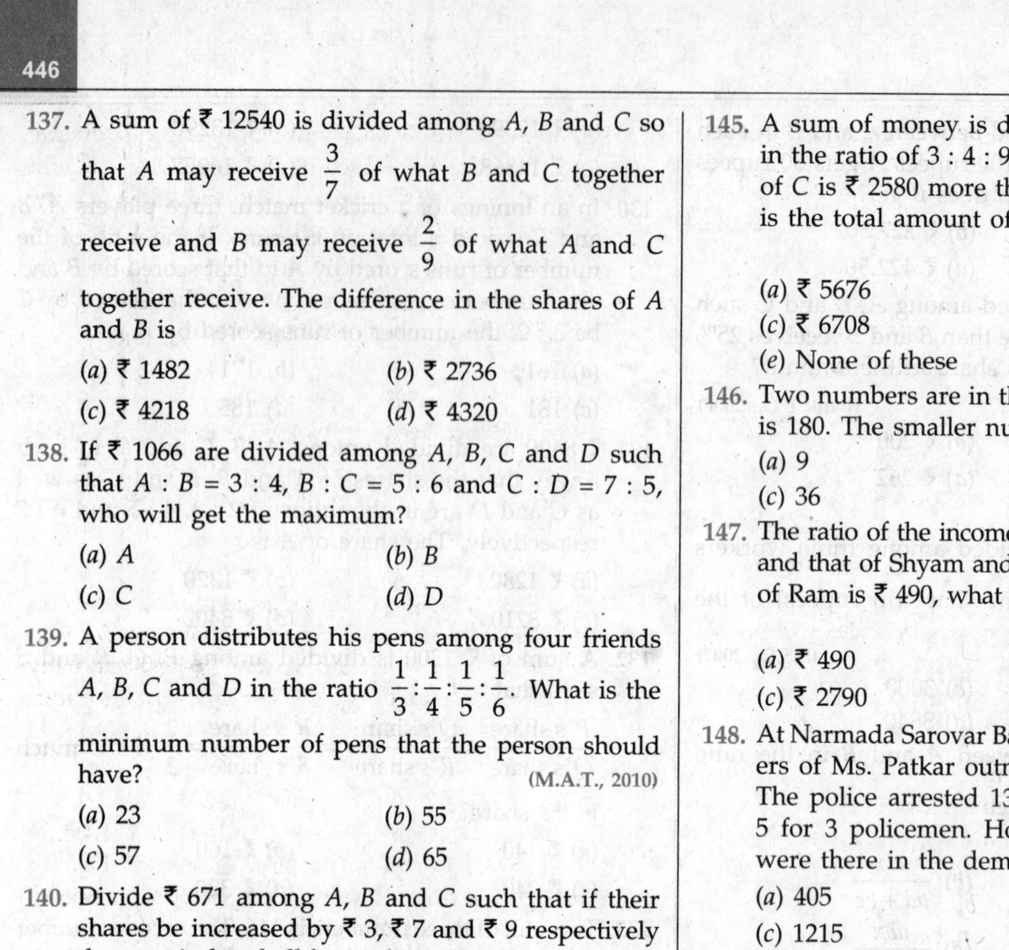

137. A sum of ₹ 12540 is divided among A, B and C so that A may receive $\frac{3}{7}$ of what B and C together receive and B may receive $\frac{2}{9}$ of what A and C together receive. The difference in the shares of A and B is

(a) ₹ 1482 (b) ₹ 2736
(c) ₹ 4218 (d) ₹ 4320

138. If ₹ 1066 are divided among A, B, C and D such that $A : B = 3 : 4$, $B : C = 5 : 6$ and $C : D = 7 : 5$, who will get the maximum?

(a) A (b) B
(c) C (d) D

139. A person distributes his pens among four friends A, B, C and D in the ratio $\frac{1}{3}:\frac{1}{4}:\frac{1}{5}:\frac{1}{6}$. What is the minimum number of pens that the person should have? (M.A.T., 2010)

(a) 23 (b) 55
(c) 57 (d) 65

140. Divide ₹ 671 among A, B and C such that if their shares be increased by ₹ 3, ₹ 7 and ₹ 9 respectively the remainder shall be in the ratio 1 : 2 : 3. (M.A.T., 2008)

(a) ₹ 110, ₹ 220, ₹ 336 (b) ₹ 112, ₹ 223, ₹ 336
(c) ₹ 105, ₹ 223, ₹ 330 (d) None of these

141. ₹ 1087 is divided among A, B and C such that if ₹ 10, ₹ 12 and ₹ 15 are diminished from the shares of A, B and C respectively, the remainders will be in the ratio of 5, 7 and 9. What is the share of B? (M.A.T., 2008)

(a) ₹ 260 (b) ₹ 355
(c) ₹ 362 (d) ₹ 465

142. Two numbers x and y are in the ratio 5 : 7 and their sum is 36. Then x is (P.C.S., 2009)

(a) 12 (b) 15
(c) 18 (d) 19

143. The ratio of income and expenditure of a person is 11 : 10. If he saves ₹ 9000 per annum, his monthly income is (S.S.C., 2010)

(a) ₹ 8000 (b) ₹ 8250
(c) ₹ 8500 (d) ₹ 8800

144. Two natural numbers are in the ratio 3 : 5 and their product is 2160. The smaller of the numbers is (S.S.C., 2010)

(a) 12 (b) 18
(c) 24 (d) 36

145. A sum of money is divided among A, B, C and D in the ratio of 3 : 4 : 9 : 10 respectively. If the share of C is ₹ 2580 more than the share of B, then what is the total amount of A and D together? (Bank P.O., 2009)

(a) ₹ 5676 (b) ₹ 6192
(c) ₹ 6708 (d) ₹ 7224
(e) None of these

146. Two numbers are in the ratio 4 : 5 and their L.C.M. is 180. The smaller number is (C.P.O., 2007)

(a) 9 (b) 15
(c) 36 (d) 45

147. The ratio of the incomes of Ram and Shyam is 7 : 17 and that of Shyam and Sohan is 7 : 17. If the income of Ram is ₹ 490, what is the income of Sohan? (R.R.B., 2007)

(a) ₹ 490 (b) ₹ 1190
(c) ₹ 2790 (d) ₹ 2890

148. At Narmada Sarovar Bachao demonstration, supporters of Ms. Patkar outnumbered the police by 9 : 1. The police arrested 135 NSB supporters averaging 5 for 3 policemen. How many supporters of NSB were there in the demonstration? (M.A.T., 2007)

(a) 405 (b) 665
(c) 1215 (d) None of these

149. The sides of a triangle are in the ratio $\frac{1}{2}:\frac{1}{3}:\frac{1}{4}$ and its perimeter is 104 cm. The length of the longest side (in cm) is (M.B.A., 2007)

(a) 26 (b) 32
(c) 48 (d) 52

150. Two numbers are in the ratio 3 : 4. If the difference of their squares is 63, then the numbers are

(a) 8, 12 (b) 9, 12
(c) 12, 15 (d) 16, 20

151. If $A : B = 4 : 5$, $B : C = 7 : 9$ and $C : D = 3 : 4$, and if A's share is ₹ 1680, the share of D is

(a) ₹ 2100 (b) ₹ 2700
(c) ₹ 2900 (d) ₹ 3600

152. The sum of the squares of three numbers is 532 and the ratio of the first and the second as also of the second and the third is 3 : 2. The third number is (M.A.T., 2010)

(a) 8 (b) 12
(c) 18 (d) 20

153. A man spends a part of his monthly income and saves a part of it. The ratio of his expenditure to his savings is 26 : 3. If his monthly income is ₹ 7250, what is the amount of his monthly savings?

(a) ₹ 290 (b) ₹ 350
(c) ₹ 750 (d) ₹ 780

154. Two numbers are in the ratio 17 : 45. One-third of the smaller is less than $\frac{1}{5}$ of the bigger by 15. The smaller number is

(a) $25\frac{1}{2}$ (b) $67\frac{1}{2}$
(c) $76\frac{1}{2}$ (d) $86\frac{1}{2}$

155. The sum of four numbers A, B, C and D is 110. C is twice A, sum of A and D is equal to that of B and C and A : B is 3 : 5. The numbers are

(a) 3, 5, 6, 8 (b) 15, 25, 30, 40
(c) 15, 25, 35, 45 (d) None of these

156. The expenses of A and B are in the ratio 2 : 3. A sum of ₹ 2800 is equally divided between them. If A saves ₹ 600, then B saves

(a) ₹ 200 (b) ₹ 300
(c) ₹ 400 (d) ₹ 500

157. Three numbers A, B and C are in the ratio of 12 : 15 : 25. If the sum of these numbers is 312, the ratio between the difference of B and A and the difference of C and B is (M.A.T., 2010)

(a) 3 : 7 (b) 5 : 1
(c) 3 : 10 (d) 10 : 3

158. Incomes of A, B and C are in the ratio 7 : 9 : 12 and their respective expenditures are in the ratio 8 : 9 : 15. If A saves $\frac{1}{4}$ of his income, then the ratio of their savings is (A.A.O. Exam., 2009)

(a) 56 : 99 : 69 (b) 33 : 19 : 23
(c) 15 : 28 : 27 (d) 56 : 69 : 99

159. The total emoluments of A and B are equal. However, A gets 65% of his basic salary as allowances and B gets 80% of his basic salary as allowances. What is the ratio of the basic salaries of A and B? (P.C.S., 2009)

(a) 5 : 7 (b) 7 : 9
(c) 12 : 11 (d) 16 : 13

160. The incomes of Mr. Gupta and Mr. Verma are in the ratio 9 : 4 and their expenditures are in the ratio 7 : 3. If each saves ₹ 2000, then Mr. Gupta's expenditure is (M.A.T., 2009)

(a) ₹ 60000 (b) ₹ 70000
(c) ₹ 80000 (d) ₹ 90000

161. A and B have incomes in the ratio 5 : 3. The expenses of A, B and C are in the ratio of 8 : 5 : 2. If C spends ₹ 2000 and B saves ₹ 700, then A's savings are

(a) ₹ 500 (b) ₹ 1000
(c) ₹ 1500 (d) ₹ 2500

162. In a bank, monthly salary of clerks and officers are in the ratio of 3 : 5. Each clerk contributes 2% and each officer contributes 3 % of his salary to the Welfare Fund. If each officer's contribution is ₹ 210, what will be the clerk's salary?

(a) ₹ 4000 (b) ₹ 4200
(c) ₹ 5200 (d) ₹ 7000
(e) None of these

163. Salaries of A and B are in the ratio of 9 : 4 respectively. When A's salary is increased by 15%, it becomes ₹ 5175. What is B's salary?

(a) ₹ 2000 (b) ₹ 2500
(c) ₹ 4000 (d) ₹ 4500
(e) None of these

164. Between two consecutive years my incomes are in the ratio of 2 : 3 and expenses in the ratio 5 : 9. If my income in the second year is ₹ 45000 and my expenses in the first year is ₹ 25000 my total savings for the two years is

(a) Nil (b) ₹ 5000
(c) ₹ 10000 (d) ₹ 15000

165. The sum of the salaries of A and B is ₹ 2100. A spends 80% of his salary and B spends 70% of his salary. If their savings are in the proportion of 4 : 3, then what is the salary of A?

(a) ₹ 700 (b) ₹ 900
(c) ₹ 1200 (d) ₹ 1400

166. The ratio of incomes of two persons is 5 : 3 and that of their expenditures is 9 : 5. If they save ₹ 2600 and ₹ 1800 respectively, their incomes are

(a) ₹ 9000, ₹ 5400 (b) ₹ 10000, ₹ 6000
(c) ₹ 6000, ₹ 3600 (d) ₹ 8000, ₹ 4800

167. The monthly incomes of A and B are in the ratio of 5 : 4, their monthly expenses are in the ratio of 19 : 21, and their monthly savings are in the ratio of 37 : 18. If the total annual savings of A and B is ₹ 66000, A's monthly income is

(a) ₹ 6000 (b) ₹ 7500
(c) ₹ 8000 (d) ₹ 9000

168. The ratio of the number of boys and girls in a school of 720 students is 7 : 5. How many more girls should be admitted to make the ratio 1 : 1? (P.C.S., 2009)

(a) 90 (b) 120
(c) 220 (d) 240

169. In a college the students in Arts and Commerce faculties were in the ratio of 4 : 5 respectively. When 65 more students joined Commerce faculty the ratio becomes 8 : 11 respectively. How many students are there in Arts faculty? (Bank P.O., 2009)

(a) 520 (b) 650
(c) 715 (d) Cannot be determined
(e) None of these

170. Two numbers are in the ratio 7 : 11. If 7 is added to each of the numbers, the ratio becomes 2 : 3. The smaller number is **(S.S.C., 2010)**
(*a*) 39 (*b*) 49
(*c*) 66 (*d*) 77

171. The ratio of boys and girls in sections *A*, *B*, *C* and *D* of class VI is respectively 7 : 5, 5 : 3, 3 : 2 and 2 : 1. If the number of students in each of the sections is equal, then maximum number of boys are enrolled in section
(*a*) *A* (*b*) *B*
(*c*) *C* (*d*) *D*

172. When a particular number is subtracted from each of 7, 9, 11 and 15, the resulting numbers are in proportion. The number to be subtracted is **(C.P.O., 2007)**
(*a*) 1 (*b*) 2
(*c*) 3 (*d*) 5

173. The ratio of milk to water in 80 litres of a mixture is 7 : 3. The water (in litres) to be added to it to make the ratio 2 : 1 is **(S.S.C., 2006)**
(*a*) 4 (*b*) 5
(*c*) 6 (*d*) 8

174. In two types of powdered detergent the ratio of soda and soap-dust is 2 : 19 and 1 : 11 respectively. If 7 kg of the first type is mixed with 4 kg of the second type, find the ratio of soda to soap-dust in the new detergent mixture.
(*a*) 1 : 9 (*b*) 9 : 1
(*c*) 1 : 10 (*d*) 20 : 1

175. What number must be added to each of the numbers 7, 11 and 19 so that the resulting numbers may be in continued proportion?
(*a*) –3 (*b*) –4
(*c*) 3 (*d*) 4

176. Two numbers are in the ratio of 3 : 5. If 9 is subtracted from each, they are in the ratio of 12 : 23. What is the larger number? **(J.M.E.T., 2010)**
(*a*) 40 (*b*) 45
(*c*) 55 (*d*) 60

177. In a certain company, the ratio of the number of managers to the number of production-line workers is 5 to 72. If 8 additional production-line workers were to be hired, the ratio of the number of managers to the production-line workers would be 5 to 74. How many managers does the company have? **(A.T.M.A., 2006)**
(*a*) 10 (*b*) 20
(*c*) 25 (*d*) 30

178. What number has to be added to the terms of 3 : 5 to make the ratio 5 : 6? **(R.R.B., 2006)**
(*a*) 6 (*b*) 7
(*c*) 12 (*d*) 13

179. The ratio of the number of ladies to that of gents at a party was 3 : 2. When 20 more gents joined the party, the ratio was reversed. The number of ladies present at the party was **(C.P.O., 2006)**
(*a*) 16 (*b*) 24
(*c*) 32 (*d*) 36

180. In a school the ratio of boys and girls is 4 : 5 respectively. When 100 girls leave the school the ratio becomes 6 : 7 respectively. How many boys are there in the school? **(Bank P.O., 2008)**
(*a*) 1300 (*b*) 1500
(*c*) 1600 (*d*) Cannot be determined
(*e*) None of these

181. Two numbers are in the ratio $1\frac{1}{2} : 2\frac{2}{3}$. When each of these is increased by 15, their ratio becomes $1\frac{2}{3} : 2\frac{1}{2}$. The greater of the numbers is **(S.S.C., 2005)**
(*a*) 27 (*b*) 36
(*c*) 48 (*d*) 64

182. Three numbers *A*, *B* and *C* are in the ratio 1 : 2 : 3. Their average is 600. If *A* is increased by 10% and *B* is decreased by 20%, then to get the average increased by 5%, *C* will be increased by
(*a*) 90 (*b*) 100
(*c*) 150 (*d*) 180

183. Two numbers are in the ratio 2 : 3. If 2 is subtracted from the first and 2 is added to the second, the ratio becomes 1 : 2. The sum of the numbers is **(S.S.C., 2007)**
(*a*) 10 (*b*) 24
(*c*) 28 (*d*) 30

184. 20 litres of a mixture contains milk and water in the ratio of 5 : 3. If four litres of this mixture is replaced by four litres of milk, then the ratio of the milk to that of the water in the new mixture will be
(*a*) 2 : 3 (*b*) 4 : 3
(*c*) 5 : 3 (*d*) 7 : 3

185. When 1 is added to each of the two given numbers, their ratio becomes 3 : 4 and when 5 is subtracted from each, the ratio becomes 7 : 10. One of the numbers is
(*a*) 11 (*b*) 15
(*c*) 26 (*d*) 36

186. The ratio of number of boys to that of girls in a group becomes 2 : 1 when 15 girls leave. But, afterwards, when 45 boys also leave, the ratio becomes 1 : 5. Originally the number of girls in the group was
(*a*) 20 (*b*) 30
(*c*) 40 (*d*) 50

187. Two vessels contain spirit of 0.5 and 0.75 concentrations. If 2 litres from the first vessel and 3 litres from the second vessel are mixed, then what will be the ratio of spirit and water in the resultant solution?

(a) 7 : 17 (b) 17 : 15
(c) 13 : 7 (d) 15 : 17

188. The least whole number which when subtracted from both the numerator and the denominator of the fractional number 6 : 7, gives a ratio less than 16 : 21, is

(a) 2 (b) 3
(c) 4 (d) 6

189. The population of a city is 9000 in a particular year. If there is an increase of 5% in men's population and 8% in women's population in the next year and the population becomes 9600, what was the ratio between the men and women in that particular year?

(a) 2 : 3 (b) 4 : 5
(c) 5 : 4 (d) Data inadequate
(e) None of these

190. A barrel contains a mixture of wine and water in the ratio 3 : 1. How much fraction of the mixture must be drawn off and substituted by water so that the ratio of wine and water in the resultant mixture in the barrel becomes 1 : 1?

(a) $\frac{1}{3}$ (b) $\frac{1}{4}$
(c) $\frac{2}{3}$ (d) $\frac{3}{4}$

191. One year ago the ratio of the ages of Sarika and Gouri was 3 : 4 respectively. One year hence the ratio of their ages will be 10 : 13 respectively. What is Sarika's present age? **(Bank P.O., 2008)**

(a) 18 years (b) 20 years
(c) 26 years (d) Cannot be determined
(e) None of these

192. The average age of three boys is 25 years and their ages are in the proportion 3 : 5 : 7. The age of the youngest boy is

(a) 9 years (b) 15 years
(c) 18 years (d) 21 years

193. A box contains 1 rupee, 50-paise and 25-paise coins in the ratio 8 : 5 : 3. If the total amount of money in the box is ₹ 112.50, the number of 50-paise coins is

(a) 30 (b) 42
(c) 50 (d) 80

194. There are 420 coins consisting of one-rupee coins, 50-paise coins and 25-paise coins. If the ratio of their values be 2 : 3 : 5, then the number of one-rupee coins is

(a) 20 (b) 30
(c) 90 (d) 300

195. Monthly consumption of kerosene oil in a certain household along with price variations is given below.

Rate of kerosene oil (in ₹)	1.5	2	3.0	4.5
Consumption (in litres)	60	45	30	20

When the price goes up to ₹ 6 per litre, what is the likely consumption of kerosene?

(a) 7.5 litres (b) 10 litres
(c) 12.5 litres (d) 15 litres

196. If A varies directly proportional to C and B also varies directly proportional to C, which one of the following is not correct? **(C.P.F., 2008)**

(a) $(A + B) \propto C$ (b) $(A - B) \propto \frac{1}{C}$
(c) $\sqrt{AB} \propto C$ (d) $\frac{A}{B}$ = constant

197. If x is inversely proportional to y and y is proportional to z, then xz **(I.A.M., 2007)**

(a) is proportional to y
(b) is inversely proportional to y
(c) is a constant
(d) is proportional to y^2

198. The falling height of an object is proportional to the square of the time. One object falls 64 cm in 2 sec then in 6 sec from how much height the object will fall? **(Campus Recruitment, 2009)**

(a) 192 cm (b) 276 cm
(c) 436 cm (d) 576 cm

199. y varies directly as $(x + 3)$ and $y = 8$ when $x = 1$. What is the value of y when $x = 2$? **(R.R.B., 2006)**

(a) 6 (b) 10
(c) 12 (d) 16

200. The ratio of the rate of flow of water in pipes varies inversely as the square of the radius of the pipes. What is the ratio of the rates of flow in two pipes of diameters 2 cm and 4 cm? **(M.A.T., 2005)**

(a) 1 : 2 (b) 2 : 1
(c) 4 : 1 (d) 1 : 8

201. Suppose y varies as the sum of two quantities of which one varies directly as x and the other inversely as x. If $y = 6$ when $x = 4$ and $y = 3\frac{1}{3}$ when $x = 3$, then the relation between x and y is **(M.B.A., 2006)**

(a) $y = 2x - \frac{8}{x}$ (b) $y = x + \frac{4}{x}$
(c) $y = 2x + \frac{4}{x}$ (d) $y = 2x + \frac{8}{x}$

202. Consider the following table of inverse variation :

M	15	–6	2	C
N	–4	A	B	60

The values of A, B and C in the above table respectively are

(a) –1, –30, 10 (b) –30, 10, –1

(c) 10, –30, –1 (d) 10, –1, 30

203. S varies directly as R and T varies inversely as R. At some particular time, $R = 20$, $S = 40$ and $T = 10$. If S is changed to 20, then the value of T would be equal to

(a) 10 (b) 20

(c) 40 (d) 80

204. x and y vary inversely with each other. When x is 12, y is 9. The pair which is not a possible pair of corresponding values of x and y is

(a) 9 and 12 (b) 18 and 6

(c) 24 and 18 (d) 36 and 3

205. The intensity of illumination on a surface from a source of light varies inversely as the square of the distance of the surface from the source. The effect of moving a piece of paper 3 times as far from the source is to

(a) multiply the intensity by 3

(b) divide the intensity by 3

(c) multiply the intensity by 9

(d) divide the intensity by 9

206. The boys and girls in a college are in the ratio 3 : 2. If 20% of the boys and 25% of the girls are adults, the percentage of students who are not adults is (P.C.S., 2009)

(a) 67.5% (b) 58%

(c) 78% (d) 82.5%

207. The cost of a table and a chair are in the ratio of 5 : 7. If the cost of chair and table is increased by 20% and 10% respectively, then what will be the new ratio? (Bank Recruitment, 2007)

(a) 16 : 17 (b) 55 : 84

(c) 60 : 77 (d) Data inadequate

(e) None of these

208. The ratio of the students in schools A, B and C is 5 : 4 : 7. If the number of students in the schools are increased by 20%, 25% and 20% respectively, what would be the new ratio of the students in schools A, B and C? (Bank P.O., 2010)

(a) 5 : 5 : 7 (b) 30 : 25 : 42

(c) 30 : 20 : 49 (d) Cannot be determined

(e) None of these

209. The expenses on rice, fish and oil of a family are in the ratio 12 : 17 : 3. The prices of these articles are increased by 20%, 30% and 50% respectively. The total expenses of family on these articles are increased by (S.S.C., 2007)

(a) $7\frac{1}{8}\%$ (b) $14\frac{1}{8}\%$

(c) $28\frac{1}{8}\%$ (d) $56\frac{1}{8}\%$

210. Ratio of earnings of A and B is 8 : 9 respectively. If the earnings of A increase by 50% and the earnings of B decrease by 25%, the new ratio of their earnings becomes 16 : 9 respectively. What are A's earnings? (Bank P.O., 2006)

(a) ₹ 22000 (b) ₹ 28500

(c) ₹ 37000 (d) Cannot be determined

(e) None of these

211. Mr. Sharma's expenditure and savings are in the ratio of 3 : 2. His income increases by 10%. His expenditure also increases by 12%. How much percent does his savings increase? (M.A.T., 2010)

(a) 6% (b) 7%

(c) 11% (d) 13%

212. The weights of two persons A and B are in the ratio of 3 : 5. A's weight increases by 20% and the total weight of A and B together becomes 80 kg, with an increase of 25%. By what percent did the weight of B increase? (M.A.T., 2008)

(a) 20% (b) 25%

(c) 28% (d) 30%

213. Mrs. Richi Rich inherits 3224 gold coins and divides them amongst her 3 daughters Lalita, Palita and Salita in a certain ratio. Out of the total coins each of them received, Lalita sells her 50 coins, Palita donates 85 of her coins and Salita makes jewellery out of her 39 coins. Now the ratio of gold coins with them is 24 : 21 : 16 respectively. How many coins did Lalita receive from her mother? (Bank Recruitment, 2009)

(a) 1050 (b) 1135

(c) 1200 (d) 1250

(e) None of these

214. A wheel that has 6 cogs is meshed with a larger wheel of 14 cogs. When the smaller wheel has made 21 revolutions, the number of revolutions made by the larger wheel will be

(a) 4 (b) 9

(c) 12 (d) 49

215. Seeta and Geeta have two glasses of equal volumes. Both have some milk in their glasses. Seeta says to Geeta. "Give me half the milk in your glass so that my glass will be full of milk." Geeta says to Seeta, "Instead you give me one-fourth of the milk in your glass so that my glass will be full of milk." Find the ratio of volumes of milk in their glasses. (S.S.C., 2006)

(*a*) 1 : 2 (*b*) 4 : 3
(*c*) 3 : 4 (*d*) 2 : 3

216. The ratio of land to water for the whole earth is 1 : 2 and 2 : 3 in the northern hemisphere. The ratio of land to water in the southern hemisphere is

(*a*) 1 : 3 (*b*) 1 : 4
(*c*) 4 : 7 (*d*) 4 : 11

217. The price of a diamond varies as the cube of its volume. A cubical variety of this diamond was worth ₹ 10,00,000. If this diamond accidentally broke into 8 equal cubical diamonds, then the total loss in value amounts to

(*a*) ₹ 9,00,000 (*b*) ₹ 9,47,532
(*c*) ₹ 9,50,000 (*d*) ₹ 9,84,375

218. ₹ 720 are divided among 2 men, 5 women and 8 boys so that the shares of a man, a woman and a boy are in the ratio of 3 : 2 : 1. How much does each boy get?

(*a*) ₹ 24 (*b*) ₹ 30
(*c*) ₹ 45 (*d*) ₹ 72

219. A person distributed two different amounts among his sons *A*, *B*, *C* and *D*. First amount was distributed in the ratio of 4 : 3 : 2 : 1 and the second amount was distributed in the ratio of 5 : 6 : 7 : 8. If the first amount is half of the second amount, then which son will get the maximum amount?

(*a*) *A* (*b*) *B*
(*c*) *C* (*d*) *D*

220. A sum of money is divided among 160 males and some females in the ratio 16 : 21. Individually each male gets ₹ 4 and a female ₹ 3. The number of females is

(*a*) 198 (*b*) 270
(*c*) 280 (*d*) 284

221. ₹ 180 are to be divided among 66 men and women. The ratio of the total amount of money received by men and women is 5 : 4. But the ratio of the money received by each man and woman is 3 : 2. The number of men is

(*a*) 20 (*b*) 24
(*c*) 30 (*d*) 36

222. Prices of foodgrains have risen by 10% and of other items of consumption by 15%. If the ratio of an employee's expenditure on foodgrains and other items is 2 : 5, by how much should his salary be increased so that he may maintain the same level of consumption as before, assuming that his present salary is ₹ 3500?

(*a*) ₹ 300 (*b*) ₹ 350
(*c*) ₹ 375 (*d*) ₹ 475

223. A student took five papers in an examination, where full marks were same on each paper. Her marks in these papers were in the proportion of 6 : 7 : 8 : 9 : 10. In all these papers together, the candidate obtained 60% of the total marks. Then the number of papers in which she got more than 50% marks is

(*a*) 2 (*b*) 3
(*c*) 4 (*d*) 5
(*e*) None of these

224. Visitors to a show were charged ₹ 15 each on the first day, ₹ 7.50 on the second day and ₹ 2.50 on the third day. The attendance on the three days was in the ratio 2 : 5 : 13. The average charge per person for the whole show was

(*a*) ₹ 5 (*b*) ₹ 6.33
(*c*) ₹ 7.50 (*d*) ₹ 9

225. In an express train, the number of passengers travelling in A.C. sleeper class, first class and sleeper class are in the ratio 1 : 2 : 3 and the fares to each of these classes are in the ratio 5 : 4 : 2. If the total income from this train is ₹ 45600, then the income from the A.C. sleeper class is

(*a*) ₹ 6000 (*b*) ₹ 8000
(*c*) ₹ 10000 (*d*) ₹ 12000

226. Railway fares of 1st, 2nd and 3rd classes between two stations were in the ratio of 8 : 6 : 3. The fares of 1st and 2nd class were subsequently reduced by $\frac{1}{6}$ and $\frac{1}{12}$ respectively. If during a year the ratio between the passengers of 1st, 2nd and 3rd classes was 9 : 12 : 26 and the total amount collected by the sale of tickets was ₹ 1088, then find the collection from the passengers of 1st class. (M.A.T., 2006)

(*a*) ₹ 260 (*b*) ₹ 280
(*c*) ₹ 300 (*d*) ₹ 320

227. 15 men, 18 women and 12 boys working together earned ₹ 2070. If the daily wages of a man, a woman and a boy are in the ratio of 4 : 3 : 2, the daily wages (in ₹) of 1 man, 2 women and 3 boys are

(*a*) 135 (*b*) 180
(*c*) 205 (*d*) 240

228. An employer reduces the number of his employees in the ratio of 9 : 8 and increases their wages in the ratio 14 : 15. The difference in the amount of the total salary bill which was originally ₹ 1890 after the above two changes will be

(*a*) ₹ 90 (*b*) ₹ 100
(*c*) ₹ 110 (*d*) ₹ 120

229. Last year, the ratio between the salaries of *A* and *B* was 3 : 4. But the ratios of their individual salaries between last year and this year were 4 : 5 and 2 : 3 respectively. If the sum of their present salaries is ₹ 4160, then how much is the salary of *A* now?

(*a*) ₹ 1040 (*b*) ₹ 1600
(*c*) ₹ 2560 (*d*) ₹ 3120

230. A man ordered 4 pairs of black socks and some pairs of brown socks. The price of a black pair is double that of a brown pair. While preparing the bill, the clerk interchanged the number of black and brown pairs by mistake which increased the bill by 50%. The ratio of the number of black and brown pairs of socks in the original order was

(*a*) 1 : 2 (*b*) 2 : 1
(*c*) 1 : 4 (*d*) 4 : 1

231. *A* and *B* are two alloys of gold and copper prepared by mixing metals in the ratio 7 : 2 and 7 : 11 respectively. If equal quantities of the alloys are melted to form a third alloy *C*, then the ratio of gold and copper in alloy *C* will be **(M.B.A. 2007; M.A.T., 2005)**

(*a*) 5 : 7 (*b*) 5 : 9
(*c*) 7 : 5 (*d*) 9 : 5

232. Two alloys contain zinc and copper in the ratio of 2 : 1 and 4 : 1. In what ratio the two alloys should be added together to get a new alloy having zinc and copper in the ratio of 3 : 1?

(*a*) 3 : 5 (*b*) 5 : 7
(*c*) 7 : 5 (*d*) None of these

233. Two vessels *A* and *B* contain milk and water mixed in the ratio 5 : 3 and 2 : 3. When these mixtures are mixed to form a new mixture containing half milk and half water, they must be taken in the ratio

(*a*) 2 : 5 (*b*) 3 : 5
(*c*) 4 : 5 (*d*) 7 : 3

234. Two glasses of equal volume respectively are half and three-fourths filled with milk. They are then filled to brim by adding water. Their contents are then poured into another vessel. What will be the ratio of milk to water in this vessel?

(*a*) 1 : 3 (*b*) 2 : 3
(*c*) 3 : 2 (*d*) 5 : 3

235. The ratio of milk to water in three containers of equal capacity is 3 : 2, 7 : 3 and 11 : 4 respectively. The contents of the three containers are mixed together. What is the ratio of milk to water after mixing? **(M.A.T., 2010)**

(*a*) 19 : 4 (*b*) 7 : 3
(*c*) 61 : 29 (*d*) 41 : 18

236. Three containers *A*, *B* and *C* are havin mixtures of milk and water in the rati 1 : 5, 3 : 5 and 5 : 7 respectively. If the capacitie of the containers are in the ratio 5 : 4 : 5, find th ratio of milk to water, if the mixtures of all the thre containers are mixed together?

(*a*) 51 : 115 (*b*) 52 : 115
(*c*) 53 : 115 (*d*) 54 : 115

237. Three glasses of equal volumes are $\frac{1}{2}, \frac{2}{3}$ and $\frac{3}{4}$ full of milk respectively. The remaining portion o all the glasses is filled up with water. The mixtur in the three glasses is poured into a container. Th ratio of milk and water in the container is

(*a*) 23 : 12 (*b*) 23 : 13
(*c*) 23 : 14 (*d*) 23 : 15

238. Six coins of gold and silver of equal weights ar melted and new coins are cast. The ratio of golc and silver in one of the coins is 2 : 1, in another twc coins 3 : 5 and 7 : 5 in the remaining coins. Wha will be the ratio between gold and silver respectively in the new coins? **(R.R.B., 2006)**

(*a*) 1 : 1 (*b*) 12 : 11
(*c*) 42 : 25 (*d*) 19 : 17

239. A company blends two varieties of tea from twc different tea gardens, one variety costing ₹ 20 pe kg and the other ₹ 25 per kg in the ratio 5 : 4. He sells the blended tea at ₹ 23 per kg. Find his profi or loss percent.

(*a*) Profit of 3.5% (*b*) No profit, no loss
(*c*) Profit of 5% (*d*) Loss of 5%

240. Tea worth ₹ 126 per kg and ₹ 135 per kg are mixed with a third variety in the ratio 1 : 1 : 2. If the mixture is worth ₹ 153 per kg, then the price of the third variety per kg will be

(*a*) ₹ 169.50 (*b*) ₹ 170
(*c*) ₹ 175.50 (*d*) ₹ 180

241. A dealer buys dry fruit at the rate of ₹ 100, ₹ 80 and ₹ 60 per kg. He bought them in the ratio 12 : 15 : 20 by weight. He in total gets 20% profit by selling the first two and at last he finds he has no gain no loss in selling the whole quantity which he had. What was the percentage loss he suffered for the third quantity? **(M.A.T., 2007)**

(*a*) 20% (*b*) 30%
(*c*) 40% (*d*) 50%

242. From a can full of milk, 10 litres of milk is taken out and replaced with water and this operation is repeated twice. If the capacity of the can is 50 litres, what is the ratio of water and milk in the can after this operation?

(*a*) 2 : 3 (*b*) 9 : 16
(*c*) 16 : 9 (*d*) None of these

243. 8 litres are drawn from a cask full of wine and is then filled with water. This operation is performed three more times. The ratio of the quantity of wine now left in the cask to that of the water is 16 : 65. How much wine did the cask hold originally?

(a) 18 litres (b) 24 litres
(c) 32 litres (d) 42 litres

244. Gold is 19 times as heavy as water and copper is 9 times as heavy as water. In what ratio should these be mixed to get an alloy 15 times as heavy as water?

(Campus Recruitment, 2010)

(a) 1 : 1 (b) 1 : 2
(c) 2 : 3 (d) 3 : 2

245. The speeds of three cars are in the ratio 5 : 4 : 6. The ratio between the time taken by them to travel the same distance is

(a) 5 : 4 : 6 (b) 6 : 4 : 5
(c) 10 : 12 : 15 (d) 12 : 15 : 10

246. Mr. X has some money with him. He has to distribute the amount among five labourers in the ratio $\frac{1}{2}:\frac{1}{3}:\frac{1}{4}:\frac{1}{5}:\frac{1}{7}$. What is the minimum amount he should have, so that each labourer gets an exact number of rupees?

(a) ₹ 358 (b) ₹ 420
(c) ₹ 512 (d) ₹ 599

247. The incomes of A, B and C are in the ratio 7 : 10 : 12 and their expenses are in the ratio 8 : 10 : 15. If A saves $\frac{1}{5}$ of his income, then B's saving is what percent more or less than that of C's?

(a) 100% more (b) $66\frac{2}{3}$% more
(c) $33\frac{1}{3}$% less (d) 40% less

248. The present ages of a mother and her son are in the ratio 11 : 5. When the son becomes as old as his mother is now, then the ratio of his father's age to that of his mother is 19 : 17. When the son becomes as old as his father is now, then the sum of his father's age and his age will be 170 years. What is the father's present age?

(a) 52 years (b) 60 years
(c) 65 years (d) 70 years

249. Six numbers a, b, c, d, e, f are such that $ab = 1$, $bc = \frac{1}{2}$, $cd = 6$, $de = 2$ and $ef = \frac{1}{2}$. What is the value of $(ad : be : cf)$?

(a) 4 : 3 : 27 (b) 6 : 1 : 9
(c) 8 : 9 : 9 (d) 72 : 1 : 9

250. A man sells 3 types of articles at 10%, 20% and 30% profit respectively. If the ratio of the cost of the articles is 1 : 2 : 3 and the ratio of the number of articles of each type sold is 3 : 2 : 1, then what is his net profit?

(a) 18% (b) 20%
(c) 24% (d) 25%

251. The respective ratio between the monthly salaries of Rene and Som is 5 : 3. Out of her monthly salary Rene gives 1/6th as rent, 1/5th to her mother, 30% as her education loan and keeps 25% aside for miscellaneous expenditure. Remaining ₹ 5000 she keeps as savings. What is Som's monthly salary?

[IBPS—RRB Officer's Gr. 'B' Exam, 2015]

(a) ₹21000 (b) ₹24000
(c) ₹27000 (d) ₹36000

252. Find the third proportional to 25 and 30.

[Indian Railway Gr. 'D' Exam, 2014]

(a) 36 (b) 32
(c) 34 (d) 38

253. The ratio of syrup and water in a mixture is 3 : 1, then the percentage of syrup in this mixture is

[SSC—CHSL (10+2) Exam, 2015]

(a) 75% (b) 25%
(c) $66\frac{2}{3}$% (d) $33\frac{1}{3}$%

254. If $a^2 + b^2 + c^2 - ab - bc - ca = 0$ then $a : b : c$ is

[SSC—CHSL (10+2) Exam, 2015]

(a) 1 : 1 : 2 (b) 1 : 1 : 1
(c) 1 : 2 : 1 (d) 2 : 1 : 1

255. 80% of a number is equal to the $\frac{4}{5}$th of the other number. What is the ratio between the first number and the second number respectively?

[United India Insurance Co. Ltd. (UIICL) Assistant (Online) Exam, 2015]

(a) 3 : 4 (b) 3 : 5
(c) 5 : 3 (d) None of these

Direction: Each of the questions below consists of a question and two statements I and II are given below it. You have to decide whether the data provided in the statements are sufficient to answer the question. Given answer–

(a) The data in statement I alone is sufficient to answer the question while II alone is not sufficient to answer the questions.
(b) Data in statement II alone is sufficient to answer the question while data in statement I alone is not sufficient to answer the question.
(c) The data in statement I alone or in statement II alone is sufficient to answer the question.
(d) The data in both statement I and II is not sufficient to answer the question.
(e) The data in both statement I and II is sufficient to answer the question.

256. What is the population of the city A?
I. The ratio of the population of males and females in city A is 27 : 23 and the difference between their populations is 100000.
II. The population of city A is 80% of that of city B. The difference of population of city A and city B is 312500.
[IDBI Bank Executive Officer's Exam, 2015]

257. 4/7th of the boys and 6/11th of girls of a school participated in marathon. If the number of participating students is 208 out of which 124 are boys, what is the total, number of students in the school?
[NICL—AAO Exam, 2015]
(a) 359 (b) 411
(c) 371 (d) 377

258. The monthly salaries of Pia and Som are in the ratio of 5 : 4. From her monthly salary, gives $\frac{3}{5}$ to her mother, 15% towards her sister's tuition fees, 18% towards a loan and she shops with the remaining amount, which is ₹ 2100. What is the monthly salary of Som?
[IBPS—RRB Officer's Gr. 'B' Exam, 2015]
(a) ₹ 25000 (b) ₹ 30000
(c) ₹ 15000 (d) ₹ 24000

259. Smita works in her office for 6 hours and Kajal works in her office for 7 hours 30 minutes. Find the ratio of their working hours.
[ESIC—UDC Exam, 2016]
(a) 3 : 5 (b) 4 : 5
(c) 6 : 7 (d) 5 : 4

260. A bag has coins of 50 paisa, 25 paisa and 10 paisa in the respective ratio of 5 : 8 : 3 whose total value is ₹ 144. Find the number of 50 paisa coins.
[ESIC—UDC Exam, 2016]
(a) 163 (b) 175
(c) 200 (d) 150

261. Express 50 paise: ₹ 4 in its simplest form.
[ESIC—UDC Exam, 2016]
(a) 1 : 8 (b) 5 : 4
(c) 4 : 5 (d) 8 : 1

262. Raj and Suraj bought a bottle of water together in which there was 2 litres of water. Raj drank $\frac{1}{4}$th part of it. The rest water was drunk by Suraj. Find the amount of water used by Suraj.
[ESIC—UDC Exam, 2016]
(a) 1.5 litres (b) 0.5 litres
(c) 2.5 litres (d) 2 litres

263. $\frac{7}{5}$ of $58 + \frac{3}{8}$ of $139.2 = ?$
[SBI—Jr. Associates (Pre.) Exam, 2016]
(a) 133.4 (b) 137.2
(c) 127.8 (d) 131.6

264. $\frac{3}{7}$ of $\frac{5}{4}$ of $3024 = ?$
[SBI—Jr. Associates (Pre.) Exam, 2016]
(a) 920 (b) 940
(c) 960 (d) 1620

265. A movie was screened for 3 days – Monday, Tuesday and Wednesday. The respective ratio between the number of spectators on Monday. Tuesday and Wednesday was 2 : 3 : 5 and the price charged for three days was in the respective ratio 2 : 3 : 4. If the difference between the amount earned on Tuesday and Wednesday was Rs. 8800. What was the total amount earned in all three days?
[CET—Maharashtra (MBA), 2016]
(a) ₹ 24800 (b) ₹ 27500
(c) ₹ 26400 (d) ₹ 22820

ANSWERS

1. (c)	2. (d)	3. (a)	4. (c)	5. (a)	6. (b)	7. (c)	8. (c)	9. (a)	10. (b)
11. (b)	12. (d)	13. (b)	14. (d)	15. (a)	16. (c)	17. (b)	18. (c)	19. (c)	20. (c)
21. (a)	22. (c)	23. (a)	24. (c)	25. (b)	26. (a)	27. (d)	28. (b)	29. (b)	30. (d)
31. (c)	32. (d)	33. (b)	34. (d)	35. (a)	36. (d)	37. (d)	38. (d)	39. (d)	40. (c)
41. (c)	42. (d)	43. (b)	44. (d)	45. (b)	46. (a)	47. (b)	48. (b)	49. (d)	50. (c)
51. (d)	52. (a)	53. (c)	54. (b)	55. (c)	56. (d)	57. (c)	58. (b)	59. (b)	60. (a)
61. (b)	62. (c)	63. (b)	64. (c)	65. (c)	66. (b)	67. (c)	68. (d)	69. (b)	70. (b)
71. (d)	72. (d)	73. (c)	74. (c)	75. (a)	76. (b)	77. (c)	78. (d)	79. (a)	80. (d)
81. (b)	82. (c)	83. (a)	84. (d)	85. (d)	86. (b)	87. (b)	88. (b)	89. (d)	90. (b)
91. (b)	92. (e)	93. (d)	94. (e)	95. (e)	96. (a)	97. (d)	98. (c)	99. (d)	100. (c)
101. (d)	102. (d)	103. (c)	104. (b)	105. (c)	106. (c)	107. (c)	108. (a)	109. (c)	110. (a)
111. (d)	112. (d)	113. (c)	114. (c)	115. (b)	116. (b)	117. (d)	118. (d)	119. (b)	120. (c)
121. (b)	122. (b)	123. (e)	124. (b)	125. (b)	126. (b)	127. (d)	128. (d)	129. (c)	130. (b)
131. (a)	132. (b)	133. (e)	134. (a)	135. (a)	136. (b)	137. (a)	138. (c)	139. (c)	140. (b)

141. (c)	142. (b)	143. (b)	144. (d)	145. (c)	146. (c)	147. (d)	148. (d)	149. (c)	150. (b)
151. (d)	152. (a)	153. (c)	154. (c)	155. (b)	156. (a)	157. (c)	158. (a)	159. (c)	160. (b)
161. (c)	162. (b)	163. (a)	164. (b)	165. (d)	166. (d)	167. (b)	168. (b)	169. (a)	170. (b)
171. (d)	172. (c)	173. (a)	174. (c)	175. (a)	176. (c)	177. (b)	178. (b)	179. (b)	180. (e)
181. (c)	182. (d)	183. (d)	184. (d)	185. (c)	186. (c)	187. (c)	188. (b)	189. (b)	190. (a)
191. (e)	192. (b)	193. (c)	194. (b)	195. (d)	196. (b)	197. (c)	198. (d)	199. (b)	200. (c)
201. (a)	202. (c)	203. (b)	204. (c)	205. (d)	206. (c)	207. (b)	208. (b)	209. (c)	210. (d)
211. (b)	212. (c)	213. (d)	214. (b)	215. (d)	216. (d)	217. (d)	218. (b)	219. (a)	220. (c)
221. (c)	222. (d)	223. (c)	224. (a)	225. (d)	226. (d)	227. (d)	228. (a)	229. (b)	230. (c)
231. (c)	232. (a)	233. (c)	234. (d)	235. (c)	236. (c)	237. (b)	238. (d)	239. (a)	240. (c)
241. (c)	242. (b)	243. (b)	244. (d)	245. (d)	246. (d)	247. (a)	248. (c)	249. (d)	250. (b)
251. (d)	252. (a)	253. (a)	254. (b)	255. (d)	256. (c)	257. (c)	258. (d)	259. (b)	260. (d)
261. (a)	262. (a)	263. (a)	264. (d)	265. (c)					

SOLUTIONS

1. Number of girls = 1200. Number of boys = 2140 − 1200 = 940.

   ∴ Required ratio = 940 : 1200 = 47 : 60.

2. Total body weight = (30000 + 10000 + 5000 + 2000 + 1000 + 1700 + 1500) g

   = 51200 g = 51 kg 200 g > 51 kg.

3. $\dfrac{\text{Weight of the liver}}{\text{Weight of the skeleton}} = \dfrac{1700}{10000} \Rightarrow$ Weight of the liver = $\dfrac{17}{100}S = 0.17S$.

4. Required ratio = $\dfrac{5000}{2000} = \dfrac{5}{2} = 2.5.$

5. Required ratio = $\dfrac{1500}{30000} = \dfrac{1}{20} = 0.05.$

6. Required ratio = $\dfrac{1500}{1000} = \dfrac{3}{2} = 1.5.$

7. ₹ 2.80 = 280 paise.

   ∴ Required ratio = 280 : 40 = 7 : 1.

8. Let the number be x. Then, required ratio

   $= x : \left(x + \dfrac{x}{5}\right) = x : \dfrac{6x}{5} = 1 : \dfrac{6}{5} = 5 : 6.$

9. Maximum possible number of tables = 6.

   [∵ 1200 × 6 = 7200].

   Number of chairs purchased = $\dfrac{8100 - 7200}{300} = \dfrac{900}{300} = 3.$

   Hence, required ratio = 3 : 6 = 1 : 2.

10. 60% of $A = \dfrac{3}{4}$ of $B \Rightarrow \dfrac{60}{100}A = \dfrac{3}{4}B \Rightarrow \dfrac{3}{5}A = \dfrac{3}{4}B$

    $\Rightarrow \dfrac{A}{B} = \dfrac{3}{4} \times \dfrac{5}{3} = \dfrac{5}{4}.$

11. $\dfrac{2}{3}A = 75\%$ of $B \Rightarrow \dfrac{2}{3}A = \dfrac{75}{100}B = \dfrac{3}{4}B$

    $\Rightarrow \dfrac{A}{B} = \dfrac{3}{4} \times \dfrac{3}{2} = \dfrac{9}{8} \Rightarrow A : B = 9 : 8.$

12. (a) $8 : a = 8 : b \Rightarrow 8a = 8b \Rightarrow a = b.$

    (b) $a : 16 = b : 4 \Rightarrow 4a = 16b \Rightarrow a = 4b.$

    (c) $a : 8 = b : 8 \Rightarrow 8b = 8a \Rightarrow b = a.$

    (d) $32 : a = b : 2 \Rightarrow ab = 64.$

13. Since the number of black and white marbles are whole numbers, so the sum of the terms of the ratio must be a factor of 10.

    1 + 4 = 5, 7 + 3 = 10 and 9 + 1 = 10, but 1 + 10 = 11, which is not a factor of 10.

14. The total number of members must be a multiple of the sum of the ratio terms. 3 + 2 = 5 and 25 is a multiple of 5.

15. $7 : 15 = \dfrac{7}{15} = 0.466$, $15 : 23 = \dfrac{15}{23} = 0.652$, $17 : 25 = \dfrac{17}{25} = 0.68$, $21 : 39 = \dfrac{21}{39} = 0.538.$

    Clearly, 7 : 15 is the lowest.

16. $5 : a :: 20 : 28 \Leftrightarrow 20a = 5 \times 28 \Leftrightarrow a = \dfrac{5 \times 28}{20} = 7.$

17. Let the missing number be x. Then, $\dfrac{1}{3} : \dfrac{1}{2} :: 27y : x \Leftrightarrow \dfrac{3}{4}x$

    $= \dfrac{1}{2} \times 27y \Leftrightarrow x = \dfrac{27y}{2} \times \dfrac{4}{3} = 18y.$

18. $x : 7.5 = 7 : 17.5 \Leftrightarrow 17.5x = 7.5 \times 7 \Leftrightarrow x = \dfrac{7.5 \times 7}{17.5} = 3.$

19. $x : 2\dfrac{1}{3} :: 21 : 50 \Leftrightarrow 50x = \dfrac{7}{3} \times 21 = 49 \Leftrightarrow x = \dfrac{49}{50}.$

20. $(x + 1) : 8 = 3.75 : 7 \Leftrightarrow 7(x + 1) = 8 \times 3.75 = 30$

    $\Leftrightarrow x + 1 = \dfrac{30}{7} \Leftrightarrow x = \dfrac{30}{7} - 1 = \dfrac{23}{7} = 3\dfrac{2}{7}.$

21. $\sqrt{2} : (1 + \sqrt{3}) :: \sqrt{6} : x \Leftrightarrow \sqrt{2}x = \sqrt{6}(1 + \sqrt{3})$

    $\Leftrightarrow x = \dfrac{\sqrt{6}(1 + \sqrt{3})}{\sqrt{2}} = \sqrt{3}(1 + \sqrt{3}) = \sqrt{3} + 3.$

22. 1 day = 24 hours. ∴ Given ratio = 3 : 24 = 1 : 8.

23. $1.5 : 2.5 = \frac{1.5}{2.5} = \frac{15}{25} = \frac{3}{5} = 3 : 5.$

24. $9^{3.04} : 9^{2.04} = \frac{9^{3.04}}{9^{2.04}} = 9^{(3.04-2.04)} = 9^1 = 9 = 9 : 1.$

25. $4^{3.5} : 2^5 = (2^2)^{3.5} : 2^5 = \frac{2^7}{2^5} = 2^{(7-5)} = 2^2 = 4 : 1.$

26. Product of 1st and 4th terms (extremes) = Product of 2nd and 3rd terms (means)

$\Rightarrow 2.5x = 40 \Rightarrow x = \frac{40}{2.5} = 16.$

27. 20% of A = 30% of B = $\frac{1}{6}$ of $C \Rightarrow \frac{20A}{100} = \frac{30B}{100} = \frac{C}{6}$

$\Rightarrow \frac{A}{5} = \frac{3B}{10} = \frac{C}{6} = k$ (say)

$\Rightarrow A = 5k,\ B = \frac{10k}{3},\ C = 6k.$

$\therefore\ A : B : C = 5k : \frac{10k}{3} : 6k = 5 : \frac{10}{3} : 6 = 15 : 10 : 18.$

28. 25% of A = 35% of $B \Rightarrow \frac{25}{100}A = \frac{35}{100}B \Rightarrow \frac{A}{4} = \frac{7B}{20}$

$\Rightarrow \frac{A}{B} = \frac{7}{20} \times 4 = \frac{7}{5} \Rightarrow A : B = 7 : 5.$

29. $x = \frac{1}{3}y = \frac{1}{3} \times \frac{1}{2}z = \frac{1}{6}z.$ Let $x = \frac{1}{3}y = \frac{1}{6}z = k.$

Then, $x = k,\ y = 3k,\ z = 6k.$

$\therefore\ x : y : z = k : 3k : 6k = 1 : 3 : 6.$

30. Let $2A = 3B = 4C = k$. Then, $A = \frac{k}{2},\ B = \frac{k}{3},\ C = \frac{k}{4}.$

$\therefore\ A : B : C = \frac{k}{2} : \frac{k}{3} : \frac{k}{4} = \frac{1}{2} : \frac{1}{3} : \frac{1}{4} = 6 : 4 : 3.$

31. $x^2 + 4y^2 = 4xy \Rightarrow x^2 - 4xy + 4y^2 = 0 \Rightarrow (x - 2y)^2 = 0 \Rightarrow x = 2y \Rightarrow \frac{x}{y} = 2 \Rightarrow x : y = 2 : 1.$

32. $5x^2 - 13xy + 6y^2 = 0 \Rightarrow 5x^2 - 10xy - 3xy + 6y^2 = 0 \Rightarrow 5x(x - 2y) - 3y(x - 2y) = 0$

$\Rightarrow (x - 2y)(5x - 3y) = 0 \Rightarrow x = 2y$ or $5x = 3y$

$\Rightarrow \frac{x}{y} = 2$ or $\frac{x}{y} = \frac{3}{5} \Rightarrow x : y = 2 : 1$ or $3 : 5.$

33. $\frac{a}{b} = \frac{7}{9}$ and $\frac{b}{c} = \frac{15}{7} \Rightarrow \frac{a}{c} = \left(\frac{a}{b} \times \frac{b}{c}\right) = \frac{7}{9} \times \frac{15}{7} = \frac{5}{3} \Rightarrow a : c = 5 : 3.$

34. $\frac{P}{Q} = \frac{2}{3}$ and $\frac{Q}{R} = \frac{4}{5} \Rightarrow \frac{P}{R} = \left(\frac{P}{Q} \times \frac{Q}{R}\right)$

$= \frac{2}{3} \times \frac{4}{5} = \frac{8}{15} \Rightarrow P : R = 8 : 15.$

35. $\frac{W_2}{W_1} = \frac{3}{2}$ and $\frac{W_1}{W_3} = \frac{1}{2}$

$\Rightarrow \frac{W_2}{W_3} = \left(\frac{W_2}{W_1} \times \frac{W_1}{W_3}\right) = \frac{3}{2} \times \frac{1}{2} = \frac{3}{4} \Rightarrow W_2 : W_3 = 3 : 4.$

36. $\frac{A}{B} = \frac{2}{3},\ \frac{B}{C} = \frac{2}{4},\ \frac{C}{D} = \frac{2}{5} \Rightarrow \frac{A}{D} = \left(\frac{A}{B} \times \frac{B}{C} \times \frac{C}{D}\right)$

$= \frac{2}{3} \times \frac{2}{4} \times \frac{2}{5} = \frac{2}{15} \Rightarrow A : D = 2 : 15.$

37. $3A = 5B$ and $4B = 6C \Rightarrow \frac{A}{B} = \frac{5}{3}$ and $\frac{B}{C} = \frac{6}{4} = \frac{3}{2}$

$\Rightarrow \frac{A}{C} = \left(\frac{A}{B} \times \frac{B}{C}\right) = \frac{5}{3} \times \frac{3}{2} = \frac{5}{2} \Rightarrow A : C = 5 : 2.$

38. $1S = 4C$ and $3C = 4D \Rightarrow \frac{S}{C} = \frac{4}{1}$ and $\frac{C}{D} = \frac{4}{3}$

$\Rightarrow \frac{S}{D} = \left(\frac{S}{C} \times \frac{C}{D}\right) = \frac{4}{1} \times \frac{4}{3} = \frac{16}{3} \Rightarrow S : D = 16 : 3.$

39. $\frac{A}{B} = \frac{2}{1},\ \frac{B}{C} = \frac{4}{3},\ \frac{C}{D} = \frac{5}{6} \Rightarrow \frac{A}{D}$

$= \left(\frac{A}{B} \times \frac{B}{C} \times \frac{C}{D}\right) = \left(\frac{2}{1} \times \frac{4}{3} \times \frac{5}{6}\right) = \frac{20}{9}$

$\Rightarrow A : D = 20 : 9.$

40. $A : B = 7 : 9$ and $B : C = 5 : 4 = \left(5 \times \frac{9}{5}\right) : \left(4 \times \frac{9}{5}\right) = 9 : \frac{36}{5}.$

$\Rightarrow A : B : C = 7 : 9 : \frac{36}{5} = 35 : 45 : 36.$

41. $A : B = 2 : 3,\ B : C = 4 : 5 = \left(4 \times \frac{3}{4}\right) : \left(5 \times \frac{3}{4}\right) = 3 : \frac{15}{4},$

$C : D = 6 : 7 = \left(6 \times \frac{5}{8}\right) : \left(7 \times \frac{5}{8}\right) = \frac{15}{4} : \frac{35}{8}.$

$\Rightarrow A : B : C : D = 2 : 3 : \frac{15}{4} : \frac{35}{8} = 16 : 24 : 30 : 35.$

42. $A : B = \frac{1}{2} : \frac{1}{3} = 3 : 2,$

$B : C = \frac{1}{2} : \frac{1}{3} = 3 : 2 = \left(3 \times \frac{2}{3}\right) : \left(2 \times \frac{2}{3}\right) = 2 : \frac{4}{3}.$

$\Rightarrow A : B : C = 3 : 2 : \frac{4}{3} = 9 : 6 : 4.$

43. $A : B = \frac{1}{2} : \frac{3}{8} = 4 : 3,\ B : C = \frac{1}{3} : \frac{5}{9} = 3 : 5,$

$C : D = \frac{5}{6} : \frac{3}{4} = 10 : 9 = 5 : \frac{9}{2}.$

$\therefore\ A : B : C : D = 4 : 3 : 5 : \frac{9}{2} = 8 : 6 : 10 : 9.$

44. $R : S = 200 : 20 = 10 : 1,\ S : A = 400 : 150 = 8 : 3$

$= \left(8 \times \frac{1}{8}\right) : \left(3 \times \frac{1}{8}\right) = 1 : \frac{3}{8}.$

$\therefore\ R : S : A = 10 : 1 : \frac{3}{8} = 80 : 8 : 3.$

45. Let the consequent be x. Then, $\frac{7}{8} = \frac{35}{x} \Rightarrow 7x = 35 \times 8$

$\Rightarrow x = \frac{35 \times 8}{7} = 40.$

46. $8a = 9b \Rightarrow a = \frac{9}{8}b.\ \therefore\ \frac{a}{9} : \frac{b}{8} = \frac{\left(\frac{9}{8}b\right)}{9} : \frac{b}{8} = \frac{b}{8} : \frac{b}{8} = 1 : 1.$

47. $\frac{x}{y}=\frac{3}{4} \Rightarrow \frac{2x+3y}{3y-2x}=\frac{2\left(\frac{x}{y}\right)+3}{3-2\left(\frac{x}{y}\right)}=\frac{2\times\frac{3}{4}+3}{3-2\times\frac{3}{4}}=\frac{9}{2}\times\frac{2}{3}=3$

$\Rightarrow (2x + 3y) : (3y - 2x) = 3 : 1.$

48. $\frac{a}{b}=\frac{2}{5} \Rightarrow \frac{2a+3b}{7a+5b}=\frac{2\left(\frac{a}{b}\right)+3}{7\left(\frac{a}{b}\right)+5}=\frac{2\times\frac{2}{5}+3}{7\times\frac{2}{5}+5}=\frac{19}{5}\times\frac{5}{39}=\frac{19}{39}$

$\Rightarrow (2a + 3b) : (7a + 5b) = 19 : 39.$

49. $\frac{x}{y}=\frac{3}{2} \Rightarrow \frac{x^2}{y^2}=\frac{9}{4} \Rightarrow \frac{2x^2+3y^2}{3x^2-2y^2}$

$=\frac{2\left(\frac{x^2}{y^2}\right)+3}{3\left(\frac{x^2}{y^2}\right)-2}=\frac{2\times\frac{9}{4}+3}{3\times\frac{9}{4}-2}=\frac{15}{2}\times\frac{4}{19}=\frac{30}{19}$

$\Rightarrow (2x^2 + 3y^2) : (3x^2 - 2y^2) = 30 : 19.$

50. $\frac{x}{y}=\frac{3}{1} \Rightarrow \frac{x^3}{y^3}=\frac{27}{1} \Rightarrow \frac{x^3-y^3}{x^3+y^3}=\frac{\left(\frac{x^3}{y^3}\right)-1}{\left(\frac{x^3}{y^3}\right)+1}=\frac{27-1}{27+1}=\frac{26}{28}=\frac{13}{14}$

$\Rightarrow (x^3 - y^3) : (x^3 + y^3) = 13 : 14.$

51. $\frac{5a+3b}{2a-3b}=\frac{23}{5} \Rightarrow 5\,(5a + 3b) = 23\,(2a - 3b)$

$\Rightarrow 25a + 15b = 46a - 69b \Rightarrow 21a = 84b \Rightarrow \frac{a}{b}=4.$

Hence, $a : b = 4 : 1$.

52. $\frac{x}{y}=\frac{7}{3} \Rightarrow \frac{xy+y^2}{x^2-y^2}=\frac{\left(\frac{x}{y}\right)+1}{\left(\frac{x^2}{y^2}\right)-1}=\frac{\frac{7}{3}+1}{\left(\frac{7}{3}\right)^2-1}=\frac{10}{3}\times\frac{9}{40}=\frac{3}{4}.$

53. $\frac{a}{b}=\frac{4}{5}$ and $\frac{b}{c}=\frac{15}{16} \Rightarrow \frac{a}{c}=\frac{a}{b}\times\frac{b}{c}=\frac{4}{5}\times\frac{15}{16}=\frac{3}{4} \Rightarrow \frac{c}{a}=\frac{4}{3}$

$\Rightarrow \frac{c^2}{a^2}=\frac{16}{9} \Rightarrow \frac{c^2-a^2}{c^2+a^2}=\frac{\frac{c^2}{a^2}-1}{\frac{c^2}{a^2}+1}=\frac{\frac{16}{9}-1}{\frac{16}{9}+1}=\frac{7}{9}\times\frac{9}{25}=\frac{7}{25}.$

54. $\frac{a}{b}=\frac{b}{c} \Rightarrow b^2=ac \Rightarrow \frac{a^4}{b^4}=\frac{a^4}{(ac)^2}=\frac{a^4}{a^2c^2}=\frac{a^2}{c^2}$

$\Rightarrow a^4 : b^4 = a^2 : c^2.$

55. $\frac{4x^2-3y^2}{2x^2+5y^2}=\frac{12}{19} \Rightarrow 19\,(4x^2 - 3y^2) = 12\,(2x^2 + 5y^2)$

$\Rightarrow 76x^2 - 57y^2 = 24x^2 + 60y^2$

$\Rightarrow 52x^2 = 117y^2 \Rightarrow 4x^2 = 9y^2$

$\Rightarrow \frac{x^2}{y^2}=\frac{9}{4} \Rightarrow \left(\frac{x}{y}\right)^2=\left(\frac{3}{2}\right)^2 \Rightarrow \frac{x}{y}=\frac{3}{2}.$

$\therefore x : y = 3 : 2.$

56. $\frac{x}{y}=\frac{3}{4}$ and $\frac{a}{b}=\frac{1}{2} \Rightarrow \frac{xa}{yb}=\frac{3}{4}\times\frac{1}{2}=\frac{3}{8}$

$\Rightarrow \frac{2xa+yb}{3yb-4xa}=\frac{2\left(\frac{xa}{yb}\right)+1}{3-4\left(\frac{xa}{yb}\right)}=\frac{2\times\frac{3}{8}+1}{3-4\times\frac{3}{8}}=\frac{7}{4}\times\frac{2}{3}=\frac{7}{6}.$

57. $a : b : c = 2 : 3 : 4 \Rightarrow \frac{1}{a}:\frac{1}{b}:\frac{1}{c}=\frac{1}{2}:\frac{1}{3}:\frac{1}{4} = 6 : 4 : 3.$

58. $\frac{1}{x}:\frac{1}{y}:\frac{1}{z} = 2 : 3 : 5 \Rightarrow x : y : z = \frac{1}{2}:\frac{1}{3}:\frac{1}{5} = 15 : 10 : 6.$

59. $\frac{(x+y)}{(x-y)}=4 \Rightarrow x + y = 4x - 4y \Rightarrow 3x = 5y$

$\Rightarrow \frac{x}{y}=\frac{5}{3}$

$\Rightarrow \frac{x^2}{y^2}=\frac{25}{9} \Rightarrow \frac{x^2+y^2}{x^2-y^2}=\frac{\frac{x^2}{y^2}+1}{\frac{x^2}{y^2}-1}=\frac{\frac{25}{9}+1}{\frac{25}{9}-1}=\frac{34}{9}\times\frac{9}{16}=\frac{17}{8}.$

$\therefore (x^2 + y^2) : (x^2 - y^2) = 17 : 8.$

60. $\frac{a}{b+c}=\frac{1}{3} \Rightarrow a=\frac{b+c}{3}.$

$\frac{c}{a+b}=\frac{5}{7} \Rightarrow 7c=5a+5b=\frac{5\,(b+c)}{3}+5b$

$\Rightarrow 7c-\frac{5}{3}c=5b+\frac{5}{3}b \Rightarrow \frac{16c}{3}=\frac{20b}{3}$

$\Rightarrow 16c = 20b \Rightarrow b=\frac{4}{5}c.$

$a=\frac{b+c}{3}=\frac{\frac{4}{5}c+c}{3}=\frac{9c}{5}\times\frac{1}{3}=\frac{3}{5}c.$

$\therefore \frac{b}{a+c}=\frac{\left(\frac{4}{5}c\right)}{\left(\frac{3}{5}c+c\right)}=\frac{4c}{5}\times\frac{5}{8c}=\frac{1}{2}=1:2.$

61. $a : b = 3 : 4,\ b : c = 4 : 7 \Rightarrow a : b : c = 3 : 4 : 7.$

Let $a = 3k,\ b = 4k,\ c = 7k$.

Then, $\frac{a+b+c}{c}=\frac{3k+4k+7k}{7k}=\frac{14k}{7k}=2.$

62. Let $A = 2k,\ B = 3k,\ C = 5k$.

$A = x\%$ of $(B + C) \Rightarrow 2k = x\%$ of $(3k + 5k) = x\%$ of $8k$

$\Rightarrow \frac{x}{100}=\frac{2k}{8k}=\frac{1}{4} \Rightarrow x=\frac{100}{4}=25.$

63. Let $\frac{x}{y}=\frac{y}{z}=\frac{z}{u}=k$. Now, $\frac{x}{u}=\frac{64}{27} \Rightarrow \frac{x}{y}\times\frac{y}{z}\times\frac{z}{u}=\frac{64}{27}$

$\Rightarrow k^3=\left(\frac{4}{3}\right)^3 \Rightarrow k=\frac{4}{3}.$

So, $x : y = y : z = z : u = 4 : 3.$

$\therefore \frac{x}{z}=\frac{x}{y}\times\frac{y}{z}=\frac{4}{3}\times\frac{4}{3}=\frac{16}{9}.$

64. Let $a = 2k$, $b = 3k$, $c = 4k$.

Then, $2a - 3b + 4c = 33$

$\Rightarrow 2 \times 2k - 3 \times 3k + 4 \times 4k = 33$

$\Rightarrow 4k - 9k + 16k = 33$

$\Rightarrow 11k = 33 \Rightarrow k = 3$.

$\therefore c = 4k = 4 \times 3 = 12$.

65. Let $p = k$, $q = 2k$, $r = 4k$.

Then, $\sqrt{5p^2 + q^2 + r^2} = \sqrt{5k^2 + (2k)^2 + (4k)^2}$

$= \sqrt{5k^2 + 4k^2 + 16k^2} = \sqrt{25k^2} = 5k = 5p$.

66. Let $A = 2k$, $B = 3k$, $C = 4k$.

Then, $\frac{A}{B} = \frac{2k}{3k} = \frac{2}{3}, \frac{B}{C} = \frac{3k}{4k} = \frac{3}{4}, \frac{C}{A} = \frac{4k}{2k} = 2$

$\Rightarrow \frac{A}{B} : \frac{B}{C} : \frac{C}{A} = \frac{2}{3} : \frac{3}{4} : 2 = 8 : 9 : 24$.

67. Let $a = 5k$, $b = 7k$. Then, $c = 2 \times 5k = 10k$, $d = 3 \times 7k = 21k$.

$ac : bd = 5k \times 10k : 7k \times 21k$

$= 50k^2 : 147k^2 = 50 : 147$.

68. Let $\frac{a}{b} = \frac{b}{c} = \frac{c}{d} = k$. Then, $a = bk$, $b = ck$, $c = dk$.

Also, $\frac{a}{b} \times \frac{b}{c} \times \frac{c}{d} = k^3 \Rightarrow k^3 = \frac{a}{d}$.

$\therefore \frac{b^3 + c^3 + d^3}{a^3 + b^3 + c^3} = \frac{b^3 + c^3 + d^3}{(bk)^3 + (ck)^3 + (dk)^3}$

$= \frac{b^3 + c^3 + d^3}{k^3 (b^3 + c^3 + d^3)} = \frac{1}{k^3} = \frac{d}{a}$.

69. $\frac{p}{q} = \frac{3}{4}, \frac{r}{s} = \frac{8}{5}, \frac{x}{y} = \frac{10}{6} \Rightarrow p = \frac{3q}{4}, r = \frac{8s}{5}, x = \frac{5y}{3}$.

$\therefore \frac{psx}{qry} = \frac{\frac{3q}{4} \times s \times \frac{5y}{3}}{q \times \frac{8s}{5} \times y} = \frac{\frac{5}{4} qsy}{\frac{8}{5} qsy} = \frac{5}{4} \times \frac{5}{8} = \frac{25}{32}$.

70. Let $\frac{x}{2} = \frac{y}{3} = \frac{z}{4} = l$. Then, $x = 2l$, $y = 3l$, $z = 4l$.

$\therefore \frac{x}{2} = \frac{2x - 3y + 5z}{k} \Rightarrow \frac{2l}{2} = \frac{2 \times 2l - 3 \times 3l + 5 \times 4l}{k}$

$\Rightarrow k = 4 - 9 + 20 = 15$.

71. Let $\frac{a}{b} = \frac{c}{d} = k$. Then, $a = bk$, $c = dk$.

$\therefore \frac{ma + nc}{mb + nd} = \frac{mbk + ndk}{mb + nd} = \frac{k(mb + nd)}{(mb + nd)} = k = \frac{a}{b}$.

72. $\frac{x}{y} = \frac{\left(\frac{a}{b}\right)}{\left(-\frac{b}{a}\right)} = -\frac{a^2}{b^2} \Rightarrow y = \left(-\frac{b^2}{a^2}\right) x$.

$\therefore x - y = \frac{a}{b} + \frac{b}{a} \Rightarrow x + \frac{b^2}{a^2} x = \frac{a^2 + b^2}{ab}$

$\Rightarrow x \left(\frac{a^2 + b^2}{a^2}\right) = \frac{a^2 + b^2}{ab} \Rightarrow x = \frac{a^2}{ab} = \frac{a}{b}$.

73. $a + b = ck$, $b + c = ak$, $c + a = bk$.

Adding, we get : $2(a + b + c) = ak + bk + ck$

$= k(a + b + c)$ or $k = 2$.

74. $a : b = 2 : 3$, $b : c = 4 : 5 = 4 \times \frac{3}{4} : 5 \times \frac{3}{4} = 3 : \frac{15}{4}$.

So, $a : b : c = 2 : 3 : \frac{15}{4} = 8 : 12 : 15$.

Let $a = 8k$, $b = 12k$, $c = 15k$. Then, $\frac{(a + b)}{(b + c)} = \frac{(8k + 12k)}{(12k + 15k)} = \frac{20k}{27k} = \frac{20}{27}$.

75. $\frac{a}{b} = \frac{c}{d} = \frac{e}{f} = \frac{1}{2} \Rightarrow b = 2a$, $d = 2c$, $f = 2e$.

$\frac{3a + 5c + 7e}{3b + 5d + 7f} = \frac{3a + 5c + 7e}{3 \times 2a + 5 \times 2c + 7 \times 2e}$

$= \frac{3a + 5c + 7e}{2(3a + 5c + 7e)} = \frac{1}{2}$.

76. $a : b = 5 : 3$, $b : c = 2 : 5 = \left(2 \times \frac{3}{2}\right) : \left(5 \times \frac{3}{2}\right) = 3 : \frac{15}{2}$.

So, $a : b : c = 5 : 3 : \frac{15}{2} = 10 : 6 : 15$.

Clearly, $b < a < c$.

77. Let $a = 10x$, $b = 6x$, $c = 15x$. Then, $15x = 50$ or $x = \frac{10}{3}$.

$\therefore a + b + c = 10x + 6x + 15x = 31x$

$= \left(31 \times \frac{10}{3}\right) = 103.33 > 103$.

78. $(c - a) = (15x - 10x) = 5x$.

I. $10(a + c) = 10(10x + 15x) = 10 \times 25x = 250x$.

II. $10a + 25b = 10 \times 10x + 25 \times 6x = 100x + 150x = 250x$.

79. Let $a + b = 6k$, $b + c = 7k$ and $c + a = 8k$.

Adding, we get : $2(a + b + c) = 21k \Rightarrow 2 \times 14 = 21k$

$\Rightarrow k = \frac{28}{21} = \frac{4}{3}$.

So, $a + b = 6k = 6 \times \frac{4}{3} = 8$.

$\therefore c = (a + b + c) - (a + b) = 14 - 8 = 6$.

80. Let the fourth proportional to 5, 8, 15 be x.

Then, $5 : 8 :: 15 : x \Leftrightarrow 5x = 8 \times 15 \Leftrightarrow x = \frac{8 \times 15}{5} = 24$.

81. Let the fourth proportional to 0.12, 0.21 and 8 be x.

Then, $0.12 : 0.21 :: 8 : x \Leftrightarrow 0.12x = 0.21 \times 8$

$\Leftrightarrow x = \frac{0.21 \times 8}{0.12} = \frac{21 \times 8}{12} = 14$.

82. Let the fourth proportional to $(a^2 - b^2)$, $(a^2 - ab)$, $(a^3 + b^3)$ be x.

Then, $(a^2 - b^2) : (a^2 - ab) :: (a^3 + b^3) : x$

$\Leftrightarrow (a^2 - b^2)\, x = (a^3 + b^3)(a^2 - ab)$

$\Leftrightarrow x = \frac{(a^3+b^3)(a^2-ab)}{(a^2-b^2)} = \frac{(a+b)(a^2-ab+b^2)\,a\,(a-b)}{(a-b)(a+b)}$
$= a(a^2 - ab + b^2)$.

83. Let the third proportional to 38 and 15 be x.

Then, $38 : 15 :: 15 : x \Leftrightarrow 38x = 15 \times 15 \Leftrightarrow x = \frac{15 \times 15}{38}$.

84. Let the third proportional to $(x^2 - y^2)$ and $(x - y)$ be t.
Then, $(x^2 - y^2) : (x - y) :: (x - y) : t$

$\Leftrightarrow (x^2-y^2)t = (x-y)^2 \Leftrightarrow t = \frac{(x-y)^2}{(x^2-y^2)} = \frac{(x-y)(x-y)}{(x-y)(x+y)} = \frac{(x-y)}{(x+y)}$.

85. Required mean proportional $= \sqrt{234 \times 104}$
$= \sqrt{13 \times 9 \times 2 \times 13 \times 8} = 13 \times 3 \times 4 = 156$.

86. Required mean proportional $= \sqrt{0.02 \times 0.32}$
$= \sqrt{0.0064} = 0.08$.

87. Required mean proportional $= \sqrt{(3+\sqrt{2})(12-\sqrt{32})}$
$= \sqrt{(3+\sqrt{2})(12-4\sqrt{2})}$
$= \sqrt{36-8} = \sqrt{28} = 2\sqrt{7}$.

88. Let the third proportional to 12 and 30 be x.
Then, $12 : 30 :: 30 : x \Leftrightarrow 12x = 30 \times 30$

$\Leftrightarrow x = \frac{(30 \times 30)}{12} = 75$.

$\therefore$ Third proportional to 12 and 30 = 75.
Mean proportional between 9 and 25 $= \sqrt{9 \times 25} = 15$.

$\therefore$ Required ratio = 75 : 15 = 5 : 1.

89. Duplicate ratio of $2a : 6b = (2a)^2 : (6b)^2$
$= 4a^2 : 36b^2 = a^2 : 9b^2$.

Reciprocal ratio of $4a^2 : 25b^2 = \frac{1}{4a^2} : \frac{1}{25b^2} = 25b^2 : 4a^2$.

$\therefore$ Required product $= \frac{a^2}{9b^2} \times \frac{25b^2}{4a^2} = \frac{25}{36}$.

90. Let the two numbers be x and y.
Then, $\sqrt{xy} = 12$ and $x : y :: y : 324$
$\Rightarrow xy = (12)^2 = 144$ and $y^2 = 324x$

$\Rightarrow x = \frac{144}{y}$ and $y^2 = 324 \times \frac{144}{y}$

$\Rightarrow y^3 = 324 \times 144 = (6 \times 3 \times 2)^3 \Rightarrow y = 6 \times 3 \times 2 = 36$

$\Rightarrow x = \frac{144}{36} = 4$.

Hence, the two numbers are 4 and 36.

91. A : B : C = 8 : 14 : 22, B : C : D = 21 : 33 : 44

$= \left(21 \times \frac{2}{3}\right) : \left(33 \times \frac{2}{3}\right) : \left(44 \times \frac{2}{3}\right) = 14 : 22 : \frac{88}{3}$.

$\therefore A : B : C : D = 8 : 14 : 22 : \frac{88}{3} = 24 : 42 : 66 : 88$
$= 12 : 21 : 33 : 44$.

92. Let the numbers be x and y.
Then, $y - 30\%$ of $x = \frac{4}{5}y \Rightarrow y - \frac{4}{5}y = \frac{30}{100}x \Rightarrow \frac{y}{5} = \frac{3x}{10}$

$\Rightarrow \frac{x}{y} = \frac{1}{5} \times \frac{10}{3} = \frac{2}{3} \Rightarrow x : y = 2 : 3$.

93. Abhinav's investment = ₹ 6000.
Sunil's investment = (100 − 30)% of ₹ 6000 = 70% of ₹ 6000 = ₹ $\left(\frac{70}{100} \times 6000\right)$ = ₹ 4200.

Rita's investment = (100 + 25)% of ₹ 4200 = 125% of ₹ 4200 = ₹ $\left(\frac{125}{100} \times 4200\right)$ = ₹ 5250.

Total amount invested = ₹ (6000 + 4200 + 5250)
= ₹ 15450.

$\therefore$ Required ratio = 5250 : 15450 = 35 : 103.

94. Let the numbers be x and y.

Then, $\frac{1}{4}$ of (60% of x) $= \frac{2}{5}$ of (20% of y)

$\Rightarrow \left(\frac{1}{4} \times \frac{60}{100} \times x\right) = \left(\frac{2}{5} \times \frac{20}{100} \times y\right) \Rightarrow \frac{3x}{20} = \frac{2y}{25}$

$\Rightarrow \frac{x}{y} = \frac{2}{25} \times \frac{20}{3} = \frac{8}{15} \Rightarrow x : y = 8 : 15$.

95. Let the number of girls be x.

Then, number of boys = 116% of $x = \frac{29}{25}x$.

$\therefore$ Required ratio $= \frac{29}{25}x : x = 29 : 25$.

96. Ratio for different heights (Section A : Section B) is as under:

$1.55 \to \frac{3}{2} = 1.5$; $1.60 \to \frac{7}{6} = 1.16$; $1.62 \to \frac{12}{14} = \frac{6}{7} = 0.86$;

$1.65 \to \frac{15}{14} = 1.07$; $1.68 \to \frac{8}{9} = 0.89$; $1.71 \to \frac{6}{5} = 1.2$;

$1.75 \to \frac{3}{4} = 0.75$.

97. Number of people having characteristic
X = (10 + 30) = 40.
Number of people having characteristic
Y = (10 + 20) = 30.
$\therefore$ Required ratio = 40 : 30 = 4 : 3.

98. $5M + 4O = 3M + 7O \Rightarrow 2M = 3O \Rightarrow \frac{M}{O} = \frac{3}{2}$

99. Required percentage
$= \left(\frac{7}{7+3} \times 100\right)\% = \left(\frac{7}{10} \times 100\right)\% = 70\%$.

100. $4A = 6B = 11C = k$ (say).

Then, $A = \frac{k}{4}$, $B = \frac{k}{6}$, $C = \frac{k}{11}$

$\Rightarrow A : B : C = \frac{1}{4} : \frac{1}{6} : \frac{1}{11} = 33 : 22 : 12$.

101. Required ratio = 120% of ₹ 30 : 110% of ₹ 20
= 36 : 22 = 18 : 11.

102. Ratio of the monthly incomes of families A and B
= Ratio of the areas of rectangles A and B
$= 5 \times 2 : 4 \times 1 = 10 : 4 = 5 : 2$.
Let the monthly income of family A be ₹ x.
Then, $5 : 2 :: x : 12000 \Leftrightarrow 2x = 5 \times 12000 = 60000$
$\Leftrightarrow x = \frac{60000}{2} = 30000$.

103. Let the number of boys be x. Then, number of girls
$= 120\%$ of $x = \frac{6x}{5}$.
$\therefore\ x + \frac{6x}{5} = 66 \Rightarrow \frac{11x}{5} = 66 \Rightarrow x = \frac{66 \times 5}{11} = 30.$
So, number of boys = 30. And, new number of girls
$= \left(\frac{6 \times 30}{5}\right) + 4 = 40.$
$\therefore$ Required ratio = 30 : 40 = 3 : 4.

104. Let C's income be ₹ x. Then, B's income = 80% of ₹ x = ₹$\left(\frac{4x}{5}\right)$.
A's income = 110% of ₹$\left(\frac{4x}{5}\right)$ = ₹$\left(\frac{110}{100} \times \frac{4x}{5}\right)$ = ₹$\left(\frac{22x}{25}\right)$.
$\therefore\ A : B : C = \frac{22x}{25} : \frac{4x}{5} : x = 22 : 20 : 25.$

105. Let the third number be x. Then, first number = 120% of $x = \frac{120}{100}x = \frac{6x}{5}$
And, second number = 150% of $x = \frac{150}{100}x = \frac{3x}{2}$.
$\therefore$ Required ratio $= \frac{6x}{5} : \frac{3x}{2} = 12 : 15 = 4 : 5.$

106. Let the terms of the ratio be x and $x + 40$.
Then, $\frac{x}{x+40} = \frac{2}{7} \Rightarrow 7x = 2x + 80 \Rightarrow 5x = 80 \Rightarrow x = 16.$
$\therefore$ Required ratio = 16 : 56.

107. $A + B = 16000,\ B = A - 4000 \Rightarrow A + (A - 4000) = 16000$
$\Rightarrow 2A = 20000 \Rightarrow A = 10000.$
So, $A = 10000,\ B = 6000.$
$\therefore\ A : B = 10000 : 6000 = 5 : 3.$

108. $x : \frac{1}{27} :: \frac{3}{11} : \frac{5}{9} \Rightarrow \frac{5}{9}x = \frac{1}{27} \times \frac{3}{11} = \frac{1}{99} \Rightarrow x = \frac{1}{99} \times \frac{9}{5} = \frac{1}{55}.$

109. Required ratio $= \frac{3}{4}x : \frac{5}{6}x = \frac{3}{4} : \frac{5}{6} = 9 : 10.$

110. Ratio of the expenditures of A, B, C and D are as under :
$A \rightarrow \frac{18}{40} = \frac{9}{20} = 0.45\ ;\ B \rightarrow \frac{21}{50} = 0.42\ ;$
$C \rightarrow \frac{24}{60} = \frac{2}{5} = 0.4\ ;\ D \rightarrow \frac{27}{70} = 0.385.$
Clearly, A has done the highest expenditure proportionate to his resources.

111. Let the two numbers be x and y.
$\frac{x+y}{2} : x = 3 : 5 \Rightarrow \frac{x+y}{2x} = \frac{3}{5} \Rightarrow 5x + 5y = 6x$
$\Rightarrow x = 5y \Rightarrow \frac{x}{y} = \frac{5}{1}.$
$\therefore$ Ratio of smaller number to larger number = 1 : 5.

112. Seema's share = ₹$\left(25000 \times \frac{3}{5}\right)$ = ₹ 15000. Meena's share = ₹$\left(25000 \times \frac{2}{5}\right)$ = ₹ 10000.
$\therefore$ Required ratio = (15000 + 5000) : (10000 + 5000)
= 20000 : 15000 = 4 : 3.

113. Number of successful candidates $= \left(\frac{9}{11} \times 132\right) = 108.$
Number of unsuccessful candidates $= \left(\frac{2}{11} \times 132\right) = 24.$
$\therefore$ Required ratio = (108 + 4) : (24 – 4) = 112 : 20 = 28 : 5.

114. Second son's share = ₹$\left(10800 \times \frac{4}{12}\right)$ = ₹ 3600.
Money distributed between the two daughters
= ₹ [3600 – (1000 + 600)] = ₹ 2000.
First daughter's share = ₹$\left(2000 \times \frac{11}{20}\right)$ = ₹ 1100.
Second daughter's share = ₹$\left(2000 \times \frac{9}{20}\right)$ = ₹ 900.

115. Sum of the angles of a triangle = 180°.
$\therefore$ Largest angle $= \left(180 \times \frac{5}{12}\right)^\circ = 75°.$

116. $x : y : z = 2 : 3 : 5.$
$\therefore\ x = \left(100 \times \frac{2}{10}\right) = 20;\ y = \left(100 \times \frac{3}{10}\right) = 30.$
$y = px - 10 \Rightarrow 30 = 20p - 10 \Rightarrow 20p = 40 \Rightarrow p = 2.$

117. When marbles are shared in the ratio 1 : 2 : 3
A's share $= \left(60 \times \frac{1}{6}\right) = 10$; B's share $= \left(60 \times \frac{2}{6}\right) = 20$;
C's share $= \left(60 \times \frac{3}{6}\right) = 30.$
When marbles are shared in the ratio 3 : 4 : 5
A's share $= \left(60 \times \frac{3}{12}\right) = 15$; B's share $= \left(60 \times \frac{4}{12}\right) = 20$;
C's share $= \left(60 \times \frac{5}{12}\right) = 25.$
Clearly, 5 marbles have been transferred from C to A.

118. Let C's share = ₹ x. Then, B's share = ₹ $(x + 8)$; A's share = ₹ $(x + 15)$.
So, $(x + 15) + (x + 8) + x = 53$
$\Rightarrow 3x = 30 \Rightarrow x = 10.$
$\therefore\ A : B : C = (x + 15) : (x + 8) : x = 25 : 18 : 10.$

119. Let the total sum be ₹ x.
Then, smallest share = ₹$\left(\frac{3}{12}x\right)$ = ₹$\frac{x}{4}$.
$\therefore$ Larger share of the two = ₹$\left(\frac{x}{4} \times \frac{2}{3}\right)$ = ₹$\frac{x}{6}$.

120. Let the second amount be ₹ x.

Then, A's share from first amount $= ₹\left(150000 \times \frac{2}{10}\right) = ₹\ 30000.$

A's share from second amount $= ₹\left(x \times \frac{5}{10}\right) = ₹\ \frac{x}{2}.$

$\therefore\ \frac{x}{2} = 30000$ or $x = 60000.$

Required ratio = 150000 : 60000 = 5 : 2.

121. Quantity of copper in 17.5 kg of alloy $= \left(17.5 \times \frac{5}{7}\right)$ kg $= 12.5$ kg.

Quantity of zinc in 17.5 kg of alloy $= \left(17.5 \times \frac{2}{7}\right)$ kg $= 5$ kg.

$\therefore$ Required ratio = 12.5 : (5 + 1.25) = 12.5 : 6.25 = 2 : 1.

122. $A + B = 100,\ A = B + 30 \Rightarrow (B + 30) + B = 100$
$\Rightarrow 2B = 70 \Rightarrow B = 35 \Rightarrow A = (100 - 35) = 65.$
$A : B = 65 : 35 = 13 : 7.$

$\therefore\ B$'s share $= ₹\left(650 \times \frac{7}{20}\right) = ₹\ 227.50.$

123. $B = 75\%$ of $C = \frac{3}{4}C$; $A = 125\%$ of

$B = 125\%$ of $\frac{3}{4}C = \left(\frac{5}{4} \times \frac{3}{4}C\right) = \frac{15}{16}C.$

$\therefore\ A : B : C = \frac{15}{16}C : \frac{3}{4}C : C = 15 : 12 : 16.$

Sum of ratio terms = (15 + 12 + 16) = 43.

C's share $= ₹\left(731 \times \frac{16}{43}\right) = ₹\ 272.$

124. Ratio of shares $= \frac{3}{5} : 2 : \frac{5}{3} = 9 : 30 : 25.$

Second worker's share $= ₹\left(6400 \times \frac{30}{64}\right) = ₹\ 3000.$

125. $A : B = \frac{a}{b} : \frac{c}{d} = \left(\frac{a}{b} \times bd\right) : \left(\frac{c}{d} \times bd\right) = ad : bc.$

$\therefore\ A$'s share $= ₹\left(\frac{adx}{ad + bc}\right).$

126. Let $\frac{1}{2}D = \frac{1}{4}W = \frac{1}{5}S = k$. Then, $D = 2k$, $W = 4k$, $S = 5k$.

So, $D : W : S = 2k : 4k : 5k = 2 : 4 : 5.$

$\therefore$ Daughter's share $= ₹\left(165000 \times \frac{2}{11}\right) = ₹\ 30000.$

127. $A = \frac{2}{9}B,\ C = \frac{3}{4}A = \left(\frac{3}{4} \times \frac{2}{9}\right)B = \frac{1}{6}B.$

$A : B : C = \frac{2}{9}B : B : \frac{1}{6}B = 4 : 18 : 3.$

C's share $= ₹\left(1250 \times \frac{3}{25}\right) = ₹\ 150.$

128. When money is divided in ratio of $\frac{1}{2} : \frac{1}{3} : \frac{1}{4}$

Ratio of shares $= \frac{1}{2} : \frac{1}{3} : \frac{1}{4} = 6 : 4 : 3.$

P's share $= ₹\left(117 \times \frac{6}{13}\right) = ₹\ 54;$

Q's share $= ₹\left(117 \times \frac{4}{13}\right) = ₹\ 36;$

R's share $= ₹\left(117 \times \frac{3}{13}\right) = ₹\ 27.$

When money is divided in ratio of 2 : 3 : 4

P's share $= ₹\left(117 \times \frac{2}{9}\right) = ₹\ 26;$

Q's share $= ₹\left(117 \times \frac{3}{9}\right) = ₹\ 39;$

R's share $= ₹\left(117 \times \frac{4}{9}\right) = ₹\ 52.$

Clearly, both Q and R gained in the transaction.

129. $A : B = 3 : 7,\ B : C = 6 : 5 = \left(6 \times \frac{7}{6}\right) : \left(5 \times \frac{7}{6}\right) = 7 : \frac{35}{6}.$

$A : B : C = 3 : 7 : \frac{35}{6}$

$= 18 : 42 : 35.$ Sum of ratio terms $= (18 + 42 + 35) = 95.$

$\therefore\ B$'s share $= ₹\left(33630 \times \frac{42}{95}\right) = ₹\ 14868.$

130. $A : B = 3 : 2,\ B : C = 3 : 2 = \left(3 \times \frac{2}{3}\right) : \left(2 \times \frac{2}{3}\right) = 2 : \frac{4}{3}.$

$A : B : C = 3 : 2 : \frac{4}{3} = 9 : 6 : 4.$

$\therefore\ A$'s score $= \left(361 \times \frac{9}{19}\right) = 171.$

131. $A : B = 2 : 3,\ B : C = 4 : 5 = \left(4 \times \frac{3}{4}\right) : \left(5 \times \frac{3}{4}\right) = 3 : \frac{15}{4},$

$C : D = 6 : 7 = \left(6 \times \frac{5}{8}\right) : \left(7 \times \frac{5}{8}\right) = \frac{15}{4} : \frac{35}{8}$

$A : B : C : D = 2 : 3 : \frac{15}{4} : \frac{35}{8} = 16 : 24 : 30 : 35.$

Sum of ratio terms = (16 + 24 + 30 + 35) = 105.

$\therefore\ A$'s share $= ₹\left(8400 \times \frac{16}{105}\right) = ₹\ 1280.$

132. $P : Q = 2 : 3,\ Q : R = 2 : 3 = \left(2 \times \frac{3}{2}\right) : \left(3 \times \frac{3}{2}\right) = 3 : \frac{9}{2},$

$R : S = 2 : 3 = \left(2 \times \frac{9}{4}\right) : \left(3 \times \frac{9}{4}\right) = \frac{9}{2} : \frac{27}{4}.$

$\therefore\ P : Q : R : S = 2 : 3 : \frac{9}{2} : \frac{27}{4} = 8 : 12 : 18 : 27.$

Sum of ratio terms = (8 + 12 + 18 + 27) = 65.

P's share $= ₹\left(1300 \times \frac{8}{65}\right) = ₹\ 160.$

133. Second : Third = 9 : 16, Third : First = 4 : 1 = 16 : 4.

$\therefore$ Second : Third : First = 9 : 16 : 4.

Second number = $\left(116 \times \frac{9}{29}\right) = 36$.

134. $A : B = 5 : 12$,

$B : C = 4 : 5.50 = 12 : 16.5 = 12 : \frac{33}{2}$.

$A : B : C = 5 : 12 : \frac{33}{2} = 10 : 24 : 33$.

Sum of ratio terms = 10 + 24 + 33 = 67.

C's share = ₹ $\left(2010 \times \frac{33}{67}\right)$ = ₹ 990.

B's share = ₹ $\left(2010 \times \frac{24}{67}\right)$ = ₹ 720.

Required difference = ₹ (990 – 720) = ₹ 270.

135. $\frac{2}{5}A + 40 = \frac{2}{7}B + 20$

$\Rightarrow \frac{2}{7}B = \frac{2}{5}A + 20 \Rightarrow B = \frac{7}{2}\left(\frac{2}{5}A + 20\right) = \frac{7}{5}A + 70.$

And, $\frac{2}{5}A + 40 = \frac{9}{17}C + 10 \Rightarrow \frac{9}{17}C = \frac{2}{5}A + 30$

$\Rightarrow C = \frac{17}{9}\left(\frac{2}{5}A + 30\right) = \frac{34}{45}A + \frac{170}{3}.$

$A + B + C = 600 \Rightarrow A + \left(\frac{7}{5}A + 70\right) + \left(\frac{34}{45}A + \frac{170}{3}\right) = 600$

$\Rightarrow \frac{142A}{45} = 600 - \frac{380}{3} = \frac{1420}{3}$

$\Rightarrow A = \frac{1420}{3} \times \frac{45}{142} = 150.$

136. $P = \frac{2}{5}(Q + R) \Rightarrow P : (Q + R) = 2 : 5.$

$\therefore$ P's share = ₹ $\left(1050 \times \frac{2}{7}\right)$ = ₹ 300.

137. $A = \frac{3}{7}(B + C);\ B = \frac{2}{9}(A + C)$

$\Rightarrow A = \frac{3}{7}\left(\frac{2}{9}A + \frac{2}{9}C + C\right) = \frac{3}{7}\left(\frac{2}{9}A + \frac{11}{9}C\right) = \frac{2}{21}A + \frac{11}{21}C$

$\Rightarrow \frac{19A}{21} = \frac{11}{21}C \Rightarrow A = \left(\frac{21}{19} \times \frac{11}{21}\right)C = \frac{11}{19}C.$

$\therefore B = \frac{2}{9}\left(\frac{11}{19}C + C\right) = \left(\frac{2}{9} \times \frac{30}{19}\right)C = \frac{20}{57}C.$

So, $A : B : C = \frac{11}{19}C : \frac{20}{57}C : C = 33 : 20 : 57$. Sum of ratio terms = (33 + 20 + 57) = 110.

A's share = ₹ $\left(12540 \times \frac{33}{110}\right)$ = ₹ 3762.

B's share = ₹ $\left(12540 \times \frac{20}{110}\right)$ = ₹ 2280.

$\therefore$ Required difference = ₹ (3762 – 2280) = ₹ 1482.

138. $A : B = 3 : 4,\ B : C = 5 : 6 = \left(5 \times \frac{4}{5}\right) : \left(6 \times \frac{4}{5}\right) = 4 : \frac{24}{5},$

$C : D = 7 : 5 = \left(7 \times \frac{24}{35}\right) : \left(5 \times \frac{24}{35}\right) = \frac{24}{5} : \frac{24}{7}.$

$\therefore A : B : C : D = 3 : 4 : \frac{24}{5} : \frac{24}{7} = 105 : 140 : 168 : 120.$

Clearly, C will get the maximum.

139. $A : B : C : D = \frac{1}{3} : \frac{1}{4} : \frac{1}{5} : \frac{1}{6} = 20 : 15 : 12 : 10.$

For each person to have a whole number of pens, th minimum number of pens required = 20 + 15 + 12 + 10 = 57.

140. Remainder = ₹ [671 + (3 + 7 + 9)] = ₹ 690.

A's share = ₹ $\left[\left(690 \times \frac{1}{6}\right) - 3\right]$ = ₹ 112.

B's share = ₹ $\left[\left(690 \times \frac{2}{6}\right) - 7\right]$ = ₹ 223.

C's share = ₹ $\left[\left(690 \times \frac{3}{6}\right) - 9\right]$ = ₹ 336.

141. Remainder = ₹ [1087 – (10 + 12 + 15)] = ₹ 1050.

$\therefore$ B's share = ₹ $\left[\left(1050 \times \frac{7}{21}\right) + 12\right]$ = ₹ 362.

142. Let $x = 5k$ and $y = 7k$. Then, $x + y = 36 \Rightarrow 5k + 7k = 3$
$\Rightarrow 12k = 36 \Rightarrow k = 3.$
$\therefore x = 5k = 5 \times 3 = 15.$

143. Let income = ₹ $11x$ and expenditure = ₹ $10x$.
Then, $11x - 10x = 9000 \Rightarrow x = 9000.$
Annual income = $11x$ = ₹ (11 × 9000) = ₹ 99000.

$\therefore$ Monthly income = ₹ $\left(\frac{99000}{12}\right)$ = ₹ 8250.

144. Let the numbers be $3x$ and $5x$.
Then, $3x.5x = 2160 \Rightarrow 15x^2 = 2160$
$\Rightarrow x^2 = 144 \Rightarrow x = 12.$
$\therefore$ Smaller number = $3x = 3 \times 12 = 36$.

145. Let the shares of A, B, C and D be ₹ $3x$, $4x$, $9x$ and 10 respectively.
$9x - 4x = 2580 \Rightarrow 5x = 2580 \Rightarrow x = 516.$
$\therefore$ Required amount = $3x + 10x = 13x$
= ₹ (13 × 516) = ₹ 6708.

146. Let the numbers be $4x$ and $5x$. Then, their L.C.M. = 20:
$20x = 180$ or $x = 9$.
$\therefore$ Smaller number = $4x = 4 \times 9 = 36$.

147. Ram : Shyam = 7 : 17

Shyam : Sohan = 7 : 17 = $\left(7 \times \frac{17}{7}\right) : \left(17 \times \frac{17}{7}\right) = 17 : \frac{289}{7}$

Ram : Shyam : Sohan = $7 : 17 : \frac{289}{7} = 49 : 119 : 289.$

Let Sohan's income be ₹ x.
Then, 49 : 289 : : 490 : x or $x = 2890$.

148. Number of policemen $= \left(\frac{135}{5} \times 3\right) = 81.$

$\therefore$ Number of supporters $= 81 \times 9 = 729.$

149. Ratio of sides $= \frac{1}{2} : \frac{1}{3} : \frac{1}{4} = 6 : 4 : 3.$

Let the sides be $6x$, $4x$ and $3x$.

Then, $6x + 4x + 3x = 104$ or $13x = 104$ or $x = 8$.

$\therefore$ Longest side $= 6x = (6 \times 8)$ m $= 48$ m.

150. Let the numbers be $3x$ and $4x$.

Then, $(4x)^2 - (3x)^2 = 63 \Rightarrow 16x^2 - 9x^2 = 63$

$\Rightarrow 7x^2 = 63 \Rightarrow x^2 = 9 \Rightarrow x = 3.$

$\therefore$ The numbers are 9 and 12.

151. $A : B = 4 : 5; B : C = 7 : 9 = \left(7 \times \frac{5}{7}\right) : \left(9 \times \frac{5}{7}\right) = 5 : \frac{45}{7};$

$C : D = 3 : 4 = \left(3 \times \frac{15}{7}\right) : \left(4 \times \frac{15}{7}\right) = \frac{45}{7} : \frac{60}{7}.$

$A : B : C : D = 4 : 5 : \frac{45}{7} : \frac{60}{7} = 28 : 35 : 45 : 60.$

Let the shares of A, B, C, D be $28x$, $35x$, $45x$, $60x$ respectively.

Then, $28x = 1680 \Rightarrow x = 60$.

$\therefore$ D's share $= 60x =$ ₹ $(60 \times 60) =$ ₹ 3600.

152. First : Second = 3 : 2, Second :

Third $= 3 : 2 = \left(3 \times \frac{2}{3}\right) : \left(2 \times \frac{2}{3}\right) = 2 : \frac{4}{3}.$

$\therefore$ Ratio between the numbers $= 3 : 2 : \frac{4}{3} = 9 : 6 : 4.$

Let the numbers be $9x$, $6x$ and $4x$. Then,

$(9x)^2 + (6x)^2 + (4x)^2 = 532 \Rightarrow 81x^2 + 36x^2 + 16x^2 = 532$

$\Rightarrow 133x^2 = 532 \Rightarrow x^2 = 4 \Rightarrow x = 2.$

So, third number $= 4x = 4 \times 2 = 8$.

153. Let the man's expenditure be ₹ $26x$ and savings be ₹ $3x$.

Then, monthly income = ₹ $(26x + 3x)$ = ₹ $(29x)$.

So, $29x = 7250$ or $x = 250$.

$\therefore$ Monthly savings = ₹ (3×250) = ₹ 750.

154. Let the numbers be $17x$ and $45x$.

Then, $\frac{1}{5}$ of $45x - \frac{1}{3}$ of $17x = 15 \Leftrightarrow 9x - \frac{17}{3}x = 15$

$\Leftrightarrow \frac{10x}{3} = 15 \Leftrightarrow x = 15 \times \frac{3}{10} = \frac{9}{2}.$

$\therefore$ Smaller number $= 17x = \left(17 \times \frac{9}{2}\right) = \frac{153}{2} = 76\frac{1}{2}.$

155. Let $A = 3x$, $B = 5x$. Then, $C = 2 \times 3x = 6x$, $A + D = B + C$

$\Rightarrow 3x + D = 5x + 6x \Rightarrow D = 8x.$

$A + B + C + D = 110 \Rightarrow 3x + 5x + 6x + 8x = 110$

$\Rightarrow 22x = 110 \Rightarrow x = 5.$

So, the numbers are (3×5), (5×5), (6×5) and (8×5) i.e., 15, 25, 30 and 40.

156. A's expenses = ₹ $(1400 - 600)$ = ₹ 800.

Let B's expenses be ₹ x.

Then, $800 : x :: 2 : 3$ or $2x = 800 \times 3$ or $x = \frac{2400}{2} = 1200.$

$\therefore$ B's saving = ₹ $(1400 - 1200)$ = ₹ 200.

157. $A : B : C = 12 : 15 : 25$. Let the numbers be $12x$, $15x$ and $25x$.

Required ratio $= (B - A) : (C - B) = (15x - 12x) : (25x - 15x) = 3x : 10x = 3 : 10.$

158. Let the incomes of A, B, C be $7x$, $9x$ and $12x$ and their expenditures be $8y$, $9y$ and $15y$ respectively.

Then, A's saving $= (7x - 8y)$.

$\therefore 7x - 8y = \frac{1}{4}$ of $7x \Rightarrow 8y = 7x - \frac{7x}{4} \Rightarrow 8y = \frac{21}{4}x$

$\Rightarrow y = \frac{21}{32}x.$

So, A's expenditure $= \left(8 \times \frac{21}{32}x\right) = \frac{168}{32}x;$

B's expenditure $= \left(9 \times \frac{21}{32}x\right) = \frac{189}{32}x;$

C's expenditure $= \left(15 \times \frac{21}{32}x\right) = \frac{315}{32}x.$

$\therefore$ A's saving $= \left(7x - \frac{168}{32}x\right) = \frac{56}{32}x;$

B's saving $= \left(9x - \frac{189}{32}x\right) = \frac{99}{32}x;$

C's saving $= \left(12x - \frac{315}{32}x\right) = \frac{69}{32}x.$

Hence, required ratio $= \frac{56}{32}x : \frac{99}{32}x : \frac{69}{32}x = 56 : 99 : 69.$

159. Let the basic salaries of A and B be ₹ x and ₹ y respectively.

Then, $x + 65\%$ of $x = y + 80\%$ of y

$\Rightarrow \frac{165}{100}x = \frac{180}{100}y \Rightarrow 165x = 180y$

$\Rightarrow \frac{x}{y} = \frac{180}{165} = \frac{12}{11}.$

$\therefore$ Required ratio = 12 : 11.

160. Let the incomes of Mr. Gupta and Mr. Verma be ₹ $9x$ and ₹ $4x$ respectively and their expenditures be ₹ $7y$ and ₹ $3y$ respectively.

Then, $9x - 7y = 4x - 3y \Rightarrow 5x = 4y \Rightarrow x = \frac{4y}{5}.$

Now, $9x - 7y = 2000 \Rightarrow 9 \times \frac{4}{5}y - 7y = 2000$

$\Rightarrow \frac{36}{5}y - 7y = 2000 \Rightarrow y = 10000.$

$\therefore$ Mr. Gupta's expenditure = ₹ (7×10000) = ₹ 70000.

161. Let the incomes of A and B be ₹ $5x$ and ₹ $3x$ respectively and the expenses of A, B and C be ₹ $8y$, ₹ $5y$ and ₹ $2y$ respectively.

Then, $2y = 2000$ or $y = 1000$.

And, $3x - 5y = 700 \Rightarrow 3x - 5000 = 700$

$\Rightarrow 3x = 5700 \Rightarrow x = 1900.$

$\therefore$ A's savings $= 5x - 8y =$ ₹ $(5 \times 1900 - 8 \times 1000)$
$=$ ₹ $(9500 - 8000) =$ ₹ 1500.

162. Let the monthly salary of a clerk and an officer be ₹ $3x$ and ₹ $5x$ respectively.

Then, 3% of $5x = 210 \Rightarrow \left(\frac{3}{100} \times 5x\right) = 210$

$\Rightarrow x = \left(\frac{210 \times 100}{15}\right) = 1400.$

$\therefore$ Clerk's salary $=$ ₹ $(3 \times 1400) =$ ₹ 4200.

163. Let the salaries of A and B be ₹ $9x$ and ₹ $4x$ respectively.

Then, 115% of $9x = 5175 \Rightarrow \frac{115}{100} \times 9x = 5175$

$\Rightarrow x = \left(\frac{5175 \times 100}{115 \times 9}\right) = 500.$

$\therefore$ B's salary $=$ ₹ $(4 \times 500) =$ ₹ 2000.

164. Let income in the first year be ₹ x and expenses in the second year be ₹ y.

Then, $\frac{x}{45000} = \frac{2}{3}$ and $\frac{25000}{y} = \frac{5}{9}$

$\Rightarrow x = \frac{2 \times 45000}{3} = 30000$ and $y = \frac{25000 \times 9}{5} = 45000.$

$\therefore$ Total savings for 2 years
$=$ ₹ $[(30000 - 25000) + (45000 - 45000)] =$ ₹ 5000.

165. Clearly, A and B save 20% and 30% of their respective salaries.

Let the salaries of A and B be x and y respectively.

Then, $\frac{20\% \text{ of } x}{30\% \text{ of } y} = \frac{4}{3} \Rightarrow \frac{x}{5} \times \frac{10}{3y} = \frac{4}{3} \Rightarrow \frac{x}{y} = 2 \Rightarrow x = 2y.$

$\therefore x + y = 2100 \Rightarrow 2y + y = 2100$

$\Rightarrow 3y = 2100 \Rightarrow y = 700.$

A's salary $= x = 2y =$ ₹ $(2 \times 700) =$ ₹ 1400.

166. Let the incomes of the two persons be $5x$ and $3x$ and their expenditures be $9y$ and $5y$ respectively.

Then, $5x - 9y = 2600$ ...(i)

and $3x - 5y = 1800$ ...(ii)

Multiplying (i) by 3 and (ii) by 5, we get :

$15x - 27y = 7800$ ...(iii)

and $15x - 25y = 9000$ ...(iv)

Subtracting (iii) from (iv), we get : $2y = 1200$ or $y = 600$.

Putting $y = 600$ in (i), we get : $5x = 8000$ or $x = 1600$.

$\therefore$ Their incomes are ₹ (5×1600) and ₹ (3×1600) i.e., ₹ 8000 and ₹ 4800 respectively.

167. Let the annual incomes of A and B be $5x$ and $4x$ and their annual expenses be $19y$ and $21y$ respectively.

Then, $\frac{5x - 19y}{4x - 21y} = \frac{37}{18} \Rightarrow 90x - 342y = 148x - 777y$

$\Rightarrow 58x = 435y \Rightarrow x = \frac{435}{58}y.$

And, $(5x - 19y) + (4x - 21y) = 66000$

$\Rightarrow 9x - 40y = 66000 \Rightarrow 9 \times \frac{435}{58}y - 40y = 66000$

$\Rightarrow 3915y - 2320y = 3828000$

$\Rightarrow 1595y = 3828000 \Rightarrow y = 2400.$

So, $x = \left(\frac{435}{58} \times 2400\right) = 18000.$

A's annual income $=$ ₹ $(5 \times 18000) =$ ₹ 90000.

$\therefore$ A's monthly income $=$ ₹ $\left(\frac{90000}{12}\right) =$ ₹ 7500.

168. Number of boys $= \left(720 \times \frac{7}{12}\right) = 420;$

Number of girls $= (720 - 420) = 300.$

Let the required number of girls be x. Then, $\frac{420}{300 + x} = 1$

$\Rightarrow 420 = 300 + x \Rightarrow x = 120.$

169. Let the number of students in Arts and Commerce faculties be $4x$ and $5x$ respectively.

Then, $\frac{4x}{5x + 65} = \frac{8}{11} \Rightarrow 44x = 8(5x + 65)$

$\Rightarrow 4x = 520 \Rightarrow x = 130.$

$\therefore$ Number of students in Arts faculty
$= (4 \times 130) = 520.$

170. Let the numbers be $7x$ and $11x$ respectively.

Then, $\frac{7x + 7}{11x + 7} = \frac{2}{3} \Rightarrow 21x + 21 = 22x + 14 \Rightarrow x = 7.$

$\therefore$ Smaller number $= 7 \times 7 = 49.$

171. Ratio of boys in the four sections is as under :

$A \to \frac{7}{12} = 0.58; B \to \frac{5}{8} = 0.625, C \to \frac{3}{5} = 0.6; D \to \frac{2}{3} = 0.66.$

Clearly, maximum number of boys are enrolled in section D.

172. Let the required number be x.

Then, $\frac{7 - x}{9 - x} = \frac{11 - x}{15 - x} \Rightarrow (7 - x)(15 - x) = (11 - x)(9 - x)$

$\Rightarrow 105 - 22x + x^2 = 99 - 20x + x^2 \Rightarrow 2x = 6 \Rightarrow x = 3.$

173. Quantity of milk $= \left(80 \times \frac{7}{10}\right)$ litres $= 56$ litres.

Quantity of water $= (80 - 56)$ litres $= 24$ litres.

Let the quantity of water to be added be x litres.

Then, $\frac{56}{24 + x} = \frac{2}{1} \Rightarrow 48 + 2x = 56 \Rightarrow 2x = 8 \Rightarrow x = 4.$

174. Quantity of soda in the mixture

$= \left(7 \times \frac{2}{21} + 4 \times \frac{1}{12}\right)$ kg $= \left(\frac{2}{3} + \frac{1}{3}\right)$ kg $= 1$ kg.

Quantity of soap-dust in the mixture
$= [(7 + 4) - 1]$ kg $= 10$ kg.

$\therefore$ Required ratio $= 1 : 10.$

175. Let the required number be x. Then,

$(7 + x) : (11 + x) :: (11 + x) : (19 + x)$

$\Rightarrow \frac{7 + x}{11 + x} = \frac{11 + x}{19 + x} \Rightarrow (7 + x)(19 + x) = (11 + x)^2$

$\Rightarrow x^2 + 26x + 133 = x^2 + 22x + 121$

$\Rightarrow 4x = -12 \Rightarrow x = -3.$

176. Let the numbers be $3x$ and $5x$.

Then, $\frac{3x-9}{5x-9}=\frac{12}{23} \Rightarrow 23(3x-9)=12(5x-9)$

$\Rightarrow 69x-207=60x-108 \Rightarrow 9x=99 \Rightarrow x=11.$

$\therefore$ Larger number $= 5 \times 11 = 55.$

177. Let the number of managers and production-line workers be $5x$ and $72x$ respectively. Then,

$\frac{5x}{72x+8}=\frac{5}{74} \Rightarrow 370x=360x+40 \Rightarrow 10x=40 \Rightarrow x=4.$

$\therefore$ Number of managers $= 5 \times 4 = 20.$

178. Let the number to be added be x.

Then, $\frac{3+x}{5+x}=\frac{5}{6} \Rightarrow 6(3+x)=5(5+x)$

$\Rightarrow 18+6x=25+5x \Rightarrow x=7.$

179. Let the number of ladies and gents at the party be $3x$ and $2x$ respectively. Then,

$\frac{3x}{2x+20}=\frac{2}{3} \Rightarrow 9x=4x+40 \Rightarrow 5x=40 \Rightarrow x=8.$

$\therefore$ Number of ladies $= 3 \times 8 = 24.$

180. Let the number of boys and girls be $4x$ and $5x$ respectively.

Then, $\frac{4x}{5x-100}=\frac{6}{7} \Rightarrow 28x=30x-600$

$\Rightarrow 2x=600 \Rightarrow x=300.$

$\therefore$ Number of boys $= 4 \times 300 = 1200.$

181. Ratio of numbers $= 1\frac{1}{2}:2\frac{2}{3}=\frac{3}{2}:\frac{8}{3}=9:16.$

Let the numbers be $9x$ and $16x$.

Then, $\frac{9x+15}{16x+15}=\frac{\left(1\frac{2}{3}\right)}{\left(2\frac{1}{2}\right)}=\frac{5}{3}\times\frac{2}{5}=\frac{2}{3}$

$\Rightarrow 27x+45=32x+30 \Rightarrow 5x=15 \Rightarrow x=3.$

$\therefore$ Greater number $= 16 \times 3 = 48.$

182. Let $A=x$, $B=2x$, $C=3x$. Then, $\frac{x+2x+3x}{3}=600$

$\Rightarrow 2x=600 \Rightarrow x=300.$

So, $A=300$, $B=600$, $C=900$.

New value of A = 110% of 300 = 330.

New value of B = 80% of 600 = 480.

New average = 105% of 600 = 630.

New value of $C = (630 \times 3)-(330+480)=1080.$

$\therefore$ Increase in value of $C = (1080-900)=180.$

183. Let the numbers be $2x$ and $3x$.

Then, $\frac{2x-2}{3x+2}=\frac{1}{2} \Rightarrow 4x-4=3x+2 \Rightarrow x=6.$

$\therefore$ Sum of the numbers $= 2x+3x=5x=5\times 6=30.$

184. Quantity of milk in the mixture

$=\left(20\times\frac{5}{8}\right)$ litres $=\frac{25}{2}$ litres $=12\frac{1}{2}$ litres.

Quantity of water in the mixture

$=\left(20-12\frac{1}{2}\right)$ litres $=7\frac{1}{2}$ litres.

Quantity of milk removed

$=\left(4\times\frac{5}{8}\right)$ litres $=\frac{5}{2}$ litres $=2\frac{1}{2}$ litres.

Quantity of water removed $=\left(4-2\frac{1}{2}\right)$ litres $=1\frac{1}{2}$ litres.

Quantity of milk in the new mixture

$=\left[\left(12\frac{1}{2}-2\frac{1}{2}\right)+4\right]$ litres $=14$ litres.

Quantity of water in the new mixture

$=\left(7\frac{1}{2}-1\frac{1}{2}\right)$ litres $=6$ litres.

$\therefore$ Required ratio $= 14:6=7:3.$

185. Let the numbers be x and y.

Then, $\frac{x+1}{y+1}=\frac{3}{4}$ and $\frac{x-5}{y-5}=\frac{7}{10}$

$\Rightarrow 4x+4=3y+3$ and $10x-50=7y-35$

$\Rightarrow 4x-3y=-1$ and $10x-7y=15$

$\Rightarrow 20x-15y=-5$ ...(*i*)

and $20x-14y=30$ ...(*ii*)

Subtracting (*i*) from (*ii*), we get : $y=35$.

Putting $y=35$ in (*i*), we get :

$20x=520$ or $x=26$.

186. Let the number of boys and girls, after leaving of 15 girls, be $2x$ and x respectively.

Then, $\frac{2x-45}{x}=\frac{1}{5} \Rightarrow 10x-225=x$

$\Rightarrow 9x=225 \Rightarrow x=25.$

$\therefore$ Original number of girls $= x+15=(25+15)=40.$

187. Quantity of spirit in the resultant solution

$=[(0.5\times 2)+(0.75\times 3)]$ litres

$=(1+2.25)$ litres $=3.25$ litres.

Quantity of water in the resultant solution

$=[(1-0.5)\times 2+(1-0.75)\times 3]$ litres

$=(1+0.75)$ litres $=1.75$ litres.

$\therefore$ Required ratio $= 3.25:1.75=13:7.$

188. Let the required number be x.

Then, $\frac{6-x}{7-x}<\frac{16}{21} \Rightarrow 21(6-x)<16(7-x)$

$\Rightarrow 126-21x<112-16x$

$\Rightarrow 5x>14 \Rightarrow x>\frac{14}{5} \Rightarrow x>2\frac{4}{5} \Rightarrow x=3.$

189. Let the number of men and women in the city be x and $(9000-x)$ respectively.

Then, 105% of x + 108% of $(9000-x)=9600$

$\Rightarrow \frac{21x}{20}+\frac{27}{25}(9000-x)=9600$

$\Rightarrow \frac{21x}{20}+9720-\frac{27x}{25}=9600$

$\Rightarrow \frac{3x}{100} = 120 \Rightarrow x = \frac{120 \times 100}{3} = 4000.$

$\therefore$ Number of men = 4000, Number of women = 5000.

Hence, required ratio = 4000 : 5000 = 4 : 5.

190. Let the quantity of wine and water in the original mixture be $3x$ and x litres only.

Total quantity of the mixture = $(3x + x)$ litres = $4x$ litres.

Let y litres of the mixture be replaced by water.

Quantity of wine in y litres of mixture = $\left(\frac{3y}{4}\right)$ litres.

Quantity of water in y litres of mixture = $\left(\frac{y}{4}\right)$ litres.

$\therefore\ 3x - \frac{3y}{4} = x - \frac{y}{4} + y \Rightarrow 2x = \frac{3y}{2} \Rightarrow 4x = 3y.$

Required fraction = $\frac{y}{4x} = \frac{1}{3}.$

191. Let Sarika's and Gauri's ages one year ago be $3x$ and $4x$ years respectively.

Sarika's age 1 year hence = $(3x + 2)$ years.

Gauri's age 1 year hence = $(4x + 2)$ years.

$\therefore\ \frac{3x+2}{4x+2} = \frac{10}{13} \Rightarrow 13\ (3x + 2) = 10\ (4x + 2)$

$\Rightarrow 39x + 26 = 40x + 20 \Rightarrow x = 6.$

Hence, Sarika's present age = $3x + 1$

= $(3 \times 6 + 1)$ years = 19 years.

192. Sum of ages of 3 boys = (25×3) years = 75 years.

$\therefore$ Age of the youngest boy

$= \left(75 \times \frac{3}{15}\right)$ years = 15 years.

193. Let the number of 1-rupee, 50-paise and 25-paise coins be $8x$, $5x$ and $3x$ respectively.

Then, sum of their values = ₹$\left(8x + \frac{50 \times 5x}{100} + \frac{25 \times 3x}{100}\right)$

= ₹$\left(8x + \frac{5}{2}x + \frac{3}{4}x\right)$ = ₹$\left(\frac{45}{4}x\right).$

$\therefore\ \frac{45x}{4} = 112.50 \Rightarrow x = \frac{112.50 \times 4}{45} = 10.$

So, number of 50-paise coins = $5x$ = 50.

194. Let the values of one-rupee, 50-paise and 25-paise coins be ₹ $2x$, ₹ $3x$ and ₹ $5x$ respectively.

Then, number of one-rupee coins = $2x$;

number of 50-paise coins = $\frac{3x}{0.5} = 6x$;

number of 25-paise coins = $\frac{5x}{0.25} = 20x$.

$\therefore\ 2x + 6x + 20x = 420 \Leftrightarrow 28x = 420 \Leftrightarrow x = 15.$

Hence, number of one-rupee coins = 2 × 15 = 30.

195. Let the required consumption be x litres.

Clearly, 1.5 × 60 = 2 × 45 = 3 × 30 = 4.5 × 20 = $6x$.

$\therefore\ 6x = 90 \Rightarrow x = 15.$

196. $A \propto C$ and $B \propto C \Rightarrow A = kC$ and $B = mC$ for some constants k and m

$\therefore\ A + B = kC + mC = (k + m)\ C \Rightarrow (A + B) \propto C.$

$A - B = kC - mC = (k - m)\ C \Rightarrow (A - B) \propto C.$

$\sqrt{AB} = \sqrt{kC \times mC} = \sqrt{kmC^2} = \sqrt{km}\,.C \Rightarrow \sqrt{AB} \propto C.$

$\frac{A}{B} = \frac{kC}{mC} = \frac{k}{m}$ = constant.

197. $x \propto \frac{1}{y}$ and $y \propto z \Rightarrow x = \frac{k}{y}$ and $y = mz$ for some constant k and m.

$\therefore\ xz = \frac{k}{y} \times \frac{y}{m} = \frac{k}{m}$ = constant.

198. $h \propto t^2 \Rightarrow h = kt^2$ for some constant k

$\Rightarrow 64 = k \times 2^2 = 4k \Rightarrow k = 16.$

Let the required height be x cm.

Then, $x = 16 \times 6^2 = (16 \times 36)$ cm = 576 cm.

199. $y \propto (x + 3) \Rightarrow y = k\ (x + 3)$ for some constant k.

When $y = 8$, $x = 1$, $y = k\ (x + 3) \Rightarrow 8 = k\ (1 + 3)$

$\Rightarrow k = 2.$

When $x = 2$, $y = 2\ (x + 3) = 2\ (2 + 3) = 2 \times 5 = 10.$

200. Rate of flow $\propto \frac{1}{r^2} \Rightarrow$ Rate of flow

$= \frac{k}{r^2}$ for some constant k.

$\therefore$ Required ratio = $\frac{k}{1^2} : \frac{k}{2^2} = \frac{k}{1} : \frac{k}{4} = 1 : \frac{1}{4} = 4 : 1.$

201. $y \propto \left(x + \frac{1}{x}\right) \Rightarrow y = kx + \frac{m}{x}$, where k and m are constants

Then, $4k + \frac{m}{4} = 6$ ...(i)

and $3k + \frac{m}{3} = \frac{10}{3}$ ...(ii)

Multiplying (i) by 3 and (ii) by 4, we get :

$12k + \frac{3m}{4} = 18$ ...(iii)

and $12k + \frac{4m}{3} = \frac{40}{3}$ ...(iv)

Subtracting (iv) from (iii), we get :

$\frac{3m}{4} - \frac{4m}{3} = 18 - \frac{40}{3} \Rightarrow -\frac{7m}{12} = \frac{14}{3} \Rightarrow m = -8.$

Putting $m = -8$ in (i), we get : $4k + \frac{(-8)}{4} = 6$

$\Rightarrow 4k = 8 \Rightarrow k = 2 \qquad \therefore\ y = 2x - \frac{8}{x}.$

202. $M \propto \frac{1}{N} \Rightarrow M = \frac{k}{N}.$

When $M = 15$, $N = -4$.

$\therefore\ 15 = \frac{k}{(-4)} \Rightarrow k = 15 \times (-4) = -60.$

When $M = -6$, $N = A$.

$\therefore\ -6 = \frac{-60}{A} \Rightarrow A = \frac{-60}{-6} = 10.$

When $M = 2, N = B$.

$\therefore\ 2 = \frac{-60}{B} \Rightarrow B = \frac{-60}{2} = -30.$

When $M = C, N = 60$.

$\therefore\ C = \frac{-60}{60} = -1.$

203. $S \propto R$ and $T \propto \frac{1}{R} \Rightarrow S = kR$ and $T = \frac{m}{R}$ for some constants k and m.

When $R = 20$, $S = 40$ and $T = 10$, $S = kR$

$\Rightarrow 40 = 20k \Rightarrow k = 2.$

And, $T = \frac{m}{R} \Rightarrow 10 = \frac{m}{20} \Rightarrow m = 10 \times 20 = 200.$

When $S = 20$, we have : $20 = 2R$ or $R = 10$.

And, $T = \frac{200}{R} = \frac{200}{10} = 20.$

204. $x \propto \frac{1}{y} \Rightarrow x = \frac{k}{y}$. When $x = 12$, $y = 9$,

$k = xy = 12 \times 9 = 108.$

Clearly, $xy \neq 108$ for $x = 24$, $y = 18$.

205. $I \propto \frac{1}{d^2} \Rightarrow I = \frac{k}{d^2}$ (where k is a constant) $\Rightarrow k = Id^2$.

$\therefore\ I_{new} = \frac{k}{(3d)^2} = \frac{Id^2}{9d^2} = \frac{I}{9}.$

206. Let the number of boys and girls be $3x$ and $2x$ respectively.

Then, number of boys and girls who are adults

$= 20\%$ of $3x + 25\%$ of $2x$

$= \left(\frac{20}{100} \times 3x\right) + \left(\frac{25}{100} \times 2x\right) = \frac{3}{5}x + \frac{x}{2} = \frac{11x}{10}.$

$\therefore$ Number of boys and girls who are not adults

$= \left[(3x + 2x) - \frac{11x}{10}\right] = 5x - \frac{11x}{10} = \frac{39x}{10}.$

Required percentage $= \left(\frac{39x}{10} \times \frac{1}{5x} \times 100\right)\% = 78\%.$

207. Let the cost of the table and chair be ₹ $5x$ and ₹ $7x$ respectively.

New cost of chair $= 120\%$ of ₹ $7x$ = ₹ $\left(\frac{6}{5} \times 7x\right)$ = ₹ $\frac{42x}{5}$.

New cost of table $= 110\%$ of ₹ $5x$ = ₹ $\left(\frac{11}{10} \times 5x\right)$ = ₹ $\frac{55x}{10}$.

$\therefore$ New ratio $= \frac{55x}{10} : \frac{42x}{5} = 55 : 84.$

208. Let the number of students in schools A, B and C be $5x$, $4x$ and $7x$ respectively.

New strength of school $A = 120\%$ of $5x = \left(\frac{6}{5} \times 5x\right) = 6x.$

New strength of school $B = 125\%$ of $4x = \left(\frac{5}{4} \times 4x\right) = 5x.$

New strength of school $C = 120\%$ of $7x$

$= \left(\frac{6}{5} \times 7x\right) = \frac{42x}{5}.$

$\therefore$ New ratio $= 6x : 5x : \frac{42x}{5} = 30 : 25 : 42.$

209. Let the original expenses on rice, fish and oil be ₹ $12x$, ₹ $17x$ and ₹ $3x$ respectively.

New expense on rice $= 120\%$ of ₹ $12x$

= ₹ $\left(\frac{6}{5} \times 12x\right)$ = ₹ $\left(\frac{72x}{5}\right)$.

New expense on fish $= 130\%$ of ₹ $17x$

= ₹ $\left(\frac{13}{10} \times 17x\right)$ = ₹ $\left(\frac{221x}{10}\right)$.

New expense on oil $= 150\%$ of ₹ $3x$ = ₹ $\left(\frac{3}{2} \times 3x\right)$ = ₹ $\left(\frac{9x}{2}\right)$.

Total original expenses = ₹ $(12x + 17x + 3x)$ = ₹ $(32x)$.

Total new expenses = ₹ $\left(\frac{72x}{5} + \frac{221x}{10} + \frac{9x}{2}\right)$ = ₹ $(41x)$.

Increase in expenses = ₹ $(41x - 32x)$ = ₹ $9x$.

$\therefore$ Increase % $= \left(\frac{9x}{32x} \times 100\right)\% = \frac{225}{8}\% = 28\frac{1}{8}\%.$

210. Let the earnings of A and B be ₹ $8x$ and ₹ $9x$ respectively.

Then, $\frac{150\% \text{ of } 8x}{75\% \text{ of } 9x} = \frac{16}{9} \Rightarrow \frac{\frac{3}{2} \times 8x}{\frac{3}{4} \times 9x} = \frac{16}{9} \Rightarrow \frac{16}{9} = \frac{16}{9}.$

Hence, A's earnings cannot be determined.

211. Let Mr. Sharma's expenditure be ₹ $3x$ and his savings be ₹ $2x$.

Income = ₹ $(3x + 2x)$ = ₹ $5x$.

Increased income $= 110\%$ of ₹ $5x$ = ₹ $5.5x$.

Increased expenditure $= 112\%$ of ₹ $3x$ = ₹ $3.36x$.

Increased savings = ₹ $(5.5x - 3.36x)$ = ₹ $2.14x$.

Increase in savings = ₹ $(2.14 - 2)\ x$ = ₹ $0.14x$.

$\therefore$ Increase % $= \left(\frac{0.14}{2x} \times 100\right)\% = 7\%.$

212. Let the initial total weight of A and B be x kg.

Then, 125% of $x = 80 \Rightarrow x = 80 \times \frac{100}{125} = 64$ kg.

A's initial weight $= \left(64 \times \frac{3}{8}\right)$ kg $= 24$ kg. B's initial weight

$= \left(64 \times \frac{5}{8}\right)$ kg $= 40$ kg.

A's new weight $= 120\%$ of 24 kg $= 28.8$ kg. B's new weight $= (80 - 28.8)$ kg $= 51.2$ kg.

Increase in B's weight $= (51.2 - 40)$ kg $= 11.2$ kg.

$\therefore$ Increase % $= \left(\frac{11.2}{40} \times 100\right)\% = 28\%.$

213. Let the number of coins with Lalita, Palita and Salita in the end be $24x$, $21x$ and $16x$ respectively.

Then, number of coins received by Lalita, Palita and Salita from their mother are $(24x + 50)$, $(21x + 85)$ and $(16x + 39)$ respectively.

So, $(24x + 50) + (21x + 85) + (16x + 39) = 3224$

$\Rightarrow 61x = 3050 \Rightarrow x = 50.$

Hence, number of coins received by Lalita from her mother $= (24 \times 50 + 50) = 1250.$

214. Let the number of revolutions made by the larger wheel be x.

Then, $6 : 14 :: x : 21$ or $14x$

$$= 6 \times 21 \text{ or } x = \frac{6 \times 21}{14} = 9.$$

215. Let the capacity of each glass be z.

Let x and y denote the quantities of milk in glasses of Seeta and Geeta respectively.

Then, $x + \frac{1}{2}y = z$ ...(i)

and $y + \frac{1}{4}x = z$ ...(ii)

So, $x + \frac{1}{2}y = y + \frac{1}{4}x \Rightarrow \frac{3}{4}x = \frac{1}{2}y \Rightarrow \frac{x}{y} = \frac{1}{2} \times \frac{4}{3} = \frac{2}{3}.$

Hence, required ratio = 2 : 3.

216. Let the area of earth be x.

Then, area of land on earth $= \frac{x}{3}$;

area of water on earth $= \frac{2x}{3}$.

Area of Northern Hemisphere $= \frac{x}{2}$.

Area of land in Northern Hemisphere $= \left(\frac{x}{2} \times \frac{2}{5}\right) = \frac{x}{5}$.

Area of water in Northern Hemisphere $= \left(\frac{x}{2} \times \frac{3}{5}\right) = \frac{3x}{10}$.

Area of land in Southern Hemisphere $= \left(\frac{x}{3} - \frac{x}{5}\right) = \frac{2x}{15}$.

Area of water in Southern Hemisphere $= \left(\frac{2x}{3} - \frac{3x}{10}\right) = \frac{11x}{30}$.

$\therefore$ Required ratio $= \frac{2x}{15} : \frac{11x}{30} = 4 : 11.$

217. Let the volume of each small piece be x cu . units.

Then, original volume of the diamond = $(8x)$ cu . units.

Original price of the diamond $= k \times (8x)^3 = 512kx^3$, where k is a constant.

$$512kx^3 = 1000000 \Rightarrow kx^3 = \frac{1000000}{512}.$$

Price of each smaller piece $= kx^3$.

Total price of the 8 pieces $= 8kx^3$.

$\therefore$ Loss in value $= (512kx^3 - 8kx^3) = 504kx^3$

$$= 504 \times \frac{1000000}{512} = 984375.$$

218. Let the share of a man, a woman and a boy be ₹ $3x$, ₹ $2x$ and ₹ x respectively.

Then, $2 \times 3x + 5 \times 2x + 8 \times x = 720$

$\Rightarrow 24x = 720 \Rightarrow x = 30.$

Hence, share of each boy = ₹ 30.

219. Let the first amount be ₹ x. Then, second amount = ₹ $(2x)$.

$$A\text{'s share} = ₹\left(\frac{4}{10} \times x + \frac{5}{26} \times 2x\right) = ₹\left(\frac{4x}{10} + \frac{5x}{13}\right) = ₹\left(\frac{102x}{130}\right).$$

$$B\text{'s share} = ₹\left(\frac{3}{10} \times x + \frac{6}{26} \times 2x\right) = ₹\left(\frac{3x}{10} + \frac{6x}{13}\right) = ₹\left(\frac{99x}{130}\right).$$

$$C\text{'s share} = ₹\left(\frac{2}{10} \times x + \frac{7}{26} \times 2x\right) = ₹\left(\frac{2x}{10} + \frac{7x}{13}\right) = ₹\left(\frac{96x}{130}\right).$$

$$D\text{'s share} = ₹\left(\frac{1}{10} \times x + \frac{8}{26} \times 2x\right) = ₹\left(\frac{x}{10} + \frac{8x}{13}\right) = ₹\left(\frac{93x}{130}\right).$$

Clearly, A got the maximum amount.

220. Let the number of females be x.

Then, $\frac{160 \times 4}{3x} = \frac{16}{21} \Rightarrow 48x = 160 \times 4 \times 21$

$\Rightarrow x = \frac{160 \times 4 \times 21}{48} = 280.$

221. Total money received by men $= ₹\left(180 \times \frac{5}{9}\right) = ₹\,100.$

Total money received by women $= ₹\left(180 \times \frac{4}{9}\right) = ₹\,80.$

Let the number of men be x.

Then, number of women $= 66 - x$.

Money received by each man $= ₹\left(\frac{100}{x}\right)$. Money received by each woman $= ₹\left(\frac{80}{66 - x}\right)$.

$\therefore \frac{100}{x} \times \frac{(66 - x)}{80} = \frac{3}{2} \Rightarrow 10(66 - x) = 12x$

$\Rightarrow 22x = 660 \Rightarrow x = 30.$

222. Let the man's original expenditure on foodgrains and other items be ₹ $2x$ and ₹ $5x$ respectively.

Then, total original expenditure = ₹ $(2x + 5x)$ = ₹ $7x$.

Total new expenditure = ₹ (110% of $2x$ + 115% of $5x$)

$$= ₹\left(\frac{110}{100} \times 2x + \frac{115}{100} \times 5x\right) = ₹\left(\frac{11x}{5} + \frac{23x}{4}\right)$$

$$= ₹\left(\frac{159x}{20}\right).$$

Ratio of increased expenditure to original expenditure

$$= \frac{159x}{20} \times \frac{1}{7x} = \frac{159}{140}.$$

$\therefore$ Required salary $= ₹\left(\frac{159}{140} \times 3500\right) = ₹\,3975.$

Desired increase in salary = ₹ (3975 – 3500) = ₹ 475.

223. Let the full marks for each paper be x.

Let the marks obtained in the five papers be $6y$, $7y$, $8y$, $9y$ and $10y$ respectively.

Then, $\frac{6y + 7y + 8y + 9y + 10y}{5x} = \frac{60}{100}$

$\Rightarrow \frac{40y}{5x} = \frac{3}{5} \Rightarrow 40y = 3x \Rightarrow x = \frac{40}{3}y$

50% of $x = \left(\frac{50}{100} \times \frac{40}{3} y\right) = \frac{20y}{3} = 6\frac{2}{3}y$.

Clearly, the student got more than 50% marks in each of the last 4 papers.

24. Let the number of visitors on the three days be $2x$, $5x$ and $13x$ respectively.

Then, total charges collected on three days
$= ₹ (15 \times 2x + 7.50 \times 5x + 2.50 \times 13)$
$= ₹ (30x + 37.50x + 32.50x) = ₹ (100x)$.

$\therefore$ Average charge per person
$= ₹\left(\frac{100x}{2x + 5x + 13x}\right) = ₹\left(\frac{100x}{20x}\right) = ₹ 5$.

25. Let the number of passengers travelling in A.C. sleeper class, first class and sleeper class be x, $2x$ and $3x$ and let their fares be $5y$, $4y$ and $2y$ respectively.

Then, $x \times 5y + 2x \times 4y + 3x \times 2y = 45600$
$\Rightarrow 5xy + 8xy + 6xy = 45600 \Rightarrow 19xy = 45600$
$\Rightarrow xy = 2400$.

$\therefore$ Income from A.C. sleeper class $= 5xy$
$= ₹ (5 \times 2400) = ₹ 12000$.

26. Let the initial fares of 1st, 2nd and 3rd class be ₹ $8x$, ₹ $6x$ and ₹ $3x$ respectively.

Revised fare of 1st class $= \frac{5}{6}$ of ₹ $8x = ₹\left(\frac{20x}{3}\right)$.

Revised fare of 2nd class $= \frac{11}{12}$ of ₹ $6x = ₹\left(\frac{11x}{2}\right)$.

Let the number of passengers of 1st, 2nd and 3rd class be $9y$, $12y$ and $26y$ respectively.

Then, $\frac{20x}{3} \times 9y + \frac{11x}{2} \times 12y + 3x \times 26y = 1088$

$\Rightarrow 60xy + 66xy + 78xy = 1088 \Rightarrow 204xy = 1088$

$\Rightarrow xy = \frac{1088}{204} = \frac{16}{3}$.

$\therefore$ Collection from passengers of 1st class $= 60xy$
$= ₹\left(60 \times \frac{16}{3}\right) = ₹ 320$.

27. Let the daily wage of a man, a woman and a boy be ₹ $4x$, ₹ $3x$ and ₹ $2x$ respectively.

Then, $15 \times 4x + 18 \times 3x + 12 \times 2x = 2070$
$\Rightarrow 60x + 54x + 24x = 2070$
$\Rightarrow 138x = 2070 \Rightarrow x = 15$.

$\therefore$ Daily wages of 1 man, 2 women and 3 boys
$= ₹ (4x + 2 \times 3x + 3 \times 2x)$
$= ₹ (4x + 6x + 6x) = ₹ 16x$
$= ₹ (16 \times 15) = ₹ 240$.

28. Let the initial number of employees be $9x$ and their wages be ₹ $14y$.

Then, reduced number of employees $= 8x$. And, increased wages $=$ ₹ $15y$.

Original wage bill $= ₹ (9x \times 14y) = ₹ (126xy)$.

$126xy = 1890 \Rightarrow xy = \frac{1890}{126} = 15$.

New wage bill $= ₹ (8x \times 15y) = ₹ (120xy)$
$= ₹ (120 \times 15) = ₹ 1800$.

Required difference $= ₹ (1890 - 1800) = ₹ 90$.

229. Let the salaries of A and B last year be ₹ $3x$ and ₹ $4x$ respectively.

Then, A's present salary $= ₹\left(\frac{5}{4} \times 3x\right) = ₹\left(\frac{15x}{4}\right)$.

B's present salary $= ₹\left(\frac{3}{2} \times 4x\right) = ₹ 6x$.

$\therefore \frac{15x}{4} + 6x = 4160 \Rightarrow 39x = 4160 \times 4 \Rightarrow x = \frac{4160 \times 4}{39}$.

So, A's present salary $= ₹\left(\frac{15}{4} \times \frac{4160 \times 4}{39}\right) = ₹ 1600$.

230. Suppose the man ordered x pairs of brown socks.

Let the price of a brown pair be ₹ y. Then, price of a black pair $= ₹ (2y)$.

Original bill $= ₹ (4 \times 2y + xy) = ₹ (8y + xy)$.

Changed bill $= ₹ (4y + x \times 2y) = ₹ (4y + 2xy)$.

$\therefore (4y + 2xy) = 150\%$ of $(8y + xy)$

$\Leftrightarrow 4y + 2xy = \frac{3}{2}(8y + xy)$

$\Leftrightarrow 8y + 4xy = 24y + 3xy$

$\Leftrightarrow xy = 16y \Leftrightarrow x = 16$.

$\therefore$ Required ratio $= 4 : 16 = 1 : 4$.

231. Gold in $C = \left(\frac{7}{9} + \frac{7}{18}\right)$ units $= \frac{7}{6}$ units.

Copper in $C = \left(\frac{2}{9} + \frac{11}{18}\right)$ units $= \frac{5}{6}$ units.

$\therefore$ Gold : Copper $= \frac{7}{6} : \frac{5}{6} = 7 : 5$.

232. Zinc in first alloy $= \frac{2}{3}$ units;

Zinc in second alloy $= \frac{4}{5}$ units.

Copper in first alloy $= \frac{1}{3}$ units;

Copper in second alloy $= \frac{1}{5}$ units.

Let the first and second alloys be mixed in the ratio $1 : y$.

Then, $\frac{\frac{2}{3} + \frac{4y}{5}}{\frac{1}{3} + \frac{y}{5}} = \frac{3}{1} \Rightarrow 10 + 12y = 3(5 + 3y)$

$\Rightarrow 10 + 12y = 15 + 9y \Rightarrow 3y = 5 \Rightarrow y = \frac{5}{3}$.

$\therefore$ Required ratio $= 1 : \frac{5}{3} = 3 : 5$.

233. Milk in $A = \frac{5}{8}$ units; Milk in $B = \frac{2}{5}$ units.

Water in $A = \frac{3}{8}$ units; Water in $B = \frac{3}{5}$ units.

Let the mixtures in A and B be taken in the ratio $1 : y$.

Then, $\frac{5}{8}+\frac{2y}{5}=\frac{3}{8}+\frac{3y}{5} \Rightarrow 25 + 16y = 15 + 24y$

$\Rightarrow 8y = 10 \Rightarrow y = \frac{5}{4}$.

$\therefore$ Required ratio $= 1 : \frac{5}{4} = 4 : 5$.

234. Milk in 1st glass $= \frac{1}{2}$ unit; Milk in 2nd glass $= \frac{3}{4}$ unit.

Water in 1st glass $= \frac{1}{2}$ unit;

Water in 2nd glass $= \frac{1}{4}$ unit.

$\therefore$ Required ratio $= \dfrac{\frac{1}{2}+\frac{3}{4}}{\frac{1}{2}+\frac{1}{4}} = \frac{5}{4}\times\frac{4}{3} = 5 : 3$.

235. Milk in the mixture $= \left(\frac{3}{5}+\frac{7}{10}+\frac{11}{15}\right)$ units $= \frac{61}{30}$ units.

Water in the mixture $= \left(\frac{2}{5}+\frac{3}{10}+\frac{4}{15}\right)$ units $= \frac{29}{30}$ units.

$\therefore$ Required ratio $= \frac{61}{30} : \frac{29}{30} = 61 : 29$.

236. Let the containers A, B and C contain $5x$, $4x$ and $5x$ litres of mixtures respectively.

Milk in $A = \left(5x \times \frac{1}{6}\right)$ litres $= \frac{5x}{6}$ litres;

Water in $A = \left(5x - \frac{5x}{6}\right)$ litres $= \frac{25x}{6}$ litres.

Milk in $B = \left(4x \times \frac{3}{8}\right)$ litres $= \frac{3x}{2}$ litres;

Water in $B = \left(4x - \frac{3x}{2}\right)$ litres $= \frac{5x}{2}$ litres.

Milk in $C = \left(5x \times \frac{5}{12}\right)$ litres $= \frac{25x}{12}$ litres;

Water in $C = \left(5x - \frac{25x}{12}\right)$ litres $= \frac{35x}{12}$ litres.

Total milk in final mixture $= \left(\frac{5x}{6}+\frac{3x}{2}+\frac{25x}{12}\right)$ litres

$= \left(\frac{53x}{12}\right)$ litres.

Total water in final mixture $= \left(\frac{25x}{6}+\frac{5x}{2}+\frac{35x}{12}\right)$ litres

$= \left(\frac{115x}{12}\right)$ litres.

$\therefore$ Required ratio of milk and water $= \frac{53x}{12} : \frac{115x}{12} = 53 : 115$.

237. Milk in 1st glass $= \frac{1}{2}$ unit; Milk in second glass $= \frac{2}{3}$ unit;

Milk in 3rd glass $= \frac{3}{4}$ unit;

Water in 1st glass $= \frac{1}{2}$ unit;

Water in second glass $= \frac{1}{3}$ unit;

Water in 3rd glass $= \frac{1}{4}$ unit.

$\therefore$ Required ratio $= \dfrac{\frac{1}{2}+\frac{2}{3}+\frac{3}{4}}{\frac{1}{2}+\frac{1}{3}+\frac{1}{4}} = \frac{6+8+9}{6+4+3} = \frac{23}{13}$.

238. Gold in new coins $= \left(\frac{2}{3}+2\times\frac{3}{8}+3\times\frac{7}{12}\right)$ units

$= \left(\frac{2}{3}+\frac{3}{4}+\frac{7}{4}\right)$ units $= \frac{19}{6}$ units.

Silver in new coins $= \left(\frac{1}{3}+2\times\frac{5}{8}+3\times\frac{5}{12}\right)$ units

$= \left(\frac{1}{3}+\frac{5}{4}+\frac{5}{4}\right)$ units $= \frac{17}{6}$ units.

$\therefore$ Required ratio $= \frac{19}{6} : \frac{17}{6} = 19 : 17$.

239. Let 5 kg of the first variety be mixed with 4 kg of second variety.

Then, C.P. of 9 kg of tea = ₹ $(20 \times 5 + 25 \times 4)$ = ₹ 200.

S.P. of 9 kg of tea = ₹ (23×9) = ₹ 207.

Profit = ₹ $(207 - 200)$ = ₹ 7.

$\therefore$ Profit % $= \left(\frac{7}{200}\times 100\right)\% = 3.5\%$.

240. Let the quantities of the three varieties taken be x kg, x kg and $2x$ kg respectively.

Let the cost of the third variety be ₹ y per kg.

Then, $126x + 135x + 2xy = 153\,(x + x + 2x)$

$\Leftrightarrow 261x + 2xy = 612x$

$\Leftrightarrow 2y = 612 - 261 = 351$

$\Leftrightarrow y = 175.50$.

241. Let the weights of the three varieties be $12x$, $15x$ and $20x$ kg respectively.

Then, total C.P. = ₹ $(100 \times 12x + 80 \times 15x + 60 \times 20x)$ = ₹ $(3600x)$.

Total S.P. = ₹ $(3600x)$.

S.P. of the first two varieties = ₹ $\left(\frac{120}{100}\times 2400x\right)$ = ₹ $(2880x)$.

S.P. of the third variety = ₹ $(3600x - 2880x)$ = ₹ $720x$.

Loss on third variety = ₹ $(1200x - 720x)$ = ₹ $480x$.

Loss% $= \left(\frac{480x}{1200x}\times 100\right)\% = 40\%$.

242. Clearly, $x = 50$ litres, $y = 10$ litres, $n = 2$.

Quantity of milk in the final mixture

$= \left[50\left(1-\frac{10}{50}\right)^2\right]$ litres $= \left[50\times\left(\frac{4}{5}\right)^2\right]$ litres

$= \left(50\times\frac{16}{25}\right)$ litres $= 32$ litres.

Quantity of water in the final mixture = (50 – 32) litres = 18 litres.

$\therefore$ Required ratio = 18 : 32 = 9 : 16.

243. Let the original quantity of the wine be x litres.

Then, $y = 8$, $n = 4$.

Quantity of wine in the final mixture $= \left[x\left(1-\frac{8}{x}\right)^4\right]$ litres

$= \frac{x(x-8)^4}{x^4}$ litres.

Quantity of water in the final mixture $= \left[x - \frac{x(x-8)^4}{x^4}\right]$ litres $= \left[\frac{x^5 - x(x-8)^4}{x^4}\right]$ litres.

$\therefore \frac{x(x-8)^4}{x^5 - x(x-8)^4} = \frac{16}{65} \Rightarrow 65x(x-8)^4$

$= 16x^5 - 16x(x-8)^4$

$\Rightarrow 81x(x-8)^4 = 16x^5$

$\Rightarrow (x-8)^4 = \frac{16}{81}x^4 = \left(\frac{2}{3}x\right)^4 \Rightarrow x - 8 = \frac{2}{3}x \Rightarrow \frac{x}{3} = 8$

$\Rightarrow x = 24$.

244. $G = 19\ W$ and $C = 9\ W$.

Let 1 gm of gold be mixed with x gm of copper to get $(1 + x)$ gm of the alloy.

(1 gm gold) + (x gm copper) = $(x + 1)$ gm of alloy

$\Leftrightarrow 19\ W + 9\ Wx = (x + 1) \times 15\ W$

$\Leftrightarrow 19 + 9x = 15(x + 1)$

$\Leftrightarrow 6x = 4 \Leftrightarrow x = \frac{2}{3}$.

$\therefore$ Ratio of gold and copper $= 1 : \frac{2}{3} = 3 : 2$.

245. Ratio of time taken $= \frac{1}{5} : \frac{1}{4} : \frac{1}{6} = 12 : 15 : 10$.

246. L.C.M. of 2, 3, 4, 5, 7 = 420.

Given ratio $= \frac{1}{2} : \frac{1}{3} : \frac{1}{4} : \frac{1}{5} : \frac{1}{7}$

$= \left(\frac{1}{2} \times 420\right) : \left(\frac{1}{3} \times 420\right) : \left(\frac{1}{4} \times 420\right) : \left(\frac{1}{5} \times 420\right) : \left(\frac{1}{7} \times 420\right)$

= 210 : 140 : 105 : 84 : 60

$\therefore$ Required minimum amount = Sum of ratio terms

= ₹ (210 + 140 + 105 + 84 + 60) = ₹ 599.

247. Let the incomes of A, B and C be ₹ $7x$, ₹ $10x$ and ₹ $12x$ respectively and their expenses be ₹ $8y$, ₹ $10y$ and ₹ $15y$ respectively.

Then, $7x - 8y = \frac{1}{5} \times 7x$

$\Rightarrow 8y = 7x - \frac{7x}{5} = \frac{28x}{5}$

$\Rightarrow 28x = 40y \Rightarrow \frac{x}{y} = \frac{40}{28} = \frac{10}{7}$.

Let $x = 10t$ and $y = 7t$.

Then, B's saving = ₹ $(10x - 10y)$ = ₹ $[10(x - y)]$

= ₹ $[10(10t - 7t)]$ = ₹ $(30t)$.

C's saving = ₹ $(12x - 15y)$ = ₹ $(120t - 105t)$ = ₹ $(15t)$.

$\therefore$ Required percentage $= \left(\frac{30t - 15t}{15t} \times 100\right)\% = 100\%$.

248. Let the present ages of the mother, son and father be $11x$, $5x$ and y years respectively.

Then, the son will become as old as his mother is now, after $(11x - 5x) = 6x$ years.

After $6x$ years, father's age = $(y + 6x)$ years; mother's age = $(11x + 6x)$ years = $17x$ years.

$\therefore \frac{y + 6x}{17x} = \frac{19}{17} \Rightarrow y + 6x = 19x \Rightarrow y = 13x$.

Again, the son will become as old as his father is now, after $(y - 5x) = (13x - 5x) = 8x$ years.

After $8x$ years, father's age = $(y + 8x)$ years = $21x$ years; son's age = $(5x + 8x)$ years = $13x$ years.

$\therefore 21x + 13x = 170 \Rightarrow 34x = 170 \Rightarrow x = 5$.

Hence, father's present age = $y = 13x$ = (13 × 5) years = 65 years.

249. $ad = \frac{ab \times cd}{bc} = \frac{1 \times 6}{(1/2)} = 12$.

$be = \frac{bc \times de}{cd} = \frac{\frac{1}{2} \times 2}{6} = \frac{1}{6}$.

$cf = \frac{cd \times ef}{de} = \frac{6 \times \frac{1}{2}}{2} = \frac{3}{2}$.

$\therefore ad : be : cf = 12 : \frac{1}{6} : \frac{3}{2} = 72 : 1 : 9$.

250. Let the C.P. of the articles be ₹ x, ₹ $2x$ and ₹ $3x$ respectively and the number of articles of each type sold be $3y$, $2y$ and y respectively. Then,

Total C.P. = ₹ $(x \times 3y + 2x \times 2y + 3x \times y)$ = ₹ $(10xy)$.

Total S.P. = ₹ $\left(\frac{110}{100} \times x \times 3y + \frac{120}{100} \times 2x \times 2y + \frac{130}{100} \times 3x \times y\right)$

= ₹ $\left(\frac{33xy}{10} + \frac{48xy}{10} + \frac{39xy}{10}\right)$ = ₹ $(12xy)$.

$\therefore$ Net gain % $= \left(\frac{2xy}{10xy} \times 100\right)\% = 20\%$.

251. Let the monthly salaries of Rene and Som be $5a$ and $3a$ respectively

Money spent by Rene

$= \left(\frac{1}{6} \text{ of } 5a + \frac{1}{5} \text{ of } 5a + 30\% \text{ of } 5a + 25\% \text{ of } 5a\right)$

According to given information

$\Rightarrow 5a - \left[5a \times \frac{1}{6} + 5a \times \frac{1}{5} + 5a \times \frac{3}{10} + \frac{5a}{4}\right] = 5000$

$\Rightarrow 5a - \left[\frac{5a}{6} + a + \frac{3a}{2} + \frac{5a}{4}\right] = 5000$

$\Rightarrow 5a - \left(\frac{55a}{12}\right) = 5000$

$\Rightarrow 60a - 55a = 60000 \Rightarrow a = 12000$

$\therefore$ Som's salary = 3 × 12000 = ₹36000

252. Let third proportional be x

$\Rightarrow 25 : 30 :: 30 : x$

$\Rightarrow 25 \times x = 30 \times 30$

$\Rightarrow x = \frac{30 \times 30}{25} = 36$

253. Ratio of syrup and water in the mixture = 3 : 1

Quantity of syrup = $\frac{3}{4}$

Quantity of water = $\frac{1}{4}$

Percentage of syrup $\frac{3}{4} \times 100 = 75\%$

254. $a^2 + b^2 + c^2 - ab - bc - ca = 0$ ...(i)

Multiple equation (i) by 2 we get

$\Rightarrow 2a^2 + 2b^2 + 2c^2 - 2ab - 2bc - 2ca = 0$

$\Rightarrow (a^2 + b^2 - 2ab) + (b^2 + c^2 - 2bc) + (c^2 + a^2 - 2ca) = 0$

$\{\because (a+b)^2 = a^2 + b^2 + 2ab\}$

$\Rightarrow (a-b)^2 + (b-c)^2 + (c-a)^2 = 0$

[If $x^2 + y^2 + z^2 = 0$ then $x = 0, y = 0, z = 0$]

$\therefore a - b = 0 \Rightarrow a = b$

$b - c = 0 \Rightarrow b = c$

$c - a = 0 \Rightarrow c = a$

$\therefore a = b = c$

$\therefore a : b : c = 1 : 1 : 1$

255. Let the first number be x and second number be y

According to the question, 80% of $x = \frac{4}{5}$ of y

$\Rightarrow \frac{80 \times x}{100} = \frac{4 \times y}{5}$

$\Rightarrow \frac{4x}{5} = \frac{4y}{5}$

$\Rightarrow x : y = 1 : 1$

256. Statement I

Let the population of males and females in city be $27x$ and $23x$ respectively and given

$27x - 23x = 100000$

$4x = 100000$

$x = 25000$

Population of males in city A = 25000 × 27 = 675000

Population of females in city A = 25000 × 23 = 575000

Total population = 12,50,000

Statement II

Population of A = $\frac{80}{100}$ of city B

Difference between the population of A and B

$\Rightarrow$ B – A = 3,12,500

$B \times \frac{20}{100} = 3,12,500$

B's population = 15,62,500

A's population = 12,50,000

The data in statement I alone or in statement II alone are sufficient to answer the question.

Hence statement C is correct.

257. Number of students participated in marathon = 208

Number of boys students participated in marathon = 124

According to given information $\frac{4}{7}$th of boys = 124

Total boys = $\frac{124 \times 7}{4} = 217$

Let total number of girls in school be x, Number of girls participated in marathon = 208 – 124 = 84

Number of girls

$\therefore \frac{6}{11}$ of $x = 84$

$\Rightarrow x = \frac{84 \times 11}{6} = 154$

Total students in school

= 217 + 154 = 371

258. Let the monthly salary of Pia and Som be $5a$ and $4a$ respectively.

Then money given by Pia to her mother $= 5a \times \frac{3}{5} = 3a$

Money given by Pia as sister's tuition fees

= 15% of $5a = \frac{15 \times 5a}{100} = \frac{75a}{100}$ 0.75a

Money given by Pia towards loan

= 18% of $5a = \frac{18 \times 5a}{100} = \frac{90a}{100} = 0.9a$

$\therefore$ Total money given = $3a + 0.75a + 0.90a = 4.65a$

$\therefore$ Remaining amount = $5a - 4.65 = 0.35a$

Pia have remaining amount = ₹ 2100

$0.35a = 2100$

$\therefore \frac{35a}{100} = 2100$

$\Rightarrow a = \frac{2100 \times 100}{35}$

a = ₹ 6000

$\therefore$ Monthly salary of Som = $4a = 4 \times 6000$ = ₹ 24000

259. Working hours of Smita = 6 hours

Working hours of Kajal = 7 hours 30 minutes = $1\frac{1}{2}$ hours

Required ratio $= 6 : 7\frac{1}{2} = 6 : \frac{15}{2}$

= 12 : 15 = 4 : 5

260. Ratio of the number of 50 paisa, 25 paisa and 10 paisa coins. = 5 : 8 : 3

Ratio of their values $= \frac{5}{2} : \frac{8}{4} : \frac{3}{10}$

LCM of 2, 4 and 10 = 20

$= \left(\frac{5}{2} \times 20\right) : \left(\frac{8}{4} \times 20\right) : \left(\frac{3}{10} \times 20\right) = 50 : 40 : 6$

Sum of the terms of ratio = 50 + 40 + 6 = 96

$\therefore$ Value of 50 paisa coins $= \frac{50}{96} \times 144 = 75$

$\therefore$ Number of 50 paisa coins = 75 × 2 = 150

261. ₹ 1 = 100 paisa

₹ 4 = 400 paisa

Required ratio

= 50 paisa : 400 paisa

= 1 : 8

262. Quantity of water in bottle = 2 liters

Part of water drank by Raj = $\frac{1}{4}$ part

Part of water drank by Suraj = $\frac{3}{4}$ part

Water taken by Suraj = $\frac{3}{4} \times 2 = 1.5$ liters.

263. Given $\frac{7}{5}$ of $58 + \frac{3}{8}$ of 139.2 = ?

$\frac{7}{5} \times 58 + \frac{3}{8} \times 139.2$

= 81.2 + 52.2 = 133.4

264. Given $\frac{3}{7}$ of $\frac{5}{4}$ of 3024 = ?

$\frac{3}{7} \times \frac{5}{4} \times 3024 = 1620$

265. Let the number of spectators on Monday, Tuesday and Wednesday be $2p$, $3p$ and $5p$, respectively.

Let the price charged on Monday, Tuesday and Wednesday be $2q$, $3q$ and $4q$ respectively.

According to the question.

$4q \times 5p \times 3p = 8800$

$20\ pq - 9\ pq = 8800$

$\Rightarrow 11pq = 8800$

$\Rightarrow pq = 800$

Now, total amount earned on all three days

$= 4\ pq + 9\ pq + 20\ pq$

$= 4 \times 800 + 9 \times 800 + 20 \times 800$

= ₹ (3200 + 7200 + 16000)

= ₹ 26400

EXERCISE

(DATA SUFFICIENCY TYPE QUESTIONS)

Directions (*Questions 1 to 15*): ***Each of the questions below consists of a statement and/or a question and two statements labelled I and II given below it. You have to decide whether the data provided in the statements is/are sufficient to answer the question. Read both the statements and***

Give answer (a) if the data in Statement I alone are sufficient to answer the question, while the data in Statement II alone are not sufficient to answer the question;

Give answer (b) if the data in Statement II alone are sufficient to answer the question, while the data in Statement I alone are not sufficient to answer the question;

Give answer (c) if the data either in Statement I or in Statement II alone are sufficient to answer the question;

Give answer (d) if the data even in both Statements I and II together are not sufficient to answer the question; and

Give answer (e) if the data in both Statements I and II are necessary to answer the question.

1. What is the value of the ratio $p : q$?

   I. $3p = 2q$

   II. $2p + q = 6$

2. What is the value of $x + y : x - y$?

   I. $x : y = 1 : 2$

   II. $x = \frac{y}{2}$ and $y - x = 3$

3. Rohan and Sachin together earn ₹ 14000 per month. How much does Rohan earn?

   I. Their salaries are in the ratio 3 : 4.

   II. Sachin earns ₹ 2000 per month more than Rohan.

4. What is the value of a?

   I. Ratio of a and b is 3 : 5, where b is positive.

   II. Ratio of $2a$ and b is 12 : 10, where a is positive.

5. What was the ratio between the ages of P and R four years ago?

   I. The ratio between the present ages of P and Q is 3 : 4.

   II. The ratio between the present ages of Q and R is 4 : 5.

6. What is the present age of the mother? **(M.A.T., 2007)**

   I. Father's age is 8 years more than the mother's age. Father got married at the age of 28 years.

   II. Present age of the father is 30 years. Four years back the ratio of mother's age to father's age was 12 : 13.

7. How many boys are there in the class? **(M.A.T., 2007)**

   I. The class has 45 children in all and ratio of boys to girls is 4 : 5.

   II. The ratio of girls to boys is 4 : 5 and boys are nine more than the girls.

8. Is $x^2 : y^2 < 1$? **(M.A.T., 2006)**

   I. $(y - x)(x + y) = 40\%$ of $60 - 120\%$ of 20

   II. $x < y$

9. Vipin's and Javed's salaries are in the proportion of 4 : 3 respectively. What is Vipin's salary? **(M.A.T., 2006)**

I. Javed's salary is 75% that of Vipin's salary.

II. Javed's salary is ₹ 4500.

10. The ages of Vinay and Sameer are in the ratio of 7 : 6. What is the age of Sameer?

I. The ages of Vinay and Ajay are in the ratio of 7 : 4.

II. After 5 years the ratio of Vinay's and Sameer's ages will be 8 : 7. (Bank P.O., 2008)

11. The ages of Tanya and Simran are in the ratio of 6 : 5. What is Simran's age?

I. The ages of Tanya and Deepti are in the ratio of 3 : 2.

II. After 6 years the ratio of Deepti's and Simran's ages will be 6 : 7.

12. What is Rajan's present age? (Bank P.O., 2009)

I. Ratio of present ages of Rajan and Madan is 3 : 4 respectively.

II. Five years hence the ratio of ages of Rajan and Madan will be 4 : 5 respectively.

13. What is the difference between the ages of Sumit and Dinesh? (Bank P.O., 2006)

I. The ratio of their ages is 7 : 9 respectively.

II. Five years hence the sum of their ages will be 58 years.

14. How many students are there in the class?

I. Boys and girls are in the ratio of 2 : 3 respectively.

II. Difference between the number of girls and the number of boys is 8 and 60% of the students are girls.

15. Aruna is twice as old as Sneha. What is the difference in their ages?

I. Five years hence, the ratio of their ages would be 9 : 5.

II. Ten years back, the ratio of their ages was 3 : 1.

ANSWERS

1. (a)	2. (c)	3. (c)	4. (d)	5. (d)	6. (b)	7. (c)	8. (c)	9. (b)	10. (b)
11. (e)	12. (e)	13. (e)	14. (b)	15. (c)					

SOLUTIONS

1. I. $3p = 2q \Rightarrow \frac{p}{q} = \frac{2}{3} \Rightarrow p : q = 2 : 3.$

II. From the given equation, we have : $2p = 6 - q$.

So, $p : q$ cannot be determined.

Thus, only I gives the answer.

∴ Correct answer is (*a*).

2. I. $\frac{x+y}{x-y} = \frac{\frac{x}{y}+1}{\frac{x}{y}-1} = \frac{\frac{1}{2}+1}{\frac{1}{2}-1} = \frac{3}{2} \times (-2) = -3.$

II. $x = \frac{y}{2}$ and $y - x = 3 \Rightarrow y - \frac{y}{2} = 3 \Rightarrow \frac{y}{2} = 3 \Rightarrow y = 6.$

So, $x = \frac{y}{2} = \frac{6}{2} = 3.$

$\therefore \frac{x+y}{x-y} = \frac{3+6}{3-6} = \frac{9}{(-3)} = -3.$

Thus, either I alone or II alone gives the answer.

∴ Correct answer is (*c*).

3. I. Let Rohan's and Sachin's salaries be ₹ $3x$ and ₹ $4x$ respectively.

Then, $3x + 4x = 14000 \Rightarrow 7x = 14000 \Rightarrow x = 2000.$

∴ Rohan earns ₹ 6000 per month.

II. Let Rohan's salary = ₹ x.

Then, Sachin's salary = ₹ $(x + 2000)$.

$x + (x + 2000) = 14000 \Rightarrow 2x = 12000 \Rightarrow x = 6000.$

Thus, either I alone or II alone gives the answer.

∴ Correct answer is (*c*).

4. I. $\frac{a}{b} = \frac{3}{5}$ II. $\frac{2a}{b} = \frac{12}{10} \Rightarrow \frac{a}{b} = \frac{1}{2} \times \frac{12}{10} = \frac{3}{5}.$

Hence, a cannot be determined even from both I and II taken together.

∴ Correct answer is (*d*).

5. From both I and II, we have :

$P : Q = 3 : 4$ and $Q : R = 4 : 5 \Rightarrow P : R = 3 : 5.$

Let the present ages of P and R be $3x$ and $5x$ respectively.

Then, ratio of their ages 4 years ago $= \frac{3x-4}{5x-4}$, which cannot be evaluated.

Thus, the answer cannot be obtained even from both I and II taken together.

∴ Correct answer is (*d*).

6. I. Let mother's present age be x years.

Then, father's present age = $(x + 8)$ years.

II. Father's age 4 years back = $(30 - 4)$ years = 26 years.

Let the mother's and father's age 4 years back be $12x$ and $13x$ years respectively.

Then, $13x = 26$ or $x = 2$.

∴ Mother's present age = $[(12 \times 2) + 4]$ years = 28 years.

Thus, II alone gives the answer.

$\therefore$ Correct answer is (*b*).

7. I. Let the number of boys and girls be $4x$ and $5x$ respectively.

Then, $4x + 5x = 45 \Rightarrow 9x = 45 \Rightarrow x = 5$.

$\therefore$ Number of boys $= (4 \times 5) = 20$.

II. Let the number of girls and boys be $4x$ and $5x$ respectively.

Then, $5x - 4x = 9 \Rightarrow x = 9$.

$\therefore$ Number of boys $= (5 \times 9) = 45$.

Thus, either I alone or II alone gives the answer.

$\therefore$ Correct answer is (*c*).

8. I. $(y - x)(y + x) = \left(\frac{40}{100} \times 60\right) - \left(\frac{120}{100} \times 20\right) = 24 - 24 = 0$

$\Rightarrow y^2 - x^2 = 0 \Rightarrow x^2 = y^2$

$\Rightarrow \frac{x^2}{y^2} = 1$. So, $x^2 : y^2 \nless 1$.

II. $x < y \Rightarrow x^2 < y^2$

$\Rightarrow \frac{x^2}{y^2} < 1 \Rightarrow x^2 : y^2 < 1$.

Thus, either I alone or II alone gives the answer.

$\therefore$ Correct answer is (*c*).

9. Let Vipin's and Javed's salaries be ₹ $4x$ and ₹ $3x$ respectively.

I. The fact stated in I is the same as that given in the question.

II. $3x = 4500 \Rightarrow x = 1500$.

So, Vipin's salary $= 4x =$ ₹ $(4 \times 1500) =$ ₹ 6000.

Thus, II alone gives the answer while I alone does not.

$\therefore$ Correct answer is (*b*).

10. Let Vinay's and Sameer's present ages be $7x$ and $6x$ years respectively.

I. Nothing can be deduced from the information given in I.

II. After 5 years, Vinay's age $= (7x + 5)$ and Sameer's age $= (6x + 5)$.

So, $\frac{7x+5}{6x+5} = \frac{8}{7} \Rightarrow 7(7x + 5) = 8(6x + 5) \Rightarrow 49x + 35 = 48x + 40 \Rightarrow x = 5$.

$\therefore$ Sameer's age $= (6 \times 5)$ years $= 30$ years.

Thus, II alone gives the answer while I alone does not.

$\therefore$ Correct answer is (*b*).

11. From both I and II, we have :

Deepti : Tanya = 2 : 3 = 4 : 6 and Tanya : Simran = 6 : 5.

So, Deepti : Tanya : Simran = 4 : 6 : 5.

Let Deepti's and Simran's present ages be $4x$ and $5x$ years respectively.

Then, $\frac{4x+6}{5x+6} = \frac{6}{7} \Rightarrow 7(4x + 6) = 6(5x + 6)$

$\Rightarrow 28x + 42 = 30x + 36 \Rightarrow 2x = 6 \Rightarrow x = 3$.

$\therefore$ Simran's age $= (5 \times 3)$ years $= 15$ years.

Thus, both I and II together give the answer.

$\therefore$ Correct answer is (*e*).

12. From both I and II, we have :

Let the present ages of Rajan and Madan be $3x$ and $4x$ years respectively.

Then, $\frac{3x+5}{4x+5} = \frac{4}{5} \Rightarrow 5(3x + 5) = 4(4x + 5)$

$\Rightarrow 15x + 25 = 16x + 20 \Rightarrow x = 5$.

So, Rajan's present age $= (3 \times 5)$ years $= 15$ years.

Thus, both I and II together give the answer.

$\therefore$ Correct answer is (*e*).

13. From both I and II, we have :

Let the present ages of Sumit and Dinesh be $7x$ and $9x$ years respectively.

Then, Sumit's age 5 years hence $= (7x + 5)$ years;

Dinesh's age 5 years hence $= (9x + 5)$ years.

So, $(7x + 5) + (9x + 5) = 58$

$\Rightarrow 16x = 48 \Rightarrow x = 3$.

$\therefore$ Required difference $= 9x - 7x = 2x$

$= (2 \times 3)$ years $= 6$ years.

Thus, both I and II together give the answer.

$\therefore$ Correct answer is (*e*).

14. I. Let the number of boys and girls be $2x$ and $3x$ respectively.

II. Let the total strength of the class be x.

Then, number of girls $= 60\%$ of $x = \frac{3x}{5}$; number of boys $= 40\%$ of $x = \frac{2x}{5}$.

So, $\frac{3x}{5} - \frac{2x}{5} = 8 \Rightarrow \frac{x}{5} = 8 \Rightarrow x = 40$.

$\therefore$ Total number of students $= 40$.

Thus, II alone gives the answer while I alone does not.

$\therefore$ Correct answer is (*b*).

15. Let the present ages of Sneha and Aruna be x and $2x$ years respectively. Then,

I. $\frac{2x+5}{x+5} = \frac{9}{5} \Rightarrow 5(2x + 5) = 9(x + 5) \Rightarrow x = 20$.

So, required difference $= 2x - x = x = 20$ years.

II. $\frac{2x-10}{x-10} = \frac{3}{1} \Rightarrow 2x - 10 = 3(x - 10) \Rightarrow 2x - 10 = 3x - 30 \Rightarrow x = 20$.

So, required difference = 20 years.

Thus, either I alone or II alone gives the answer.

$\therefore$ Correct answer is (*c*).

14 Partnership

IMPORTANT FACTS

I. Partnership: When two or more than two persons run a business jointly, they are called partners and the deal is known as partnership.

II. Ratio of Division of Gains:

(i) **Simple Partnership:** *A simple partnership is the one in which the capitals of all the partners are invested for the same time.*

In this partnership, the gain or loss is distributed among the partners in the ratio of their investments.

Suppose A and B invest ₹ x and ₹ y respectively for a year in a business, then at the end of the year:

(A's share of profit) : (B's share of profit) = $x : y$.

(ii) **Compound Partnership:** *A compound partnership is the one in which the capitals of the partners are invested for different time periods.*

In this partnership, the equivalent capitals are calculated for a unit of time by taking (capital × number of units of time). Now, gain or loss is divided in the ratio of these capitals.

Suppose A invests ₹ x for p months and B invests ₹ y for q months, then

(A's share of profit) : (B's share of profit) = $xp : yq$.

III. Working and Sleeping Partners: *A partner who manages the business is known as a working partner and the one who simply invests the money is a sleeping partner.*

SOLVED EXAMPLES

Ex. 1. ***A, B and C started a business by investing ₹ 120000, ₹ 135000 and ₹ 150000 respectively. Find the share of each, out of an annual profit of ₹ 56700.***

Sol. Ratio of shares of A, B and C = Ratio of their investments

$= 120000 : 135000 : 150000 = 8 : 9 : 10.$

$\therefore$ A's share $= ₹ \left(56700 \times \frac{8}{27}\right) = ₹\ 16800$; B's share $= ₹ \left(56700 \times \frac{9}{27}\right) = ₹\ 18900$;

C's share $= ₹ \left(56700 \times \frac{10}{27}\right) = ₹\ 21000.$

Ex. 2. ***Alfred started a business investing ₹ 45000. After 3 months, Peter joined him with a capital of ₹ 60000. After another 6 months, Ronald joined them with a capital of ₹ 90000. At the end of the year, they made a profit of ₹ 16500. Find the share of each.***

Sol. Clearly, Alfred invested his capital for 12 months, Peter for 9 months and Ronald for 3 months.

So, ratio of their capitals $= (45000 \times 12) : (60000 \times 9) : (90000 \times 3)$

$= 540000 : 540000 : 270000 = 2 : 2 : 1.$

$\therefore$ Alfred's share $= ₹ \left(16500 \times \frac{2}{5}\right) = ₹\ 6600$; Peter's share $= ₹ \left(16500 \times \frac{2}{5}\right) = ₹\ 6600$;

Ronald's share $= ₹ \left(16500 \times \frac{1}{5}\right) = ₹\ 3300.$

Ex. 3. ***A, B and C start a business each investing ₹ 20000. After 5 months A withdrew ₹ 5000, B withdrew ₹ 4000 and C invests ₹ 6000 more. At the end of the year, a total profit of ₹ 69900 was recorded. Find the share of each.*** **(SNAP, 2005)**

Sol. Ratio of the capitals of A, B and C

$= 20000 \times 5 + 15000 \times 7 : 20000 \times 5 + 16000 \times 7 : 20000 \times 5 + 26000 \times 7$

$= 205000 : 212000 : 282000 = 205 : 212 : 282.$

$\therefore$ A's share $= ₹\left(69900 \times \frac{205}{699}\right) = ₹\ 20500;$ B's share $= ₹\left(69900 \times \frac{212}{699}\right) = ₹\ 21200;$

C's share $= ₹\left(69900 \times \frac{282}{699}\right) = ₹\ 28200.$

Ex. 4. ***A, B and C enter into partnership. A invests 3 times as much as B invests and B invests two-thirds of what C invests. At the end of the year, the profit earned is ₹ 6600. What is the share of B?***

Sol. Let C's capital = ₹ x. Then, B's capital = ₹ $\frac{2}{3}x$. A's capital $= ₹\left(3 \times \frac{2}{3}x\right) = ₹\ 2x.$

$\therefore$ Ratio of their capitals $= 2x : \frac{2}{3}x : x = 6 : 2 : 3.$

Hence, B's share $= ₹\left(6600 \times \frac{2}{11}\right) = ₹\ 1200.$

Ex. 5. ***A, B and C enter into a partnership with capitals in the ratio $\frac{7}{2} : \frac{4}{3} : \frac{6}{5}$. After 4 months A increases his share of capital by 50%. If at the end of the year the total profit earned is ₹ 2430, find the share of each in the profit.***

Sol. Ratio of capitals $= \frac{7}{2} : \frac{4}{3} : \frac{6}{5} = \left(\frac{7}{2} \times 30\right) : \left(\frac{4}{3} \times 30\right) : \left(\frac{6}{5} \times 30\right) = 105 : 40 : 36.$

Let the initial capitals of A, B and C be ₹ $105x$, ₹ $40x$ and ₹ $36x$ respectively.

Then, ratio of profits $= [105x \times 4 + (150\% \text{ of } 105x) \times 8] : (40x \times 12) : (36x \times 12)$

$= 1680 : 480 : 432 = 35 : 10 : 9.$

$\therefore$ A's share $= ₹\left(2430 \times \frac{35}{54}\right) = ₹\ 1575;$ B's share $= ₹\left(2430 \times \frac{10}{54}\right) = ₹\ 450;$

C's share $= ₹\left(2430 \times \frac{9}{54}\right) = ₹\ 405.$

Ex. 6. ***A, B and C enter into partnership with capitals of ₹ 25000, ₹ 30000 and ₹ 15000 respectively. A is the working partner and he gets 30% of the profit for managing the business. The balance profit is distributed in proportion to the capital investment. At the year-end, A gets ₹ 200 more than B and C together. Find the total profit and the share of each.***

Sol. Let the total profit be ₹ x.

Amount obtained by A for managing $= ₹\left(\frac{30x}{100}\right) = ₹\left(\frac{3x}{10}\right).$

Balance profit $= ₹\left(x - \frac{3x}{10}\right) = ₹\left(\frac{7x}{10}\right).$

Ratio of capitals $= 25000 : 30000 : 15000 = 5 : 6 : 3.$

$\therefore$ A's share $= ₹\left[\left(\frac{7x}{10} \times \frac{5}{14}\right) + \frac{3x}{10}\right] = ₹\left(\frac{11x}{20}\right);$ B's share $= ₹\left(\frac{7x}{10} \times \frac{6}{14}\right) = ₹\left(\frac{3x}{10}\right);$

C's share $= ₹\left(\frac{7x}{10} \times \frac{3}{14}\right) = ₹\left(\frac{3x}{20}\right).$

$\therefore \frac{3x}{10}+\frac{3x}{20}+200=\frac{11x}{20} \Rightarrow x=2000.$

So, total profit = ₹ 2000.

$\therefore$ A's share = ₹ $\left(\frac{11\times 2000}{20}\right)$ = ₹ 1100; B's share = ₹ $\left(\frac{3\times 2000}{10}\right)$ = ₹ 600;

C's share = ₹ $\left(\frac{3\times 2000}{20}\right)$ = ₹ 300.

Ex. 7. ***Four milkmen rented a pasture. A grazed 24 cows for 3 months; B 10 cows for 5 months; C 35 cows for 4 months and D 21 cows for 3 months. If A's share of rent is ₹ 720, find the total rent of the field.***

Sol. Ratio of shares of A, B, C, D = (24 × 3) : (10 × 5) : (35 × 4) : (21 × 3)
= 72 : 50 : 140 : 63.

Let total rent be ₹ x. Then, A's share = ₹ $\frac{72x}{325}$.

$\therefore \frac{72x}{325}=720 \Leftrightarrow x=\frac{720\times 325}{72}=3250.$

Hence, total rent of the field is ₹ 3250.

Ex. 8. ***Two persons A and B take a field on rent. A put on it 21 horses for 3 months and 15 cows for 2 months; B puts 15 cows for 6 months and 40 sheep for $7\frac{1}{2}$ months. If, in one day, 3 horses eat as much as 5 cows eat and 6 cows as much as 10 sheep, what part of the rent should A pay?***

Sol. 6 cows ≡ 10 sheep $\Rightarrow$ 1 cow ≡ $\frac{5}{3}$ sheep.

3 horses ≡ 5 cows $\Rightarrow$ 1 horse ≡ $\frac{5}{3}$ cows ≡ $\left(\frac{5}{3}\times\frac{5}{3}\right)$ sheep ≡ $\frac{25}{9}$ sheep.

$\therefore$ Ratio of shares of A and B

$$=\left[\left(21\times\frac{25}{9}\times 3\right)+\left(15\times\frac{5}{3}\times 2\right)\right]:\left[\left(15\times\frac{5}{3}\times 6\right)+\left(40\times\frac{15}{2}\right)\right]=225:450=1:2.$$

Hence, part of the rent paid by A = $\frac{1}{3}$.

Ex. 9. ***A, B and C took a house on rent for one year for ₹ 13824. They remained together for 4 months and then C left the house. After 5 more months, B also left the house. How much rent should each pay?***

(S.S.C., 2006)

Sol. Monthly rent = ₹ $\left(\frac{13824}{12}\right)$ = ₹ 1152.

Rent for first 4 months = ₹ (1152 × 4) = ₹ 4608.
It is to be divided equally among A, B and C.

$\therefore$ Share of each = ₹ $\left(\frac{4608}{3}\right)$ = ₹ 1536.

Rent for next 5 months = ₹ (1152 × 5) = ₹ 5760.
It is to be divided equally between A and B.

$\therefore$ Share of each = ₹ $\left(\frac{5760}{2}\right)$ = ₹ 2880.

Rent for last 3 months = ₹ (1152 × 3) = ₹ 3456.
It is to be paid by A only.

$\therefore$ Total rent paid by A = ₹ (1536 + 2880 + 3456) = ₹ 7872.
Total rent paid by B = ₹ (1536 + 2880) = ₹ 4416.
Total rent paid by C = ₹ 1536.

Ex. 10. ***A invested ₹ 76000 in a business. After few months, B joined him with ₹ 57000. At the end of the year, the total profit was divided between them in the ratio 2 : 1. After how many months did B join?***

Sol. Suppose B joined after x months.

Then, B's money was invested for $(12 - x)$ months.

$$\therefore \frac{76000 \times 12}{57000 \times (12 - x)} = \frac{2}{1} \Leftrightarrow 912000 = 114000\,(12 - x)$$

$$\Leftrightarrow 114\,(12 - x) = 912$$

$$\Leftrightarrow (12 - x) = 8 \quad \Leftrightarrow \quad x = 4.$$

Hence, B joined after 4 months.

Ex. 11. ***The ratio of investments of two partners A and B is 11 : 12 and the ratio of their profits is 2 : 3. If A invested the money for 8 months, then for how much time B invested his money?*** (S.S.C., 2008)

Sol. Suppose A invested ₹ $11x$ for 8 months and B invested ₹ $12x$ for y months.

Then, $\frac{11x \times 8}{12x \times y} = \frac{2}{3} \Rightarrow 24y = 264 \Rightarrow y = 11.$

Hence, B invested the money for 11 months.

Ex. 12. ***A, B and C are partners in a business. A, whose money has been used for 4 months, claims $\frac{1}{8}$ of the profit. B, whose money has been used for 6 months, claims $\frac{1}{3}$ of the profit. C had invested ₹ 1560 for 8 months. How much money did A and B contribute?***

Sol. Let the total profit be ₹ x.

Then, A's share = ₹ $\frac{x}{8}$; B's share = ₹ $\frac{x}{3}$;

C's share = ₹ $\left[x - \left(\frac{x}{8} + \frac{x}{3}\right)\right]$ = ₹ $\left(x - \frac{11x}{24}\right)$ = ₹ $\left(\frac{13x}{24}\right)$.

$\therefore$ Ratio of shares of A, B and C = $\frac{x}{8} : \frac{x}{3} : \frac{13x}{24} = 3 : 8 : 13.$

Suppose A invested ₹ y for 4 months and B invested ₹ z for 6 months.

Then, $\frac{y \times 4}{1560 \times 8} = \frac{3}{13} \Rightarrow 52y = 37440 \Rightarrow y = 720.$

And, $\frac{z \times 6}{1560 \times 8} = \frac{8}{13} \Rightarrow 78z = 99840 \Rightarrow z = 1280.$

Hence, A's contribution = ₹ 720 ; B's contribution = ₹ 1280.

Ex. 13. ***A, B and C enter into a partnership by investing in the ratio of 3 : 2 : 4. After one year, B invests another ₹ 270000 and C, at the end of 2 years, also invests ₹ 270000. At the end of three years, profits are shared in the ratio of 3 : 4 : 5. Find the initial investment of each.***

Sol. Let the initial investments of A, B and C be ₹ $3x$, ₹ $2x$ and ₹ $4x$ respectively.

Then, $(3x \times 36) : [(2x \times 12) + (2x + 270000) \times 24] : [(4x \times 24) + (4x + 270000) \times 12] = 3 : 4 : 5$

$\Leftrightarrow 108x : (72x + 6480000) : (144x + 3240000) = 3 : 4 : 5$

$$\therefore \frac{108x}{72x + 6480000} = \frac{3}{4} \Leftrightarrow 432x = 216x + 19440000 \Leftrightarrow 216x = 19440000 \Leftrightarrow x = 90000.$$

Hence, A's initial investment = $3x$ = ₹ 270000;

B's initial investment = $2x$ = ₹ 180000;

C's initial investment = $4x$ = ₹ 360000.

Ex. 14. ***A, B and C enter into a partnership. Their capital contribution is in the ratio 21 : 18 : 14. At the end of the business term they share profits in the ratio 15 : 8 : 9. Find the ratio of time for which they invest their capitals.***

Sol. Suppose A, B and C invest ₹ $21x$ for p months, ₹ $18x$ for q months and ₹ $14x$ for r months.

Then, $21x \times p : 18x \times q : 14x \times r = 15 : 8 : 9 \Rightarrow 21p : 18q : 14r = 15 : 8 : 9$.

Now, $\frac{21p}{18q} = \frac{15}{8} \Rightarrow p = \left(\frac{15}{8} \times \frac{18}{21}\right) q = \frac{45}{28} q$. And, $\frac{18q}{14r} = \frac{8}{9} \Rightarrow q = \left(\frac{8}{9} \times \frac{14}{18}\right) r = \frac{56}{81} r$.

$\therefore \quad p = \frac{45}{28} q = \left(\frac{45}{28} \times \frac{56}{81}\right) r = \frac{10}{9} r$.

So, required ratio $= p : q : r = \frac{10}{9} r : \frac{56}{81} r : r = \frac{10}{9} : \frac{56}{81} : 1 = 90 : 56 : 81$.

EXERCISE

(OBJECTIVE TYPE QUESTIONS)

Directions: ***Mark* (✓) *against the correct answer:***

1. Rahul, Arun and Sumit started a business. Rahul invested $\frac{1}{2}$ part, Arun $\frac{1}{3}$ part and rest of the capital was invested by Sumit. The ratio of their profits will be **(P.C.S., 2006)**

   (*a*) 2 : 3 : 1 (*b*) 3 : 2 : 1
   (*c*) 2 : 3 : 6 (*d*) 3 : 2 : 5

2. P and Q started a business investing ₹ 85000 and ₹ 15000 respectively. In what ratio the profit earned after 2 years be divided between P and Q respectively?

   (*a*) 3 : 4 (*b*) 3 : 5
   (*c*) 15 : 23 (*d*) 17 : 23
   (*e*) None of these

3. Anand and Deepak started a business investing ₹ 22500 and ₹ 35000 respectively. Out of a total profit of ₹ 13800, Deepak's share is

   (*a*) ₹ 5400 (*b*) ₹ 7200
   (*c*) ₹ 8400 (*d*) ₹ 9600

4. Samaira, Mahira and Kiara rented a set of DVDs at a rent of ₹ 578. If they used it for 8 hours, 12 hours and 14 hours respectively, what is Kiara's share of rent to be paid? **(Bank P.O., 2008)**

   (*a*) ₹ 192 (*b*) ₹ 204
   (*c*) ₹ 215 (*d*) ₹ 238
   (*e*) None of these

5. P, Q and R invested ₹ 45000, ₹ 70000 and ₹ 90000 respectively to start a business. At the end of 2 years, they earned a profit of ₹ 164000. What will be Q's share in the profit? **(Bank P.O., 2009)**

   (*a*) ₹ 36000 (*b*) ₹ 56000
   (*c*) ₹ 64000 (*d*) ₹ 72000
   (*e*) None of these

6. Prakash, Sachin and Anil started a business jointly investing ₹ 11 lakh, ₹ 16.5 lakh and ₹ 8.25 lakh respectively. The profit earned by them in the business at the end of 3 years was ₹ 19.5 lakh. What will be 50% of Anil's share in the profit? **(Bank P.O., 2009)**

   (*a*) ₹ 2.25 lakh (*b*) ₹ 2.5 lakh
   (*c*) ₹ 3.75 lakh (*d*) ₹ 4.5 lakh
   (*e*) None of these

7. Two friends invested ₹ 1500 and ₹ 2500 in a business. They earned a profit of ₹ 800. One-half of the profit was divided equally between them and the other half was divided in proportion to their capitals. How much did each of them receive? **(Campus Recruitment, 2009)**

   (*a*) ₹ 350 and ₹ 450 (*b*) ₹ 360 and ₹ 440
   (*c*) ₹ 370 and ₹ 430 (*d*) ₹ 375 and ₹ 425

8. Three persons stared a placement business with a capital of ₹ 3000. B invests ₹ 600 less than A and C invests ₹ 300 less than B. What is B's share in a profit of ₹ 886? **(Campus Recruitment, 2010)**

   (*a*) ₹ 443 (*b*) ₹ 354.40
   (*c*) ₹ 265.80 (*d*) ₹ 177.20

9. Reena and Shaloo are partners in a business. Reena invests ₹ 35000 for 8 months and Shaloo invests ₹ 42000 for 10 months. Out of a profit of ₹ 31570, Reena's share is :

   (*a*) ₹ 9471 (*b*) ₹ 12,628
   (*c*) ₹ 18,040 (*d*) ₹ 18942

10. Shankar started a business with an investment of ₹ 120,000. After three months, Aniket joined him with an investment of ₹ 190,000. They earned a profit of ₹ 17,50,000 after one year. What is Aniket's share in the profit? **(Bank P.O., 2008)**

    (*a*) ₹ 800000 (*b*) ₹ 850000
    (*c*) ₹ 900000 (*d*) ₹ 950000
    (*e*) None of these

11. Arun started a business investing ₹ 38000. After 5 months Bakul joined him with a capital of ₹ 55000. At the end of the year the total profit was ₹ 22000. What is the approximate difference between the shares of profits of Arun and Bakul? **(Bank P.O., 2007)**

    (*a*) ₹ 1007 (*b*) ₹ 1192
    (*c*) ₹ 1568 (*d*) ₹ 1857
    (*e*) ₹ 1928

12. Gautam started a business with a sum of ₹ 60000. Jatin joined him 8 months later with a sum of ₹ 35000. At what respective ratio will the two share the profit after two years? **(Bank P.O., 2008)**

(*a*) 2 : 1 (*b*) 3 : 1
(*c*) 18 : 7 (*d*) 37 : 14
(*e*) None of these

13. Simran started a software business by investing ₹ 50000. After six months, Nanda joined her with a capital of ₹ 80000. After 3 years, they earned a profit of ₹ 24500. What was Simran's share in the profit? **(Bank P.O., 2004)**

(*a*) ₹ 9423 (*b*) ₹ 10,250
(*c*) ₹ 12500 (*d*) ₹ 14000
(*e*) None of these

14. Dilip, Ram and Avtar started a shop by investing ₹ 2700, ₹ 8100 and ₹ 7200 respectively. At the end of one year, the profit earned was distributed. If Ram's share was ₹ 3600, what was their total profit? **(R.R.B., 2006)**

(*a*) ₹ 8000 (*b*) ₹ 10800
(*c*) ₹ 11600 (*d*) Data inadequate

15. A and B started a business in partnership investing ₹ 20000 and ₹ 15000 respectively. After six months, C joined them with ₹ 20000. What will be B's share in the total profit of ₹ 25000 earned at the end of 2 years from the starting of the business?

(*a*) ₹ 7500 (*b*) ₹ 9000
(*c*) ₹ 9500 (*d*) ₹ 10000
(*e*) None of these

16. Aman started a business investing ₹ 70000. Rakhi joined him after six months with an amount of ₹ 105000 and Sagar joined them with ₹ 1.4 lakhs after another six months. The amount of profit earned should be distributed in what ratio among Aman, Rakhi and Sagar respectively, 3 years after Aman started the business?

(*a*) 7 : 6 : 10 (*b*) 12 : 15 : 16
(*c*) 42 : 45 : 56 (*d*) Cannot be determined
(*e*) None of these

17. Sonia started a business investing ₹ 60000. After 6 months Vivek joined him with an amount of ₹ 140000. After 1 year Kirti also joined them with ₹ 120000. After 2 years the business yielded a total profit of ₹ 450000. What is the share of Vivek in the profit? **(Bank P.O., 2005)**

(*a*) ₹ 140000 (*b*) ₹ 198500
(*c*) ₹ 210000 (*d*) ₹ 215000
(*e*) None of these

18. Arun, Kamal and Vinay invested ₹ 8000, ₹ 4000 and ₹ 8000 respectively in a business. Arun left after six months. If after eight months, there was a gain of ₹ 4005, then what will be the share of Kamal?

(*a*) ₹ 890 (*b*) ₹ 1335
(*c*) ₹ 1602 (*d*) ₹ 1780

19. P and Q started a business in the ratio of 2 : 3. After 1 year P left the business but Q continues. After 2 years he had the profit of ₹ 26000. What is the profit of Q? **(Bank Recruitment, 2007)**

(*a*) ₹ 10400 (*b*) ₹ 13000
(*c*) ₹ 15600 (*d*) ₹ 18500
(*e*) None of these

20. A, B and C enter into a partnership. A invests some money at the beginning, B invests double the amount after six months and C invests thrice the amount after eight months. If the annual profit be ₹ 27000; C's share (in ₹) is **(G.B.O., 2007)**

(*a*) ₹ 8625 (*b*) ₹ 9000
(*c*) ₹ 10800 (*d*) ₹ 11250

21. A, B and C enter into a partner ship. They invest ₹ 40000, ₹ 80000 and ₹ 120000 respectively. At the end of the first year, B withdraws ₹ 40,000, while at the end of the second year, C withdraws ₹ 80000. In what ratio will the profit be shared at the end of 3 years?

(*a*) 2 : 3 : 5 (*b*) 3 : 4 : 7
(*c*) 4 : 5 : 9 (*d*) None of these

22. A, B and C enter into a partnership. A initially invests ₹ 25 lakhs and adds another ₹ 10 lakhs after one year. B initially invests ₹ 35 lakhs and withdraws ₹ 10 lakhs after 2 years and C invests ₹ 30 lakhs. In what ratio should the profits be divided at the end of 3 years?

(*a*) 10 : 10 : 9 (*b*) 20 : 20 : 19
(*c*) 20 : 19 : 18 (*d*) None of these

23. Subhash starts a business by investing ₹ 25000. 6 months later Aditya joins him by investing ₹ 15000. After another 6 months Aditya invests an additional amount of ₹ 15000. At the end of 3 years they earn a profit of ₹ 247000. What is Aditya's share in the profit? **(Bank P.O., 2006)**

(*a*) ₹ 105000 (*b*) ₹ 111500
(*c*) ₹ 123000 (*d*) ₹ 130000
(*e*) None of these

24. Shekhar started a business investing ₹ 25000 in 2009. In 2010, he invested an additional amount of ₹ 10000 and Rajeev joined him with an amount of ₹ 35000. In 2011, Shekhar invested another additional amount of ₹ 10000 and Jatin joined them with an amount of ₹ 35000. What will be Rajeev's share in the profit of ₹ 150000 earned at the end of 3 years from the start of the business in 2009?

(*a*) ₹ 45000 (*b*) ₹ 50000
(*c*) ₹ 70000 (*d*) ₹ 75000
(*e*) None of these

25. A and B entered into a partnership investing ₹ 16000 and ₹ 12000 respectively. After 3 months, A withdrew ₹ 5000 while B invested ₹ 5000 more. After 3 more months, C joins the business with a capital of ₹ 21000. The share of B exceeds that of C, out of a total profit of ₹ 26,400 after one year by

(a) ₹ 2400 (b) ₹ 3000
(c) ₹ 3600 (d) ₹ 4800

26. A and B start a business with investments of ₹ 5000 and ₹ 4500 respectively. After 4 months, A takes out half of his capital. After two more months, B takes out one-third of his capital while C joins them with a capital of ₹ 7000. At the end of a year, they earn a profit of ₹ 5080. Find the share of each member in the profit. (Bank P.O., 2003)

(a) A – ₹ 1400, B – ₹ 1900, C – ₹ 1780
(b) A – ₹ 1600, B – ₹ 1800, C – ₹ 1680
(c) A – ₹ 1800, B – ₹ 1500, C – ₹ 1780
(d) A – ₹ 1680, B – ₹ 1600, C – ₹ 1800
(e) None of these

27. A, B, C subscribe ₹ 50000 for a business. A subscribes ₹ 4000 more than B and B ₹ 5000 more than C. Out of a total profit of ₹ 35000, A receives: (M.A.T., 2005)

(a) ₹ 8400 (b) ₹ 11900
(c) ₹ 13600 (d) ₹ 14700

28. A, B and C are three partners. They altogether invested ₹ 14000 in business. At the end of the year, A got ₹ 337.50, B ₹ 1125 and C ₹ 637.50 as profit. The difference between the investments of B and A was (M.A.T., 2010)

(a) ₹ 2200 (b) ₹ 3200
(c) ₹ 4200 (d) ₹ 5250

29. A, B and C started a business investing amounts in the ratio of 5 : 6 : 8 respectively. After one year, C withdrew 50% of the amount and A invested an additional amount of 60% of the original amount invested by him. In what ratio, the profit earned at the end of 2 years should be distributed among A, B and C respectively? (Bank P.O., 2004)

(a) 2 : 3 : 3
(b) 4 : 3 : 2
(c) 13 : 12 : 12
(d) Cannot be determined
(e) None of these

30. John, Mona and Gordon, three US based business partners, jointly invested in a business project to supply nuclear fuel to India. As per their share in the investment, Gordon will receive $\frac{2}{3}$ of the profits whereas John and Mona divide the remainder equally. It is estimated that the income of John will increase by $ 60 million when the rate of profit rises from 4% to 7%. What is Mona's capital? (M.B.A., 2009)

(a) $ 2000 million (b) $ 3000 million
(c) $ 5000 million (d) $ 8000 million

31. Anu is a working partner and Bimla is a sleeping partner in a business. Anu puts in ₹ 5000 and Bimla puts in ₹ 6000. Anu receives 12.5% of the profit for managing the business and the rest is divided in proportion to their capitals. What does each get out of a profit of ₹ 880? (M.A.T., 2010)

(a) ₹ 400, ₹ 480 (b) ₹ 450, ₹ 430
(c) ₹ 460, ₹ 420 (d) ₹ 470, ₹ 410

32. Two partners invested ₹ 125000 and ₹ 85000 respectively in a business. They distribute 60% of the profit equally and decide to distribute the remaining 40% as the interest on their capitals. If one partner received ₹ 3000 more than the other, the total profit is

(a) ₹ 42250 (b) ₹ 39375
(c) ₹ 38840 (d) ₹ 36575

33. Three partners A, B, C start a business. Twice A's capital is equal to thrice B's capital and B's capital is four times C's capital. Out of a total profit of ₹ 16500 at the end of the year, B's share is :

(a) ₹ 4000 (b) ₹ 6000
(c) ₹ 7500 (d) ₹ 6600

34. If 4 (A's capital) = 6 (B's capital) = 10 (C's capital), then out of a profit of ₹ 4650, C will receive

(a) ₹ 465 (b) ₹ 900
(c) ₹ 1550 (d) ₹ 2250

35. Ninad, Vikas and Manav enter into a partnership. Ninad invests some amount at the beginning, Vikas invests double the amount after 6 months and Manav invests thrice the amount invested by Ninad after 8 months. They earn a profit of ₹ 45000 at the end of the year. What is Manav's share in the profit? (S.B.I.P.O., 2008)

(a) ₹ 9000 (b) ₹ 12000
(c) ₹ 15000 (d) ₹ 25000
(e) None of these

36. Four milkmen rented a pasture. A grazed 15 cows for 4 months, B grazed 12 cows for 2 months, C grazed 18 cows for 6 months and D grazed 16 cows for 5 months. If A's share of rent is ₹ 1020, what is C's share of rent? (Bank P.O., 2008)

(a) ₹ 816
(b) ₹ 1360
(c) ₹ 1836
(d) Cannot be determined
(e) None of these

37. A, B and C enter into a partnership by making investments in the ratio 3 : 5 : 7. After a year, C invests another ₹ 337600 while A withdraws ₹ 45600. The ratio of investments then changes to 24 : 59 : 16.7. How much did A invest initially?

(a) ₹ 45600 (b) ₹ 96000
(c) ₹ 141600 (d) None of these

38. A, B and C are partners in a business. Their shares are in the proportion of $\frac{1}{3}:\frac{1}{4}:\frac{1}{5}$. A withdraws half of his capital after 15 months and after another 15 months, a profit of ₹ 4340 is divided. The share of C is (M.B.A., 2004)

(a) ₹ 1240 (b) ₹ 1245
(c) ₹ 1360 (d) ₹ 1550

39. A, B, C started a business with their investments in the ratio 1 : 3 : 5. After 4 months, A invested the same amount as before and B as well as C withdrew half of their investments. The ratio of their profits at the end of the year is : (L.I.C.A.A.O., 2007)

(a) 4 : 3 : 5 (b) 5 : 6 : 10
(c) 6 : 5 : 10 (d) 10 : 5 : 6

40. A and B entered into partnership with capitals in the ratio 4 : 5. After 3 months, A withdrew $\frac{1}{4}$ of his capital and B withdrew $\frac{1}{5}$ of his capital. The gain at the end of 10 months was ₹ 760. A's share in this profit is :

(a) ₹ 330 (b) ₹ 360
(c) ₹ 380 (d) ₹ 430

41. In a partnership, A invests $\frac{1}{6}$ of the capital for $\frac{1}{6}$ of the time, B invests $\frac{1}{3}$ of the capital for $\frac{1}{3}$ of the time and C, the rest of the capital for the whole time. Out of a profit of ₹ 4600, B's share is (M.B.A., 2004)

(a) ₹ 650 (b) ₹ 800
(c) ₹ 960 (d) ₹ 1000

42. A, B and C jointly thought of engaging themselves in a business venture. It was agreed that A would invest ₹ 6500 for 6 months, B, ₹ 8400 for 5 months and C, ₹ 10,000 for 3 months. A wants to be the working member for which he was to receive 5% of the profits. The profit earned was ₹ 7400. Calculate the share of B in the profit.

(a) ₹ 1900 (b) ₹ 2660
(c) ₹ 2800 (d) ₹ 2840

43. Manick received ₹ 6000 as his share out of the total profit of ₹ 9000 which he and Raunaq earned at the end of one year. If Manick invested ₹ 20000 for 6 months, whereas Raunaq invested his amount for the whole year, what was the amount invested by Raunaq?

(a) ₹ 4000 (b) ₹ 5000
(c) ₹ 6000 (d) ₹ 10,000

44. A, B and C entered into a partnership. A invested ₹ 2560 and B invested ₹ 2000. At the end of the year, they gained ₹ 1105, out of which A got ₹ 320. C's capital was (S.S.C., 2006)

(a) ₹ 2840 (b) ₹ 4028
(c) ₹ 4280 (d) ₹ 4820

45. A, B and C enter into a partnership. A contributes one-third of the capital while B contributes as much as A and C together contribute. If the profit at the end of the year amounts to ₹ 900, what would C receive? (P.C.S., 2008)

(a) ₹ 100 (b) ₹ 150
(c) ₹ 200 (d) ₹ 300

46. A and B started a business jointly. A's investment was thrice the investment of B and the period of his investment was two times the period of investment of B. If B received ₹ 4000 as profit, then their total profit is:

(a) ₹ 16000 (b) ₹ 20000
(c) ₹ 24000 (d) ₹ 28000

47. A started a business with ₹ 21000 and is joined afterwards by B with ₹ 36000. After how many months did B join if the profits at the end of the year are divided equally?

(a) 3 (b) 4
(c) 5 (d) 6

48. A began a business with ₹ 85000. He was joined afterwards by B with ₹ 42500. For how much period does B join, if the profits at the end of the year are divided in the ratio of 3 : 1? (N.I.F.T., 2003)

(a) 4 months (b) 5 months
(c) 6 months (d) 8 months

49. A starts business with ₹ 3500 and after 5 months, B joins with A as his partner. After a year, the profit is divided in the ratio 2 : 3. What is B's contribution in the capital?

(a) ₹ 7500 (b) ₹ 8000
(c) ₹ 8500 (d) ₹ 9000

50. A and B enter into a partnership with ₹ 50000 and ₹ 60000 respectively. C joins them after x months, contributing ₹ 70000 and B leaves x months before the end of the year. If they share the profit in the ratio of 20 : 18 : 21, then the value of x is (M.A.T., 2008)

(a) 3 (b) 6
(c) 8 (d) 9

51. In a business A invests ₹ 600 more than B. The capital of B remained invested for $7\frac{1}{2}$ months, while the capital of A remained invested for 2 more months. If the total profit be ₹ 620 and B gets ₹ 140 less than what A gets, then A's capital is
(a) ₹ 2400 (b) ₹ 2800
(c) ₹ 3000 (d) ₹ 3200

52. A and B start a business jointly. A invests ₹ 16000 for 8 months and B remains in the business for 4 months. Out of the total profit, B claims $\frac{2}{7}$ of the profit. How much money was contributed by B?
(a) ₹ 10500 (b) ₹ 11900
(c) ₹ 12800 (d) ₹ 13600

53. Two friends P and Q started a business investing in the ratio of 5 : 6. R joined them after six months investing an amount equal to that of Q's. At the end of the year, 20% profit was earned which was equal to ₹ 98,000. What was the amount invested by R?
(a) ₹ 105000 (b) ₹ 175000
(c) ₹ 210000 (d) Data inadequate
(e) None of these

54. Three partners shared the profit in a business in the ratio 5 : 7 : 8. They had partnered for 14 months, 8 months and 7 months respectively. What was the ratio of their investments?
(a) 5 : 7 : 8 (b) 28 : 49 : 64
(c) 38 : 28 : 21 (d) None of these

55. A, B and C invested their capitals in the ratio 3 : 4 : 6. However their shares of profit are equal. The durations of their investments must be in the ratio
(a) 4 : 3 : 2 (b) 6 : 4 : 3
(c) 3 : 4 : 6 (d) 1 : 1 : 1

56. A and B invest in a business in the ratio 3 : 2. If 5% of the total profit goes to charity and A's share is ₹ 855, the total profit is
(a) ₹ 1425 (b) ₹ 1500
(c) ₹ 1537.50 (d) ₹ 1576

57. Swati and Rajni enter into a partnership with their capitals in the ratio 5 : 6. At the end of 7 months Swati withdraws her capital. If they receive the profit in the ratio of 5 : 9, find how long was Rajni's capital used. (I.I.F.T., 2005, R.R.B., 2008)
(a) 10 months (b) 12 months
(c) 14 months (d) None of these

58. *X* and *Y* are partners in a business. *X* contributed $\frac{1}{3}$ of the capital for 9 months and *Y* received $\frac{2}{5}$ of the profits. For how long was *Y*'s money used in the business? (M.A.T., 2010)
(a) 2 months (b) 3 months
(c) 4 months (d) 5 months

59. A and B started a business with initial investments in the respective ratio of 18 : 7. After four months from the start of the business, A invested ₹ 2000 more and B invested ₹ 7000 more. At the end of one year, if the profit was distributed among them in the ratio of 2 : 1 respectively, what was the total initial investment with which A and B started the business?
[IBPS—RRB Officers Gr.'B' Exam, 2015]
(a) ₹ 50000 (b) ₹ 25000
(c) ₹ 150000 (d) ₹ 75000

60. Anil, Kamal and Vini Invested ₹ 8000, ₹ 4000 and ₹ 8000 respectively in a business. Anil left after six months. If after eight months, there was a gain of ₹ 4005, then what will be the share of Kamal?
[RBI Gr. 'B' (Phase I) Exam, 2015]
(a) ₹ 800 (b) ₹ 890
(c) ₹ 500 (d) ₹ 900

61. A starts a business by investing ₹ 28,000. After 2 months, B joins with ₹ 20,000 and after another two months C joins with ₹ 18,000. At the end of 10 months from the start of the business, if B withdraws ₹ 2,000 and C withdraws ₹ 2,000, in what ratio should the profit be distributed among A, B and C at the end of the year? [IBPS—Bank Spl. Officer (IT) Exam, 2015]
(a) 12 : 7 : 5 (b) 12 : 9 : 5
(c) 12 : 6 : 3 (d) 14 : 7 : 5

62. In a business, B invests half the amount invested by A. After 6 months from the start of the business, C joins the business with an amount equal to twice of B's investment. After 8 months from the start of the business B withdraws completely from the business. If at the end of the year, C's share in the profit was ₹ 2460, what was the total profit received that year?
[United India Insurance Co. Ltd. (UIICL)—Assistant (Online) Exam 2015]
(a) ₹ 11200 (b) ₹ 9600
(c) ₹ 9020 (d) ₹ 12000

63. A, B and C entered in to a partnership by investing ₹ 15,400, ₹ 18,200 and ₹ 12,600 respectively. B left after 6 months. If after 8 months, there was a profit of ₹ 28,790, then what is the share of C in the profit?
[NICL—AAO Exam, 2015]
(a) ₹ 8712 (b) ₹ 9432
(c) ₹ 8352 (d) ₹ 8568

64. A and B started a business by investing ₹ 2400 and ₹ 3600 respectively. At the end of 4th month from the start of the business, C joined with ₹ 'X'. After 8 months from the start of the business, B withdrew ₹600. If C's share is ₹ 8000 in the annual profit of ₹ 22500, what was the amount C invested in the business?
[CET—Maharashtra (MBA) Exam, 2016]
(a) ₹ 7200 (b) ₹ 5800
(c) ₹ 4000 (d) ₹ 4800

ANSWERS

1. (b)	2. (e)	3. (c)	4. (d)	5. (b)	6. (a)	7. (a)	8. (c)	9. (b)	10. (d)
11. (d)	12. (c)	13. (e)	14. (a)	15. (a)	16. (b)	17. (c)	18. (a)	19. (e)	20. (b)
21. (b)	22. (d)	23. (e)	24. (b)	25. (c)	26. (b)	27. (d)	28. (d)	29. (c)	30. (a)
31. (c)	32. (b)	33. (b)	34. (b)	35. (c)	36. (c)	37. (c)	38. (a)	39. (b)	40. (a)
41. (b)	42. (b)	43. (b)	44. (c)	45. (b)	46. (d)	47. (c)	48. (d)	49. (d)	50. (a)
51. (c)	52. (c)	53. (c)	54. (d)	55. (a)	56. (b)	57. (d)	58. (b)	59. (a)	60. (b)
61. (a)	62. (c)	63. (a)	64. (d)						

SOLUTIONS

1. Let the total capital be ₹ x. Then, Rahul's share = ₹ $\frac{x}{2}$,

Arun's share = ₹ $\frac{x}{3}$.

Sumit's share = ₹ $\left[x-\left(\frac{x}{2}+\frac{x}{3}\right)\right]$ = ₹ $\frac{x}{6}$.

∴ Required ratio = $\frac{x}{2}:\frac{x}{3}:\frac{x}{6}=\frac{1}{2}:\frac{1}{3}:\frac{1}{6}=3:2:1$.

2. P : Q = 85000 : 15000 = 85 : 15 = 17 : 3.

3. Ratio of their shares = 22500 : 35000 = 9 : 14. Deepak's share = ₹ $\left(13800\times\frac{14}{23}\right)$ = ₹ 8400.

4. Ratio of shares = 8 : 12 : 14 = 4 : 6 : 7.

∴ Kiara's share = ₹ $\left(578\times\frac{7}{17}\right)$ = ₹ 238.

5. P : Q : R = 45000 : 70000 : 90000 = 9 : 14 : 18.

∴ Q's share = ₹ $\left(164000\times\frac{14}{41}\right)$ = ₹ 56000.

6. Ratio of shares = 11 : 16.5 : 8.25 = 4 : 6 : 3.

Anil's share = ₹ $\left(19.5\times\frac{3}{13}\right)$ lakh = ₹ 4.5 lakh.

∴ Required amount = 50% of ₹ 4.5 lakh = ₹ 2.25 lakh.

7. Ratio of shares = 1500 : 2500 = 3 : 5.

Share of first friend = ₹ $\left[\frac{400}{2}+\left(400\times\frac{3}{8}\right)\right]$

= ₹ (200 + 150) = ₹ 350.

Share of second friend = ₹ $\left[\frac{400}{2}+\left(400\times\frac{5}{8}\right)\right]$

= ₹ (200 + 250) = ₹ 450.

8. Let A's capital = ₹ x. Then, B's capital = ₹ $(x - 600)$.

C's capital = ₹ $[(x - 600) - 300]$ = ₹ $(x - 900)$.

∴ $x + (x - 600) + (x - 900) = 3000$

⇒ $3x = 4500 \Rightarrow x = 1500$.

So, A : B : C = 1500 : 900 : 600 = 5 : 3 : 2.

Hence, B's share = ₹ $\left(886\times\frac{3}{10}\right)$ = ₹ 265.80.

9. Ratio of their shares = (35000 × 8) : (42000 × 10) = 2 : 3.

Reena's share = ₹ $\left(31570\times\frac{2}{5}\right)$ = ₹ 12628.

10. Shankar : Aniket = (120000 × 12) : (190000 × 9)
= 1440000 : 1710000 = 16 : 19.

∴ Aniket's share = ₹ $\left(1750000\times\frac{19}{35}\right)$ = ₹ 950000.

11. Arun : Bakul = (38000 × 12) : (55000 × 7)
= 456000 : 385000 = 456 : 385.

Required difference = ₹ $\left[22000\times\left(\frac{456}{841}-\frac{385}{841}\right)\right]$

= ₹ $\left(22000\times\frac{71}{841}\right)$ = ₹ 1857.31 ≈ ₹ 1857.

12. Gautam : Jatin = (60000 × 12) : (35000 × 8)
= 720000 : 280000 = 18 : 7.

13. Simran : Nanda = (50000 × 36) : (80000 × 30)
= 1800000 : 2400000 = 3 : 4.

∴ Simran's share = ₹ $\left(24500\times\frac{3}{7}\right)$ = ₹ 10500.

14. Dilip : Ram : Avtar = 2700 : 8100 : 7200 = 3 : 9 : 8.

Let the total profit be ₹ x.

Then, Ram's share = ₹ $\left(\frac{9}{20}x\right)$.

∴ $\frac{9}{20}x=3600 \Rightarrow x=\left(\frac{3600\times20}{9}\right)=8000$.

Hence, total profit = ₹ 8000.

15. A : B : C = (20000 × 24) : (15000 × 24) : (20000 × 18)
= 4 : 3 : 3.

∴ B's share = ₹ $\left(25000\times\frac{3}{10}\right)$ = ₹ 7500.

16. Aman : Rakhi : Sagar = (70000 × 36) : (105000 × 30) : (140000 × 24) = 12 : 15 : 16.

17. Sonia : Vivek : Kirti
= (60000 × 24) : (140000 × 18) : (120000 × 12)
= 1440000 : 2520000 : 1440000 = 4 : 7 : 4.

∴ Vivek's share = ₹ $\left(450000\times\frac{7}{15}\right)$ = ₹ 210000.

18. Arun : Kamal : Vinay = (8000 × 6) : (4000 × 8) : (8000 × 8)
= 48 : 32 : 64 = 3 : 2 : 4.

∴ Kamal's share = ₹ $\left(4005 \times \frac{2}{9}\right)$ = ₹ 890.

19. Let the initial capitals of P and Q be ₹ $2x$ and ₹ $3x$ respectively.
Then, Ratio of profits = $(2x \times 12) : (3x \times 24)$
= $24x : 72x$ = 1 : 3.

∴ Q's share = ₹ $\left(26000 \times \frac{3}{4}\right)$ = ₹ 19500.

20. Let the money invested by A, B and C be ₹ x, ₹ $2x$ and ₹ $3x$ respectively.
Then, A : B : C = $(x \times 12) : (2x \times 6) : (3x \times 4)$
= $12x : 12x : 12x$ = 1 : 1 : 1.

∴ C's share = ₹ $\left(27000 \times \frac{1}{3}\right)$ = ₹ 9000.

21. A : B : C = (40000 × 36) : (80000 × 12 + 40000 × 24) : (120000 × 24 + 40000 × 12)
= 144 : 192 : 336 = 3 : 4 : 7.

22. A : B : C = (25 lakhs × 1 + 35 lakhs × 2) : (35 lakhs × 2 + 25 lakhs × 1) : (30 lakhs × 3)
= 95 lakhs : 95 lakhs : 90 lakhs = 19 : 19 : 18.

23. Subhash : Aditya = (25000 × 36) : (15000 × 6 + 30000 × 24)
= 900000 : 810000 = 10 : 9.

∴ Aditya's share = ₹ $\left(247000 \times \frac{9}{19}\right)$ = ₹ 117000.

24. Shekhar : Rajeev : Jatin
= (25000 × 12 + 35000 × 12 + 45000 × 12) : (35000 × 24) : (35000 × 12)
= 1260000 : 840000 : 420000 = 3 : 2 : 1.

∴ Rajeev's share = ₹ $\left(150000 \times \frac{2}{6}\right)$ = ₹ 50000.

25. A : B : C = (16000 × 3 + 11000 × 9) : (12000 × 3 + 17000 × 9) : (21000 × 6)
= 147 : 189 : 126 = 7 : 9 : 6.

∴ Difference between B's and C's shares

= ₹ $\left(26400 \times \frac{9}{22} - 26400 \times \frac{6}{22}\right)$ = ₹ 3600.

26. A : B : C = (5000 × 4 + 2500 × 8) : (4500 × 6 + 3000 × 6) : (7000 × 6)
= 40000 : 45000 : 42000 = 40 : 45 : 42.

∴ A's share = ₹ $\left(5080 \times \frac{40}{127}\right)$ = ₹ 1600;

B's share = ₹ $\left(5080 \times \frac{45}{127}\right)$ = ₹ 1800;

C's share = ₹ $\left(5080 \times \frac{42}{127}\right)$ = ₹ 1680.

27. Let C = x. Then, B = x + 5000 and A = x + 5000 + 4000 = x + 9000.
So, $x + x + 5000 + x + 9000 = 50000$
⇔ $3x = 36000$ ⇔ $x = 12000$.
A : B : C = 21000 : 17000 : 12000 = 21 : 17 : 12.

∴ A's share = ₹ $\left(35000 \times \frac{21}{50}\right)$ = ₹ 14,700.

28. Ratio of investments of A, B and C = Ratio of their profits
= 337.50 : 1125 : 637.50 = 9 : 30 : 17.

∴ A's investment = ₹ $\left(14000 \times \frac{9}{56}\right)$ = ₹ 2250.

B's investment = ₹ $\left(14000 \times \frac{30}{56}\right)$ = ₹ 7500.

Hence, required difference = ₹ (7500 – 2250) = ₹ 5250.

29. Let the initial investments of A, B and C be $5x$, $6x$ and $8x$ respectively. Then,
A : B : C = $[5x \times 12 + (160\% \text{ of } 5x) \times 12] : (6x \times 24) : (8x \times 12 + 4x \times 12)$
= $156x : 144x : 144x$ = 13 : 12 : 12.

30. Fraction of profit received by each one of John and Mona

= $\frac{\left(1-\frac{2}{3}\right)}{2} = \frac{1}{6}$.

Ratio of capitals of John, Mona and Gordon = Ratio of their profits = $\frac{1}{6} : \frac{1}{6} : \frac{2}{3} = 1:1:4$.

Let the total capital be ₹ x.

Then, $\frac{1}{6}$ of (7% of x – 4% of x) = $ 60 million

⇒ 3% of x = $ 360 million

⇒ x = $ $\left(\frac{360 \times 100}{3}\right)$ million = $ 12000 million.

∴ Mona's capital = $\left(\frac{1}{6} \times \$\,12000 \text{ million}\right)$

= $ 2000 million.

31. Anu : Bimla = 5000 : 6000 = 5 : 6.
Anu's share for managing business = 12.5% of ₹ 880 = ₹ 110.
Net profit = ₹ (880 – 110) = ₹ 770.

Anu's share = ₹ $\left(770 \times \frac{5}{11}\right)$ = ₹ 350.

Anu's total share = ₹ (110 + 350) = ₹ 460.

Bimla's share = ₹ $\left(770 \times \frac{6}{11}\right)$ = ₹ 420.

32. Let the total profit be ₹ x.

Then, 60% of the profit = ₹ $\left(\frac{60}{100} \times x\right)$ = ₹ $\left(\frac{3x}{5}\right)$.

From this part of the profit each gets = ₹ $\left(\frac{3x}{10}\right)$.

40% of total profit = ₹ $\left(\frac{40}{100} \times x\right)$ = ₹ $\left(\frac{2x}{5}\right)$.

Now, this amount of ₹ $\left(\frac{2x}{5}\right)$ has been divided in the ratio of capitals, which is 125000 : 85000 or 25 : 17 as interests.

$\therefore$ Interest on first capital = ₹ $\left(\frac{2x}{5} \times \frac{25}{42}\right)$ = ₹ $\left(\frac{5x}{21}\right)$.

Interest on second capital = ₹ $\left(\frac{2x}{5} \times \frac{17}{42}\right)$ = ₹ $\left(\frac{17x}{105}\right)$.

Total money received by first partner = ₹ $\left(\frac{3x}{10} + \frac{5x}{21}\right)$

= ₹ $\left(\frac{113x}{210}\right)$.

Total money received by second partner

= ₹ $\left(\frac{3x}{10} + \frac{17x}{105}\right)$ = ₹ $\left(\frac{97x}{210}\right)$.

$\therefore \frac{113x}{210} - \frac{97x}{210} = 3000$ or $x = 39375$.

Hence, total profit = ₹ 39375.

33. Let C = x. Then, B = $4x$ and $2A = 3 \times 4x = 12x$ or A = $6x$.

$\therefore$ A : B : C = $6x : 4x : x = 6 : 4 : 1$.

So, B's share = ₹ $\left(16500 \times \frac{4}{11}\right)$ = ₹ 6000.

34. Let 4A = 6B = 10C = k.

Then, $A = \frac{k}{4}$, $B = \frac{k}{6}$ and $C = \frac{k}{10}$.

$\therefore$ A : B : C = $\frac{k}{4} : \frac{k}{6} : \frac{k}{10} = 15 : 10 : 6$.

Hence, C's share = ₹ $\left(4650 \times \frac{6}{31}\right)$ = ₹ 900.

35. Let Ninad's investment be ₹ x.

Then, Ratio of capitals = $(x \times 12) : (2x \times 6) : (3x \times 4)$

$= 12x : 12x : 12x = 1 : 1 : 1$.

$\therefore$ Manav's share = ₹ $\left(45000 \times \frac{1}{3}\right)$ = ₹ 15000.

36. A : B : C : D = 15 × 4 : 12 × 2 : 18 × 6 : 16 × 5

= 60 : 24 : 108 : 80 = 15 : 6 : 27 : 20.

Let the total rent be ₹ x.

Then, A's share = ₹ $\left(\frac{15x}{68}\right)$.

$\therefore \frac{15x}{68} = 1020 \Rightarrow x = \left(\frac{1020 \times 68}{15}\right) = 4624$.

Hence, C's share = ₹ $\left(4624 \times \frac{27}{68}\right)$ = ₹ 1836.

37. Let the initial investments of A, B, C, be ₹ $3x$, ₹ $5x$ and ₹ $7x$ respectively. Then,

$(3x - 45600) : 5x : (7x + 337600) = 24 : 59 : 167$.

$\therefore \frac{3x - 45600}{5x} = \frac{24}{59} \Rightarrow 177x - 2690400 = 120x \Rightarrow 57x$

$= 2690400 \Rightarrow x = 47200$.

Hence, A's initial investment = ₹ (47200 × 3) = ₹ 141600.

38. Ratio of initial investments = $\frac{1}{3} : \frac{1}{4} : \frac{1}{5} = 20 : 15 : 12$.

Let their initial investments be $20x$, $15x$ and $12x$ respectively.

A : B : C = $(20x \times 15 + 10x \times 15) : (15x \times 30) : (12x \times 30)$

$= 450x : 450x : 360x = 5 : 5 : 4$.

$\therefore$ C's share = ₹ $\left(4340 \times \frac{4}{14}\right)$ = ₹ 1240.

39. Let their initial investments be x, $3x$ and $5x$ respectively. Then,

$A:B:C = (x \times 4 + 2x \times 8) : \left(3x \times 4 + \frac{3x}{2} \times 8\right) : \left(5x \times 4 + \frac{5x}{2} \times 8\right)$

$= 20x : 24x : 40x = 5 : 6 : 10$.

40. A : B

$= \left[4x \times 3 + \left(4x - \frac{1}{4} \times 4x\right) \times 7\right] : \left[5x \times 3 + \left(5x - \frac{1}{5} \times 5x\right) \times 7\right]$

$= (12x + 21x) : (15x + 28x) = 33x : 43x = 33 : 43$.

$\therefore$ A's share = ₹ $\left(760 \times \frac{33}{76}\right)$ = ₹ 330.

41. Suppose A invests ₹ $\frac{x}{6}$ for $\frac{y}{6}$ months.

Then, B invests ₹ $\frac{x}{3}$ for $\frac{y}{3}$ months.

C invests $\left[x - \left(\frac{x}{6} + \frac{x}{3}\right)\right]$, i.e., ₹ $\frac{x}{2}$ for y months.

$\therefore$ A : B : C = $\left(\frac{x}{6} \times \frac{y}{6}\right) : \left(\frac{x}{3} \times \frac{y}{3}\right) : \left(\frac{x}{2} \times y\right)$

$= \frac{1}{36} : \frac{1}{9} : \frac{1}{2} = 1 : 4 : 18$.

Hence, B's share = ₹ $\left(4600 \times \frac{4}{23}\right)$ = ₹ 800.

42. For managing, A receives = 5% of ₹ 7400 = ₹ 370.

Balance = ₹ (7400 – 370) = ₹ 7030.

Ratio of their investments = (6500 × 6) : (8400 × 5) : (10000 × 3)

= 39000 : 42000 : 30000 = 13 : 14 : 10.

$\therefore$ B's share = ₹ $\left(7030 \times \frac{14}{37}\right)$ = ₹ 2660.

43. Suppose Raunaq invested ₹ x.

Then, Manick : Raunaq = (20000 × 6) : (x × 12)

$\therefore \frac{120000}{12x} = \frac{6000}{3000}$ or $x = \frac{120000}{24} = 5000$.

44. Let C's capital be ₹ x.

Then, A : B : C = 2560 : 2000 : x.

A's share = ₹ $\left(1105 \times \frac{2560}{4560 + x}\right)$.

$\therefore 1105 \times \frac{2560}{4560 + x} = 320$

$\Rightarrow 320x + 1459200 = 2828800$

$\Rightarrow 320x = 1369600$

$\Rightarrow x = 4280.$

45. Let total capital = ₹ x. Then, A's capital = ₹ $\left(\frac{x}{3}\right)$.

B's capital = (A + C)'s capital $\Rightarrow$ 2(B's capital) = (A + B + C)'s capital = ₹ x

$\Rightarrow$ B's capital = ₹ $\left(\frac{x}{2}\right)$.

C's capital = ₹ $\left[x - \left(\frac{x}{3} + \frac{x}{2}\right)\right]$ = ₹ $\frac{x}{6}$.

$\therefore$ A : B : C = $\frac{x}{3} : \frac{x}{2} : \frac{x}{6} = 2 : 3 : 1$.

So, C's share = ₹ $\left(900 \times \frac{1}{6}\right)$ = ₹ 150.

46. Suppose B invested ₹ x for y months.
Then, A invested ₹ $3x$ for $2y$ months.
So, A : B = $(3x \times 2y) : (x \times y) = 6xy : xy = 6 : 1$.
$\therefore$ B's profit : Total profit = 1 : 7.
Let the total profit be ₹ x.

Then, $\frac{1}{7} = \frac{4000}{x}$ or $x = 28000$.

47. Suppose B joined after x months.
Then, $21000 \times 12 = 36000 \times (12 - x)$
$\Leftrightarrow 36x = 180 \Leftrightarrow x = 5$.
Hence, B joined after 5 months.

48. Suppose B joined for x months.

Then, $\frac{85000 \times 12}{42500 \times x} = \frac{3}{1}$ or $x = \frac{85000 \times 12}{42500 \times 3} = 8$.

So, B joined for 8 months.

49. Let B's capital be ₹ x.

Then, $\frac{3500 \times 12}{7x} = \frac{2}{3} \Leftrightarrow 14x = 126000 \Leftrightarrow x = 9000$.

50. Clearly, A invested his capital for 12 months while each one of B and C invested his capital for $(12 - x)$ months.
Ratio of profits of A, B and C
$= (50000 \times 12) : [60000 \times (12 - x)] : [70000 \times (12 - x)]$
$= 60 : 6(12 - x) : 7(12 - x)$
$= 60 : (72 - 6x) : (84 - 7x)$
But ratio of profits = 20 : 18 : 21 = 60 : 54 : 63.
$\therefore$ $60 : (72 - 6x) : (84 - 7x) = 60 : 54 : 63$
So, $72 - 6x = 54 \Rightarrow 6x = 18 \Rightarrow x = 3$.

51. Let B's capital be ₹ x.
Then, A's capital = ₹ $(x + 600)$.

$\therefore$ A : B = $\left[(x + 600) \times \frac{19}{2}\right] : \left(x \times \frac{15}{2}\right)$

$= (19x + 11400) : 15x$.

A's share = ₹ $\left[620 \times \frac{(19x + 11400)}{(34x + 11400)}\right]$;

B's share = ₹ $\left[620 \times \frac{15x}{(34x + 11400)}\right]$.

$\therefore$ $620 \left[\frac{19x + 11400}{34x + 11400} - \frac{15x}{34x + 11400}\right] = 140$

$\Rightarrow 62(4x + 11400) = 14(34x + 11400)$
$\Rightarrow 248x + 706800 = 476x + 159600$
$\Rightarrow 228x = 547200 \Rightarrow x = 2400$.
Hence, A's capital = ₹ (2400 + 600) = ₹ 3000.

52. Let the total profit be ₹ x.

Then, B = $\frac{2x}{7}$ and A = $\left(x - \frac{2x}{7}\right) = \frac{5x}{7}$.

So, A : B = $\frac{5x}{7} : \frac{2x}{7} = 5 : 2$.

Let B's capital be ₹ y.

Then, $\frac{16000 \times 8}{y \times 4} = \frac{5}{2} \Leftrightarrow y = \left(\frac{16000 \times 8 \times 2}{5 \times 4}\right) = 12800$.

53. Let the total investment be ₹ z.

Then, 20% of $z = 98000 \Leftrightarrow z = \left(\frac{98000 \times 100}{20}\right) = 490000$.

Let the capitals of P, Q and R be ₹ $5x$, ₹ $6x$ and ₹ $6x$ respectively.
Then, $(5x \times 12) + (6x \times 12) + (6x \times 6) = 490000 \times 12$

$\Leftrightarrow 168x = 490000 \times 12 \Leftrightarrow x = \left(\frac{490000 \times 12}{168}\right) = 35000$.

$\therefore$ R's investment = $6x$ = ₹ (6 × 35000) = ₹ 210000.

54. Let their investments be ₹ x for 14 months; ₹ y for 8 months and ₹ z for 7 months respectively.
Then, $14x : 8y : 7z = 5 : 7 : 8$.

Now, $\frac{14x}{8y} = \frac{5}{7} \Leftrightarrow 70x = 40y \Leftrightarrow y = \frac{7}{4}x$.

And, $\frac{14x}{7z} = \frac{5}{8} \Leftrightarrow 112x = 35z \Leftrightarrow z = \frac{112}{35}x = \frac{16}{5}x$.

$\therefore$ $x : y : z = x : \frac{7}{4}x : \frac{16}{5}x = 20 : 35 : 64$.

55. Let their investments be ₹ $3x$ for p months; ₹ $4x$ for q months and ₹ $6x$ for r months respectively.
Then, $3xp : 4xq : 6xr = 1 : 1 : 1$
$\Rightarrow 3p : 4q : 6r = 1 : 1 : 1$

So, $3p = 4q \Rightarrow q = \frac{3p}{4}$. And, $4q = 6r \Rightarrow r = \frac{2q}{3} = \left(\frac{2}{3} \times \frac{3}{4}p\right) = \frac{p}{2}$.

$\therefore$ $p : q : r = p : \frac{3p}{4} : \frac{p}{2} = 4 : 3 : 2$.

56. Let the total profit be ₹ 100.

After paying to charity, A's share = ₹ $\left(95 \times \frac{3}{5}\right)$ = ₹ 57.

If A's share is ₹ 57, total profit = ₹ 100.

If A's share is ₹ 855, total profit = $\left(\frac{100}{57} \times 855\right) = 1500$.

57. Suppose Swati invested ₹ $5x$ for 7 months and Rajni invested ₹ $6x$ for y months. Then,

$\frac{5x \times 7}{6x \times y} = \frac{5}{9} \Rightarrow 30y = 315 \Rightarrow y = 10\frac{1}{2}$.

Hence, Rajni's capital was used for $10\frac{1}{2}$ months.

58. Let the total profit be ₹ z. Then, Y's share = ₹ $\left(\frac{2z}{5}\right)$, X's share = ₹ $\left(z - \frac{2z}{5}\right)$ = ₹ $\left(\frac{3z}{5}\right)$.

$\therefore$ X : Y = $\frac{3z}{5} : \frac{2z}{5} = 3:2.$

Let the total capital be ₹ x and suppose Y's money was used for y months. Then,

$$\frac{\frac{1}{3}x \times 9}{\frac{2}{3}x \times y} = \frac{3}{2} \Rightarrow 18x = 6xy \Rightarrow y = 3.$$

Hence, Y's money was used for 3 months.

59. Let the initial investment of A and B is $18x$ and $7x$. After four months from the start of business, A invest ₹ 2000 more for each eight months. Then total investment of A

= $18x \times 4 + (18x + 2000) \times 8$

= $72x + 144x + 16000$

= $216x + 16000$

After four months, from the start of business, B invest ₹ 7000 more for each eight months.

Total investment by B

= $7x \times 4 + (7x + 7000) \times 8$

= $28x + 56x + 56000$

= $84x + 56000$

According to the questions.

$\frac{216x + 16000}{84x + 56000} = \frac{2}{1}$

$\Rightarrow 216x + 16000 = 168x + 112000$

$\Rightarrow 216x - 168x = 112000 - 16000$

$48x = 96000 \Rightarrow x = \frac{96000}{48} = 2000$

Total initial investment of A and B

= (18 + 7) × 2000 = ₹ 50000

60. Ratio of profit of Anil : Kamal : Vini

= (8000 × 6) : (4000 × 8) : (8000 × 8) = 48000 : 32000 : 64000

= 48 : 32 : 64

= 3 : 2 : 4

$\therefore$ Kamal's share = ₹ $\left(4005 \times \frac{2}{9}\right)$ = ₹ 890

61. A invests money for 12 months

B invests money for 10 months

C invests money for 8 months

Ratio of profit of A to B to C

= 28000 × 12 : 20000 × 8 + 18000 × 2 : 18000 × 6 + 16000 × 2

= 28 × 12 × 1000 : (160 + 36) × 1000 : (108 + 32) × 1000

= 28 × 12 : 160 + 36 : 108 + 32

= 336 : 196 : 140 = 12 : 7 : 5

62. Let B's investment be ₹ x

$\therefore$ A's investment = ₹ $2x$

$\therefore$ C's investment = ₹ $2x$

A invests money for 12 months

B invests money for 8 months

C invests money for 6 months.

Ratio of the equivalent capitals of A, B and C for 1 month

= $2x \times 12 : x \times 8 : 2x \times 6$ = 6 : 2 : 3

Sum of the terms of ratio

= 6 + 2 + 3 = 11

If the total profit at the end of the year be ₹ a, then

Share of $c = \frac{3a}{11} = 2460$

$\Rightarrow 3a = 2460 \times 11$

$\Rightarrow a = \frac{2460 \times 11}{3}$ = ₹ 9020

63. Investment of A for 8 months = ₹ 15400

Investment of B for 6 months = ₹ 18200

Investment of C for 8 months = ₹ 12600

Ratio of the share of A, B and C

= 15400 × 8 : 18200 × 6 : 12600 × 8

= 154 × 8 : 182 × 6 : 126 × 8

= 44 : 39 : 36

Sum of the terms of ratio = 44 + 39 + 36 = 119

Share of C = ₹ $\left(\frac{36}{119} \times 28790\right)$ = ₹ 8710 ≈ ₹ 8712

64. A invests ₹ 2400 for 12 months

B invests ₹ 3600 for 8 months

And ₹ 3000 for 4 months

C invests ₹ X for 8 months

Ratio of profit of A, B and C

= Profit of A : Profit of B : Profit of C

= 2400 × 12 : (3600 × 8) + (3000 × 4) : X × 8

= 28800 : 40800 : 8X = 3600 : 5100 : X

Given profit of C = ₹ 8000

and total profit of A, B and C = ₹ 22,500

$\therefore \frac{X \times 22500}{3600 + 5100 + X} \Rightarrow \frac{X \times 22500}{8700 + X} = 8000$

$\Rightarrow$ 22500X = 69600000 + 8000X

$\Rightarrow$ 14500X = 69600000 $\Rightarrow$ X = ₹ 4800

EXERCISE

(DATA SUFFICIENCY TYPE QUESTIONS)

Directions (*Questions 1 – 5*): *Each of the questions given below consists of a statement and/or a question and two statements numbered I and II given below it. You have to decide whether the data provided in the statement(s) is/are sufficient to answer the question. Read both the statements and:*

Give answer (a) if the data in Statement I alone are sufficient to answer the question, while the data in Statement II alone are not sufficient to answer the question;

Give answer (b) if the data in Statement II alone are sufficient to answer the question, while the data in

Statement I alone are not sufficient to answer the question;

Give answer (c) if the data either in Statement I or in Statement II alone are sufficient to answer the question;

Give answer (d) if the data even in both Statements I and II together are not sufficient to answer the question;

Give answer (e) if the data in both Statements I and II together are necessary to answer the question.

1. Ravi, Gagan and Nitin are running a business firm in partnership. What is Gagan's share in the profit earned by them? (M.B.A., 2002)
   I. Ravi, Gagan and Nitin invested the amounts in the ratio of 2 : 4 : 7.
   II. Nitin's share in the profit is ₹ 8750.
2. A and B start a business jointly. What is A's share out of an annual profit of ₹ 23,800?
   I. B's investment is $12\frac{1}{2}$% more than A's investment.
   II. A's investment is ₹ 1,20,000.
3. A and B are in a partnership business of one year. At the end of the year, a profit of ₹ 20,000 was earned. What is A's share?
   I. A invested ₹ 50,000.
   II. B withdrew his capital after 8 months.
4. Rahul, Anurag and Vivek started a business together. In what proportion would the annual profit be distributed among them?
   I. Rahul got one-fourth of the profit.
   II. Rahul and Vivek contributed 75% of the total investment.
5. What is Nikita's share in the profit of ₹ 50000 earned in the business run by her in partnership with Shalini? (Bank P.O., 2009)
   I. Nikita invested an amount 150% of the amount invested by Shalini.
   II. Amount invested by Shalini is two-thirds of the amount invested by Nikita.

Directions (*Questions 6–10*): ***Each of the questions given below consists of a question followed by three statements. You have to study the question and the statements and decide which of the statement(s) is/are necessary to answer the given question.***

6. What is R's share of profit in a joint venture?
   I. Q started business investing ₹ 80000.
   II. R joined him after 3 months.
   III. P joined after 4 months with a capital of ₹ 120000 and got ₹ 6000 as his share of profit.
   (*a*) All I, II and III
   (*b*) I and III only
   (*c*) II and III only
   (*d*) Even with all I, II, and III, the answer cannot be arrived at
   (*e*) None of these
7. What is the difference in the shares of profit between P and Q in a joint business at the end of one year? (M.B.A., 2007)
   I. P invested ₹ 80000 and withdrew ₹ 20000 after 6 months.
   II. Q joined four months after the start of business.
   III. Q's amount was 80% of P's amount during the last six months.
   (*a*) I and II only
   (*b*) II and III only
   (*c*) All I, II and III
   (*d*) Even with all I, II and III together, the answer cannot be arrived at.
   (*e*) None of these
8. A, B and C together start a business with a total investment of ₹ 15,000. At the end of the year, the total profit is ₹ 3000. What is A's share in the profit?
   I. A's contribution is $\frac{3}{2}$ times B's.
   II. B's contribution is twice that of C.
   III. A's contribution is thrice that of C.
   (*a*) I and II only
   (*b*) II and III only
   (*c*) All I, II and III
   (*d*) Any two of the three
   (*e*) None of these
9. What will be the share of R in the profit earned by V, R and A together?
   I. They together invested an amount of ₹ 54000 for a period of 1 year.
   II. R's investment was 25% less than V's and 50% more than A's.
   III. The profit of V is ₹ 4000 more than that of A. (M.A.T., 2006)
   (*a*) Only I and II together
   (*b*) Only II
   (*c*) Only II and III together
   (*d*) II and either I or III only
10. How much did Rohit get as profit at the year-end in the business done by Nitin, Rohit and Kunal?
    I. Kunal invested ₹ 8000 for nine months, his profit was $\frac{3}{2}$ times that of Rohit's and his investment was four times that of Nitin.
    II. Nitin and Rohit invested for one year in the proportion 1 : 2 respectively.
    III. The three together got ₹ 1000 as profit at the year end.
    (*a*) Only I and II
    (*b*) Only I and III

(c) Question cannot be answered even with the information in all the three statements
(d) All I, II and III
(e) None of these

Directions (*Questions 11-13*): *Each of these questions is followed by three statements. You have to study the question and all the three statements given to decide whether any information provided in the statement(s) is redundant and can be dispensed with while answering the given question.*

11. Three friends P, Q and R started a partnership business investing money in the ratio of 5 : 4 : 2 respectively for a period of 3 years. What is the amount received by P as his share in the total profit?
    I. Total amount invested in the business is ₹ 22000.
    II. Profit earned at the end of 3 years is $\frac{3}{8}$ of the total investment.
    III. The average amount of profit earned per year is ₹ 2750.
    (a) I or II or III
    (b) Either III only, or I and II together
    (c) Any two of the three
    (d) All I, II and III are required
    (e) None of these

12. What will be the percentage share of Y in the profit earned by X, Y and Z together?
    I. X, Y and Z invested a total amount of ₹ 25,000 for a period of two years.
    II. The profit earned at the end of 2 years is 30%.
    III. The amount invested by Y is equal to the amount invested by X and Z together.
    (a) I and II only
    (b) II and III only
    (c) Any two of the three
    (d) All I, II and III are required
    (e) Question cannot be answered even with information in all the three statements.

13. What is Neeta's share in the profit of ₹ 50000 earned at the end of 2 years in a joint business run by Neeta, Seeta and Geeta?
    I. Neeta invested ₹ 85000 to start the business.
    II. Seeta and Geeta joined Neeta's business after six months, investing amounts in the ratio of 3 : 5.
    III. Total amount invested by Seeta and Geeta is ₹ 2.5 lakh.
    (a) Only II
    (b) Only III
    (c) Only either II or III
    (d) Information in all the three statements is required to answer the question
    (e) The question cannot be answered even with the information in all the three statements

ANSWERS

1. (e)	2. (a)	3. (d)	4. (e)	5. (c)	6. (d)	7. (d)	8. (d)	9. (c)	10. (d)
11. (b)	12. (a)	13. (d)							

SOLUTIONS

1. Let us name Ravi, Gagan and Nitin by R, G and N respectively.
   I. R : G : N = 2 : 4 : 7.
   II. N = 8750.
   From I and II, we get :
   When N = 7, then G = 4. When N = 8750, then
   $G = \left(\frac{4}{7} \times 8750\right) = 5000.$
   Thus, both I and II are needed to get the answer.
   ∴ Correct answer is (*e*).

2. Annual profit = ₹ 23800.
   I. Let A's investment = ₹ *x*.
   Then, B's investment = $112\frac{1}{2}\%$ of ₹ x = ₹ $\left(\frac{9x}{8}\right)$.
   $\therefore\ A : B = x : \frac{9x}{8} = 8 : 9.$
   A's share = ₹ $\left(23800 \times \frac{8}{17}\right)$ = ₹ 11200.
   Thus, I only gives the answer.
   II. A's investment = ₹ 120000. This is not sufficient to get the answer.
   Thus, I gives the answer but II is not sufficient to get the answer.
   ∴ Correct answer is (*a*).

3. Since B's investment is not given, both the statements together also do not give the answer.
   ∴ Correct answer is (*d*).

4. Let the total investment be ₹ *x*. Then, $R = \frac{x}{4}$.
   $R + V = \left(\frac{75}{100} \times x\right) = \frac{3x}{4} \Rightarrow V = \left(\frac{3x}{4} - \frac{x}{4}\right) = \frac{x}{2}.$
   $\therefore\ A = x - \left(\frac{x}{4} + \frac{x}{2}\right) = \frac{x}{4}.$
   $R : A : V = \frac{x}{4} : \frac{x}{4} : \frac{x}{2} = 1 : 1 : 2.$
   Thus, both I and II are needed to get the answer.
   ∴ Correct answer is (*e*).

5. I. Let Shalini's capital = ₹ x.

Then, Nikita's capital = 150% of ₹ x = ₹ $\frac{3x}{2}$.

∴ Nikita : Shalini = $\frac{3x}{2} : x = 3 : 2$.

∴ Nikita's share = ₹ $\left(50000 \times \frac{3}{5}\right)$ = ₹ 30000.

II. Let Nikita's captial = ₹ x.

Then, Shalini's capital = ₹ $\left(\frac{2x}{3}\right)$.

Nikita : Shalini = $x : \frac{2x}{3} = 3 : 2$.

Again, Nikita's share can be calculated.

Thus, either I alone or II alone is sufficient to get the answer.

∴ Correct answer is (*c*).

6. From I, II and III, we get P : Q : R = (120000 × 8) : (80000 × 12) : (x × 9).

Since R's investment is not given, the above ratio cannot be determined.

∴ Given data is inadequate. ∴ Correct answer is (*d*).

7. I. P's investment = (80000 × 6 + 60000 × 6) = 840000 for 1 month.

II & III. Q's investment = 80% of ₹ 60000 for 8 months = ₹ (48000 × 8) for 1 month = 384000 for 1 month

P : Q = 840000 : 384000 = 35 : 16.

But, the total profit is not given, so data is inadequate.

∴ Correct answer is (*d*).

8. Let C's contribution be ₹ x.

From I and II, we get : C = ₹ x,

B = ₹ $2x$ and A = ₹ $\left(\frac{3}{2} \times 2x\right)$ = ₹ $3x$.

From II and III, we get C = ₹ x, B = ₹ $2x$ and A = ₹ $3x$.

From I and III, we get C = ₹ x,

A = ₹ $3x$ and B = ₹ $\left(\frac{2}{3} \times 3x\right)$ = ₹ $2x$.

Thus, A : B : C = $3x : 2x : x = 3 : 2 : 1$.

A's share = ₹ $\left(3000 \times \frac{3}{6}\right)$ = ₹ 1500.

Thus, any two of the three give the answer.

∴ Correct answer is (*d*).

9. From II and III, we have :

Let A's investment = ₹ x.

Then, R's investment = 150% of ₹ x = ₹ $\left(\frac{3x}{2}\right)$.

Now, 75% of V's investment = $\frac{3x}{2}$

⇒ V's investment = $\left(\frac{3x}{2} \times \frac{100}{75}\right)$ = ₹ $2x$.

V : R : A = $2x : \frac{3x}{2} : x = 4 : 3 : 2$.

Let the total profit be ₹ P.

Then, V's share = ₹ $\left(\frac{4P}{9}\right)$ and A's share = ₹ $\left(\frac{2P}{9}\right)$.

So, $\frac{4P}{9} - \frac{2P}{9} = 4000$ ⇒ $P = \left(\frac{4000 \times 9}{2}\right) = 18000$.

R's share = ₹ $\left(18000 \times \frac{3}{9}\right)$ = ₹ 6000.

Thus, both II and III together give the answer.

∴ Correct answer is (*c*).

10. I and II give, K = ₹ (8000 × 9) for 1 month = ₹ 72000 for 1 month.

N = ₹ $\left(\frac{1}{4} \times 8000 \times 12\right)$ for 1 month = ₹ 24000 for 1 month.

R = ₹ 48000 for 1 month.

∴ K : N : R = 72000 : 24000 : 48000 = 3 : 1 : 2.

III gives, total profit = ₹ 1000.

∴ Rohit's share = ₹ $\left(1000 \times \frac{2}{6}\right)$ = ₹ $333\frac{1}{3}$.

∴ Correct answer is (*d*).

11. I and II give, profit after 3 years = ₹ $\left(\frac{3}{8} \times 22000\right)$ = ₹ 8250.

From III also, profit after 3 years = ₹ (2750 × 3) = ₹ 8250.

∴ P's share = ₹ $\left(8250 \times \frac{5}{11}\right)$ = ₹ 3750.

Thus, (either III is redundant) or (I and II are redundant).

∴ Correct answer is (*b*).

12. From III, Y = X + Z ⇒ Y's investment is 50%.

∴ Share of Y is 50%.

Thus, I and II are redundant.

∴ Correct answer is (*a*).

13. All the three statements I, II and III are required to calculate the ratio of profits of Neeta, Seeta and Geeta, as shown below :

Neeta's investment = ₹ 85000.

Seeta's investment = ₹ $\left(250000 \times \frac{3}{8}\right)$ = ₹ 93750.

Geeta's investment = ₹ (250000 − 93750) = ₹ 156250.

∴ Neeta : Seeta : Geeta = (85000 × 24) : (93750 × 18) : (156250 × 18)

= 2040000 : 1687500 : 2812500 = 272 : 225 : 375.

So, Neeta's share = ₹ $\left(50000 \times \frac{272}{872}\right)$.

∴ Correct answer is (*d*).

15 Chain Rule

IMPORTANT FACTS

I. Direct Proportion: *Two quantities are said to be directly proportional, if on the increase (or decrease) of the one, the other increases (or decreases) to the same extent.*

Ex. 1. ***Cost is directly proportional to the number of articles.*** *(More Articles, More Cost)*

Ex. 2. ***Work done is directly proportional to the number of men working on it.*** *(More Men, More Work)*

II. Indirect Proportion: *Two quantities are said to be indirectly proportional, if on the increase of the one, the other decreases to the same extent and vice-versa.*

Ex. 1. ***The time taken by a car in covering a certain distance is inversely proportional to the speed of the car.*** *(More speed, Less is the time taken to cover a distance)*

Ex. 2. ***Time taken to finish a work is inversely proportional to the number of persons working at it.*** *(More persons, Less is the time taken to finish a job)*

Remark: In solving questions by chain rule, we compare every item with the term to be found out.

SOLVED EXAMPLES

Ex. 1. ***A canteen requires 105 kgs of wheat for a week. How many kgs of wheat will it require for 58 days?*** **(L.I.C.A.D.O., 2007)**

Sol. Let the required quantity be x kg. Then,

More days, More cost ***(Direct Proportion)***

$\therefore \quad 7 : 58 :: 105 : x \Leftrightarrow 7 \times x = 58 \times 105 \Leftrightarrow x = \left(\frac{58 \times 105}{7}\right) = 870.$

Hence, the canteen will require 870 kg of wheat for 58 days.

Ex. 2. ***If 36 men can do a piece of work in 25 hours, in how many hours will 15 men do it?***

Sol. Let the required number of hours be x. Then,

Less men, More hours ***(Indirect Proportion)***

$\therefore \quad 15 : 36 :: 25 : x \quad \Leftrightarrow \quad (15 \times x) = (36 \times 25) \Leftrightarrow x = \frac{36 \times 25}{15} = 60.$

Hence, 15 men can do it in 60 hours.

Ex. 3. ***35 women can do a piece of work in 15 days. How many women would be required to do the same work in 25 days?*** **(Bank P.O., 2008)**

Sol. Let the required number of women be x. Then,

More days, Less women ***(Indirect Proportion)***

$\therefore 25 : 15 :: 35 : x \Leftrightarrow (25 \times x) = (15 \times 35) \Leftrightarrow x = \left(\frac{15 \times 35}{25}\right) = 21.$

Hence, 21 women can do the work in 25 days.

Ex. 4. ***A certain number of people were supposed to complete a work in 24 days. The work, however, took 32 days since 9 people were absent throughout. How many people were supposed to be working originally?*** **(M.A.T., 2004)**

Sol. Originally, let there be x people.

Less people, More days ***(Indirect Proportion)***

$\therefore (x - 9) : x :: 24 : 32 \Leftrightarrow (x - 9) \times 32 = x \times 24 \Leftrightarrow 8x = 288 \Leftrightarrow x = 36.$

Hence, 36 people were supposed to be working originally..

Ex. 5. ***If 5 students utilize 18 pencils in 9 days, how long, at the same rate, will 66 pencils last for 15 students?*** **(M.A.T., 2010)**

Sol. Let the required number of days be x.

More students, Less days ***(Indirect Proportion)***

More pencils, More days ***(Direct Proportion)***

$$\left.\begin{array}{ll}\text{Students} & 15:5 \\ \text{Pencils} & 18:66\end{array}\right\} :: 9 : x$$

$$\therefore (15 \times 18 \times x) = (5 \times 66 \times 9) \Leftrightarrow x = \left(\frac{5 \times 66 \times 9}{15 \times 18}\right) = 11.$$

Hence, the required number of days is 11.

Ex. 6. ***If 20 men can build a wall 56 metres long in 6 days, what length of a similar wall can be built by 35 men in 3 days?***

Sol. Let the required length be x metres.

More men, More length built ***(Direct Proportion)***

Less days, Less length built ***(Direct Proportion)***

$$\left.\begin{array}{ll}\text{Men} & 20:35 \\ \text{Days} & 6:3\end{array}\right\} :: 56 : x$$

$$\therefore (20 \times 6 \times x) = (35 \times 3 \times 56) \Leftrightarrow x = \frac{(35 \times 3 \times 56)}{120} = 49.$$

Hence, the required length is 49 m.

Ex. 7. ***8 men working for 9 hours a day complete a piece of work in 20 days. In how many days can 7 men working for 10 hours a day complete the same piece of work?*** **(Bank P.O., 2006)**

Sol. Let the required number of days be x.

Less men, More days ***(Indirect Proportion)***

More hours per day, Less days ***(Indirect Proportion)***

$$\left.\begin{array}{ll}\text{Men} & 7:8 \\ \text{Hours per day} & 10:9\end{array}\right\} :: 20 : x$$

$$\therefore (7 \times 10 \times x) = (8 \times 9 \times 20) \Leftrightarrow x = \left(\frac{8 \times 9 \times 20}{7 \times 10}\right) = \frac{144}{7} = 20\frac{4}{7}.$$

Hence, required number of days $= 20\frac{4}{7}$.

Ex. 8. ***If 12 men or 18 women can do a work in 14 days, then in how many days will 8 men and 16 women do the same work?*** **(R.R.B., 2007)**

Sol. Let the required number of days be x.

$$12 \text{ men} \equiv 18 \text{ women} \Rightarrow 8 \text{ men} \equiv \left(\frac{18}{12} \times 8\right) \text{women} = 12 \text{ women}.$$

More women, Less days ***(Indirect Proportion)***

$$\therefore 28 : 18 :: 14 : x \Leftrightarrow (28 \times x) = (18 \times 14) \Leftrightarrow x = \left(\frac{18 \times 14}{28}\right) = 9.$$

Hence, required number of days = 9.

Ex. 9. ***5 press compositors can set 625 pages of a manuscript in 16 days of $10\frac{1}{2}$ hours each. Each page has 60 lines and each line has 40 letters. In how many days of 8 hours each, will 10 compositors set 1000 pages of a manuscript, each page having 45 lines with 50 letters in each line?***

Sol. Let the required number of days be x.

More compositors, Less days (Indirect Proportion)
More pages, More days (Direct Proportion)
Less hours per day, More days (Indirect Proportion)
Less lines per page, Less days (Direct Proportion)
More letters per line, More days (Direct Proportion)

$$\left.\begin{array}{ll}\text{Compositors} & 10:5 \\ \text{Pages} & 625:1000 \\ \text{Hours per day} & 8:\frac{21}{2} \\ \text{Lines per page} & 60:45 \\ \text{Letters per line} & 40:50\end{array}\right\} :: 16 : x$$

$\therefore$ $10 \times 625 \times 8 \times 60 \times 40 \times x = 5 \times 1000 \times \frac{21}{2} \times 45 \times 50 \times 16$

$\Rightarrow x = \frac{5 \times 1000 \times 21 \times 45 \times 50 \times 16}{2 \times 10 \times 625 \times 8 \times 60 \times 40} = \frac{63}{4} = 15\frac{3}{4}$.

Hence, required number of days $= 15\frac{3}{4}$.

Ex. 10. ***Rocky can walk a certain distance in 40 days when he rests 9 hours a day. How long will he take to walk twice the distance, twice as fast and rest twice as long each day?***

Sol. Let the distance in the two cases be y and $2y$ respectively and the speed be z and $2z$ respectively. Let the required number of days be x.

More distance, More days (Direct Proportion)
More speed, Less days (Indirect Proportion)
More resting time, More days (Direct Proportion)

$$\left.\begin{array}{ll}\text{Distance} & y:2y \\ \text{Speed} & 2z:z \\ \text{Resting time} & 9:18\end{array}\right\} :: 40 : x$$

$\therefore$ $y \times 2z \times 9 \times x = 2y \times z \times 18 \times 40 \Rightarrow x = \frac{2y \times z \times 18 \times 40}{y \times 2z \times 9} = 80$.

Hence, required number of days = 80.

Ex. 11. ***15 persons working 8 hours a day can complete a work in 21 days. How many days will 14 persons take to complete a work $1\frac{1}{2}$ times as great, if they work 6 hours a day?*** (S.S.C., 2006)

Sol. Let the required number of days be x.

Less persons, More days (Indirect Proportion)
Less hours per day, More days (Indirect Proportion)
More work, More days Direct Proportion)

$$\left.\begin{array}{ll}\text{Persons} & 14:15 \\ \text{Hours per day} & 6:8 \\ \text{Work} & y:\frac{3}{2}y\end{array}\right\} :: 21 : x$$

$\therefore$ $14 \times 6 \times y \times x = 15 \times 8 \times \frac{3}{2}y \times 21 \Leftrightarrow x = \frac{15 \times 8 \times 3y \times 21}{2 \times 14 \times 6 \times y} = 45$.

Hence, required number of days = 45.

Ex. 12. ***A contract is to be completed in 50 days and 105 men were set to work, each working 8 hours a day. After 25 days, $\frac{2}{5}$ of the work is finished. How many additional men be employed so that the work may be completed on time, each man now working 9 hours a day?*** (SNAP., 2010)

Sol. Let the required number of additional men be x.

Remaining work = $\left(1-\frac{2}{5}\right)=\frac{3}{5}$.

More days, less men **(Indirect Proportion)**
More working hours per day, Less men **(Indirect Proportion)**
More work, More men **(Direct Proportion)**

$$\left.\begin{array}{ll}\text{Days} & 25:25\\ \text{Working hours} & 9:8\\ \text{Work} & \frac{2}{5}:\frac{3}{5}\end{array}\right\} :: 105:(105+x)$$

$\therefore$ $25 \times 9 \times \frac{2}{5} \times (105 + x) = 25 \times 8 \times \frac{3}{5} \times 105$

$\Leftrightarrow (105 + x) = 8\times\frac{3}{5}\times105\times\frac{5}{2}\times\frac{1}{9} = 140 \Leftrightarrow x = 35.$

Hence, additional number of men required = 35.

Ex. 13. ***If 9 engines consume 24 metric tonnes of coal, when each is working 8 hours a day; how much coal will be required for 8 engines, each running 13 hours a day, it being given that 3 engines of former type consume as much as 4 engines of latter type?***

Sol. Let 3 engines of former type consume 1 unit in 1 hour.
Then, 4 engines of latter type consume 1 unit in 1 hour.

$\therefore$ 1 engine of former type consumes $\frac{1}{3}$ unit in 1 hour.

1 engine of latter type consumes $\frac{1}{4}$ unit in 1 hour.

Let the required consumption of coal be x units.

Less engines, Less coal consumed **(Direct Proportion)**
More working hours, More coal consumed **(Direct Proportion)**
Less rate of consumption, Less coal consumed **(Direct Proportion)**

$$\left.\begin{array}{ll}\text{Number of engines} & 9:8\\ \text{Working hours} & 8:13\\ \text{Rate of consumption} & \frac{1}{3}:\frac{1}{4}\end{array}\right\} :: 24:x$$

$\therefore$ $\left(9\times8\times\frac{1}{3}\times x\right)=\left(8\times13\times\frac{1}{4}\times24\right) \Leftrightarrow 24x = 624 \Leftrightarrow x = 26.$

Hence, the required consumption of coal = 26 metric tonnes.

Ex. 14. ***A garrison of 3300 men had provisions for 32 days, when given at the rate of 850 gms per head. At the end of 7 days, a reinforcement arrives and it was found that the provisions will last 17 days more, when given at the rate of 825 gms per head. What is the strength of the reinforcement?***

Sol. **The problem becomes :**
3300 men taking 850 gms per head have provisions for (32 – 7) or 25 days. How many men taking 825 gms each have provisions for 17 days?

Less ration per head, More men **(Indirect Proportion)**
Less days, More men **(Indirect Proportion)**

$$\left.\begin{array}{ll}\text{Ration} & 825:850\\ \text{Days} & 17:25\end{array}\right\} :: 3300:x$$

$\therefore$ $825 \times 17 \times x = 850 \times 25 \times 3300$ or $x = \frac{850\times25\times3300}{825\times17} = 5000.$

$\therefore$ Strength of reinforcement = (5000 – 3300) = 1700.

Ex. 15. ***Two coal loading machines each working 12 hours per day for 8 days handle 9000 tonnes of coal with an efficiency of 90% while 3 other coal loading machines at an efficiency of 80% are set to handle 12000 tonnes of coal in 6 days. Find how many hours per day each should work.*** **(M.A.T., 2008)**

Sol. Let the number of working hours per day be x.

More machines, Less working hours per day *(Indirect Proportion)*
Less days, More working hours per day *(Indirect Proportion)*
More coal, More working hours per day *(Direct Proportion)*
Less efficiency, More working hours per day *(Indirect Proportion)*

$$\left.\begin{array}{lr} \text{Machines} & 3:2 \\ \text{Days} & 6:8 \\ \text{Coal} & 9000:12000 \\ \text{Efficiency} & 80:90 \end{array}\right\} :: 12 : x$$

$$\therefore \quad 3 \times 6 \times 9000 \times 80 \times x = 2 \times 8 \times 12000 \times 90 \times 12 \Leftrightarrow x = \frac{2 \times 8 \times 12000 \times 90 \times 12}{3 \times 6 \times 9000 \times 80} = 16.$$

Hence, each machine should work for 16 hours per day.

EXERCISE

(OBJECTIVE TYPE QUESTIONS)

Directions: ***Mark (✓) against the correct answer:***

1. If the cost of x metres of wire is d rupees, then what is the cost of y metres of wire at the same rate? **(M.B.A., 2002)**
   (a) ₹ $\left(\frac{xy}{d}\right)$ (b) ₹ (xd)
   (c) ₹ (yd) (d) ₹ $\left(\frac{yd}{x}\right)$
2. The price of 5.5 dozen pens is ₹ 1287. What is the price of 16 such pens?
   (a) ₹ 212 (b) ₹ 296
   (c) ₹ 312 (d) ₹ 412
   (e) None of these
3. The price of 357 mangoes is ₹ 1517.25. What will be the approximate price of 49 dozens of such mangoes?
   (a) ₹ 3000 (b) ₹ 3500
   (c) ₹ 4000 (d) ₹ 2500
4. If a quarter kg of potato costs 60 paise, how many paise will 200 gm cost?
   (a) 48 paise (b) 54 paise
   (c) 56 paise (d) 72 paise
5. If 11.25 m of a uniform iron rod weighs 42.75 kg, what will be the weight of 6 m of the same rod?
   (a) 22.8 kg (b) 25.6 kg
   (c) 28 kg (d) 26.5 kg
6. On a scale of map, 0.6 cm represents 6.6 km. If the distance between the points on the map is 80.5 cm, the actual distance between these points is
   (a) 9 km (b) 72.5 km
   (c) 190.75 km (d) 885.5 km
7. An industrial loom weaves 0.128 metres of cloth every second. Approximately, how many seconds will it take for the loom to weave 25 metres of cloth? **(M.B.A., 2003)**
   (a) 178 (b) 195
   (c) 204 (d) 488
8. A recipe for stew that feeds 4 people calls for $1\frac{1}{2}$ teaspoons of salt. If 3 teaspoons = 1 tablespoon, then how many tablespoons of salt will be needed to make enough stew for 18 people?
   (a) 2.25 (b) 3.25
   (c) 4.5 (d) 6
9. A snapshot $1\frac{7}{8}'' \times 2\frac{1}{2}''$ is to be enlarged so that the longer dimension is 4". What will be the dimension of the shorter side? **(DMRC, 2003)**
   (a) $2\frac{3}{8}''$ (b) $2\frac{1}{2}''$
   (c) 3" (d) $3\frac{3}{8}''$
10. A canteen requires 651 bananas for a week. Totally, how many bananas will it require for the months of April, May and June? **(Bank Recruitment, 2009)**
    (a) 8463 (b) 8547
    (c) 9086 (d) 9284
    (e) None of these

11. If $\frac{4}{9}$th of a bucket is filled in 1 minute, the rest of it will be filled in (Hotel Management, 2010)

(a) 1 min (b) $\frac{9}{4}$ min
(c) $\frac{5}{4}$ min (d) $\frac{4}{5}$ min

12. On a certain map of India the actual distance of 1450 km between two cities Delhi and Kolkata is shown as 5 cm. What scale is used to draw the map? (A.T.M.A., 2004)

(a) $1 : 15 \times 10^6$ (b) $1 : 20 \times 10^6$
(c) $1 : 25 \times 10^6$ (d) $1 : 29 \times 10^6$

13. A flagstaff 17.5 m high casts a shadow of length 40.25 m. The height of the building, which casts a shadow of length 28.75 m under similar conditions will be (M.B.A., 2002)

(a) 10 m (b) 12.5 m
(c) 17.5 m (d) 21.25 m

14. A TV tower 36 metres high casts a shadow of 24 metres at a particular time of a day. What is the height of a minar with a three metre high flagstaff atop it, if both of these together cast a shadow of 50 metres at the same time of the day?

(a) 64 m (b 72 m
(c) 75 m (d) None of these

15. A man completes $\frac{5}{8}$ of a job in 10 days. At this rate, how many more days will it take him to finish the job? (M.B.A., 2003)

(a) 5 (b) 6
(c) 7 (d) $7\frac{1}{2}$

16. 56 men can complete a piece of work in 24 days. In how many days can 42 men complete the same piece of work? (Bank P.O., 2008)

(a) 18 (b) 32
(c) 48 (d) 98
(e) None of these

17. 30 men can do a piece of work in 16 days. How many men would be required to do the same work in 20 days? (Bank P.O., 2008)

(a) 12 (b) 24
(c) 36 (d) 48
(e) None of these

18. A group of workers promise to complete a piece of work in 10 days, but five of them do not report for work. If it took the remaining workers 12 days to complete the work, then the number of workers originally hired was

(a) 15 (b) 25
(c) 30 (d) 45

19. A wheel that has 6 cogs is meshed with a larger wheel of 14 cogs. When the smaller wheel has made 21 revolutions, then the number of revolutions made by the larger wheel is

(a) 4 (b) 9
(c) 12 (d) 49

20. In a camp, there is a meal for 120 men or 200 children. If 150 children have taken the meal, how many men will be catered to with the remaining meal?

(a) 20 (b) 30
(c) 40 (d) 50

21. The cost of 16 packets of salt, each weighing 900 grams is ₹ 28. What will be the cost of 27 packets, if each packet weighs 1 kg?

(a) ₹ 52.50 (b) ₹ 56
(c) ₹ 58.50 (d) ₹ 64.75

22. 4 mat-weavers can weave 4 mats in 4 days. At the same rate, how many mats would be woven by 8 mat-weavers in 8 days? (S.S.C., 2004)

(a) 4 (b) 8
(c) 12 (d) 16

23. If 7 maids with 7 mops cleaned 7 floors in 7 hours, how long would it take 3 maids to mop 3 floors with 3 mops? (M.A.T., 2005)

(a) $\frac{7}{3}$ hours (b) 3 hours
(c) $\frac{49}{3}$ hours (d) 7 hours

24. Four gardeners with four grass mowers mow 400 sq. m of ground in 4 hours. How long would it take for eight gardeners with eight grass mowers to mow 800 sq. m of ground? (CLAT, 2010)

(a) 4 hours (b) 6 hours
(c) 8 hours (d) 12 hours

25. Runnning at the same constant rate, 6 identical machines can produce a total of 180 bottles per hour. How many bottles could 15 such machines produce in 30 minutes? (SNAP, 2010)

(a) 225 (b) 250
(c) 300 (d) 350

26. If 6 persons working 8 hours a day earn ₹ 8400 per week, then 9 persons working 6 hours a day will earn per week (S.S.C., 2003)

(a) ₹ 8400 (b) ₹ 9450
(c) ₹ 16200 (d) ₹ 16800

27. If 5 workers can collect 60 kg wheat in 3 days, how many kilograms of wheat will 8 workers collect in 5 days? (Bank P.O., 2007)

(a) 80 kg (b) 100 kg
(c) 120 kg (d) 160 kg

28. 50 people consume 350 kg of rice in 30 days. In how many days will 35 people consume 50 kg of rice? **(NABARD, 2008)**

(*a*) 2 days (*b*) 3 days
(*c*) 5 days (*d*) 7 days
(*e*) None of these

29. In a dairy farm, 40 cows eat 40 bags of husk in 40 days. In how many days one cow will eat one bag of husk?

(*a*) 1 (*b*) $\frac{1}{40}$
(*c*) 40 (*d*) 80

30. Working 8 hours a day, 12 men can do a work in 30 days. Working 4 hours a day, 18 men can do the work in **(P.C.S., 2006)**

(*a*) 30 days (*b*) 40 days
(*c*) 45 days (*d*) 50 days

31. 12 men working 8 hours per day complete a piece of work in 10 days. To complete the same work in 8 days, working 15 hours a day, the number of men required, is:

(*a*) 4 (*b*) 5
(*c*) 6 (*d*) 8

32. 5 persons can prepare an admission list in 8 days working 7 hours a day. If 2 persons join them so as to complete the work in 4 days, they need to work per day for **(S.S.C., 2004)**

(*a*) 8 hours (*b*) 9 hours
(*c*) 10 hours (*d*) 12 hours

33. 3 pumps, working 8 hours a day, can empty a tank in 2 days. How many hours a day must 4 pumps work to empty the tank in 1 day?

(*a*) 9 (*b*) 10
(*c*) 11 (*d*) 12

34. If 8 men can reap 80 hectares in 24 days, then how many hectares can 36 men reap in 30 days?

(*a*) 350 (*b*) 400
(*c*) 425 (*d*) 450

35. A certain number of persons can dig a trench 100 m long, 50 m broad and 10 m deep in 10 days. The same number of persons can dig another trench 20 m broad and 15 m deep in 30 days. The length of the second trench is

(*a*) 400 m (*b*) 500 m
(*c*) 800 m (*d*) 900 m

36. If 5 men or 7 women can earn ₹ 5250 per day, how much would 7 men and 13 women earn per day? **(S.S.C., 2010)**

(*a*) ₹ 11600 (*b*) ₹ 11700
(*c*) ₹ 16100 (*d*) ₹ 17100

37. 3 men or 6 women can do a piece of work in 20 days. In how many days will 12 men and 8 women do the same work? **(P.C.S., 2008)**

(*a*) $3\frac{1}{2}$ days (*b*) $3\frac{3}{4}$ days
(*c*) 4 days (*d*) 5 days

38. If 5 men or 9 women can do a piece of work in 19 days, then in how many days will 3 men and 6 women do the same work?

(*a*) 12 (*b*) 15
(*c*) 18 (*d*) 21

39. 49 pumps can empty a reservoir in $6\frac{1}{2}$ days, working 8 hours a day. If 196 pumps are used for 5 hours each day, then the same work will be completed in

(*a*) 2 days (*b*) $2\frac{1}{2}$ days
(*c*) $2\frac{3}{5}$ days (*d*) 3 days

40. 30 labourers, working 7 hours a day can finish a piece of work in 18 days. If the labourers work 6 hours a day, then the number of labourers to finish the same piece of work in 30 days, will be:

(*a*) 15 (*b*) 21
(*c*) 22 (*d*) 25

41. If 18 pumps can raise 2170 tonnes of water in 10 days, working 7 hours a day; in how many days will 16 pumps raise 1736 tonnes of water, working 9 hours a day?

(*a*) 6 (*b*) 7
(*c*) 8 (*d*) 9

42. If 80 lamps can be lighted, 5 hours per day for 10 days for ₹ 21.25, then the number of lamps, which can be lighted 4 hours daily for 30 days, for ₹ 76.50, is

(*a*) 100 (*b*) 120
(*c*) 150 (*d*) 160

43. If 12 carpenters, working 6 hours a day, can make 460 chairs in 24 days, how many chairs will 18 carpenters make in 36 days, each working 8 hours a day?

(*a*) 1260 (*b*) 1320
(*c*) 920 (*d*) 1380

44. If 5 spiders can catch five flies in five minutes, how many flies can hundred spiders catch in 100 minutes? **(SNAP, 2005)**

(*a*) 100 (*b*) 500
(*c*) 1000 (*d*) 2000

45. 2 persons working 2 hours a day assemble 2 machines in 2 days. The number of machines assembled by 6 persons working 6 hours a day in 6 days is (A.A.O., 2009)

(a) 6 (b) 18
(c) 27 (d) 54

46. The work done by a man is double the work done by a woman in the same time. If 10 men can do a piece of work in 8 days, then in how many days that work can be done by 3 men and 4 women?

(a) 4 (b) $7\frac{3}{11}$
(c) 8 (d) 16

47. A wall of 100 metres can be built by 7 men or 10 women in 10 days. How many days will 14 men and 20 women take to build a wall of 600 metres?

(a) 15 (b) 20
(c) 25 (d) 30

48. If 10 men or 20 boys can make 260 mats in 20 days, then how many mats will be made by 8 men and 4 boys in 20 days? (C.P.O., 2007)

(a) 240 (b) 260
(c) 280 (d) 520

49. If 600 men dig a 5.5 m wide, 4 m deep and 405 m long canal in half an hour, then how long a canal will 2500 men, working for 6 hours, dig if it is 10 m wide and 8 m deep?

(a) $2694\frac{1}{3}$ m (b) 4082 m
(c) $5568\frac{3}{4}$ m (d) 6452 m

50. 64 persons can dig a trench 50 m long, 2 m wide and 2 m deep in 5 days, working 12 hours daily. In how many days, working 8 hours daily, will 80 persons dig another trench 75 m long, 4 m wide and 3 m deep?

(a) 18 (b) 27
(c) 36 (d) 45

51. 21 binders can bind 1400 books in 15 days. How many binders will be required to bind 800 books in 20 days? (Bank P.O., 2009)

(a) 7 (b) 9
(c) 12 (d) 14
(e) None of these

52. A certain number of artisans can complete a shoe fabrication consignment in 16 days. 8 additional artisans had to be deployed for the same consignment and together they completed it in 4 days less than the earlier estimate. The number of artisans initially employed was

(a) 18 (b) 20
(c) 24 (d) None of these

53. If 9 examiners can examine a certain number of answer books in 12 days, working 5 hours a day; for how many hours a day would 4 examiners have to work in order to examine twice the number of answer books in 30 days?

(a) 6 (b) 8
(c) 9 (d) 10

54. If 17 labourers can dig a ditch 20 m long in 18 days, working 8 hours a day; how many more labourers should be engaged to dig a similar ditch 39 m long in 6 days, each labourer working 9 hours a day?

(a) 34 (b) 51
(c) 68 (d) 85

55. 20 men complete one-third of a piece of work in 20 days. How many more men should be employed to finish the rest of the work in 25 more days? (G.B.O., 2007)

(a) 10 (b) 12
(c) 15 (d) 20

56. A rope makes 70 rounds of the circumference of a cylinder whose radius of the base is 14 cm. How many times can it go round a cylinder with radius 20 cm?

(a) 40 (b) 49
(c) 100 (d) None of these

57. If x men, working x hours per day, can do x units of work in x days, then y men, working y hours per day would be able to complete how many units of work in y days?

(a) $\frac{x^2}{y^3}$ (b) $\frac{x^3}{y^2}$
(c) $\frac{y^2}{x^3}$ (d) $\frac{y^3}{x^2}$

58. A contract is to be completed in 46 days and 117 men were set to work, each working 8 hours a day. After 33 days, $\frac{4}{7}$ of the work is completed. How many additional men may be employed so that the work may be completed in time, each man now working 9 hours a day? (M.A.T., 2005)

(a) 80 (b) 81
(c) 82 (d) 83

59. The normal dosage of a particular medicine is t tablets per day for each patient. A hospital's current supply of these tablets will last p patients for d days. If the recommended dosage increases by 20% and the number of patients decreases by one-third, then for how many days will the hospital's supply last?

(a) $\frac{5d}{4}$ (b) $\frac{4d}{5}$
(c) $\frac{4pt}{5}$ (d) Cannot be determined

60. Some persons can do a piece of work in 12 days. Two times the number of such persons will do half of that work in :
(a) 6 days (b) 4 days
(c) 3 days (d) 12 days

61. 12 persons can do a piece of work in 4 days. How many persons are required to complete 8 times the work in half the time? (S.S.C., 2004)
(a) 144 (b) 180
(c) 190 (d) 192

62. If 5 engines consume 6 metric tonnes of coal when each is running 9 hours a day, how many metric tonnes of coal will be needed for 8 engines, each running 10 hours a day, it being given that 3 engines of the former type consume as much as 4 engines of the latter type? (M.A.T., 2008)
(a) $3\frac{1}{8}$ (b) 8
(c) $8\frac{8}{9}$ (d) $6\frac{12}{25}$

63. If 9 men working $7\frac{1}{2}$ hours a day can finish a piece of work in 20 days, then how many days will be taken by 12 men, working 6 hours a day to finish the work? It is being given that 2 men of latter type work as much as 3 men of the former type. (L.I.C.A.A.O., 2007)
(a) $9\frac{1}{2}$ (b) 11
(c) $12\frac{1}{2}$ (d) 13

64. If a certain number of workmen can do a piece of work in 25 hours, in how many hours will another set of an equal number of men, do a piece of work, twice as great, supposing that 2 men of the first set can do as much work in an hour, as 3 men of the second set do in an hour?
(a) 60 (b) 75
(c) 90 (d) 105

65. 15 men take 21 days of 8 hours each to do a piece of work. How many days of 6 hours each would 21 women take, if 3 women do as much work as 2 men?
(a) 18 (b) 20
(c) 25 (d) 30

66. A contractor employed 30 men to do a piece of work in 38 days. After 25 days, he employed 5 men more and the work was finished one day earlier. How many days he would have been behind, if he had not employed additional men?
(a) 1 (b) $1\frac{1}{4}$
(c) $1\frac{3}{4}$ (d) $1\frac{1}{2}$

67. In a barrack of soldiers there was stock of food for 190 days for 4000 soldiers. After 30 days 800 soldiers left the barrack. For how many days shall the left over food last for the remaining soldiers? (P.C.S., 2006)
(a) 175 days (b) 200 days
(c) 225 days (d) 250 days

68. A garrison of 500 men had provisions for 27 days. After 3 days a reinforcement of 300 men arrived. For how many more days will the remaining food last now? (M.B.A., 2006)
(a) 15 (b) 16
(c) $17\frac{1}{2}$ (d) 18

69. A garrison had provisions for a certain number of days. After 10 days, $\frac{1}{5}$ of the men desert and it is found that the provisions will now last just as long as before. How long was that? (M.B.A., 2003)
(a) 15 days (b) 25 days
(c) 35 days (d) 50 days

70. A fort has provisions for 50 days. If after 10 days they are strengthened by 500 men and the food lasts for 35 days longer, the number of men originally in the fort were
(a) 2500 (b) 3000
(c) 3500 (d) 4000

71. A garrison of 2000 men has provision of ration for 66 days. At the end of a fortnight, reinforcement arrives and it is found that ration will last only for 20 days more. The strength of the reinforcement is
(a) 2000 (b) 2200
(c) 2600 (d) 3200

72. A team of workers was employed by a contractor who undertook to finish 360 pieces of an article in a certain number of days. Making four more pieces per day than was planned, they could complete the job a day ahead of schedule. How many days did they take to complete the job? (M.A.T., 2007)
(a) 8 days (b) 9 days
(c) 10 days (d) 12 days

73. The work done by a woman in 8 hours is equal to the work done by a man in 6 hours and by a boy in 12 hours. If working 6 hours per day 9 men can complete a work in 6 days, then in how many days can 12 men, 12 women and 12 boys together finish the same work, working 8 hours per day? (M.A.T., 2007)
(a) $1\frac{1}{2}$ days (b) 3 days
(c) $3\frac{2}{3}$ days (d) $4\frac{1}{2}$ days

74. 12 men and 18 boys, working $7\frac{1}{2}$ hours a day, can do a piece of work in 60 days. If a man works equal to 2 boys, then how many boys will be required to help 21 men to do twice the work in 50 days, working 9 hours a day?
(a) 30 (b) 42
(c) 48 (d) 90

75. If 3 men or 6 boys can do a piece of work in 10 days, working 7 hours a day; how many days will it take to complete a piece of work twice as large with 6 men and 2 boys working together for 8 hours a day?
(a) 6 (b) $7\frac{1}{2}$
(c) $8\frac{1}{2}$ (d) 9

76. 2 men and 7 boys can do a piece of work in 14 days; 3 men and 8 boys can do the same in 11 days. Then, 8 men and 6 boys can do three times the amount of this work in :
(a) 18 days (b) 21 days
(c) 24 days (d) 30 days

77. Large, medium and small ships are used to bring water. 4 large ships carry as much water as 7 small ships, 3 medium ships carry the same amount of water as 2 large ships and 1 small ship. 15 large, 7 medium and 14 small ships, each made 36 journeys and brought a certain quantity of water. In how many journeys would 12 large, 14 medium and 21 small ships bring the same quantity? (M.A.T., 2007)
(a) 25 (b) 29
(c) 32 (d) 49

78. If 2 m. 60 cm cloth is required for one shirt, then the cloth required for 7 shirts is [APTET, 2011]
(a) 14 m 80 cm (b) 18 m 20 cm
(c) 15 m 20 cm (d) 16 m 80 cm

79. The cost of 4 dozen papers is ₹ 24. The cost of 1 score of papers (in rupees) is [APTET, 2011]
(a) 40 (b) 20
(c) 10 (d) 42

80. The cost of 8 fans and 14 ovens is ₹ 36,520. What is the cost of 12 fans and 21 ovens? [SBI—Clerk Level, 2012]
(a) ₹ 56,800 (b) ₹ 54,780
(c) ₹ 57,950 (d) Cannot be determined

81. The cost of 5 kgs of apples is ₹ 450. The cost of 12 dozen mangoes is ₹ 4,320 and the cost of 4 kgs of oranges is ₹ 240. What is the total cost of 8 kg of apples, 8 dozens of mangoes and 8 kg of oranges? [MAT—2012]
(a) ₹ 4,020 (b) ₹ 4,080
(c) ₹ 4,050
(d) Other than those given as options

82. The cost of 21 pencils and 9 clippers is ₹ 819. The cost price of 7 pencils and 3 clippers is [DMRC—Train Operator (Station Controller), 2012]
(a) ₹ 204 (b) ₹ 409
(c) ₹ 273 (d) ₹ 208

ANSWERS

1. (d)	2. (c)	3. (d)	4. (a)	5. (a)	6. (d)	7. (b)	8. (a)	9. (c)	10. (a)
11. (c)	12. (d)	13. (b)	14. (b)	15. (b)	16. (b)	17. (b)	18. (c)	19. (b)	20. (b)
21. (a)	22. (d)	23. (d)	24. (a)	25. (a)	26. (b)	27. (d)	28. (e)	29. (c)	30. (b)
31. (d)	32. (c)	33. (d)	34. (d)	35. (b)	36. (d)	37. (b)	38. (b)	39. (c)	40. (b)
41. (b)	42. (b)	43. (d)	44. (d)	45. (d)	46. (d)	47. (a)	48. (b)	49. (c)	50. (b)
51. (b)	52. (c)	53. (c)	54. (b)	55. (b)	56. (b)	57. (d)	58. (b)	59. (a)	60. (c)
61. (d)	62. (b)	63. (c)	64. (b)	65. (d)	66. (a)	67. (b)	68. (a)	69. (d)	70. (c)
71. (d)	72. (c)	73. (a)	74. (b)	75. (b)	76. (b)	77. (b)	78. (b)	79. (c)	80. (b)
81. (b)	82. (c)								

SOLUTIONS

1. Cost of x metres = ₹ d. Cost of 1 metre = ₹ $\left(\frac{d}{x}\right)$

Cost of y metres = ₹ $\left(\frac{d}{x} \times y\right)$ = ₹ $\left(\frac{yd}{x}\right)$.

2. 5.5 dozen pens = (5.5 × 12) pens = 66 pens. Let the cost of 16 pens be ₹ x.
Less pens, Less cost *(Direct Proportion)*

∴ 66 : 16 : : 1287 : x ⇔ $66x = 16 \times 1287$

⇔ $x = \left(\frac{16 \times 1287}{66}\right)$ = ₹ 312.

3. Let the required price be ₹ x.
Then,
More mangoes, More price *(Direct Proportion)*
∴ 357 : (49 × 12) : : 1517.25 : x
⇔ $357x = (49 \times 12 \times 1517.25)$

$\Leftrightarrow x = \frac{(49 \times 12 \times 1517.25)}{357} \Leftrightarrow x = 2499.$

Hence, the approximate price is ₹ 2500.

4. Let the required cost be x paise.

Less weight, Less cost ***(Direct Proportion)***

$\therefore\ 250 : 200 :: 60 : x$

$\Leftrightarrow\ 250 \times x = (200 \times 60)$

$\Leftrightarrow x = \frac{(200 \times 60)}{250} \Leftrightarrow x = 48.$

5. Let the required weight be x kg. Then,

Less length, Less weight ***(Direct Proportion)***

$\therefore\ 11.25 : 6 :: 42.75 : x$

$\Leftrightarrow 11.25 \times x = 6 \times 42.75$

$\Leftrightarrow x = \frac{(6 \times 42.75)}{11.25}$

$\Leftrightarrow x = 22.8.$

6. Let the actual distance be x km. Then,

More distance on the map, More is the actual distance ***(Direct Proportion)***

$\therefore\ 0.6 : 80.5 :: 6.6 : x$

$\Leftrightarrow 0.6\ x = 80.5 \times 6.6$

$\Leftrightarrow x = \frac{80.5 \times 6.6}{0.6} \Leftrightarrow x = 885.5.$

7. Let the required time be x seconds.

Then,

More metres, More time ***(Direct Proportion)***

$\therefore\ 0.128 : 25 :: 1 : x$

$\Leftrightarrow 0.128 \times x = 25 \times 1$

$\Leftrightarrow x = \frac{25}{0.128} = \frac{25 \times 1000}{128} \Leftrightarrow x = 195.31.$

$\therefore$ Required time = 195 sec (approximately).

8. 3 teaspoons = 1 tablespoon

$\Rightarrow 1\frac{1}{2}$ teaspoons $= \frac{1}{2}$ tablespoon.

Let the number of tablespoons required be x.

More people, More salt required ***(Direct Proportion)***

$\therefore 4 : 18 :: \frac{1}{2} : x \Leftrightarrow 4x = 18 \times \frac{1}{2} = 9 \Leftrightarrow x = \frac{9}{4} = 2.25.$

9. Let the dimension of the shorter side be x.

More is the longer side, More is the shorter side ***(Direct Proportion)***

$\therefore\ 2\frac{1}{2} : 4 :: 1\frac{7}{8} : x \Leftrightarrow \frac{5}{2}x = 4 \times \frac{15}{8} \Leftrightarrow x = \left(\frac{15}{2} \times \frac{2}{5}\right) = 3.$

10. Total number of days $= (\overset{\text{Apr}}{30} + \overset{\text{May}}{31} + \overset{\text{Jun}}{30}) = 91.$

Let the number of bananas be x.

More days, More bananas ***(Direct Proportion)***

$\therefore 7 : 91 :: 651 : x \Leftrightarrow 7x = 91 \times 651$

$\Leftrightarrow x = \left(\frac{91 \times 651}{7}\right) = 8463.$

11. Remaining part $= \left(1 - \frac{4}{9}\right) = \frac{5}{9}.$

Let the required time be x minutes.

More volume to be filled, More time taken ***(Direct Proportion)***

$\therefore\ \frac{4}{9} : \frac{5}{9} :: 1 : x \Leftrightarrow \frac{4}{9}x = \frac{5}{9} \Leftrightarrow x = \left(\frac{5}{9} \times \frac{9}{4}\right) = \frac{5}{4}.$

12. 5 cm on the map represents 1450 km.

$\therefore$ 1 cm on the map represents $\left(\frac{1450}{5}\right)$ km = 290 km.

Hence, the scale is 1 cm : 290 km *i.e.*, $1 : 29 \times 10^6$.

$[\because 290 \text{ km} = (29 \times 10^6) \text{ cm}]$

13. Let the height of the building be x metres.

Less lengthy shadow, Less is the height ***(Direct Proportion)***

$\therefore\ 40.25 : 28.75 :: 17.5 : x$

$\Leftrightarrow\ 40.25 \times x = 28.75 \times 17.5$

$\Leftrightarrow x = \frac{(28.75 \times 17.5)}{40.25} \Leftrightarrow x = 12.5.$

14. Let the height of the minar with flagstaff be x metres.

More lengthy shadow, More is the height ***(Direct Proportion)***

$\therefore 24 : 50 :: 36 : x \Leftrightarrow 24x = 50 \times 36$

$\Leftrightarrow x = \left(\frac{50 \times 36}{24}\right) = 75.$

Hence, height of the minar = (75 – 3) m = 72 m.

15. Work done $= \frac{5}{8}$. Balance work $= \left(1 - \frac{5}{8}\right) = \frac{3}{8}.$

Less work, Less days ***(Direct Proportion)***

Let the required number of days be x.

Then,

$\frac{5}{8} : \frac{3}{8} :: 10 : x \Leftrightarrow \frac{5}{8} \times x = \frac{3}{8} \times 10 \Leftrightarrow x = \left(\frac{3}{8} \times 10 \times \frac{8}{5}\right) = 6.$

16. Let the required number of days be x.

Less men, More days ***(Indirect Proportion)***

$\therefore 42 : 56 :: 24 : x$

$\Leftrightarrow 42\ x = 56 \times 24 \Leftrightarrow x = \left(\frac{56 \times 24}{42}\right) = 32.$

17. Let the required number of men be x.

More days, Less men ***(Indirect Proportion)***

$\therefore 20 : 16 :: 30 : x \Leftrightarrow 20x = 16 \times 30$

$\Leftrightarrow x = \left(\frac{16 \times 30}{20}\right) = 24.$

18. Let the number of workers originally hired be x.

Less workers, More days ***(Indirect Proportion)***

$(x - 5) : x :: 10 : 12$

$\Leftrightarrow 12\ (x - 5) = 10\ x \Leftrightarrow 2x = 60 \Leftrightarrow x = 30.$

19. Let the required number of revolutions made by larger wheel be x.

Then, ***More cogs, Less revolutions*** ***(Indirect Proportion)***

$\therefore\ 14 : 6 :: 21 : x$

$\Leftrightarrow\ 14 \times x = 6 \times 21 \Leftrightarrow x = \left(\frac{6 \times 21}{14}\right) = 9.$

20. There is a meal for 200 children. 150 children have taken the meal.

Remaining meal is to be catered to 50 children.

Now, 200 children ≡ 120 men

$$50 \text{ children} \equiv \left(\frac{120}{200} \times 50\right) \text{men} = 30 \text{ men}.$$

21. Let the required cost be ₹ x. Then,

More packets, More cost *(Direct Proportion)*

More weight, More cost *(Direct Proportion)*

$$\left.\begin{array}{ll}\text{Packets} & 16:27 \\ \text{Weight} & 900:1000\end{array}\right\} :: 28 : x$$

$\therefore \quad (16 \times 900 \times x) = (27 \times 1000 \times 28)$

$$\Leftrightarrow \quad x = \frac{(27 \times 1000 \times 28)}{16 \times 900} = \frac{105}{2} = 52.50.$$

22. Let the required number of mats be x.

More weavers, More mats *(Direct Proportion)*

More days, More mats *(Direct Proportion)*

$$\left.\begin{array}{ll}\text{Weavers} & 4:8 \\ \text{Days} & 4:8\end{array}\right\} :: 4 : x$$

$$\therefore 4 \times 4 \times x = 8 \times 8 \times 4 \Leftrightarrow x = \frac{(8 \times 8 \times 4)}{(4 \times 4)} = 16.$$

23. Since each maid would work with one mop, so we shall consider 1 maid and 1 mop as 1 unit. Let the required time be x hours.

Less maids and mops, More time *(Indirect Proportion)*

Less floors, Less time *(Direct Proportion)*

$$\left.\begin{array}{ll}\text{Maids \& Mops} & 3:7 \\ \text{Floors} & 7:3\end{array}\right\} :: 7 :: x$$

$$\therefore 3 \times 7 \times x = 7 \times 3 \times 7 \Leftrightarrow x = \frac{7 \times 3 \times 7}{3 \times 7} = 7.$$

24. Since each gardener would work with one grass mower, so we shall consider 1 gardener and 1 grass mower as one unit. Let the required time be x hours.

More gardeners and grass mowers,

Less time *(Indirect Proportion)*

More area, More time *(Direct Proportion)*

$$\left.\begin{array}{ll}\text{Gardeners \& grass mowers} & 8:4 \\ \text{Area} & 400:800\end{array}\right\} :: 4 : x$$

$\therefore 8 \times 400 \times x = 4 \times 800 \times 4$

$$\Leftrightarrow x = \left(\frac{4 \times 800 \times 4}{8 \times 400}\right) = 4.$$

25. Let the required number of bottles be x.

More machines,

More bottles produced *(Direct Proportion)*

Less time, Less bottles produced *(Direct Proportion)*

$$\left.\begin{array}{ll}\text{Machines} & 6:15 \\ \text{Time} & 60:30\end{array}\right\} :: 180 : x$$

$\therefore 6 \times 60 \times x = 15 \times 30 \times 180$

$$\Leftrightarrow x = \left(\frac{15 \times 30 \times 180}{6 \times 60}\right) = 225.$$

26. Let the weekly earning be ₹ x.

More persons, More earning *(Direct Proportion)*

Less working hours, Less earning *(Direct Proportion)*

$$\left.\begin{array}{ll}\text{Persons} & 6:9 \\ \text{Working hours} & 8:6\end{array}\right\} :: 8400 : x$$

$\therefore 6 \times 8 \times x = 9 \times 6 \times 8400$

$$\Leftrightarrow x = \left(\frac{9 \times 6 \times 8400}{6 \times 8}\right) = 9450.$$

27. Let the required quantity be x kg.

More workers, More quantity *(Direct Proportion)*

More days, More quantity *(Direct Proportion)*

$$\left.\begin{array}{ll}\text{Workers} & 5:8 \\ \text{Days} & 3:5\end{array}\right\} :: 60 : x$$

$\therefore 5 \times 3 \times x = 8 \times 5 \times 60$

$$\Leftrightarrow x = \left(\frac{8 \times 5 \times 60}{5 \times 3}\right) = 160.$$

28. Let the required number of days be x.

Less people, More days *(Indirect Proportion)*

Less quantity, Less days *(Direct Proportion)*

$$\left.\begin{array}{ll}\text{People} & 35:50 \\ \text{Quantity} & 350:50\end{array}\right\} :: 30 : x$$

$\therefore 35 \times 350 \times x = 50 \times 50 \times 30$

$$\Leftrightarrow x = \left(\frac{50 \times 50 \times 30}{35 \times 350}\right) = \frac{300}{49} = 6\frac{6}{49}.$$

29. Let the required number of days be x.

Less cows, More days *(Indirect Proportion)*

Less bags, Less days *(Direct Proportion)*

$$\left.\begin{array}{ll}\text{Cows} & 1:40 \\ \text{Bags} & 40:1\end{array}\right\} :: 40 : x$$

$$\therefore 1 \times 40 \times x = 40 \times 1 \times 40 \Leftrightarrow x = 40.$$

30. Let the required number of days be x.

Less working hours,

More days *(Indirect Proportion)*

More men, Less days *(Indirect Proportion)*

$$\left.\begin{array}{ll}\text{Working hours} & 4:8 \\ \text{Men} & 18:12\end{array}\right\} :: 30 : x$$

$\therefore 4 \times 18 \times x = 8 \times 12 \times 30$

$$\Leftrightarrow x = \left(\frac{8 \times 12 \times 30}{4 \times 18}\right) = 40.$$

31. Let the required number of men be x.

Less days, More men *(Indirect Proportion)*

More working hrs per day,

Less men *(Indirect Proportion)*

$$\left.\begin{array}{ll}\text{Days} & 8:10 \\ \text{Working Hrs} & 15:8\end{array}\right\} :: 12 : x$$

$\therefore 8 \times 15 \times x = 10 \times 8 \times 12$

$$\Leftrightarrow x = \frac{10 \times 8 \times 12}{8 \times 15} \Leftrightarrow x = 8.$$

32. Let the number of working hours per day be x.

More persons, Less working hours **(Indirect Proportion)**
Less days, More working hours **(Indirect Proportion)**

$$\left.\begin{matrix}\text{Persons} & 7:5\\ \text{Days} & 4:8\end{matrix}\right\}::7:x$$

$\therefore 7 \times 4 \times x = 5 \times 8 \times 7 \Leftrightarrow x = \left(\frac{5\times8\times7}{7\times4}\right) = 10.$

33. Let the required number of working hours per day be x.
More pumps, Less working hours per day **(Indirect Proportion)**
Less days, More working hours per day **(Indirect Proportion)**

$$\left.\begin{matrix}\text{Pumps} & 4:3\\ \text{Days} & 1:2\end{matrix}\right\}::8:x$$

$\therefore 4 \times 1 \times x = 3 \times 2 \times 8$

$\Leftrightarrow x = \frac{3\times2\times8}{4} \Leftrightarrow x = 12.$

34. Let the required number of hectares be x. Then,
More men, More hectares **(Direct Proportion)**
More days, More hectares **(Direct Proportion)**

$$\left.\begin{matrix}\text{Men} & 8:36\\ \text{Days} & 24:30\end{matrix}\right\}::80:x$$

$\therefore 8 \times 24 \times x = 36 \times 30 \times 80$

$\Leftrightarrow x = \frac{(36\times30\times80)}{(8\times24)} \Leftrightarrow x = 450.$

35. Let the required length be x metres.
Less breadth, More length **(Indirect Proportion)**
More depth, Less length **(Indirect Proportion)**
More days, More length **(Direct Proportion)**

$$\left.\begin{matrix}\text{Breadth} & 20:50\\ \text{Depth} & 15:10\\ \text{Days} & 10:30\end{matrix}\right\}::100:x$$

$\therefore 20 \times 15 \times 10 \times x = 50 \times 10 \times 30 \times 100$

$\Leftrightarrow x = \frac{(50\times10\times30\times100)}{(20\times15\times10)} \Leftrightarrow x = 500.$

36. Let the required earning be ₹ x.

5 men ≡ 7 women ⇔ 7 men ≡ $\left(\frac{7}{5}\times7\right)$ women $= \frac{49}{5}$ women.

∴ (7 men and 13 women) ≡ $\left(\frac{49}{5}+13\right)$ women $= \frac{114}{5}$ women.

Now, *More women, More earning* **(Direct Proportion)**

$\therefore 7 : \frac{114}{5} :: 5250 : x \Leftrightarrow 7x = \left(\frac{114}{5}\times5250\right) = 119700$

$\Leftrightarrow x = \frac{119700}{7} = 17100.$

37. Let the required number of days be x.

3 men ≡ 6 women ⇔ 12 men ≡ (2 × 12) women = 24 women.

∴ (12 men and 8 women) ≡ (24 + 8) women = 32 women.

Now, *More women, Less days* **(Indirect Proportion)**

$\therefore 32 : 6 :: 20 : x \Leftrightarrow 32x = 6 \times 20$

$\Leftrightarrow x = \left(\frac{6\times20}{32}\right) = \frac{15}{4} = 3\frac{3}{4}.$

38. Let the required number of days be x.

5 men ≡ 9 women ⇔ 3 men ≡ $\left(\frac{9}{5}\times3\right)$ women $= \frac{27}{5}$ women.

∴ (3 men and 6 women) ≡ $\left(\frac{27}{5}+6\right)$ women $= \frac{57}{5}$ women.

Now,
More women, Less days **(Indirect Proportion)**

$\therefore \frac{57}{5} : 9 :: 19 : x \Leftrightarrow \frac{57}{5}\times x = 9\times19$

$\Leftrightarrow x = \left(9\times19\times\frac{5}{57}\right) = 15.$

39. Let the required number of days be x. Then,
More pumps, Less days **(Indirect Proportion)**
Less working hrs/day, More days **(Indirect Proportion)**

$$\left.\begin{matrix}\text{Pumps} & 196:49\\ \text{Working Hrs/Day} & 5:8\end{matrix}\right\}::\frac{13}{2}:x$$

$\therefore 196\times5\times x = 49\times8\times\frac{13}{2} \Leftrightarrow x = \left(49\times8\times\frac{13}{2}\times\frac{1}{196\times5}\right)$

$\Leftrightarrow x = \frac{13}{5} = 2\frac{3}{5}.$

40. Let the required number of labourers be x. Then,
Less working hrs/day, More labourers **(Indirect Proportion)**
More days, Less labourers **(Indirect Proportion)**

$$\left.\begin{matrix}\text{Working Hrs/Day} & 6:7\\ \text{Days} & 30:18\end{matrix}\right\}::30:x$$

$\therefore 6 \times 30 \times x = 7 \times 18 \times 30 \Leftrightarrow 6x = 126 \Leftrightarrow x = 21.$

41. Let the required number of days be x. Then,
Less pumps, More days **(Indirect Proportion)**
Less weight, Less days **(Direct Proportion)**
More hours/day, Less days **(Indirect Proportion)**

$$\left.\begin{matrix}\text{Pumps} & 16:18\\ \text{Weight} & 2170:1736\\ \text{Hours/Day} & 9:7\end{matrix}\right\}::10:x$$

$\therefore (16 \times 2170 \times 9 \times x) = (18 \times 1736 \times 7 \times 10)$

$\Leftrightarrow x = \frac{18\times1736\times7\times10}{16\times2170\times9} = 7.$

42. Let the required number of lamps be x.
Less hours per day, More lamps **(Indirect Proportion)**
More money, More lamps **(Direct Proportion)**
More days, Less lamps **(Indirect Proportion)**

$$\left.\begin{matrix}\text{Hours per day} & 4:5\\ \text{Money} & 21.25:76.50\\ \text{Number of days} & 30:10\end{matrix}\right\}::80:x$$

$\therefore 4 \times 21.25 \times 30 \times x = 5 \times 76.50 \times 10 \times 80$

$\Leftrightarrow x = \frac{5\times76.50\times10\times80}{4\times21.25\times30} \Leftrightarrow x = 120.$

43. Let the required number of chairs be x. Then,

More carpenters, More chairs (Direct Proportion)
More hours per day, More chairs (Direct Proportion)
More days, More chairs (Direct Proportion)

$$\left.\begin{array}{ll}\text{Carpenters} & 12:18\\ \text{Hours per day} & 6:8\\ \text{Days} & 24:36\end{array}\right\}::460:x$$

$\therefore \quad (12 \times 6 \times 24 \times x) = (18 \times 8 \times 36 \times 460)$

$\Leftrightarrow \quad x = \dfrac{(18\times8\times36\times460)}{(12\times6\times24)} = 1380.$

$\therefore$ Required number of chairs = 1380.

44. Let the required number of flies be x.

More spiders, More flies (Direct Proportion)
More time, More flies (Direct Proportion)

$$\left.\begin{array}{ll}\text{Spiders} & 5:100\\ \text{Minutes} & 5:100\end{array}\right\}::5:x$$

$\therefore 5 \times 5 \times x = 100 \times 100 \times 5$

$\Leftrightarrow x = \left(\dfrac{100\times100\times5}{5\times5}\right) = 2000.$

45. Let the required number of machines be x.

More persons, More machines (Direct Proportion)
More working hours, More machines (Direct Proportion)
More days, More machines (Direct Proportion)

$$\left.\begin{array}{ll}\text{Persons} & 2:6\\ \text{Working hours} & 2:6\\ \text{Days} & 2:6\end{array}\right\}::2:x \quad \therefore 2 \times 2 \times 2 \times x$$

$= 6 \times 6 \times 6 \times 2$

$\Leftrightarrow x = \left(\dfrac{6\times6\times6\times2}{2\times2\times2}\right) = 54.$

46. 2 women ≡ 1 man ⇔ 4 women ≡ 2 men.

$\therefore$ (3 men and 4 women) ≡ (3 + 2) men = 5 men.

Let the required number of days be x.

Less Men, More days (Indirect Proportion)

$\therefore 5 : 10 :: 8 : x \Leftrightarrow 5x = 10 \times 8 \Leftrightarrow x = 16.$

47. Let the required number of days be x.

7 men ≡ 10 women

⇒ 14 men ≡ 20 women

$\therefore$ (14 men and 20 women) ≡ (20 + 20) women = 40 women.

More length, More days (Direct Proportion)
More women, Less days (Indirect Proportion)

$$\left.\begin{array}{ll}\text{Length} & 100:600\\ \text{Women} & 40:10\end{array}\right\}::10:x$$

$\therefore 100 \times 40 \times x = 600 \times 10 \times 10$

$\Leftrightarrow x = \left(\dfrac{600\times10\times10}{100\times40}\right) = 15.$

48. Let the required number of mats be x.

10 men ≡ 20 boys ⇒ 1 man ≡ 2 boys

⇒ 8 men ≡ 16 boys

⇒ (8 men + 4 boys) ≡ (16 + 4) boys = 20 boys.

$\therefore$ 8 men and 4 boys can make as many mats as 20 boys i.e., 260 mats.

49. Let the required length be x metres.

More men, More length (Direct Proportion)
More width, Less length (Indirect Proportion)
More depth, Less length (Indirect Proportion)
More time, More length (Direct Proportion)

$$\left.\begin{array}{ll}\text{Men} & 600:2500\\ \text{Width} & 10:5.5\\ \text{Depth} & 8:4\\ \text{Hours} & \frac{1}{2}:6\end{array}\right\}::405:x$$

$\therefore 600 \times 10 \times 8 \times \dfrac{1}{2} \times x = 2500 \times 5.5 \times 4 \times 6 \times 405$

$\Leftrightarrow x = \left(\dfrac{2500\times5.5\times4\times6\times405\times2}{600\times10\times8}\right) = \dfrac{22275}{4} = 5568\dfrac{3}{4}.$

50. Let the required number of days be x.

More persons, Less days (Indirect Proportion)
More length, More days (Direct Proportion)
More width, More days (Direct Proportion)
More depth, More days (Direct Proportion)
Less working hrs, More days (Indirect Proportion)

$$\left.\begin{array}{ll}\text{Persons} & 80:64\\ \text{Length} & 50:75\\ \text{Width} & 2:4\\ \text{Depth} & 2:3\\ \text{Working hrs} & 8:12\end{array}\right\}::5:x$$

$\therefore 80\times50\times2\times2\times8\times x = 64\times75\times4\times3\times12\times5$

$\Leftrightarrow x = \left(\dfrac{64\times75\times4\times3\times12\times5}{80\times50\times2\times2\times8}\right) = 27.$

51. Let the required number of binders be x.

Less books, Less binders (Direct Proportion)
More days, Less binders (Indirect Proportion)

$$\left.\begin{array}{ll}\text{Books} & 1400:800\\ \text{Days} & 20:15\end{array}\right\}::21:x$$

$\therefore 1400 \times 20 \times x = 800 \times 15 \times 21$

$\Leftrightarrow x = \left(\dfrac{800\times15\times21}{1400\times20}\right) = 9.$

52. Let the original number of artisans be x.

More artisans, Less days (Indirect Proportion)

$\therefore (x + 8) : x :: 16 : 12 \Leftrightarrow 12\,(x + 8) = 16\,x$

$\Leftrightarrow 4x = 96 \Leftrightarrow x = 24.$

53. Let the required number of working hours per day be x.

Less examiners, More working hours per day (Indirect Proportion)
More days, Less working hours per day (Indirect Proportion)
More answer books,

More working hours per day **(Direct Proportion)**

$$\begin{rmatrix} \text{Examiners} & 4:9 \\ \text{Days} & 30:12 \\ \text{Answer books} & 1:2 \end{rmatrix} :: 5 : x$$

$\therefore$ $(4 \times 30 \times 1 \times x) = (9 \times 12 \times 2 \times 5)$

$\Leftrightarrow 120x = 1080 \Leftrightarrow x = 9.$

54. Let the total number of men to be engaged be x.

More length, More labourers **(Direct Proportion)**

Less days, More labourers **(Indirect Proportion)**

More hours per day, Less labourers **(Indirect Proportion)**

$$\left.\begin{matrix} \text{Length} & 26:39 \\ \text{Days} & 6:18 \\ \text{Hours per day} & 9:8 \end{matrix}\right\} :: 17 : x$$

$\therefore$ $(26 \times 6 \times 9 \times x) = (39 \times 18 \times 8 \times 17)$

$\Leftrightarrow x = \frac{(39 \times 18 \times 8 \times 17)}{(26 \times 6 \times 9)} = 68.$

$\therefore$ Number of more labourers $= (68 - 17) = 51.$

55. Let the total number of men be x.

Work done $= \frac{1}{3}$, Remaining work $= \left(1 - \frac{1}{3}\right) = \frac{2}{3}.$

More work, More men **(Direct Proportion)**

More days, Less men **(Indirect Proportion)**

$$\left.\begin{matrix} \text{Work} & \frac{1}{3} : \frac{2}{3} \\ \text{Days} & 25:20 \end{matrix}\right\} :: 20 : x$$

$\therefore$ $\left(\frac{1}{3} \times 25 \times x\right) = \left(\frac{2}{3} \times 20 \times 20\right) \Leftrightarrow x = \frac{800}{25} = 32.$

$\therefore$ More men to be employed $= (32 - 20) = 12.$

56. Let the required number of rounds be x.

More radius, Less rounds **(Indirect Proportion)**

$\therefore$ $20 : 14 :: 70 : x \Leftrightarrow (20 \times x) = (14 \times 70)$

$\Leftrightarrow x = \frac{14 \times 70}{20} \Leftrightarrow x = 49.$

Hence, the required number of rounds $= 49.$

57. Let the required number of units of work be z.

More men, More work **(Direct Proportion)**

More working hours, More work **(Direct Proportion)**

More days, More work **(Direct Proportion)**

$$\left.\begin{matrix} \text{Men} & x:y \\ \text{Hours per day} & x:y \\ \text{Days} & x:y \end{matrix}\right\} :: x : z$$

$\therefore$ $(x \times x \times x \times z) = (y \times y \times y \times x) \Leftrightarrow z = \frac{y^3}{x^2}.$

58. Remaining work $= \left(1 - \frac{4}{7}\right) = \frac{3}{7}.$ Remaining period $= (46 - 33)$ days $= 13$ days.

Let the total men working at it be x.

Less work, Less men **(Direct Proportion)**

Less days, More men **(Indirect Proportion)**

More Hrs/Day, Less men **(Indirect Proportion)**

$$\left.\begin{matrix} \text{Work} & \frac{4}{7} : \frac{3}{7} \\ \text{Days} & 13:33 \\ \text{Hrs/Day} & 9:8 \end{matrix}\right\} :: 117 : x$$

$\therefore$ $\frac{4}{7} \times 13 \times 9 \times x = \frac{3}{7} \times 33 \times 8 \times 117$ or x

$= \left(\frac{3 \times 33 \times 8 \times 117}{4 \times 13 \times 9}\right) = 198.$

$\therefore$ Additional men to be employed $= (198 - 117) = 81.$

59. New dosage $= 120\%$ of $t = \frac{6}{5}t.$ Number of patients $= \frac{2}{3}p.$

Let the required number of days be x.

More dosage, Less days **(Indirect Proportion)**

Less patients, More days **(Indirect Proportion)**

$$\left.\begin{matrix} \text{Dosage} & \frac{6}{5}t : t \\ \text{Patients} & \frac{2}{3}p : p \end{matrix}\right\} :: d : x$$

$\therefore$ $\frac{6}{5}t \times \frac{2}{3}p \times x = t \times p \times d \Leftrightarrow x = \left(\frac{3}{2} \times \frac{5}{6} \times d\right) = \frac{5d}{4}.$

60. Let x men can do the work in 12 days and the required number of days be z.

More men, Less days **(Indirect Proportion)**

Less work, Less days **(Direct Proportion)**

$$\left.\begin{matrix} \text{Men} & 2x : x \\ \text{Work} & 1 : \frac{1}{2} \end{matrix}\right\} :: 12 : z$$

$\therefore$ $(2x \times 1 \times z) = \left(x \times \frac{1}{2} \times 12\right)$

$\Leftrightarrow 2xz = 6x \Leftrightarrow z = 3.$

61. Let the required number of persons be x.

Less days, More persons **(Indirect Proportion)**

More work, More persons **(Direct Proportion)**

$$\left.\begin{matrix} \text{Days} & 2:4 \\ \text{Work} & 1:8 \end{matrix}\right\} :: 12 : x$$

$\therefore$ $2 \times 1 \times x = 4 \times 8 \times 12$

$\Leftrightarrow x = \left(\frac{4 \times 8 \times 12}{2}\right) = 192.$

62. Let the required quantity of coal be x metric tonnes.

More engines, More coal **(Direct Proportion)**

More hours per day, More coal **(Direct Proportion)**

More rate, More coal **(Direct Proportion)**

$$\left.\begin{matrix} \text{Engines} & 5:8 \\ \text{Hours per day} & 9:10 \\ \text{Rate} & \frac{1}{3} : \frac{1}{4} \end{matrix}\right\} :: 6 : x$$

$\therefore$ $\left(5 \times 9 \times \frac{1}{3} \times x\right) = \left(8 \times 10 \times \frac{1}{4} \times 6\right) \Leftrightarrow 15x = 120 \Leftrightarrow x = 8.$

63. Let the required number of days be x.

2 men of latter type

$\equiv$ 3 men of former type

$\Rightarrow$ 12 men of latter type $\equiv \left(\frac{3}{2}\times 12\right)$

$=$ 18 men of former type

More men, Less days ***(Indirect Proportion)***

Less working hrs, More days ***(Indirect Proportion)***

$$\left.\begin{array}{ll}\text{Men} & 18:9 \\ \text{Working hrs} & 6:\frac{15}{2}\end{array}\right\}::20:x$$

$\therefore 18\times 6\times x = 9\times\frac{15}{2}\times 20 \Leftrightarrow 108x = 1350 \Leftrightarrow x = \frac{25}{2} = 12\frac{1}{2}$.

64. Let the required number of hours be x.

Speeds of working of first and second type of men are $\frac{1}{2}$ and $\frac{1}{3}$.

More work, More time ***(Direct Proportion)***

Less speed, More time ***(Indirect Proportion)***

$$\left.\begin{array}{ll}\text{Work} & 1:2 \\ \text{Speed} & \frac{1}{3}:\frac{1}{2}\end{array}\right\}::25:x$$

$\therefore \quad \left(1\times\frac{1}{3}\times x\right) = \left(2\times\frac{1}{2}\times 25\right) \Leftrightarrow x = 75.$

65. 3 women $\equiv$ 2 men.

So, 21 women $\equiv$ 14 men.

Less men, More days ***(Indirect Proportion)***

Less hours per day, More days ***(Indirect Proportion)***

$$\left.\begin{array}{ll}\text{Men} & 14:15 \\ \text{Hours per day} & 6:8\end{array}\right\}::21:x$$

$\therefore \quad (14 \times 6 \times x) = (15 \times 8 \times 21)$

$\Leftrightarrow x = \frac{(15\times 8\times 21)}{(14\times 6)} = 30.$

$\therefore$ Required number of days = 30.

66. After 25 days, 35 men complete the work in 12 days.

Thus, 35 men can finish the remaining work in 12 days.

$\therefore$ 30 men can do it in $\frac{(12\times 35)}{30} = 14$ days,

which is 1 day behind.

67. Let the remaining food last for x days.

4000 soldiers had provisions for 160 days. 3200 soldiers had provisions for x days.

Less men, More days ***(Indirect Proportion)***

$\therefore$ 3200 : 4000 : : 160 : x

$\Leftrightarrow 3200x = 4000 \times 160$

$\Leftrightarrow x = \left(\frac{4000\times 160}{3200}\right) = 200.$

68. Let the remaining food last for x days.

500 men had provisions for (27 – 3) = 24 days.

(500 + 300) men had provisions for x days.

More men, Less days ***(Indirect Proportion)***

$\therefore \quad$ 800 : 500 : : 24 : x

$\Leftrightarrow \quad (800 \times x) = (500 \times 24)$

$\Leftrightarrow \quad x = \left(\frac{500\times 24}{800}\right) = 15.$

69. Initially, let there be x men having food for y days.

After 10 days, x men had food for $(y - 10)$ days. Also, $\left(x - \frac{x}{5}\right)$ men had food for y days.

$\therefore x(y - 10) = \frac{4x}{5}\times y$

$\Leftrightarrow 5xy - 50x = 4xy \Leftrightarrow xy - 50x = 0$

$\Leftrightarrow x(y - 50) = 0 \Leftrightarrow y - 50 = 0 \Leftrightarrow y = 50.$

70. Let there be x men originally.

So, x men had provisions for 40 days whereas $(x + 500)$ men consumed it in 35 days.

More men, Less days ***(Indirect Proportion)***

$\therefore (x + 500) : x : : 40 : 35$

$\Leftrightarrow 35(x + 500) = 40x \Leftrightarrow 5x = 35 \times 500$

$\Leftrightarrow x = \left(\frac{35\times 500}{5}\right) = 3500.$

71. Let the strength of the reinforcement be x men.

Then, 2000 men had provisions for (66 – 14) = 52 days while $(2000 + x)$ men consumed it in 20 days.

More men, Less days ***(Indirect Proportion)***

$\therefore (2000 + x) : 2000 : : 52 : 20$

$\Leftrightarrow 20(2000 + x) = 2000 \times 52$

$\Leftrightarrow (2000 + x) = \left(\frac{2000\times 52}{20}\right) = 5200 \Leftrightarrow x = 3200.$

72. Let the team take x days to finish 360 pieces.

Then, number of pieces made each day $= \frac{360}{x}$.

More number of pieces per day, Less days ***(Indirect Proportion)***

$\therefore \left(\frac{360}{x} + 4\right) : \frac{360}{x} : : x : (x - 1)$

$\Leftrightarrow \left(\frac{360}{x} + 4\right)(x - 1) = \frac{360}{x}\times x = 360$

$\Leftrightarrow 360 - \frac{360}{x} + 4x - 4 = 360$

$\Leftrightarrow 4x - \frac{360}{x} - 4 = 0 \Leftrightarrow x - \frac{90}{x} - 1 = 0$

$\Leftrightarrow \quad x^2 - x - 90 = 0 \Leftrightarrow (x - 10)(x + 9) = 0 \Leftrightarrow x = 10.$

73. Ratio of time taken by a woman, a man and a boy

$= 8 : 6 : 12 = 4 : 3 : 6.$

So, 4 women $\equiv$ 3 men $\equiv$ 6 boys.

(12 men + 12 women + 12 boys)

$= \left[12 + \left(\frac{3}{4}\times 12\right) + \left(\frac{3}{6}\times 12\right)\right]$ men

$= (12 + 9 + 6)$ men $= 27$ men.

Let the required number of days be x.

More men, Less days ***(Indirect Proportion)***

More working hours, Less days ***(Indirect Proportion)***

$$\left.\begin{array}{ll}\text{Men} & 27:9 \\ \text{Working hrs} & 8:6\end{array}\right\}::6:x$$

$\therefore 27 \times 8 \times x = 9 \times 6 \times 6$

$\Leftrightarrow x = \left(\frac{9\times 6\times 6}{27\times 8}\right) = \frac{3}{2} = 1\frac{1}{2}.$

74. 1 man ≡ 2 boys ⇔ (12 men + 18 boys)
≡ (12 × 2 + 18) boys = 42 boys.

Let required number of boys = x.

21 men + x boys ≡ (21 × 2 + x) boys = (42 + x) boys.

Less days, More boys ***(Indirect Proportion)***
More hrs per day, Less boys ***(Indirect Proportion)***
More work, More boys ***(Direct Proportion)***

$$\left.\begin{array}{ll}\text{Days} & 50:60\\ \text{Hours per day} & 9:\frac{15}{2}\\ \text{Work} & 1:2\end{array}\right\}::42:(42+x)$$

$\therefore$ $[50 \times 9 \times 1 \times (42 + x)] = \left(60\times\frac{15}{2}\times2\times42\right)$

$\Leftrightarrow (42+x)=\frac{37800}{450} \Leftrightarrow 42+x=84 \Leftrightarrow x=42.$

75. 3 men ≡ 6 boys ⇔ (6 men + 2 boys) ≡ 14 boys.

More work, More days ***(Direct Proportion)***
More boys, Less days ***(Indirect Proportion)***
More hours per day, Less days ***(Indirect Proportion)***

$$\left.\begin{array}{ll}\text{Work} & 1:2\\ \text{Boys} & 14:6\\ \text{Hours per day} & 8:7\end{array}\right\}::10:x$$

$\therefore (1 \times 14 \times 8 \times x) = (2 \times 6 \times 7 \times 10)$

$\Leftrightarrow x = \frac{840}{112}=7\frac{1}{2}.$

76. (2 × 14) men + (7 × 14) boys
≡ (3 × 11) men + (8 × 11) boys

⇔ 5 men ≡ 10 boys ⇔ 1 man ≡ 2 boys.

$\therefore$ (2 men + 7 boys) ≡ (2 × 2 + 7) boys = 11 boys.
(8 men + 6 boys) ≡ (8 × 2 + 6) boys = 22 boys.

Let the required number of days be x.

Now, ***More boys, Less days*** ***(Indirect Proportion)***
More work, More days ***(Direct Proportion)***

$$\left.\begin{array}{ll}\text{Boys} & 22:11\\ \text{Work} & 1:3\end{array}\right\}::14:x$$

$\therefore (22 \times 1 \times x) = (11 \times 3 \times 14)$

$\therefore x = \frac{462}{22}=21.$

77. 4 large ships ≡ 7 small ships

$\Leftrightarrow$ 15 large ships = $\left(\frac{7}{4}\times15\right)$ small ships = $\frac{105}{4}$ small ships.

Also, 2 large ships = $\left(\frac{7}{4}\times2\right)$ small ships = $\frac{7}{2}$ small ships.

3 medium ships ≡ 2 large ships + 1 small ship

≡ $\left(\frac{7}{2}+1\right)$ small ships = $\frac{9}{2}$ small ships.

⇔ 7 medium ships

= $\left(\frac{9}{2}\times\frac{1}{3}\times7\right)$ small ships = $\frac{21}{2}$ small ships.

$\therefore$ (15 large + 7 medium + 14 small) ships

≡ $\left(\frac{105}{4}+\frac{21}{2}+14\right)$ small ships = $\frac{203}{4}$ small ships.

(12 large + 14 medium + 21 small) ships

≡ $\left[\left(\frac{7}{4}\times12\right)+\left(\frac{21}{2}\times2\right)+21\right]$ small ships

= (21 + 21 + 21) small ships = 63 small ships.

Let the required number of journeys be x.

More ships, Less journeys ***(Indirect Proportion)***

$\therefore 63:\frac{203}{4}::36:x \Leftrightarrow 63x=\frac{203}{4}\times36=1827 \Leftrightarrow x=\frac{1827}{63}=29.$

78. Cloth is required for 1 shirt = 2m, 60cm or 260cm

Cloth is required for 7 shirts = 260 × 7 = 1,820 cm

Or 18m 20cm.

79. 1 score of papers = 20 papers.

Cost of 4 dozen papers = ₹ 24

Cost of 20 papers = $\frac{24}{4\times12}\times20=$ ₹ 10

80. Cost of 8 fans and 14 oven's is ₹ 36.520

Cost of 4 fans and 7 oven's is = $\frac{36.520}{2}$ = ₹ 18.260

Cost of 12 fans and 21 oven's = 18.260 × 3 = ₹ 54.780.

81. Cost of 5 apples = ₹ 450

Cost of 1kg apples = $\frac{450}{5}$

Cost of 8 kg apples = $\frac{450}{5}\times8=$ ₹ 720

Cost of 12 dozen mangoes = ₹ 4,320

Cost of 1 dozen mangoes = $\frac{4320}{12}$

Cost of 8 dozen mangoes = $\frac{4320}{12}\times8=$ ₹ 2880

Cost of 4kg oranges = ₹ 240

Cost of 1kg orange = $\frac{240}{4}$

Cost of 8 kg orange = $\frac{240}{4}\times8=$ ₹ 480

Total cost = 720 + 2880 + 480 = ₹ 4080

82. Cost of 21 pencils and 9 clippers = ₹ 819

Cost of 7 pencils and 3 clippers = $\frac{819}{3}=$ ₹ 273

16 Pipes and Cisterns

IMPORTANT FACTS AND FORMULAE

I. Inlet: *A pipe connected with a tank or a cistern or a reservoir, that fills it, is known as an* ***inlet.***

Outlet: *A pipe connected with a tank or a cistern or a reservoir, emptying it, is known as an* ***outlet.***

II. (*i*) If a pipe can fill a tank in x hours, then part filled in 1 hour $= \frac{1}{x}$.

(*ii*) If a pipe can empty a full tank in y hours, then part emptied in 1 hour $= \frac{1}{y}$.

(*iii*) If a pipe can fill a tank in x hours and another pipe can empty the full tank in y hours (where $y > x$), then on opening both the pipes, the net part filled in 1 hour $= \left(\frac{1}{x} - \frac{1}{y}\right)$.

(*iv*) If a pipe can fill a tank in x hours and another pipe can empty the full tank in y hours (where $x > y$), then on opening both the pipes, the net part emptied in 1 hour $= \left(\frac{1}{y} - \frac{1}{x}\right)$.

ILLUSTRATIVE EXAMPLES

Ex. 1. ***A tank 9 ft by 5 ft by 2ft is fitted with an inlet pipe and an exhaust pipe. The inlet pipe pours in 576 cu. inch of water per minute and the exhaust pipe can empty the full tank in 3 hours. If the tank is full and both pipes are open, how many hours will it take to empty it?***

Sol. Volume of the tank $= (9 \times 5 \times 2)$ cu. *ft* = 90 cu. ft.

$= (90 \times 12 \times 12 \times 12)$ cu. inch.

Volume of water drained by the exhaust pipe in one minute

$= \left(\frac{90 \times 12 \times 12 \times 12}{3 \times 60}\right)$ cu. inch = 864 cu. inch.

Net volume drained in one minute, when both the pipes are opened = (864 – 576) cu. inch = 288 cu. inch.

$\therefore$ Required time $= \left(\frac{90 \times 12 \times 12 \times 12}{288 \times 60}\right)$ hrs = 9 hrs.

Ex. 2. ***Pipe A can fill a tank in 30 hours and pipe B in 45 hours. If both the pipes are opened in an empty tank, how much time will they take to fill it?***

Sol. Part filled by A in 1 hour $= \frac{1}{30}$; Part filled by B in 1 hour $= \frac{1}{45}$.

Part filled by (A + B) in 1 hour $= \left(\frac{1}{30} + \frac{1}{45}\right) = \frac{10}{180} = \frac{1}{18}$.

Hence, pipes A and B together will fill the tank in 18 hours.

Ex. 3. ***A cistern can be filled by pipes A and B in 4 hours and 6 hours respectively. When full, the cistern can be emptied by pipe C in 8 hours. If all the pipes were turned on at the same time, in how much time will the cistern be filled?***

Sol. Net part filled in 1 hour $= \left(\frac{1}{4} + \frac{1}{6} - \frac{1}{8}\right) = \frac{7}{24}$.

$\therefore$ The cistern will be full in $\frac{24}{7}$ hrs, i.e. $3\frac{3}{7}$ hrs.

Ex. 4. ***A pipe can empty a tank in 40 minutes. A second pipe with diameter twice as much as that of the first is also attached with the tank to empty it. How much time will the two pipes together take to empty the tank?*** **(C.P.O., 2005)**

Sol. Let the diameters of the pipes be d and $2d$ and the times taken by them to empty the tank be t and T minutes respectively.

Since the time taken to fill or empty a tank is inversely proportional to the square of the diameter of the pipe, we have:

$$t \propto \frac{1}{d^2} \Rightarrow t = \frac{k}{d^2} \Rightarrow \frac{k}{d^2} = 40.$$

Again, $$T \propto \frac{1}{(2d)^2} \Rightarrow T = \frac{k}{4d^2} \Rightarrow T = \frac{1}{4} \times \frac{k}{d^2} = \frac{1}{4} \times 40 = 10.$$

Thus, net part emptied in 1 min $= \left(\frac{1}{40} + \frac{1}{10}\right) = \frac{5}{40} = \frac{1}{8}$.

Hence, the two pipes together will empty the tank in 8 minutes.

Ex. 5. ***A tap can fill a tank in 10 minutes and another can empty it in 6 minutes. If the tank is already two-fifths full and both the taps are opened together, will the tank be filled or emptied? How long will it take before the tank is either filled completely or emptied completely, as the case may be?*** **(M.A.T., 2004, 05; S.S.C., 2004)**

Sol. Clearly, the outlet pipe is faster than the inlet pipe and so, the tank will be emptied.

Part to be emptied $= \frac{2}{5}$.

Net part emptied in 1 minute $= \left(\frac{1}{6} - \frac{1}{10}\right) = \frac{2}{30} = \frac{1}{15}$.

$\therefore \quad \frac{1}{15} : \frac{2}{5} :: 1 : x$ or $x = \left(\frac{2}{5} \times 1 \times 15\right) = 6$ min.

So, the tank will be emptied in 6 minutes.

Ex. 6. ***A cistern has two taps which fill it in 12 minutes and 15 minutes respectively. There is also a waste pipe in the cistern. When all the three are opened, the empty cistern is full in 20 minutes. How long will the waste pipe take to empty the full cistern?*** **(M.A.T., 2005)**

Sol. Work done by the waste pipe in 1 minute

$$= \frac{1}{20} - \left(\frac{1}{12} + \frac{1}{15}\right) = -\frac{1}{10} \qquad \text{[–ve sign means emptying]}$$

$\therefore$ Waste pipe will empty the full cistern in 10 minutes.

Ex. 7. ***An electric pump can fill a tank in 3 hours. Because of a leak in the tank it took $3\frac{1}{2}$ hours to fill the tank. If the tank is full, how much time will the leak take to empty it?***

Sol. Work done by the leak in 1 hour $= \left[\frac{1}{3} - \frac{1}{\left(\frac{7}{2}\right)}\right] = \left(\frac{1}{3} - \frac{2}{7}\right) = \frac{1}{21}$.

$\therefore$ The leak will empty the tank in 21 hours.

Ex. 8. ***Two pipes can fill a cistern in 14 hours and 16 hours respectively. The pipes are opened simultaneously and it is found that due to leakage in the bottom it took 32 minutes more to fill the cistern. When the cistern is full, in what time will the leak empty it?*** **(I.I.F.T., 2005)**

Sol. Work done by the two pipes in 1 hour $= \left(\frac{1}{14} + \frac{1}{16}\right) = \frac{15}{112}$.

$\therefore$ Time taken by these pipes to fill the tank $= \frac{112}{15}$ hrs = 7 hrs 28 min.

Due to leakage, time taken = 7 hrs 28 min + 32 min = 8 hrs.

$\therefore$ Work done by (two pipes + leak) in 1 hour $= \frac{1}{8}$.

Work done by the leak in 1 hour $= \left(\frac{15}{112} - \frac{1}{8}\right) = \frac{1}{112}$.

Hence, the leak will empty the full cistern in 112 hours.

Ex. 9. ***If two pipes function simultaneously, the reservoir will be filled in 12 hours. The second pipe fills the reservoir 10 hours faster than the first. How many hours does it take the second pipe to fill the reservoir?***

Sol. Let the reservoir be filled by first pipe in x hours.

Then, second pipe will fill it in $(x + 10)$ hours.

$$\therefore \quad \frac{1}{x} + \frac{1}{(x+10)} = \frac{1}{12} \Leftrightarrow \frac{x+10+x}{x(x+10)} = \frac{1}{12} \Leftrightarrow x^2 - 14x - 120 = 0$$

$$\Leftrightarrow (x-20)(x+6) = 0 \Leftrightarrow x = 20 \quad \text{[Neglecting –ve value of } x\text{]}$$

So, the second pipe will take $(20 + 10)$ *i.e.* 30 hrs to fill the reservoir.

Ex. 10. ***A tank is fitted with two inlet pipes A and B, and an outlet pipe C. A is twice as efficient as B which in turn is twice as efficient as C. The empty tank gets filled in 16 hours when all the three pipes are opened. How many hours will be taken to fill the empty tank if B is plugged and the other two pipes are opened?***

Sol. Suppose A alone takes x hours to fill the tank. Then, B alone takes $2x$ hours to fill the tank and C alone takes $4x$ hours to empty the tank.

[∵ time taken to fill or empty a tank is inversely proportional to the efficiency of the pipe]

$$\therefore \quad \frac{1}{x} + \frac{1}{2x} - \frac{1}{4x} = \frac{1}{16} \Leftrightarrow \frac{8+4-2}{8x} = \frac{1}{16} \Leftrightarrow x = \left(\frac{10 \times 16}{8}\right) = 20.$$

Net part filled by A and C in 1 hour $= \left(\frac{1}{x} - \frac{1}{4x}\right) = \frac{3}{4x} = \frac{3}{80}$.

Hence, A and C will fill the tank in $\frac{80}{3}$ hrs. *i.e.* $26\frac{2}{3}$ hrs. or 26 hrs 40 mins.

Ex. 11. ***Two pipes A and B can fill a tank in 12 minutes and 15 minutes respectively while a third pipe C can empty the full tank in 20 minutes. All the three pipes are opened in the beginning. However, pipe C is closed 6 minutes before the tank is filled. In what time will the tank be full?***

Sol. Let the tank be full in x minutes.

Then, pipes A and B worked for x minutes, while pipe C worked for $(x - 6)$ minutes.

$$\therefore \quad \frac{x}{12} + \frac{x}{15} - \frac{(x-6)}{20} = 1 \Leftrightarrow \frac{5x + 4x - 3(x-6)}{60} = 1 \Leftrightarrow 6x + 18 = 60 \Leftrightarrow 6x = 42 \Leftrightarrow x = 7.$$

Hence, the tank will be full in 7 minutes.

Ex. 12. ***Pipes A and B can completely fill a water tank in 4 hours and 5 hours respectively. A pipe C can empty a tank filled completely with water in 3 hours. Initially, the tank is empty and all pipes are closed. Pipe A is opened first at time t = 0 and pipe C is opened at the instant when the tank is exactly half filled with water. Pipe B is opened after pipe C and at the instant when the tank is exactly one-fourth filled with water. Find the total time taken to fill the tank completely counting from t = 0.***

Sol. The whole process involves 3 steps:

Step 1: *Pipe A alone fills half the tank.*

Let time taken be t_1. Then, $t_1 = 2$ hrs.

Step 2: *Pipe A and C together empty* $\left(\frac{1}{2} - \frac{1}{4}\right) = \frac{1}{4}$ *of the tank.*

Let time taken be t_2.

Work alone by A and C in 1 hour $= \left(\frac{1}{4} - \frac{1}{3}\right) = -\frac{1}{12}$. [– ve sign means emptying]

$$\therefore \quad \frac{1}{12} : \frac{1}{4} :: 1 : t_2 \text{ or } t_2 = \frac{1}{4} \times 12 = 3 \text{ hrs.}$$

Step 3: *Pipes A, B and C together fill* $\left(1 - \frac{1}{4}\right) = \frac{3}{4}$ *of the tank.*

Let time taken be t_3.

Work done by A, B and C in 1 hour $= \left(\frac{1}{4} + \frac{1}{5} - \frac{1}{3}\right) = \frac{7}{60}$.

$\therefore \quad \frac{7}{60} : \frac{3}{4} :: 1 : t_3$ or $t_3 = \frac{3}{4} \times \frac{60}{7} = \frac{45}{7} = 6\frac{3}{7}$ hrs.

Hence, total time taken $= (t_1 + t_2 + t_3) = \left(2 + 3 + 6\frac{3}{7}\right)$ hrs. $= 11\frac{3}{7}$ hrs.

Ex. 13. ***A cistern has three pipes A, B and C. A and B can fill it in 3 hours and 4 hours respectively while C can empty the completely filled cistern in 1 hour. If the pipes are opened in order at 3, 4 and 5 p.m. respectively, at what time will the cistern be empty?*** **(S.S.C., 2007)**

Sol. Let the cistern be emptied t hours after 3 p.m.

Then, work done by pipe A in t hours + work done by pipe B in $(t - 1)$ hours + work done by pipe C in $(t - 2)$ hours = 0

$\Rightarrow \frac{t}{3} + \frac{(t-1)}{4} - \frac{(t-2)}{1} = 0 \Rightarrow 4t + 3(t - 1) - 12(t - 2) = 0$

$\Rightarrow -5t + 21 = 0 \Rightarrow 5t = 21 \Rightarrow t = 4\frac{1}{5}$ hrs = 4 hrs 12 min.

So, the cistern will be emptied 4 hrs 12 min after 3 p.m. i.e. 7 : 12 p.m.

Ex. 14. ***Three pipes A, B and C are attached to a tank. A and B can fill it in 20 and 30 minutes respectively while C can empty it in 15 minutes. If A, B and C are kept open successively for 1 minute each, how soon will the tank be filled?*** **(Campus Recruitment, 2006)**

Sol. (A + B + C)'s 3 minutes' work when opened alternately $= \left(\frac{1}{20} + \frac{1}{30} - \frac{1}{15}\right) = \frac{1}{60}$.

Part filled in (3 × 55) i.e. 165 min $= \frac{55}{60} = \frac{11}{12}$. Remaining part $= \left(1 - \frac{11}{12}\right) = \frac{1}{12}$.

Now it is A's turn.

Part filled by A in 1 min $= \frac{1}{20}$. Remaining part $= \left(\frac{1}{12} - \frac{1}{20}\right) = \frac{1}{30}$, which is filled by B in the next minute.

So, total time taken = (165 + 2) min = 167 min = 2 hrs 47 min.

Ex. 15. ***Two pipes A and B can fill a tank in 24 minutes and 32 minutes respectively. If both the pipes are opened simultaneously, after how much time B should be closed so that the tank is full in 18 minutes?*** **(S.S.C., 2006)**

Sol. Let B be closed after x minutes. Then,

Part filled by (A + B) in x min + part filled by A in $(18 - x)$ min = 1

$\therefore \quad x\left(\frac{1}{24} + \frac{1}{32}\right) + (18 - x) \times \frac{1}{24} = 1 \Leftrightarrow \frac{7x}{96} + \frac{18 - x}{24} = 1 \Leftrightarrow 7x + 4(18 - x) = 96 \Leftrightarrow x = 8.$

Hence, B must be closed after 8 minutes.

Ex. 16. ***A keg is fitted with 3 taps – A, B and C. All the three taps, if opened together, can drain the full keg in $1\frac{1}{2}$ minutes. Taps B and C together take 2 minutes to drain the keg while taps A and C together take $2\frac{4}{13}$ minutes to drain it. How long will taps A and B together take to drain the keg?***

Sol. Let taps A, B and C individually take, x, y and z minutes respectively to drain the keg.

Then, $\frac{1}{x} + \frac{1}{y} + \frac{1}{z} = \frac{2}{3}$; $\frac{1}{y} + \frac{1}{z} = \frac{1}{2}$; $\frac{1}{x} + \frac{1}{z} = \frac{13}{30}$.

(A + B)'s 1 minute's work $= \frac{1}{x} + \frac{1}{y} = 2\left(\frac{1}{x} + \frac{1}{y} + \frac{1}{z}\right) - \left(\frac{1}{y} + \frac{1}{z}\right) - \left(\frac{1}{x} + \frac{1}{z}\right)$

$= 2 \times \frac{2}{3} - \frac{1}{2} - \frac{13}{30} = \frac{4}{3} - \frac{1}{2} - \frac{13}{30} = \frac{12}{30} = \frac{2}{5}.$

Hence, A and B together can drain the keg in $\frac{5}{2}$ i.e., $2\frac{1}{2}$ minutes.

EXERCISE
(OBJECTIVE TYPE QUESTIONS)

Directions: ***Mark (√) against the correct answer:***

1. In 1 minute, $\frac{3}{7}$ of a bucket is filled. The rest of the bucket can be filled in (R.R.B., 2006)

(a) $\frac{7}{3}$ minutes (b) $\frac{7}{4}$ minutes
(c) $\frac{4}{3}$ minutes (d) None of these

2. The petrol tank of an automobile can hold *g* litres. If *a* litres was removed when the tank was full, what part of the full tank was removed? (Campus Recruitment, 2008)

(a) $g - a$ (b) $\frac{g}{a}$
(c) $\frac{a}{g}$ (d) $\frac{(g-a)}{a}$
(e) $\frac{(g-a)}{g}$

3. Water is continuously supplied from a reservoir to a locality at the steady rate of 10,000 litres per hour. When delivery exceeds demand the excess water is stored in a tank. If the demand for 8 consecutive three-hour periods is 10000, 10000, 45000, 25000, 40000, 15000, 60000 and 35000 litres respectively, what will be the minimum capacity required of the water tank (in thousand litres) to meet the demand and avoid any wastage? (Campus Recruitment, 2004)

(a) 10 (b) 30
(c) 40 (d) 50

4. Two pipes A and B can fill a tank in 20 and 30 minutes respectively. If both the pipes are used together, how long will it take to fill the tank? (M.A.T., 2003; C.P.O., 2003)

(a) 12 minutes (b) 15 minutes
(c) 25 minutes (d) 50 minutes

5. A pipe can fill a tank in *x* hours and another pipe can empty it in *y* ($y > x$) hours. If both the pipes are open, in how many hours will the tank be filled? (S.S.C., 2007)

(a) $(x - y)$ hours (b) $(y - x)$ hours
(c) $\frac{xy}{x-y}$ hours (d) $\frac{xy}{y-x}$ hours

6. A tap can completely fill a water tank in 8 hours. The water tank has a hole in it through which the water leaks out. The leakage will cause the full water tank to get empty in 12 hours. How much time will it take for the tap to fill the tank completely with the hole? (R.B.I., 2004)

(a) 16 hours (b) 18 hours
(c) 24 hours (d) None of these

7. A tap can fill a tank in 48 minutes whereas another tap can empty it in 2 hours. If both the taps are opened at 11 : 40 A.M, then the tank will be filled at (JMET, 2004)

(a) 12 : 40 P.M. (b) 1 : 00 P.M
(d) 1 : 20 P.M (d) 1 : 30 P.M.

8. A tank with capacity T litres is empty. If water flows into the tank from pipe X at the rate of *x* litres per minute and water is pumped out by Y at the rate of *y* litres per minute and $x > y$, then in how many minutes will the tank be filled? (M.B.A., 2002)

(a) $(x - y)$ 60 T (b) $(T - x)y$
(c) $\frac{T}{(x-y)}$ (d) $\frac{T}{(y-x)}$

9. Pipes A and B can fill a tank in 20 hours and 30 hours respectively and pipe C can empty the full tank in 40 hours. If all the pipes are opened together, how much time will be needed to make the tank full? (D.E.T. Exam, 2004)

(a) $10\frac{3}{7}$ hours (b) $12\frac{4}{5}$ hours
(c) $17\frac{1}{7}$ hours (d) $19\frac{1}{4}$ hours

10. A pipe can fill a tank in 3 hours. There are two outlet pipes from the tank which can empty it in 7 and 10 hours respectively. If all the three pipes are opened simultaneously, then the tank will be filled in (M.B.A., 2002)

(a) 8 hours (b) 9 hours
(c) 10 hours (d) 11 hours

11. In what time would a cistern be filled by three pipes whose diameters are 1 cm, $1\frac{1}{3}$ cm and 2 cm running together, when the largest alone will fill it in 61 minutes, the amount of water flowing in by each pipe, being proportional to the square of its diameter? (Railways, 2006)

(a) 25 minutes (b) 30 minutes
(c) 36 minutes (d) 40 minutes

12. A tap can fill a tank in 6 hours. After half the tank is filled, three more similar taps are opened. What is the total time taken to fill the tank completely?

(a) 3 hrs 15 min (b) 3 hrs 45 min
(c) 4 hrs (d) 4 hrs 15 min

13. A cistern has two pipes. One can fill it with water in 8 hours and other can empty it in 5 hours. In how many hours will the cistern be emptied if both the pipes are opened together when $\frac{3}{4}$ of the cistern is already full of water?

(*a*) $3\frac{1}{3}$ hours (*b*) 6 hours

(*c*) 10 hours (*d*) $13\frac{1}{3}$ hours

14. A vessel has three pipes connected to it, two to supply liquid and one to draw liquid. The first alone can fill the vessel in $4\frac{1}{2}$ hours, the second in 3 hours and the third can empty it in $1\frac{1}{2}$ hours. If all the pipes are opened simultaneously when the vessel is half full, how soon will it be emptied? **(M.B.A., 2007)**

(*a*) $4\frac{1}{2}$ hours (*b*) $5\frac{1}{2}$ hours

(*c*) $6\frac{1}{2}$ hours (*d*) None of these

15. Two pipes A and B can separately fill a cistern in 60 minutes and 75 minutes respectively. There is a third pipe in the bottom of the cistern to empty it. If all the three pipes are simultaneously opened then the cistern is full in 50 minutes. In how much time, the third pipe alone can empty the cistern?

(*a*) 90 min (*b*) 100 min

(*c*) 110 min (*d*) 120 min

16. Eight pipes are fitted to a water tank. Some of these are water pipes to fill the tank and the remaining are waste pipes used to empty the tank. Each water pipe can fill the tank in 12 hours and each waste pipe can empty it in 36 hours. On opening all the pipes an empty tank is filled in 3 hours. The number of waste pipes is

(*a*) 2 (*b*) 3

(*c*) 4 (*d*) 5

17. A pump can fill a tank with water in 2 hours. Because of a leak, it took $2\frac{1}{3}$ hours to fill the tank. The leak can drain all the water of the tank in **(C.P.O., 2006; S.S.C., 2002)**

(*a*) $4\frac{1}{3}$ hours (*b*) 7 hours

(*c*) 8 hours (*d*) 14 hours

18. Two taps A and B can fill a tank in 5 hours and 20 hours respectively. If both the taps are open then due to a leakage, it took 30 minutes more to fill the tank. If the tank is full, how long will it take for the leakage alone to empty the tank?

(*a*) $4\frac{1}{2}$ hrs (*b*) 9 hrs

(*c*) 18 hrs (*d*) 36 hrs

19. Three pipes A, B and C can fill a tank from empty to full in 30 minutes, 20 minutes and 10 minutes respectively. When the tank is empty, all the three pipes are opened. A, B and C discharge chemical solutions P, Q and R respectively. What is the proportion of solution R in the liquid in the tank after 3 minutes? **(D.M.R.C., 2003)**

(*a*) $\frac{5}{11}$ (*b*) $\frac{6}{11}$

(*c*) $\frac{7}{11}$ (*d*) $\frac{8}{11}$

20. Two pipes A and B together can fill a cistern in 4 hours. Had they been opened separately, then B would have taken 6 hours more than A to fill the cistern. How much time will be taken by A alone to fill the cistern?

(*a*) 1 hr (*b*) 2 hrs

(*c*) 6 hrs (*d*) 8 hrs

21. One pipe can fill a tank three times as fast as another pipe. If together the two pipes can fill the tank in 36 minutes, then the slower pipe alone will be able to fill the tank in **(C.B.I., 2003)**

(*a*) 81 min (*b*) 108 min

(*c*) 144 min (*d*) 192 min

22. A tank is filled in 5 hours by three pipes A, B and C. The pipe C is twice as fast as B and B is twice as fast as A. How much time will pipe A alone take to fill the tank?

(*a*) 20 hrs (*b*) 25 hrs

(*c*) 35 hrs (*d*) Cannot be determined

(*e*) None of these

23. A swimming pool is filled by three pipes with uniform flow. The first two pipes operating simultaneously fill the pool in the same time during which the pool is filled by the third pipe alone. The second pipe fills the pool 5 hours faster than the first pipe and 4 hours slower than the third pipe. The time required by the first pipe is **(M.B.A., 2002; M.A.T., 2006)**

(*a*) 6 hrs (*b*) 10 hrs

(*c*) 15 hrs (*d*) 30 hrs

24. 12 buckets of water fill a tank when the capacity of each bucket is 13.5 litres. How many buckets will be needed to fill the same tank, if the capacity of each bucket is 9 litres?

(*a*) 8 (*b*) 15

(*c*) 16 (*d*) 18

25. Bucket P has thrice the capacity as bucket Q. It takes 60 turns for bucket P to fill the empty drum. How many turns will it take for both the buckets P and Q, having each turn together to fill the empty drum?
(*a*) 30 (*b*) 40
(*c*) 45 (*d*) 90

26. Two pipes A and B can fill a tank in 12 minutes and 15 minutes respectively. If both the pipes are opened simultaneously and pipe A is closed after 3 minutes, then how much more time will it take to fill the tank by pipe B? **(C.D.S., 2002; Bank P.O., 2006)**
(*a*) 7 min 15 sec (*b*) 7 min 45 sec
(*c*) 8 min 5 sec (*d*) 8 min 15 sec

27. Two pipes A and B can fill a tank in 15 minutes and 20 minutes respectively. Both the pipes are opened together but after 4 minutes, pipe A is turned off. What is the total time required to fill the tank?
(*a*) 10 min 20 sec (*b*) 11 min 45 sec
(*c*) 12 min 30 sec (*d*) 14 min 40 sec

28. Two pipes A and B can fill a tank in 15 hours and 20 hours respectively while a third pipe C can empty the full tank in 25 hours. All the three pipes are opened in the beginning. After 10 hours, C is closed. In how much time will the tank be full?
(*a*) 12 hrs (*b*) 13 hrs
(*c*) 16 hrs (*d*) 18 hrs

29. A large tanker can be filled by two pipes A and B in 60 minutes and 40 minutes respectively. How many minutes will it take to fill the tanker from empty state if B is used for half the time and A and B fill it together for the other half? **(D.M.R.C., 2003)**
(*a*) 15 min (*b*) 20 min
(*c*) 27.5 min (*d*) 30 min

30. Two pipes A and B can fill a cistern in 12 minutes and 15 minutes respectively while a third pipe C can empty the full cistern in 6 minutes. A and B are kept open for 5 minutes in the beginning and then C is also opened. In what time is the cistern emptied? **(M.A.T., 2005)**
(*a*) 30 min (*b*) 33 min
(*c*) $37\frac{1}{2}$ min (*d*) 45 min

31. Two pipes A and B can fill a tank in 20 and 30 hours respectively. Both the pipes are opened to fill the tank but when the tank is one-third full, a leak develops in the tank through which one-third water supplied by both the pipes goes out. The total time taken to fill the tank is **(M.A.T., 2006)**
(*a*) 12 hours (*b*) 14 hours
(*c*) 16 hours (*d*) 18 hours

32. Four pipes can fill a reservoir in 15, 20, 30 and 60 hours respectively. The first pipe was opened at 8 a.m, second at 9 a.m., third at 10 a.m. and fourth at 11 a.m. When will the reservoir be full?
(*a*) 1 p.m. (*b*) 2 p.m.
(*c*) 2.30 p.m. (*d*) 3 p.m.

33. Two pipes can fill a tank with water in 15 and 12 hours respectively and a third pipe can empty it in 4 hours. If the pipes be opened in order at 8, 9 and 11 a.m. respectively, the tank will be emptied at **(S.S.C., 2005)**
(*a*) 11 : 40 a.m. (*b*) 12 : 40 p.m.
(*c*) 1 : 40 p.m. (*d*) 2 : 40 p.m.

34. Tap A fills a tank in 4 hours whereas tap B empties the full tank in 24 hours. A and B are opened alternately for 1 hour each. Every 2 hours the level of water is found to increase by 0.5 m. The depth of the tank is
(*a*) 2.4 m (*b*) 4.8 m
(*c*) 6.4 m (*d*) 24 m

35. Two pipes A and B can fill a tank in 6 hours and 4 hours respectively. If they are opened on alternate hours and if pipe A is opened first, in how many hours, the tank shall be full? **(Campus Recruitment, 2003)**
(*a*) 4 (*b*) $4\frac{1}{2}$
(*c*) 5 (*d*) $5\frac{1}{2}$

36. Three taps A, B and C can fill a tank in 12, 15 and 20 hours respectively. If A is open all the time and B and C are open for one hour each alternately, the tank will be full in
(*a*) 6 hrs (*b*) $6\frac{2}{3}$ hrs
(*c*) 7 hrs (*d*) $7\frac{1}{2}$

37. Pipe A can fill a tank in 10 hours. Pipe B can fill the same tank in 15 hours. Pipe C can empty the full tank in 20 hours. Pipes A, B and C are opened alternatively for one hour each. If A is opened first, then how many hours will they take to fill the empty tank? **(M.B.A., 2004)**
(*a*) 24 hrs (*b*) $24\frac{2}{3}$ hrs
(*c*) 25 hrs (*d*) 26 hrs

38. A booster pump can be used for filling as well as for emptying a tank. The capacity of the tank is 2400 m^3. The emptying capacity of the tank is 10 m^3 per minute higher than its filling capacity and the pump needs 8 minutes lesser to empty the tank than it needs to fill it. What if the filling capacity of the pump?
(*a*) 50 m^3/min (*b*) 60 m^3/min
(*c*) 72 m^3/min (*d*) None of these

39. A leak in the bottom of a tank can empty the full tank in 8 hours. An inlet pipe fills water at the rate of 6 litres a minute. When the tank is full, the inlet is opened and due to the leak, the tank is empty in 12 hours. How many litres does the tank hold? **(M.A.T., 2005)**

(*a*) 7580 (*b*) 7960
(*c*) 8290 (*d*) 8640

40. Two pipes can fill a tank in 20 and 24 minutes respectively and a waste pipe can empty 3 gallons per minute. All the three pipes working together can fill the tank in 15 minutes. The capacity of the tank is :

(*a*) 60 gallons (*b*) 100 gallons
(*c*) 120 gallons (*d*) 180 gallons

41. Two pipes A and B can fill a cistern in $37\frac{1}{2}$ minutes and 45 minutes respectively. Both the pipes are opened. The cistern will be filled in just half an hour, if the pipe B is turned off after **(S.S.C., 2004)**

(*a*) 5 min (*b*) 9 min
(*c*) 10 min (*d*) 15 min

42. A cistern can be filled by two pipes filling separately in 12 and 16 minutes separately. Both the pipes are opened together for a certain time but being clogged, only $\frac{7}{8}$ of the full quantity of water flows through the former and only $\frac{5}{6}$ through the latter pipe. The obstructions, however, being suddenly removed, the cistern is filled in 3 minutes from that moment. How long was it before the full flow began? **(M.A.T., 2006)**

(*a*) $2\frac{1}{2}$ min (*b*) $3\frac{1}{2}$ min
(*c*) $4\frac{1}{2}$ min (*d*) $5\frac{1}{2}$ min

43. Three pipes can fill a reservoir in 10, 15 and 20 hours respectively. If the three taps are opened one after another in the given order, with a certain fixed time gap between them, the reservoir fills in 5 hours. The time gap is

(*a*) 15 min (*b*) 30 min
(*c*) 45 min (*d*) 1 hr

44. Three pipes A, B and C can fill a tank in 6 hours. After working at it together for 2 hours, C is closed and A and B can fill the remaining part in 7 hours. The number of hours taken by C alone to fill the tank is **(L.I.C.A.A.O., 2003)**

(*a*) 10 (*b*) 12
(*c*) 14 (*d*) 16

45. A bath can be filled by the cold water pipe in 10 minutes and by the hot water pipe in 15 minutes. A person leaves the bathroom after turning on both the pipes. He returns just when the bath should have been full. Finding however, the waste pipe was open, he closes it. In 4 minutes more, the bath is full. In what time will the waste water pipe empty it?

(*a*) 6 minutes (*b*) 8 minutes
(*c*) 9 minutes (*d*) None of these

46. A large fresh water reservoir is fitted with two types of feeder pipes – hot water pipes and cold water pipes. Six cold water pipes alone can fill the reservoir in 12 hours. 3 cold water pipes and 9 hot water pipes together can fill the reservoir in 8 hours. How long will 5 hot water pipes alone take to fill the reservoir?

(*a*) 18 hrs 36 min (*b*) 20 hrs 45 min
(*c*) 21 hrs 36 min (*d*) None of these

47. A town is supplied with water from a big overhead tank which is fed with a constant volume of water regularly. When the tank is full, if 32000 gallons are used daily, the supply fails in 50 days. However, if 37000 gallons are used daily, the supply lasts for 40 days only. How much water can be used daily without the supply ever failing?

(*a*) 12000 gallons (*b*) 15000 gallons
(*c*) 18000 gallons (*d*) 20000 gallons

48. Water flows through a cylindrical pipe of internal diameter 7 cm at the rate of 5 m/s. The time, in minutes, the pipe would take to fill an empty rectangular tank 4m × 3m × 2.31m is **[CDS, 2016]**

(*a*) 28 (*b*) 24
(*c*) 20 (*d*) 12

49. An outlet pipe can empty a cistern in 3 hours. In what time will it empty $\frac{2}{3}$rd of the cistern?

[DMRC—Customer Relationship Assistant (CRA) Exam, 2016]

(*a*) 3 hours (*b*) 5 hours
(*c*) 2 hours (*d*) 4 hours

50. Two pipes A and B can fill a tank in 24 hours and 30 hours respectively. If both the pipes are opened simultaneously in the empty tank, how much time will be taken by them to fill it?

[UPSSC—Lower Subordinate (Pre.) Exam, 2016]

(*a*) 13 hours 20 min (*b*) 12 hours 10 min
(*c*) 14 hours (*d*) 10 hours 5 min

51. A tank is 7 metre long and 4 metre wide. At what speed should water run through a pipe 5 cm broad and 4 cm deep so that in 6 hours and 18 minutes water level in the tank rises by 4.5 metre?

[DMRC—Train Operator (Station Controller) Exam, 2016]

(*a*) 10 km/hr. (*b*) 12 km/hr.
(*c*) 8 km/hr. (*d*) None of these

52. Two pieces A and B can fill a tank in 18 hours and 6 hours respectively. If both the pipes are opened simultaneously, how much time will be taken to fill the tank?

[Indian Railway Gr. 'D' Exam, 2014]

(*a*) $4\frac{1}{2}$ hours (*b*) 7 hours

(*c*) 6 hours (*d*) 10 hours

53. Two pipes can fill a tank in 12 hours and 16 hours respectively. A third pipe can empty the tank in 30 hours. If all three pipes are opened and function simultaneously, how much time will the tank take to be full? (in hours)

[United India Insurance (UIICL) Assistant (Online) Exam, 2015]

(*a*) $10\frac{4}{9}$ (*b*) $9\frac{1}{2}$

(*c*) $8\frac{8}{9}$ (*d*) $7\frac{2}{9}$

54. A tank has two outlets A and B, which together take 6 hours to empty a full tank when they are opened simultaneously. The tank was initially half-full and both the outlets were opened. After an hour, an inlet pipe 'X' was also opened. If the inlet alone can fill an empty tank in 4 hours, how much time will it now take to fill the tank completely? (in hours)

[CET—Maharashtra (MBA) Exam, 2016]

(*a*) 8 (*b*) 7

(*c*) $8\frac{1}{2}$ (*d*) 9

ANSWERS

1. (*c*)	2. (*c*)	3. (*c*)	4. (*a*)	5. (*d*)	6. (*c*)	7. (*b*)	8. (*c*)	9. (*c*)	10. (*d*)
11. (*c*)	12. (*b*)	13. (*c*)	14. (*a*)	15. (*b*)	16. (*b*)	17. (*d*)	18. (*d*)	19. (*b*)	20. (*c*)
21. (*c*)	22. (*c*)	23. (*c*)	24. (*d*)	25. (*c*)	26. (*d*)	27. (*d*)	28. (*a*)	29. (*d*)	30. (*d*)
31. (*c*)	32. (*d*)	33. (*d*)	34. (*a*)	35. (*c*)	36. (*c*)	37. (*b*)	38. (*a*)	39. (*d*)	40. (*c*)
41. (*b*)	42. (*c*)	43. (*b*)	44. (*c*)	45. (*c*)	46. (*c*)	47. (*a*)	48. (*b*)	49. (*a*)	50. (*a*)
51. (*a*)	52. (*a*)	53. (*c*)	54. (*d*)						

SOLUTIONS

1. Time taken to fill the whole bucket = $\frac{7}{3}$ min.

$\therefore$ Required time $= \left(\frac{7}{3}-1\right)$ minutes $= \frac{4}{3}$ minutes.

2. Required part $= \frac{\text{Quantity removed}}{\text{Total capacity}} = \frac{a}{g}$.

3. We have the following table:

Period	Supply	Demand	Excess Qty. in tank
0–3 hrs	30000	10000	20000
3–6 hrs	30000	10000	40000
6–9 hrs	30000	45000	25000
9–12 hrs	30000	25000	30000
12–15 hrs	30000	40000	20000
15–18 hrs	30000	15000	35000
18–21 hrs	30000	60000	5000
21–24 hrs	30000	35000	0

The excess quantity in tank at any time does not exceed 40000 litres, which is the required minimum capacity to avoid wastage.

4. Part filled by A in 1 min $= \frac{1}{20}$; Part filled by B in 1 min $= \frac{1}{30}$.

Part filled by (A + B) in 1 min $= \left(\frac{1}{20}+\frac{1}{30}\right) = \frac{1}{12}$.

$\therefore$ Both the pipes can fill the tank in 12 minutes.

5. Net part filled in 1 hour $= \left(\frac{1}{x}-\frac{1}{y}\right) = \left(\frac{y-x}{xy}\right)$.

$\therefore$ The tank will be filled in $\left(\frac{xy}{y-x}\right)$ hours.

6. Net part filled in 1 hour $= \left(\frac{1}{8}-\frac{1}{12}\right) = \frac{1}{24}$.

$\therefore$ The tank will be filled in 24 hours.

7. Net part filled in 1 hour $= \left(\frac{1}{48}-\frac{1}{120}\right) = \frac{3}{240} = \frac{1}{80}$.

$\therefore$ The tank will be filled 80 mins i.e. 1 hour 20 min. after 11 : 40 A.M. i.e. at 1 P.M.

8. Net volume filled in 1 minute = $(x - y)$ litres. $\therefore$ Time taken to fill the tank $= \frac{T}{(x-y)}$ minutes.

9. Net part filled in 1 hour $= \left(\frac{1}{20}+\frac{1}{30}-\frac{1}{40}\right) = \frac{7}{120}$.

$\therefore$ The tank will be full in $\frac{120}{7}$ i.e. $17\frac{1}{7}$ hours.

10. Net part filled in 1 hour $= \frac{1}{3}-\left(\frac{1}{7}+\frac{1}{10}\right) = \frac{1}{3}-\frac{17}{70} = \frac{19}{210}$.

$\therefore$ The tank will be filled in $\frac{210}{19}$ hrs i.e. $11\frac{1}{19}$ hrs $\cong$ 11 hrs.

11. Let t_1, t_2 and t_3 be the times taken by pipes with diameters 1 cm, $\frac{4}{3}$ cm and 2 cm respectively.

Since time taken to fill the tank is inversely proportional to the amount of water flowing through it, we have

$t_3 \propto \frac{1}{r^2}$ or $t_3 = \frac{k}{r^2} \Rightarrow 61 = \frac{k}{4} \Rightarrow k = 244.$

Thus, $t_1 = \frac{k}{(1)^2} = 244;\ t_2 = \frac{k}{\left(\frac{4}{3}\right)^2} = \frac{9}{16} \times 244 = \frac{549}{4}.$

Net part filled in 1 min $= \frac{1}{244} + \frac{1}{61} + \frac{4}{549}$

$= \frac{1}{61}\left(\frac{1}{4} + 1 + \frac{4}{9}\right) = \frac{1}{61}\left(\frac{9+36+16}{36}\right)$

$= \frac{1}{61} \times \frac{61}{36} = \frac{1}{36}.$

Hence, all the three pipes together would fill the tank in 36 minutes.

12. Time taken by one tap to fill half the tank = 3 hrs.

Part filled by the four taps in one hour $= \left(4 \times \frac{1}{6}\right) = \frac{2}{3}.$

Remaining part $= \frac{1}{2}.$

$\therefore \frac{2}{3} : \frac{1}{2} :: 1 : x$ or $x = \left(\frac{1}{2} \times 1 \times \frac{3}{2}\right) = \frac{3}{4}$ hrs i.e. 45 min.

So, total time taken = 3 hrs 45 min.

13. Net part emptied in one hour $= \left(\frac{1}{5} - \frac{1}{8}\right) = \frac{3}{40}.$

$\therefore \frac{3}{40} : \frac{3}{4} :: 1 : x$ or $x = \left(\frac{3}{4} \times 1 \times \frac{40}{3}\right) = 10$ hrs.

So, the cistern will be emptied in 10 hrs.

14. Net part emptied in 1 hour $= \frac{2}{3} - \left(\frac{2}{9} + \frac{1}{3}\right) = \left(\frac{2}{3} - \frac{5}{9}\right)$

$= \frac{1}{9}.$

$\therefore \frac{1}{9} : \frac{1}{2} :: 1 : x$ or $x = \left(\frac{1}{2} \times 9\right) = 4\frac{1}{2}$ hours.

So, the tank will be emptied in $4\frac{1}{2}$ hours.

15. Work done by the third pipe in 1 min.

$= \frac{1}{50} - \left(\frac{1}{60} + \frac{1}{75}\right) = \left(\frac{1}{50} - \frac{3}{100}\right) = -\frac{1}{100}.$

[– ve sign means emptying]

$\therefore$ The third pipe alone can empty the cistern in 100 min.

16. Let there be x water pipes and $(8 - x)$ waste pipes.

Now, part filled by each water pipe $= \frac{1}{12}$; part emptied by each waste pipe $= \frac{1}{36}.$

$\therefore \frac{x}{12} - \frac{(8-x)}{36} = \frac{1}{3} \Leftrightarrow 3x - (8 - x) = 12 \Leftrightarrow 4x = 20$

$\Leftrightarrow x = 5.$

So, number of waste pipes = (8 – 5) = 3.

17. Work done by the leak in 1 hour $= \left(\frac{1}{2} - \frac{3}{7}\right) = \frac{1}{14}.$

$\therefore$ Leak will empty the tank in 14 hours.

18. Part filled by (A + B) in 1 hour $= \left(\frac{1}{5} + \frac{1}{20}\right) = \frac{1}{4}.$

So, A and B together can fill the tank in 4 hours.

Work done by the leak in 1 hour $= \left(\frac{1}{4} - \frac{2}{9}\right) = \frac{1}{36}.$

$\therefore$ Leak will empty the tank in 36 hours.

19. Part filled by (A + B + C) in 3 minutes

$= 3\left(\frac{1}{30} + \frac{1}{20} + \frac{1}{10}\right) = \left(3 \times \frac{11}{60}\right) = \frac{11}{20}.$

Part filled by C in 3 minutes $= \frac{3}{10}.$

$\therefore$ Required ratio $= \left(\frac{3}{10} \times \frac{20}{11}\right) = \frac{6}{11}.$

20. Let the cistern be filled by pipe A alone in x hour. Then, pipe B will fill it in $(x + 6)$ hours.

$\therefore \frac{1}{x} + \frac{1}{(x+6)} = \frac{1}{4} \Leftrightarrow \frac{x+6+x}{x(x+6)} = \frac{1}{4}$

$\Leftrightarrow x^2 - 2x - 24 = 0$

$\Leftrightarrow (x - 6)(x + 4) = 0 \Leftrightarrow x = 6.$

[Neglecting – ve value of x]

So, A alone will fill the cistern in 6 hrs.

21. Let the slower pipe alone fill the tank in x minutes.

Then, faster pipe alone will fill it in $\frac{x}{3}$ minutes.

$\therefore \frac{1}{x} + \frac{3}{x} = \frac{1}{36} \Leftrightarrow \frac{4}{x} = \frac{1}{36} \Leftrightarrow x = 144.$

So, slower pipe alone will fill the tank in 144 min.

22. Suppose pipe A alone takes x hours to fill the tank.

Then, pipes B and C will take $\frac{x}{2}$ and $\frac{x}{4}$ hours respectively to fill the tank.

$\therefore \frac{1}{x} + \frac{2}{x} + \frac{4}{x} = \frac{1}{5} \Leftrightarrow \frac{7}{x} = \frac{1}{5} \Leftrightarrow x = 35.$

So, pipe A alone takes 35 hours to fill the tank.

23. Suppose first pipe alone takes x hours to fill the tank. Then, second and third pipes will take $(x - 5)$ and $(x - 9)$ hours respectively to fill the tank.

$\therefore \frac{1}{x} + \frac{1}{(x-5)} = \frac{1}{(x-9)} \Leftrightarrow \frac{x-5+x}{x(x-5)} = \frac{1}{(x-9)}$

$\Leftrightarrow (2x - 5)(x - 9) = x(x - 5)$

$\Leftrightarrow x^2 - 18x + 45 = 0$

$\Leftrightarrow (x - 15)(x - 3) = 0$

$\Leftrightarrow x = 15.$ [neglecting $x = 3$]

So, first pipe alone takes 15 hrs to fill the tank.

24. Capacity of the tank = (12 × 13.5) litres = 162 litres.

Capacity of each bucket = 9 litres.

Number of buckets needed $= \left(\frac{162}{9}\right) = 18.$

25. Let capacity of bucket P be x litres. Then, capacity of bucket $Q = \left(\frac{x}{3}\right)$ litres.

Capacity of the drum = 60 x litres.

$\therefore$ Required number of turns = $\frac{60x}{\left(x+\frac{x}{3}\right)} = \left(60x \times \frac{3}{4x}\right) = 45.$

26. Part filled in 3 min = $3\left(\frac{1}{12}+\frac{1}{15}\right) = \left(3 \times \frac{9}{60}\right) = \frac{9}{20}.$

Remaining part = $\left(1-\frac{9}{20}\right) = \frac{11}{20}.$

Part filled by B in 1 min = $\frac{1}{15}.$

$\frac{1}{15}:\frac{11}{20}::1:x$ or $x = \left(\frac{11}{20}\times 1 \times 15\right) = 8\frac{1}{4}$ min

= 8 min 15 sec.

$\therefore$ Remaining part is filled by B in 8 min 15 sec.

27. Part filled in 4 minutes = $4\left(\frac{1}{15}+\frac{1}{20}\right) = \frac{7}{15}.$

Remaining part = $\left(1-\frac{7}{15}\right) = \frac{8}{15}.$

Part filled by B in 1 minute = $\frac{1}{20}.$ $\frac{1}{20}:\frac{8}{15}::1:x$

or $x = \left(\frac{8}{15}\times 1 \times 20\right) = 10\frac{2}{3}$ min = 10 min 40 sec.

$\therefore$ The tank will be full in (4 min + 10 min 40 sec) = 14 min 40 sec.

28. Part filled in 10 hours = $10\left(\frac{1}{15}+\frac{1}{20}-\frac{1}{25}\right) = \frac{23}{30}.$

Remaining part = $\left(1-\frac{23}{30}\right) = \frac{7}{30}.$

(A + B)'s 1 hour's work = $\left(\frac{1}{15}+\frac{1}{20}\right) = \frac{7}{60}.$ $\frac{7}{60}:\frac{7}{30}::1:x$

or $x = \left(\frac{7}{30}\times 1 \times \frac{60}{7}\right) = 2$ hours.

$\therefore$ The tank will be full in (10 + 2) hrs = 12 hrs.

29. Part filled by (A + B) in 1 minute = $\left(\frac{1}{60}+\frac{1}{40}\right) = \frac{1}{24}.$

Suppose the tank is filled in x minutes.

Then, $\frac{x}{2}\left(\frac{1}{24}+\frac{1}{40}\right) = 1 \Leftrightarrow \frac{x}{2}\times\frac{1}{15} = 1 \Leftrightarrow x = 30.$

30. Part filled in 5 min = $5\left(\frac{1}{12}+\frac{1}{15}\right) = \left(5\times\frac{9}{60}\right) = \frac{3}{4}.$

Part emptied in 1 min when all the pipes are opened

$= \frac{1}{6} - \left(\frac{1}{12}+\frac{1}{15}\right) = \left(\frac{1}{6}-\frac{3}{20}\right) = \frac{1}{60}.$

Now, $\frac{1}{60}$ part is emptied in 1 min.

$\therefore$ $\frac{3}{4}$ part will be emptied in $\left(60\times\frac{3}{4}\right) = 45$ min.

31. Part filled by (A + B) in 1 hour = $\left(\frac{1}{20}+\frac{1}{30}\right) = \frac{1}{12}.$

So, A and B together can fill the tank in 12 hrs. $\frac{1}{3}$ part is filled by (A + B) in $\left(\frac{1}{3}\times 12\right) = 4$ hrs.

Since the leak empties one - third water, so time taken to fill the tank = Time taken by (A + B) to fill the whole tank + Time taken by (A + B) to fill one - third tank = (12 + 4) hrs = 16 hrs.

32. Let the time be t hours after 8 a.m.

Then, the first pipe worked for t hours; second pipe for $(t-1)$ hours; third for $(t-2)$ hours and fourth for $(t-3)$ hours.

$\therefore$ $\frac{t}{15}+\frac{(t-1)}{20}+\frac{(t-2)}{30}+\frac{(t-3)}{60} = 1 \Leftrightarrow 4t + 3(t-1) + 2(t-2) + (t-3) = 60 \Leftrightarrow 10t = 70 \Leftrightarrow t = 7.$

So, the reservoir will be full 7 hours after 8 a.m. i.e. at 3 p.m.

33. Let the tank be emptied t hours after 8 a.m. Then,

Work done by first pipe in t hours + work done by second pipe in $(t-1)$ hours + work done by third pipe in $(t-3)$ hours = 0

$\Rightarrow \frac{t}{15}+\frac{(t-1)}{12}-\frac{(t-3)}{4} = 0$

$\Rightarrow 4t + 5(t-1) - 15(t-3) = 0$

$\Rightarrow -6t + 40 = 0 \Rightarrow 6t = 40 \Rightarrow t = 6\frac{2}{3}$ hrs = 6 hrs 40 min.

So, the tank will be emptied 6 hrs 40 min after 8 a.m. i.e., at 2 : 40 p.m.

34. Part filled in 2 hours = $\left(\frac{1}{4}-\frac{1}{24}\right) = \frac{5}{24}.$

Let the depth of the tank be h metres.

Then, $\frac{5}{24}h = 0.5 \Rightarrow h = \left(\frac{0.5\times 24}{5}\right) = 2.4$ m.

35. (A + B)'s 2 hours' work when opened alternately

$= \left(\frac{1}{6}+\frac{1}{4}\right) = \frac{5}{12}.$

Part filled in 4 hrs = $\frac{10}{12} = \frac{5}{6}.$

Remaining part = $\left(1-\frac{5}{6}\right) = \frac{1}{6}.$

Now it is A's turn and $\frac{1}{6}$ part is filled by A in 1 hour.

$\therefore$ Total time taken to fill the tank = (4 + 1) hrs = 5 hrs.

36. (A + B)'s 1 hour's work = $\left(\frac{1}{12}+\frac{1}{15}\right) = \frac{9}{60} = \frac{3}{20}.$

(A + C)'s 1 hour's work = $\left(\frac{1}{12}+\frac{1}{20}\right) = \frac{8}{60} = \frac{2}{15}.$

Part filled in 2 hrs = $\left(\frac{3}{20}+\frac{2}{15}\right) = \frac{17}{60}$; Part filled in 6 hrs

$= \left(3 \times \frac{17}{60}\right) = \frac{17}{20}.$

Remaining part $= \left(1 - \frac{17}{20}\right) = \frac{3}{20}.$

Now, it is the turn of A and B and $\frac{3}{20}$ part is filled by A and B in 1 hour.

$\therefore$ Total time taken to fill the tank = (6 + 1) hrs = 7 hrs.

37. (A + B + C)'s 3 hours' work when opened alternately

$= \left(\frac{1}{10} + \frac{1}{15} - \frac{1}{20}\right) = \frac{7}{60}.$

Part filled in (3 × 8) i.e. 24 hrs $= \left(\frac{7}{60} \times 8\right) = \frac{14}{15}.$

Remaining part $= \left(1 - \frac{14}{15}\right) = \frac{1}{15}.$

Now it is A's turn. $\frac{1}{10}$ part is filled by A in 1 hr.

$\frac{1}{15}$ part will be filled by A in $\left(10 \times \frac{1}{15}\right)$hrs $= \frac{2}{3}$ hr.

So, total time taken $= 24\frac{2}{3}$ hrs.

38. Let the filling capacity of the pump be x m³/min. Then, emptying capacity of the pump = $(x + 10)$ m³/min.

So, $\frac{2400}{x} - \frac{2400}{(x+10)} = 8 \Leftrightarrow x^2 + 10x - 3000 = 0 \Leftrightarrow (x - 50)(x + 60) = 0 \Leftrightarrow x = 50.$

[neglecting – ve value of x]

Hence, filling capacity of the pump = 50 m³/min.

39. Work done by the inlet in 1 hour $= \left(\frac{1}{8} - \frac{1}{12}\right) = \frac{1}{24}.$

Work done by the inlet in 1 min $= \left(\frac{1}{24} \times \frac{1}{60}\right) = \frac{1}{1440}.$

$\therefore$ Volume of $\frac{1}{1440}$ part = 6 litres.

Volume of whole tank = (1440 × 6) litres = 8640 litres.

40. Work done by the waste pipe in 1 minute

$= \frac{1}{15} - \left(\frac{1}{20} + \frac{1}{24}\right) = \left(\frac{1}{15} - \frac{11}{120}\right) = -\frac{1}{40}.$

[– ve sign means emptying]

$\therefore$ Volume of $\frac{1}{40}$ part = 3 gallons.

Volume of whole tank = (3 × 40) gallons = 120 gallons.

41. Let B be turned off after x minutes. Then,

Part filled by (A + B) in x min + Part filled by A in $(30 - x)$ min = 1

$\therefore \quad x\left(\frac{2}{75} + \frac{1}{45}\right) + (30 - x).\frac{2}{75} = 1$

$\Leftrightarrow \frac{11x}{225} + \frac{(60 - 2x)}{75} = 1$

$\Leftrightarrow 11x + 180 - 6x = 225.$

$\Leftrightarrow 5x = 45 \Leftrightarrow x = 9.$

42. Suppose the full flow began after x minutes.

Then, part filled by both pipes with obstruction in x min + part filled by both pipes with full flow in 3 min = 1

$\Rightarrow x\left(\frac{7}{8} \times \frac{1}{12} + \frac{5}{6} \times \frac{1}{16}\right) + 3\left(\frac{1}{12} + \frac{1}{16}\right) = 1$

$\Rightarrow x\left(\frac{7}{96} + \frac{5}{96}\right) + 3 \times \frac{7}{48} = 1 \Rightarrow \frac{x}{8} = \frac{9}{16}$

$\Rightarrow x = \frac{9}{2} = 4\frac{1}{2}.$

43. Let the fixed time gap be x hrs. Then, Part filled by first pipe in 5 hrs + part filled by second pipe in $(5 - x)$ hrs + part filled by third pipe in $(5 - 2x)$ hrs = 1

$\Rightarrow \frac{5}{10} + \frac{(5-x)}{15} + \frac{(5-2x)}{20} = 1$

$\Rightarrow 30 + 4(5 - x) + 3(5 - 2x) = 60 \Rightarrow 10x = 5 \Rightarrow x = \frac{1}{2}.$

Hence, the fixed time gap is $\frac{1}{2}$ hr i.e. 30 min.

44. Part filled in 2 hours $= \frac{2}{6} = \frac{1}{3},$

Remaining part $= \left(1 - \frac{1}{3}\right) = \frac{2}{3}.$

(A + B)'s 7 hours' work $= \frac{2}{3}$; (A + B)'s 1 hour's work $= \frac{2}{21}.$

$\therefore$ C's 1 hour's work = [(A + B + C)'s 1 hour's work – (A + B)'s 1 hour's work] $= \left(\frac{1}{6} - \frac{2}{21}\right) = \frac{1}{14}.$

Hence, C alone can fill the tank in 14 hours.

45. Part filled by two inlet pipes in 1 min $= \frac{1}{10} + \frac{1}{15} = \frac{1}{6}.$

Part filled by two inlet pipes in 4 min $= \left(4 \times \frac{1}{6}\right) = \frac{2}{3}.$

Time after which the waste pipe is closed = Time taken by two inlets to fill the bath = 6 min.

Part filled by (2 inlets + 1 waste pipe) in 6 min

$= \left(1 - \frac{2}{3}\right) = \frac{1}{3}.$

Part filled by (2 inlets + 1 waste pipe) in 1 min

$= \left(\frac{1}{3} \times \frac{1}{6}\right) = \frac{1}{18}.$

$\therefore$ Work done by waste pipe in 1 min $= \left(\frac{1}{18} - \frac{1}{6}\right) = -\frac{1}{9}.$

[– ve sign means emptying]

Hence, the waste pipe can empty the cistern in 9 minutes.

46. Let one cold water pipe and one hot water pipe individually take x and y hours respectively to fill the reservoir.

Then, $\frac{6}{x} = \frac{1}{12}$ or $x = 72.$

Also, $\frac{3}{x}+\frac{9}{y}=\frac{1}{8} \Rightarrow \frac{3}{72}+\frac{9}{y}=\frac{1}{8}$

$\Rightarrow \frac{9}{y}=\frac{1}{8}-\frac{1}{24}=\frac{1}{12} \Rightarrow y=108.$

Work done by 5 hot water pipes in 1 hr = $\frac{5}{y}=\frac{5}{108}$.

So, 5 hot water pipes alone will take $\frac{108}{5}$ hrs, i.e. $21\frac{3}{5}$ hrs or 21 hrs 36 min to fill the reservoir.

47. Let the volume of the overhead tank be x litres and the constant volume being fed per day to the tank be y litres. Then, $x + 50y = 32000 \times 50 \Rightarrow x + 50y = 1600000$ ...(i)

$x + 40y = 37000 \times 40 \Rightarrow x + 40y = 1480000$ ...(*ii*)

Subtracting (*ii*) from (*i*), we get $10y = 120000$ or $y = 12000$.

Clearly, the supply won't ever fail if the regular demand is equal to the regular supply, which is 12000 gallons.

48. Volume of water in a rectangular tank

$= 400 \times 300 \times 231$ cc

Volume of cylinder = $\pi r^2 h = \pi\times\left(\frac{7}{2}\right)^2\times 500$

Required time

$=\frac{400\times300\times231}{\pi\times\left(\frac{7}{2}\right)^2\times500}$

$=\frac{400\times300\times231\times4\times7}{22\times49\times500}$

= 1440 seconds = 24 minutes

49. The outlet pipe empties the one complete cistern in 3 hours.

$\therefore$ Time taken to empty $\frac{2}{3}$ Part of the cistern

$=\frac{2}{3}\times3=2$ hours.

50. A's 1 hour work = $\frac{1}{24}$

B's 1 hour work = $\frac{1}{30}$

LCM of 24 and 30 = 120

1 hour work of together A and B's

$=\frac{1}{24}+\frac{1}{30}=\frac{5+4}{120}=\frac{9}{120}=\frac{3}{40}$

$\therefore$ Total time to fill the tank = $\frac{40}{3}$

$= 13\frac{1}{3}$ hour = 13 hours 20 minutes

51. Rate of flow of water = x cm/minute

$\therefore$ Volume of water that flowed in the tank in 1 minutes $= 5 \times 4 \times x = 20x$ cu.cm.

$\therefore$ Volume of water that flowed in the tank in 6 hours 18 minutes.

i.e. $(6 \times 60 + 18) = 378$ minutes

$= 2x \times 378$ cu.cm.

According to the question, $20x \times 378 = 700 \times 400 \times 450$

$\Rightarrow x=\left(\frac{700\times400\times450}{20\times378}\right)$ cm/minutes

$=\left(\frac{700\times400\times450\times60}{100000\times20\times378}\right)$ km/hour.

= 10 km/hour.

52. Part of tank filled by A in 1 hour = $\frac{1}{18}$ part

Part of tank filled by B in 1 hour = $\frac{1}{6}$ part

Part of tank filled by pipes A and B in 1 hour = $\frac{1}{18}+\frac{1}{6}$

$=\frac{1+3}{18}=\frac{4}{18}=\frac{2}{9}$

$\therefore$ Required time taken by pipe A and B = $\frac{9}{2}$ hours

$=4\frac{1}{2}$ hours

53. First pipe fill the tank in 1 hour = $\frac{1}{12}$ part of tank

Second pipe fill the tank in 1 hour = $\frac{1}{16}$ part of tank

Third pipe empty the tank in 1 hour = $\frac{1}{30}$ part of tank.

When all three pipes are opened simultaneously, part of the tank filled in 1 hour

$=\frac{1}{12}+\frac{1}{16}-\frac{1}{30}$

LCM of 12, 16 and 30 = 240

$=\frac{20+15-8}{240}=\frac{27}{240}$

$\therefore$ Required time taken by all the three pipes = $\frac{240}{27}$

$=\frac{80}{9}=8\frac{8}{9}$ Hours

54. Part of the tank filled by inlet in 1h. = $\frac{1}{4}$

Part of the tank emptied by outlets A and B together in $1h = \frac{1}{6}$

Let the time taken to fill the tank completely = ah

$\therefore \left(\frac{a-1}{4}\right)-\frac{a}{6}=\frac{1}{2}$

$\Rightarrow \frac{6a-6-4a}{24}=\frac{1}{2}$

$\Rightarrow 2a-6=12$

$\Rightarrow 2a=18$

$\Rightarrow a=9h$

EXERCISE

(DATA SUFFICIENCY TYPE QUESTIONS)

Directions (*Questions 1–4*): ***Each of the questions given below consists of a statement and/or a question and two statements numbered I and II given below it. You have to decide whether the data provided in the statement(s) is/are sufficient to answer the given question. Read both the statements and:***

Give answer (a) if the data in Statement I alone are sufficient to answer the question, while the data in Statement II alone are not sufficient to answer the question;

Give answer (b) if the data in Statement II alone are sufficient to answer the question, while the data in Statement I alone are not sufficient to answer the question;

Give answer (c) if the data either in Statement I or in Statement II alone are sufficient to answer the question;

Give answer (d) if the data even in both Statements I and II together are not sufficient to answer the question;

Give answer (e) if the data in both Statements I and II together are necessary to answer the question.

1. How long will it take to empty the tank if both the inlet pipe A and the outlet pipe B are opened simultaneously?
   I. A can fill the tank in 16 minutes.
   II. B can empty the full tank in 8 minutes.

2. Two taps A and B, when opened together, can fill a tank in 6 hours. How long will it take for the pipe A alone to fill the tank?
   I. B alone takes 5 hours more than A to fill the tank.
   II. The ratio of the time taken by A to that taken by B to fill the tank is 2 : 3.

3. A tank is fitted with two inlet pipes A and B. Both the pipes are kept open for 10 minutes so that the tank is two-thirds full and then pipe A is closed. How much time will pipe B take to fill the remaining part of the tank?
   I. Pipe A is thrice as fast as pipe B.
   II. Pipe B alone can fill the tank in 60 minutes.

4. How much time will the leak take to empty the full cistern?
   I. The cistern is normally filled in 9 hours.
   II. It takes one hour more than the usual time to fill the cistern because of a leak in the bottom.

Directions (*Questions 5-6*): ***Each of the questions below consists of a question followed by three statements. You have to study the question and the statements and decide which of the statement(s) is/are necessary to answer the question:***

5. A tank is fitted with two taps A and B. In how much time will the tank be full if both the taps are opened together? (SNAP, 2005)
   I. A is 50% more efficient than B.
   II. A alone takes 16 hours to fill the tank.
   III. B alone takes 24 hours to fill the tank.
   (*a*) II and III only (*b*) All I, II and III
   (*c*) I and II only (*d*) I and III only
   (*e*) Any two of the three

6. If both the pipes are opened, how many hours will be taken to fill the tank?
   I. The capacity of the tank is 400 litres.
   II. The pipe A fills the tank in 4 hours.
   III. The pipe B fills the tank in 6 hours.
   (*a*) Only I and II (*b*) Only II and III
   (*c*) All I, II and III (*d*) Any two of the three
   (*e*) Even with all the three statements, answer cannot be given.

Directions: ***The question given below is followed by three statements. You have to decide whether any information given in the statement(s) is not required.***

7. A water tank has been filled with two filler taps P and Q and a drain pipe R. Taps P and Q fill at the rate of 5 litres per minute and 9 litres per minute respectively. What is the capacity of the tank? (M.A.T., 2006)
   I. Tap R drains out at the rate of 6 litres per minute.
   II. If all the three taps are opened simultaneously, then the tank is filled in $4\frac{1}{2}$ hours.
   III. Tap R drains the filled tank in 15 hours.
   (*a*) II and either I or III (*b*) Either I or II
   (*c*) II and III together (*d*) Any one of them

ANSWERS

1. (*e*) 2. (*c*) 3. (*c*) 4. (*e*) 5. (*e*) 6. (*b*) 7. (*b*)

SOLUTIONS

1. I. A's 1 minute's filling work $= \frac{1}{16}$.

II. B's 1 minute's emptying work $= \frac{1}{8}$.

(A + B)'s 1 minute's emptying work $= \left(\frac{1}{8}-\frac{1}{16}\right) = \frac{1}{16}$

$\therefore$ Tank will be emptied in 16 minutes. Thus, both I and II are necessary to answer the question.

Hence, correct answer is (*e*).

2. (A + B)'s 1 hour filling work $= \frac{1}{6}$.

I. Suppose A takes x hours to fill the tank. Then, B takes $(x + 5)$ hours to fill the tank.

$\therefore$ (A's 1 hour work) + (B's 1 hour work) = (A + B)'s 1 hour work

$\Leftrightarrow \frac{1}{x}+\frac{1}{(x+5)}=\frac{1}{6} \Leftrightarrow \frac{(x+5)+x}{x(x+5)}=\frac{1}{6}$

$\Leftrightarrow x^2 + 5x = 12x + 30 \Leftrightarrow x^2 - 7x - 30 = 0$

$\Leftrightarrow x^2 - 10x + 3x - 30 = 0$

$\Leftrightarrow x(x - 10) + 3(x - 10) = 0$

$\Leftrightarrow (x - 10)(x + 3) = 0 \Leftrightarrow x = 10.$

So, A alone takes 10 hours to fill the tank.

II. Suppose A takes $2x$ hours and B takes $3x$ hours to fill the tank. Then, $\frac{1}{2x}+\frac{1}{3x} = \frac{1}{6}$

$\Leftrightarrow \left(\frac{1}{2}+\frac{1}{3}\right)\cdot\frac{1}{x} = \frac{1}{6} \Leftrightarrow \frac{5}{6x} = \frac{1}{6} \Leftrightarrow x = 5.$

So, A alone takes $(2 \times 5) = 10$ hours to fill the tank.

Thus, each one of I and II alone gives the answer. Hence, correct answer is (*c*).

3. I. Let B's 1 min. work $= \frac{1}{x}$. Then, A's 1 min. work $= \frac{3}{x}$.

(A + B)'s 1 min. work $= \left(\frac{1}{x}+\frac{3}{x}\right) = \frac{4}{x}$. (A + B)'s 10 min. work $= \left(\frac{4}{x}\times 10\right) = \frac{40}{x}$

$\therefore \quad \frac{40}{x} = \frac{2}{3} \Leftrightarrow x = 60.$

$\therefore$ B's 1 min. work $= \frac{1}{60}$

$\frac{1}{60}$ part is filled by B in 1 min. $\frac{1}{3}$ part is filled by B in $\left(60\times\frac{1}{3}\right)$ min. = 20 min.

II. B's 1 min. work $= \frac{1}{60}$.

$\frac{1}{60}$ part is filled by B in 1 min. $\frac{1}{3}$ part is filled by B in $\left(60\times\frac{1}{3}\right)$ min. = 20 min.

Hence, correct answer is (*c*).

4. I. Time taken to fill the cistern without leak = 9 hours.

Part of cistern filled without leak in 1 hour $= \frac{1}{9}$.

II. Time taken to fill the cistern in presence of leak = 10 hours.

Net filling in 1 hour $= \frac{1}{10}$. Work done by leak in 1 hour $= \left(\frac{1}{9}-\frac{1}{10}\right) = \frac{1}{90}$

$\therefore$ Leak will empty the full cistern in 90 hours.

Clearly, both I and II are necessary to answer the question.

$\therefore$ Correct answer is (*e*).

5. II. A's 1 hour work $= \frac{1}{16}$.

Suppose B fills the tank in x hours. Then, B's 1 hour work $= \frac{1}{x}$.

I. Work done by A in 1 hour = 150% of $\frac{1}{x}$

$= \left(\frac{1}{x}\times\frac{150}{100}\right) = \frac{3}{2x}$.

$\therefore \quad \frac{3}{2x} = \frac{1}{16} \Leftrightarrow x = 24.$

So, B can fill the tank in 24 hours.

(A + B)'s 1 hour work $= \left(\frac{1}{16}+\frac{1}{24}\right) = \frac{5}{48}$.

$\therefore$ (A + B) can fill the tank in $\frac{48}{5}$ hrs. Thus, I & II give the answer.

III. Work done by B in 1 hour $= \frac{1}{24}$.

From II & III, we get the same answer.

From III & I, we get : A's 1 hour work = 150% of $\frac{1}{24}$

$= \left(\frac{1}{24}\times\frac{150}{100}\right) = \frac{1}{16}$

Thus, from III & I, we get the same answer.

$\therefore$ Correct answer is (*e*).

6. II. Part of the tank filled by A in 1 hour $= \frac{1}{4}$.

III. Part of the tank filled by B in 1 hour $= \frac{1}{6}$.

(A + B)'s 1 hour's work $= \left(\frac{1}{4}+\frac{1}{6}\right) = \frac{5}{12}$.

∴ When both A and B are opened together, they will fill the tank in $\frac{12}{5}$ hrs = 2 hrs 24 min.

So, II and III are needed. ∴ Correct answer is (*b*).

7. I and III.

Capacity of the tank = $(6 \times 60 \times 15)$ litres = 5400 litres.

∴ II is not required.

II and III.

Work done by P and Q in 1 hour

$$= \left(\frac{2}{9} - \frac{1}{15}\right) = \frac{(10-3)}{45} = \frac{7}{45}.$$

∴ P and Q together can fill it in $\frac{45}{7}$ hrs.

Volume flown through P and Q in 1 hr = $\{(6 + 8) \times 60\}$ litres. = 840 litres.

Capacity of the tank = $\left(840 \times \frac{45}{7}\right)$ litres = 5400 litres.

∴ I is not required.

Thus, either I or II is not required. Hence, correct answer is (*b*).

17 Time and Work

IMPORTANT FACTS AND FORMULAE

I. If A can do a piece of work in n days, then A's 1 day's work $= \frac{1}{n}$.

II. If A's 1 day's work $= \frac{1}{n}$, then A can finish the work in n days.

II. If A is thrice as good a workman as B, then :

Ratio of work done by A and B = 3 : 1.

Ratio of times taken by A and B to finish a work = 1 : 3.

ILLUSTRATIVE EXAMPLES

Ex. 1. ***If Roger can do a piece of work in 8 days and Antony can complete the same work in 5 days, in how many days will both of them together complete it?*** **(L.I.C., 2008)**

Sol. Roger's 1 day's work $= \frac{1}{8}$; Antony's 1 day's work $= \frac{1}{5}$.

(Roger + Antony)'s 1 day's work $= \left(\frac{1}{8}+\frac{1}{5}\right)=\frac{13}{40}$.

$\therefore$ Both Roger and Antony will complete the work in $\frac{40}{13}=3\frac{1}{13}$ days.

Ex. 2. ***A and B together can complete a piece of work in 15 days and B alone in 20 days. In how many days can A alone complete the work?*** **(S.S.C., 2010)**

Sol. (A + B)'s 1 day's work $= \frac{1}{15}$; B's 1 day's work $= \frac{1}{20}$.

$\therefore$ A's 1 day's work $= \left(\frac{1}{15}-\frac{1}{20}\right)=\frac{1}{60}$.

Hence, A alone can complete the work in 60 days.

Ex. 3. ***A alone can complete a piece of work of ₹ 300 in 6 days; but by engaging an assistant, the work is completed in 4 days. Find the share to be received by the assistant.*** **(Section Officer's, 2008)**

Sol. Assistant's 1 day's work $= \frac{1}{4}-\frac{1}{6}=\frac{1}{12}$.

$\therefore$ A's share : Assistant's share = Ratio of their 1 day's work $= \frac{1}{6}:\frac{1}{12}=2:1$.

Hence, assistant's share $=$ ₹$\left(300\times\frac{1}{3}\right)=$ ₹ 100.

Ex. 4. ***A can do a work in 4 days, B in 5 days and C in 10 days. Find the time taken by A, B and C to do the work together.*** **(P.C.S., 2006)**

Sol. A's 1 day's work $= \frac{1}{4}$; B's 1 day's work $= \frac{1}{5}$; C's 1 day's work $= \frac{1}{10}$.

(A + B + C) 's 1 day's work $= \left(\frac{1}{4}+\frac{1}{5}+\frac{1}{10}\right)=\frac{11}{20}$.

Hence, A, B and C together can do the work in $\frac{20}{11}=1\frac{9}{11}$ days.

Ex.5. ***A and B undertake to do a piece of work for ₹ 600. A alone can do it in 6 days while B alone can do it in 8 days. With the help of C, they finish it in 3 days. Find the share of each.***

Sol. C's 1 day's work $=\frac{1}{3}-\left(\frac{1}{6}+\frac{1}{8}\right)=\frac{1}{24}$.

$\therefore$ A : B : C = Ratio of their 1 day's work $\frac{1}{6}:\frac{1}{8}:\frac{1}{24}=4:3:1$.

$\therefore$ A's share = ₹ $\left(600\times\frac{4}{8}\right)$ = ₹ 300, B's share = ₹ $\left(600\times\frac{3}{8}\right)$ = ₹ 225.

C's share = ₹ [600 − (300 + 225)] = ₹ 75.

Ex. 6. ***A can do a piece of work in 7 days of 9 hours each and B can do it in 6 days of 7 hours each. How long will they take to do it, working together $8\frac{2}{5}$ hours a day?***

Sol. A can complete the work in $(7 \times 9) = 63$ hours.

B can complete the work in $(6 \times 7) = 42$ hours.

$\therefore$ A's 1 hour's work $=\frac{1}{63}$ and B's 1 hour's work $=\frac{1}{42}$.

(A + B)'s 1 hour's work $=\left(\frac{1}{63}+\frac{1}{42}\right)=\frac{5}{126}$.

$\therefore$ Both will finish the work in $\left(\frac{126}{5}\right)$ hrs.

Number of days of $8\frac{2}{5}$ hrs each $=\left(\frac{126}{5}\times\frac{5}{42}\right)=3$ days.

Ex. 7. ***Rahul takes twice as much time as Manick and thrice as much time as Sachin to complete a job. If working together, they can complete the job in 4 days, find the time taken by each of them separately to complete the work.*** **(I.I.F.T., 2005)**

Sol. Suppose Rahul takes x hours to complete the job.

Then, Manick takes $\frac{x}{2}$ hours and Sachin takes $\frac{x}{3}$ hours to do the job.

Rahul's 1 hour's work $=\frac{1}{x}$; Manick's 1 hour's work $=\frac{2}{x}$; Sachin's 1 hour's work $=\frac{3}{x}$.

$\therefore \quad 4\left(\frac{1}{x}+\frac{2}{x}+\frac{3}{x}\right)=1 \Rightarrow \frac{6}{x}=\frac{1}{4} \Rightarrow x=24.$

Hence, Rahul takes 24 hours, Manick takes 12 hours and Sachin takes 8 hours to complete the job.

Ex. 8. ***A and B can do a piece of work in 9 days; B and C can do it in 12 days; A and C can do it in 18 days. In how many days will A, B and C finish it, working together and separately?*** **(S.S.C., 2007)**

Sol. (A + B)'s 1 day's work $=\frac{1}{9}$; (B + C)'s 1 day's work $=\frac{1}{12}$;

(A + C)'s 1 day's work $=\frac{1}{18}$.

Adding, we get: 2 (A + B + C)'s 1 day's work $=\left(\frac{1}{9}+\frac{1}{12}+\frac{1}{18}\right)=\frac{9}{36}=\frac{1}{4}$.

$\therefore$ (A + B + C)'s 1 day's work $=\frac{1}{8}$.

Thus, A, B and C together can finish the work in 8 days.

Now, A's 1 day's work = [(A + B + C)'s 1 day's work − (B + C)'s 1 day's work]

$= \left(\frac{1}{8} - \frac{1}{12}\right) = \frac{1}{24}$.

$\therefore$ A alone can finish the work in 24 days.

Similarly, B's 1 day's work

$= [(A + B + C)\text{'s 1 day's work} - (A + C)\text{'s 1 day's work}] = \left(\frac{1}{8} - \frac{1}{18}\right) = \frac{5}{72}$.

$\therefore$ B alone can finish the work in $\frac{72}{5} = 14\frac{2}{5}$ days.

And, C's 1 day's work

$= [(A + B + C)\text{'s 1 day's work} - (A + B)\text{'s 1 day's work}] = \left(\frac{1}{8} - \frac{1}{9}\right) = \frac{1}{72}$.

$\therefore$ C alone can finish the work in 72 days.

Ex. 9. ***A is twice as good a workman as B and together they finish a piece of work in 18 days. In how many days will A alone finish the work ?***

Sol. (A's 1 day's work) : (B's 1 day's work) = 2 : 1.

(A + B)'s 1 day's work $= \frac{1}{18}$. Divide $\frac{1}{18}$ in the ratio 2 : 1.

$\therefore$ A's 1 day's work $= \left(\frac{1}{18} \times \frac{2}{3}\right) = \frac{1}{27}$.

Hence, A alone can finish the work in 27 days.

Ex. 10. ***A can do a certain job in 12 days. B is 60% more efficient than A. How many days does B alone take to do the same job ?***

Sol. Ratio of times taken by A and B = 160 : 100 = 8 : 5.

Suppose B alone takes x days to do the job.

Then, $8 : 5 :: 12 : x \Rightarrow 8x = 5 \times 12 \Rightarrow x = 7\frac{1}{2}$ days.

Ex. 11. ***A can do a piece of work in 80 days. He works at it for 10 days and then B alone finishes the remaining work in 42 days. In how much time will A and B, working together, finish the work ?***

Sol. Work done by A in 10 days $= \left(\frac{1}{80} \times 10\right) = \frac{1}{8}$. Remaining work $= \left(1 - \frac{1}{8}\right) = \frac{7}{8}$.

Now, $\frac{7}{8}$ work is done by B in 42 days.

Whole work will be done by B in $\left(42 \times \frac{8}{7}\right) = 48$ days.

$\therefore$ A's 1 day's work $= \frac{1}{80}$ and B's 1 day's work $= \frac{1}{48}$.

$\therefore$ (A + B)'s 1 day's work $= \left(\frac{1}{80} + \frac{1}{48}\right) = \frac{8}{240} = \frac{1}{30}$.

Hence, both will finish the work in 30 days.

Ex. 12. ***A can do a piece of work in 10 days and B in 20 days. They work together but 2 days before the completion of the work, A leaves. In how many days was the work completed ?*** **(S.S.C., 2008)**

Sol. B's 2 days' work $= \left(\frac{1}{20} \times 2\right) = \frac{1}{10}$. Remaining work $= \left(1 - \frac{1}{10}\right) = \frac{9}{10}$.

(A + B)'s 1 day's work $= \left(\frac{1}{10} + \frac{1}{20}\right) = \frac{6}{40} = \frac{3}{20}$.

Now, $\frac{3}{20}$ work is done by A and B in 1 day.

$\therefore \quad \frac{9}{10}$ work is done by A and B in $\left(\frac{20}{3} \times \frac{9}{10}\right) = 6$ days.

Hence, total time taken = (2 + 6) days = 8 days.

Ex. 13. ***A can complete a work in 10 days, B in 12 days and C in 15 days. All of them began the work together, but A had to leave the work after 2 days of the start and B, 3 days before the completion of the work. How long did the work last?*** (S.S.C., 2005)

Sol. A, B and C work together for 2 days. C alone works for 3 days and the remaining work is done by B and C together.

Now, (A + B + C)'s 2 days' work = $2\left(\frac{1}{10}+\frac{1}{12}+\frac{1}{15}\right)=\left(2 \times \frac{15}{60}\right)=\frac{1}{2}$.

C's 3 days' work = $\left(3 \times \frac{1}{15}\right)=\frac{1}{5}$. Remaining work = $1-\left(\frac{1}{2}+\frac{1}{5}\right)=\frac{3}{10}$.

But, (B + C)'s 1 day's work = $\left(\frac{1}{12}+\frac{1}{15}\right)=\frac{27}{180}=\frac{3}{20}$.

Now, $\frac{3}{20}$ work is done by (B + C) in 1 day.

$\therefore \quad \frac{3}{10}$ work is done by (B + C) in $\left(\frac{20}{3} \times \frac{3}{10}\right)=2$ days.

Hence, total time taken = (2 + 3 + 2) days = 7 days.

Ex. 14. ***A and B can do a piece of work in 45 and 40 days respectively. They began the work together but A leaves after some days and B finished the remaining work in 23 days. After how many days did A leave?*** (M.B.A., 2009)

Sol. B's 23 days' work = $\left(23 \times \frac{1}{40}\right)=\frac{23}{40}$. Remaining work = $\left(1-\frac{23}{40}\right)=\frac{17}{40}$.

Now, (A + B)'s 1 day's work = $\left(\frac{1}{45}+\frac{1}{40}\right)=\frac{17}{360}$.

Thus, $\frac{17}{360}$ work is done by (A + B) in 1 day.

$\therefore \quad \frac{17}{40}$ work is done by (A + B) in $\left(\frac{360}{17} \times \frac{17}{40}\right)=9$ days.

Hence, A left after 9 days.

Ex. 15. ***A and B working separately can do a piece of work in 9 and 12 days respectively. If they work for a day alternately, A beginning, in how many days, the work will be completed ?***

Sol. (A + B)'s 2 days' work = $\left(\frac{1}{9}+\frac{1}{12}\right)=\frac{7}{36}$.

Work done in 5 pairs of days = $\left(5 \times \frac{7}{36}\right)=\frac{35}{36}$.

Remaining work = $\left(1-\frac{35}{36}\right)=\frac{1}{36}$.

On 11th day, it is A's turn. $\frac{1}{9}$ work is done by him in 1 day.

$\frac{1}{36}$ work is done by him in $\left(9 \times \frac{1}{36}\right)=\frac{1}{4}$ day.

$\therefore \quad$ Total time taken = $\left(10+\frac{1}{4}\right)$ days $=10\frac{1}{4}$ days.

Ex. 16. ***A can do a piece of work in 120 days and B can do it in 150 days. They work together for 20 days. Then, B leaves and A alone continues the work. 12 days after that C joins A and the work is completed in 48 days more. In how many days can C do it, if he works alone?***

Sol. [(A + B)'s 20 days' work] + (A's 12 days' work) $= 20\left(\frac{1}{120}+\frac{1}{150}\right)+\left(12\times\frac{1}{120}\right)=\frac{2}{5}$.

Remaining work $=\left(1-\frac{2}{5}\right)=\frac{3}{5}$ = (A + C)'s 48 days' work.

$\therefore$ (A + C)'s 1 day's work $=\left(\frac{3}{5}\times\frac{1}{48}\right)=\frac{1}{80}$. C's 1 day's work $=\left(\frac{1}{80}-\frac{1}{120}\right)=\frac{1}{240}$.

Hence, C alone can finish the work in 240 days.

Ex. 17. ***A and B can do a piece of work in 12 days. B and C together can do it in 15 days. If A is twice as good a workman as C, find in what time B alone can do it.***

Sol. A's 1 day's work = C's 2 days' work.

$\therefore$ (A + B)'s 1 day's work = (B's 1 day's work) + (C's 2 days' work)

$\Rightarrow$ (B's 1 day's work) + (C's 2 days' work) $=\frac{1}{12}$ ...(*i*)

But (B's 1 day's work) + (C's 1 day's work) $=\frac{1}{15}$ ...(*ii*)

Subtracting (*ii*) from (*i*), we get: C's 1 day's work $=\left(\frac{1}{12}-\frac{1}{15}\right)=\frac{1}{60}$.

$\therefore$ B's 1 day's work $=\left(\frac{1}{15}-\frac{1}{60}\right)=\frac{3}{60}=\frac{1}{20}$.

Hence, B alone can finish the work in 20 days.

Ex. 18. ***45 men can complete a work in 16 days. Six days after they started working, 30 more men joined them. How many days will they now take to complete the remaining work?***

Sol. (45 × 16) men can complete the work in 1 day.

$\therefore$ 1 man's 1 day's work $=\frac{1}{720}$. 45 men's 1 days' work $=\frac{45}{720}=\frac{1}{16}$

45 men's 6 days' work $=\left(\frac{1}{16}\times 6\right)=\frac{3}{8}$. Remaining work $=\left(1-\frac{3}{8}\right)=\frac{5}{8}$.

75 men's 1 day's work $=\frac{75}{720}=\frac{5}{48}$.

Now, $\frac{5}{48}$ work is done by them in 1 day.

$\therefore$ $\frac{5}{8}$ work is done by them in $\left(\frac{48}{5}\times\frac{5}{8}\right)=6$ days.

Ex. 19. ***10 persons begin to work together on a job but after some days 4 persons leave. As a result, the job which could have been completed in 40 days is completed in 50 days. How many days after the commencement of the work did the 4 persons leave?*** (S.S.C., 2004)

Sol. 10 persons can complete the work in 40 days.

$\therefore$ 1 person's 1 day's work $=\frac{1}{40\times 10}=\frac{1}{400}$.

Suppose 4 persons left after x days.

Then, $\frac{1}{400}\times 10\times x+\frac{1}{400}\times 6\times(50-x)=1 \Rightarrow \frac{1}{40}x+\frac{3}{200}(50-x)=1$

$\Rightarrow \frac{1}{40}x+\frac{3}{4}-\frac{3}{200}x=1 \Rightarrow \frac{1}{100}x=\frac{1}{4} \Rightarrow x=25.$

Hence, 4 persons left 25 days after the commencement of the work.

Ex. 20. ***9 children can complete a piece of work in 360 days. 18 men can complete the same piece of work in 72 days and 12 women can complete it in 162 days. In how many days can 4 men, 12 women and 10 children together complete the piece of work?*** (Bank. P.O., 2006)

Sol. 1 man's 1 day's work = $\frac{1}{72 \times 18} = \frac{1}{1296}$.

1 woman's 1 day's work = $\frac{1}{162 \times 12} = \frac{1}{1944}$.

1 child's 1 day's work = $\frac{1}{360 \times 9} = \frac{1}{3240}$.

(4 men + 12 women + 10 children)'s 1 day's work

$= \left(4 \times \frac{1}{1296} + 12 \times \frac{1}{1944} + 10 \times \frac{1}{3240}\right) = \left(\frac{1}{324} + \frac{1}{162} + \frac{1}{324}\right) = \frac{4}{324} = \frac{1}{81}$.

Hence, 4 men, 12 women and 10 children can complete the work in 81 days.

Ex. 21. ***2 men and 3 boys can do a piece of work in 10 days while 3 men and 2 boys can do the same work in 8 days. In how many days can 2 men and 1 boy do the work?***

Sol. Let 1 man's 1 day's work = x and 1 boy's 1 day's work = y.

Then, $2x + 3y = \frac{1}{10}$ and $3x + 2y = \frac{1}{8}$.

Solving, we get : $x = \frac{7}{200}$ and $y = \frac{1}{100}$.

$\therefore$ (2 men + 1 boy)'s 1 day's work = $\left(2 \times \frac{7}{200} + 1 \times \frac{1}{100}\right) = \frac{16}{200} = \frac{2}{25}$.

So, 2 men and 1 boy together can finish the work in $\frac{25}{2} = 12\frac{1}{2}$ days.

Ex. 22. ***3 men and 4 women can earn ₹ 3780 in 7 days. 11 men and 13 women can earn ₹ 15040 in 8 days. In what time will 7 men and 9 women earn ₹ 12400?***

Sol. Let 1 man's 1 day's earning be ₹ x and 1 woman's 1 day's earning be ₹ y.

Then, $3x + 4y = \frac{3780}{7} = 540$ ... (*i*)

And, $11x + 13y = \frac{15040}{8} = 1880$ ...(*ii*)

Solving (*i*) and (*ii*), we get: $x = 100$, $y = 60$.

(7 men + 9 women)'s 1 day's earning = ₹ (7 × 100 + 9 × 60) = ₹ 1240.

Hence, required time = $\left(\frac{12400}{1240}\right)$ days = 10 days.

EXERCISE

(OBJECTIVE TYPE QUESTIONS)

Directions: ***Mark (✓) against the correct answer:***

1. Ayesha can complete a piece of work in 16 days. Amita can complete the same piece of work in 8 days. If both of them work together in how many days can they complete the same piece of work? **(Bank P.O., 2010)**

   (*a*) $4\frac{2}{5}$ days (*b*) $5\frac{1}{3}$ days
   (*c*) 6 days (*d*) 12 days
   (*e*) None of these

2. A can complete a certain work in 4 minutes, *B* in 5 minutes, *C* in 6 minutes, *D* in 10 minutes and *E* in 12 minutes. The average number of units of work completed by them per minute will be **(P.C.S., 2009)**

   (*a*) 0.16 (*b*) 0.40
   (*c*) 0.80 (*d*) None of these

3. A can finish a work in 18 days and B can do the same work in half the time taken by A. Then, working together, what part of the same work they can finish in a day ? **(S.S.C., 2002)**

   (*a*) $\frac{1}{6}$ (*b*) $\frac{1}{9}$
   (*c*) $\frac{2}{5}$ (*d*) $\frac{2}{7}$

4. A tyre has two punctures. The first puncture alone would have made the tyre flat in 9 minutes and the second alone would have done it in 6 minutes. If air leaks out at a constant rate, how long does it take both the punctures together to make it flat ?

(a) $1\frac{1}{2}$ minutes (b) $3\frac{1}{2}$ minutes
(c) $3\frac{3}{5}$ minutes (d) $4\frac{1}{4}$ minutes

5. A can knit a pair of socks in 3 days. B can knit the same pair in 9 days. If they are knitting together, then in how many days will they knit two pairs of socks? **(R.R.B., 2004)**

(a) 3 days (b) 4 days
(c) $4\frac{1}{2}$ days (d) 5 days

6. A can complete a work in 6 days while B can complete the same work in 12 days. If they work together and complete it, the portion of the work done by A is

(a) $\frac{1}{3}$ (b) $\frac{1}{4}$
(c) $\frac{1}{2}$ (d) $\frac{2}{3}$

7. A can do a piece of work in 8 days and B can do the same piece of work in 12 days. A and B together complete the same piece of work and get ₹ 200 as the combined wages. B's share of the wages will be

(a) ₹ 75 (b) ₹ 80
(c) ₹ 85 (d) ₹ 90

8. George takes 8 hours to copy a 50-page manuscript while Sonia can copy the same manuscript in 6 hours. How many hours would it take them to copy a 100-page manuscript, if they work together? **(M.A.T., 2005)**

(a) $6\frac{6}{7}$ (b) 9
(c) $9\frac{5}{7}$ (d) 14

9. A and B together complete a piece of work in T days. If A alone completes the work in T + 3 days and B alone completes the piece of work in T + 12 days, what is T? **(S.B.I.P.O., 2008)**

(a) 3 days (b) 9 days
(c) 12 days (d) Cannot be determined
(e) None of these

10. Reena, Aastha and Shloka can independently complete a piece of work in 6 hours, 4 hours and 12 hours respectively. If they work together, how much time will they take to complete that piece of work? **(Bank P.O., 2004)**

(a) 2 hours (b) 5 hours
(c) 6 hours (d) 8 hours
(e) None of these

11. A man can do a job in 15 days. His father takes 20 days and his son finishes it in 25 days. How long will they take to complete the job if they all work together?

(a) Less than 6 days
(b) Exactly 6 days
(c) Approximately 6.4 days
(d) More than 10 days

12. Amit and Sumit can plough a field in 4 days. Sumit alone can plough the field in 6 days. In how many days will Amit alone plough the field? **(R.R.B., 2006)**

(a) 10 days (b) 12 days
(c) 14 days (d) 15 days

13. Two spinning machines A and B can together produce 3,00,000 metres of cloth in 10 hours. If machine B alone can produce the same amount of cloth in 15 hours, then how much cloth can machine A produce alone in 10 hours? **(M.A.T., 2005)**

(a) 50,000 metres (b) 1,00,000 metres
(c) 1,50,000 metres (d) 2,00,000 metres

14. X, Y and Z complete a work in 6 days. X or Y alone can do the same work in 16 days. In how many days Z alone can finish the same work? **(R.R.B., 2006)**

(a) 12 (b) 16
(c) 24 (d) 36

15. A can lay railway track between two given stations in 16 days and B can do the same job in 12 days. With the help of C, they did the job in 4 days only. Then, C alone can do the job in : **(S.S.C., 2003)**

(a) $9\frac{1}{5}$ days (b) $9\frac{2}{5}$ days
(c) $9\frac{3}{5}$ days (d) 10 days

16. A can complete $\frac{1}{3}$ of a work in 5 days and B, $\frac{2}{5}$ of the work in 10 days. In how many days both A and B together can complete the work? **(S.S.C., 2010; P.C.S., 2009)**

(a) $7\frac{1}{2}$ (b) $8\frac{4}{5}$
(c) $9\frac{3}{8}$ (d) 10

17. X can do $\frac{1}{4}$ of a work in 10 days, Y can do 40% of the work in 40 days and Z can do $\frac{1}{3}$ of the work in 13 days. Who will complete the work first ?

(a) X (b) Y
(c) Z (d) X and Z both

18. A man and a boy together can do a certain amount of digging in 40 days. Their speeds in digging are in the ratio of 8 : 5. How many days will the boy take to complete the work if engaged alone? **(R.R.B., 2005)**

(a) 52 days (b) 68 days
(c) 80 days (d) 104 days

19. A takes twice as much time as B or thrice as much time as C to finish a piece of work. Working together, they can finish the work in 2 days. B can do the work alone in : **(S.S.C., 2002)**

(a) 4 days (b) 6 days
(c) 8 days (d) 12 days

20. Work done by A in one day is half of the work done by B in one day. Work done by B is half of the work done by C in one day. If C alone can complete the work in 7 days, in how many days can A, B and C together complete the work? **(S.B.I.P.O., 2008)**

(a) 4 (b) 14
(c) 21 (d) 28
(e) None of these

21. Rosa can eat 32 rosogollas in one hour. Her sister Lila needs three hours to eat the same number. How much time will they take to eat 32 rosogollas together? **(R.R.B., 2005)**

(a) 45 minutes (b) 75 minutes
(c) 90 minutes (d) None of these

22. A conveyor belt delivers baggage at the rate of 3 tons in 5 minutes and a second conveyor belt delivers baggage at the rate of 1 ton in 2 minutes. How much time will it take to get 33 tons of baggage delivered using both the conveyor belts together? **(P.C.S., 2006)**

(a) 25 min 30 sec (b) 30 min
(c) 35 min (d) 45 min

23. A manufacturer builds a machine which will address 500 envelopes in 8 minutes. He wishes to build another machine so that when both are operating together they will address 500 envelopes in 2 minutes. The equation used to find how many minutes x it would require the second machine to address 500 envelopes alone, is **(M.B.A., 2011)**

(a) $8 - x = 2$ (b) $\frac{1}{8} + \frac{1}{x} = \frac{1}{2}$
(c) $\frac{500}{8} + \frac{500}{x} = 500$ (d) $\frac{x}{2} + \frac{x}{8} = 1$

24. Computer A takes 3 minutes to process an input while computer B takes 5 minutes. If computers A, B and C can process an average of 14 inputs in one hour, how many minutes does computer C alone take to process one input? **(M.C.A., 2009)**

(a) 4 (b) 6
(c) 10 (d) None of these

25. Bob and David are two typists. One afternoon, they were each given 40 pages for typing. They divided the work equally but David finished 20 minutes before Bob who took 2 hours for the same. The next afternoon, they were again given 77 pages to type. However, this time they decided to divide the work such that they finished typing simultaneously. How many pages did Bob have to type?

(a) 35 (b) 36
(c) 40 (d) 42

26. P, Q and R are three typists who working simultaneously can type 216 pages in 4 hours. In one hour, R can type as many pages more than Q as Q can type more than P. During a period of five hours, R can type as many pages as P can during seven hours. How many pages does each of them type per hour ? **(M.A.T., 2005)**

(a) 14, 17, 20 (b) 15, 17, 22
(c) 15, 18, 21 (d) 16, 18, 22

27. Ronald and Elan are working on an assignment. Ronald takes 6 hours to type 32 pages on a computer, while Elan takes 5 hours to type 40 pages. How much time will they take, working together on two different computers to type an assignment of 110 pages? **(SCMHRD, 2002)**

(a) 7 hours 30 minutes (b) 8 hours
(c) 8 hours 15 minutes (d) 8 hours 25 minutes

28. Cloth Makers Inc. has p spindles, each of which can produce q metres of cloth on an average in r minutes. If the spindles are made to run with no interruption, then how many hours will it take for 20,000 metres of cloth to be produced? **(M.A.T., 2004)**

(a) $\frac{20000\,pq}{r}$ (b) $\frac{20000\,rq}{p}$
(c) $\frac{20000\,r}{pq}$ (d) $\frac{20000\,r}{60\,pq}$

29. Two workers A and B are engaged to do a work. A working alone takes 8 hours more to complete the job than if both worked together. If B worked alone, he would need $4\frac{1}{2}$ hours more to complete the job than they both working together. What time would they take to do the work together ? **(M.A.T., 2010)**

(a) 4 hours (b) 5 hours
(c) 6 hours (d) 7 hours

30. Three friends Anne, Bob and Chris work together to do a certain job. The time it takes them to do the work together is 6 hours less than Anne would have take alone, 1 hour less than Bob would have taken alone and half the time Chris would have taken working alone. How long did it take them to complete the job, working together? (M.B.A., 2010)

(a) 20 min (b) 30 min
(c) 40 min (d) 50 min

31. To do a piece of work, B takes 3 times as long as A and C together and C twice as long as A and B together. If A, B and C together can complete the work in 10 days, how long would A take alone to complete it?

(a) 24 days (b) 30 days
(c) 36 days (d) 40 days

32. P can complete a work in 12 days working 8 hours a day. Q can complete the same work in 8 days working 10 hours a day. If both P and Q work together, working 8 hours a day, in how many days can they complete the work ?

(a) $5\frac{5}{11}$ (b) $5\frac{6}{11}$
(c) $6\frac{5}{11}$ (d) $6\frac{6}{11}$
(e) None of these

33. A and B together can complete a work in 12 days, B and C together can complete the same work in 8 days and A and C together can complete it in 16 days. In total, how many days do A, B and C together take to complete the same work? (Bank P.O., 2009)

(a) $3\frac{5}{12}$ (b) $3\frac{9}{13}$
(c) $7\frac{5}{12}$ (d) $7\frac{5}{13}$
(e) None of these

34. A can do a piece of work in 4 hours, B and C together in 3 hours, and A and C together in 2 hours. How long will B alone take to do it? (S.S.C., 2005)

(a) 8 hours (b) 10 hours
(c) 12 hours (d) 24 hours

35. A and B can do a work in 8 days, B and C can do the same work in 12 days. A, B and C together can finish it in 6 days. A and C together will do it in (S.S.C., 2006)

(a) 4 days (b) 6 days
(c) 8 days (d) 12 days

36. A and B together can do a job in 2 days; B and C can do it in 4 days; A and C in $2\frac{2}{5}$ days. The number of days required for A to do the job alone is (M.B.A., 2011)

(a) 1 (b) 3
(c) 6 (d) 12

37. A and B can do a piece of work in 5 days; B and C can do it in 7 days; A and C can do it in 4 days. Who among these will take the least time if put to do it alone ?

(a) A (b) B
(c) C (d) Data inadequate

38. A and B can do a piece of work in 12 days, B and C in 8 days and C and A in 6 days. How long would B take to do the same work alone? (S.S.C., 2007)

(a) 24 days (b) 32 days
(c) 40 days (d) 48 days

39. A can build a wall in the same time in which B and C together can do it. If A and B together could do it in 25 days and C alone in 35 days, in what time could B alone do it? (N.M.A.T., 2008)

(a) 90 days (b) 100 days
(c) 175 days (d) None of these

40. Madhu takes twice as much time as Uma to complete a work and Rahul does it in the same time as Madhu and Uma together. If all three working together can finish the work in 6 days, then the time taken by Madhu to finish the work is (M.A.T., 2010)

(a) 12 days (b) 14 days
(c) 36 days (d) 40 days

41. A takes 5 days more than B to do a certain job and 9 days more than C; A and B together can do the job in the same time as C. How many days A would take to do it?

(a) 5 (b) 10
(c) 15 (d) 20

42. A works twice as fast as B. If B can complete a work in 12 days independently, the number of days in which A and B can together finish the work is

(a) 4 days (b) 6 days
(c) 8 days (d) 18 days

43. A is twice as good a workman as B. If they work together, they can complete a job in 18 days. If A alone does the job, in how many days he will complete the job? (Hotel Management, 2010)

(a) 27 days (b) 36 days
(c) 40 days (d) 54 days

44. David and Michael together can finish a job in 4 days 19 hrs 12 min. If David works at two-thirds Michael's speed, how long does it take Michael alone to finish the same job?

(a) 8 days (b) 12 days
(c) 15 days (d) None of these

45. A is thrice as good a workman as B and so takes 60 days less than B for doing a job. The time in which they can do the job together is

(A.A.O. Exam, 2010; M.A.T., 2010)

(a) $22\frac{1}{2}$ days (b) 30 days
(c) 45 days (d) 60 days

46. A and B can do a job together in 7 days. A is $1\frac{3}{4}$ times as efficient as B. The same job can be done by A alone in : (S.S.C., 2003)

(a) $9\frac{1}{3}$ days (b) 11 days
(c) $12\frac{1}{4}$ days (d) $16\frac{1}{3}$ days

47. Kamal can do a work in 15 days. Bimal is 50% more efficient than Kamal. The number of days, Bimal will take to do the same piece of work, is (C.P.O., 2006)

(a) $7\frac{1}{2}$ (b) 10
(c) 12 (d) 14

48. A does 20% less work than B. If A can complete a piece of work in $7\frac{1}{2}$ hours, then B can do it in (S.S.C., 2006)

(a) 5 hours (b) $5\frac{1}{2}$ hours
(c) 6 hours (d) $6\frac{1}{2}$ hours

49. A is 30% more efficient than B. How much time will they, working together, take to complete a job which A alone could have done in 23 days ?

(a) 11 days (b) 13 days
(c) $20\frac{3}{17}$ days (d) None of these

50. A can do a piece of work in 10 days working 8 hours per day. If B is two-thirds as efficient as A, then in how many days can B alone do the same piece of work, working 5 hours per day?

(a) 15 (b) 18
(c) 20 (d) 24

51. *A* does half as much work as *B* in one-sixth of the time. If together they take 10 days to complete a work, how much time shall *B* alone take to do it? (S.S.C., 2005)

(a) 30 days (b) 40 days
(c) 50 days (d) 70 days

52. A is 50% as efficient as B. C does half of the work done by A and B together. If C alone does the work in 40 days, then A, B and C together can do the work in:

(a) $13\frac{1}{3}$ days (b) 15 days
(c) 20 days (d) 30 days

53. Two workers A and B working together completed a job in 5 days. If A worked twice as efficiently as he actually did and B worked $\frac{1}{3}$ as efficiently as he actually did, the work would have been completed in 3 days. A alone could complete the work in :

(a) $5\frac{1}{4}$ days (b) $6\frac{1}{4}$ days
(c) $7\frac{1}{2}$ days (d) None of these

54. A can do a work in 15 days and B in 20 days. If they work on it together for 4 days, then the fraction of the work that is left is :

(a) $\frac{1}{4}$ (b) $\frac{1}{10}$
(c) $\frac{7}{15}$ (d) $\frac{8}{15}$

55. A can do a piece of work in 15 days, which B can do in 10 days. B worked at it for 8 days. A can finish the remaining work in (R.R.B., 2004)

(a) 2 days (b) 3 days
(c) 5 days (d) 10 days

56. A and B can complete a work in 18 days and 15 days respectively. They started doing the work together but after 3 days *A* had to leave and *B* alone completed the remaining work. The whole work was completed in

(a) $9\frac{3}{4}$ days (b) $10\frac{1}{4}$ days
(c) $12\frac{1}{2}$ days (d) $12\frac{3}{4}$ days

57. A, B and C can separately do a work in 12, 15 and 20 days respectively. They started to work together but C left after 2 days. The remaining work will be finished in (R.R.B., 2006)

(a) 4 days (b) 5 days
(c) 6 days (d) 15 days

58. A can complete a piece of work in 18 days, B in 20 days and C in 30 days. B and C together start the work and are forced to leave after 2 days. The time taken by A alone to complete the remaining work is (S.S.C., 2010)

(a) 10 days (b) 12 days
(c) 15 days (d) 16 days

59. A can complete a piece of work in 10 days, B in 15 days and C in 20 days. A and C worked together for 2 days and then A was replaced by B. In how many days, altogether, was the work completed? (C.P.O., 2007)

(a) 6 (b) 8
(c) 10 (d) 12

60. A machine P can print one lakh books in 8 hours, machine Q can print the same number of books in 10 hours while machine R can print them in 12 hours. All the machines are started at 9 a.m. while machine P is closed at 11 a.m. and the remaining two machines complete the work. Approximately at what time will the work be finished ?
(*a*) 11 : 30 a.m. (*b*) 12 noon
(*c*) 12 : 30 p.m. (*d*) 1 p.m.

61. A and B can do a piece of work in 30 days, while B and C can do the same work in 24 days and C and A in 20 days. They all work together for 10 days when B and C leave. How many days more will A take to finish the work ?
(*a*) 18 days (*b*) 24 days
(*c*) 30 days (*d*) 36 days

62. X and Y can do a piece of work in 20 days and 12 days respectively. X started the work alone and then after 4 days Y joined him till the completion of the work. How long did the work last ?
(*a*) 6 days (*b*) 10 days
(*c*) 15 days (*d*) 20 days

63. A completes $\frac{7}{10}$ of a work in 15 days. Then he completes the remaining work with the help of B in 4 days. The time required for A and B together to complete the entire work is **(S.S.C., 2005)**
(*a*) $8\frac{1}{4}$ days (*b*) $10\frac{1}{2}$ days
(*c*) $12\frac{2}{3}$ days (*d*) $13\frac{1}{3}$ days

64. A man and a boy can do a piece of work in 24 days. If the man works alone for the last 6 days, it is completed in 26 days. How long would the boy take to do it alone? **(S.S.C., 2005)**
(*a*) 20 days (*b*) 24 days
(*c*) 36 days (*d*) 72 days

65. A and B can together finish a work in 30 days. They worked together for 20 days and then B left. After another 20 days, A finished the remaining work. In how many days A alone can finish the job ? **(S.S.C., 2003)**
(*a*) 40 (*b*) 50
(*c*) 54 (*d*) 60

66. X can do a piece of work in 40 days. He works at it for 8 days and then Y finished it in 16 days. How long will they together take to complete the work ?
(*a*) $13\frac{1}{3}$ days (*b*) 15 days
(*c*) 20 days (*d*) 56 days

67. A, B and C together can complete a piece of work in 10 days. All the three started working at it together and after 4 days A left. Then B and C together completed the work in 10 more days. A alone could complete the work in :
(*a*) 15 days (*b*) 16 days
(*c*) 25 days (*d*) 50 days

68. A does $\frac{4}{5}$ of a work in 20 days. He then calls in B and they together finish the remaining work in 3 days. How long B alone would take to do the whole work ?
(*a*) 23 days (*b*) 37 days
(*c*) $37\frac{1}{2}$ days (*d*) 40 days

69. *A* and *B* together can do a piece of work in 30 days. A having worked for 16 days, *B* finishes the remaining work alone in 44 days. In how many days shall B finish the whole work alone ?
(*a*) 30 days (*b*) 40 days
(*c*) 60 days (*d*) 70 days

70. A and B together can do a piece of work in 12 days, which B and C together can do in 16 days. After A has been working at it for 5 days and B for 7 days, C finishes it in 13 days. In how many days C alone will do the work ?
(*a*) 16 (*b*) 24
(*c*) 36 (*d*) 48

71. A and B can do a piece of work in 28 and 35 days respectively. They began to work together but A leaves after some time and B completed the remaining work in 17 days. After how many days did A leave?
(*a*) $7\frac{5}{9}$ days (*b*) 8 days
(*c*) 9 days (*d*) $14\frac{2}{5}$ days

72. A can build up a wall in 8 days while B can break it in 3 days. A has worked for 4 days and then B joined to work with A for another 2 days only. In how many days will A alone build up the remaining part of the wall? **(M.A.T., 2006)**
(*a*) $6\frac{1}{3}$ days (*b*) 7 days
(*c*) $7\frac{1}{3}$ days (*d*) $13\frac{1}{3}$ days

73. Anuj and Manoj can together paint their house in 30 days. After working for 20 days, Anuj has to go out and Manoj finishes the remaining work in the next 30 days. If Manoj had gone away after 20 days

instead of Anuj, then Anuj would have completed the remaining work in (M.B.A., 2006)

(*a*) 15 days (*b*) 20 days
(*c*) 25 days (*d*) 35 days

74. A started a work and left after working for 2 days. Then B was called and he finished the work in 9 days. Had A left the work after working for 3 days, B would have finished the remaining work in 6 days. In how many days can each of them, working alone, finish the whole work? (N.M.A.T., 2005)

(*a*) 2.5 days, 7.5 days (*b*) 5 days, 8.5 days
(*c*) 5 days, 15 days (*d*) None of these

75. Working together, Asha and Sudha can complete an assigned task in 20 days. However, if Asha worked alone and completed half the work and then Sudha takes over the task and completes the second half of the task, the task will be completed in 45 days. How long will Asha take to complete the task if she worked alone? Assume that Sudha is more efficient than Asha. (M.A.T., 2010)

(*a*) 25 days (*b*) 30 days
(*c*) 60 days (*d*) 65 days

76. A can do a piece of work in 14 days which B can do in 21 days. They begin together but 3 days before the completion of the work, A leaves off. The total number of days to complete the work is (G.B.O., 2007)

(*a*) $6\frac{3}{5}$ (*b*) $8\frac{1}{2}$
(*c*) $10\frac{1}{5}$ (*d*) $13\frac{1}{2}$

77. A, B and C can complete a work separately in 24, 36 and 48 days respectively. They started together but C left after 4 days of start and A left 3 days before the completion of the work. In how many days will the work be completed ?

(*a*) 15 days (*b*) 22 days
(*c*) 25 days (*d*) 35 days

78. A, B and C can complete a work in 10, 12 and 15 days respectively. They started the work together. But A left the work 5 days before its completion. B also left the work 2 days after A left. In how many days was the work completed? (C.P.O., 2007)

(*a*) 4 (*b*) 5
(*c*) 7 (*d*) 8

79. A, B and C together earn ₹ 300 per day, while A and C together earn ₹ 188 and B and C together earn ₹ 152. The daily earning of C is :

(*a*) ₹ 40 (*b*) ₹ 68
(*c*) ₹ 112 (*d*) ₹ 150

80. A, B and C are employed to do a piece of work for ₹ 529. A and B together are supposed to do $\frac{19}{23}$ of the work and B and C together $\frac{8}{23}$ of the work. What amount should A be paid ?

(*a*) ₹ 315 (*b*) ₹ 345
(*c*) ₹ 355 (*d*) ₹ 375

81. Kim can do a work in 3 days while David can do the same work in 2 days. Both of them finish the work together and get ₹ 150. What is the share of Kim ?

(*a*) ₹ 30 (*b*) ₹ 60
(*c*) ₹ 70 (*d*) ₹ 75

82. If A can do $\frac{1}{4}$ of a work in 3 days and B can do $\frac{1}{6}$ of the same work in 4 days, how much will A get if both work together and are paid ₹ 180 in all?

(*a*) ₹ 36 (*b*) ₹ 60
(*c*) ₹ 108 (*d*) ₹ 120

83. A man and a boy received ₹ 800 as wages for 5 days for the work they did together. The man's efficiency in the work was three times that of the boy. What are the daily wages of the boy? (S.S.C., 2005)

(*a*) ₹ 40 (*b*) ₹ 44
(*c*) ₹ 56 (*d*) ₹ 76

84. Two men undertake to do a piece of work for ₹ 1400. The first man alone can do this work in 7 days while the second man alone can do this work in 8 days. If they working together complete this work in 3 days with the help of a boy, how should the money be divided? (M.A.T., 2007)

(*a*) ₹ 600, ₹ 550, ₹ 250 (*b*) ₹ 600, ₹ 525, ₹ 275
(*c*) ₹ 600, ₹ 500, ₹ 300 (*d*) ₹ 500, ₹ 525, ₹ 375

85. A sum of money is sufficient to pay A's wages for 21 days and B's wages for 28 days. The same money is sufficient to pay the wages of both for : (ICET, 2005; G.B.O., 2007)

(*a*) 12 days (*b*) $12\frac{1}{4}$ days
(*c*) 14 days (*d*) $24\frac{1}{2}$ days

86. A can do a piece of work in 10 days; B in 15 days. They work for 5 days. The rest of the work was finished by C in 2 days. If they get ₹ 1500 for the whole work, the daily wages of B and C are (M.A.T., 2005)

(*a*) ₹ 150 (*b*) ₹ 225
(*c*) ₹ 250 (*d*) ₹ 300

87. The daily wages of a worker are ₹ 100. Five workers can do a work in 10 days. If you pay ₹ 20 more daily, they agree to do 25% more work daily. If the proposal is accepted, then the total amount that could be saved is

(*a*) ₹ 200 (*b*) ₹ 250
(*c*) ₹ 300 (*d*) ₹ 500

88. A and B together can complete a work in 12 days. A alone can complete it in 20 days. If B does the work only for half a day daily, then in how many days A and B together will complete the work ?

(*a*) 110 days (*b*) 11 days
(*c*) 15 days (*d*) 20 days

89. *A, B* and *C* completed a work costing ₹ 1800. *A* worked for 6 days, *B* for 4 days and *C* for 9 days. If their daily wages are in the ratio of 5 : 6 : 4, how much amount will be received by *A*? **(S.S.C., 2007)**

(*a*) ₹ 600 (*b*) ₹ 750
(*c*) ₹ 800 (*d*) ₹ 900

90. *A* and *B* can complete a piece of work in 12 and 18 days respectively. A begins to do the work and they work alternatively one at a time for one day each. The whole work will be completed in **(S.S.C., 2007)**

(*a*) $14\frac{1}{3}$ days (*b*) $15\frac{2}{3}$ days
(*c*) $16\frac{1}{3}$ days (*d*) $18\frac{2}{3}$ days

91. A, B and C can do a piece of work in 11 days, 20 days and 55 days respectively, working alone. How soon can the work be done if A is assisted by B and C on alternate days?

(*a*) 7 days (*b*) 8 days
(*c*) 9 days (*d*) 10 days

92. A, B and C can do a piece of work in 20, 30 and 60 days respectively. In how many days can A do the work if he is assisted by B and C on every third day?

(*a*) 12 days (*b*) 15 days
(*c*) 16 days (*d*) 18 days

93. A can do a piece of work in 90 days, B in 40 days and C in 12 days. They work for a day each in turn i.e., first day A does it alone, B does it the second day and C the third day. After that A does it for another day, and so on. After finishing the work they get ₹ 240. If the wages are divided in proportion to the work done by them, find what each will get. **(M.A.T., 2006)**

(*a*) A ₹ 24, B ₹ 54 and C ₹ 162
(*b*) A ₹ 22, B ₹ 50 and C ₹ 132
(*c*) A ₹ 26, B ₹ 52 and C ₹ 142
(*d*) A ₹ 20, B ₹ 44 and C ₹ 182

94. A and B can finish a work, working on alternate days, in 19 days, when A works on the first day. However, they can finish the work, working on alternate days, in $19\frac{5}{6}$ days, when B works on the first day. How many days does A alone take to finish the work?

(*a*) $11\frac{1}{2}$ days (*b*) 15 days
(*c*) 18 days (*d*) 21 days

95. A and B can separately do a piece of work in 20 and 15 days respectively. They worked together for 6 days, after which B was replaced by C. If the work was finished in next 4 days, then the number of days in which C alone could do the work will be

(*a*) 30 (*b*) 35
(*c*) 40 (*d*) 60

96. A, B and C can do a piece of work in 36, 54 and 72 days respectively. They started the work but A left 8 days before the completion of the work while B left 12 days before the completion. The number of days for which C worked is

(*a*) 4 (*b*) 8
(*c*) 12 (*d*) 24

97. Twenty women can do a work in sixteen days. Sixteen men can complete the same work in fifteen days. What is the ratio between the capacity of a man and a woman ?

(*a*) 3 : 4 (*b*) 4 : 3
(*c*) 5 : 3 (*d*) Data inadequate

98. 10 men can complete a piece of work in 15 days and 15 women can complete the same work in 12 days. If all the 10 men and 15 women work together, in how many days will the work get completed ?

(*a*) 6 (*b*) $6\frac{1}{3}$
(*c*) $6\frac{2}{3}$ (*d*) $7\frac{2}{3}$

99. A job can be done by 3 skilled worksmen in 20 days or by 5 boys in 30 days. How many days will they take if they work together? **(M.A.T., 2009)**

(*a*) 8 days (*b*) 10 days
(*c*) 11 days (*d*) 12 days

100. Five men are working to complete a work in 15 days. After five days 10 women are accompanied by them to complete the work in next 5 days. If the work is to be done by women only, then in how many days could the work be over if 10 women have started it ? **(Bank Recruitment, 2007)**

(*a*) 10 days (*b*) 12 days
(*c*) 15 days (*d*) 18 days

101. A contractor undertakes to do a piece of work in 40 days. He engages 100 men at the beginning and 100 more after 35 days and completes the work in stipulated time. If he had not engaged the additional men, how many days behind the schedule the work should have been finished? **(G.B.O., 2007)**

(*a*) 5 (*b*) 6
(*c*) 7 (*d*) 8

102. Seven men can complete a work in 12 days. They started the work and after 5 days, two men left. In how many days will the work be completed by the remaining men ?

(*a*) 5 (*b*) 6
(*c*) 7 (*d*) 8
(*e*) None of these

103. 12 men complete a work in 9 days. After they have worked for 6 days, 6 more men join them. How many days will they take to complete the remaining work ?

(*a*) 2 days (*b*) 3 days
(*c*) 4 days (*d*) 5 days
(*e*) None of these

104. Three men, four women and six children can complete a work in seven days. A woman does double the work a man does and a child does half the work a man does. How many women alone can complete this work in 7 days ?

(*a*) 7 (*b*) 8
(*c*) 12 (*d*) Cannot be determined
(*e*) None of these

105. A man, a woman and a boy can complete a job in 3, 4 and 12 days respectively. How many boys must assist 1 man and 1 woman to complete the job in $\frac{1}{4}$ of a day ?

(*a*) 1 (*b*) 4
(*c*) 19 (*d*) 41

106. 10 men and 15 women together can complete a work in 6 days. It takes 100 days for one man alone to complete the same work. How many days will be required for one woman alone to complete the same work ?

(*a*) 90 (*b*) 125
(*c*) 145 (*d*) 150
(*e*) None of these

107. A child can do a piece of work 15 hours slower than a woman. The child works for 18 hours on the job and then the woman takes charge for 6 hours. In this manner, $\frac{3}{5}$ of the work can be completed. To complete the job now, how much time will the woman take? **(M.A.T., 2005)**

(*a*) 12 hours (*b*) 1 hours
(*c*) 24 hours (*d*) 3 hours

108. A group of workers having eual efficiency can complete a job in 4 days. But itso happened that every alternate day starting fror the second day, 3 workers are withdrawn from ie job and every alternate day starting from the thid day, 2 workers are added to the group. If it nowtakes 7 days to complete the job, find the numberof workers who started the job.

(*a*) 4 (*b*) 5
(*c*) 6 (*d*) 8

109. A man, a woman and a boy can do piece of work in 6, 9 and 18 days respectively. Hw many boys must assist one man and one womano do the work in 1 day? **(N.M.A.T., 2006)**

(*a*) 5 (*b*) 6
(*c*) 9 (*d*) 13

110. If 3 men or 9 boys can finish a piee of work in 21 days, in how many days can 5 me and 6 boys together do the same piece of work? **(Bank Reuitment, 2010)**

(*a*) 8 days (*b*) 12 days
(*c*) 14 days (*d*) Cannot bdetermined
(*e*) None of these

111. If 2 men or 6 women or 4 boys can finis a work in 99 days, how many days will one man, ne woman and one boy together take to finish the sme work? **(Bank Recrutment, 2010)**

(*a*) 44 days (*b*) 54 days
(*c*) 64 days (*d*) 104 days
(*e*) None of these

112. 8 men can complete a piece of work in 0 days. 8 women can complete the same work in 3 days. In how many days will 5 men and 8 womei together complete the same work? **(BankP.O., 2010)**

(*a*) 10 days (*b*) 12 days
(*c*) 14 days (*d*) 16 days
(*e*) None of these

113. 18 men can complete a piece of work in 63days. 9 women take 189 days to complete the sane piece of work. How many days will 4 men, 9 wonen and 12 children together take to complete the piece of work if 7 children alone can complete the piece of work in 486 days? **(I.R.M.A., 2007)**

(*a*) 54 (*b*) 63
(*c*) 76 (*d*) 81
(*e*) None of these

114. 16 men can fiish a work in 24 days and 48 boys can finish the ame work in 16 days. 12 men started the work andafter 4 days 12 boys joined them. In how many d*a*s can they finish the remaining work? **(R.R.B., 2008)**

(*a*) 6 (*b*) 12
(*c*) 16 (*d*) None of these

115. 12 men can omplete a piece of work in 4 days, while 15 women an complete the same work in 4 days. 6 men star working on the job and after working for 2 days, ll of them stopped working. How many women sbuld be put on the job to complete the remainingwork, if it is to be completed in 3 days?

(*a*) 15 (*b*) 18
(*c*) 22 (*d*) Data inadequate
(*e*) None of these

116. Twelve hildren take sixteen days to complete a work wich can be completed by eight adults in twelve dys. Sixteen adults started working and after three d*a*s ten adults left and four children joined them. How many days will they take to complete the remining work ?

(*a*) 3 (*b*) 4
(*c*) 6 (*d*) 8
(*e*) Noe of these

117. Sixteei men can complete a work in twelve days. Twen*t*-four children can complete the same work in eigteen days. Twelve men and eight children startel working and after eight days three more childen joined them. How many days will they now ake to complete the remaining work ?

(*a*) 2 lays (*b*) 4 days
(*c*) 6 lays (*d*) 8 days
(*e*) None of these

118. Twety-four men can complete a work in sixteen days Thirty-two women can complete the same wor in twenty-four days. Sixteen men and sixteen wonen started working and worked for twelve days. Hov many more men are to be added to complete theremaining work in 2 days ?

(*a*)16 (*b*) 24
(*c*)36 (*d*) 48
(*e*)None of these

119. 5 men and 2 boys working together can do four tines as much work as a man and a boy. Working capacities of a man and a boy are in the ratio :

(*a*) 1 : 2 (*b*) 2 : 1
(*c*) 1 : 3 (*d*) 3 : 1

120. If 12 mn and 16 boys can do a piece of work in 5 days; 1 men and 24 boys can do it in 4 days, then the ratio of the daily work done by a man to that of a boy is

(*a*) 2 : 1 (*b*) 3 : 1
(*c*) 3 : 2 (*d*) 5 : 4

121. 4 men and 6 women can complete a work in 8 days, while 3 men and 7 women can complete it in 10 days. In how many days will 10 women complete it ?

(*a*) 35 (*b*) 40
(*c*) 45 (*d*) 50

122. 4 men and 10 women were put on a work. They completed $\frac{1}{3}$ of the work in 4 days. After this 2 men and 2 women were increased. They completed $\frac{2}{9}$ more of the work in 2 days. If the remaining work is to be completed in 3 days, then how many more women must be increased? **(M.A.T., 2006)**

(*a*) 8 (*b*) 32
(*c*) 50 (*d*) 55

123. One man, 3 women and 4 boys can do a piece of work in 96 hours, 2 men and 8 boys can do it in 80 hours, 2 men and 3 women can do it in 120 hours. 5 men and 12 boys can do it in :

(*a*) $39\frac{1}{11}$ hours (*b*) $42\frac{7}{11}$ hours
(*c*) $43\frac{7}{11}$ hours (*d*) 44 hours

124. If 6 men and 8 boys can do a piece of work in 10 days while 26 men and 48 boys can do the same in 2 days, the time taken by 15 men and 20 boys in doing the same type of work will be

(*a*) 4 days (*b*) 5 days
(*c*) 6 days (*d*) 7 days

125. If 5 men and 3 women can reap 18 acre of crop in 4 days; 3 men and 2 women can reap 22 acre of crop in 8 days, then how many men are required to join 21 women to reap 54 acre of crop in 6 days? **(M.C.A., 2005)**

(*a*) 5 (*b*) 6
(*c*) 10 (*d*) 12

126. 25 men with 10 boys can do in 6 days as much work as 21 men with 30 boys can do in 5 days. How many boys must help 40 men to do the same work in 4 days? **(R.R.B., 2008)**

(*a*) 5 (*b*) 10
(*c*) 20 (*d*) 40

127. 40 men can complete a piece of work in 15 days. 20 more men join them after 5 days they start doing work. How many days will be required by them to finish the remaining work? **[ESIC—UDC, Exam 2016]**

(a) $7\frac{2}{3}$ days (b) $6\frac{1}{5}$ days

(c) $8\frac{1}{4}$ days (d) $6\frac{2}{3}$ days

128. 12 men can do a piece of work in 24 days. How many days are needed to complete the work, if 8 men do this work? **[Indian Railway Gr. 'D' Exam, 2014]**

(a) 28 (b) 36

(c) 48 (d) 52

129. A can do in one day three times the work done by B in one day. They together finish $\frac{2}{5}$ of the work in 9 days. The number of days by which B can do the work alone is **[SSC—CHSL (10+2) Exam , 2015]**

(a) 90 days (b) 120 days

(c) 100 days (d) 30 days

130. A, B and C can complete a piece of work in 24, 5 and 12 days respectively. Working together, they will complete the same work in

[SSC—CHSL (10+2) Exam, 2015]

(a) $\frac{7}{24}$ days (b) $3\frac{3}{7}$ days

(c) 4 days (d) $3\frac{1}{13}$ days

131. X can do a piece of work in 24 days. When he had worked for 4 days, Y joined him. If complete work was finished in 16 days, Y can alone finish that work in **[SSC—CHSL (10+2) Exam, 2015]**

(a) 18 days (b) 27 days

(c) 36 days (d) 42 days

132. 6 men can complete a piece of work in 12 days, 8 women can complete the same piece of work in 18 days and 18 children can do it in 10 days. 4 men, 12 women and 20 children do the work for 2 days. If the remaining work be completed by men only in 1 day, how many men will be required?

[RBI Officer Gr. 'B' (Phase-1) Online Exam, 2015]

(a) 36 (b) 24

(c) 18 (d) Cannot be determined

133. 16 men can finish a piece of work in 49 days. 14 men started working and in 8 days they could finish certain amount of work. If it is required to finish the remaining work in 24 days. How many more men should be added to the existing workforce?

[IBPS—RRB Office Assistant (Online) Exam, 2015]

(a) 21 (b) 28

(c) 16 (d) 14

ANSWERS

1. (b)	2. (a)	3. (a)	4. (c)	5. (c)	6. (d)	7. (b)	8. (a)	9. (e)	10. (a)
11. (c)	12. (b)	13. (b)	14. (c)	15. (c)	16. (c)	17. (c)	18. (d)	19. (b)	20. (a)
21. (a)	22. (b)	23. (b)	24. (b)	25. (a)	26. (c)	27. (c)	28. (d)	29. (c)	30. (c)
31. (a)	32. (a)	33. (d)	34. (c)	35. (c)	36. (b)	37. (a)	38. (d)	39. (c)	40. (c)
41. (c)	42. (a)	43. (a)	44. (a)	45. (a)	46. (b)	47. (b)	48. (c)	49. (b)	50. (d)
51. (b)	52. (a)	53. (b)	54. (d)	55. (b)	56. (c)	57. (a)	58. (c)	59. (b)	60. (d)
61. (a)	62. (b)	63. (d)	64. (d)	65. (d)	66. (a)	67. (c)	68. (c)	69. (c)	70. (b)
71. (b)	72. (c)	73. (a)	74. (c)	75. (c)	76. (c)	77. (a)	78. (c)	79. (a)	80. (b)
81. (b)	82. (d)	83. (a)	84. (b)	85. (a)	86. (b)	87. (a)	88. (c)	89. (a)	90. (a)
91. (b)	92. (b)	93. (a)	94. (a)	95. (c)	96. (d)	97. (b)	98. (c)	99. (d)	100. (c)
101. (a)	102. (e)	103. (a)	104. (a)	105. (d)	106. (e)	107. (a)	108. (c)	109. (d)	110. (e)
111. (e)	112. (d)	113. (d)	114. (d)	115. (a)	116. (c)	117. (b)	118. (b)	119. (b)	120. (a)
121. (b)	122. (a)	123. (c)	124. (a)	125. (a)	126. (b)	127. (d)	128. (b)	129. (a)	130. (d)
131. (c)	132. (a)	133. (d)							

SOLUTIONS

1. Ayesha's 1 day's work = $\frac{1}{16}$. Amita's 1 day's work = $\frac{1}{8}$.

(Ayesha + Amita)'s 1 day's work = $\left(\frac{1}{16}+\frac{1}{8}\right)=\frac{3}{16}$.

$\therefore$ Both together can complete the work in $\frac{16}{3}=5\frac{1}{3}$ days.

2. Required average

$$= \frac{\left(\frac{1}{4}+\frac{1}{5}+\frac{1}{6}+\frac{1}{10}+\frac{1}{12}\right)}{5}=\left(\frac{48}{60}\times\frac{1}{5}\right)=\frac{4}{25}=0.16.$$

3. A's 1 day's work = $\frac{1}{18}$ and B's 1 day's work = $\frac{1}{9}$.

$\therefore$ (A + B)'s 1 day's work = $\left(\frac{1}{18}+\frac{1}{9}\right)=\frac{1}{6}$.

4. 1 minute's work of both the punctures = $\left(\frac{1}{9}+\frac{1}{6}\right)=\frac{5}{18}$.

So, both the punctures will make the tyre flat in $\frac{18}{5}=3\frac{3}{5}$ min.

5. Number of pairs knit by A and B together in 1 day $=\left(\frac{1}{3}+\frac{1}{9}\right)=\frac{4}{9}$.

$\therefore$ Required number of days $=\left(2\div\frac{4}{9}\right)=\left(2\times\frac{9}{4}\right)=\frac{9}{2}=4\frac{1}{2}$.

6. (A + B)'s 1 day's work = $\left(\frac{1}{6}+\frac{1}{12}\right)=\frac{3}{12}=\frac{1}{4}$.

$\therefore$ Both A and B together can complete the work in 4 days.

Part of the work done by A = $\left(\frac{1}{6}\times 4\right)=\frac{2}{3}$.

7. A's share : B's share = Ratio of their 1 day's work $=\frac{1}{8}:\frac{1}{12}=3:2$.

$\therefore$ B's share = ₹$\left(200\times\frac{2}{5}\right)$ = ₹ 80.

8. Number of pages typed by George in 1 hour = $\frac{50}{8}=\frac{25}{4}$.

Number of pages typed by Sonia in 1 hour = $\frac{50}{6}=\frac{25}{3}$.

Number of pages typed by George and Sonia together in 1 hour = $\left(\frac{25}{4}+\frac{25}{3}\right)=\left(\frac{75+100}{12}\right)=\frac{175}{12}$.

$\therefore$ Required time = $\left(100\div\frac{175}{12}\right)$ hrs $=\left(\frac{100\times 12}{175}\right)$ hrs

$=\frac{48}{7}$ hrs $=6\frac{6}{7}$ hrs.

9. A's 1 day's work = $\frac{1}{T+3}$;

B's 1 day's work = $\frac{1}{T+12}$.

(A + B)'s 1 day's work = $\frac{1}{T}$.

$\therefore \frac{1}{T+3}+\frac{1}{T+12}=\frac{1}{T} \Rightarrow \frac{2T+15}{(T+3)(T+12)}=\frac{1}{T}$

$\Rightarrow 2T^2 + 15T = T^2 + 15T + 36$

$\Rightarrow T^2 = 36 \Rightarrow T = 6$.

10. Reena's 1 hour's work = $\frac{1}{6}$;

Aastha's 1 hour's work = $\frac{1}{4}$;

Shloka's 1 hour's work = $\frac{1}{12}$.

(Reena + Aastha + Shloka)'s 1 hour's work $=\frac{1}{4}+\frac{1}{6}+\frac{1}{12}=\frac{6}{12}=\frac{1}{2}$.

Hence, Reena, Aastha and Shloka together take 2 hours to complete the work.

11. 1 day's work of the three persons = $\left(\frac{1}{15}+\frac{1}{20}+\frac{1}{25}\right)=\frac{47}{300}$.

So, all the three together will complete the work in $\frac{300}{47}\simeq 6.4$ days.

12. Amit's 1 day's work = $\left(\frac{1}{4}-\frac{1}{6}\right)=\frac{1}{12}$.

$\therefore$ Amit alone can plough the field in 12 days.

13. Length of cloth produced by A and B in 10 hrs = 3,00,000 m.

Length of cloth produced by B in 10 hrs = $\left(\frac{300000}{15}\times 10\right)$ m = 200000 m.

$\therefore$ Length of cloth produced by A in 10 hrs = (300000 – 200000) m = 100000 m.

14. (X + Y)'s 1 day's work = $\left(\frac{1}{16}+\frac{1}{16}\right)=\frac{2}{16}=\frac{1}{8}$.

Z's 1 day's work = (X + Y + Z)'s 1 day's work – (X + Y)'s 1 day's work = $\frac{1}{6}-\frac{1}{8}=\frac{1}{24}$.

$\therefore$ Z alone can finish the work in 24 days.

15. (A + B + C)'s 1 day's work = $\frac{1}{4}$,

A's 1 day's work = $\frac{1}{16}$,

B's 1 day's work = $\frac{1}{12}$.

$\therefore$ C's 1 day's work = $\frac{1}{4}-\left(\frac{1}{16}+\frac{1}{12}\right)=\left(\frac{1}{4}-\frac{7}{48}\right)=\frac{5}{48}$.

So, C alone can do the work in $\frac{48}{5}=9\frac{3}{5}$ days.

16. Whole work will be done by A in (5 × 3) = 15 days.

Whole work will be done by B in $\left(10\times\frac{5}{2}\right)$ = 25 days.

A's 1 day's work = $\frac{1}{15}$; B's 1 day's work = $\frac{1}{25}$.

(A + B)'s 1 day's work = $\left(\frac{1}{15}+\frac{1}{25}\right)=\frac{16}{150}=\frac{8}{75}$.

$\therefore$ A and B together can complete the work in $\frac{75}{8}=9\frac{3}{8}$ days.

17. Whole work will be done by X in (10 × 4) = 40 days.

Whole work will be done by Y in $\left(40\times\frac{100}{40}\right)$ = 100 days.

Whole work will be done by Z in (13 × 3) = 39 days.

$\therefore$ Z will complete the work first.

18. Ratio of digging speeds of man and boy = 8 : 5.
Ratio of times taken by man and boy = 5 : 8.
Suppose the man takes $5x$ days while the boy takes $8x$ days to complete the work alone.

Then, $\frac{1}{5x}+\frac{1}{8x}=\frac{1}{40} \Rightarrow \frac{13}{40x}=\frac{1}{40} \Rightarrow x=13.$

Hence, time taken by the boy to complete the work alone = (8 × 13) days = 104 days.

19. Suppose A, B and C take x, $\frac{x}{2}$ and $\frac{x}{3}$ days respectively to finish the work.

Then, $\left(\frac{1}{x}+\frac{2}{x}+\frac{3}{x}\right)=\frac{1}{2} \Rightarrow \frac{6}{x}=\frac{1}{2} \Rightarrow x=12.$

So, B takes 6 days to finish the work.

20. C's 1 day's work = $\frac{1}{7}$; B's 1 day's work = $\left(\frac{1}{2}\times\frac{1}{7}\right)=\frac{1}{14}$;

A's 1 day's work = $\left(\frac{1}{2}\times\frac{1}{14}\right)=\frac{1}{28}.$

$\therefore$ (A + B + C)'s 1 day's work = $\left(\frac{1}{28}+\frac{1}{14}+\frac{1}{7}\right)=\frac{7}{28}=\frac{1}{4}.$

Hence, A, B and C together can complete the work in 4 days.

21. Number of rosogollas eaten by Rosa in 1 minute = $\frac{32}{60}$.

Number of rosogollas eaten by Lila in 1 minute = $\frac{32}{180}$.

Number of rosogollas eaten by Rosa and Lila together in 1 minute = $\left(\frac{32}{60}+\frac{32}{180}\right)=\frac{128}{180}.$

$\therefore$ Required time = $\left(32\div\frac{128}{180}\right)=\left(\frac{32\times180}{128}\right)$ min = 45 min.

22. Baggage delivered by first belt in 1 min = $\left(\frac{3}{5}\right)$ tons.

Baggage delivered by second belt in 1 min = $\left(\frac{1}{2}\right)$ ton.

Baggage delivered by both belts in 1 min

$= \left(\frac{3}{5}+\frac{1}{2}\right)$ ton $=\frac{11}{10}$ tons.

$\therefore$ Required time = $\left(33\div\frac{11}{10}\right)$ min $=\left(\frac{33\times10}{11}\right)$ min

= 30 min.

23. Number of envelopes addressed by first machine in 1 min = $\frac{500}{8}$.

Number of envelopes addressed by second machine in 1 min = $\frac{500}{x}$.

Number of envelopes addressed by both machines in 1 min = $\frac{500}{2}$.

$\therefore \frac{500}{8}+\frac{500}{x}=\frac{500}{2} \Rightarrow \frac{1}{8}+\frac{1}{x}=\frac{1}{2}.$

24. Number of units processed by computer A in 1 min $=\frac{1}{3}$.

Number of units processed by computer B in 1 min = $\frac{1}{5}$.

Number of units processed by A, B and C in 1 min

$=\frac{14\times3}{60}=\frac{7}{10}.$

$\therefore$ Number of units processed by computer C in 1 min

$=\frac{7}{10}-\left(\frac{1}{3}+\frac{1}{5}\right)=\frac{7}{10}-\frac{8}{15}=\frac{5}{30}=\frac{1}{6}.$

Hence, computer C takes 6 minutes to process one input alone.

25. Time taken by Bob to type 20 pages = 2 hrs = 120 min.
Time taken by David to type 20 pages = 1 hr 40 min = 100 min.

Time taken by Bob to type 1 page = $\left(\frac{120}{20}\right)$ min = 6 min.

Time taken by David to type 1 page = $\left(\frac{100}{20}\right)$ min = 5 min.

Bob's 1 minute's work = $\frac{1}{6}$;

David's 1 minute's work = $\frac{1}{5}$.

$\therefore$ Ratio of division of work = $\frac{1}{6}:\frac{1}{5}=5:6.$

Hence, number of pages to be typed by Bob

$=\left(77\times\frac{5}{11}\right)=35.$

26. Let the number of pages typed in one hour by P, Q and R be x, y and z respectively.

Then, $x+y+z=\frac{216}{4}$

$\Rightarrow x+y+z=54$ ...(*i*)

$z-y=y-x$

$\Rightarrow 2y=x+z$ ...(*ii*)

$5z=7x$

$\Rightarrow x=\frac{5}{7}z$ ...(*iii*)

Solving (*i*), (*ii*) and (*iii*), we get $x=15$, $y=18$, $z=21$.

27. Number of pages typed by Ronald in 1 hour = $\frac{32}{6}=\frac{16}{3}$.

Number of pages typed by Elan in 1 hour = $\frac{40}{5}=8$.

Number of pages typed by both in 1 hour = $\left(\frac{16}{3}+8\right)=\frac{40}{3}$.

$\therefore$ Time taken by both to type 110 pages

$=\left(110\times\frac{3}{40}\right)$ hrs $=8\frac{1}{4}$ hrs = 8 hrs 15 min.

28. Length of cloth produced in 1 hour

$=\left(\frac{pq}{r}\times60\right)$ m $=\left(\frac{60\,pq}{r}\right)$ m.

$\therefore$ Required time $= \left(20000 \div \dfrac{60\,pq}{r}\right)$ hrs $= \left(\dfrac{20000\,r}{60\,pq}\right)$ hrs.

29. Let A and B together take x hours to complete the work. Then, A alone takes $(x + 8)$ hrs and B alone takes $\left(x+\dfrac{9}{2}\right)$ hrs to complete the work.

Then, $\dfrac{1}{(x+8)}+\dfrac{1}{\left(x+\dfrac{9}{2}\right)}=\dfrac{1}{x}$

$\Rightarrow \dfrac{1}{(x+8)}+\dfrac{2}{(2x+9)}=\dfrac{1}{x}$

$\Rightarrow x(4x + 25) = (x + 8)(2x + 9)$

$\Rightarrow 2x^2 = 72 \Rightarrow x^2 = 36 \Rightarrow x = 6.$

30. Let the time taken by the three friends together to do the work be x hours.

Then, time taken by Anne alone = $(x + 6)$ hrs;
time taken by Bob alone = $(x + 1)$ hrs;
time taken by Chris alone = $2x$ hrs.

$\therefore \dfrac{1}{x+6}+\dfrac{1}{x+1}+\dfrac{1}{2x}=\dfrac{1}{x}$

$\Rightarrow \dfrac{2x(x+1)+2x(x+6)+(x+1)(x+6)}{2x(x+6)(x+1)}=\dfrac{1}{x}$

$\Rightarrow 5x^2 + 21x + 6 = 2(x^2 + 7x + 6)$

$\Rightarrow 3x^2 + 7x - 6 = 0 \Rightarrow (x + 3)(3x - 2) = 0 \Rightarrow x = \dfrac{2}{3}$ $[\because x \neq -3]$

$\therefore$ Required time $= \dfrac{2}{3}$ hrs $= \left(\dfrac{2}{3}\times 60\right)$ min $= 40$ min.

31. 3 (B's 1 day's work) = (A + C)'s 1 day's work

$\Rightarrow$ 4 (B's 1 day's work) = (A + B + C)'s 1 day's work

$\Rightarrow$ B's 1 day's work $= \left(\dfrac{1}{4}\times\dfrac{1}{10}\right)=\dfrac{1}{40}$

2 (C's 1 day's work) = (A + B)'s 1 day's work

$\Rightarrow$ 3 (C's 1 day's work) = (A + B + C)'s 1 day's work

$\Rightarrow$ C's 1 day's work $= \left(\dfrac{1}{3}\times\dfrac{1}{10}\right)=\dfrac{1}{30}.$

$\therefore$ A's 1 day's work = (A + B + C)'s 1 day's work – (B + C)'s 1 day's work

$= \dfrac{1}{10}-\left(\dfrac{1}{40}+\dfrac{1}{30}\right)=\dfrac{1}{10}-\dfrac{7}{120}=\dfrac{5}{120}=\dfrac{1}{24}.$

Hence, A alone would take 24 days to complete the work.

32. P can complete the work in (12×8) hrs = 96 hrs.
Q can complete the work in (8×10) hrs = 80 hrs.

$\therefore$ P's 1 hour's work $= \dfrac{1}{96}$

and Q's 1 hour's work $= \dfrac{1}{80}$.

(P + Q)'s 1 hour's work $= \left(\dfrac{1}{96}+\dfrac{1}{80}\right)=\dfrac{11}{480}.$

So, both P and Q will finish the work in $\left(\dfrac{480}{11}\right)$ hrs.

$\therefore$ Number of days of 8 hours each

$= \left(\dfrac{480}{11}\times\dfrac{1}{8}\right)=\dfrac{60}{11}$ days $= 5\dfrac{5}{11}$ days.

33. (A + B)'s 1 day's work $= \dfrac{1}{12}$;

(B + C)'s 1 day's work $= \dfrac{1}{8}$;

(A + C)'s 1 day's work $= \dfrac{1}{16}$.

Adding, we get: 2 (A + B + C)'s 1 day's work

$= \left(\dfrac{1}{12}+\dfrac{1}{8}+\dfrac{1}{16}\right)=\dfrac{13}{48}.$

$\therefore$ (A + B + C)'s 1 day's work $= \dfrac{13}{96}.$

So, A, B and C together can complete the work in $\dfrac{96}{13}=7\dfrac{5}{13}$ days.

34. A's 1 hour's work $= \dfrac{1}{4}$;

(B + C)'s 1 hour's work $= \dfrac{1}{3}$;

(A + C)'s 1 hour's work $= \dfrac{1}{2}$.

(A + B + C)'s 1 hour's work $= \dfrac{1}{4}+\dfrac{1}{3}=\dfrac{7}{12}.$

$\therefore$ B's 1 hour's work = (A + B + C)'s 1 hour's work – (A + C)'s 1 hour's work $= \dfrac{7}{12}-\dfrac{1}{2}=\dfrac{1}{12}.$

So, B alone can complete the work in 12 hours.

35. (A + B + C)'s 1 day's work $= \dfrac{1}{6}$;

(A + B)'s 1 day's work $= \dfrac{1}{8}$;

(B + C)'s 1 day's work $= \dfrac{1}{12}$.

$\therefore$ (A + C)'s 1 day's work

$= \left(2\times\dfrac{1}{6}\right)-\left(\dfrac{1}{8}+\dfrac{1}{12}\right)=\left(\dfrac{1}{3}-\dfrac{5}{24}\right)=\dfrac{3}{24}=\dfrac{1}{8}.$

So, A and C together will do the work in 8 days.

36. (A + B)'s 1 day's work $= \dfrac{1}{2}$;

(B + C)'s 1 day's work $= \dfrac{1}{4}$;

(A + C)'s 1 day's work $= \dfrac{5}{12}$.

Adding, we get: 2 (A + B + C)'s 1 day's work

$= \left(\dfrac{1}{2}+\dfrac{1}{4}+\dfrac{5}{12}\right)=\dfrac{14}{12}=\dfrac{7}{6}$

$\Rightarrow$ (A + B + C)'s 1 day's work $= \dfrac{7}{12}.$

So, A's 1 day's work $= \left(\dfrac{7}{12}-\dfrac{1}{4}\right)=\dfrac{4}{12}=\dfrac{1}{3}.$

$\therefore$ A alone can do the work in 3 days.

37. (A + B)'s 1 day's work $= \frac{1}{5}$;

(B + C)'s 1 day's work $= \frac{1}{7}$;

(A + C)'s 1 day's work $= \frac{1}{4}$.

Adding, we get : 2 (A + B + C)'s 1 day's work

$= \left(\frac{1}{5}+\frac{1}{7}+\frac{1}{4}\right) = \frac{83}{140}$.

(A + B + C)'s 1 day's work $= \frac{83}{280}$.

A's 1 day's work $= \left(\frac{83}{280}-\frac{1}{7}\right) = \frac{43}{280}$;

B's 1 day's work $= \left(\frac{83}{280}-\frac{1}{4}\right) = \frac{13}{280}$;

C's 1 day's work $= \left(\frac{83}{280}-\frac{1}{5}\right) = \frac{27}{280}$.

Thus time taken by A, B, C is $\frac{280}{43}$ days, $\frac{280}{13}$ days, $\frac{280}{27}$ days respectively.

Clearly, the time taken by A is least.

38. (A + B)'s 1 day's work $= \frac{1}{12}$;

(B + C)'s 1 day's work $= \frac{1}{8}$;

(A + C)'s 1 day's work $= \frac{1}{6}$.

[(A + B)'s 1 day's work + (B + C)'s 1 day's work] – (A + C)'s 1 day's work $= \frac{1}{12}+\frac{1}{8}-\frac{1}{6} = \frac{1}{24}$.

$\Rightarrow$ 2 (B's 1 day's work) $= \frac{1}{24}$

$\Rightarrow$ B's 1 day's work $= \frac{1}{48}$.

Hence, *B* alone can do the work in 48 days.

39. (A + B)'s 1 day's work $= \frac{1}{25}$; C's 1 day's work $= \frac{1}{35}$.

(A + B + C)'s 1 day's work $= \left(\frac{1}{25}+\frac{1}{35}\right) = \frac{12}{175}$. ...(*i*)

Also, A's 1 day's work = (B + C)'s 1 day's work. ...(*ii*)

From (*i*) and (*ii*), we get: 2 × (A's 1 day's work) $= \frac{12}{175}$

$\Rightarrow$ A's 1 day's work $= \frac{6}{175}$.

$\therefore$ B's 1 day's work $= \left(\frac{1}{25}-\frac{6}{175}\right) = \frac{1}{175}$.

40. Suppose Uma takes x days to complete a work.

Then, Madhu takes $2x$ days to complete the work.

Uma's 1 day's work $= \frac{1}{x}$;

Madhu's 1 day's work $= \frac{1}{2x}$.

Rahul's 1 day's work = (Madhu + Uma)'s 1 day's work

$= \frac{1}{2x}+\frac{1}{x} = \frac{3}{2x}$.

(Rahul + Madhu + Uma)'s 1 day's work

$= \frac{3}{2x}+\frac{1}{2x}+\frac{1}{x} = \frac{6}{2x} = \frac{3}{x}$.

$\therefore \quad \frac{3}{x} = \frac{1}{6} \Rightarrow x = 18.$

Hence, Madhu takes (2 × 18) = 36 days to complete the work.

41. Suppose A takes x days to do the job alone.

Then, B takes $(x - 5)$ days and C takes $(x - 9)$ days.

(A + B)'s 1 day's work = C's 1 day's work

$\Rightarrow \frac{1}{x}+\left(\frac{1}{x-5}\right) = \frac{1}{x-9} \Rightarrow \frac{(x-5)+x}{x(x-5)} = \frac{1}{(x-9)}$

$\Rightarrow (2x-5)(x-9) = x(x-5)$

$\Rightarrow 2x^2 - 23x + 45 = x^2 - 5x$

$\Rightarrow x^2 - 18x + 45 = 0 \Rightarrow (x-3)(x-15) = 0 \Rightarrow x = 15.$ $[\because x \neq 3]$

Hence, A alone would take 15 days to do the job.

42. Ratio of rates of working of A and B = 2 : 1.

So, ratio of times taken = 1 : 2.

$\therefore$ A's 1 day's work $= \frac{1}{6}$; B's 1 day's work $= \frac{1}{12}$.

(A + B)'s 1 day's work $= \left(\frac{1}{6}+\frac{1}{12}\right) = \frac{3}{12} = \frac{1}{4}$.

So, A and B together can finish the work in 4 days.

43. (A's 1 day's work) : (B's 1 day's work) = 2 : 1.

(A + B)'s 1 day's work $= \frac{1}{18}$.

$\therefore$ A's 1 day's work $= \left(\frac{1}{18}\times\frac{2}{3}\right) = \frac{1}{27}$.

Hence, *A* alone can finish the work in 27 days.

44. Total time taken by David and Michael together

= 4 days 19 hrs 12 min = 4 days $19\frac{1}{5}$ hrs

$= 4 \text{ days} + \left(\frac{96}{5}\times\frac{1}{24}\right) \text{days} = 4\frac{4}{5} \text{ days} = \frac{24}{5} \text{ days}.$

(David + Michael)'s 1 day's work $= \frac{5}{24}$.

(David's 1 day's work) : (Michael's 1 day's work)

$= \frac{2}{3} : 1 = 2 : 3.$

$\therefore$ Michael's 1 day's work $= \left(\frac{5}{24}\times\frac{3}{5}\right) = \frac{1}{8}$.

Hence, Michael alone can finish the job in 8 days.

45. Ratio of times taken by A and B = 1 : 3.

If difference of time is 2 days, B takes 3 days.

If difference of time is 60 days, B takes $\left(\frac{3}{2}\times 60\right) = 90$ days.

So, A takes 30 days to do the work.

A's 1 day's work = $\frac{1}{30}$; B's 1 day's work = $\frac{1}{90}$.

(A + B)'s 1 day's work = $\left(\frac{1}{30}+\frac{1}{90}\right)=\frac{4}{90}=\frac{2}{45}$.

$\therefore$ A and B together can do the work in $\frac{45}{2}=22\frac{1}{2}$ days.

46. (A's 1 day's work) : (B's 1 day's work) = $\frac{7}{4}:1=7:4$.

Let A's and B's 1 day's work be $7x$ and $4x$ respectively.

Then, $7x + 4x = \frac{1}{7} \Rightarrow 11x=\frac{1}{7} \Rightarrow x=\frac{1}{77}$.

$\therefore$ A's 1 day's work = $\left(\frac{1}{77}\times 7\right)=\frac{1}{11}$.

Hence, A alone can do the job in 11 days.

47. Ratio of times taken by Kamal and Bimal = 150 : 100 = 3 : 2

Suppose Bimal takes x days to do the work.

$3 : 2 :: 15 : x \Rightarrow x = \left(\frac{2\times 15}{3}\right) \Rightarrow x = 10$ days.

48. Ratio of times taken by A and B = 100 : 80 = 5 : 4.

Suppose B takes x hours to do the work.

$5 : 4 :: \frac{15}{2} : x \Rightarrow x=\left(\frac{4\times 15}{2\times 5}\right) \Rightarrow x = 6$ hours.

49. Ratio of times taken by A and B = 100 : 130 = 10 : 13.

Suppose B takes x days to do the work.

Then, $10:13::23:x \Rightarrow x=\left(\frac{23\times 13}{10}\right) \Rightarrow x=\frac{299}{10}$.

A's 1 day's work = $\frac{1}{23}$; B's 1 day's work = $\frac{10}{299}$.

(A + B)'s 1 day's work = $\left(\frac{1}{23}+\frac{10}{299}\right)=\frac{23}{299}=\frac{1}{13}$.

$\therefore$ A and B together can complete the job in 13 days.

50. Time taken by A alone to do the work = (10 × 8) hrs = 80 hrs.

Since B is two-thirds as efficient as A, so time taken by B to do the work

$=\left(80\times\frac{3}{2}\right)$ hrs = 120 hrs.

$\therefore$ Required time = $\left(\frac{120}{5}\right)$ days = 24 days.

51. Suppose B takes x days to do the work.

$\therefore$ A takes $\left(2\times\frac{1}{6}x\right)=\frac{1}{3}x$ days to do it.

(A + B)'s 1 day's work = $\frac{1}{10}$.

$\therefore \frac{1}{x}+\frac{3}{x}=\frac{1}{10} \Rightarrow \frac{4}{x}=\frac{1}{10} \Rightarrow x = 40.$

52. (A's 1 day's work) : (B's 1 day's work) = 150 : 100 = 3 : 2.

Let A's and B's 1 day's work be $3x$ and $2x$ respectively.

Then, C's 1 day's work = $\left(\frac{3x+2x}{2}\right)=\frac{5x}{2}$.

$\therefore \frac{5x}{2}=\frac{1}{40}$ or $x=\left(\frac{1}{40}\times\frac{2}{5}\right)=\frac{1}{100}$.

A's 1 day's work = $\frac{3}{100}$; B's 1 day's work = $\frac{1}{50}$;

C's 1 day's work = $\frac{1}{40}$.

(A + B + C)'s 1 day's work = $\left(\frac{3}{100}+\frac{1}{50}+\frac{1}{40}\right)=\frac{15}{200}=\frac{3}{40}$.

So, A, B and C together can do the work in $\frac{40}{3}=13\frac{1}{3}$ days.

53. Let A's 1 day's work = x and B's 1 day's work = y.

Then, $x+y=\frac{1}{5}$ and $2x+\frac{1}{3}y=\frac{1}{3}$.

Solving, we get : $x=\frac{4}{25}$ and $y=\frac{1}{25}$.

$\therefore$ A's 1 day's work = $\frac{4}{25}$.

So, A alone could complete the work in $\frac{25}{4}=6\frac{1}{4}$ days.

54. A's 1 day's work = $\frac{1}{15}$; B's 1 day's work = $\frac{1}{20}$.

(A + B)'s 1 day's work = $\left(\frac{1}{15}+\frac{1}{20}\right)=\frac{7}{60}$.

(A + B)'s 4 days' work = $\left(\frac{7}{60}\times 4\right)=\frac{7}{15}$.

$\therefore$ Remaining work = $\left(1-\frac{7}{15}\right)=\frac{8}{15}$.

55. B's 8 days' work = $\left(\frac{1}{10}\times 8\right)=\frac{4}{5}$;

Remaining work = $\left(1-\frac{4}{5}\right)=\frac{1}{5}$.

Now, $\frac{1}{15}$ work is done by A in 1 day.

$\therefore \frac{1}{5}$ work is done by A in $\left(15\times\frac{1}{5}\right)=3$ days.

56. (A + B)'s 1 day's work = $\left(\frac{1}{18}+\frac{1}{15}\right)=\frac{11}{90}$.

(A + B)'s 3 days' work = $\left(\frac{11}{90}\times 3\right)=\frac{11}{30}$.

Remaining work = $\left(1-\frac{11}{30}\right)=\frac{19}{30}$.

Now, $\frac{1}{15}$ work is done by B in 1 day.

$\therefore$ $\frac{19}{30}$ work will be done by B in $\left(15\times\frac{19}{30}\right)=\frac{19}{2}$ days

$= 9\frac{1}{2}$ days.

Hence, total time taken = $\left(3+9\frac{1}{2}\right)$ days $= 12\frac{1}{2}$ days.

57. (A + B + C)'s 1 day's work = $\left(\frac{1}{12}+\frac{1}{15}+\frac{1}{20}\right)=\frac{12}{60}=\frac{1}{5}$.

(A + B + C)'s 2 days' work = $\left(\frac{1}{5}\times 2\right)=\frac{2}{5}$.

Remaining work = $\left(1-\frac{2}{5}\right)=\frac{3}{5}$.

(A + B)'s 1 day's work = $\left(\frac{1}{12}+\frac{1}{15}\right)=\frac{9}{60}=\frac{3}{20}$.

Now, $\frac{3}{20}$ work is done by A and B in 1 day.

$\therefore$ $\frac{3}{5}$ work will be done by A and B in $\left(\frac{20}{3}\times\frac{3}{5}\right)=4$ days.

58. (B + C)'s 1 day's work = $\left(\frac{1}{20}+\frac{1}{30}\right)=\frac{5}{60}=\frac{1}{12}$.

(B + C)'s 2 day's work = $\left(\frac{1}{12}\times 2\right)=\frac{1}{6}$.

Remaining work = $\left(1-\frac{1}{6}\right)=\frac{5}{6}$.

$\frac{1}{18}$ work is done by A in 1 day.

$\frac{5}{6}$ work will be done by A in $\left(18\times\frac{5}{6}\right)$ = 15 days.

59. (A + C)'s 1 day's work = $\left(\frac{1}{10}+\frac{1}{20}\right)=\frac{3}{20}$.

(A + C)'s 2 days' work = $\left(\frac{3}{20}\times 2\right)=\frac{3}{10}$.

Remaining work = $\left(1-\frac{3}{10}\right)=\frac{7}{10}$.

(B + C)'s 1 day's work = $\left(\frac{1}{15}+\frac{1}{20}\right)=\frac{7}{60}$.

$\frac{7}{60}$ work is done by B and C in 1 day.

$\frac{7}{10}$ work will be done by B and C in $\left(\frac{60}{7}\times\frac{7}{10}\right)=6$ days.

Hence, total time taken = (2 + 6) days = 8 days.

60. (P + Q + R)'s 1 hour's work = $\left(\frac{1}{8}+\frac{1}{10}+\frac{1}{12}\right)=\frac{37}{120}$.

Work done by P, Q and R in 2 hours = $\left(\frac{37}{120}\times 2\right)=\frac{37}{60}$.

Remaining work = $\left(1-\frac{37}{60}\right)=\frac{23}{60}$.

(Q + R)'s 1 hour's work = $\left(\frac{1}{10}+\frac{1}{12}\right)=\frac{11}{60}$.

Now, $\frac{11}{60}$ work is done by Q and R in 1 hour.

So, $\frac{23}{60}$ work will be done by Q and R in $\left(\frac{60}{11}\times\frac{23}{60}\right)=\frac{23}{11}$ hours

≈ 2 hours.

So, the work will be finished approximately 2 hours after 11 a.m., *i.e.*, around 1 p.m.

61. 2 (A + B + C)'s 1 day's work = $\left(\frac{1}{30}+\frac{1}{24}+\frac{1}{20}\right)=\frac{15}{120}=\frac{1}{8}$.

$\Rightarrow$ (A + B + C)'s 1 day's work = $\frac{1}{16}$.

Work done by A, B and C in 10 days = $\frac{10}{16}=\frac{5}{8}$.

Remaining work = $\left(1-\frac{5}{8}\right)=\frac{3}{8}$.

A's 1 day's work = $\left(\frac{1}{16}-\frac{1}{24}\right)=\frac{1}{48}$.

Now, $\frac{1}{48}$ work is done by A in 1 day.

So, $\frac{3}{8}$ work will be done by A in $\left(48\times\frac{3}{8}\right)$ = 18 days.

62. Work done by X in 4 days = $\left(\frac{1}{20}\times 4\right)=\frac{1}{5}$.

Remaining work = $\left(1-\frac{1}{5}\right)=\frac{4}{5}$.

(X + Y)'s 1 day's work = $\left(\frac{1}{20}+\frac{1}{12}\right)=\frac{8}{60}=\frac{2}{15}$.

Now, $\frac{2}{15}$ work is done by X and Y in 1 day.

So, $\frac{4}{5}$ work will be done by X and Y in $\left(\frac{15}{2}\times\frac{4}{5}\right)=6$ days.

Hence, total time taken = (6 + 4) days = 10 days.

63. (A + B)'s 4 days' work = $\left(1-\frac{7}{10}\right)=\frac{3}{10}$.

(A + B)'s 1 day's work = $\left(\frac{3}{10}\times\frac{1}{4}\right)=\frac{3}{40}$.

Hence, A and B together take $\frac{40}{3}=13\frac{1}{3}$ days to complete the entire work.

64. (M + B)'s 1 days' work = $\frac{1}{24}$.

(M + B)'s 20 days' work + M's 6 days' work = 1

$\Rightarrow$ M's 6 days' work = $\left(1-\frac{1}{24}\times 20\right)=\frac{4}{24}=\frac{1}{6}$

$\Rightarrow$ M's 1 day's work = $\frac{1}{6}\times\frac{1}{6}=\frac{1}{36}$.

$\therefore$ B's 1 day's work = $\frac{1}{24}-\frac{1}{36}=\frac{1}{72}$.

Hence, the boy alone can do the work in 72 days.

65. (A + B)'s 20 days' work $= \left(\frac{1}{30} \times 20\right) = \frac{2}{3}$.

Remaining work $= \left(1 - \frac{2}{3}\right) = \frac{1}{3}$.

Now, $\frac{1}{3}$ work is done by A in 20 days.

Whole work will be done by A in $(20 \times 3) = 60$ days.

66. Work done by X in 8 days $= \left(\frac{1}{40} \times 8\right) = \frac{1}{5}$.

Remaining work $= \left(1 - \frac{1}{5}\right) = \frac{4}{5}$.

Now, $\frac{4}{5}$ work is done by Y in 16 days.

Whole work will be done by Y in $\left(16 \times \frac{5}{4}\right) = 20$ days.

$\therefore$ X's 1 day's work $= \frac{1}{40}$, Y's 1 day's work $= \frac{1}{20}$.

(X + Y)'s 1 day's work $= \left(\frac{1}{40} + \frac{1}{20}\right) = \frac{3}{40}$.

Hence, X and Y will together complete the work in $\frac{40}{3} = 13\frac{1}{3}$ days.

67. Work done by A, B and C in 4 days $= \left(\frac{1}{10} \times 4\right) = \frac{2}{5}$.

Remaining work $= \left(1 - \frac{2}{5}\right) = \frac{3}{5}$.

Now, $\frac{3}{5}$ work is done by B and C in 10 days.

Whole work will be done by B and C in $\left(10 \times \frac{5}{3}\right) = \frac{50}{3}$ days.

(A + B + C)'s 1 day's work $= \frac{1}{10}$,

(B + C)'s 1 day's work $= \frac{3}{50}$.

A's 1 day's work $= \left(\frac{1}{10} - \frac{3}{50}\right) = \frac{2}{50} = \frac{1}{25}$.

$\therefore$ A alone could complete the work in 25 days.

68. Whole work is done by A in $\left(20 \times \frac{5}{4}\right) = 25$ days.

Now, $\left(1 - \frac{4}{5}\right)$ *i.e.,* $\frac{1}{5}$ work is done by A and B in 3 days.

Whole work will be done by A and B in $(3 \times 5) = 15$ days.

A's 1 day's work $= \frac{1}{25}$, (A + B)'s 1 day's work $= \frac{1}{15}$.

$\therefore$ B's 1 day's work $= \left(\frac{1}{15} - \frac{1}{25}\right) = \frac{4}{150} = \frac{2}{75}$.

So, B alone would do the work in $\frac{75}{2} = 37\frac{1}{2}$ days.

69. Let A's 1 day's work = x and B's 1 day's work = y.

Then, $x + y = \frac{1}{30}$ and $16x + 44y = 1$.

Solving these two equations, we get : $x = \frac{1}{60}$ and $y = \frac{1}{60}$.

$\therefore$ B's 1 day's work $= \frac{1}{60}$.

Hence, B alone shall finish the whole work in 60 days.

70. A's 5 days' work + B's 7 days' work + C's 13 days' work = 1

$\Rightarrow$ (A + B)'s 5 days' work + (B + C)'s 2 days' work + C's 11 days' work = 1

$\Rightarrow$ $\frac{5}{12} + \frac{2}{16} +$ C's 11 days' work = 1

$\Rightarrow$ C's 11 days' work $= 1 - \left(\frac{5}{12} + \frac{2}{16}\right) = \frac{11}{24}$

$\Rightarrow$ C's 1 day's work $= \left(\frac{11}{24} \times \frac{1}{11}\right) = \frac{1}{24}$.

$\therefore$ C alone can finish the work in 24 days.

71. (A + B)'s 1 day's work $= \left(\frac{1}{28} + \frac{1}{35}\right) = \frac{9}{140}$.

Work done by B in 17 days $= \left(\frac{1}{35} \times 17\right) = \frac{17}{35}$.

Remaining work $= \left(1 - \frac{17}{35}\right) = \frac{18}{35}$.

Now, $\frac{9}{140}$ work was done by (A + B) in 1 day.

So, $\frac{18}{35}$ work was done by (A + B) in $\left(\frac{140}{9} \times \frac{18}{35}\right) = 8$ days.

$\therefore$ A left after 8 days.

72. Part of wall built by A in 1 day $= \frac{1}{8}$.

Part of wall broken by B in 1 day $= \frac{1}{3}$.

Part of wall built by A in 4 days $= \left(\frac{1}{8} \times 4\right) = \frac{1}{2}$.

Part of wall broken by (A + B) in 2 days $= 2\left(\frac{1}{3} - \frac{1}{8}\right) = \frac{5}{12}$.

Part of wall built in 6 days $= \left(\frac{1}{2} - \frac{5}{12}\right) = \frac{1}{12}$.

Remaining part to be built $= \left(1 - \frac{1}{12}\right) = \frac{11}{12}$.

Now, $\frac{1}{8}$ wall is built by A in 1 day.

$\therefore$ $\frac{11}{12}$ wall will be built by A in $\left(8 \times \frac{11}{12}\right)$

$= \frac{22}{3}$ days $= 7\frac{1}{3}$ days.

73. (Anuj + Manoj)'s 20 days' work = $\left(\frac{1}{30} \times 20\right) = \frac{2}{3}$.

Remaining work = $\left(1 - \frac{2}{3}\right) = \frac{1}{3}$.

Manoj's 30 days' work = $\frac{1}{3}$.

$\therefore$ Manoj's 1 days' work = $\frac{1}{90}$.

Anuj's 1 days' work = $\left(\frac{1}{30} - \frac{1}{90}\right) = \frac{2}{90} = \frac{1}{45}$.

If Manoj had gone away after 20 days, then the remaining $\frac{1}{3}$ work would have been done by Anuj.

$\frac{1}{45}$ work is done by Anuj in 1 day.

$\frac{1}{3}$ work would be done by Anuj in $\left(45 \times \frac{1}{3}\right)$ = 15 days.

74. Suppose A takes x days to finish the work alone and B takes y days to finish the work alone.

Then, $\frac{2}{x} + \frac{9}{y} = 1$ ...(*i*)

And, $\frac{3}{x} + \frac{6}{y} = 1 \Leftrightarrow \frac{1}{x} + \frac{2}{y} = \frac{1}{3} \Leftrightarrow \frac{2}{x} + \frac{4}{y} = \frac{2}{3}$ ...(*ii*)

Subtracting (*ii*) from (*i*), we get: $\frac{5}{y} = \frac{1}{3}$ or $y = 15$.

Putting $y = 15$ in (*i*), we get: $\frac{2}{x} = \frac{2}{5}$ or $x = 5$.

Hence, A alone takes 5 days while B alone takes 15 days to finish the work.

75. Suppose Asha takes x days to complete the task alone while Sudha takes y days to complete it alone.

Since Sudha is more efficient than Asha, we have $x > y$.

Asha's 1 day's work = $\frac{1}{x}$; Sudha's 1 day's work = $\frac{1}{y}$.

(Asha + Sudha)'s 1 day's work = $\frac{1}{x} + \frac{1}{y} = \frac{x+y}{xy}$.

If Asha and Sudha each does half of the work alone, time taken = $\left(\frac{x}{2} + \frac{y}{2}\right)$ days $= \left(\frac{x+y}{2}\right)$ days.

$\therefore \frac{x+y}{2} = 45 \Rightarrow x + y = 90$

From (*i*) and (*ii*), we have: $\frac{xy}{20} = 90$ or $xy = 1800$.

Now, $xy = 1800$ and $x + y = 90 \Rightarrow x = 60$, $y = 30$. $[\because x > y]$

Hence, Asha alone will take 60 days to complete the task.

76. B's 3 days' work = $\left(\frac{1}{21} \times 3\right) = \frac{1}{7}$.

Remaining work = $\left(1 - \frac{1}{7}\right) = \frac{6}{7}$.

(A + B)'s 1 day's work = $\left(\frac{1}{14} + \frac{1}{21}\right) = \frac{5}{42}$.

Now, $\frac{5}{42}$ work is done by A and B in 1 day.

$\therefore \frac{6}{7}$ work is done by A and B in $\left(\frac{42}{5} \times \frac{6}{7}\right) = \frac{36}{5}$ days.

Hence, total time taken = $\left(3 + \frac{36}{5}\right)$ days $= 10\frac{1}{5}$ days.

77. (A + B + C)'s 1 day's work = $\left(\frac{1}{24} + \frac{1}{36} + \frac{1}{48}\right) = \frac{13}{144}$.

Work done by (A + B + C) in 4 days = $\left(\frac{13}{144} \times 4\right) = \frac{13}{36}$.

Work done by B in 3 days = $\left(\frac{1}{36} \times 3\right) = \frac{1}{12}$.

Remaining work = $\left[1 - \left(\frac{13}{36} + \frac{1}{12}\right)\right] = \frac{5}{9}$.

(A + B)'s 1 day's work = $\left(\frac{1}{24} + \frac{1}{36}\right) = \frac{5}{72}$.

Now, $\frac{5}{72}$ work is done by A and B in 1 day.

So, $\frac{5}{9}$ work is done by A and B in $\left(\frac{72}{5} \times \frac{5}{9}\right) = 8$ days.

Hence, total time taken = (4 + 3 + 8) days = 15 days.

78. C's 3 days' work = $\left(\frac{1}{15} \times 3\right) = \frac{1}{5}$.

(B + C)'s 2 days' work = $\left[\left(\frac{1}{12} + \frac{1}{15}\right) \times 2\right] = \left(\frac{3}{20} \times 2\right) = \frac{3}{10}$.

Remaining work = $\left[1 - \left(\frac{1}{5} + \frac{3}{10}\right)\right] = \left(1 - \frac{1}{2}\right) = \frac{1}{2}$.

(A + B + C)'s 1 day's work = $\left(\frac{1}{10} + \frac{1}{12} + \frac{1}{15}\right) = \frac{15}{60} = \frac{1}{4}$.

$\frac{1}{4}$ work is done by A, B and C in 1 day.

$\therefore \frac{1}{2}$ work is done by A, B and C in $\left(4 \times \frac{1}{2}\right)$ = 2 days.

Total number of days = (3 + 2 + 2) = 7.

79. B's daily earning = ₹ (300 – 188) = ₹ 112.
A's daily earning = ₹ (300 – 152) = ₹ 148.
C's daily earning = ₹ [300 – (112 + 148)] = ₹ 40.

80. Work done by A = $\left(1 - \frac{8}{23}\right) = \frac{15}{23}$.

$\therefore$ A : (B + C) = $\frac{15}{23} : \frac{8}{23} = 15 : 8$.

So, A's share = ₹ $\left(\frac{15}{23} \times 529\right)$ = ₹ 345.

81. Kim's wages : David's wages
= Kim's 1 day's work : David's 1 day's work
$= \frac{1}{3} : \frac{1}{2} = 2 : 3$.

$\therefore$ Kim's share = ₹$\left(\frac{2}{5}\times 150\right)$ = ₹ 60.

82. Whole work is done by A in (3 × 4) = 12 days.
Whole work is done by B in (4 × 6) = 24 days.
A's wages : B's wages
= A's 1 day's work : B's 1 day's work = $\frac{1}{12}:\frac{1}{24} = 2:1.$

$\therefore$ A's share = ₹$\left(\frac{2}{3}\times 180\right)$ = ₹ 120.

83. Ratio of 1 day's work of man and boy = 3 : 1.

Total wages of the boy = ₹$\left(800\times\frac{1}{4}\right)$ = ₹ 200.

$\therefore$ Daily wages of the boy = ₹$\left(\frac{200}{5}\right)$ = ₹ 40.

84. Boy's 1 day's work = $\frac{1}{3}-\left(\frac{1}{7}+\frac{1}{8}\right)=\left(\frac{1}{3}-\frac{15}{56}\right)=\frac{11}{168}.$

$\therefore$ Ratio of wages of the first man, second man and boy

$= \frac{1}{7}:\frac{1}{8}:\frac{11}{168} = 24:21:11.$

First man's share = ₹$\left(\frac{24}{56}\times 1400\right)$ = ₹ 600;

Second man's share = ₹$\left(\frac{21}{56}\times 1400\right)$ = ₹ 525;

Boy's share = ₹ [1400 – (600 + 525)] = ₹ 275.

85. Let total money be ₹ x. A's 1 day's wages = ₹$\frac{x}{21}$,

B's 1 day's wages = ₹$\frac{x}{28}$.

$\therefore$ (A + B)'s 1 day's wages = ₹$\left(\frac{x}{21}+\frac{x}{28}\right)$ = ₹$\frac{x}{12}$.

$\therefore$ Money is sufficient to pay the wages of both for 12 days.

86. Part of the work done by A = $\left(\frac{1}{10}\times 5\right)=\frac{1}{2}.$

Part of the work done by B = $\left(\frac{1}{15}\times 5\right)=\frac{1}{3}.$

Part of the work done by C = $1-\left(\frac{1}{2}+\frac{1}{3}\right)=\frac{1}{6}.$

So, (A's share) : (B's share) : (C's share) = $\frac{1}{2}:\frac{1}{3}:\frac{1}{6}=3:2:1.$

$\therefore$ A's share = ₹$\left(\frac{3}{6}\times 1500\right)$ = ₹ 750,

B's share = ₹$\left(\frac{2}{6}\times 1500\right)$ = ₹ 500,

C's share = ₹$\left(\frac{1}{6}\times 1500\right)$ = ₹ 250.

A's daily wages = ₹$\left(\frac{750}{5}\right)$ = ₹ 150;

B's daily wages = ₹$\left(\frac{500}{5}\right)$ = ₹ 100;

C's daily wages = ₹$\left(\frac{250}{2}\right)$ = ₹ 125.

$\therefore$ Daily wages of B and C = ₹ (100 + 125) = ₹ 225.

87. 5 workers' 1 day's work = $\frac{1}{10}$.

5 workers' 1 day's work on increasing wages

$= 125\% \text{ of } \frac{1}{10} = \left(\frac{125}{100}\times\frac{1}{10}\right)=\frac{1}{8}.$

So, now the work is done in 8 days.
Original wage bill = ₹ (100 × 5 × 10) = ₹ 5000.
New wage bill = ₹ (120 × 5 × 8) = ₹ 4800.
$\therefore$ Amount saved = ₹ (5000 – 4800) = ₹ 200.

88. B's 1 day's work = $\left(\frac{1}{12}-\frac{1}{20}\right)=\frac{2}{60}=\frac{1}{30}.$

Now, (A + B)'s 1 day's work = $\left(\frac{1}{20}+\frac{1}{60}\right)=\frac{4}{60}=\frac{1}{15}.$

[$\because$ B works for half day only]

So, A and B together will complete the work in 15 days.

89. Let the daily wages of A, B and C be ₹ $5x$, ₹ $6x$ and ₹ $4x$ respectively.
Then, ratio of their amounts = ($5x$ × 6) : ($6x$ × 4) : ($4x$ × 9) = 30 : 24 : 36 = 5 : 4 : 6.

$\therefore$ A's amount = ₹$\left(1800\times\frac{5}{15}\right)$ = ₹ 600.

90. (A + B)'s 2 days' work = $\left(\frac{1}{12}+\frac{1}{18}\right)=\frac{5}{36}.$

Work done in 7 pairs of days = $\left(\frac{5}{36}\times 7\right)=\frac{35}{36}.$

Remaining work = $\left(1-\frac{35}{36}\right)=\frac{1}{36}.$

On 15th day, it is A's turn.

$\frac{1}{12}$ work is done by A in 1 day.

$\frac{1}{36}$ work is done by A in $\left(12\times\frac{1}{36}\right)=\frac{1}{3}$ day.

$\therefore$ Total time taken = $14\frac{1}{3}$ days.

91. (A + B)'s 1 day's work = $\left(\frac{1}{11}+\frac{1}{20}\right)=\frac{31}{220}.$

(A + C)'s 1 day's work = $\left(\frac{1}{11}+\frac{1}{55}\right)=\frac{6}{55}.$

Work done in 2 days = $\left(\frac{31}{220}+\frac{6}{55}\right)=\frac{55}{220}=\frac{1}{4}.$

Now, $\frac{1}{4}$ work is done in 2 days.

$\therefore$ Whole work will be done in (2 × 4) = 8 days.

92. A's 2 days' work = $\left(\frac{1}{20} \times 2\right) = \frac{1}{10}$.

(A + B + C)'s 1 day's work = $\left(\frac{1}{20} + \frac{1}{30} + \frac{1}{60}\right) = \frac{6}{60} = \frac{1}{10}$.

Work done in 3 days = $\left(\frac{1}{10} + \frac{1}{10}\right) = \frac{1}{5}$.

Now, $\frac{1}{5}$ work is done in 3 days.

$\therefore$ Whole work will be done in (3 × 5) = 15 days.

93. (A + B + C)'s 3 days' work = $\frac{1}{90} + \frac{1}{40} + \frac{1}{12} = \frac{43}{360}$.

(A + B + C)'s 24 days' work = $\frac{43}{360} \times 8 = \frac{344}{360}$.

Remaining work = $\left(1 - \frac{344}{360}\right) = \frac{16}{360} = \frac{4}{90}$.

On 25th day, it is A's turn.

A's 1 day's work = $\frac{1}{90}$.

Remaining work = $\left(\frac{4}{90} - \frac{1}{90}\right) = \frac{3}{90} = \frac{1}{30}$.

On 26th day, it is B's turn.

B's 1 day's work = $\frac{1}{40}$.

Remaining work = $\left(\frac{1}{30} - \frac{1}{40}\right) = \frac{1}{120}$.

On 27th day, it is C's turn.

$\frac{1}{12}$ work is done by C in 1 day.

$\frac{1}{120}$ work is done by C in $\left(12 \times \frac{1}{120}\right) = \frac{1}{10}$ day.

Hence, the whole work is completed in $26\frac{1}{10}$ days out of which A worked for 9 days, B worked for 9 days and C worked for $8\frac{1}{10}$ days.

Ratio of wages of A, B and C = Ratio of work done by A, B and C

$= \left(\frac{1}{90} \times 9\right) : \left(\frac{1}{40} \times 9\right) : \left(\frac{1}{12} \times 8\frac{1}{10}\right) = \frac{1}{10} : \frac{9}{40} : \frac{27}{40}$

= 4 : 9 : 27.

A's share = ₹$\left(\frac{4}{40} \times 240\right)$ = ₹ 24;

B's share = ₹$\left(\frac{9}{40} \times 240\right)$ = ₹ 54;

C's share = ₹$\left(\frac{27}{40} \times 240\right)$ = ₹ 162.

94. Let the time taken by A alone and B alone to complete the work be x days and y days respectively.

When A works on the first day:

In this case, A works for 10 days while B works for 9 days.

$\therefore \quad \frac{10}{x} + \frac{9}{y} = 1$ ...(*i*)

When B works on the first day:

In this case, A works for $9\frac{5}{6}$ days $\left(= \frac{59}{6} \text{ days}\right)$ while B works for 10 days.

$\therefore \quad \frac{59}{6x} + \frac{10}{y} = 1$ ...(*ii*)

Multiplying (*i*) by 10 and (*ii*) by 9 and then subtracting, we get: $x = \frac{23}{2} = 11\frac{1}{2}$.

Hence, A alone takes $11\frac{1}{2}$ days to complete the work.

95. (A + B)'s 6 days' work = $6\left(\frac{1}{20} + \frac{1}{15}\right) = \frac{7}{10}$;

(A + C)'s 4 days' work = $\left(1 - \frac{7}{10}\right) = \frac{3}{10}$;

(A + C)'s 1 day's work = $\frac{3}{40}$. A's 1 day's work = $\frac{1}{20}$.

$\therefore$ C's 1 day's work = $\left(\frac{3}{40} - \frac{1}{20}\right) = \frac{1}{40}$.

Hence, C alone can finish the work in 40 days.

96. Suppose the work was finished in x days.

Then, A's $(x - 8)$ days' work + B's $(x - 12)$ days' work + C's x days' work = 1

$\Rightarrow \quad \frac{(x-8)}{36} + \frac{(x-12)}{54} + \frac{x}{72} = 1$

$\Leftrightarrow \quad 6(x - 8) + 4(x - 12) + 3x = 216.$

$\therefore \quad 13x = 312$ or $x = 24$.

97. (20 × 16) women can complete the work in 1 day.

$\therefore$ 1 woman's 1 day's work = $\frac{1}{320}$.

(16 × 15) men can complete the work in 1 day.

$\therefore$ 1 man's 1 day's work = $\frac{1}{240}$.

So, required ratio = $\frac{1}{240} : \frac{1}{320} = 4 : 3$.

98. 10 men's 1 day's work = $\frac{1}{15}$;

15 women's 1 day's work = $\frac{1}{12}$.

(10 men + 15 women)'s 1 day's work = $\left(\frac{1}{15} + \frac{1}{12}\right) = \frac{9}{60} = \frac{3}{20}$.

$\therefore$ 10 men and 15 women will complete the work in $\frac{20}{3} = 6\frac{2}{3}$ days.

99. 3 men's 1 day's work $= \frac{1}{20}$;

5 boys' 1 day's work $= \frac{1}{30}$.

(3 men + 5 boys)'s 1 day's work $= \left(\frac{1}{20}+\frac{1}{30}\right)=\frac{5}{60}=\frac{1}{12}$.

$\therefore$ 3 men and 5 boys will complete the work in 12 days.

100. 5 men's 15 days' work = 5 men's 10 days' work + 10 women's 5 days' work

$\Rightarrow$ 5 men's 5 days' work = 10 women's 5 days' work

$\Rightarrow$ 10 women's 5 days' work $= \left(\frac{1}{15}\times 5\right)=\frac{1}{3}$

$\Rightarrow$ 10 women's 1 day's work $= \frac{1}{15}$.

$\therefore$ 10 women can complete the work in 15 days.

101. 100 men's 40 days' work + 100 men's 5 days' work = 1

$\Rightarrow$ 100 men's 45 days' work = 1

So, if the contractor had not engaged additional men, 100 men would have finished the work in 45 days.

Difference in time = (45 – 40) days = 5 days.

102. (7 × 12) men can complete the work in 1 day.

$\therefore$ 1 man's 1 day's work $= \frac{1}{84}$.

7 men's 5 days' work $= \left(\frac{1}{12}\times 5\right)=\frac{5}{12}$.

Remaining work $= \left(1-\frac{5}{12}\right)=\frac{7}{12}$.

5 men's 1 day's work $= \left(\frac{1}{84}\times 5\right)=\frac{5}{84}$.

$\frac{5}{84}$ work is done by them in 1 day.

$\frac{7}{12}$ work is done by them in $\left(\frac{84}{5}\times\frac{7}{12}\right)=\frac{49}{5}$ days $=9\frac{4}{5}$ days.

103. 1 man's 1 day's work $= \frac{1}{108}$.

12 men's 6 days' work $= \left(\frac{1}{9}\times 6\right)=\frac{2}{3}$.

Remaining work $= \left(1-\frac{2}{3}\right)=\frac{1}{3}$.

18 men's 1 day's work $= \left(\frac{1}{108}\times 18\right)=\frac{1}{6}$.

$\frac{1}{6}$ work is done by them in 1 day.

$\therefore$ $\frac{1}{3}$ work is done by them in $\left(6\times\frac{1}{3}\right)=2$ days.

104. Let 1 woman's 1 day's work = x.

Then, 1 man's 1 day's work $= \frac{x}{2}$ and 1 child's 1 day's work $= \frac{x}{4}$.

So, $\left(\frac{3x}{2}+4x+\frac{6x}{4}\right)=\frac{1}{7} \Rightarrow \frac{28x}{4}=\frac{1}{7}$

$\Rightarrow x=\left(\frac{1}{7}\times\frac{4}{28}\right)=\frac{1}{49}$.

$\therefore$ 1 woman alone can complete the work in 49 days.

So, to complete the work in 7 days, number of women required $= \left(\frac{49}{7}\right)=7$.

105. (1 man + 1 woman)'s 1 day's work $= \left(\frac{1}{3}+\frac{1}{4}\right)=\frac{7}{12}$.

Work done by 1 man and 1 woman in $\frac{1}{4}$ day $= \left(\frac{7}{12}\times\frac{1}{4}\right)=\frac{7}{48}$.

Remaining work $= \left(1-\frac{7}{48}\right)=\frac{41}{48}$.

Work done by 1 boy in $\frac{1}{4}$ day $= \left(\frac{1}{12}\times\frac{1}{4}\right)=\frac{1}{48}$.

$\therefore$ Number of boys required $= \left(\frac{41}{48}\times 48\right)=41$.

106. 1 man's 1 day's work $= \frac{1}{100}$.

(10 men + 15 women)'s 1 day's work $= \frac{1}{6}$.

15 women's 1 day's work $= \left(\frac{1}{6}-\frac{10}{100}\right)=\left(\frac{1}{6}-\frac{1}{10}\right)=\frac{1}{15}$.

1 woman's 1 day's work $= \frac{1}{225}$.

$\therefore$ 1 woman alone can complete the work in 225 days.

107. Suppose the woman takes x hours to do the job. Then, the child takes $(x + 15)$ hours to do the job.

Woman's 1 hours' work $= \frac{1}{x}$.

Child's 1 hours' work $= \frac{1}{(x+15)}$.

Child's 18 hours' work + Woman's 6 hours' work $= \frac{3}{5}$

$\Rightarrow \frac{18}{(x+15)}+\frac{6}{x}=\frac{3}{5} \Rightarrow \frac{18x+6(x+15)}{x(x+15)}=\frac{3}{5}$

$\Rightarrow 5(24x+90)=3(x^2+15x)$

$\Rightarrow 120x+450=3x^2+45x$

$\Rightarrow 3x^2-75x-450=0 \Rightarrow x^2-25x-150=0$

$\Rightarrow x^2-30x+5x-150=0$

$\Rightarrow x(x-30)+5(x-30)=0$

$\Rightarrow (x-30)(x+5)=0 \Rightarrow x=30$.

Remaining work $= \left(1-\frac{3}{5}\right)=\frac{2}{5}$.

$\frac{1}{30}$ work is done by the woman in 1 hour.

$\therefore$ $\frac{2}{5}$ work will be done by the woman in $\left(30\times\frac{2}{5}\right)$

= 12 hours.

108. Let the number of workers who started the job be n.

Then, n workers' 1 day's work = $\frac{1}{4}$

$\Rightarrow$ 1 worker's 1 day's work = $\frac{1}{4n}$.

Now, n workers worked on first day, $(n-3)$ on 2nd day, $(n-3+2)$ *i.e.*, $(n-1)$ on 3rd day, ... and so on.

Thus, we have:

$[n + (n-3) + (n-1) + (n-4) + (n-2) + (n-5) + (n-3)] \times \frac{1}{4n} = 1$

$\Rightarrow 7n - 18 = 4n \Rightarrow 3n = 18 \Rightarrow n = 6.$

Hence, 6 workers started the job.

109. (1 man + 1 woman)'s 1 day's work = $\frac{1}{6}+\frac{1}{9}=\frac{5}{18}$.

Remaining work = $\left(1-\frac{5}{18}\right)=\frac{13}{18}$.

Work done by 1 boy in 1 day = $\frac{1}{18}$.

$\therefore$ Number of boys required = $\left(\frac{13}{18}\times 18\right)=13$.

110. 1 man's 1 day's work = $\frac{1}{21\times 3}=\frac{1}{63}$;

1 boy's 1 day's work = $\frac{1}{21\times 9}=\frac{1}{189}$

(5 men + 6 boys)'s 1 day's work

$=\frac{5}{63}+\frac{6}{189}=\frac{5}{63}+\frac{2}{63}=\frac{7}{63}=\frac{1}{9}$.

Hence, 5 men and 6 boys together can do the work in 9 days.

111. 1 man's 1 day's work = $\frac{1}{99\times 2}=\frac{1}{198}$;

1 woman's 1 day's work = $\frac{1}{99\times 6}=\frac{1}{594}$;

1 boy's 1 day's work = $\frac{1}{99\times 4}=\frac{1}{396}$.

(1 man + 1 woman + 1 boy)'s 1 day's work

$=\left(\frac{1}{198}+\frac{1}{594}+\frac{1}{396}\right)=\frac{11}{1188}=\frac{1}{108}$.

Hence, 1 man, 1 woman and 1 boy together take 108 days to finish the same work.

112. 1 man's 1 day's work = $\frac{1}{20\times 8}=\frac{1}{160}$;

1 woman's 1 day's work = $\frac{1}{32\times 8}=\frac{1}{256}$.

(5 men + 8 women)'s 1 day's work

$=\left(\frac{5}{160}+\frac{8}{256}\right)=\frac{1}{32}+\frac{1}{32}=\frac{1}{16}$.

Hence, 5 men and 8 women together can complete the work in 16 days.

113. 1 man's 1 day's work = $\frac{1}{63\times 18}=\frac{1}{1134}$;

1 woman's 1 day's work = $\frac{1}{189\times 9}=\frac{1}{1701}$;

1 child's 1 day's work = $\frac{1}{486\times 7}=\frac{1}{3402}$.

(4 men + 9 women + 12 children)'s 1 days' work

$=\left(\frac{4}{1134}+\frac{9}{1701}+\frac{12}{3402}\right)=\frac{42}{3402}=\frac{1}{81}$.

Hence, 4 men, 9 women and 12 children together will complete the work in 81 days.

114. 1 man's 1 day's work = $\frac{1}{24\times 16}=\frac{1}{384}$;

1 boy's 1 day's work = $\frac{1}{16\times 48}=\frac{1}{768}$.

12 men's 4 days' work = $\left(\frac{12}{384}\times 4\right)=\frac{1}{8}$.

Remaining work = $\left(1-\frac{1}{8}\right)=\frac{7}{8}$.

(12 men + 12 boys)'s 1 day's work

$=\left(\frac{12}{384}+\frac{12}{768}\right)=\left(\frac{1}{32}+\frac{1}{64}\right)=\frac{3}{64}$.

$\frac{3}{64}$ work is done by (12 men + 12 boys) in 1 day.

$\therefore$ $\frac{7}{8}$ work is done by them in $\left(\frac{64}{3}\times\frac{7}{8}\right)=\frac{56}{3}$ days

$= 18\frac{2}{3}$ days.

115. 1 man's 1 day's work = $\frac{1}{48}$;

1 woman's 1 day's work = $\frac{1}{60}$.

6 men's 2 days' work = $\left(\frac{6}{48}\times 2\right)=\frac{1}{4}$.

Remaining work = $\left(1-\frac{1}{4}\right)=\frac{3}{4}$.

Now, $\frac{1}{60}$ work is done in 1 day by 1 woman.

So, $\frac{3}{4}$ work will be done in 3 days by $\left(60\times\frac{3}{4}\times\frac{1}{3}\right)$

= 15 women

116. 1 child's 1 day's work = $\frac{1}{192}$;

1 adult's 1 day's work = $\frac{1}{96}$.

Work done in 3 days = $\left(\frac{1}{96}\times 16\times 3\right)=\frac{1}{2}$.

Remaining work = $\left(1-\frac{1}{2}\right)=\frac{1}{2}$.

(6 adults + 4 children)'s 1 day's work = $\left(\frac{6}{96}+\frac{4}{192}\right)=\frac{1}{12}$.

$\frac{1}{12}$ work is done by them in 1 day.

$\frac{1}{2}$ work is done by them in $\left(12\times\frac{1}{2}\right)$ = 6 days.

117. 1 man's 1 day's work = $\frac{1}{192}$;

1 child's 1 day's work = $\frac{1}{432}$.

Work done in 8 days = $8\left(\frac{12}{192}+\frac{8}{432}\right)=8\left(\frac{1}{16}+\frac{1}{54}\right)=\frac{35}{54}$.

Remaining work = $\left(1-\frac{35}{54}\right)=\frac{19}{54}$.

(12 men + 11 children)'s 1 day's work = $\left(\frac{12}{192}+\frac{11}{432}\right)=\frac{19}{216}$.

Now, $\frac{19}{216}$ work is done by them in 1 day.

$\therefore$ $\frac{19}{54}$ work will be done by them in $\left(\frac{216}{19}\times\frac{19}{54}\right)$ = 4 days.

118. 1 man's 1 day's work = $\frac{1}{384}$;

1 woman's 1 day's work = $\frac{1}{768}$.

Work done in 12 days = $12\left(\frac{16}{384}+\frac{16}{768}\right)=\left(12\times\frac{3}{48}\right)=\frac{3}{4}$.

Remaining work = $\left(1-\frac{3}{4}\right)=\frac{1}{4}$.

(16 men + 16 women)'s 2 days' work

$= 2\left(\frac{16}{384}+\frac{16}{768}\right)=\left(2\times\frac{1}{16}\right)=\frac{1}{8}$.

Remaining work = $\left(\frac{1}{4}-\frac{1}{8}\right)=\frac{1}{8}$.

$\frac{1}{384}$ work is done in 1 day by 1 man.

$\therefore$ $\frac{1}{8}$ work will be done in 2 days by $\left(384\times\frac{1}{8}\times\frac{1}{2}\right)$

= 24 men.

119. Let 1 man's 1 day's work = x and 1 boy's 1 day's work = y.

Then, $5x+2y=4(x+y) \Rightarrow x=2y \Rightarrow \frac{x}{y}=\frac{2}{1}$.

120. Let 1 man's 1 day's work = x and 1 boy's 1 day's work = y.

Then, $12x+16y=\frac{1}{5}$ and $13x+24y=\frac{1}{4}$.

Solving these two equations, we get: $x=\frac{1}{100}$ and $y=\frac{1}{200}$.

$\therefore$ Required ratio = $x:y=\frac{1}{100}:\frac{1}{200}=2:1$.

121. Let 1 man's 1 day's work = x and 1 woman's 1 day's work = y.

Then, $4x+6y=\frac{1}{8}$ and $3x+7y=\frac{1}{10}$.

Solving these two equations, we get : $x=\frac{11}{400}$, $y=\frac{1}{400}$.

$\therefore$ 1 woman's 1 day's work = $\frac{1}{400}$.

$\Rightarrow$ 10 women's 1 day's work = $\left(\frac{1}{400}\times 10\right)=\frac{1}{40}$.

Hence, 10 women will complete the work in 40 days.

122. Let 1 man's 1 day's work = x and 1 woman's 1 day's work = y.

Then, $4x+10y=\frac{1}{3}\times\frac{1}{4}=\frac{1}{12}\Rightarrow 2x+5y=\frac{1}{24}$ ...(i)

And, $6x+12y=\frac{1}{9}\Rightarrow 2x+4y=\frac{1}{27}$ ...(ii)

Subtracting (ii) from (i), we get: $y=\frac{1}{24}-\frac{1}{27}=\frac{1}{216}$.

Now, (6 men + 12 women)'s 3 days' work = $\left(\frac{1}{9}\times 3\right)=\frac{1}{3}$.

Work completed = $\left(\frac{1}{3}+\frac{2}{9}+\frac{1}{3}\right)=\frac{8}{9}$.

Remaining work = $\left(1-\frac{8}{9}\right)=\frac{1}{9}$.

1 woman's 3 days' work = $\left(\frac{1}{216}\times 3\right)=\frac{1}{72}$.

In 3 days, $\frac{1}{72}$ work is done by 1 woman.

$\therefore$ In 3 days, $\frac{1}{9}$ work is done by $\left(72\times\frac{1}{9}\right)$ = 8 women.

123. Let 1 man's 1 hour's work = x;
1 woman's 1 hour's work = y
and 1 boy's 1 hour's work = z.

Then, $x+3y+4z=\frac{1}{96}$ ... (i)

$2x+8z=\frac{1}{80}$ ... (ii)

$2x+3y=\frac{1}{120}$ ... (iii)

Adding (ii) and (iii) and subtracting (i) from it,

we get : $3x+4z=\frac{1}{96}$ ...(iv)

From (ii) and (iv), we get $x=\frac{1}{480}$.

Substituting, we get : $y=\frac{1}{720}$, $z=\frac{1}{960}$.

(5 men + 12 boys)'s 1 hour's work

$= \left(\frac{5}{480}+\frac{12}{960}\right)=\left(\frac{1}{96}+\frac{1}{80}\right)=\frac{11}{480}.$

$\therefore$ 5 men and 12 boys can do the work in $\frac{480}{11}$

i.e., $43\frac{7}{11}$ hours.

124. Let 1 man's 1 day's work = x

and 1 boy's 1 day's work = y.

Then, $6x+8y=\frac{1}{10}$ and $26x+48y=\frac{1}{2}$.

Solving these two equations, we get : $x=\frac{1}{100}$ and $y=\frac{1}{200}$.

(15 men + 20 boys)'s 1 day's work = $\left(\frac{15}{100}+\frac{20}{200}\right)=\frac{1}{4}$.

$\therefore$ 15 men and 20 boys can do the work in 4 days.

125. Acreage reaped by 5 men and 3 women in 1 day = $\frac{18}{4}=\frac{9}{2}$.

Acreage reaped by 3 men and 2 women in 1 day

$=\frac{22}{8}=\frac{11}{4}$.

Suppose 1 man can reap x acres in 1 day and 1 woman can reap y acres in 1 day.

$\therefore$ $5x + 3y = \frac{9}{2} \Rightarrow 10x + 6y = 9$ ...(*i*)

$3x + 2y = \frac{11}{4} \Rightarrow 9x + 6y = \frac{33}{4}$ ...(*ii*)

Subtracting (*ii*) from (*i*), we get : $x = 9-\frac{33}{4}=\frac{3}{4}$.

Putting $x=\frac{3}{4}$ in (*i*), we get: $6y = 9-\frac{15}{2}=\frac{3}{2}\Rightarrow y=\frac{1}{4}$.

Acreage reaped by 21 women in 6 days $=\left(\frac{1}{4}\times 21\times 6\right)=\frac{63}{2}$.

Remaining acreage to be reaped $=\left(54-\frac{63}{2}\right)=\frac{45}{2}$.

Acreage reaped by 1 man in 6 days $=\left(\frac{3}{4}\times 6\right)=\frac{9}{2}$.

In 6 days, $\frac{9}{2}$ acre is reaped by 1 man.

$\therefore$ In 6 days, $\frac{45}{2}$ acre is reaped by $\left(\frac{2}{9}\times\frac{45}{2}\right)$ men = 5 men.

126. Let 1 man's 1 day's work = x

and 1 boy's 1 day's work = y.

Then, $6(25x + 10y) = 5(21x + 30y)$

$\Rightarrow 150x + 60y = 105x + 150y \Rightarrow 45x = 90y \Rightarrow x = 2y$.

Let the required number of boys be z.

Then, $4(40x + zy) = 6(25x + 10y) \Rightarrow 4(80y + zy)$

$= 6(50y + 10y)$ $[\because x = 2y]$

$\Rightarrow 80 + z = \frac{6\times 60}{4} = 90 \Rightarrow z = 10.$

127. Work done by 40 men in 5 days $=\frac{1}{3}$ (as if whole work is completed in 15 days then in 5 days 1/3rd of the work will be finished)

Remaining work $=1-\frac{1}{3}=\frac{2}{3}$

$\because$ 40 men do 1 work in 15 days.

60 men can do $\frac{2}{3}$ work in x day

$\frac{M_1D_1}{W_1}=\frac{M_2D_2}{W_2}$

$M_1 = 40$ $M_2 = 60$

$D_1 = 15$ $D_2 = x$

$W_1 = 1$ $W_2=\frac{2}{3}$

$\Rightarrow \frac{40\times 15}{1}=\frac{60\times x}{\frac{2}{3}}$

$\Rightarrow \frac{2}{3}(40\times 15)=60x$

$\Rightarrow 2\times 40\times 5 = 60x$

$\Rightarrow x=\frac{20}{3}=6\frac{2}{3}$ days

128. 12 men can do a piece of work in 24 days

$\Rightarrow M_1 = 12$ and $D_1 = 24$

8 men can do this work in D_2 days

$\Rightarrow M_2 = 8$

$M_1 D_1 = M_2 D_2$

$\Rightarrow 12\times 24 = 8\times D_2$

$\Rightarrow D_2=\frac{12\times 24}{8}=36$ days

129. Let time taken by A alone in doing work be x days.

$\therefore$ Time taken by B alone = $3x$ days

A's 1 day's work $=\frac{1}{x}$

B's 1 day's work $=\frac{1}{3x}$

$\because$ A and B together finish $=\frac{2}{5}$ work in 9 days.

$\therefore$ Time taken by A and B in doing whole work

$=\frac{9\times 5}{2}=\frac{45}{2}$ days

According to given information we get

$\therefore \frac{1}{x}+\frac{1}{3x}=\frac{2}{45}$

$\Rightarrow \frac{3+1}{3x}=\frac{2}{45}$

$\Rightarrow \frac{4}{3x}=\frac{2}{45}$

By cross-multiply we get

$\Rightarrow 2\times 3x = 4\times 45$

$\Rightarrow x=\frac{4\times 45}{2\times 3}=30$ days

Time taken by A = x days = 30 days

$\therefore$ Time taken by B = $3x$ days

= 3 × 30 = 90 days

130. A's 1 days work = $\frac{1}{24}$

B's 1 days work = $\frac{1}{5}$

C's 1 days work = $\frac{1}{12}$

$\therefore$ (A + B + C)'s 1 days work

$= \frac{1}{24} + \frac{1}{5} + \frac{1}{12}$

LCM of 24, 5 and 12

2	24 – 5 – 12
2	12 – 5 – 6
3	6 – 5 – 3
	2 – 5 – 1

2 × 2 × 3 × 2 × 5 = 120

$= \frac{5+24+10}{120}$

$= \frac{39}{120} = \frac{13}{40}$

Time taken by A, B and C to complete the work, working together

$= \frac{40}{13} = 3\frac{1}{13}$ days

131. X's 1 day's work = $\frac{1}{24}$

X's 16 day's work = $\frac{16}{24}$

Let Y alone complete the work in x days.

Y's 12 days work = $\frac{12}{x}$

According to the question,

Complete work done by X and Y = 1

X's 16 days work + Y's 12 days work = 1

$\Rightarrow \frac{16}{24} + \frac{12}{x} = 1$

$\Rightarrow \frac{2}{3} + \frac{12}{x} = 1$

$\Rightarrow \frac{12}{x} = 1 - \frac{2}{3} = \frac{1}{3}$

$\Rightarrow x = 12 \times 3 = 36$ days

132. 6 men will complete the work in 12 days

1 man will complete the work in = 6 × 12 = 72 days

8 women can complete two work in 18 day

1 woman will complete the work in = 8 × 18 = 144 days

18 children can complete the work in 10 days.

1 child will complete the work in = 18 × 10 = 180 days

1 men's 1 day's work = $\frac{1}{72}$

1 women's 1 day's work = $\frac{1}{144}$

1 children's 1 day's work = $\frac{1}{180}$

4 men + 12 women + 20 children's 2 days' work

$= 2\left(\frac{4}{72} + \frac{12}{144} + \frac{20}{180}\right)$

$= 2\left(\frac{1}{18} + \frac{1}{12} + \frac{1}{9}\right)$

LCM of 18, 12 and 9 = 36

$\frac{2(2+3+4)}{36} = \frac{1}{2}$

$\therefore$ Remaining work = $\frac{1}{2}$

$\therefore$ Required number of men = $72 \times \frac{1}{2} = 36$

133. Given $M_1 = 16$; $D_1 = 49$; $W_1 = 1$

$M_2 = ?$; $D_2 = 24$; $W_2 = ?$

According to the question

$\frac{M_1D_1}{W_1} = \frac{M_2D_2}{W_2}$

$\Rightarrow \frac{16 \times 49}{1} = \frac{14 \times 8}{W_2}$

$\Rightarrow W_2 = \frac{14 \times 8}{16 \times 49} = \frac{1}{7}$

Remaining work = $1 - \frac{1}{7} = \frac{6}{7}$

Again, $\frac{M_1D_1}{W_1} = \frac{M_2D_2}{W_2}$

$\Rightarrow \frac{16 \times 49}{1} = \frac{M_2 \times 24}{\frac{6}{7}}$

$\Rightarrow 16 \times 49 = \frac{M_2 \times 24 \times 7}{6}$

$\Rightarrow 16 \times 49 = M_2 \times 4 \times 7$

$\Rightarrow M_2 = \frac{16 \times 49}{4 \times 7} = 28$

Number of additional men = 28 – 14 = 14

EXERCISE

(DATA SUFFICIENCY TYPE QUESTIONS)

Directions (*Questions 1–11*): ***Each of the questions given below consists of a statement and/or a question followed by two statements labelled I and II. Read both the statements and***

Give answer (a) if the data in Statement I alone are sufficient to answer the question, while the data in Statement II alone are not sufficient to answer the question;

Give answer (b) if the data in Statement II alone are sufficient to answer the question, while the data in Statement I alone are not sufficient to answer the question;

Give answer (c) if the data either in Statement I or in Statement II alone are sufficient to answer the question;

Give answer (d) if the data even in both Statements I and II together are not sufficient to answer the question;

Give answer (e) if the data in both Statements I and II together are necessary to answer the question.

1. Will Q take more than 8 hours to complete the job alone?
   I. P works faster than Q.
   II. P and Q can together finish the job in 5 hours. **(J.M.E.T., 2005)**
2. In how many days can Mohan alone complete the work?
   I. Mohan and Prakash together can complete the work in 17 days.
   II. Rakesh works double as fast as Mohan and can alone complete the work in 10 days. **(Bank P.O., 2006)**
3. In how many days can B alone complete the work? **(Bank P.O., 2009)**
   I. B and C together can complete the work in 8 days.
   II. A and B together can complete the work in 12 days.
4. How long will Machine Y, working alone, take to produce x candles ? **(M.B.A., 2002)**
   I. Machine X produces x candles in 5 minutes.
   II. Machine X and Machine Y working at the same time produce x candles in 2 minutes.
5. B alone can complete a work in 12 days. How many days will A, B and C together take to complete the work ? **(SNAP, 2005)**
   I. A and B together can complete the work in 3 days.
   II. B and C together can complete the work in 6 days.
6. Is it cheaper to employ X to do a certain job than to employ Y ?
   I. X is paid 20% more per hour than Y, but Y takes 2 hours longer to complete the job.
   II. X is paid ₹ 80 per hour.
7. A and B together can complete a task in 7 days. B alone can do it in 20 days. What part of the work was carried out by A ?
   I. A completed the job alone after A and B worked together for 5 days.
   II. Part of the work done by A could have been done by B and C together in 6 days.
8. Who is the slowest among the three workers P, Q and R? **(M.A.T., 2009)**
   I. P and Q together fence a garden of perimeter 800 m in 11 hours.
   II. P, Q and R together can fence a garden of perimeter 800 m in 5 hours.
9. How many women can complete a piece of work in 15 days? **(Bank P.O., 2009)**
   I. 12 women can complete the same piece of work in 20 days.
   II. 10 men can complete the same piece of work in 12 days.
10. In how many days 10 men will finish the work while working together? **(Bank P.O., 2008)**
    I. Only 12 women can finish the work in 16 days.
    II. 4 men and 6 women can finish the work in 16 days.
11. How many women can complete the work in 10 days? **(Bank P.O., 2009)**
    I. Work done by one woman in one day is 75% of the work done by one man in one day.
    II. Work done by one woman in one day is 150% of the work done by one child in one day.

Directions (*Questions 12–19*): ***Each of the following questions consists of a question followed by three statements I, II and III. You have to study the question and the statements and decide which of the statement(s) is/are necessary to answer the question.***

12. In how many days can A and B working together complete a job ?
    I. A alone can complete the job in 30 days.
    II. B alone can complete the job in 40 days.
    III. B takes 10 days more than A to complete the job.
    (*a*) I and II only (*b*) II and III only
    (*c*) I and III only (*d*) Any two of the three
    (*e*) All I, II and III
13. In how many days A alone can complete a work?
    I. A and B can complete the work in 8 days.
    II. B takes twice the time taken by A in completing the work.
    III. A and B together take $\frac{1}{3}$ of the time taken by B alone in completing the work. **(Bank P.O., 2004)**
    (*a*) Only I and III (*b*) Only II and III
    (*c*) All I, II and III (*d*) Any two of the three
    (*e*) None of these
14. In how many days can the work be completed by A and B together ? **(M.A.T., 2005)**

I. A alone can complete the work in 8 days.

II. If A alone works for 5 days and B alone works for 6 days, the work gets completed.

III. B alone can complete the work in 16 days.

(*a*) I and II only
(*b*) II and III only
(*c*) Any two of the three
(*d*) II and either I or III
(*e*) None of these

15. In how many days will B alone complete the work?

I. A and B together can complete the work in 8 days.

II. B and C together can complete the work in 10 days.

III. A and C together can complete the work in 12 days.

(*a*) Only I and II
(*b*) Only II and III
(*c*) All I, II and III
(*d*) Question cannot be answered with the information in all the three statements
(*e*) None of these

16. How many workers are required for completing the construction work in 10 days?

I. 20% of the work can be completed by 8 workers in 8 days.

II. 20 workers can complete the work in 16 days.

III. One-eighth of the work can be completed by 8 workers in 5 days.

(*a*) I only
(*b*) II and III only
(*c*) III only
(*d*) I and III only
(*e*) Any one of the three

17. In how many days can 16 men and 8 women together complete the piece of work? **(Bank P.O., 2006)**

I. 8 men complete the piece of work in 10 days.

II. 16 women complete the piece of work in 10 days.

III. 5 women take 32 days to complete the piece of work.

(*a*) Only I and II
(*b*) Only II and III
(*c*) Only I and III
(*d*) Only I and either II or III
(*e*) Any two of the three

18. In how many days can the work be done by 9 men and 15 women ?

I. 6 men and 5 women can complete the work in 6 days.

II. 3 men and 4 women can complete the work in 10 days.

III. 18 men and 15 women can complete the work in 2 days.

(*a*) III only
(*b*) All I, II and III
(*c*) Any two of the three
(*d*) Any one of the three
(*e*) None of these

19. In how many days can 10 women finish a work? **(N.M.A.T. 2005; R.B.I., 2002)**

I. 10 men can complete the work in 6 days.

II. 10 men and 10 women together can complete the work in $3\frac{3}{7}$ days.

III. If 10 men work for 3 days and thereafter 10 women replace them, the remaining work is completed in 4 days.

(*a*) Any two of the three
(*b*) I and II only
(*c*) II and III only
(*d*) I and III only
(*e*) None of these

Directions (*Questions 20-21*): *Each of these questions is followed by three statements. You have to study the question and all the three statements given to decide whether any information provided in the statement(s) is/are redundant and can be dispensed with while answering the given question.*

20. In how many days can the work be completed by A, B and C together?

I. A and B together can complete the work in 6 days.

II. B and C together can complete the work in $3\frac{3}{4}$ days.

III. A and C together can complete the work in $3\frac{1}{3}$ days.

(*a*) Any one of the three
(*b*) I only
(*c*) II only
(*d*) III only
(*e*) Information in all the three statements is necessary to answer the question.

21. 8 men and 14 women are working together in a field. After working for 3 days, 5 men and 8 women leave the work. How many more days will be required to complete the work ?

I. 19 men and 12 women together can complete the work in 18 days.

II. 16 men can complete two-thirds of the work in 16 days.

III. In a day, the work done by three men is equal to the work done by four women. (M.A.T., 2006)

(a) I only
(b) II only
(c) III only
(d) I or II or III
(e) II or III only

ANSWERS

1. (e)	2. (b)	3. (d)	4. (e)	5. (e)	6. (d)	7. (a)	8. (d)	9. (a)	10. (e)
11. (d)	12. (d)	13. (e)	14. (c)	15. (c)	16. (e)	17. (d)	18. (c)	19. (a)	20. (e)
21. (d)									

SOLUTIONS

1. From II, we can conclude that if P and Q worked with equal efficiency, each of them alone would do the job in 10 hours. But according to I, Q is slower than P. So Q alone would take more than 10 hours to complete the job. Thus, both I and II together are necessary to get the answer.

$\therefore$ Correct answer is (e).

2. From II, it is clear that Mohan alone takes double the time as taken by Rakesh alone to do the work i.e., 20 days. I is insufficient.

Thus, II alone gives the answer.

$\therefore$ Correct answer is (b).

3. I. gives, (B + C)'s 1 day's work $= \frac{1}{8}$ ...(i)

II. gives, (A + B)'s 1 day's work $= \frac{1}{12}$ ...(ii)

We cannot find B's 1 day's work using (i) and (ii). Thus, both I and II together are not sufficient.

$\therefore$ Correct answer is (d).

4. I. gives, Machine X produces $\frac{x}{5}$ candles in 1 min.

II. gives, Machines X and Y produce $\frac{x}{2}$ candles in 1 min.

From I and II, Y produces $\left(\frac{x}{2}-\frac{x}{5}\right)=\frac{3x}{10}$ candles in 1 min.

$\frac{3x}{10}$ candles are produced by Y in 1 min.

x candles will be produced by Y in

$\left(\frac{10}{3x}\times x\right)$ min $=\frac{10}{3}$ min.

Thus, I and II both are necessary to get the answer.

$\therefore$ Correct answer is (e).

5. Given : B's 1 day's work $= \frac{1}{12}$.

I. gives, (A + B)'s 1 day's work $= \frac{1}{3}$

$\Rightarrow$ A's 1 day's work $= \left(\frac{1}{3}-\frac{1}{12}\right)=\frac{3}{12}=\frac{1}{4}$.

II. gives, (B + C)'s 1 day's work $= \frac{1}{6}$

$\Rightarrow$ C's 1 day's work $= \left(\frac{1}{6}-\frac{1}{12}\right)=\frac{1}{12}$.

$\therefore$ (A + B + C)'s 1 day's work $= \left(\frac{1}{4}+\frac{1}{12}+\frac{1}{12}\right)=\frac{5}{12}$.

Hence, they all finish the work in $\frac{12}{5}=2\frac{2}{5}$ days.

Thus, I and II both are necessary to get the answer.

$\therefore$ Correct answer is (e).

6. Suppose X takes x hours and Y takes $(x + 2)$ hours to complete the job.

II. X is paid ₹ 80 per hour.
Total payment to X = ₹ $(80x)$.

I. X = 120% of Y $= \frac{120}{100}Y=\frac{6}{5}Y \Rightarrow Y=\frac{5}{6}X$.

$\therefore$ Y is paid ₹$\left(\frac{5}{6}\times 80\right)$ per hour

$\Rightarrow$ Y is paid ₹$\left[\frac{200}{3}(x+2)\right]$.

We cannot compare $(80x)$ and $\frac{200}{3}(x+2)$.

$\therefore$ Correct answer is (d).

7. B's 1 day's work $= \frac{1}{20}$. (A + B)'s 1 day's work $= \frac{1}{7}$.

I. (A + B)'s 5 days' work $= \frac{5}{7}$.

Remaining work $= \left(1-\frac{5}{7}\right)=\frac{2}{7}$.

$\therefore$ $\frac{2}{7}$ work was carried by A.

II. is irrelevant.

$\therefore$ Correct answer is (a).

8. Clearly, using I and II, we can find only R's 1 hour's work while the same cannot be found for P and Q.

Hence, the speeds of P, Q and R cannot be compared. Thus, correct answer is (*d*).

9. **I.** gives, 1 woman's 1 day's work $= \frac{1}{20 \times 12} = \frac{1}{240}$.

$\therefore$ 1 woman's 15 days' work $= \left(\frac{1}{240} \times 15\right) = \frac{1}{16}$.

So, 16 women can complete the work in 15 days.

Thus, I alone gives the answer. While II is irrelevant.

$\therefore$ Correct answer is (*a*).

10. **I.** gives, 1 woman's 1 day's work $= \frac{1}{16 \times 12} = \frac{1}{192}$.

II. gives, $(4M + 6W) = 12W \Rightarrow 4M = 6W \Rightarrow M = \frac{3}{2}W$.

So, 1 man's 1 day's work $= \left(\frac{3}{2} \times \frac{1}{192}\right) = \frac{1}{128}$.

10 men's 1 day's work $= \left(\frac{1}{128} \times 10\right) = \frac{5}{64}$.

Hence, 10 men together take $\frac{64}{5}$ *i.e.*, $12\frac{4}{5}$ days to finish the work.

Thus, both I and II are necessary to answer the question.

$\therefore$ Correct answer is (*e*).

11. Both I and II tell us about the comparative efficiencies of a man, a woman and a child. From the given information, the answer cannot be obtained.

$\therefore$ Correct answer is (*d*).

12. **I.** A can complete the job in 30 days.

$\therefore$ A's 1 day's work $= \frac{1}{30}$.

II. B can complete the job in 40 days.

$\therefore$ B's 1 day's work $= \frac{1}{40}$.

III. B takes 10 days more than A to complete the job.

I and II gives, (A + B)'s 1 day's work $= \left(\frac{1}{30} + \frac{1}{40}\right) = \frac{7}{120}$.

$\therefore$ I and III also give the same answer.

II and III also give the same answer.

$\therefore$ Correct answer is (*d*).

13. **I.** (A + B)'s 1 day's work $= \frac{1}{8}$.

II. Suppose A takes x days to complete the work.

Then, B takes $2x$ days to complete it.

$\therefore \frac{1}{x} + \frac{1}{2x} = \frac{1}{8} \Rightarrow \frac{3}{2x} = \frac{1}{8} \Leftrightarrow x = \frac{3 \times 8}{2} = 12$.

So, A alone takes 12 days to complete the work.

III. B alone takes (3 × 8) = 24 days to complete the work.

$\therefore$ A's 1 day's work $= \frac{1}{8} - \frac{1}{24} = \frac{2}{24} = \frac{1}{12}$.

So, A alone takes 12 days to complete the work.

Thus, (I and II) or (I and III) give the answer.

$\therefore$ Correct answer is (*e*).

14. **I.** A can complete the job in 8 days.

So, A's 1 day's work $= \frac{1}{8}$.

II. A works for 5 days, B works for 6 days and the work is completed.

III. B can complete the job in 16 days.

So, B's 1 day's work $= \frac{1}{16}$.

I and III : (A + B)'s 1 day's work $= \left(\frac{1}{8} + \frac{1}{16}\right) = \frac{3}{16}$.

$\therefore$ Both can finish the work in $\frac{16}{3}$ days.

II and III : Suppose A takes x days to finish the work.

Then, $\frac{5}{x} + \frac{6}{16} = 1 \Rightarrow \frac{5}{x} = \left(1 - \frac{3}{8}\right) = \frac{5}{8} \Rightarrow x = 8$.

$\therefore$ (A + B)'s 1 day's work $= \left(\frac{1}{8} + \frac{1}{16}\right) = \frac{3}{16}$.

$\therefore$ Both can finish it in $\frac{16}{3}$ days.

I and II : A's 1 day's work $= \frac{1}{8}$. Suppose B takes x days to finish the work.

Then from II, $\left(5 \times \frac{1}{8} + 6 \times \frac{1}{x} = 1\right) \Leftrightarrow \frac{6}{x} = \left(1 - \frac{5}{8}\right)$

$= \frac{3}{8} \Rightarrow x = \left(\frac{8 \times 6}{3}\right) = 16$.

$\therefore$ (A + B)'s 1 day's work $= \left(\frac{1}{8} + \frac{1}{16}\right) = \frac{3}{16}$.

$\therefore$ Both can finish it in $\frac{16}{3}$ days.

Hence, the correct answer is (*c*).

15. **I.** (A + B)'s 1 day's work $= \frac{1}{8}$. ...(*i*)

II. (B + C)'s 1 day's work $= \frac{1}{10}$. ...(*ii*)

III. (A + C)'s 1 day's work $= \frac{1}{12}$. ...(*iii*)

Adding (*i*), (*ii*) and (*iii*), we get:

2 (A + B + C)'s 1 day's work $= \frac{1}{8} + \frac{1}{10} + \frac{1}{12} = \frac{37}{120}$

$\Rightarrow$ (A + B + C)'s 1 day's work $= \frac{37}{240}$

$\therefore$ B's 1 day's work $= \left(\frac{37}{240} - \frac{1}{12}\right) = \frac{17}{240}$.

Hence, B alone can complete the work in $\frac{240}{17}$ *i.e.*, $14\frac{2}{17}$ days.

Thus, I, II and III together give the answer.

$\therefore$ Correct answer is (*c*).

16. **I.** $\frac{20}{100}$ work can be completed by (8×8) workers in 1 day.

$\Rightarrow$ Whole work can be completed by $(8 \times 8 \times 5)$ workers in 1 day

$= \frac{8 \times 8 \times 5}{10}$ worke rs in 10 days = 32 workers in 10 days.

II. (20×16) workers can finish it in 1 day

$\Rightarrow \frac{(20 \times 16)}{10}$ workers can finish it in 10 days

$\Rightarrow$ 32 workers can finish it in 10 days.

III. $\frac{1}{8}$ work can be completed by (8×5) workers in 1 day

$\Rightarrow$ Whole work can be completed by $(8 \times 5 \times 8)$ workers in 1 day

$= \frac{8 \times 5 \times 8}{10}$ workers in 10 days = 32 workers in 10 days.

$\therefore$ Any one of the three gives the answer.
$\therefore$ Correct answer is (*e*).

17. **I.** 1 man's 1 day's work $= \frac{1}{10 \times 8} = \frac{1}{80}$.

II. 1 woman's 1 day's work $= \frac{1}{10 \times 16} = \frac{1}{160}$.

III. 1 woman's 1 day's work $= \frac{1}{32 \times 5} = \frac{1}{160}$.

Since II and III give the same information, either of them may be used.
(16 men + 8 women)'s 1 day's work

$= \left(\frac{1}{80} \times 16 + \frac{1}{160} \times 8\right) = \frac{1}{5} + \frac{1}{20} = \frac{5}{20} = \frac{1}{4}$.

$\therefore$ 16 men and 8 women together can complete the work in 4 days.
Thus, I and either II or III give the answer.
$\therefore$ Correct answer is (*d*).

18. Clearly, any two of the three will give two equations in x and y, which can be solved simultaneously.
$\therefore$ Correct answer is (*c*).

$\left[\text{For example I and II together give } \left(6x + 5y = \frac{1}{6}, 3x + 4y = \frac{1}{10}\right)\right]$.

19. **I.** (10×6) men can complete the work in 1 day

$\Rightarrow$ 1 man's 1 day's work $= \frac{1}{60}$.

II. $\left(10 \times \frac{24}{7}\right)$ men + $\left(10 \times \frac{24}{7}\right)$ women can complete the work in 1 day.

$\Rightarrow \left(\frac{240}{7}\right)$ men's 1 day's work + $\left(\frac{240}{7}\right)$ women's 1 day's work = 1

$\Rightarrow \left(\frac{240}{7} \times \frac{1}{60}\right) + \left(\frac{240}{7}\right)$ women's 1 day's work = 1.

$\Rightarrow \left(\frac{240}{7}\right)$ women's 1 day's work $= \left(1 - \frac{4}{7}\right) = \frac{3}{7}$

$\Rightarrow$ 10 women's 1 day's work $= \left(\frac{3}{7} \times \frac{7}{240} \times 10\right) = \frac{1}{8}$.

So, 10 women can finish the work in 8 days.

III. (10 men's work for 3 days) + (10 women's work for 4 days) = 1

$\Rightarrow$ (10×3) men's 1 day's work + (10×4) women's 1 day's work = 1

$\Rightarrow$ 30 men's 1 day's work + 40 women's 1 day's work = 1.
Thus, I and III will give us the answer. And, II and III will give us the answer.
$\therefore$ Correct answer is (*a*).

20. **I.** (A + B)'s 1 day's work $= \frac{1}{6}$.

II. (B + C)'s 1 day's work $= \frac{4}{15}$.

III. (A + C)'s 1 day's work $= \frac{3}{10}$.

Adding, we get 2 (A + B + C)'s 1 day's work

$= \left(\frac{1}{6} + \frac{4}{15} + \frac{3}{10}\right) = \frac{22}{30}$

$\Rightarrow$ (A + B + C)'s 1 day's work $= \left(\frac{1}{2} \times \frac{22}{30}\right) = \frac{11}{30}$.

Thus, A, B and C together can finish the work in $\frac{30}{11}$ days.
Hence I, II and III are necessary to answer the question.
$\therefore$ Correct answer is (*e*).

21. Clearly, I only gives the answer.
Similarly, II only gives the answer.
And, III only gives the answer.
$\therefore$ Correct answer is (*d*).

18 Time and Distance

IMPORTANT FACTS AND FORMULAE

I. Speed $= \left(\frac{\text{Distance}}{\text{Time}}\right)$, Time $= \left(\frac{\text{Distance}}{\text{Speed}}\right)$, Distance = (Speed × Time)

II. x km/hr $= \left(x \times \frac{5}{18}\right)$ m/sec

III. x m/sec $= \left(x \times \frac{18}{5}\right)$ km/hr

IV. If the ratio of the speeds of A and B is $a : b$, then the ratio of the times taken by them to cover the same distance is $\frac{1}{a} : \frac{1}{b}$ or $b : a$.

V. Suppose a man covers a certain distance at x km/hr and an equal distance at y km/hr. Then, the average speed during the whole journey is $\left(\frac{2xy}{x+y}\right)$ km/hr.

VI. Suppose two men are moving in the same direction at u m/s and v m/s respectively, where $u > v$, then their relative speed = $(u - v)$ m/s.

VII. Suppose two men are moving in opposite directions at u m/s and v m/s respectively, then their relative speed = $(u + v)$ m/s.

VIII. If two persons A and B start at the same time in opposite directions from two points and after passing each other they complete the journeys in a and b hours respectively, then
A's speed: B's speed = $\sqrt{b} : \sqrt{a}$.

SOLVED EXAMPLES

Ex. 1. ***A train travels 82.6 km/hr. How many metres will it travel in 15 minutes?*** **(E.S.I.C., 2006)**

Sol. Distance travelled in 1 min $= \left(\frac{82.6}{60}\right)$ km.

$\therefore$ Distance travelled in 15 min. $= \left(\frac{82.6}{60} \times 15\right)$ km $= 20.65$ km $= (20.65 \times 1000)$ m

$= 20650$ m.

Ex. 2. ***How many minutes does Aditya take to cover a distance of 400 m, if he runs at a speed of 20 km/hr?***

Sol. Aditya's speed = 20 km/hr $= \left(20 \times \frac{5}{18}\right)$ m/sec $= \frac{50}{9}$ m/sec.

$\therefore$ Time taken to cover 400 m $= \left(400 \times \frac{9}{50}\right)$ sec $= 72$ sec $= 1\frac{12}{60}$ min $= 1\frac{1}{5}$ min.

Ex. 3. ***A cyclist covers a distance of 750 m in 2 min 30 sec. What is the speed in km/hr of the cyclist?***

Sol. Speed $= \left(\frac{750}{150}\right)$ m/sec $= 5$ m/sec $= \left(5 \times \frac{18}{5}\right)$ km/hr $= 18$ km/hr.

[$\because$ 2 min 30 sec = 150 sec]

Ex. 4. *A man walked at a speed of 4 km/hr from point A to B and came back from point B to A at the speed of 6 km/hr. What would be the ratio of the time taken by the man in walking from point A to B to that from point B to A?*

Sol. Ratio of speeds = 4 : 6 = 2 : 3.

$\therefore$ Ratio of times taken $= \frac{1}{2} : \frac{1}{3} = 3 : 2.$

Ex. 5. *A dog takes 4 leaps for every 5 leaps of a hare but 3 leaps of a dog are equal to 4 leaps of the hare. Compare their speeds.* (M.B.A., 2007)

Sol. Let the distance covered in 1 leap of the dog be x and that covered in 1 leap of the hare be y.

Then, $3x = 4y \Rightarrow x = \frac{4}{3}y \Rightarrow 4x = \frac{16}{3}y.$

$\therefore$ Ratio of speeds of dog and hare

= Ratio of distances covered by them in the same time

$= 4x : 5y = \frac{16}{3}y : 5y = \frac{16}{3} : 5 = 16 : 15.$

Ex. 6. *While covering a distance of 24 km, a man noticed that after walking for 1 hour and 40 minutes, the distance covered by him was $\frac{5}{7}$ of the remaining distance. What was his speed in metres per second?*

Sol. Let the speed be x km / hr.

Then, distance covered in 1 hr. 40 min. *i.e.*, $1\frac{2}{3}$ hrs $= \frac{5x}{3}$ km.

Remaining distance $= \left(24 - \frac{5x}{3}\right)$ km.

$\therefore \frac{5x}{3} = \frac{5}{7}\left(24 - \frac{5x}{3}\right) \Leftrightarrow \frac{5x}{3} = \frac{5}{7}\left(\frac{72 - 5x}{3}\right) \Leftrightarrow 7x = 72 - 5x$

$\Leftrightarrow 12x = 72 \Leftrightarrow x = 6.$

Hence, speed $= 6$ km/hr $= \left(6 \times \frac{5}{18}\right)$ m/sec $= \frac{5}{3}$ m/sec $= 1\frac{2}{3}$ m/sec.

Ex. 7. *A trip to a destination is made in the following way : 900 km by train at an average speed of 60 km/hr, 3000 km by plane at an average speed of 500 km/hr, 400 km by boat at an average speed of 25 km/hr, 15 km by taxi at an average speed of 45 km/hr. What is the average speed for the entire journey?* (I.A.S., 2008)

Sol. Total distance travelled = (900 + 3000 + 400 + 15) km = 4315 km.

Total time taken $= \left(\frac{900}{60} + \frac{3000}{500} + \frac{400}{25} + \frac{15}{45}\right)$ hr

$= \left(15 + 6 + 16 + \frac{1}{3}\right)$ hr $= 37\frac{1}{3}$ hr $= \frac{112}{3}$ hr.

$\therefore$ Average speed for the whole journey

$= \left(4315 \times \frac{3}{112}\right)$ km/hr $= 115\frac{65}{112}$ km/hr.

Ex. 8. *Peter can cover a certain distance in 1 hr. 24 min. by covering two-third of the distance at 4 kmph and the rest at 5 kmph. Find the total distance.*

Sol. Let the total distance be x km. Then,

$\frac{\frac{2}{3}x}{4} + \frac{\frac{1}{3}x}{5} = \frac{7}{5} \Leftrightarrow \frac{x}{6} + \frac{x}{15} = \frac{7}{5} \Leftrightarrow 7x = 42 \Leftrightarrow x = 6.$

$\therefore$ Total distance = 6 km.

Ex. 9. ***One-third of a certain journey was covered at the speed of 20 km/hr, one-fourth at 30 km/hr and the re at the speed of 50 km/hr. Find the average speed per hour for the whole journey.*** **(A.A.O. Exam., 200**

Sol. Let the total distance be x km. Then,

Distance covered at 20 km/hr = $\frac{x}{3}$ km; Distance covered at 30 km/hr = $\frac{x}{4}$ km;

Distance covered at 50 km/hr = $\left[x - \left(\frac{x}{3} + \frac{x}{4}\right)\right]$ km $= \frac{5x}{12}$ km.

Total time taken = $\left[\frac{(x/3)}{20} + \frac{(x/4)}{30} + \frac{(5x/12)}{50}\right]$ hrs

$= \left(\frac{x}{60} + \frac{x}{120} + \frac{x}{120}\right)$ hrs $= \frac{4x}{120}$ hrs $= \frac{x}{30}$ hrs.

$\therefore$ Average speed for the whole journey = $\left(x \times \frac{30}{x}\right)$ km/hr = 30 km/hr.

Ex. 10. ***A man travelled from the village to the post-office at the rate of 25 kmph and walked back at the rate 4 kmph. If the whole journey took 5 hours 48 minutes, find the distance of the post-office from th village.***

Sol. Average speed = $\left(\frac{2xy}{x+y}\right)$ km/hr = $\left(\frac{2 \times 25 \times 4}{25+4}\right)$ km/hr = $\frac{200}{29}$ km/hr.

Distance travelled in 5 hours 48 minutes, i.e., $5\frac{4}{5}$ hrs = $\left(\frac{200}{29} \times \frac{29}{5}\right)$ km = 40 km.

$\therefore$ Distance of the post-office from the village = $\left(\frac{40}{2}\right)$ = 20 km.

Ex. 11. ***An aeroplane flies along the four sides of a square at the speeds of 100, 200, 300 and 400 km/hr. Find th average speed of the plane around the field.*** **(P.C.S., 200**

Sol. Let each side of the square be x km and let the average speed of the plane around the field be y km/h

Then, $\frac{x}{100} + \frac{x}{200} + \frac{x}{300} + \frac{x}{400} = \frac{4x}{y} \Leftrightarrow \frac{25x}{1200} = \frac{4x}{y} \Leftrightarrow y = \left(\frac{1200 \times 4}{25}\right) = 192.$

$\therefore$ Average speed = 192 km/hr.

Ex. 12. ***A fast train takes 3 hours less than a slow train for a journey of 600 km. If the speed of the slow train 10 km/hr less than that of the fast train, then find the speeds of the two trains.*** **(M.A.T., 200**

Sol. Let the speed of the fast train be x km/hr.

The, speed of the slow train = $(x - 10)$ km/hr.

$\therefore \frac{600}{(x-10)} - \frac{600}{x} = 3 \Leftrightarrow 600x - 600(x - 10) = 3x(x - 10)$

$\Leftrightarrow x^2 - 10x - 2000 = 0 \Leftrightarrow x^2 - 50x + 40x - 2000 = 0$

$\Leftrightarrow x(x - 50) + 40(x - 50) = 0 \Leftrightarrow (x - 50)(x + 40) = 0 \Leftrightarrow x = 50.$

Hence, speed of fast train = 50 km/hr and speed of slow train = 40 km/hr.

Ex. 13. ***By walking at $\frac{3}{4}$ of his usual speed, a man reaches his office 20 minutes later than his usual time. Fin the usual time taken by him to reach his office.*** **(S.S.C., 201**

Sol. New speed = $\frac{3}{4}$ of usual speed.

$\therefore$ New time taken = $\frac{4}{3}$ of usual time.

So, $\left(\frac{4}{3}\text{ of the usual time}\right) - (\text{usual time}) = 20$ min

$\Rightarrow \frac{1}{3}$ of the usual time = 20 min $\Rightarrow$ Usual time = 60 min = 1 hr.

Ex. 14. ***A person reaches his destination 40 minutes late if his speed is 3 km/hr; and reaches 30 minutes before time if his speed is 4 km/hr. Find the distance of his destination from his starting point.*** **(S.S.C., 2007)**

Sol. Let the required distance be x km.

Difference in the times taken at two speeds = 70 min = $\frac{7}{6}$ hr.

$\therefore \quad \frac{x}{3} - \frac{x}{4} = \frac{7}{6} \Leftrightarrow 4x - 3x = 14 \Leftrightarrow x = 14.$

Hence, the required distance is 14 km.

Ex. 15. ***A carriage driving in a fog passed a man who was walking at the rate of 3 kmph in the same direction. He could see the carriage for 4 minutes and it was visible to him upto a distance of 100 m. What was the speed of the carriage?***

Sol. Let the speed of the carriage be x kmph. Then, relative speed = $(x - 3)$ kmph.

Distance covered in 4 min *i.e.*, $\frac{1}{15}$ hr at relative speed = 100 m = $\frac{1}{10}$ km.

$\therefore \quad (x - 3) = \frac{1}{10} \times 15 = \frac{3}{2} \Leftrightarrow x = 3 + \frac{3}{2} = \frac{9}{2} = 4\frac{1}{2}.$

Hence, speed of the carriage = $4\frac{1}{2}$ kmph.

Ex. 16. ***A train after travelling 150 km meets with an accident and then proceeds at $\frac{3}{5}$ of its former speed and arrives at its destination 8 hours late. Had the accident occurred 360 km further, it would have reached the destination 4 hours late. What is the total distance travelled by the train?*** **(M.A.T., 2007)**

Sol. Let the original speed of the train be x km/hr.

Then, $\frac{360}{\left(\frac{3}{5}x\right)} - \frac{360}{x} = 4 \Leftrightarrow \frac{600}{x} - \frac{360}{x} = 4 \Leftrightarrow \frac{240}{x} = 4 \Leftrightarrow x = 60.$

Let the total distance travelled by the train be y km.

Then, $\left[\frac{150}{60} + \frac{(y-150)}{\left(\frac{3}{5} \times 60\right)}\right] - \frac{y}{60} = 8 \Leftrightarrow \frac{5}{2} + \frac{(y-150)}{36} - \frac{y}{60} = 8 \Leftrightarrow 2x = 1740 \Leftrightarrow x = 870.$

Hence, required distance = 870 km.

Ex. 17. ***A ship 77 km from the shore, springs a leak which admits $2\frac{1}{4}$ tonnes of water in $5\frac{1}{2}$ minutes. 92 tonnes of water would sink it. But the pumps can throw out 12 tonnes of water per hour. Find the average rate of sailing so that the ship may just reach the shore as it begins to sink.***

Sol. Quantity of water let in by the leak in 1 min

$$= \left(\frac{2\frac{1}{4}}{5\frac{1}{2}}\right) \text{tonnes} = \left(\frac{9}{4} \times \frac{2}{11}\right) \text{tonnes} = \frac{9}{22} \text{ tonnes.}$$

Quantity of water thrown out by the pumps in 1 min = $\left(\frac{12}{60}\right)$ tonnes = $\frac{1}{5}$ tonnes.

Net quantity of water filled in the ship in 1 min = $\left(\frac{9}{22} - \frac{1}{5}\right)$ tonnes = $\frac{23}{110}$ tonnes.

$\frac{23}{110}$ tonnes water is filled in 1 min.

92 tonnes water is filled in $\left(\frac{110}{23} \times 92\right)$ min = 440 min = $\frac{22}{3}$ hrs.

Hence, required speed $= \frac{77}{(22/3)}$ km/hr $= \left(77 \times \frac{3}{22}\right)$ km/hr $= 10.5$ km/hr.

Ex. 18. ***Excluding the stoppages, the speed of a bus is 64 km/hr and including the stoppages, the speed of the bus is 48 km/hr. For how many minutes does the bus stop per hour?*** **(Bank P.O., 2009)**

Sol. Due to stoppage, the bus covers $(64 - 48) = 16$ km less per hour.

Time taken to cover 16 km $= \left(\frac{16}{64} \times 60\right)$ min $= 15$ min.

Hence, stoppage time per hour = 15 min.

Ex. 19. ***An aeroplane started 30 minutes later than the scheduled time from a place 1500 km away from its destination. To reach the destination at the scheduled time the pilot had to increase the speed by 250 km/hr. What was the speed of the aeroplane per hour during the journey?*** **(P.C.S., 2006)**

Sol. Let the original speed of the aeroplane be x km/hr.

$\therefore \frac{1500}{x} - \frac{1500}{(x+250)} = \frac{1}{2} \Leftrightarrow 3000(x+250) - 3000x = x(x+250)$

$\Leftrightarrow x^2 + 250x - 750000 = 0$

$\Leftrightarrow x^2 + 1000x - 750x - 750000 = 0$

$\Leftrightarrow x(x + 1000) - 750(x + 1000) = 0$

$\Leftrightarrow (x + 1000)(x - 750) = 0 \Leftrightarrow x = 750.$

Hence, speed of the aeroplane during the journey = (750 + 250) km/hr = 1000 km/hr.

Ex. 20. ***Two boys A and B start at the same time to ride from Delhi to Meerut, 60 km away. A travels 4 km an hour slower than B. B reaches Meerut and at once turns back meeting A 12, km from Meerut. Find A's speed.*** **(M.B.A., 2011)**

Sol. Let A's speed = x km/hr. Then, B's speed = $(x + 4)$ km/hr.

Clearly, time taken by B to cover (60 + 12), i.e., 72 km = time taken by A to cover (60 – 12) *i.e.,* 48 km

$\therefore \frac{72}{x+4} = \frac{48}{x} \Leftrightarrow 72x = 48x + 192 \Leftrightarrow 24x = 192 \Leftrightarrow x = 8.$

Hence, A's speed = 8 km/hr.

Ex. 21. ***A man covers a certain distance on a toy train. Had the train moved 4 km/hr faster, it would have taken 30 minutes less. If it moved 2 km/hr slower, it would have taken 20 minutes more. Find the distance.*** **(M.A.T., 2010)**

Sol. Let the distance be x km and initial speed be y km/hr.

Then, $\frac{x}{y} - \frac{x}{y+4} = \frac{30}{60} = \frac{1}{2} \Leftrightarrow \frac{4x}{y(y+4)} = 2 \Leftrightarrow 8x = y^2 + 4y \Leftrightarrow x = \frac{y^2 + 4y}{8}$ ...(i)

And, $\frac{x}{y-2} - \frac{x}{y} = \frac{20}{60} = \frac{1}{3} \Leftrightarrow \frac{2x}{y(y-2)} = \frac{1}{3} \Leftrightarrow 6x = y^2 - 2y \Leftrightarrow x = \frac{y^2 - 2y}{6}$ ...(ii)

From (*i*) and (*ii*), we have :

$\frac{y^2 + 4y}{8} = \frac{y^2 - 2y}{6} \Leftrightarrow 6y^2 + 24y = 8y^2 - 16y \Leftrightarrow 2y^2 = 40y \Leftrightarrow 2y = 40 \Leftrightarrow y = 20.$

Putting $y = 20$ in (*i*), we get : $x = 60$.

Hence, required distance = 60 km.

Ex. 22. ***A and B are two stations 390 km apart. A train starts from A at 10 a.m. and travels towards B at 65 kmph. Another train starts from B at 11 a.m. and travels towards A at 35 kmph. At what time do they meet?*** **(M.B.A., 2002)**

Sol. Suppose they meet x hours after 10 a.m. Then,

(Distance moved by first in x hrs) + [Distance moved by second in $(x - 1)$ hrs] = 390

$\therefore \quad 65x + 35(x - 1) = 390 \Rightarrow 100x = 425 \Rightarrow x = 4\frac{1}{4}.$

So, they meet 4 hrs. 15 min. after 10 a.m., i.e., at 2.15 p.m.

Ex. 23. ***A goods train leaves a station at a certain time and at a fixed speed. After 6 hours, an express train leaves the same station and moves in the same direction at a uniform speed of 90 kmph. This train catches up the goods train in 4 hours. Find the speed of the goods train.***

Sol. Let the speed of the goods train be x kmph.

Distance covered by goods train in 10 hours = Distance covered by express train in 4 hours

$\therefore \quad 10x = 4 \times 90$ or $x = 36$.

So, speed of goods train = 36 kmph.

Ex. 24. ***A thief is spotted by a policeman from a distance of 100 metres. When the policeman starts the chase, the thief also starts running. If the speed of the thief be 8 km/hr and that of the policeman 10 km/hr, how far the thief will have run before he is overtaken?***

Sol. Relative speed of the policeman = (10 – 8) km / hr = 2 km / hr.

Time taken by policeman to cover 100 m = $\left(\frac{100}{1000} \times \frac{1}{2}\right)$ hr = $\frac{1}{20}$ hr.

In $\frac{1}{20}$ hrs, the thief covers a distance of $\left(8 \times \frac{1}{20}\right)$ km = $\frac{2}{5}$ km = 400 m.

Ex. 25. ***Two places A and B are 80 km apart from each other on a highway. A car starts from A and another from B at the same time. If they move in the same direction they meet each other in 8 hours. If they move in opposite directions towards each other, they meet in 1 hour 20 minutes. Determine the speeds of the cars.*** **(S.S.C., 2006)**

Sol. Let their speeds be x kmph and y kmph respectively.

Then, $\frac{80}{x - y} = 8 \Rightarrow x - y = 10$ ...(i)

And, $\frac{80}{x + y} = 1\frac{1}{3} = \frac{4}{3} \Rightarrow x + y = 60$ ...(ii)

Adding (i) and (ii), we get : $2x = 70$ or $x = 35$.

Putting $x = 35$ in (i), we get : $y = 25$.

Hence, the speeds of the two cars are 35 kmph and 25 kmph.

Ex. 26. ***A man takes 6 hours 30 min in going by a cycle and coming back by scooter. He would have lost 2 hours 10 min by going on cycle both ways. How long would it take him to go by scooter both ways?*** **(M.A.T., 2006)**

Sol. Let the distance be x km. Then,

(Time taken to cover x km by cycle) + (Time taken to cover x km by scooter) = 6 hr 30 min

$\Rightarrow$ (Time taken to cover $2x$ km by cycle) + (Time taken to cover $2x$ km by scooter) = 13 hrs

But, time taken to cover $2x$ km by cycle = 8 hr 40 min.

$\therefore$ Time taken to cover $2x$ km by scooter = 13 hrs – 8 hr 40 min = 4 hr 20 min.

Hence, required time = 4 hr 20 min.

Ex. 27. ***Sneha is picked up by her father by car from college everyday. The college gets over at 4 p.m. daily. One day, the college got over an hour earlier than usual. Sneha started walking towards her house. Her father, unaware of this fact, leaves his house as usual, meets his daughter on the way, picks her up and they reach the house 15 minutes earlier than usual. What is the ratio of the father's driving speed to Sneha's walking speed?***

Sol. Since 15 minutes are saved, it means that Sneha's father drives from the meeting point to the college and back to the meeting point in 15 min. i.e. he can drive from the meeting point to the college in $\left(\frac{15}{2}\right) = 7.5$ min.

But he reaches the college daily at 4 p.m. So Sneha and her father meet on the way at $3:52\frac{1}{2}$ p.m.

Thus, Sneha walked for 52.5 min and covered the same distance as covered by her father in 7.5 min.

Since speed varies inversely as time taken to cover a distance, we have:

$$\frac{\text{Father's driving speed}}{\text{Sneha's walking speed}} = \frac{52.5}{7.5} = \frac{7}{1}.$$

Hence, required ratio = 7 : 1.

EXERCISE

(OBJECTIVE TYPE QUESTIONS)

Directions: ***Mark (✓) against the correct answer:***

1. A speed of 30.6 km/hr is the same as **(R.R.B., 2008)**
   (*a*) 5.1 m/sec (*b*) 8.5 m/sec
   (*c*) 110.16 m/sec (*d*) None of these
2. A man riding his bicycle covers 150 metres in 25 seconds. What is his speed in km per hour? **(S.S.C., 2005)**
   (*a*) 20 (*b*) 21.6
   (*c*) 23 (*d*) 25
3. A bus covers a distance of 2924 km in 43 hours. What is the speed of the bus? **(Bank Recruitment, 2008)**
   (*a*) 60 km/hr
   (*b*) 68 km/hr
   (*c*) 72 km/hr
   (*d*) Cannot be determined
   (*e*) None of these
4. *A* is travelling at 72 km per hour on a highway while *B* is travelling at a speed of 25 metres per second. What is the difference in their speeds in metres per second? **(Campus Recruitment, 2010)**
   (*a*) $1\frac{1}{2}$ m/sec (*b*) 2 m/sec
   (*c*) 3 m/sec (*d*) 5 m/sec
5. A motorist travelled between two towns, which are 65 km apart, in 2 hours and 10 minutes. Find the speed in metres per minute. **(R.R.B., 2006)**
   (*a*) 200 (*b*) 500
   (*c*) 600 (*d*) 700
6. In track meets both 100 yards and 100 metres are used as distances. By how many metres is 100 metres longer than 100 yards?
   (*a*) 0.0856 m (*b*) 0.856 m
   (*c*) 1 m (*d*) 8.56 m
7. Which of the following trains is the fastest?
   (*a*) 25 m/sec (*b*) 1500 m/min
   (*c*) 90 km/hr (*d*) None of these
8. A person crosses a 600 m long street in 5 minutes. What is his speed in km per hour?
   (*a*) 3.6 (*b*) 7.2
   (*c*) 8.4 (*d*) 10
9. A car covers a distance of 432 km at the speed of 48 km/hr. In how many hours will the car cover this distance? **(Bank Recruitment, 2009)**
   (*a*) 6 hours (*b*) 7 hours
   (*c*) 9 hours (*d*) 12 hours
   (*e*) None of these
10. A man covered a distance of 180 km in 4 hours on a bike. How much distance will be cover on bicycle in 8 hours if he rides the bicycle at one-sixth the speed of the bike? **(Bank Recruitment, 2010)**
    (*a*) 54 km (*b*) 60 km
    (*c*) 72 km (*d*) 84 km
    (*e*) None of these
11. The ratio of the speeds of a car, a train and a bus is 5 : 9 : 4. The average speed of the car, the bus and the train is 72 km/hr. What is the average speed of the car and the train together? **(Bank P.O., 2010)**
    (*a*) 78 km/hr
    (*b*) 82 km/hr
    (*c*) 84 km/hr
    (*d*) Cannot be determined
    (*e*) None of these
12. Car A travels at the speed of 65 km/hr and reaches its destination in 8 hours. Car B travels at the speed of 70 km/hr and reaches its destination in 4 hours. What is the ratio of the distance covered by car A and car B respectively? **(Bank P.O., 2010)**
    (*a*) 7 : 11 (*b*) 13 : 7
    (*c*) 7 : 13 (*d*) 11 : 7
    (*e*) None of these
13. The average speed of a bus is one-third of the speed of a train. The train covers 1125 km in 15 hours. How much distance will the bus cover in 36 minutes? **(Bank Recruitment, 201**
    (*a*) 12 km (*b*) 18 km
    (*c*) 21 km (*d*) 75 km
    (*e*) None of these

14. The mileage of a motorbike *A* and a motorbike *B* is 42 km per litre and 52 km per litre respectively. Motorbike *A* covered 294 km and motorbike *B* covered 208 km. If the cost of 1 litre of petrol is ₹ 48, how much amount would be spent on petrol to cover the total distance by both the motor bikes together? **(Bank P.O., 2010)**

(*a*) ₹ 480
(*b*) ₹ 528
(*c*) ₹ 576
(*d*) Cannot be determined
(*e*) None of these

15. A train leaves Delhi at 4.10 P.M. and reaches Aligarh at 7.25 P.M. The average speed of the train is 40 km/hr. What is the distance from Delhi to Aligarh? **(R.R.B., 2006)**

(*a*) 120 km (*b*) 130 km
(*c*) 135 km (*d*) 140 km

16. *A* is 10 miles west of *B*. *C* is 30 miles north of *B*. *D* is 20 miles east of *C*. What is the distance from *A* to *D*? **(M.B.A., 2006)**

(*a*) 10 miles (*b*) 30 miles
(*c*) $10\sqrt{10}$ miles (*d*) $10\sqrt{13}$ miles
(*e*) $30\sqrt{2}$ miles

17. A plane flying north at 500 mph passes over a city at 12 noon. A plane flying east at the same altitude passes over the same city at 12 : 30 P.M. The plane is flying east at 400 mph. To the nearest hundred miles, how far apart are the two planes at 2 P.M.?

(*a*) 600 miles (*b*) 1000 miles
(*c*) 1100 miles (*d*) 1200 miles
(*e*) 1300 miles

18. A train travels at the speed of 65 km/hr and halts at 8 junctions for a certain time. It covers a distance of 1300 km in 1 day (24 hours). How long does the train stop at each junction, if it halts for the same period of time at all the junctions? **(Bank P.O., 2006)**

(*a*) 20 minutes (*b*) 30 minutes
(*c*) 40 minutes (*d*) 60 minutes
(*e*) None of these

19. Jane travelled $\frac{4}{7}$ as many miles on foot as by water and $\frac{2}{5}$ as many miles on horseback as by water. If she covered a total of 3036 miles, how many miles did she travel on foot? **(SNAP, 2005)**

(*a*) 1540 (*b*) 880
(*c*) 756 (*d*) 616

20. A star is 8.1×10^{13} km away from the earth. Suppose light travels at the speed of 3.0×10^5 km per second. How long will it take the light from the star to reach the earth? **(R.R.B., 2005)**

(*a*) 7.5×10^3 hours (*b*) 7.5×10^4 hours
(*c*) 2.7×10^{10} seconds (*d*) 2.7×10^{11} seconds

21. Akash leaves home for school which is 12 km from his house. After the school, he goes to his club which is 7 km from his school. If his house, school and club all fall in a line, then what is the minimum distance he has to travel to get back home?

(*a*) 5 km (*b*) 7 km
(*c*) 12 km (*d*) 17 km
(*e*) 19 km

22. A train covers a distance of $193\frac{1}{3}$ km in $4\frac{1}{4}$ hours with one stoppage of 10 minutes, two of 5 minutes and one of 3 minutes on the way. The average speed of the train is

(*a*) 48 km/hr (*b*) 50 km/hr
(*c*) 55 km/hr (*d*) 60 km/hr

23. Deepa rides her bike at an average speed of 30 km/hr and reaches her destination in 6 hours. Hema covers the same distance in 4 hours. If Deepa increases her average speed by 10 km/hr and Hema increases her average speed by 5 km/hr, what would be the difference in their time taken to reach the destination?

(*a*) 40 minutes (*b*) 45 minutes
(*c*) 54 minutes (*d*) 1 hour
(*e*) None of these

24. A monkey climbing up a pole ascends 6 metres and slips 3 metres in alternate minutes. If the pole is 60 metres high, how long will it take the monkey to reach the top? **(Campus Recruitment, 2010)**

(*a*) 31 min (*b*) 33 min
(*c*) 35 min (*d*) 37 min

25. An aeroplane flies twice as fast as a train which covers 60 miles in 80 minutes. What distance will the aeroplane cover in 20 minutes? **(E.S.I.C., 2006)**

(*a*) 30 miles (*b*) 35 miles
(*c*) 40 miles (*d*) 50 miles

26. A boy is running at a speed of p kmph to cover a distance of 1 km. But, due to the slippery ground, his speed is reduced by q kmph ($p > q$). If he takes r hours to cover the distance, then **(M.B.A., 2006)**

(*a*) $\frac{1}{r} = p - q$ (*b*) $r = p - q$
(*c*) $\frac{1}{r} = p + q$ (*d*) $r = p + q$

27. Ravi can walk a certain distance in 40 days when he rests 9 hours a day. How long will he take to walk twice the distance, twice as fast and rest twice as long each day? **(A.A.O. Exam, 2010)**

(*a*) 40 days (*b*) 50 days
(*c*) 80 days (*d*) 100 days

28. A car is driven at the speed of 100 km/hr and stops for 10 minutes at the end of every 150 km. To cover a distance of 1000 km, it will take

(*a*) 9 hours (*b*) 10 hours
(*c*) 11 hours (*d*) 12 hours

29. A man takes 50 minutes to cover a certain distance at a speed of 6 km/hr. If he walks with a speed of 10 km/hr, he covers the same distance in

(*a*) 10 minutes (*b*) 20 minutes
(*c*) 30 minutes (*d*) 40 minutes

30. A truck covers a distance of 550 metres in 1 minute whereas a bus covers a distance of 33 kms in 45 minutes. The ratio of their speeds is

(*a*) 3 : 4 (*b*) 4 : 3
(*c*) 3 : 5 (*d*) 50 : 3

31. The ratio between the speeds of two trains is 7 : 8. If the second train runs 400 kms in 4 hours, then the speed of the first train is

(*a*) 70 km/hr (*b*) 75 km/hr
(*c*) 84 km/hr (*d*) 87.5 km/hr

32. A train travels at an average of 50 miles per hour for $2\frac{1}{2}$ hours and then travels at a speed of 70 miles per hour for $1\frac{1}{2}$ hours. How far did the train travel in the entire 4 hours?

(*a*) 120 miles (*b*) 150 miles
(*c*) 200 miles (*d*) 230 miles

33. A man in a train notices that he can count 21 telephone posts in one minute. If they are known to be 50 metres apart, then at what speed is the train travelling?

(*a*) 55 km/hr (*b*) 57 km/hr
(*c*) 60 km/hr (*d*) 63 km/hr

34. Sound is said to travel in air at about 1100 feet per second. A man hears the axe striking the tree, $\frac{11}{5}$ seconds after he sees it strike the tree. How far is the man from the wood chopper? **(M.B.A., 2002)**

(*a*) 2197 ft (*b*) 2420 ft
(*c*) 2500 ft (*d*) 2629 ft

35. An express train travelled at an average speed of 100 km/hr, stopping for 3 minutes after every 75 km. How long did it take to reach its destination 600 km from the starting point? **(M.A.T., 2003)**

(*a*) 6 hrs 21 min (*b*) 6 hrs 24 min
(*c*) 6 hrs 27 min (*d*) 6 hrs 30 min

36. A certain distance is covered by a cyclist at a certain speed. If a jogger covers half the distance in double the time, the ratio of the speed of the jogger to that of the cyclist is :

(*a*) 1 : 2 (*b*) 2 : 1
(*c*) 1 : 4 (*d*) 4 : 1

37. A motor car starts with the speed of 70 km/hr with its speed increasing every two hours by 10 kmph. In how many hours will it cover 345 kms?

(*a*) $2\frac{1}{4}$ hrs
(*b*) 4 hrs 5 min
(*c*) $4\frac{1}{2}$ hrs
(*d*) Cannot be determined
(*e*) None of these

38. A bus moving at a speed of 24 m/s begins to slow at a rate of 3 m/s each second. How far does it go before stopping? **(N.D.A., 2007)**

(*a*) 48 m (*b*) 60 m
(*c*) 72 m (*d*) 96 m

39. A boy goes three equal distances, each of length x km, with a speed of y km/hr, $\frac{3y}{5}$ km/hr and $\frac{2y}{5}$ km/hr respectively. If the total time taken is 1 hour, then $x : y$ is equal to

(*a*) 6 : 13 (*b*) 6 : 23
(*c*) 6 : 31 (*d*) 6 : 37

40. A long distance runner runs 9 laps of a 400 metres track everyday. His timings (in min) for four consecutive days are 88, 96, 89 and 87 respectively. On an average, how many metres/minute does the runner cover? **(M.A.T., 2008)**

(*a*) 17.78 (*b*) 40
(*c*) 90 (*d*) None of these

41. An express train travelled at an average speed of 100 kmph, stopping for 3 minutes after 75 km. A local train travelled at a speed of 50 kmph, stopping for 1 minute after every 25 km. If the trains began travelling at the same time, how many kilometres did the local train travel in the time it took the express train to travel 600 km? **(M.A.T., 2005)**

(*a*) 287.5 km (*b*) 307.5 km
(*c*) 325 km (*d*) 396 km

42. A car starts running with the initial speed of 40 kmph, with its speed increasing every hour by 5 kmph. How many hours will it take to cover a distance of 385 km? **(M.A.T., 2007)**

(*a*) 7 hours (*b*) $8\frac{1}{2}$ hours
(*c*) 9 hours (*d*) $9\frac{1}{2}$ hours

43. The speed of a car increases by 2 kms after every one hour. If the distance travelled in the first one hour was 35 kms, what was the total distance travelled in 12 hours?

(*a*) 456 kms (*b*) 482 kms
(*c*) 552 kms (*d*) 556 kms
(*e*) None of these

44. A bus started its journey from Ramgarh and reached Devgarh in 44 minutes at its average speed of 50 km/hr. If the average speed of the bus is increased by 5 km/hr, how much time will it take to cover the same distance? **(Bank P.O., 2009)**

(*a*) 31 min (*b*) 36 min
(*c*) 38 min (*d*) 40 min
(*e*) 49 min

45. The speeds of three cars are in the ratio 2 : 3 : 4. The ratio of the times taken by these cars to travel the same distance is **(S.S.C., 2005)**

(*a*) 2 : 3 : 4 (*b*) 4 : 3 : 2
(*c*) 4 : 3 : 6 (*d*) 6 : 4 : 3

46. The speeds of *A* and *B* are in the ratio 3 : 4. *A* takes 20 minutes more than B to reach a destination. In what time does A reach the destination? **(S.S.C., 2007)**

(*a*) $1\frac{1}{3}$ hours (*b*) $1\frac{2}{3}$ hours
(*c*) 2 hours (*d*) $2\frac{2}{3}$ hours

47. The speed of electric train is 25% more than that of steam engine train. What is the time taken by an electric train to cover a distance which a steam engine takes 4 hours 25 minutes to cover? **(P.C.S., 2004)**

(*a*) $3\frac{1}{10}$ hr (*b*) $3\frac{11}{15}$ hr
(*c*) $3\frac{11}{12}$ hr (*d*) $3\frac{8}{15}$ hr

48. *A* takes 2 hours more than *B* to walk *d* km, but if *A* doubles his speed, then he can make it in 1 hour less than *B*. How much time does *B* require for walking *d* km? **(R.R.B., 2005)**

(*a*) $\frac{d}{2}$ hours (*b*) 3 hours
(*c*) 4 hours (*d*) $\frac{2d}{3}$ hours

49. A train covers a distance of 10 km in 12 minutes. If its speed is decreased by 5 km/hr, the time taken by it to cover the same distance will be

(*a*) 10 min (*b*) 11 min 20 sec
(*c*) 13 min (*d*) 13 min 20 sec

50. Anna left for city *A* from city *B* at 5.20 a.m. She travelled at the speed of 80 km/hr for 2 hours 15 minutes. After that the speed was reduced to 60 km/hr. If the distance between two cities is 350 kms, at what time did Anna reach city *A*?

(*a*) 9.20 a.m. (*b*) 9.25 a.m.
(*c*) 9.35 a.m. (*d*) 10.05 a.m.
(*e*) None of these

51. An aeroplane covers a certain distance at a speed of 240 kmph in 5 hours. To cover the same distance in $1\frac{2}{3}$ hours, it must travel at a speed of

(*a*) 300 kmph (*b*) 360 kmph
(*c*) 600 kmph (*d*) 720 kmph

52. A salesman travels a distance of 50 km in 2 hours and 30 minutes. How much faster, in kilometres per hour, on an average, must he travel to make such a trip in $\frac{5}{6}$ hour less time? **(Hotel Management, 2002)**

(*a*) 10 (*b*) 20
(*c*) 30 (*d*) None of these

53. A person has to cover a distance of 6 km in 45 minutes. If he covers one-half of the distance in two-thirds of the total time; to cover the remaining distance in the remaining time, his speed (in km/hr) must be

(*a*) 6 (*b*) 8
(*c*) 12 (*d*) 15

54. A man performs $\frac{3}{5}$ of the total journey by rail, $\frac{7}{20}$ by bus and the remaining 6.5 km on foot. His total journey is

(*a*) 65 km (*b*) 100 km
(*c*) 120 km (*d*) 130 km

55. A person wishes to reach his destination 90 km away in 3 hours but for the first half of the journey his speed was 20 km/hr. His average speed for the rest of the journey should be **(P.C.S., 2008)**

(*a*) 40 km/hr (*b*) 0.75 km/min
(*c*) 1 km/min (*d*) None of these

56. A train is scheduled to cover the distance between two stations 46 km apart in one hour. If it travels 25 km at a speed of 40 km/hr, find the speed for the remaining journey to complete it in the scheduled time. **(M.A.T., 2009)**

(*a*) 36 km/hr (*b*) 46 km/hr
(*c*) 56 km/hr (*d*) 66 km/hr

57. How long must a driver take to drive the final 70 miles of a trip if he wants to average 50 miles an hour for the entire trip and during the first part of the trip he drove 50 miles in $1\frac{1}{2}$ hours? **(M.B.A., 2006)**

(*a*) 54 min (*b*) 1 hour
(*c*) 66 min (*d*) 70 min

58. A can complete a journey in 10 hours. He travels first half of the journey at the rate of 21 km/hr and second half at the rate of 24 km/hr. Find the total journey in km.

(*a*) 220 km (*b*) 224 km
(*c*) 230 km (*d*) 234 km

59. A motorcyclist completes a certain journey in 5 hours. He covers one-third distance at 60 km/hr and the rest at 80 km/hr. The length of the journey is

(*a*) 180 km (*b*) 240 km
(*c*) 300 km (*d*) 360 km

60. A person travels equal distances with speeds of 3 km/hr, 4 km/hr and 5 km/hr and takes a total time of 47 minutes. The total distance (in km) is

(*a*) 2 (*b*) 3
(*c*) 4 (*d*) 5

61. A person travels 285 km in 6 hours in two stages. In the first part of the journey, he travels by bus at the speed of 40 km per hour. In the second part of the journey, he travels by train at the speed of 55 km per hour. How much distance did he travel by train? **(M.A.T., 2007)**

(*a*) 145 km (*b*) 165 km
(*c*) 185 km (*d*) 205 km

62. *A* is faster than *B*. *A* and *B* each walk 24 km. The sum of their speeds is 7 km/hr and the sum of times taken by them is 14 hours. Then, *A*'s speed is equal to

(*a*) 3 km/hr (*b*) 4 km/hr
(*c*) 5 km/hr (*d*) 7 km/hr

63. A person travels from *P* to *Q* at a speed of 40 kmph and returns by increasing his speed by 50%. What is his average speed for both the trips? **(M.B.A., 2003)**

(*a*) 36 kmph (*b*) 45 kmph
(*c*) 48 kmph (*d*) 50 kmph

64. An aeroplane flies from place A to place B at the speed of 500 km/hr. On the return journey, its speed is 700 km/hr. The average speed of the aeroplane for the entire journey is **(P.C.S. 2009)**

(*a*) $566\frac{2}{3}$ km/hr (*b*) $583\frac{1}{3}$ km/hr
(*c*) $583\frac{2}{3}$ km/hr (*d*) 600 km/hr

65. A car covers a distance from Town I to Town II at the speed of 56 km/hr and from Town II to Town I at the speed of 53 km/hr. What is the average speed of the car? **(Bank Recruitment, 2007)**

(*a*) 53.5 km/hr (*b*) 54 km/hr
(*c*) 55 km/hr (*d*) 55.5 km/hr
(*e*) None of these

66. A man can walk uphill at the rate of $2\frac{1}{2}$ km/hr and downhill at the rate of $3\frac{1}{4}$ km/hr. If the total time required to walk a certain distance up the hill and return to the starting point was 4 hr 36 min, then what was the distance walked up the hill by the man? **(C.D.S., 2005)**

(*a*) 4 km (*b*) $4\frac{1}{2}$ km
(*c*) $5\frac{1}{2}$ km (*d*) $6\frac{1}{2}$ km

67. A man drives 150 km to the seashore in 3 hours 20 min. He returns from the shore to the starting point in 4 hours 10 min. Let *r* be the average rate for the entire trip. Then the average rate for the trip going exceeds *r*, in kilometres per hour, by **(M.B.A., 2010)**

(*a*) 2 (*b*) 4
(*c*) $4\frac{1}{2}$ (*d*) 5

68. The average speed of a train in the onward journey is 25% more than that in the return journey. The train halts for one hour on reaching the destination. The total time taken for the complete to and fro journey is 17 hours, covering a distance of 800 km. The speed of the train in the onward journey is

(*a*) 45 km/hr (*b*) 47.5 km/hr
(*c*) 52 km/hr (*d*) 56.25 km/hr

69. I started on my bicycle at 7 a.m. to reach a certain place. After going a certain distance, my bicycle went out of order. Consequently, I rested for 35 minutes and came back to my house walking all the way. I reached my house at 1 p.m. If my cycling speed is 10 kmph and my walking speed is 1 kmph, then on my bicycle I covered a distance of

(*a*) $4\frac{61}{66}$ km (*b*) $13\frac{4}{9}$ km
(*c*) $14\frac{3}{8}$ km (*d*) $15\frac{10}{21}$ km

70. A, B and C are on a trip by a car. A drives during the first hour at an average speed of 50 km/hr. B drives during the next 2 hours at an average speed of 48 km/hr. C drives for the next 3 hours at an average speed of 52 km/hr. They reached their destination after exactly 6 hours. Their mean speed was :

(*a*) 50 km/hr (*b*) $50\frac{1}{3}$ km/hr
(c) $51\frac{1}{3}$ km/hr (*d*) 52 km/hr

71. A car covers the first 39 kms of its journey in 45 minutes and covers the remaining 25 km in 35 minutes. What is the average speed of the car? **(Bank P.O., 2007)**

(*a*) 40 km/hr (*b*) 48 km/hr
(*c*) 49 km/hr (*d*) 64 km/hr
(*e*) None of these

72. A train travels at a speed of 30 km/hr for 12 minutes and at a speed of 45 km/hr for the next 8 minutes. The average speed of the train for this journey is **(S.S.C., 2005)**

(*a*) 30 km/hr (*b*) 36 km/hr
(*c*) 37.5 km/hr (*d*) 48 km/hr

73. A man on tour travels 160 km by car at 64 km/hr and another 160 km by bus at 80 km/hr. The average speed for the whole journey is **(L.I.C.A.D.O., 2008)**

(*a*) 35.55 km/hr (*b*) 36 km/hr
(*c*) 71.11 km/hr (*d*) 71 km/hr

74. A boy rides his bicycle 10 km at an average speed of 12 km/hr and again travels 12 km at an average speed of 10 km/hr. His average speed for the entire trip is approximately **(M.B.A., 2008)**

(*a*) 10.4 km/hr (*b*) 10.8 km/hr
(*c*) 11 km/hr (*d*) 12.2 km/hr

75. A man travels 600 km by train at 80 km/hr, 800 km by ship at 40 km/hr, 500 km by aeroplane at 400 km/hr and 100 km by car at 50 km/hr. What is the average speed for the entire distance? **(Teachers' Exam., 2009)**

(*a*) 60 km/hr (*b*) $60\frac{5}{123}$ km/hr
(*c*) 62 km/hr (*d*) $65\frac{5}{123}$ km/hr

76. A cyclist rides 24 km at 16 kmph and further 36 km at 15 kmph. Find his average speed for the journey. **(R.R.B., 2008)**

(*a*) 15.38 kmph (*b*) 15.5 kmph
(*c*) 16 kmph (*d*) None of these

77. A person travels three equal distances at a speed of x km/hr, y km/hr and z km/hr respectively. What is the average speed for the whole journey? **(S.C.C., 2007)**

(*a*) $\frac{xyz}{3(xy+yz+zx)}$ (*b*) $\frac{xyz}{(xy+yz+zx)}$
(*c*) $\frac{(xy+yz+zx)}{xyz}$ (*d*) $\frac{3xyz}{(xy+yz+zx)}$

78. A car travels the first one-third of a certain distance with a speed of 10 km/hr, the next one-third distance with a speed of 20 km/hr, and the last one-third distance with a speed of 60 km/hr. The average speed of the car for the whole journey is

(*a*) 18 km/hr (*b*) 24 km/hr
(*c*) 30 km/hr (*d*) 36 km/hr

79. A motorist covers a distance of 39 km in 45 minutes by moving at a speed of x kmph for the first 15 minutes, then moving at double the speed for the next 20 minutes and then again moving at his original speed for the rest of the journey. Then, x is equal to :

(*a*) 31.2 (*b*) 36
(*c*) 40 (*d*) 52

80. Mary jogs 9 km at a speed of 6 km per hour. At what speed would she need to jog during the next 1.5 hours to have an average of 9 km per hour for the entire jogging session?

(*a*) 9 kmph (*b*) 10 kmph
(*c*) 12 kmph (*d*) 14 kmph

81. A family, planning a weekend trip, decides to spend not more than a total of 8 hours driving. By leaving early in the morning, they can average 40 miles per hour on the way to their destination. Due to the heavy Sunday traffic, they average only 30 miles per hour on the return trip. What is the farthest distance from home they can plan to go? **(Campus Recruitment, 2010)**

(*a*) 120 miles or less
(*b*) Between 120 and 140 miles
(*c*) 140 miles
(*d*) Between 140 and 160 miles
(*e*) 160 miles or more

82. A car travelling with $\frac{5}{7}$ of its actual speed covers 42 km in 1 hr 40 min 48 sec. Find the actual speed of the car. **(S.S.C., 2005)**

(*a*) $17\frac{6}{7}$ km/hr (*b*) 25 km/hr
(*c*) 30 km/hr (*d*) 35 km/hr

83. A train running at $\frac{7}{11}$ of its own speed reached a place in 22 hours. How much time could be saved if the train would have run at its own speed?

(*a*) 7 hours (*b*) 8 hours
(*c*) 14 hours (*d*) 16 hours

84. A man can reach a certain place in 30 hours. If he reduces his speed by $\frac{1}{15}$th, he goes 10 km less in that time. Find his speed. (S.S.C., 2002)
(*a*) 4 km/hr (*b*) 5 km/hr
(c) $5\frac{1}{2}$ km/hr (*d*) 6 km/hr

85. Walking $\frac{6}{7}$th of his usual speed, a man is 12 minutes too late. The usual time taken by him to cover that distance is
(*a*) 1 hour (*b*) 1 hr 12 min
(*c*) 1 hr 15 min (*d*) 1 hr 20 min

86. The average speed of a train is 20% less on the return journey than on the onward journey. The train halts for half an hour at the destination station before starting on the return journey. If the total time taken for the to and fro journey is 23 hours, covering a distance of 1000 km, the speed of the train on the return journey is (M.A.T., 2010)
(*a*) 40 km/hr (*b*) 50 km/hr
(*c*) 55 km/hr (*d*) 60 km/hr

87. A train increases its normal speed by 12.5% and reaches its destination 20 minutes earlier. What is the actual time taken by the train in the journey? (P.C.S., 2008)
(*a*) 145 min (*b*) 160 min
(*c*) 180 min (*d*) 220 min

88. A student walks from his house at a speed of $2\frac{1}{2}$ km per hour and reaches his school 6 minutes late. The next day he increases his speed by 1 km per hour and reaches 6 minutes before school time. How far is the school from his house? (S.S.C., 2007)
(*a*) $1\frac{1}{4}$ km (*b*) $1\frac{3}{4}$ km
(*c*) $2\frac{1}{4}$ km (*d*) $2\frac{3}{4}$ km

89. With an average speed of 50 km/hr, a train reaches its destination in time. If it goes with an average speed of 40 km/hr, it is late by 24 minutes. The total journey is (N.M.A.T., 2008)
(*a*) 30 km (*b*) 40 km
(*c*) 70 km (*d*) 80 km

90. If a train runs at 40 kmph, it reaches its destination late by 11 minutes but if it runs at 50 kmph, it is late by 5 minutes only. The correct time for the train to complete its journey is
(*a*) 13 min (*b*) 15 min
(*c*) 19 min (*d*) 21 min

91. Robert is travelling on his cycle and has calculated to reach point A at 2 P.M. if he travels at 10 kmph; he will reach there at 12 noon if he travels at 15 kmph. At what speed must he travel to reach A at 1 P.M.? (D.M.R.C., 2003)
(*a*) 8 kmph (*b*) 11 kmph
(*c*) 12 kmph (*d*) 14 kmph

92. Ravi walks to and fro to a shopping mall. He spends 30 minutes shopping. If he walks at a speed of 10 km an hour, he returns home at 19.00 hours. If he walks at 15 km an hour, he returns home at 18.30 hours. How far must he walk in order to return home at 18.15 hours? (M.B.A., 2009)
(*a*) 17 km/hr (*b*) 17.5 km/hr
(*c*) 18 km/hr (*d*) 19 km/hr
(*e*) None of these

93. A person travels 285 km in 6 hours in two stages. In the first part of the journey, he travels by bus at the speed of 40 km/hr. In the second part of the journey, he travels by train at the speed of 55 km/hr. How much distance does he travel by train? (M.A.T., 2007)
(*a*) 145 km (*b*) 165 km
(*c*) 185 km (*d*) 205 km

94. A man covered a certain distance at some speed. Had he moved 3 kmph faster, he would have taken 40 minutes less. If he had moved 2 kmph slower, he would have taken 40 minutes more. The distance (in km) is
(*a*) 35 (*b*) $36\frac{2}{3}$
(*c*) $37\frac{1}{2}$ (*d*) 40

95. A train covered a certain distance at a uniform speed. If the train had been 6 km/hr faster, then it would have taken 4 hours less than the scheduled time. And, if the train were slower by 6 km/hr, then the train would have taken 6 hours more than the scheduled time. The length of the journey is (M.A.T., 2006)
(*a*) 700 km (*b*) 720 km
(*c*) 740 km (*d*) 760 km

96. A car travels from *P* to *Q* at a constant speed. If its speed were increased by 10 km/hr, it would have taken one hour lesser to cover the distance. It would have taken further 45 minutes lesser if the speed was further increased by 10 km/hr. What is the distance between the two cities?
(*a*) 420 km (*b*) 540 km
(*c*) 600 km (*d*) 650 km

97. A train can travel 50% faster than a car. Both start from point A at the same time and reach point B 75 kms away from A at the same time. On the way, however, the train lost about 12.5 minutes while stopping at the stations. The speed of the car is **(M.A.T., 2003)**

(*a*) 100 kmph (*b*) 110 kmph
(*c*) 120 kmph (*d*) 130 kmph

98. Excluding stoppages, the speed of a bus is 54 kmph and including stoppages, it is 45 kmph. For how many minutes does the bus stop per hour?

(*a*) 9 (*b*) 10
(*c*) 12 (*d*) 20

99. A flight of Jet Airways from Delhi to Mumbai has an average speed of 700 km/hr without any stoppage, whereas a flight of Kingfisher from Delhi to Mumbai has an average speed of 560 km/hr with stoppage at Baroda. What is the average stoppage time per hour of Kingfisher flight if both the planes fly at the same speed? **(M.B.A., 2009)**

(*a*) 8 min (*b*) 12 min
(*c*) 16 min (*d*) 24 min

100. A bus covered a certain distance from village A to village B at the speed of 60 km/hr. However on its return journey it got stuck in traffic and covered the same distance at the speed of 40 km/hr and took 2 hours more to reach its destination. What is the distance covered between villages A and B? **(Bank P.O., 2010)**

(*a*) 200 km (*b*) 240 km
(*c*) 260 km (*d*) Cannot be determined
(*e*) None of these

101. A train covers a distance between two stations A and B in 45 minutes. If the speed of the train is reduced by 5 km/hr, then it covers the distance in 48 minutes. The distance between the stations A and B is **(P.C.S., 2009)**

(*a*) 55 km (*b*) 60 km
(*c*) 64 km (*d*) 80 km

102. A train travels a distance of 600 km at a constant speed. If the speed of the train is increased by 5 km/hr, the journey would take 4 hours less. Find the speed of the train. **(M.A.T., 2010)**

(*a*) 25 km/hr (*b*) 50 km/hr
(*c*) 100 km/hr (*d*) None of these

103. A car takes 15 minutes less to cover a distance of 75 km, if it increases its speed by 10 km/hr from its usual speed. How much time would it take to cover a distance of 300 km using this speed? **(M.A.T., 2010)**

(*a*) 5 hours (*b*) $5\frac{1}{2}$ hours
(*c*) 6 hours (*d*) $6\frac{1}{2}$ hours

104. With a uniform speed a car covers the distance in 8 hours. Had the speed been increased by 4 km/hr, the same distance could have been covered in $7\frac{1}{2}$ hours. What is the distance covered?

(*a*) 420 km
(*b*) 480 km
(*c*) 640 km
(*d*) Cannot be determined
(*e*) None of these

105. Two men start together to walk to a certain destination, one at 3 kmph and another at 3.75 kmph. The latter arrives half an hour before the former. The distance is

(*a*) 6 km (*b*) 7.5 km
(*c*) 8 km (*d*) 9.5 km

106. If a person walks at 14 km/hr instead of 10 km/hr, he would have walked 20 km more. The actual distance travelled by him is

(*a*) 50 km (*b*) 56 km
(*c*) 70 km (*d*) 80 km

107. In covering a certain distance, the speeds of A and B are in the ratio of 3 : 4. A takes 30 minutes more than B to reach the destination. The time taken by A to reach the destination is

(*a*) 1 hour (*b*) $1\frac{1}{2}$ hours
(*c*) 2 hours (*d*) $2\frac{1}{2}$ hours

108. In covering a distance of 30 km, Abhay takes 2 hours more than Sameer. If Abhay doubles his speed, then he would take 1 hour less than Sameer. Abhay's speed is

(*a*) 5 kmph (*b*) 6 kmph
(*c*) 6.25 kmph (*d*) 7.5 kmph

109. Three persons are walking from a place A to another place B. Their speeds are in the ratio of 4 : 3 : 5. The time ratio to reach B by these persons will be

(*a*) 4 : 3 : 5 (*b*) 5 : 3 : 4
(*c*) 15 : 9 : 20 (*d*) 15 : 20 : 12

110. A journey of 192 km between two cities takes 2 hours less by a fast train than by a slow train. If the average speed of the slow train is 16 km/hr less than that of the fast train, then the average speed of the fast train is

(*a*) 32 km/hr (*b*) 36 km/hr
(*c*) 48 km/hr (*d*) 64 km/hr

111. In a flight of 6000 km, an aircraft was slowed down due to bad weather. The average speed for the trip was reduced by 400 kmph and the time of flight increased by 30 minutes. The original planned duration of the flight was **(M.A.T., 2006)**

(a) $2\frac{1}{2}$ hours (b) $3\frac{1}{3}$ hours
(c) $4\frac{1}{3}$ hours (d) $5\frac{1}{3}$ hours

112. An aeroplane first flew with a speed of 440 kmph and covered a certain distance. It still had to cover 770 km less than what it had already covered, but it flew with a speed of 660 kmph. The average speed for the entire flight was 500 kmph. Find the total distance covered. (M.A.T., 2005)
(a) 1375 km (b) 2750 km
(c) 3250 km (d) 4400 km

113. Two boys *A* and *B* start at the same time to ride from Delhi to Meerut, 60 km away. A travels 4 km an hour slower than *B*, *B* reaches Meerut and at once turns back meeting A, 12 km from Meerut. A's rate was (M.B.A., 2011)
(a) 4 km/hr (b) 8 km/hr
(c) 12 km/hr (d) 16 km/hr

114. A cyclist drove one kilometre, with the wind in his back, in 3 minutes and drove the same way back, against the wind, in 4 minutes. If we assume that the cyclist always puts constant force on the pedals, how much time would it take him to drive 1 km without wind? (SNAP, 2008)
(a) $2\frac{1}{3}$ min (b) $2\frac{3}{7}$ min
(c) $3\frac{3}{7}$ min (d) $3\frac{7}{12}$ min

115. Ramesh travels 760 km to his home, partly by train and partly by car. He takes 8 hours, if he travels 160 km by train and the rest by car. He takes 12 minutes more, if he travels 240 km by train and the rest by car. What are the speeds of the car and the train respectively? (M.A.T., 2006)
(a) 90 km/hr, 60 km/hr (b) 100 km/hr, 80 km/hr
(c) 80 km/hr, 70 km/hr (d) 100 km/hr, 90 km/hr

116. Two sea trawlers left a sea port simultaneously in two mutually perpendicular directions. Half an hour later, the shortest distance between them was 17 km, and another 15 minutes later, one sea trawler was 10.5 km farther from the origin than the other. Find the speed of each sea trawler. (SNAP, 2008)
(a) 16 km/hr, 30 km/hr (b) 18 km/hr, 24 km/hr
(c) 20 km/hr, 22 km/hr (d) 18 km/hr, 36 km/hr

117. *A* runs twice as fast as *B* and *B* runs thrice as fast as C. The distance covered by C in 72 minutes, will be covered by *A* in (C.P.O., 2007; R.R.B., 2006)
(a) 12 minutes (b) 16 minutes
(c) 18 minutes (d) 24 minutes

118. A ship, 40 kilometres from the shore, springs a leak which admits $3\frac{3}{4}$ tonnes of water in 12 minutes. 60 tonnes would suffice to sink her, but the ship's pumps can throw out 12 tonnes of water in one hour. Find the average rate of sailing, so that she may reach the shore just as she begins to sink. (M.A.T. 2006, 2008)
(a) $1\frac{1}{2}$ km per hour (b) $2\frac{1}{2}$ km per hour
(c) $3\frac{1}{2}$ km per hour (d) $4\frac{1}{2}$ km per hour

119. Amit travelled back to home in a car, after visiting his friend in a distant village. When he started at his friend's house the car had exactly 18 litres of petrol in it. He travelled along at a steady 40 kilometres per hour and managed a 10 kilometres per litre of petrol. As the car was old, the fuel tank lost fuel at the rate of half a litre per hour. Amit was lucky as his car stopped just in front of his home because it had run out of fuel and he only just made it. How far was it from his friend's home to Amit's home? (I.I.F.T., 2005)
(a) 150 km (b) 170 km
(c) 180 km (d) None of these

120. Two men starting from the same place walk at the rate of 5 kmph and 5.5 kmph respectively. What time will they take to be 8.5 km apart, if they walk in the same direction?
(a) 4 hrs 15 min (b) 8 hrs 30 min
(c) 16 hrs (d) 17 hrs

121. A walks around a circular field at the rate of one round per hour while B runs around it at the rate of six rounds per hour. They start in the same direction from the same point at 7.30 a.m. They shall first cross each other at :
(a) 7.42 a.m. (b) 7.48 a.m.
(c) 8.10 a.m. (d) 8.30 a.m.

122. *A* and *B* start from the same point and in the same direction at 7 a.m. to walk around a rectangular field 400 m × 300 m. *A* and *B* walk at the rate of 3 km/hr and 2.5 km/hr respectively. How many times shall they cross each other if they continue to walk till 12 : 30 p.m.? (Civil Services, 2004)
(a) Not even once (b) Once
(c) Twice (d) Thrice

123. There are 8 equidistant points *A*, *B*, *C*, *D*, *E*, *F*, *G* and *H* in the clockwise direction on the periphery of a circle. In a time interval *t*, a person reaches from *A* to C with uniform motion while another person reaches the point E from the point B during the same time interval with uniform motion. Both the persons move in the same direction along the circumference of the circle and start at the same instant. How much time after the start, will the two persons meet each other? (Civil Services, 2006)

(*a*) 4*t* (*b*) 7*t*
(*c*) 9*t* (*d*) Never

124. *A* walks at 4 kmph and 4 hours after his start, *B* cycles after him at 10 kmph. How far from the start does *B* catch up with *A*?

(*a*) 16.7 km (*b*) 18.6 km
(*c*) 21.5 km (*d*) 26.7 km

125. Paschim Express left Delhi for Mumbai at 14.30 hrs travelling at a speed of 60 kmph and August Kranti Express left Delhi for Mumbai on the same day at 16.30 hrs travelling at a speed of 80 kmph. How far away from Delhi will the two trains meet (excluding stoppages)? (M.B.A., 2004)

(*a*) 120 km (*b*) 360 km
(*c*) 480 km (*d*) 500 km

126. A thief is noticed by a policeman from a distance of 200 m. The thief starts running and the policeman chases him. The thief and the policeman run at the rate of 10 km and 11 km per hour respectively. What is the distance between them after 6 minutes?

(*a*) 100 m (*b*) 150 m
(*c*) 190 m (*d*) 200 m

127. A bus is moving with a speed of 30 km/hr ahead of a car with a speed of 50 km/hr. How many kilometres apart are they if it takes 15 minutes for the car to catch up with the bus?

(*a*) 5 km (*b*) 7.5 km
(*c*) 12.5 km (*d*) 15 km

128. A thief running at 8 km/hr is chased by a policeman whose speed is 10 km/hr. If the thief is 100 metres ahead of the policeman, then the time required for the policeman to catch the thief will be

(*a*) 2 minutes (*b*) 3 minutes
(*c*) 6 minutes (*d*) 10 minutes

129. A thief steals a car at 2.30 p.m. and drives it at 60 kmph. The theft is discovered at 3 p.m. and the owner sets off in another car at 75 kmph. When will he overtake the thief?

(*a*) 4.30 p.m. (*b*) 4.45 p.m.
(*c*) 5 p.m. (*d*) 5.15 p.m.

130. Aryan runs at a speed of 40 metres/minute. Rahul follows him after an interval of 5 minutes and runs at a speed of 50 metres/minute. Rahul's dog runs at a speed of 60 metres/minute and starts along with Rahul. The dog reaches Aryan and then comes back to Rahul, and continues to do so till Rahul reaches Aryan. What is the total distance covered by the dog? (Civil Services, 2005)

(*a*) 600 m (*b*) 750 m
(*c*) 980 m (*d*) 1200 m

131. A thief, pursued by a policeman, was 100 m ahead at the start. If the ratio of the speed of the policeman to that of the thief was 5 : 4, then how far could the thief go before he was caught by the policeman? (S.S.C., 2005)

(*a*) 80 m (*b*) 200 m
(*c*) 400 m (*d*) 600 m

132. A walks at a uniform rate of 4 km an hour; and 4 hours after his start, *B* bicycles after him at the uniform rate of 10 km an hour. How far from the starting point will B catch A? (C.P.O., 2005)

(*a*) 16.7 km (*b*) 18.6 km
(*c*) 21.5 km (*d*) 26.7 km

133. A passenger train runs at the rate of 80 kmph. It starts from the station, 6 hours after a goods train leaves the station. The passenger train overtakes the goods train after 4 hours. The speed of goods train is (R.R.B., 2008)

(*a*) 32 km/hr (*b*) 45 km/hr
(*c*) 50 km/hr (*d*) 64 km/hr

134. An athlete claimed that his timing for a 100 m dash should be corrected because the starting signal was given by a gun fired from a point 10 m away from him and the timekeeper was standing close to the gun. The error due to this could be (in seconds)

[Given: speed of sound = 300 m/s]

(*a*) 0.03 (*b*) 0.1
(*c*) 0.5 (*d*) 0.7

135. Sound waves travel at 300 m/s. Sound produced at a point is heard by a person after 5 seconds while the same sound is heard by another person after 6 seconds. What could be the maximum and minimum distance between the two persons?

(*a*) 1.8 km, 0.15 km (*b*) 2.2 km, 0.20 km
(*c*) 2.8 km, 0.25 km (*d*) 3.3 km, 0.3 km

136. Two guns were fired from the same place at an interval of 8 minutes, A person approaching the place observes that 5 minutes 52 seconds have elapsed between the hearing of the sound of the two guns. If the velocity of the sound is 330 m/sec, the man was approaching the place at what speed (in km/hr)? (S.S.C., 2007)

(*a*) 24 (*b*) 27
(*c*) 30 (*d*) 36

137. Two cyclists start from the same place in opposite directions. One goes towards north at 18 kmph and the other goes towards south at 20 kmph. What time will they take to be 47.5 km apart?

(*a*) $1\frac{1}{4}$ hrs (*b*) $2\frac{1}{4}$ hrs
(*c*) 2 hrs. 23 min. (*d*) $2\frac{1}{2}$ hrs

138. A and B are two stations 10 km apart. A man, P starts from A and travels towards B at the rate of 3 km/hr, whereas another man Q starts from B and travels to wards. A at the rate of 2 km/hr. When and where do they meet? (P.C.S., 2008)

(a) After 2 hours, 6 km from A

(b) After 3 hours, 9 km from A

(c) After $2\frac{1}{2}$ hours, 7.5 km from A

(d) After 2 hours, 4 km from A

139. Two cars X and Y start from places A and B respectively which are 700 km apart at 9 a.m. Both the cars run at an average speed of 60 km/hr. Car X stops at 10 a.m. and again starts at 11 a.m. while the other car continues to run without stopping. The two cars cross each other at (P.C.S., 2009)

(a) 2 : 40 p.m (b) 3 : 20 p.m

(c) 4 : 10 p.m (d) 4 : 20 p.m

140. A train started from station A and proceeded towards station B at a speed of 48 km/hr. Forty-five minutes later another train started from station B and proceeded towards station a at 50 km/hr. If the distance between the two stations is 232 km, at what distance from station A will the trains meet? (M.A.T., 2009)

(a) 108 km (b) 132 km

(c) 144 km (d) None of these

141. The jogging track in a sports complex is 726 metres in circumference. Deepak and his wife start from the same point and walk in opposite directions at 4.5 km/hr and 3.75 km/hr respectively. They will meet for the first time in

(a) 4.9 min (b) 5.28 min

(c) 5.5 min (d) 6 min

142. A and B walk around a circular track. They start at 8 a.m. from the same point in the opposite directions. A and B walk at a speed of 2 rounds per hour and 3 rounds per hour respectively. How many times shall they cross each other before 9.30 a.m.?

(a) 5 (b) 6

(c) 7 (d) 8

143. Two cyclists start on a circular track from a given point but in opposite directions with speeds of 7 m/sec and 8 m/sec respectively. If the circumference of the circle is 300 metres, after what time will they meet at the starting point? (M.A.T., 2007)

(a) 20 sec (b) 100 sec

(c) 200 sec (d) 300 sec

144. A distance of 425 km separates two trains moving towards each other at a speed of 200 km/hr each. What will be the distance between them after 1 hr 30 min, if they reduce their speed by half, every half an hour?

(a) 75 km (b) 120 km

(c) 150 km (d) 200 km

Directions (*Questions 145 to 147*): ***These questions are based on the following information:***

P and Q are 120 km apart. A starts from P towards Q at 6 a.m. B starts from Q towards P at 11 a.m. on the same day. A is 50 % faster than B. They cross each other at 8 p.m.

145. At what time will A reach his destination?

(a) Midnight (b) 2 a.m. the next day

(c) 11 p.m. (d) 11 a.m. the next day

146. In reaching his destination, how many more hours than A, will B take?

(a) 8 (b) 9

(c) 10 (d) 12

147. A's speed (in km/hr) is

(a) 4 (b) 4.5

(c) 5 (d) 6

148. Train X leaves New York at 1 A.M. and travels east at a constant speed of x mph. If train Z leaves New York at 2 A.M. and travels east, at what constant rate of speed will train Z have to travel in order to catch train X at exactly 5 : 30 A.M.? (M.B.A., 2006)

(a) $\frac{5}{6}x$ (b) $\frac{9}{8}x$

(c) $\frac{6}{5}x$ (d) $\frac{9}{7}x$

(e) $\frac{3}{2}x$

149. Two ladies simultaneously leave cities A and B connected by a straight road and travel towards each other. The first lady travels 2 km/hr faster than the second lady and reaches B one hour before the second lady reaches A. The two cities A and B are 24 km apart. How many kilometres does each lady travel in one hour?

(a) 5 km, 3 km (b) 7 km, 5 km

(c) 8 km, 6 km (d) 6 km, 14 km

150. Buses start from a bus terminal with a speed of 20 km/hr at intervals of 10 minutes. What is the speed of a man coming from the opposite direction towards the bus terminal if he meets the buses at intervals of 8 minutes? (S.S.C., 2010)

(a) 3 km/hr (b) 4 km/hr

(c) 5 km/hr (d) 7 km/hr

151. Two men at points R and S, 76 km apart, set out at the same time to walk towards each other. The man at R walks uniformly at the rate of $4\frac{1}{2}$ km/hr ; the man at S walks at the constant rate of $3\frac{1}{4}$ km/hr for the first hour, at $3\frac{3}{4}$ km/hr for the second hour, and so on, in arithmetic progression. If the men meet x km nearer R than S in an integral number of hours, then x is **(M.B.A., 2010)**

(*a*) 4 (*b*) 6
(*c*) 8 (*d*) 10

152. Two planes move along a circle of circumference 1.2 kms with constant speeds. When they move in different directions, they meet every 15 seconds and when they move in the same direction one plane overtakes the other every 60 seconds. The speed of the slower plane is **(M.B.A., 2004)**

(*a*) 0.02 km/s (*b*) 0.03 km/s
(*c*) 0.04 km/s (*d*) 0.05 km/s

153. Two cyclists, k kilometres apart, and starting at the same time, would be together in r hours if they travelled in the same direction, but would pass each other in t hours if they travelled in opposite directions. The ratio of the speed of the faster cyclist to that of the slower is **(M.B.A., 2011)**

(*a*) $\frac{r+t}{r-t}$ (*b*) $\frac{r}{r-t}$
(*c*) $\frac{r+t}{r}$ (*d*) $\frac{r}{t}$

154. A bus left X for point Y. Two hours later a car left point X for Y and arrived at Y at the same time as the bus. If the car and the bus left simultaneously from the opposite ends X and Y towards each other, they would meet $1\frac{1}{3}$ hours after the start. How much time did it take the bus to travel from X to Y?

(*a*) 2 hours (*b*) 4 hours
(*c*) 6 hours (*d*) 8 hours

155. Two trains starting at the same time from two stations 200 km apart and going in opposite directions cross each other at a distance of 110 km from one of the stations. What is the ratio of their speeds?

(*a*) 9 : 20 (*b*) 11 : 9
(*c*) 11 : 20 (*d*) None of these

156. Two trains start from stations A and B and travel towards each other at a speed of 50 kmph and 60 kmph respectively. A the time of their meeting, the second train had travelled 120 km more than the first. The distance between A and B is **(R.R.B. 2006 ; C.P.O. 2005 ; M.A.T. 2009 ; Bank P.O. 2008)**

(*a*) 600 km (*b*) 1320 km
(*c*) 1440 km (*d*) 1660 km

157. Train A leaves Ludhiana for Delhi at 11 a.m, running at the speed of 60 km/hr. Train B leaves Ludhiana for Delhi by the same route at 2 p.m. on the same day, running at the speed of 72 km/hr. At what time will the two trains meet each other? **(M.A.T., 2008)**

(*a*) 2 a.m. on the next day (*b*) 5 a.m. on the next day
(*c*) 5 p.m. on the next day (*d*) None of these

158. A train M leaves station X at 5 a.m and reaches station Y at 9 a.m. Another train N leaves station Y at 7 a.m. and reaches station X at 10.30 a.m. At what time do the two trains cross each other? **(M.A.T., 2006)**

(*a*) 7.36 a.m (*b*) 7.56 a.m
(*c*) 8.36 a.m (*d*) 8.56 a.m

159. Train A travelling at 60 km/hr leaves Mumbai for Delhi at 6 p.m. Train B travelling at 90 km/hr also leaves Mumbai for Delhi at 9 p.m. Train C leaves Delhi for Mumbai at 9 p.m. If all the three trains meet at the same time between Mumbai and Delhi, then what is the speed of train C if the distance between Delhi and Mumbai is 1260 km?

(*a*) 60 km/hr (*b*) 90 km/hr
(*c*) 120 km/hr (*d*) 135 km/hr

160. Amit starts from a point A and walks to another point B and then returns from B to A by his car and thus takes a total time of 6 hours and 45 minutes. If he had driven both ways in his car, he would have taken 2 hours less. How long would it take for him to walk both ways? **(Civil Services, 2007)**

(*a*) 7 hours 45 minutes (*b*) 8 hours 15 minutes
(*c*) 8 hours 30 minutes (*d*) 8 hours 45 minutes

161. Reena leaves office at 6.00 p.m. and catches a 6.30 p.m. local train that arrives in her town at 7.00 p.m. Her father leaves home to pick her up at 7.00 p.m. from the station as she gets off the train. Yesterday, Reena left her office early and took a 6.00 p.m. train and arrived at 6.30 p.m. As her father was not there to pick her up, she started walking towards home. Her father left home at the usual time, saw her daughter walking, turned around, picked her up and drove home, arriving there 10 minutes earlier than the usual. For how long did Reena walk before her father picked her up?

(*a*) 10 min (*b*) 15 min
(*c*) 20 min (*d*) 25 min

162. On return from a business trip, Mr X was to be picked up from the railway station by his coachman. However, his meeting having finished before schedule, he left his destination earlier by catching an earlier train as a result of which he arrived 2 hours early. Immediately on arrival he rang up home for the coach and was told that it had just left in order to be exactly in time for the train by which he was scheduled to come. To save time he started walking home ward a 4 mph. On the way he met the coachman who brought him home an hour before schedule. How far is Mr X's house from the railway station?

(*a*) 12 miles (*b*) 16 miles
(*c*) 18 miles (*d*) 24 miles

163. A train approaches a tunnel *AB*. Inside the tunnel is a cat located at a point that is $\frac{3}{8}$ of the distance *AB* measured from the entrance *A*. When the train whistles, that cat runs. If the cat moves to the entrance *A* of the tunnel, the train catches the cat exactly at the entrance. If the cat moves to the exit *B*, the train catches the cat at exactly the exit. The ratio of the speed of the train to that of the cat is of the order

(*a*) 3 : 1 (*b*) 4 : 1
(*c*) 5 : 1 (*d*) None of these

164. The speed of a railway engine is 42 km/hr when no compartment is attached and the reduction in speed is directly proportional to the square root of the number of compartments attached. If the speed of the train carried by this engine is 24 km/hr with 9 compartments attached, the maximum number of compartments that the engine can pull is

(*a*) 35 (*b*) 41
(*c*) 48 (*d*) None of these

Direction (*Questions 165-166*): *These questions are based on the following information:* (C.A.T., 2005)

Ram and Shyam run a race between points *A* and *B*, 5 km apart. Ram starts at 9 a.m. from *A* at a speed of 5 km/hr, reaches *B* and returns to *A* at the same speed. Shyam starts at 9 : 45 a.m. from *A* at a speed of 10 km/hr, reaches *B* and comes back to A at the same speed.

165. At what time do Ram and Shyam meet each other?

(*a*) 10 a.m. (*b*) 10 : 10 a.m.
(*c*) 10 : 20 a.m. (*d*) 10 : 30 a.m.

166. At what time does Shyam overtake Ram?

(*a*) 10 : 20 a.m. (*b*) 10 : 30 a.m.
(*c*) 10 : 40 a.m. (*d*) 10 : 50 a.m.

167. A man can walk up a 'moving-up' escalator in 30 seconds. The same man can walk down this 'moving-up' escalator in 90 seconds. Assume that his walking speed is same upwards and downwards. How much time will he take to walk up the escalator, when it is not moving?

(*a*) 30 sec (*b*) 45 sec
(*c*) 60 sec (*d*) 90 sec

168. A hare pursued by a hound is 60 of her own leaps before him. When the hare takes 4 leaps, the hound takes 3. In one leap, the hare goes $1\frac{3}{4}$ metres and the hound $2\frac{3}{4}$ metres. In how many leaps will the hound overtake the hare?

(*a*) 84 (*b*) 188
(*c*) 252 (*d*) 356

169. Arun had ridden one-third the total distance of his trip when his scooter got punctured. He finished the journey on foot, spending twenty times as long walking as he had spent riding. What was the ratio of his riding speed to his walking speed?

(*a*) 4 : 1 (*b*) 5 : 1
(*c*) 10 : 1 (*d*) 20 : 1

170. A car overtakes a bus travelling from Delhi to Jaipur at 4 : 30 p.m. The car reaches Jaipur at 6 : 00 p.m. After stopping there for 1 hour, it starts back towards Delhi and meets the same bus at 7 : 30 p.m. which was moving towards Jaipur at that time. If both the bus and the car were travelling with uniform speeds on the same route, at what time would the bus reach Jaipur?

(*a*) 8 : 30 p.m. (*b*) 9 : 00 p.m.
(*c*) 9 : 15 p.m. (*d*) 9 : 30 p.m.

171. If Karan travels at a speed of 60 kmph and covers a distance in 9 hrs., then how much time will he take to travel the same distance at a speed of 90 kmph? **[Indian Railway Gr. 'D' Exam, 2014]**

(*a*) 8 hrs (*b*) 6 hrs
(*c*) 12 hrs (*d*) 9 hrs

172. The speed of a bus is 72 kmph. The distance covered by the bus in 5 sec is **[Indian Railway Gr. 'D' Exam, 2014]**

(*a*) 50 m (*b*) 74.5 m
(*c*) 100 m (*d*) 60 m

173. A man travels for 5 hours 15 minutes. If he covers the first half of the journey at 60km/h and rest at 45km/h. Find the total distance travelled by him. **[SSC—CHSL (10 + 2) Exam, 2015]**

(*a*) $1028\frac{6}{7}$ km (*b*) 189 km
(*c*) 378 km (*d*) 270 km

174. Ashok left from place A for place B at 8 a.m. and Rahul left place B for place A at 10.00 a.m. the distance between place A and B is 637 km. If Ashok and Rahul are travelling at a uniform speed of 39kmph and 47 kmph respectively, at what time will they meet? **[IBPS—Bank Spl. Officers (IT) Exam, 2015]**

(*a*) 5 : 30 pm (*b*) 4 : 30 pm
(*c*) 5 pm (*d*) 4 pm

175. A car goes 20 metres in a second. Find its speed in km/hr **[SSC—CHSL (10+2) Exam, 2015]**
(*a*) 18 (*b*) 72
(*c*) 36 (*d*) 20

176. Two men P and Q start a journey from the same place at a speed of 3 km/hr and $3\frac{1}{2}$ km/hr respectively. If they move in the same direction then what is the distance between them after 4 hours? **[IDBI—Executive Officer's Exam, 2015]**
(*a*) 3 km (*b*) $2\frac{1}{2}$ km
(*c*) 2 km (*d*) $\frac{1}{2}$ km

177. Rohan covers $\frac{2}{3}$rd of a certain distance in 2 hours 30 minutes at the rate of x kmph. He covers the remaining distance at the rate of $(x + 2)$ kmph in 50 minutes. What is the total distance? **[RBI Officer's Gr. 'B' (Phase I) Exam, 2015]**
(*a*) 21 km (*b*) 18 km
(*c*) 16 km (*d*) 15 km

178. To reach point B from point A at 4pm, Sara will have to travel at an average speed of 18 kmph. She will reach point B at 3 pm if she travels at an average speed of 24 kmph. At what average speed should Sara travel to reach point B at 2pm? **[IBPS—Bank PO/MT (Pre.) Exam, 2015]**
(*a*) 36 kmph (*b*) 28 kmph
(*c*) 25 kmph (*d*) 30 kmph

179. A student goes to school at the rate of $2\frac{1}{2}$ km/h and reaches 6 min late. If he travels at the speed of 3km/h he is 10 min early. What is the distance to the school? **[SSC—CHSL (10+2) Exam, 2015]**
(*a*) 4 km (*b*) $3\frac{1}{4}$ km
(*c*) 1 km (*d*) $3\frac{1}{2}$ km

180. Kim and Om are travelling from points A to B, which are 400 km apart. Travelling at a certain speed Kim takes one hour more than Om to reach point B. If Kim doubles her speed she will take 1 hour 30 mins less than Om to reach point B. At what speed was Kim driving from point A to B? (In kmph) **[IBPS—Bank PO (Pre.) Exam, 2015]**
(*a*) 90 kmph (*b*) 70 kmph
(*c*) 160 kmph (*d*) 80 kmph

181. A car covers 650 kms in 12 hours and the other 850 kms in 18 hours. Find the average speed of the car. **[ESIC—UDC Exam, 2016]**
(*a*) 47 kmph (*b*) 50 kmph
(*c*) 48 kmph (*d*) 52 kmph

182. A vehicle travels at the rate of 80 kmph. What distance will it travel in 15 minutes? **[ESIC—UDC Exam, 2016]**
(*a*) 20000 metre (*b*) 25000 metre
(*c*) 24000 metre (*d*) 22000 metre

183. Aryan covers a certain distance in 1 hour 30 minutes. He covers two thirds of it at the rate of 4 kmph and remaining distance at the rate of 5 kmph. Find the total distance. **[ESIC—UDC Exam, 2016]**
(*a*) 6.5 km (*b*) 6.6 km
(*c*) 6.3 km (*d*) 6.4 km

184. Rani goes to school from her house in 30 minutes. Raja takes 45 minutes in covering the same distance. Find the ratio between time taken by Rani and Raja. **[ESIC—UDC Exam, 2016]**
(*a*) 2 : 3 (*b*) 4 : 3
(*c*) 3 : 2 (*d*) 1 : 3

185. The speeds of John and Max are 30 km/h and 40 km/h. Initially Max is at a place L and John is at a place M. The distance between L and M is 650 kms. John started his journey 3 hours earlier than Max to meet each other. If they meet each other at a place P somewhere between L and M, then the distance between P and M is: **[SBI—Jr. Associates (Pre.) Exam, 2016]**
(*a*) 220 km (*b*) 250 km
(*c*) 330 km (*d*) 320 km

186. A car travels the first one third of a certain distance with a speed of 10 km/hr, the next one third distance with a speed of 20 km/hr and the last one third distance with a speed of 60 km/hr. The average speed of the car for the whole journey is **[CDS, 2016]**
(*a*) 18 km/hr (*b*) 24 km/hr
(*c*) 30 km/hr (*d*) 36 km/hr

187. With a uniform speed, a car covers a distance in 8 hours. Had the speed been increased by 4 km/hr, the same distance could have been covered in 7 hours and 30 minutes. What is the distance covered? **[CDS, 2016]**
(*a*) 420 km (*b*) 480 km
(*c*) 520 km (*d*) 640 km

188. A thief is noticed by a policeman from a distance of 200 m. The thief starts running and the policeman chases him. The thief and the policeman run at the speed of 10km/hr and 11 km/hr respectively. What is the distance between them after 6 minutes? [CDS, 2016]

(*a*) 100m (*b*) 120m
(*c*) 150m (*d*) 160m

189. A man performs 2/15 of the total journey by rail, 9/20 by bus and the remaining 10 km, on the cycle. His total journey is

[UPSSSC—Lower Subordinate (Pre.) Exam, 2016]

(*a*) 31.2 km (*b*) 38.4 km
(*c*) 32.8 km (*d*) 24 km

190. Ramesh is walking at a speed of 10 kilometres per hour. After every kilometer he takes rest for 5 minutes. The time taken to cover a distance of 5 kilometres by Ramesh is

[DMRC—Customer Relationship Assistant (CRA) Exam, 2016]

(*a*) 30 minutes (*b*) 35 minutes
(*c*) 50 minutes (*d*) 55 minutes

191. If a runner takes as much time in running 20 metres as the car takes in covering 50 metres. The distance covered by the runner during the time the car covers 1 km is

[DMRC—Jr. Engineer (Electrical) Exam, 2016]

(*a*) 400 metres (*b*) 40 metres
(*c*) 440 metres (*d*) None of these

ANSWERS

1. (*b*)	2. (*b*)	3. (*b*)	4. (*d*)	5. (*b*)	6. (*d*)	7. (*d*)	8. (*b*)	9. (*c*)	10. (*b*)
11. (*c*)	12. (*b*)	13. (*e*)	14. (*b*)	15. (*b*)	16. (*e*)	17. (*d*)	18. (*b*)	19. (*b*)	20. (*b*)
21. (*a*)	22. (*b*)	23. (*c*)	24. (*d*)	25. (*a*)	26. (*a*)	27. (*c*)	28. (*c*)	29. (*c*)	30. (*a*)
31. (*d*)	32. (*d*)	33. (*c*)	34. (*b*)	35. (*a*)	36. (*c*)	37. (*c*)	38. (*d*)	39. (*c*)	40. (*b*)
41. (*b*)	42. (*a*)	43. (*c*)	44. (*d*)	45. (*d*)	46. (*a*)	47. (*d*)	48. (*c*)	49. (*d*)	50. (*e*)
51. (*d*)	52. (*a*)	53. (*c*)	54. (*d*)	55. (*c*)	56. (*c*)	57. (*a*)	58. (*b*)	59. (*d*)	60. (*b*)
61. (*b*)	62. (*b*)	63. (*c*)	64. (*b*)	65. (*e*)	66. (*d*)	67. (*d*)	68. (*d*)	69. (*a*)	70. (*b*)
71. (*b*)	72. (*b*)	73. (*c*)	74. (*b*)	75. (*d*)	76. (*a*)	77. (*d*)	78. (*a*)	79. (*b*)	80. (*c*)
81. (*b*)	82. (*d*)	83. (*b*)	84. (*b*)	85. (*b*)	86. (*a*)	87. (*c*)	88. (*b*)	89. (*d*)	90. (*c*)
91. (*c*)	92. (*e*)	93. (*b*)	94. (*d*)	95. (*b*)	96. (*a*)	97. (*c*)	98. (*b*)	99. (*b*)	100. (*b*)
101. (*b*)	102. (*a*)	103. (*a*)	104. (*b*)	105. (*b*)	106. (*a*)	107. (*c*)	108. (*a*)	109. (*d*)	110. (*c*)
111. (*a*)	112. (*b*)	113. (*b*)	114. (*c*)	115. (*b*)	116. (*a*)	117. (*a*)	118. (*d*)	119. (*d*)	120. (*d*)
121. (*a*)	122. (*b*)	123. (*b*)	124. (*d*)	125. (*c*)	126. (*a*)	127. (*a*)	128. (*b*)	129. (*c*)	130. (*d*)
131. (*c*)	132. (*d*)	133. (*a*)	134. (*a*)	135. (*d*)	136. (*b*)	137. (*a*)	138. (*a*)	139. (*b*)	140. (*b*)
141. (*b*)	142. (*c*)	143. (*d*)	144. (*a*)	145. (*b*)	146. (*c*)	147. (*d*)	148. (*d*)	149. (*c*)	150. (*c*)
151. (*a*)	152. (*b*)	153. (*a*)	154. (*b*)	155. (*b*)	156. (*b*)	157. (*b*)	158. (*b*)	159. (*c*)	160. (*d*)
161. (*d*)	162. (*d*)	163. (*b*)	164. (*c*)	165. (*b*)	166. (*b*)	167. (*b*)	168. (*c*)	169. (*c*)	170. (*b*)
171. (*b*)	172. (*c*)	173. (*d*)	174. (*b*)	175. (*b*)	176. (*c*)	177. (*d*)	178. (*a*)	179. (*a*)	180. (*d*)
181. (*b*)	182. (*a*)	183. (*d*)	184. (*a*)	185. (*c*)	186. (*a*)	187. (*b*)	188. (*a*)	189. (*d*)	190. (*c*)
191. (*c*)									

SOLUTIONS

1. 30.6 km/hr $= \left(30.6 \times \frac{5}{18}\right)$ m/sec $= \frac{153}{18}$ m/sec = 8.5 m/sec.

2. Speed $= \left(\frac{150}{25}\right)$ m/sec = 6 m/sec

$= \left(6 \times \frac{18}{5}\right)$ km/hr $= \left(\frac{108}{5}\right)$ km/hr = 21.6 km/hr.

3. Speed $= \left(\frac{2924}{43}\right)$ km/hr = 68 km/hr.

4. *A*'s speed = 72 km/hr $= \left(72 \times \frac{5}{18}\right)$ m/sec = 20 m/sec.

B's speed = 25 m/sec.

Difference = (25 – 20) m/sec = 5 m/sec.

5. Distance covered = 65 km = 65000 m.

Time taken = 2 hrs 10 min

= [(2 × 60) + 10] min = 130 min.

$\therefore$ Speed $= \left(\frac{65000}{130}\right)$ m/min = 500 m/min.

6. 1 yard = 0.9144 m $\Rightarrow$ 100 yards = (100 × 0.9144) m = 91.44 m.

$\therefore$ Required difference = (100 – 91.44) m = 8.56 m.

7. 25 m/sec $= \left(25 \times \frac{18}{5}\right)$ km/hr = 90 km/hr.

And, 25 m/sec = (25 × 60) m/min = 1500 m/min.

So, all the three speeds are equal.

8. Speed $= \left(\frac{600}{5 \times 60}\right)$ m/sec = 2 m/sec

$= \left(2 \times \frac{18}{5}\right)$ km/hr = 7.2 km/hr.

9. Required time = $\left(\frac{432}{48}\right)$ hours = 9 hours.

10. Speed of the bike = $\left(\frac{180}{4}\right)$ km/hr = 45 km/hr.

Speed of the bicycle = $\left(\frac{1}{6} \times 45\right)$ km/hr = 7.5 km/hr.

$\therefore$ Required distance = (7.5 × 8) km = 60 km.

11. Let the speeds of the car, train and bus be $5x$, $9x$ and $4x$ km/hr respectively.

Then, $\frac{5x + 9x + 4x}{3} = 72 \Leftrightarrow 6x = 72 \Leftrightarrow x = 12.$

$\therefore$ Speed of the car = 60 km/hr ;

speed of the train = 108 km/hr.

Average speed of car and train

$= \left(\frac{60 + 108}{2}\right)$ km/hr = 84 km/hr.

12. Required ratio = (65 × 8) : (70 × 4) = 520 : 280 = 13 : 7.

13. Speed of the train = $\left(\frac{1125}{15}\right)$ km/hr = 75 km/hr.

Speed of the bus = $\left(\frac{1}{3} \times 75\right)$ km/hr = 25 km/hr.

Distance covered by the bus in 60 min = 25 km.

Distance covered by the bus in 36 min

$= \left(\frac{25}{60} \times 36\right)$ km = 15 km.

14. Quantity of petrol consumed by both the motorbikes

$= \left(\frac{294}{42} + \frac{208}{52}\right)$ litres = 11 litres.

$\therefore$ Total amount spent on petrol = Rs (48 × 11) = ₹ 528.

15. Time taken = 3 hrs 15 min = $3\frac{1}{4}$ hrs = $\frac{13}{4}$ hrs.

$\therefore$ Required distance = $\left(40 \times \frac{13}{4}\right)$ km = 130 km.

16. Required distance

$= AD \sqrt{(AE)^2 + (DE)^2}$

$= \sqrt{(30)^2 + (30)^2}$

$= \sqrt{900 + 900} = \sqrt{1800}$

$= 30\sqrt{2}$ miles.

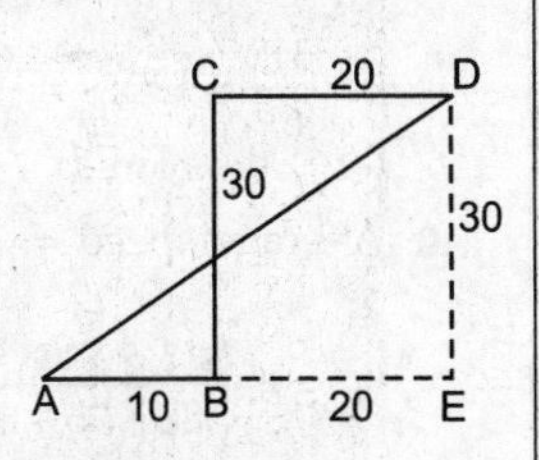

17. Distance covered by the first plane till 2 P.M., i.e., in 2 hrs = (500 × 2) miles = 1000 miles.

Distance covered by the second plane till 2 P.M., i.e., in $1\frac{1}{2}$ hrs = $\left(400 \times \frac{3}{2}\right)$ miles = 600 miles.

$\therefore$ Required distance

$= AB = \sqrt{(1000)^2 + (600)^2}$

$= \sqrt{1000000 + 360000}$

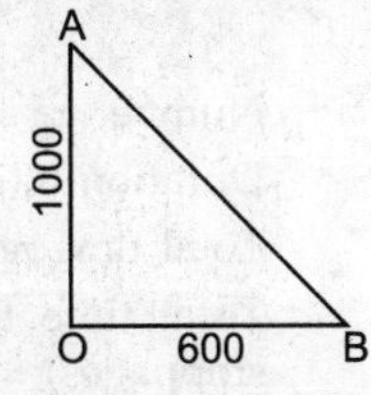

$= \sqrt{1360000}$ miles $= 200\sqrt{34}$ miles

= 1166 miles ≈ 1200 miles.

18. Time taken to cover 1300 km = $\left(\frac{1300}{65}\right)$ hrs = 20 hrs.

Halt time = (24 – 20) hrs = 4 hrs.

Halting time at each junction = $\left(\frac{4 \times 60}{8}\right)$ min = 30 min.

19. Suppose Jane travelled x miles by water, $\left(\frac{4x}{7}\right)$ miles on foot and $\left(\frac{2x}{5}\right)$ miles on horseback.

Then, $x + \frac{4x}{7} + \frac{2x}{5} = 3036 \Leftrightarrow \frac{69x}{35} = 3036$

$\Leftrightarrow x = \left(\frac{3036 \times 35}{69}\right) = 1540.$

$\therefore$ Distance travelled on foot = $\left(\frac{4}{7} \times 1540\right)$ miles = 880 miles.

20. Required time = $\left(\frac{8.1 \times 10^{13}}{3.0 \times 10^5}\right)$ seconds $= 2.7 \times 10^8$ sec

$= \left(\frac{2.7 \times 10^8}{60 \times 60}\right)$ hrs $= 7.5 \times 10^4$ hrs.

21. For the distance to be minimum, the club must lie between Akash's home and school.

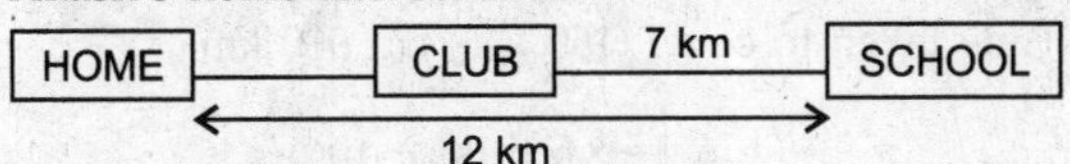

Hence, required distance = (12 – 7) km = 5 km.

22. Actual time taken for the journey

= 4 hrs 15 min – (10 + 2 × 5 + 3) min

= 4 hrs 15 min – 23 min = 3 hrs 52 min = $3\frac{26}{30}$ hrs = $\frac{116}{30}$ hrs.

$\therefore$ Average speed = $\left(\frac{580}{3} \times \frac{30}{116}\right)$ km/hr = 50 km/hr.

23. Deepa's original speed = 30 km/hr.

Deepa's new speed = (30 + 10) km/hr = 40 km/hr.

Distance = (30 × 6) km = 180 km.

Hema's original speed = $\left(\frac{180}{4}\right)$ km/hr = 45 km/hr.

Hema's new speed

= (45 + 5) km/hr = 50 km/hr.

Difference in time

$= \left(\frac{180}{40} - \frac{180}{50}\right)$ hrs $= \frac{9}{10}$ hrs $= \left(\frac{9}{10} \times 60\right)$ min = 54 min.

24. Net height ascended in 2 min = (6 – 3) m = 3 m.

Net height ascended in 36 min = $\left(\frac{3}{2} \times 36\right)$ m = 54 m.

In the 37th min, the monkey ascends 6 m and reaches the top.

Hence, total time taken = 37 minutes.

25. Time taken to cover 60 miles = 80 min = $\frac{4}{3}$ hrs.

$\therefore$ Speed of the train = $\left(60 \times \frac{3}{4}\right)$ mph = 45 mph.

Speed of the aeroplane = (2 × 45) mph = 90 mph.

Distance covered by the aeroplane in 60 min = 90 miles.

Distance covered by the aeroplane in 20 min

$= \left(\frac{90}{60} \times 20\right)$ miles = 30 miles.

26. Speed = $\frac{\text{Distance}}{\text{Time}} \Rightarrow p - q = \frac{1}{r}$.

27. Let the required number of days be x.

More distance, More days required **(Direct Proportion)**

More speed, Less days required **(Indirect Proportion)**

More resting hours, More days required **(Direct Proportion)**

$$\left.\begin{array}{lc} \text{Distance} & 1 : 2 \\ \text{Speed} & 2 : 1 \\ \text{Resting hours} & 9 : 18 \end{array}\right\} :: 40 : x$$

$\therefore \quad 1 \times 2 \times 9 \times x =$

$2 \times 1 \times 18 \times 40 \Leftrightarrow x = \frac{2 \times 18 \times 40}{2 \times 9} = 80.$

28. Time taken to cover 150 km = (1 hr 30 min + 10 min)

$= 1$ hr 40 min $= 1\frac{2}{3}$ hr $= \frac{5}{3}$ hr.

Time taken to cover (150 × 6) *i.e.*, 900 km

$= \left(\frac{5}{3} \times 6\right)$ hrs. = 10 hrs.

Remaining 100 km is covered in 1 hour.

Total time taken = (10 + 1) hrs = 11 hrs.

29. Distance = Speed x Time = $\left(6 \times \frac{50}{60}\right)$ km = 5 km.

$\therefore$ Required time = $\frac{\text{Distance}}{\text{Speed}} = \left(\frac{5}{10}\right)$ hrs $= \frac{1}{2}$ hr = 30 min.

30. Ratio of speeds = $\left(\frac{550}{60} \times \frac{18}{5}\right) : \left(\frac{33}{45} \times 60\right) = 33 : 44 = 3 : 4.$

31. Let the speeds of two trains be $7x$ and $8x$ km/hr.

Then, $8x = \frac{400}{4} = 100 \Rightarrow x = \left(\frac{100}{8}\right) = 12.5.$

$\therefore$ Speed of first train = (7 × 12.5) km/hr = 87.5 km/hr.

32. Total distance travelled $= \left[\left(50 \times 2\frac{1}{2}\right) + \left(70 \times 1\frac{1}{2}\right)\right]$

miles = (125 + 105) miles = 230 miles.

33. Number of gaps between 21 telephone posts = 20.

Distance travelled in 1 minute = (50 × 20) m = 1000 m = 1 km.

$\therefore$ Speed = 60 km/hr.

34. Distance = $\left(1100 \times \frac{11}{5}\right)$ feet = 2420 feet.

35. Time taken to cover 600 km = $\left(\frac{600}{100}\right)$ hrs = 6 hrs.

Number of stoppages = $\frac{600}{75} - 1 = 7.$

Total time of stoppage = (3 × 7) min = 21 min.

Hence, total time taken = 6 hrs 21 min.

36. Let the distance covered by the cyclist be x and the time taken be y. Then,

Required ratio $= \frac{\frac{1}{2}x}{2y} : \frac{x}{y} = \frac{1}{4} : 1 = 1 : 4.$

37. Distance covered in first 2 hours = (70 × 2) km = 140 km.

Distance covered in next 2 hours = (80 × 2) km = 160 km.

Remaining distance = 345 − (140 + 160) = 45 km.

Speed in the fifth hour = 90 km/hr.

Time taken to cover 45 km = $\left(\frac{45}{90}\right)$ hr $= \frac{1}{2}$ hr.

$\therefore$ Total time taken = $\left(2 + 2 + \frac{1}{2}\right) = 4\frac{1}{2}$ hrs.

38. This is a question on uniform retardation (as it is given that the car slows down at a fixed rate)

If v is the final velocity, u is the initial velocity, a is the uniform acceleration (or retardation), t is the time and s is the distance covered, we have :

$v = u + at$ and $s = ut + \frac{1}{2}at^2$

Here, $v = 0$, $u = 24$ m/s, $a = -3$ m/s^2

$\therefore \quad 0 = 24 - 3t \Rightarrow 3t = 24 \Rightarrow t = 8.$

And, $s = \left[24 \times 8 + \frac{1}{2} \times (-3) \times 8^2\right]$ m = (192 − 96) m = 96 m.

39. Total time taken

$= \left[\frac{x}{y} + \frac{x}{\left(\frac{3y}{5}\right)} + \frac{x}{\left(\frac{2y}{5}\right)}\right]$ hours

$= \left(\frac{x}{y} + \frac{5x}{3y} + \frac{5x}{2y}\right)$ hours $= \left(\frac{6x + 10x + 15x}{6y}\right)$ hours

$= \left(\frac{31x}{6y}\right)$ hours.

$\therefore \quad \frac{31x}{6y} = 1 \Leftrightarrow \frac{x}{y} = \frac{6}{31}.$

40. Average speed = $\frac{\text{Total distance covered}}{\text{Total time taken}}$

$= \left(\frac{4 \times 9 \times 400}{88 + 96 + 89 + 87}\right)$ m/min $= \left(\frac{14400}{360}\right)$ m/min

= 40 m/min.

41. Time taken by the express train to cover 600 km

$= \left(\frac{600}{100}\right)$ hrs = 6 hrs.

Number of stoppages = (600 ÷ 75) − 1 = 7.

Duration of stoppage = (3 × 7) min = 21 min.

Total time taken = 6 hrs 21 min.

Total time taken by local train to cover 50 km (with stoppages) = 1 hr 2 min.

So, the local train covers (50 × 6) = 300 km in 6 hr 12 min.

In remaining 9 min, it covers $\left(\frac{50}{60}\times 9\right)\text{km} = 7.5\text{ km}.$

∴ Required distance = (300 + 7.5) km = 307.5 km.

42. Let the required number of hours be n.

Clearly, the car covers 40 km in first hour, 45 km in the second hour, 50 km in the third hour, and so on.

Thus, we have :
40 + 45 + 50 + ... upto n terms = 385.

This is an A.P. with first term a = 40, common difference d = 5.

$\therefore S_n = \frac{n}{2}[2\times 40 + (n-1)5]$

So, $\frac{n}{2}[80 + 5(n-1)] = 385 \Leftrightarrow 80n + 5n^2 - 5n = 770 \Leftrightarrow$

$5n^2 + 75n - 770 = 0$

$\Leftrightarrow n^2 + 15n - 154 = 0 \Leftrightarrow n^2 + 22n - 7n - 154 = 0$

$\Leftrightarrow n(n+22) - 7(n+22) = 0 \Leftrightarrow (n+22)(n-7) = 0 \Leftrightarrow n = 7.$

Hence, required number of hours = 7.

43. Total distance travelled in 12 hours = (35 + 37 + 39 + ... upto 12 terms).

This is an A.P. with first term, a = 35, number of terms, n = 12, common difference, d = 2.

∴ Required distance

$= \frac{12}{2}[2\times 35 + (12-1)\times 2] = 6(70+22) = 552\text{ km}.$

44. Time taken to cover a distance is inversely proportional to the speed.

Let the required time be x min.

Then, $50 : 55 :: x : 44 \Leftrightarrow 55x = 50 \times 44$

$\Leftrightarrow x = \left(\frac{50\times 44}{55}\right)\text{min} = 40\text{ min}.$

45. Ratio of speeds = 2 : 3 : 4.

∴ Ratio of times taken $= \frac{1}{2}:\frac{1}{3}:\frac{1}{4} = 6:4:3.$

46. Ratio of speeds = 3 : 4.

Ratio of times taken $= \frac{1}{3}:\frac{1}{4} = 4:3.$

Let A and B take $4x$ and $3x$ minutes respectively to reach a destination.

Then, $4x - 3x = 20 \Leftrightarrow x = 20.$

∴ Time taken by $A = 4x = (4\times 20)\text{ min} = 80\text{ min} = 1\frac{1}{3}\text{ hr}.$

47. Let the speed of steam engine train be x.

Then, speed of electric train = 125% of $x = \frac{5x}{4}$.

Time taken by steam engine = 4 hr 25 min $= 4\frac{25}{60}\text{ hr} = 4\frac{5}{12}\text{ hr}$

Let the time taken by electric train be t hours.

Then, $x : \frac{5x}{4} :: t : 4\frac{5}{12} \Leftrightarrow 1 : \frac{5}{4} :: t : \frac{53}{12}$

$\Leftrightarrow \frac{5}{4}t = \frac{53}{12} \Leftrightarrow t = \left(\frac{53}{12}\times\frac{4}{5}\right) = \frac{53}{15} = 3\frac{8}{15}\text{ hr}.$

48. Suppose B takes x hours to walk d km.

Then, A takes $(x + 2)$ hours to walk d km.

A's speed $= \left(\frac{d}{x+2}\right)$ km/hr and B's speed $= \left(\frac{d}{x}\right)$ km/hr.

A's new speed $= \left(\frac{2d}{x+2}\right)$ km/hr.

$\therefore \frac{d}{\left(\frac{d}{x}\right)} - \frac{d}{\left(\frac{2d}{x+2}\right)} = 1 \Leftrightarrow x - \left(\frac{x+2}{2}\right) = 1$

$\Leftrightarrow x - 2 = 2 \Leftrightarrow x = 4.$

49. Speed $= \left(10\times\frac{60}{12}\right)$ km/hr = 50 km/hr.

New speed = (50 – 5) km/hr = 45 km/hr.

∴ Time taken $= \left(\frac{10}{45}\right)\text{hr} = \left(\frac{2}{9}\times 60\right)\text{min} = 13\frac{1}{3}\text{ min}$

= 13 min 20 sec.

50. Distance covered in 2 hrs 15 min, i.e.,

$2\frac{1}{4}\text{ hrs} = \left(80\times\frac{9}{4}\right)\text{hrs} = 180\text{ hrs}.$

Time taken to cover remaining distance

$= \left(\frac{350-180}{60}\right)\text{hrs} = \frac{17}{6}\text{ hrs} = 2\frac{5}{6}\text{ hrs} = 2\text{ hrs }50\text{ min}.$

Total time taken = (2 hrs 15 min + 2 hrs 50 min) = 5 hrs 5 min.

So, Anna reached city A at 10.25 a.m.

51. Distance = (240 × 5) km = 1200 km.

∴ Required speed $= \left(1200\times\frac{3}{5}\right)$ km/hr = 720 km/hr.

52. Time required = (2 hrs 30 min – 50 min)

$= 1\text{ hr }40\text{ min} = 1\frac{2}{3}\text{ hrs}.$

∴ Required speed $= \left(50\times\frac{3}{5}\right)$ km/hr = 30 km/hr.

Original speed $= \left(50\times\frac{2}{5}\right)$ km/hr = 20 km/hr.

∴ Difference in speed = (30 – 20) km/hr = 10 km/hr.

53. Remaining distance = 3 km

and Remaining time $= \left(\frac{1}{3}\times 45\right)\text{min} = 15\text{ min} = \frac{1}{4}\text{ hour}.$

∴ Required speed = (3 × 4) km/hr = 12 km/hr.

54. Let the total journey be x km.

Then, $\frac{3x}{5} + \frac{7x}{20} + 6.5 = x \Leftrightarrow 12x + 7x + 20\times 6.5$

$= 20x \Leftrightarrow x = 130$ km.

55. Time taken to travel 45 km $= \left(\frac{45}{20}\right)\text{hr} = \frac{9}{4}\text{ hr} = 2\frac{1}{4}\text{ hr}$

= 2 hr 15 min.

Remaining time = (3 hr – 2 hr 15 min) = 45 min.

Hence, required speed = $\left(\frac{45}{45}\right)$ km/min = 1 km/min.

56. Time taken to travel 25 km = $\left(\frac{25}{40}\right)$ hr = $\frac{5}{8}$ hr.

Remaining time = $\left(1-\frac{5}{8}\right)$ hr = $\frac{3}{8}$ hr.

∴ Required speed = $\left(21\times\frac{8}{3}\right)$ km/hr = 56 km/hr.

57. Total distance = (70 + 50) miles = 120 miles.

Average speed = 50 miles/hour.

Required time of journey = $\left(\frac{120}{50}\right)$ hr = $\frac{12}{5}$ = hr $2\frac{2}{5}$ hr

= 2 hr 24 min.

Time taken to cover 50 miles

= $1\frac{1}{2}$ hr = 1 hr 30 min.

∴ Remaining time = (2 hr 24 min – 1 hr 30 min) = 54 min.

58. Let the total distance be x km. Then,

$$\frac{\frac{1}{2}x}{21}+\frac{\frac{1}{2}x}{24}=10 \Rightarrow \frac{x}{21}+\frac{x}{24}=20$$

$$\Rightarrow 15x = 168\times20 \Rightarrow x = \left(\frac{168\times20}{15}\right) = 224 \text{ km.}$$

59. Let the length of the journey be x km. Then,

$$\frac{\frac{1}{3}x}{60}+\frac{\frac{2}{3}x}{80}=5 \Rightarrow \frac{x}{180}+\frac{x}{120}=5 \Rightarrow \frac{5x}{360}=5 \Rightarrow x=360.$$

60. Let the total distance be $3x$ km.

Then, $\frac{x}{3}+\frac{x}{4}+\frac{x}{5}=\frac{47}{60} \Leftrightarrow \frac{47x}{60}=\frac{47}{60} \Leftrightarrow x = 1.$

∴ Total distance = (3 × 1) km = 3 km.

61. Let the distance travelled by the train be x km.

Then, distance travelled by bus = (285 – x) km.

$$\therefore \left(\frac{285-x}{40}\right)+\frac{x}{55}=6 \Leftrightarrow \frac{(285-x)}{8}+\frac{x}{11}=30$$

$$\Leftrightarrow \frac{11(285-x)+8x}{88}=30$$

$\Leftrightarrow$ 3135 – 11x + 8x = 2640 $\Leftrightarrow$ 3x = 495 $\Leftrightarrow$ x = 165.

Hence, distance travelled by train = 165 km.

62. Let A's speed = x km/hr. Then, B's speed = (7 – x) km/hr.

So, $\frac{24}{x}+\frac{24}{(7-x)}=14 \Leftrightarrow 24(7-x)+24x=14x(7-x)$

$\Leftrightarrow$ $14x^2 - 98x + 168 = 0$

$\Leftrightarrow$ $x^2 - 7x + 12 = 0$

$\Leftrightarrow$ $(x-3)(x-4) = 0$

$\Leftrightarrow$ $x = 3$ or $x = 4$.

Since A is faster than B, so A's speed = 4 km/hr and B's speed = 3 km/hr.

63. Speed on return trip = 150% of 40 = 60 kmph.

∴ Average speed

= $\left(\frac{2\times40\times60}{40+60}\right)$ km/hr = $\left(\frac{4800}{100}\right)$ km/hr = 48 km/hr.

64. Average speed = $\left(\frac{2\times500\times700}{500+700}\right)$ km/hr = $\left(\frac{1750}{3}\right)$ km/hr

= $583\frac{1}{3}$ km/hr.

65. Average speed = $\left(\frac{2\times56\times53}{56+53}\right)$ km/hr = $\left(\frac{5936}{109}\right)$ km/hr

= 54.45 km/hr ≈ 54.5 km/hr.

66. Average speed

$$= \frac{\left(2\times\frac{5}{2}\times\frac{13}{4}\right)}{\left(\frac{5}{2}+\frac{13}{4}\right)} \text{ km/hr} = \left(\frac{65}{4}\times\frac{4}{23}\right) \text{ km/hr} = \left(\frac{65}{23}\right) \text{ km/hr.}$$

Total time taken = 4 hr 36 min = $4\frac{36}{60}$ hr = $4\frac{3}{5}$ hr = $\frac{23}{5}$ hr.

Total distance covered uphill and downhill

= $\left(\frac{65}{23}\times\frac{23}{5}\right)$ km = 13 km.

∴ Distance walked uphill = $\left(\frac{13}{2}\right)$ km = $6\frac{1}{2}$ km.

67. Time taken to cover 150 km in going trip

= 3 hr 20 min = $3\frac{20}{60}$ hr = $3\frac{1}{3}$ hr = $\frac{10}{3}$ hr.

Speed in going trip = $\left(150\times\frac{3}{10}\right)$ km/hr = 45 km/hr.

Time taken to cover 150 km in return trip = 4 hr 10 min.

= $4\frac{1}{6}$ hr = $\frac{25}{6}$ hr.

Speed in return trip = $\left(150\times\frac{6}{25}\right)$ km/hr = 36 km/hr.

∴ Average speed

= $\left(\frac{2\times45\times36}{45+36}\right)$ km/hr = $\left(\frac{2\times45\times36}{81}\right)$ km/hr = 40 km/hr.

Required difference = (45 – 40) km/hr = 5 km/hr.

68. Let the speed in return journey be x km/hr.

Then, speed in onward journey = $\frac{125}{100}x = \left(\frac{5}{4}x\right)$ km/hr.

Average speed = $\left(\frac{2\times\frac{5}{4}x\times x}{\frac{5}{4}x+x}\right)$ km/hr = $\left(\frac{10x}{9}\right)$ km/hr.

∴ $\left(800\times\frac{9}{10x}\right)=16 \Leftrightarrow x=\left(\frac{800\times9}{16\times10}\right)=45.$

So, speed in onward journey

= $\left(\frac{5}{4}\times45\right)$ km/hr = 56.25 km/hr.

69. Time taken = 5 hrs 25 min = $\frac{65}{12}$ hrs.

Let the required distance be x km.

Then, $\frac{x}{10}+\frac{x}{1}=\frac{65}{12} \Leftrightarrow 11x=\frac{650}{12} \Leftrightarrow x=\frac{325}{66}=4\frac{61}{66}$ km.

70. Total distance travelled = $(50 \times 1 + 48 \times 2 + 52 \times 3)$ km = 302 km.

Total time taken = 6 hrs.

$\therefore$ Mean speed = $\left(\frac{302}{6}\right)$ km/hr = $50\frac{1}{3}$ km/hr.

71. Total distance travelled = $(39 + 25)$ km = 64 km.

Total time taken = $(45 + 35)$ min = 80 min = $\frac{4}{3}$ hr.

$\therefore$ Average speed = $\left(64\times\frac{3}{4}\right)$ km/hr = 48 km/hr.

72. Total distance travelled = $\left(30\times\frac{12}{60}+45\times\frac{8}{60}\right)$ km = 12 km.

Total time taken = $(12 + 8)$ min = 20 min = $\frac{1}{3}$ hr.

$\therefore$ Average speed = (12×3) km/hr = 36 km/hr.

73. Total time taken = $\left(\frac{160}{64}+\frac{160}{80}\right)$ hrs = $\frac{9}{2}$ hrs.

$\therefore$ Average speed = $\left(320\times\frac{2}{9}\right)$ km/hr = 71.11 km/hr.

74. Total distance travelled = $(10 + 12)$ km/hr = 22 km/hr.

Total time taken = $\left(\frac{10}{12}+\frac{12}{10}\right)$ hrs = $\frac{61}{30}$ hrs.

$\therefore$ Average speed = $\left(22\times\frac{30}{61}\right)$ km/hr = 10.8 km/hr.

75. Total distance travelled = $(600 + 800 + 500 + 100)$ km = 2000 km.

Total time taken = $\left(\frac{600}{80}+\frac{800}{40}+\frac{500}{400}+\frac{100}{50}\right)$ hrs = $\frac{123}{4}$ hrs.

$\therefore$ Average speed = $\left(2000\times\frac{4}{123}\right)$ km/hr = $\left(\frac{8000}{123}\right)$ km/hr = $65\frac{5}{123}$ km/hr.

76. Total distance travelled = $(24 + 36)$ km = 60 km.

Total time taken = $\left(\frac{24}{16}+\frac{36}{15}\right)$ hr = $\left(\frac{3}{2}+\frac{12}{5}\right)$ hr = $\frac{39}{10}$ hrs.

$\therefore$ Average speed = $\left(60\times\frac{10}{39}\right)$ km/hr = $\left(\frac{200}{13}\right)$ km/hr = 15.38 km/hr.

77. Let each distance be equal to d. Then,

Total distance travelled = $3d$.

Total time taken = $\left(\frac{d}{x}+\frac{d}{y}+\frac{d}{z}\right)$ hr = $\frac{d(xy+yz+zx)}{xyz}$ hr.

$\therefore$ Average speed = $\left[3d\times\frac{xyz}{d(xy+yz+zx)}\right]$ km/hr = $\frac{3xyz}{(xy+yz+zx)}$ km/hr.

78. Let the whole distance travelled be x km and the average speed of the car for the whole journey be y km/hr.

Then, $\frac{(x/3)}{10}+\frac{(x/3)}{20}+\frac{(x/3)}{60}=\frac{x}{y}$

$\Leftrightarrow \frac{x}{30}+\frac{x}{60}+\frac{x}{180}=\frac{x}{y} \Leftrightarrow \frac{1}{18}y=1 \Leftrightarrow y=18$ km/hr.

79. $x\times\frac{15}{60}+2x\times\frac{20}{60}+x\times\frac{10}{60}=39$

$\Rightarrow \frac{x}{4}+\frac{2x}{3}+\frac{x}{6}=39 \Rightarrow 3x+8x+2x=468 \Rightarrow x=36.$

80. Let speed of jogging be x km/hr.

Total time taken = $\left(\frac{9}{6}\text{ hrs}+1.5\text{ hrs}\right)$ = 3 hrs.

Total distance covered = $(9 + 1.5x)$ km.

$\therefore \frac{9+1.5x}{3}=9 \Leftrightarrow 9+1.5x=27 \Leftrightarrow \frac{3}{2}x=18$

$\Leftrightarrow x=\left(18\times\frac{2}{3}\right)=12$ kmph.

81. Ratio of speeds while going and returning = 40 : 30 = 4 : 3.

Ratio of times taken while going and returning = 3 : 4.

Time taken while going = $\left(\frac{3}{7}\times8\right)$ hr = $\frac{24}{7}$ hr.

Time taken while returning = $\left(\frac{4}{7}\times8\right)$ hr = $\frac{32}{7}$ hr.

$\therefore$ Required distance = $\left(40\times\frac{24}{7}\right)$ miles = $\frac{960}{7}$ miles = 137.14 miles.

82. Time taken = 1 hr 40 min 48 sec

= 1 hr $40\frac{4}{5}$ min = $1\frac{51}{75}$ hrs = $\frac{126}{75}$ hrs.

Let the actual speed be x km/hr.

Then, $\frac{5}{7}x\times\frac{126}{75}=42$ or $x=\left(\frac{42\times7\times75}{5\times126}\right)=35$ km/hr.

83. New speed = $\frac{7}{11}$ of usual speed.

$\therefore$ New time = $\frac{11}{7}$ of usual time.

So, $\frac{11}{7}$ of usual time = 22 hrs

$\Rightarrow$ usual time = $\left(\frac{22\times7}{11}\right)$ = 14 hrs.

Hence, time saved = $(22 - 14)$ = 8 hrs.

84. Let the speed be x km/hr.

Then, $30x-30\times\frac{14}{15}x=10 \Leftrightarrow 2x=10 \Leftrightarrow x=5$ km/hr.

85. New speed = $\frac{6}{7}$ of usual speed.

New time = $\frac{7}{6}$ of usual time

$\therefore \left(\frac{7}{6}\text{ of usual time}\right) - (\text{usual time}) = \frac{1}{5}\text{ hr.}$

$\Rightarrow \frac{1}{6}\text{ of usual time} = \frac{1}{5}\text{ hr}$

$\Rightarrow$ usual time $= \frac{6}{5}\text{ hr} = 1\text{ hr }12\text{ min.}$

86. Let the average speed on the onward journey be x km/hr. Then, average speed on return journey

$= (80\% \text{ of } x)\text{ km/hr} = \left(\frac{4x}{5}\right)\text{km/hr.}$

$\therefore \frac{500}{x} + \frac{500}{\left(\frac{4x}{5}\right)} + \frac{1}{2} = 23 \Rightarrow \frac{500}{x} + \frac{625}{x} = \frac{45}{2}$

$\Rightarrow \frac{1125}{x} = \frac{45}{2} \Rightarrow x = \frac{1125 \times 2}{45} = 50.$

Hence, speed on return journey

$= \left(\frac{4x}{5}\right) = \left(\frac{4 \times 50}{5}\right)\text{km/hr} = 40\text{ km/hr.}$

87. Let the normal speed of the train be x km/hr.

Then, new speed $= \left(112\frac{1}{2}\%\text{ of } x\right)\text{ km/hr}$

$= \left(\frac{225}{2} \times \frac{1}{100} \times x\right)\text{km/hr} = \left(\frac{9}{8}x\right)\text{km/hr.}$

Let the distance covered be d km.

Then, $\frac{d}{x} - \frac{d}{\left(\frac{9x}{8}\right)} = \frac{20}{60} = \frac{1}{3} \Rightarrow \frac{d}{x} - \frac{8d}{9x} = \frac{1}{3}$

$\Rightarrow \frac{d}{9x} = \frac{1}{3} \Rightarrow d = 3x.$

$\therefore$ Actual time taken $= \frac{d}{x} = \frac{3x}{x} = 3\text{ hours} = 180\text{ min.}$

88. Let the distance be x km.

Difference in timings $= 12\text{ min} = \frac{12}{60}\text{ hr} = \frac{1}{5}\text{ hr.}$

$\therefore \frac{x}{\left(\frac{5}{2}\right)} - \frac{x}{\left(\frac{7}{2}\right)} = \frac{1}{5} \Leftrightarrow \frac{2x}{5} - \frac{2x}{7} = \frac{1}{5}$

$\Leftrightarrow 14x - 10x = 7 \Leftrightarrow x = 1\frac{3}{4}\text{ km.}$

89. Difference between timings $= 24\text{ min} = \frac{24}{60}\text{ hr} = \frac{2}{5}\text{ hr.}$

Let the length of the journey be x km.

Then, $\frac{x}{40} - \frac{x}{50} = \frac{2}{5} \Leftrightarrow \frac{x}{200} = \frac{2}{5} \Leftrightarrow x = \left(\frac{2}{5} \times 200\right) = 80\text{ km.}$

90. Let the correct time to complete the journey be x min.

Distance covered in $(x + 11)$ min. at 40 kmph

= Distance covered in $(x + 5)$ min. at 50 kmph

$\therefore \frac{(x+11)}{60} \times 40 = \frac{(x+5)}{60} \times 50 \Leftrightarrow x = 19\text{ min.}$

91. Let the distance travelled be x km.

Then, $\frac{x}{10} - \frac{x}{15} = 2 \Leftrightarrow 3x - 2x = 60 \Leftrightarrow x = 60\text{ km.}$

Time taken to travel 60 km at 10 km/hr $= \left(\frac{60}{10}\right)\text{hrs} = 6\text{ hrs.}$

So, Robert started 6 hours before 2 P.M. *i.e.*, at 8 A.M.

$\therefore$ Required speed $= \left(\frac{60}{5}\right)\text{kmph} = 12\text{ kmph.}$

92. Let the to and fro distance to the mall be x km.

Then, $\frac{x}{10} - \frac{x}{15} = \frac{30}{60} = \frac{1}{2} \Rightarrow \frac{x}{30} = \frac{1}{2} \Rightarrow x = 15.$

Time taken to travel 15 km at 10 km/hr

$= \left(\frac{15}{10}\right)\text{hr} = \frac{3}{2}\text{ hrs} = 1\frac{1}{2}\text{ hrs.}$

Since 30 minutes were spent in shopping, so Ravi started for the mall 2 hours before 19.00 hrs *i.e.*, at 17.00 hrs.

Now, required time for to and fro journey

$= (18.15\text{ hrs} - 17.00\text{ hrs}) - 30\text{ min} = 45\text{ min} = \frac{3}{4}\text{ hrs.}$

Hence, required speed $= \left(15 \times \frac{4}{3}\right)\text{km/hr} = 20\text{ km/hr.}$

93. Let the distance travelled by bus be x km.

Then, distance travelled by train $= (285 - x)$ km.

$\therefore \frac{x}{40} + \frac{(285-x)}{55} = 6 \Rightarrow \frac{11x + 8(285-x)}{440} = 6$

$\Rightarrow 11x - 8x + 2280 = 2640 \Rightarrow 3x = 360 \Rightarrow x = 120.$

Hence, distance travelled by train $= (285 - 120)$ km $= 165$ km.

94. Let distance $= x$ km and usual rate $= y$ kmph.

$\frac{x}{y} - \frac{x}{y+3} = \frac{40}{60}$ or $2y(y+3) = 9x$ ...(*i*)

And, $\frac{x}{y-2} - \frac{x}{y} = \frac{40}{60}$ or $y(y-2) = 3x$ ...(*ii*)

On dividing (*i*) by (*ii*), we get :

$2(y + 3) = 3(y - 2) \Rightarrow y = 12.$

$\therefore$ Distance $= x = \frac{2y(y+3)}{9} = \left(\frac{2 \times 12 \times 15}{9}\right)\text{km} = 40\text{ km.}$

95. Let distance $= x$ km and usual speed $= y$ kmph.

$\frac{x}{y} - \frac{x}{y+6} = 4 \Rightarrow 6x = 4y(y+6)$ ...(*i*)

And, $\frac{x}{y-6} - \frac{x}{y} = 6 \Rightarrow 6x = 6y(y-6)$ ...(*ii*)

From (i) and (ii), we get :

$4y(y + 6) = 6y(y - 6) \Rightarrow 2(y + 6) = 3(y - 6) \Rightarrow y = 30.$

$\therefore$ Length of the journey $= x = \frac{4y(y+6)}{6} = \left(\frac{4 \times 30 \times 36}{6}\right)\text{km}$

96. Let distance $= x$ km and usual rate $= y$ kmph.

Then, $\frac{x}{y} - \frac{x}{y+10} = 1$ or $y(y+10) = 10x$ ...(*i*)

And $\frac{x}{y} - \frac{x}{y+20} = \frac{7}{4}$ or $y(y+20) = \frac{80x}{7}$ ...(*ii*)

On dividing (*i*) by (*ii*), we get : $y = 60.$

Substituting $y = 60$ in (*i*), we get : $x = 420$ km.

97. Let speed of the car be x kmph.

Then, speed of the train $= \frac{150}{100}x = \left(\frac{3}{2}x\right)$ kmph.

$\therefore \frac{75}{x} - \frac{75}{\frac{3}{2}x} = \frac{125}{10 \times 60} \Leftrightarrow \frac{75}{x} - \frac{50}{x}$

$= \frac{5}{24} \Leftrightarrow x = \left(\frac{25 \times 24}{5}\right) = 120$ kmph.

98. Due to stoppages, it covers 9 km less.

Time taken to cover 9 km $= \left(\frac{9}{54} \times 60\right)$ min $= 10$ min.

99. Due to stoppage, Kingfisher flight covers $(700 - 560)$ $= 140$ km less per hour.

Time taken to cover 140 km $= \left(\frac{140}{700} \times 60\right)$ min $= 12$ min.

Hence, stoppage time per hour = 12 min.

100. Let the distance between village A and B be x km.

Then, $\frac{x}{40} - \frac{x}{60} = 2 \Rightarrow x = 240.$

101. Let the distance between the stations A and B be x km.

Time taken = 45 min $= \frac{3}{4}$ hr.

$\therefore$ Original speed $= \left(x \times \frac{4}{3}\right)$ km/hr $= \frac{4x}{3}$ km/hr.

New speed $= \left(\frac{4x}{3} - 5\right)$ km/hr $= \left(\frac{4x - 15}{3}\right)$ km/hr.

$\therefore \frac{x}{\left(\frac{4x - 15}{3}\right)} = \frac{48}{60} \Rightarrow \frac{3x}{4x - 15} = \frac{4}{5}$

$\Rightarrow 15x = 16x - 60 \Rightarrow x = 60.$

102. Let the speed of the train be x km/hr.

Then, $\frac{600}{x} - \frac{600}{x + 5} = 4 \Leftrightarrow 4x\,(x + 5) = 3000$

$\Leftrightarrow 4x^2 + 20x - 3000 = 0 \Leftrightarrow x^2 + 5x - 750 = 0$

$\Leftrightarrow (x + 30)\,(x - 25) = 0 \Leftrightarrow x = 25.$

$\therefore$ Speed of the train = 25 km/hr.

103. Let the usual speed be x km/hr.

Then, $\frac{75}{x} - \frac{75}{x + 10} = \frac{15}{60} \Leftrightarrow x(x + 10) = 3000$

$\Leftrightarrow x^2 + 10x - 3000 = 0 \Leftrightarrow (x + 60)\,(x - 50) = 0 \Leftrightarrow x = 50.$

$\therefore$ Required time $= \left(\frac{300}{60}\right)$ hrs $= 5$ hrs.

104. Let the distance be x km.

Then, $\frac{x}{7\frac{1}{2}} - \frac{x}{8} = 4 \Leftrightarrow \frac{2x}{15} - \frac{x}{8} = 4 \Leftrightarrow x = 480$ km.

105. Let the distance be x km.

Then, $\frac{x}{3} - \frac{x}{3.75} = \frac{1}{2} \Leftrightarrow 2.5x - 2x = 3.75$

$\Leftrightarrow \quad x = \frac{3.75}{0.50} = \frac{15}{2} = 7.5$ km.

106. Let the actual distance travelled be x km.

Then, $\frac{x}{10} = \frac{x + 20}{14} \Leftrightarrow 14x = 10x + 200$

$\Leftrightarrow \quad 4x = 200 \Leftrightarrow x = 50$ km.

107. Ratio of speeds = 3 : 4. Ratio of times taken = 4 : 3.

Suppose A takes $4x$ hrs and B takes $3x$ hrs to reach the destination. Then,

$4x - 3x = \frac{30}{60} = \frac{1}{2}$ or $x = \frac{1}{2}.$

$\therefore$ Time taken by $A = 4x$ hrs $= \left(4 \times \frac{1}{2}\right)$ hrs $= 2$ hrs.

108. Let Abhay's speed be x km/hr.

Then, $\frac{30}{x} - \frac{30}{2x} = 3 \Leftrightarrow 6x = 30 \Leftrightarrow x = 5$ km/hr.

109. Ratio of speeds = 4 : 3 : 5.

$\therefore$ Ratio of times taken $= \frac{1}{4} : \frac{1}{3} : \frac{1}{5} = 15 : 20 : 12.$

110. Let the speed of the fast train be x km/hr.

Then, speed of the slow train $= (x - 16)$ km/hr.

$\therefore \frac{192}{x - 16} - \frac{192}{x} = 2 \Rightarrow \frac{1}{x - 16} - \frac{1}{x} = \frac{1}{96}$

$\Leftrightarrow \quad x^2 - 16x - 1536 = 0 \Leftrightarrow (x - 48)\,(x + 32) = 0 \Leftrightarrow x = 48.$

111. Let the original planned duration of the flight be x hours.

Then, $\frac{6000}{x} - \frac{6000}{\left(x + \frac{1}{2}\right)} = 400 \Leftrightarrow \frac{6000}{x} - \frac{12000}{(2x + 1)} = 400$

$\Leftrightarrow \quad \frac{15}{x} - \frac{30}{(2x + 1)} = 1 \Leftrightarrow 2x^2 + x - 15 = 0$

$\Leftrightarrow \quad (x + 3)\,(2x - 5) = 0 \Leftrightarrow x = \frac{5}{2} = 2\frac{1}{2}.$

112. Let the distance covered at 440 kmph be x km.

Then, distance covered at 660 kmph $= (x - 770)$ km.

Total distance covered $= (x + x - 770)$ km

$= (2x - 770)$ km.

$\therefore \frac{2x - 770}{500} = \frac{x}{440} + \frac{x - 770}{660} \Leftrightarrow \frac{2x - 770}{25} = \frac{x}{22} + \frac{(x - 770)}{33}$

$\Leftrightarrow \quad 66\,(2x - 770) = 25\,(5x - 1540)$

$\Leftrightarrow \quad 7x = 12320 \Leftrightarrow x = 1760.$

Hence, total distance covered $= (2x - 770)$

$= (2 \times 1760 - 770)$ km $= 2750$ km.

113. Let A's speed $= x$ km/hr.

Then, B's speed $= (x + 4)$ km/hr.

Clearly, time taken by B to cover $(60 + 12)$ *i.e.*, 72 km

= Time taken by A to cover $(60 - 12)$ *i.e.*, 48 km

$\therefore \frac{72}{x + 4} = \frac{48}{x} \Rightarrow 72x = 48x + 192 \Rightarrow 24x = 192 \Rightarrow x = 8.$

Hence, A's speed = 8 km/hr.

114. Let the cyclist's speed without wind be x km/hr and the speed of the wind be y km/hr.

Then, $\frac{1}{x+y}=\frac{3}{60} \Rightarrow x+y=20$ ...(i)

And, $\frac{1}{x-y}=\frac{4}{60} \Rightarrow x-y=15$ ...(ii)

Adding (i) and (ii), we get : $2x = 35$ or $x = 17.5$.
Putting $x = 17.5$ in (i), we get : $y = 2.5$.
Time taken to drive 17.5 km without wind = 1 hr.
Time taken to drive 1 km without wind

$=\left(\frac{1}{17.5}\right)\text{hr}=\left(\frac{1}{17.5}\times 60\right)\text{min}=3\frac{3}{7}\text{ min}.$

115. Let the speeds of the train and the car be x km/hr and y km/hr respectively.

Then, $\frac{160}{x}+\frac{600}{y}=8 \Rightarrow \frac{20}{x}+\frac{75}{y}=1$ ...(i)

And, $\frac{240}{x}+\frac{520}{y}=8\frac{1}{5} \Rightarrow \frac{240}{x}+\frac{520}{y}=\frac{41}{5}$ ...(ii)

Multiplying (i) by 12 and subtracting (ii) from it, we get :

$\frac{380}{y}=12-\frac{41}{5}=\frac{19}{5} \Rightarrow y=\left(380\times\frac{5}{19}\right)=100.$

Putting $y = 100$ in (i), we get : $\frac{20}{x}+\frac{3}{4}=1 \Rightarrow \frac{20}{x}=\frac{1}{4} \Rightarrow x=80.$

Hence, speed of car = 100 km/hr, speed of train = 80 km/hr

116. Suppose the two trawlers start from a point O and move in the directions OA and OB respectively.
Let the speeds of the two sea trawlers be x km/hr and y km/hr. respectively.

Then, $\left(x\times\frac{1}{2}\right)^2+\left(y\times\frac{1}{2}\right)^2=(17)^2$

$\Rightarrow \frac{x^2}{4}+\frac{y^2}{4}=289 \Rightarrow x^2+y^2=1156$ ...(i)

And, $\left(x\times\frac{3}{4}\right)-\left(y\times\frac{3}{4}\right)=10.5 \Rightarrow x-y=10.5\times\frac{4}{3}=14$ ...(ii)

Now, $(x + y)^2 + (x - y)^2 = 2(x^2 + y^2)$
$\Rightarrow (x + y)^2 = 2 \times 1156 - (14)^2 = 2312 - 196 = 2116$
$\Rightarrow x + y = \sqrt{2116} = 46$ ...(iii)

Adding (ii) and (iii), we get : $2x = 60$ or $x = 30$.
Putting $x = 30$ in (ii), we get : $y = 16$.
Hence, the speeds of the two sea-trawlers are 30 km/hr and 16 km/hr.

117. Let C's speed = x km/hr. Then, B's speed = $3x$ km/hr and A's speed = $6x$ km/hr.
∴ Ratio of speeds of A, B, C = $6x : 3x : x = 6 : 3 : 1$.

Ratio of times taken = $\frac{1}{6}:\frac{1}{3}:1=1:2:6.$

If C takes 6 min, then A takes 1 min.

If C takes 72 min, then A takes $\left(\frac{1}{6}\times 72\right)\text{min}=12\text{ min}.$

118. Qua]ntity of water let in by the leak in 1 min

$=\left(\frac{3\frac{3}{4}}{12}\right)\text{tonnes}=\left(\frac{15}{4}\times\frac{1}{12}\right)\text{tonnes}=\frac{15}{48}\text{ tonnes.}$

Quantity of water thrown out by the pumps in 1 min

$=\left(\frac{12}{60}\right)\text{tonnes}=\frac{1}{5}\text{ tonnes.}$

Net quantity of water filled in the ship in 1 min

$=\left(\frac{15}{48}-\frac{1}{5}\right)\text{tonnes}=\frac{27}{240}\text{ tonnes.}$

$\frac{27}{240}$ tonnes water is filled in 1 min.

60 tonnes water is filled in $\left(\frac{240}{27}\times 60\right)$ min

$=\frac{1600}{3}\text{ min}=\frac{80}{9}\text{ hrs.}$

Hence, required speed = $\frac{40}{(80/9)}$ km/hr

$=\left(40\times\frac{9}{80}\right)\text{km/hr}=\frac{9}{2}\text{ km/hr}=4\frac{1}{2}\text{ km/hr.}$

119. Quantity of petrol consumed in 1 hour

$=\left(\frac{40}{10}+\frac{1}{2}\right)\text{litres} = 4\frac{1}{2}\text{ litres.}$

Time for which the fuel lasted = $\left[\frac{18}{\left(4\frac{1}{2}\right)}\right]$ hrs

$=\left(18\times\frac{2}{9}\right)\text{hrs}=4\text{ hrs.}$

∴ Required distance = (40 × 4) km = 160 km.

120. To be 0.5 km apart, they take 1 hour.

To be 8.5 km apart, they take $\left(\frac{1}{0.5}\times 8.5\right)$ hrs = 17 hrs.

121. Since A and B move in the same direction along the circle, so they will first meet each other when there is a difference of one round between the two.
Relative speed of A and B = (6 – 1) = 5 rounds per hour.
Time taken to complete one round at this speed

$=\frac{1}{5}\text{ hr}=12\text{ min.}$

122. Perimeter of the field = 2(400 + 300) m = 1400 m = 1.4 km.
Since A and B move in the same direction, so they will first meet each other when there is a difference of one round *i.e.*, 1.4 km between the two.
Relative speed of A and B = (3 – 2.5) km/hr = 0.5 km/hr.

Time take to cover 1.4 km at this speed = $\left(\frac{1.4}{0.5}\right)$ hr

$=2\frac{4}{5}\text{ hr}=2\text{ hr }48\text{ min.}$

So they shall first cross each other at 9 : 48 a.m. and again, 2 hr 48 min after 9 : 48 a.m. *i.e.*, 12 : 36 p.m.
Thus, till 12 : 30 p.m. they will cross each other once.

123. Distance covered by first person in time t

$=\left(\frac{2}{8}\right)\text{rounds}=\frac{1}{4}\text{ round.}$

Distance covered by second person in time $t = \frac{3}{8}$ round.

Speed of first person $= \frac{1}{4t}$;

Speed of second person $= \frac{3}{8t}$.

Since the two persons start from A and B respectively, so they shall meet each other when there is a difference of $\frac{7}{8}$ round between the two.

Relative speed of A and $B = \left(\frac{3}{8t} - \frac{1}{4t}\right) = \frac{1}{8t}$.

Time taken to cover $\frac{7}{8}$ round at this speed $= \left(\frac{7}{8} \times 8t\right) = 7t$.

124. Suppose after x km from the start B catches up with A. Then, the difference in the time taken by A to cover x km and that taken by B to cover x km is 4 hours.

$\therefore \frac{x}{4} - \frac{x}{10} = 4$ or $x = 26.7$ km.

125. Suppose the two trains meet x km from Delhi.

Then, $\frac{x}{60} - \frac{x}{80} = 2 \Leftrightarrow x = 480$.

126. Relative speed of the thief and policeman
$= (11 - 10)$ km/hr $= 1$ km/hr.

Distance covered in 6 minutes $= \left(\frac{1}{60} \times 6\right)$ km

$= \frac{1}{10}$ km $= 100$ m.

$\therefore$ Distance between the thief and policeman
$= (200 - 100)$ m $= 100$ m.

127. Relative speed of the car w.r.t. bus $= (50 - 30)$ km/hr
$= 20$ km/hr.

Required distance = Distance covered in 15 min at relative speed $= \left(20 \times \frac{1}{4}\right)$ km $= 5$ km.

128. Relative speed $= (10 - 8)$ km/hr $= 2$ km/hr.

Required time = Time taken to cover 100 m at relative speed

$= \left(\frac{100}{2000}\right)$ hr $= \frac{1}{20}$ hr $= \left(\frac{1}{20} \times 60\right)$ min $= 3$ min.

129. Suppose the thief is overtaken x hrs after 2.30 p.m.

Then, Distance covered by the thief in x hrs = Distance covered by the owner in $\left(x - \frac{1}{2}\right)$ hrs.

$\therefore 60x = 75\left(x - \frac{1}{2}\right) \Leftrightarrow 15x = \frac{75}{2} \Leftrightarrow x = \frac{5}{2}$ hrs.

So, the thief is overtaken at 5 p.m.

130. Distance covered by Aryan in 5 min $= (40 \times 5)$ m $= 200$ m.

Relative speed of Rahul w.r.t. Aryan $= (50 - 40)$ m/min
$= 10$ m/min.

Time taken to cover 200 m at relative speed

$= \left(\frac{200}{10}\right)$ min $= 20$ min.

Distance covered by the dog in 20 min $= (60 \times 20)$ m
$= 1200$ m.

131. Let the thief be caught x metres from the place where the policeman started running.

Let the speed of the policeman and the thief be $5y$ m/s and $4y$ m/s respectively.

Then, time taken by the policeman to cover x metres
= time taken by the thief to cover $(x - 100)$ m

$\Rightarrow \frac{x}{5y} = \frac{(x-100)}{4y} \Rightarrow 4x = 5(x - 100) \Rightarrow x = 500$.

So, the thief ran $(500 - 100)$ i.e. 400 m before being caught.

132. Distance covered by A in 4 hrs $= (4 \times 4)$ km $= 16$ km.

Relative speed of B w.r.t. A $= (10 - 4)$ km/hr $= 6$ km/hr.

Time taken to cover 16 km at relative speed

$= \left(\frac{16}{6}\right)$ hrs $= \frac{8}{3}$ hrs.

Distance covered by B in $\frac{8}{3}$ hrs $= \left(10 \times \frac{8}{3}\right)$ km $= \left(\frac{80}{3}\right)$ km

$= 26.7$ km.

133. Let the speed of the goods train be x km/hr. Then, relative speed $= (80 - x)$ km/hr.

Distance covered by goods train in 6 hrs at x km/hr
= Distance covered by passenger train in 4 hrs at $(80 - x)$ km/hr

$\Rightarrow 6x = 4(80 - x) \Rightarrow 10x = 320 \Rightarrow x = 32$ km/hr.

134. Error = Time taken to cover 10 m at 300 m/sec

$= \left(\frac{10}{300}\right)$ sec $= \frac{1}{30}$ sec ≈ 0.03 sec.

135. Clearly, the two persons would be maximum distance apart when they stand in opposite directions to the point at which sound is produced, and minimum distance apart when they stand in the same direction.

$\therefore$ Maximum distance between the two persons
= Distance covered by sound in $(6 + 5)$ seconds, i.e. 11 sec
$= (300 \times 11)$ m $= 3300$ m $= 3.3$ km.

And, minimum distance between the two persons
= Distance covered by sound in $(6 - 5)$ sec., i.e. 1 sec
$= 300$ m $= 0.3$ km.

136. Let the speed of the man be x m/sec.

Then, Distance travelled by the man in 5 min 52 sec
= Distance travelled by sound in 8 sec

$\Leftrightarrow x \times 352 = 330 \times 8$

$\Leftrightarrow x = \left(\frac{330 \times 8}{352}\right)$ m/sec.

$= \left(\frac{330 \times 8}{352} \times \frac{18}{5}\right)$ km/hr $= 27$ km/hr.

137. To be $(18 + 20)$ km apart, they take 1 hour.

To be 47.5 km apart, they take $\left(\frac{1}{38} \times 47.5\right)$ hrs $= 1\frac{1}{4}$ hrs.

138. Suppose they meet after x hours. Then,

Distance travelled by P in x hrs + Distance travelled by Q in x hrs = 10 km

$\Leftrightarrow 3x + 2x = 10 \Rightarrow 5x = 10 \Rightarrow x = 2$ hrs.

Distance travelled by P in 2 hrs = (3×2) km = 6 km.

139. Suppose they meet x hrs after 9 a.m. Then,

Distance travelled by car X in $(x - 1)$ hrs + Distance travelled by car Y in x hrs = 700 km

$\Rightarrow 60(x - 1) + 60x = 700 \Rightarrow 120x = 760$

$\Rightarrow x = \frac{760}{120} = \frac{19}{3}$ hrs = 6 hr 20 min.

So, they cross each other 6 hr 20 min after 9 a.m. *i.e.*, at 3 : 20 p.m.

140. Suppose the trains meet after x hrs. Then,

Distance covered by 1st train in x hrs

+ Distance covered by 2nd train in $\left(x - \frac{3}{4}\right)$ hrs = 232 km

$\Rightarrow 48x + 50\left(x - \frac{3}{4}\right) = 232$

$\Rightarrow 98x = 232 + \frac{75}{2} = \frac{539}{2} \Rightarrow x = \frac{539}{196}$ hrs.

Required distance

= Distance travelled by 1st train in $\left(\frac{539}{196}\right)$ hrs.

$= \left(48 \times \frac{539}{196}\right)$ km = 132 km.

141. Clearly, the two will meet when they are 726 m apart.

To be $(4.5 + 3.75) = 8.25$ km apart, they take 1 hour.

To be 726 m apart, they take $\left(\frac{100}{825} \times \frac{726}{1000}\right)$ hrs

$= \left(\frac{242}{2750} \times 60\right)$ min = 5.28 min.

142. Relative speed = $(2 + 3)$ = 5 rounds per hour.

So, they cross each other 5 times in an hour and 2 times in half an hour.

Hence, they cross each other 7 times before 9.30 a.m.

143. Time taken by the two cyclists to cover one round of the track is $\frac{300}{7}$ sec and $\frac{300}{8}$ sec respectively.

$\therefore$ Required time = L.C.M. of $\frac{300}{7}$ and $\frac{300}{8}$ = 300 sec.

144. Relative speed = $(200 + 200)$ km/hr = 400 km/hr.

Distance covered in 1 hr 30 min

$= \left(400 \times \frac{1}{2} + 200 \times \frac{1}{2} + 100 \times \frac{1}{2}\right)$ km

$= (200 + 100 + 50)$ km = 350 km.

[$\because$ speed reduces by half every half an hour]

Hence, distance between the trains

$= (425 - 350)$ km = 75 km.

Questions 145 to 147

Let B's speed = x km/hr.

Then, A's speed = (150% of x) km/hr = $\left(\frac{3x}{2}\right)$ km/hr.

Clearly, A and B cross each other when A has travelled for 14 hours and B for 9 hours.

So, distance travelled by A in 14 hrs + distance travelled by B in 9 hrs = 120 km

$\Rightarrow \left(\frac{3x}{2} \times 14\right) + 9x = 120 \Rightarrow 30x = 120 \Rightarrow x = 4.$

$\therefore$ A's speed = $\left(\frac{3 \times 4}{2}\right)$ km/hr

= 6 km/hr & B's speed = 4 km/hr.

145. Time taken by A to cover 120 km = $\left(\frac{120}{6}\right)$ hrs = 20 hrs.

So, A will reach his destination 20 hrs after 6 a.m., i.e., at 2 a.m. the next day.

146. Required difference = $\left(\frac{120}{4} - \frac{120}{6}\right)$ hrs

= $(30 - 20)$ hrs = 10 hrs.

147. A's speed = 6 km/hr.

148. Let the speed of train Z be z mph.

Distance travelled by train X in 1 hr = x miles.

Relative speed of train Z w.r.t. train X = $(z - x)$ mph.

To catch train X at 5 : 30 A.M., train Z will have to cover x miles at relative speed in 3 hr 30 min, i.e. $\frac{7}{2}$ hrs.

$\therefore \quad (z - x) \times \frac{7}{2} = x \Rightarrow \frac{7}{2}z = \frac{9}{2}x \Rightarrow z = \left(\frac{9}{2} \times \frac{2}{7}\right)x = \frac{9}{7}x.$

149. Let the speed of the second lady be x km/hr.

Then, speed of first lady = $(x + 2)$ km/hr.

$\therefore \quad \frac{24}{x} - \frac{24}{(x+2)} = 1 \Rightarrow x(x+2) = 48$

$\Rightarrow \quad x^2 + 2x - 48 = 0 \Rightarrow x^2 + 8x - 6x - 48 = 0$

$\Rightarrow \quad x(x + 8) - 6(x + 8) = 0 \Rightarrow (x + 8)(x - 6) = 0$

$\Rightarrow \quad x = 6.$

Hence, speed of first lady = 8 km/hr; speed of second lady = 6 km/hr.

150. Let the speed of the man be x km/hr.

Then, Distance covered by the bus in 2 min = Distance covered by the man in 8 min

$\Rightarrow 20 \times \frac{2}{60} = x \times \frac{8}{60} \Rightarrow x = \left(\frac{2}{3} \times \frac{60}{8}\right) = 5$ km/hr.

151. Suppose the two men meet in n hours.

Then Sum of distances covered by two men in n hours = 76

$\Rightarrow 4\frac{1}{2}n + \left(3\frac{1}{4} + 3\frac{3}{4} + \text{.........} \text{ upto } n \text{ terms}\right) = 76$

$\Rightarrow \frac{9}{2}n + \frac{n}{2}\left[2 \times \frac{13}{4} + (n-1) \times \frac{1}{2}\right] = 76$

[Sum to n terms of an A.P.]

$\Rightarrow \frac{9n}{2} + \frac{n}{2}\left[\frac{13}{2} + \frac{1}{2}n - \frac{1}{2}\right] = 76$

$\Rightarrow \frac{9n}{2} + \frac{n}{2}\left(6 + \frac{n}{2}\right) = 76$

$\Rightarrow \frac{9n}{2}+\frac{6n}{2}+\frac{n^2}{4}=76 \Rightarrow \frac{15n}{2}+\frac{n^2}{4}=76$

$\Rightarrow 30n + n^2 = 304 \Rightarrow n^2 + 30n - 304 = 0$

$\Rightarrow (n + 38)(n - 8) = 0 \Rightarrow n = 8.$

Distance travelled by first man in 8 hours

$= \left(\frac{9}{2}\times 8\right)\text{km} = 36 \text{ km}.$

Distance travelled by second man = (76 – 36) km = 40 km.

Thus, the meeting point is 36 km from R and 40 km from S, i.e. (40 – 36) = 4 km nearer to R than S.

Hence, $x = 4$.

152. Let their speeds be x m/sec and y m/sec respectively.

Then, $\frac{1200}{x+y}=15 \Rightarrow x+y=80$ ...(*i*)

And, $\frac{1200}{x-y}=60 \Rightarrow x-y=20$ ..(*ii*)

Adding (*i*) and (*ii*), we get : $2x = 100$ or $x = 50$.

Putting $x = 50$ in (*i*), we get : $y = 30$.

Hence, speed of slower plane = 30m/s = 0.03 km/s.

153. Let the speed of the faster and slower cyclists be x km/hr and y km/hr respectively,

Then, $\frac{k}{x-y}=r \Rightarrow (x-y)r=k$ ...(*i*)

And, $\frac{k}{x+y}=t \Rightarrow (x+y)t=k$ ...(*ii*)

From (*i*) and (*ii*), we have :

$(x - y)r = (x + y)t \Rightarrow xr - yr = xt + yt \Rightarrow xr - xt = yr + yt$

$\Rightarrow x(r - t) = y(r + t) \Rightarrow \frac{x}{y}=\frac{r+t}{r-t}.$

154. Let the distance between points X and Y be d km.

Suppose the bus takes x hours to travel from X to Y.

Then, speed of bus = $\frac{d}{x}$ and speed of car = $\frac{d}{x-2}$.

Now, sum of distances travelled by car and bus in $1\frac{1}{3}$ hrs *i.e.* $\frac{4}{3}$ hrs $= d$

$\Rightarrow \left(\frac{d}{x}\times\frac{4}{3}\right)+\left(\frac{d}{x-2}\times\frac{4}{3}\right)=d$

$\Rightarrow \frac{4}{3x}+\frac{4}{3(x-2)}=1$

$\Rightarrow 4(x - 2) + 4x = 3x(x - 2)$

$\Rightarrow 3x^2 - 14x + 8 = 0$

$\Rightarrow 3x^2 - 12x - 2x + 8 = 0 \Rightarrow 3x(x - 4) - 2(x - 4) = 0$

$\Rightarrow (x - 4)(3x - 2) = 0 \Rightarrow x = 4 \quad \left[\because x \neq \frac{2}{3}\right]$

$\therefore$ Required time = 4 hours.

155. In the same time, they cover 110 km and 90 km respectively.

$\therefore$ Ratio of their speeds = 110 : 90 = 11 : 9.

156. At the time of meeting, let the distance travelled by the first train be x km.

Then, distance covered by the second train = $(x + 120)$ km.

$\therefore \frac{x}{50}=\frac{x+120}{60} \Leftrightarrow 60x = 50x + 6000$

$\Leftrightarrow 10x = 6000 \Leftrightarrow x = 600.$

So, distance between A and B = $(x + x + 120)$ km = 1320 km.

157. Distance covered by train A from 11 a.m. to 2 p.m. *i.e.*, in 3 hrs = (60 × 3) = 180 km.

Relative speed = (72 – 60) km/hr = 12 km/hr.

Time taken to cover 180 km at relative speed

$= \left(\frac{180}{12}\right)\text{hrs} = 15 \text{ hrs}.$

So, the two trains will meet 15 hrs after 2 p.m. *i.e.*, at 5 a.m. on the next day.

158. Let the distance between stations X and Y be x km and let the trains meet y hours after 7 a.m.

Clearly, M covers x km in 4 hrs and N covers x km in (7/2) hrs.

$\therefore$ Speed of $M = \frac{x}{4}$ kmph, Speed of $N = \frac{2x}{7}$ kmph.

Distance covered by M in $(y + 2)$ hrs + Distance covered by N in y hrs = x.

$\therefore \frac{x}{4}(y+2)+\frac{2x}{7}\times y = x \Leftrightarrow \frac{(y+2)}{4}+\frac{2y}{7}=1$

$\Leftrightarrow y = \frac{14}{15}\text{ hrs} = \left(\frac{14}{15}\times 60\right)\text{ min.} = 56 \text{ min.}$

Hence, the trains meet at 7.56 a.m.

159. Suppose the three trains meet x hours after 9 p.m.

Let the speed of train C be y km/hr.

Distance travelled by Train A in $(x + 3)$ hrs = Distance travelled by Train B in x hrs

$\Rightarrow 60(x + 3) = 90x \Rightarrow 30x = 180 \Rightarrow x = 6.$

Also, dist. travelled by Train B in x hrs + Dist. travelled by train C in x hrs = 1260 km

$\Rightarrow 90x + yx = 1260 \Rightarrow 540 + 6y = 1260 \Rightarrow 6y = 720 \Rightarrow y = 120.$

Hence, speed of Train C = 120 km/hr.

160. Let the distance be x km. Then,

(Time taken to walk x km) + (Time taken to drive x km) $= \frac{27}{4}$ hrs

$\Rightarrow$ (Time taken to walk $2x$ km) + (Time taken to drive $2x$ km) $= \frac{27}{2}$ hrs.

But time taken to drive $2x$ km $= \frac{19}{4}$ hrs.

$\therefore$ Time taken to walk $2x$ km $= \left(\frac{27}{2}-\frac{19}{4}\right)$hrs

$= \frac{35}{4}\text{ hrs} = 8 \text{ hrs } 45 \text{ min.}$

161. Since 10 minutes are saved, it means that Reena's father drives from the meeting point to the station and back to the meeting point in 10 min *i.e.* he can drive from the meeting point to the station in $\left(\frac{10}{2}\right) = 5$ min.

But he reaches the station daily at 7 p.m. So Reena and her father meet on the way at 6 : 55 p.m. Thus, Reena walked for 25 min before her father picked her up.

162. Clearly, the coachman needed 2 hours to reach the station from Mr X's house or 4 hours for the entire round trip. But now he took (4 – 1) = 3 hours for the round trip.

Thus he went one way in $1\frac{1}{2}$ hrs *i.e.*,

Mr X walked for $1\frac{1}{2}$ hrs.

Distance covered in $1\frac{1}{2}$ hrs while walking

$= \left(4 \times \frac{3}{2}\right)$ miles = 6 miles.

But this distance would have been covered by the coachman in $\left(2 - 1\frac{1}{2}\right)$ hr $= \frac{1}{2}$ hr.

Speed of the coachman $= \left(6 \div \frac{1}{2}\right)$ mph = 12 mph.

∴ Distance between the house and the station
= Distance covered by coachman in 2 hrs
= (12 × 2) miles = 24 miles.

163. Let length $AB = x$.

Then, if C is the position of the

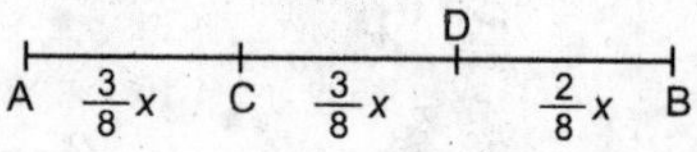

cat, we have $AC = \frac{3}{8}x$.

When the cat runs towards the entrance, the train catches it at the entrance. This means that when the train reaches the entrance, the cat has travelled a distance of $\frac{3}{8}x$.

Let us now consider the case when the cat runs towards the exit.

So, when the train reaches A, the cat reaches a point D such that $CD = \frac{3}{8}x$.

Then, $BD = \left[x - \left(\frac{3}{8}x + \frac{3}{8}x\right)\right] = \frac{x}{4}$.

Since the train catches the cat at the exit, so the train covers distance x (= AB) in the same time in which the cat covers distance $\frac{x}{4}$ (= BD).

∴ Required ratio $= x : \frac{x}{4} = 4 : 1$.

164. On attaching 9 compartments to the engine, we have : reduction in speed $= k\sqrt{9}$, $= 3k$ where k is a constant.

∴ $42 - 3k = 24$ or $3k = 18$ or $k = 6$.

For the speed of the engine to be zero, let the number of compartments attached be x.

Then, $42 - 6\sqrt{x} = 0 \Rightarrow 6\sqrt{x} = 42 \Rightarrow \sqrt{x} = 7 \Rightarrow x = 49$.

Hence, maximum number of compartments that the engine can pull = (49 – 1) = 48.

165. Since A and B are 5 km apart and Ram's speed is 5 km/hr, so Ram reaches B in 1 hour *i.e.*, at 10 a.m.

Thus, when Ram reaches B, Shyam has travelled from 9 : 45 a.m. to 10 a.m. *i.e.* 15 min.

So, distance covered by Shyam when Ram reaches $B = \left(10 \times \frac{15}{60}\right)$ km $= \frac{5}{2}$ km.

Now, Ram starts travelling from B to A.

So, relative speed = (10 + 5) km/hr = 15 km/hr.

Distance between Ram and Shyam $= \left(5 - \frac{5}{2}\right)$ km $= \frac{5}{2}$ km.

Time taken to cover $\frac{5}{2}$ km at relative speed

$= \left(\frac{5}{2} \times \frac{1}{15}\right)$ hr $= \frac{1}{6}$ hr = 10 min.

Hence, Ram and Shyam meet each other 10 minutes after 10 a.m. *i.e.*, at 10 : 10 a.m.

166. Time taken by Shyam to reach B from A

$= \left(\frac{5}{10}\right)$ hr $= \frac{1}{2}$ hr = 30 min.

So, Shyam reaches B at 10 : 15 a.m.

Now, Shyam starts travelling from B to A.

Distance between Ram and Shyam
= Distance travelled by Ram in 15 min

$= \left(5 \times \frac{1}{4}\right)$ km $= \frac{5}{4}$ km.

Relative speed = (10 – 5) km/hr = 5 km/hr.

∴ Time taken to cover $\frac{5}{4}$ km at 5 km/hr

$= \left(\frac{5}{4} \times \frac{1}{5}\right)$ hr $= \frac{1}{4}$ hr = 15 min.

Hence, Shyam overtakes Ram at 15 min past 10 : 15 a.m. *i.e.*, at 10 : 30 a.m.

167. Suppose the escalator has n steps.

Let man's speed be x steps per sec. and the speed of the escalator be y steps per sec.

Then, $x + y = \frac{n}{30}$ and $x - y = \frac{n}{90}$.

Adding, we get : $2x = \frac{4n}{90} = \frac{2n}{45}$ or $x = \frac{n}{45}$.

∴ Required time $= \frac{n}{(n/45)} = 45$ sec.

168. 60 leaps of the hare $= \left(60 \times 1\frac{3}{4}\right)$ m = 105 m.

So, the hound should gain 105 m over the hare.

When the hound travels $\left(3 \times 2\frac{3}{4}\right)$ m $= \frac{33}{4}$ m, the hare travels $\left(4 \times 1\frac{3}{4}\right)$ m = 7m.

In 3 leaps of the hound, the hound gains $\left(\frac{33}{4} - 7\right)$ m $= \frac{5}{4}$ m.

$\therefore$ Number of leaps required = $\left(105\times\frac{4}{5}\times 3\right) = 252.$

169. Let the total distance be x km and time spent in riding be y hours.

Then, distance covered by riding = $\left(\frac{x}{3}\right)$km.

Distance covered by walking = $\left(x-\frac{x}{3}\right)$km $= \frac{2x}{3}$ km.

Time spent in walking = (20 y) hrs.

Riding speed = $\left(\frac{\frac{x}{3}}{y}\right)$km/hr $=\left(\frac{x}{3y}\right)$km/hr.

Walking speed = $\left(\frac{\frac{2x}{3}}{20\,y}\right)$km/hr $=\left(\frac{x}{30\,y}\right)$km/hr.

$\therefore$ Required ratio = $\frac{x}{3y}:\frac{x}{30\,y} = 1:\frac{1}{10} = 10:1.$

170. Suppose after meeting the bus, the car travelled x km to reach Jaipur.

Then, it travelled x km in $1\frac{1}{2}$ hours.

Again, it travelled back to meet the bus again in $1\frac{1}{2}$ hours.

Now, distance travelled in $\frac{1}{2}$ hour $= \frac{x}{3}$ km.

The bus travelled $\left(x-\frac{x}{3}\right) = \frac{2x}{3}$ km in 3 hours.

So, it will travel x km in $\left(3\times\frac{3}{2x}\times x\right)$hrs $= \frac{9}{2}$ hrs $= 4\frac{1}{2}$ hrs.

Hence, the bus will reach Jaipur

$4\frac{1}{2}$ hours after 4 : 30 p.m. *i.e.* at 9 p.m.

171. Speed of Karan = 60kmph

Time = 9 hrs.

Distance = Speed × Time = 60 × 9 = 540 km.

$\therefore$ Time taken to cover 540 km at 90 km/ph

$= \frac{540}{90} = 6$ hours.

172. Speed of bus = 72 km/ph $=\left(\frac{72\times 5}{18}\right)$m/sec. = 20 m/sec.

Let distance covered by bus in 5 sec be x

$\therefore$ Distance = Speed × Time

$\Rightarrow x = 20 \times 5 = 100$ meter

173. Let the distance covered be $2x$ km.

Time = $\frac{\text{Distance}}{\text{Speed}}$

Time taken to covers the first half and second half of the journey in t_1 and t_1 hours

$\Rightarrow \frac{a}{60} = t_1$ ....(i)

$\Rightarrow \frac{a}{45} = t_2$ ....(ii)

Adding (i) and (ii) we get

$\frac{a}{60}+\frac{a}{45} = t_1+t_2$

$\frac{a}{60}+\frac{a}{45} = 5\frac{15}{60} = 5\frac{1}{4}$

$\Rightarrow \frac{3a+4a}{180} = \frac{21}{4}$

$\Rightarrow 7a = \frac{21}{4}\times 180$

$\Rightarrow a = \frac{21\times 180}{4\times 7} = 135$ km.

$\therefore$ Length of total journey.

= 2 × 135 = 270 km.

174. Speed of Ashok = 39 km/ph

Speed of Rahul = 47 km/ph

Distance between place A and B = 637 km

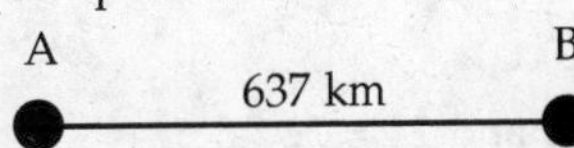

Distance covered by Ashok (from 8 am to 10 am) in 2 hours = 2 × 39 = 78 km

$\therefore$ Remaining distance = 637 – 78 = 559

Relative speed = 39 + 47 = 86 km/ph

$\therefore$ Time taken to travel 559 km = $\frac{559}{86}$ = 6.5 hours

So, they meet at = (10 a.m.+ 6.5) hours = 4:30 pm

175. 1 m/sec = $\frac{18}{5}$ km/ph

Car cover 20 metres in a second

$\therefore$ 20 m/sec = $\frac{20\times 18}{5}$ = 72 km/ph

176. Distance between the Speed of P and Q

$= 3\frac{1}{2} - 3 = \frac{7}{2} - 3 = \frac{1}{2}$ km/hr.

So, Distance = Speed × Time

Time = 4 hours

$\Rightarrow D = \frac{1}{2}\times 4 = 2$ km

177. Let the total distance be covered $3a$ km

$2a$ km distance covered in 2 hours 30 minutes at the rate of k km/ph.

According to the question

Speed × Time = Distance

$x\times 2\frac{30}{60} = 2a$

$\Rightarrow x\times 2\frac{1}{2} = 2a$

$\therefore x\times\frac{5}{2} = 2a$

$\Rightarrow 5x = 4a$ ....(*i*)

Then, 'a' km distance covered in 50 minutes at the rate of (x + 2) km/ph.

$(x+2)\times\frac{50}{60} = a$

$\Rightarrow (x + 2) \times 5 = 6a$ ....(ii)

On dividing equation (ii) by (i).

$\frac{(x+2)\times 5}{5x} = \frac{6a}{4a}$

$\Rightarrow \frac{x+2}{x} = \frac{3}{2}$

$\Rightarrow 3x = 2x + 4$

$\Rightarrow x + 4$

From equation (i)

$5 \times 4 = 4a$

$\Rightarrow a = 5$

$\therefore$ Total distance = $3a = 3 \times 5 = 15$ km.

178. Difference between time = 1 hour

Distance between point AB = x km

According to the question

$\frac{x}{18} - \frac{x}{24} = 1$

LCM of 18 and 24 = 72

$\Rightarrow \frac{4x - 3x}{72} = 1$

$\Rightarrow x = 72$ km

Time taken at 18 km/ph to cover 72 km

$= \frac{72}{18} = 4$ hours

$\therefore$ Speed to cover 72 km in 2 hours

$= \frac{72}{2} = 36$ km/ph.

179. Let the distance between school and home be = D

According to the given information

$\frac{D}{2\frac{1}{2}} - \frac{D}{3} = 16$ minutes

$\therefore \frac{2D}{5} - \frac{D}{3} = \frac{16}{60}$

$\Rightarrow \frac{6D - 5D}{15} = \frac{16}{60}$

$\Rightarrow D = \frac{16}{60} \times 15 = 4$ km

180.

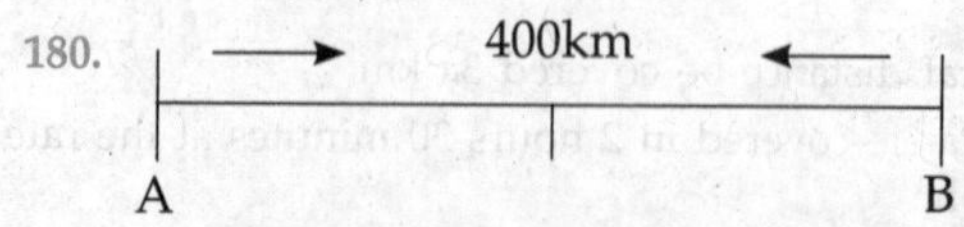

Let the speed of Kim be a and that of Om be b.

Distance between point A and B = 400 *km*

Then, $\frac{400}{a} - \frac{400}{b} = 1$

Let, $\frac{1}{a} = x$ and $\frac{1}{b} = y$

$400\,x - 500\,y = 1$ ....(i)

Speed of km doubles and she will take lets time *i.e.* 1 hour 30 minutes than 0 meter

Again, $\frac{400}{b} - \frac{400}{2b} = \frac{3}{2}$

$\therefore 400y - 200x = \frac{3}{2}$

$800y - 400x = 3$

Solving (i) and (ii), we get

$400x - 400y = 1$

$-400x + 800y = 3$

$400y = 4$

$\therefore y = \frac{4}{400} = \frac{1}{100}$ km

$\therefore b = 100$ km

Now, $\frac{400}{a} - \frac{400}{100} = 4$

Or, $\frac{400}{a}$

$\therefore a = 80$ kmph.

181. Let distance covered be x in 15 minutes

Average speed $= \frac{\text{Time distance}}{\text{Time taken}}$

$= \left(\frac{650 + 850}{12 + 18}\right)$kmph

$= \left(\frac{1500}{30}\right)$kmph

$= 50$ kmph

182. Speed of vehicle = 80 kmph

$= \left(\frac{80 \times 1000}{60}\right)$m/min.

$= \left(\frac{4000}{3}\right)$m/min.

$\therefore$ Required distance $x = \frac{4000}{3} \times 15 = 20000$ meter

183. According to given information

$\frac{\frac{2x}{3}}{4} + \frac{3}{5} = \frac{3}{2}$

$\Rightarrow \frac{2x}{12} + \frac{x}{15} = \frac{3}{2}$

$\Rightarrow \frac{x}{6} + \frac{x}{15} = \frac{3}{2}$

$\Rightarrow \frac{5x + 2x}{30} = \frac{3}{2}$

$\Rightarrow \frac{7x}{30} = \frac{3}{2}$

$\Rightarrow 14x = 90$

$\Rightarrow x = \frac{90}{14} = 6.4$ km.

184. Rani goes to school from her house = 30 minutes

Raja goes to school from her house = 45 minutes

Required ratio = 30 : 45 = 2 : 3

185. Speed of John = 30 km/h

Speed of Max = 40 km/h

Distance between L and M = 650 km

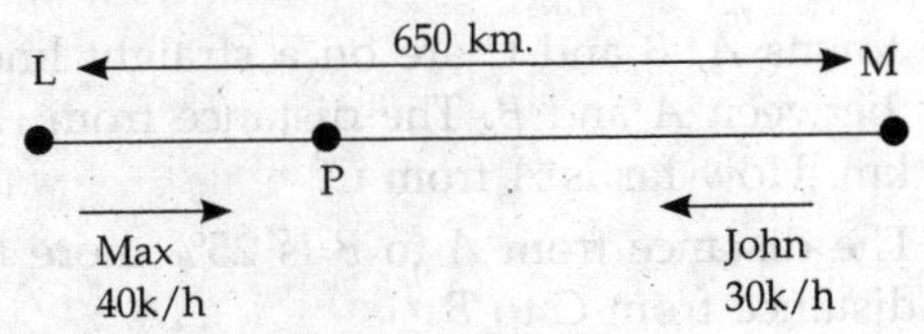

Distance travelled by John in 3 hrs. = 30 × 3 = 90 kms

Time taken by Max and John to travel remaining (650 – 90 = 560)

$= \frac{560}{40+30} = 8$ hours.

Distance travelled by John to reach point P = 8 × 30 = 240 kms

Distance between P and M = 240 + 90 = 330 kms

186. Let the distance travelled by a car be x km.

First $\frac{x}{3}$ km distance cover at speed of 10 km/hr

Second $\frac{x}{3}$ km distance cover at speed = 20 km/hr

Third $\frac{x}{3}$ km distance cover at speed = 60 km/hr

According to given information

Total time $= \frac{x}{3\times10} + \frac{x}{3\times20} + \frac{x}{3\times60}$

$= \frac{x}{30} + \frac{x}{60} + \frac{x}{180}$

$= \frac{6x+3x+x}{180}$

$= \frac{10x}{180} = \frac{x}{18}$

Average speed $= \frac{x\times18}{x}$ km/hr. = 18 km/hr

187. Let the speed of car be x km/hr

Distance = speed × time

Distance = $8x$ km

According to given information

$(x + 4) \times 7.5 = 8x$

$\Rightarrow 7.5x + 30 = 8x$

$\Rightarrow 8x - 7.5x = 30$

$30 = 0.5x$

$x = \frac{30}{0.5} = 60$ km/hr

Required distance = 8 × 60 = 480 km.

188. Speed of thief = 10 km/hr

Speed of policeman = 11 km/hr

Relative speed of policeman with respect to thief = (11 – 10) km/hr = 1 km/hr

Thief is noticed by a policeman from a distance of 200m

Distance covered in 6 minutes $\frac{1000}{60}\times6 = 100$ m

Distance between them after 6 minutes = 200 – 100 = 100 m

189. Let total distance covered by man be x km

Journey covered by rail $= \frac{2x}{15}$

Journey covered by bus $= \frac{9x}{20}$

Remaining covered by Cycle = 10 km

$\therefore x\left(1 - \frac{2}{15} - \frac{9}{20}\right) = 10$

LCM of 15 and 20 = 60

$x\left(\frac{60-8-27}{60}\right) = 10$

$\Rightarrow x\left(\frac{25}{60}\right) = 10$

$x = \frac{10\times60}{25} = 24$ km.

190. Speed of Ramesh = 10 kmph

Ramesh will take rest four times during his journey

∴ Required time

$= \left(5\times\frac{1}{10}\times60\right)$ minutes + (5 × 4) minutes

= (30 + 20) minutes

≐ 50 minutes

Ramesh takes time to cover a distance of 5 kms

191. According to the question,

∴ 50m = 20m

∴ 1m $= \frac{20}{50}$ m

∴ 1000m $= \left(\frac{20}{50}\times1000\right)$ m ≡ 400 m

EXERCISE

(DATA SUFFICIENCY TYPE QUESTIONS)

Directions (*Questions 1 to 12*): ***Each of the questions below consists of a statement and/or a question and two statements numbered I and II given below it. You have to decide whether the data provided in the statements is/are sufficient to answer the question. Read both the statements and***

Give answer (a) if the data in Statement I alone are sufficient to answer the question, while the data in Statement II alone are not sufficient to answer the question;

Give answer (b) if the data in Statement II alone are sufficient to answer the question, while the data in Statement I alone are not sufficient to answer the question;

Give answer (c) if the data either in Statement I or in Statement II alone are sufficient to answer the question;

Give answer (d) if the data even in both Statements I and II together are not sufficient to answer the question; and

Give answer (e) if the data in both Statements I and II together are necessary to answer the question.

1. How much time did X take to reach the destination?
   I. The ratio between the speeds of X and Y is 3 : 4.
   II. *Y* takes 36 minutes to reach the same destination.
2. Shweta walked from her home to the bus stop and back again. How long did it take her to make the entire trip?
   I. She walked from home to the bus stop at the rate of 3 km/hr.
   II. She walked back to home @ 5 km/hr.
3. What is the distance between City *A* and City *B*?
   I. Bus starting from A reaches B at 6 : 15 p.m. at an average speed of 60 kmph.
   II. Bus at an average speed of 40 kmph reaches *A* at 4 : 35 p.m. if it starts from *B* exactly at noon. **(Bank P.O., 2009)**
4. What is the usual speed of the train? **(M.B.A., 2002)**
   I. The speed of the train is increased by 25 km/hr to reach the destination 150 km away in time.
   II. The train is late by 30 minutes.
5. Two towns are connected by railway. Can you find the distance between them?
   I. The speed of mail train is 12 km/hr more than that of an express train.
   II. A mail train takes 40 minutes less than an express train to cover the distance.
6. Sachin jogs at a constant rate for 80 minutes along the same route everyday. How long is the route? **(M.A.T., 2006)**
   I. Yesterday, Sachin began jogging at 5 : 00 p.m.
   II. Yesterday, Sachin had jogged 5 miles by 5 : 40 p.m. and 8 miles by 6 : 04 p.m.
7. The towns *A*, *B* and *C* are on a straight line. Town C is between *A* and *B*. The distance from *A* to *B* is 100 km. How far is *A* from C? **(M.B.A., 2003)**
   I. The distance from *A* to *B* is 25% more than the distance from C to *B*.
   II. The distance from *A* to C is $\frac{1}{4}$ of the distance from C to *B*.
8. What is the average speed of the car over the entire distance?
   I. The car covers the whole distance in four equal stretches at speeds of 10 kmph, 20 kmph, 30 kmph and 60 kmph respectively.
   II. The total time taken is 36 minutes.
9. How long will it take for a jeep to travel a distance of 250 km? **(M.B.A., 2005)**
   I. The relative speed of the jeep with respect to the car moving in the same direction at 40 kmph is 50 kmph.
   II. The car started at 3.00 a.m. in the morning.
10. A car and a bus start from city *A* at the same time. How far is the city *B* from city *A* ?
    I. The car travelling at an average speed of 40 km/hr reaches city *B* at 4 : 35 p.m.
    II. The bus reaches city *B* at 6 : 15 p.m. at an average speed of 60 km/hr.
11. Two cars pass each other in opposite directions. How long would they take to be 500 km apart?
    I. The sum of their speeds is 135 km/hr.
    II. The difference of their speeds is 25 km/hr.
12. Jacob's house is 60 miles from the town. On Sunday, he went to town and returned home. How long did the entire trip take?
    I. He travelled at a uniform rate for the round trip of 30 miles per hour.
    II. If Jacob travelled 10 miles per hour faster, it would have taken $\frac{3}{4}$ of the time for the round trip.

ANSWERS

1. (*e*)	2. (*d*)	3. (*b*)	4. (*e*)	5. (*d*)	6. (*b*)	7. (*c*)	8. (*a*)	9. (*a*)	10. (*e*)
11. (*a*)	12. (*c*)								

SOLUTIONS

1. I. If *Y* takes 3 min, then X takes 4 min.

   II. If Y takes 36 min, then *X* takes $\left(\frac{4}{3}\times 36\right)$ min = 48 min.

   Thus, I and II together give the answer.

   ∴ Correct answer is (*e*).

2. Since the distance between the house and the bus stop is not given, the duration of the trip cannot be calculated.

   ∴ Correct answer is (*d*).

3. I. Only the reaching time is given. So, the duration of the journey and hence the distance between City A and City B cannot be calculated.

II. Required distance $= \left(40 \times 4\frac{35}{60}\right)$ km $= 183\frac{1}{3}$ km.

$\therefore$ II alone gives the answer. $\therefore$ Correct answer is (*b*).

4. Let the usual speed of the train be x kmph.

Time taken to cover 150 km at usual speed $= \frac{150}{x}$ hrs.

I. Time taken at increased speed $= \frac{150}{(x+25)}$ hrs.

II. $\frac{150}{x} - \frac{150}{(x+25)} = \frac{30}{60} \Leftrightarrow \frac{1}{x} - \frac{1}{(x+25)} = \frac{1}{300}$

$\Leftrightarrow [(x+25) - x] \times 300 = x(x+25)$

$\Leftrightarrow x^2 + 25x - 7500 = 0 \Leftrightarrow (x+100)(x-75) = 0$

$\Leftrightarrow x = 75.$

Thus, I and II together give the answer.

$\therefore$ Correct answer is (*e*).

5. Let the distance between the two stations be x km.

I. Let the speed of the express train be y km/hr.

Then, speed of the mail train = $(y + 12)$ km/hr.

II. $\frac{x}{y} - \frac{x}{(y+12)} = \frac{40}{60}.$

Thus, even I and II together do not give x.

$\therefore$ Correct answer is (*d*).

6. From II, we have :

Distance covered by Sachin from 5 : 40 p.m. to 6 : 04 p.m *i.e.*, in 24 min = 3 miles.

$\therefore$ Length of the route = Distance covered in 80 min

$= \left(\frac{3}{24} \times 80\right)$ miles $= 10$ miles.

So, II alone gives the answer while I alone does not.

$\therefore$ Correct answer is (*b*).

7. Let AC = x km.

Then, CB = $(100 - x)$km   A —x— C —$(100 - x)$— B

I. AB = 125% of CB

$\Leftrightarrow 100 = \frac{125}{100} \times (100 - x) \Leftrightarrow 100 - x$

$= \frac{100 \times 100}{125} = 80 \Leftrightarrow x = 20$ km.

$\therefore AC = 20$ km.

Thus, I alone gives the answer.

II. $AC = \frac{1}{4} CB \Leftrightarrow x = \frac{1}{4}(100 - x) \Leftrightarrow 5x = 100 \Leftrightarrow x = 20.$

$\therefore AC = 20$ km.

Thus, II alone gives the answer.

$\therefore$ Correct answer is (*c*).

8. Let the whole distance be $4x$ km.

I. Total time taken

$= \left(\frac{x}{10} + \frac{x}{20} + \frac{x}{30} + \frac{x}{60}\right) = \frac{(6x + 3x + 2x + x)}{60} = \frac{12x}{60} = \frac{x}{5}.$

$\therefore$ Speed $= \frac{\text{Distance}}{\text{Time}} = \frac{4x}{(x/5)}$ kmph $= 20$ km/hr.

$\therefore$ I alone is sufficient to answer the question.

II. alone does not give the answer.

$\therefore$ Correct answer is (*a*).

9. I. Speed of the jeep = (40 + 50) kmph = 90 kmph.

$\therefore$ Required time $= \left(\frac{250}{90}\right)$ hrs $= \frac{25}{9}$ hrs $= 2\frac{7}{9}$ hrs.

So, I alone gives the answer while II alone does not.

$\therefore$ Correct answer is (*a*).

10. Let $AB = x$ km. From I and II, we get :

$\frac{x}{40} - \frac{x}{60} = 1\frac{40}{60}$ [(6 : 15 p.m.) – (4 : 35 p.m.) = 1 hr 40 min]

$\Leftrightarrow \frac{x}{40} - \frac{x}{60} = \frac{100}{60}$. This gives x.

$\therefore$ Correct answer is (*e*).

11. I. gives, relative speed = 135 km/hr.

$\therefore$ Time taken $= \frac{500}{135}$ hrs.

II. does not give the relative speed.

$\therefore$ I alone gives the answer and II is irrelevant.

$\therefore$ Correct answer is (*a*).

12. I. Time taken for the round trip $= \left(\frac{120}{30}\right)$ hrs = 4 hrs.

II. Let the time taken for the round trip be x hours.

Then, $\frac{120}{\left(\frac{3}{4}x\right)} - \frac{120}{x} = 10 \Leftrightarrow \frac{160}{x} - \frac{120}{x} = 10$

$\Leftrightarrow 10x = 40 \Leftrightarrow x = 4.$

Thus, I alone or II alone gives the answer.

$\therefore$ Correct answer is (*c*).

19 Boats and Streams

IMPORTANT FACTS AND FORMULAE

I. In water, the direction along the stream is called ***downstream***. And, the direction against the stream is called ***upstream***.

II. If the speed of a boat in still water is u km/hr and the speed of the stream is v km/hr, then :

$$\textit{Speed downstream} = (u + v) \text{ km/hr}$$

$$\textit{Speed upstream} = (u - v) \text{ km/hr}$$

III. If the speed downstream is a km/hr and the speed upstream is b km/hr, then:

$$\textit{Speed in still water} = \frac{1}{2}(a + b) \text{ km/hr}$$

$$\textit{Rate of stream} = \frac{1}{2}(a - b) \text{ km/hr}$$

IV. Suppose a man can swim in still water at the rate of u km/hr, the speed of current/stream is v km/hr and the man wishes to cross the stream (of width x metres) straight along its width, then time taken to cross the river is the same as time taken to swim x metres at u km/hr.

[**Note** : This is because the stream sways the man such that both the distance and the effective velocity increase and the time taken to cross the river remains unaffected.]

V. A man can swim directly across a stream of width x km in t hours when there is no current and in t' hours when there is a current. Then, the rate of the current is

$$\left(x\sqrt{\frac{1}{t^2} - \frac{1}{t'^2}}\right) \text{ km/hr.}$$

SOLVED EXAMPLES

Ex. 1. ***The speed of a boat when travelling downstream is 32 km/hr, whereas when travelling upstream it is 28 km/hr, what is the speed of the boat in still water and the speed of the stream?*** **(S.B.I.P.O., 2010)**

Sol. Speed of boat in still water $= \frac{1}{2}(32 + 28) \text{ km/hr} = 30 \text{ km/hr}.$

Speed of stream $= \frac{1}{2}(32 - 28) \text{ km/hr} = 2 \text{ km/hr}.$

Ex. 2. ***A man takes 3 hours 45 minutes to row a boat 15 km downstream of a river and 2 hours 30 minutes to cover a distance of 5 km upstream. Find the speed of the river current in km/hr.***

Sol. Rate downstream $= \left(\frac{15}{3\frac{3}{4}}\right) \text{ km/hr} = \left(15 \times \frac{4}{15}\right) \text{ km/hr} = 4 \text{ km/hr}.$

Rate upstream $= \left(\frac{5}{2\frac{1}{2}}\right) \text{ km/hr} = \left(5 \times \frac{2}{5}\right) \text{ km/hr} = 2 \text{ km/hr}.$

$\therefore$ Speed of current $= \frac{1}{2}(4 - 2) \text{ km/hr} = 1 \text{ km/hr}.$

Ex. 3. ***The speed of a motor boat is that of the current of water as 36 : 5. The boat goes along with the current in 5 hours 10 minutes. How much time will it take to come back?*** **(S.S.C., 2007)**

Sol. Let the speed of the motor boat and that of the current be $36x$ km/hr and $5x$ km/hr respectively.
Then, speed downstream = $(36x + 5x)$ km/hr = $41x$ km/hr.
Speed upstream = $(36x - 5x)$ km/hr = $31x$ km/hr.
Let the distance be d km.

Then, $\frac{d}{41x} = 5\frac{10}{60} = 5\frac{1}{6} = \frac{31}{6} \Rightarrow d = \left(\frac{31 \times 41}{6}\right)x = \frac{1271x}{6}$.

$\therefore$ Time taken while coming back = $\frac{d}{31x} = \left(\frac{1271x}{6} \times \frac{1}{31x}\right)$ hrs $= \frac{41}{6}$ hrs $= 6\frac{5}{6}$ hrs

= 6 hrs 50 min.

Ex. 4. ***A man can row 6 km/hr in still water. It takes him twice as long to row up as to row down the river. Find the rate of stream.*** **(A.T.M.A., 2007)**

Sol. Let man's rate upstream be x km/hr.
Then, his rate downstream = $2x$ km/hr.

$\therefore$ Rate in still water = $\frac{1}{2}(x + 2x)$ km/hr $= \frac{3x}{2}$ km/hr.

So, $\frac{3x}{2} = 6$ or $x = 4$.

$\therefore$ Rate upstream = 4 km/hr, Rate downstream = 8 km/hr.

Hence, rate of stream = $\frac{1}{2}(8 - 4)$ km/hr = 2 km/hr.

Ex. 5. ***There is a road beside a river. Two friends started from a place A, moved to a temple situated at another place B and then returned to A again. One of them moves on a cycle at a speed of 12 km/hr, while the other sails on a boat at a speed of 10 km/hr. If the river flows at the speed of 4 km/hr, which of the two friends will return to place A first?***

Sol. Clearly, the cyclist moves both ways at a speed of 12 km/hr.
So, average speed of the cyclist = 12 km/hr.
The boat sailor moves downstream @ (10 + 4) *i.e.,* 14 km/hr and upstream @ (10 – 4) *i.e.,* 6 km/hr.

So, average speed of the boat sailor = $\left(\frac{2 \times 14 \times 6}{14 + 6}\right)$ km/hr $= \frac{42}{5}$ km/hr

= 8.4 km/hr.

Since the average speed of the cyclist is greater, he will return to A first.

Ex. 6. ***A man can row $7\frac{1}{2}$ kmph in still water. If in a river running at 1.5 km an hour, it takes him 50 minutes to row to a place and back, how far off is the place?*** **(P.C.S., 2009)**

Sol. Speed downstream = (7.5 + 1.5) kmph = 9 kmph;
Speed upstream = (7.5 – 1.5) kmph = 6 kmph.
Let the required distance be x km. Then,

$\frac{x}{9} + \frac{x}{6} = \frac{50}{60} \Leftrightarrow 2x + 3x = \left(\frac{5}{6} \times 18\right) \Leftrightarrow 5x = 15 \Leftrightarrow x = 3.$

Hence, the required distance is 3 km.

Ex. 7. ***A boat goes 8 km upstream and then returns. Total time taken is 4 hrs 16 minutes. If the velocity of current is 1 km/hr, find the actual velocity of the boat.*** **(Hotel Management, 2007)**

Sol. Let the actual velocity of the boat be x km/hr. Then,
Speed downstream = $(x + 1)$ km/hr; Speed upstream = $(x - 1)$ km/hr.

$\therefore \quad \frac{8}{x+1} + \frac{8}{x-1} = 4\frac{16}{60} = 4\frac{4}{15} = \frac{64}{15} \Leftrightarrow \frac{(x-1)+(x+1)}{(x+1)(x-1)} = \frac{8}{15} \Leftrightarrow 30x = 8(x^2 - 1)$

$\Leftrightarrow 4x^2 - 15x - 4 = 0 \Leftrightarrow 4x^2 - 16x + x - 4 = 0 \Leftrightarrow 4x(x - 4) + (x - 4) = 0$
$\Leftrightarrow (x - 4)(4x + 1) = 0 \Leftrightarrow x = 4.$

Hence, actual velocity of the boat = 74 km/hr.

Ex. 8. ***A boatman rows to a place 45 km distant and back in 20 hours. He finds that he can row 12 km with the stream in the same time as 4 km against the stream. Find the speed of the stream.*** **(M.A.T., 2007)**

Sol. Suppose he moves 12 km downstream in x hours. Then,

Speed downstream = $\left(\frac{12}{x}\right)$ km/hr, Speed upstream = $\left(\frac{4}{x}\right)$ km/hr

$$\therefore \quad \frac{45}{(12/x)} + \frac{45}{(4/x)} = 20 \Rightarrow \frac{x}{12} + \frac{x}{4} = \frac{20}{45} = \frac{4}{9} \Rightarrow \frac{x}{3} = \frac{4}{9} \Rightarrow x = \frac{4}{3}.$$

So, Speed downstream = $\left(12 \times \frac{3}{4}\right)$ km/hr = 9 km/hr,

Speed upstream = $\left(4 \times \frac{3}{4}\right)$ km/hr = 3 km/hr.

$\therefore$ Speed of the stream = $\frac{1}{2}(9 - 3)$ km/hr = 3 km/hr.

Ex. 9. ***A man can row 40 km upstream and 55 km downstream in 13 hours. Also, he can row 30 km upstream and 44 km downstream in 10 hours. Find the speed of the man in still water and the speed of the current.***

Sol. Let rate upstream = x km/hr and rate downstream = y km/hr.

Then, $\frac{40}{x} + \frac{55}{y} = 13$ ...(*i*) and $\frac{30}{x} + \frac{44}{y} = 10$ ...(*ii*)

Multiplying (*ii*) by 4 and (*i*) by 3 and subtracting, we get : $\frac{11}{y} = 1$ or $y = 11$.

Substituting $y = 11$ in (*i*), we get : $x = 5$.

$\therefore$ Rate in still water = $\frac{1}{2}(11 + 5)$ kmph = 8 kmph.

Rate of current = $\frac{1}{2}(11 - 5)$ kmph = 3 kmph.

EXERCISE

(OBJECTIVE TYPE QUESTIONS)

Directions: ***Mark (✓) against the correct answer:***

1. A boat goes 8 km in one hour along the stream and 2 km in one hour against the stream. The speed in km/hr of the stream is **(S.S.C., 2005)**
   (*a*) 2 (*b*) 3
   (*c*) 4 (*d*) 5

2. In one hour, a boat goes 11 km along the stream and 5 km against the stream. The speed of the boat in still water (in km/hr) is **(B.Ed Entrance, 2009)**
   (*a*) 3 (*b*) 5
   (*c*) 8 (*d*) 9

3. A man rows downstream 32 km and 14 km upstream. If he takes 6 hours to cover each distance, then the velocity (in kmph) of the current is **(R.R.B., 2008)**
   (*a*) $\frac{1}{2}$ (*b*) 1
   (*c*) $1\frac{1}{2}$ (*d*) 2

4. A boatman rows 1 km in 5 minutes, along the stream and 6 km in 1 hour against the stream. The speed of the stream is **(S.S.C., 2010)**
   (*a*) 3 kmph (*b*) 6 kmph
   (*c*) 10 kmph (*d*) 12 kmph

5. A boat takes half time in moving a certain distance downstream than upstream. What is the ratio between the rate in still water and the rate of current? **(R.R.B., 2006)**
   (*a*) 1 : 2 (*b*) 2 : 1
   (*c*) 1 : 3 (*d*) 3 : 1

6. If a man goes 18 km downstream in 4 hours and returns against the stream in 12 hours, then the speed of the stream in km/hr is **(S.S.C., 2008)**
   (*a*) 1 (*b*) 1.5
   (*c*) 1.75 (*d*) 3

7. A boatman goes 2 km against the current of the stream in 1 hour and goes 1 km along the current in 10 minutes. How long will it take to go 5 km in stationary water?

(a) 40 minutes (b) 1 hour
(c) 1 hr 15 min (d) 1 hr 30 min

8. A man can row $\frac{3}{4}$ of a km against the stream in $11\frac{1}{4}$ minutes and returns in $7\frac{1}{2}$ minutes. Find the speed of the man in still water. **(M.A.T., 2008)**
(a) 3 km/hr (b) 4 km/hr
(c) 5 km/hr (d) 6 km/hr

9. A boat, while going downstream in a river covered a distance of 50 miles at an average speed of 60 miles per hour. While returning, because of the water resistance, it took 1 hour 15 minutes to cover the same distance. What was the average speed during the whole journey? **(M.A.T., 2004)**
(a) 40 mph (b) 48 mph
(c) 50 mph (d) 55 mph

10. A man swimming in a stream which flows $1\frac{1}{2}$ km/hr finds that in a given time he can swim twice as far with the stream as he can against it. At what rate does he swim? **(M.A.T., 2008)**
(a) $4\frac{1}{2}$ km/hr (b) $5\frac{1}{2}$ km/hr
(c) $7\frac{1}{2}$ km/hr (d) None of these

11. A boat running upstream takes 8 hours 48 minutes to cover a certain distance, while it takes 4 hours to cover the same distance running downstream. What is the ratio between the speed of the boat and speed of the water current respectively ?
(a) 2 : 1
(b) 3 : 2
(c) 8 : 3
(d) Cannot be determined
(e) None of these

12. If a boat goes 7 km upstream in 42 minutes and the speed of the stream is 3 kmph, then the speed of the boat in still water is : **(Bank Rec., 2010)**
(a) 4.2 km/hr (b) 9 km/hr
(c) 13 km/hr (d) 21 km/hr

13. A man's speed with the current is 15 km / hr and the speed of the current is 2.5 km / hr. The man's speed against the current is :
(a) 8.5 km/hr (b) 9 km/hr
(c) 10 km/hr (d) 12.5 km/hr

14. If a man rows at the rate of 5 kmph in still water and his rate against the current is 3.5 kmph, then the man's rate along the current is :
(a) 4.25 kmph (b) 6 kmph
(c) 6.5 kmph (d) 8.5 kmph

15. A motorboat in still water travels at a speed of 36 km/hr. It goes 56 km upstream in 1 hour 45 minutes. The time taken by it to cover the same distance down the stream will be **(C.P.O., 2007)**
(a) 1 hour 24 minutes (b) 2 hour 21 minutes
(c) 2 hour 25 minutes (d) 3 hour

16. Speed of a boat in standing water is 9 kmph and the speed of the stream is 1.5 kmph. A man rows to a place at a distance of 105 km and comes back to the starting point. The total time taken by him is :
(a) 16 hours (b) 18 hours
(c) 20 hours (d) 24 hours

17. The speed of a boat in still water is 15 km / hr and the rate of current is 3 km / hr. The distance travelled downstream in 12 minutes is :
(a) 1.2 km (b) 1.8 km
(c) 2.4 km (d) 3.6 km

18. A man can row at 5 kmph in still water. If the velocity of current is 1 kmph and it takes him 1 hour to row to a place and come back, how far is the place? **(S.S.C., 2004)**
(a) 2.4 km (b) 2.5 km
(c) 3 km (d) 3.6 km

19. A boat takes 19 hours for travelling downstream from point A to point B and coming back to a point C midway between A and B. If the velocity of the stream is 4 kmph and the speed of the boat in still water is 14 kmph, what is the distance between A and B?
(a) 160 km (b) 180 km
(c) 200 km (d) 220 km

20. P, Q and R are three towns on a river which flows uniformly. Q is equidistant from P and R. I row from P to Q and back in 10 hours and I can row from P to R in 4 hours. Compare the speed of my boat in still water with that of the river. **(M.A.T., 2005)**
(a) 4 : 3 (b) 5 : 3
(c) 6 : 5 (d) 7 : 3

21. A man can row $9\frac{1}{3}$ kmph in still water and finds that it takes him thrice as much time to row up than as to row down the same distance in the river. The speed of the current is :
(a) $3\frac{1}{3}$ km/hr (b) $3\frac{1}{9}$ km/hr
(c) $4\frac{2}{3}$ km/hr (d) $4\frac{1}{2}$ km/hr

22. A boat takes 8 hours to cover a distance while travelling upstream, whereas while travelling downstream it takes 6 hours. If the speed of the current is 4 kmph, what is the speed of the boat in still water? (Bank P.O., 2006)
(a) 12 kmph
(b) 16 kmph
(c) 28 kmph
(d) Cannot be determined
(e) None of these

23. A motor boat can travel at 10 km/hr in still water. It travelled 91 km downstream in a river a then returned taking altogether 20 hours. Find the rate of flow of the river. (M.A.T., 2008)
(a) 3 km/hr (b) 5 km/hr
(c) 6 km/hr (d) 8 km/hr

24. The speed of a boat in still water is 10 km / hr. If it can travel 26 km downstream and 14 km upstream in the same time, the speed of the stream is :
(a) 2 km/hr (b) 2.5 km/hr
(c) 3 km/hr (d) 4 km/hr

25. A boat takes 90 minutes less to travel 36 miles downstream than to travel the same distance upstream. If the speed of the boat in still water is 10 mph, the speed of the stream is :
(a) 2 mph (b) 2.5 mph
(c) 3 mph (d) 4 mph

26. A man rows to a place 48 km distant and back in 14 hours. He finds that he can row 4 km with the stream in the same time as 3 km against the stream. The rate of the stream is : (M.A.T., 2005)
(a) 1 km / hr (b) 1.5 km / hr
(c) 1.8 km / hr (d) 3.5 km / hr

27. A boat covers 24 km upstream and 36 km downstream in 6 hours while it covers 36 km upstream and 24 km downstream in $6\frac{1}{2}$ hours. The velocity of the current is
(a) 1 km/hr (b) 1.5 km/hr
(c) 2 km/hr (d) 2.5 km/hr

28. A boat goes 30 km upstream and 44 km downstream in 10 hours. In 13 hours, it can go 40 km upstream and 55 km downstream. The speed of the boat in still water is (I.I.F.T., 2008)
(a) 3 km/hr (b) 4 km/hr
(c) 8 km/hr (d) None of these

29. At his usual rowing rate, Rahul can travel 12 miles downstream in a certain river in 6 hours less than it takes him to travel the same distance upstream. But if he could double his usual rowing rate for his 24-mile round trip, the downstream 12 miles would then take only one hour less than the upstream 12 miles. What is the speed of the current in miles per hour? (M.A.T., 2001)
(a) $1\frac{1}{3}$ (b) $1\frac{2}{3}$
(c) $2\frac{1}{3}$ (d) $2\frac{2}{3}$

30. A man can swim in still water at a rate of 4 km/hr. The width of the river is 1 km. How long will he take to cross the river straight, if the speed of the current is 3 km/hr? (R.R.B., 2009)
(a) 10 min (b) 15 min
(c) 18 min (d) 20 min

31. A man wishes to cross a river perpendicularly. In still water he takes 4 minutes to cross the river, but in flowing river he takes 5 minutes. If the river is 100 metres wide, the velocity of the flowing water of the river is (M.A.T., 2004)
(a) 10 m/min (b) 15 m/min
(c) 20 m/min (d) 30 m/min

32. A man can row upstream at 10 kmph and downstream at 18 kmph. Find the man's rate in still water? [Indian Railways Gr. 'D' Exam, 2014]
(a) 14 kmph (b) 4 kmph
(c) 12 kmph (d) 10 kmph

33. A man takes 2.2 times as long to row a distance upstream as to row the same distance downstream. If he can row 55 km downstream in 2 hours 30 minutes, what is the speed of the boat in still water? [IBPS—RRB Officers Gr. 'B' Exam, 2015]
(a) 40 km/h (b) 8 km/h
(c) 16 km/h (d) 24 km/h

34. Boat A travels downstream from Point X to Point Y in 3 hours less than the time taken by Boat B to travel upstream from Point Y to Point Z. The distance between X and Y is 20 km, which is half of the distance between Y and Z. The speed of Boat B in still water is 10 km/h and the speed of Boat A in still water is equal to the speed of Boat B upstream. What is the speed of Boat A in still water? (Consider the speed of the current to be the same.) [RBI Gr. 'B' (Phase I) Exam, 2015]
(a) 10 km/h (b) 16 km/h
(c) 12 km/h (d) 8 km/h

35. The speed of the boat in still water is 5 times that of the current, it takes 1.1 hours to row to point B form point A downstream. The distance between point A and point B is 13.2km. How much distance (in km) will it cover in 312 minutes upstream? [IBPS—Bank Spl. Officer (IT) Exam, 2015]
(a) 43.2 (b) 48
(c) 41.6 (d) 44.8

36. A boat can travel 36 km upstream in 5 hours. If the speed of the stream is 2.4 kmph, how much

time will the boat take to cover a distance of 78 km downstream? (in hours)

(a) 5 (b) 6.5
(c) 5.5 (d) 8

[United India Insurance Co. Ltd. (UIICL) Assistant (Online) Exam, 2015]

Direction (*Question No. 37*): The following question is followed by two statements number I and II are given. You have to read both the statements and then give the answer.

a. If the data given in Statement I alone are sufficient to answer the question whereas the data given in Statement II alone are not sufficient to answer the questions.

b. If the data given in Statement II alone are sufficient to answer the question I alone are not sufficient to answer the question.

c. If the data in either Statement I alone or in Statement II alone are sufficient to answer the question.

d. If the data in both the statement I and II are not sufficient to answer the question.

e. If the data given in both the Statements I and II are necessary to answer the question.

37. What is the speed of the boat in still water? (in km/hr)

I. The boat takes total time of 4*h* to travel 14 km upstream and 35 km downstream together.

II. The boat takes total time of 5*h* to travel 29 km upstream and 24 km downstream together.

[CET—Maharashtra (MBA) Exam, 2016]

ANSWERS

1. (b)	2. (c)	3. (c)	4. (a)	5. (d)	6. (b)	7. (c)	8. (c)	9. (b)	10. (a)
11. (c)	12. (c)	13. (c)	14. (c)	15. (a)	16. (d)	17. (d)	18. (a)	19. (b)	20. (b)
21. (c)	22. (c)	23. (a)	24. (c)	25. (a)	26. (a)	27. (c)	28. (c)	29. (d)	30. (b)
31. (b)	32. (a)	33. (c)	34. (d)	35. (c)	36. (b)	37. (e)			

SOLUTIONS

1. Speed of the stream $= \frac{1}{2}(8-2)$ km/hr $= 3$ km/hr.

2. Speed of the boat in still water $= \frac{1}{2}(11+5)$ km/hr $= 8$ km/hr.

3. Rate downstream $= \left(\frac{32}{6}\right)$ kmph;

Rate upstream $= \left(\frac{14}{6}\right)$ kmph.

Velocity of current $= \frac{1}{2}\left(\frac{32}{6}-\frac{14}{6}\right)$ kmph

$= \frac{3}{2}$ kmph $= 1\frac{1}{2}$ kmph.

4. Rate downstream $= \left(\frac{1}{5}\times 60\right)$ kmph $= 12$ kmph;

Rate upstream $= 6$ kmph.

Speed of the stream $= \frac{1}{2}(12-6)$ kmph $= 3$ kmph.

5. Ratio of times taken (Downstream : Upstream) = 1 : 2.

$\therefore$ Speed downstream : Speed upstream = 2 : 1.

Let speed downstream = $2x$ kmph and speed upstream = x kmph.

Required ratio $= \frac{\text{Rate in still water}}{\text{Rate of current}} = \frac{\frac{1}{2}(2x+x)}{\frac{1}{2}(2x-x)} = 3:1.$

6. Speed downstream $= \left(\frac{18}{4}\right)$ km/hr $= 4.5$ km/hr ;

Speed upstream $= \left(\frac{18}{12}\right)$ km/hr $= 1.5$ km/hr.

$\therefore$ Speed of the stream $= \frac{1}{2}(4.5-1.5)$ km/hr $= 1.5$ km/hr.

7. Rate downstream

$= \left(\frac{1}{10}\times 60\right)$ km/hr $= 6$ km/hr; Rate upstream $= 2$ km/hr.

Speed in still water $= \frac{1}{2}(6+2)$ km/hr $= 4$ km/hr.

$\therefore$ Required time $= \left(\frac{5}{4}\right)$ hrs $= 1\frac{1}{4}$ hrs $= 1$ hr 15 min.

8. Rate upstream $= \left(\frac{750}{675}\right)$ m/sec $= \frac{10}{9}$ m/sec;

Rate downstream $= \left(\frac{750}{450}\right)$ m/sec $= \frac{5}{3}$ m/sec.

$\therefore$ Rate in still water

$= \frac{1}{2}\left(\frac{10}{9}+\frac{5}{3}\right)$ m/sec $= \frac{25}{18}$ m/sec $= \left(\frac{25}{18}\times\frac{18}{5}\right)$ km/hr

$= 5$ km/hr.

9. Time taken to cover 50 miles downstream $= \left(\frac{50}{60}\right)$ hr $= \frac{5}{6}$ hr.

Time taken to cover 50 miles upstream

$= 1$ hr 15 min $= 1\frac{1}{4}$ hrs $= \frac{5}{4}$ hrs.

Total time taken to cover 100 miles $= \left(\frac{5}{6}+\frac{5}{4}\right)$ hrs $= \frac{25}{12}$ hrs.

$\therefore$ Average speed

$= \frac{100}{\left(\frac{25}{12}\right)}$ mph $= \left(\frac{100 \times 12}{25}\right)$ mph $= 48$ mph.

10. Let speed upstream $= x$ km/hr.

Then, speed downstream $= 2x$ km/hr.

Speed of stream $= \frac{1}{2}(2x - x)$ km/hr $= \frac{x}{2}$ km/hr.

$\therefore \frac{x}{2} = 1\frac{1}{2} \Leftrightarrow \frac{x}{2} = \frac{3}{2} \Leftrightarrow x = 3.$

So, speed upstream = 3 km/hr;

Speed downstream = 6 km/hr.

Hence, rate of swimming $= \frac{1}{2}(3+6)$ km/hr $= 4\frac{1}{2}$ km/hr.

11. Let the man' rate upstream be x kmph and that downstream be y kmph. Then, Distance covered upstream in 8 hrs 48 min. = Distance covered downstream in 4 hrs.

$\Rightarrow \left(x \times 8\frac{4}{5}\right) = (y \times 4) \Rightarrow \frac{44}{5}x = 4y \Rightarrow y = \frac{11}{5}x.$

$\therefore$ Required ratio

$= \left(\frac{y+x}{2}\right) : \left(\frac{y-x}{2}\right) = \left(\frac{16x}{5} \times \frac{1}{2}\right) : \left(\frac{6x}{5} \times \frac{1}{2}\right) = \frac{8}{5} : \frac{3}{5} = 8:3.$

12. Rate upstream $= \left(\frac{7}{42} \times 60\right)$ kmph $= 10$ kmph.

Speed of stream = 3 kmph.

Let speed in still water be x km/hr.

Then, speed upstream $= (x - 3)$ km/hr.

$\therefore$ $x - 3 = 10$ or $x = 13$ km/hr.

13. Man's rate in still water = (15 – 2.5) km/hr = 12.5 km/hr.

Man's rate against the current = (12.5 – 2.5) km/hr

= 10 km/hr.

14. Let the rate along the current be x kmph.

Then, $\frac{1}{2}(x + 3.5) = 5$ or $x = 6.5$ kmph.

15. Speed upstream

$= \left(\frac{56}{1\frac{3}{4}}\right)$ km/hr $= \left(56 \times \frac{4}{7}\right)$ km/hr $= 32$ km/hr.

Let speed downstream be x km/hr.

Then, speed of boat in still water $= \frac{1}{2}(x + 32)$ km/hr.

$\therefore \frac{1}{2}(x + 32) = 36 \Rightarrow x = 40.$

Hence, required time $= \left(\frac{56}{40}\right)$ hrs $= 1\frac{2}{5}$ hrs = 1 hr 24 min.

16. Speed upstream = 7.5 kmph; Speed downstream = 10.5 kmph.

$\therefore$ Total time taken $= \left(\frac{105}{7.5} + \frac{105}{10.5}\right)$ hours = 24 hours.

17. Speed downstream = (15 + 3) kmph = 18 kmph.

Distance travelled $= \left(18 \times \frac{12}{60}\right)$ km $= 3.6$ km.

18. Speed downstream = (5 + 1) kmph = 6 kmph;

Speed upstream = (5 – 1) kmph = 4 kmph.

Let the required distance be x km.

Then, $\frac{x}{6} + \frac{x}{4} = 1 \Leftrightarrow 2x + 3x = 12$

$\Leftrightarrow 5x = 12 \Leftrightarrow x = 2.4$ km.

19. Speed downstream = (14 + 4) km/hr = 18 km/hr;

Speed upstream = (14 – 4) km/hr = 10 km/hr.

Let the distance between A and B be x km.

Then, $\frac{x}{18} + \frac{(x/2)}{10} = 19 \Leftrightarrow \frac{x}{18} + \frac{x}{20} = 19$

$\Leftrightarrow \frac{19x}{180} = 19 \Leftrightarrow x = 180$ km.

20. Let $PQ = QR = x$ km.

Let speed downstream $= a$ km/hr,

and speed upstream $= b$ km/hr.

downstream

P x Q y R

upstream

Then, $\frac{x}{a} + \frac{x}{b} = 10 \Rightarrow x = \frac{10ab}{a+b}$ ...(i)

And, $\frac{2x}{a} = 4 \Rightarrow x = \frac{4a}{2} = 2a$ ...(ii)

From (i) and (ii), we have :

$2a = \frac{10ab}{a+b} \Rightarrow 5b = a + b \Rightarrow a = 4b.$

$\therefore$ Required ratio $= \frac{\text{Speed in still water}}{\text{Speed of river}}$

$= \frac{\frac{1}{2}(a+b)}{\frac{1}{2}(a-b)} = \frac{(a+b)}{(a-b)} = \frac{4b+b}{4b-b} = \frac{5}{3}.$

21. Let speed upstream be x kmph.

Then, speed downstream $= 3x$ kmph.

Speed in still water $= \frac{1}{2}(3x + x)$ kmph $= 2x$ kmph.

$\therefore 2x = \frac{28}{3} \Rightarrow x = \frac{14}{3}.$

So, Speed upstream $= \frac{14}{3}$ km/hr;

Speed downstream = 14 km/hr.

Hence, speed of the current

$\frac{1}{2}\left(14 - \frac{14}{3}\right)$ km/hr $= \frac{14}{3}$ km/hr $= 4\frac{2}{3}$ km/hr.

22. Let the speed of the boat in still water be x kmph.

Then, Speed downstream $= (x + 4)$ kmph,

Speed upstream = $(x - 4)$ kmph.

$\therefore\ (x + 4) \times 6 = (x - 4) \times 8$

$\Rightarrow 6x + 24 = 8x - 32 \Rightarrow 2x = 56 \Rightarrow x = 28$ kmph.

23. Let the rate of flow of the river be x km/hr. Then,

Speed downstream = $(10 + x)$ km/hr;

Speed upstream = $(10 - x)$ km/hr

$\therefore\ \dfrac{91}{(10+x)} + \dfrac{91}{(10-x)} = 20 \Rightarrow 91\left[\dfrac{20}{(10+x)(10-x)}\right] = 20$

$\Rightarrow (10 + x)(10 - x) = 91$

$\Rightarrow 100 - x^2 = 91 \Rightarrow x^2 = 9 \Rightarrow x = 3.$

Hence, rate of flow of the river = 3 km/hr.

24. Let the speed of the stream be x km/hr.

Then, Speed downstream = $(10 + x)$ km/hr,

Speed upstream = $(10 - x)$ km/hr.

$\therefore\ \dfrac{26}{(10+x)} = \dfrac{14}{(10-x)} \Leftrightarrow 260 - 26x = 140 + 14x \Leftrightarrow 40x = 120 \Leftrightarrow x = 3$ km/hr.

25. Let the speed of the stream be x mph.

Then, Speed downstream = $(10 + x)$ mph,

Speed upstream = $(10 - x)$ mph.

$\therefore\ \dfrac{36}{(10-x)} - \dfrac{36}{(10+x)} = \dfrac{90}{60} \Leftrightarrow 72x \times 60 = 90(100 - x^2)$

$\Leftrightarrow x^2 + 48x + 100 = 0$

$\Leftrightarrow (x + 50)(x - 2) = 0 \Leftrightarrow x = 2$ mph.

26. Suppose he moves 4 km downstream in x hours.

Then, Speed downstream = $\left(\dfrac{4}{x}\right)$ km/hr.

$=$ Speed upstream = $\left(\dfrac{3}{x}\right)$ km/hr.

$\therefore\ \dfrac{48}{(4/x)} + \dfrac{48}{(3/x)} = 14$ or $x = \dfrac{1}{2}$.

So, Speed downstream = 7 km/hr,

Speed upstream = 6 km/hr

Rate of the stream = $\dfrac{1}{2}(8-6)$ km/hr $= 1$ km/hr.

27. Let rate upstream = x kmph and rate downstream = y kmph.

Then, $\dfrac{24}{x} + \dfrac{36}{y} = 36$ ...(*i*)

and $\dfrac{36}{x} + \dfrac{24}{y} = \dfrac{13}{2}$ ...(*ii*)

Adding (*i*) and (*ii*), we get :

$60\left(\dfrac{1}{x} + \dfrac{1}{y}\right) = \dfrac{25}{2}$ or $\dfrac{1}{x} + \dfrac{1}{y} = \dfrac{5}{24}$ ...(*iii*)

Subtracting (*i*) from (*ii*), we get :

$12\left(\dfrac{1}{x} - \dfrac{1}{y}\right) = \dfrac{1}{2}$ or $\dfrac{1}{x} - \dfrac{1}{y} = \dfrac{1}{24}$ ...(*iv*)

Adding (*iii*) and (*iv*), we get : $\dfrac{2}{x} = \dfrac{6}{24}$ or $x = 8$.

So, $\dfrac{1}{8} + \dfrac{1}{y} = \dfrac{5}{24} \Leftrightarrow \dfrac{1}{y} = \left(\dfrac{5}{24} - \dfrac{1}{8}\right) = \dfrac{1}{12} \Leftrightarrow y = 12.$

$\therefore$ Speed upstream = 8 kmph,

Speed downstream = 12 kmph.

Hence, rate of current = $\dfrac{1}{2}(12-8)$ kmph $= 2$ kmph.

28. Let rate upstream = x km/hr and rate downstream = y km/hr.

Then, $\dfrac{30}{x} + \dfrac{44}{y} = 10$ ...(*i*)

and $\dfrac{40}{x} + \dfrac{55}{y} = 13$ ...(*ii*)

Multiplying (*i*) by 4 and (*ii*) by 3 and subtracting, we get : $\dfrac{11}{y} = 1$ or $y = 11$.

Putting $y = 11$ in (*i*), we get : $x = 5$.

Hence, speed in still water = $\dfrac{1}{2}(11+5)$ km/hr $= 8$ km/hr.

29. Let the speed in still water be x mph and the speed of the current be y mph. Then,

Speed upstream = $(x - y)$;

Speed downstream = $(x + y)$

$\therefore\ \dfrac{12}{(x-y)} - \dfrac{12}{(x+y)} = 6 \Leftrightarrow 6(x^2 - y^2) = 24y$

$\Leftrightarrow x^2 - y^2 = 4y \Leftrightarrow x^2 = (4y + y^2)$ ...(*i*)

And, $\dfrac{12}{(2x-y)} - \dfrac{12}{(2x+y)} = 1$

$\Leftrightarrow 4x^2 - y^2 = 24y \Leftrightarrow x^2 = \dfrac{24y + y^2}{4}$ ...(*ii*)

From (*i*) and (*ii*), we have :

$4y + y^2 = \dfrac{24y + y^2}{4} \Leftrightarrow 16y + 4y^2 = 24y + y^2$

$\Leftrightarrow 3y^2 = 8y \Leftrightarrow y = \dfrac{8}{3}.$

$\therefore$ Speed of the current = $\dfrac{8}{3}$ mph $= 2\dfrac{2}{3}$ mph.

30. Required time = Time taken to cover 1 km @ 4 kmph

$= \left(\dfrac{1}{4} \times 60\right)$ min $= 15$ min.

31. Velocity of the river = $\left(100\sqrt{\dfrac{1}{4^2} - \dfrac{1}{5^2}}\right)$ m/min

$= \left(100\sqrt{\dfrac{1}{16} - \dfrac{1}{25}}\right)$ m/min

$= 100\sqrt{\dfrac{9}{400}}$ m/min $= \left(100 \times \dfrac{3}{20}\right)$ m/min

$= 15$ m/min.

32. Speed of boatman in still water

$= \dfrac{1}{2}$ (Rate downstream + Rate upstream)

$= \dfrac{1}{2}(18 + 10) = \dfrac{28}{2} = 14$ kmph

33. Speed of the boat in downstream $=\frac{55}{2.2}=\frac{55\times10}{2.5}=22$ km/h

Then, speed of the boat in upstream

$=\frac{22}{2.2}=\frac{22\times10}{22}=10$ km/h

$\therefore$ Speed of boat in still water $=\frac{22+10}{2}=16$ km/h

34. Let the speed of current in water = s *km/h*

The time taken by boat A = t_a

And the time taken by boat B = t_b

Distance between point X to point Y = 20 km

Distance between point Y to Point Z = 40 km

According to the question

$\frac{40}{t_b}=10+s$ ...(i)

$t_a = t_b$ 3

The speed of boat A in still water

= The speed of boat B in upstream = (10 + s) km/h

So, t_a = 20/10 = 2 hours

Hence, $t_b=t_a+3=2+3=5$ hours.

By using equation (i)

$\frac{40}{5}=10+S$

$\Rightarrow$ 8 = 10 + S

S = 2 *km/h*

The speed of boat A in still water = (10 – 2) = 8 km/h

35. Let the speed of the current be x kmph.

Then speed of the boat in still water = $5x$

$\therefore$ Downstream speed = $(5x + x) = 6x$ kmph

Upstream speed = $(5x - x) = 4x$ kmph

Now,

13.2km

A ———— B

According to the question,

$1.1 \times 6x = 13.2$

$\Rightarrow$ $6.6x = 13.2$

$\Rightarrow x=\frac{13.2}{6.6}$

$\therefore$ x = 2 kmph

$\therefore$ Upstream speed = $4x = 4 \times 2 = 8$ kmph

$\therefore$ 312 minutes = $5\frac{1}{5}$ hours = $\frac{26}{5}$ hours

$\therefore$ Required distance travelled upstream = Speed × Time

$=8\times\frac{26}{5}=41.6$ km

36. Distance covered by a boat in 5 hours = 36 km

Rate upstream of boat $=\frac{36}{5}=7.2$ kmph

Speed of stream = 2.4 kmph

$\therefore$ Speed of boat in still water

= (7.2 + 2.4) kmph

= 9.6 kmph

$\therefore$ Rate downstream of boat

= (9.6 + 2.4) kmph

= 12 kmph

$\therefore$ Time taken in covering 78 km distance $=\frac{78}{12}=6.5$ hours.

37. Let upstream speed be a km/hr and downstream speed be b km/hr

Statement I = $\frac{14}{a}+\frac{35}{b}=4$

Statement II $\frac{29}{a}+\frac{24}{b}=5$

Let, $\frac{1}{a}=m$, $\frac{1}{b}=n$

$\Rightarrow 14m + 35b = 4$ ....(i)

and $29m + 24b = 5$....(ii)

Solving Equations (i) and (ii), we get

$m=\frac{79}{679}$ and $n=\frac{46}{679}$

$\therefore$ $a=\frac{1}{m}=\frac{679}{79}$ and $b=\frac{1}{n}=\frac{679}{46}$

Hence, data in both the statements I and II will give the answer.

Hence, option (e) is correct.

EXERCISE

(DATA SUFFICIENCY TYPE QUESTIONS)

Directions (*Questions 1 to 8*): *Each of the questions given below consists of a statement and/ or a question and two statements numbered I and II given below it. You have to decide whether the data provided in the statement(s) is/ are sufficient to answer the question. Read both the statements and*

Give answer (a) if the data in Statement I alone are sufficient to answer the question, while the data in Statement II alone are not sufficient to answer the question;

Give answer (b) if the data in Statement II alone are sufficient to answer the question while the data in statement I alone are not sufficient to answer the question;

Give answer (c) if the data either in Statement I or in Statement II alone are sufficient to answer the question;

Give answer (d) if the data even in both Statements I and II together are not sufficient to answer the question;

Give answer (e) if the data in both Statements I and II together are necessary to answer the question.

1. What is the speed of the boat in still water? (Bank P.O., 2003)
   I. It takes 2 hours to cover the distance between A and B downstream.
   II. It takes 4 hours to cover the distance between A and B upstream.
2. What is the speed of the stream?
   I. The ratio of the speed upstream to the speed downstream of a boat is 2 : 3.
   II. The distance travelled upstream in 2 hours by the boat is more than the distance travelled by it downstream in 1 hour by 4 km.
3. What is the speed of the boat in still water? (Bank P.O., 2008)
   I. The boat covers a distance of 48 kms in 6 hours while running upstream.
   II. The boat covers the same distance in 4 hours while running downstream.
4. What is the speed of the boat in still water? (Bank P.O., 2006)
   I. The boat running downstream takes 6 hours from A to B.
   II. The boat running upstream takes 8 hours from B to C.
5. What is the man's speed in still water?
   I. The speed of the stream is one-third of the man's speed in still water.
   II. In a given time, the man can swim twice as far with the stream as he can against it.
6. A boat takes a total time of three hours to travel downstream from P to Q and upstream back from Q to P. What is the speed of the boat in still water?
   I. The speed of the river current is 1 km per hour.
   II. The distance between P and Q is 4 km.
7. What is the speed of the boat in still water?
   I. The speed downstream of the boat is thrice the speed upstream.
   II. The sum of the speeds of the boat, upstream and downstream is 12 kmph.
8. What is the speed of the boat in still water? (Bank P.O., 2007)
   I. Speed of the current is 2 kmph.
   II. Time taken by the boat to cover a distance of 24 km running upstream is one hour more than the time taken to cover the same distance running downstream.

Directions (*Questions 9-11*): ***Each of the questions given below consists of a question followed by three statements. You have to study the question and the statements and decide which of the statement (s) is/are necessary to answer the questions.***

9. What is the speed of the current? (R.B.I., 2004)
   I. Speed of the boat is 4 km/hr in still water.
   II. The boat runs at a speed of 6 km/hr downstream.
   III. The difference between the speeds of the boat while travelling in still water and downstream is 2 km/hr.

   (*a*) Only I and II
   (*b*) Only III
   (*c*) Any one of the three
   (*d*) Only I and either II or III
   (*e*) Either I and II together or only III
10. What is the speed of the boat in still water?
   I. The speed downstream is 12 kmph.
   II. The speed upstream is 4 kmph.
   III. In a to and fro journey between two points, the average speed of the boat was 6 kmph.

   (*a*) I and II only
   (*b*) All I, II and III
   (*c*) III, and either I or II
   (*d*) Any two of the three
   (*e*) None of these
11. What is the speed of stream? (Bank P.O., 2004)
   I. The boat covers 24 km in 6 hours moving upstream.
   II. The boat covers 24 km in 3 hours moving downstream.
   III. The ratio between the speed of boat and stream is 3 : 1 respectively.

   (*a*) Any two of the three
   (*b*) I and II only
   (*c*) II and III only
   (*d*) I and III only
   (*e*) All I, II and III

ANSWERS

1. (*d*)	2. (*e*)	3. (*e*)	4. (*d*)	5. (*d*)	6. (*e*)	7. (*b*)	8. (*e*)	9. (*e*)	10. (*d*)
11. (*a*)									

SOLUTIONS

1. Let AB = x km. Then,

I. Speed downstream = $\frac{x}{2}$ km/hr.

II. Speed upstream = $\frac{x}{4}$ km/hr.

$\therefore$ Speed of the boat in still water

$= \frac{1}{2}\left(\frac{x}{2}+\frac{x}{4}\right)$ km/hr $= \frac{3x}{8}$ km/hr

Thus, I and II both even do not give the answer.
Hence, the correct answer is (*d*).

2. I. Let speed upstream = $2x$ km/hr and speed downstream = $3x$ km/hr.

II. $(2 \times 3x) - (1 \times 2x) = 4 \Rightarrow 4x = 4 \Rightarrow x = 1.$

$\therefore$ Speed upstream = 2 km/hr and
Speed downstream = 3 km/hr.

Speed of the stream = $\frac{1}{2}$ (3 – 2) km/hr

$= \frac{1}{2}$ km/hr.

Thus, I and II together give the answer.
Hence, the correct answer is (*e*).

3. I. Speed upstream = $\frac{48}{6}$ km/hr = 8 km/hr.

II. Speed downstream = $\frac{48}{4}$ km/hr = 12 km/hr.

Speed of the boat in still water

$= \frac{1}{2}(8+12)$ km/hr $= 10$ km/hr.

Thus, I and II together give the answer.
Hence, the correct answer is (*e*).

4. I. Let the distance AB be x km.

Then, speed downstream = $\frac{x}{6}$ km/hr.

II. Let the distance BC be y km.

Then, Speed upstream = $\frac{y}{8}$ km/hr.

Speed of the boat in still water $\frac{1}{2}\left(\frac{x}{6}+\frac{y}{8}\right)$ km/hr.

Thus, I and II together do not give the answer.
Hence, the correct answer is (*d*).

5. Let the man's speed in still water be x km/hr.

I. Speed of the stream = $\frac{x}{3}$ km/hr.

Speed downstream = $\left(x+\frac{x}{3}\right)$ km/hr $= \frac{4x}{3}$ km/hr.

Speed upstream = $\left(x-\frac{x}{3}\right)$ km/hr $= \frac{2x}{3}$ km/hr.

Suppose that the fixed time is t hours. Then,

II. Gives : $2\left(\frac{4x}{3}\times t\right)=\left(\frac{2x}{3}\times t\right)$, which does not give x.

Hence, the correct answer is (*d*).

6. I. Speed of the current = 1 km/hr.

II. PQ = 4 km. Let the speed of the boat in still water be x km/hr.

Then, $\frac{4}{(x+1)}+\frac{4}{(x-1)} = 3$. This gives x.

Hence, the correct answer is (*e*).

7. Let the speed upstream be x km/hr. Then,

I. Speed downstream = $3x$ km/hr.

II. Gives, speed of the boat in still water

$= \left(\frac{1}{2}\times 12\right)$ km/hr $= 6$ km/hr.

So, II only gives the correct answer.
Hence, the correct answer is (*b*).

8. Let the speed of the boat in still water be x km/hr.

I. Speed downstream = $(x + 2)$ km/hr,
Speed upstream = $(x - 2)$ km/hr.

II. Gives : $\frac{24}{(x-2)}=\frac{24}{(x+2)}+1$

$\Rightarrow$ $24(x + 2) = 24(x - 2) + (x^2 - 4)$

$\Rightarrow$ $x^2 = 100 \Rightarrow x = 10$

$\therefore$ The speed of the boat in still water is 10 km/hr.

Thus, both I and II are necessary to get the correct answer.
Hence, the correct answer is (*e*).

9. Let the speed of the current be x km/hr. Then,

I. Speed downstream = $(x + 4)$ km/hr,
Speed upstream = $(x - 4)$ km/hr.

II. $x + 4 = 6 \Rightarrow x = 2.$

III. Let the speed of the boat in still water be y.
Then, $(y + x) - y = 2 \Rightarrow x = 2.$

$\therefore$ Either I and II together or only III are required.
Hence, the correct answer is (*e*).

10. **From I and II:** Speed of boat in still water

$= \frac{1}{2}(12+4)$ km/hr $= 8$ km/hr.

From II and III, we get

$\frac{2\times 4\times y}{4+y} = 6 \Rightarrow 8y = 24 + 6y \Rightarrow 2y = 24 \Rightarrow y = 12.$

$\left[\because \text{Average speed} = \frac{2xy}{(x+y)}\right]$

$\therefore$ Required speed $= \frac{1}{2}(12+4)$ km/hr $= 8$ km/hr.

Thus, II and III give the answer.
Similarly, I and III give the answer.
Hence, the correct answer is (*d*).

11. I. Speed upstream = $\frac{24}{3}$ km/hr = 4 km/hr.

II. Speed downstream = $\frac{24}{3}$ km/hr = 8 km/hr.

III. Let the speed of the boat in still water be $3x$ km/hr.
Then, speed of the stream is x km/hr.

$\therefore$ Speed downstream = $\frac{1}{2}(3x + x)$ km/hr = $2x$ km/hr.

Speed upstream = $\frac{1}{2}(3x - x)$ km/hr = x km/hr.

From I and II: Speed of stream = $\frac{1}{2}$ (8 – 4) km/hr = 2 km/hr.

From II and III: We get $2x = 8 \Rightarrow x = 4$.

$\therefore$ Speed downstream = (2 × 4) km/hr = 8 km/hr.

$\therefore$ Speed of the stream = $\frac{1}{2}$ (8 – 4) km/hr = 2 km/hr.

From I and III: We get $x = 4$ and $2x = 8$.

$\therefore$ Speed of the stream = $\frac{1}{2}$ (8 – 4) km/hr = 2 km/hr.

Thus, any two of the three will give the answer.
Hence, the correct answer is (*a*).

20 Problems on Trains

IMPORTANT FACTS AND FORMULAE

I. a km/hr $= \left(a \times \frac{5}{18}\right)$ m/s. II. a m/s $= \left(a \times \frac{18}{5}\right)$ km/hr.

III. Time taken by a train of length l metres to pass a pole or a standing man or a signal post is equal to the time taken by the train to cover l metres.

IV. Time taken by a train of length l metres to pass a stationary object of length b metres is the time taken by the train to cover $(l + b)$ metres.

V. Suppose two trains or two bodies are moving in the same direction at u m/s and v m/s, where $u > v$, then their relative speed $= (u - v)$ m/s.

VI. Suppose two trains or two bodies are moving in opposite directions at u m/s and v m/s, then their relative speed $= (u + v)$ m/s.

VII. If two trains of length a metres and b metres are moving in opposite directions at u m/s and v m/s, then time taken by the trains to cross each other $= \frac{(a+b)}{(u+v)}$ sec.

VIII. If two trains of length a metres and b metres are moving in the same direction at u m/s and v m/s, then the time taken by the faster train to cross the slower train $= \frac{(a+b)}{(u-v)}$ sec.

IX. If two trains (or bodies) start at the same time from points A and B towards each other and after crossing they take a and b sec in reaching B and A respectively, then **(A's speed) : (B's speed) = $(\sqrt{b} : \sqrt{a})$.**

SOLVED EXAMPLES

Ex. 1. ***A 100-m long train is running at the speed of 30 km/hr. Find the time taken by it to pass a man standing near the railway line.***

Sol. Speed of the train $= \left(30 \times \frac{5}{18}\right)$ m/sec $= \left(\frac{25}{3}\right)$ m/sec.

Distance moved in passing the standing man = 100 m.

Required time taken $= \frac{100}{\left(\frac{25}{3}\right)} = \left(100 \times \frac{3}{25}\right)$ sec $= 12$ sec.

Ex. 2. ***A train is moving at a speed of 132 km/hr. If the length of the train is 110-m, how long will it take to cross a railway platform 165-m long?***

Sol. Speed of train $= \left(132 \times \frac{5}{18}\right)$ m/sec $= \left(\frac{110}{3}\right)$ m/sec.

Distance covered in passing the platform = (110 + 165) m = 275 m.

$\therefore$ Time taken $= \left(275 \times \frac{3}{110}\right)$ sec $= \frac{15}{2}$ sec $= 7\frac{1}{2}$ sec.

Ex. 3. ***A 160-m long train crosses a 160-m long platform in 16 seconds. Find the speed of the train.*** (R.R.B., 2009)

Sol. Distance covered in passing the platform = (160 + 160) m = 320 m.

$\therefore$ Speed of train $= \left(\frac{320}{16}\right)$ m/sec $= 20$ m/sec $= \left(20 \times \frac{18}{5}\right)$ km/hr $= 72$ km/hr.

Ex. 4. ***A person standing on a railway platform noticed that a train took 21 seconds to completely pass through the platform which was 84 m long and it took 9 seconds in passing him. Find the speed of the train in km/hr.*** **(C.P.O., 2006)**

Sol. Let the length of the train be x metres.

Then, the train covers x metres in 9 seconds and $(x + 84)$ metres in 21 seconds.

So, length of the train = 63 m.

$$\text{Speed of the train} = \left(\frac{63}{9}\right) \text{m/sec} = 7\text{m/sec} = \left(7 \times \frac{18}{5}\right) \text{km/hr} = \left(\frac{126}{5}\right) \text{km/hr} = 25.2 \text{ km/hr.}$$

Ex. 5. ***A train travelling with constant speed crosses a 90 m long platform in 12 seconds and a 120 m long platform in 15 seconds. Find the length of the train and its speed.*** **(P.C.S., 2009)**

Sol. Let the length of the train be x metres.

Then, $\frac{x+90}{12} = \frac{x+120}{15} \Leftrightarrow 15(x+90) = 12(x+120)$

$\Leftrightarrow 15x + 1350 = 12x + 1440$

$\Leftrightarrow 3x = 90 \Leftrightarrow x = 30.$

$$\text{Speed of the train} = \left(\frac{30+90}{12}\right) \text{m/sec} = 10 \text{ m/sec} = \left(10 \times \frac{18}{5}\right) \text{km/hr} = 36 \text{ km/hr.}$$

Hence, lenght of train = 30 m, speed of train = 36 km/hr.

Ex. 6. ***A 150-m long train is running with a speed of 68 kmph. In what time will it pass a man who is running at 8 kmph in the same direction in which the train is going?***

Sol. Speed of the train relative to man = (68 – 8) kmph

$$= \left(60 \times \frac{5}{18}\right) \text{m/sec} = \left(\frac{50}{3}\right) \text{m/sec.}$$

Time taken by the train to cross the man

$$= \text{Time taken by it to cover 150 m at } \left(\frac{50}{3}\right) \text{m/sec} = \left(150 \times \frac{3}{50}\right) \text{sec} = 9 \text{ sec.}$$

Ex. 7. ***A 220-m long train is running with a speed of 59 kmph. In what time will it pass a man who is running at 7 kmph in the direction opposite to that in which the train is going?***

Sol. Speed of the train relative to man = (59 + 7) kmph

$$= \left(66 \times \frac{5}{18}\right) \text{m/sec} = \left(\frac{55}{3}\right) \text{m/sec.}$$

Time taken by the train to cross the man

$$= \text{Time taken by it to cover 220 m at } \left(\frac{55}{3}\right) \text{m/sec} = \left(220 \times \frac{3}{55}\right) \text{sec} = 12 \text{ sec.}$$

Ex. 8. ***Two trains 240 metres and 270 metres in length are running towards each other on parallel lines, one at the rate of 60 kmph and another at 48 kmph. How much time will they take to cross each other?*** **(S.B.I.P.O., 2009)**

Sol. Relative speed of the two trains

= (60 + 48) kmph

$$= 108 \text{ kmph} = \left(108 \times \frac{5}{18}\right) \text{m/sec} = 30 \text{ m/sec.}$$

Time taken by the trains to pass each other

$$= \text{Time taken to cover (240 + 270) m at 30 m/sec} = \left(\frac{510}{3}\right) \text{sec} = 17 \text{ sec.}$$

Ex. 9 ***A 300-m long train passed a man walking along the line in the same direction at the rate of 3 km/hr in 33 seconds. Find the speed of the train in km/hr.*** (S.S.C., 2010)

Sol. Speed of the train relative to man $= \left(\frac{300}{33}\right) \text{m/s} = \left(\frac{100}{11}\right) \text{m/sec}$

$= \left(\frac{100}{11} \times \frac{18}{5}\right) \text{km/hr} = \left(\frac{360}{11}\right) \text{km/hr}.$

Let the speed of the train be x km/hr. Then, relative speed = $(x - 3)$ km/hr.

$\therefore \quad x - 3 = \frac{360}{11} \Leftrightarrow x = \frac{360}{11} + 3 = \frac{393}{11} = 35\frac{8}{11}.$

Hence, speed of train = $35\frac{8}{11}$ km/hr.

Ex. 10. ***Two trains 100 metres and 120 metres long are running in the same direction with speeds of 72 km/hr and 54 km/hr. In how much time will the first train cross the second?***

Sol. Relative speed of the trains = $(72 - 54)$km/hr = 18 km/hr $= \left(18 \times \frac{5}{18}\right) \text{m/sec} = 5 \text{ m/sec}.$

Time taken by the trains to pass each other

= Time taken to cover $(100 + 120)$ m at 5 m/sec $= \left(\frac{220}{5}\right) \text{sec} = 44 \text{ sec}.$

Ex. 11. ***A 100 m long train, takes*** $7\frac{1}{5}$ ***seconds to cross a man walking at the rate of 5 km/hr in the direction opposite to that of the train. What is the speed of the train?*** (Section Officers', 2005)

Sol. Let the speed of the train be x km/hr.

Speed of the train relative to man = $(x + 5)$ km/hr $= \left[(x+5) \times \frac{5}{18}\right]$

$\therefore \quad \frac{100}{(x+5) \times \frac{5}{18}} = \frac{36}{5} \Leftrightarrow 10x + 50 = 500 \Leftrightarrow 10x = 450 \Leftrightarrow x = 45.$

Hence, speed of the train = 45 km/hr.

Ex. 12. ***A train 100 m long travelling at 60 km/hr passes another train, twice as fast as this train and travelling in opposite direction, in 10 seconds. Find the length of the seocnd train.*** (S.S.C., 2008)

Sol. Relative speed = $(60 + 120)$ km/hr $= \left(180 \times \frac{5}{18}\right) \text{m/sec} = 50 \text{ m/sec}.$

Let the length of the second train be x metres.

Then, $\frac{x + 100}{10} = 50 \Rightarrow x + 100 = 500 \Rightarrow x = 400.$

Hence, length of second train = 400 m.

Ex. 13. ***A train running at 54 kmph takes 20 seconds to pass a platform. Next it takes 12 seconds to pass a man walking at 6 kmph in the same direction in which the train is going. Find the length of the train and the length of the platform.***

Sol. Let the length of train be x metres and the length of platform be y metres.

Speed of the train relative to man = $(54 - 6)$ kmph = 48 kmph

$= \left(48 \times \frac{5}{18}\right) \text{m/sec} = \frac{40}{3} \text{ m/sec}.$

In passing a man, the train covers its own length with relative speed.

$\therefore \quad$ Length of train = (Relative speed × Time) $= \left(\frac{40}{3} \times 12\right) \text{m} = 160 \text{ m}.$

Also, speed of the train $= \left(54 \times \frac{5}{18}\right) \text{m/sec} = 15 \text{ m/sec}.$

$\therefore \quad \frac{x + y}{15} = 20 \Leftrightarrow x + y = 300 \Leftrightarrow y = (300 - 160) \text{ m} = 140 \text{ m}.$

Ex. 14. ***A moving train, 66 metres long, overtakes another train 88 metres long, moving in the same direction, in 0.168 minutes. If the second train is moving at 30 km per hour, at what speed is the first train moving?*** **(C.P.O., 2003)**

Sol. Let the speed of the first train be x km/hr.

Then, sum of lengths of trains = (66 + 88) m = 154 m.

Relative speed of two trains = $(x - 30)$ kmph = $\left[(x-30)\times\frac{5}{18}\right]$ m/sec.

$$\therefore \quad \frac{154}{(x-30)\times\frac{5}{18}} = 0.168\times 60 \Leftrightarrow 5(x-30) = \frac{154\times 18}{10.08} = 275 \Leftrightarrow x - 30 = 55 \Leftrightarrow x = 85.$$

Hence, speed of the first train = 85 km/hr.

Ex. 15. ***A man sitting in a train which is travelling at 50 kmph observes that a goods train, travelling in opposite direction, takes 9 seconds to pass him. If the goods train is 280 m long, find its speed.***

Sol. Relative speed = $\left(\frac{280}{9}\right)$ m/sec $= \left(\frac{280}{9}\times\frac{18}{5}\right)$ kmph = 112 kmph.

$\therefore$ Speed of goods train = (112 – 50) kmph = 62 kmph.

EXERCISE

(OBJECTIVE TYPE QUESTIONS)

Directions: *Mark (✓) against the correct answer:*

1. A train moves with a speed of 108 kmph. Its speed in metres per second is

(a) 10.8 m/sec. (b) 18 m/sec.
(c) 30 m/sec. (d) 38.8 m/sec.

2. A speed of 14 metres per second is the same as

(a) 28 km/hr (b) 46.6 km/hr
(c) 50.4 km/hr (d) 70 km/hr

3. A man sitting in a train is counting the pillars of electricity. The distance between two pillars is 60 metres, and the speed of the train is 42 km/hr. In 5 hours, how many pillars will he count? **(R.R.B., 2009)**

(a) 3501 (b) 3600
(c) 3800 (d) None of these

4. In what time will a train 100 metres long cross an electric pole, if its speed be144 km/hr?

(a) 2.5 seconds (b) 4.25 seconds
(c) 5 seconds (d) 12.5 seconds

5. A train 280 m long, running with a speed of 63 km/hr will pass a tree in:

(a) 15 sec (b) 16 sec
(c) 18 sec (d) 20 sec

6. A 100 m long train is going at a speed of 60 km/hr. It will cross a 140 m long railway bridge in **(G.I.C., 2009)**

(a) 3.6 sec (b) 7.2 sec
(c) 14.4 sec (d) 21.6 sec

7. A 120 metre long train is running at a speed of 90 km/hr. It will cross a railway platform 230 m long in **(S.S.C., 2005)**

(a) $4\frac{4}{5}$ seconds (b) 7 seconds
(c) $9\frac{1}{5}$ seconds (d) 14 seconds

8. A train travelling at a speed of 75 mph enters a tunnel $3\frac{1}{2}$ miles long. The train is $\frac{1}{4}$ mile long. How long does it take for the train to pass through the tunnel from the moment the front enters to the moment the rear emerges?

(a) 2.5 min (b) 3 min
(c) 3.2 min (d) 3.5 min

9. A train running at the speed of 60 km/hr crosses a pole in 9 seconds. What is the length of the train?

(a) 120 metres (b) 180 metres
(c) 324 metres
(d) Cannot be determined (e) None of these

10. A train 132 m long passes a telegraph pole in 6 seconds. Find the speed of the train.

(a) 70 km/hr (b) 72 km/hr
(c) 79.2 km/hr (d) 80 km/hr

11. A train covers a distance of 12 km in 10 minutes. If it takes 6 seconds to pass a telegraph post, then the length of the train is

(a) 90 m (b) 100 m
(c) 120 m (d) 140 m

12. A train 240 m long passed a pole in 24 seconds. How long will it take to pass a platform 650 m long?
(*a*) 65 sec (*b*) 89 sec
(*c*) 100 sec (*d*) 150 sec

13. A 50-metre long train passes over a bridge at the speed of 30 km per hour. If it takes 36 seconds to cross the brige, what is the length of the bridge? **(P.C.S., 2009)**
(*a*) 200 metres (*b*) 250 metres
(*c*) 300 metres (*d*) 350 metres

14. A train takes 5 minutes to cross a telegraphic post. Then the time taken by another train whose length is just double of the first train and moving with same speed to cross a platform of its own length is **(Hotel Management, 2007)**
(*a*) 10 minutes (*b*) 15 minutes]
(*c*) 20 minutes (*d*) Data inadequate

15. The length of the bridge, which a train 130 metres long and travelling at 45 km/hr can cross in 30 seconds, is
(*a*) 200 m (*b*) 225 m
(*c*) 245 m (*d*) 250 m

16. A train 800 metres long is running at a speed of 78 km/hr. If it crosses a tunnel in 1 minute, then the length of the tunnel (in metres) is :
(*a*) 130 (*b*) 360
(*c*) 500 (*d*) 540

17. A train running at the speed of 60 kmph crosses a 200 m long platform in 27 seconds. What is the length of the train? **(Bank Recruitment, 2009)**
(*a*) 200 metres (*b*) 240 metres
(*c*) 250 metres (*d*) 450 metres
(*e*) None of these

18. A train running at a speed of 90 km/hr crosses a platform double its length in 36 seconds. What is the length of the platform in metres? **(Bank Recruitment, 2007)**
(*a*) 200 (*b*) 300
(*c*) 450
(*d*) Cannot be determined (*e*) None of these

19. A train of length 150 metres takes 40.5 seconds to cross a tunnel of length 300 metres. What is the speed of the train in km/hr?
(*a*) 13.33 (*b*) 26.67
(*c*) 40 (*d*) 66.67

20. A 280-metre long train crosses a platform thrice its length in 50 seconds. What is the speed of the train in km/hr? **(M.B.A.–C.E.T., 2008)**
(*a*) 60.48 (*b*) 64.86
(*c*) 80.64 (*d*) 82.38
(*e*) None of these

21. A train passes a station platform in 36 seconds and a man standing on the platform in 20 seconds. If the speed of the train is 54 km/hr, what is the length of the platform? **(M.A.T., 2008)**
(*a*) 225 m (*b*) 240 m
(*c*) 230 m (*d*) 235 m

22. Train A crosses a stationary train B in 50 seconds and a pole in 20 seconds with the same speed. The length of the train A is 240 metres. What is the length of the stationary train *B*? **(Bank. P.O., 2010)**
(*a*) 260 metres (*b*) 300 metres
(*c*) 360 metres
(*d*) Cannot be determined (*e*) None of these

23. A train speeds past a pole in 20 seconds and speeds past a platform 100 metres in length in 30 seconds. What is the length of the train? **(Bank P.O., 2010)**
(*a*) 100 m (*b*) 150 m
(*c*) 180 m (*d*) 200 m
(*e*) None of these

24. A train crosses a platform 100 m long in 60 seconds at a speed of 45 km/hr. The time taken by the train to cross an electric pole is:
(*a*) 8 sec (*b*) 52 sec
(*c*) 1 minute (*d*) Data inadequate

25. A train, 150 m long, takes 30 seconds to cross a bridge 500 m long. How much time will the train take to cross a platform 370 m long? **(S.S.C., 2007)**
(*a*) 18 sec (*b*) 24 sec
(*c*) 30 sec (*d*) 36 sec

26. A train passes a platform 90 m long in 30 seconds and a man standing on the platform in 15 seconds. The speed of the train is **(C.P.O., 2007)**
(*a*) 12.4 km/hr (*b*) 14.6 km/hr
(*c*) 18.4 km/hr (*d*) 21.6 km/hr

27. A train running at a certain speed takes 20 seconds to cross a signal post and 50 seconds to cross a bridge. Which of the following statements is correct about the length of the bridge?
(*a*) 1.5 times the length of the train
(*b*) 2.5 times the length of the train
(*c*) 30 metres more than the length of the train
(*d*) Cannot be determined

28. A train travelling with a constant speed crosses a 96-metre long platform in 12 seconds and another 141-metre long platform in 15 seconds. The length of the train and its speed are **(R.R.B., 2006)**
(*a*) 84 metres and 54 km/hr
(*b*) 64 metres and 44 km/hr
(*c*) 64 metres and 54 km/hr
(*d*) 84 metres and 60 km/hr

29. The time taken by a train 180 m long, travelling at 42 kmph, in passing a person walking in the same direction at 6 kmph, will be **(S.S.C., 2005)**

(*a*) 18 sec (*b*) 21 sec
(*c*) 24 sec (*d*) 25 sec

30. A train with 90 km/hr crosses a bridge in 36 seconds. Another train 100 metres shorter crosses the same bridge at 45 km/hr. What is the time taken by the second train to cross the bridge? **(M.A.T., 2006)**

(*a*) 61 seconds (*b*) 62 seconds
(*c*) 63 seconds (*d*) 64 seconds

31. A jogger running at 9 kmph alongside a railway track is 240 metres ahead of the engine of a 120 metre long train running at 45 kmph in the same direction. In how much time will the train pass the jogger?

(*a*) 3.6 sec (*b*) 18 sec
(*c*) 36 sec (*d*) 72 sec

32. A train 110 metres long is running with a speed of 60 kmph. In what time will it pass a man who is running at 6 kmph in the direction opposite to that in which the train is going? **(M.A.T., 2002)**

(*a*) 5 sec (*b*) 6 sec
(*c*) 7 sec (*d*) 10 sec

33. Two trains 200 metres and 150 metres long are running on parallel rails in the same direction at speeds of 40 km/hr and 45 km/hr respectively. Time taken by the faster train to cross the slowed train will be **(P.C.S., 2009)**

(*a*) 72 seconds (*b*) 132 seconds
(*c*) 192 seconds (*d*) 252 seconds

34. Two trains A and B start running together from the same point in the same direction, at the speeds of 60 kmph and 72 kmph respectively. If the length of each of the trains is 240 metres, how long will it take for train B to cross train A? **(Bank P.O., 2005)**

(*a*) 1 min 12 secs (*b*) 1 min 24 secs
(*c*) 2 min 12 secs (*d*) 2 min 24 secs

35. Two trains are moving in opposite directions @ 60 km/hr and 90 km/hr. Their lengths are 1.10 km and 0.9 km respectively. The time taken by the slower train to cross the faster train in seconds is **(M.B.A., 2002)**

(*a*) 36 (*b*) 45
(*c*) 48 (*d*) 49

36. Two trains of lengths 120 m and 90 m are running with speeds of 80 km/hr and 55 km/hr respectively towards each other on parallel lines. If they are 90 m apart, after how many seconds they will cross each other? **(Hotel Management, 2010)**

(*a*) 5.6 sec. (*b*) 7.2 sec.
(*c*) 8 sec. (*d*) 9 sec.

37. Two trains are coming from opposite directions with speeds of 75 km/hr and 100 km/hr on two parallel tracks. At some moment the distance between them is 100 km. After T hours, distance between them is again 100 km. T is equal to **(I.A.M., 2007)**

(*a*) 1 hr (*b*) $1\frac{1}{7}$ hr
(*c*) $1\frac{1}{2}$ hr (*d*) 2 hrs

38. A train 125 m long passes a man, running at 5 kmph in the same direction in which the train is going, in 10 seconds. The speed of the train is: **(A.A.O. Exam., 2003)**

(*a*) 45 km/hr (*b*) 50 km/hr
(*c*) 54 km/hr (*d*) 55 km/hr

39. A train 400 m long overtook a man walking along the line in the same direction as the train, at the rate of 5 kmph and passed him in 40 seconds. The train reached the station in 20 minutes after passing the man. In what time did the man reach the station?

(*a*) 2 hr 24 min (*b*) 2 hr 30 min 40 sec
(*c*) 2 hr 36 min 48 sec (*d*) 2 hr 48 min 48 sec

40. A train, 240 m long, crosses a man walking along the line in opposite direction at the rate of 3 kmph in 10 seconds. The speed of the train is **(S.S.C., 2010)**

(*a*) 63 kmph (*b*) 75 kmph
(*c*) 83.4 kmph (*d*) 86.4 kmph

41. A train 75 m long overtook a person who was walking at the rate of 6 km/hr in the same direction and passed him in $7\frac{1}{2}$ seconds. Subsequently, it overtook a second person and passed him in $6\frac{3}{4}$ seconds. At what rate was the second person travelling? **(M.A.T., 2008)**

(*a*) 1 km/hr (*b*) 2 km/hr
(*c*) 4 km/hr (*d*) 5 km/hr

42. If a train takes 1.75 sec to cross a telegraphic post and 1.5 sec to overtake a cyclist racing along a road parallel to the track @ 10 metres per second, then the length of the train is

(*a*) 105 m (*b*) 115 m
(*c*) 125 m (*d*) 135 m

43. Two trains of equal length are running on parallel lines in the same direction at 46 km/hr and 36 km/hr. The faster train passes the slower train in 36 seconds. The length of each train is **(M.A.T., 2003)**

(*a*) 50 m (*b*) 72 m
(*c*) 80 m (*d*) 82 m

44. A 270 m long train running at the speed of 120 kmph crosses another train running in opposite direction at the speed of 80 kmph in 9 seconds. What is the length of the other train? (*a*) 230 m
(*b*) 240 m
(*c*) 260 m (*d*) 320 m
(*e*) None of these

45. Two trains are running in opposite directions with the same speed. If the length of each train is 120 metres and they cross each other in 12 seconds, then the speed of each train (in km/hr) is (S.S.C., 2003)
(*a*) 10 (*b*) 18
(*c*) 36 (*d*) 72

46. A 180-metre long train crosses another 270-metre long train running in the opposite direction in 10.8 seconds. If the speed of the first train is 60 kmph, what is the speed of the second train in kmph? (Bank P.O., 2010)
(*a*) 80 (*b*) 90
(*c*) 150
(*d*) Cannot be determined
(*e*) None of these

47. Two trains of equal lengths take 10 seconds and 15 seconds respectively to cross a telegraph post. If the length of each train be 120 metres, in what time (in seconds) will they cross each other travelling in opposite direction? (S.S.C., 2004)
(*a*) 10 (*b*) 12
(*c*) 15 (*d*) 20

48. A train 108 m long moving at a speed of 50 km/hr crosses a train 112 m long coming from opposite direction in 6 seconds. The speed of the second train is (M.A.T., 2005, SNAP, 2010)
(*a*) 48 km/hr (*b*) 54 km/hr
(*c*) 66 km/hr (*d*) 82 km/hr

49. A train B speeding with 120 kmph crosses another train C running in the same direction, in 2 minutes. If the lengths of the trains B and C be 100 m and 200 m respectively, what is the speed (in kmph) of the train C? (L.I.C.A.A.O., 2007)
(*a*) 111 km (*b*) 123 km
(*c*) 127 km (*d*) 129 km

50. One local and another express train were proceeding in the same direction on parallel tracks at 29 km/hr and 65 km/hr respectively. The driver of the farmer noticed that it took exactly 16 seconds for the faster train to pass by him. What is the length of the faster train?
(*a*) 60 m (*b*) 120 m
(*c*) 160 m (*d*) 240 m

51. Two trains travel in opposite directions at 36 kmph and 45 kmph and a man sitting in slower train passes the faster train in 8 seconds. The length of the faster train is:
(*a*) 80 m (*b*) 100 m
(*c*) 120 m (*d*) 180 m

52. A train overtakes two persons who are walking in the same direction in which the train is going, at the rate of 2 kmph and 4 kmph and passes them completely in 9 and 10 seconds respectively. The length of the train is :
(*a*) 45 m (*b*) 50 m
(*c*) 54 m (*d*) 72 m

53. A train overtakes two persons walking along a railway track. The first one walks at 4.5 km/hr. The other one walks at 5.4 km/hr. The train needs 8.4 and 8.5 seconds respectively to overtake them. What is the speed of the train if both the persons are walking in the same direction as the train?
(*a*) 66 km/hr (*b*) 72 km/hr
(*c*) 78 km/hr (*d*) 81 km/hr

54. Two men are running in the same direction with speeds of 6 km per hour and $7\frac{1}{2}$ km per respectively. A train running in the same direction crosses them in 5 sec and $5\frac{1}{2}$ sec respectively. The length and the speed of the train are respectively.
(*a*) 22.92 m (approximately) and 22 km per hour
(*b*) 22 m (approximately) and 22.5 km per hour
(*c*) 22.90 m (approximately) and 20.5 km per hour
(*d*) 22.92 m (approximately) and 22.5 km per hour

55. What is the speed of a train if it overtakes two persons who are walking in the same direction at the rate of a m/s and $(a + 1)$ m/s and passes them completely in b seconds and $(b + 1)$ seconds respectively? (C.D.S., 2004)
(*a*) $(a + b)$ m/s (*b*) $(a + b + 1)$ m/s
(*c*) $(2a + 1)$ m/s (*d*) $\frac{(2a+1)}{2}$ m/s

56. Two trains, each 100 m long, moving in opposite directions, cross each other in 8 seconds. If one is moving twice as fast the other, then the speed of the faster train is :
(*a*) 30 km/hr (*b*) 45 km/hr
(*c*) 60 km/hr (*d*) 75 km/hr

57. A 150 m long train crosses a milestone in 15 seconds and a train of same length coming from the opposite direction in 12 seconds. The speed of the othe train is (R.R.B., 2006)
(*a*) 36 kmph (*b*) 45 kmph
(*c*) 50 kmph (*d*) 54 kmph

58. A train moving at 15 m/sec takes 20 seconds to pass a cyclist moving in the same direction as that of the train. How much time will the train need to pass the cyclist, if the cyclist moves in a direction opposite to that of the train and if the speed of the cyclist is 5 m/sec and the length of the cycle is 1 m?

(*a*) 9.95 sec (*b*) 10 sec
(*c*) 10.05 sec (*d*) 12 sec

59. A man standing on a platform finds that a train takes 3 seconds to pass him and another train of the same length moving in the opposite direction takes 4 seconds. The time taken by the trains to pass each other will be **(C.P.O., 2006)**

(*a*) $2\frac{3}{7}$ seconds (*b*) $3\frac{3}{7}$ seconds
(*c*) $4\frac{3}{7}$ seconds (*d*) $5\frac{3}{7}$ seconds

60. A train travelling at 48 kmph completely crosses another train having half its length and travelling in opposite direction at 42 kmph, in 12 seconds. It also passes a railway platform in 45 seconds. The length of the platform is

(*a*) 400 m (*b*) 450 m
(*c*) 560 m (*d*) 600 m

61. Two trains running in opposite directions cross a man standing on the platform in 27 seconds and 17 seconds respectively and they cross each other in 23 seconds. The ratio of their speeds is :

(*a*) 1 : 3 (*b*) 3 : 2
(*c*) 3 : 4 (*d*) None of these

62. Two trains, 130 and 110 metres long, are going in the same direction. The faster train takes one minute to pass the other completely. If they are moving in opposite directions, they pass each other completely in 3 seconds. Find the speed of the faster train. **(M.A.T., 2008)**

(*a*) 38 m/sec (*b*) 42 m/sec
(*c*) 46 m/sec (*d*) 50 m/sec

63. Two identical trains A and B running in opposite directions at same speed take 2 minutes to cross each other completely. The number of bogies of A are increased from 12 to 16. How much more time would they now require to cross each other? **(SNAP, 2007)**

(*a*) 20 sec (*b*) 40 sec
(*c*) 50 sec (*d*) 60 sec

64. Two stations A and B are 110 km apart on a straight line. One train starts from A at 7 a.m. and travels towards B at 20 kmph. Another train starts from B at 8 a.m. and travels towards A at a speed of 25 kmph. At what time will they meet?

(*a*) 9 a.m. (*b*) 10 a.m.
(*c*) 10.30 a.m. (*d*) 11 a.m.

65. A train X starts from Meerut at 4 p.m. and reaches Ghaziabad at 5 p.m. while another train Y starts from Ghaziabad at 4 p.m. and reaches Meerut at 5.30 p.m. The two trains will cross each other at

(*a*) 4.36 p.m. (*b*) 4.42 p.m.
(*c*) 4.48 p.m. (*d*) 4.50 p.m.

66. The Ghaziabad-Hapur-Meerut EMU and the Meerut-Hapur-Ghaziabad EMU start at the same time from Ghaziabad and Meerut and proceed towards each other at 16 km/hr and 21 km/hr respectively. When they meet, it is found that one train has travelled 60 km more than the other. The distance between two stations is **(I.I.F.T., 2007)**

(*a*) 440 km (*b*) 444 km
(*c*) 445 km (*d*) 450 km

67. Two trains, one from Howrah to Patna and the other from Patna to Howrah, start simultaneously. After they meet, the trains reach their destinations after 9 hours and 16 hours respectively. The ratio of their speeds is :

(*a*) 2 : 3 (*b*) 4 : 3
(*c*) 6 : 7 (*d*) 9 : 16

68. Two trains start simultaneously (with uniform speeds) from two stations 270 km apart, each to the opposite station; they reach their destinations in $6\frac{1}{4}$ hours and 4 hours after they meet. The rate at which the slower train travels is **(ATMA, 2005)**

(*a*) 16 km/hr. (*b*) 24 km/hr.
(*c*) 25 km/hr. (*d*) 30 km/hr.

69. A train which is moving at an average speed of 40km/h reaches its destination on time. When its average speed reduces to 35 km/h, then it reaches its destination 15 minutes late. The distance travelled by the train, is **[CLAT Exam, 2016]**

(*a*) 70km (*b*) 80km
(*c*) 40km (*d*) 30km

70. A train takes 9 sec to cross a pole: If the speed of the train is 48 kmph, then length of the train is **[Indian Railway Group 'D' Exam, 2014]**

(*a*) 150 m (*b*) 120 m
(*c*) 90 m (*d*) 80 m

71. Two trains start at the same time form A and B and proceed toward each other at the speed of 75 km/hr and 50 km/hr respectively. when both meet at a point in between, one train was found to have travelled 175 km more than the other. Find the distance between A and B. **[SSC—CHSL (10+2) Exam, 2015]**

(a) 875 km (b) 785 km
(c) 758 km (d) 857 km

72. A train passes two bridges of lengths 500 m and 250 m in 100 seconds and 60 seconds respectively. The length of the train is [SSC—CHSL (10+2) Exam, 2015]
(a) 152 m (b) 125 m
(c) 250 m (d) 120 m

73. Train A passes a lamp post in 9 seconds and 700 meter long platform in 30 seconds. How much time will the same train take to cross a platform which is 800 meters long? (in seconds)
[United India Insurance Co. Ltd. (UIICL) Assistant (Online) Exam, 2015]
(a) 32 (b) 31
(c) 33 (d) 30

74. Train A travelling at 63 kmph can cross a platform 199.5 m long in 21 seconds. How much time would train A take to completely cross (from the moment they meet) train B, 157m long and travelling at 54 kmph in opposite direction which train A is travelling? (in seconds)
[IBPS—RRB Office Assistant (Online) Exam, 2015]
(a) 16 (b) 18
(c) 12 (d) 10

ANSWERS

1. (c)	2. (c)	3. (a)	4. (a)	5. (b)	6. (c)	7. (d)	8. (b)	9. (e)	10. (c)
11. (c)	12. (b)	13. (b)	14. (c)	15. (c)	16. (c)	17. (c)	18. (e)	19. (c)	20. (c)
21. (b)	22. (c)	23. (d)	24. (b)	25. (b)	26. (d)	27. (a)	28. (a)	29. (a)	30. (d)
31. (c)	32. (b)	33. (d)	34. (d)	35. (c)	36. (c)	37. (b)	38. (b)	39. (d)	40. (c)
41. (b)	42. (a)	43. (a)	44. (a)	45. (c)	46. (b)	47. (b)	48. (d)	49. (d)	50. (c)
51. (d)	52. (b)	53. (d)	54. (d)	55. (b)	56. (c)	57. (d)	58. (b)	59. (b)	60. (a)
61. (b)	62. (b)	63. (a)	64. (b)	65. (a)	66. (b)	67. (b)	68. (b)	69. (a)	70. (b)
71. (a)	72. (b)	73. (c)	74. (d)						

SOLUTIONS

1. 108 kmph $= \left(108 \times \frac{5}{18}\right)$ m / sec = 30 m / sec.

2. 14 m/s sec $= \left(14 \times \frac{18}{5}\right)$ km / hr = 50.4 km/hr.

3. Distance covered by the train in 5 hours $= (42 \times 5)$ km = 210 km = 210000 m.

$\therefore$ Number of pillars counted by the man
$= \left(\frac{210000}{60} + 1\right) = (3500 + 1) = 3501.$

4. Speed $= \left(144 \times \frac{5}{18}\right)$ m/sec = 40 m/sec.

Time taken $= \left(\frac{100}{40}\right)$ sec = 2.5 sec.

5. Speed $= \left(63 \times \frac{5}{18}\right)$ m/sec $= \frac{35}{2}$ m/sec.

Time taken $= \left(280 \times \frac{2}{35}\right)$ sec = 16 sec.

6. Speed $= \left(60 \times \frac{5}{18}\right)$ m/sec $= \frac{50}{3}$ m/sec.

Total distance covered = (100 + 140) m = 240 m.

$\therefore$ Required time $= \left(240 \times \frac{3}{50}\right)$ sec $= \frac{72}{5}$ sec = 14.4 sec.

7. Speed $= \left(90 \times \frac{5}{18}\right)$ m/sec = 25 m/sec.

Total distance covered = (120 + 230) m = 350 m.

$\therefore$ Required time $= \left(\frac{350}{25}\right)$ sec = 14 sec.

8. Total distance covered $= \left(\frac{7}{2} + \frac{1}{4}\right)$ miles $= \frac{15}{4}$ miles.

$\therefore$ Time taken $= \left(\frac{15}{4 \times 75}\right)$ hrs $= \frac{1}{20}$ hrs
$= \left(\frac{1}{20} \times 60\right)$ min. = 3 min.

9. Speed $= \left(60 \times \frac{5}{18}\right)$ m/sec $= \left(\frac{50}{3}\right)$ m/sec.

Length of the train = (Speed × Time) $= \left(\frac{50}{3} \times 9\right)$ m = 150 m.

10. Speed $= \left(\frac{132}{6}\right)$ m/sec $= \left(22 \times \frac{18}{5}\right)$ km/hr = 79.2 km/hr.

11. Speed $= \left(\frac{12}{10} \times 60\right)$ km/hr $= \left(72 \times \frac{5}{18}\right)$ m/sec = 20 m/sec.

Length of the train = (Speed × Time) = (20 × 6) m = 120 m.

12. Speed $= \left(\frac{240}{24}\right)$ m/sec = 10 m/sec.

$\therefore$ Required time $= \left(\frac{240 + 650}{10}\right)$ sec = 89 sec.

13. Speed $= \left(30 \times \frac{5}{18}\right)$ m/sec $= \left(\frac{25}{3}\right)$ m/sec.

Time = 36 sec.

Let the length of the bridge be x metres.

Then, $\frac{50+x}{36} = \frac{25}{3} \Leftrightarrow 3\ (50 + x) = 900$

$\Leftrightarrow 50 + x = 300 \Leftrightarrow x = 250$ m.

14. Let the length of the train be x metres.

Time taken to cover x metres = 5 min

$= (5 \times 60)$ sec = 300 sec.

Speed of the train $= \left(\frac{x}{300}\right)$ m/sec.

Length of the second train = $(2x)$ metres.

Length of the platform = $(2x)$ metres.

$\therefore$ Required time $= \left[\frac{2x+2x}{\left(\frac{x}{300}\right)}\right]$ sec $= \left(\frac{4x \times 300}{x}\right)$ sec

$= 1200$ sec $= \left(\frac{1200}{60}\right)$ min = 20 min.

15. Speed $= \left(45 \times \frac{5}{18}\right)$ m/sec $= \left(\frac{25}{2}\right)$ m/sec; Time = 30 sec.

Let the length of bridge be x metres.

Then, $\frac{130+x}{30} = \frac{25}{2}$

$\Leftrightarrow 2\ (130 + x) = 750$

$\Leftrightarrow x = 245$ m.

16. Speed $= \left(78 \times \frac{5}{18}\right)$ m/sec $= \left(\frac{65}{3}\right)$ m/sec.

Time = 1 minute = 60 sec.

Let the length of the tunnel be x metres.

Then, $\frac{800+x}{60} = \frac{65}{3}$

$\Leftrightarrow 3\ (800 + x) = 3900$

$\Leftrightarrow x = 500$.

17. Speed $= \left(60 \times \frac{5}{18}\right)$ m/sec $= \left(\frac{50}{3}\right)$ m/sec.

Time = 27 sec.

Let the length of the train be x metres.

Then, $\frac{x+200}{27} = \frac{50}{3} \Leftrightarrow x + 200 = \left(\frac{50}{3} \times 27\right) = 450$

$\Leftrightarrow x = 250$.

18. Let the length of the train be x metres. Then, length of the platform = $(2x)$ metres.

Speed of the train $= \left(90 \times \frac{5}{18}\right)$ m/sec = 25 m/sec.

$\therefore \frac{x+2x}{25} = 36 \Leftrightarrow 3x = 900 \Leftrightarrow x = 300$.

Hence, length of platform = $2x = (2 \times 300)$ m = 600 m.

19. Speed $= \left(\frac{150+300}{40.5}\right)$ m/sec

$= \left(\frac{450}{40.5} \times \frac{18}{5}\right)$ km/hr = 40 km/hr.

20. Length of train = 280 m. Length of platform $= (3 \times 280)$ m = 840 m.

$\therefore$ Speed of train $= \left(\frac{280+840}{50}\right)$ m/sec $= \frac{1120}{50}$ m/sec

$= \left(\frac{1120}{50} \times \frac{18}{5}\right)$ km/hr = 80.64 km/hr.

21. Speed $= \left(54 \times \frac{5}{18}\right)$ m/sec = 15 m/ sec.

Length of the train = (15×20) m = 300 m.

Let the length of the platform be x metres.

Then, $\frac{x+300}{36} = 15 \Leftrightarrow x + 300 = 540 \Leftrightarrow x = 240$ m.

22. Speed of train A $= \left(\frac{240}{20}\right)$ m/sec = 12 m/sec.

Let the length of train B be x metres. Then, $\frac{240+x}{12} = 50$

$\Leftrightarrow 240 + x = 600$

$\Leftrightarrow x = 360$ m.

23. Let the length of the train be x metres and its speed be y m/sec. Then, $\frac{x}{y} = 20 \Rightarrow y = \frac{x}{20}$.

$\therefore \frac{x+100}{30} = \frac{x}{20} \Leftrightarrow 30x = 20x + 2000$

$\Leftrightarrow 10x = 2000 \Leftrightarrow x = 200$ m.

24. Speed $= \left(45 \times \frac{5}{18}\right)$ m/sec $= \left(\frac{25}{2}\right)$ m / sec.

Let the length of the train be x metres. Then, $\frac{x+100}{\left(\frac{25}{2}\right)}$

= 60 or $x = 650$ m.

$\therefore$ Time taken by the train to cross an electric pole

$= \left(650 \times \frac{2}{25}\right)$ sec = 52 sec.

25. Speed of the train $= \left(\frac{150+500}{30}\right)$ m/sec $= \left(\frac{65}{3}\right)$ m/sec.

$\therefore$ Required time $= \left[\frac{150+370}{\left(\frac{65}{3}\right)}\right]$ sec $= \left(520 \times \frac{3}{65}\right)$ sec

= 24 sec.

26. Let the length of the train be x metres and its speed be y m/sec.

Then, $\frac{x}{y} = 15 \Rightarrow x = 15\ y$. Now, $\frac{x+90}{30} = y$

$\Leftrightarrow 15\ y + 90 = 30y \Leftrightarrow 15y = 90 \Leftrightarrow y = 6$.

$\therefore$ Speed = 6 m/sec $= \left(6 \times \frac{18}{5}\right)$ km/hr = 21.6 km/hr.

27. Let the lengths of the train and the bridge be x metres and y metres respectively.

Let the speed of the train be z m/sec.

Then, $\frac{x}{20} = z$ ...(*i*)

and $\frac{x+y}{50} = z$ ...(ii)

From (i) and (ii), we have: $\frac{x}{20} = \frac{x+y}{50}$

$\Leftrightarrow 50x = 20x + 20y$

$\Leftrightarrow 30x = 20y$

$\Leftrightarrow y = \frac{3}{2} = 1.5x.$

28. Let the length of the train be x metres.

$\therefore \frac{x+96}{12} = \frac{x+141}{15}$

$\Leftrightarrow 15(x + 96) = 12(x + 141)$

$\Leftrightarrow 3x = 1692 - 1440 = 252$

$\Leftrightarrow x = 84$ m.

Speed of the train $= \left(\frac{x+96}{12}\right)$ m/sec $= \left(\frac{84+96}{12}\right)$ m/sec

$= 15$ m/sec

$= \left(15 \times \frac{18}{5}\right)$ km/hr $= 54$ km/hr.

29. Speed of train relative to man = (42 – 6) kmph = 36 kmph

$= \left(36 \times \frac{5}{18}\right)$ m/sec $= 10$ m/sec.

$\therefore$ Time taken to pass the man $= \left(\frac{180}{10}\right)$ sec $= 18$ sec.

30. Let the lengths of the train and the bridge be x metres and y metres respectively.

Speed of the first train = 90 km/hr $= \left(90 \times \frac{5}{18}\right)$ m/sec

$= 25$ m/sec.

Speed of the second train = 45 km/hr

$= \left(45 \times \frac{5}{18}\right)$ m/sec $= \frac{25}{2}$ m/sec.

Then, $\frac{x+y}{36} = 25 \Leftrightarrow x + y = 900$ ...(i)

$\therefore$ Required time $= \left[\frac{(x-100)+y}{\left(\frac{25}{2}\right)}\right]$ sec $= \left[\frac{(x+y)-100}{\left(\frac{25}{2}\right)}\right]$

sec $= \left(800 \times \frac{2}{25}\right)$ sec $= 64$ sec.

31. Speed of train relative to jogger = (45 – 9) km / hr = 36 km / hr $= \left(36 \times \frac{5}{18}\right)$ m/sec $= 10$ m/sec.

Distance to be covered = (240 + 120) m = 360 m.

$\therefore$ Time taken $= \left(\frac{360}{10}\right)$ sec $= 36$ sec.

32. Speed of train relative to man = (60 + 6) km / hr = 66 km / hr $= \left(66 \times \frac{5}{18}\right)$ m/sec $= \left(\frac{55}{3}\right)$ m/sec.

$\therefore$ Time taken to pass the man $= \left(110 \times \frac{3}{55}\right)$ sec $= 6$ sec.

33. Relative speed = (45 – 40) km/hr = 5 km/hr

$= \left(5 \times \frac{5}{18}\right)$ m/sec $= \left(\frac{25}{18}\right)$ m/sec.

Total distance covered = Sum of lengths of trains = (200 + 150) m = 350 m.

$\therefore$ Time taken $= \left(350 \times \frac{18}{25}\right)$ sec $= 252$ sec.

34. Relative speed = (72 – 60) km/hr = 12 km/hr

$= \left(12 \times \frac{5}{18}\right)$ m/sec $= \left(\frac{10}{3}\right)$ m/sec.

Total distance covered = Sum of lengths of trains = (240 + 240) m = 480 m.

$\therefore$ Time taken $= \left(480 \times \frac{3}{10}\right)$ sec = 144 sec = 2 min 24 sec.

35. Relative speed = (60 + 90) km/hr

$= \left(150 \times \frac{5}{18}\right)$ m/sec $= \left(\frac{125}{3}\right)$ m/sec.

Distance covered = (1.10 + 0.9) km = 2 km = 2000 m.

Required time $= \left(2000 \times \frac{3}{125}\right)$ sec $= 48$ sec.

36. Relative speed = (80 + 55) km/hr = 135 km/hr

$= \left(135 \times \frac{5}{18}\right)$ m/sec $= \left(\frac{75}{2}\right)$ m/sec.

Distance covered = (120 + 90 + 90) m = 300 m.

Required time $= \left(300 \times \frac{2}{75}\right)$ sec $= 8$ sec.

37. Relative speed = (75 + 100) km/hr = 175 km/hr.

Time taken to cover 175 km at relative speed = 1 hr.

$\therefore$ T = Time taken to cover 200 km

$= \left(\frac{1}{175} \times 200\right)$ hr $= \frac{8}{7}$ hr $= 1\frac{1}{7}$ hr

38. Speed of the train relative to man

$= \left(\frac{125}{10}\right)$ m/sec $= \left(\frac{25}{2}\right)$ m/sec

$= \left(\frac{25}{2} \times \frac{18}{5}\right)$ km/hr $= 45$ km/hr.

Let the speed of the train be x kmph. Then, relative speed $= (x - 5)$ kmph.

$\therefore x - 5 = 45$ or $x = 50$ kmph.

39. Speed of the train relative to man

$= \left(\frac{400}{40}\right)$ m/sec $= 10$ m/sec $= \left(10 \times \frac{18}{5}\right)$ km/hr $= 36$ km/hr.

Let the speed of the train be x kmph. Then, relative speed $= (x - 5)$ kmph.

$\therefore x - 5 = 36$ or $x = 41$ kmph.

Distance covered by the station in 20 min

$= \left(41 \times \frac{20}{60}\right)$ km $= \frac{41}{3}$ km.

Distance to be covered by the man to reach the station

$= \left(\frac{41}{3} + \frac{400}{1000}\right) \text{km} = \left(\frac{41}{3} + \frac{2}{5}\right) \text{km} = \frac{211}{15} \text{ km.}$

$\therefore$ Required time $= \left(\frac{211}{15} \times \frac{1}{5} \times 60\right) \text{min}$

$= \frac{844}{5} \text{ min} = 168\frac{4}{5} \text{ min} = 2 \text{ hr } 48 \text{ min } 48 \text{ sec.}$

40. Speed of the train relative to man $= \left(\frac{240}{10}\right) \text{m/sec} = 24$ m/sec $= \left(24 \times \frac{18}{5}\right) \text{km/hr} = \frac{432}{5}$ km/hr.

Let the speed of the train be x kmph. Then, relative speed $= (x + 3)$ kmph.

$\therefore x + 3 = \frac{432}{5} \Leftrightarrow x = \frac{432}{5} - 3 = \frac{417}{5} = 83.4 \text{ kmph.}$

41. Speed of the train relative to first man

$= \left(\frac{75}{7.5}\right) \text{m/sec} = 10 \text{ m/sec}$

$= \left(10 \times \frac{18}{5}\right) \text{km/hr} = 36 \text{ km/hr.}$

Let the speed of the train be x km/hr. Then, relative speed $= (x - 6)$ km/hr.

$\therefore x - 6 = 36 \Leftrightarrow x = 42$ km/hr.

Speed of the train relative to second man

$= \left(\frac{75}{6\frac{3}{4}}\right) \text{m/sec} = \left(75 \times \frac{4}{27}\right) \text{m/sec}$

$= \left(\frac{100}{9}\right) \text{m/sec} = \left(\frac{100}{9} \times \frac{18}{5}\right) \text{km} = 40 \text{ km/hr.}$

Let the speed of the second man be y kmph. Then, relative speed $= (42 - y)$ kmph.

$\therefore 42 - y = 40 \Leftrightarrow y = 2$ km/hr.

42. Let the length of the train be x metres and its speed be y m/sec.

Then, $\frac{x}{y} = 1.75$

$\Leftrightarrow x = 1.75\, y.$ ...(i)

Since the train takes less time to pass a moving object than a stationary object, it means that the cyclist is moving in a direction opposite to that of the train.

$\therefore \frac{x}{y + 10} = 1.5$

$\Leftrightarrow x = 1.5\, y + 15$

$\Leftrightarrow 1.75\, y = 1.5\, y + 15$

$\Leftrightarrow 0.25\, y = 15 \Leftrightarrow y = \frac{15}{0.25} = 60.$

Length of the train $= 1.75\, y = (1.75 \times 60)$ m $= 105$ m.

43. Let the length of each train be x metres.

Then, distance covered $= 2x$ metres.

Relative speed $= (46 - 36)$ km/hr

$= \left(10 \times \frac{5}{18}\right) \text{m/sec} = \left(\frac{25}{9}\right) \text{m/sec.}$

$\therefore \frac{2x}{36} = \frac{25}{9} \Leftrightarrow 2x = 100 \Leftrightarrow x = 50.$

44. Relative speed $= (120 + 80)$ km/hr

$= \left(200 \times \frac{5}{18}\right) \text{m/sec} = \left(\frac{500}{9}\right) \text{m/sec.}$

Let the length of the other train be x metres.

Then, $\frac{x + 270}{9} = \frac{500}{9}$

$\Leftrightarrow x + 270 = 500 \Leftrightarrow x = 230.$

45. Let the speed of each train be x m/sec. Then, relative speed of the two trains $= 2x$ m/sec.

So, $2x = \frac{(120 + 120)}{12} \Leftrightarrow 2x = 20 \Leftrightarrow x = 10.$

$\therefore$ Speed of each train $= 10$ m/sec

$= \left(10 \times \frac{18}{5}\right) \text{km/hr} = 36 \text{ km/hr.}$

46. Let the speed of the second train be x m/sec.

Speed of the first train $= 60$ kmph

$= \left(60 \times \frac{5}{18}\right) \text{m/sec.} = \left(\frac{50}{3}\right) \text{m/sec.}$

Relative speed of the two trains $= \left(x + \frac{50}{3}\right) \text{m/sec.}$

$\therefore x + \frac{50}{3} = \frac{180 + 270}{10.8} \Leftrightarrow \frac{3x + 50}{3} = \frac{4500}{108}$

$\Leftrightarrow 3x + 50 = \left(\frac{4500}{108} \times 3\right) = 125$

$\Leftrightarrow 3x = 75 \Leftrightarrow x = 25.$

Hence, speed of second train $= 25$ m/sec

$= \left(25 \times \frac{18}{5}\right) \text{kmph} = 90 \text{ kmph.}$

47. Speed of the first train $= \left(\frac{120}{10}\right) \text{m/sec} = 12 \text{ m/sec.}$

Speed of the second train $= \left(\frac{120}{15}\right) \text{m/sec} = 8 \text{ m/sec.}$

Relative speed $= (12 + 8)$ m/sec $= 20$ m/sec.

$\therefore$ Required time $= \frac{(120 + 120)}{20} \text{ sec} = 12 \text{ sec.}$

48. Let the speed of the second train be x km/hr.

Relative speed $= (x + 50)$ km/hr

$= \left[(x + 50) \times \frac{5}{18}\right] \text{m/sec} = \left(\frac{250 + 5x}{18}\right) \text{m/sec.}$

Distance covered $= (108 + 112) = 220$ m.

$\therefore \frac{220}{\left(\frac{250 + 5x}{18}\right)} = 6 \Leftrightarrow 250 + 5x = 660 \Leftrightarrow x = 82 \text{ km/hr.}$

49. Relative speed of the trains

$= \left(\frac{100 + 200}{2 \times 60}\right) \text{m/sec} = \left(\frac{5}{2}\right) \text{m/sec.}$

Speed of train B = 120 kmph

$= \left(120 \times \frac{5}{18}\right) \text{m/sec} = \left(\frac{100}{3}\right) \text{m/sec.}$

Let the speed of second train be x m/sec.

Then, $x - \frac{100}{3} = \frac{5}{2} \Leftrightarrow x = \left(\frac{5}{2} + \frac{100}{3}\right) = \left(\frac{215}{6}\right) \text{m/sec.}$

$\therefore$ Speed of second train $= \left(\frac{215}{6} \times \frac{18}{5}\right) \text{kmph} = 129$ mph.

50. Relative speed = (65 – 29) km/hr = 36 km/hr

$= \left(36 \times \frac{5}{18}\right) \text{m/sec} = 10 \text{ m/sec.}$

Length of faster train = (10 × 16) m = 160 m.

51. Relative speed = (36 + 45) km/hr

$= \left(81 \times \frac{5}{18}\right) \text{m/sec} = \left(\frac{45}{2}\right) \text{m/sec.}$

Length of train $= \left(\frac{45}{2} \times 8\right) \text{m} = 180$ m.

52. 2 kmph $= \left(2 \times \frac{5}{18}\right) \text{m/sec} = \frac{5}{9}$ m/sec

and 4 kmph $= \frac{10}{9}$ m/sec.

Let the length of the train be x metres and its speed be y m/sec.

Then, $\frac{x}{\left(y - \frac{5}{9}\right)} = 9$ and $\frac{x}{\left(y - \frac{10}{9}\right)} = 10.$

$\therefore$ $9y - 5 = x$ and $10(9y - 10) \Rightarrow 9y - x = 9x = 5$

and $90y - 9x = 100$.

On solving, we get: $x = 50$.

$\therefore$ Length of the train is 50 m.

53. $4.5 \text{ km/hr} = \left(4.5 \times \frac{5}{18}\right) \text{m/sec} = \frac{5}{4} \text{ m/sec} = 1.25$ m/sec, and

$5.4 \text{ km/hr} = \left(5.4 \times \frac{5}{18}\right) \text{m/sec} = \frac{3}{2} \text{ m/sec} = 1.5$ m/sec.

Let the speed of the train be x m/sec.

Then, $(x - 1.25) \times 8.4 = (x - 1.5) \times 8.5$

$\Leftrightarrow 8.4x - 10.5 = 8.5x - 12.75$

$\Leftrightarrow 0.1x = 2.25 \Leftrightarrow x = 22.5.$

$\therefore$ Speed of the train $= \left(22.5 \times \frac{18}{5}\right) \text{km/hr} = 81$ km/hr.

54. Let the length of the train be x metres and its speed by m/sec.

Speed of first man = 6 km/hr $= \left(6 \times \frac{5}{18}\right) \text{m/sec} = \frac{5}{3}$ m/sec.

Speed of second man

$= 7\frac{1}{2} \text{ km/hr} = \left(\frac{15}{2} \times \frac{5}{18}\right) \text{m/sec} = \left(\frac{25}{12}\right) \text{m/sec.}$

Then, $\frac{x}{\left(y - \frac{5}{3}\right)} = 5$ and $\frac{x}{\left(y - \frac{25}{12}\right)} = \frac{11}{2}$

$\Leftrightarrow x = 5y - \frac{25}{3}$ and $x = \frac{11}{2}y - \frac{275}{24}$

$\Leftrightarrow 5y - \frac{25}{3} = \frac{11}{2}y - \frac{275}{24}$

$\Leftrightarrow \frac{y}{2} = \frac{275}{24} - \frac{25}{3} = \frac{75}{24} = \frac{25}{8} \Leftrightarrow y = \frac{25}{4}.$

$\therefore x = 5 \times \frac{25}{4} - \frac{25}{3} = \frac{125}{4} - \frac{25}{3} = \frac{375 - 100}{12} = \frac{275}{12}.$

Hence, length of train $= \left(\frac{275}{12}\right) \text{m} = 22.916$ m.

Speed of train $= \left(\frac{25}{4}\right) \text{m/sec} = \left(\frac{25}{4} \times \frac{18}{5}\right) \text{km/hr}$

$= \left(\frac{45}{2}\right) \text{km/hr}$

= 22.5 km/hr.

55. Let the length of the train be x metres and its speed be y m/s.

Then, $\frac{x}{y - a} = b$ and $\frac{x}{y - (a+1)} = (b + 1)$

$\Leftrightarrow x = b(y - a)$ and $x = (b + 1)(y - a - 1)$

$\Leftrightarrow b(y - a) = (b + 1)(y - a - 1)$

$\Leftrightarrow by - ba = by - ba - b + y - a - 1$

$\Leftrightarrow y = (a + b + 1).$

56. Let the speed of the slower train be x m/sec.

Then, speed of the faster train = $2x$ m/sec.

Relative speed = $(x + 2x)$ m/sec = $3x$ m/sec.

$\therefore \frac{(100 + 100)}{8} = 3x \Leftrightarrow 24x = 200 \Leftrightarrow x = \frac{25}{3}.$

So, speed of the faster train

$= \frac{50}{3} \text{ m/sec} = \left(\frac{50}{3} \times \frac{18}{5}\right) \text{km/hr} = 60$ km/hr.

57. Speed of first train $= \left(\frac{150}{15}\right) \text{m/sec} = 10$ m/sec.

Let the speed of second train be x m/sec.

Relative speed = $(10 + x)$ m/sec.

$\therefore \frac{300}{10 + x} = 12 \Leftrightarrow 300 = 120 + 12x$

$\Leftrightarrow 12x = 180$

$\Leftrightarrow x = \frac{180}{12} = 15$ m/sec.

Hence, speed of other train $= \left(15 \times \frac{18}{5}\right) \text{kmph} = 54$ kmph.

58. Let the length of the train be x metres.

Then, distance covered in passing the cyclist = $(x + 1)$ m.

$\therefore x + 1 = (15 - 5) \times 20 = 200 \Leftrightarrow x = 199$ m.

So, required time $= \left[\frac{(x+1)}{15+5}\right] \text{sec} = \left(\frac{200}{20}\right) \text{sec} = 10$ sec.

59. Let the length of each train be x metres.

Then, speed of first train $= \left(\frac{x}{3}\right)$ m/sec. Speed of second train $= \left(\frac{x}{4}\right)$ m/sec.

$\therefore$ Required time $= \left[\frac{x+x}{\left(\frac{x}{3}+\frac{x}{4}\right)}\right]$ sec $= \left[\frac{2x}{\left(\frac{7x}{12}\right)}\right]$ sec

$= \left(2\times\frac{12}{7}\right)$ sec $= \frac{24}{7}$ sec $= 3\frac{3}{7}$ sec.

60. Let the length of the first train be x metres.

Then, the length of second train is $\left(\frac{x}{2}\right)$ metres.

Relative speed = (48 + 42) kmph

$= \left(90\times\frac{5}{18}\right)$ m/sec = 25 m/sec.

$\therefore \frac{\left(x+\frac{x}{2}\right)}{25} = 12$ or $\frac{3x}{2} = 300$ or $x = 200$.

$\therefore$ Length of first train = 200 m.

Let the length of platform be y metres.

Speed of the first train $= \left(48\times\frac{5}{18}\right)$ m/sec $= \frac{40}{3}$ m/sec.

$\therefore (200+y)\times\frac{3}{40} = 45$

$\Leftrightarrow 600 + 3y = 1800 \Leftrightarrow y = 400$ m.

61. Let the speed of the two trains be x m/sec and y m/sec respectively. Then, length of the first train = $27x$ metres, and length of the second train = $17y$ metres.

$\therefore \frac{27x+17y}{x+y} = 23$

$\Leftrightarrow 27x + 17y = 23x + 23y$

$\Leftrightarrow 4x = 6y \Leftrightarrow \frac{x}{y} = \frac{3}{2}$.

62. Let the speeds of the faster and slower trains be x m/sec and y m/sec respectively.

Then, $\frac{240}{x-y} = 60 \Leftrightarrow x - y = 4$ ...(i)

And, $\frac{240}{x+y} = 3 \Leftrightarrow x + y = 80$ ...(ii)

Adding (i) and (ii), we get: $2x = 84$ or $x = 42$. Putting $x = 42$ in (i), we get: $y = 38$.

Hence, speed of faster train = 42 m/sec.

63. Let the length of each train be x metres and let the speed of each of them by y m/sec.

Then, $\frac{2x}{2y} = 120 \Leftrightarrow \frac{x}{y} = 120$ ...(i)

New length of train $A = \left(\frac{16}{12}x\right)$ m $= \left(\frac{4x}{3}\right)$ m.

$\therefore$ Time taken by trains to cross each other

$= \left(\frac{x+\frac{4x}{3}}{2y}\right)$ sec $= \frac{7x}{6y} = \frac{7}{6}\times\frac{x}{y} = \left(\frac{7}{6}\times120\right)$ sec = 140 sec.

Hence, difference in times taken

= (140 – 120) sec = 20 sec.

64. Suppose they meet x hours after 7 a.m.

Distance covered by A in x hours = $20x$ km.

Distance covered by B in $(x - 1)$ hours = $25(x - 1)$ km.

$\therefore \quad 20x + 25(x-1) = 110 \Leftrightarrow 45x = 135 \Leftrightarrow x = 3$.

So, they meet at 10 a.m.

65. Suppose, the distance between Meerut and Ghaziabad is x km.

Time taken by X to cover x km = 1 hour.

Time taken by Y to cover x km $= \frac{3}{2}$ hours.

$\therefore$ Speed of X = x kmph, Speed of Y $= \left(\frac{2x}{3}\right)$ kmph.

Let them meet y hours after 4 p.m. Then,

$xy + \frac{2xy}{3} = x \Leftrightarrow y\left(1+\frac{2}{3}\right) = 1$

$\Leftrightarrow y = \frac{3}{5}$ hours $= \left(\frac{3}{5}\times60\right)$ min = 36 min.

So, the two trains meet at 4.36 p.m.

66. At the time of meeting, let the distance travelled by the first train be x km.

Then, distance travelled by the second train is $(x + 60)$ km.

$\therefore \frac{x}{16} = \frac{x+60}{21} \Rightarrow 21x = 16x + 960$

$\Rightarrow 5x = 960 \Rightarrow x = 192$.

Hence, distance between two stations = (192 + 192 + 60) km = 444 km.

67. Let us name the trains as A and B. Then,

(A's speed) : (B's speed) $= \sqrt{b}:\sqrt{a} = \sqrt{16}:\sqrt{9} = 4:3$.

68. Ratio of speeds $= \sqrt{4}:\sqrt{6\frac{1}{4}} = \sqrt{4}:\sqrt{\frac{25}{4}} = 2:\frac{5}{2} = 4:5$.

Let the speeds of the two trains be $4x$ and $5x$ km/hr respectively.

Then, time taken by trains to meet each other

$= \left(\frac{270}{4x+5x}\right)$ hr $= \left(\frac{270}{9x}\right)$ hr $= \left(\frac{30}{x}\right)$ hr.

Time taken by slower train to travel 270 km $= \left(\frac{270}{4x}\right)$ hr.

$\therefore \frac{270}{4x} = \frac{30}{x} + 6\frac{1}{4} \Rightarrow \frac{270}{4x} - \frac{30}{x} = \frac{25}{4} \Rightarrow \frac{150}{4x} = \frac{25}{4}$

$\Rightarrow 100x = 600 \Rightarrow x = 6$.

Hence, speed of slower train = $4x$ = 24 km/hr.

69. Average speed of train = 40 km/h

Reach at its destination at on time

New average speed of train = 35 km/h

Time = 15 minutes = $\frac{15}{60}$ hours

Then distance travelled = $\frac{40\times35}{40-35}\times\frac{15}{60}$

$= \frac{40\times35}{5}\times\frac{15}{60} = 70$ km.

70. Time taken by train to cross a pole = 9 sec.
Distance covered in crossing a pole = length of train
Speed of train = 48 km/h

$= \left(\frac{48\times5}{18}\right)$m/sec

$= \frac{40}{3}$m/sec

$\therefore$ Length of train = speed × time = $\frac{40}{3}\times9$

= 120 m

71. Let the trains meet after t hours.
Speed of train A = 75 km/hr
Speed of train B = 50 km/hr
Distance covered by train A = 75 × t = 75t
Distance covered by train B = 50 × t = 50t
Distance = Speed × Time
According to the question,
75t – 50t = 175
⇒ 25t = 175

⇒ $t = \frac{175}{25} = 7$ hours

$\therefore$ Distance between A and B

= 75t + 50t = 125t

= 125 × 7 = 875 km.

72. Let the length of train x m

Speed of train = $\frac{\text{(Length of train + length of bridge)}}{\text{Time taken in crossing}}$

According to information we get

⇒ $\frac{x+500}{100} = \frac{x+250}{60}$

⇒ 60 (x + 500) = 100 (x + 250)

3 (x + 500) = 5 (x + 250)

⇒ $5x+1250 = 3x+1500$

⇒ $5x-3x = 1500-1250$

⇒ $2x = 250$

⇒ $x = \frac{250}{2} = 125$ m

73. Let the length of train be x m.
When a train crosses a light post in 9 second the distance covered = length of train

⇒ speed of train = $\frac{x}{9}$

Distance covered in crossing a 700 meter platform in 30 seconds = Length of platform + length of train

speed of train = $\frac{x+700}{9}$

$= \frac{x}{9} = \frac{x+700}{30}$ $\left[\because \text{Speed} = \frac{\text{Distance}}{\text{Time}}\right]$

⇒ $\frac{x}{3} = \frac{x+700}{10}$

⇒ $10x = 3x+2100$

⇒ $10x-3x = 2100$

⇒ $7x = 2100$

⇒ $x = \frac{2100}{7} = 300$ m

When the length of the platform be 800 m, then time 'T' be taken by train to cross 800 m long platform

$\frac{x}{9} = \frac{x+800}{T}$

⇒ Tx = 9x + 7200

⇒ 300T = 2700 + 7200

⇒ 300T = 9900

⇒ T = $\frac{9900}{300} = 33$ seconds

74. Speed of train A = 63 kmph = $\left(\frac{63\times5}{18}\right)$m/sec.

= 17.5 m/sec

Speed of train B = 54 kmph

$= \left(\frac{54\times5}{18}\right)$m/sec = 15 m/sec

If the length of train A be x meter, then
Speed of train A

$= \frac{\text{Length of train + length of platform}}{\text{Time taken in crossing}}$

⇒ $17.5 = \frac{x+199.5}{21}$

⇒ $17.5\times21 = x+199.5$

⇒ $367.5 = x+199.5$

⇒ $x = 367.5-199.5$

⇒ 168 meters

Relative speed = (Speed of train A + speed of train B)

= (17.5 + 15) m/sec.

= 32.5 m/sec.

$\therefore$ Required time

$= \frac{\text{length of trains A + Length of train B}}{\text{Relative speed}}$

$= \left(\frac{168+157}{32.5}\right)$seconds

$= \frac{325}{32.5} = 10$ seconds.

EXERCISE

(DATA SUFFICIENCY TYPE QUESTIONS)

1. A train running at a certain speed crosses a stationary engine in 20 seconds. To find out the speed of the train, which of the following information is necessary?
   (a) Only the length of the train
   (b) Only the length of the engine
   (c) Either the length of the train or the length of the engine
   (d) Both the length of the train and the length of the engine

2. A train running at a certain speed crosses another train running in the opposite direction in 4.8 seconds. To find out the speed of the first train, which of the following information P and Q is sufficient?
   P : The length of the first train
   Q : The length of the second train
   (a) Only P is sufficient
   (b) Only Q is sufficient
   (c) Either P or Q is sufficient
   (d) Both P and Q are needed
   (e) Both P and Q are not sufficient

Directions (*Questions 3–16*) : *Each of the questions given below consists of a statement and/or a question and two statements numbered I and II given below it. You have to decide whether the data provided in the statement(s) is/are sufficient to answer the given question. Read both the statements and*

Give answer (a) if the data in Statement I alone are sufficient to answer the question, while the data in Statement II alone are not sufficient to answer the question;

Give answer (b) if the data in Statement II alone are sufficient to answer the question, while the data in Statement I alone are not sufficient to answer the question;

Give answer (c) if the data either in Statement I or in Statement II alone are sufficient to answer the question;

Give answer (d) if the data even in both Statements I and II together are not sufficient to answer the question;

Give answer (e) if the data in both Statements I and II together are necessary to answer the question.

3. A train crosses a signal post in x seconds. What is the length of the train? **(NABARD, 2002)**
   I. The train crosses a platform of 100 metres in y seconds.
   II. The train is running at the speed of 80 km/hr.

4. What was the speed of the running train? **(Bank P.O., 2000)**
   I. Length of the train was 120 metres.
   II. The train crossed the other stationary train whose length was 180 m in 4 seconds.

5. What is the speed of a running train which takes 9 seconds to cross a signal post?
   I. The length of the train is 90 metres.
   II. The train takes 27 seconds to cross a platform of 180 metres.

6. What is the speed of the running train? **(Bank P.O., 2006)**
   I. The length of the train is 180 metres.
   II. The train crosses another stationary train of 120 metres length in 60 seconds.

7. What is the length of a running train?
   I. The train crosses a man in 9 seconds.
   II. The train crosses a 240 metre long platform in 24 seconds.

8. What is the speed of the train? **(Bank P.O., 2003)**
   I. 280 metres long train crosses a signal pole in 18 seconds.
   II. 280 metres long train crosses a platform in 45 seconds.

9. What was the speed of a running train X?
   I. The relative speed of train X and another train Y running in opposite direction is 160 kmph.
   II. The train Y crosses a signal post in 9 seconds.

10. What was the length of a running train crossing another 180 metre long train running in the opposite direction?
    I. The relative speed of the two trains was 150 kmph.
    II. The trains took 9 seconds to cross each other.

11. A train crosses another train running in the opposite direction in x seconds. What is the speed of the train? **(S.B.I.P.O., 2003)**
    I. Both the trains have the same length and are running at the same speed.
    II. One train crosses a pole in 5 seconds.

12. A train crosses another train running in the same direction in one minute. What is the speed of the faster train? **(R.B.I., 2003)**
    I. The speed of the slower train is 80 kmph.
    II. The sum of the lengths of both the trains is 300 m.

13. What is the speed of a running train?
    I. The train crosses a signal post in 6 seconds.
    II. The train crosses another train running in the opposite direction in 15 seconds.

14. What is the relative speed of two trains with respect to each other? **(JMET, 2007)**

I. The speed of the first train is 120% more than the speed of the second train.

II. The speed of the second train is 80 km/hr.

15. A train crosses a pole in 10 seconds. What is the length of the train? **(Bank P.O., 2003)**

I. The train crosses another train running in opposite direction with a speed of 80 km / hr in 22 seconds.

II. The speed of the train is 108 km / hr.

16. What is the speed of the train whose length is 210 metres? **(Bank P.O., 2003)**

I. The train crosses another train of 300 metres length running in opposite direction in 10 seconds.

II. The train crosses another train running in the same direction at the speed of 60 km / hr in 30 seconds.

Directions (*Questions 17 to 23*) : *Each of the questions given below consists of a question followed by three statements. You have to study the question and the statements and decide which of the statement(s) is/are necessary to answer the question.*

17. What is the speed of the train? **(S.B.I.P.O., 2002)**

I. The train crosses a tree in 13 seconds.

II. The train crosses a platform of length 250 metres in 27 seconds.

III. The train crosses another train running in the same direction in 32 seconds.

(*a*) I and II only (*b*) II and III only
(*c*) I and III only (*d*) Any two of the three
(*e*) None of these

18. What is the speed of the train? **(M.B.A., 2002)**

I. The train crosses 300 metres long platform in 21 seconds.

II. The train crosses another stationary train of equal length in $19\frac{1}{2}$ seconds.

III. The train crosses a signal pole in $9\frac{3}{4}$ seconds.

(*a*) I and II only
(*b*) I and either II or III only
(*c*) II and either I or III only
(*d*) III and either I or II only
(*e*) None of these

19. What is the speed of the train? **(Bank P.O., 2008)**

I. The train crosses a signal pole in 18 seconds.

II. The train crosses a platform of equal length in 36 seconds.

III. Length of the train is 330 metres.

(*a*) I and II only (*b*) II and III only
(*c*) I and III only
(*d*) III and either I or II only
(*e*) Any two of the three

20. What is the length of the train *X*?

I. Train *X* crosses a telegraph post in 20 seconds

II. Train *X* crosses a platform of length 800 m in 100 seconds.

III. Train *X* passes through a tunnel 400 m long in 60 seconds.

(*a*) I and either II or III only
(*b*) II and III only
(*c*) II and either I or III only
(*d*) III and either I or II only
(*e*) Any two of the three

21. What is the speed of the train?

I. The train passes a man walking at the rate of 3 kmph in 9 seconds.

II. The train passes a man walking at the rate of 6 kmph in 10 seconds.

III. The train is moving in the same direction in which the two men are moving.

(*a*) I and III only (*b*) II and III only
(*c*) I and II only (*d*) All I, II and III
(*e*) Question cannot be answered even with information in all the three statements.

22. What is the length of the train? **(Bank P.O., 2004)**

I. The train cosses a 280 m long platform in 18 sec.

II. The train crosses a man standing on the platform in 10.5 sec.

III. Speed of the train is 96 kmph.

(*a*) I and II only (*b*) I and III only
(*c*) All I, II and III
(*d*) Any two of the three (*e*) None of these

23. What is the speed of train? **(Bank P.O. 2004)**

I. The train crosses a signal post in 20 seconds.

II. The train crosses a 260 metre long platform in 33 seconds.

III. The train crosses another stationary train of same length in 40 seconds.

(*a*) Only I and II
(*b*) Any two of the three
(*c*) All I, II and III
(*d*) II and either I or III
(*e*) Even with all three statements answer cannot be given.

Directions (*Questions 24–26*): *Each of these questions is followed by three statements. You have to study the question and all the three statements given to decide whether any information provided in the statement(s) is redundant and can be dispensed with while answering the given question.*

24. How much time will the train A take to cross another train B running in opposite direction?

I. Train A crosses a signal pole in 6 seconds.

II. Ratio of the speeds of trains A and B is 3 : 2.

III. Length of the two trains together is 500 metres.

(*a*) I only (*b*) II only

(*c*) III only (*d*) I or II only

(*e*) Question cannot be answered even with the information in all the three statements.

25. What is the length of a running train *P* crossing another running train *Q*?

I. These two trains take 18 seconds to cross each other.

II. These trains are running in opposite directions.

III. The length of train Q is 180 metres.

(*a*) I only (*b*) II only

(*c*) III only

(*d*) All I, II and III are required

(*e*) Even with I, II and III, the answer cannot be obtained.

26. At what time will the train reach city X from city Y?

I. The train crosses another train of equal length of 200 metres and running in opposite direction in 15 seconds.

II. The train leaves city *Y* at 7.15 a.m. for city *X* situated at a distance of 558 km.

III. The 200 metre long train crosses a signal pole in 10 seconds.

(*a*) I only (*b*) II only

(*c*) III only (*d*) I or III only

(*e*) All I, II and III are required

ANSWERS

1. (*d*)	2. (*e*)	3. (*c*)	4. (*e*)	5. (*a*)	6. (*e*)	7. (*e*)	8. (*a*)	9. (*d*)	10. (*e*)
11. (*d*)	12. (*e*)	13. (*d*)	14. (*d*)	15. (*b*)	16. (*e*)	17. (*a*)	18. (*b*)	19. (*d*)	20. (*e*)
21. (*d*)	22. (*d*)	23. (*d*)	24. (*e*)	25. (*e*)	26. (*a*)				

SOLUTIONS

1. Time taken by the train to cross a stationary engine

$$= \frac{\text{(Length of train + Length of engine)}}{\text{(Speed of the train)}}$$

$$\Rightarrow \frac{\text{(Length of train + Length of engine)}}{\text{(Speed of the train)}} = 20 \text{ (given)}$$

Hence, to find the speed of the train, the length of the train and the length of the engine both must be known.

$\therefore$ The correct answer is (*d*).

2. Let two trains of lengths *a* and *b* metres be moving in opposite directions at u m/s and v m/s.

Time taken by the trains to cross each other $= \frac{(a+b)}{(u+v)}$ sec.

$\therefore \frac{a+b}{u+v} = 4.8.$

In order to find *u*, we must know *a*, *b* and *v*, *i.e.*, length of first train, length of second train and the speed of the second train.

Thus, *P* and *Q* are not sufficient. $\therefore$ The correct answer is (*e*).

3. Let the length of the train be *l* metres.

Time taken to cross a signal post

$$= \frac{\text{Length of the train}}{\text{Speed of the train}} \Rightarrow x = \frac{l}{\text{Speed.}} \quad ...(i)$$

Time taken to cross the platform

$$= \frac{(l+100)}{\text{Speed}} \Rightarrow y = \frac{l+100}{\text{Speed}} \quad ...(ii)$$

Thus, from (*i*) and (*ii*), we can find *l*.

Also, II gives, speed $= \left(80 \times \frac{5}{18}\right) \text{m/s} = \frac{200}{9}$ m/s.

Thus, the data in I or II alone are sufficient to answer the question.

$\therefore$ The correct answer is (*c*).

4. Speed of the first train

$$= \frac{\text{(sum of the lengths of the two trains)}}{\text{Time taken}}$$

$$= \frac{(120+180)}{4} \text{ m/s} = 75 \text{ m/s}.$$

So, both the statements are necessary to get the answer.

$\therefore$ The correct answer is (*e*).

5. Speed of the train $= \frac{\text{Length of the train}}{\text{Time taken to cross the post}}$

$$= \frac{90}{9} \text{ m/s} = 10 \text{ m/s}.$$

Thus, I alone gives the answer.

Time taken to cross a platform

$$= \frac{\text{(Length of train + Length of platform)}}{\text{Speed of the train}}$$

$$\Rightarrow \text{Speed} = \frac{(l+180)}{27}.$$

But, *l* is not given. So, speed cannot be obtained.

So, II alone does not give the answer.

$\therefore$ The correct answer is (*a*).

6. Speed of the running train

$= \frac{\text{Sum of the lengths of two trains}}{\text{Time taken to cross stationary train}}$

$= \frac{(180+120)}{60}$ m/s = 5 m/s.

So, both the statements are necessary to get the answer.

∴ The correct answer is (*e*).

7. Time taken by train to cross a man

$= \frac{\text{Length of train}}{\text{Speed of train}} \Rightarrow \text{Speed} = \frac{l}{9}$ ...(*i*)

Time taken by train to cross a platform

$= \frac{(\text{Length of train} + \text{Length of platform})}{\text{Speed of the train}}$

$\Rightarrow \text{Speed} = \frac{l+240}{24}$ ...(*ii*)

From (*i*) and (*ii*), we get $\frac{l}{9} = \frac{l+240}{24}$.

Thus, l can be obtained. So both I and II are necessary to get the answer.

∴ The correct answer is (*e*).

8. Speed $= \frac{\text{Length of the train}}{\text{Time taken to cross the pole}} = \frac{280}{18}$ m/s

$= \frac{140}{9}$ m/s.

∴ I alone gives the answer.

$\Rightarrow \text{Speed} = \frac{(280+p)}{45}$ m/s.

But, p = length of platform, is not given.

∴ II is not sufficient to give the answer.

∴ The correct answer is (*a*).

9. Let the two trains of length a metres and b metres be moving in opposite directions at u m/s and v m/s. Then,

I gives, $u + v = 160$. II gives, $v = \frac{b}{9}$.

From these equations, we cannot obtain u.

∴ The correct answer is (*d*).

10. Let the two trains of length a metres and b metres be moving in opposite directions at u m/s and v m/s.

Time taken to cross each other $= \frac{(a+b)}{(u+v)}$ sec.

Now, $b = 180$, $u + v = \left(150 \times \frac{5}{18}\right)$ m/sec $= \frac{125}{3}$ m/sec

$\Rightarrow 9 = \frac{a+180}{(125/3)} \Rightarrow a = (375 - 180) = 195$ m.

Thus, both I and II are necessary to get the answer.

∴ The correct answer is (*e*).

11. Let the two trains of length a metres and b metres be moving in opposite directions at u m/s and v m/s.

Time taken to cross each other

$= \frac{(a+b)}{(u+v)}$ m/sec $\Rightarrow x = \frac{(a+a)}{(u+u)} = \frac{a}{u}$. ...(*i*)

Time taken to cross the pole

$= \frac{\text{Length of the train}}{\text{Speed of the train}} = \frac{a}{u} \Rightarrow \frac{a}{u} = 5$ ...(*ii*)

From (*i*) and (*ii*) also, we cannot find u.

∴ The correct answer is (*d*).

12. Let the speed of the faster train be x m/sec.

Speed of slower train = 80 kmph

$= \left(80 \times \frac{5}{18}\right)$ m/sec $= \left(\frac{200}{9}\right)$ m/sec.

Time taken by the trains to cross each other

$= \frac{\text{Sum of the lengths of trains}}{\text{Relative speed}}$

$\Rightarrow \frac{300}{x - \frac{200}{9}} = 60.$

Thus, the value of x can be determined. So, both I and II together give the answer.

∴ The correct answer is (*e*).

13. Since the lengths of the trains are not given, it is not possible to determine the speed of the train from both I and II together.

∴ The correct answer is (*d*).

14. Speed of second train = 80 km/hr.

Speed of first train = (80 + 120% of 80) km/hr = 176 km/hr.

I and II give us the speeds of both the trains but to find the relative speed, we need to know whether the trains are moving in same or opposite directions, which is not given.

Thus, even both I and II together do not give the answer.

∴ The correct answer is (*d*).

15. Time taken to cross a pole

$= \frac{\text{Length of train}}{\text{Speed of train}} \Rightarrow 10 = \frac{\text{Length of train}}{\left(108 \times \frac{5}{18}\right)}$

$\Rightarrow$ Length of the train = 300 m.

Clearly, II is sufficient to get the answer. Also, I is not sufficient to get the answer.

∴ The correct answer is (*b*).

16. Time taken to cross the train, running in opposite directions $= \frac{(l_1 + l_2)}{(u+v)}$ sec.

$\Rightarrow 10 = \frac{(210+300)}{(u+v)} \Rightarrow u + v = 51.$

Time taken to cross the train, running in same direction

$= \frac{(l_1 + l_2)}{(u-v)}$ sec.

$\Rightarrow 30 = \frac{(210+300)}{\left(u - 60 \times \frac{5}{18}\right)} \Rightarrow u = \left(17 + \frac{50}{3}\right)$ m/sec.

Thus, u and v can be obtained.

∴ Correct answer is (*e*).

17. Let the speed of the train be x metres / sec.

Time taken to cross a tree $= \dfrac{\text{Length of the train}}{\text{Speed of the train}}$.

Time taken to cross a platform

$= \dfrac{\text{(Length of train + Length of platform)}}{\text{Speed of the train}}$ ...(*ii*)

I gives, $13 = \dfrac{1}{x} \Rightarrow l = 13x$.

II gives, 27

$= \dfrac{l+250}{x} \Rightarrow \dfrac{13x+250}{x} = 24$

$\Rightarrow x = \dfrac{125}{7}$ m/sec.

Thus I and II give the speed of the train.

∴ The correct answer is (*a*).

18. Let the speed of the train be x m / sec.

Time taken to cross a platform

$= \dfrac{\text{(Length of train + Length of platform)}}{\text{Speed of the train}}$

Time taken by the train to cross a stationary train

$= \dfrac{\text{(Sum of the lengths of the trains)}}{\text{Speed of moving train}}$

Time taken to cross a signal pole $= \dfrac{\text{Length of train}}{\text{Speed of train}}$

I gives, $21 = \dfrac{(l+300)}{x}$; **II** gives, $\dfrac{39}{2} = \dfrac{2l}{x}$; **III** gives, $\dfrac{39}{4} = \dfrac{l}{x}$.

Thus, (I and II) or (I and III) give x.

∴ Correct answer is (*b*).

19. Let the speed of the train be x m / sec.

Time taken to cross a signal pole $= \dfrac{\text{Length of train}}{\text{Speed of train}}$.

Time taken to cross a platform

$= \dfrac{\text{(Length of train + Length of platform)}}{\text{Speed of the train}}$

Length of train = 330 m.

I and III give, $18 = \dfrac{330}{x} \Rightarrow x = \dfrac{330}{18}$ m/s $= \dfrac{55}{3}$ m/s.

II and III give, $36 = \dfrac{2 \times 330}{x} \Rightarrow x = \dfrac{660}{36}$ m/s $= \dfrac{55}{3}$ m/s.

∴ Correct answer is (*d*).

20. Time taken to cross a pole

$= \dfrac{\text{Length of train}}{\text{Its speed}} \Rightarrow 20 = \dfrac{l}{\text{speed}}$

$\Rightarrow \text{speed} = \dfrac{l}{20}$ ...(*i*)

Time taken to cross a platform $= \dfrac{(l+800)}{\text{speed}}$

$\Rightarrow 100 = \dfrac{(l+800)}{\text{speed}} \Rightarrow \text{speed} = \dfrac{(l+800)}{100}$ ...(*ii*)

Time taken to pass through a tunnel $= \dfrac{(l+400)}{60}$

$\Rightarrow 60 = \dfrac{(l+400)}{\text{speed}} \Rightarrow \text{speed} = \dfrac{(l+400)}{60}$ ...(*iii*)

Equating any two out of three will give us l.

∴ Correct answer is (*e*).

21. Let the speed of the train be x m / sec.

III gives that the men are moving in the same direction.

I gives, time taken to pass a man

$= \dfrac{l}{\left(x - 3 \times \dfrac{5}{18}\right)} = \left(\dfrac{6l}{6x-5}\right)$ sec.

∴ $\dfrac{6l}{6x-5} = 9 \Rightarrow 54x - 6l = 45$

$\Rightarrow 18x - 2l = 15$ ...(*i*)

II gives, time taken to pass another man

$= \dfrac{l}{\left(x - 6 \times \dfrac{5}{18}\right)}$ sec $= \dfrac{3l}{(3x-5)}$ sec.

∴ $\dfrac{3l}{(3x-5)} = 10 \Rightarrow 30x - 3l = 50$ ...(*ii*)

On solving (*i*) and (*ii*), we get : $x = \dfrac{55}{6}$ m/sec.

Thus, all I, II, III are needed to get the answer.

∴ (*d*) is correct.

22. Let the length of the train be x metres and its speed be y m/sec.

From I, we have : $\dfrac{x+280}{y} = 18$ ...(*i*) From II, we have:

$\dfrac{x}{y} = 10.5$ ...(*ii*)

From III, we have: $y = 96$ kmph

$= \left(96 \times \dfrac{5}{18}\right)$ m/sec $= \dfrac{80}{3}$ m/sec ...(*iii*)

Clearly, the value of x can be found by solving any two equations out of (*i*), (*ii*) and (*iii*) simulaneously.

So, any two of the three give the answer.

∴ The correct answer is (*d*).

23. Let the length of the train be x metres and its speed be y m/sec.

From I, we have: $\dfrac{x}{y} = 20$ ...(*i*)

From II, we have: $y = \dfrac{x+260}{33}$ ...(*ii*)

From III, we have: $y = \dfrac{2x}{40}$ or $\dfrac{x}{y} = 20$ ...(*iii*)

Thus, the value of y can be found by solving (*ii*) with either (*i*) or (*iii*) simultaneously.

∴ II and either I or III together give the answer.

Hence, the correct answer is (*d*).

24. II. Let the speeds of A and B be $3x$ m / sec and $2x$ m / sec.

I. Length of train $A = (3x \times 6)$ m $= 18x$ metres.

III. Length of train B $= (500 - 18x)$ m.

Relative speed $= (3x + 2x)$ m / sec $= 5x$ m / sec.

$$\text{Time taken } A \text{ to cross } B = \frac{\text{Sum of their lengths}}{\text{Relative speed}} = \frac{500}{5x} \text{ sec.}$$

Thus, even with the information in all the three statements, question cannot be answered.

$\therefore$ Correct answer is (*e*).

25. Let the length of train P be x metres.

II. These trains are running in opposite directions.

III. Length of train Q is 180 m.

$$\text{I. Time taken by } P \text{ to cross Q} = \frac{(180 + x)}{\text{Relative speed}}$$

$$\Rightarrow 18 = \frac{(180 + x)}{\text{Relative speed}}.$$

Thus, even with I, II and III, the answer cannot be obtained.

$\therefore$ Correct answer is (*e*).

26. III. gives, speed

$$= \frac{200}{10} \text{ m/s} = 20 \text{ m/s}$$

$$= \left(20 \times \frac{18}{5}\right) \text{km/hr} = 72 \text{ km/hr. t}$$

II. gives, time taken

$$= \left(\frac{558}{72}\right) \text{hrs} = \frac{31}{4} \text{ hrs} = 7\frac{3}{4} \text{ hrs} = 7 \text{ hrs } 45 \text{ min.}$$

So, the train will reach city X at 3 p.m.

Hence, I is redundant.

$\therefore$ Correct answer is (*a*).

21 Alligation or Mixture

IMPORTANT FACTS AND FORMULAE

I. Alligation: It is the rule that enables us to find the ratio in which two or more ingredients at the given price must be mixed to produce a mixture of a desired price.

II. Mean Price: The cost price of a unit quantity of the mixture is called the mean price.

III. Rule of Alligation: If two ingredients are mixed, then

$$\left(\frac{\text{Quantity of cheaper}}{\text{Quantity of dearer}}\right)=\frac{(\text{C.P. of dearer})-(\text{Mean price})}{(\text{Mean price})-(\text{C.P. of cheaper})}.$$

We present as under :

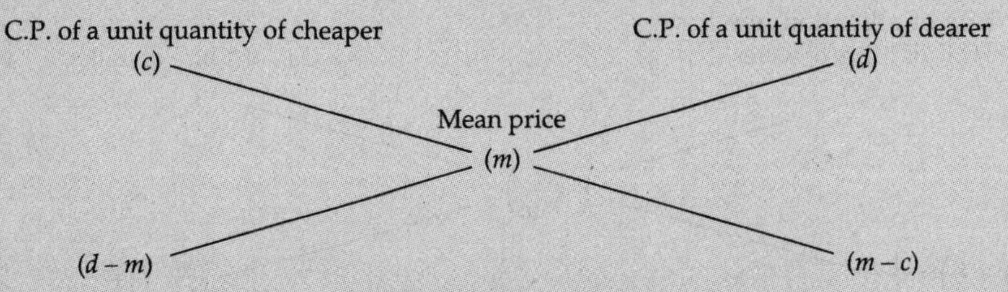

∴ (Cheaper quantity) : (Dearer quantity) = $(d - m) : (m - c)$.

IV. Suppose a container contains x units of liquid from which y units are taken out and replaced by water.

After n operations, the quantity of pure liquid = $\left[x\left(1-\frac{y}{x}\right)^n\right]$ units.

SOLVED EXAMPLES

Ex. 1. ***In what ratio must rice at ₹ 9.30 per kg be mixed with rice at ₹ 10.80 per kg so that the mixture be worth ₹ 10 per kg ?***

Sol. By the rule of alligation, we have :

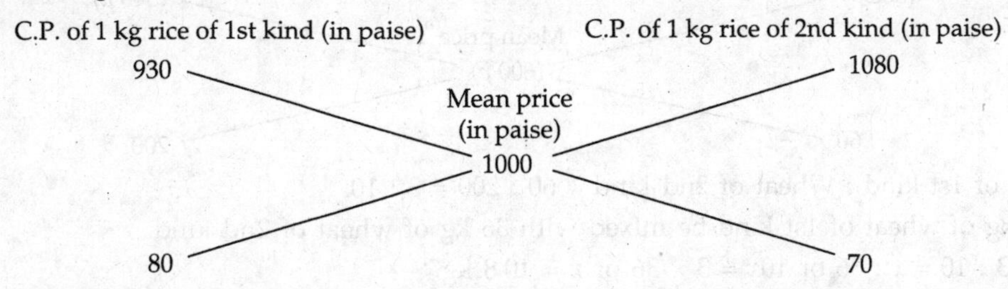

∴ Required ratio = 80 : 70 = 8 : 7.

Ex. 2. ***How much water must be added to 60 litres of milk at $1\frac{1}{2}$ litres for ₹ 20 so as to have a mixture worth ₹ $10\frac{2}{3}$ a litre ?***

Sol. C.P. of 1 litre of milk = ₹$\left(20\times\frac{2}{3}\right)$ = ₹ $\frac{40}{3}$.

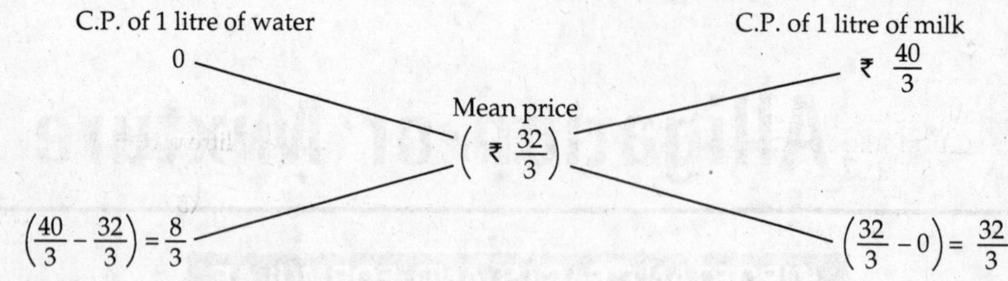

Ratio of water and milk $= \frac{8}{3} : \frac{32}{3} = 8 : 32 = 1 : 4.$

$\therefore$ Quantity of water to be added to 60 litres of milk $= \left(\frac{1}{4} \times 60\right)$ litres = 15 litres.

Ex. 3. ***In what ratio must water be mixed with milk to gain 20% by selling the mixture at cost price ?***

Sol. Let C.P. of milk be ₹ 1 per litre. Then, S.P. of 1 litre of mixture = ₹ 1. Gain obtained = 20%.

$\therefore$ C.P. of 1 litre of mixture = = ₹ $\left(\frac{100}{120} \times 1\right)$ = ₹ $\frac{5}{6}$.

By the rule of alligation, we have :

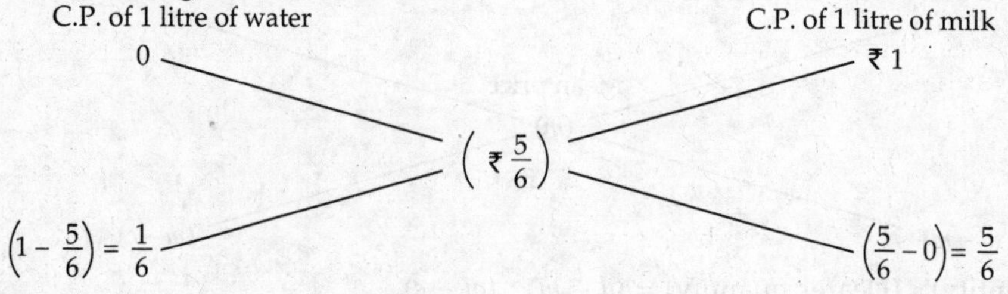

$\therefore$ Ratio of water and milk $= \frac{1}{6} : \frac{5}{6} = 1 : 5.$

Ex. 4. ***How many kgs. of wheat costing ₹ 8 per kg must be mixed with 36 kg of rice costing ₹ 5.40 per kg so that 20% gain may be obtained by selling the mixture at ₹ 7.20 per kg ?***

Sol. S.P. of 1 kg mixture = ₹ 7.20, Gain = 20%.

$\therefore$ C.P. of 1 kg mixture = ₹ $\left(\frac{100}{120} \times 7.20\right)$ = ₹ 6.

By the rule of alligation, we have :

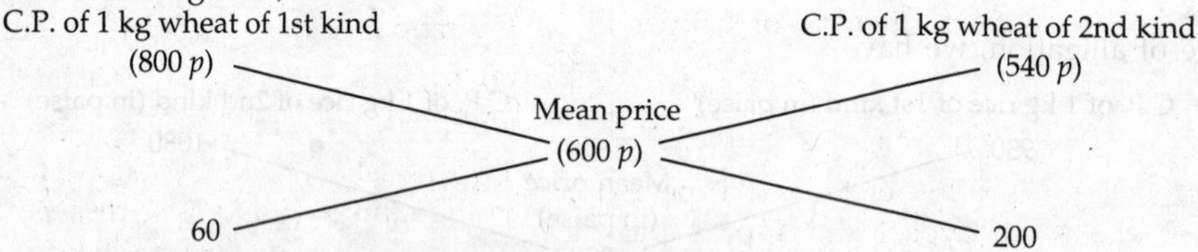

Wheat of 1st kind : Wheat of 2nd kind = 60 : 200 = 3 : 10.

Let x kg of wheat of 1st kind be mixed with 36 kg of wheat of 2nd kind.

Then, 3 : 10 = x : 36 or $10x = 3 \times 36$ or $x = 10.8$ kg.

Ex. 5. ***The milk and water in two vessels A and B are in the ratio 4 : 3 and 2 : 3 respectively. In what ratio, the liquids in both the vessels be mixed to obtain a new mixture in vessel C containing half milk and half water ?***

Sol. Let the C.P. of milk be ₹ 1 per litre.

Milk in 1 litre mixture of A $= \frac{4}{7}$ litre; Milk in 1 litre mixture of B $= \frac{2}{5}$ litre;

Milk in 1 litre mixture of C $= \frac{1}{2}$ litre.

$\therefore$ C.P. of 1 litre mixture in A = ₹ $\frac{4}{7}$; C.P. of 1 litre mixture in B = ₹ $\frac{2}{5}$.

Mean price = ₹ $\frac{1}{2}$.

By the rule of alligation, we have :

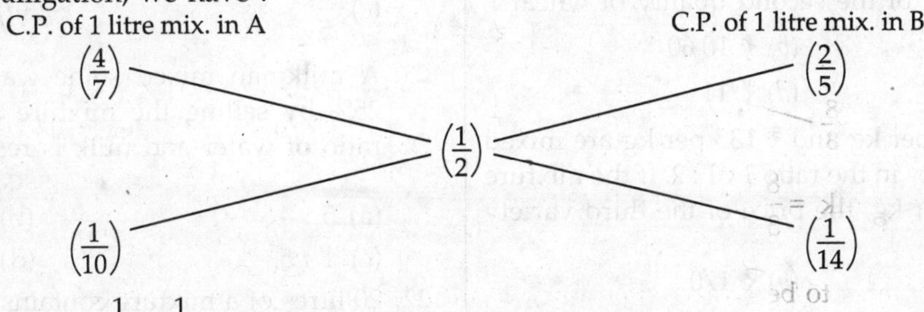

$\therefore$ Required ratio $= \frac{1}{10} : \frac{1}{14} = 7 : 5.$

EXERCISE

(OBJECTIVE TYPE QUESTIONS)

Directions: ***Mark* (3) *against the correct answer:***

1. In what ratio must a grocer mix two varieties of pulses costing ₹ 15 and ₹ 20 per kg respectively so as to get a mixture worth ₹ 16.50 per kg ? **(R.R.B., 2008)**

   (*a*) 3 : 7 (*b*) 5 : 7
   (*c*) 7 : 3 (*d*) 7 : 5

2. Find the ratio in which rice at ₹ 7.20 a kg be mixed with rice at ₹ 5.70 a kg to produce a mixture worth ₹ 6.30 a kg.

   (*a*) 1 : 3 (*b*) 2 : 3
   (*c*) 3 : 4 (*d*) 4 : 5

3. In what ratio must tea at ₹ 62 per kg be mixed with tea at ₹ 72 per kg so that the mixture must be worth ₹ 64.50 per kg ?

   (*a*) 3 : 1 (*b*) 3 : 2
   (*c*) 4 : 3 (*d*) 5 : 3

4. In what ratio must water be mixed with milk costing ₹ 12 per litre to obtain a mixture worth of ₹ 8 per litre ?

   (*a*) 1 : 2 (*b*) 2 : 1
   (*c*) 2 : 3 (*d*) 3 : 2

5. The cost of Type 1 rice is ₹ 15 per kg and Type 2 rice is ₹ 20 per kg. If both Type 1 and Type 2 are mixed in the ratio of 2 : 3, then the price per kg of the mixed variety of rice is

   (*a*) ₹ 18 (*b*) ₹ 18.50
   (*c*) ₹ 19 (*d*) ₹ 19.50

6. In what ratio must a grocer mix two varieties of tea worth ₹ 60 a kg and ₹ 65 a kg so that by selling the mixture at ₹ 68.20 a kg he may gain 10%?

   (*a*) 3 : 2 (*b*) 3 : 4
   (*c*) 3 : 5 (*d*) 4 : 5

7. How many kilograms of sugar costing ₹ 9 per kg must be mixed with 27 kg of sugar costing ₹ 7 per kg so that there may be a gain of 10% by selling the mixture at ₹ 9.24 per kg ?

   (*a*) 36 kg (*b*) 42 kg
   (*c*) 54 kg (*d*) 63 kg

8. In what ratio must water be mixed with milk to gain $16\frac{2}{3}\%$ on selling the mixture at cost price ?

   (*a*) 1 : 6 (*b*) 6 : 1
   (*c*) 2 : 3 (*d*) 4 : 3

9. A dishonest milkman professes to sell his milk at cost price but he mixes it with water and thereby gains 25%. The percentage of water in the mixture is

   (*a*) 4% (*b*) $6\frac{1}{4}\%$
   (*c*) 20% (*d*) 25%

10. Two vessels A and B contain spirit and water mixed in the ratio 5 : 2 and 7 : 6 respectively. Find the ratio in which these mixtures be mixed to obtain a new mixture in vessel C containing spirit and water in the ratio 8 : 5 ?

    (*a*) 4 : 3 (*b*) 3 : 4
    (*c*) 5 : 6 (*d*) 7 : 9

11. Two vessels A and B contain milk and water mixed in the ratio 8 : 5 and 5 : 2 respectively. The ratio in which these two mixtures be mixed to get a new mixture containing $69\frac{3}{13}\%$ milk, is

    (*a*) 2 : 7 (*b*) 3 : 5
    (*c*) 5 : 2 (*d*) 5 : 7

12. A milk vendor has 2 cans of milk. The first contains 25% water and the rest milk. The second contains 50% water. How much milk should he mix from each of the containers so as to get 12 litres of milk such that the ratio of water to milk is 3 : 5 ?

    (*a*) 4 litres, 8 litres (*b*) 6 litres, 6 litres
    (*c*) 5 litres, 7 litres (*d*) 7 litres, 5 litres

13. One quality of wheat at ₹ 9.30 per kg is mixed with another quality at a certain rate in the ratio 8 : 7. If the mixture so formed be worth ₹ 10 per kg, what is the rate per kg of the second quality of wheat ?
(a) ₹ 10.30 (b) ₹ 10.60
(c) ₹ 10.80 (d) ₹ 11

14. Tea worth ₹ 126 per kg and ₹ 135 per kg are mixed with a third variety in the ratio 1 : 1 : 2. If the mixture is worth ₹ 153 per kg, the price of the third variety per kg will be :
(a) ₹ 169.50 (b) ₹ 170
(c) ₹ 175.50 (d) ₹ 180

15. A merchant has 1000 kg of sugar, part of which he sells at 8% profit and the rest at 18% profit. He gains 14% on the whole. The quantity sold at 18% profit is
(a) 400 kg (b) 560 kg
(c) 600 kg (d) 640 kg

16. A jar full of whisky contains 40% alcohol. A part of this whisky is replaced by another containing 19% alcohol and now the percentage of alcohol was found to be 26%. The quantity of whisky replaced is :
(a) $\frac{1}{3}$ (b) $\frac{2}{3}$
(c) $\frac{2}{5}$ (d) $\frac{3}{5}$

17. A container contains 40 litres of milk. From this container 4 litres of milk was taken out and replaced by water. This process was repeated further two times. How much milk is now contained by the container ?
(a) 26.34 litres (b) 27.36 litres
(c) 28 litres (d) 29.16 litres

18. 8 litres are drawn from a cask full of wine and is then filled with water. This operation is performed three more times. The ratio of the quantity of wine now left in cask to that of the water is 16 : 65. How much wine did the cask hold originally ?
(a) 18 litres (b) 24 litres
(c) 32 litres (d) 42 litres

19. A can contains a mixture of two liquids A and B in the ratio 7 : 5. When 9 litres of mixture are drawn off and the can is filled with B, the ratio of A and B becomes 7 : 9. How many litres of liquid A was contained by the can initially?
(a) 10 (b) 20
(c) 21 (d) 25

20. A vessel is filled with liquid, 3 parts of which are water and 5 parts syrup. How much of the mixture must be drawn off and replaced with water so that the mixture may be half water and half syrup ?
(a) $\frac{1}{3}$ (b) $\frac{1}{4}$
(c) $\frac{1}{5}$ (d) $\frac{1}{7}$

21. A milkman mixed some water with milk to gain 25% by selling the mixture at the cost price. The ratio of water and milk is respectively
[SSC—CHSL (10+2) Exam, 2015]
(a) 5 : 4 (b) 4 : 5
(c) 1 : 5 (d) 1 : 4

22. 20 litres of a mixture contains milk and water in the ratio 3 : 1. Then the amount of milk to be added to the mixture so as to have milk and water in ratio 4 : 1 is **[SSC—CHSL (10+2) Exam, 2015]**
(a) 7 litres (b) 4 litres
(c) 5 litres (d) 6 litres

23. A vessel contains a mixture of Grape, Pineapple and Banana juices in the respective ratio of 4 : 6 : 5. 15 litres of this mixture is taken out and 8 litres of grape juice and 2 litres of pineapple juice is added to the vessel. If the resultant quantity of grape juice is 10 litres less than the resultant quantity of pineapple juice, what was the initial quantity of mixture in the vessel? (in litres)
[IBPS—Bank PO/MT (Pre.) Exam, 2015]
(a) 120 (b) 150
(c) 105 (d) 135

24. The respective ratio of milk and water in the mixture is 4 : 3. If 6 Litres of water is added to this mixture, the respective ratio of milk and water becomes 8 : 7. What is the quantity of milk in the original mixture?
[IBPS—RRB Office Assistant (Online) Exam, 2015]
(a) 36 litres (b) 84 litres
(c) 48 litres (d) None of these

25. 35 kg of type A sandal powder, which costs ₹ 614 per kg, was mixed with a certain amount of type B sandal powder, which costs ₹ 695 per kg. Then the mixture was sold at the rate of ₹ 767 per kg and 18% profit was earned. What was the amount (in kg) of type B sandal powder in the mixture?
[IBPS—Bank Spl. Officer (IT) Exam, 2015]
(a) 24 (b) 28
(c) 32 (d) 36

26. How many liters of water should be added to a 30 litre mixture of milk and water containing milk and water in the ratio of 7 : 3 such that the resultant mixture has 40% water in it?
[SSC—Junior Associates (Pre.) Exam, 2016]
(a) 5 (b) 2
(c) 3 (d) 8

ANSWERS

1. (*c*)	2. (*b*)	3. (*a*)	4. (*a*)	5. (*a*)	6. (*a*)	7. (*d*)	8. (*a*)	9. (*c*)	10. (*d*)
11. (*a*)	12. (*b*)	13. (*c*)	14. (*c*)	15. (*c*)	16. (*b*)	17. (*d*)	18. (*b*)	19. (*c*)	20. (*c*)
21. (*d*)	22. (*c*)	23. (*d*)	24. (*d*)	25. (*b*)	26. (*a*)				

SOLUTIONS

1. By the rule of alligation :

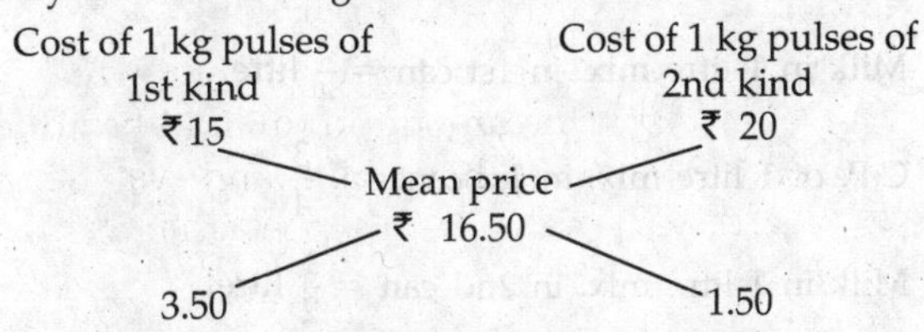

∴ Required rate = 3.50 : 1.50 = 35 : 15 = 7 : 3.

2. By the rule of alligation :

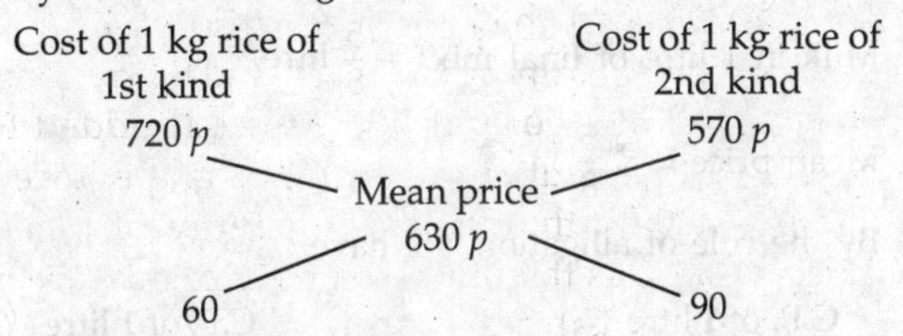

∴ Required ratio = 60 : 90 = 2 : 3.

3. By the rule of alligation :

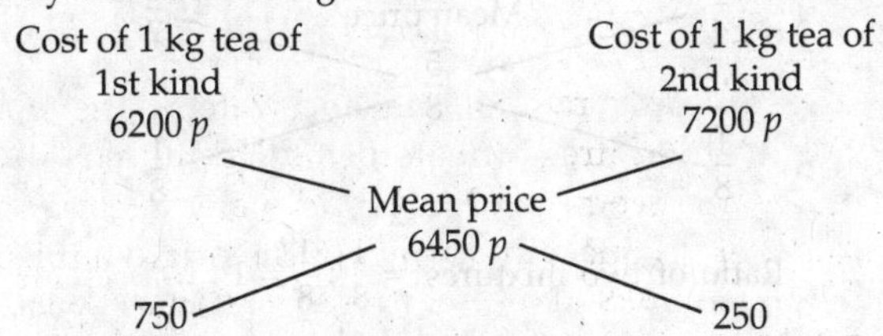

∴ Required ratio = 750 : 250 = 3 : 1.

4. By the rule of alligation :

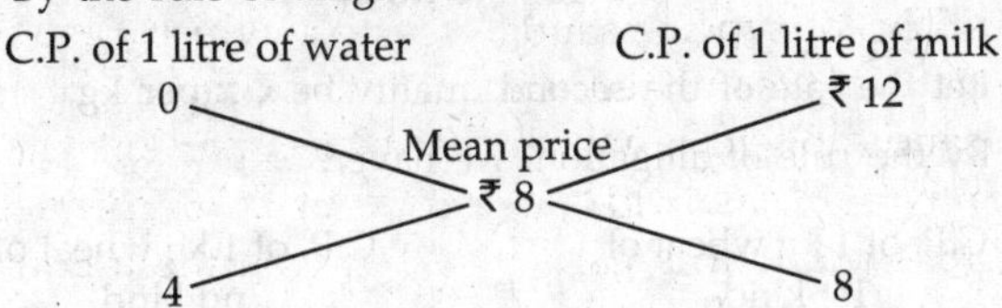

Ratio of water to milk = 4 : 8 = 1 : 2.

5. Let the price of the mixed variety be ₹ x per kg.

By the rule of alligation, we have :

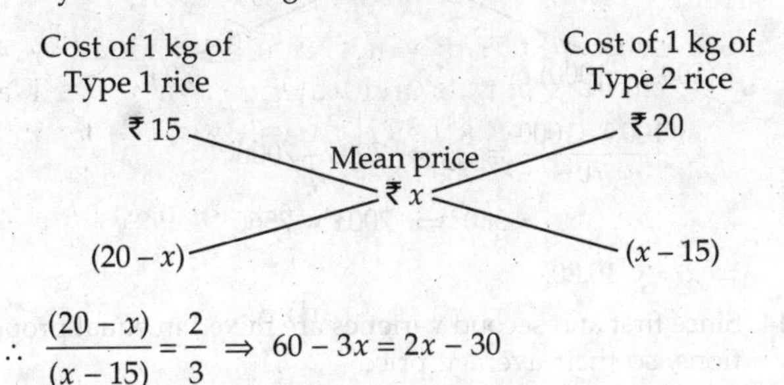

$\therefore \quad \frac{(20-x)}{(x-15)} = \frac{2}{3} \Rightarrow 60 - 3x = 2x - 30$

$\Rightarrow 5x = 90 \Rightarrow x = 18.$

So, price of the mixture is ₹ 18 per kg.

6. S.P. of 1 kg of the mixture = ₹ 68.20, Gain = 10 %.

C.P. of 1 kg of the mixture = ₹ $\left(\frac{100}{110} \times 68.20\right)$ = ₹ 62.

By the rule of alligation, we have :

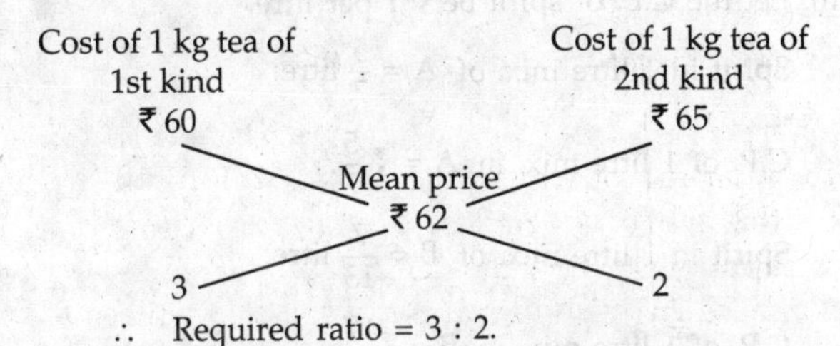

∴ Required ratio = 3 : 2.

7. S.P. of 1 kg of mixture = ₹ 9.24, Gain = 10%.

∴ C.P. of 1 kg of mixture = ₹ $\left(\frac{100}{110} \times 9.24\right)$ = ₹ 8.40.

By the rule of alligation, we have :

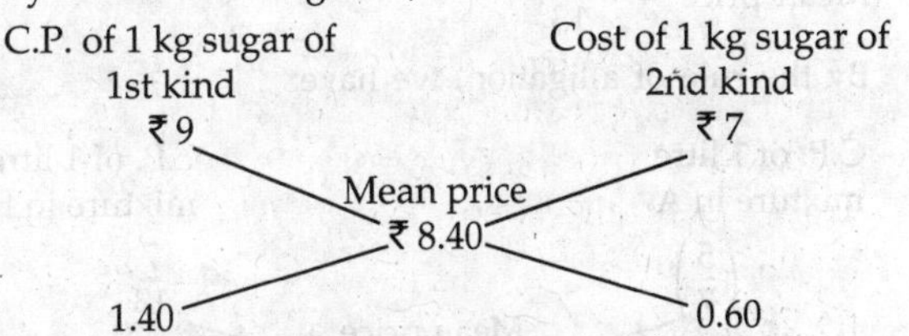

∴ Ratio of quantities of 1st and 2nd kind= 14 : 6 = 7 : 3.

Let x kg of sugar of 1st kind be mixed with 27 kg of 2nd kind.

Then, 7 : 3 = x : 27 or $x = \left(\frac{7 \times 27}{3}\right)$ = 63 kg.

8. Let C.P. of 1 litre milk be ₹ 1.

S.P. of 1 litre of mixture = ₹ 1, Gain = $\frac{50}{3}$%.

∴ C.P. of 1 litre of mixture = $\left(100 \times \frac{3}{350} \times 1\right)$ = ₹ $\frac{6}{7}$.

By the rule of alligation, we have :

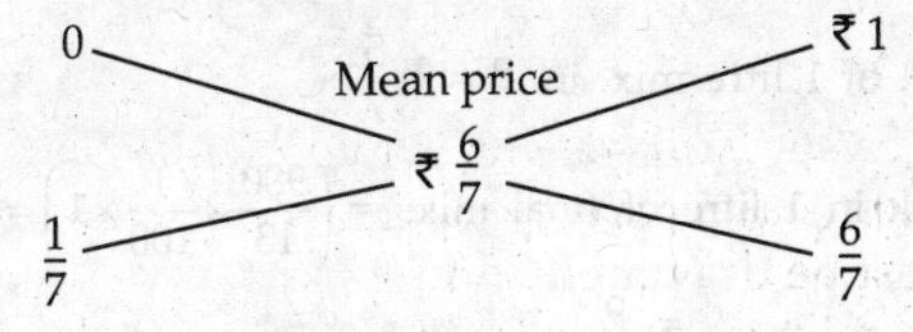

∴ Ratio of water and milk = $\frac{1}{7} : \frac{6}{7}$ = 1 : 6.

9. Let C.P. of 1 litre milk be ₹ 1.

Then, S.P. of 1 litre of mixture = ₹ 1, Gain = 25%.

C.P. of 1 litre mixture = ₹ $\left(\frac{100}{125}\times 1\right)$ = ₹ $\frac{4}{5}$.

C.P. of 1 litre of milk C.P. of 1 litre of water

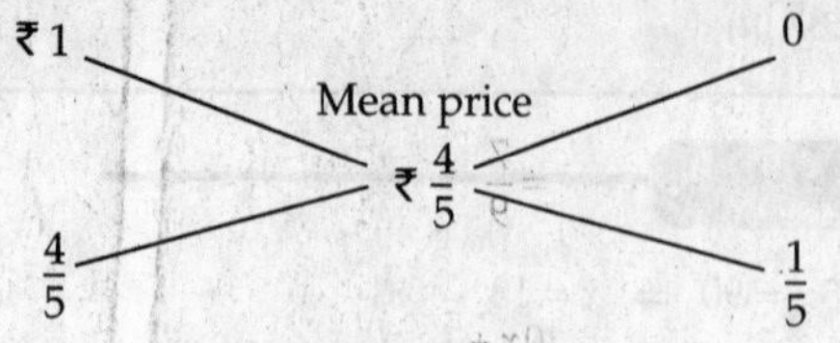

∴ Ratio of milk to water = $\frac{4}{5}:\frac{1}{5}$ = 4 : 1.

Hence, percentage of water in the mixture

$= \left(\frac{1}{5}\times 100\right)\% = 20\%.$

10. Let the C.P. of spirit be ₹ 1 per litre.

Spirit in 1 litre mix. of A = $\frac{5}{7}$ litre;

C.P. of 1 litre mix. in A = ₹ $\frac{5}{7}$.

Spirit in 1 litre mix. of B = $\frac{7}{13}$ litre;

C.P. of 1 litre mix. in B = ₹ $\frac{7}{13}$.

Spirit in 1 litre mix. of C = $\frac{8}{13}$ litre;

Mean price = ₹ $\frac{8}{13}$.

By the rule of alligation, we have:

C.P. of 1 litre mixture in A C.P. of 1 litre mixture in B

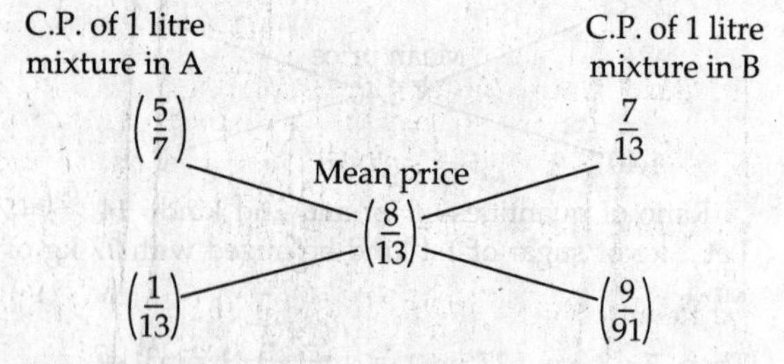

∴ Required ratio = $\frac{1}{13}:\frac{9}{91}$ = 7 : 9.

11. Let cost of 1 litre milk be ₹ 1.

Milk in 1 litre mix. in A = $\frac{8}{13}$ litre,

C.P. of 1 litre mix. in A = ₹ $\frac{8}{13}$.

Milk in 1 litre mix. in B = $\frac{5}{7}$ litre,

C.P. of 1 litre mix. in B = ₹ $\frac{5}{7}$.

Milk in 1 litre of final mix. = $\left(\frac{900}{13}\times\frac{1}{100}\times 1\right) = \frac{9}{13}$ litre;

Mean price = ₹ $\frac{9}{13}$.

By the rule of alligation, we have :

C.P. of 1 litre mixture in A C.P. of 1 litre mixture in B

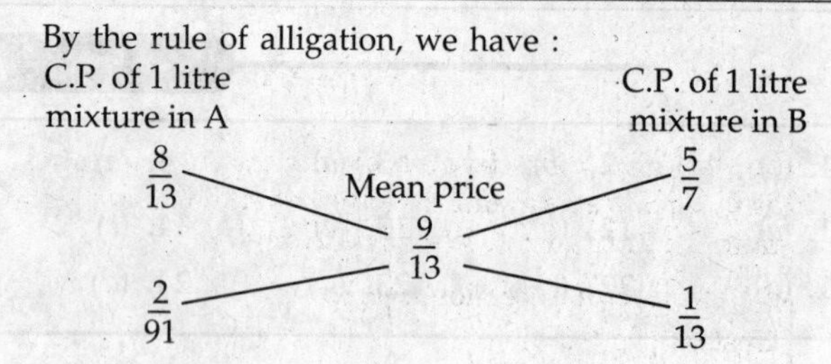

∴ Required ratio = $\frac{2}{91}:\frac{1}{13}$ = 2 : 7.

12. Let cost of 1 litre milk be ₹ 1.

Milk in 1 litre mix. in 1st can = $\frac{3}{4}$ litre,

C.P. of 1 litre mix. in 1st can = ₹ $\frac{3}{4}$.

Milk in 1 litre mix. in 2nd can = $\frac{1}{2}$ litre,

C.P. of 1 litre mix. in 2nd can = ₹ $\frac{1}{2}$.

Milk in 1 litre of final mix. = $\frac{5}{8}$ litre,

Mean price = ₹ $\frac{5}{8}$.

By the rule of alligation, we have :

C.P. of 1 litre mixture in 1st can C.P. of 1 litre mixture in 2nd can

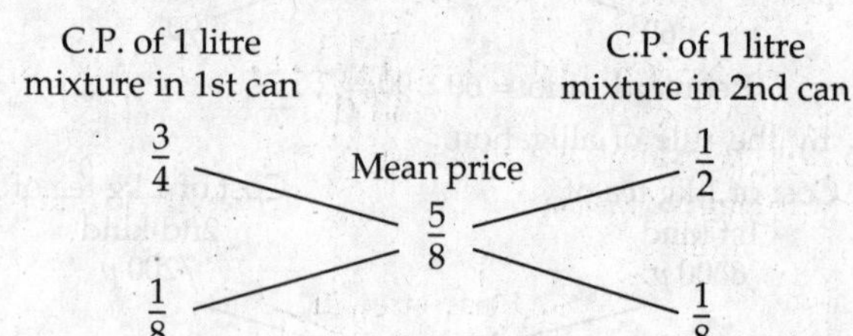

∴ Ratio of two mixtures = $\frac{1}{8}:\frac{1}{8}$ = 1 : 1.

So, quantity of mixture taken from each can

$= \left(\frac{1}{2}\times 12\right) = 6$ litres.

13. Let the rate of the second quality be ₹ x per kg.

By the rule of alligation, we have :

C.P. of 1 kg wheat of 1st kind C.P. of 1 kg wheat of 2nd kind

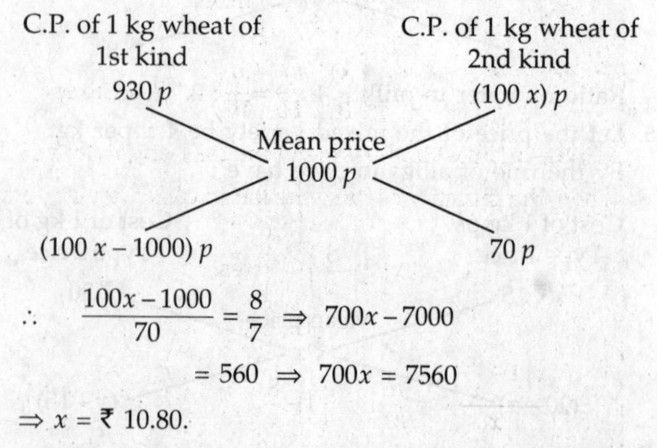

∴ $\frac{100x-1000}{70} = \frac{8}{7} \Rightarrow 700x - 7000$

$= 560 \Rightarrow 700x = 7560$

$\Rightarrow x =$ ₹ 10.80.

14. Since first and second varieties are mixed in equal proportions, so their average price

$= ₹\left(\frac{126+135}{2}\right) = ₹\ 130.50.$

So, the mixture is formed by mixing two varieties, one at ₹ 130.50 per kg and the other at say, ₹ x per kg in the ratio 2 : 2, *i.e.*, 1 : 1. We have to find x.

By the rule of alligation, we have :

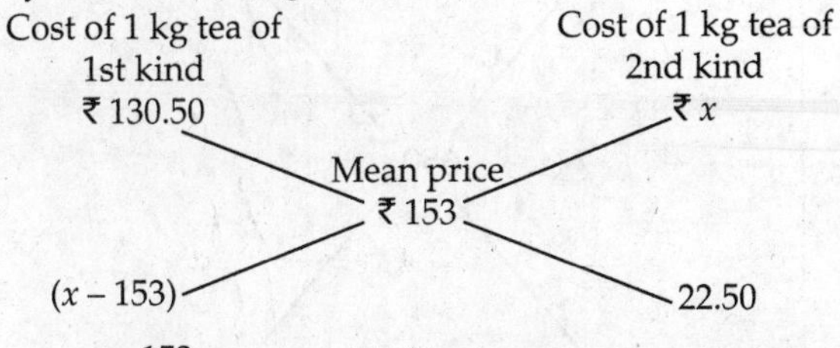

$\therefore \quad \frac{x-153}{22.50} = 1 \Rightarrow x - 153 = 22.50 \Rightarrow x = 175.50.$

Hence, price of the third variety = ₹ 175.50 per kg.

15. By the rule of alligation, we have :

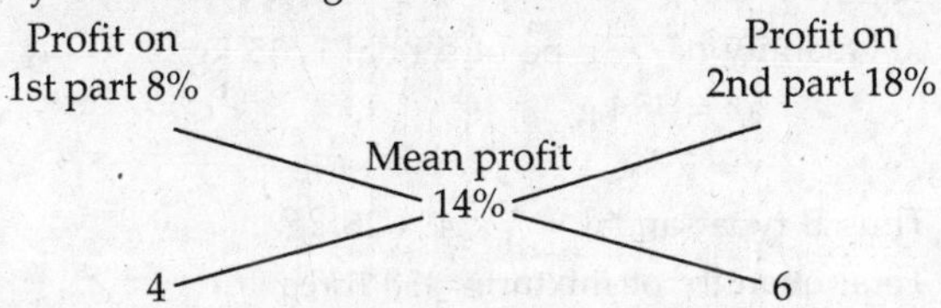

Ratio of 1st and 2nd parts = 4 : 6 = 2 : 3.

$\therefore \quad$ Quantity of 2nd kind $= \left(\frac{3}{5}\times 1000\right)$ kg = 600 kg.

16. By the rule of alligation, we have :

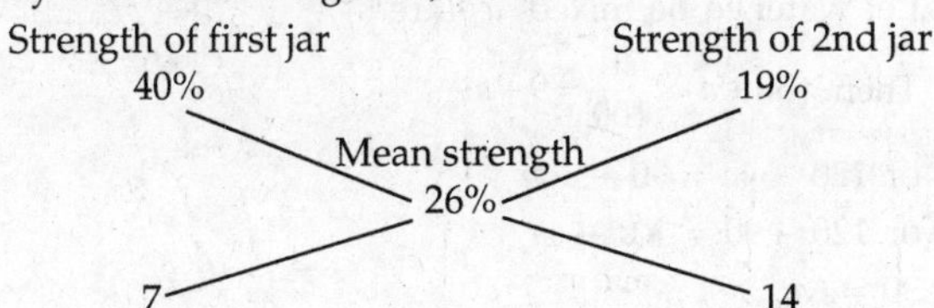

So, ratio of 1st and 2nd quantities = 7 : 14 = 1 : 2.

$\therefore \quad$ Required quantity replaced $= \frac{2}{3}.$

17. Amount of milk left after 3 operations

$= \left[40\left(1-\frac{4}{40}\right)^3\right]$ litres

$= \left(40\times\frac{9}{10}\times\frac{9}{10}\times\frac{9}{10}\right) = 29.16$ litres.

18. Let the quantity of the wine in the cask originally be x litres. Then, the quantity of the wine left in cask after 4 operations

$= \left[x\left(1-\frac{8}{x}\right)^4\right]$ litres.

$\therefore \quad \frac{x\left(1-\frac{8}{x}\right)^4}{x} = \frac{16}{81} \Rightarrow \left(1-\frac{8}{x}\right)^4 = \left(\frac{2}{3}\right)^2 \Rightarrow \left(\frac{x-8}{x}\right) = \frac{2}{3}$

$\Rightarrow 3x - 24 = 2x \Rightarrow x = 24.$

19. Suppose the can initially contains $7x$ and $5x$ litres of mixtures A and B respectively.

Quantity of A in mixture left

$= \left(7x - \frac{7}{12}\times 9\right)$ litres $= \left(7x - \frac{21}{4}\right)$ litres.

Quantity of B in mixture left

$= \left(5x - \frac{5}{12}\times 9\right)$ litres $= \left(5x - \frac{15}{4}\right)$ litres.

$\therefore \quad \frac{\left(7x-\frac{21}{4}\right)}{\left(5x-\frac{15}{4}\right)+9} = \frac{7}{9} \Rightarrow \frac{28x-21}{20x+21} = \frac{7}{9}$

$\Rightarrow 252x - 189 = 140x + 147$

$\Rightarrow 112x = 336 \Rightarrow x = 3.$

So, the can contained 21 litres of A.

20. Suppose the vessel initially contains 8 litres of liquid. Let x litres of this liquid be replaced with water.

Quantity of water in new mixture $= \left(3 - \frac{3x}{8} + x\right)$ litres.

Quantity of syrup in new mixture $= \left(5 - \frac{5x}{8}\right)$ litres.

$\therefore \quad \left(3 - \frac{3x}{8} + x\right) = \left(5 - \frac{5x}{8}\right)$

$\Rightarrow 5x + 24 = 40 - 5x$

$\Rightarrow 10x = 16 \Rightarrow x = \frac{8}{5}.$

So, part of the mixture replaced $= \left(\frac{8}{5}\times\frac{1}{8}\right) = \frac{1}{5}.$

21. C.P. of 1 litres of milk = ₹ 100

$\therefore$ Mixture sold for ₹ 125

$= \frac{125}{100} = \frac{5}{4}$ liters

$\therefore$ Quantity of mixture $= \frac{5}{4}$ liters

$\therefore$ Quantity of milk = 1 liters

$\therefore$ Quantity of water $= \frac{5}{4} - 1 = \frac{1}{4}$ liters

$\therefore$ Required ratio $= \frac{1}{4} : 1$

$= 1 : 4$

22. In 20 litres of mixture.

Quantity of Milk $\Rightarrow \frac{3}{4}\times 20 = 15$ liters

Quantity of Water $\Rightarrow \frac{1}{4}\times 20 = 5$ liters

Let the quantity of milk added be x liters.

According to the question,

$\frac{15+x}{5} = \frac{4}{1}$

$\Rightarrow 15 + x = 4 \times 5$

$\Rightarrow x = 20 - 15 = 5$ liters

23. Let quantity of grape, pineapple and banana juice in the mixture be $4x$, $6x$ and $5x$ respectively

Total initial quantity of juice in the vessel

$= 4x + 6x + 5x = 15x$ liters

In 15 liters of juice,
Grape's juice = 4 liters
Pineapple's juice = 6 liters
Banana's juice = 5 liters
Resultant quantity of grape juice is 10 liters less than the resultant quantity of pineapple juice.

$\Rightarrow (6x-6+2)-(4x-4+8)=10$

$\Rightarrow 6x-4-4x-4=10$

$\Rightarrow 2x-8=10$

$\Rightarrow 2x=10+8=18$

$\Rightarrow x=9$

$\therefore$ Initial quantity of mixture = $15x$
= 15 × 9 = 135 liters

24. Let the quantity of milk and water in initial mixture be $4x$ and $3x$ liters.
Quantity of water = $3x$ liters
On adding 6 liters of water, we get

$\frac{4x}{3x+6}=\frac{8}{7}$

$\Rightarrow 28x = 24x + 48$

$\Rightarrow 28x - 24x = 48$

$\Rightarrow 4x = 48$

$\Rightarrow x=\frac{48}{4}=12$

$\therefore$ Required quantity of milk
= $4x$ = 4 × 12 = 48 liters.

25. Cost price of mixture

$=\frac{\text{Sale price}}{(100+\text{gain\%})}\times 100=\frac{767}{118}\times 100=₹\,650$

By using allegation method:

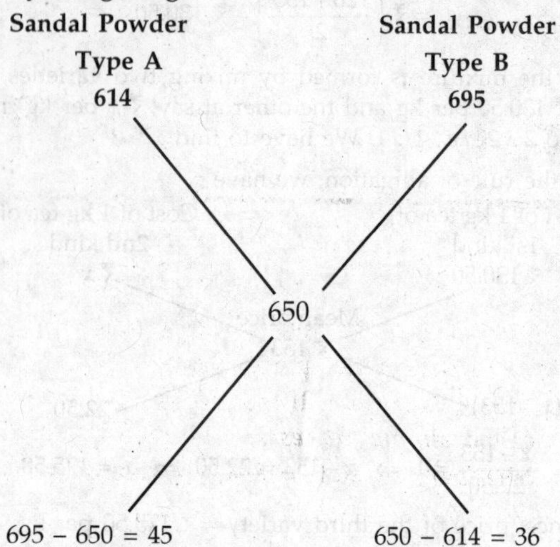

695 – 650 = 45 650 – 614 = 36

Ratio = 5 : 4

$\therefore$ Quantity of A type of sandal is 35 kg

$\therefore$ $5x = 35$ kg

$\therefore$ $x = 7$ kg

Thus B type sandal = 7 × 4 = 28 kg

26. Total quantity of mixture = 30 litres

Quantity Milk in the mixture = $\frac{7}{7+3}\times 30$ litre = 21 litres

and quantity water in the mixture = $\frac{3}{7+3}\times 30$ litre = 9 litres

Let water to be mixed 'a' litre

Then $(30+a)\times\frac{40}{100}=9+a$

or $120 + 4a = 90 + 10a$

or $120 - 90 = 10a - 4a$

$30 = 6a$

$\Rightarrow a = 5$

Hence, 5 litres water mixed in the mixture.

22 Simple Interest

IMPORTANT FACTS AND FORMULAE

I. **Principal:** The money borrowed or lent out for a certain period is called the ***principal*** or the ***sum.***

II. **Interest:** Extra money paid for using other's money is called ***interest.***

III. **Simple Interest (S.I.):** If the interest on a sum borrowed for a certain period is reckoned uniformly, then it is called ***simple interest.***

Let Principal = P, Rate = R% per annum (p.a.) and Time = T years.

Then, (i) $\text{S.I.} = \left(\frac{P \times R \times T}{100}\right)$.

(ii) $P = \left(\frac{100 \times S.I.}{R \times T}\right)$; $R = \left(\frac{100 \times S.I.}{P \times T}\right)$ and $T = \left(\frac{100 \times S.I.}{P \times R}\right)$.

SOLVED EXAMPLES

Ex. 1. ***Find the simple interest on ₹ 68000 at $16\frac{2}{3}$% per annum for 9 months.***

Sol. $P = ₹\ 68000$, $R = \frac{50}{3}$% p.a. and $T = \frac{9}{12}$ years $= \frac{3}{4}$ years.

$\therefore$ $\text{S.I.} = \left(\frac{P \times R \times T}{100}\right) = ₹\left(68000 \times \frac{50}{3} \times \frac{3}{4} \times \frac{1}{100}\right) = ₹\ 8500.$

Ex. 2. ***Find the simple interest on ₹ 3000 at $6\frac{1}{4}$% per annum for the period from 4th Feb., 2009 to 18th April, 2009.***

Sol. Time = (24 + 31 + 18) days = 73 days = $\frac{73}{365}$ year $= \frac{1}{5}$ year.

$P = ₹\ 3000$ and $R = 6\frac{1}{4}$% p.a. $= \frac{25}{4}$% p.a.

$\therefore$ $\text{S.I.} = ₹\left(3000 \times \frac{25}{4} \times \frac{1}{5} \times \frac{1}{100}\right) = ₹\ 37.50.$

Remark : The day on which money is deposited is not counted while the day on which money is withdrawn is counted.

Ex. 3. ***A sum at simple interest at $13\frac{1}{2}$% per annum amounts to ₹ 2502.50 after 4 years. Find the sum.***

Sol. Let sum be ₹ x. Then, $\text{S.I.} = ₹\left(x \times \frac{27}{2} \times 4 \times \frac{1}{100}\right) = ₹\ \frac{27x}{50}$.

$\therefore$ Amount $= ₹\left(x + \frac{27x}{50}\right) = ₹\ \frac{77x}{50}$.

$\therefore$ $\frac{77x}{50} = 2502.50 \Leftrightarrow x = \frac{2502.50 \times 50}{77} = 1625.$

Hence, sum = ₹ 1625.

Ex. 4. ***The simple interest accrued on an amount of ₹ 2500 at the end of 6 years is ₹ 1875. What would be the simple interest accrued on an amount of ₹ 6875 at the same rate and for the same period?*** **(Bank P.O., 2009)**

Sol. P = ₹ 2500, T = 6 years, S.I. = ₹ 1875.

$\therefore$ Rate $= \left(\frac{100 \times 1875}{2500 \times 6}\right)\% = 12\frac{1}{2}\%$.

Now, P = ₹ 6875, T = 6 years, $R = 12\frac{1}{2}\%$.

$\therefore$ S.I. = ₹ $\left(\frac{6875 \times 25 \times 6}{100 \times 2}\right)$ = ₹ 5156.25.

Ex. 5. ***A sum of ₹ 800 amounts to ₹ 920 in 3 years at simple interest. If the interest rate is increased by 3%, it would amount to how much ?***

Sol. S.I. = ₹ (920 – 800) = ₹ 120; P = ₹ 800, T = 3 years

$\therefore$ $R = \left(\frac{100 \times 120}{800 \times 3}\right)\% = 5\%$. New rate = (5 + 3)% = 8%.

New S.I. = ₹ $\left(\frac{800 \times 8 \times 3}{100}\right)$ = ₹ 192.

$\therefore$ New amount = ₹ (800 + 192) = ₹ 992.

Ex. 6. ***Adam borrowed some money at the rate of 6% p.a. for the first two years, at the rate of 9% p.a. for the next three years, and at the rate of 14% p.a. for the period beyond five years. If he pays a total interest of ₹ 11400 at the end of nine years, how much money did he borrow?***

Sol. Let the sum borrowed be x. Then,

$$\left(\frac{x \times 6 \times 2}{100}\right) + \left(\frac{x \times 9 \times 3}{100}\right) + \left(\frac{x \times 14 \times 4}{100}\right) = 11400$$

$$\Leftrightarrow \left(\frac{3x}{25} + \frac{27x}{100} + \frac{14x}{25}\right) = 11400 \Leftrightarrow \frac{95x}{100} = 11400 \Leftrightarrow x = \left(\frac{11400 \times 100}{95}\right) = 12000.$$

Hence, sum borrowed = ₹ 12,000.

Ex. 7. ***A certain sum of money amounts to ₹ 1008 in 2 years and to ₹ 1164 in $3\frac{1}{2}$ years. Find the sum and the rate of interest.***

Sol. S.I. for $1\frac{1}{2}$ years = ₹ (1164 – 1008) = ₹ 156.

S.I. for 2 years = ₹ $\left(156 \times \frac{2}{3} \times 2\right)$ = ₹ 208.

$\therefore$ Principal = ₹ (1008 – 208) = ₹ 800.

Now, P = ₹ 800, T = 2 years and S.I. = ₹ 208

$\therefore$ Rate $= \left(\frac{100 \times 208}{800 \times 2}\right)\% = 13\%$.

Ex. 8. ***At what rate of simple interest a certain sum will be doubled in 15 years?*** **(R.R.B., 2005)**

Sol. Let principal = P. Then, S.I. = P and T = 15 yrs.

$\therefore$ Rate $= \left(\frac{100 \times P}{P \times 15}\right)\% = 6\frac{2}{3}\%$.

Ex. 9. *On a certain sum, the simple interest at the end of $12\frac{1}{2}$ years becomes $\frac{3}{4}$ of the sum. What is the rate of interest p.c.p.a?* **(Bank P.O., 2009)**

Sol. Let principal = P. Then, S.I. = $\frac{3}{4}P$ and $T = 12\frac{1}{2}$ yrs.

$$\therefore \quad \text{Rate} = \left(\frac{100 \times \frac{3}{4}P}{P \times \frac{25}{2}}\right)\% = \left(\frac{100 \times 3 \times 2}{4 \times 25}\right)\% = 6\%.$$

Ex. 10. *In how many years will a sum of money double itself at $6\frac{1}{4}\%$ simple interest per annum?* **(S.S.C., 2010)**

Sol. Let principal = P. Then, S.I. = P and $R = 6\frac{1}{4}\%$.

$$\therefore \quad \text{Time} = \left(\frac{100 \times P}{P \times \frac{25}{4}}\right)\text{yrs} = \left(\frac{100 \times 4}{25}\right)\text{yrs} = 16 \text{ yrs}.$$

Ex. 11. *A certain sum of money becomes three times of itself in 20 years at simple interest. In how many years does it become double of itself at the same rate of simple interest?* **(C.P.O., 2005)**

Sol. Let principal = P. Then, S.I. = $2P$ and T = 20 yrs.

$$\therefore \quad \text{Rate} = \left(\frac{100 \times 2P}{P \times 20}\right)\% = 10\%.$$

Now, principal = P, S.I. = P, R = 10%.

$$\therefore \quad \text{Time} = \left(\frac{100 \times P}{P \times 10}\right)\text{yrs} = 10 \text{ yrs}.$$

Ex. 12. *The simple interest on a sum of money is $\frac{4}{9}$ of the principal. Find the rate percent and time, if both are numerically equal.* **(S.S.C., 2000)**

Sol. Let sum = ₹ x. Then, S.I. = ₹ $\frac{4x}{9}$.

Let rate = R% and time = R years.

Then, $\left(\frac{x \times R \times R}{100}\right) = \frac{4x}{9}$ or $R^2 = \frac{400}{9}$ or $R = \frac{20}{3} = 6\frac{2}{3}$.

$\therefore$ Rate = $6\frac{2}{3}\%$ and Time = $6\frac{2}{3}$ yrs = 6 yrs 8 months.

Ex. 13. *The simple interest on a certain sum of money for $2\frac{1}{2}$ years at 12% per annum is ₹ 40 less than the simple interest on the same sum for $3\frac{1}{2}$ years at 10% per annum. Find the sum.*

Sol. Let the sum be ₹ x. Then, $\left(\frac{x \times 10 \times 7}{100 \times 2}\right) - \left(\frac{x \times 12 \times 5}{100 \times 2}\right) = 40$

$$\Leftrightarrow \quad \frac{7x}{20} - \frac{3x}{10} = 40 \quad \Leftrightarrow \quad x = (40 \times 20) = 800.$$

Hence, the sum is ₹ 800.

Ex. 14. ***A sum was put at simple interest at a certain rate for 3 years. Had it been put at 2% higher rate, it would have fetched ₹ 360 more. Find the sum.***

Sol. Let sum = P and original rate = R. Then, $\left[\frac{P\times(R+2)\times 3}{100}\right]-\left[\frac{P\times R\times 3}{100}\right]=360$

$\Leftrightarrow\ 3PR + 6P - 3PR = 36000 \ \Leftrightarrow\ 6P = 36000 \ \Leftrightarrow\ P = 6000.$

Hence, sum = ₹ 6000.

Ex. 15. ***What annual instalment will discharge a debt of ₹ 1092 due in 3 years at 12% simple interest ?***

Sol. Let each instalment be ₹ x. Then, $\left(x+\frac{x\times 12\times 1}{100}\right)+\left(x+\frac{x\times 12\times 2}{100}\right)+x=1092$

$\Leftrightarrow\ \frac{28x}{25}+\frac{31x}{25}+x = 1092 \Leftrightarrow (28x + 31x + 25x) = (1092 \times 25)$

$\Leftrightarrow\ x = \left(\frac{1092\times 25}{84}\right)=325.$

$\therefore$ Each instalment = ₹ 325.

Ex. 16. ***A sum of ₹ 1550 is lent out into two parts, one at 8% and another one at 6%. If the total annual income is ₹ 106, find the money lent at each rate.***

Sol. Let the sum lent at 8% be ₹ x and that at 6% be ₹ $(1550 - x)$.

$\therefore\ \left[\frac{x\times 8\times 1}{100}\right]+\left[\frac{(1550-x)\times 6\times 1}{100}\right]=106$

$\Leftrightarrow\ 8x + 9300 - 6x = 10600 \ \Leftrightarrow\ 2x = 1300 \ \Leftrightarrow\ x = 650.$

$\therefore$ Money lent at 8% = ₹ 650. Money lent at 6% = ₹ (1550 − 650) = ₹ 900.

Ex. 17. ***Ashish borrowed a sum of money from a nationalised bank at 12% simple interest per annum and the same amount at 10% simple interest per annum both for the same period. He cleared the first loan 6 months before the scheduled date of repayment and repaid the second loan just at the end of the scheduled period. If in each case he had to pay ₹ 3250 as amount then how much and for what time did he borrow?*** (P.C.S., 2006)

Sol. Let each sum = ₹ x.

Let first sum be invested for T years and the second sum for $\left(T-\frac{1}{2}\right)$ years.

Then, $x+\frac{x\times 12\times\left(T-\frac{1}{2}\right)}{100} = 3250$

$\Rightarrow\ 100x + 12xT - 6x = 3250000$

$\Rightarrow\ 94x + 12xT = 32500$ ...(i)

And, $x+\frac{x\times 10\times T}{100} = 3250 \Rightarrow 100x + 10xT = 325000$ ...(ii)

From (i) and (ii), we get: $94x + 12xT = 100x + 10xT \Rightarrow 6x = 2xT$

$\Rightarrow\ 2T = 6 \Rightarrow T = 3.$

Putting $T = 3$ in (i), we get: $94x + 36x = 325000 \Rightarrow 130x = 325000 \Rightarrow x = 2500.$

Ex. 18. ***A person lends out ₹ 9000 on the condition that the loan is payable in 10 months by 10 monthly equal instalments of ₹ 1000 each. Find the rate of simple interest charged.*** (S.S.C., 2006)

Sol. We have:

₹ 9000 + S.I. on ₹ 9000 for 10 months

= ₹ 10000 + S.I. on ₹ 1000 for (1 + 2 +...+ 9) months.

$\Rightarrow$ ₹ 9000 + S.I. on ₹ 1000 for 90 months

= ₹ 10000 + S.I. on ₹ 1000 for 45 months

$\Rightarrow$ S.I. on ₹ 1000 for 45 months = ₹ 1000.

$\therefore\ \text{Rate} = \left(\frac{100\times 1000\times 12}{1000\times 45}\right)\% = \frac{80}{3}\% = 26\frac{2}{3}\%.$

Ex. 19. *A man invested $\frac{1}{3}$ of his capital at 7%; $\frac{1}{4}$ at 8% and the remainder at 10%. If his annual income is ₹ 561, find the capital.* (M.B.A., 2006)

Sol. Let the total capital be ₹ x.

Then, $\left(\frac{x}{3}\times\frac{7}{100}\times 1\right)+\left(\frac{x}{4}\times\frac{8}{100}\times 1\right)+\left[\left\{1-\left(\frac{1}{3}+\frac{1}{4}\right)\right\}x\times\frac{10}{100}\times 1\right] = 561$

$\Rightarrow \frac{7x}{300}+\frac{x}{50}+\frac{x}{24} = 561 \Rightarrow 51x = 561 \times 600 \Rightarrow x = \left(\frac{561\times 600}{51}\right) = 6600.$

Hence, capital = ₹ 6600.

EXERCISE

(OBJECTIVE TYPE QUESTIONS)

Directions: *Mark (✓) against the correct answer:*

1. What would be the simple interest obtained on an amount of ₹ 5760 at the rate of 6 p.c.p.a. after 3 years.? (Bank Recruitment, 2007)
(a) ₹ 1036.80 (b) ₹ 1063.80
(c) ₹ 1336.80 (d) ₹ 1666.80
(e) None of these

2. A farmer borrowed ₹ 3600 at 15% simple interest per annum. At the end of 4 years, he cleared this account by paying ₹ 4000 and a cow. The cost of the cow is (Civil Services, 2006)
(a) ₹ 1000 (b) ₹ 1200
(c) ₹ 1550 (d) ₹ 1760

3. Ram borrows ₹ 520 from Gaurav at a simple interest of 13% per annum. What amount of money should Ram pay to Gaurav after 6 months to be absolved of the debt? (CLAT, 2010)
(a) ₹ 353.80 (b) ₹ 453.80
(c) ₹ 552.80 (d) ₹ 553.80

4. At the rate of $8\frac{1}{2}$% p.a. simple interest, a sum of ₹ 4800 will earn how much interest in 2 years 3 months?
(a) ₹ 796 (b) ₹ 816
(c) ₹ 918 (d) ₹ 956

5. What will be the simple interest earned on an amount of ₹ 16,800 in 9 months at the rate of $6\frac{1}{4}$% p.a. ?
(a) ₹ 787.50 (b) ₹ 812.50
(c) ₹ 860 (d) ₹ 887.50

6. The simple interest on ₹ 1820 from March 9, 2012 to May 21, 2012 at $7\frac{1}{2}$% rate will be
(a) ₹ 22.50 (b) ₹ 27.30
(c) ₹ 28.80 (d) ₹ 29

7. A shopkeeper with an overdraft facility at 18 percent with a bank borrowed ₹ 15000 on Jan 8, 2011 and returned the money on June 3, 2011 so as to clear the debt. The amount that he paid was
(a) ₹ 16080 (b) ₹ 16280
(c) ₹ 16400 (d) None of these

8. A person borrows ₹ 5000 for 2 years at 4% p.a. simple interest. He immediately lends it to another person at $6\frac{1}{4}$% p.a. for 2 years. Find his gain in the transaction per year. (S.S.C., 2005)
(a) ₹ 112.50 (b) ₹ 125
(c) ₹ 150 (d) ₹ 167.50

9. Ramakant invested amounts in two different schemes A and B for five years in the ratio of 5 : 4 respectively. Scheme A offers 8% simple interest and bonus equal to 20% of the amount of interest earned in 5 years on maturity. Scheme B offers 9% simple interest. If the amount invested in scheme A was ₹ 20000, what was the total amount received on maturity from both the schemes? (Bank P.O., 2005)
(a) ₹ 50800 (b) ₹ 51200
(c) ₹ 52800 (d) ₹ 58200
(e) None of these

10. ₹ 1000 is invested at 5% per annum simple interest. If the interest is added to the principal after every 10 years, the amount will become ₹ 2000 after (S.S.C., 2007)
(a) 15 years (b) $16\frac{2}{3}$ years
(c) 18 years (d) 20 years

11. How much time will it take for an amount of ₹ 450 to yield ₹ 81 as interest at 4.5% per annum of simple interest ? (IGNOU, 2003)
(a) 3.5 years (b) 4 years
(c) 4.5 years (d) 5 years

12. Asmita invests an amount of ₹ 9534 @ 4 p.c.p.a. to obtain a total amount of ₹ 11442 on simple interest after a certain period. For how many years did she invest the amount to obtain the total sum?
(M.A.T., 2009)
(a) 2 years (b) 4 years
(c) 5 years (d) 10 years

13. Deepak invested an amount of ₹ 21250 for 6 years. At what rate of simple interest will be obtain the total amount of ₹ 26350 at the end of 6 years?
(Bank Recruitment, 2008)
(a) 5 p.c.p.a (b) 6 p.c.p.a
(c) 8 p.c.p.a (d) 12 p.c.p.a
(e) None these

14. A sum of ₹ 1600 gives a simple interest of ₹ 252 in 2 years and 4 months. The rate of interest per annum is
(a) 6% (b) $6\frac{1}{4}\%$
(c) $6\frac{1}{2}\%$ (d) $6\frac{3}{4}\%$

15. At what rate of simple interest per annum can an amount of ₹ 1553.40 be obtained on the principal amount of ₹ 8630 after 3 years? (Bank Recruitment, 2007)
(a) 4 p.c.p.a (b) 5 p.c.p.a
(c) 7 p.c.p.a (d) 8 p.c.p.a
(e) None of these

16. If simple interest on ₹ 600 for 4 years and on ₹ 600 for 2 years combined together is ₹ 180, find the rate of interest. (R.R.B., 2009)
(a) 4% (b) 5%
(c) 5.5% (d) 6.25%

17. Veena obtained an amount of ₹ 8376 as simple interest on a certain amount at 8 p.c.p.a. after 6 years. What is the amount invested by Veena?
(S.B.I.P.O., 2008)
(a) ₹ 16660 (b) ₹ 17180
(c) ₹ 17450 (d) ₹ 18110
(e) None of these

18. At which sum the simple interest at the rate of $3\frac{3}{4}\%$ per annum will be ₹ 210 in $2\frac{1}{3}$ years?
(R.R.B., 2006)
(a) ₹ 1580 (b) ₹ 2400
(c) ₹ 2800 (d) None of these

19. What is the present worth of ₹ 132 due in 2 years at 5% simple interest per annum?
(a) ₹ 112 (b) ₹ 118.80
(c) ₹ 120 (d) ₹ 122

20. A sum fetched a total simple interest of ₹ 4016.25 at the rate of 9 p.c.p.a. in 5 years. What is the sum?
(a) ₹ 4462.50 (b) ₹ 8032.50
(c) ₹ 8900 (d) ₹ 8925
(e) None of these

21. The simple interest at x% for x years will be ₹ x on a sum of :
(a) ₹ x (b) ₹ $\left(\frac{100}{x}\right)$
(c) ₹ $100x$ (d) ₹ $\left(\frac{100}{x^2}\right)$

22. In 4 years, ₹ 6000 amounts to ₹ 8000. In what time at the same rate will ₹ 525 amount to ₹ 700?
(a) 2 years (b) 3 years
(c) 4 years (d) 5 years

23. ₹ 6200 amounts to ₹ 9176 in 4 years at simple interest. If the interest rate is increased by 3% it would amount to how much? (E.S.I.C., 2006)
(a) ₹ 8432 (b) ₹ 9820
(c) ₹ 9920 (d) ₹ 10920

24. Simple interest on ₹ 500 for 4 years at 6.25% per annum is equal to the simple interest on ₹ 400 at 5% per annum for a certain period of time. The period of time is (S.S.C., 2007)
(a) 4 years (b) 5 years
(c) $6\frac{1}{4}$ years (d) $8\frac{2}{3}$ years

25. A certain amount earns simple interest of ₹ 1750 after 7 years. Had the interest been 2% more, how much more interest would it have earned ?
(a) ₹ 35 (b) ₹ 245
(c) ₹ 350 (d) Cannot be determined
(e) None of these

26. ₹ 6000 becomes ₹ 7200 in 4 years at a certain rate of simple interest. If the rate becomes 1.5 times of itself, the amount of the same principal in 5 years will be (S.S.C., 2007)
(a) ₹ 8000 (b) ₹ 8250
(c) ₹ 9000 (d) ₹ 9250

27. In how many years, ₹ 150 will produce the same interest @ 8% as ₹ 800 produce in 3 years @ $4\frac{1}{2}\%$?
(a) 6 (b) 8
(c) 9 (d) 12

28. The simple interest accrued on a certain principal in 5 years at the rate of 12 p.c.p.a. is ₹ 1536. What amount of simple interest would one get if one invests ₹ 1000 more than the previous principal for 2 years and at the same rate p.c.p.a.?
(Bank Recruitment, 2010)

(*a*) ₹ 614.40 (*b*) ₹ 845.40
(*c*) ₹ 1536 (*d*) ₹ 2136
(*e*) None of these

29. If ₹ 64 amounts to ₹ 83.20 in 2 years, what will ₹ 86 amount to in 4 years at the same rate percent per annum ?
(*a*) ₹ 114.80 (*b*) ₹ 124.70
(*c*) ₹ 127.40 (*d*) ₹ 137.60

30. The simple interest on a certain sum of money at the rate of 5% p.a. for 8 years is ₹ 840. At what rate of interest the same amount of interest can be received on the same sum after 5 years ?
(*a*) 6% (*b*) 8%
(*c*) 9% (*d*) 10%

31. The interest on a certain deposit at 4.5% p.a. is ₹ 202.50 in one year. How much will the additional interest in one year be on the same deposit at 5% p.a. ?
(*a*) ₹ 20.25 (*b*) ₹ 22.50
(*c*) ₹ 25 (*d*) ₹ 42.75

32. A sum invested at 5% simple interest per annum grows to ₹ 504 in 4 years. The same amount at 10% simple interest per annum in $2\frac{1}{2}$ years will grow to :
(*a*) ₹ 420 (*b*) ₹ 450
(*c*) ₹ 525 (*d*) ₹ 550

33. If *x*, *y*, *z* are three sums of money such that *y* is the simple interest on *x*, *z* is the simple interest on *y* for the same time and at the same rate of interest, then we have **(G.B.O., 2007)**
(*a*) $x^2 = yz$ (*b*) $y^2 = xz$
(*c*) $z^2 = xy$ (*d*) $xyz = 1$

34. What will be the ratio of simple interest earned by certain amount at the same rate of interest for 6 years and that for 9 years ?
(*a*) 1 : 3 (*b*) 1 : 4
(*c*) 12 : 3 (*d*) Data inadequate
(*e*) None of these

35. Arun borrowed a sum of money from Jayant at the rate of 8% per annum simple interest for the first four years, 10% per annum for the next 6 years and 12% per annum for the period beyond 10 years. If he pays a total of ₹ 12160 as interest only at the end of 15 years, how much money did be borrow? **(N.M.A.T., 2005)**
(*a*) ₹ 8000 (*b*) ₹ 9000
(*c*) ₹ 10000 (*d*) ₹ 12000

36. Kruti took a loan at simple interest rate of 6 p.c.p.a. in the first year and it increased by 1.5 p.c.p.a. every year. If she pays ₹ 8190 as interest at the end of 3 years, what was her loan amount? **(Bank P.O., 2010)**
(*a*) ₹ 35400 (*b*) ₹ 36000
(*c*) ₹ 36800 (*d*) Cannot be determined
(*e*) None of these

37. A person deposited ₹ 400 for 2 years, ₹ 550 for 4 years and ₹ 1200 for 6 years. He received the total simple interest of ₹ 1020. The rate of interest per annum is **(S.S.C., 2007)**
(*a*) 5% (*b*) 10%
(*c*) 15% (*d*) 20%

38. The simple interest on a sum of money will be ₹ 600 after 10 years. If the principal is trebled after 5 years, what will be the total interest at the end of the tenth year?
(*a*) ₹ 600 (*b*) ₹ 900
(*c*) ₹ 1200 (*d*) ₹ 1500
(*e*) Data inadequate

39. The simple interest on ₹ 10 for 4 months at the rate of 3 paise per rupee per month is
(*a*) ₹ 1.20 (*b*) ₹ 1.60
(*c*) ₹ 2.40 (*d*) ₹ 3.60

40. An automobile financier claims to be lending money at simple interest, but he includes the interest every six months for calculating the principal. If he is charging an interest of 10%, the effective rate of interest becomes
(*a*) 10% (*b*) 10.25%
(*c*) 10.5% (*d*) None of these

41. A sum of money at simple interest amounts to ₹ 815 in 3 years and to ₹ 854 in 4 years. The sum is
(*a*) ₹ 650 (*b*) ₹ 690
(*c*) ₹ 698 (*d*) ₹ 700

42. A sum of money lent out at simple interest amounts to ₹ 720 after 2 years and to ₹ 1020 after a further period of 5 years. The sum is **(S.S.C., 2004)**
(*a*) ₹ 500 (*b*) ₹ 600
(*c*) ₹ 700 (*d*) ₹ 710

43. A sum of money amounts to ₹ 5200 in 5 years and to ₹ 5680 in 7 years at simple interest. The rate of interest per annum is : **(S.S.C., 2007)**
(*a*) 3% (*b*) 4%
(*c*) 5% (*d*) 6%

44. A sum of money becomes ₹ 20925 in 2 years and ₹ 24412.50 in 5 years. Find the rate of interest and the sum of money. **(R.R.B., 2006)**
(*a*) 6.25%, ₹ 18600 (*b*) 6.75%, ₹ 17775
(*c*) 7%, ₹ 18000 (*d*) 8%, ₹ 17560

45. A certain sum of money at simple interest amounts to ₹ 1012 in $2\frac{1}{2}$ years and to ₹ 1067.20 in 4 years.

The rate of interest per annum is

(a) 2.5% (b) 3%

(c) 4% (d) 5%

46. In how many years will a sum of money double itself at 18.75% per annum simple interest? (R.R.B., 2006)

(a) 4 years 5 months (b) 5 years 4 months

(c) 6 years 2 months (d) 6 years 5 months

47. At what rate percent of simple interest will a sum of money double itself in 12 years?

(a) $8\frac{1}{4}\%$ (b) $8\frac{1}{3}\%$

(c) $8\frac{1}{2}\%$ (d) $9\frac{1}{2}\%$

48. The rate at which a sum becomes four times of itself in 15 years at S.I., will be

(a) 15% (b) $17\frac{1}{2}\%$

(c) 20% (d) 25%

49. A sum of money at a simple rate of interest i_1, doubles in 5 years. At another simple rate of interest i_2, it becomes three times in 12 years. Then, the two rates of interest i_1 and i_2 respectively are

(a) 10%, $16\frac{2}{3}\%$ (b) 10%, 20%

(c) 20%, $16\frac{2}{3}\%$ (d) 20%, 30%

50. A sum of money at simple interest doubles in 7 years. It will become four times in: (R.R.B., 2006)

(a) 18 years (b) 21 years

(c) 38 years (d) 42 years

51. A sum of money trebles itself in 15 years 6 months. In how many years would it double itself ?

(a) 6 years 3 months (b) 7 years 9 months

(c) 8 years 3 months (d) 9 years 6 months

52. If a sum doubles in 6 years, how much will it be in 8 years? (R.R.B., 2006)

(a) $1\frac{1}{2}$ times (b) $1\frac{1}{3}$ times

(c) $1\frac{1}{4}$ times (d) $1\frac{3}{4}$ times

53. Consider the following statements

If a sum of money is lent at simple interest, then the

1. money gets doubled in 5 years if the rate of interest is $16\frac{2}{3}\%$
2. money gets doubled in 5 years if the rate of interest is 20%.
3. money becomes four times in 10 years if it gets doubled in 5 years.

Of these statements,

(a) 1 and 3 are correct (b) 2 alone is correct

(c) 3 alone is correct (d) 2 and 3 are correct

54. The simple interest on a sum of money at 8% per annum for 6 years is half the sum. The sum is :

(a) ₹ 4800 (b) ₹ 6000

(c) ₹ 8000 (d) Data inadequate

55. At what rate percent per annum will the simple interest on a sum of money be $\frac{2}{5}$ of the amount in 10 years ?

(a) 4% (b) $5\frac{2}{3}\%$

(c) 6% (d) $6\frac{2}{3}\%$

56. In how much time would the simple interest on a certain sum be 0.125 times the principal at 10% per annum ? (Assistant Grade, 1997)

(a) $1\frac{1}{4}$ years (b) $1\frac{3}{4}$ years

(c) $2\frac{1}{4}$ years (d) $2\frac{3}{4}$ years

57. How long will it take a sum of money invested at 5% p.a. S.I. to increase its value by 40%?

(a) 5 years (b) 6 years

(c) 7 years (d) 8 years

58. A sum of money becomes $\frac{7}{6}$ of itself in 3 years at a certain rate of simple interest. The rate per annum is

(a) $5\frac{5}{9}\%$ (b) $6\frac{5}{9}\%$

(c) 18% (d) 25%

59. If the simple interest for 6 years be equal to 30% of the principal, it will be equal to the principal after (Bank P.O., 2006)

(a) 10 years (b) 20 years

(c) 22 years (d) 30 years

60. Simple interest on a certain sum at a certain annual rate of interest is $\frac{1}{9}$ of the sum. If the numbers representing rate percent and time in years be equal, then the rate of interest is

(a) $3\frac{1}{3}\%$ (b) 5%

(c) $6\frac{2}{3}\%$ (d) 10%

61. Simple interest on a certain amount is $\frac{9}{16}$ of the principal. If the numbers representing the rate of interest in percent and time in years be equal, then time, for which the principal is lent out, is

(a) $5\frac{1}{2}$ years (b) $6\frac{1}{2}$ years
(c) 7 years (d) $7\frac{1}{2}$ years

62. A lends ₹ 2500 to B and a certain sum to C at the same time at 7% p.a. simple interest. If after 4 years, A altogether receives ₹ 1120 as interest from B and C, then the sum lent to C is :

(a) ₹ 700 (b) ₹ 1500
(c) ₹ 4000 (d) ₹ 6500

63. Two equal sums of money were lent at simple interest at 11% p.a. for $3\frac{1}{2}$ years and $4\frac{1}{2}$ years respectively. If the difference in interests for two periods was ₹ 412.50, then each sum is:

(a) ₹ 3250 (b) ₹ 3500
(c) ₹ 3750 (d) ₹ 4250

64. If the simple interest on a certain sum for 15 months at $7\frac{1}{2}$% per annum exceeds the simple interest on the same sum for 8 months at $12\frac{1}{2}$% per annum by ₹ 32.50, then the sum (in ₹) is :

(a) ₹ 3000 (b) ₹ 3060
(c) ₹ 3120 (d) ₹ 3250

65. Sujata invested ₹ 7500 at simple interest @ 11 p.c.p.a. She further invested some amount at simple interest @ 15 p.c.p.a. Total interest earned at the end of the year became 12 p.c.p.a. Find the amount invested at the rate of 15 p.c.p.a.

(a) ₹ 2000 (b) ₹ 2500
(c) ₹ 3000 (d) ₹ 3500

66. A man invests a certain sum of money at 6% p.a. simple interest and another sum at 7% p.a. simple interest. His income from interest after 2 years was ₹ 354. One-fourth of the first sum is equal to one-fifth of the second sum. The total sum invested was:

(a) ₹ 2600 (b) ₹ 2700
(c) ₹ 2880 (d) ₹ 2900

67. Rahul borrowed a sum of ₹ 1150 from Amit at the simple interest rate of 6 p.c.p.a. for 3 years. He then added some more money to the borrowed sum and lent it to Sachin for the same time at 9 p.c.p.a. simple interest. If Rahul gains ₹ 274.95 by way of interest on borrowed sum as well as his own amount from the whole transaction, then what is the sum lent by him to Sachin? **(Bank P.O., 2008)**

(a) ₹ 1200 (b) ₹ 1285
(c) ₹ 1690 (d) ₹ 1785
(e) None of these

68. A person invested some amount at the rate of 12% simple interest and a certain amount at the rate of 10% simple interest. He received yearly interest of ₹ 130. But if he had interchanged the amounts invested, he would have received ₹ 4 more as interest. How much did he invest at 12% simple interest? **(M.A.T., 2010)**

(a) ₹ 400 (b) ₹ 500
(c) ₹ 700 (d) ₹ 800

69. A person borrowed ₹ 500 @ 3% per annum S.I. and ₹ 600 @ $4\frac{1}{2}$% per annum on the agreement that the whole sum will be returned only when the total interest becomes ₹ 126. The number of years, after which the borrowed sum is to be returned, is :

(a) 2 years (b) 3 years
(c) 4 years (d) 5 years

70. Two equal sums of money are lent at the same time at 8% and 7% per annum simple interest. The former is recovered 6 months earlier than the latter and the amount in each case is ₹ 2560. The sum and the time for which the sums of money are lent out are **(M.A.T., 2005)**

(a) ₹ 2000, 3.5 years × 4 years
(b) ₹ 1500, 3.5 years × 4 years
(c) ₹ 2000, 4 years × 5.5 years
(d) ₹ 3000, 4 years × 4.5 years

71. A lent ₹ 5000 to B for 2 years and ₹ 3000 to C for 4 years on simple interest at the same rate of interest and received ₹ 2200 in all from both of them as interest. The rate of interest per annum is

(a) 5% (b) 7%
(c) $7\frac{1}{8}$% (d) 10%

72. A sum of ₹ 725 is lent in the beginning of a year at a certain rate of interest. After 8 months, a sum of ₹ 362.50 more is lent but at the rate twice the former. At the end of the year, ₹ 33.50 is earned as interest from both the loans. What was the original rate of interest ?

(a) 3.6% (b) 4.5%
(c) 5% (d) 6%
(e) None of these

73. The difference between the simple interest received from two different sources on ₹ 1500 for 3 years is ₹ 13.50. The difference between their rates of interest is
(a) 0.1% (b) 0.2%
(c) 0.3% (d) 0.4%
(e) None of these

74. Peter invested an amount of ₹ 12,000 at the rate of 10 p.c.p.a. simple interest and another amount at the rate of 20 p.c.p.a. simple interest. The total interest earned at the end of one year on the total amount invested became 14 p.c.p.a. Find the total amount invested.
(a) ₹ 20,000 (b) ₹ 22,000
(c) ₹ 24,000 (d) ₹ 25,000
(e) None of these

75. A man invested ₹ 5000 at some rate of simple interest and ₹ 4000 at 1 percent higher rate of interest. If the interest in both the cases after 4 years is same, the rate of interest in the former case is (A.T.M.A., 2004)
(a) 4% p.a. (b) 5% p.a.
(c) $6\frac{1}{4}$% p.a. (d) $8\frac{1}{3}$% p.a.

76. What should be the least number of years in which the simple interest on ₹ 2600 at $6\frac{2}{3}$% will be an exact number of rupees ?
(a) 2 years (b) 3 years
(c) 4 years (d) 5 years

77. The rates of simple interest in two banks A and B are in the ratio 5 : 4. A person wants to deposit his total savings in two banks in such a way that he received equal half-yearly interest from both. He should deposit the savings in banks A and B in the ratio:
(a) 2 : 5 (b) 4 : 5
(c) 5 : 2 (d) 5 : 4

78. A sum was put at simple interest at a certain rate for 3 years. Had it been put at 1% higher rate, it would have fetched ₹ 5100 more. The sum is (M.A.T., 2010)
(a) ₹ 1,20,000 (b) ₹ 1,25,000
(c) ₹ 1,50,000 (d) ₹ 1,70,000

79. If the annual rate of simple interest increases from 10% to $12\frac{1}{2}$%, a man's yearly income increases by ₹ 1250. His principal (in ₹) is (S.S.C., 2004)
(a) ₹ 45,000 (b) ₹ 50,000
(c) ₹ 60,000 (d) ₹ 65,000

80. A moneylender finds that due to a fall in the annual rate of interest from 8% to $7\frac{3}{4}$%, his yearly income diminishes by ₹ 61.50. His capital is
(a) ₹ 22,400 (b) ₹ 23,800
(c) ₹ 24,600 (d) ₹ 26,000

81. What equal instalment of annual payment will discharge a debt which is due as ₹ 848 at the end of 4 years at 4% per annum simple interest ? (C.P.O., 2007)
(a) ₹ 200 (b) ₹ 212
(c) ₹ 225 (d) ₹ 250

82. A sum of ₹ 10 is lent to be returned in 11 monthly instalments of ₹ 1 each, interest being simple. The rate of interest is :
(a) $9\frac{1}{11}$% (b) 10%
(c) 11% (d) $21\frac{9}{11}$%

83. A person takes a loan of ₹ 200 at 5% simple interest. He returns ₹ 100 at the end of 1 year. In order to clear his dues at the end of 2 years, he would pay :
(a) ₹ 105 (b) ₹ 110
(c) ₹ 115 (d) ₹ 115.50

84. The price of a T.V. set worth ₹ 20,000 is to be paid in 20 instalments of ₹ 1000 each. If the rate of interest be 6% per annum, and the first instalment be paid at the time of purchase, then the value of the last instalment covering the interest as well will be :
(a) ₹ 1050 (b) ₹ 2050
(c) ₹ 3000 (d) None of these

85. A computer is available for ₹ 39000 cash or ₹ 17000 as cash down payment followed by five monthly instalments of ₹ 4800 each. What is the rate of interest under the instalment plan? (M.A.T., 2006)
(a) 35.71% p.a (b) 36.71% p.a.
(c) 37.71% p.a. (d) 38.71% p.a.

86. If the rate increases by 2%, the simple interest received on a sum of money increases by ₹ 108. If the time period is increased by 2 years, the simple interest on the same sum increases by ₹ 180. The sum is:
(a) ₹ 1800 (b) ₹ 3600
(c) ₹ 5400 (d) Data inadequate
(e) None of these

87. Vishwas borrowed a total amount of ₹ 30000, part of it on simple interest rate of 12 p.c.p.a. and remaining on simple interest rate of 10 p.c.p.a. If at the end of 2 years he paid in all ₹ 36480 to settle the loan amount, what was the amount borrowed at 12 p.c.p.a.? (Bank P.O., 2008)
(a) ₹ 12000 (b) ₹ 16000
(c) ₹ 17500 (d) ₹ 18000

88. A man divided his share between his sons A and B in such a way that the interest received by A at

15% p.a. for 3 years is double the interest received by B at 12% p.a. for 5 years. In what ratio was his share divided? **(M.A.T., 2010)**

(*a*) $\frac{2}{3}$ (*b*) $\frac{3}{2}$

(*c*) $\frac{3}{8}$ (*d*) $\frac{8}{3}$

89. A sum of ₹ 18750 is left by a will by a father to be divided between the two sons, 12 and 14 years of age, so that when they attain maturity at 18, the amount (principal + interest) received by each at 5 per cent simple interest will be the same. Find the sum allotted at present to each son. **(N.M.A.T., 2005)**

(*a*) ₹ 9500, ₹ 9250 (*b*) ₹ 8000, ₹ 1750

(*c*) ₹ 9000, ₹ 9750 (*d*) None of these

90. A certain sum of money is invested at an interest rate of 5% per annum and a second sum, twice as large as the first, is invested at 5.5% p.a. The total amount of interest earned from the two investments together is ₹ 1000 per year and the interest is withdrawn every year. The second sum invested is **(J.M.E.T., 2007)**

(*a*) ₹ 6250 (*b*) ₹ 10500

(*c*) ₹ 12500 (*d*) ₹ 15000

91. I had ₹ 10000 with me. Out of this money I lent some money to A for 2 years @ 15% simple interest. I lent the remaining money to B for an equal number of years @ 18% simple interest. After 2 years, I found that A had given me ₹ 360 more as interest as compared to B. The amount of money which I had lent to B must have been

(*a*) ₹ 2000 (*b*) ₹ 3000

(*c*) ₹ 4000 (*d*) ₹ 5000

92. A sum of ₹ 2600 is lent out in two parts in such a way that the interest on one part at 10% for 5 years is equal to that on another at 9% for 6 years. The sum lent out at 10% is :

(*a*) ₹ 1150 (*b*) ₹ 1250

(*c*) ₹ 1350 (*d*) ₹ 1450

93. A sum of ₹ 1550 was lent partly at 5% and partly at 8% p.a. simple interest. The total interest received after 3 years was ₹ 300. The ratio of the money lent at 5% to that lent at 8% is : **(R.R.B., 2008)**

(*a*) 5 : 8 (*b*) 8 : 5

(*c*) 16 : 15 (*d*) 31 : 6

94. A man lends ₹ 10,000 in four parts. If he gets 8% on ₹ 2000; $7\frac{1}{2}$% on ₹ 4000 and $8\frac{1}{2}$% on ₹ 1400; what percent must he get for the remainder, if his average annual interest is 8.13% ?

(*a*) 7% (*b*) 9%

(*c*) $9\frac{1}{4}$% (*d*) $10\frac{1}{2}$%

95. An amount of ₹ 1,00,000 is invested in two types of shares. The first yields an interest of 9% p.a. and the second, 11% p.a. If the total interest at the end of one year is $9\frac{3}{4}$%, then the amount invested in each share was **(M.B.A., 2007)**

(*a*) ₹ 52,500; ₹ 47,500 (*b*) ₹ 62,500; ₹ 37,500

(*c*) ₹ 72,500; ₹ 27,500 (*d*) ₹ 82,500; ₹ 17,500

96. David invested certain amount in three different schemes A, B and C with the rate of interest 10% p.a., 12% p.a. and 15% p.a. respectively. If the total interest accrued in one year was ₹ 3200 and the amount invested in Scheme C was 150% of the amount invested in Scheme A and 240% of the amount invested in Scheme B, what was the amount invested in Scheme B ?

(*a*) ₹ 5000 (*b*) ₹ 6500

(*c*) ₹ 8000 (*d*) Cannot be determined

(*e*) None of these

97. A sum of ₹ 1440 is lent out in three parts in such a way that the interests on first part at 2% for 3 years, second part at 3% for 4 years and third part at 4% for 5 years are equal. Then the difference between the largest and the smallest sum is **(N.M.A.T., 2005)**

(*a*) ₹ 200 (*b*) ₹ 400

(*c*) ₹ 460 (*d*) ₹ 560

98. A person invests money in three different schemes for 6 years, 10 years and 12 years at 10 percent, 12 percent and 15 percent simple interest respectively. At the completion of each scheme, he gets the same interest. The ratio of his investments is **(S.S.C., 2006)**

(*a*) 2 : 3 : 4 (*b*) 4 : 3 : 2

(*c*) 3 : 4 : 6 (*d*) 6 : 3 : 2

99. Divide ₹ 2379 into 3 parts so that their amounts after 2, 3 and 4 years respectively may be equal, the rate of interest being 5% per annum at simple interest. The first part is

(*a*) ₹ 759 (*b*) ₹ 792

(*c*) ₹ 818 (*d*) ₹ 828

100. A man invested $\frac{1}{3}$ of his capital at 7%; $\frac{1}{4}$ at 8% and the remainder at 10%. If his annual income is ₹ 561, the capital is

(M.B.A., 2006; Hotel Management, 2010)

(*a*) ₹ 5400 (*b*) ₹ 6000

(*c*) ₹ 6600 (*d*) ₹ 7200

101. Find the amount to be received after 2 years 6 months at the rate of 5% p.a. of simple interest on a sum of ₹ 3200. **[ESIC—UDC Exam, 2016]**

(*a*) ₹ 3800 (*b*) ₹ 3500
(*c*) ₹ 3600 (*d*) ₹ 3900

102. A man buys a TV priced at ₹ 16000. He pays ₹ 4000 at once and the rest after 15 months on which he is charged a simple interest at the rate of 12% per year. The total amount he pays for the TV is **[SSC—CHSL (10+2) Exam, 2015]**

(*a*) ₹ 18200 (*b*) ₹ 17800
(*c*) ₹ 17200 (*d*) ₹ 16800

103. A sum becomes its double in 10 years. Find the annual rate of simple interest. **[Indian Railway Gr. 'D' Exam, 2014]**

(*a*) 8% (*b*) 5%
(*c*) 10% (*d*) 20%

104. The interest earned on ₹ 4000 when invested in Scheme A for two years at 7% p.a. simple interest is half of the interest earned when ₹ 'X' is invested for five years in the same scheme at the same rate of interest. What is the value of X?

(a) 2000 (b) 2800
(c) 3000 (d) 3200
(e) 3600

[IBPS Mktg Off. (Scale-I), Exam, 2016]

105. The interest earned on ₹ 15000 in 3 years at simple interest is ₹ 5400. Find the rate of interest per annum **(IBPS—RRB Office Assistant (Online) Exam, 2015]**

(a) 11.5% (b) 12%
(c) 12.5% (d) 15%

106. The sum invested in Scheme B is thrice the sum invested in Scheme A. The investment in Scheme A is made for 4 years at 8% p.a. simple interest and in Scheme B for 2 years at 13% p.a. simple interest. The total interest earned from both the schemes is ₹ 1320. How much amount was invested in Scheme A? **[IBPS—Bank PO/PT Exam, 2015]**

(a) ₹ 1200 (b) ₹ 1140
(c) ₹ 960 (d) ₹ 1500

ANSWERS

1. (*a*)	2. (*d*)	3. (*d*)	4. (*c*)	5. (*a*)	6. (*b*)	7. (*a*)	8. (*a*)	9. (*c*)	10. (*b*)
11. (*b*)	12. (*c*)	13. (*e*)	14. (*d*)	15. (*e*)	16. (*b*)	17. (*c*)	18. (*b*)	19. (*c*)	20. (*d*)
21. (*b*)	22. (*c*)	23. (*c*)	24. (*c*)	25. (*d*)	26. (*b*)	27. (*c*)	28. (*e*)	29. (*d*)	30. (*b*)
31. (*b*)	32. (*c*)	33. (*b*)	34. (*c*)	35. (*a*)	36. (*e*)	37. (*b*)	38. (*c*)	39. (*a*)	40. (*b*)
41. (*c*)	42. (*b*)	43. (*d*)	44. (*a*)	45. (*c*)	46. (*b*)	47. (*b*)	48. (*c*)	49. (*c*)	50. (*b*)
51. (*b*)	52. (*a*)	53. (*b*)	54. (*d*)	55. (*a*)	56. (*a*)	57. (*d*)	58. (*a*)	59. (*b*)	60. (*a*)
61. (*d*)	62. (*b*)	63. (*c*)	64. (*c*)	65. (*b*)	66. (*b*)	67. (*d*)	68. (*b*)	69. (*b*)	70. (*a*)
71. (*d*)	72. (*e*)	73. (*c*)	74. (*a*)	75. (*a*)	76. (*b*)	77. (*b*)	78. (*d*)	79. (*b*)	80. (*c*)
81. (*a*)	82. (*d*)	83. (*c*)	84. (*d*)	85. (*d*)	86. (*d*)	87. (*a*)	88. (*d*)	89. (*c*)	90. (*c*)
91. (*c*)	92. (*c*)	93. (*c*)	94. (*b*)	95. (*b*)	96. (*a*)	97. (*d*)	98. (*d*)	99. (*d*)	100. (*c*)
101. (*c*)	102. (*b*)	103. (*c*)	104. (*d*)	105 (*b*)	106. (*a*)				

SOLUTIONS

1. $P = ₹\ 5760,\ R = 6\%,\ T = 3$ yrs.

$\therefore$ S.I. $= ₹\left(\dfrac{5760 \times 6 \times 3}{100}\right) = ₹\ 1036.80.$

2. $P = ₹\ 3600,\ R = 15\%,\ T = 4$ yrs.

$\therefore$ S.I. $= ₹\left(\dfrac{3600 \times 15 \times 4}{100}\right) = ₹\ 2160.$

Hence, amount after 4 years = ₹ (3600 + 2160) = ₹ 5760.

$\therefore$ Cost of the cow = ₹ (5760 – 4000) = ₹ 1760.

3. $P = ₹\ 520,\ R = 13\%,\ T = \dfrac{1}{2}$ yr.

$\therefore$ S.I. $= ₹\left(\dfrac{520 \times 13}{100 \times 2}\right) = ₹\ 33.80.$

Hence, amount after 6 months = ₹ (520 + 33.80) = ₹ 553.80.

4. $P = ₹\ 4800,\ R = 8\frac{1}{2}\% = \dfrac{17}{2}\%,$

$T = 2$ yrs 3 mths $= 2\frac{1}{4}$ yrs $= \dfrac{9}{4}$ yrs.

$\therefore$ S.I. $= ₹\left(4800 \times \dfrac{17}{2} \times \dfrac{9}{4} \times \dfrac{1}{100}\right) = ₹\ 918.$

5. $P = ₹\ 16800,\ R = 6\frac{1}{4}\% = \dfrac{25}{4}\%,\ T = 9$ mths $= \dfrac{3}{4}$ yr.

$\therefore$ S.I. $= ₹\left(16800 \times \dfrac{25}{4} \times \dfrac{3}{4} \times \dfrac{1}{100}\right) = ₹\ 787.50.$

6. Time = $(\overset{Mar}{22} + \overset{Apr}{30} + \overset{May}{21})$ days $= 73$ days $= \frac{1}{5}$ year.

$\therefore$ S.I. $= ₹\left(1820 \times \frac{15}{2} \times \frac{1}{5} \times \frac{1}{100}\right) = ₹\, 27.30.$

7. Time = $(\overset{Jan}{23} + \overset{Feb}{28} + \overset{Mar}{31} + \overset{Apr}{30} + \overset{May}{31} + \overset{Jun}{3})$ days 146 days

$= \frac{2}{5}$ years.

$\therefore$ S.I. $= ₹\left(15000 \times 18 \times \frac{2}{5} \times \frac{1}{100}\right) = ₹\, 1080.$

Hence, amount paid = ₹ (15000 + 1080) = ₹ 16080.

8. Gain in 2 yrs $= \left[\left(5000 \times \frac{25}{4} \times \frac{2}{100}\right) - \left(\frac{5000 \times 4 \times 2}{100}\right)\right]$

= ₹ (625 – 400) = ₹ 225.

$\therefore$ Gain in 1 year $= ₹\left(\frac{225}{2}\right) = ₹\, 112.50.$

9. Let the amounts invested in Schemes A and B be ₹ $5x$ and ₹ $4x$ respectively. Then,

$5x = 20000 \Rightarrow x = 4000.$

$\therefore$ Amount invested in Scheme B = ₹ 16000.

Total interest received on maturity

$= ₹\left[120\% \text{ of} \left(\frac{20000 \times 8 \times 5}{100}\right) + \left(\frac{16000 \times 9 \times 5}{100}\right)\right]$

= ₹ (120% of 8000 + 7200) = ₹ (9600 + 7200)

= ₹ 16800.

$\therefore$ Total amount = ₹ (20000 + 16000 + 16800) = ₹ 52800.

10. Amount after 10 years $= ₹\left[1000 + \frac{1000 \times 5 \times 10}{100}\right] = ₹\, 1500.$

Now, S.I. = ₹ (2000 – 1500) = ₹ 500, P = ₹ 1500, R = 5%.

$\therefore$ Time $= \left(\frac{500 \times 100}{1500 \times 5}\right)$ yrs $= 6\frac{2}{3}$ yrs.

Hence, required time $= \left(10 + 6\frac{2}{3}\right)$ yrs $= 16\frac{2}{3}$ yrs.

11. P = ₹ 450, S.I. = ₹ 81, R = 4.5%.

Time $= \left(\frac{100 \times 81}{450 \times 4.5}\right)$ years = 4 years.

12. P = ₹ 9534, S.I. = ₹ (11442 – 9534) = ₹ 1908, R = 4%.

$\therefore$ Time $= \left(\frac{100 \times 1908}{9534 \times 4}\right)$ yrs $= \left(\frac{47700}{9534}\right)$ yrs ≈ 5 yrs.

13. P = ₹ 21250, S.I. = ₹ (26350 – 21250) = ₹ 5100, T = 6 years.

$\therefore$ Rate $= \left(\frac{100 \times 5100}{21250 \times 6}\right)\% = 4\%.$

14. Time = 2 years 4 months $= 2\frac{1}{3}$ years $= \frac{7}{3}$ years,

S.I. = ₹ 252, P = ₹ 1600.

Rate $= \left(\frac{100 \times 252 \times 3}{1600 \times 7}\right)\% = 6\frac{3}{4}\%.$

15. P = ₹ 8630, S.I. = ₹ 1553.40, T = 3 yrs.

$\therefore$ Rate $= \left(\frac{100 \times 1553.40}{8630 \times 3}\right)\% = 6\%.$

16. Let the rate of be R% p.a.

Then, $\left(\frac{600 \times R \times 4}{100}\right) + \left(\frac{600 \times R \times 2}{100}\right) = 180$

$\Rightarrow 2400R + 1200R = 18000 \Rightarrow 3600R = 18000$

$\Rightarrow R = 5\%.$

17. S.I. = ₹ 8376, R = 8%, T = 6 yrs.

$\therefore$ Sum $= ₹\left(\frac{100 \times 8376}{8 \times 6}\right) = ₹\, 17450.$

18. S.I. = ₹ 210, $R = 3\frac{3}{4}\% = \frac{15}{4}\%$, $T = 2\frac{1}{3}$ yrs $= \frac{7}{3}$ yrs.

$\therefore$ Sum $= ₹\left(\frac{100 \times 210}{\frac{15}{4} \times \frac{7}{3}}\right) = ₹\left(\frac{100 \times 210 \times 4 \times 3}{15 \times 7}\right) = ₹\, 2400.$

19. Let the present worth be ₹ x. Then, S.I. = ₹ $(132 - x)$.

$\therefore \left(\frac{x \times 5 \times 2}{100}\right) = 132 - x \Leftrightarrow 10x = 13200 - 100x$

$\Leftrightarrow 110x = 13200 \Leftrightarrow x = 120.$

20. Principal $= ₹\left(\frac{100 \times 4016.25}{9 \times 5}\right) = ₹\left(\frac{401625}{45}\right) = ₹\, 8925.$

21. Sum $= \left(\frac{100 \times \text{S.I.}}{R \times T}\right) = ₹\left(\frac{100 \times x}{x \times x}\right) = ₹\left(\frac{100}{x}\right).$

22. P = ₹ 6000, S.I. = ₹ (8000 – 6000) = ₹ 2000, T = 4 years.

$\therefore$ Rate $= \left(\frac{100 \times 2000}{6000 \times 4}\right)\% = \frac{25}{3}\% = 8\frac{1}{3}\%.$

Now, P = ₹ 525, S.I. = ₹ (700 – 525) = ₹ 175, $R = 8\frac{1}{3}\%.$

$\therefore$ Time $= \left(\frac{175 \times 100 \times 3}{525 \times 25}\right)$ years = 4 years.

23. P = ₹ 6200, S.I. = ₹ (9176 – 6200) = ₹ 2976, T = 4 years.

$\therefore$ Rate $= \left(\frac{100 \times 2976}{6200 \times 4}\right)\% = 12\%.$

New rate = (12 + 3)% = 15%.

New S.I. $= ₹\left(\frac{6200 \times 15 \times 4}{100}\right) = 3720.$

Now amount = ₹ (6200 + 3720) = ₹ 9920.

24. Let the required time be T years.

Then, $\frac{500 \times 6.25 \times 4}{100} = \frac{400 \times 5 \times T}{100}$

$\Rightarrow T = \left(\frac{500 \times 6.25 \times 4}{400 \times 5}\right)$ yrs $= 6\frac{1}{4}$ yrs.

25. We need to known the S.I; principal and time to find the rate. Since the principal is not given, so data is inadequate.

26. P = ₹ 6000, S.I. = ₹ (7200 – 6000) = ₹ 1200, T = 4 yrs.

$\therefore$ Rate $= \left(\frac{100 \times 1200}{6000 \times 4}\right)\% = 5\%.$

New rate = (1.5 × 5)% = 7.5%.

New S.I. = ₹$\left(\frac{6000 \times 7.5 \times 5}{100}\right)$ = ₹ 2250.

∴ New amount = ₹ (6000 + 2250) = ₹ 8250.

27. P = ₹ 800, $R = 4\frac{1}{2}\% = \frac{9}{2}\%$, T = 3 years.

Then, S.I. = ₹$\left(800 \times \frac{9}{2} \times \frac{3}{100}\right)$ = ₹ 108.

Now, P = ₹ 150, S.I. = ₹ 108, R = 8%.

∴ Time = $\left(\frac{100 \times 108}{150 \times 8}\right)$ years = 9 years.

28. Sum = ₹$\left(\frac{100 \times 1536}{12 \times 5}\right)$ = ₹ 2560.

Now, P = ₹ (2560 + 1000) = ₹ 3560, T = 2 yrs, R = 12%.

∴ S.I. = ₹$\left(\frac{3560 \times 12 \times 2}{100}\right)$ = ₹ 854.40.

29. P = ₹ 64, S.I. = ₹ (83.20 – 64) = ₹ 19.20, T = 2 years.

So, rate = $\left(\frac{100 \times 19.20}{64 \times 2}\right)\%$ = 15%.

Now, P = ₹ 86, R = 15%, T = 4 years.

∴ S.I. ₹$\left(\frac{86 \times 15 \times 4}{100}\right)$ = ₹ 51.60.

Amount = ₹ (86 + 51.60) = ₹ 137.60.

30. S.I. = ₹ 840, R = 5%, T = 8 years.

Principal = ₹$\left(\frac{100 \times 840}{5 \times 8}\right)$ = ₹ 2100.

Now, P = ₹ 2100, S.I. = ₹ 840, T = 5 years.

∴ Rate = $\left(\frac{100 \times 840}{2100 \times 5}\right)\%$ = 8%.

31. S.I. = ₹ 202.50, R = 4.5%, T = 1 year.

Principal = ₹$\left(\frac{100 \times 202.50}{4.5 \times 1}\right)$ = ₹ 4500.

Now, P = ₹ 4500, R = 5%, T = 1 year.

S.I. = ₹$\left(\frac{4500 \times 5 \times 1}{100}\right)$ = ₹ 225.

∴ Difference in interest = ₹ (225 – 202.50) = ₹ 22.50.

32. Let the sum be ₹ x. Then, S.I. = ₹ (504 – x).

∴ $\left(\frac{x \times 5 \times 4}{100}\right) = 504 - x \Leftrightarrow 20x = 50400 - 100x$

$\Leftrightarrow 120x = 50400 \Leftrightarrow x = 420.$

Now, P = ₹ 420, R = 10%, $T = \frac{5}{2}$ years.

S.I. = ₹$\left(\frac{420 \times 10}{100} \times \frac{5}{2}\right)$ = ₹ 105.

∴ Amount = ₹ (420 + 105) = ₹ 525.

33. Let time be T years and rate be R% p.a.

Then, y is the S.I. on $x \Rightarrow \frac{x\,RT}{100} = y$ ... (*i*)

And, z is the S.I. on $y \Rightarrow \frac{y\,RT}{100} = z \Rightarrow y = \frac{100\,z}{RT}$ ... (*ii*)

From (*i*) and (*ii*) we have: $\frac{x\,RT}{100} = \frac{100\,z}{RT}$

$\Rightarrow \frac{xR^2T^2}{(100)^2} = z \Rightarrow \frac{y^2}{x} = z \Rightarrow y^2 = xz.$

34. Let the principal be P and rate of interest be R%

∴ Required ratio = $\left[\frac{\left(\frac{P \times R \times 6}{100}\right)}{\left(\frac{P \times R \times 9}{100}\right)}\right] = \frac{6PR}{9PR} = \frac{6}{9} = 2:3.$

35. Let the sum be ₹ x. Then,

$\left(\frac{x \times 8 \times 4}{100}\right) + \left(\frac{x \times 10 \times 6}{100}\right) + \left(\frac{x \times 12 \times 5}{100}\right) = 12160$

$\Rightarrow 32x + 60x + 60x = 1216000$

$\Rightarrow 152x = 1216000 \Rightarrow x = 8000.$

36. Let the loan amount be ₹ x. Then,

$\frac{6x}{100} + \frac{7.5x}{100} + \frac{9x}{100} = 8190 \Rightarrow 22.5\,x = 819000 \Rightarrow = x = 36400$

37. Let the rate of interest be R% p.a.

Then, $\left(\frac{400 \times R \times 2}{100}\right) + \left(\frac{550 \times R \times 4}{100}\right) + \left(\frac{1200 \times R \times 6}{100}\right) = 1020$

$\Rightarrow 800R + 220R + 7200R = 102000$

$\Rightarrow 10200R = 102000$

$\Rightarrow R = 10.$

38. Let the sum be ₹ x. Now, S.I. = ₹ 600, T = 10 years.

Rate = $\left(\frac{100 \times 600}{x \times 10}\right)\% = \left(\frac{6000}{x}\right)\%.$

S.I. for first 5 years = ₹$\left(\frac{x \times 5 \times 6000}{x \times 100}\right)$ = ₹ 300.

S.I. for last 5 years = ₹$\left(3x \times 5 \times \frac{6000}{x \times 100}\right)$ = ₹ 900.

∴ Total interest = ₹ 1200.

39. S.I. = ₹$\left(10 \times \frac{3}{100} \times 4\right)$ = ₹ 1.20.

40. Let the sum be ₹ 100. Then,

S.I. for first 6 months = ₹$\left(\frac{100 \times 10 \times 1}{100 \times 2}\right)$ = ₹ 5.

S.I. for last 6 months = ₹$\left(\frac{105 \times 10 \times 1}{100 \times 2}\right)$ = ₹ 5.25.

So, amount at the end of 1 year = ₹ (100 + 5 + 5.25) = ₹ 110.25.

∴ Effective rate = (110.25 – 100) = 10.25%.

41. S.I. for 1 year = ₹ (854 – 815) = ₹ 39.

S.I. for 3 years = ₹ (39 × 3) = ₹ 117.

∴ Principal = ₹ (815 – 117) = ₹ 698.

42. S.I. for 5 years = ₹ (1020 – 720) = ₹ 300.

S.I. for 2 years = ₹$\left(\frac{300}{5} \times 2\right)$ = ₹ 120.

∴ Principal = ₹ (720 – 120) = ₹ 600.

43. S.I. for 2 years = ₹ (5680 – 5200) = ₹ 480.

S.I. for 5 years = ₹ $\left(\frac{480}{2} \times 5\right)$ = ₹ 1200.

∴ Principal = ₹ (5200 – 1200) = ₹ 4000.

Hence, rate = $\left(\frac{100 \times 1200}{4000 \times 5}\right)\% = 6\%$.

44. S.I. for 3 years = ₹ (24412.50 – 20925) = ₹ 3487.50.

S.I. for 2 years = ₹ $\left(\frac{3487.50}{3} \times 2\right)$ = ₹ 2325.

∴ Principal = ₹ (20925 – 2325) = ₹ 18600.

Hence, rate = $\left(\frac{100 - 2325}{18600 \times 2}\right)\% = 6.25\%$.

45. S.I. for $1\frac{1}{2}$ years = ₹ (1067.20 – 1012) = ₹ 55.20.

S.I. for $2\frac{1}{2}$ years = ₹ $\left(55.20 \times \frac{2}{3} \times \frac{5}{2}\right)$ = ₹ 92.

∴ Principal = ₹ (1012 – 92) = ₹ 920.

Hence, rate = $\left(\frac{100 \times 92 \times 2}{920 \times 5}\right)\% = 4\%$.

46. Let sum = ₹ x. Then, S.I. = ₹ x.

∴ Time = $\left(\frac{100 \times \text{S.I.}}{P \times R}\right) = \left(\frac{100 \times x}{x \times 18.75}\right)$ years $= \frac{26}{3}$ years

$= 5\frac{1}{3}$ years = 5 years 4 months.

47. Let sum = ₹ x. Then, S.I. = ₹ x.

∴ Rate = $\left(\frac{100 \times \text{S.I.}}{P \times T}\right) = \left(\frac{100 \times x}{x \times 12}\right)\% = \frac{25}{3}\% = 8\frac{1}{3}\%$.

48. Let sum = ₹ x. Then, S.I. = ₹ $3x$.

∴ Rate = $\left(\frac{100 \times \text{S.I.}}{P \times T}\right) = \left(\frac{100 \times 3x}{x \times 15}\right)\% = 20\%$.

49. **Case I.** Let sum = ₹ x. Then, S.I. = ₹ x.

∴ Rate = $\left(\frac{100 \times \text{S.I.}}{P \times T}\right) = \left(\frac{100 \times x}{x \times 5}\right)\% = 20\%$.

Case II. Let sum = ₹ x. Then, S.I. = ₹ $2x$.

∴ Rate = $\left(\frac{100 \times \text{S.I.}}{P \times T}\right) = \left(\frac{100 \times 2x}{x \times 12}\right)\% = \frac{50}{3}\% = 16\frac{2}{3}\%$.

50. Let sum = ₹ x. Then, S.I. = ₹ x.

∴ Rate = $\left(\frac{100 \times x}{x \times 7}\right)\% = \frac{100}{7}\%$.

Now, sum = ₹ x, S.I. = ₹ $3x$, Rate = $\frac{100}{7}\%$.

∴ Time = $\left(\frac{100 \times 3x}{x \times \frac{100}{7}}\right)$ yrs = 21 years.

51. Let sum = ₹ x.

Then, S.I. = ₹ $2x$, Time = $15\frac{1}{2}$ years $= \frac{31}{2}$ years.

∴ Rate = $\left(\frac{100 \times 2x}{x \times \frac{31}{2}}\right)\% = \frac{400}{31}\%$.

Now, sum = ₹ x, S.I. = ₹ x, Rate = $\frac{400}{31}\%$.

∴ Time = $\frac{100 \times x}{x \times \frac{400}{31}} = \frac{31}{4}$ years = 7 years 9 months.

52. Let sum = ₹ x. Then, S.I. = ₹ x, Time = 16 years.

∴ Rate = $\left(\frac{100 \times x}{x \times 16}\right)\% = \frac{25}{4}\% = 6\frac{1}{4}\%$.

Now, sum = ₹ x, Time = 8 years, Rate = $6\frac{1}{4}\%$.

∴ S.I. = ₹ $\left(\frac{x \times 25 \times 8}{100 \times 4}\right)$ = ₹ $\frac{x}{2}$.

So, amount = ₹ $\left(x + \frac{x}{2}\right)$ = ₹ $\frac{3x}{2} = 1\frac{1}{2}$ times

53. Let sum be x. Then, S.I. = x.

1. Time = $\frac{100 \times x}{x \times \frac{50}{3}} = 6$ years (False)

2. Time = $\frac{100 \times x}{x \times 20} = 5$ years (True)

3. Suppose sum = x. Then, S.I. = x and Time = 5 years.

Rate = $\left(\frac{100 \times x}{x \times 5}\right)\% = 20\%$.

Now, sum = x, S.I. = $3x$ and Rate = 20%.

∴ Time = $\left(\frac{100 \times 3x}{x \times 20}\right)$ years = 15 years (False)

So, 2 alone is correct.

54. Let sum = x.

Then, S.I. = $\frac{x}{2}$.

∴ $\frac{x}{2} = \frac{x \times 8 \times 6}{100}$. Clearly, data is inadequate.

55. Let sum = x. Then, S.I. = $\frac{2x}{5}$, Time = 10 years.

∴ Rate = $\left(\frac{100 \times 2x}{x \times 5 \times 10}\right)\% = 4\%$.

56. Let sum = x. Then, S.I. = $0.125x = \frac{1}{8}x$, $R = 10\%$.

∴ Rate = $\left(\frac{100 \times x}{x \times 8 \times 10}\right)$ years $= \frac{5}{4}$ years $= 1\frac{1}{4}$ years.

57. Let the sum be x.

Then, S.I. = 40% of $x = \frac{2x}{5}$; Rate = 5%.

∴ Time = $\left(100 \times \frac{2x}{5} \times \frac{1}{x \times 5}\right) = 8$ years.

58. Let sum = x. Then, amount = $\frac{7x}{6}$.

S.I. = $\left(\frac{7x}{6} - x\right) = \frac{x}{6}$; Time = 3 years.

$\therefore$ Rate = $\left(\frac{100 \times x}{x \times 6 \times 3}\right)\% = \frac{50}{9}\% = 5\frac{5}{9}\%$.

59. Let sum = ₹ x. Then, S.I. = 30% of ₹ x = ₹ $\frac{3x}{10}$.

Time = 6 years.

$\therefore$ Rate = $\left(\frac{100 \times 3x}{10 \times x \times 6}\right)\% = 5\%$.

Now, sum = ₹ x, S.I. = ₹ x, Rate = 5%.

$\therefore$ Time = $\left(\frac{100 \times x}{x \times 5}\right)$ years = 20 years.

60. Let sum = x. Then, S.I. = $\frac{x}{9}$.

Let rate = R% and time = R years.

$\therefore \left(\frac{x \times R \times R}{100}\right) = \frac{x}{9} \Leftrightarrow R^2 = \frac{100}{9} \Leftrightarrow R = \frac{10}{3} = 3\frac{1}{3}$.

Hence, rate = $3\frac{1}{3}\%$.

61. Let sum = x. Then, S.I. = $\frac{9}{16}x$.

Let rate = R% and time = R years.

$\therefore \left(\frac{x \times R \times R}{100}\right) = \frac{9x}{16} \Leftrightarrow R^2 = \frac{900}{16} \Leftrightarrow R = \frac{30}{4} = 7\frac{1}{2}$.

Hence, time = $7\frac{1}{2}$ years.

62. Let the sum lent to C be ₹ x.

Then, $\left(\frac{2500 \times 7 \times 4}{100}\right) + \left(\frac{x \times 7 \times 4}{100}\right) = 1120$

$\Leftrightarrow \frac{7}{25}x = (1120 - 700) \Rightarrow x = \left(\frac{420 \times 25}{7}\right) = 1500$.

63. Let each sum be ₹ x.

Then, $\left(\frac{x \times 11 \times 9}{100 \times 2}\right) - \left(\frac{x \times 11 \times 7}{100 \times 2}\right) = 412.50$

$\Leftrightarrow (99x - 77x) = 82500 \Leftrightarrow 22x = 82500 \Leftrightarrow x = 3750$.

64. Let the sum be ₹ x.

Then, $\left(x \times \frac{15}{2} \times \frac{5}{4} \times \frac{1}{100}\right) - \left(x \times \frac{25}{2} \times \frac{2}{3} \times \frac{1}{100}\right) = 32.50$

$\Leftrightarrow \frac{75x}{8} - \frac{25x}{3} = 3250 \Leftrightarrow 25x = (3250 \times 24)$

$\Leftrightarrow x = \left(\frac{3250 \times 24}{25}\right) = 3120$.

65. Let the required sum be ₹ x.

Then, 11% of 7500 + 15% of x = 12% of (7500 + x)

$\Rightarrow \left(\frac{11}{100} \times 7500\right) + \left(\frac{15}{100}x\right) = \frac{12}{100}(7500 + x)$

$\Rightarrow 82500 + 15x = 90000 + 12x \Rightarrow 3x = 7500$

$\Rightarrow x = 2500$.

Hence, required sum = ₹ 2500.

66. Let the sums be x and y.

$\frac{x \times 6 \times 2}{100} + \frac{y \times 7 \times 2}{100} = 354$ or $6x + 7y = 17700$. ...(i)

Also, $\frac{x}{4} = \frac{y}{5}$ or $5x - 4y = 0$ ...(ii)

Solving (i) and (ii), we get : $x = 1200$ and $y = 1500$.

$\therefore$ Total sum = ₹ 2700.

67. Let the money added by Rahul be ₹ x.

Then, $\frac{(1150 + x) \times 9 \times 3}{100} - \frac{1150 \times 6 \times 3}{100} = 274.95$

$\Leftrightarrow 1150 \times 27 + 27x - 1150 \times 18 = 27495$

$\Leftrightarrow 27x + 1150 \times (27 - 18) = 27495$

$\Rightarrow 27x = 27495 - 10350 = 17145 \Rightarrow x = 635$.

So, sum lent by Rahul to Sachin = ₹ (1150 + 635) = ₹ 1785.

68. Let the amount invested at 12% be ₹ x and that invested at 10% be ₹ y.

Then, 12% of x + 10% of y = 130

$\Rightarrow 12x + 10y = 13000 \Rightarrow 6x + 5y = 6500$ ... (i)

And, 10% of x + 12% of y = 134

$\Rightarrow 10x + 12y = 13400 \Rightarrow 5x + 6y = 6700$ ... (ii)

Adding (i) and (ii), we get: $11(x + y) = 13200$

$\Rightarrow x + y = 1200$ ... (iii)

Subtracting (i) from (ii), we get: $-x + y = 200$ ... (iv)

Adding (iii) and (iv), we get: $2y = 1400$ or $y = 700$.

Hence, amount invested at 12% = (1200 − 700) = ₹ 500.

69. Let the time be x years.

Then, $\left(\frac{500 \times 3 \times x}{100}\right) + \left(\frac{600 \times 9 \times x}{100 \times 2}\right) = 126$

$\Leftrightarrow 15x + 27x = 126 \Leftrightarrow 42x = 126 \Leftrightarrow x = 3$.

$\therefore$ Required time = 3 years.

70. Let each sum = ₹ x.

Let the first sum be invested for $\left(T - \frac{1}{2}\right)$ years and the second sum for T years.

Then, $x + \frac{x \times 8 \times \left(T - \frac{1}{2}\right)}{100} = 2560$

$\Rightarrow 100x + 8xT - 4x = 256000$

$\Rightarrow 96x + 8xT = 256000$ ... (i)

And, $x + \frac{x \times 7 \times T}{100} = 2560 \Rightarrow 100x + 7xT = 256000$ ... (ii)

From (i) and (ii), we get: $96x + 8xT = 100x + 7xT$

$\Rightarrow 4x = xT \Rightarrow T = 4$.

Putting $T = 4$ in (i), we get: $96x + 32x = 256000$

$\Rightarrow 128x = 256000 \Rightarrow x = 2000$.

Hence, each sum = ₹ 2000; time periods = 4 yrs and $3\frac{1}{2}$ yrs.

71. Let the rate be R% p.a. Then,

$$\left(\frac{5000 \times R \times 2}{100}\right)+\left(\frac{3000 \times R \times 4}{100}\right)=2200$$

$\Leftrightarrow$ $100R + 120R = 2200 \Rightarrow R = \left(\frac{2200}{220}\right)=10.$

$\therefore$ Rate = 10%.

72. Let the original rate be R%. Then, new rate = $(2R)$%.

$$\therefore \left(\frac{725 \times R \times 1}{100}\right)+\left(\frac{362.50 \times 2R \times 1}{100 \times 3}\right)=33.50$$

$\Leftrightarrow$ $(2175 + 725)\ R = 33.50 \times 100 \times 3 = 10050$

$\Leftrightarrow$ $R = \frac{10050}{2900}=3.46.$

$\therefore$ Original rate = 3.46%.

73. $\left(\frac{1500 \times R_1 \times 3}{100}\right)-\left(\frac{1500 \times R_2 \times 3}{100}\right)=13.50$

$\Leftrightarrow$ $4500\ (R_1 - R_2) = 1350 \Leftrightarrow R_1 - R_2 = \frac{1350}{4500}=0.3\%.$

74. Let the second amount be ₹ x. Then,

$$\left(\frac{12000 \times 10 \times 1}{100}\right)+\left(\frac{x \times 20 \times 1}{100}\right)=\left[\frac{(12000+x) \times 14 \times 1}{100}\right]$$

$\Leftrightarrow$ $12000 + 20x = 168000 + 14x$

$\Leftrightarrow$ $6x = 48000 \quad \Leftrightarrow x = 8000.$

$\therefore$ Total investment = ₹ (12000 + 8000) = ₹ 20000.

75. Let the rates of interest in the former and latter cases be R% and $(R + 1)$% p.a.

Then, $5000 \times R \times 4 = 4000 \times (R + 1) \times 4$

$\Rightarrow$ $\frac{R+1}{R}=\frac{5000 \times 4}{4000 \times 4} \Rightarrow 1+\frac{1}{R}=1+\frac{1}{4} \Rightarrow R=4.$

Hence, required rate = 4% p.a.

76. S.I. = ₹$\left(2600 \times \frac{20}{3} \times \frac{1}{100} \times T\right)$ = ₹$\left(\frac{520}{3} \times T\right)$,

which is an exact number of rupees when T = 3 years.

77. Let the savings be X and Y and the rates of simple interest be $5x$ and $4x$ respectively.

Then, $X \times 5x \times \frac{1}{2} \times \frac{1}{100}=Y \times 4x \times \frac{1}{2} \times \frac{1}{100}$

or $\frac{X}{Y}=\frac{4}{5}$, *i.e.*, $X : Y = 4 : 5.$

78. Let the sum be ₹ x and original rate be R%.

Then, $\frac{x \times (R+1) \times 3}{100}-\frac{x \times R \times 3}{100}=5100$

$\Rightarrow$ $3Rx + 3x - 3Rx = 510000$

$\Rightarrow$ $3x = 510000 \Rightarrow x = 170000.$

Hence, sum = ₹ 170000.

79. Let the sum be ₹ x.

Then, $\left(x \times \frac{25}{2} \times \frac{1}{100}\right)-\left(\frac{x \times 10 \times 1}{100}\right)=1250$

$\Leftrightarrow$ $25x - 20x = 250000 \quad \Leftrightarrow \quad 5x = 250000 \Leftrightarrow x = 50000.$

80. Let the capital be ₹ x.

Then, $\left(\frac{x \times 8 \times 1}{100}\right)-\left(x \times \frac{31}{4} \times \frac{1}{100}\right)=61.50$

$\Leftrightarrow$ $32x - 31x = 6150 \times 4 \quad \Leftrightarrow \quad x = 24600.$

81. Let the annual instalment be ₹ x.

Then, $\left[x+\left(\frac{x \times 3 \times 4}{100}\right)\right]+\left[x+\left(\frac{x \times 2 \times 4}{100}\right)\right]+\left[x+\left(\frac{x \times 1 \times 4}{100}\right)\right]+x=848$

$\Leftrightarrow$ $\frac{28x}{25}+\frac{27x}{25}+\frac{26x}{25}+x = 848$

$\Leftrightarrow$ $106x = 848 \times 25 = 21200 \Leftrightarrow x = 200.$

Short Cut Method: *The annual payment that will discharge a debt of ₹ A due in t years at the rate of interest r% p.a. is* $\frac{100\,A}{100t+\frac{rt\,(t-1)}{2}}$.

$\therefore$ Annual instalment

$$= ₹\left[\frac{100 \times 848}{100 \times 4+\frac{4 \times 4 \times 3}{2}}\right]= ₹\left(\frac{100 \times 848}{424}\right)= ₹\ 200.$$

82. ₹ 10 + S.I. on ₹ 10 for 11 months

= ₹ 11 + S.I. on ₹ 1 for (1 + 2 + 3 + 4 + ...+ 10) months

$\Rightarrow$ ₹ 10 + S.I. on ₹ 1 for 110 months

= ₹ 11 + S.I. on ₹ 1 for 55 months

$\Rightarrow$ S.I. on ₹ 1 for 55 months = ₹ 1.

$\therefore$ Rate = $\left(\frac{100 \times 12}{1 \times 55}\right)\% = 21\frac{9}{11}\%.$

83. Amount to be paid = ₹$\left(100+\frac{200 \times 5 \times 1}{100}+\frac{100 \times 5 \times 1}{100}\right)$

= ₹ 115.

84. Money paid in cash = ₹ 1000.

Balance payment = ₹ (20000 – 1000) = ₹ 19000.

85. Total cost of the computer = ₹ 39000.

Down payment = ₹ 17000

Balance = ₹ (39000 – 17000) = ₹ 22000.

Let the rate of interest be R% p.a.

Amount of ₹ 22000 for 5 months

$$= ₹\left(22000+22000 \times \frac{5}{12} \times \frac{R}{100}\right) = ₹\left(22000+\frac{275R}{3}\right).$$

The customer pays the shopkeeper ₹ 4800 after 1 month, ₹ 4800 after 2 months,...... and ₹ 4800 after 5 months.

Thus, the shopkeeper keeps ₹ 4800 for 4 months, ₹ 4800 for 3 months, ₹ 4800 for 2 months, ₹ 4800 for 1 month and gets ₹ 4800 at the end.

$\therefore$ Sum of the amounts of these instalments

= (₹ 4800 + S.I. on ₹ 4800 for 4 months) + (₹ 4800 + S.I. on ₹ 4800 for 3 months)+ ... + (₹ 4800 + S.I. on ₹ 4800 for 1 month + ₹ 4800

= ₹ (4800 × 5) + S.I. on ₹ 4800 for (4 + 3 + 2 + 1) months

= ₹ 24000 + S.I. on ₹ 4800 for 10 months

$= ₹\left(24000 + 4800 \times R \times \frac{10}{12} \times \frac{1}{100}\right) = ₹(24000 + 40R).$

$\therefore \quad 22000 + \frac{275R}{3} = 24000 + 40R$

$\Rightarrow \quad \frac{155R}{3} = 2000 \Rightarrow R = \frac{2000 \times 3}{155} = 38.71\%$ p.a.

86. Let the sum be ₹ x, rate be R% p.a. and time be T years.

Then, $\left[\frac{x \times (R+2) \times T}{100}\right] - \left(\frac{x \times R \times T}{100}\right) = 108$

$\Leftrightarrow \quad 2xT = 10800 \quad \ldots (i)$

And, $\left[\frac{x \times R \times (T+2)}{100}\right] - \left(\frac{x \times R \times T}{100}\right) = 180$

$\Leftrightarrow \quad 2xR = 18000 \quad \ldots (ii)$

Clearly, from (*i*) and (*ii*), we cannot find the value of x. So, the data is inadequate.

87. Let the sum borrowed at 12% p.a. be ₹ x and that borrowed at 10% p.a. be ₹ (30000 – x).

S.I. at the end of 2 years = ₹ (36480 – 30000) = ₹ 6480.

$\therefore \quad \left(\frac{x \times 12 \times 2}{100}\right) + \left[\frac{(30000 - x) \times 10 \times 2}{100}\right] = 6480$

$\Leftrightarrow \quad 24x + 600000 - 20x = 648000$

$\Leftrightarrow \quad 4x = 48000 \Leftrightarrow x = 12000.$

88. Let A's share = ₹ x and B's share = ₹ y.

Then, $\frac{x \times 15 \times 3}{100} = 2 \times \frac{y \times 12 \times 5}{100} \Rightarrow 45x = 120\,y$

$\Rightarrow \quad \frac{x}{y} = \frac{120}{45} = \frac{8}{3}.$

89. Let the two sums be ₹ x and ₹ (18750 – x).

Then, $x + \frac{x \times 5 \times 6}{100} = (18750 - x) + \frac{(18750 - x) \times 5 \times 4}{100}$

$\Leftrightarrow \quad x + \frac{30x}{100} = (18750 - x) + 3750 - \frac{20x}{100}$

$\Leftrightarrow \quad 2x + \frac{x}{2} = 22500 \Leftrightarrow \frac{5x}{2} = 22500$

$\Leftrightarrow \quad x = \left(\frac{22500 \times 2}{5}\right) = 9000.$

Hence, the two sums are ₹ 9000 and ₹ 9750.

90. Let the two sums be ₹ x and ₹ $2x$.

Then, $\frac{x \times 5}{100} + \frac{2x \times 5.5}{100} = 1000$

$\Rightarrow \quad 5x + 11x = 100000$

$\Rightarrow \quad 16x = 100000 \Rightarrow x = 6250.$

Hence, second sum ₹ (6250 × 2) = ₹ 12500.

91. Let the sum lent to A be ₹ x and that lent to B be ₹ (10000 – x).

Then, $\frac{x \times 15 \times 2}{100} - \frac{(10000 - x) \times 18 \times 2}{100} = 360$

$\Rightarrow \quad 30x - 360000 + 36x = 36000 \Rightarrow 66x = 396000$

$\Rightarrow \quad x = 6000.$

Hence, sum lent to B = ₹ (10000 – 6000) = ₹ 4000.

92. Let the sum lent at 10% be ₹ x and that lent at 9% be ₹ (2600 – x). Then,

$\left(\frac{x \times 10 \times 5}{100}\right) = \frac{(2600 - x) \times 9 \times 6}{100}$

$\Leftrightarrow \quad 50x = (2600 \times 54) - 54x$

$\Rightarrow \quad x = \left(\frac{2600 \times 54}{104}\right) = 1350.$

$\therefore$ Sum lent at 10% = ₹ 1350.

93. Let the sum lent at 5% be ₹ x and that lent at 8% be ₹ (1550 – x). Then,

$\left(\frac{x \times 5 \times 3}{100}\right) + \left[\frac{(1550 - x) \times 8 \times 3}{100}\right] = 300$

$\Leftrightarrow \quad 15x - 24x + (1550 \times 24) = 30000$

$\Leftrightarrow \quad 9x = 7200 \Leftrightarrow x = 800.$

$\therefore$ Required ratio = 800 : 750 = 16 : 15.

94. Let the required rate be R. Then,

$\left(\frac{2000 \times 8 \times 1}{100}\right) + \left(4000 \times \frac{15}{2} \times \frac{1}{100}\right) + \left(1400 \times \frac{17}{2} \times \frac{1}{100}\right) + \left(2600 \times R \times \frac{1}{100}\right)$

$= \left(\frac{813}{10000} \times 10000\right)$

$\Leftrightarrow \quad 160 + 300 + 119 + 26R = 813 \Leftrightarrow R = 9.$

95. Let the sum invested at 9% be ₹ x and that invested at 11% be ₹ (100000 – x).

Then, $\left(\frac{x \times 9 \times 1}{100}\right) + \left[\frac{(100000 - x) \times 11 \times 1}{100}\right]$

$= \left(100000 \times \frac{39}{4} \times \frac{1}{100}\right)$

$\Leftrightarrow \quad \frac{9x + 1100000 - 11x}{100} = \frac{39000}{4} = 9750$

$\Leftrightarrow \quad 2x = (1100000 - 975000) = 125000 \Leftrightarrow x = 62500.$

$\therefore$ Sum invested at 9% = ₹ 62500.

Sum invested at 11% = ₹ (100000 – 62500) = ₹ 37500.

96. Let x, y and z be the amounts invested in schemes A, B and C respectively. Then,

$\left(\frac{x \times 10 \times 1}{100}\right) + \left(\frac{y \times 12 \times 1}{100}\right) + \left(\frac{z \times 15 \times 1}{100}\right) = 3200$

$\Leftrightarrow \quad 10x + 12y + 15z = 320000 \quad \ldots (i)$

Now, $z = 240\%$ of $y = \frac{12}{5}y \quad \ldots (ii)$

And, $z = 150\%$ of $x = \frac{3}{2}x$

$\Rightarrow \quad x = \frac{2}{3}z = \left(\frac{2}{3} \times \frac{12}{5}\right)y = \frac{8}{5}y$ ... (*iii*)

From (*i*), (*ii*) and (*iii*), we have:

$16y + 12y + 36y = 320000 \Leftrightarrow 64y = 320000 \Leftrightarrow y = 5000.$

$\therefore$ Sum invested in Scheme B = ₹ 5000.

97. Let the parts be ₹ x, ₹ y and ₹ $[1440 - (x + y)]$. Then,

$$\frac{x \times 2 \times 3}{100} = \frac{y \times 3 \times 4}{100} = \frac{[1440 - (x+y)] \times 4 \times 5}{100}$$

$\therefore \quad 6x = 12y$ or $x = 2y$.

So, $\frac{x \times 2 \times 3}{100} = \frac{[1400 - (x+y)] \times 4 \times 5}{100}$

$\Rightarrow \quad 12y = (1440 - 3y) \times 20 \Rightarrow 72y = 28800 \Rightarrow y = 400.$

First part = $x = 2y$ = ₹ 800, Second part = ₹ 400,

Third part = ₹ [1440 – (800 + 400)] = ₹ 240.

$\therefore$ Required difference = ₹ (800 – 240) = ₹ 560.

98. Let the three amounts be ₹ x, ₹ y and ₹ z.

Then, $\frac{x \times 10 \times 6}{100} = \frac{y \times 12 \times 10}{100} = \frac{z \times 15 \times 12}{100}$

$\Rightarrow \quad 60x = 120y = 180z \Rightarrow x = 2y = 3z = k$ (say)

$\Rightarrow \quad x = k, y = \frac{k}{2}, z = \frac{k}{3}$

$\Rightarrow \quad x : y : z = k : \frac{k}{2} : \frac{k}{3} = 1 : \frac{1}{2} : \frac{1}{3} = 6 : 3 : 2.$

99. Let the parts be x, y and z.

$$x + \left(x \times 2 \times \frac{5}{100}\right) = y + \left(y \times 3 \times \frac{5}{100}\right) = z + \left(z \times 4 \times \frac{5}{100}\right)$$

$\Rightarrow \quad \frac{11x}{10} = \frac{23y}{20} = \frac{6z}{5} = k \Rightarrow x = \frac{10k}{11}, y = \frac{20k}{23}, z = \frac{5k}{6}.$

But $x + y + z = 2379$

$\Rightarrow \quad \frac{10k}{11} + \frac{20k}{23} + \frac{5k}{6} = 2379$

$\Rightarrow \quad 1380k + 1320k + 1265k = 2379 \times 11 \times 23 \times 6$

$\Rightarrow \quad k = \frac{2379 \times 11 \times 23 \times 6}{3965} = \frac{3 \times 11 \times 23 \times 6}{5}$

$x = \left(\frac{10}{11} \times \frac{3 \times 11 \times 23 \times 6}{5}\right) = 828.$

Hence, the first part is ₹ 828.

100. Let total capital be ₹ x.

Then, $\left(\frac{x}{3} \times \frac{7}{100} \times 1\right) + \left(\frac{x}{4} \times \frac{8}{100} \times 1\right) + \left(\frac{5x}{12} \times \frac{10}{100} \times 1\right) = 561$

$\Leftrightarrow \quad \frac{7x}{300} + \frac{x}{50} + \frac{x}{24} = 561 \Leftrightarrow 51x = (561 \times 600)$

$\Leftrightarrow \quad x = \left(\frac{561 \times 600}{51}\right) = 6600.$

101. Rate of interest = 5% p.a.

Sum = ₹ 3200

Time = 2 years 6 months = $2\frac{1}{2}$ years = $\frac{5}{2}$ years

S.I. = $\frac{\text{Principal} \times \text{Time} \times \text{Rate}}{100} = \frac{3200 \times 5 \times 5}{2 \times 100}$ = ₹ 400

$\therefore$ Amount = ₹ Sum + S.I. = (3200 + 400) = ₹ 3600

102. Price paid = ₹ 4000

Rest price = ₹ 12000

Rate = 12%

$\therefore = \frac{12000 \times 12 \times 5}{100 \times 12}$ = ₹ 1800

$\therefore$ Amount paid after 15 months

= 12000 + 1800 = 13800

$\therefore$ Total amount paid for TV = 4000 + 13800 = 17800

103. Let sum be ₹ x and let S.I. = ₹ x

Time = 10 years

$\therefore$ Rate = $\frac{\text{S.I.} \times 100}{\text{Principal} \times \text{Time}}$

$= \frac{x \times 100}{x \times 10} = 10\%$ per annum.

104. Simple Interest earned in scheme

A = $\frac{PRT}{100}$

$= \frac{4000 \times 7 \times 2}{100}$ = ₹ 560

Interest earned in scheme B = 560 × 2

= ₹ 1120

Let 'A' be the principal amount invested in scheme B

Interest = $\frac{\text{Principal} \times \text{Rate} \times \text{Time}}{100}$

$1120 = \frac{A \times 7 \times 5}{100}$

A = ₹ 3200

105. Rate = $\frac{\text{S.I.} \times 100}{\text{Principal} \times \text{Time}} = \frac{5400 \times 100}{15000 \times 3}$

= 12% per annum.

106. Let the amount invested in scheme A be ₹ x and that in B be ₹ $3x$.

Then, $\frac{x \times 4 \times 8}{100} + \frac{3x \times 2 \times 13}{100} = 1320$

or, $\frac{32x}{100} + \frac{78x}{100} = 1320$

or, $\frac{110x}{100} = 1320$

$\therefore \quad x = \frac{1320 \times 100}{110}$ = ₹ 1200

EXERCISE

(DATA SUFFICIENCY TYPE QUESTIONS)

Directions (*Questions 1–8*): *Each of the questions given below consists of a statement and/or a question and two statements numbered I and II given below it. You have to decide whether the data provided in the statement(s) is/are sufficient to answer the question. Read both the statements and*

Give answer (a) if the data in Statement I alone are sufficient to answer the question, while the data in Statement II alone are not sufficient to answer the question;

Give answer (b) if the data in Statement II alone are sufficient to answer the question, while the data in Statement I alone are not sufficient to answer the question;

Give answer (c) if the data either in Statement I or in Statement II alone are sufficient to answer the question;

Give answer (d) if the data in both Statements I and II together are not sufficient to answer the question;

Give answer (e) if the data in both Statements I and II together are necessary to answer the question.

1. What is the rate of simple interest ?
   I. The total interest earned was ₹ 4000.
   II. The sum was invested for 4 years.
2. The simple interest on a sum of money is ₹ 50. What is the sum ? **(R.B.I., 2003)**
   I. The interest rate is 10% p.a.
   II. The sum earned simple interest in 10 years.
3. How much money did X invest ?
   I. An increase in the rate of interest from $4\frac{7}{8}\%$ to $5\frac{1}{8}\%$ per annum increases his yearly income by ₹ 25.
   II. The sum invested gets doubled, when invested at 8% p.a. for $12\frac{1}{2}$ years.
4. What percentage of simple interest per annum did Anand pay to Deepak ?
   I. Anand borrowed ₹ 8000 from Deepak for four years.
   II. Anand returned ₹ 8800 to Deepak at the end of two years and settled the loan.
5. A man borrowed a total sum of ₹ 24000 from two moneylenders. For one loan, he paid interest @ $7\frac{1}{2}\%$ p.a. and for the other 9% p.a. How much money did he borrow at each rate ?
   I. The sum of the interests after one year was ₹ 2025.
   II. The interest on one sum was twice that on the other.
6. What is the sum which earned interest ?
   I. The total simple interest was ₹ 7000 after 7 years.
   II. The total of sum and simple interest was double of the sum after 5 years.
7. How much money did Gagan borrow from a bank?
   I. Gagan paid a total simple interest of ₹ 32000 at the end of 5 years.
   II. The interest at the end of 2 years was one-tenth of the money be borrowed.
8. What is the rate of interest p.c.p.a.? **(Bank P.O., 2009)**
   I. The amount doubles itself in 10 years.
   II. The simple interest accrued in 5 years is ₹ 5000.

Directions (*Questions 9-12*): *Each of the questions given below consists of a question followed by three statements. You have to study the question and the statements and decide which of the statement(s) is/are necessary to answer the question.*

9. What is the principal sum ?
   I. The sum amounts to ₹ 690 in 3 years at S.I.
   II. The sum amounts to ₹ 750 in 5 years at S.I.
   III. The rate of interest is 5% p.a.
   (*a*) I and III only
   (*b*) II and III only
   (*c*) I and II only
   (*d*) I and III only, or II and III only
   (*e*) Any two of the three
10. In how many years will a sum of money put at simple interest treble itself ?
   I. The interest earned in 4 years is half the sum.
   II. The rate of interest is $12\frac{1}{2}\%$.
   III. The sum doubles itself in 8 years at simple interest.
   (*a*) Any one of the three (*b*) Any two of the three
   (*c*) All I, II and III (*d*) II and III only
   (*e*) I and II only
11. What is the principal sum? **(SNAP, 2005)**
   I. The interest amount after 30 months is half the interest amount after 5 years.
   II. The sum amounts to ₹ 1050 in 5 years at simple interest rate.
   III. The rate of interest is 8% p.a.
   (*a*) I and II only
   (*b*) II and III only
   (*c*) I and III only
   (*d*) I and III only, or II and III only

12. What is the rate of simple interest per annum? **(R.B.I., 2004)**
    - I. An amount of ₹ 7500 increases by ₹ 1125 at the end of one year.
    - II. The principal amount of ₹ 6000 increases by three times in 20 years.
    - III. Interest accrued on an amount of ₹ 5200 in 3 years is ₹ 2340.

    (a) Any one of the three
    (b) Only I
    (c) Only III
    (d) Either I and II or III only
    (e) None of these

ANSWERS

1. (d)	2. (e)	3. (a)	4. (e)	5. (c)	6. (e)	7. (e)	8. (a)	9. (e)	10. (a)
11. (b)	12. (a)								

SOLUTIONS

1. We know that, $R = \left(\frac{100 \times \text{S.I.}}{P \times T}\right)$.

   Now, I. gives, S.I. = ₹ 4000. II. gives, T = 4 years.
   But, P is unknown.
   So, we cannot find R. So, given data is insufficient to get R.
   ∴ Correct answer is (d).

2. Given : S.I. = ₹ 50.
   I. gives, R = 10% p.a. II. gives, T = 10 years.
   $\therefore$ Sum $= \left(\frac{100 \times \text{S.I.}}{T \times R}\right) = ₹\left(\frac{100 \times 50}{10 \times 10}\right) = ₹\,50.$
   Thus, I and II together give the answer.
   ∴ Correct answer is (e).

3. Suppose X invests ₹ x.
   I. gives : $R_1 = \frac{39}{8}\%$, $R_2 = \frac{41}{8}\%$. Increase in S.I. = ₹ 25.
   $$\Rightarrow \left(\frac{x \times 1 \times \frac{41}{8}}{100}\right) - \left(\frac{x \times 1 \times \frac{39}{8}}{100}\right) = 25$$
   $\Rightarrow (41x - 39x) = (25 \times 800) \Rightarrow x = \left(\frac{25 \times 800}{2}\right) = 10000.$
   Thus, I only gives the answer.
   II. gives, S.I. = ₹ x, R = 8% and $T = \frac{25}{2}$ years.
   $$P = \frac{100 \times S.I.}{R \times T} = \left(\frac{100 \times x}{8 \times 25} \times 2\right)$$
   Thus, P is not obtained.
   ∴ I alone is sufficient to get the answer and II is not sufficient to get the answer.
   ∴ Correct answer is (a).

4. Let the rate be R% p.a.
   I. gives, P = ₹ 8000 and T = 4 years.
   II. gives, S.I. = ₹ (8800 − 8000) = ₹ 800.
   $$\therefore R = \frac{100 \times S.I.}{P \times T} = \left(\frac{100 \times 800}{8000 \times 4}\right)\% = 2\frac{1}{2}\% \text{ p.a.}$$
   Thus, I and II both are needed to get the answer.
   ∴ Correct answer is (e).

5. Suppose he borrowed ₹ x at $7\frac{1}{2}$% p.a. and ₹ $(24000 - x)$ at 9% p.a.
   I. gives, total interest = ₹ 2025.
   $$\therefore \left(x \times 1 \times \frac{15}{2} \times \frac{1}{100}\right) + \left\{(24000 - x) \times 1 \times \frac{9}{100}\right\} = 2025.$$
   This gives x.
   II. gives, Interest on ₹ $(24000 - x)$ = 2 × (interest on ₹ x)
   $$\Rightarrow (24000 - x) \times \frac{9}{100} \times 1 = \left(2 \times x \times \frac{15}{2} \times \frac{1}{100}\right)$$
   This gives x.
   Thus, data in I as well as in II are sufficient to answer the question.
   ∴ Correct answer is (c).

6. Let the sum be ₹ x.
   I. gives, S.I. = ₹ 7000 and T = 7 years.
   II. gives, Sum + S.I. for 5 years = 2 × Sum
   ⇒ Sum = S.I. for 5 years
   Now, S.I. for 7 years = ₹ 7000
   $\therefore$ S.I. for 1 year $= ₹\frac{7000}{7} = ₹\,1000.$
   S.I. for 5 years = ₹ (1000 × 5) = ₹ 5000.
   Thus, I and II both are needed to get the answer.
   ∴ Correct answer is (e).

7. Let the sum be ₹ x.
   I. gives, S.I. = ₹ 32000, T = 5 yrs.
   II. gives, S.I. $= ₹\frac{x}{10}$, T = 2 yrs.
   From II, we have: $R = \left(\frac{100 \times \text{S.I.}}{P \times T}\right) = \left(\frac{100 \times \frac{x}{10}}{x \times 2}\right)\% = 5\%.$
   Using I, we get: $x = ₹\left(\frac{100 \times 32000}{5 \times 5}\right) = ₹\,128000.$
   Thus, I and II together give the answer.
   ∴ Correct answer is (e).

8. I. gives, $P = ₹\, x$, S.I. = ₹ x, $T = 10$ yrs.

$\therefore$ Rate $= \left(\frac{S.I. \times 100}{P \times T}\right) = \left(\frac{x \times 100}{x \times 10}\right)\% = 10\%.$

II. gives, S.I. = 5000, $T = 5$ yrs.

Since P is still unknown, R cannot be calculated. Thus, only I gives the answer.

$\therefore$ Correct answer is (*a*).

9. Let the sum be ₹ x.

From **I** and **III**, we have: $A = ₹\, 690$, $T = 3$ yrs, $R = 5\%$.

$\therefore \quad x + \frac{x \times 5 \times 3}{100} = 690 \Rightarrow x + \frac{3x}{20} = 690 \Rightarrow \frac{23x}{20} = 750$

$\Rightarrow x = \frac{690 \times 20}{23} = 600$

From **II** and **III**, we have: $A = ₹\, 750$, $T = 5$ yrs, $R = 5\%$

$\therefore \quad x + \frac{x\, 5 \times 5 \times 5}{100} = 750 \Rightarrow x + \frac{x}{4} = 750 \Rightarrow \frac{5x}{4} = 750$

$\Rightarrow x = \frac{750 \times 4}{5} = 600.$

From **I** and **II**, we have:

Let the rate be R% p.a.

Then, $x + \frac{x \times R \times 3}{100} = 690 \Rightarrow x\left(1 + \frac{3R}{100}\right) = 690$ ... (*i*)

And, $x + \frac{x \times R \times 5}{100} = 750 \Rightarrow x\left(1 + \frac{5R}{100}\right) = 750$ ... (*ii*)

Dividing (*ii*) by (*i*), we get: $\frac{\left(1 + \frac{5R}{100}\right)}{\left(1 + \frac{3R}{100}\right)} = \frac{750}{690}$

$\Rightarrow$ 69 (1000 + 5R) = 75 (1000 + 3R)

$\Rightarrow$ 120R = 600 $\Rightarrow$ R = 5.

Putting $R = 5$ in (*i*), we get: $x\left(1 + \frac{15}{100}\right) = 690$

$\Rightarrow \quad x = \frac{690 \times 100}{115} = 600.$

Clearly, any two of the three will give us the answer.

$\therefore$ Correct answer is (*e*).

10. Let sum be ₹ x. Then, S.I. = ₹ $(3x - x)$ = ₹ $2x$, T = ?

I. gives : When $T = 4$, then

$\therefore \quad R = \frac{100 \times S.I.}{P \times T} = \left(100 \times \frac{x}{2} \times \frac{1}{x} \times \frac{1}{4}\right) = 12\frac{1}{2}\%$ p.a.

Now, Sum = ₹ x, S.I. = ₹ $2x$, T = ?

$\therefore \quad T = \frac{100 \times S.I.}{P \times R} = \left(\frac{100 \times 2x}{x \times 25} \times 2\right) = 16$ years.

Thus, *I* only gives the answer.

II. gives, $R = \frac{25}{2}\%$ p.a.

$\therefore \quad T = \frac{100 \times S.I.}{P \times R} = \left(\frac{100 \times 2x}{x \times 25} \times 2\right) = 16$ years.

Thus, II only also gives the answer.

III. gives, $R = 5\%$ p.a.

$\therefore \quad T = \frac{100 \times S.I.}{P \times R} = \left(\frac{100 \times 2x}{x \times 5}\right) = 40$ years

Thus, III only also gives the answer.

$\therefore$ Correct answer is (*a*).

11. Let the sum be ₹ x

Clearly, the fact given in I always hold true, irrespective of the sum. So, I does not give us the answer.

From II and III, we have: $A = ₹\, 750$, $T = 5$ yrs, $R = 8\%$.

$\therefore \quad x + \frac{x \times 8 \times 5}{100} = 1050 \Rightarrow x + \frac{2x}{5} = 1050 \Rightarrow \frac{7x}{5} = 1050$

$\Rightarrow \quad x = \left(\frac{1050 \times 5}{7}\right) = 750.$

Thus, II and III together give the answer.

$\therefore$ Correct answer is (*b*).

12. I. gives, $P = ₹\, 7500$, S.I. = ₹ 1125, $T = 1$ year.

$\therefore \quad R = \left(\frac{100 - S.I.}{P \times T}\right) = \left(\frac{100 \times 1125}{7500 \times 1}\right)\% = 15\%.$

Thus, I only gives the answer.

II. gives, $P = ₹\, 6000$, S.I. = ₹ 18000, T = 20 yrs.

$\therefore \quad R = \left(\frac{100 \times 18000}{6000 \times 20}\right)\% = 15\%.$

Thus, II only gives the answer.

III. gives, $P = ₹\, 5200$, S.I. = ₹ 2340, $T = 3$ yrs.

$\therefore \quad R = \left(\frac{100 \times 2340}{5200 \times 3}\right)\% = 15\%.$

Thus, III only gives the answer.

$\therefore$ Correct answer is (*a*).

23 Compound Interest

Compound Interest: Sometimes it so happens that the borrower and the lender agree to fix up a certain unit of time, say *yearly* or *half-yearly* or *quarterly* to settle the previous account.

In such cases, the amount after first unit of time becomes the principal for the second unit, the amount after second unit becomes the principal for the third unit and so on.

After a specified period, *the difference between the amount and the money borrowed is called the* ***Compound Interest*** *(abbreviated as C.I.) for that period.*

IMPORTANT FACTS AND FORMULAE

Let Principal = P, Rate = R% per annum, Time = n years.

I. When interest is compounded Annually:

$$\text{Amount} = P\left(1+\frac{R}{100}\right)^n$$

II. When interest is compounded Half-yearly:

$$\text{Amount} = P\left[1+\frac{(R/2)}{100}\right]^{2n}$$

III. When interest is compounded Quarterly:

$$\text{Amount} = P\left[1+\frac{(R/4)}{100}\right]^{4n}$$

IV. When interest is compounded Annually but time is in fraction, say $3\frac{2}{5}$ years.

$$\text{Amount} = P\left(1+\frac{R}{100}\right)^3 \times \left(1+\frac{\frac{2}{5}R}{100}\right)$$

V. When rates are different for different years, say R_1%, R_2%, R_3% for 1st, 2nd and 3rd year respectively.

$$\text{Then, Amount} = P\left(1+\frac{R_1}{100}\right)\left(1+\frac{R_2}{100}\right)\left(1+\frac{R_3}{100}\right).$$

VI. Present worth of ₹ x due n years hence is given by:

$$\text{Present Worth} = \frac{x}{\left(1+\frac{R}{100}\right)^n}.$$

SOLVED EXAMPLES

Ex. 1. ***After 3 years, how much compound interest will be obtained on ₹ 7800 at the interest rate of 5% per annum?*** **(R.R.B., 2009)**

Sol. Amount $= ₹\left[7800\times\left(1+\frac{5}{100}\right)^3\right] = ₹\left(7800\times\frac{21}{20}\times\frac{21}{20}\times\frac{21}{20}\right)$

$= ₹\left(\frac{361179}{40}\right) = ₹\ 9029.475.$

$\therefore$ C.I. = ₹ (9029.475 – 7800) = ₹ 1229. 475.

Ex. 2. ***Find the compound interest on ₹ 8000 at 15% per annum for 2 years 4 months, compounded annually.*** **(C.P.O., 200**

Sol. Time = 2 years 4 months = $2\frac{4}{12}$ years = $2\frac{1}{3}$ years.

$$\therefore \text{ Amount} = ₹\left[8000 \times \left(1+\frac{15}{100}\right)^2 \times \left(1+\frac{\frac{1}{3}\times 15}{100}\right)\right] = ₹\left(8000 \times \frac{23}{20} \times \frac{23}{20} \times \frac{21}{20}\right) = ₹\ 11109.$$

$\therefore$ C.I. = ₹ (11109 – 8000) = ₹ 3109.

Ex. 3. ***Find the compound interest on ₹ 10,000 in 2 years at 4% per annum, the interest being compounded half-yearly.*** **(S.S.C., 200**

Sol. Principal = ₹ 10000; Rate = 2% per half-year; Time = 2 years = 4 half-years.

$$\therefore \text{ Amount} = ₹\left[10000 \times \left(1+\frac{2}{100}\right)^4\right] = ₹\left(10000 \times \frac{51}{50} \times \frac{51}{50} \times \frac{51}{50} \times \frac{51}{50}\right) = ₹\ 10824.32.$$

$\therefore$ C.I. = ₹ (10824.32 – 10000) = ₹ 824.32.

Ex. 4. ***Find the compound interest on ₹ 16000 at 20% per annum for 9 months, compounded quarterly.*** **(C.P.O., 20**

Sol. Principal = ₹ 16000; Time = 9 months = 3 quarters;

Rate = 20% per annum = 5% per quarter.

$$\therefore \text{ Amount} = ₹\left[16000 \times \left(1+\frac{5}{100}\right)^3\right] = ₹\left(16000 \times \frac{21}{20} \times \frac{21}{20} \times \frac{21}{20}\right) = ₹\ 18522.$$

$\therefore$ C.I. = ₹ (18522 – 16000) = ₹ 2522.

Ex. 5. ***The simple interest accrued on an amount of ₹ 40000 at the end of four years is ₹ 24000. What would b the compound interest accrued on the same amount at the same rate in the same period?*** **(Bank P.O., 200**

Sol. Clearly, Principal = ₹ 40000, Time = 4 years, S.I. = ₹ 24000.

So, Rate = $\left(\frac{100 \times 24000}{40000 \times 4}\right)\%$ = 15%.

$$\text{Amount} = ₹\left[40000 \times \left(1+\frac{15}{100}\right)^4\right] = ₹\left(40000 \times \frac{23}{20} \times \frac{23}{20} \times \frac{23}{20} \times \frac{23}{20}\right) = ₹\left(\frac{279841}{4}\right) = ₹\ 69960.25.$$

$\therefore$ C.I. = ₹ (69960.25 – 40000) = ₹ 29960.25.

Ex. 6. ***Rohit invested a certain amount at the rate of 6 p.c.p. a and obtained a simple interest of ₹ 8730 at th end of 3 years. What amount of compound interest would he obtain on the same amount at the same ra of interest at the end of 2 years?*** **(Bank P.O., 201**

Sol. Clearly, Rate = 6% p.a; Time = 3 years, S.I. = ₹ 8730.

So, Principal = ₹ $\left(\frac{100 \times 8730}{3 \times 6}\right)$ = ₹ 48500.

$$\text{Amount} = ₹\left[48500 \times \left(1+\frac{6}{100}\right)^2\right] = ₹\left(48500 \times \frac{53}{50} \times \frac{53}{50}\right) = ₹\ 54494.60.$$

$\therefore$ C.I. = ₹ (54494.60 – 48500) = ₹ 5994.60.

Ex. 7. ***In how many years ₹ 100000 will become ₹ 1,33,100 at compound interest rate of 10% per annum?*** **(P.C.S., 200**

Sol. Principal = ₹ 100000, Amount

= ₹ 133100, Rate = 10% p.a.

Let the time be n years. Then,

$$100000\left(1+\frac{10}{100}\right)^n = 133100 \Rightarrow \left(\frac{11}{10}\right)^n = \left(\frac{1331}{1000}\right) = \left(\frac{11}{10}\right)^3 \Rightarrow n = 3.$$

Hence, required time = 3 years.

Ex. 8. ***At what rate percent per annum of compound interest will ₹ 1600 amount to ₹ 1852.20 in 3 years?*** **(S.S.C., 2007)**

Sol. Let the rate be R% per annum. Then,

$$1600\left(1+\frac{R}{100}\right)^3 = 1852.20$$

$$\Rightarrow \left(1+\frac{R}{100}\right)^3 = \frac{1852.20}{1600} = \frac{18522}{16000}$$

$$\Rightarrow \left(1+\frac{R}{100}\right)^3 = \frac{9261}{8000} = \left(\frac{21}{20}\right)^3$$

$$\Rightarrow 1+\frac{R}{100} = \frac{21}{20} \Rightarrow \frac{R}{100} = \frac{1}{20} \Rightarrow R = 5.$$

Hence, rate = 5% p.a.

Ex. 9. ***Find the sum of money which will amount to ₹ 26010 in 6 months at the rate of 8% per annum when the interest is compounded quarterly.*** **(Section Officers', 2006)**

Sol. Amount = ₹ 26010; Time = 6 months = 2 quarters;

Rate = 8% p.a. = 2% per quarter.

Let the sum be ₹ x. Then,

$$x \times \left(1+\frac{2}{100}\right)^2 = 26010 \Rightarrow \left(x \times \frac{51}{50} \times \frac{51}{50}\right) = 26010$$

$$\Rightarrow x = \left(\frac{26010 \times 10 \times 50 \times 50}{51 \times 51}\right) = 25000.$$

Hence, required sum = ₹ 25000.

Ex. 10. ***If the compound interest on a certain sum at $16\frac{2}{3}$% for 3 years is ₹ 1270, find the simple interest on the same sum at the same rate and for the same period.***

Sol. Let the sum be ₹ x. Then,

$$\text{C.I.} = \left[x \times \left(1+\frac{50}{3 \times 100}\right)^3 - x\right] = \left(\frac{343x}{216} - x\right) = \frac{127x}{216}$$

$$\therefore \frac{127x}{216} = 1270 \text{ or } x = \frac{1270 \times 216}{127} = 2160.$$

Thus, the sum is ₹ 2160.

$$\therefore \text{S.I.} = ₹\left(2160 \times \frac{50}{3} \times 3 \times \frac{1}{100}\right) = ₹ 1080.$$

Ex. 11. ***The compound interest accrued on an amount of ₹ 22000 at the end of two years is ₹ 5596.80. What would be the simple interest accrued on the same amount at the same rate in the same period?*** **(Bank P.O., 2008)**

Sol. Let the rate be R% p.a. Then,

$$22000\left(1+\frac{R}{100}\right)^2 = (22000 + 5596.80) = 27596.80$$

$$\Rightarrow \left(1+\frac{R}{100}\right)^2 = \frac{275968}{220000} = \left(\frac{28}{25}\right)^2$$

$$\Rightarrow \left(1+\frac{R}{100}\right) = \frac{28}{25} \Rightarrow \frac{R}{100} = \frac{3}{25} \Rightarrow R = 12.$$

$$\therefore \text{S.I.} = ₹\left(\frac{22000 \times 12 \times 2}{100}\right) = ₹ 5280.$$

Ex. 12. ***If the difference between the compound and simple interests on a certain sum of money for 3 years at 5% per annum is ₹ 15.25, find the sum.*** (C.P.O., 2006)

Sol. Let the sum be ₹ x. Then,

$$\text{C.I.} = x\left(1+\frac{5}{100}\right)^3 - x = \frac{9261}{8000}x - x = \frac{1261}{8000}x.$$

$$\text{S.I.} = \left(\frac{x\times5\times3}{100}\right) = \frac{3x}{20}.$$

$$\therefore \quad (\text{C.I.}) - (\text{S.I.}) = \left(\frac{1261}{8000}x - \frac{3x}{20}\right) = \frac{61x}{8000}.$$

$$\text{So, } \frac{61x}{8000} = 15.25$$

$$\Leftrightarrow x = \frac{15.25\times8000}{61} = 2000.$$

Hence, required sum = ₹ 2000.

Ex. 13. ***The difference between the compound interest and the simple interest accrued on an amount of ₹ 18,000 in 2 years was ₹ 405. What was the rate of interest p.c.p.a.?***

Sol. Let the rate be R% p.a. Then,

$$\left[18000\left(1+\frac{R}{100}\right)^2 - 18000\right] - \left(\frac{18000\times R\times2}{100}\right) = 405$$

$$\Leftrightarrow 18000\left[\frac{(100+R)^2}{10000} - 1 - \frac{2R}{100}\right] = 405$$

$$\Leftrightarrow 18000\left[\frac{(100+R)^2 - 10000 - 200R}{10000}\right] = 405$$

$$\Leftrightarrow \quad \frac{9}{5}R^2 = 405 \Leftrightarrow R^2 = \left(\frac{405\times5}{9}\right) = 225 \Leftrightarrow R = 15.$$

$\therefore$ Rate = 15%.

Ex. 14. ***The difference between compound and simple interests on a certain sum of money at the interest rate of 10% per annum for $1\frac{1}{2}$ years is ₹ 183, when the interest is compounded semi-annually. Find the sum of money.*** (S.S.C., 2007)

Sol. Let the sum be ₹ x. Then,

$$\text{C.I.} = ₹\left[x\left(1+\frac{5}{100}\right)^3 - x\right] = ₹\left[\left(x\times\frac{21}{20}\times\frac{21}{20}\times\frac{21}{20}\right) - x\right]$$

$$= ₹\left(\frac{9261x}{8000} - x\right) = ₹\left(\frac{1261x}{8000}\right).$$

$$\text{S.I.} = ₹\left(\frac{x\times10\times3}{100\times2}\right) = ₹\ \frac{3x}{20}.$$

$$\therefore \quad \frac{1261x}{8000} - \frac{3x}{20} = 183 \Rightarrow \frac{61x}{8000} = 183$$

$$\Rightarrow x = \left(\frac{183\times8000}{61}\right) = 24000.$$

Hence, required sum = ₹ 24000.

Ex. 15. ***Divide ₹ 1301 between A and B, so that the amount of A after 7 years is equal to the amount of B after 9 years, the interest being compounded at 4% per annum.***

Sol. Let the two parts be ₹ x and ₹ $(1301 - x)$.

$$x\left(1+\frac{4}{100}\right)^7 = (1301-x)\left(1+\frac{4}{100}\right)^9$$

$$\Leftrightarrow \frac{x}{(1301-x)} = \left(1+\frac{4}{100}\right)^2 = \left(\frac{26}{25}\times\frac{26}{25}\right).$$

$\Leftrightarrow 625x = 676\ (1301 - x)$

$\Leftrightarrow 1301x = 676 \times 1301 \Leftrightarrow x = 676.$

So, the two parts are ₹ 676 and ₹ (1301 – 676) i.e. ₹ 676 and ₹ 625.

Ex. 16. ***A certain sum amounts to ₹ 7350 in 2 years and to ₹ 8575 in 3 years. Find the sum and rate percent.*** **(Campus Recruitment, 2010)**

Sol. S.I. on ₹ 7350 for 1 year = ₹ (8575 – 7350) = ₹ 1225.

$$\therefore \quad \text{Rate} = \left(\frac{100\times1225}{7350\times1}\right)\% = 16\frac{2}{3}\%.$$

Let the sum be ₹ x. Then,

$$x\left(1+\frac{50}{3\times100}\right)^2 = 7350 \Leftrightarrow x\times\frac{7}{6}\times\frac{7}{6} = 7350 \Leftrightarrow x = \left(7350\times\frac{36}{49}\right) = 5400.$$

$\therefore$ Sum = ₹ 5400.

Ex. 17. ***A sum of money becomes ₹ 13380 after 3 years and ₹ 20070 after 6 years on compound interest. Find the sum.*** **(L.I.C.A.A.O., 2007)**

Sol. Let the sum be ₹ P. Then,

$$P\left(1+\frac{R}{100}\right)^3 = 13380 \qquad ...(i)$$

$$\text{and} \quad P\left(1+\frac{R}{100}\right)^6 = 20070 \qquad ...(ii)$$

On dividing, we get: $\left(1+\frac{R}{100}\right)^3 = \frac{20070}{13380} = \frac{3}{2}.$

Substituting this value in *(i)*, we get;

$$P\times\frac{3}{2} = 13380 \quad \text{or} \quad P = \left(13380\times\frac{2}{3}\right) = 8920.$$

Hence, required sum = ₹ 8920.

Ex. 18. ***A sum of money doubles itself at compound interest in 15 years. In how many years will it become eight times?***

Sol. $P\left(1+\frac{R}{100}\right)^{15} = 2P \Rightarrow \left(1+\frac{R}{100}\right)^{15} = \frac{2P}{P} = 2 \qquad ...(i)$

Let $P\left(1+\frac{R}{100}\right)^n = 8P \Rightarrow \left(1+\frac{R}{100}\right)^n = 8 = 2^3 = \left\{\left(1+\frac{R}{100}\right)^{15}\right\}^3$ [using *(i)*]

$$\Rightarrow \left(1+\frac{R}{100}\right)^n = \left(1+\frac{R}{100}\right)^{45} \Rightarrow n = 45.$$

Thus, the required time = 45 years.

Ex. 19. ***What annual payment will discharge a debt of ₹ 7620 due in 3 years at $16\frac{2}{3}$% per annum compound interest?*** **(G.B.O., 2007)**

Sol. Let each instalment be ₹ x. Then,

(P.W. of ₹ x due 1 year hence) + (P.W. of ₹ x due 2 years hence) + (P.W. of ₹ x due 3 years hence) = 7620.

$$\therefore \frac{x}{\left(1+\frac{50}{3\times100}\right)}+\frac{x}{\left(1+\frac{50}{3\times100}\right)^2}+\frac{x}{\left(1+\frac{50}{3\times100}\right)^3}=7620$$

$$\Leftrightarrow \frac{6x}{7}+\frac{36x}{49}+\frac{216x}{343}=7620 \Leftrightarrow 294x+252x+216x=7620\times343$$

$$\Leftrightarrow x=\left(\frac{7620\times343}{762}\right)=3430.$$

∴ Amount of each instalment = ₹ 3430.

Ex. 20. ***A T.V. set is available for ₹ 19650 cash payment or for ₹ 3100 cash down payment and three equal annual instalments. If the shopkeeper charges interest at the rate of 10% per annum compounded annually, calculate the amount of each instalment.*** (S.S.C., 2008)

Sol. Total cost of the T.V. set = ₹ 19650. Down payment = ₹ 3100.

Balance = ₹ (19650 – 3100) = ₹ 16550.

Let the value of each instalment be ₹ x. Then,

(P. W. of ₹ x due 1 year hence) + (P. W. of ₹ x due 2 years hence) + (P. W. of ₹ x due 3 years hence) = ₹ 16550.

$$\therefore \frac{x}{\left(1+\frac{10}{100}\right)}+\frac{x}{\left(1+\frac{10}{100}\right)^2}+\frac{x}{\left(1+\frac{10}{100}\right)^3}=16550 \Rightarrow \frac{10x}{11}+\frac{100x}{121}+\frac{1000x}{1331}=16550$$

$$\Rightarrow 1210x + 1100x + 1000x = 16550 \times 1331 \Rightarrow 3310x = 16550 \times 1331$$

$$\Rightarrow x=\left(\frac{16550\times1331}{3310}\right)=6655.$$

Hence, value of each instalment = ₹ 6655.

EXERCISE

(OBJECTIVE TYPE QUESTIONS)

Directions: ***Mark (✓) against the correct answer:***

1. What would be the compound interest accrued on an amount of ₹ 8000 at the rate of 15 p.c.p.a. in 3 years? (Bank P.O., 2009)
   (*a*) ₹ 4051 (*b*) ₹ 4167
   (*c*) ₹ 4283 (*d*) ₹ 4325
   (*e*) None of these
2. What would be the compound interest accrued on an amount of ₹ 8400 @ 12.5 p.c.p.a. at the end of 3 years? (Bank P.O., 2010)
   (*a*) ₹ 2584.16 (*b*) ₹ 3560.16
   (*c*) ₹ 3820.14 (*d*) ₹ 4205.62
   (*e*) None of these
3. The compound interest on ₹ 2800 for 18 months at 10% p.a. is (L.I.C.A.D.O., 2008)
   (*a*) ₹ 420 (*b*) ₹ 434
   (*c*) ₹ 436.75 (*d*) ₹ 441.35
4. The compound interest on ₹ 20,480 at $6\frac{1}{4}$% per annum for 2 years 73 days, is
   (*a*) ₹ 2929 (*b*) ₹ 3000
   (*c*) ₹ 3131 (*d*) ₹ 3636
5. A man saves ₹ 200 at the end of each year and lends the money at 5% compound interest. How much will it become at the end of 3 years ?
   (*a*) ₹ 565.25 (*b*) ₹ 635
   (*c*) ₹ 662.02 (*d*) ₹ 666.50
6. If the rate of interest be 4% per annum for first year, 5% per annum for second year and 6% per annum for third year, then the compound interest of ₹ 10000 for 3 years will be (C.P.O., 2006)
   (*a*) ₹ 1575.20 (*b*) ₹ 1600
   (*c*) ₹ 1625.80 (*d*) ₹ 2000
7. What will be the compound interest accrued on an amount of ₹ 10000 @ 20 p.c.p.a. in 2 years if the interest is compounded half-yearly? (Bank P.O., 2009)
   (*a*) ₹ 4400 (*b*) ₹ 4600
   (*c*) ₹ 4641 (*d*) ₹ 4680
   (*e*) None of these
8. A bank offers 5% compound interest calculated on half-yearly basis. A customer deposits ₹ 1600 each on 1st January and 1st July of a year. At the end of the year, the amount he would have gained by way of interest is:
   (*a*) ₹ 120 (*b*) ₹ 121
   (*c*) ₹ 122 (*d*) ₹ 123

9. What is the difference between the compound interests on ₹ 5000 for $1\frac{1}{2}$ years at 4% per annum compounded yearly and half-yearly?
(a) ₹ 2.04 (b) ₹ 3.06
(c) ₹ 4.80 (d) ₹ 8.30

10. Mr Duggal invested ₹ 20000 with rate of interest @ 20 p.c.p.a. The interest was compounded half-yearly for first one year and in the next year it was compounded yearly. What will be the total interest earned at the end of 2 years? **(Bank P.O., 2009)**
(a ₹ 8040 (b) ₹ 8800
(c) ₹ 9040 (d) ₹ 9800
(e) None of these

11. Find the compound interest on ₹ 15625 for 9 months at 16% per annum compounded quarterly.
(a) ₹ 1851 (b) ₹ 1941
(c) ₹ 1951 (d) ₹ 1961

12. A man gets a simple interest of ₹ 1000 on a certain principal at the rate of 5 p.c.p.a. in 4 years. What compound interest will the man get on twice the principal in 2 years at the same rate? **(Bank P.O., 2010)**
(a) ₹ 1000 (b) ₹ 1005
(c) ₹ 10125 (d) ₹ 11025
(e) None of these

13. The simple interest accrued on an amount of ₹ 20000 at the end of 3 years is ₹ 7200. What would be the compound interest accrued on the same amount at the same rate in the same period? **(Bank P.O., 2008)**
(a) ₹ 8098.56 (b) ₹ 8112.86
(c) ₹ 8246.16 (d) ₹ 8342.36
(e) None of these

14. The difference between simple interest and compound interest on ₹ *P* at *R*% p.a. in 2 years is **(Compus Recruitment, 2010)**
(a) ₹ $\frac{PR}{100}$ (b) ₹ $\frac{2PR}{100}$
(c) ₹ $\frac{PR^2}{100}$ (d) ₹ $\frac{PR^2}{(100)^2}$

15. What will be the difference between the simple interest and compound interest accrued on an amount of ₹ 19200 at the end of 3 years @ 12 p.c.p.a.? **(S.B.I.P.O., 2008)**
(a) ₹ 722.6826 (b) ₹ 798.1824
(c) ₹ 802.5144 (d) ₹ 862.6176
(e) None of these

16. What will be the difference between S.I. and C.I. on a sum of ₹ 15000 for 2 years at the same rate of interest of $12\frac{1}{2}$% per annum? **(R.R.B., 2006)**
(a) ₹ 230.550 (b) ₹ 234.375
(c) ₹ 250.129 (d) ₹ 324.357

17. The difference between simple interest and compound interest on ₹ 1200 for one year at 10% per annum reckoned half-yearly is
(a) ₹ 2.50 (b) ₹ 3
(c) ₹ 3.75 (d) ₹ 4
(e) None of these

18. A man borrows ₹ 4000 at 15% compound rate of interest. At the end of each year he pays back ₹ 1500. How much amount should be pay at the end of the third year to clear all his dues? **(N.M.A.T., 2005)**
(a) ₹ 874.75 (b) ₹ 824.50
(c) ₹ 924.25 (d) ₹ 974.25

19. A man invests ₹ 5000 for 3 years at 5% p.a. compound interest reckoned yearly. Income tax at the rate of 20% on the interest earned is deducted at the end of each year. Find the amount at the end of the third year. **(M.A.T., 2004)**
(a) ₹ 5624.32 (b) ₹ 5627.20
(c) ₹ 5630.50 (d) ₹ 5788.125

20. The compound interest on ₹ 30,000 at 7% per annum is ₹ 4347. The period (in years) is **(L.I.C.A.A.O., 2003)**
(a) 2 years (b) $2\frac{1}{2}$ years
(c) 3 years (d) 4 years

21. Compound interest accrued on an amount of ₹ 26500 in two years is ₹ 9775.85. What is the rate of interest p.c.p.a.? **(Bank P.O., 2010)**
(a) 12% (b) 15%
(c) 17% (d) 22%
(e) None of these

22. ₹ 2000 amounts to ₹ 2226.05 in 2 years at compound interest. What will be the rate of interest? **(E.S.I.C., 2006)**
(a) 5% (b) 5.25%
(c) 5.5% (d) 6%

23. A man invests ₹ 4000 for 3 years at compound interest. After one year the money amounts to ₹ 4320. What will be the amount (to the nearest rupee) due at the end of 3 years? **(R.R.B., 2006)**
(a) ₹ 4939 (b) ₹ 5039
(c) ₹ 5789 (d) ₹ 6129

24. An amount of ₹ 10000 becomes ₹ 14641 in 2 years if the interest is compounded half-yearly. What is the rate of compound interest p.c.p.a.? **(Bank P.O. 2009)**
(a) 10% (b) 12%
(c) 16% (d) 20%
(e) None of these

25. The principal that amounts to ₹ 4913 in 3 years at $6\frac{1}{4}$% per annum compound interest compounded annually, is (S.S.C., 2005)
(a) ₹ 3096 (b) ₹ 4076
(c) ₹ 4085 (d) ₹ 4096

26. The present worth of ₹ 169 due in 2 years at 4% per annum compound interest is
(a) ₹ 150.50 (b) ₹ 154.75
(c) ₹ 156.25 (d) ₹ 158

27. The compound interest accrued on an amount at the end of 3 years @ 15 p.c.p.a. is ₹ 6500.52. What is the amount? (S.B.I.P.O., 2008)
(a) ₹ 10500 (b) ₹ 12480
(c) ₹ 13620 (d) ₹ 14800
(e) None of these

28. In how many years will a sum of ₹ 800 at 10% per annum compounded semi-annually become ₹ 926.10? (S.S.C., 2010)
(a) $1\frac{1}{3}$ years (b) $1\frac{1}{2}$ years
(c) $2\frac{1}{3}$ years (d) $2\frac{1}{2}$ years

29. If the compound interest on a sum for 2 years at $12\frac{1}{2}$% per annum is ₹ 510, the simple interest on the same sum at the same rate for the same period of time is : (S.S.C., 2004)
(a) ₹ 400 (b) ₹ 450
(c) ₹ 460 (d) ₹ 480

30. The compound interest on a certain sum for 2 years at 10% per annum is ₹ 525. The simple interest on the same sum for double the time at half the rate percent per annum is
(a) ₹ 400 (b) ₹ 500
(c) ₹ 600 (d) ₹ 800

31. The simple interest on a certain sum of money for 3 years at 8% per annum is half the compound interest on ₹ 4000 for 2 years at 10% per annum. The sum placed on simple interest is
(a) ₹ 1550 (b) ₹ 1650
(c) ₹ 1750 (d) ₹ 2000

32. There is 60% increase in an amount in 6 years at simple interest. What will be the compound interest of ₹ 12,000 after 3 years at the same rate?
(a) ₹ 2160 (b) ₹ 3120
(c) ₹ 3972 (d) ₹ 6240
(e) None of these

33. The compound interest earned by Sachin on a certain amount at the end of two years at the rate of 8 p.c.p.a. was ₹ 1414.40. What was the total amount that Sachin got back at the end of 2 years in the form of principal plus interest earned (S.B.I.P.O., 2010)
(a) ₹ 8914.40 (b) ₹ 9014.40
(c) ₹ 9414.40 (d) ₹ 9914.40
(e) None of these

34. The compound interest accrued on an amount of ₹ 25500 at the end of 3 years is ₹ 8440.50. What would be the simple interest accrued on the same amount at the same rate in the same period? (Bank P.O., 2009)
(a) ₹ 4650 (b) ₹ 5650
(c) ₹ 6650 (d) ₹ 7650
(e) None of these

35. Sriram invested equal sums of money in two schemes. Under scheme X, the compound interest rate was 10 p.c.p.a. and under scheme Y, the compound interest rate was 12 p.c.p.a. The interest after 2 years on the sum invested in scheme X was ₹ 63. How much is the interest earned under scheme Y after 2 years? (Bank P.O., 2006)
(a) ₹ 70.56 (b) ₹ 76.32
(c) ₹ 79.0272
(d) ₹ Cannot be determined
(e) None of these

36. The difference between the amount the amount of compound interest and simple interest accrued on an amount of ₹ 26000 at the end of 3 years is ₹ 2994.134. What is the rate of interest p.c.p.a.? (Bank P.O., 2005)
(a) 17% (b) 19%
(c) 22%
(d) Cannot be determined
(e) None of these

37. The difference between compound interest and simple interest on a sum for 2 years at 8 per cent is ₹ 768. The sum is
(a) ₹ 100000 (b) ₹ 110000
(c) ₹ 120000 (d) ₹ 170000

38. The compound interest on a sum of money for 2 years is ₹ 832 and the simple interest on the same sum for the same period is ₹ 800. The difference between the compound interest and the simple interest for 3 years will be
(a) ₹ 48 (b) ₹ 66.56
(c) ₹ 98.56 (d) None of these

39. The difference between the simple interest on a certain sum at the rate of 10% per annum for 2 years and compound interest which is compounded every 6 months is ₹ 124.05. What is the principal sum?
(*a*) ₹ 6000 (*b*) ₹ 8000
(*c*) ₹ 10,000 (*d*) ₹ 12,000
(*e*) None of these

40. The difference between compound interest and simple interest on a sum for 2 years at 10% per annum, when the interest is compounded annually is ₹ 16. If the interest were compounded half-yearly, the difference in two interests would be
(*a*) ₹ 24.81 (*b*) ₹ 26.90
(*c*) ₹ 31.61 (*d*) ₹ 32.40

41. A money-lender borrows money at 4% per annum and pays the interest at the end of the year. He lends it at 6% per annum compound interest compounded half-yearly and receives the interest at the end of the year. In this way, he gains ₹ 104.50 a year. The amount of money be borrows, is (S.S.C., 2007)
(*a*) ₹ 4500 (*b*) ₹ 5000
(*c*) ₹ 5500 (*d*) ₹ 6000

42. A sum of money lent at compound interest for 2 years at 20% per annum would fetch ₹ 482 more, if the interest was payable half-yearly than if it was payable annually. The sum is :
(*a*) ₹ 10,000 (*b*) ₹ 20,000
(*c*) ₹ 40,000 (*d*) ₹ 50,000

43. On a sum of money, the simple interest for 2 years is ₹ 660, while the compound interest is ₹ 696.30, the rate of interest being the same in both the cases. The rate of interest is
(*a*) 10% (*b*) 10.5%
(*c*) 12% (*d*) None of these

44. The effective annual rate of interest corresponding to a nominal rate of 6% per annum payable half-yearly is (S.S.C., 2005)
(*a*) 6.06% (*b*) 6.07%
(*c*) 6.08% (*d*) 6.09%

45. A person lent out a certain sum on simple interest and the same sum on compound interest at a certain rate of interest per annum. He noticed that the ratio between the difference of compound interest and simple interest of 3 years and that of 2 years is 25 : 8. The rate of interest per annum is (M.A.T., 2005)
(*a*) 10% (*b*) 11%
(*c*) 12% (*d*) $12\frac{1}{2}$%

46. A father left a will of ₹ 16400 for his two sons aged 17 and 18 years. They must get equal amounts when they are 20 years, at 5% compound interest. Find the present share of the younger son. (R.R.B., 2008)
(*a*) ₹ 8000 (*b*) ₹ 8200
(*c*) ₹ 8400 (*d*) ₹ 8800

47. Divide ₹ 8840 between A and B so that the amount received by A at the end of 8 years may be equal to the amount received by B at the end of 10 years, compound interest being at 10% per annum. (S.S.C., 2007)
(*a*) ₹ 4640, ₹ 4200 (*b*) ₹ 4840, ₹ 4000
(*c*) ₹ 5000, ₹ 3840 (*d*) ₹ 5240, ₹ 3600

48. Mr. Dua invested money in two schemes A and B offering compound interest @ 8 p.c.p.a. and 9 p.c.p.a. respectively. If the total amount of interest accrued through two schemes together in two years was ₹ 4818.30 and the total amount invested was ₹ 27,000, what was the amount invested in Scheme A?
(*a*) ₹ 12,000 (*b*) ₹ 13,500
(*c*) ₹ 15,000
(*d*) Cannot be determined
(*e*) None of these

49. A sum of money put at compound interest amounts in 2 years to ₹ 672 and in 3 years to ₹ 714. The rate of interest per annum is (P.C.S., 2009)
(*a*) 5.5% (*b*) 6.0%
(*c*) 6.25% (*d*) 6.75%

50. A sum of money invested at compound interest amounts to ₹ 4624 in 2 years and to ₹ 4913 in 3 years. The sum of money is :
(*a*) ₹ 4096 (*b*) ₹ 4260
(*c*) ₹ 4335 (*d*) ₹ 4360

51. A sum of ₹ 12,000 deposited at compound interest becomes double after 5 years. After 20 years, it will become : (S.S.C., 2010)
(*a*) ₹ 96,000 (*b*) ₹ 1,20,000
(*c*) ₹ 1,24,000 (*d*) ₹ 1,92,000

52. A sum of money at compound interest doubles itself in 15 years. It will become eight times of itself in (S.S.C., 2010)
(*a*) 45 years (*b*) 48 years
(*c*) 54 years (*d*) 60 years

53. A finance company declares that, at a certain compound interest rate, a sum of money deposited by anyone will become 8 times in 3 years. If the same amount is deposited at the same compound rate of interest, then in how many years will it become 16 times? (M.A.T., 2007)
(*a*) 4 years (*b*) 5 years
(*c*) 6 years (*d*) 7 years

54. A sum of money lent out at compound interest increases in value by 50% in 5 years. A person wants to lend three different sums x, y and z for 10, 15 and 20 years respectively at the above rate in such a way that he gets back equal sums at the end of their respective periods. The ratio $x : y : z$ is (A.O. Exam, 2010)

(a) 6 : 9 : 4 (b) 9 : 4 : 6
(c) 9 : 6 : 4 (d) 6 : 4 : 9

55. The least number of complete years in which a sum of money put out at 20% compound interest will be more than doubled is (N.I.F.T., 2003)

(a) 3 (b) 4
(c) 5 (d) 6

56. A man borrows ₹ 2550 to be paid back with compound interest at the rate of 4% per annum by the end of 2 years in two equal yearly instalments. How much will each instalment be?

(a) ₹ 1275 (b) ₹ 1283
(c) ₹ 1352 (d) ₹ 1377

57. Under the Rural Housing Scheme, the Delhi Development Authority (DDA) allotted a house to Kamal Raj for ₹ 1,26,100. This payment is to be made in three equal annual instalments. If the money is reckoned at 5% per annum compound interest, then how much is to be paid by Kamal Raj in each instalment? (M.A.T., 2006)

(a) ₹ 45205 (b) ₹ 46305
(c) ₹ 47405 (d) ₹ 48505

58. A taperecorder is sold for ₹ 3500 cash, or ₹ 1000 cash down payment and the balance in three equal easy instalments. If $12\frac{1}{2}$% is the rate of interest compounded annually, find the amount of instalment. (R.R.B., 2005)

(a) ₹ 1000.35 (b) ₹ 1049.85
(c) ₹ 1050.65 (d) ₹ 1100.45

59. One can purchase a flat from a house building society for ₹ 55000 cash or on the terms that he should pay ₹ 4275 as cash down payment and the rest in three equal instalments. The society charges interest at the rate of 16% per annum compounded half-yearly. If the flat is purchased under instalment plan, find the value of each instalment. (N.M.A.T., 2005)

(a) ₹ 18756 (b) ₹ 19292
(c) ₹ 19683 (d) ₹ 20285

60. What annual payment will discharge a debt of ₹ 1025 due in 2 years at the rate of 5% compound interest?

(a) ₹ 550 (b) ₹ 551.25
(c) ₹ 560 (d) ₹ 560.75

61. A man borrows ₹ 12,500 at 20% compound interest. At the end of every year he pays ₹ 2000 as part repayment. How much does he still owe after three such instalments?

(a) ₹ 12,000 (b) ₹ 12,864
(c) ₹ 15,600 (d) None of these

62. A sum of money is borrowed and paid back in two annual instalments of ₹ 882 each allowing 5% compound interest. The sum borrowed was

(a) ₹ 1620 (b) ₹ 1640
(c) ₹ 1680 (d) ₹ 1700

63. The sum of money which when given on compound interest at 18% per annum would fetch ₹ 960 more when the interest is payable half yearly than when it was payable annually for 2 years is [SSC—CHSL (10+2) Exam, 2015]

(a) ₹ 60,000 (b) ₹ 30,000
(c) ₹ 40,000 (d) ₹ 50,000

64. On what sum of money will the difference between simple interest and compound interest for 2 years at 5% per annum be equal to ₹ 63? [SSC—CHSL (10 + 2) Exam, 2015]

(a) ₹ 24600 (b) ₹ 24800
(c) ₹ 25200 (d) ₹ 25500

65. At what rate of compound interest per annum will a sum of ₹ 1200 become ₹ 1348.32 in 2 years? [SSC—CHSL (10+2) Exam, 2015]

(a) 7.5% (b) 6.5%
(c) 7% (d) 6%

66. The compound interest on a certain sum of money for 2 years at 10% per annum is ₹ 525. The simple interest on the same sum of money for double the time at half the rate percent per annum is? [RBI Gr. 'B' (Phase I) Exam, 2015]

(a) ₹ 1000 (b) ₹ 500
(c) ₹ 200 (d) ₹ 800

67. Shashi had a certain amount of money. He invested $\frac{2}{3}$ of the total money in scheme A for 6 years and rest of the money he invested in scheme B for 2 years. Scheme A offers simple interest at a rate of 12% p.a. and scheme B offers compound interest (compounded annually) at a rate of 10% p.a. If the total interest obtained from both the schemes is ₹ 2,750, what was the total amount invested by him in scheme A and scheme B together? (Approximate value) [IBPS—Bank Spl. Officers (IT) Exam, 2015]

(a) ₹ 4500 (b) ₹ 4200
(c) ₹ 4050 (d) ₹ 5000

68. The difference between CI and SI on a certain sum of money for 3 years at 5% p.a. is ₹ 122. Find the sum invested. [IBPS—RRB Office Assistant (Online) Exam, 2015]

(*a*) ₹ 10000 (*b*) ₹ 12000
(*c*) ₹ 16000 (*d*) ₹ 20000

69. What is the difference between the compound interests on ₹ 5000 for 1 year at 4% per annum compounded yearly and half yearly?

[SSC—Junior Associates (Pre.) Exam, 2016]

(*a*) 2 (*b*) 3
(c) 4 (e) None of these

ANSWERS

1. (*b*)	2. (*b*)	3. (*b*)	4. (*a*)	5. (*c*)	6. (*a*)	7. (*c*)	8. (*b*)	9. (*a*)	10. (*c*)
11. (*c*)	12. (*e*)	13. (*a*)	14. (*d*)	15. (*d*)	16. (*b*)	17. (*b*)	18. (*a*)	19. (*a*)	20. (*a*)
21. (*e*)	22. (*c*)	23. (*b*)	24. (*d*)	25. (*d*)	26. (*c*)	27. (*b*)	28. (*b*)	29. (*d*)	30. (*b*)
31. (*c*)	32. (*c*)	33. (*d*)	34. (*d*)	35. (*b*)	36. (*b*)	37. (*c*)	38. (*c*)	39. (*b*)	40. (*a*)
41. (*b*)	42. (*b*)	43. (*d*)	44. (*d*)	45. (*d*)	46. (*a*)	47. (*b*)	48. (*a*)	49. (*c*)	50. (*a*)
51. (*d*)	52. (*a*)	53. (*a*)	54. (*c*)	55. (*b*)	56. (*c*)	57. (*b*)	58. (*b*)	59. (*c*)	60. (*b*)
61. (*d*)	62. (*b*)	63. (*d*)	64. (*c*)	65. (*d*)	66. (*b*)	67. (*d*)	68. (*c*)	69. (*a*)	

SOLUTIONS

1. Amount $= ₹\left[8000\times\left(1+\frac{15}{100}\right)^3\right]$

$= ₹\left(8000\times\frac{23}{20}\times\frac{23}{20}\times\frac{23}{20}\right) = ₹\ 12167.$

$\therefore$ C.I. $= ₹\ (12167 - 8000) = ₹\ 4167.$

2. Amount $= ₹\left[8400\times\left(1+\frac{25}{2\times100}\right)^3\right] = ₹\left(8400\times\frac{9}{8}\times\frac{9}{8}\times\frac{9}{8}\right)$

$= ₹\left(\frac{382725}{32}\right) = ₹\ 11960.156 \approx ₹\ 11960.16.$

$\therefore$ C.I. $= ₹\ (11960.16 - 8400) = ₹\ 3560.16.$

3. Amount $= ₹\left[2800\times\left(1+\frac{10}{100}\right)\left(1+\frac{5}{100}\right)\right]$

$= ₹\left(2800\times\frac{11}{10}\times\frac{21}{20}\right) = ₹\ 3234.$

$\therefore$ C.I. $= ₹\ (3234 - 2800) = ₹\ 434.$

4. Time $= 2\frac{73}{365}$ years $= 2\frac{1}{5}$ years.

$\therefore$ Amount $= ₹\left[20480\times\left(1+\frac{25}{4\times100}\right)^2\left(1+\frac{\frac{1}{5}\times\frac{25}{4}}{100}\right)\right]$

$= ₹\left(20480\times\frac{17}{16}\times\frac{17}{16}\times\frac{81}{80}\right) = ₹\ 23409.$

$\therefore$ C.I. $= ₹\ (23409 - 20480) = ₹\ 2929.$

5. Amount

$= ₹\left[200\left(1+\frac{5}{100}\right)^3 + 200\left(1+\frac{5}{100}\right)^2 + 200\left(1+\frac{5}{100}\right)\right]$

$= ₹\left[200\times\frac{21}{20}\times\frac{21}{20}\times\frac{21}{20} + 200\times\frac{21}{20}\times\frac{21}{20} + 200\times\frac{21}{20}\right]$

$= ₹\left[200\times\frac{21}{20}\left(\frac{21}{20}\times\frac{21}{20}+\frac{21}{20}+1\right)\right] = ₹\ 662.02.$

6. Amount $= ₹\ 10000\left[\left(1+\frac{4}{100}\right)\left(1+\frac{5}{100}\right)\left(1+\frac{6}{100}\right)\right]$

$= ₹\left(10000\times\frac{26}{25}\times\frac{21}{20}\times\frac{53}{50}\right) = ₹\left(\frac{57876}{5}\right) = ₹\ 11575.20$

$\therefore$ C.I. $= ₹\ (11575.20 - 10000) = ₹\ 1575.20.$

7. $P = ₹\ 10000$, $R = 20\%$ p.a. $= 10\%$ per half-year; $T = 2$ years $= 4$ half-years.

Amount $= ₹\left[10000\times\left(1+\frac{10}{100}\right)^4\right]$

$= ₹\left(10000\times\frac{11}{10}\times\frac{11}{10}\times\frac{11}{10}\times\frac{11}{10}\right) = ₹\ 14641.$

$\therefore$ C. I. $= ₹\ (14641 - 10000) = ₹\ 4641.$

8. Amount $= ₹\left[1600\times\left(1+\frac{5}{2\times100}\right)^2 + 1600\times\left(1+\frac{5}{2\times100}\right)\right]$

$= ₹\left[1600\times\frac{41}{40}\times\frac{41}{40} + 1600\times\frac{41}{40}\right]$

$= ₹\left[1600\times\frac{41}{40}\left(\frac{41}{40}+1\right)\right] = ₹\left(\frac{1600\times41\times81}{40\times40}\right)$

$= ₹\ 3321.$

$\therefore$ C.I. $= ₹\ (3321 - 3200) = ₹\ 121.$

9. C.I. when interest is compounded yearly

$= ₹\left[5000\times\left(1+\frac{4}{100}\right)\times\left(1+\frac{\frac{1}{2}\times4}{100}\right)\right]$

$= ₹\left(5000\times\frac{26}{25}\times\frac{51}{50}\right) = ₹\ 5304.$

C.I. when interest is compounded half-yearly

$= ₹\left[5000\times\left(1+\frac{2}{100}\right)^3\right] = ₹\left(5000\times\frac{51}{50}\times\frac{51}{50}\times\frac{51}{50}\right)$

$= ₹\ 5306.04.$

$\therefore$ Difference $= ₹\ (5306.04 - 5304) = ₹\ 2.04.$

10. Amount = ₹ $\left[20000\left(1+\frac{10}{100}\right)^2\left(1+\frac{20}{100}\right)\right]$

$= ₹ \left(20000\times\frac{11}{10}\times\frac{11}{10}\times\frac{6}{5}\right) = ₹\ 29040.$

$\therefore$ C. I. = ₹ (29040 – 20000) = ₹ 9040.

11. P = ₹ 15625, n = 9 months = 3 quarters, R = 16% p.a. = 4% per quarter.

Amount = ₹ $\left[15625\times\left(1+\frac{4}{100}\right)^3\right]$

$= ₹ \left(15625\times\frac{26}{25}\times\frac{26}{25}\times\frac{26}{25}\right) = ₹\ 17576.$

$\therefore$ C.I. = ₹ (17576 – 15625) = ₹ 1951.

12. Principal = ₹ $\left(\frac{100\times1000}{5\times4}\right)$ = ₹ 5000.

Now, P = ₹ 10000, T = 2 years, R = 5%.

Amount= ₹ $\left[10000\left(1+\frac{5}{100}\right)^2\right]$

$= ₹ \left(10000\times\frac{21}{20}\times\frac{21}{20}\right) = ₹\ 11025.$

$\therefore$ C.I. = ₹ (11025 – 10000) = ₹ 1025.

13. Rate = $\left(\frac{100\times7200}{20000\times3}\right)\%$ = 12%

Now, = ₹ 20000, R = 12%, T = 3 years.

Amount = ₹ $\left[20000\left(1+\frac{12}{100}\right)^3\right]$

$= ₹ \left(20000\times\frac{28}{25}\times\frac{28}{25}\times\frac{28}{25}\right)$

$= ₹ \left(\frac{702464}{25}\right) = ₹\ 28098.56.$

$\therefore$ C.I. = ₹ (28098.56 – 20000) = ₹ 8098.56.

14. S.I. = ₹ $\left(\frac{P\times R\times2}{100}\right)$ = ₹ $\left(\frac{2PR}{100}\right)$.

C.I. = ₹ $\left[P\times\left(1+\frac{R}{100}\right)^2-P\right]$ = ₹ $\left[\frac{PR^2}{(100)^2}+\frac{2PR}{100}\right]$.

$\therefore$ Difference = ₹ $\left[\left\{\frac{PR^2}{(100)^2}+\frac{2PR}{100}\right\}-\frac{2PR}{100}\right]$ = ₹ $\left[\frac{PR^2}{(100)^2}\right]$.

15. S.I. = ₹ $\left(\frac{19200\times12\times3}{100}\right)$ = ₹ 6912.

C.I. = ₹ $\left[19200\times\left(1+\frac{12}{100}\right)^3-19200\right]$

$= ₹ \left[\left(19200\times\frac{28}{25}\times\frac{28}{25}\times\frac{28}{25}\right)-19200\right]$

$= ₹ \left(\frac{16859136}{625}-19200\right)$

= ₹ (26974.6176 – 19200) = ₹ 7774.6176.

$\therefore$ Difference = ₹ (7774.6176 – 6912) = ₹ 862.6176.

16. S.I. = ₹ $\left(15000\times\frac{25}{2}\times2\times\frac{1}{100}\right)$ = ₹ 3750.

C.I. = ₹ $\left[15000\left(1+\frac{25}{2\times100}\right)^2-15000\right]$

$= ₹ \left(15000\times\frac{9}{8}\times\frac{9}{8}-15000\right)$

= ₹ (18984.375 – 15000) = ₹ 3984.375.

$\therefore$ Difference = ₹ (3984.375 – 3750) = ₹ 234.375.

17. S.I. = ₹ $\left(\frac{1200\times10\times1}{100}\right)$ = ₹ 120.

C.I. = ₹ $\left[1200\times\left(1+\frac{5}{100}\right)^2-1200\right]$ = ₹ 123.

Difference = ₹ (123 – 120) = ₹ 3.

18. Amount after 1st year = ₹ $\left[4000\left(1+\frac{15}{100}\right)-1500\right]$

$= ₹ \left[\left(4000\times\frac{23}{20}\right)-1500\right]$

= ₹ (4600 – 1500) = ₹ 3100.

Amount after 2nd year = ₹ $\left[3100\left(1+\frac{15}{100}\right)-1500\right]$

$= ₹ \left[\left(3100\times\frac{23}{20}\right)-1500\right]$

= ₹ (3565 – 1500) = ₹ 2065.

Amount after 3rd year = ₹ $\left[2065\left(1+\frac{15}{100}\right)-1500\right]$

$= ₹ \left[\left(2065\times\frac{23}{20}\right)-1500\right]$

= ₹ (2374.75 – 1500) = ₹ 874.75.

19. C.I. earned during 1st year = ₹ $\left[5000\left(1+\frac{5}{100}\right)-5000\right]$

= ₹ (5250 – 5000) = ₹ 250.

Amount after 1st year = ₹ (5250 – 20% of 250) = ₹ (5250 – 50) = ₹ 5200.

C.I. earned during 2nd year = ₹ $\left[5200\left(1+\frac{5}{100}\right)-5200\right]$

= ₹ (5460 – 5200) = ₹ 260.

Amount after 2nd year = ₹ (5460 – 20% of 260) = ₹ (5460 – 52) = ₹ 5408.

C.I. earned during 3rd year = ₹ $\left[5408\left(1+\frac{5}{100}\right)-5408\right]$

= ₹ (5678.40 – 5408) = ₹ 270.40.

Amount after 3rd year = ₹ (5678.40 – 20% of 270.40) = ₹ (5678.40 – 54.08) = ₹ 5624.32.

20. Amount = ₹ (30000 + 4347) = ₹ 34347.

Let the time be n years.

Then, $30000\left(1+\frac{7}{100}\right)^n = 34347$

$\Leftrightarrow \left(\frac{107}{100}\right)^n = \frac{34347}{30000} = \frac{11449}{10000} = \left(\frac{107}{100}\right)^2$.

$\therefore n = 2$ years.

21. Let the rate be R% p.a.

Then, $26500\left(1+\frac{R}{100}\right)^2 = 26500 + 9775.85 = 36275.85$

$\Rightarrow \left(1+\frac{R}{100}\right)^2 = \frac{3627585}{2650000} = \frac{13689}{10000} = \left(\frac{117}{100}\right)^2$

$\Rightarrow 1 + \frac{R}{100} = \frac{117}{100} \Rightarrow \frac{R}{100} = \frac{17}{100} \Rightarrow R = 17\%$.

22. Let the rate be R% p.a.

Then, $2000\left(1+\frac{R}{100}\right)^2 = 2226.05$

$\Rightarrow \left(1+\frac{R}{100}\right)^2 = \frac{222605}{200000} = \frac{44521}{40000} = \left(\frac{211}{200}\right)^2$

$\Rightarrow 1+\frac{R}{100} = \frac{211}{200} \Rightarrow \frac{R}{100} = \frac{11}{200} \Rightarrow R = \frac{11}{2}\% = 5.5\%$.

23. Let the rate be R% p.a.

Then, $4000\left(1+\frac{R}{100}\right) = 4320$

$\Rightarrow 1 + \frac{R}{100} = \frac{4320}{4000} = \frac{108}{100} \Rightarrow \frac{R}{100} = \frac{8}{100} \Rightarrow R = 8$.

$\therefore$ Amount after 3 years = ₹ $\left[4000\left(1+\frac{8}{100}\right)^3\right]$

= ₹ $\left(4000 \times \frac{27}{25} \times \frac{27}{25} \times \frac{27}{25}\right)$ = ₹ $\left(\frac{629856}{125}\right)$

= ₹ 5038.848 ≈ 5039.

24. Let the rate be R% p.a. Then, $10000\left(1+\frac{R}{2\times 100}\right)^4 = 14641$

$\Rightarrow \left(1+\frac{R}{200}\right)^4 = \frac{14641}{10000} = \left(\frac{11}{10}\right)^4 \Rightarrow 1+\frac{R}{200} = \frac{11}{10}$

$\Rightarrow \frac{R}{200} = \frac{1}{10} \Rightarrow R = 20\%$.

25. Principal = ₹ $\left[\frac{4913}{\left(1+\frac{25}{4\times 100}\right)^3}\right]$

= ₹ $\left(4913 \times \frac{16}{17} \times \frac{16}{17} \times \frac{16}{17}\right)$ = ₹ 4096.

26. Present worth = ₹ $\left[\frac{169}{\left(1+\frac{4}{100}\right)^2}\right]$

= ₹ $\left(169 \times \frac{25}{26} \times \frac{25}{26}\right)$ = ₹ 156.25.

27. Let the sum be ₹ x. Then,

$x\left(1+\frac{15}{100}\right)^3 - x = 6500.52$

$\Rightarrow x \times \frac{23}{20} \times \frac{23}{20} \times \frac{23}{20} - x = 6500.52$

$\Rightarrow \frac{12167}{8000}x - x = 6500.52$

$\Rightarrow \frac{4167x}{8000} = 6500.52$

$\Rightarrow x = \left(\frac{6500.52 \times 8000}{4167}\right) = 12480$.

28. Let the time be n years. Then,

$800 \times \left(1+\frac{5}{100}\right)^{2n} = 926.10$ or $\left(1+\frac{5}{100}\right)^{2n} = \frac{9261}{8000}$

or $\left(\frac{21}{20}\right)^{2n} = \left(\frac{21}{20}\right)^3$ or $2n = 3$ or $n = \frac{3}{2}$.

$\therefore n = 1\frac{1}{2}$ years.

29. Let the sum be ₹ P. Then,

$\left[P\left(1+\frac{25}{2\times 100}\right)^2 - P\right] = 510$

$\Rightarrow P\left[\left(\frac{9}{8}\right)^2 - 1\right] = 510 \Rightarrow P = \left(\frac{510 \times 64}{17}\right) = 1920$.

$\therefore$ Sum = ₹ 1920.

So, S.I. = ₹ $\left(\frac{1920 \times 25 \times 2}{2 \times 100}\right)$ = ₹ 480.

30. Let the sum be ₹ P.

Then, $\left[P\left(1+\frac{10}{100}\right)^2 - P\right] = 525$

$\Rightarrow P\left[\left(\frac{11}{10}\right)^2 - 1\right] = 525$

$\Rightarrow P = \left(\frac{525 \times 100}{21}\right) = 2500$. $\therefore$ Sum = ₹ 2500.

So, S.I. = ₹ $\left(\frac{2500 \times 5 \times 4}{100}\right)$ = ₹ 500.

31. C.I. = ₹ $\left[4000 \times \left(1+\frac{10}{100}\right)^2 - 4000\right]$

= ₹ $\left(4000 \times \frac{11}{10} \times \frac{11}{10} - 4000\right)$ = ₹ 840.

$\therefore$ Sum = ₹ $\left(\frac{420 \times 100}{3 \times 8}\right)$ = ₹ 1750.

32. Let P = ₹ 100. Then, S.I. = ₹ 60 and T = 6 years.

$\therefore R = \frac{100 \times 60}{100 \times 6} = 10\%$ p.a.

Now, P = ₹ 12000, T = 3 years and R = 10% p.a.

$\therefore$ C.I. = ₹ $\left[12000 \times \left\{\left(1+\frac{10}{100}\right)^3 - 1\right\}\right]$ = ₹ $\left(12000 \times \frac{331}{1000}\right)$

= ₹ 3972.

33. Let the sum be ₹ P. Then,

$$P\left(1+\frac{8}{100}\right)^2 - P = 1414.40$$

$$\Rightarrow \left(P\times\frac{27}{25}\times\frac{27}{25}\right) - P = 1414.40$$

$$\Rightarrow \frac{729}{625}P - P = 1414.40$$

$$\Rightarrow \frac{104}{625}P = 1414.40$$

$$\Rightarrow P = \left(\frac{1414.40\times625}{104}\right) = 8500.$$

Hence, total amount = ₹ (8500 + 1414.40) = ₹ 9914.40.

34. Let the rate be ₹ R% p.a. Then,

$$25500\left(1+\frac{R}{100}\right)^3 = 25500 + 8440.50 = 33940.50$$

$$\Rightarrow \left(1+\frac{R}{100}\right)^3 = \frac{33940.50}{25500} = \frac{1331}{1000} = \left(\frac{11}{10}\right)^3$$

$$\Rightarrow 1+\frac{R}{100} = \frac{11}{10} \Rightarrow \frac{R}{100} = \frac{1}{10} \Rightarrow R = 10\%.$$

$$\therefore \text{ S.I.} = ₹\left(\frac{25500\times10\times3}{100}\right) = ₹\ 7650.$$

35. Let each sum be ₹ P. Then,

$$P\left(1+\frac{10}{100}\right)^2 - P = 63$$

$$\Rightarrow \left(P\times\frac{11}{10}\times\frac{11}{10}\right) - P = 63$$

$$\Rightarrow \frac{121}{100}P - P = 63$$

$$\Rightarrow \frac{21}{100}P = 63$$

$$\Rightarrow P = \left(\frac{63\times100}{21}\right) = 300.$$

$$\text{Hence, C.I.} = ₹\left[300\left(1+\frac{12}{100}\right)^2 - 300\right]$$

$$= ₹\left[\left(300\times\frac{28}{25}\times\frac{28}{25}\right) - 300\right] = ₹\ 76.32.$$

36. Let the rate be R% p.a. Then

$$\left[26000\times\left(1+\frac{R}{100}\right)^3 - 26000\right] - \left(\frac{26000\times R\times3}{100}\right) = 2994.134$$

$$\Rightarrow 26000\left[\left(1+\frac{R}{100}\right)^3 - 1 - \frac{3R}{100}\right] = 2994.134$$

$$\Rightarrow 26000\left[\frac{(100+R)^3 - 1000000 - 30000R}{1000000}\right] = 2994.134$$

$\Rightarrow$ 26 {[1000000 + R^3 + 300R (100 + R)} − 1000000 − 30000R} = 2994134

$$\Rightarrow R^3 + 300R^2 = \frac{2994134}{26} = 115159$$

$$\Rightarrow R^2(R + 300) = 115159 \Rightarrow R = 19\%.$$

37. Let the sum be ₹ x. Then,

$$\text{C.I.} = ₹\left[x\left(1+\frac{8}{100}\right)^2 - x\right]$$

$$= ₹\left(\frac{729}{625}x - x\right) = ₹\left(\frac{104x}{625}\right).$$

$$\text{S.I.} = ₹\left(\frac{x\times8\times2}{100}\right) = ₹\left(\frac{4x}{25}\right).$$

$$\therefore \frac{104x}{625} - \frac{4x}{25} = 768$$

$$\Rightarrow \frac{4x}{625} = 768$$

$$\Rightarrow x = \left(\frac{768\times625}{4}\right) = 120000.$$

38. Difference in C.I. and S.I. for 2 years = ₹ 32.

S.I. for 1 year = ₹ 400.

∴ S.I. on ₹ 400 for one year = ₹ 32.

$$\text{So, Rate} = \left(\frac{100\times32}{400\times1}\right)\% = 8\%.$$

Hence, difference in C.I. and S.I. for 3rd year = S.I. on

$$₹\ 832 = ₹\left(\frac{832\times8\times1}{100}\right) = ₹\ 66.56.$$

Total difference = ₹ (32 + 66.56) = ₹ 98.56.

39. Let the sum be ₹ P. Then

$$P\left[\left(1+\frac{5}{100}\right)^4 - 1\right] - \frac{P\times10\times2}{100} = 124.05$$

$$\Rightarrow P\left[\left(\frac{21}{20}\right)^4 - 1 - \frac{1}{5}\right] = 124.05$$

$$\Rightarrow P\left[\frac{194481}{160000} - \frac{6}{5}\right] = \frac{12405}{100}$$

$$\Rightarrow P\left[\frac{194481 - 192000}{160000}\right] = \frac{12405}{100}$$

$$\Rightarrow P = \left(\frac{12405}{100}\times\frac{160000}{2481}\right) = 8000.$$

40. For first year, S.I. = C.I.

Now, ₹ 16 is the S.I. on S.I. for 1 year.

₹ 10 is S.I. on ₹ 100.

$$\therefore ₹\ 16 \text{ is S.I. on } ₹\left(\frac{100}{10}\times16\right) = ₹\ 160.$$

So, S.I. on principal for 1 year at 10% is ₹ 160.

$$\therefore \text{ Principal} = ₹\left(\frac{100\times160}{10\times1}\right) = ₹\ 1600.$$

Amount for 2 years compounded half yearly

$$= ₹\left[1600\times\left(1+\frac{5}{100}\right)^4\right] = ₹\ 1944.81.$$

∴ C.I. = ₹ (1944.81 − 1600) = ₹ 344.81.

$$\text{S.I.} = ₹\left(\frac{1600\times10\times2}{100}\right) = ₹\ 320.$$

∴ (C.I.) − (S.I.) = ₹ (344.81 − 320) = ₹ 24.81.

41. Let the sum be ₹ x. Then

C.I. when compounded half-yearly $= ₹\left[x \times \left(1+\frac{3}{100}\right)^2 - x\right]$

$= ₹\left(\frac{10609}{10000}x - x\right) = ₹\left(\frac{609x}{10000}\right).$

C.I. when compounded yearly $= ₹\left[x\left(1+\frac{4}{100}\right) - x\right]$

$= ₹\left(\frac{26x}{25} - x\right) = ₹\left(\frac{x}{25}\right).$

$\therefore \frac{609x}{10000} - \frac{x}{25} = 104.50$

$\Rightarrow \frac{209x}{10000} = 104.50$

$\Rightarrow x = \left(\frac{104.50 \times 10000}{209}\right) = 5000.$

42. Let the sum be ₹ x. Then,

C.I. when compounded half-yearly

$= \left[x \times \left(1+\frac{10}{100}\right)^4 - x\right] = \frac{4641}{10000}x.$

C.I. when compounded annually

$= \left[x \times \left(1+\frac{20}{100}\right)^2 - x\right] = \frac{11}{25}x.$

$\therefore \frac{4641}{10000}x - \frac{11}{25}x = 482$

or $x = \frac{482 \times 10000}{241} = 20000.$

43. Difference in C.I. and S.I. for 2 years

$= ₹ (696.30 - 660) = ₹ 36.30.$

S.I. for one year = ₹ 330.

$\therefore$ S.I. on ₹ 330 for 1 year = ₹ 36.30.

$\therefore$ Rate $= \left(\frac{100 \times 36.30}{330 \times 1}\right)\% = 11\%.$

44. Amount of ₹ 100 for 1 year when compounded half-yearly $= ₹\left[100 \times \left(1+\frac{3}{100}\right)^2\right] = ₹ 106.09.$

$\therefore$ Effective rate = (106.09 − 100)% = 6.09%.

45. Let the principal be ₹ P and the rate of interest be R% per annum.

Difference of C.I. and S.I. for 2 years

$= \left[P \times \left(1+\frac{R}{100}\right)^2 - P\right] - \left(\frac{P \times R \times 2}{100}\right) = \frac{PR^2}{10^4}.$

Difference of C.I. and S.I. for 3 years

$= \left[P \times \left(1+\frac{R}{100}\right)^3 - P\right] - \left(\frac{P \times R \times 3}{100}\right)$

$= \frac{PR^2}{10^4}\left(\frac{300+R}{100}\right).$

$\therefore \frac{\frac{PR^2}{10^4}\left(\frac{300+R}{100}\right)}{\frac{PR^2}{10^4}} = \frac{25}{8}$

$\Rightarrow \left(\frac{300+R}{100}\right) = \frac{25}{8}$

$\Rightarrow R = \frac{100}{8} = 12\frac{1}{2}\%.$

46. Let the shares of the younger and elder sons be ₹ x and ₹ (16400 − x).

Then, Amount of ₹ x after 3 years = Amount of ₹ (16400 − x) after 2 years

$\Rightarrow x\left(1+\frac{5}{100}\right)^3 = (16400 - x)\left(1+\frac{5}{100}\right)^2$

$\Rightarrow x\left(1+\frac{5}{100}\right) = (16400 - x)$

$\Rightarrow \frac{21x}{20} + x = 16400$

$\Rightarrow \frac{41x}{20} = 16400$

$\Rightarrow x = \left(\frac{16400 \times 20}{41}\right) = 8000.$

47. Let A's share = ₹ x and B's share = ₹ (8840 − x).

$\therefore x\left(1+\frac{10}{100}\right)^8 = (8840 - x)\left(1+\frac{10}{100}\right)^{10}$

$\Rightarrow x = (8840 - x)\left(1+\frac{10}{100}\right)^2$

$\Rightarrow x = \frac{121}{100}(8840 - x)$

$\Rightarrow 221x = 121 \times 8840$

$\Rightarrow x = \left(\frac{121 \times 8840}{221}\right) = 4840.$

Hence, the two parts are ₹ 4840 and ₹ 4000.

48. Let the investment in scheme A be ₹ x.

Then, investment in scheme B = ₹ (27000 − x).

$\therefore \left[x \times \left\{\left(1+\frac{8}{100}\right)^2 - 1\right\} + (27000 - x)\left\{\left(1+\frac{9}{100}\right)^2 - 1\right\}\right]$

$= 4818.30$

$\Leftrightarrow \left(x \times \frac{104}{625}\right) + \frac{1881(27000 - x)}{10000} = \frac{481830}{100}$

$\Leftrightarrow 1664x + 1881(27000 - x) = 48183000$

$\Leftrightarrow (1881x - 1664x) = (50787000 - 48183000)$

$\Leftrightarrow 217x = 2604000$

$\Leftrightarrow x = \frac{2604000}{217} = 12000.$

49. S.I. on ₹ 672 for 1 year

$= ₹ (714 - 672) = ₹ 42.$

$\therefore$ Rate $= \left(\frac{100 \times 42}{672 \times 1}\right)\% = 6.25\%.$

50. S.I. on ₹ 4624 for 1 year = ₹ (4913 − 4624) = ₹ 289.

$\therefore$ Rate = $\left(\frac{100 \times 289}{4624 \times 1}\right)\% = 6\frac{1}{4}\%$.

Now, $x\left(1+\frac{25}{4 \times 100}\right)^2 = 4624$ or $x \times \frac{17}{16} \times \frac{17}{16} = 4624$

or $x = \left(4624 \times \frac{16}{17} \times \frac{16}{17}\right) =$ ₹ 4096.

51. $12000 \times \left(1+\frac{R}{100}\right)^5 = 24000 \Rightarrow \left(1+\frac{R}{100}\right)^5 = 2$

$\therefore \left[\left(1+\frac{R}{100}\right)^5\right]^4 = 2^4 = 16$

$\Rightarrow \left(1+\frac{R}{100}\right)^{20} = 16$

$\Rightarrow P\left(1+\frac{R}{100}\right)^{20} = 16P$

$\Rightarrow 12000\left(1+\frac{R}{100}\right)^{20} = 16 \times 12000 = 192000.$

52. $P\left(1+\frac{R}{100}\right)^{15} = 2P \Rightarrow \left(1+\frac{R}{100}\right)^{15} = 2$ ...(i)

Let $P\left(1+\frac{R}{100}\right)^n = 8P$

$\Rightarrow \left(1+\frac{R}{100}\right)^n = 8 = 2^3 = \left\{\left(1+\frac{R}{100}\right)^{15}\right\}^3$

$\Rightarrow \left(1+\frac{R}{100}\right)^n = \left(1+\frac{R}{100}\right)^{45} \Rightarrow n = 45.$

$\therefore$ Required time = 45 years.

53. $P\left(1+\frac{R}{100}\right)^3 = 8P \Rightarrow \left(1+\frac{R}{100}\right)^3 = 8.$

Let $P\left(1+\frac{R}{100}\right)^n = 16P \Rightarrow \left(1+\frac{R}{100}\right)^n = 16 = 2^4 = (2^3)^{4/3}$

$\Rightarrow \left(1+\frac{R}{100}\right)^n = (8)^{4/3} = \left\{\left(1+\frac{R}{100}\right)^3\right\}^{4/3} = \left(1+\frac{R}{100}\right)^4.$

$\Rightarrow n = 4.$

$\therefore$ Required time = 4 years.

54. $P\left(1+\frac{R}{100}\right)^5 = 150\%$ of $P = \frac{3}{2}P \Rightarrow \left(1+\frac{R}{100}\right)^5 = \frac{3}{2}.$

$x\left(1+\frac{R}{100}\right)^{10} = y\left(1+\frac{R}{100}\right)^{15} = z\left(1+\frac{R}{100}\right)^{20}$

$\Rightarrow x\left\{\left(1+\frac{R}{100}\right)^5\right\}^2 = y\left\{\left(1+\frac{R}{100}\right)^5\right\}^3 = z\left\{\left(1+\frac{R}{100}\right)^5\right\}^4$

$\Rightarrow x \times \left(\frac{3}{2}\right)^2 = y \times \left(\frac{3}{2}\right)^3 = z \times \left(\frac{3}{2}\right)^4$

$\Rightarrow \frac{9x}{4} = \frac{27y}{8} = \frac{81z}{16} = k$ (say)

$\Rightarrow x = \frac{4k}{9}, y = \frac{8k}{27}, z = \frac{16k}{81}$

$\Rightarrow x : y : z = \frac{4k}{9} : \frac{8k}{27} : \frac{16k}{81}$

$= 36 : 24 : 16 = 9 : 6 : 4.$

55. $P\left(1+\frac{20}{100}\right)^n > 2P$ or $\left(\frac{6}{5}\right)^n > 2.$

Now, $\left(\frac{6}{5} \times \frac{6}{5} \times \frac{6}{5} \times \frac{6}{5}\right) > 2.$ So, $n = 4$ years.

56. Let the value of each instalment be ₹ x. Then,

(P.W. of ₹ x due 1 year hence)

+ (P.W. of ₹ x due 2 years hence) = ₹ 2550

$\Leftrightarrow \frac{x}{\left(1+\frac{4}{100}\right)} + \frac{x}{\left(1+\frac{4}{100}\right)^2} = 2550$

$\Leftrightarrow \frac{25x}{26} + \frac{625x}{676} = 2550$

$\Leftrightarrow 1275x = 2550 \times 676$

$\Leftrightarrow x = \left(\frac{2550 \times 676}{1275}\right) = 1352.$

$\therefore$ Value of each instalment = ₹ 1352.

57. Let the value of each instalment be ₹ x. Then,

(P.W. of ₹ x due 1 year hence) + (P.W. of ₹ x due 2 years hence) + (P.W. of ₹ x due 3 years hence) = ₹ 126100

$\Rightarrow \frac{x}{\left(1+\frac{5}{100}\right)} + \frac{x}{\left(1+\frac{5}{100}\right)^2} + \frac{x}{\left(1+\frac{5}{100}\right)^3} = 126100$

$\Rightarrow \frac{20x}{21} + \frac{400x}{441} + \frac{8000x}{9261} = 126100$

$\Rightarrow \frac{8820x + 8400x + 8000x}{9261} = 126100$

$\Rightarrow \frac{25220\,x}{9261} = 126100 \Rightarrow x = \left(\frac{126100 \times 9261}{25220}\right) = 46305.$

58. Total cost of taperecorder = ₹ 3500.

Down payment = ₹ 1000.

Balance = ₹ (3500 − 1000) = ₹ 2500.

Let the value of each instalment be ₹ x.

P.W. of ₹ x due 1 year hence + P.W. of ₹ x due 2 years hence + P.W. of ₹ x due 3 years hence = 2500

$\Rightarrow \frac{x}{\left(1+\frac{25}{2 \times 100}\right)} + \frac{x}{\left(1+\frac{25}{2 \times 100}\right)^2} + \frac{x}{\left(1+\frac{25}{2 \times 100}\right)^3} = 2500$

$\Rightarrow \frac{8x}{9} + \frac{64x}{81} + \frac{512x}{729} = 2500 \Rightarrow \frac{1736x}{729} = 2500$

$\Rightarrow x = \frac{2500 \times 729}{1736} = 1049.83 \approx 1049.85.$

59. Total cost of the flat = ₹ 55000.

Down payment = ₹ 4275.

Balance = ₹ (55000 − 4275) = ₹ 50725.

Rate of interest = 8% per half-year.

Let the value of each instalment be ₹ x.

P.W. of ₹ x due 6 months hence + P.W. of ₹ x due 1 year hence + P.W. of ₹ x due $1\frac{1}{2}$ years hence = 50725

$$\Rightarrow \frac{x}{\left(1+\frac{8}{100}\right)}+\frac{x}{\left(1+\frac{8}{100}\right)^2}+\frac{x}{\left(1+\frac{8}{100}\right)^3}=50725$$

$$\Rightarrow \frac{25x}{27}+\frac{625x}{729}+\frac{15625x}{19683}=50725$$

$$\Rightarrow \frac{50725x}{19683}=50725$$

$$\Rightarrow x=\left(\frac{50725\times19683}{50725}\right)=19683.$$

60. Let each instalment be ₹ x. Then,

$$\frac{x}{\left(1+\frac{5}{100}\right)}+\frac{x}{\left(1+\frac{5}{100}\right)^2}=1025$$

$$\Leftrightarrow \frac{20x}{21}+\frac{400x}{441}=1025$$

$$\Leftrightarrow 820x = 1025\times441$$

$$\Leftrightarrow x=\left(\frac{1025\times441}{820}\right)=551.25.$$

So, value of each instalment = ₹ 551.25.

61. Balance

$$= ₹\left[\left\{12500\times\left(1+\frac{20}{100}\right)^3\right\}-\left\{2000\times\left(1+\frac{20}{100}\right)^2+2000\times\left(1+\frac{20}{100}\right)+2000\right\}\right]$$

$$= ₹\left[\left(12500\times\frac{6}{5}\times\frac{6}{5}\times\frac{6}{5}\right)-\left(2000\times\frac{6}{5}\times\frac{6}{5}+2000\times\frac{6}{5}+2000\right)\right]$$

= ₹ [21600 − (2880 + 2400 + 2000)] = ₹ 14320.

62. Principal

= (P.W. of ₹ 882 due 1 year hence) + (P.W. of ₹ 882 due 2 years hence)

$$=\left[\frac{882}{\left(1+\frac{5}{100}\right)}+\frac{882}{\left(1+\frac{5}{100}\right)^2}\right]$$

$$=\left(\frac{882\times20}{21}+\frac{882\times400}{441}\right)=₹\ 1640.$$

63. Rate of interest = 18%

Time = 2 years

When the interest is payable half yearly.

Then, rate of interest = 9% per half annum.

Time = 4 half years.

Let the principal be ₹ x

$$\therefore \text{C.I.} = x\left[\left(1+\frac{R}{100}\right)^T-1\right]$$

$$= x\left[\left(1+\frac{9}{100}\right)^4-1\right]$$

$$= x\left[\left(\frac{109}{100}\right)^4-1\right]$$

$= x$ [1.4116 − 1] = ₹ $0.4116x$

According to the question.

$$= x\left[\left(1+\frac{18}{100}\right)^2-1\right]$$

$$= x\left[\left(\frac{118}{100}\right)^2-1\right]$$

$$= x\left[(1.18)^2-1\right]$$

$= x$ (1.3924 − 1) = ₹ 0.3924 x

According to the question.

$0.4116x - 0.3924x = 960$

$\Rightarrow 0.0192x = 960$

$$\Rightarrow x=\frac{960}{0.0192}$$

$$x=\frac{960\times10000}{192}=₹\ 50{,}000$$

Hence, sum of money = ₹ 50,000

64. Time = 2 years

Rate of interest = 5% per annum

According to question,

$$P\left[\left(1+\frac{r}{100}\right)^n-1\right]-\frac{P\times r\times t}{100}=63$$

$$P\left[\left(1+\frac{5}{100}\right)^2-1\right]-\frac{P\times5\times2}{100}=63$$

$$\Rightarrow P\left[\left(1+\frac{5}{100}\right)^2-1\right]-\frac{10P}{100}=63$$

$$\Rightarrow P\left[\left(\frac{105}{100}\right)^2-1\right]-\frac{10P}{100}=63$$

$$\Rightarrow P\left(\frac{11025-10000}{10000}\right)-\frac{10P}{100}=63$$

$$\Rightarrow \frac{1025P}{10000}-\frac{10P}{100}=63$$

$$\Rightarrow \frac{1025P-1000P}{10000}=63$$

$\Rightarrow$ 25P = ₹ 630000

$$\Rightarrow P=\frac{630000}{25}=₹\ 25200$$

Hence, sum = ₹ 25200

65. Given amount = ₹ 1348.32

Principal = ₹ 1200

And time = 2 years

$A = P\left(1+\frac{R}{100}\right)^T$

$\Rightarrow 1348.32 = 1200\left(1+\frac{R}{100}\right)^2$

$\Rightarrow \frac{1348.32}{1200} = \left(1+\frac{R}{100}\right)^2$

$\Rightarrow \frac{134832}{120000} = \left(1+\frac{R}{100}\right)^2$

$\Rightarrow \frac{11236}{10000} = \left(1+\frac{R}{100}\right)^2$

$\Rightarrow \left(\frac{106}{100}\right)^2 = \left(1+\frac{R}{100}\right)^2$

$\Rightarrow 1+\frac{6}{100} = 1+\frac{R}{100}$

$\Rightarrow$ R = 6% per annum.

66. Let the sum of money be ₹ P

Then $\left[P\left(1+\frac{R}{100}\right)^t - P\right] = CI$

$\left[P\left(1+\frac{10}{100}\right)^2 - P\right] = 525$

$\Rightarrow \left(\frac{11}{10}\right)^2 - 1 = 525$

$\Rightarrow P\left(\frac{121}{100} - 1\right) = 525$

$\Rightarrow P\left(\frac{21}{100}\right) = 525$

$\Rightarrow P = \left(\frac{525 \times 100}{21}\right) = ₹\ 2500$

∴ Sum of money = ₹ 2500.

Simple interest on the same sum ₹ 2500 for 4 (double the time) years at 5% (half the rate of percent per annum) is

So, S.I. = ₹ $\left(\frac{2500 \times 5 \times 4}{100}\right) = ₹\ 500$

67. Let the total sum of money invested by Shashi be ₹ x.

In scheme A money invested at simple interest for 6 years at a rate of 12% p.a.

$\therefore \frac{2}{3}$ of $x \times \frac{12 \times 6}{100} = \frac{48x}{100}$ ...(i)

In scheme B money invested at compound interest for 2 years at a rate of 10% p.a. $\frac{x}{3}\left(1+\frac{10}{100}\right)^2 - \frac{x}{3}$

$\Rightarrow \frac{x}{3}\left(1+\frac{10}{100}\right)^2 - \frac{x}{3} = \frac{7x}{100}$

According to given information we get

$\Rightarrow \frac{48x}{100} + \frac{7x}{100} = 2750$

$55x = 2750 \times 100$

$x = \frac{2750 \times 100}{55}$

x = ₹ 5000

68. Rate of interest = 5% p.c.p.a.

If time 3 years then CI – SI = $P\left[\left(\frac{R}{100}\right)^3 + 3\left(\frac{R}{100}\right)^2\right]$

$\Rightarrow 122 = P\left[\left(\frac{5}{100}\right)^3 + 3\left(\frac{5}{100}\right)^2\right]$

$\Rightarrow 122 = P\left(\frac{125}{1000000} + \frac{75}{10000}\right)$

$\Rightarrow 122 = P\left[\frac{125+7500}{1000000}\right]$

$\Rightarrow 122 = P\left[\frac{7525}{1000000}\right]$

$\Rightarrow P = \frac{122 \times 1000000}{7625}$

= ₹ 16000

69. Interest compounded half yearly = $5000\left(1+\frac{2}{100}\right)^2$

$= 5000\left(\frac{102}{100}\right)^2$

$= 5000(1.02)^2$ .....(i)

As we know $A = P\left(1+\frac{R}{100}\right)^t$

Interest compounded yearly = $5000\left(1+\frac{4}{100}\right)^1$

$= 5000\left(\frac{104}{100}\right) = 5000(1.04)$ ....(ii)

From (i) and (ii)

Required difference = $5000(1.02)^2 - 5000(1.04)^1$

$= 5000(1.0404) - 5000(1.04)$

$= 5202 - 5200 = ₹\ 2$

EXERCISE

(DATA SUFFICIENCY TYPE QUESTIONS)

1. The difference between the compound interest and the simple interest earned on a sum of money at the end of 4 years is ₹ 256.40. To find out the sum, which of the following informations given in the statements P and Q is/are necessary?

P : Amount of simple interest accrued after 4 years.

Q : Rate of interest per annum.

(*a*) Only P is necessary

(*b*) Only Q is necessary

(*c*) Either P or Q is necessary

(*d*) Neither P nor Q is necessary

(*e*) Both P and Q are necessary

Directions (*Questions 2 to 15*): ***Each of the questions given below consists of a statement and/or a question and two statements numbered I and II given below it. You have to decide whether the data provided in the statement(s) is/are sufficient to answer the given question. Read both the statements and:***

Give answer (a) if the data in Statement I alone are sufficient to answer the question, while the data in Statement II alone are not sufficient to answer the question;

Give answer (b) if the data in Statement II alone are sufficient to answer the question, while the data in Statement I alone are not sufficient to answer the question;

Give answer (c) if the data either in Statement I or in Statement II alone are sufficient to answer the question;

Give answer (d) if the data even in both Statements I and II together are not sufficient to answer the question;

Give answer (e) if the data in both Statements I and II together are necessary to answer the question.

2. What is the rate of compound interest? **(Bank P.O., 2003)**
   I. The principal was invested for 4 years.
   II. The earned interest was ₹ 1491.
3. What will be the compounded amount?
   I. ₹ 200 were borrowed for 192 months at 6% compounded annually.
   II. ₹ 200 were borrowed for 16 years at 6%.
4. What is the compound interest earned by Robert at the end of 2 years?
   I. Simple interest at the same rate for one year is ₹ 1020 and the rate of interest is 12 p.c.p.a.
   II. The amount invested is ₹ 8500.
5. What is the rate of compound interest on a sum of money? **(Bank P.O., 2009)**
   I. The total simple interest at the same rate on ₹ 6000 at the end of 3 years is ₹ 1800.
   II. The total compound interest on ₹ 6000 at the end of 2 years is ₹ 1260.
6. What is the total compound interest accrued on a sum of money after 5 years?
   I. The sum was ₹ 20,000.
   II. The total amount of simple interest on the sum after 5 years was ₹ 4000.
7. What was the total compound interest on a sum after 3 years?
   I. The interest after one year was ₹ 100 and the sum was ₹ 1000.
   II. The difference between simple and compound interest on a sum of ₹ 1000 at the end of 2 years was ₹ 10.
8. What will be the compound interest after 3 years?
   I. Rate of interest is 5 percent.
   II. The difference between the total simple interest and the total compound interest after 2 years is ₹ 20.
9. What is the rate of interest? **(Bank Recruitment, 2007)**
   I. Simple interest accrued on an amount of ₹ 25000 in 2 years is less than the compound interest for the same period by ₹ 250.
   II. Simple interest accrued in 10 years is equal to the principal.
10. An amount of money was lent for 3 years. What will be the difference between the simple and the compound interest earned on it at the same rate?
    I. The rate of interest was 8 p.c.p.a.
    II. The total amount of simple interest was ₹ 1200.
11. What is the rate of interest p.c.p.a.? **(Bank P.O. 2004)**
    I. Difference between compound interest and the simple interest accrued on an amount of ₹ 15000 in 3 years is ₹ 673.92.
    II. In 2 years, an amount of ₹ 6500 fetches simple interest of ₹ 1560.
12. What is the rate of interest p.c.p.a.? **(Bank P.O., 2005)**
    I. The amount doubles itself on simple interest in 10 years.
    II. Compound interest on any amount in 2 years is more than the simple interest in 2 years by an amount equal to 1% of the principal amount.
13. What was the rate of interest on a sum of money?
    I. The sum fetched a total of ₹ 2522 as compound interest at the end of 3 years.
    II. The difference between the simple interest and the compound interest at the end of 2 years at the same rate was ₹ 40.
14. What is the total compound interest accrued on a sum of money after 10 years? **(Bank P.O., 2010)**
    I. The difference between the simple and compound interest at the end of 2 years was ₹ 200.
    II. The total amount of simple interest at the same rate at the end of 10 years was ₹ 20000.
15. What is the rate of compound interest on a sum of money? **(M.A.T., 2006)**
    I. The difference between C.I. and S.I. at the same rate of interest for two years is ₹ 43.20 and S.I. at the end of five years is ₹ 3600.
    II. The difference between C.I. and S.I. at the same rate of interest on ₹ 12000 for 3 years is ₹ 132.192.

Directions (*Questions 16 to 22*): ***Each of the questions given below consists of a question followed by three statements. You have to study the question and the statements and decide which of the statement(s) is/are necessary to answer the question.***

16. What is the rate of interest p.c.p.a.? **(Bank P.O., 2006)**
    I. Simple interest earned per annum is ₹ 5300.
    II. The difference between the compound and simple interest on an amount is ₹ 1060 at the end of 2 years.
    III. An amount doubles itself in 5 years with simple interest.
    (*a*) All of these (*b*) Only III
    (*c*) Either II or III (*d*) Only III or I and II
    (*e*) Question cannot be answered even with the information

17. What is the rate of interest p.c.p.a.? **(Bank P.O. 2005)**
    I. Difference between compound inteest and simple interest for 2 years is ₹ 100.
    II. The amount doubles itself in 10 years on simple interest.
    III. The amount invested is ₹ 10000.
    (*a*) Only I and II (*b*) Only I and III
    (*c*) Only III and either I or II
    (*d*) Either only II or only I and III
    (*e*) None of these

18. What is the rate of interest p.c.p.a.? **(Bank P.O. 2009)**
    I. I.An amount doubles itself at simple interest in 10 years.
    II. Difference between the compound interest and simple interest on an amount of ₹ 15000 in 2 years is ₹ 150.
    III. The compound interest accrued in 8 years is more than the principal.
    (*a*) Only I (*b*) Only II
    (*c*) Only either I or II (*d*) Only II and III
    (*e*) Only I and III

19. A sum of money is put at compound interest. What is the rate of interest?
    I. The sum amounts to ₹ 5290 in 2 years.
    II. The sum amounts to ₹ 6083.50 in 3 years.
    III. The sum is ₹ 4000.
    (*a*) I and II only (*b*) II and III only
    (*c*) I and III only
    (*d*) Any two of the three
    (*e*) I and III only, or II and III only

20. What will be the compound interest earned on an amount of ₹ 5000 in 2 years?
    I. The simple interest on the same amount at the same rate of interest in 5 years is ₹ 2000.
    II. The compound interest and the simple interest earned in one year is the same.
    III. The amount becomes more than double on compound interest in 10 years.
    (*a*) I only (*b*) I and II only
    (*c*) II and III only (*d*) I and III only
    (*e*) None of these

21. What will be the difference between the total simple interest and the total compound interest at the end of 8 years on a certain sum at the same rate of interest?
    I. The total simple interest on the same sum at the end of 3 years is ₹ 750.
    II. The total compound interest on the same sum at the end of 2 years is ₹ 512.50.
    III. The rate of interest is 5 p.c.p.a.
    (*a*) I and II only (*b*) II and III only
    (*c*) Any two of I, II and III
    (*d*) All I, II and III are required
    (*e*) None of these

22. A sum of money is placed at compound interest. In how many years will it amount to sixteen times of itself?
    I. The sum doubles itself in 4 years.
    II. The sum amounts to eight times of itself in 12 years.
    III. The sum amounts to four times of itself in 8 years.
    (*a*) I only (*b*) I and II only
    (*c*) II and III only (*d*) I and III only
    (*e*) Any one of the three

Directions (*Questions 23 to 27*) : *In each of the following questions, a question is asked and is followed by three statements. While answering the question, you may or may not require the data provided in all the statements. You have to read the question and the three statements and then decide whether the question can be answered with any one or two of the statements or all the three statements are required to answer the question. The answer number bearing the statements, which can be dispensed with, if any, while answering the question is your answer.*

23. What would be the difference between the simple interest and the compound interest on a sum of money at the end of four years ?
    I. The rate of interest is 5 p.c.p.a.
    II. The sum fetches a total of ₹ 2000 as simple interest at the end of 8 years.
    III. The difference between the simple interest and the compound interest at the end of 2 years is ₹ 12.50.
    (*a*) II only (*b*) III only

(*c*) II or III only
(*d*) All I, II and III are required
(*e*) None of these

24. Mr. Gupta borrowed a sum of money on compound interest. What will be the amount to be repaid if he is repaying the entire amount at the end of 2 years?

I. The rate of interest is 5% p.a.
II. Simple interest fetched on the same amount in one year is ₹ 600.
III. The amount borrowed is 10 times the simple interest in 2 years.

(*a*) I only (*b*) III only
(*c*) I or II only (*d*) I or III only
(*e*) All I, II and III are required

25. What is the total compound interest earned at the end of 3 years?

I. Simple interest earned on that amount at the same rate and for the same period is ₹ 4500.
II. The rate of interest is 10 p.c.p.a.
III. Compound interest for 3 years is more than the simple interest for that period by ₹ 465.

(*a*) I and II only (*b*) II and III only
(*c*) I and III only (*d*) Either II or III only
(*e*) Any two of the three

26. What is the rate of interest per annum?

I. The amount becomes ₹ 11,025 with compound interest after 2 years.
II. The same amount with simple interest becomes ₹ 11,000 after 2 years.
III. The amount invested is ₹ 10,000.

(*a*) I or II only (*b*) II or III only
(*c*) I or III only (*d*) I or II or III only
(*e*) All I, II and III are required

27. The difference between the compound interest and the simple interest at the same rate on a certain amount at the end of 2 years is ₹ 12.50. What is the rate of interest?

I. Simple interest for 2 years is ₹ 500.
II. Compound interest for 2 years is ₹ 512.50.
III. Amount on simple interest after 2 years becomes ₹ 5500.

(*a*) I or II only (*b*) III only
(*c*) I or III only
(*d*) Any two of I, II and III
(*e*) Any two of I, II and III

ANSWERS

1. (*b*)	2. (*d*)	3. (*c*)	4. (*a*)	5. (*c*)	6. (*e*)	7. (*c*)	8. (*e*)	9. (*c*)	10. (*e*)
11. (*c*)	12. (*c*)	13. (*e*)	14. (*e*)	15. (*c*)	16. (*d*)	17. (*d*)	18. (*c*)	19. (*d*)	20. (*a*)
21. (*c*)	22. (*e*)	23. (*c*)	24. (*d*)	25. (*d*)	26. (*d*)	27. (*d*)			

SOLUTIONS

1. To find the sum, difference between C.I. and S.I., the time and the rate of interest are needed.
∴ Only *Q* is necessary. So correct answer is (*b*).

2. Let Principal = ₹ *P* and Rate = *R*% p.a. Then,

$$\text{C.I.} = P\left[\left(1+\frac{R}{100}\right)^4 - 1\right] \Rightarrow P\left[\left(1+\frac{R}{100}\right)^4 - 1\right] = 1491.$$

Clearly, it does not give the answer.
∴ Correct answer is (*d*).

3. Clearly, 192 months ≡ 16 years. So, both I and II provide the same information.
From each one of I and II, we have:

$$\text{Amount} = ₹\left[200\times\left(1+\frac{6}{100}\right)^{16}\right].$$

Thus, I alone or II alone gives the answer.
∴ Correct answer is (*c*).

4. I. S.I. = ₹ 1020, *R* = 12% p.a. and *T* = 1 year.

$$\therefore P = \frac{100\times S.I.}{R\times T}$$

$$\Rightarrow P = ₹\left(\frac{100\times 1020}{12\times 1}\right) = ₹\ 8500.$$

$$\therefore \text{C.I. for 2 years} = ₹\left[8500\times\left\{\left(1+\frac{12}{100}\right)^2 - 1\right\}\right].$$

= ₹ 2162.40.

So, I alone gives the answer.

II. gives : only *P* and *T*.
∴ II alone does not give the answer.
∴ Correct answer is (*a*).

5. I. *P* = ₹ 6000, *T* = 3 yrs, S.I. = ₹ 1800.

$$\therefore \text{Rate} = \left(\frac{100\times 1800}{6000\times 3}\right)\% = 10\%.$$

II. *P* = ₹ 6000, *T* = 2 yrs, C.I. = ₹ 1260.

$$6000\left(1+\frac{R}{100}\right)^2 = 6000 + 1260 = 7260$$

$$\Rightarrow \left(1+\frac{R}{100}\right)^2 = \frac{7260}{6000} = \frac{121}{100} = \left(\frac{11}{10}\right)^2 \Rightarrow 1+\frac{R}{100} = \frac{11}{10}$$

$$\Rightarrow \frac{R}{100} = \frac{1}{10} \Rightarrow R = 10\%.$$

Thus, either I alone or II alone gives the answer.

∴ Correct answer is (*c*).

6. Given : Time = 5 years.

I. gives : Sum = ₹ 20000.

II. gives : S.I. = ₹ 4000.

Let the rate be R% p.a. Then,

$$R = \frac{100 \times S.I.}{P \times T} = \left(\frac{100 \times 4000}{5 \times 20000}\right) = 4\% \text{ p.a.}$$

$$\therefore \text{ C.I.} = ₹ \left[20000 \times \left\{\left(1 + \frac{4}{100}\right)^5 - 1\right\}\right]$$

∴ Both I and II are needed to get the answer.

So, the correct answer is (*e*).

7. I. gives : P = ₹ 1000 and S.I. for 1 year = ₹ 100.

$$\therefore \text{ Rate} = \frac{100 \times S.I.}{P \times T} = \left(\frac{100 \times 100}{1000 \times 1}\right) = 10\% \text{ p.a.}$$

Thus, P = ₹ 1000, T = 3 years and R = 10% p.a.

∴ C.I. may be obtained.

II. Sum = ₹ 1000, [(C.I.) – (S.I.)] for 2 years = ₹ 10.

Let the rate be R% p.a.

$$1000 \times \left[\left(1 + \frac{R}{100}\right)^2 - 1\right] - \left(\frac{1000 \times R \times 2}{100}\right) = 10.$$

From this, we can find R.

Thus P, T and R are given and therefore,

C.I. may be calculated.

Thus, I alone as well as II alone is sufficient to get the answer.

∴ Correct answer is (*c*).

8. I. $R = 5\%$

II. Let the sum be ₹ P. Then,

$$\left[P\left(1 + \frac{R}{100}\right)^2 - P\right] - \left(\frac{P \times R \times 2}{100}\right) = 20$$

$$\Rightarrow P + \frac{PR^2}{10000} + \frac{2PR}{100} - P - \frac{2PR}{100} = 20$$

$$\Rightarrow \frac{PR^2}{10000} = 20 \Rightarrow P = \frac{20 \times 10000}{R^2} = \frac{20 \times 10000}{25} = 8000.$$

$$\therefore \text{ C.I.} = ₹ \left[8000\left(1 + \frac{5}{100}\right)^3 - 8000\right] = ₹\ 1261.$$

Thus, both I and II are required to get the answer.

∴ Correct answer is (*e*).

9. I. Let rate = R% p.a.

$$\text{Then, } \left[25000\left(1 + \frac{R}{100}\right)^2 - 25000\right] - \left(\frac{25000 \times R \times 2}{100}\right) = 250$$

$$\Rightarrow \frac{25000 \times R^2}{10000} = 250 \Rightarrow R^2 = 100 \Rightarrow R = 10\%.$$

II. Let Principal = ₹ P. Then, S.I. = ₹ P.

$$\therefore \text{ Rate} = \left(\frac{100 \times P}{P \times 10}\right)\% = 10\%.$$

Thus, I alone as well as II alone is sufficient to get the answer.

∴ Correct answer is (*c*).

10. Given : T = 3 years.

I. gives : R = 8% p.a.

II. gives : S.I. = ₹ 1200.

Thus, P = ₹ 5000, R = 8% p.a. and T = 3 years.

∴ Difference between C.I. and S.I. may be obtained.

So, the correct answer is (*e*).

11. I. C.I. – S.I. = ₹ 673.92

$$\Rightarrow \left[15000\left(1 + \frac{R}{100}\right)^3 - 15000\right] - \left(\frac{15000 \times R \times 3}{100}\right) = 673.92$$

$$\Rightarrow \frac{15000}{1000000}(100 + R)^3 - 15000 - 450R = 673.92$$

$$\Rightarrow \frac{15}{1000}(1000000 + R^3 + 30000R + 300R^2) - 15000 - 450R = 673.92$$

$$\Rightarrow 15R^3 + 4500R^2 = 673920$$

$$\Rightarrow R^3 + 300R^2 = 44928 = R = 12\%.$$

II. P = ₹ 6500, S.I. = ₹ 1560, T = 2 years

$$\therefore R = \left(\frac{100 \times 1560}{6500 \times 2}\right)\% = 12\%.$$

Thus, I alone as well as II alone is sufficient to answer the question.

∴ Correct answer is (*c*).

12. I. Let sum = ₹ P. Then, S.I. = ₹ P, T = 10 years.

$$\therefore \text{ Rate} = \left(\frac{100 \times P}{P \times 10}\right)\% = 10\%.$$

II. Let principal = ₹ P and rate = R% p.a. Then,

$$\left[P\left(1 + \frac{R}{100}\right)^2 - P\right] - \left(\frac{P \times R \times 2}{100}\right) = 1\% \text{ of } P$$

$$\Rightarrow \left(1 + \frac{R}{100}\right)^2 - 1 - \frac{2R}{100} = \frac{1}{100} \Rightarrow \frac{R^2}{10000} = \frac{1}{100}$$

$$\Rightarrow R^2 = 100 \Rightarrow R = 10\%.$$

Thus, I alone as well as II alone is sufficient to answer the question.

∴ Correct answer is (*c*).

13. I. gives : C.I. for 3 years = ₹ 2522.

II. gives : (C.I.) – (S.I.) for 2 years at same rate is ₹ 40.

$$P\left[\left(1 + \frac{R}{100}\right)^3 - 1\right] = 2522 \quad ...(i)$$

$$P\left[\left(1 + \frac{R}{100}\right)^2 - 1\right] - \frac{P \times R \times 2}{100} = 40 \quad ...(ii)$$

On dividing (*i*) by (*ii*) we get:

$$\frac{\left(1 + \frac{R}{100}\right)^3 - 1}{\left(1 + \frac{R}{100}\right)^2 - 1 - \frac{R}{50}} = \frac{2522}{40}$$

$\Rightarrow \dfrac{\dfrac{R^3}{1000000}+\dfrac{3R}{100}+\dfrac{3R^2}{10000}}{\dfrac{R^2}{10000}} = \dfrac{1261}{20}$

$\Rightarrow \dfrac{R}{100}+\dfrac{300}{R} = \dfrac{1201}{20} \Rightarrow R^2 - 6005R + 30000 = 0$

$\Rightarrow R^2 - 6000R - 5R + 30000 = 0$

$\Rightarrow R(R - 6000) - 5(R - 6000) = 0$

$\Rightarrow (R - 5)(R - 6000) = 0 \Rightarrow R = 5.$

$\therefore$ Both I and II are needed to get R.

$\therefore$ Correct answer is (*e*).

14. I. Let Principal = ₹ P and Rate = R% p.a.

Then, $\left[P\left(1+\dfrac{R}{100}\right)^2 - P\right] - \left(\dfrac{P\times R\times 2}{100}\right) = 200$

$\Rightarrow \dfrac{PR^2}{10000} = 200$ ...(*i*)

II. $P = \left(\dfrac{100\times \text{S.I.}}{R\times T}\right) = \left(\dfrac{100\times 20000}{R\times 10}\right)$ ...(*ii*)

From (*i*) and (*ii*) we have: $\left(\dfrac{100\times 20000}{R\times 10}\right)\times\dfrac{R^2}{10000} = 200$

$\Rightarrow 20R = 200 \Rightarrow R = 10\%.$

Putting $R = 10$ in (*i*), we get: P = ₹ 20000.

$\therefore$ C.I. = ₹ $\left[20000\left(1+\dfrac{10}{100}\right)^{10} - 20000\right]$.

Thus, both I and II together give the answer.

$\therefore$ Correct answer is (*e*).

15. I. Let Principal = ₹ P and Rate = R% p.a.

Then, $P = \left(\dfrac{100\times \text{S.I.}}{R\times T}\right)$

$\Rightarrow P = \left(\dfrac{100\times 3600}{R\times 5}\right) = \dfrac{72000}{R}$ ...(*i*)

And, $\left[P\left(1+\dfrac{R}{100}\right)^2 - P\right] - \left(\dfrac{P\times R\times 2}{100}\right) = 43.20$

$\Rightarrow \dfrac{PR^2}{10000} = 43.20$

$\Rightarrow PR^2 = 432000$

$\Rightarrow \dfrac{72000}{R}\times R^2 = 432000$

$\Rightarrow R = \dfrac{432000}{72000} = 6\%.$

II. $12000\left(1+\dfrac{R}{100}\right)^3 - 12000 - \left(\dfrac{12000\times 3\times R}{100}\right) = 132.192$

$\Rightarrow \dfrac{12000}{1000000}(100 + R)^3 - 12000 - 360R = 132.192$

$\Rightarrow 12R^3 + 3600R^2 = 132192$

$\Rightarrow R^3 + 300R^2 = \dfrac{132192}{12} = 11016$

$\Rightarrow R = 6\%.$

Thus, I alone as well as II alone is sufficient to answer the question.

$\therefore$ Correct answer is (*c*).

16. I. $\dfrac{P\times R\times 1}{100} = 5300 \Rightarrow PR = 530000.$

II. $P\left(1+\dfrac{R}{100}\right)^2 - P - \dfrac{P\times R\times 2}{100} = 1060 \Rightarrow PR^2 = 10600000.$

III. $\dfrac{P\times R\times 5}{100} = P \Rightarrow R = 20\%.$

From I and II, we have: $\dfrac{PR^2}{PR} = \dfrac{10600000}{530000}$

$\Rightarrow R = 20\%.$

Thus, III only or (I and II) give the answer.

$\therefore$ Correct answer is (*d*).

17. I. $P\left(1+\dfrac{R}{100}\right)^2 - P - \dfrac{P\times R\times 2}{100} = 100 \Rightarrow PR^2 = 1000000.$

II. $\dfrac{P\times R\times 10}{100} = P \Rightarrow R = 10\%.$

III. $P = 10000.$

From I and III, we have: $\dfrac{PR^2}{P} = \dfrac{1000000}{10000}$

$\Rightarrow R^2 = 100 \Rightarrow R = 10\%.$

Thus, II only or (I and III) give the answer.

$\therefore$ Correct answer is (*d*).

18. I. $\dfrac{P\times R\times 10}{100} = P \Rightarrow R = 10\%.$

II. $15000\left(1+\dfrac{R}{100}\right)^2 - 15000 - \left(\dfrac{15000\times R\times 2}{100}\right) = 150$

$\Rightarrow 15000R^2 = 1500000 \Rightarrow R^2 = 100 \Rightarrow R = 10\%.$

III. $P\left(1+\dfrac{R}{100}\right)^2 - P > P.$

Thus, either I alone or II alone gives the answer.

$\therefore$ Correct answer is (*c*).

19. I. $P\left(1+\dfrac{R}{100}\right)^2 = 5290$ ...(*i*)

II. $P\left(1+\dfrac{R}{100}\right)^3 = 6083.50$ ...(*ii*)

On dividing (*ii*) by (*i*), we get :

$\left(1+\dfrac{R}{100}\right) = \dfrac{608350}{529000} = \dfrac{23}{20}$

$\Rightarrow \dfrac{R}{100} = \left(\dfrac{23}{20}-1\right) = \dfrac{3}{20} \Rightarrow R = 15.$

Thus, I and II to gether give the answer.

III. gives $P = 4000$.

Putting this value of P in (*i*), we get the answer.

Putting this value of P in (*ii*), we get the answer.

$\therefore$ (I & II) or (I & III) or (II & III) all give the answer.

Hence, the correct answer is (*d*).

20. P = ₹ 5000 & T = 2 years.

I. S.I. on ₹ 5000 in 5 years is ₹ 2000.

$$\frac{5000 \times R \times 5}{100} = 2000 \Rightarrow R = 8.$$

II. C.I. for 1 year = S.I. for 1 year, always holds true.

III. $P\left(1+\frac{R}{100}\right)^{10} > 2P.$

Thus, only I alone gives the answer.

$\therefore$ Correct answer is (*a*).

21. From I and III, we have: $P = \left(\frac{100 \times \text{S.I.}}{R \times T}\right)$

$$= ₹\left(\frac{100 \times 750}{5 \times 3}\right) = ₹\ 5000.$$

$\therefore$ Required difference

$$= ₹\left[\left\{5000\left(1+\frac{5}{100}\right)^8 - 5000\right\} - \left(\frac{5000 \times 5 \times 8}{100}\right)\right].$$

From II and III, we have: $P\left[\left(1+\frac{5}{100}\right)^2 - 1\right] = 512.50$

$$\Rightarrow \quad = \frac{512.50 \times 400}{41} = 5000.$$

Agan, the difference between C.I. and S.I. may be calculated as above.

From I and II, we have: $P = \left(\frac{100 \times 750}{R \times 3}\right)$

$$\Rightarrow P = \frac{25000}{R}.$$

And, $P\left[\left(1+\frac{R}{100}\right)^2 - 1\right] = 512.50$

$$\Rightarrow P\left[\frac{R^2}{10000} + \frac{2R}{100}\right] = 512.50$$

$$\Rightarrow \frac{25000}{R}\left(\frac{R^2}{10000} + \frac{2R}{100}\right) = 512.50$$

$$\Rightarrow \frac{5}{2} R = 12.50 \Rightarrow R = \frac{12.50 \times 2}{5} = 5\%.$$

$$\therefore P = \frac{25000}{5} = 5000.$$

Again, the difference between C.I. and S.I. may be calculated.

Thus, any two of the three together give the answer.

$\therefore$ Correct answer is (*c*).

22. I. $P\left(1+\frac{R}{100}\right)^4 = 2P \Rightarrow \left(1+\frac{R}{100}\right)^4 = 2$ ...(*i*)

II. $P\left(1+\frac{R}{100}\right)^{12} = 8P \Rightarrow \left(1+\frac{R}{100}\right)^{12} = 8$ ...(*ii*)

III. $P\left(1+\frac{R}{100}\right)^8 = 4P \Rightarrow \left(1+\frac{R}{100}\right)^8 = 4$ ...(*iii*)

Let the given sum become 16 times in n years.

Then,

$P\left(1+\frac{R}{100}\right)^n = 16P \Rightarrow \left(1+\frac{R}{100}\right)^n = 16$ ...(*iv*)

$\therefore$ Any one of (*i*), (*ii*) and (*iii*) with (*iv*) will give the value of n.

$\therefore$ Correct answer is (*e*).

23. I and II will give us, R, S.I. and T.

$$\therefore \quad P = \frac{100 \times \text{S.I.}}{R \times T} = \left(\frac{100 \times 2000}{5 \times 8}\right) = 5000.$$

[(C.I.) – (S.I.)] for 4 years may be calculated. In this case, III is redundant.

I and III give us R and P, using

$$P\left[\left(1+\frac{5}{100}\right)^2 - 1\right] - \frac{P \times 5 \times 2}{100} = 12.50$$

So, [(C.I.) – (S.I.)] for 4 years may be calculated.

$\therefore$ Correct answer is (*c*).

24. I. gives, Rate = 5% p.a.

II. gives, S.I. for 1 year = ₹ 600.

III. gives, sum = 10 × (S.I. for 2 years).

Now, I and II give the sum.

For this sum, C.I. and hence amount can be obtained.

Thus, III is redundant.

Again, II gives S.I. for 2 years = ₹ (600 × 2) = ₹ 1200.

Now, from III, Sum = ₹ (10 × 1200) = ₹ 12000.

$$\text{Thus, Rate} = \frac{100 \times 1200}{2 \times 12000} = 5\% \text{ p.a.}$$

Thus, C.I. for 2 years and therefore, amount can be obtained. Thus, I is redundant.

Hence, I or III is redundant.

$\therefore$ Correct answer is (*d*).

25. I. gives, S.I. for 3 years = ₹ 4500.

II. gives, Rate = 10% p.a.

III. gives, (C.I.) – (S.I.) = ₹ 465.

Clearly, using I and III we get C.I. = ₹ (465 + 4500).

Thus, II is redundant.

Also, from I and II, we get sum

$$= \left(\frac{100 \times 4500}{10 \times 3}\right) = 15000.$$

Now C.I. on ₹ 15000 at 10% p.a. for 3 years may be obtained. Thus, III is redundant.

$\therefore$ Either II or III is redundant.

$\therefore$ Correct answer is (*d*).

26. I. gives, Amount after 2 years = ₹ 11025, when compounded.

II. gives, Amount after 2 years at S.I. = ₹ 11000.

III. gives, Principal = ₹ 10000.

From II and III, we have :

Principal = ₹ 10000,

S.I. = ₹ (11000 – 10000) = ₹ 1000 and Time = 2 years.

Hence, Rate can be obtained.

$\therefore$ I is redundant.

From I and III, we get 11025 = 10000 × $\left(1+\frac{R}{100}\right)^2$.

This gives R.

∴ II is redundant.

From I and II, we have

$$P\left(1+\frac{R}{100}\right)^2 = 1102 \qquad ...(i)$$

$$\text{and } P\left[1+\frac{R\times 2}{100}\right] = 11000 \qquad ...(ii)$$

On dividing (*i*) by (*ii*), we get $\frac{\left(1+\frac{R}{100}\right)^2}{(50+R)} = \frac{11025}{550000}$.

This gives R. Thus, III is redundant.

Hence I or II or III is redundant.

∴ Correct answer is (*d*).

27. We have:

$$P\left(1+\frac{R}{100}\right)^2 - P - \frac{P\times R\times 2}{100} = 12.50$$

$$\Rightarrow \frac{PR^2}{10000} = 12.50$$

$$\Rightarrow PR^2 = 125000 \qquad ...(i)$$

I. $P = \left(\frac{100\times 500}{R\times 2}\right) = \frac{25000}{R}$ ...(*ii*)

II. $P\left[\left(1+\frac{R}{100}\right)^2 - 1\right] = 512.50$

$$\Rightarrow P = \frac{512.50\times 400}{41} = 5000 \qquad ...(iii)$$

III. $\frac{P\times R\times 2}{100} + P = 5500$

$$\Rightarrow 100\,P + 2PR = 550000$$

$$\Rightarrow P = \frac{550000}{100+2R} \qquad ...(iv)$$

From (*i*) and (*ii*),

we have: $\frac{25000}{R} \times R^2 = 125000$

$\Rightarrow R = 5\%$.

From (*i*) and (*iii*), we have: $R^2 = 25 \Rightarrow R = 5\%$.

From (*i*) and (*iv*), we have: $\left(\frac{550000}{100+2R}\right) \times R^2 = 125000$

$\Rightarrow 550000\,R^2 = 12500000 + 250000\,R$

$\Rightarrow 11\,R^2 - 5R\ 250 = 0$

$\Rightarrow (11R + 50)\,(R - 5) = 0 \Rightarrow R = 5\%$.

Thus, any one of the three statements gives the answer *i.e.*, any two of the three statements can be dispensed with.

∴ Correct answer is (*d*).

24 Area

FUNDAMENTAL CONCEPTS

I. Results on Triangles:

1. Sum of the angles of a triangle is 180°.
2. The sum of any two sides of a triangle is greater than the third side.
3. **Pythagoras' Theorem:** In a right-angled triangle,

$$(\text{Hypotenuse})^2 = (\text{Base})^2 + (\text{Height})^2$$

4. The line joining the mid-point of a side of a triangle to the opposite vertex is called the **median.**
5. The point where the three medians of a triangle meet, is called **centroid.** The centroid divides each of the medians in the ratio 2 : 1.
6. In an isosceles triangle, the altitude from the vertex bisects the base.
7. The median of a triangle divides it into two triangles of the same area.
8. The line joining the mid-points of any two sides of a triangle is parallel to the third side and equal to half of it.
9. The four triangles formed by joining the mid-points of the sides of a given triangle are equal in area, each equal to one-fourth of the given triangle.
10. The ratio of the areas of two similar triangles is equal to the ratio of the squares of their
    (i) corresponding sides (ii) corresponding altitudes

II. Results on Quadrilaterals:

1. The diagonals of a parallelogram bisect each other.
2. Each diagonal of a parallelogram divides it into two triangles of the same area.
3. The diagonals of a rectangle are equal and bisect each other.
4. The diagonals of a square are equal and bisect each other at right angles.
5. The diagonals of a rhombus are unequal and bisect each other at right angles.
6. A parallelogram and a rectangle on the same base and between the same parallels are equal in area.
7. Of all the parallelograms of given sides, the parallelogram which is a rectangle has the greatest area.
8. The line joining the mid-points of the non-parallel sides of a trapezium is parallel to each of the parallel sides and equal to half of their sum.
9. The line joining the mid-points of the diagonals of a trapezium is parallel to each of the parallel sides and equal to half of their difference.

IMPORTANT FORMULAE

I. 1. Area of a rectangle = (Length × Breadth).

$\therefore$ Length $= \left(\dfrac{\text{Area}}{\text{Breadth}}\right)$ and Breath $= \left(\dfrac{\text{Area}}{\text{Lengdth}}\right)$

2. Perimeter of a rectangle = 2 (Length + Breadth).

II. Area of a square $= (\text{side})^2 = \dfrac{1}{2}(\text{diagonal})^2$.

III. Area of 4 walls of a room = 2 (Length + Breadth) × Height.

IV. 1. Area of a triangle $= \dfrac{1}{2} \times \text{Base} \times \text{Height}$.

2. Area of a triangle $= \sqrt{s(s-a)(s-b)(s-c)}$,

where a, b, c are the sides of the triangle and $s = \frac{1}{2}(a+b+c)$

3. Area of an equilateral triangle $= \frac{\sqrt{3}}{4} \times (\text{side})^2$.
4. Area of a triangle $= \frac{1}{2} ab \sin \theta$, where a and b are the lengths of any two sides of the triangle and θ is the angle between them.
5. Radius of incircle of an equilateral triangle of side a $= \frac{a}{2\sqrt{3}}$.
6. Radius of circumcircle of an equilateral triangle of side a $= \frac{a}{\sqrt{3}}$.
7. Radius of incircle of a triangle of area Δ and semi-perimeter s $= \frac{\Delta}{s}$.
8. Radius of circumcircle of a triangle $= \frac{\text{Product of sides}}{4\Delta}$.

V. 1. Area of a parallelogram = (Base × Height).
2. Area of a rhombus $= \frac{1}{2} \times$ (Product of diagonals).
3. Area of a trapezium $= \frac{1}{2} \times$ (sum of parallel sides) × (distance between them)

VI. 1. Area of a circle $= \pi R^2$, where R is the radius
2. Circumference of a circle $= 2\pi R$
3. Length of an arc $= \frac{2\pi R\theta}{360}$, where θ is the central angle
4. Area of a sector $= \frac{1}{2}(\text{arc length} \times R) = \frac{\pi R^2 \theta}{360}$.

VII. 1. Area of a semi-circle $= \frac{\pi R^2}{2}$.
2. Circumference of semi-circle $= \pi R$.
3. Perimeter of a semi-circle $= \pi R + 2R$.

VIII. 1. Area of a regular polygon of N sides, with a as the length of each side $= \frac{a^2 N}{4 \tan\left(\frac{180}{N}\right)}$.
2. Area of a regular hexagon of side a $= \frac{3\sqrt{3}}{2} a^2$.
3. Area of a regular pentagon of side a $= 1.72\, a^2$.
4. The area enclosed between the circumcircle and incircle of a regular polygon of side $a = \frac{\pi a^2}{4}$.

SOLVED EXAMPLES

Ex. 1. ***Find the maximum distance between two points on the perimeter of a rectangular garden whose length and breadth are 100 m and 50 m.*** **(Hotel Management, 2007)**

Sol. Clearly, the two points which are maximum distance apart are the end-points of a diagonal.

$\therefore$ Reqd. distance = Length of the diagonal $= \sqrt{(100)^2 + (50)^2}$ m

$= \sqrt{1000 + 2500}$ m $= \sqrt{12500}$ m

$= 50\sqrt{5}$ m $= (50 \times 2.236) = 111.8$ m.

Ex. 2. ***One side of a rectangular field is 15 m and one of its diagonals is 17 m. Find the area of the field.***

Sol. Other side = $\sqrt{(17)^2-(15)^2}=\sqrt{289-225}=\sqrt{64}=8$ m.

$\therefore$ Area = $(15\times 8)\ m^2 = 120\ m^2$.

Ex. 3. ***A lawn is in the form of a rectangle having its sides in the ratio 2 : 3. The area of the lawn is $\frac{1}{6}$ hectares. Find the length and breadth of the lawn.***

Sol. Let length = $2x$ metres and breadth = $3x$ metres.

Now, area = $\left(\frac{1}{6}\times 1000\right)m^2=\left(\frac{5000}{3}\right)m^2$.

So, $2x\times 3x=\frac{5000}{3}\Leftrightarrow x^2=\frac{2500}{9}\Leftrightarrow x=\left(\frac{50}{3}\right)$.

$\therefore$ Length = $2x=\frac{100}{3}\ m=33\frac{1}{3}$ m and Breadth = $3x=\left(3\times\frac{50}{3}\right)m=50$ m.

Ex. 4. ***Find the cost of carpeting a room 13 m long and 9 m broad with a carpet 75 cm wide at the rate of ₹ 12.40 per square metre.*** **(M.B.A., 2011)**

Sol. Area of the carpet = Area of the room = $(13\times 9)\ m^2 = 117\ m^2$.

Length of the carpet = $\left(\frac{\text{Area}}{\text{Width}}\right)=\left(117\times\frac{4}{3}\right)m=156$ m.

$\therefore$ Cost of carpeting = ₹ (156×12.40) = ₹ 1934.40.

Ex. 5. ***The length of a rectangle is twice its breadth. If its length is decreased by 5 cm and breadth is increased by 5 cm, the area of the rectangle is increased by 75 sq. cm. Find the length of the rectangle.***

Sol. Let breadth = x. Then, length = $2x$. Then,

$(2x-5)(x+5)-2x\times x=75\Leftrightarrow 5x-25=75\Leftrightarrow x=20$.

$\therefore$ Length of the rectangle = 20 cm.

Ex. 6. ***A rectangular carpet has an area of 120 sq. metres and a perimeter of 46 metres. Find the length of its diagonal.*** **(L.I.C. A.A.O., 2007)**

Sol. Let the length and breadth of the rectangle be l and b metres respectively.

Then, $2(l+b)=46\Rightarrow l+b=23\Rightarrow b=(23-l)$.

And, $lb=120\Rightarrow l(23-l)=120\Rightarrow 23l-l^2=120\Rightarrow l^2-23l+120=0$

$\Rightarrow l^2-15l-8l+120=0$

$\Rightarrow l(l-15)-8(l-15)=0$

$\Rightarrow (l-15)(l-8)=0\Rightarrow l=15$.

So, $l=15$ and $b=8$.

$\therefore$ Length of diagonal = $\sqrt{l^2+b^2}=\sqrt{(15)^2+8^2}\ m=\sqrt{289}\ m=17$ m.

Ex. 7. ***The length of a rectangle is increased by 30%. By what percent would the breadth have to be decreased to maintain the same area?*** **(M.B.A., 2008)**

Sol. Let the length and breadth of the rectangle be l and b units respectively.

Then, area of rectangle = (lb) sq. units.

New length = 160% of $l=\frac{8l}{5}$ units.

Desired breadth = $\frac{\text{Area}}{\text{New length}}=\frac{lb}{\left(\frac{8l}{5}\right)}=\frac{5b}{8}$ units.

Decrease in breadth = $\left(b-\frac{5b}{8}\right)$ units $=\frac{3b}{8}$ units.

$\therefore$ Decrease% = $\left(\frac{3b}{8}\times\frac{1}{b}\times 100\right)\%=\frac{75}{2}\%=37.5\%$.

Ex. 8. ***In measuring the sides of a rectangular plot, one side is taken 5% in excess and the other 6% in deficit. Find the error percent in area calculated, of the plot.*** **(M.A.T., 2010)**

Sol. Let the length and breadth of the rectangle be l and b units respectively.

Then, correct area = (lb) sq. units.

Calculated area = $\left(\frac{105\,l}{100}\times\frac{94\,b}{100}\right)=\left(\frac{987\,lb}{1000}\right)$ sq. units.

Error in measurement = $\left(lb-\frac{987}{1000}lb\right)$ sq. units $=\left(\frac{13lb}{1000}\right)$ sq.units.

$\therefore$ Error% = $\left(\frac{13lb}{1000}\times\frac{1}{lb}\times 100\right)\% = 1.3\%$.

Ex. 9. ***Instead of walking along two adjacent sides of a rectangular field, a boy took a shor-cut along the diagonal of the field and saved a distance equal to half of the longer side. Find the ratio of the shorter side of the rectangle to the longer side.*** **(M.B.A., 2011)**

Sol. Let the length of the longer side of the field be l and that of the shorter side be b.

Then, diagonal = $\sqrt{l^2+b^2}$.

$\therefore \quad (l+b)-\sqrt{l^2+b^2}=\frac{1}{2}l \Rightarrow \sqrt{l^2+b^2}=\frac{l}{2}+b$

$\Rightarrow 2\sqrt{l^2+b^2}=l+2b \Rightarrow 4(l^2+b^2)=l^2+4b^2+4lb$

$\Rightarrow 3l^2=4lb \Rightarrow 3l=4b \Rightarrow \frac{b}{l}=\frac{3}{4}$.

Hence, required ratio = 3 : 4.

Ex. 10. ***Two perpendicular cross roads of equal width run through the middle of a rectangular field of length 80 m and breadth 60 m. If the area of the cross roads is 675 m², find the width of the roads.***

Sol. Let $ABCD$ and $EFGH$ denote the cross roads, each of width x metres.

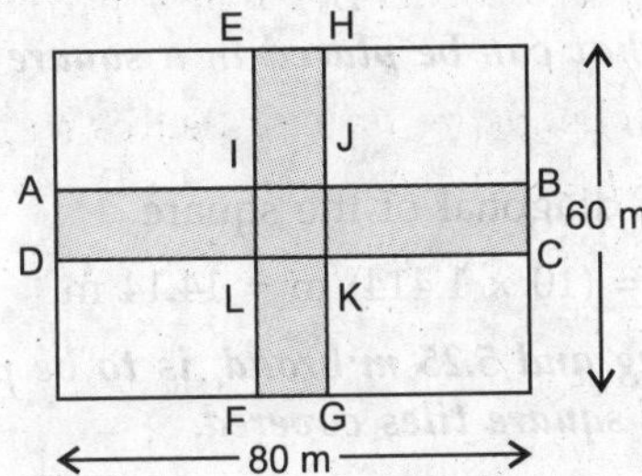

Then, area of the cross-roads

= area of rectangle $ABCD$ + area of rectangle $EFGH$ – area of square $IJKL$

= $(80x + 60x - x^2) = 140x - x^2$.

$\therefore \quad 140x - x^2 = 675 \Rightarrow x^2 - 140x + 675 = 0$

$\Rightarrow x^2 - 135x + 5x - 675 = 0 \quad \Rightarrow \quad x(x-135) - 5(x-135) = 0$

$\Rightarrow (x-135)(x-5) = 0 \Rightarrow x = 5. \qquad [\because x \neq 135]$

So, width of road = 5m.

Ex. 11. ***A rectangular grassy plot 110 m by 65 m has a gravel path 2.5 m wide all round it on the inside. Find the cost of gravelling the path at 80 paise per sq. metre.***

Sol. Area of the plot = (110×65) m² = 7150 m².

Area of the plot excluding the path = $[(110-5)\times(65-5)]$ m² = 6300 m².

$\therefore$ Area of the path = $(7150 - 6300)$ m² = 850 m².

Cost of gravelling the path = ₹$\left(850\times\frac{80}{100}\right)$ = ₹ 680.

Ex. 12. ***The diagonal of a rectangular field is 15 m and its area is 108 sq. m. What will be the total expenditure in fencing the field at the rate of ₹ 5 per metre?***

Sol. Let the length and breadth of the rectangle be l and b metres respectively.

Then, $\sqrt{l^2 + b^2} = 15$ and $lb = 108 \Rightarrow l^2 + b^2 = 225$ and $lb = 108$

$\Rightarrow (l + b)^2 = (l^2 + b^2) + 2lb = 225 + 216 = 441$

$\Rightarrow l + b = \sqrt{441} = 21.$

$\therefore$ Perimeter of the field $= 2(l + b) = (2 \times 21)$ m $= 42$ m.

Hence, cost of fencing = ₹ (42×5) = ₹ 210.

Ex. 13. ***The perimeters of two squares are 40 cm and 32 cm. Find the perimeter of a third square whose area is equal to the difference of the areas of the two squares.***

Sol. Side of first square $= \left(\frac{40}{4}\right)$ cm $= 10$ cm; Side of second square $= \left(\frac{32}{4}\right)$ cm $= 8$ cm.

Area of third square $= [(10)^2 - (8)^2]$ cm^2 $= (100 - 64)$ cm^2 $= 36$ cm^2.

Side of third square $= \sqrt{36}$ cm $= 6$ cm.

$\therefore$ Required perimeter $= (6 \times 4)$ cm $= 24$ cm.

Ex. 14. ***The length of a rectangle R is 10% more than the side of a square S. The width of the rectangle R is 10% less than the side of the square S. What is the ratio of the area of R to that of S?***

Sol. Let each side of the square S be x units.

Then, length of rectangle R = 110% of $x = \left(\frac{11x}{10}\right)$ units.

And, width of rectangle R = 90% of $x = \left(\frac{9x}{10}\right)$ units.

$\therefore$ Ratio of areas of R and $S = \left(\frac{11x}{10} \times \frac{9x}{10}\right) : x^2 = \frac{99x^2}{100} : x^2 = 99 : 100.$

Ex. 15. ***Find the largest size of a bamboo that can be placed in a square of area 100 sq. m.*** (P.C.S., 2009)

Sol. Side of the square $= \sqrt{100}$ m $= 10$ m.

Largest size of bamboo = Length of diagonal of the square

$= 10\sqrt{2}$ m. $= (10 \times 1.414)$ m $= 14.14$ m.

Ex. 16. ***A rectangular courtyard, 3.78 m long and 5.25 m broad, is to be paved exactly with square tiles, all of the same size. Find the least number of square tiles covered.*** (M.A.T., 2007)

Sol. Area of the room $= (378 \times 525)$ cm^2.

Size of largest square tile = H.C.F. of 378 cm and 525 cm = 21 cm.

Area of 1 tile $= (21 \times 21)$ cm^2.

$\therefore$ Number of tiles required $= \left(\frac{378 \times 525}{21 \times 21}\right) = 450.$

Ex. 17. ***Find the area of a square, one of whose diagonals is 3.8 m long.***

Sol. Area of the square $= \frac{1}{2} \times (\text{diagonal})^2 = \left(\frac{1}{2} \times 3.8 \times 3.8\right) \text{m}^2 = 7.22 \text{ m}^2.$

Ex. 18. ***The diagonals of two squares are in the ratio of 2 : 5. Find the ratio of their areas.*** (Section Officers', 2003)

Sol. Let the diagonals of the squares be $2x$ and $5x$ respectively.

$\therefore$ Ratio of their areas $= \frac{1}{2} \times (2x)^2 : \frac{1}{2} \times (5x)^2 = 4x^2 : 25x^2 = 4 : 25.$

Ex. 19. ***If each side of a square is increased by 25%, find the percentage change in its area.***

Sol. Let each side of the square be a. Then, area $= a^2$.

New side $= \frac{125a}{100} = \frac{5a}{4}$. New area $= \left(\frac{5a}{4}\right)^2 = \frac{25a^2}{16}$.

Increase in area $= \left(\frac{25a^2}{16} - a^2\right) = \frac{9a^2}{16}$.

$\therefore$ Increase% $= \left(\frac{9a^2}{16} \times \frac{1}{a^2} \times 100\right)\% = 56.25\%$.

Ex. 20. ***If the diagonal of a square is decreased by 15%, find the percentage decrease in its area.***

Sol. Let the length of the diagonal of the square be x. Then, area $= \frac{x^2}{2}$.

New diagonal = 85% of $x = \frac{17x}{20}$.

New area $= \frac{1}{2} \times \left(\frac{17x}{20}\right)^2 = \frac{289x^2}{800}$.

Decrease in area $= \left(\frac{x^2}{2} - \frac{289x^2}{800}\right) = \frac{111x^2}{800}$.

$\therefore$ Decrease% $= \left(\frac{111x^2}{800} \times \frac{2}{x^2} \times 100\right)\% = 27.75\%$.

Ex. 21. ***A square park is surrounded by a path of uniform width 2 metres all around it. The area of the path is 288 sq. metres. Find the perimeter of the park.*** (R.R.B., 2009)

Sol. Let the length of each side of the square park be x metres.

Then, area of the path $= [(x + 4)^2 - x^2]\ m^2 = (16 + 8x)\ m^2$.

$16 + 8x = 288 \Rightarrow 8x = 272 \Rightarrow x = 34$ m.

$\therefore$ Perimeter of the park $= (4 \times 34)$ m $= 136$ m.

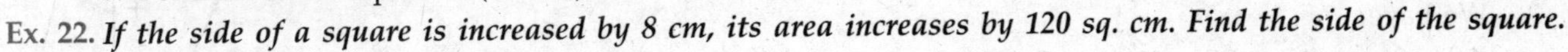

Ex. 22. ***If the side of a square is increased by 8 cm, its area increases by 120 sq. cm. Find the side of the square.***

Sol. Let the length of a side of the square be x cm. Then,

$(x + 8)^2 - x^2 = 120 \Rightarrow 64 + 16x = 120 \Rightarrow 16x = 56 \Rightarrow x = \frac{56}{16} = \frac{7}{2} = 3.5$ cm.

Hence, side of square = 3.5 cm.

Ex. 23. ***If the length of a certain rectangle is decreased by 4 cm and the width is increased by 3 cm, a square with the same area as the original rectangle would result. Find the perimeter of the original rectangle.***

Sol. Let x and y be the length and breadth of the rectangle respectively.

Then, $x - 4 = y + 3$ or $x - y = 7$ ...(*i*)

Area of the rectangle $= xy$; Area of the square $= (x - 4)(y + 3)$

$\therefore (x - 4)(y + 3) = xy \Leftrightarrow 3x - 4y = 12$ ...(*ii*)

Solving (*i*) and (*ii*), we get $x = 16$ and $y = 9$.

$\therefore$ Perimeter of the rectangle $= 2(x + y) = [2(16 + 9)]$ cm $= 50$ cm.

Ex. 24. ***The dimensions of a room are 12.5 metres by 9 metres by 7 metres. There are 2 doors and 4 windows in the room; each door measures 2.5 metres by 1.2 metres and each window 1.5 metres by 1 metre. Find the cost of painting the walls at ₹ 36.50 per square metre.*** (M.A.T., 2006)

Sol. Area of 4 walls $= 2(l + b) \times h = 2[(12.5 + 9) \times 7]\ m^2 = 301\ m^2$.

Area of 2 doors and 4 windows $= [2(2.5 \times 1.2) + 4(1.5 \times 1)]\ m^2 = 12\ m^2$.

Area to be painted $= (301 - 12)\ m^2 = 289\ m^2$.

$\therefore$ Cost of painting = ₹ (289 × 36.50) = ₹ 10548.50.

Ex. 25. ***A room is half as long again as it is broad. The cost of carpeting the room at ₹ 5 per sq. m is ₹ 270 and the cost of papering the four walls at ₹ 10 per m² is ₹ 1720. If a door and 2 windows occupy 8 sq. m, find the dimensions of the room.***

Sol. Let breadth $= x$ metres, length $= \frac{3x}{2}$ metres, height $= H$ metres.

Area of the floor = $\left(\frac{\text{Total cost of carpeting}}{\text{Rate/m}^2}\right) m^2 = \left(\frac{270}{5}\right) m^2 = 54\ m^2.$

$\therefore\ x \times \frac{3x}{2} = 54 \Leftrightarrow x^2 = \left(54 \times \frac{2}{3}\right) = 36 \Leftrightarrow x = 6.$

So, breadth = 6 m and length = $\left(\frac{3}{2} \times 6\right)$ m = 9 m.

Now, papered area = $\left(\frac{1720}{10}\right) m^2 = 172\ m^2.$

Area of 1 door and 2 windows = 8 m^2.

Total area of 4 walls = (172 + 8) m^2 = 180 m^2.

$\therefore\ 2(9 + 6) \times H = 180 \Leftrightarrow H = \left(\frac{180}{30}\right) = 6$ m.

Ex. 26. ***The readings in a field book are as given below:***

To B (in metres)

24 to E	***96***	
	48	
	24	***12 to D***
	12	***6 to C***

From A

Calculate the area.

Sol. The field may be drawn as shown in the adjoining figure.

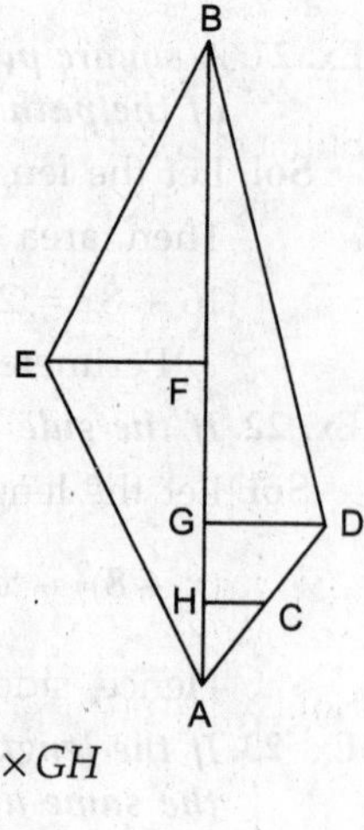

We have:

$AB = 96$ m, $AF = BF = 48$ m, $AG = 24$ m,

$AH = 12$ m, $CH = 6$ m,

$DG = 12$ m, $EF = 24$ m.

Area of the field = ar (ΔBFE) + ar (ΔAFE) + ar (ΔAHC) + ar (ΔBGD) + ar (trap. $CDGH$)

$= \frac{1}{2} \times BF \times EF + \frac{1}{2} \times AF \times EF \times \frac{1}{2} \times AH \times CH + \frac{1}{2} \times BG \times GD + \frac{1}{2} \times (GD + CH) \times GH$

$= \left[\frac{1}{2} \times 48 \times 24 + \frac{1}{2} \times 48 \times 24 + \frac{1}{2} \times 12 \times 6 + \frac{1}{2} \times 72 \times 12 + \frac{1}{2} \times (12 + 6) \times 12\right] m^2$

$= (576 + 576 + 36 + 432 + 108)\ m^2 = 1728\ m^2.$

Ex. 27. ***Find the area of a triangle whose sides measure 15 cm, 16 cm and 17 cm.***

Sol. Let a = 15 cm, b = 16 cm and c = 17 cm. Then, $s = \frac{1}{2}(a + b + c) = 24.$

$\therefore\ (s - a)$ = 9 cm, $(s - b)$ = 8 cm and $(s - c)$ = 7 cm.

Area = $\sqrt{s(s-a)(s-b)(s-c)} = \sqrt{24 \times 9 \times 8 \times 7}\ cm^2 = 24\sqrt{21}\ cm^2.$

Ex. 28. ***Find the area of a right-angled triangle with hypotenuse 65 cm and one side 25 cm.***

Sol. Other side = $\sqrt{(65)^2 - (25)^2}$ cm = $\sqrt{3600}$ cm = 60 cm.

$\therefore$ Area of the triangle = $\frac{1}{2} \times$ product of sides containing the right angle

$= \left(\frac{1}{2} \times 60 \times 25\right) cm^2 = 750$ cm.

Ex. 29. ***The base of a triangular field is three times its altitude. If the cost of cultivating the field at ₹ 24.68 per hectare be ₹ 333.18, find its base and height.***

Sol. Area of the field = $\frac{\text{Total cost}}{\text{Rate}} = \left(\frac{333.18}{24.68}\right)$ hectares = 13.5 hectares

= (13.5×10000) m^2 = 135000 m^2.

Let altitude = x metres and base = $3x$ metres.

Then, $\frac{1}{2} \times 3x \times x = 135000 \Leftrightarrow x^2 = 90000 \Leftrightarrow x = 300$.

$\therefore$ Base = 900 m and Altitude = 300 m.

Ex. 30. ***The cost of fencing an equilateral triangular park and a square park is the same. If the area of the triangular park is $16\sqrt{3}$ m^2, find the length of the diagonal of the diagonal of the square park.*** **(Hotel Management, 2010)**

Sol. Let the length of each side of the triangular park be a cm.

Then, $\frac{\sqrt{3}}{4} a^2 = 16\sqrt{3} \Rightarrow a^2 = 64 \Rightarrow a = 8$ m.

Perimeter of the square park = Perimeter of the triangular park = (3×8) m = 24 m.

Side of the square park = $\left(\frac{24}{4}\right)$ cm = 6 m.

$\therefore$ Length of diagonal of the square park = $6\sqrt{2}$ m.

Ex. 31. ***The altitude drawn to the base of an isosceles triangle is 8 cm and the perimeter is 32 cm. Find the area of the triangle.***

Sol. Let ABC be the isosceles triangle and AD be the altitude.

Let AB = $AC = x$. Then, BC = $(32 - 2x)$.

Since, in an isosceles triangle, the altitude bisects the base, so $BD = DC = (16 - x)$.

In ΔADC, $AC^2 = AD^2 + DC^2 \Rightarrow x^2 = (8)^2 + (16 - x)^2 \Rightarrow 32x = 320 \Rightarrow x = 10$.

$\therefore$ BC = $(32 - 2x) = (32 - 20)$ cm = 12 cm.

Hence, required area = $\left(\frac{1}{2} \times BC \times AD\right) = \left(\frac{1}{2} \times 12 \times 10\right)$ cm^2 = 60 cm^2.

A, x, x, B, D, C

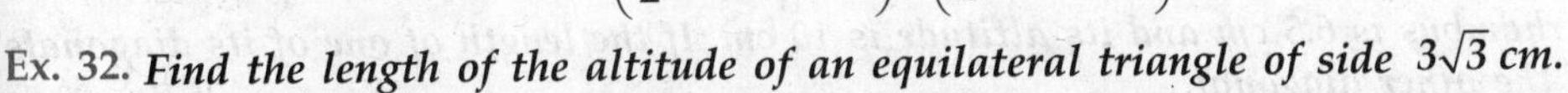

Ex. 32. ***Find the length of the altitude of an equilateral triangle of side $3\sqrt{3}$ cm.***

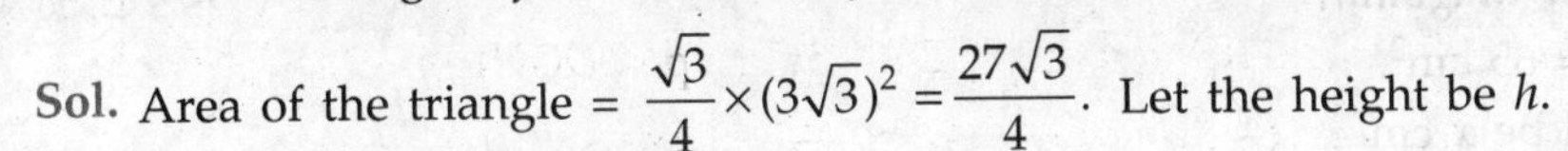

Sol. Area of the triangle = $\frac{\sqrt{3}}{4} \times (3\sqrt{3})^2 = \frac{27\sqrt{3}}{4}$. Let the height be h.

Then, $\frac{1}{2} \times 3\sqrt{3} \times h = \frac{27\sqrt{3}}{4} \Leftrightarrow h = \frac{27\sqrt{3}}{4} \times \frac{2}{3\sqrt{3}} = \frac{9}{2} = 4.5$ cm.

Ex. 33. ***The base and altitude of a right angled triangle are 12 cm and 5 cm respectively. Find the perpendicular distance of its hypotenuse from the opposite vertex.*** **(S.S.C., 2006)**

Sol. Area of the triangle = $\left(\frac{1}{2} \times 12 \times 5\right)$ cm^2 = 30 cm^2.

Hypotenuse = $\sqrt{(12)^2 + 5^2}$ cm = $\sqrt{169}$ cm = 13 cm.

Let the perpendicular distance of the hypotenuse from the opposite vertex be h cm.

Then, $\frac{1}{2} \times 13 \times h = 30 \Rightarrow h = \frac{60}{13} = 4\frac{8}{13}$ cm.

Ex. 34. ***In two triangles, the ratio of the areas is 4 : 3 and the ratio of their heights is 3 : 4. Find the ratio of their bases.***

Sol. Let the bases of the two triangles be x and y and their heights be $3h$ and $4h$ respectively.

Then, $\frac{\frac{1}{2} \times x \times 3h}{\frac{1}{2} \times y \times 4h} = \frac{4}{3} \Leftrightarrow \frac{x}{y} = \left(\frac{4}{3} \times \frac{4}{3}\right) = \frac{16}{9}$.

$\therefore$ Required ratio = 16 : 9.

Ex. 35. ***If the height of a triangle is increased by 30% and its base is decreased by 20%, what will be the effect on its area?***

Sol. Let the base and height of the triangle be x and y units respectively.

Then, area of the triangle $= \left(\frac{1}{2}xy\right)$ sq. units.

New, area $= \left[\frac{1}{2}(80\% \text{ of } x)(130\% \text{ of } y)\right]$ sq. units.

$= \left(\frac{1}{2} \times \frac{4x}{5} \times \frac{13y}{10}\right)$ sq.units $= \left(\frac{13xy}{25}\right)$ sq.units.

Increase in area $= \left(\frac{13xy}{25} - \frac{xy}{2}\right)$ sq.units $= \left(\frac{xy}{50}\right)$ sq.units.

$\therefore$ Increase% $= \left(\frac{xy}{50} \times \frac{2}{xy} \times 100\right)\% = 4\%$.

Ex. 36. ***The base of a parallelogram is twice its height. If the area of the parallelogram is 72 sq. cm, find its height.***

Sol. Let the height of the parallelogram be x cm. Then, base = $(2x)$ cm.

$\therefore$ $2x \times x = 72 \Leftrightarrow 2x^2 = 72 \Leftrightarrow x^2 = 36 \Leftrightarrow x = 6$.

Hence, height of the parallelogram = 6 cm.

Ex. 37. ***Find the area of a rhombus one side of which measures 20 cm and one diagonal 24 cm.***

Sol. Let other diagonal = $2x$ cm.

Since diagonals of a rhombus bisect each other at right angles, we have :

$(20)^2 = (12)^2 + x^2 \Leftrightarrow x = \sqrt{(20)^2 - (12)^2} = \sqrt{256} = 16$ cm.

So, other diagonal = 32 cm.

$\therefore$ Area of rhombus $= \frac{1}{2} \times$ (Product of diagonals) $= \left(\frac{1}{2} \times 24 \times 32\right) \text{cm}^2 = 384 \text{ cm}^2$.

Ex. 38. ***The length of one side of a rhombus is 6.5 cm and its altitude is 10 cm. If the length of one of its diagonals is 26 cm, find the length of the other diagonal.*** (S.S.C., 2005)

Sol. Area of rhombus = (6.5×10) cm^2 = 65 cm^2.

Let the length of the other diagonal be x cm.

Then, $\frac{1}{2} \times 26 \times x = 65$ or $x = 5$ cm.

Hence, length of the other diagonal = 5 cm.

Ex. 39. ***The difference between two para lel sides of a trapezium is 4 cm. The perpendicular distance between them is 19 cm. If the area of the trapezium is 475 cm², find the lengths of the parallel sides.*** (R.R.B., 2002)

Sol. Let the two parallel sides of the trapezium be a cm and b cm.

Then, $a - b = 4$ ...(i)

And, $\frac{1}{2} \times (a + b) \times 19 = 475 \Leftrightarrow (a + b) = \left(\frac{475 \times 2}{19}\right) \Leftrightarrow a + b = 50$ ...(ii)

Solving (i) and (ii), we get : $a = 27$, $b = 23$.

So, the two parallel sides are 27 cm and 23 cm.

Ex. 40. ***Find the length of a rope by which a cow must be tethered in order that it may be able to graze an area of 9856 sq. metres.*** (M.B.A. 2009)

Sol. Clearly, the cow will graze a circular field of area 9856 sq. metres and radius equal to the length of the rope.

Let the length of the rope be R metres.

Then, $\pi R^2 = 9856 \Leftrightarrow R^2 = \left(9856 \times \frac{7}{22}\right) = 3136 \Leftrightarrow R = 56$.

$\therefore$ Length of the rope = 56 m.

Ex. 41. ***The area of a circular field is 13.86 hectares. Find the cost of fencing it at the rate of ₹ 4.40 per metre.*** **(A.A.O. Exam, 2010)**

Sol. Area = $(13.86 \times 10000)\ m^2 = 138600\ m^2$.

$\pi R^2 = 138600 \Leftrightarrow R^2 = \left(138600 \times \frac{7}{22}\right) \Leftrightarrow R = 210$ m.

Circumference = $2\pi R = \left(2 \times \frac{22}{7} \times 210\right)$ m = 1320 m.

∴ Cost of fencing = ₹ (1320 × 4.40) = ₹ 5808.

Ex. 42. ***The ratio of the circumferences of two circles is 2 : 3. What is the ratio of their areas?*** **(J.M.E.T., 2004)**

Sol. Let the radius of the circles be r and R respectively.

Then, $\frac{2\pi r}{2\pi R} = \frac{2}{3} \Rightarrow \frac{r}{R} = \frac{2}{3} \Rightarrow \frac{r^2}{R^2} = \left(\frac{2}{3}\right)^2 \Rightarrow \frac{\pi r^2}{\pi R^2} = \frac{4}{9}$.

Hence, ratio of areas = 4 : 9.

Ex. 43. ***If a wire of 440 metres length is moulded in the form of a circle and a square turn by turn, find the ratio of the area of the circle to that of the square.***

Sol. Let the radius of the circle be r metres and the side of the square be a metres.

Then, $2\pi r = 440 \Rightarrow r = \left(\frac{440 \times 7}{2 \times 22}\right) = 70$ m. And, $4a = 440 \Rightarrow a = \left(\frac{440}{4}\right) = 110$ m.

∴ Required ratio = $\pi r^2 : a^2 = \left(\frac{22}{7} \times 70 \times 70\right) : (110)^2$ = 15400 : 12100 = 14 : 11.

Ex. 44. ***A circular wire of diameter 42 cm is bent in the form of a rectangle whose sides are in the ratio 6 : 5. Find the area of the rectangle.*** **(S.S.C., 2007)**

Sol. We have: $r = 21$ cm.

Perimeter of the rectangle = Circumference of the circle

$= \left(2 \times \frac{22}{7} \times 21\right)$ cm = 132 cm.

Let the sides of the rectangle be $6x$ and $5x$.

Then, $2(6x + 5x) = 132 \Rightarrow 11x = 66 \Rightarrow x = 6$.

So, the sides of the rectangle are 36 cm and 30 cm.

∴ Area of the rectangle = $(36 \times 30)\ cm^2 = 1080\ cm^2$.

Ex. 45. ***The diameter of the driving wheel of a bus is 140 cm. How many revolutions per minute must the wheel make in order to keep a speed of 66 kmph?***

Sol. Distance to be covered in 1 min. = $\left(\frac{66 \times 1000}{60}\right)$ m = 1100 m.

Circumference of the wheel = $\left(2 \times \frac{22}{7} \times 0.70\right)$ m = 4.4 m.

∴ Number of revolutions per min. = $\left(\frac{1100}{4.4}\right) = 250$.

Ex. 46. ***A wheel makes 1000 revolutions in covering a distance of 88 km. Find the radius of the wheel.***

Sol. Distance covered in one revolution = $\left(\frac{88 \times 1000}{1000}\right)$ m = 88 m.

∴ $2\pi R = 88 \Leftrightarrow 2 \times \frac{22}{7} \times R = 88 \Leftrightarrow R = \left(88 \times \frac{7}{44}\right) = 14$ m.

Ex. 47. ***A circular grassy plot of land, 42 m in diameter, has a path 3.5 m wide running round it outside. Find the cost of gravelling the path at ₹ 4 per square metre.*** **(M.A.T., 2005)**

Sol. Radius of plot, $r = \left(\frac{42}{2}\right) \text{m} = 21 \text{ m}.$

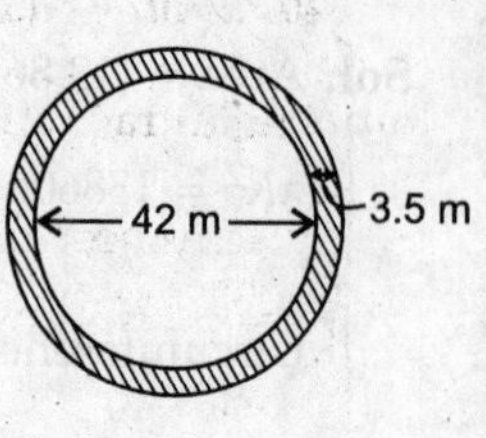

Radius of (plot + path), $R = (21 + 3.5)$ m $= 24.5$ m.

Area of path $= \pi\,(R^2 - r^2) = \pi[(24.5)^2 - (21)^2]$

$$= \frac{22}{7} \times (24.5 + 21)\,(24.5 - 21) = \left(\frac{22}{7} \times 45.5 \times 3.5\right) \text{m}^2 = 500.5 \text{ m}^2.$$

∴ Cost of gravelling = ₹ (500.5 × 4) = ₹ 2002.

Ex. 48. ***The inner circumference of a circular race track, 14 m wide, is 440 m. Find the radius of the outer circle.***

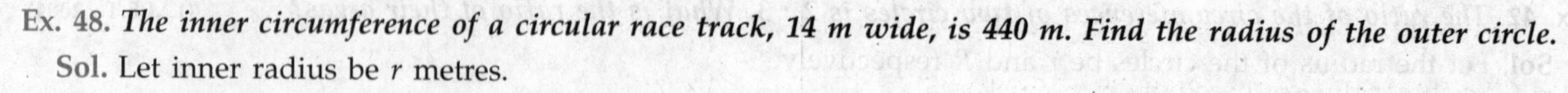

Sol. Let inner radius be r metres.

Then, $2\pi r = 440 \Rightarrow r = \left(440 \times \frac{7}{44}\right) = 70$ m.

∴ Radius of outer circle = (70 + 14) m = 84 m.

Ex. 49. ***Two concentric circles form a ring. The inner and outer circumferences of the ring ar $50\frac{2}{7}$ m and $75\frac{3}{7}$ m respectively. Find the width of the ring.***

Sol. Let the inner and outer radii be r and R metres.

Then, $2\pi r = \frac{352}{7} \Rightarrow r = \left(\frac{352}{7} \times \frac{7}{22} \times \frac{1}{2}\right) = 8$ m.

$2\pi R = \frac{528}{7} \Rightarrow R = \left(\frac{528}{7} \times \frac{7}{22} \times \frac{1}{2}\right) = 12$ m.

∴ Width of the ring = $(R - r)$ = (12 – 8) m = 4 m.

Ex. 50. ***If the cost of gardening is ₹ 85 per square metre then what will be the cost of gardening 1.4 metre wide strip inside around a circular field having an area of 1386 square metres?*** **(Bank P.O., 2007)**

Sol. Let the radius of the circular field be R metres.

Then, $\pi R^2 = 1386 \Rightarrow R^2 = \frac{1386 \times 7}{22} = 441 \Rightarrow R = \sqrt{441} = 21$ m.

Radius of field excluding strip, $r = (21 - 1.4)$ m $= 19.6$ m.

Area of strip $= \pi\,(R^2 - r^2) = \pi\,[(21)^2 - (19.6)^2]$

$$= \left[\frac{22}{7}(441 - 384.16)\right] \text{m}^2 = \left(\frac{22}{7} \times 56.84\right) \text{m}^2 = 178.64 \text{ m}^2.$$

∴ Cost of gardening = ₹ (178.64 × 85) = ₹ 15184.40.

Ex. 51. ***The radii of three concentric circles are in the ratio 1 : 2 : 3. Find the ratio of the area between the two inner circles to that between the two outer circles.*** **(S.S.C., 2008)**

Sol. Let the radii of the three concentric circles be r, $2r$ and $3r$ respectively.

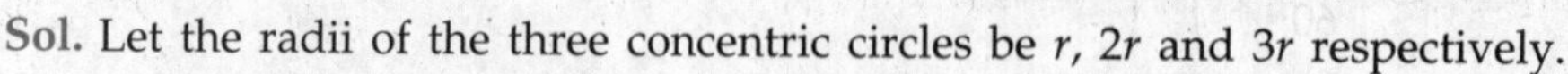

∴ Required ratio $= \pi[(2r)^2 - r^2] : \pi[(3r)^2 - (2r)^2]$

$= 3\pi r^2 : 5\pi r^2 = 3 : 5.$

Ex. 52. ***In a circle of radius 28 cm, an arc subtends an angle of 72° at the centre. Find the length of the arc and the area of the sector so formed.*** **(S.S.C., 2008)**

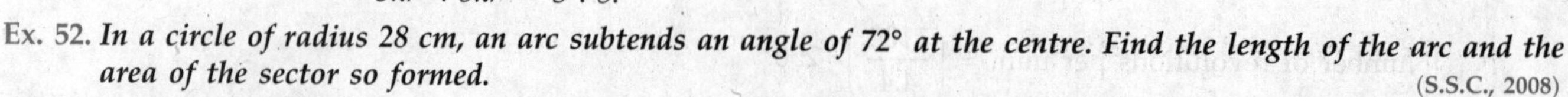

Sol. $r = 28$ cm, $\theta = 72°$.

∴ Length of arc $= \left(2 \times \frac{22}{7} \times 28 \times \frac{72}{360}\right)$ cm $= 35.2$ cm.

Area of the sector $= \left(\frac{22}{7} \times 28 \times 28 \times \frac{72}{360}\right) \text{cm}^2 = 492.8 \text{ cm}^2.$

Ex. 53. ***The minute hand of a clock is 1.5 cm long. What is the distance travelled by its tip during an interval of 40 minutes? (Take π = 3.14)***

Sol. Angle traced in 40 min = $\left(\frac{360}{60} \times 40\right)^\circ = 240°$.

∴ Distance travelled by the tip of the hand

= Length of arc of a circle with radius 1.5 cm and central angle 240°

$= \left(2 \times 3.14 \times 1.5 \times \frac{240}{360}\right) \text{cm}^2 = 6.28 \text{ cm}^2.$

Ex. 54. ***A sector of 120°, cut out from a circle, has an area of $9\frac{3}{7}$ sq. cm. Find the radius of the circle.***

Sol. Let the radius of the circle be r cm. Then,

$\frac{\pi r^2 \theta}{360} = \frac{66}{7} \Leftrightarrow \frac{22}{7} \times r^2 \times \frac{120}{360} = \frac{66}{7} \Leftrightarrow r^2 = \left(\frac{66}{7} \times \frac{7}{22} \times 3\right) = 9 \Leftrightarrow r = 3.$

Hence, radius = 3 cm.

Ex. 55. ***Find the area of the largest circle that can be drawn inside a rectangle with sides 7 m by 6 m.***

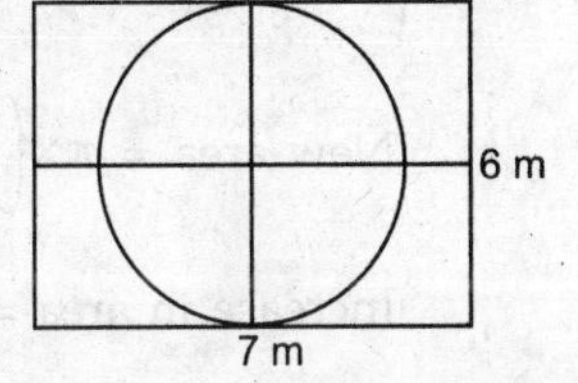

Sol. Radius of the required circle = $\left(\frac{1}{2} \times 6\right) \text{m} = 3 \text{ m}.$

∴ Area of the circle = $\left(\frac{22}{7} \times 3 \times 3\right) \text{m}^2$

$= \left(\frac{198}{7}\right) \text{m}^2 = 28\frac{2}{7} \text{ m}^2.$

Ex. 56. ***Find the ratio of the areas of the incircle and circumcircle of a square.***

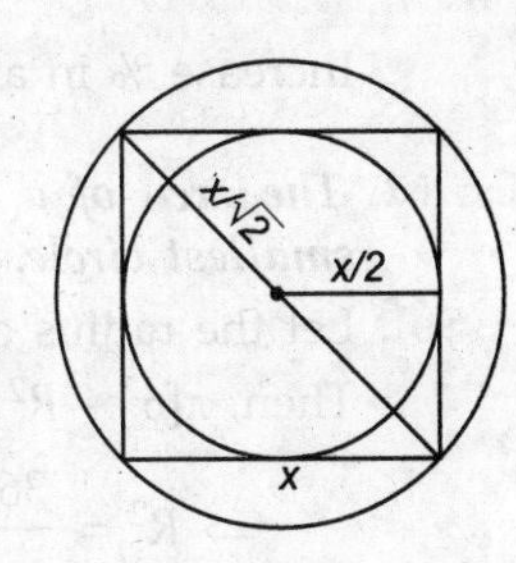

Sol. Let the side of the square be x. Then, its diagonal = $\sqrt{2}\, x$.

Radius of incircle = $\frac{x}{2}$ and radius of circumcircle = $\frac{\sqrt{2}\, x}{2} = \frac{x}{\sqrt{2}}$.

∴ Required ratio = $\left(\frac{\pi x^2}{4} : \frac{\pi x^2}{2}\right) = \frac{1}{4} : \frac{1}{2} = 1 : 2.$

Ex. 57. ***Four horses are tied on the four corners of a square field of length 14 m so that each horse can just touch the other two horses. They were able to graze in the area accessible to them for 11 days. For how many days is the ungrazed area sufficient for them?*** **(M.A.T., 2006)**

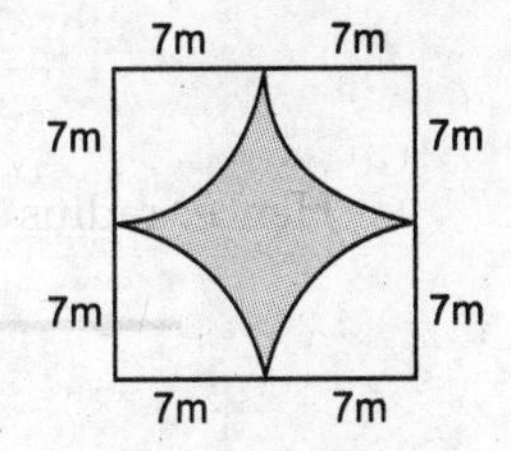

Sol. Area of the square field = (14 × 14) m² = 196 m².

Area accessible to the horses for grazing

= 4 × Area of a quadrant with r = 7 m

= Area of a circle with r = 7 m = $\left(\frac{22}{7} \times 7 \times 7\right) \text{m}^2 = 154 \text{ m}^2.$

Ungrazed area = (196 − 154) m² = 42 m².

154 m² area feeds the horses for 11 days.

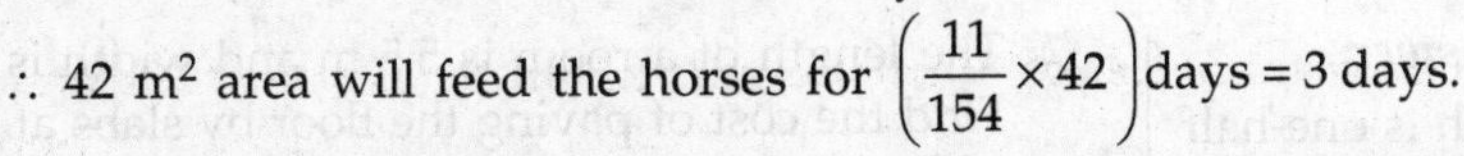

∴ 42 m² area will feed the horses for $\left(\frac{11}{154} \times 42\right)$ days = 3 days.

Ex. 58. ***If the radius of a circle is decreased by 50%, find the percentage decrease in its area.*** **(M.A.T., 2008)**

Sol. Let original radius = R. New radius = $\frac{50}{100} R = \frac{R}{2}$.

Original area = πR^2 and New area = $\pi \left(\frac{R}{2}\right)^2 = \frac{\pi R^2}{4}$.

∴ Decrease in area = $\left(\frac{3\pi R^2}{4} \times \frac{1}{\pi R^2} \times 100\right)\% = 75\%.$

Ex. 59. ***If the radius of a circle is increased by 20% then by how much will its area be increased?*** **(M.B.A. 2011)**

Sol. Let original radius = R. New radius = $\frac{120}{100}R = \frac{6R}{5}$.

Original area = πR^2 and New area = $\pi\left(\frac{6R}{5}\right)^2 = \frac{36\pi R^2}{25}$.

Increase in area = $\left(\frac{36\pi R^2}{25} - \pi R^2\right) = \frac{11\pi R^2}{25}$.

$\therefore$ Increase% = $\left(\frac{11\pi R^2}{25} \times \frac{1}{\pi R^2} \times 100\right)\% = 44\%$.

Ex. 60. ***The radius of a cricle is so increased that its circumference increased by 5%. Find the percentage increase in its area.*** **(SNAP, 2010)**

Sol. Let the original radius of the circle be r. Then, original circumference = $2\pi r$.

New circumference = 105% of $(2\pi r)$ = $\left(\frac{105}{100} \times 2\pi r\right) = 2\pi\left(\frac{21}{20}r\right)$.

$\therefore$ New radius = $\frac{21}{20}r$.

New area = $\pi \times \left(\frac{21}{20}r\right)^2 = \frac{441}{400}\pi r^2$.

Increase in area = $\left(\frac{441}{400}\pi r^2 - \pi r^2\right) = \frac{41}{400}\pi r^2$.

Increase % in area = $\left(\frac{41}{400}\pi r^2 \times \frac{1}{\pi r^2} \times 100\right)\% = 10.25\%$.

Ex. 61. ***The area of a circle whose radius is 6 cm, is trisected by two concentric circles. Find the radius of the smallest circle.*** **(C.P.O., 2008)**

Sol. Let the radius of the smallest circle be r and that of the middle circle be R.

Then, $\pi[6^2 - R^2] = \pi[R^2 - r^2] \Rightarrow 6^2 - R^2 = R^2 - r^2 \Rightarrow 2R^2 = 36 + r^2$

$\Rightarrow R^2 = \frac{36 + r^2}{2}$ ...(i)

And, $\pi[R^2 - r^2] = \pi r^2 \Rightarrow R^2 - r^2 = r^2 \Rightarrow R^2 = 2r^2$

$\Rightarrow \frac{36 + r^2}{2} = 2r^2 \Rightarrow 3r^2 = 36$

$\Rightarrow r^2 = 12 \Rightarrow r = \sqrt{12} = 2\sqrt{3}$ cm.

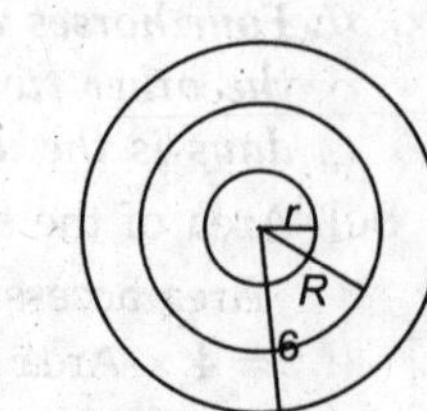

Hence, radius of the smallest circle = $2\sqrt{3}$ cm.

EXERCISE – A

(OBJECTIVE TYPE QUESTIONS)

Directions: ***Mark (✓) against the correct answer:***

1. If a rectangle has length L and the width is one-half of the length, then the area of the rectangle is **(M.B.A., 2006)**
   (a) L (b) L^2 (c) $\frac{1}{2}L^2$ (d) $\frac{1}{4}L^2$ (e) 2L

2. The length of a room is 5.5 m and width is 3.75 m. Find the cost of paving the floor by slabs at the rate of ₹ 800 per sq. metre. **(B.Ed Entrance, 2008)**
   (a) ₹ 15,000 (b) ₹ 15,550 (c) ₹ 15,600 (d) ₹ 16,500

3. The area of a rectangular field is 2100 sq. metres. If the field is 60 metres long, what is its perimeter? **(Bank Recruitment, 2007)**
   (a) 180 m (b) 210 m (c) 240 m (d) Cannot be determined (e) None of these

4. The length of a rectangle is 18 cm and its breadth is 10 cm. When the length is increased to 25 cm, what will be the breadth of the rectangle if the area remains the same?
(*a*) 7 cm (*b*) 7.1 cm
(*c*) 7.2 cm (*d*) 7.3 cm

5. A rectangular plot measuring 90 metres by 50 metres is to be enclosed by wire fencing. If the poles of the fence are kept 5 metres apart, how many poles will be needed?
(*a*) 55 (*b*) 56
(*c*) 57 (*d*) 58

6. The length of a rectangular plot is 60% more than its breadth. If the difference between the length and the breadth of that rectangle is 24 cm, what is the area of that rectangle?
(*a*) 2400 sq. cm (*b*) 2480 sq. cm
(*c*) 2560 sq. cm (*d*) Data inadequate
(*e*) None of these

7. A rectangular parking space is marked out by painting three of its sides. If the length of the unpainted side is 9 feet, and the sum of the lengths of the painted sides is 37 feet, then what is the area of the parking space in square feet?
(*a*) 46 (*b*) 81
(*c*) 126 (*d*) 252

8. The difference between the length and breadth of a rectangle is 23 m. If its perimeter is 206 m, then its area is **(Section Officers', 2003)**
(*a*) 1520 m^2 (*b*) 2420 m^2
(*c*) 2480 m^2 (*d*) 2520 m^2

9. The total cost of flooring a room at ₹ 8.50 per square metre is ₹ 510. If the length of the room is 8 m, its breadth is **(R.R.B. 2006)**
(*a*) 7.5 m (*b*) 8.5 m
(*c*) 10.5 m (*d*) 12.5 m

10. The length of a rectangular plot is thrice its breadth. If the area of the rectangular plot is 7803 sq. metres, What is the breadth of the rectangular plot? **(Bank P.O. 2009)**
(*a*) 51 m (*b*) 88 m
(*c*) 104 m (*d*) 153 m
(*e*) None of these

11. The perimeter of a rectangle is 60 metres. If its length is twice its breadth, then its area is **(R.R.B. 2008)**
(*a*) 160 m^2 (*b*) 180 m^2
(*c*) 200 m^2 (*d*) 220 m^2

12. A man is walking in a rectangular field whose perimeter is 6 km. If the area of the rectangular field be 2 sq. km, then what is the difference between the length and breadth of the rectangle? **(R.R.B. 2006; P.C.S. 2009)**
(*a*) $\frac{1}{2}$ km (*b*) 1 km
(*c*) $1\frac{1}{2}$ km (*d*) 2 km

13. The area of a rectangle is 252 cm^2 and its length and breadth are in the ratio of 9 : 7 respectively. What is its perimeter? **(Bank. P.O., 2009)**
(*a*) 64 cm (*b*) 68 cm
(*c*) 96 cm (*d*) 128 cm

14. The length of a rectangular plot is 20 metres more than its breadth. If the cost of fencing the plot @ ₹ 26.50 per metre is ₹ 5300, what is the length of the plot in metres?
(*a*) 40 (*b*) 50
(*c*) 120 (*d*) Data inadequate
(*e*) None of these

15. A carpenter is designing a table. The table will be in the form of a rectangle whose length is 4 feet more than its width. How long should the table be if the carpenter wants the area of the table to be 45 sq ft? **(J.M.E.T., 2010)**
(*a*) 6 ft (*b*) 9 ft
(*c*) 11 ft (*d*) 13 ft

16. The perimeter of a rectangular field is 480 metres and the ratio between the length and the breadth is 5 : 3. The area is **(M.A.T., 2008)**
(*a*) 1350 sq. m (*b*) 1550 sq. m
(*c*) 13500 sq. m (*d*) 15500 sq. m

17. A rectangular farm has to be fenced on one long side, one short side and the diagonal. If the cost of fencing is ₹ 100 per m, the area of the farm is 1200 m^2 and the short side is 30 m long, how much would the job cost? **(M.A.T., 2009)**
(*a*) ₹ 7000 (*b*) ₹ 12000
(*c*) ₹ 14000 (*d*) ₹ 15000

18. The breadth of a rectangular field is 60% of its length. If the perimeter of the field is 800 m, what is the area of the field?
(*a*) 18750 sq. m (*b*) 37500 sq. m
(*c*) 40000 sq. m (*d*) 48000 sq. m

19. The ratio between the length and the perimeter of a rectangular plot is 1 : 3. What is the ratio between the length and breadth of the plot?
(*a*) 1 : 2 (*b*) 2 : 1
(*c*) 3 : 2 (*d*) Data inadequate

20. The ratio between the length and the breadth of a rectangular park is 3 : 2. If a man cycling along the boundary of the park at the speed of 12 km / hr completes one round in 8 minutes, then the area of the park (in sq. m) is
(*a*) 15360 sq. m (*b*) 153600 sq. m
(*c*) 30720 sq. m (*d*) 307200 sq. m

21. The area of a rectangle is 460 square metres. If the length is 15% more than the breadth, what is the breadth of the rectangular field?

(*a*) 15 metres (*b*) 26 metres
(*c*) 34.5 metres (*d*) Cannot be determined
(*e*) None of these

22. The area of a rectangular field is 52000 m^2. This rectangular area has been drawn on a map to the scale 1 cm to 100 m. The length is shown as 3.25 cm on the map. The breadth of the rectangular field is **(M.B.A. 2006)**

(*a*) 150 m (*b*) 160 m
(*c*) 200.5 m (*d*) 300.5 m

23. A rectangular field is to be fenced on three sides leaving a side of 20 feet uncovered. If the area of the field is 680 sq. feet, how many feet of fencing will be required?

(*a*) 34 (*b*) 40
(*c*) 68 (*d*) 88

24. A farmer wishes to start a 100 sq. m rectangular vegetable garden. Since he has only 30 m barbed wire, he fences three sides of the garden letting his house compound wall act as the fourth side fencing. The dimension of the garden is:

(*a*) 15 m × 6.67 m (*b*) 20 m × 5 m
(*c*) 30 m × 3.33 m (*d*) 40 m × 2.5 m

25. The ratio of length and breadth of a rectangle is 3 : 2 respectively. The respective ratio of its perimeter and area is 5 : 9. What is the breadth of the rectangle in metres? **(Bank Recruitment, 2007)**

(*a*) 6 m (*b*) 8 m
(*c*) 9 m (*d*) 13 m
(*e*) None of these

26. A rectangle of certain dimensions is chopped off from one corner of a larger rectangle as shown. AB = 8 cm and BC = 4 cm. The perimeter of the figure $ABCPQRA$ (in cm) is

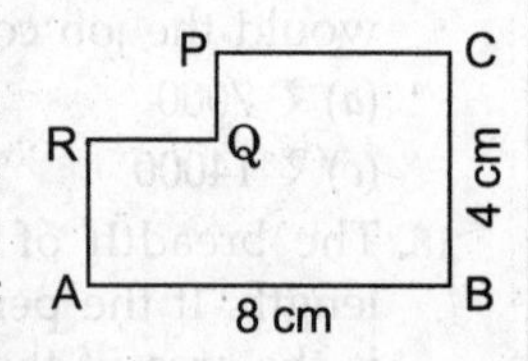

(*a*) 24 (*b*) 28
(*c*) 36 (*d*) 48

27. A large field of 700 hectares is divided into two parts. The difference of the areas of the two parts is one-fifth of the average of the two areas. What is the area of the smaller part in hectares?

(*a*) 225 (*b*) 280
(*c*) 300 (*d*) 315

28. A rectangular paper, when folded into two congruent parts had a perimeter of 34 cm for each part folded along one set of sides and the same is 38 cm when folded along the other set of sides. What is the area of the paper?

(*a*) 140 cm^2 (*b*) 240 cm^2
(*c*) 560 cm^2 (*d*) None of these

29. A rectangular plot is half as long again as it is broad and its area is $\frac{2}{3}$ hectares. Then, its length is

(*a*) 100 m (*b*) 33.33 m
(*c*) 66.66 m (*d*) $\frac{100\sqrt{3}}{3}$ m

30. An artist has completed one-fourth of a rectangular oil painting. When he will paint another 100 square centimetres of the painting, he would complete three-quarters of the painting. If the height of the oil painting is 10 cm, determine the length (in cm) of the oil painting. **(J.M.E.T., 2008)**

(*a*) 10 (*b*) 15
(*c*) 20 (*d*) 25

31. A courtyard 25 m long and 16 m broad is to be paved with bricks of dimensions 20 cm by 10 cm. The total number of bricks required is

(*a*) 18000 (*b*) 20000
(*c*) 25000 (*d*) None of these

32. How many metres of carpet 63 cm wide will be required to cover the floor of a room 14 m by 9 m? **(R.R.B. ,2008)**

(*a*) 185 m (*b*) 200 m
(*c*) 210 m (*d*) 220 m

33. The cost of carpeting a room 18 m long with a carpet 75 cm wide at ₹ 4.50 per metre is ₹ 810. The breadth of the room is

(*a*) 7 m (*b*) 7.5 m
(*c*) 8 m (*d*) 8.5 m

34. The diagonal of the floor of a rectangular closet is $7\frac{1}{2}$ feet. The shorter side of the closet is $4\frac{1}{2}$ feet. What is the area of the closet in square feet?

(*a*) $5\frac{1}{4}$ (*b*) $13\frac{1}{2}$
(*c*) 27 (*d*) 37

35. The length of a rectangle is three times of its width. If the length of the diagonal is $8\sqrt{10}$ cm, then the perimeter of the rectangle is

(*a*) $15\sqrt{10}$ cm (*b*) $16\sqrt{10}$ cm
(*c*) $24\sqrt{10}$ cm (*d*) 64 cm

36. The diagonal of a rectangle is thrice its smaller side. The ratio of the length to the breadth of the rectangle is

(*a*) 3 : 1 (*b*) $\sqrt{3} : 1$
(*c*) $\sqrt{2} : 1$ (*d*) $2\sqrt{2} : 1$

37. The diagonal of a rectangle is 10 cms and is twice the length of one of the sides. What is the area of the rectangle in sq. cm? (R.R.B. 2006)
(a) $10\sqrt{3}$ (b) 25
(c) $25\sqrt{3}$ (d) 100

38. The diagonal of a rectangular field is 15 metres and the difference between its length and width is 3 metres. The area of the rectangular field is (M.A.T., 2007)
(a) 9 m^2 (b) 12 m^2
(c) 21 m^2 (d) 108 m^2

39. A rectangular carpet has an area of 120 sq. metres and a perimeter of 46 metres. The length of its diagonal is
(a) 15 m (b) 16 m
(c) 17 m (d) 20 m

40. The diagonal of a rectangle is $\sqrt{41}$ cm and its area is 20 sq. cm. The perimeter of the rectangle must be (Hotel Management, 2002)
(a) 9 cm (b) 18 cm
(c) 20 cm (d) 41 cm

41. If the area of a rectangle is $\sqrt{3}\, d^2$, where $2d$ is the length of its diagonal, then its perimeter is equal to
(a) $4\sqrt{3}\, d$ (b) $2\sqrt{3}\, d$
(c) $4(\sqrt{3}+1)\, d$ (d) $2(\sqrt{3}+1)\, d$

42. If the diagonal and the area of a rectangle are 25 m and 168 m^2, what is the length of the rectangle?
(a) 12 m (b) 17 m
(c) 24 m (d) 31 m

43. A took 15 seconds to cross a rectanglar field diagonally walking at the rate of 52 m / min and B took the same time to cross the same field along its sides walking at the rate of 68 m / min. The area of the field is
(a) 30 m^2 (b) 40 m^2
(c) 50 m^2 (d) 60 m^2

44. A rectangular carpet has an area of 60 sq. m. If its diagonal and longer side together equal 5 times the shorter side, the length of the carpet is
(a) 5 m (b) 12 m
(c) 13 m (d) 14.5 m

45. The ratio between the length and the breadth of a rectangular field is 3 : 2. If only the length is increased by 5 metres, the new area of the field will be 2600 sq. metres. What is the breadth of the rectangular field?
(a) 40 metres (b) 60 metres
(c) 65 metres (d) Cannot be determined
(e) None of these

46. The cost of carpeting a room is ₹ 120. If the width had been 4 metres less, the cost of the carpet would have been ₹ 20 less. The width of the room is
(a) 18.5 m (b) 20 m
(c) 24 m (d) 25 m

47. The length of a rectangular blackboard is 8 m more than its breadth. If its length is increased by 7m and its breath is decreased by 4 m, its area remains unchanged. The length and breadth of the rectangular blackboard is (M.A.T. 2009)
(a) 24 m, 16 m (b) 20 m, 24 m
(c) 28 m, 16 m (d) 28 m, 20 m

48. The area of a grassy plot is 480 sq. m. If each side had been 5 m longer, the area would have been increased by 245 sq. m. Find the length of the fence to surround it. (M.B.A. 2007)
(a) 87 m (b) 88 m
(c) 90 m (d) None of these

49. The area of a rectangle gets reduced by 9 m^2 if its length is reduced by 5 m and breadth is increased by 3 m. If we increase the length by 3 m and breadth by 2 m, the area is increased by 67 m^2. The length of the rectangle is
(a) 9 m (b) 15.6 m
(c) 17 m (d) 18.5 m

50. If each side of a rectangle is increased by 50%, its area will increase by (R.R.B. 2005; P.C.S., 2008)
(a) 50% (b) 125%
(c) 150% (d) 200%

51. An order was placed for supply of carpet of breadth 3 metre, the length of carpet was 1.44 times of breadth. Subsequently the breadth and length were increased by 25 and 40 percent respectively. At the rate of 45 per square metre, what would be the increase in the cost of the carpet? (Bank P.O., 2009)
(a) ₹ 398.80 (b) ₹ 437.40
(c) ₹ 583.20 (d) ₹ 1020.60
(e) None of these

52. If the length of a rectangle is increased by 10% and its breadth is decreased by 10%, the change in its area will be (S.S.C. 2007, 2010; P.C.S. 2009; Hotel Managment, 2010)
(a) 1% increase (b) 1% decrease
(c) 10% increase (d) No change

53. Two sides of a rectangle were measured. One of the sides (length) was measured 10% more than its actual length and the other side (width) was measured 5% less than its actual length. The percentage error in measure obtained for the area of the rectangle is (P.C.S. 2009)
(a) 4.5% (b) 5%
(c) 7.56% (d) 15%

54. If the length of a rectangle is increased by 50% and breadth is decreased by 25%, what is the percentage change in its area? **(Campus Recruitment, 2010)**

(*a*) 12.5% increase (*b*) 10% increase
(*c*) 25% increase (*d*) 20% decrease

55. A towel, when bleached, was found to have lost 20% of its length and 10% of its breadth. The percentage of decrease in area is **(R.R.B. 2008)**

(*a*) 10% (*b*) 10.08%
(*c*) 20% (*d*) 28%

56. The length of a rectangle is halved, while its breadth is tripled. What is the percentage change in area?

(*a*) 25% increase (*b*) 50% increase
(*c*) 50% decrease (*d*) 75% decrease

57. The length of a rectangle is decreased by r%, and the breadth is increased by $(r + 5)$%. Find r, if the area of the rectangle is unaltered. **(SCMHRD, 2002)**

(*a*) 5 (*b*) 8
(*c*) 10 (*d*) 15
(*e*) 20

58. The length of a rectangle is increased by 60%. By what percent would the width have to be decreased so as to maintain the same area? **(M.B.A., 2006)**

(*a*) $37\frac{1}{2}$% (*b*) 60%
(*c*) 75% (*d*) 120%

59. If the area of a rectangular plot increases by 30% while its breadth remains the same, what will be the ratio of the areas of new and old figures?

(*a*) 1 : 3 (*b*) 3 : 1
(*c*) 4 : 7 (*d*) 10 : 13
(*e*) None of these

60. If the breadth of a rectangle is decreased by 50%, then to double the area, its length is required to be increased by

(*a*) 150% (*b*) 200%
(*c*) 300% (*d*) 400%

61. If the length and breadth of a rectangular field are increased, the area increases by 50%. If the increase in length was 20%, by what percentage was the breadth increased? **(Bank Recruitment, 2007)**

(*a*) 20% (*b*) 25%
(*c*) 30% (*d*) Date inadequate
(*e*) None of these

62. The length of a rectangle is reduced by 20% and breadth is kept constant, and the new figure that is formed is a square.

Consider the following statements:

1. The area of square is 25% less than the area of rectangle.
2. The perimeter of square is approximately 11% less than the perimeter of rectangle.
3. The diagonal of square is approximately 12% less than the diagonal of rectangle.

Which of the statements given above is/are correct?

(*a*) 1 only (*b*) 1 and 2
(*c*) 2 and 3 (*d*) 1, 2 and 3

63. A typist uses a paper 30 cm by 15 cm. He leaves a margin of 2.5 cm at the top and bottom and 1.25 cm on either side. What percentage of paper area is approximately available for typing? **(R.R.B., 2006)**

(*a*) 60% (*b*) 65%
(*c*) 70% (*d*) 80%

64. A room 5 m × 8 m is to be carpeted leaving a margin of 10 cm from each wall. If the cost of the carpet is ₹ 18 per Sq. metre, the cost of carpeting the room will be **(M.A.T., 2007)**

(*a*) ₹ 673.92 (*b*) ₹ 682.46
(*c*) ₹ 691.80 (*d*) ₹ 702.60

65. A lawn is in the shape of a rectangle of 80 m length and 50 m width. Outside the lawn there is a footpath of uniform 1 m width bordering the lawn. The area of the footpath is

(*a*) 264 m^2 (*b*) 284 m^2
(*c*) 4000 m^2 (*d*) 4264 m^2

66. The breadth of a rectangular field is $\frac{3}{4}$ of its length and its area is 300 sq. metres. What will be the area (in sq. metres) of the garden of breadth 1.5 metres developed around the field? **(Bank P.O., 2008)**

(*a*) 96 (*b*) 105
(*c*) 114 (*d*) Cannot be determined
(*e*) None of these

67. What will be the cost of gardening 1 metre broad boundary around a rectangular plot having perimeter of 340 metres at the rate of ₹ 10 per square metre?

(*a*) ₹ 1700 (*b*) ₹ 3400
(*c*) ₹ 3440 (*d*) Cannot be determined
(*e*) None of these

68. 2 metres broad pathway is to be constructed around a rectangular plot on the inside. The area of the plot is 96 sq. m. The rate of construction is ₹ 50 per square metre. Find the total cost of the construction.

(*a*) ₹ 2400 (*b*) ₹ 4000
(*c*) ₹ 4800 (*d*) Data inadequate
(*e*) None of these

69. A path of uniform width runs round the inside of a rectangular field 38 m long and 32 m wide. If the path occupies 600 m^2, then the width of the path is **(S.S.C., 2007)**

(*a*) 5 m (*b*) 10 m
(*c*) 18.75 m (*d*) 30 m

70. Within a rectangular garden 10 m wide and 20 m long, we wish to pave a walk around the borders of uniform width so as to leave an area of 96 m^2 for flowers. How wide should the walk be?

(a) 1 m (b) 2 m
(c) 2.1 m (d) 2.5 m

71. A rectangular garden (60 m × 40 m) is surrounded by a road of width 2 m, the road is covered by tiles and the garden is fenced. If the total expenditure is ₹ 51600 and rate of fencing is ₹ 50 per metre, then the cost of covering 1 sq. m of road by tiles is (Hotel Management, 2007)

(a) ₹ 10 (b) ₹ 50
(c) ₹ 100 (d) ₹ 150

72. A rectangular lawn 80 metres by 60 metres has two roads each 10 m wide running in the middle of it, one parallel to the length and the other parallel to the breadth. Find the cost of gravelling them at ₹ 30 per square metre. (M.A.T., 2005)

(a) ₹ 3600 (b) ₹ 3900
(c) ₹ 36000 (d) ₹ 39000

73. A rectangular field has dimensions 25 m by 15 m. Two mutually perpendicular passages, 2 m wide have been left in its central part and grass has been grown in rest of the field. The area (in sq. metres) under the grass is (G.B.O., 2007)

(a) 295 (b) 299
(c) 300 (d) 375

74. A rectangular park 60 m long and 40 m wide has two concrete crossroads running in the middle of the park and rest of the park has been used as a lawn. If the area of the lawn is 2109 sq. m, then what is the width of the road?

(a) 2.91 m (b) 3 m
(c) 5.82 m (d) None of these

75. Nine playing cards are set up to form a rectangle as shown in the adjoining figure. If the area of the rectangle so formed is 180 square inches, what is its perimeter?

(a) 48 inches (b) 56 inches
(c) 58 inches (d) 60 inches

76. A garden is 24 m long and 14 m wide. There is a path 1 m wide outside the garden along its sides. If the path is to be constructed with square marble tiles 20 cm × 20 cm, the number of tiles required to cover the path is (M.A.T., 2007)

(a) 200 (b) 1800
(c) 2000 (d) 2150

77. The dimensions of a rectangle are 51 m and 49 m respectively while side of a square is 50 m. Which of the following statements is correct?

(a) Diagonals of the square and the rectangle are equal.
(b) Diagonals of both the geometrical figures intersect at right angles.
(c) The perimeters of both the geometrical figures are equal.
(d) Both the geometrical figures are of the same area.

78. A housing society has been allotted a square piece of land measuring 2550.25 sq. m. What is the side of the plot?

(a) 50.25 m (b) 50.5 m
(c) 50.65 m (d) None of these

79. The area of a square with perimeter 48 cm is (P.C.S., 2007)

(a) 144 sq. cm (b) 156 sq. cm
(c) 170 sq. cm (d) 175 sq. cm

80. The length of the side of a square whose area is four times the area of a square with side 25 m is

(a) 12.5 m (b) 50 m
(c) 100 m (d) 125 m

81. The area of a square is three-fifths the area of a rectangle. The length of the rectangle is 25 cm and its breadth is 10 cm less than its length. What is the perimeter of the square? (Bank Recruitment, 2010)

(a) 44 cm (b) 60 cm
(c) 80 cm (d) Cannot be determined
(e) None of these

82. The area of a square is 1024 sq. cm. What is the ratio of the length to the breadth of a rectangle whose length is twice the side of the square and breadth is 12 cm less than the side of this square? (Bank P.O., 2010)

(a) 5 : 18 (b) 16 : 7
(c) 14 : 5 (d) 32 : 5
(e) None of these

83. ABCD is a square and AEFG is a rectangle. Area of each of them is 36 sq. m. E is the mid-point of AB. The perimeter of the rectangle AEFG is (Hotel Management, 2007)

(a) 12 m (b) 18 m
(c) 30 m (d) 36 m

84. The cost of cultivating a square field at the rate of ₹ 685 per hectare is ₹ 6165. The cost of putting a fence around it at the rate of ₹ 48.75 per metre would be

(a) ₹ 23400 (b) ₹ 52650
(c) ₹ 58500 (d) ₹ 117000

85. The perimeter of a square and a rectangle is the same. If the rectangle is 12 cm by 10 cm, then by

what percentage is the area of the square more than that of the rectangle?

(a) $\frac{2}{3}$ (b) 1

(c) $1\frac{1}{3}$ (d) $1\frac{1}{6}$

(e) None of these

86. The following squares represent the monthly incomes of two families

(P.C.S., 2008)

If the monthly income of family A is ₹ 40000, the monthly income of family B is

(a) ₹ 50000 (b) ₹ 60000

(c) ₹ 90000 (d) ₹ 120000

87. *ABJH, JDEF, ACEG* are squares.

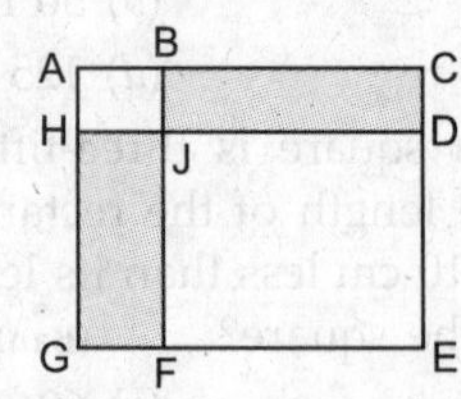

$\frac{BC}{AB} = 3. \frac{\text{Area BCDJ}}{\text{Area HJFG}} = ?$

(a) $\frac{1}{9}$ (b) $\frac{1}{3}$

(c) 1 (d) 3

88. The perimeters of five squares are 24 cm, 32 cm, 40 cm, 76 cm and 80 cm respectively. The perimeter of another square equal in area to the sum of the areas of these squares is

(a) 31 cm (b) 62 cm

(c) 124 cm (d) 961 cm

89. Total area of 64 small squares of a chessboard is 400 sq. cm. There is 3 cm wide border around the chess board. What is the length of the side of the chessboard? (M.A.T., 2006; R.R.B., 2006)

(a) 17 cm (b) 20 cm

(c) 23 cm (d) 26 cm

90. The adjoining figure contains three squares with areas of 100, 16 and 49 lying side by side as shown. By how much should the area of the middle square be reduced in order that the total length *PQ* of the resulting three squares is 19?

100 16 49

(a) $\sqrt{2}$ (b) 2

(c) 4 (d) 12

91. A coaching institute wants to execute tiling work fo one of its teaching halls 60 m long and 40 m wid with a square tile of 0.4 m side. If each tile cost ₹ 5, the total cost of tiles would be (M.B.A. 2007, 2005

(a) ₹ 60000 (b) ₹ 65000

(c) ₹ 70000 (d) ₹ 75000

92. The number of marble slabs of size 20 cm × 30 cn required to pave the floor of a square room of sid 3 metres is

(a) 100 (b) 150

(c) 225 (d) 250

93. 50 square stone slabs of equal size were needed t cover a floor area of 72 sq. m. The length of eac stone slab is

(a) 102 cm (b) 120 cm

(c) 201 cm (d) 210 cm

94. How many squares with side $\frac{1}{2}$ inch long are needec to cover a rectangle that is 4 feet long and 6 fee wide? (Campus Recruitment, 2010

(a) 24 (b) 96

(c) 3456 (d) 13824

(e) 14266

95. The length and breadth of the floor of the roon are 20 feet and 10 feet respectively. Square tiles o 2 feet length of different colours are to be laid o the floor. Black tiles are laid in the first row on a sides. If white tiles are laid in the one-third of th remaining and blue tiles in the rest, how many blu tiles will be there?

(a) 16 (b) 24

(c) 32 (d) 48

(e) None of these

96. A big rectangular plot of area 4320 m² is divided int 3 square-shaped smaller plots by fencing parallel t the smaller side of the plot. However some area o land was still left as a square could not be formed So, 3 more square-shaped plots were formed b fencing parallel to the longer side of the origina plot such that no area of the plot was left surplus What are the dimensions of the original plot?

(I.A.S., 2005

(a) 160 m × 27 m (b) 240 m × 18 m

(c) 120 m × 36 m (d) 135 m × 32 m

97. Three plots having areas 110, 130 and 190 squar metres are to be subdivided into flower beds o equal size. If the breadth of a bed is 2 metre, th maximum length of a bed can be (P.C.S., 2008

(a) 5 m (b) 11 m

(c) 13 m (d) 19 m

98. A room is $12\frac{1}{4}$ m long and 7 m wide. The maximum length of a square tile to fill the floor of the room with whole number of tiles should be (R.R.B., 2008)
(a) 125 cm (b) 150 cm
(c) 175 cm (d) 200 cm

99. What is the minimum number of identical square tiles required to tile a floor of length 6 m 24 cm and width 4 m 80 cm? (M.B.A., 2011)
(a) 122 (b) 130
(c) 148 (d) 165
(e) None of these

100. A rectangular room can be partitioned into two equal square rooms by a partition 7 metres long. What is the area of the rectangular room in square metres?
(a) 49 (b) 147
(c) 196 (d) None of these

101. Perimeter of a rectangular field is 160 metres and the difference between its two adjacent sides is 48 metres. The side of a square field, having the same area as that of the rectangle, is (S.S.C. 2005)
(a) 4 m (b) 8 m
(c) 16 m (d) 32 m

102. The area of the shaded portion is
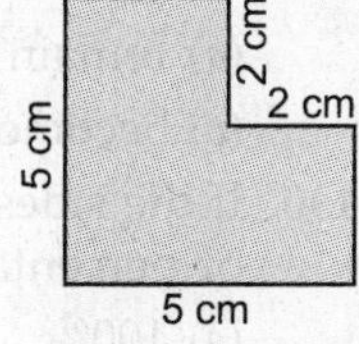

(a) 10 sq cm
(b) 14 sq cm
(c) 21 sq cm
(d) 25 sq cm

103. The perimeter of a square is 48 cm. The area of a rectangle is 4 cm^2 less than the area of the square. If the length of the rectangle is 14 cm, then its perimeter is
(a) 24 cm (b) 48 cm
(c) 50 cm (d) 54 cm

104. The area of a rectangle is thrice that of a square. If the length of the rectangle is 40 cm and its breadth is $\frac{3}{2}$ times that of the side of the square, then the side of the square is
(a) 15 cm (b) 20 cm
(c) 30 cm (d) 60 cm

105. The perimeter of a rectangle and a square are 160 m each. The area of the rectangle is less than that of the square by 100 sq. m. The length of the rectangle is
(a) 30 m (b) 40 m
(c) 50 m (d) 60 m

106. The area of a rectangle is four times the area of a square. The length of the rectangle is 90 cm and the breadth of the rectangle is $\frac{2}{3}$rd the side of the square. What is the side of the square? (Bank Recruitment, 2008)
(a) 9 cm (b) 10 cm
(c) 20 cm (d) Cannot be determined
(e) None of these

107. The cost of fencing a square field @ ₹ 20 per metre is ₹ 10,080. How much will it cost to lay a three metre wide pavement along the fencing inside the field @ ₹ 50 per sq. metre?
(a) ₹ 37,350 (b) ₹ 73,800
(c) ₹ 77,400 (d) None of these

108. A park square in shape has a 3 metre wide road inside it running along its sides. The area occupied by the road is 1764 square metres. What is the perimeter along the outer edge of the road?
(a) 576 metres (b) 600 metres
(c) 640 metres (d) Data inadequate
(e) None of these

109. A man walked diagonally across a square lot. Approximately, what was the percent saved by not walking along the edges?
(a) 20 (b) 24
(c) 30 (d) 33

110. If the length of diagonal AC of a square ABCD is 5.2 cm, then the area of the square is (L.I.C.A.D.O., 2008)
(a) 10.52 sq.cm (b) 11.52 sq.cm
(c) 12.52 sq.cm (d) 13.52 sq.cm

111. A man walking at the speed of 4 kmph crosses a square field diagonally in 3 minutes. The area of the field is
(a) 18000 m^2 (b) 19000 m^2
(c) 20000 m^2 (d) 25000 m^2

112. If the length of the diagonal of a square is 20 cm, then its perimeter must be
(a) $10\sqrt{2}$ cm (b) 40 cm
(c) $40\sqrt{2}$ cm (d) 200 cm

113. The area of a square field is 69696 cm^2. Its diagonal will be equal to
(a) 313.296 m (b) 353.296 m
(c) 373.296 m (d) 393.296 m

114. What will be the length of the diagonal of that square plot whose area is equal to the area of a rectangular plot of length 45 metres and breadth 40 metres?
(a) 42.5 metres (b) 60 metres
(c) 75 metres (d) Data inadequate
(e) None of these

115. The area of a square field is 0.5 hectare. Its diagonal would be

(a) 50 m (b) $50\sqrt{2}$ m
(c) 100 m (d) 250 m

116. Area of a square natural lake is 50 sq. kms. A diver wishing to cross the lake diagonally, will have to swim a distance of (SNAP, 2007)

(a) 10 miles (b) 12 miles
(c) 15 miles (d) None of these

117. The length of a rectangle is 20% more than its breadth. What will be the ratio of the area of a rectangle to that of a square whose side is equal to the breadth of the rectangle?

(a) 2 : 1 (b) 5 : 6
(c) 6 : 5 (d) Data inadequate
(e) None of these

118. A square and a rectangle have equal areas. If their perimeters are p_1 and p_2 respectively, then

(a) $p_1 < p_2$ (b) $p_1 = p_2$
(c) $p_1 > p_2$ (d) None of these

119. If the perimeters of a square and a rectangle are the same, then the areas A and B enclosed by them would satisfy the condition

(a) A < B (b) A ≤ B
(c) A > B (d) A ≥ B

120. The diagonal of a square is $4\sqrt{2}$ cm. The diagonal of another square whose area is double that of the first square, is (SNAP, 2010; S.S.C., 2005; B.Ed., 2007)

(a) 8 cm (b) $8\sqrt{2}$ cm
(c) $4\sqrt{2}$ cm (d) 16 cm

121. The ratio of the area of a square to that of the square drawn on its diagonal, is (Campus Recruitment, 2008, 2010; Hotel Management, 2010; I.A.M., 2009)

(a) 1 : 1 (b) $1 : \sqrt{2}$
(c) 1 : 2 (d) 1 : 4

122. A square S_1 encloses another square S_2 in such a manner that each corner of S_2 is at the mid-point of the side of S_1. If A_1 is the area of S_1 and A_2 is the area of S_2, then

(a) $A_1 = 4\,A_2$ (b) $A_1 = 2\,A_2$
(c) $A_2 = 2\,A_1$ (d) $A_1 = A_2$

123. If a square of area $\frac{A}{2}$ is cut off from a given square of area A, then the ratio of diagonal of the cut off square to that of the given square is

(a) 1 : 5 (b) $1 : 2\sqrt{5}$
(c) $1 : \sqrt{5}$ (d) $1 : \sqrt{2}$

124. The ratio of the areas of two squares, one having its diagonal double than the other, is

(a) 2 : 1 (b) 2 : 3
(c) 3 : 1 (d) 4 : 1

125. If the ratio of areas of two squares is 225 : 256, then the ratio of their perimeters is

(a) 225 : 256 (b) 256 : 225
(c) 15 : 16 (d) 16 : 15

126. Of the two square fields, the area of one is 1 hectare while the other one is broader by 1%. The difference in their areas is (M.A.T., 2006)

(a) 100 m^2 (b) 101 m^2
(c) 200 m^2 (d) 201 m^2

127. If each side of a square is increased by 10%, its area will be increased by (S.S.C. 2010; J.M.E.T., 2004)

(a) 10% (b) 21%
(c) 44% (d) 100%

128. If each side of a square is increased by 50%, the ratio of the area of the resulting square to that of the given square is (M.B.A. 2005; 2007)

(a) 4 : 5 (b) 5 : 4
(c) 4 : 9 (d) 9 : 4

129. What happens to the area of a square when its side is halved? Its area will

(a) remain same (b) become half
(c) become one-fourth (d) become double

130. If the sides of a square be doubled find the increase of percentage in area. (P.C.S., 2008)

(a) 100% (b) 200%
(c) 300% (d) 400%

131. An error of 2% in excess is made while measuring the side of a square. The percentage of error in the calculated area of the square is

(a) 2% (b) 2.02%
(c) 4% (d) 4.04%

132. If the area of a square increases by 69%, then the side of the square increases by

(a) 13% (b) 30%
(c) 39% (d) 69%

133. If the diagonal of a square is made 1.5 times, then the ratio of the areas of two squares is

(a) 4 : 3 (b) 4 : 5
(c) 4 : 7 (d) 4 : 9

134. The length and breadth of a square are increased by 40% and 30% respectively. The area of the resulting rectangle exceeds the area of the square by (M.B.A., 2004, 2006)

(a) 35% (b) 42%
(c) 62% (d) 82%

135. The length of one pair of opposite sides of a square is increased by 5 cm on each side; the ratio of the length and the breadth of the newly formed rectangle becomes 3 : 2. What is the area of the original square?

(*a*) 25 sq. cm (*b*) 81 sq. cm
(*c*) 100 sq. cm (*d*) 225 sq. cm
(*e*) None of these

136. If the length of a certain rectangle is decreased by 4 cm and the width is increased by 3 cm, a square with the same area as the original rectangle would result. The perimeter of the original rectangle (in cm) is

(*a*) 44 (*b*) 46
(*c*) 48 (*d*) 50

137. A rectangle becomes a square when its length is reduced by 10 units and its breadth is increased by 5 units. But by this process the area of the rectangle is reduced by 210 sq. units. The area of the rectangle (*a*) in square units is (M.A.T., 2006)

(*a*) $2950 > A < 2900$ (*b*) $2900 > A > 2875$
(*c*) $2925 < A > 2875$ (*d*) $2925 > A > 2900$

138. If the side of a square is increased by 5 cm, the area increases by 165 sq. cm. The side of the square is

(*a*) 12 cm (*b*) 13 cm
(*c*) 14 cm (*d*) 15 cm

139. The difference of the areas of two squares drawn on two line segments of different lengths is 32 sq. cm. Find the length of the greater line segment if one is longer than the other by 2 cm.

(*a*) 7 cm (*b*) 9 cm
(*c*) 11 cm (*d*) 16 cm

140. The areas of a square and a rectangle are equal. The length of the rectangle is greater than the length of any side of the square by 5 cm and the breadth is less by 3 cm. Find the perimeter of the rectangle. (S.S.C. 2005)

(*a*) 17 cm (*b*) 26 cm
(*c*) 30 cm (*d*) 34 cm

141. The area of a square is twice that of a rectangle. The perimeter of the rectangle is 10 cm. If its length and breadth each is increased by 1 cm, the area of the rectangle becomes equal to the area of the square. The length of side of the square is (Hotel Management, 2007)

(*a*) $2\sqrt{3}$ cm (*b*) $3\sqrt{2}$ cm
(*c*) $4\sqrt{3}$ cm (*d*) 12 cm

142. Twenty-nine times the area of a square is one square metre less than six times the area of the second square and nine times its side exceeds the perimeter of other square by 1 metre. The difference in the sides of these squares is (M.A.T., 2010)

(*a*) 5 m (*b*) $\frac{54}{11}$ m
(*c*) 6 m (*d*) 11 m

143. A rectangular plank $\sqrt{2}$ metre wide is placed symmetrically on the diagonal of a square of side 8 metres as shown in the figure. The area of the plank is

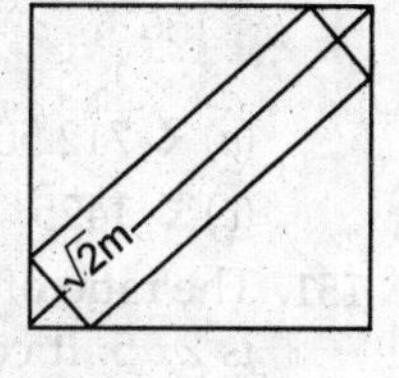

(*a*) $7\sqrt{2}$ sq. m (*b*) 14 sq. m
(*c*) 98 sq. m (*d*) $(16\sqrt{2} - 3)$ sq. m

144. What will be the area of 4 metre high wall on all four sides of a rectangular hall having perimeter 64 m? (Bank P.O., 2008)

(*a*) 256 m^2 (*b*) 328 m^2
(*c*) 384 m^2 (*d*) Cannot be determined
(*d*) None of these

145. The area of the four walls of a room is 120 m^2 and the length is twice the breadth. If the height of the room is 4 m, then the area of the floor is (M.A.T., 2007)

(*a*) 48 m^2 (*b*) 49 m^2
(*c*) 50 m^2 (*d*) 52 m^2

146. A tank is 25 m long, 12 m wide and 6 m deep. The cost of plastering its walls and bottom at 75 paise per sq. m, is

(*a*) ₹ 456 (*b*) ₹ 458
(*c*) ₹ 558 (*d*) ₹ 568

147. The length of a room is double its breadth. The cost of colouring the ceiling at ₹ 25 per sq. m is ₹ 5000 and the cost of painting the four walls at ₹ 240 per sq. m is ₹ 64800. Find the height of the room. (M.A.T., 2005)

(*a*) 3.5 m (*b*) 4 m
(*c*) 4.5 m (*d*) 5 m

148. The dimensions of a room are 12.5 metres by 9 metres by 7 metres. There are 2 doors and 4 windows in the room; each door measures 2.5 metres by 1.2 metres and each window 1.5 metres by 1 metre. Find the cost of painting the walls at ₹ 3.50 per square metre.

(*a*) ₹ 1050.50 (*b*) ₹ 1011.50
(*c*) ₹ 1101.50 (*d*) Cannot be determined

149. A hall, whose length is 16 m and the breadth is twice its height, takes 168 m of paper with 2 m as its width to cover its four walls. The area of the floor is

(*a*) 96 m^2 (*b*) 190 m^2
(*c*) 192 m^2 (*d*) 216 m^2

150. The cost of papering the four walls of a room is ₹ 475. Each one of the length, breadth and height of another room is double that of this room. The cost of papering the walls of this new room is (M.B.A., 2006)

(a) ₹ 712.50 (b) ₹ 950
(c) ₹ 1425 (d) ₹ 1900

151. The ratio of the height of a room to its semi-perimeter is 2 : 5. It costs ₹ 260 to paper the walls of the room with paper 50 cm wide at ₹ 2 per metre allowing an area of 15 sq. m for doors and windows. The height of the room is

(a) 2.6 m (b) 3.9 m
(c) 4 m (d) 4.2 m

152. The length, breadth and height of the room are in the ratio 3 : 2 : 1. The breadth and height of the room are halved and length of the room is doubled. The area of the four walls of the room will (SNAP, 2010)

(a) decrease by 13.64% (b) decrease by 15%
(c) decrease by 18.75% (d) decrease by 30%

153. Consider the following:

I. 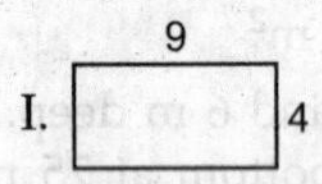

II. 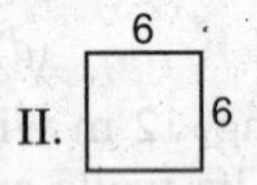

III. 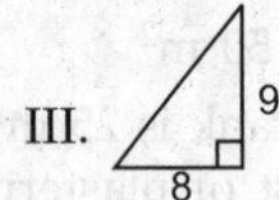

Which one of the following conclusions can be drawn form these figures?

(a) The areas of the three figures are all different.
(b) The areas of all the three figures are equal.
(c) The perimeters of the three figures are equal.
(d) The perimeters of figures I and II are equal.

154. The base of a triangle is 15 cm and height is 12 cm. The height of another triangle of double the area having the base 20 cm is

(a) 8 cm (b) 9 cm
(c) 12.5 cm (d) 18 cm

155. The area of a right-angled triangle is 40 times its base. What is its height?

(a) 45 cm (b) 60 cm
(c) 80 cm (d) Data inadequate
(e) None of these

156. The area of a triangle is p sq. cm and its base is x cm. What is the height of the triangle (in cm)? (M.C.A., 2005)

(a) $\frac{2p}{x}$ (b) $\frac{x}{2p}$
(c) $\frac{p}{2x}$ (d) $\frac{2x}{p}$

157. The area of an equilateral triangle whose side is 8 cm is

(a) $32\sqrt{3}$ cm^2 (b) $\frac{16}{3}$ cm^2
(c) $16\sqrt{3}$ cm^2 (d) 16 cm^2

158. The ratio of the areas of a square of side 6 cm and an equilateral triangle of side 6 cm is (S.S.C., 2007)

(a) $3:\sqrt{3}$ (b) $8:\sqrt{3}$
(c) $6:\sqrt{3}$ (d) $4:\sqrt{3}$

159. *ABCD* is a rectangle and *ABE* is a triangle whose vertex *E* lies on *CD*. If *AB* = 5 cm and the area of the triangle is 10 sq. cm, then the perimeter of the rectangle is

(a) 14 cm (b) 15 cm
(c) 18 cm (d) 20 cm

160. The area of a triangle is equal to the area of a square whose each side is 60 metres. The height of the triangle is 90 metres. The base of the triangle will be (R.R.B., 2006)

(a) 65 m (b) 75 m
(c) 80 m (d) 85 m

161. What is the area of the given figure? (R.R.B., 2006)

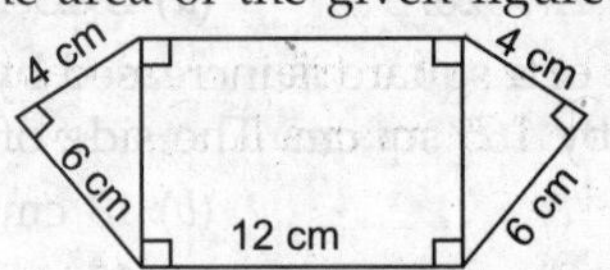

(a) 98.8 cm^2 (b) 110.4 cm^2
(c) 120 cm^2 (d) 132.6 cm^2

162. In ΔPQR, side PQ = 32 cm and side PR = 25 cm. What is the measure of side QR ? (M.B.A., 2011)

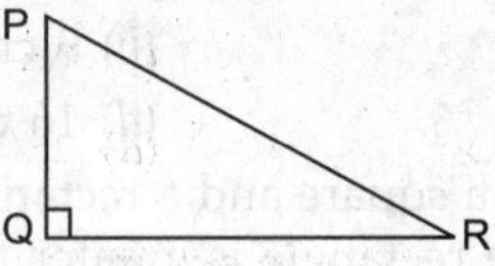

(a) $4\sqrt{154}$ cm (b) $2\sqrt{308}$ cm
(c) $4\sqrt{308}$ cm (d) Cannot be determined
(e) None of these

163. What is the area of ΔPQR, shown in Q. 162? (M.B.A., 2011)

(a) $2\sqrt{154}$ sq. cm (b) $3\sqrt{154}$ sq. cm
(c) $4\sqrt{308}$ sq. cm (d) Cannot be determined
(e) None of these

164. Out of a square of side 8 cm, a triangle is drawn with base as one side of the square and third vertex at any point on the opposite side of the square. What is the area of the remaining portion of the square if the triangle is taken out?

(a) 16 sq. cm (b) 32 sq. cm
(c) 64 sq. cm (d) Cannot be determined
(e) None of these

165. Consider the given figure.

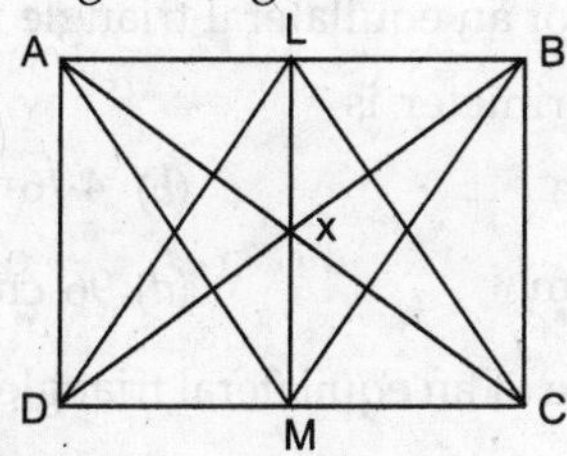

If the areas of the triangles LDC, BMC and AMC are denoted by x, y and z respectively, then

(a) $x = y = z$ (b) $x = 2y = 2z$
(c) $y = 2x = 2z$ (d) $z = 2x = 2y$

166. If the area of a triangle is 1176 cm^2 and base : corresponding altitude is 3 : 4, then the altitude of the triangle is

(a) 42 cm (b) 52 cm
(c) 54 cm (d) 56 cm

167. The area of a triangle whose sides are of lengths 3 cm, 4 cm and 5 cm is (P.C.S., 2008; E.S.I.C., 2007; R.R.B., 2009)

(a) 8 cm^2 (b) 6 cm^2
(c) 10 cm^2 (d) None of these

168. The three sides of a triangular field are 20 metres, 21 metres and 29 metres long respectively. The area of the field is (I.I.F.T., 2005)

(a) 210 sq. m (b) 215 sq. m
(c) 230 sq. m (d) None of these

169. The perimeter of an isosceles triangle is equal to 14 cm and the lateral side is to the base in the ratio 5 : 4. The area of the triangle is (M.B.A., 2008)

(a) 21 cm^2 (b) $0.5\sqrt{21}$ cm^2
(c) $1.5\sqrt{21}$ cm^2 (d) $2\sqrt{21}$ cm^2

170. The sides of a triangle are in the ratio of $\frac{1}{2}:\frac{1}{3}:\frac{1}{4}$. If the perimeter is 52 cm, then the length of the smallest side is (M.A.T., 2005)

(a) 9 cm (b) 10 cm
(c) 11 cm (d) 12 cm

171. The sides of a triangle are consecutive integers. The perimeter of the triangle is 120 cm. Find the length of the greatest side. (M.C.A., 2007)

(a) 39 cm (b) 40 cm
(c) 41 cm (d) 42 cm

172. The area of a triangle is 216 cm^2 and its sides are in the ratio 3 : 4 : 5. The perimeter of the triangle is (S.S.C., 2004)

(a) 6 cm (b) 12 cm
(c) 36 cm (d) 72 cm

173. If three sides of a triangle are 6 cm, 8 cm and 10 cm, then the altitude of the triangle, using the largest side as its base, will be

(a) 4.4 cm (b) 4.8 cm
(c) 6 cm (d) 8 cm

174. The sides of a triangle are 3 cm, 4 cm and 5 cm. The area (in cm^2) of the triangle formed by joining the mid-points of the sides of this triangle is

(a) $\frac{3}{4}$ (b) $\frac{3}{2}$
(c) 3 (d) 6

175. If D, E and F are the mid-points of the sides of a ΔABC, the ratio of the areas of the triangles DEF and DCE is

(a) 1.1 : 1 (b) 1 : 1.1
(c) 1 : 1 (d) 0.9 : 1

176. The sides of a triangle are 5 cm, 6 cm, and 7 cm. One more triangle is formed by joining the mid-points of the sides. The perimeter of the second triangle in cm is

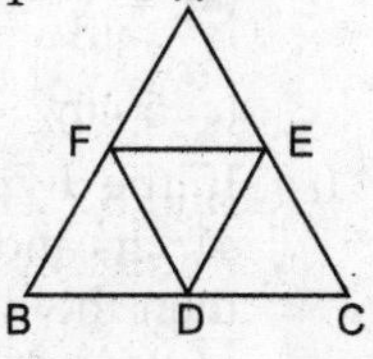

(a) 6 (b) 9
(c) 12 (d) 18
(e) None of these

177. In a triangle ABC, a line XY is drawn parallel to BC meeting AB in X and AC in Y. The area of the triangle AXY is half of the area of the triangle ABC. XY divides AB in the ratio of (Campus Recruitment, 2009)

(a) $1 : \sqrt{2}$ (b) $\sqrt{2} : (\sqrt{2}-1)$
(c) $1 : (\sqrt{2}-1)$ (d) $\sqrt{2} : \sqrt{3}$

178. The areas of two similar triangles are 12 cm^2 and 48 cm^2. If the height of the smaller one is 2.1 cm, then the corresponding height of the bigger one is (M.B.A., 2006)

(a) 0.525 cm (b) 4.2 cm
(c) 4.41 cm (d) 8.4 cm

179. A triangle of area 9 y cm^2 has been drawn such that its area is equal to the area of an equilateral triangle of side 6 cm. The value of y would be (M.B.A. 2005, 2007)

(a) $\sqrt{2}$ (b) $\sqrt{3}$
(c) 2 (d) 3

180. The hypotenuse of a right-angled isosceles triangle is 5 cm. The area of the triangle is

(a) 5 cm^2 (b) 6.25 cm^2
(c) 6.5 cm^2 (d) 12.5 cm^2

181. One side of a right-angled triangle is twice the other, and the hypotenuse is 10 cm. The area of the triangle is

(a) 20 cm^2 (b) $33\frac{1}{3}$ cm^2
(c) 40 cm^2 (d) 50 cm^2

182. The area of a right-angled triangle is 20 sq. cm and one of the sides containing the right angle is 4 cm. The altitude on the hypotenuse is **(R.R.B., 2006)**

(*a*) $\frac{41}{\sqrt{34}}$ cm (*b*) $\sqrt{\frac{41}{40}}$ cm

(*c*) $\frac{29}{\sqrt{20}}$ cm (*d*) $\frac{20}{\sqrt{29}}$ cm

183. The base and altitude of a right-angled triangle are 12 cm and 5 cm respectively. The perpendicular distance of its hypotenuse from the opposite vertex is **(S.S.C., 2007)**

(*a*) $4\frac{4}{13}$ cm (*b*) $4\frac{8}{13}$ cm

(*c*) 5 cm (*d*) 7 cm

184. If the hypotenuse of a right-angled triangle is 41 cm and the area of the triangle is 180 sq. cm, then the difference between the lengths of the legs of the triangle must be

(*a*) 22 cm (*b*) 25 cm

(*c*) 27 cm (*d*) 31 cm

185. The perimeter of a right-angled triangle is 60 cm. Its hypotenuse is 26 cm. The area of the triangle is

(*a*) 120 cm^2 (*b*) 240 cm^2

(*c*) 390 cm^2 (*d*) 780 cm^2

186. If the perimeter of a right-angled isosceles triangle is $(4\sqrt{2}+4)$ cm, the length of the hypotenuse is **(C.P.O., 2007)**

(*a*) 4 cm (*b*) 6 cm

(*c*) 8 cm (*d*) 10 cm

187. If the perimeter of an isosceles right triangle is $(6+3\sqrt{2})$ m, then the area of the triangle is

(*a*) 4.5 m^2 (*b*) 5.4 m^2

(*c*) 9 m^2 (*d*) 81 m^2

188. The perimeter of an isosceles right-angled triangle having an area of 162 cm^2 is

(*a*) 40 cm (*b*) 56.5 cm

(*c*) 61.38 cm (*d*) 68.2 cm

189. In an isosceles triangle, the measure of each of the equal sides is 10 cm and the angle between them is 45°. The area of the triangle is **(C.P.O., 2006)**

(*a*) 25 cm^2 (*b*) $\frac{25}{2}\sqrt{2}$ cm^2

(*c*) $25\sqrt{2}$ cm^2 (*d*) $25\sqrt{3}$ cm^2

190. The perimeter of a triangle is 30 cm and its area is 30 cm^2. If the largest side measures 13 cm, then what is the length of the smallest side of the triangle?

(*a*) 3 cm (*b*) 4 cm

(*c*) 5 cm (*d*) 6 cm

191. If the area of an equilateral triangle is $24\sqrt{3}$ sq. cm, then its perimeter is

(*a*) $2\sqrt{6}$ cm (*b*) $4\sqrt{6}$ cm

(*c*) $12\sqrt{6}$ cm (*d*) 96 cm

192. The altitude of an equilateral triangle of side $2\sqrt{3}$ cm is **(M.B.A., 2005, 2008)**

(*a*) $\frac{1}{2}$ cm (*b*) $\frac{\sqrt{3}}{4}$ cm

(*c*) $\frac{\sqrt{3}}{2}$ cm (*d*) 3 cm

193. The height of an equilateral triangle is 10 cm. Its area is

(*a*) $\frac{100}{3}$ cm^2 (*b*) 30 cm^2

(*c*) 100 cm^2 (*d*) $\frac{100}{\sqrt{3}}$ cm^2

194. The areas of two equilateral triangles are in the ratio 25 : 36. Their altitudes will be in the ratio **(C.P.O., 2007)**

(*a*) 25 : 36 (*b*) 36 : 25

(*c*) 5 : 6 (*d*) $\sqrt{5}:\sqrt{6}$

195. From a point within an equilateral triangle, perpendiculars drawn to the three sides are 6 cm, 7 cm, and 8 cm respectively. The length of the side of the triangle is

(*a*) 7 cm (*b*) 10.5 cm

(*c*) $14\sqrt{3}$ cm (*d*) $\frac{14\sqrt{3}}{3}$ cm

196. If x is the length of a median of an equilateral triangle, then its area is

(*a*) x^2 (*b*) $\frac{1}{2}x^2$

(*c*) $\frac{\sqrt{3}}{2}x^2$ (*d*) $\frac{\sqrt{3}}{3}x^2$

197. *ABCD* is a square. *E* is the mid-point of *BC* and *F* is the mid--point of *CD*. The ratio of the area of triangle *AEF* to the area of the square *ABCD* is **(Campus Recruitment, 2009)**

(*a*) 1 : 2 (*b*) 1 : 3

(*c*) 1 : 4 (*d*) 3 : 8

198. If the area of a square with side *a* is equal to the area of a triangle with base *a*, then the altitude of the triangle is

(*a*) $\frac{a}{2}$ (*b*) a

(*c*) $2a$ (*d*) $4a$

199. An equilateral triangle is described on the diagonal of a square. What is the ratio of the area of the triangle to that of the square?

(a) $2 : \sqrt{3}$ (b) $4 : \sqrt{3}$
(c) $\sqrt{3} : 2$ (d) $\sqrt{3} : 4$

200. What will be the ratio between the area of a rectangle and the area of a triangle with one of the sides of the rectangle as base and a vertex on the opposite side of the rectangle?

(a) 1 : 2 (b) 2 : 1
(c) 3 : 1 (d) Data inadequate
(e) None of these

201. If an equilateral triangle of area X and a square of area Y have the same perimeter, then X is (C.D.S., 2003)

(a) equal to Y (b) greater than Y
(c) less than Y (d) less than or equal to Y

202. A square and an equilateral triangle have equal perimeters. If the diagonal of the square is $12\sqrt{2}$ cm, then the area of the triangle is

(a) $24\sqrt{2}$ cm^2 (b) $24\sqrt{3}$ cm^2
(c) $48\sqrt{3}$ cm^2 (d) $64\sqrt{3}$ cm^2

203. The ratio of bases of two triangles is $x : y$ and that of their areas is $a : b$. Then the ratio of their corresponding altitudes will be (S.S.C. 2004)

(a) $ax : by$ (b) $\frac{a}{x} : \frac{b}{y}$
(c) $ay : bx$ (d) $\frac{x}{a} : \frac{b}{y}$

204. If the sides of a triangle be in the ratio 2 : 3 : 4, the ratio of the corresponding altitudes is

(a) 6 : 5 : 3 (b) 4 : 5 : 6
(c) 5 : 4 : 3 (d) 6 : 4 : 3

205. If the side of an equilateral triangle is decreased by 20%, its area is decreased by

(a) 36% (b) 40%
(c) 60% (d) 64%

206. If the height of a triangle is decreased by 40% and its base is increased by 40%, what will be the effect on its area?

(a) No change (b) 8% decrease
(c) 16% increase (d) 16 % decrease

207. If every side of a triangle is doubled, the area of the new triangle is K times the area of the old one. K is equal to (R.R.B., 2003)

(a) $\sqrt{2}$ (b) 2
(c) 3 (d) 4

208. Two isosceles triangles have equal vertical angles and their corresponding sides are in the ratio 3 : 5. What is the ratio of their areas?

(a) 3 : 5 (b) 6 : 10
(c) 9 : 25 (d) None of these

209. If an angle of a triangle remains unchanged but each of its two including sides is doubled, then by what factor does the area get multiplied?

(a) 2 (b) 3
(c) 4 (d) 6

210. In the given figure, ABCD is a rectangle with AD = 4 units and AE = EB. EF is perpendicular to DB and is half of DF. If the area of the triangle DEF is 5 sq. units, then what is the area of ABCD?

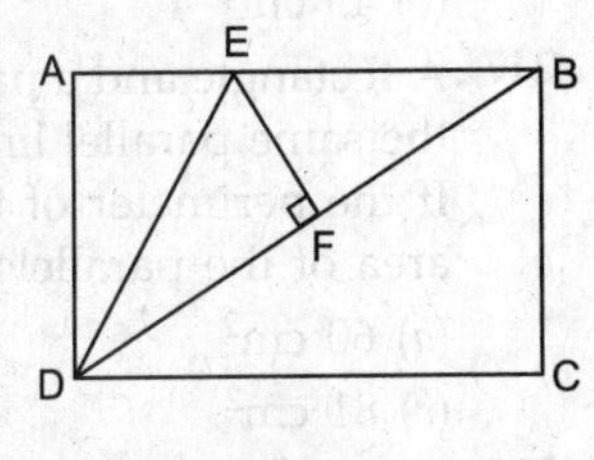

(a) $18\sqrt{3}$ sq. units (b) 20 sq. units
(c) 24 sq. units (d) 28 sq. units

211. Four equilateral triangles are described on the four sides of a rectangle with perimeter 12 cm. If the sum of the areas of the four triangles is $10\sqrt{3}$ cm^2, what is the area of the rectangle?

(a) 5 cm^2 (b) 8 cm^2
(c) 9 cm^2 (d) 6.75 cm^2

212. The dimensions of the field shown in the given figure are
AC = 150 m, AH = 120 m,
AG = 80 m, AF = 50 m,
EF = 30 m, GB = 50 m,
HD = 20 m
The area of this field is

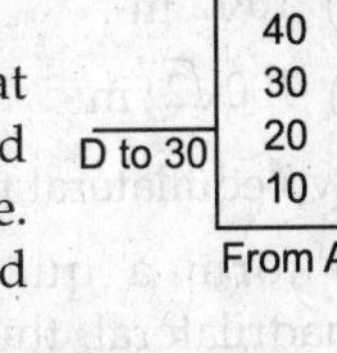

(a) 6500 m^2 (b) 6550 m^2
(c) 6600 m^2 (d) 6650 m^2

213. The readings in a field book are:
It is subsequently realised that the distances to C and D had been interchanged by mistake. The are of the actual field would be

To B (in metres)

	40	
	30	30 to E
D to 30	20	
	10	20 to C

From A

(a) 1300 sq. m (b) 1500 sq. m
(c) 1800 sq. m (d) 2000 sq. m

214. The measurements of a field are as shown
If the total area of the field is 27500 sq. m, then the value of x is equal to

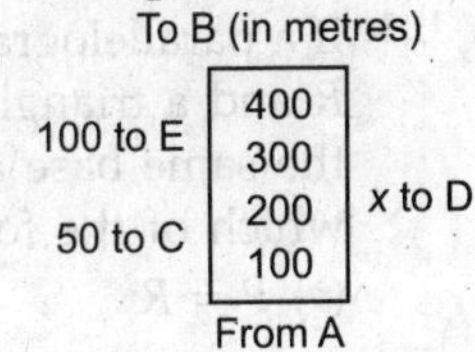

(a) 25 m (b) 30 m
(c) 50 m (d) 75 m

215. A field in the form of a parallelogram has one side 150 metres and its distance from the opposite side is 80 metres. The cost of watering the field at the rate of 50 paise per square metre is (R.R.B., 2006)
(*a*) ₹ 3500 (*b*) ₹ 5000
(*c*) ₹ 6000 (*d*) ₹ 7000

216. Let *ABCD* be a parallelogram and *ABEF* be a rectangle with *EF* lying along the line *CD*. If *AB* = 7 cm and BE = 6.5 cm, then the area of the parallelogram is
(*a*) 11.375 cm^2 (*b*) 22.75 cm^2
(*c*) 45 cm^2 (*d*) 45.5 cm^2

217. A rectangle and a parallelogram are drawn between the same parallel lines on a common base of 10 cm. If the perimeter of the rectangle is 36 cm, then the area of the parallelogram is
(*a*) 60 cm^2 (*b*) 80 cm^2
(*c*) 81 cm^2 (*d*) 100 cm^2

218. A rectangle and a parallelogram have equal areas. If the sides of the rectangle are 10 m and 12 m and the base of the parallelogram is 20 m, then the altitude of the parallelogram is
(*a*) 3 m (*b*) 5 m
(*c*) 6 m (*d*) 7 m

219. A parallelogram has sides 30 m and 14 m and one of its diagonals is 40 m long. Then, its area is
(*a*) 168 m^2 (*b*) 336 m^2
(*c*) 372 m^2 (*d*) 480 m^2

220. One diagonal of a parallelogram is 70 cm and the perpendicular distance of this diagonal from either of the outlying vertices is 27 cm. The area of the parallelogram (in sq. cm) is
(*a*) 1800 (*b*) 1836
(*c*) 1890 (*d*) 1980

221. A triangle and a parallelogram are constructed on the same base such that their areas are equal. If the altitude of the parallelogram is 100 m, then the altitude of the triangle is
(*a*) $10\sqrt{2}$ m (*b*) 100 m
(*c*) $100\sqrt{2}$ m (*d*) 200 m

222. Two equilateral triangles of side $2\sqrt{3}$ cm are joined to form a quadrilateral. The altitude of the quadrilateral, thus formed, is equal to
(*a*) 3 cm (*b*) 4 cm
(*c*) 6 cm (*d*) 8 cm

223. If a parallelogram with area *P*, a rectangle with area *R* and a triangle with area *T* are all constructed on the same base and all have the same altitude, then which of the following statements is false?
(*a*) $P = R$ (*b*) $P + T = 2R$
(*c*) $P = 2T$ (*d*) $T = \frac{1}{2}R$

224. The area of a rhombus is 150 cm^2. The length of one of its diagonals is 10 cm. The length of the other diagonal is
(*a*) 25 cm (*b*) 30 cm
(*c*) 35 cm (*d*) 40 cm

225. One of the diagonals of a rhombus is double the other diagonal. Its area is 25 sq. cm. The sum of the diagonals is
(*a*) 10 cm (*b*) 12 cm
(*c*) 15 cm (*d*) 16 cm

226. The perimeter of a rhombus is 56 m and its height is 5 m. Its area is
(*a*) 64 sq. m (*b*) 70 sq. m
(*c*) 78 sq. m (*d*) 84 sq. m

227. If the diagonals of a rhombus are 24 cm and 10 cm, the area and the perimeter of the rhombus are respectively (S.S.C., 2005)
(*a*) 120 cm^2, 52 cm (*b*) 120 cm^2, 64 cm
(*c*) 240 cm^2, 52 cm (*d*) 240 cm^2, 64 cm

228. Each side of a rhombus is 26 cm and one of its diagonals is 48 cm long. The area of the rhombus is
(*a*) 2400 cm^2 (*b*) 3000 cm^2
(*c*) 3600 cm^2 (*d*) 4800 cm^2

229. A diagonal of a rhombus is 6 cm. If its area is 24 cm^2 then the length of each side of the rhombus is
(*a*) 5 cm (*b*) 6 cm
(*c*) 7 cm (*d*) 8 cm

230. If each side of a rhombus is 20 metres and its shorter diagonal is three-fourths of its longer diagonal, then the area of this rhombus must be
(*a*) 375 sq. m (*b*) 380 sq. m
(*c*) 384 sq. m (*d*) 395 sq. m

231. The length of one diagonal of a rhombus is 80% of the other diagonal. The area of the rhombus is how many times the square of the length of the other diagonal?
(*a*) $\frac{4}{5}$ (*b*) $\frac{2}{5}$
(*c*) $\frac{3}{4}$ (*d*) $\frac{1}{4}$

232. If a square and a rhombus stand on the same base, then the ratio of the areas of the square and the rhombus is
(*a*) greater than 1 (*b*) equal to 1
(*c*) equal to $\frac{1}{2}$ (*d*) equal to $\frac{1}{4}$

233. The two parallel sides of a trapezium are 1.5 m and 2.5 m respectively. If the perpendicular distance between them is 6.5 metres, the area of the trapezium is

(*a*) 10 m^2 (*b*) 13 m^2
(*c*) 20 m^2 (*d*) 26 m^2

234. If the area of the trapezium whose parallel sides are 6 cm and 10 cm is 32 sq. cm, then the distance between the parallel sides is

(*a*) 2 cm (*b*) 4 cm
(*c*) 5 cm (*d*) 8 cm

235. The distance between the parallel sides of a trapezium = The distance between the mid-points of the slant sides = 4 cm. What is the area of the trapezium?

(*a*) 4 cm^2 (*b*) 8 cm^2
(*c*) 16 cm^2 (*d*) 20 cm^2

236. *ABCD* is a rectangle and *E* and *F* are the mid-points of *AD* and *DC* respectively. Then the ratio of the areas of *EDF* and *AEFC* would be

(*a*) 1 : 2 (*b*) 1 : 3
(*c*) 1 : 4 (*d*) 2 : 3

237. The area of a field in the shape of a trapezium measures 1440 m^2. The perpendicular distance between its parallel sides is 24 m. If the ratio of the parallel sides is 5 : 3, the length of the longer parallel side is

(*a*) 45 m (*b*) 60 m
(*c*) 75 m (*d*) 120 m

238. The cross-section of a canal is trapezium in shape. The canal is 12 m wide at the top and 8 m wide at the bottom. If the area of the cross-section is 840 sq. m, the depth of the canal is

(*a*) 8.75 m (*b*) 42 m
(*c*) 63 m (*d*) 84 m

239. Which two figure have an equal area?

14 cm | 12 cm, 10 cm | 12 cm, 12 cm | 14 cm, 12 cm
A B C D

(*a*) A and B (*b*) B and D
(*c*) A and C (*d*) A and D

240. Which of the following figures has the longest perimeter? (P.C.S., 2009; R.R.B., 2006)

(*a*) A square of side 10 cm
(*b*) A rectangle of sides 12 cm and 9 cm
(*c*) A circle of radius 7 cm
(*d*) A rhombus of side 9 cm

241. Which one of the following has a greater perimeter than the rest?

(*a*) A square with an area of 36 sq. cm
(*b*) An equilateral triangle with a side of 9 cm
(*c*) A rectangle with 10 cm as length and 40 sq. cm as area
(*d*) A circle with a radius of 4 cm

242. The diameter of a circle is 3.5 cm. What is the circumference of the circle? (Bank Recruitment, 2010)

(*a*) 11 cm (*b*) 22 cm
(*c*) 38.5 cm (*d*) 45.2 cm
(*e*) None of these

243. Area of a rectangle is equal to the area of a circle whose radius is 14 cm. If the breadth of the rectangle is 22 cm, what is its length?

(*a*) 24 cm (*b*) 26 cm
(*c*) 28 cm (*d*) Cannot be determined
(*d*) None of these

244. The area of a circle of radius 5 is numerically what percent of its circumference?

(*a*) 200 (*b*) 225
(*c*) 240 (*d*) 250

245. A man runs round a circular field of radius 50 m at the speed of 12 km / hr. What is the time taken by the man to take twenty rounds of the field?

(*a*) 30 min. (*b*) 32 min.
(*c*) 34 min. (*d*) None of these

246. From a circular sheet of paper with radius 20 cm, four circles of radius 5 cm each are cut out. What is the ratio of the uncut to the cut portion?

(*a*) 1 : 3 (*b*) 3 : 1
(*c*) 4 : 1 (*d*) 4 : 3

247. A cow is tethered in the middle of a field with a 14 feet long rope. If the cow grazes 100 sq. ft. per day, then approximately what time will be taken by the cow to graze the whole field?

(*a*) 2 days (*b*) 6 days
(*c*) 18 days (*d*) 24 days
(*e*) None of these

248. A circle and a rectangle have the same perimeter. The sides of the rectangle are 18 cm and 26 cm. What is the area of the circle? (M.A.T., 2005)

(*a*) 88 cm^2 (*b*) 154 cm^2
(*c*) 1250 cm^2 (*d*) Cannot be determined
(*e*) None of these

249. The area of a circular field is equal to the area of a rectangular field. The ratio of the length and the breadth of the rectangular field is 14 : 11 respectively and perimeter is 100 metres. What is the diameter of the circular field?

(*a*) 14 m (*b*) 22 m
(*c*) 24 m (*d*) 28 m
(*e*) None of these

250. The circumference of a circle, whose area is 24.64 m^2, is (Bank P.O., 2009)

(*a*) 14.64 m (*b*) 16.36 m
(*c*) 17.60 m (*d*) 18.40 m

251. What will be the cost of building a fence around a circular field with area equal to 18634 sq. metres if the cost of building the fence per metre is ₹ 365?

(*a*) ₹ 1,76,660 (*b*) ₹ 2,43,250
(*c*) ₹ 56,60,220 (*d*) ₹ 68,01,410
(*e*) None of these

252. The circumference of a circular plot is 396 metres. what is the area of the circular plot?

(*a*) 9446 sq. m (*b*) 9856 sq. m
(*c*) 12474 sq. m (*d*) 18634 sq. m
(*e*) None of these

253. What is the area of a circle whose circumference is 1047.2 metres?

(*a*) 69843.23 sq. m (*b*) 78621.47 sq. m
(*c*) 79943.82 sq. m (*d*) 85142.28 sq. m
(*e*) 87231.76 sq. m

254. The circumferences of two circles are 132 metres and 176 metres respectively. What is the difference between the area of the larger circle and the smaller circle?

(*a*) 1048 sq. m (*b*) 1076 sq. m
(*c*) 1078 sq. m (*d*) 1090 sq. m
(*e*) None of these

255. Cost of fencing a circular plot at the rate of ₹ 15 per metre is ₹ 3300. What will be the cost of flooring the plot at the rate of ₹ 100 per square metre? (Bank P.O., 2010)

(*a*) ₹ 2,20,000 (*b*) ₹ 3,50,000
(*c*) ₹ 3,85,000 (*d*) Cannot be determined
(*e*) None of these

256. If the circumference and the area of a circle are numerically equal, then the diameter is equal to

(*a*) $\frac{\pi}{2}$ (*b*) 2π
(*c*) 2 (*d*) 4

257. The magnitude of the area of a circle is seven times that of its circumference. What is the circumference (in units) of the circle? (Bank P.O., 2006)

(*a*) 88 (*b*) 132
(*c*) 616 (*d*) Cannot be determined
(*e*) None of these

258. The difference between the circumference and the radius of a circle is 37 cm. The area of the circle is

(*a*) 111 cm^2 (*b*) 148 cm^2
(*c*) 154 cm^2 (*d*) 259 cm^2

259. Two small circular parks of diameters 16 m and 12 m are to be replaced by a Bigger circular park. What would be the radius of this new park, If the new park has to occupy the same space as the two small parks? (M.A.T., 2008)

(*a*) 10 m (*b*) 15 m
(*c*) 20 m (*d*) 25 m

260. The sum of areas of two circles *A* and *B* is equal to the area of a third circle C whose diameter is 30 cm. If the diameter of circle A is 18 cm, then the radius of circle B is

(*a*) 10 cm (*b*) 12 cm
(*c*) 15 cm (*d*) 18 cm

261. The sum of radii of two circles is 140 cm and the difference of their circumferences is 88 cm. The diameters of the circles are

(*a*) 77 cm, 63 cm (*b*) 150 cm, 120 cm
(*c*) 154 cm, 126 cm (*d*) 160 cm, 120 cm

262. The radius of a circle is 20% more than the height of a right-angled triangle. The base of the triangle is 36 cm. If the area of triangle and circle be equal, what will be the area of circle? (Bank P.O., 2007)

(*a*) 72 cm^2 (*b*) 128 cm^2
(*c*) 144 cm^2 (*d*) 216 cm^2
(*e*) Cannot be determined

263. A circular pond has area equal to 616 m^2. A circular stage is made at the centre of the pond whose radius is equal to half the radius of the pond. What is the area where water is present? (R.R.B., 2008)

(*a*) 454 sq. m (*b*) 462 sq. m
(*c*) 532 sq. m (*d*) 564 sq. m

264. Between a square of perimeter 44 cm and a circle of circumference 44 cm, which figure has larger area and by how much?

(*a*) Both have equal area (*b*) Square, 33 cm^2
(*c*) Circle, 33 cm^2 (*d*) Square, 495 cm^2

265. The perimeter of a circular field and a square field are equal. If the area of the square field is 12100 m^2, the area of the circular field will be (R.R.B., 2006)

(*a*) 15200 m^2 (*b*) 15300 m^2
(*c*) 15400 m^2 (*d*) 15500 m^2

266. If the perimeter of a square is equal to the radius of a circle whose area is 39424 sq. m. What is the are area of the square? (Bank P.O., 2009)

(*a*) 441 sq.m (*b*) 784 sq.m
(*c*) 1225 sq.m (*d*) Cannot be determined
(*e*) None of these

267. A wire can be bent in the form of a circle of radius 56 cm. If it is bent in the form of a square, then its area will be (R.R.B., 2002)

(*a*) 3520 cm^2 (*b*) 6400 cm^2
(*c*) 7744 cm^2 (*d*) 8800 cm^2

268. The circumference of a circle is equal to the side of a square whose area measures 407044 sq. cm. What is the area of the circle? (Bank P.O., 2010)
(*a*) 22583.2 sq. cm (*b*) 32378.5 sq. cm
(*c*) 39483.4 sq. cm (*d*) 41263.5 sq. cm
(*e*) Cannot be determined

269. A wire when bent in the form of a square encloses an area of 484 sq. cm. What will be the enclosed area when the same wire is bent into the form of a circle?
(*a*) 462 sq. cm (*b*) 539 sq. cm
(*c*) 616 sq. cm (*d*) 693 sq. cm

270. A circular wire of diameter 42 cm is bent in the form of a rectangle whose sides are in the ratio 6 : 5. The area of the rectangle is
(*a*) 540 cm^2 (*b*) 1080 cm^2
(*c*) 2160 cm^2 (*d*) 4320 cm^2

271. A square lawn with side 100 m long has a circular flower bed in the centre. If the area of the lawn, excluding the flower bed, is 8614 m^2, the radius of the circular flower bed is
(*a*) 21 m (*b*) 31 m
(*c*) 41 m (*d*) None of these

272. There is a rectangular tank of length 180 m and breadth 120 m in a circular field. If the area of the land portion of the field is 40000 m^2, what is the radius of the field?
(*a*) 130 m (*b*) 135 m
(*c*) 140 m (*d*) 145 m

273. If the ratio between the areas of two circles is 4 : 1 then the ratio between their radii will be (P.C.S., 2008)
(*a*) 1 : 2 (*b*) 2 : 1
(*c*) 1 : 3 (*d*) 4 : 1

274. The areas of two circular fields are in the ratio 16 : 49. If the radius of the latter is 14 m, then what is the radius of the former? (IGNOU, 2003)
(*a*) 4 m (*b*) 8 m
(*c*) 18 m (*d*) 32 m

275. The ratio of the radii of two circles is 3 : 2. What is the ratio of their circumferences? (S.S.C., 2010)
(*a*) 2 : 3 (*b*) 3 : 2
(*c*) 4 : 9 (*d*) None of these

276. The ratio of the radii of two circles is 1 : 3. Then the ratio of their areas is (B.Ed Entrance, 2010)
(*a*) 1 : 3 (*b*) 1 : 6
(*c*) 1 : 9 (*d*) None of these

277. The ratio of the circumferences of two circles is 2 : 3. What is the ratio of their areas? (M.B.A., 2008)
(*a*) 2 : 3 (*b*) 4 : 9
(*c*) 9 : 4 (*d*) None of these

278. The perimeter of a circle is equal to the perimeter of a square. Then, their areas are in the ratio
(*a*) 4 : 1 (*b*) 11 : 7
(*c*) 14 : 11 (*d*) 22 : 7

279. A circle and a square have the same area. The ratio of the side of the square and the radius of the circle is
(*a*) $\sqrt{22} : \sqrt{7}$ (*b*) $\sqrt{\pi} : 1$
(*c*) $1 : \pi$ (*d*) $\sqrt{7} : \sqrt{22}$

280. If the areas of a circle and a square are equal then the ratio of their perimeters is
(*a*) 1 : 1 (*b*) $2 : \pi$
(*c*) $\pi : 2$ (*d*) $\sqrt{\pi} : 2$

281. The diameter of a wheel is 1.26 m. How far will it travel in 500 revolutions?
(*a*) 1492 m (*b*) 1980 m
(*c*) 2530 m (*d*) 2880 m

282. The number of revolutions made by a wheel of diameter 56 cm in covering a distance of 1.1 km is:
(*a*) 31.25 (*b*) 56.25
(*c*) 62.5 (*d*) 625

283. The diameter of the driving wheel of a bus is 140 cm. How many revolutions per minute must the wheel make in order to keep a speed of 66 km per hour?
(*a*) 200 (*b*) 250
(*c*) 300 (*d*) 350

284. If the wheel of the engine of a train $4\frac{2}{7}$ metres in circumference makes 7 revolutions in 4 seconds, then the speed (in km/hr) of the train is (G.B.O., 2007)
(*a*) 27 (*b*) 28
(*c*) 29 (*d*) 30

285. The radius of the wheel of a vehicle is 70 cm. The wheel makes 10 revolutions in 5 seconds. The speed of the vehicle is (M.B.A., 2008)
(*a*) 29.46 km/hr (*b*) 31.68 km/hr
(*c*) 32.72 km/hr (*d*) 36.25 km/hr

286. The diameter of a cycle wheel is 70 cm. A cyclist takes 30 hours to reach a destination at the speed of 22 km/hr. How many revolutions will the wheel make during this journey?
(*a*) 3 lakh (*b*) 4 lakh
(*c*) 30 million (*d*) None of these

287. Wheels of diameters 7 cm and 14 cm start rolling simultaneously from X and Y, which are 1980 cm apart, towards each other in opposite directions. Both of them make the same number of revolutions per second. If both of them meet after 10 seconds, the speed of the smaller wheel is (M.A.T., 2005)
(*a*) 22 cm/sec (*b*) 44 cm/sec
(*c*) 66 cm/sec (*d*) 132 cm/sec

288. A toothed wheel of diameter 50 cm is attached to a smaller wheel of diameter 30 cm. How many revolutions will the smaller wheel make when the larger one makes 15 revolutions? (M.B.A., 2005, 2007)

(a) 18 (b) 20
(c) 25 (d) 30

289. A small ring of negligible thickness and radius 2 cm moves on a bigger rung of radius 10 cm. How many rotations will the small ring take on the bigger ring to make a complete round? (Hotel Management, 2010)

(a) 5 (b) 6
(c) 7 (d) 10

290. Find the diameter of a wheel that makes 113 revolutions to go 2 km 26 decameters.

(a) $4\frac{4}{13}$ m (b) $6\frac{4}{11}$ m
(c) $12\frac{4}{11}$ m (d) $12\frac{8}{11}$ m

291. The circumference of the front wheel of a cart is 40 ft long and that of the back wheel is 48 ft long. What is the distance travelled by the cart, when the front wheel has done five more revolutions than the rear wheel? (M.B.A., 2011)

(a) 850 ft (b) 950 ft
(c) 1200 ft (d) 1450 ft

292. The radii of the front wheel and the rear wheel of a bike are 14 cm and 21 cm respectively. Rahul puts a red mark on the point of contact of each of the wheels with the ground when the bike is stationary. Once the bike starts moving, then after what distance will the two red marks touch the ground again simultaneously?

(a) 42 cm (b) 84 cm
(c) 264 cm (d) 294 cm

293. The circumferences of the front and rear wheels of a bicycle are 3.5 m and 3 m respectively. If the vehicle is moving at a speed of 15 m/sec, the shortest time in which both the wheels will make a whole number of turns is (R.R.B., 2008)

(a) 1.4 seconds (b) 2.1 seconds
(c) 4 seconds (d) 6.4 seconds

294. The circumference of the back-sided wheel of a vehicle is 1 m greater than that of front side wheel. To travel 600 m, the front wheel rotates 30 times more than the back wheel. The circumference of the front wheel is (Hotel Management, 2007)

(a) 2 m (b) 4 m
(c) 5 m (d) None of these

295. Two boys are running on two different circular paths with same centre. If their radii are 5 m and 10 m, the maximum possible distance between them is (I.A.M., 2007)

(a) 5 m (b) 10 m
(c) 15 m (d) 20 m

296. A circular ground whose diameter is 35 metres, has a 1.4 m broad garden around it. What is the area of the garden in square meters?

(a) 160.16 (b) 176.16
(c) 196.16 (d) Data inadequate
(e) None of these

297. A circular grassy plot of land, 42 cm in diameter, has a path 3.5 m wide running around it outside. The cost of gravelling the path at ₹ 4 per square metre is (M.A.T., 2007)

(a) ₹ 1002 (b) ₹ 1802
(c) ₹ 2002 (d) ₹ 3002

298. A circle of radius 5 cm is drawn and another circle of 3 cm radius is cut out of this circle. What is the radius of a circle which has the same area as the area of the bigger circle excluding the cut one?

(a) 2 cm (b) 3 cm
(c) 4 cm (d) 4.5 cm

299. The circumference of a circular ground is 88 metres. A strip of land, 3 metres wide, inside and along the circumference of the ground is to be levelled. What is the budgeted expenditure if the levelling costs ₹ 7 per square metre? (M.A.T., 2006)

(a) ₹ 1050 (b) ₹ 1125
(c) ₹ 1325 (d) ₹ 1650

300. The areas of two concentric circles forming a ring are 154 sq. cm and 616 sq. cm. The breadth of the ring is

(a) 7 cm (b) 14 cm
(c) 21 cm (d) 28 cm

301. A circular road runs around a circular garden. If the difference between the circumference of the outer circle and the inner circle is 44 m, the width of the road is (M.A.T., 2007)

(a) 3.5 m (b) 4 m
(c) 7 m (d) 7.5 m

302. A small disc of radius r is cut out from a disc of radius R. The weight of the disc which now has a hole in it, is reduced to $\frac{24}{25}$ of the original weight. If $R = xr$, what is the value of x?

(a) 4 (b) 4.5
(c) 24 (d) 25
(e) None of these

303. A circular swimming pool is surrounded by a concrete wall 4 ft. wide. If the area of the concrete wall surrounding the pool is $\frac{11}{25}$ that of the pool, then the radius of the pool is

(a) 8 ft (b) 16 ft
(c) 20 ft (d) 30 ft

304. The ratio of the outer and the inner perimeters of a circular path is 23 : 22. If the path is 5 metres wide, the diameter of the inner circle is (S.S.C., 2004)

(a) 55 m (b) 110 m
(c) 220 m (d) 230 m

305. If a region bounded by a circle C is to be divided into three regions of equal areas by drawing two circles concentric with C, then the ratio of the radii of the two circles must be

(a) 1 : 3 (b) $1 : \sqrt{3}$
(c) 1 : 2 (d) $1 : \sqrt{2}$

306. The area of a circle is increased by 22 sq. cm if its radius is increased by 1 cm. The original radius of the circle is (S.S.C., 2007)

(a) 3 cm (b) 3.2 cm
(c) 3.5 cm (d) 6 cm

307. The perimeter of a square is equal to twice the perimeter of a rectangle of length 8 cm and breadth 7 cm. What is the circumference of a semi-circle whose diameter is equal to the side of the square? (rounded off to two decimal places) (Bank P.O., 2010)

(a) 23.57 cm (b) 38.57 cm
(c) 42.46 cm (d) 47.47 cm
(e) None of these

308. What will be the area of a semi-circle of 14 m diameter?

(a) 22 m^2 (b) 77 m^2
(c) 154 m^2 (d) 308 m^2
(e) None of these

309. A semi-circular shaped window has diameter of 63 cm. Its perimeter equals

(a) 126 cm (b) 162 cm
(c) 198 cm (d) 251 cm

310. A vertical rod of height 33 metres is bent to form a semi-circular shape so that the top touches the ground. The distance between the top head and the base on the ground is (I.A.M., 2007)

(a) 10.5 m (b) 12 m
(c) 21 m (d) 33 m

311. What will be the area of a semi-circle whose perimeter is 36 cm? (R.R.B., 2009)

(a) 154 cm^2 (b) 168 cm^2
(c) 308 cm^2 (d) Data inadequate
(e) None of these

312. If the area of a semi-circular plot is 11088 m^2, then its perimeter is

(a) 264 m (b) 348 m
(c) 432 m (d) 452 m

313. If a wire is bent into the shape of a square, then the area of the square is 81 sq. cm. When the wire is bent into a semi-circular shape, then the area of the semi-circle will be

(a) 22 cm^2 (b) 44 cm^2
(c) 77 cm^2 (d) 154 cm^2

314. If $MN = x$, then what is the area of the shaded region?

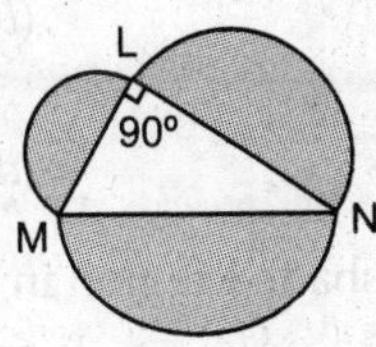

(a) πx^2 (b) $\frac{\pi x^2}{2}$
(c) $\frac{\pi x^2}{2}$ (d) $\frac{\pi x^2}{4}$

315. In the given figure, ABC is a right-angled triangle with B as the right angle. Three semi-circles are drawn with AB, BC and AC as diameters. What is the area of the shaded portion if the area of the triangle ABC is 12 square units?

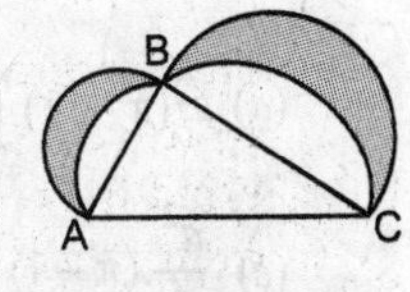

(a) 6 square units
(b) 12 square units
(c) 24 square units
(d) Cannot be determined as the data is insufficient

316. If in the given figure OP = OQ = 14 cm and OP, PQ and OQ are all joined by semi-circles, then the perimeter of the shaded are a is equal to

(a) 88 cm (b) 176 cm
(c) 264 cm (d) 352 cm

317. In the given diagram, ABCD is a square and semi-circular regions have been added to it by drawing two semi-circles with AB and CD as diameters. If the total area of the three regions is 350 sq. cm, then the length of the side of the square is equal to

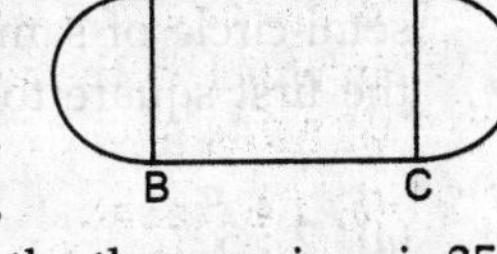

(a) $5\sqrt{7}$ cm (b) 7 cm
(c) 13 cm (d) 14 cm

318. If r and R and the respective radii of the smaller and the bigger semi-circles then the area of the shaded portion in the given figure is :

(a) πr^2 sq. units (b) $\pi R^2 - \pi r^2$ sq. units
(c) $\pi R^2 + \pi r^2$ sq. units (d) πR^2 sq. units

319. Two circular wheels of the same radius r have their central hubs at a distance of a from one another. The minimum length of a fan belt which will pass around both the wheels is

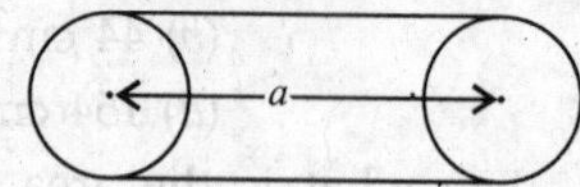

(a) $2(a + \pi r)$ (b) $a + \frac{\pi r}{2}$
(c) $2a + \pi r)$ (d) $\frac{a + \pi r}{2}$

320. The area of the shaded region in the adjoining figure is (S.S.C., 2007)

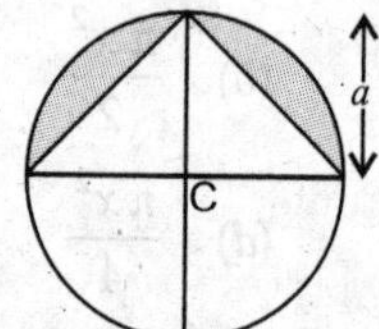

(a) $a^2(\pi - 1)$ sq. units (b) $a^2\left(\frac{\pi}{2} - 1\right)$ sq. units
(c) $\frac{a^2}{2}(\pi - 1)$ sq. units (d) $\frac{a^2}{2}\left(\frac{\pi}{2} - 1\right)$ sq. units

321. An athletic track 14 m wide consists of two straight sections 120 m long joining semi-circular ends whose inner radius is 35 m. The area of the track is (M.A.T., 2006)

(a) 7026 m^2 (b) 7036 m^2
(c) 7046 m^2 (d) 7056 m^2

322. A square of area 40 sq. cm is inscribed in a circle as shown in the figure. The area (in sq.cm) of the semi-circle is (A.A.O., 2009)

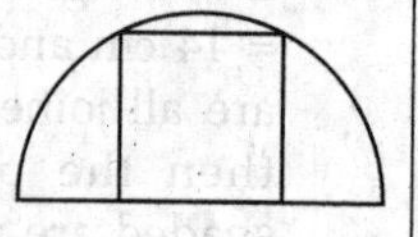

(a) 20 π (b) 25 π
(c) 30 π (d) 40 π

323. A square is inscribed in a circle and another in a semi-circle of same radius. The ratio of the area of the first square to the area of the second square is (Hotel Management, 2010)

(a) 2 : 5 (b) 5 : 2
(c) 4 : 5 (d) 5 : 4

324. Semi-circular lawns are attached to the edges of a rectangular field measuring 42 m × 35 m. The area of the total field is

(a) 1358 m^2 (b) 3818.5 m^2
(c) 5813 m^2 (d) 8318 m^2

325. The area of a sector of a circle of radius 5 cm, formed by an arc of length 3.5 cm, is

(a) 7.5 cm^2 (b) 7.75 cm^2
(c) 8.5 cm^2 (d) 8.75 cm^2

326. In a circle of radius 7 cm, an arc subtends an angle of 108° at the centre. The area of the sector is

(a) 43.2 cm^2 (b) 44.2 cm^2
(c) 45.2 cm^2 (d) 46.2 cm^2

327. A sector of 56° has an area of 17.6 cm^2. The its radius will be

(a) 1.5 cm (b) 3 cm
(c) 4.2 cm (d) 6 cm

328. There are three circles each of radius $\sqrt{7}$ cm. A triangle is formed by joining their centres. The angles at the centre made by the triangle are shown in the figure. The area of the shaded portion is

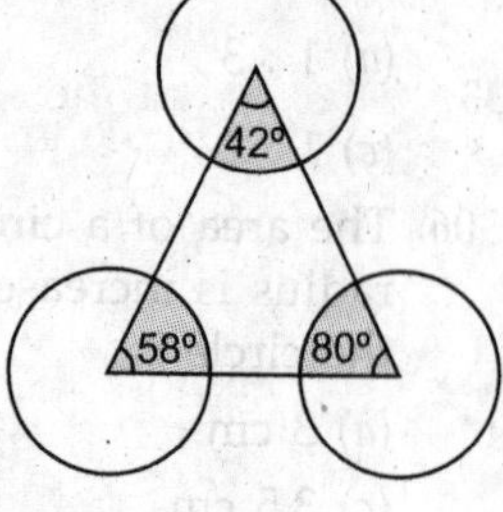

(a) $\frac{4}{7}$ cm^2 (b) $\frac{11}{7}$ cm^2
(c) $\frac{22}{7}$ cm^2 (d) 11 cm^2

329. The minute hand of a clock is 7 cm long. Find the area of the sector made by the minute hand between 7 a.m. and 7.05 a.m. (R.R.B., 2006)

(a) 11.5 cm^2 (b) 12.8 cm^2
(c) 15.4 cm^2 (d) None of these

330. A horse is tied at the corner of a rectangular field whose length is 20 m and width is 16 m, with a rope whose length is 14 m. Find the area which the horse can graze: (R.R.B., 2006)

(a) 144 sq. m (b) 154 sq. m
(c) 156 sq. m (d) 164 sq. m

331. Area of the segment of a circle is

(a) $\frac{1}{2} l r$ (b) $\frac{\pi r \theta}{180°}$
(c) $r^2\left(\frac{\pi\theta}{360°} - \frac{1}{2}\sin\theta\right)$ (d) None of these

332. If in a circle of radius 21 cm, an arc subtends an angle of 56° at the centre, the length of the arc is

(a) 15.53 cm (b) 16.53 cm
(c) 18.53 cm (d) 20.53 cm

333. If the circumference of a circle is 100 units, then what will be the length of the arc described by an angle of 20 degrees? (Campus Recruitment, 2010)

(a) 5.55 units (b) 4.86 units
(c) 5.85 units (d) None of these

334. The area of the greatest circle which can be inscribed in a square whose perimeter is 120 cm, is (S.S.C., 2004)

(a) $\frac{22}{7} \times \left(\frac{7}{2}\right)^2$ cm^2 (b) $\frac{22}{7} \times \left(\frac{9}{2}\right)^2$ cm^2
(c) $\frac{22}{7} \times \left(\frac{15}{2}\right)^2$ cm^2 (d) $\frac{22}{7} \times (15)^2$ cm^2

335. The area of the largest circle, that can be drawn inside a rectangle with sides 18 cm by 14 cm, is (S.S.C., 2007)

(*a*) 49 cm^2 (*b*) 154 cm^2
(*c*) 378 cm^2 (*d*) 1078 cm^2

336. The sides of a rectangle are 8 cm and 6 cm. The corners of the rectangle lie on a circle. Find the area of the circle without the rectangle. (S.S.C., 2007)

(*a*) 30.6 cm^2 (*b*) 39 cm^2
(*c*) 42.4 cm^2 (*d*) 65.3 cm^2

337. The area of the rectangle circumscribed by a circle is 32 cm^2 and the length of one side of the rectangle is 8 cm. The length of the diameter of the circle is

(*a*) 16 cm (*b*) 12 cm
(*c*) $5\sqrt{2}$ cm (*d*) $4\sqrt{5}$ cm

338. The area of a circle is 220 sq. cm. The area of a square inscribed in this circle will be

(*a*) 49 cm^2 (*b*) 70 cm^2
(*c*) 140 cm^2 (*d*) 150 cm^2

339. A square is inscribed in a circle whose radius is 4 cm. The area of the portion between the circle and the square is :

(*a*) $(8\pi - 16)$ (*b*) $(8\pi - 32)$
(*c*) $(16\pi - 16)$ (*d*) $(16\pi - 32)$

340. The circumference of a circle is 100 cm. The side of a square inscribed in the circle is

(*a*) $50\sqrt{2}$ cm^2 (*b*) $\frac{100}{\pi}$ cm^2
(*c*) $\frac{50\sqrt{2}}{\pi}$ cm^2 (*d*) $\frac{100\sqrt{2}}{\pi}$ cm^2

341. A circle is inscribed in a square of side 54 cms and another circle circumscribes the same square. Then the ratio of circumferences of the bigger circle to the smaller circle is

(*a*) $1 : \sqrt{2}$ (*b*) $\sqrt{2} : 1$
(*c*) $\sqrt{3} : 1$ (*d*) None of these

342. A circle is circumscribed around a square as shown in the figure. The area of one of the four shaded portions is equal to $\frac{4}{7}$.

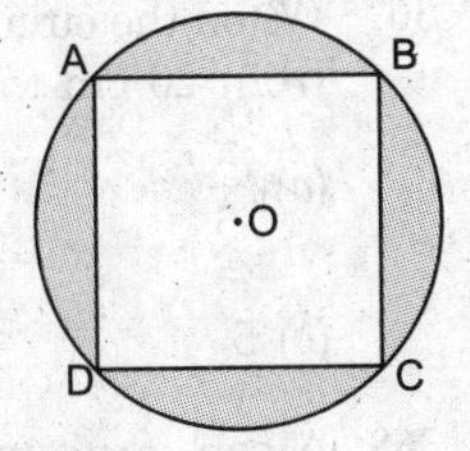

The radius of the circle is (R.R.B., 2006)

(*a*) $\sqrt{2}$ (*b*) $\frac{1}{\sqrt{2}}$
(*c*) 2 (*d*) 3

343. The ratio of the areas of the incircle and the circumcircle of a square is (S.S.C., 2008)

(*a*) 1 : 2 (*b*) $\sqrt{2} : 1$
(*c*) $1 : \sqrt{2}$ (*d*) 2 : 1

344. A square circumscribes a circle and another square is inscribed in this circle with one vertex at the point of contact. The ratio of the areas of the circumscribed and the inscribed squares is

(*a*) 1 (*b*) 2 : 1
(*c*) 3 (*d*) 4

345. What is the area of the shaded region?

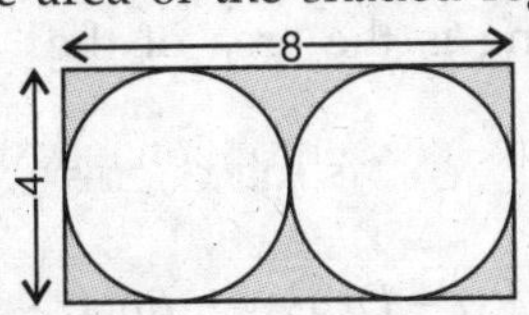

(*a*) $32 - 4\pi$ sq. units (*b*) $32 - 8\pi$ sq. units
(*c*) $16 - 4\pi$ sq. units (*d*) $16 - 8\pi$ sq. units

346. Four equal sized maximum circular plates are cut off from a square paper sheet of area 784 cm^2. The circumference of each plate is

(*a*) 22 cm (*b*) 44 cm
(*c*) 66 cm (*d*) 88 cm

347. There are 4 semi-circular gardens on each side of a square-shaped pond with each side 21 m. The cost of fencing the entire plot at the rate of ₹ 12.50 per metre is

(*a*) ₹ 1560 (*b*) ₹ 1650
(*c*) ₹ 3120 (*d*) ₹ 3300

348. The circumradius of an equilateral triangle is 8 cm. The inradius of the triangle

(*a*) 3.25 cm (*b*) 4 cm
(*c*) 3.5 cm (*d*) 4.25 cm

349. The ratio of the areas of the incircle and circumcircle of an equilateral triangle is

(*a*) 1 : 2 (*b*) 1 : 3
(*c*) 1 : 4 (*d*) 1 : 9

350. The radius of the circumcircle of an equilateral triangle of side 12 cm is

(*a*) $\frac{4\sqrt{2}}{3}$ cm (*b*) $4\sqrt{2}$ cm
(*c*) $\frac{4\sqrt{3}}{3}$ cm (*d*) $4\sqrt{3}$ cm

351. The area of the incircle of an equilateral triangle of side 42 cm is

(*a*) $22\sqrt{3}$ cm^2 (*b*) 231 cm^2
(*c*) 462 cm^2 (*d*) 924 cm^2

352. The area of a circle inscribed in an equilateral triangle is 154 cm^2. Find the perimeter of the triangle. (M.B.A., 2006)

(*a*) 71.5 cm (*b*) 71.7 cm
(*c*) 72.3 cm (*d*) 72.7 cm

353. A circle is inscribed in a square. An equilateral triangle of side $4\sqrt{3}$ cm is inscribed in that circle. The length of the diagonal of the square is

(a) $4\sqrt{2}$ cm (b) 8 cm
(c) $8\sqrt{2}$ cm (d) 16 cm

354. In the given figure, ABC is an equilateral triangle which is inscribed inside a circle and whose radius is r. Which of the following is the area of the triangle?

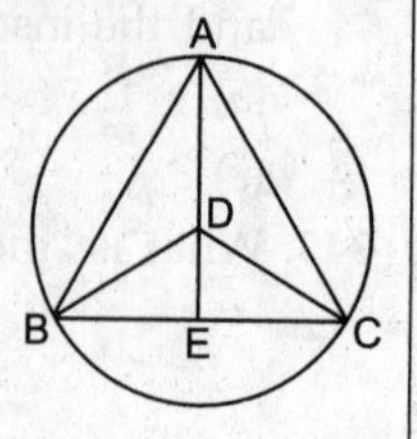

(S.B.I.P.O., 2005)

(a) $(r + DE)^{\frac{1}{2}} (r - DE)^{\frac{3}{2}}$ (b) $(r - DE)^{\frac{1}{2}} (r + DE)^2$
(c) $(r - DE)^2 (r + DE)^2$ (d) $(r - DE)^{\frac{1}{2}} (r + DE)^{\frac{3}{2}}$

355. Three boys are standing on a circular boundary of a fountain. They are at equal distance from each other. If the radius of the boundary is 5 m, the shortest distance between any two boys is (Hotel Management, 2010)

(a) $\frac{5\sqrt{3}}{2}$ m (b) $5\sqrt{3}$ m
(c) $\frac{15\sqrt{3}}{2}$ m (d) $\frac{10\pi}{3}$ m

356. What is the area of an equilateral triangle inscribed in a circle of unit radius?

(a) $3\sqrt{3}$ sq. units (b) $\frac{3\sqrt{3}}{2}$ sq. units
(c) $\frac{3\sqrt{3}}{4}$ sq. units (d) $\frac{3\sqrt{3}}{16}$ sq. units

357. The sides of a triangle are 6 cm, 11 cm and 15 cm. The radius of its incircle is

(a) $3\sqrt{2}$ cm (b) $\frac{4\sqrt{2}}{5}$ cm
(c) $\frac{5\sqrt{2}}{4}$ cm (d) $6\sqrt{2}$ cm

358. The product of the lengths of three sides of a triangle is 196 and the radius of its circumscribe is 2.5 cm. The area of the triangle is

(a) 19.6 cm^2 (b) 39.2 cm^2
(c) 61.25 cm^2 (d) 122.5 cm^2

359. A triangle with sides 13 cm, 14 cm and 15 cm is inscribed in a circle. The radius of the circle is (M.B.A., 2007)

(a) 2 cm (b) 3 cm
(c) 4 cm (d) 8.125 cm

360. The perimeter of a triangle is 30 cm and the circumference of its incircle is 88 cm. The area of the triangle is

(a) 70 cm^2 (b) 140 cm^2
(c) 210 cm^2 (d) 420 cm^2

361. If in a triangle, the area is numerically equal to the perimeter, then the radius of the inscribed circle of the triangle is

(a) 1 (b) 1.5
(c) 2 (d) 3

362. An equilateral triangle, a square and a circle have equal perimeters. If T denotes the area of the triangle, S, the area of the square and C, the area of the circle, then

(a) $S < T < C$ (b) $T < C < S$
(c) $T < S < C$ (d) $C < S < T$

363. A circle, a square and an equilateral triangle have the same area. The correct increasing order of the perimeters will be

(a) triangle, square, circle
(b) triangle, circle, square
(c) circle, triangle, square
(d) circle, square, triangle

364. The area of the largest triangle that can be inscribed in a semi-circle of radius r, is (B.Ed Entrance, 2011)

(a) r^2 (b) $2r^2$
(c) r^3 (d) $2r^3$

365. ABC is a right-angled triangle with right angle at B. If the semi-circle on AB with AB as diameter encloses an area of 81 sq. cm and the semi-circle on BC with BC as diameter encloses an area of 36 sq. cm, then the area of the semi-circle on AC with AC as diameter will be

(a) 117 cm^2 (b) 121 cm^2
(c) 217 cm^2 (d) 221 cm^2

366. If the radius of a circle is increased by 75%, then its circumference will increase by

(a) 25% (b) 50%
(c) 75% (d) 100%

367. When the circumference of a toy balloon is increased from 20 cm to 25 cm, its radius is increased by

(a) $\frac{\pi}{5}$ (b) $\frac{5}{\pi}$
(c) 5 (d) $\frac{5}{2\pi}$

368. A can go round a circular path 8 times in 40 minutes. If the diameter of the circle is increased to 10 times the original diameter, then the time required by A to go round the new path once, travelling at the same speed as before, is

(a) 20 min. (b) 25 min.
(c) 50 min. (d) 100 min.

369. If the radius of a circle is increased by 6%, then the area is increased by
(a) 6% (b) 12%
(c) 12.36% (d) 16.64%

370. If the radius of a circle is increased by 200%, then its area will increase by (P.C.S. 2009)
(a) 200% (b) 400%
(c) 800% (d) 900%

371. If the radius of a circle is diminished by 10%, then its area is diminished by
(a) 10% (b) 19%
(c) 20% (d) 36%

372. If the radius of a circle is doubled, its area is increased by
(a) 100% (b) 200%
(c) 300% (d) 400%

373. If the radius of a circle is increased to 3 times, then how many times will its circumference be increased?
(a) $\frac{1}{3}$ times (b) 2 times
(c) 3 times (d) 9 times

374. If the circumference of a circle increases form 4π to 8π, what change occurs in its area?
(a) It is halved. (b) It doubles.
(c) it triples. (d) It quadruples.

375. If the circumference of a circle is increased by 20%, what will be the effect on the circle? (Bank P.O., 2008)
(a) 40% increase (b) 44% increase
(c) 48% increase (d) Cannot be determined
(e) None of these

376. If the circumference of a circle is decreased by 50% then the percentage of decrease in its area is (S.S.C., 2010)
(a) 25 (b) 50
(c) 60 (d) 75

377. Three equal circles are described with vertices of the triangles as centres. If the radius of each circle is r, the sum of areas of the portions of the circles intercepted in a triangle is (Campus Recuritment, 2010)
(a) $2\pi r^2$ (b) $\frac{3}{2}\pi r^2$
(c) πr^2 (d) $\frac{1}{2}\pi r^2$

378. Three circles of radius 3.5 cm are placed in such a way that each circle touches the other two. The area of the portion enclosed by the circles is (S.S.C., 2003)
(a) 1.967 cm² (b) 1.975 cm²
(c) 19.67 cm² (d) 21.21 cm²

379. Four circles each of radius 'a' units touch one another. The area enclosed between them in square units is
(a) $\frac{a^2}{7}$ (b) $3a^2$
(c) $\frac{6a^2}{7}$ (d) $\frac{41a^2}{7}$

380. Four horses are tethered at four corners of a square plot of side 63 metres so that they just cannot reach one another. The area left ungrazed is
(a) 675.5 m² (b) 780.6 m²
(c) 785.8 m² (d) 850.5 m²

381. In the adjoining figure, if the radius of each of the four outer circles is r, what is the radius of the inner circle?

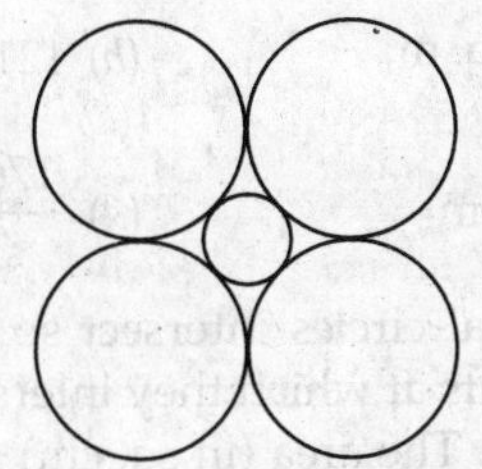

(a) $\frac{2}{\sqrt{2}+1}r$ (b) $\frac{1}{\sqrt{2}}r$
(c) $(\sqrt{2}-1)r$ (d) $\sqrt{2}r$

382. Four equal circles are described at the four corners of a square so that each touches two of the others. The area enclosed by the circumferences of the circles is $13\frac{5}{7}$ sq. cm. Find the radius of the circle.
(a) 2.5 cm (b) 4 cm
(c) 6 cm (d) 7.5 cm

383. In order to reach his office on time, Mr. Roy goes through the middle passage of a round fort which he takes 14 minutes to pass through. However, on a certain day, due to repairs, the straight road being blocked, he had to take the roundabout way as a result of which he reached his office late. How late was he?
(a) 6 min (b 8 min
(c) 12 min (d) $7\frac{1}{2}$ min

384. A kite-shaped quadrilateral of the largest possible area is cut from a circular sheet of paper. If the lengths of the sides of the kite are in the ratio 3 : 3 : 4 : 4, what percentage of the circular sheet is wasted?
(a) 34% (b) 39%
(c) 42% (d) 47%

Directions (Questions 385-386): ***These questions are based on the following in formation:***

A cow is tethered at point A by a rope. Neither the rope nor the cow is allowed to enter the triangle ABC. $\angle BAC = 30°$, $AB = AC = 10$ m.

385. What is the area that can be grazed by the cow if the length of the rope is 8?

(a) $\frac{133\pi}{6}$ sq. m (b) 121π sq. m

(c) 132π sq. m (d) $\frac{176\pi}{3}$ sq. m

386. What is the area that can be grazed by the cow if the length of the rope is 12 m?

(a) $134\frac{1}{3}\pi$ sq. m (b) 121π sq.m

(c) 132π sq.m (d) $\frac{176\pi}{3}$ sq. m

387. Two identical circles intersect so that their centres, and the points at which they intersect, form a square of side 1 cm. The area (in sq. cm) of the portion that is common to the circles is

(a) $\frac{\pi}{4}$ (b) $\frac{\pi}{2}-1$

(c) $\frac{\pi}{5}$ (d) $\sqrt{2}-1$

388. A one-rupee coin is placed on a plain paper. How many coins of the same size can be placed round it so that each one touches the centre and adjacent coins? (R.R.B., 2006)

(a) 3 (b) 4

(c) 6 (d) 7

389. A skating champion moves along the circumference of a circle of radius 28 m in 44 sec. How many seconds will it take her to move along the perimeter of a hexagon of side 48 m? (M.B.A., 2011)

(a) 48 (b) 68

(c) 72 (d) 84

(e) 90

390. Each side of a regular hexagon is 1 cm. The area of the hexagon is

(a) $3\sqrt{2}$ cm^2 (b) $4\sqrt{3}$ cm^2

(c) $\frac{3\sqrt{3}}{4}$ cm^2 (d) $\frac{3\sqrt{3}}{2}$ cm^2

391. The difference between the areas of the circumcircle and the incircle of a regular polygon of n sides with each side of length $2a$, is

(a) πa^2 (b) $(2n+1)\pi a^2$

(c) $\pi n a^2$ (d) $2\pi n a^2$

392. If a circle touching all the n sides of a polygon of perimeter $2p$ has radius r, then the area of the polygon is

(a) $(p-n)r$ (b) pr

(c) $(2p-n)r$ (d) $(p+n)r$

393. Two equal circles are drawn in square in such a way that a side of the square forms diameter of each circle. If the remaining area of the square is 42 cm^2, how much will the diameter of the circle measure? [IBPS—RRB Officers Gr. 'B' Exam, 2015]

(a) 3.5 cm (b) 4 cm

(c) 14 cm (d) 7.5 cm

394. If radius of a circle is 3cm, what is the area of the circle in sq. cm.? [Indian Railway Gr. 'D' Exam, 2014]

(a) 6π (b) 9π

(c) $\frac{3\pi}{2}$ (d) $9\pi^2$

395. A plate on square base made of brass is of length x c and width 1 mm. The plate weighs 4725 gm. If 1 cubic cm of brass weighs 8.4 grams, then the value of x is [SSC—CHSL (10+2) Exam, 2015]

(a) 75 (b) 76

(c) 72 (d) 74

396. Area of a rectangle is 150 sq. metre When the breadth of the same rectangle is increased by 2 metres and the length decreased by 5 metres the area of the rectangle decreases by 30 square metres. What is the perimeter of the square whose sides are equal to the length of the rectangle? [RBI Officers Gr. 'B' (Phase I) Exam, 2015]

(a) 76 m (b) 72 m

(c) 120 m (d) 60 m

397. The area of a circle whose radius is the diagonal of a square whose area is 4 sq. units is

(a) 16π sq. units (b) 4π sq. units

(c) 6π sq. units (d) 8π sq. units

[SSC—CHSL (10+2) Exam, 2015]

398. The ratio of circumference and diameter of a circle is 22 : 7. If the circumference be $1\frac{4}{7}$ m, then the radius of the circle is [SSC—CHSL (10+2) Exam, 2015]

(a) $\frac{1}{3}$ m (b) $\frac{1}{2}$ m

(c) $\frac{1}{4}$ m (d) 1m

399. A rectangular carpet has an area of 120 m^2 and a perimeter of 46 metre. The length of its diagonal is

(*a*) 23 metre (*b*) 13 metre
(*c*) 17 metre (*d*) 21 metre

[SSC—CHSL (10+2) Exam, 2015]

400. The total surface area of a right circular cylinder with radius of the base 7 cm and height 20 cm is

[SSC—CHSL (10+2) Exam, 2015]

(*a*) 900 cm^2 (*b*) 140 cm^2
(*c*) 1000 cm^2 (*d*) 1188 cm^2

401. The height of a triangle is equal to the perimeter of a square whose diagonal is $8\sqrt{2}$ metre and the base of the same triangle is equal to the side of a square whose area is 729sq. metre. What is the area of the triangle? (In sq. metre)

[United India Insurance (UIICL) Assistant (Online) Exam, 2015]

(*a*) 378 (*b*) 206
(*c*) 472 (*d*) 432

402. A boundary wall around a rectangular plot is constructed at a total cost of ₹ 46000 at the rate of ₹ 200 per metre. What is the area of the plot if the respective ratio between the bradth and the length of the plot is 10 : 13? (in sq. metre)

[United India Insurance (UIICL) Assistant (Online) Exam, 2015]

(*a*) 3750 (*b*) 3250
(*c*) 3000 (*d*) 3900

403. Four circles having equal radii are drawn with centres at the four corners of a square. Each circle touches the other two adjacent circles. If the remaining area of the square is 168 cm^2, what is the size of the radius of the circle?(in centimeters)

[RBI Officers Gr. 'B' (Phase I) Exam, 2015]

(*a*) 14 (*b*) 1.4
(*c*) 35 (*d*) 21

404. A courtyard is 25m long and 16m broad is to be paved with bricks of dimensions 20cm by 10cm. What is the total number of bricks required?

[IBPS—RRB Office Assistant (Online) Exam, 2015]

(*a*) 16000 (*b*) 18000
(*c*) 20000 (*d*) 22000

405. The diameter of a circle is equal to the perimeter of a square whose area is 3136 cm^2. What is the circumference of the circle?

[IBPS—RRB Office Assistant (Online) Exam, 2015]

(*a*) 352 cm (*b*) 704 cm
(*c*) 39424 cm (*d*) 1024 cm

406. The base of triangle is 15 cm and height is 12 cm. the height of another triangle of double the area having base 20cm is

[IBPS—RRB Office Assistant (Online) Exam, 2015]

(*a*) 22 cm (*b*) 20 cm
(*c*) 18 cm (*d*) 10 cm

407. The base of an isosceles is 14 cm and its perimeter is 36 cm. Find its area.

(*a*) $42\sqrt{2}$ sq. cm. (*b*) 42 sq. cm
(*c*) 84 sq. cm (*d*) 48 sq. cm

[ESIC—UDC Exam, 2016]

408. What would be the area of a rectangle whose area is equal to the area of a circle of radius 7 cm?

[SBI Jr. Associates (Pre.) Exam, 2016]

(*a*) 77 cm^2 (*b*) 154 cm^2
(*c*) 184 cm^2 (*d*) 180 cm^2

409. If the total surface area of a cube is 864 square cm, find the volume of the cube:

(*a*) 1728 cm^3 (*b*) 1624 cm^3
(*c*) 144 cm^3 (*d*) 1684 cm^3

[DMRC—Train Operator/Station Controller Exam, 2016]

410. The circumference of a circle is 10% more than the perimeter of a square. If the difference between the area of the circle and that of the square is 216 cm^2, how much does the diagonal of the square measure? (in cm)

[CET—Maharashtra (MBA), 2016]

(*a*) $14\sqrt{2}$ (*b*) 14
(*c*) 20 (*d*) $20\sqrt{2}$

411. A circular park, 42 m in diameter, has a path 3.5 m wide running around it on the outside. Find the cost of gravelling the path at ₹ 4 per sq. m.

[CLAT, 2016]

(*a*) ₹ 2048 (*b*) ₹ 1652
(*c*) ₹ 1672 (*d*) ₹ 2002

Direction: In the question below there is a question-statement and two statements numbered I and II. You have to decide whether the data given in the statements are sufficient to answer the questions. Read with the statements and given answer:

(*a*) If the data in statement I alone are sufficient to answer the question, while the data in statement II alone are not sufficient to answer the question.

(*b*) If the data in statement II alone are sufficient to answer the question, while the data in statement I alone are not sufficient to answer the question.

(*c*) If the data either in Statement I alone or statement II alone are sufficient to answer the question.

(*d*) If the data given in both Statements I and II together are not sufficient to answer the question.

(E) If the data in both Statements I and II together are necessary to answer the question.

412. What is the area of the circle?

I. Perimeter of the circle is 88 cm

II. Diameter of the circle is 28 cm

[IBPS—Bank Spl. Officer (Marketing) Exam, 2016]

413. The area of a rhombus with side 13 cm and one diagonal 10 cm will be **[CDS, 2016]**

(*a*) 140 cm^2 (*b*) 130 cm^2

(*c*) 120 cm^2 (*d*) 110 cm^2

414. A piece of wire when bent to form a circle will have a radius of 84 cm. If the wire is bent to form a square, the length of a side of the square is

[DMRC—Customer Relationship Assistant (CRA) Exam, 2016]

(*a*) 216 cm (*b*) 133 cm

(*c*) 132 cm (*d*) 168 cm

415. A hall 50m long and 45m broad is to be paved with square tiles. Find the largest tile as well as its number in the given options so that the tiles exactly fit in the hall.

[DMRC—Junior Engineer (Electrical) Exam, 2016]

(*a*) 36 sq. m and 80 tiles (*b*) 16 sq m and 80 tiles

(*c*) 25 sq. m and 90 tiles (*d*) 36 sq. m and 90 tiles

416. The perimeters of a square and a regular hexagon are equal. The ratio of the area of the hexagon to the area of the square is

[DMRC—Junior Engineer (Electrical) Exam, 2016]

(*a*) $2\sqrt{3}:1$ (*b*) $2\sqrt{3}:3$

(*c*) $3\sqrt{3}:2$ (*d*) $\sqrt{2}:3$

ANSWERS

1. (*c*)	2. (*d*)	3. (*e*)	4. (*c*)	5. (*b*)	6. (*c*)	7. (*c*)	8. (*d*)	9. (*a*)	10. (*a*)
11. (*c*)	12. (*b*)	13. (*a*)	14. (*e*)	15. (*b*)	16. (*c*)	17. (*b*)	18. (*b*)	19. (*b*)	20. (*b*)
21. (*e*)	22. (*b*)	23. (*d*)	24. (*b*)	25. (*a*)	26. (*a*)	27. (*d*)	28. (*a*)	29. (*a*)	30. (*c*)
31. (*b*)	32. (*b*)	33. (*b*)	34. (*c*)	35. (*d*)	36. (*d*)	37. (*c*)	38. (*d*)	39. (*c*)	40. (*b*)
41. (*d*)	42. (*c*)	43. (*d*)	44. (*b*)	45. (*a*)	46. (*c*)	47. (*d*)	48. (*b*)	49. (*c*)	50. (*b*)
51. (*b*)	52. (*b*)	53. (*a*)	54. (*a*)	55. (*d*)	56. (*b*)	57. (*e*)	58. (*a*)	59. (*e*)	60. (*c*)
61. (*b*)	62. (*c*)	63. (*c*)	64. (*a*)	65. (*a*)	66. (*c*)	67. (*c*)	68. (*d*)	69. (*a*)	70. (*b*)
71. (*c*)	72. (*d*)	73. (*b*)	74. (*b*)	75. (*c*)	76. (*c*)	77. (*c*)	78. (*b*)	79. (*a*)	80. (*b*)
81. (*b*)	82. (*e*)	83. (*c*)	84. (*c*)	85. (*e*)	86. (*c*)	87. (*c*)	88. (*c*)	89. (*d*)	90. (*d*)
91. (*d*)	92. (*d*)	93. (*b*)	94. (*d*)	95. (*a*)	96. (*c*)	97. (*a*)	98. (*c*)	99. (*b*)	100. (*d*)
101. (*d*)	102. (*c*)	103. (*b*)	104. (*b*)	105. (*a*)	106. (*e*)	107. (*b*)	108. (*b*)	109. (*c*)	110. (*d*)
111. (*c*)	112. (*c*)	113. (*c*)	114. (*b*)	115. (*c*)	116. (*d*)	117. (*c*)	118. (*a*)	119. (*c*)	120. (*a*)
121. (*c*)	122. (*b*)	123. (*d*)	124. (*d*)	125. (*c*)	126. (*d*)	127. (*b*)	128. (*d*)	129. (*c*)	130. (*c*)
131. (*d*)	132. (*b*)	133. (*d*)	134. (*d*)	135. (*d*)	136. (*d*)	137. (*d*)	138. (*c*)	139. (*b*)	140. (*d*)
141. (*a*)	142. (*c*)	143. (*b*)	144. (*a*)	145. (*c*)	146. (*c*)	147. (*c*)	148. (*b*)	149. (*c*)	150. (*d*)
151. (*c*)	152. (*d*)	153. (*b*)	154. (*d*)	155. (*c*)	156. (*a*)	157. (*c*)	158. (*d*)	159. (*c*)	160. (*c*)
161. (*b*)	162. (*e*)	163. (*b*)	164. (*b*)	165. (*b*)	166. (*d*)	167. (*b*)	168. (*a*)	169. (*d*)	170. (*d*)
171. (*c*)	172. (*d*)	173. (*b*)	174. (*b*)	175. (*c*)	176. (*b*)	177. (*c*)	178. (*b*)	179. (*b*)	180. (*b*)
181. (*a*)	182. (*d*)	183. (*b*)	184. (*d*)	185. (*a*)	186. (*a*)	187. (*a*)	188. (*c*)	189. (*c*)	190. (*c*)
191. (*c*)	192. (*d*)	193. (*d*)	194. (*c*)	195. (*c*)	196. (*d*)	197. (*d*)	198. (*c*)	199. (*c*)	200. (*b*)
201. (*c*)	202. (*d*)	203. (*c*)	204. (*d*)	205. (*a*)	206. (*e*)	207. (*d*)	208. (*c*)	209. (*c*)	210. (*c*)
211. (*b*)	212. (*b*)	213. (*a*)	214. (*a*)	215. (*c*)	216. (*d*)	217. (*b*)	218. (*c*)	219. (*b*)	220. (*c*)
221. (*d*)	222. (*a*)	223. (*b*)	224. (*b*)	225. (*c*)	226. (*b*)	227. (*a*)	228. (*a*)	229. (*a*)	230. (*c*)

231. (a)	232. (b)	233. (b)	234. (b)	235. (c)	236. (b)	237. (c)	238. (d)	239. (d)	240. (c)
241. (c)	242. (a)	243. (c)	244. (d)	245. (d)	246. (b)	247. (b)	248. (e)	249. (d)	250. (c)
251. (a)	252. (c)	253. (e)	254. (c)	255. (c)	256. (d)	257. (a)	258. (c)	259. (a)	260. (b)
261. (c)	262. (a)	263. (b)	264. (c)	265. (c)	266. (b)	267. (c)	268. (b)	269. (c)	270. (b)
271. (a)	272. (c)	273. (b)	274. (b)	275. (b)	276. (c)	277. (b)	278. (c)	279. (b)	280. (d)
281. (b)	282. (d)	283. (b)	284. (a)	285. (b)	286. (a)	287. (a)	288. (c)	289. (a)	290. (b)
291. (c)	292. (c)	293. (a)	294. (b)	295. (c)	296. (e)	297. (c)	298. (c)	299. (d)	300. (a)
301. (c)	302. (e)	303. (c)	304. (c)	305. (d)	306. (a)	307. (a)	308. (b)	309. (b)	310. (c)
311. (e)	312. (c)	313. (c)	314. (c)	315. (b)	316. (a)	317. (d)	318. (d)	319. (a)	320. (b)
321. (d)	322. (b)	323. (b)	324. (b)	325. (d)	326. (d)	327. (d)	328. (d)	329. (b)	330. (b)
331. (c)	332. (d)	333. (a)	334. (d)	335. (b)	336. (a)	337. (d)	338. (c)	339. (d)	340. (c)
341. (b)	342. (a)	343. (a)	344. (a)	345. (b)	346. (b)	347. (b)	348. (b)	349. (c)	350. (d)
351. (c)	352. (d)	353. (c)	354. (d)	355. (b)	356. (c)	357. (c)	358. (a)	359. (d)	360. (c)
361. (c)	362. (c)	363. (d)	364. (a)	365. (a)	366. (c)	367. (d)	368. (c)	369. (c)	370. (c)
371. (b)	372. (c)	373. (c)	374. (d)	375. (b)	376. (d)	377. (d)	378. (a)	379. (c)	380. (d)
381. (c)	382. (b)	383. (b)	384. (b)	385. (d)	386. (a)	387. (b)	388. (c)	389. (c)	390. (d)
391. (a)	392. (b)	393. (c)	394. (b)	395. (a)	396. (d)	397. (d)	398. (c)	399. (c)	400. (d)
401. (d)	402. (b)	403. (a)	404. (c)	405. (b)	406. (c)	407. (a)	408. (b)	409. (a)	410. (d)
411. (d)	412. (c)	413. (c)	414. (c)	415. (c)	416. (b)				

SOLUTIONS

1. Length = L, Width = $\frac{L}{2}$. $\therefore$ Area = $L \times \frac{L}{2} = \frac{1}{2}L^2$.

2. Area of the floor = (5.5×3.75) m^2 = 20.625 m^2.

   $\therefore$ Cost of paving = ₹ (800×20.625) = ₹ 16500.

3. Breadth = $\frac{\text{Area}}{\text{Length}} = \left(\frac{2100}{60}\right)$ m = 35 m.

   $\therefore$ Perimeter = 2(60 + 35) m = 190 m.

4. Let the breadth be b. Then,

   $25 \times b = 18 \times 10 \Leftrightarrow b = \left(\frac{18 \times 10}{25}\right)$ cm = 7.2 cm.

5. Perimeter of the plot = 2(90 + 50) = 280 m.

   $\therefore$ Number of poles = $\left(\frac{280}{5}\right) = 56$

6. Let breadth = x cm. Then, length = $\left(\frac{160}{100}x\right)$ cm $= \frac{8}{5}x$ cm.

   So, $\frac{8}{5}x - x = 24 \Leftrightarrow \frac{3}{5}x = 24 \Leftrightarrow x = \left(\frac{24 \times 5}{3}\right) = 40$.

   $\therefore$ Length = 64 cm, Breadth = 40 cm.

   Area = (64×40) cm^2 = 2560 cm^2.

7. Clearly, we have : $l = 9$ and $l + 2b = 37$ or $b = 14$.

   $\therefore$ Area = $(l \times b)$ = (9×14) sq. ft. = 126 sq. ft.

8. We have : $(l - b) = 23$ and $2(l + b) = 206$ or $(l + b) = 103$.

   Solving the two equations, we get : $l = 63$ and $b = 40$.

   $\therefore$ Area = $(l \times b)$ = (63×40) m^2 = 2520 m^2.

9. Area of the floor = $\left(\frac{510}{8.50}\right)$ m^2 = 60 m^2.

   $\therefore$ Breadth of the room = $\left(\frac{60}{8}\right)$ m = 7.5 m.

10. Let the breadth of the plot be x metres. Then, length of the plot = $(3x)$ meters.

    $x \times 3x = 7803 \Rightarrow 3x^2 = 7803 \Rightarrow x^2 = 2601$

    $\Rightarrow x = \sqrt{2601} = 51$ m.

11. Let the breadth of the rectangle be x metres. Then, length of the rectangle = $(2x)$ metres.

    $2(2x + x) = 60 \Rightarrow 6x = 60 \Rightarrow x = 10$.

    So, length = 20 m, breadth = 10 m.

    $\therefore$ Area = (20×10) m^2 = 200 m^2.

12. Let the length and breadth of the field be l and b km respectively.

    Then, $2(l + b) = 6$ or $l + b = 3$ and $lb = 2$.

    $(l - b)^2 = (l + b)^2 - 4\,lb = 3^2 - 4 \times 2 = 1 \Rightarrow (l - b) = 1$ m

13. Let the length and breadth of the rectangle be $(9x)$ cm and $(7x)$ cm respectively.

    Then, $9x \times 7x = 252 \Rightarrow 63x^2 = 252 \Rightarrow x^2 = 4 \Rightarrow x = 2$.

    So, length = 18 cm, breadth = 14 cm.

    $\therefore$ Perimeter = 2 (18 + 14) cm = 64 cm.

14. Let breadth = x metres. Then, length = $(x + 20)$ metres

    Perimeter = $\left(\frac{5300}{26.50}\right)$ m = 200 m.

    $\therefore 2[(x + 20) + x] = 200 \Leftrightarrow 2x + 20 = 100 \Leftrightarrow 2x = 80$

    $\Leftrightarrow x = 40$.

    Hence, length = $x + 20$ = 60 m.

15. Let the width of the table be x feet. Then, length of the table = $(x + 4)$ ft.

    $\therefore x(x + 4) = 45 \Rightarrow x^2 + 4x - 45 = 0$

    $\Rightarrow x^2 + 9x - 5x - 45 = 0$

    $\Rightarrow x(x + 9) - 5(x - 9) = 0$

    $\Rightarrow (x + 9)(x - 5) = 0 \Rightarrow x = 5$.

    Hence, length of the table = (5 + 4) ft = 9 ft.

16. Let the length and breadth of the field be $(5x)$ metres and $(3x)$ metres respectively.

Then, $2(5x + 3x) = 480 \Rightarrow 8x = 240 \Rightarrow x = 30$.

So, length = 150 m, breadth = 90 m.

$\therefore$ Area of the field = (150×90) sq. m = 13500 sq. m.

17. Length $= \left(\frac{1200}{30}\right) \text{m} = 40$ m.

Diagonal $= \sqrt{(40)^2 + (30)^2}$ m $= 50$ m.

Length to be fenced = $(40 + 30 + 50)$ m = 120 m.

$\therefore$ Cost of fencing = ₹ (120×100) = ₹ 12000.

18. Let length = x metres.

Then, breadth $= \left(\frac{60}{100}x\right)$ metres $= \left(\frac{3x}{5}\right)$ metres.

Perimeter $= \left[2\left(x + \frac{3x}{5}\right)\right]$ m $= \left(\frac{16x}{5}\right)$ m.

$\therefore \frac{16x}{5} = 800 \Leftrightarrow x = \left(\frac{800 \times 5}{16}\right) = 250$ m.

So, length = 250 m; breadth = 150 m.

$\therefore$ Area = (250×150) m^2 = 37500 m^2.

19. $\frac{l}{2(l+b)} = \frac{1}{3} \Rightarrow 3l = 2l + 2b \Rightarrow l = 2b \Rightarrow \frac{l}{b} = \frac{2}{1} = 2 : 1$.

20. Perimeter = Distance covered in 8 min.

$= \left(\frac{12000}{60} \times 8\right)$ m = 1600 m.

Let length = $3x$ metres and breadth = $2x$ metres.

Then, $2(3x + 2x) = 1600$ or $x = 160$.

Length = 480 m and Breadth = 320 m.

$\therefore$ Area = (480×320) m^2 = 153600 m^2.

21. Let breadth = x metres. Then, length $= \left(\frac{115x}{100}\right)$ metres.

$\therefore x \times \frac{115x}{100} = 460 \Leftrightarrow x^2 = \left(\frac{460 \times 100}{115}\right) = 400 \Leftrightarrow x = 20$.

22. Length of the field = (3.25×100) m = 325 m.

$\therefore$ Breadth of the field $= \left(\frac{52000}{325}\right)$ m $= 160$ m.

23. We have : $l = 20$ ft and $lb = 680$ sq. ft. So, $b = 34$ ft.

$\therefore$ Length of fencing = $(l + 2b) = (20 + 68)$ ft = 88 ft.

24. We have : $2b + l = 30 \Rightarrow l = 30 - 2b$.

Area = 100 m^2 $\Rightarrow l \times b = 100 \Rightarrow b(30 - 2b) = 100$

$\Rightarrow b^2 - 15b + 50 = 0$

$\Rightarrow (b - 10)(b - 5) = 0$

$\Rightarrow b = 10$ or $b = 5$.

When $b = 10$, $l = 10$ and when $b = 5$, $l = 20$.

Since the garden is rectangular, so its dimension is 20 m × 5 m.

25. Let the length and breadth of the rectangle be $3x$ and $2x$ respectively.

Then, perimeter = $2(3x + 2x) = 10x$.

And, area = $(3x \times 2x) = 6x^2$.

$\therefore \frac{10x}{6x^2} = \frac{5}{9} \Rightarrow 30x = 90 \Rightarrow x = 3$.

So, breadth = (2×3) m = 6 m.

26. Required perimeter = (AB + BC + CP + PQ + QR + RA) = AB + BC + (CP + QR) + (PQ + RA) = AB + BC + AB + BC = 2 (AB + BC)

= [2 (8 + 4)] cm = 24 cm.

27. Let the areas of the two parts be x and $(700 - x)$ hectares respectively. Then,

$[x - (700 - x)] = \frac{1}{5} \times \left[\frac{x + (700 - x)}{2}\right]$

$\Leftrightarrow 2x - 700 = 70 \Leftrightarrow x = 385$.

So, area of smaller part = $(700 - 385)$ hectares = 315 hectares.

28. When folded along breadth, we have :

$2\left(\frac{l}{2} + b\right) = 34$ or $l + 2b = 34$ ...(*i*)

When folded along length, we have :

$2\left(l + \frac{b}{2}\right) = 38$ or $2l + b = 38$ ...(*ii*)

Solving (*i*) and (*ii*), we get : $l = 14$ and $b = 10$.

$\therefore$ Area of the paper = (14×10) cm^2 = 140 cm^2.

29. Let breadth = x metres.

Then, length $= \left(\frac{3}{2}x\right)$ metres. Area $= \left(\frac{2}{3} \times 10000\right)$ m^2.

$\therefore \frac{3}{2}x \times x = \frac{2}{3} \times 10000 \Leftrightarrow x^2 = \frac{4}{9} \times 10000 \Leftrightarrow x = \frac{2}{3} \times 100$.

$\therefore$ Length $= \frac{3}{2}x = \left(\frac{3}{2} \times \frac{2}{3} \times 100\right)$ m = 100 m.

30. Let the area of the whole painting be x cm^2.

Then, $\frac{1}{4}x + 100 = \frac{3}{4}x \Rightarrow \frac{1}{2}x = 100 \Rightarrow x = 200$.

$\therefore$ Area of painting = 200 cm^2. Height = 10 cm.

Length of painting $= \left(\frac{200}{10}\right)$ cm = 20 cm.

31. Number of bricks $= \left(\frac{\text{Area of courtyard}}{\text{Area of 1 brick}}\right)$

$= \left(\frac{2500 \times 1600}{20 \times 10}\right) = 20000$.

32. Area of the floor = (14×9) m^2 = 126 m^2.

$\therefore$ Length of the carpet $= \left(\frac{126}{63} \times 100\right)$ m = 200 m

33. Length of the carpet $= \left(\frac{\text{Total cost}}{\text{Rate/m}}\right) = \left(\frac{8100}{45}\right)$ m = 180 m.

Area of the room = Area of the carpet

$= \left(180 \times \frac{75}{100}\right)$ m^2 = 135 m^2.

$\therefore$ Breadth of the room $= \left(\frac{\text{Area}}{\text{Length}}\right) = \left(\frac{135}{18}\right)$ m = 7.5 m.

34. Other side

$= \sqrt{\left(\frac{15}{2}\right)^2 - \left(\frac{9}{2}\right)^2}$ ft $= \sqrt{\frac{225}{4} - \frac{81}{4}}$ ft $= \sqrt{\frac{144}{4}}$ ft = 6 ft.

$\therefore$ Area of the closet = (6×4.5) sq. ft = 27 sq. ft.

35. Let breadth = x cm. Then, length = $3x$ cm.
$x^2 + (3x)^2 = (8\sqrt{10})^2 \Rightarrow 10x^2 = 640 \Rightarrow x^2 = 64 \Rightarrow x = 8.$
So, length = 24 cm and breadth = 8 cm.
$\therefore$ Perimeter = [2 (24 + 8)] cm = 64 cm.

36. $\sqrt{l^2 + b^2} = 3b \Rightarrow l^2 + b^2 = 9b^2 \Rightarrow l^2 = 8b^2$
$\Rightarrow \frac{l^2}{b^2} = 8 \Rightarrow \frac{l}{b} = \sqrt{8} = 2\sqrt{2} = \sqrt{2} : 1.$

37. Length of one side = $\frac{10}{2}$ cm = 5 cm.
Let the length of the other side be x cm.
Then, $x^2 + 5^2 = (10)^2 \Rightarrow x^2 = 75 \Rightarrow x = 5\sqrt{3}.$
$\therefore$ Area of the rectangle = $(5 \times 5\sqrt{3})\text{ cm}^2 = 25\sqrt{3}\text{ cm}^2.$

38. Let l and b be the length and breadth of the rectangle respectively.
Then, $\sqrt{l^2 + b^2} = 15 \Rightarrow (l^2 + b^2) = (15)^2 = 225.$
And, $l + b = 3 \Rightarrow (l - b)^2 = 9 \Rightarrow l^2 + b^2 - 2\,lb = 9$
$\Rightarrow 225 - 2lb = 9 \Rightarrow 2lb = 216 \Rightarrow lb = 108.$
Hence, area of the field = lb = 108 m².

39. $2(l + b) = 46$ or $l + b = 23$. Also, $lb = 120$.
$\therefore$ Diagonal = Diagonal = $\sqrt{l^2 + b^2} = \sqrt{(l+b)^2 - 2lb}$
$= \sqrt{(23)^2 - 240} = \sqrt{289} = 17$ m.

40. $\sqrt{l^2 + b^2} = \sqrt{41}$ or $l^2 + b^2 = 41$. Also, $lb = 20$.
$(l + b)^2 = (l^2 + b^2) + 2lb = 41 + 40 = 81 \Rightarrow (l + b) = 9.$
$\therefore$ Perimeter = $2(l + b)$ = 18 cm.

41. $\sqrt{l^2 + b^2} = 2d \Rightarrow l^2 + b^2 = 4d^2$. Also, $lb = \sqrt{3}\,d^2$.
$(l + b)^2 = (l^2 + b^2) + 2lb = 4d^2 + 2\sqrt{3}\,d^2$
$\Rightarrow (l + b) = \sqrt{(4 + 2\sqrt{3})d^2} = \sqrt{[(1)^2 + (\sqrt{3})^2 + 2\sqrt{3}]d^2}$
$= \sqrt{(\sqrt{3} + 1)^2 d^2} = (\sqrt{3} + 1)d.$
$\therefore$ Perimeter = $2(l + b) = 2(\sqrt{3} + 1)\,d.$

42. Let the length of the rectangle be x metres. Then, breadth of the rectangle = $\left(\frac{168}{x}\right)$ m.
$\therefore \sqrt{x^2 + \left(\frac{168}{x}\right)^2} = 25 \Rightarrow \sqrt{x^2 + \frac{28224}{x^2}} = 25$
$\Rightarrow x^2 + \frac{28224}{x^2} = 625$
$\Rightarrow x^4 - 625x^2 + 28224 = 0$
$\Rightarrow x^4 - 576x^2 - 49x^2 + 28224 = 0$
$\Rightarrow x^2(x^2 - 576) - 49(x^2 - 576) = 0$
$\Rightarrow (x^2 - 576)(x^2 - 49) = 0$
$\Rightarrow x^2 = 576$ or $x^2 = 49 \Rightarrow x = 24$ or $x = 7$.
Hence, length = 24 m and breadth = 7 m.

43. Length of diagonal = $\left(52 \times \frac{15}{60}\right)$ m = 13 m.
Sum of length and breadth = $\left(68 \times \frac{15}{60}\right)$ m = 17 m.
$\therefore \sqrt{l^2 + b^2} = 13$ or $l^2 + b^2 = 169$ and $l + b = 17$.
Area $= lb = \frac{1}{2}(2\,lb)$
$= \frac{1}{2}[(l+b)^2 - (l^2 + b^2)] = \frac{1}{2}[(17)^2 - 169]$
$= \frac{1}{2}(289 - 169) = 60\text{ m}^2.$

44. We have : $lb = 60$ and $\sqrt{l^2 + b^2} + l = 5b$.
Now, $l^2 + b^2 = (5b - l)^2$
$\Rightarrow 24b^2 - 10lb = 0$
$\Rightarrow 24b^2 - 600 = 0$
$\Rightarrow b^2 = 25 \Rightarrow b = 5.$
$\therefore l = \left(\frac{60}{5}\right)$ m = 12 m. So, length of the carpet = 12 m.

45. Let length = $(3x)$ metres and breadth = $(2x)$ metres.
Then, $(3x + 5) \times 2x = 2600$
$\Leftrightarrow 6x^2 + 10x - 2600 = 0$
$\Leftrightarrow 3x^2 + 5x - 1300 = 0$
$\Leftrightarrow (3x + 65)(x - 20) = 0 \Leftrightarrow x = 20.$
$\therefore$ Breadth = $2x$ = 40 m.

46. Let the length and breadth of the carpet be l and b metres respectively and let the rate of carpeting be ₹ x per metre.
Then, $lbx = 120$ ...(*i*)
And, $l(b - 4)x = \Rightarrow lbx - 4lx = 100 \Rightarrow 4lx = 20$ ...(*ii*)
Dividing (*i*) by (*ii*), we get: $\frac{lbx}{4lx} = \frac{120}{20} \Rightarrow b = 24$ m.

47. Let breadth = x cm. Then, length = $(x + 8)$ m.
$\therefore (x + 8)\,x = (x + 15)(x - 4)$
$\Leftrightarrow x^2 + 8x = x^2 + 11x - 60$
$\Leftrightarrow x = 20.$
So, length = 28 m and breadth = 20 m.

48. Let the length and breadth of the plot be l and b metres respectively.
Then, $lb = 480$
And, $(l + 5)(b + 5) = 725 \Rightarrow lb + 5(l + b) + 25 = 725$
$\Rightarrow 5(l + b) + 505 = 725 \Rightarrow (l + b) = \frac{220}{5} = 44.$ [$\because lb = 480$]
$\therefore$ Length of the fence = $2(l + b) = (2 \times 44)$ m = 88 m.

49. Let the length and breadth of the rectangle be l and b metres respectively.
Then, area of the rectangle = lb.
$lb - (l - 5)(b + 3) = 9$
$\Rightarrow lb - (lb + 3l - 5b - 15) = 9$
$\Rightarrow lb - lb - 3l + 5b + 15 = 9$
$\Rightarrow 3l - 5b = 6$ ...(*i*)
And, $(l + 3)(b + 2) - lb = 67$

$\Rightarrow lb + 2l + 3b + 6 - lb = 67$

$\Rightarrow 2l + 3b = 61$ ...(ii)

Multiplying (i) by 2 and (ii) by 3 and subtracting, we get: $-19b = -171$ or $b = 9$.

Putting $b = 9$ in (i) we get: $3l = 51$ or $l = 17$ m.

50. Let original length = l metres and original breadth = b metres.

Original area = (lb) m^2.

New length = $\left(\frac{150}{100}l\right)$ m $= \left(\frac{3}{2}l\right)$ m;

New breadth = $\left(\frac{150}{100}b\right)$ m $= \left(\frac{3}{2}b\right)$ m.

New area = $\left(\frac{3}{2}l \times \frac{3}{2}b\right)$ m^2 $= \left(\frac{9}{4}lb\right)$ m^2.

$\therefore$ Increase % = $\left(\frac{5}{4}lb \times \frac{1}{lb} \times 100\right)\% = 125\%$.

51. Original breadth = 3 m,

Original length = (1.44×3) m = 4.32 m.

New breadth = (125% of 3) m = $\left(\frac{125}{100} \times 3\right)$ m = 3.75 m.

New length = (140% of 4.32) m = $\left(\frac{140}{100} \times 4.32\right)$ m = 6.048 m.

Original area = (4.32×3) m^2 = 12.96 m^2.

New area = (6.048×3.75) m^2 = 22.68 m^2.

Increase in area = $(22.68 - 12.96)$ m^2 = 9.72 m^2.

$\therefore$ Increase in cost = ₹ (9.72×45) = ₹ 437.40.

52. Let the original length and breadth of the rectangle be l and b respectively.

Then, original area = lb.

New length = 110% of $l = \frac{11}{10}l$;

New breadth = 90% of $b = \frac{9}{10}b$.

New area = $\left(\frac{11}{10}l \times \frac{9}{10}b\right) = \frac{99}{100}lb$.

Decrease in area = $\left(lb - \frac{99}{100}lb\right) = \frac{lb}{100}$.

$\therefore$ Decrease % = $\left(\frac{lb}{100} \times \frac{1}{lb} \times 100\right)\% = 1\%$.

53. Let the actual length and width of the rectangle be l and b respectively.

Then, measured length = 110% of $l = \frac{11}{10}l$;

measured width = 95% of $b = \frac{19}{20}b$.

Actual area = lb.

Measured area = $\left(\frac{11}{10}l \times \frac{19}{20}b\right) = \frac{209}{200}lb$.

Error in measurement = $\left(\frac{209}{200}lb - lb\right) = \frac{9}{200}lb$.

$\therefore$ Error% = $\left(\frac{9}{200}lb \times \frac{1}{lb} \times 100\right)\% = 4.5\%$.

54. Let the original length and breadth of the rectangle be l and b respectively.

New length = 150% of $l = \frac{3}{2}l$;

New breadth = 75% of $b = \frac{3}{4}b$.

Original area = lb. New area = $\left(\frac{3}{2}l \times \frac{3}{4}b\right) = \frac{9}{8}lb$.

Increase in area = $\left(\frac{9}{8}lb - lb\right) = \frac{lb}{8}$.

$\therefore$ Increase % = $\left(\frac{lb}{8} \times \frac{1}{lb} \times 100\right)\% = 12.5\%$.

55. Let original length = x and original breadth = y.

Decrease in area = $xy - \left(\frac{80}{100}x \times \frac{90}{100}y\right)$

$= \left(xy - \frac{18}{25}xy\right) = \frac{7}{25}xy$.

$\therefore$ Decrease% = $\left(\frac{7}{25}xy \times \frac{1}{xy} \times 100\right)\%$ = 28%.

56. Let original length = x and original breadth = y. Then, original area = xy.

New length = $\frac{x}{2}$; New breadth = $3y$;

New area = $\left(\frac{x}{2} \times 3y\right) = \frac{3}{2}xy$.

$\therefore$ Increase% = $\left(\frac{1}{2}xy \times \frac{1}{xy} \times 100\right)\%$ = 50%.

57. Let original length = x and original breadth = y.

Then, original area = xy.

New area = $\left[\frac{(100-r)}{100} \times x\right]\left[\frac{(105+r)}{100} \times y\right]$

$= \left[\left(\frac{10500 - 5r - r^2}{10000}\right)xy\right]$

$\therefore \left(\frac{10500 - 5r - r^2}{10000}\right)xy = xy$

$\Leftrightarrow r^2 + 5r - 500 = 0 \Leftrightarrow (r + 25)(r - 20) = 0 \Leftrightarrow r = 20$.

58. Let original length = x and original breadth = y. Then original area = xy.

New length = $\frac{160x}{100} = \frac{8x}{5}$. Let new breadth = z.

Then, $\frac{8x}{5} \times z = xy \Rightarrow z = \frac{5y}{8}$.

$\therefore$ Decrease in breadth = $\left(\frac{3y}{8} \times \frac{1}{y} \times 100\right)\% = 37\frac{1}{2}\%$.

59. Let original length = x and original breadth = y. Then, original area = xy.

New length = $\frac{130}{100}x = \frac{13x}{10}$. New breadth = y.

New area $= \left(\frac{13x}{10} \times y\right) = \frac{13xy}{10}.$

$\therefore$ Required ratio $= \left(\frac{\frac{13xy}{10}}{xy}\right) = \frac{13}{10} = 13 : 10.$

60. Let the original length and breadth of the rectangle be l and b respectively
Then, original area $= lb$.
New area $= 2lb$.

New breadth $= 50\%$ of $b = \frac{b}{2}$. New length $= \frac{2lb}{\left(\frac{b}{2}\right)} = 4l.$

Increase in length $= (4l - l) = 3l$.

$\therefore$ Increase % $= \left(3l \times \frac{1}{l} \times 100\right)\% = 300\%$.

61. Let the original length and breadth of the rectangle be l and b respectively.
Then, original area $= lb$.

New length $= 120\%$ of $l = \frac{6}{5}l$. New area $= 150\%$ of $lb = \frac{3lb}{2}$.

New breadth $= \left(\frac{3lb}{2} \times \frac{5}{6l}\right) = \frac{5b}{4}.$

Increase in breadth $= \left(\frac{5b}{4} - b\right) = \frac{b}{4}.$

$\therefore$ Increase% $= \left(\frac{b}{4} \times \frac{1}{b} \times 100\right)\% = 25\%$

62. Let the length and breadth of the rectangle be l and b respectively.

Then, 80% of $l = b \Rightarrow b = \frac{4}{5}l.$

(1) Area of rectangle $= lb = \left(l \times \frac{4}{5}l\right) = \frac{4}{5}l^2.$

Area of square $= \left(\frac{4}{5}l\right)^2 = \frac{16}{25}l^2.$

Difference $= \left(\frac{4}{5}l^2 - \frac{16}{25}l^2\right) = \frac{4l^2}{25}.$

$\therefore$ Percentage difference $= \left(\frac{4l^2}{25} \times \frac{5}{4l^2} \times 100\right)\% = 20\%.$

(2) Perimeter of square $= 4 \times \frac{4}{5}l = \frac{16}{5}l.$

Perimeter of rectangle $= 2\left(l + \frac{4}{5}l\right) = \frac{18}{5}l.$

Difference $= \left(\frac{18}{5}l - \frac{16}{5}l\right) = \frac{2}{5}l.$

$\therefore$ Percentage difference $= \left(\frac{2}{5}l \times \frac{5}{18l} \times 100\right)\% = 11\frac{1}{9}\%$

(3) Diagonal of square $= \sqrt{\left(\frac{4}{5}l\right)^2 + \left(\frac{4}{5}l\right)^2} = \sqrt{\frac{32}{25}l^2} = \frac{4\sqrt{2}}{5}l$

$= \frac{4 \times 1.414}{5}l = 1.13l.$

Diagonal of rectangle $= \sqrt{l^2 + \left(\frac{4}{5}l\right)^2} = \sqrt{l^2 + \frac{16}{25}l^2}$

$= \sqrt{\frac{41}{25}l^2} = \frac{\sqrt{41}}{5}l = \frac{6.403}{5}l = 1.28\,l.$

Difference $= (1.28\,l - 1.13\,l) = 0.15\,l.$

Percentage difference $= \left(\frac{0.15\,l}{1.28\,l} \times 100\right)\% = 11.72\% \approx 12\%.$

63. Area of the sheet $= (30 \times 15)$ cm² $= 45$ cm².
Area used for typing $= [(30 - 5) \times (15 - 2.5)]$ cm² $= 312.5$ cm².

$\therefore$ Required percentage $= \left(\frac{312.5}{450} \times 100\right)\% = 69.4\% \approx 70\%.$

64. Area of the carpet $= [(5 - 0.20) \times (8 - 0.20)]$ m² $= (4.8 \times 7.8)$ m² $= 37.44$ m².
$\therefore$ Cost of carpeting = ₹ (37.44 × 18) = ₹ 673.92.

65. Area of the footpath $= [\{(80 + 2) \times (50 + 2\} - (80 \times 50)]$ m²
$= [(82 \times 52) - (80 \times 50)]$ m² $= (4264 - 4000)$ m² $= 264$ m².

66. Let the length of the field be x metres. Then, breadth of the field $= \left(\frac{3}{4}x\right)$ metres.

$x \times \frac{3}{4}x = 300 \Rightarrow x^2 = 300 \times \frac{4}{3} = 400 \Rightarrow x = 20.$

So. length = 20 m, breadth = 15 m.
$\therefore$ Area of the garden
$= [\{(20 + 3) \times (15 + 3)\} - (20 \times 15)]$ m²
$= [(23 \times 18) - (20 \times 15)]$ m² $= (414 - 300)$ m² $= 114$ m².

67. $2(l + b) = 340$ (Given).
Area of the boundary
$= [(l + 2)(b + 2) - lb] = 2(l + b) + 4 = 344.$
$\therefore$ Cost of gardening = ₹ (344 × 10) = ₹ 3440.

68. $lb = 96$ (Given)
Area of pathway $= [(l - 4)(b - 4) - lb] = 16 - 4(l + b)$, which cannot be determined.
So, data is inadequate.

69. Let the width of the path be x.
Then, $[(38 \times 32) - \{(38 - 2x)(32 - 2x)\}] = 600$
$\Rightarrow [1216 - (1216 - 140x + 4x^2)]$
$\Rightarrow 4x^2 - 140x + 600 = 0 \Rightarrow x^2 - 35x + 150 = 0$
$\Rightarrow x^2 - 30x - 5x + 150 = 0 \Rightarrow (x - 30)(x - 5) = 0$
$\Rightarrow x = 5$ m. $[\because x \neq 30]$

70. Let the width of walk be x metres. Then,
$(20 - 2x)(10 - 2x) = 96 \Leftrightarrow 4x^2 + 60x - 104 = 0$
$\Leftrightarrow x^2 + 15x - 26 = 0$
$\Leftrightarrow (x - 13)(x - 2) = 0 \Leftrightarrow x = 2$ $[\because x \neq 13]$

71. Length of the fence $= 2(60 + 40)$ m $= 200$ m.
Cost of fencing = ₹ (200 × 50) = ₹ 10000.
Area of the road $= [(64 \times 44) - (60 \times 40)]$ m²
$= (2816 - 2400)$ m² $= 416$ m².

Let the cost of tiling the rood be ₹ x per sq. m.
$\therefore 416x + 10000 = 51600 \Rightarrow 416x = 41600 \Rightarrow x =$ ₹ 100.

72. Area of the roads = $(80 \times 10 + 60 \times 10 - 10 \times 10)\ m^2$
$= 1300\ m^2$.
$\therefore$ Cost of gravelling = ₹ (1300×30) = ₹ 39000.

73. Area of the field = $(25 \times 15)\ m^2 = 375\ m^2$.
Area of the passages = $(25 \times 2 + 15 \times 2 - 2 \times 2)\ m^2$
$= 76\ m^2$.
Area under grass = $(375 - 76)\ m^2 = 299\ m^2$.

74. Area of the park = $(60 \times 40)\ m^2 = 2400\ m^2$.
Area of the lawn = $2109\ m^2$.
$\therefore$ Area of the crossroads = $(2400 - 2109)\ m^2 = 291\ m^2$.
Let the width of the road be x metres. Then,
$60x + 40x - x^2 = 291 \Leftrightarrow x^2 - 100x + 291 = 0 \Leftrightarrow (x - 97)(x - 3) = 0 \Leftrightarrow x = 3$ $[\because x \neq 97]$.

75. Let the length and breadth of each card be l and b inches respectively.
Then, area of each card = (lb) sq.inches
Area of the rectangle = Sum of areas of 9 cards = $(9\ lb)$ sq. inches.
So, $9\ lb = 180 \Rightarrow lb = 20$ ...(*i*)
Length of rectangle = $(5b)$ inches. Breadth of rectangle = $(l + b)$ inches.
Area of rectangle = $5b(l + b)$ sq. inches
$\therefore\ 5b(l + b) = 180 \Rightarrow lb + b^2 = 36$
$\Rightarrow b^2 = 36 - 20 = 16 \Rightarrow b = 4$.
Putting $b = 4$ in (*i*), we get: $l = 5$.
So, length of rectangle = (5×4) inches = 20 inches.
Breadth of rectangle = $(5 + 4)$ inches = 9 inches.
Perimeter of rectangle = $2(20 + 9)$ inches = 58 inches.

76. Area of the path = $[(26 \times 16) - (24 \times 14)]\ m^2 = (416 - 336)\ m^2 = 80\ m^2$.
$\therefore$ Number of tiles required to cover the path
$$= \frac{\text{Area of path}}{\text{Area of each tile}} = \left(\frac{80 \times 100 \times 100}{20 \times 20}\right) = 2000.$$

77. (*a*) Diagonal of the rectangle =
$\sqrt{(51)^2 + (49)^2}\ m = \sqrt{2601 + 2401}\ m = \sqrt{5002}\ m$.
Diagonal of the square = $50\sqrt{2}\ m = \sqrt{5000}\ m$.
(*b*) Diagonals of a square intersect at right angles but those of a rectangle do not.
(*c*) Perimeter of rectangle = $2(51 + 49)$ m = 200 m.
Perimeter of square = (4×50) m = 200 m.
(*d*) Area of rectangle = $(50 \times 50)\ m^2 = 2500\ m^2$.

78. $\text{Side} = \sqrt{2550.25} = \sqrt{\frac{255025}{100}} = \frac{505}{10} = 50.5\ m.$

79. Side of the square = $\left(\frac{48}{4}\right) cm = 12\ cm.$
Area of the square = $(12 \times 12)\ cm^2 = 144\ cm^2$.

80. Area of given square = $(25 \times 25)\ m^2 = 625\ m^2$.
Area of new square = $(625 \times 4)\ m^2 = 2500\ m^2$.
$\therefore$ Side of new square = $\sqrt{2500}\ m = 50\ m$.

81. Length of rectangle = 25 cm;
Breadth of rectangle = 15 cm.
Area of rectangle = $(25 \times 15)\ cm^2 = 375\ cm^2$.
$\therefore$ Area of square = $\left(\frac{3}{5} \times 375\right) cm^2 = 225\ cm^2$ Side of square
$= \sqrt{225}\ cm = 15\ cm.$
Perimeter of square = (4×15) cm = 60 cm.

82. Area of square = $\sqrt{1024}\ cm = 32\ cm.$
Length of rectangle = (2×32) cm = 64 cm. Breadth of rectangle = $(32 - 12)$ cm = 20 cm.
$\therefore$ Required ratio = 64 : 20 = 16 : 5.

83. Area of square $ABCD = 36\ m^2$. $AB = \sqrt{36}\ m = 6\ m.$
$AE = \frac{1}{2} \times AB = 3\ m.$
Area of rectangle $AEFG = 36\ m^2$.
$\therefore\ AE \times EF = 36 \Rightarrow EF = \left(\frac{36}{3}\right) = 12\ m.$
Perimeter of rectangle $AEFG = 2(AE + EF)$
$= [2\ (3 + 12)]$ m = 30 m.

84. $\text{Area} = \frac{\text{Total cost}}{\text{Rate}} = \left(\frac{6165}{685}\right) \text{hectares} = (9 \times 10000)\ m^2.$
$\therefore$ Side of the square = $\sqrt{90000}\ m = 300\ m.$
Perimeter of the field = (300×4) m = 1200 m.
Cost of fencing = ₹ (1200×48.75) = ₹ 58500.

85. Perimeter of the square = Perimeter of the rectangle
$= 2(12 + 10)$ cm = 44 cm.
Side of the square = $\left(\frac{44}{4}\right) cm = 11\ cm$
Area of the rectangle = $(12 \times 10)\ cm^2 = 120\ cm^2$.
Area of the square = $(11 \times 11)\ cm^2 = 121\ cm^2$.
$\therefore$ Required percentage = $\left(\frac{1}{120} \times 100\right)\% = \frac{5}{6}\%.$

86. $\frac{\text{Monthly income of family A}}{\text{Monthly income of family B}} = \frac{\text{Area of square A}}{\text{Area of square B}}$
$\Rightarrow \frac{40000}{x} = \frac{2^2}{3^2} \Rightarrow x = \left(\frac{40000 \times 9}{4}\right) = 90000.$

87. Let $AB = x$. Then $BC = 3x$.
$BJ = AB = x$, $HJ = AB = x$,
$HG = BC = 3x$.
$\frac{\text{Area } BCDJ}{\text{Area } HJFG} = \frac{BC \times BJ}{HG \times HJ} = \frac{3x \times x}{3x \times x} = 1.$

88. The sides of the five squares are
$\left(\frac{24}{4}\right), \left(\frac{32}{4}\right), \left(\frac{40}{4}\right), \left(\frac{76}{4}\right), \left(\frac{80}{4}\right)$
i.e., 6 cm, 8 cm, 10 cm, 19 cm, 20 cm.
$\therefore$ Area of the new square = $[6^2 + 8^2 + (10)^2 + (19)^2 + (20)^2]$
$= (36 + 64 + 100 + 361 + 400)\ cm^2 = 961\ cm^2$.
Side of the new square = $\sqrt{961}$ cm = 31 cm.
Perimeter of the new square = (4×31) cm = 124 cm.

89. Area of each small square = $\left(\frac{400}{64}\right) cm^2 = 6.25 \ cm^2$.

Side of each small square = $\sqrt{6.25}$ cm = 2.5 cm.

Since there are 8 squares along each side of the chessboard, we have :

Side = [(8 × 2.5) + 6] cm = 26 cm.

90. PQ = $\sqrt{100} + \sqrt{16} + \sqrt{49} = (10 + 4 + 7) = 21$.

Side of middle square = $\sqrt{16} = 4$.

Reduction in PQ = (21 – 19) = 2.

New side of middle square = (4 – 2) = 2.

∴ Reduction in area of middle square = $(4^2 - 2^2) = 12$.

91. Number of tiles required

$= \frac{\text{Area of hall}}{\text{Area of each tile}} = \left(\frac{60 \times 40}{0.4 \times 0.4}\right) = 15000.$

∴ Total cost of tiles = ₹ (15000 × 5) ₹ 75000.

92. Number of marbles = $\left(\frac{300 \times 300}{20 \times 30}\right) = 150$.

93. Area of each slab = $\left(\frac{72}{50}\right) m^2 = 1.44 \ m^2$.

∴ Length of each slab = $\sqrt{1.44}$ m = 1.2 m = 120 cm.

94. Length of rectangle = 4 ft = (4 × 12) inch = 48 inch.

Width of rectangle = 6 ft = (6 × 12) inch = 72 inch.

∴ Number of squares = $\frac{48 \times 72}{\frac{1}{2} \times \frac{1}{2}} = 13824$.

95. Area left after laying black tiles = [(20 – 4) × (10 – 4)] sq. ft = 96 sq. ft.

Area under white tiles = $\left(\frac{1}{3} \times 96\right)$ sq. ft = 32 sq. ft

Area under blue tiles = (96 – 32) sq. ft = 64 sq. ft.

Number of blue tiles = $\frac{64}{(2 \times 2)} = 16$.

96. Let the side of each square formed by fencing parallel to breadth be x metres and that of each square formed by fencing parallel to length be y metres.

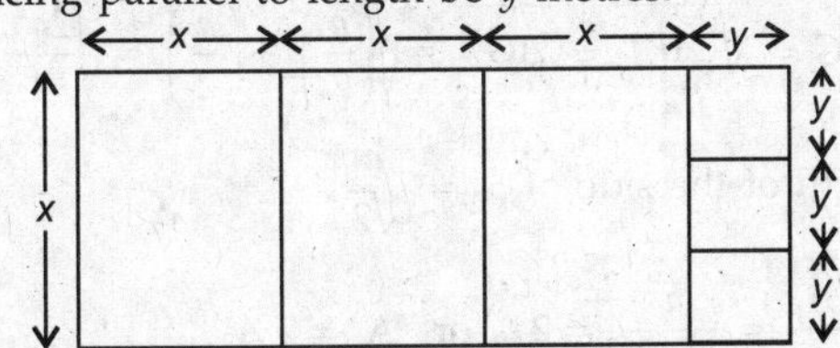

Then, $3x^2 + 3y^2 = 4320 \Rightarrow x^2 + y^2 = 1440$ ...(i)

And, $x(3x + y) = 4320 \Rightarrow 3x^2 + xy = 3(x^2 + y^2)$

$\Rightarrow xy = 3y^2 \Rightarrow x = 3y$ ...(ii)

From (i) and (ii), we have: $(3y)^2 + y^2 = 1440 \Rightarrow 10y^2 = 1440 \Rightarrow y^2 = 144 \Rightarrow y = 12$

So, x = 36.

Length of rectangular plot = $3x + y$ = (3 × 36 + 12) m = 120 m.

Breadth of rectangular plot = x = 36 m.

97. Maximum possible size of a flower bed = (H.C.F of 110, 130, 190) sq. m = 10 sq. m

∴ Maximum possible length = $\left(\frac{10}{2}\right)$ m = 5 m.

98. Length of largest tile = H.C.F. of $12\frac{1}{4}$ m and 7 m = H.C.F. of 12.25 m and 7 m

= H.C.F. of 1225 cm and 700 cm = 175 cm.

99. Length of largest lile = H.C.F. of 624 cm and 480 cm = 48 cm.

Area of each tile = $(48 \times 48) \ cm^2$.

∴ Required number of tiles = $\left(\frac{624 \times 480}{48 \times 48}\right) = 130$.

100. Length of the room = (7 + 7) m = 14 m. Breadth of the room = 7 m.

∴ Area of the room = $(14 \times 7) \ m^2 = 98 \ m^2$.

101. Let the sides of the rectangle be x metres and $(x + 48)$ metres.

Then, $2(x + x + 48) = 160 \Rightarrow 4x + 96 = 160 \Rightarrow 4x = 64 \Rightarrow x = 16$.

So, sides of the rectangle are 16 m and 64 m.

Area of the rectangle = $(16 \times 64) \ m^2 = 1024 \ m^2$. Area of the square = $1024 \ m^2$.

∴ Side of the square = $\sqrt{1024}$ m = 32 m.

102. Required area = $[(2 \times 3) + (3 \times 3) + (2 \times 3)] \ cm^2 = (6 + 9 + 6) \ cm^2 = 21 \ cm^2$.

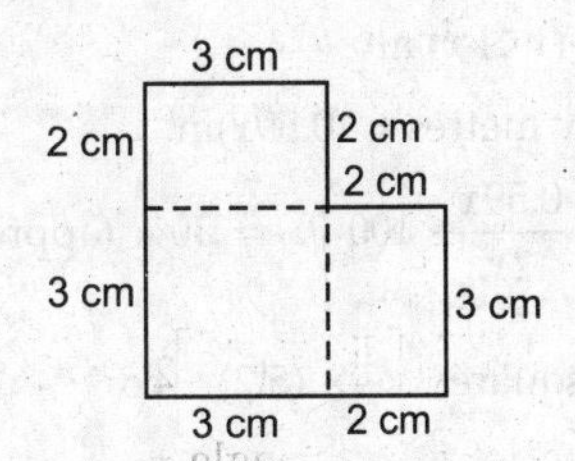

103. Side of the square = 12 cm

Area of rectangle = $[(12 \times 12) - 4] \ cm^2 = 140 \ cm^2$.

∴ Breadth = $\frac{\text{Area}}{\text{Length}} = \frac{140}{14} = 10$ cm.

Hence, perimeter = $2(l + b)$ = 2 (14 + 10) cm = 48 cm.

104. Let the side of the square be x cm. Then, its area = $x^2 \ cm^2$.

Area of the rectangle = $(3x^2) \ cm^2$.

∴ $40 \times \frac{3}{2} \times x = 3x^2 \Leftrightarrow x = 20$.

105. Perimeter of square = 160 m.

Side of square = $\left(\frac{160}{4}\right)$ m = 40 m.

Area of square = $(40 \times 40) \ m^2 = 1600 \ m^2$

Area of rectangle = $(1600 - 100) \ m^2 = 1500 \ m^2$.

Let the length and breadth of the rectangle be l and b respectively.

Then, $2(l + b) = 160 \Rightarrow l + b = 80 \Rightarrow b = 80 - l$.

∴ $lb = 1500 \Rightarrow l(80 - l) = 1500 \Rightarrow 80l - l^2 = 1500$

$\Rightarrow l^2 - 80l + 1500 = 0 \Rightarrow (l - 50)(l - 30) = 0$

$\Rightarrow l = 50$.

Hence, length = 50 m, breadth = 30 m.

106. Let the side of the square be x cm. Then, breadth of the rectangle $= \left(\frac{2}{3}x\right)$ cm. $90 \times \frac{2}{3}x = 4x^2 \Rightarrow 6x = 90 \Rightarrow x = 15$ cm.

107. Perimeter $= \frac{\text{Total cost}}{\text{Cost per m}} = \frac{10080}{20}$ m = 504 m.

Side of the square $= \frac{504}{4}$ m = 126 m.

Breadth of the pavement = 3 m.

Side of inner square = (126 – 6) m = 120 m.

Area of the pavement $= [(126 \times 126) - (120 \times 120)]\ \text{m}^2$

$= [(126 + 120)(126 - 120)]\ \text{m}^2$

$= (246 \times 6)\ \text{m}^2$.

∴ Cost of pavement = ₹ (246 × 6 × 50) = ₹ 73800.

108. Let the length of the outer edge be x metres. Then, length of the inner edge = $(x - 6)$ m.

$\therefore x^2 - (x-6)^2 = 1764 \Leftrightarrow x^2 - (x^2 - 12x + 36) = 1764$

$\Leftrightarrow 12x = 1800 \Leftrightarrow x = 150.$

∴ Required perimeter = $(4x)$ m = (4 × 150) m = 600 m.

109. Let the side of the square be x metres.

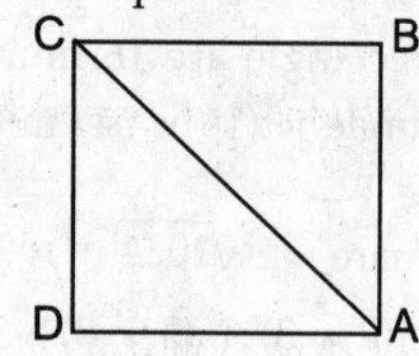

Then, $AB + BC = 2x$ metres.

$AC = \sqrt{2}\,x = (1.41\,x)$ m

Saving on $2x$ metres = $(0.59x)$m.

Saving% $= \left(\frac{0.59x}{2x} \times 100\right)\%$ = 30% (approx.).

110. Area of the square $= \left[\frac{1}{2} \times (5.2)^2\right] \text{cm}^2$

$= \left(\frac{1}{2} \times 27.04\right) \text{cm}^2 = 13.52\ \text{cm}^2.$

111. Speed of the man $= \left(4 \times \frac{5}{18}\right)$ m/s $= \frac{10}{9}$ m/s.

Time taken = (3 × 60) sec = 180 sec.

Length of diagonal = (speed × time) $= \left(\frac{10}{9} \times 180\right)$ m = 200 m.

Area of the field $= \frac{1}{2} \times (\text{diagonal})^2$

$= \left(\frac{1}{2} \times 200 \times 200\right) \text{m}^2 = 20000\ \text{m}^2.$

112. $d = \sqrt{2} \times l \Rightarrow l = \frac{20}{\sqrt{2}}.$

∴ Perimeter = $(4l)$ cm $= \left(\frac{4 \times 20}{\sqrt{2}} \times \frac{\sqrt{2}}{\sqrt{2}}\right)$ cm $= 40\sqrt{2}$ cm.

113. Side $= \sqrt{69696}$ cm = 264 cm.

$\therefore d = \sqrt{2} \times \text{side} = (264\sqrt{2})$ cm = (264 × 1.414) cm = 373.296 cm.

114. Area $= (45 \times 40)\ \text{m}^2 \Leftrightarrow \frac{1}{2} \times (\text{diagonal})^2$

$= 1800 \Leftrightarrow$ diagonal = 60 m.

115. Area = 0.5 hectare = (0.5 × 10000) m² = 5000 m².

$\therefore \frac{1}{2}(\text{diagonal})^2 = 5000 \Rightarrow \text{diagonal} = \sqrt{10000} = 100$ m.

116. Let the length of the diagonal be x km.

Then, $\frac{1}{2}x^2 = 50 \Rightarrow x^2 = 100 \Rightarrow x = \sqrt{100} = 10$ km

$= \left(\frac{10}{1.6}\right)$ miles = 6.25 miles [∵ 1 mile = 1.609 km]

117. Let breadth be x metres.

Then, length = 120% of $x = \left(\frac{120}{100}x\right) = \frac{6x}{5}$ m.

Required ratio $= \left(\frac{6x}{5} \times x \times \frac{1}{x \times x}\right) = 6 : 5.$

118. A square and a rectangle with equal areas will satisfy the relation $p_1 < p_2$.

119. Take a square of side 4 cm and a rectangle having l = 6 cm, b = 2 cm.

Then, perimeter of square = perimeter of rectangle.

Area of square = 16 cm², area of rectangle = 12 cm².

∴ A > B.

120. $d_1 = 4\sqrt{2}$ cm $\Rightarrow$ area $= \frac{1}{2}d_1^2 = \frac{1}{2} \times (4\sqrt{2})^2 = 16\ \text{cm}^2.$

Area of new square = (2 × 16) cm² = 32 cm².

$\therefore \frac{1}{2}d_2^2 = 32 \Rightarrow d_2^2 = 64 \Rightarrow d_2 = 8$ cm.

121. Required ratio $= \frac{a^2}{(\sqrt{2}\,a)^2} = \frac{a^2}{2a^2} = \frac{1}{2} = 1 : 2.$

122. Let $ABCD$ be the square S_1 and $EFGH$ be the square S_2.

Let the length of each side of S_1 be a.

Then, $AF = AG = \frac{a}{2}$.

So $FG = \sqrt{(AF)^2 + (AG)^2} = \sqrt{\left(\frac{a}{2}\right)^2 + \left(\frac{a}{2}\right)^2} = \sqrt{\frac{2a^2}{4}} = \frac{a}{\sqrt{2}}.$

Length of the side of $S_2 = \frac{a}{\sqrt{2}}$.

$\therefore \frac{A_1}{A_2} = \frac{a^2}{\left(\frac{a}{\sqrt{2}}\right)^2} = 2$ or $A_1 = 2A_2$.

123. Let the length of diagonal of the bigger square be x and that of the smaller square be y.

Then, $A = \frac{1}{2}x^2$ or $x = \sqrt{2A}$.

And, $\frac{A}{2} = \frac{1}{2}y^2$ or $y = \sqrt{A}$.

$\therefore$ Required ratio $= \frac{y}{x} = \frac{\sqrt{A}}{\sqrt{2A}} = 1 : \sqrt{2}.$

124. Let the diagonals be $2d$ and d.

Then, ratio of their areas $= \dfrac{\frac{1}{2}\times(2d)^2}{\frac{1}{2}\times d^2} = \dfrac{4d^2}{d^2} = \dfrac{4}{1} = 4:1.$

125. $\dfrac{a^2}{b^2} = \dfrac{225}{256} = \dfrac{(15)^2}{(16)^2} \Leftrightarrow \dfrac{a}{b} = \dfrac{15}{16} \Leftrightarrow \dfrac{4a}{4b} = \dfrac{4\times15}{4\times16} = \dfrac{15}{16}.$

$\therefore$ Ratio of perimeter = 15 : 16.

126. Area = 1 hect. = 10000 sq. m. $\Rightarrow$ side $= \sqrt{10000}$ m = 100 m.

Side of the other square = 101 m.

Difference in their areas $= [(101)^2 - (100)^2]$ m^2
$= [(101 + 100)(101 - 100)]$ m^2
$= 201$ m^2.

127. Let original length of side be x.

Then, new length = (110% of x) $= \dfrac{11x}{10}$.

Original area $= x^2$ New area $= \left(\dfrac{11x}{10}\right)^2 = \dfrac{121x^2}{100}$.

Increase in area $= \left(\dfrac{121x^2}{100} - x^2\right) = \dfrac{21x^2}{100}$.

$\therefore$ Increase% $= \left(\dfrac{21x^2}{100}\times\dfrac{1}{x^2}\times100\right)\% = 21\%$.

128. Let the original length of each side be x.

Then, new length = 150 % of $x = \left(\dfrac{150}{100}x\right) = \dfrac{3x}{2}$.

$\therefore$ Required ratio $= \dfrac{\left(\frac{3x}{2}\right)^2}{x^2} = \dfrac{9}{4} = 9:4.$

129. $A_1 = x^2$ and $A_2 = \left(\dfrac{1}{2}x\right)^2 = \dfrac{1}{4}x^2 = \dfrac{1}{4}A_1.$

130. $A_1 = x^2$ and $A_2\ (2x)^2 = 4x^2$.

Increase in area $= (4x^2 - x^2) = 3x^2$.

Increase % $= \left(\dfrac{3x^2}{x^2}\times100\right)\% = 300\%.$

131. 100 cm is read as 102 cm.

$\therefore A_1 = (100\times100)$ cm^2 and $A_2 = (102\times102)$ cm^2.

$(A_2 - A_1) = [(102)^2 - (100)^2] = (102 + 100)(102 - 100)$
$= 404$ cm^2.

$\therefore$ Percentage error $= \left(\dfrac{404}{100\times100}\times100\right)\% = 4.04\%.$

132. Let original area = 100 cm^2. Then, new area = 169 cm^2.

$\Rightarrow$ Original side = 10 cm,

New side = 13 cm. Increase on 10 cm = 3 cm.

Increase% $= \left(\dfrac{3}{10}\times100\right)\% = 30\%.$

133. Given diagonal $= d$. New diagonal $= \dfrac{3}{2}d.$

Original area $= \dfrac{1}{2}d^2$, New area $= \dfrac{1}{2}\times\left(\dfrac{3}{2}d\right)^2 = \dfrac{9}{8}d^2.$

$\therefore$ Required ratio $= \dfrac{1}{2}d^2 : \dfrac{9}{8}d^2 = \dfrac{1}{2} : \dfrac{9}{8} = 4:9.$

134. Let length $= l$ metres and breadth $= b$ metres.

Then, original area $= (lb)$ m^2.

New length = (140% of l) m $= \left(\dfrac{140}{100}\times l\right)$ m $= \dfrac{7l}{5}$ m.

New breadth = (130% of b) m $= \left(\dfrac{130}{100}\times b\right)$ m $= \dfrac{13b}{10}$ m.

New area $= \left(\dfrac{7l}{5}\times\dfrac{13b}{10}\right) = \left(\dfrac{91}{50}lb\right)$ m^2.

Increase $= \left(\dfrac{91}{50}lb - lb\right) = \dfrac{41}{50}lb.$

$\therefore$ Increase% $= \left(\dfrac{41}{50}\times lb\times\dfrac{1}{lb}\times100\right)\% = 82\%.$

135. Let original length of each side $= x$ cm. Then, its area $= (x^2)$ cm^2.

Length of rectangle formed $= (x + 5)$ cm and its breadth $= x$ cm.

$\therefore \dfrac{x+5}{x} = \dfrac{3}{2} \Leftrightarrow 2x + 10 = 3x \Leftrightarrow x = 10.$

$\therefore$ Original length of each side = 10 cm

and its area = 100 cm^2.

136. Let the length and width of the rectangle be l cm and b cm respectively.

Then, $(l - 4)(b + 3) = lb \Rightarrow lb + 3l - 4b - 12 = lb$

$\Rightarrow 3l - 4b = 12$ ...(i)

And, $l - 4 = b + 3 \Rightarrow l - b = 7$ ...(ii)

Multiplying (ii) by 4 and subtracting (i) from it, we get : $l = 16$.

Putting $l = 16$ in (ii), we get : $b = 9$.

$\therefore$ Perimeter of the original rectangle
$= 2(l + b) = [2(16 + 9)]$ cm = 50 cm.

137. Let the length and breadth of the rectangle be l and b units respectively. Then,

$l - 10 = b + 5$

$\Rightarrow l - b = 15$ ...(i)

And, $lb - (l - 10)(b + 5) = 210$

$\Rightarrow lb - (lb + 5l - 10b - 50) = 210$

$\Rightarrow -5l + 10b = 160 \Rightarrow -l + 2b = 32$ ...(ii)

Adding (i) and (ii), we get: $b = 47$. Putting $b = 47$ in (i), we get: $l = 62$.

Hence, area of the rectangle $= lb = (62\times47)$ sq. units = 2914 sq.units.

Clearly, 2925 > A > 2900.

138. Let original side $= x$ cm. Then, new side $= (x + 5)$ cm.

$\therefore (x + 5)^2 - x^2 = 165 \Leftrightarrow x^2 + 10x + 25 - x^2 = 165$
$\Leftrightarrow 10x = 140 \Leftrightarrow x = 14.$

Hence, the side of the square is 14 cm.

139. Let the lengths of the line segments be x cm and $(x + 2)$ cm.

Then, $(x + 2)^2 - x^2 = 32 \Leftrightarrow x^2 + 4x + 4 - x^2 = 32$
$\Leftrightarrow 4x = 28$
$\Leftrightarrow x = 7.$

$\therefore$ Length of longer line segment = (7 + 2) cm = 9 cm.

140. Let the length of each side of the square be x cm.
Then, length of rectangle = $(x + 5)$ cm and its breadth = $(x - 3)$ cm.

$\therefore (x + 5)(x - 3) = x^2 \Leftrightarrow x^2 + 2x - 15 = x^2 \Leftrightarrow x = \frac{15}{2}$.

$\therefore$ Length $= \left(\frac{15}{2} + 5\right)$ cm $= \frac{25}{2}$ cm, breadth

$= \left(\frac{15}{2} - 3\right)$ cm $= \frac{9}{2}$ cm.

Hence, perimeter $= 2(l + b) = 2\left(\frac{25}{2} + \frac{9}{2}\right)$ cm = 34 cm

141. Let the length and breadth of the rectangle be l cm and b cm respectively.
Then, $2(l + b) = 10 \Rightarrow l + b = 5 \Rightarrow b = (5 - l)$ cm.
Area of the rectangle $= l(5 - l)$ cm^2 $= (5l - l^2)$ cm^2.
Area of the square $= 2(5l - l^2)$ cm^2 $= (10l - 2l^2)$ cm^2.
$\therefore (l + 1)(6 - l) = (10l - 2l^2) \Rightarrow l^2 - 5l + 6 = 0$
$\Rightarrow (l - 3)(l - 2) = 0 \Rightarrow l = 3$.
Area of the square $= (10 \times 3 - 2 \times 9)$ cm^2 = 12 cm^2.

$\therefore$ Side of the square $= \sqrt{2}$ cm $= 2\sqrt{3}$ cm.

142. Let the sides of the two squares be x metres and y metres respectively.
Then, $29x^2 = 6y^2 - 1$ ...(i)

And, $9x - 4y = 1 \Rightarrow 4y = 9x - 1 \Rightarrow y = \frac{9x - 1}{4}$ ...(ii)

From (i) and (ii), we get:

$$29x^2 = 6\left(\frac{9x - 1}{4}\right)^2 - 1 \Rightarrow 29x^2 = 6\left(\frac{81x^2 + 1 - 18x}{16}\right) - 1$$

$\Rightarrow 243x^2 + 3 - 54x - 8 = 232x^2$
$\Rightarrow 11x^2 - 54x - 5 = 0 \Rightarrow (x - 5)(11x + 1) = 0 \Rightarrow x = 5$ m.

$\therefore y = \frac{9x - 1}{4} = \frac{9 \times 5 - 1}{4} = 11$ m.

Required difference = (11 – 5) m = 6 m.

143. Let $AP = AQ = x$ metres.

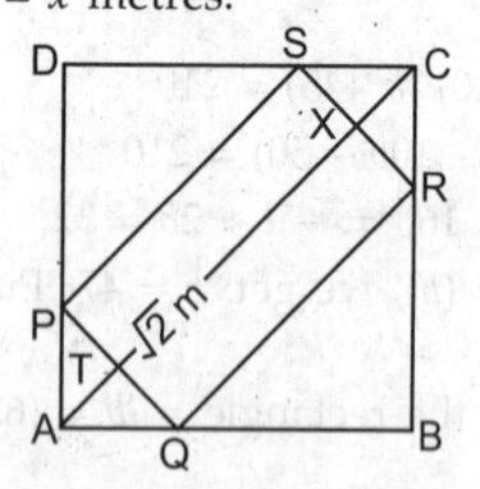

Then, $x^2 + x^2 = (\sqrt{2})^2 \Rightarrow 2x^2 = 2 \Rightarrow x^2 = 1 \Rightarrow x = 1$ m.

So, ΔPAQ is isosceles.

$\therefore PT = QT = \left(\frac{\sqrt{2}}{2}\right)$ m $= \left(\frac{1}{\sqrt{2}}\right)$ m.

In ΔPTA, we have: $\angle PTA = 90°$.

$\therefore AT^2 = AP^2 - PT^2 = 1^2 - \left(\frac{1}{\sqrt{2}}\right)^2 = 1 - \frac{1}{2} = \frac{1}{2}$

or $AT = \left(\frac{1}{\sqrt{2}}\right)$ m.

Similarly, $CX = \left(\frac{1}{\sqrt{2}}\right)$ m.

$\therefore PS = QR = XT = AC - 2 \times AT = \left[8\sqrt{2} - \left(2 \times \frac{1}{\sqrt{2}}\right)\right]$ m

$= \left(8\sqrt{2} - \frac{2}{\sqrt{2}}\right)$ m $= \frac{14}{\sqrt{2}}$ m.

Area of the plank $= \left(\frac{14}{\sqrt{2}} \times \sqrt{2}\right)$ m^2 = 14 m^2.

144. Perimeter = 64 m $\Rightarrow 2(l + b) = 64$.
$\therefore$ Area of 4 walls $= 2(l + b) \times h = (64 \times 4)$m^2 = 256 m^2.

145. Let breadth = x metres and length = $(2x)$ metres.
Area of 4 walls $= [2(2x + x) \times 4]$ m^2 $= (24x)$ m^2.
$\therefore 24x = 120 \Rightarrow x = 5$.
So, length = 10 m, breadth = 5 m.
Area of the floor $= (10 \times 5)$ m^2 = 50 m^2.

146. Area to be plastered $= [2(l + b) \times h] + (l \times b)$
$= \{[2(25 + 12) \times 6] + (25 \times 12)\}$ m^2
$= (444 + 300)$ m^2 = 744 m^2.

$\therefore$ Cost of plastering = Rs. $\left(744 \times \frac{75}{100}\right)$ = Rs. 558.

147. Let the breadth and height of the room be b metres and h metres respectively.
Then, length of the room = $(2b)$ metres.
Area of the ceiling $= (2b \times b)$ $m = (2b^2)$ m^2.

$2b^2 = \frac{5000}{25} = 200 \Rightarrow b^2 = 100 \Rightarrow b = 10$.

So, length = 20 m, breadth = 10 m. Area of 4 walls $= [2(20 + 10) \times h]$ m^2 $= (60h)$ m^2.

$\therefore 60h = \frac{64800}{240} = 270 \Rightarrow h = \frac{270}{60} = 4.5$ m.

148. Area of 4 walls $= 2(l + b) \times h$
$= [2(12.5 + 9) \times 7]$ m^2 = 301 m^2.
Area of 2 doors and 4 windows
$= [2(2.5 \times 1.2) + 4(1.5 \times 1)]$ m^2 = 12 m^2.
$\therefore$ Area to be painted $= (301 - 12)$ m^2 = 289 m^2.
Cost of painting = ₹(289 × 3.50) = ₹ 1011.50.

149. Let the height of the room be x metres. Then, breadth of the room = $(2x)$ metres.
Area of 4 walls $= [2(16 + 2x) \times x]$ m^2 $= (32x + 4x^2)$ m^2.
$\therefore 32x + 4x^2 = 168 \times 2 \Rightarrow x^2 + 8x - 84 = 0$
$\Rightarrow x^2 + 14x - 6x - 84 = 0 \Rightarrow x(x + 14) - 6(x + 14) = 0$
$\Rightarrow (x + 14)(x - 6) = 0 \Rightarrow x = 6$.
Area of the floor $= (16 \times 12)$ m^2 = 192 m^2

150. $A_1 = 2(l + b) \times h$; $A_2 = 2(2l + 2b) \times 2h = 8(l + b) \times h = 4A_1$.
$\therefore$ Required cost = ₹ (4 × 475) = ₹ 1900.

151. Let $h = 2x$ metres and $(l + b) = 5x$ metres.

Length of the paper $= \frac{\text{Total cost}}{\text{Rate per m}} = \frac{260}{2}$ m = 130 m.

Area of the paper $= \left(130 \times \frac{50}{100}\right)$ m^2 = 65 m^2.

Total area of 4 walls $= (65 + 15)$ m^2 = 80 m^2.
$\therefore 2(l + b) \times h = 80 \Leftrightarrow 2 \times 5x \times 2x = 80$
$\Leftrightarrow x^2 = 4 \Leftrightarrow x = 2$.

Height of the room = 4 m.

152. Let the length, breadth and height of the room be $3x$, $2x$ and x respectively.

Area of 4 walls $= 2(l + b) \times h = 2(3x + 2x) \times x = 10x^2$.

New length $= 6x$, New breadth $= x$, New height $= \frac{x}{2}$.

New area of four walls $= \left[2(6x + x) \times \frac{x}{2}\right] = 7x^2$.

Decrease in area $= (10x^2 - 7x^2) = 3x^2$.

$\therefore$ Decrease% $= \left(\frac{3x^2}{10x^2} \times 100\right)\% = 30\%$.

153. I. Area $= (9 \times 4)$ sq. units $= 36$ sq. units.

Perimeter $= [2(9 + 4)]$ units $= 26$ units.

II. Area $= (6 \times 6)$ sq. units $= 36$ sq. units.

Perimeter $= (4 \times 6)$ units $= 24$ units.

III. Area $= \left(\frac{1}{2} \times 8 \times 9\right)$ sq. units $= 36$ sq. units

Third side $= \sqrt{8^2 + 9^2} = \sqrt{64 + 81} = \sqrt{145}$ units.

$\therefore$ Perimeter $= (8 + 9 + \sqrt{145})$ units $= (17 + \sqrt{145})$ units.

Hence, the area of all the three figure area equal.

154. $A_1 = \left(\frac{1}{2} \times 15 \times 12\right)$ cm^2 $= 90$ cm^2. $A_2 = 2A_1 = 180$ cm^2.

$\therefore \frac{1}{2} \times 20 \times h = 180 \Leftrightarrow h = 18$ cm.

155. $\Delta = \frac{1}{2} \times \text{Base} \times \text{Height} \Rightarrow 40 \times \text{Base}$

$= \frac{1}{2} \times \text{Base} \times \text{Height} \Rightarrow \text{Height} = 80$ cm.

156. $\frac{1}{2} \times \text{Base} \times \text{Height} = p \Rightarrow \frac{1}{2} x \times \text{Height} = p \Rightarrow \text{Height} = \frac{2p}{x}$.

157. Area of equilateral triangle $= \left(\frac{\sqrt{3}}{4} \times 8 \times 8\right)$ cm^2 $= 16\sqrt{3}$ cm^2.

158. Required ratio $= (6 \times 6) : \left(\frac{\sqrt{3}}{4} \times 6 \times 6\right) = 4 : \sqrt{3}$.

159. Area of $\Delta ABE = \frac{1}{2} \times AB \times EF = \frac{1}{2} \times AB \times BC$.

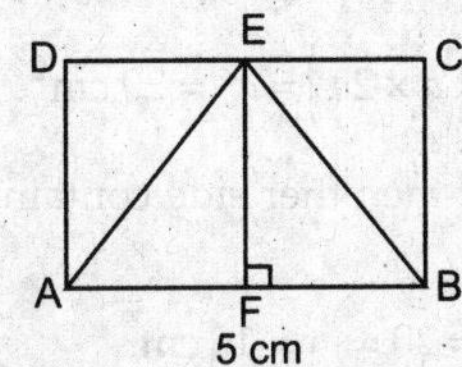

$\therefore \frac{1}{2} \times AB \times BC = 10 \Rightarrow \frac{1}{2} \times 5 \times BC = 10 \Rightarrow BC = \frac{2 \times 10}{5} = 4$.

Perimeter of rectangle $ABCD = 2(AB + BC) = [2(5 + 4)]$ cm $= 18$ cm.

160. $\frac{1}{2} \times \text{Base} \times \text{Height} = 60 \times 60 \Rightarrow \frac{1}{2} \times \text{Base} \times 90 = 3600$

$\Rightarrow \text{Base} = \left(\frac{3600 \times 2}{90}\right) = 80$ m.

161. $AD = \sqrt{4^2 + 6^2}$ cm $= \sqrt{52}$ cm

$= 2\sqrt{13}$ cm $= (2 \times 3.6)$ cm $= 7.2$ cm.

$BC = AD = 7.2$ cm.

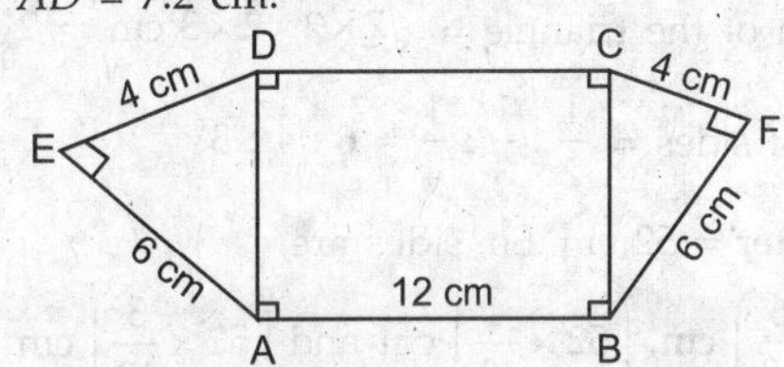

Area of the whole figure

$=$ area(ΔAED) + area(rect. ABCD) + area(ΔBFC)

$= \left[\left(\frac{1}{2} \times 4 \times 6\right) + (12 \times 7.2) + \left(\frac{1}{2} \times 4 \times 6\right)\right]$ cm^2

$= (24 + 86.4)$ cm^2 $= 110.4$ cm^2.

162. $QR = \sqrt{(PR)^2 - (PQ)^2} = \sqrt{(25)^2 - 3^2}$ cm

$= \sqrt{625 - 9}$ cm $= \sqrt{616}$ cm $= 2\sqrt{154}$ cm.

163. Area of ΔPQR

$= \frac{1}{2} \times QR \times PQ = \left(\frac{1}{2} \times 2\sqrt{154} \times 3\right)$ cm^2 $= 3\sqrt{154}$ cm^2.

164. Base of the triangle $= 8$ cm. Height of the triangle $= 8$ cm.

Area of the triangle $= \left(\frac{1}{2} \times 8 \times 8\right)$ cm^2 $= 32$ cm^2.

Area of the square $= (8 \times 8)$ cm^2 $= 64$ cm^2.

$\therefore$ Required area $= (64 - 32)$ cm^2 $= 32$ cm^2.

165. $x = \frac{1}{2} \times CD \times LM$; $y = \frac{1}{2} \times CM \times BC = \frac{1}{2} \times \left(\frac{1}{2} CD\right) \times LM$

$= \frac{1}{4} \times CD \times LM = \frac{1}{2} x$;

$z = \frac{1}{2} \times CM \times LM = \frac{1}{2} \times \left(\frac{1}{2} CD\right) \times LM = \frac{1}{4} \times CD \times LM = \frac{1}{2} x$.

$\therefore x = 2y = 2z$.

166. Let base $= 3x$ cm and altitude $= 4x$ cm.

Then, $\frac{1}{2} \times 3x \times 4x = 1176 \Leftrightarrow 12x^2 = 2352$

$\Leftrightarrow x^2 = 196 \Leftrightarrow x = 14$ cm.

$\therefore$ Altitude $= (4 \times 14)$ cm $= 56$ cm.

167. Since $3^2 + 4^2 = 5^2$, so it is a right-angled triangle with Base $= 3$ cm and Height $= 4$ cm.

$\therefore$ Area $= \left(\frac{1}{2} \times 3 \times 4\right)$ cm^2 $= 6$ cm^2.

168. Since $(20)^2 + (21)^2 = (29)^2$, so it is a right-angled triangle with Base $= 20$ m Height $= 21$ m.

$\therefore$ Area $= \left(\frac{1}{2} \times 20 \times 21\right)$ m^2 $= 210$ m^2.

169. Let the sides of the triangle be $5x$, $5x$ and $4x$ cm respectively.

Then, $5x + 5x = 4x + 14$ or $14x = 14$ or $x = 1$.

So, $a = 5$ cm, $b = 5$ cm, $c = 4$ cm.

$s = \frac{a+b+c}{2} = \left(\frac{14}{2}\right) \text{cm} = 7 \text{ cm}$. $(s - a) = 2$ cm, $(s - b)$ $= 2$ cm, $(s - c) = 3$ cm.

$\therefore$ Area of the triangle $= \sqrt{7 \times 2 \times 2 \times 3} \text{ cm}^2 = 2\sqrt{21} \text{ cm}^2$.

170. Ratio of sides $= \frac{1}{2} : \frac{1}{3} : \frac{1}{4} = 6 : 4 : 3$.

Perimeter = 52 cm. So, sides are

$\left(52 \times \frac{6}{13}\right)$ cm, $\left(52 \times \frac{4}{13}\right)$ cm and $\left(52 \times \frac{3}{13}\right)$ cm.

So, $a = 24$ cm, $b = 16$ cm, $c = 12$ cm.

$\therefore$ Length of smallest side = 12 cm.

171. Let the sides of the triangle be x cm, $(x + 1)$ cm and $(x + 2)$ cm respectively.

Then, $x + (x + 1) + (x + 2) = 120 \Rightarrow 3x + 3 = 120 \Rightarrow 3x = 117 \Rightarrow x = 39$.

$\therefore$ Length of greatest side = $(39 + 2)$ cm = 41 cm.

172. Let $a = 3x$ cm, $b = 4x$ cm and $c = 5x$ cm. Then, $s = 6x$ cm.

$A = \sqrt{s(s-a)(s-b)(s-c)}$

$= \sqrt{6x \times 3x \times 2x \times x} = (6x^2) \text{ cm}^2$.

$\therefore 6x^2 = 216 \Leftrightarrow x^2 = 36 \Leftrightarrow x = 6$.

So $a = 18$ cm, $b = 24$ cm and $c = 30$ cm.

Perimeter = $(18 + 24 + 30)$ cm = 72 cm.

173. $a = 6$ cm, $b = 8$ cm, $c = 10$ cm. So, $s = \frac{6+8+10}{2} = 12$ cm.

Area of the triangle $= \sqrt{12 \times 6 \times 4 \times 2} \text{ cm}^2 = 24 \text{ cm}^2$.

Let the length of the required altitude be x cm.

Then, $\frac{1}{2} \times 10 \times x = 24 \Rightarrow x = \frac{24 \times 2}{10} = \left(\frac{48}{10}\right)$ cm = 4.8 cm.

174. **Note:** If the mid-points of three sides of a triangle are joined, the whole triangle is divided into four triangles of equal area.

$a = 3$ cm, $b = 4$ cm and $c = 5$ cm.

It is a right-angle triangle with base = 3 cm and height = 4 cm.

$\therefore$ Its area $= \left(\frac{1}{2} \times 3 \times 4\right) \text{cm}^2 = 6 \text{ cm}^2$.

Area of required triangle $= \left(\frac{1}{4} \times 6\right) \text{cm}^2 = \frac{3}{2} \text{ cm}^2$.

175. Keeping the above note in mind, we have: Required ratio = 1 : 1

176. **Note:** The line segment joining the mid-points of two sides of a triangle is parallel to the third side and equal to half of it.

Then, perimeter of the second triangle

$= \frac{1}{2}(5 + 6 + 7) \text{ cm} = 9 \text{ cm}$.

177. **Note:** The ratio of the areas of two similar triangles is equal to the ratio of the squares of their corresponding sides.

Since XY || BC, we have:

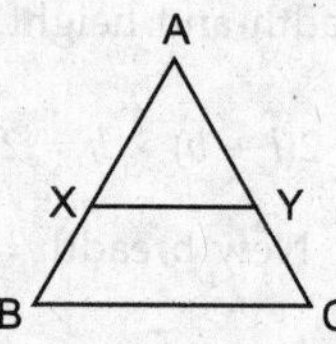

$\angle AXY = \angle ABC$ and $\angle AYX = \angle ACB$.

Also, $\angle A = \angle A$ (common)

So, $\Delta AXY \sim \Delta ABC$.

Let area $(\Delta ABC) = x$ sq. units.

Then, area $(\Delta XY) = \frac{x}{2}$ sq.units $\frac{(AB)^2}{(AX)^2} = \frac{x}{(x/2)}$

$\Rightarrow \frac{AB}{AX} = \sqrt{2} \Rightarrow \frac{AX + BX}{AX} = \sqrt{2} \Rightarrow 1 + \frac{BX}{AX} = \sqrt{2}$

$\Rightarrow \frac{BX}{AX} = (\sqrt{2} - 1) \Rightarrow \frac{AX}{BX} = \frac{1}{(\sqrt{2} - 1)}$.

178. **Note :** The areas of two similar triangles are in the ratio of the squares of the corresponding altitudes. Let the length of the required altitude be x cm.

Then, $\frac{12}{48} = \frac{(2.1)^2}{x^2} \Rightarrow x^2 = (4.41 \times 4) \Rightarrow x = 2.1 \times 2 = 4.2$ cm.

179. $9y = \frac{\sqrt{3}}{4} \times 6 \times 6 \Rightarrow y = \left(\frac{\sqrt{3}}{4} \times 6 \times 6 \times \frac{1}{9}\right) = \sqrt{3}$.

180. Let the length of each side containing the right angle be x cm.

Then, $x^2 + x^2 = 5^2 \Rightarrow 2x^2 = 25 \Rightarrow x^2 = \frac{25}{2} \Rightarrow x = \frac{5}{\sqrt{2}}$.

$\therefore$ Area of the triangle $= \left(\frac{1}{2} \times \frac{5}{\sqrt{2}} \times \frac{5}{\sqrt{2}}\right) \text{cm}^2$

$= \left(\frac{25}{4}\right) \text{cm}^2 = 6.25 \text{ cm}^2$.

181. Let the sides be a cm and $2a$ cm.

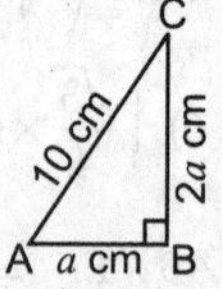

Then, $a^2 + (2a)^2 = (10)^2 \Leftrightarrow 5a^2 = 100 \Leftrightarrow a^2 = 20$.

$\therefore$ Area $= \left(\frac{1}{2} \times a \times 2a\right) = a^2 = 20 \text{ cm}^2$.

182. Let the length of the other side containing the right angle be x cm.

Then, $\frac{1}{2} \times 4 \times x = 20 \Rightarrow x = 10$ cm.

Hypotenuse $= \sqrt{(10)^2 + 4^2} \text{ cm} = \sqrt{116} \text{ cm} = 2\sqrt{29}$ cm.

Let the altitude on the hypotenuse be h cm.

Then, $\frac{1}{2} \times 2\sqrt{29} \times h = 20 \Rightarrow h = \frac{20}{\sqrt{29}}$ cm.

183. Area of the triangle $= \left(\frac{1}{2} \times 12 \times 5\right) \text{cm}^2 = 30 \text{ cm}^2$.

Hypotenuse $= \sqrt{(12)^2 + 5^2} \text{ cm} = \sqrt{169} \text{ cm} = 13$ cm.

Let the perpendicular distance of the hypotenuse from the opposite vertex be x cm.

Then, $\frac{1}{2}\times 13\times x = 30 \Rightarrow x = \frac{60}{13} = 4\frac{8}{13}$ cm.

184. Let the base be b cm and height be h cm.

Then, $\frac{1}{2}bh = 180 \Rightarrow bh = 360.$

And, $b^2 + h^2 = (41)^2 \Rightarrow b^2 + h^2 = 1681.$

$\therefore \quad (b-h)^2 = b^2 + h^2 - 2bh = 1681 - 720 = 961$

$\Rightarrow (b-h) = \sqrt{961} = 31$ cm.

185. Let Base = b cm and Height = h cm.

$b + h + 26 = 60 \Leftrightarrow b + h = 34 \Leftrightarrow (b+h)^2 = (34)^2$ ...(*i*)

Also, $b^2 + h^2 = (26)^2$ ...(*ii*)

$\therefore (b+h)^2 - (b^2 + h^2) = (34)^2 - (26)^2$

$\Leftrightarrow 2bh = (34 + 26)(34 - 26) = 480$

$\Leftrightarrow bh = 240 \Leftrightarrow \frac{1}{2}bh = 120.$

$\therefore$ Area = 120 cm^2.

186. Let the length of each of the sides containing the right angle be x cm.

Then, hypotenuse = $\sqrt{x^2 + x^2}$ cm $= \sqrt{2x^2}$ cm $= \sqrt{2}x$ cm.

Perimeter of the triangle = $(x + x + \sqrt{2}x)$ cm $= (2x + \sqrt{2}x)$ cm

$= \sqrt{2}x(\sqrt{2}+1)$ cm.

$\therefore \sqrt{2}x(\sqrt{2}+1) = (4\sqrt{2}+4) = 4(\sqrt{2}+1) \Rightarrow \sqrt{2}x = 4 \Rightarrow x = 2\sqrt{2}.$

Hence, hypotenuse = $(\sqrt{2}\times 2\sqrt{2})$ cm = 4 cm.

187. Let the sides be a metres, a metres and b metres.

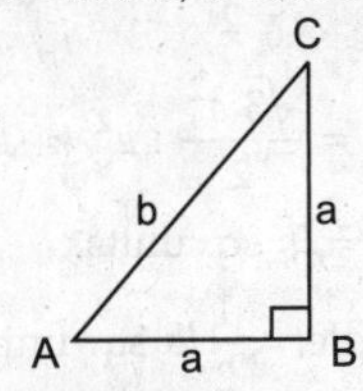

Then, $2a + b = 6 + 3\sqrt{2}$ and $b^2 = a^2 + a^2 = 2a^2 \Leftrightarrow b = \sqrt{2}\,a.$

$\therefore \quad 2a + \sqrt{2}\,a = 6 + 3\sqrt{2} \Leftrightarrow a = 3.$

$\therefore \quad$ Area $= \left(\frac{1}{2}\times 3\times 3\right)$ m^2 = 4.5 m^2.

188. Let the length of the base and height be x cm each.

Then, $\frac{1}{2}x^2 = 162 \Rightarrow x^2 = 324 \Rightarrow x = \sqrt{324} = 18$ cm.

Hypotenuse = $\sqrt{(18)^2 + (18)^2}$ cm $= \sqrt{648}$ cm $= 18\sqrt{2}$ cm.

$\therefore$ Perimeter = $(18 + 18 + 18\sqrt{2})$ cm $= 18(2+\sqrt{2})$ cm

= 18(2 + 1.41) cm = (18 × 3.41) cm

= 61.38 cm.

189. Area of the triangle = $\frac{1}{2}ab\sin\theta = \left(\frac{1}{2}\times 10\times 10\times \sin 45^\circ\right)$ cm^2

$= \left(\frac{1}{2}\times 10\times 10\times \frac{1}{\sqrt{2}}\right)$ cm$^2 = \left(\frac{50}{\sqrt{2}}\times\frac{\sqrt{2}}{\sqrt{2}}\right)$ cm$^2 = 25\sqrt{2}$ cm^2.

190. Let the smallest side be x cm. Then, other sides are 13 cm and $(17 - x)$ cm.

Let $a = 13$, $b = x$ and $c = (17 - x)$. So, $s = 15$.

Area = $\sqrt{s(s-a)(s-b)(s-c)}$

$= \sqrt{15\times 2\times (15-x)(x-2)} = \sqrt{30(15-x)(x-2)}.$

$\therefore 30(15 - x)(x - 2) = (30)^2$

$\Leftrightarrow (15 - x)(x - 2) = 30 \Leftrightarrow x^2 - 17x + 60 = 0$

$\Leftrightarrow (x - 12)(x - 5) = 0 \Leftrightarrow x = 12$ or $x = 5$.

$\therefore$ Smallest side = 5 cm.

191. Area of an equilateral triangle of side a cm $= \left(\frac{\sqrt{3}}{4}a^2\right)$ cm^2.

$\therefore \frac{\sqrt{3}}{4}a^2 = 24\sqrt{3} \Leftrightarrow a^2 = 96 \Leftrightarrow a = 4\sqrt{6}$ cm.

$\therefore$ Perimeter = 3a = 12 $12\sqrt{6}$ cm.

192. Let ABC be the equilateral triangle and AD be the altitude on base BC.

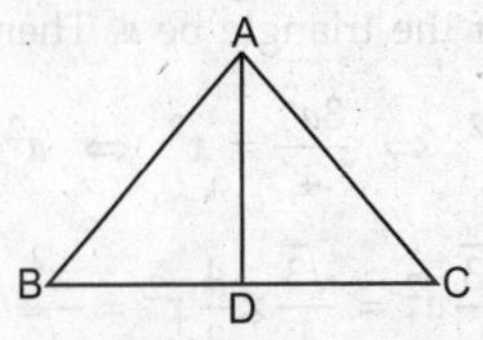

In an equilateral triangle, the altitude and the median coincide.

So, BC = DC = $\left(\frac{2\sqrt{3}}{2}\right)$ cm $= \sqrt{3}$ cm.

Let the length of the altitude AD be x cm.

Then, in right angled ΔADB,

$AB^2 = AD^2 + BD^2 \Rightarrow (2\sqrt{3})^2 = x^2 + (\sqrt{3})^2 \Rightarrow x^2 = (12 - 3)$

$= 9 \Rightarrow x = 3$ cm.

193. Let each side be a cm. Then,

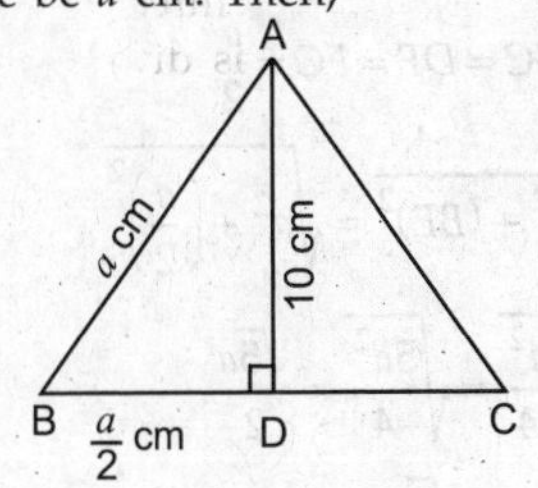

$\left(\frac{a}{2}\right)^2 + (10)^2 = a^2 \Leftrightarrow \left(a^2 - \frac{a^2}{4}\right) = 100$

$\Leftrightarrow \frac{3a^2}{4} = 100 \Leftrightarrow a^2 = \frac{400}{3}.$

$\therefore$ Area $= \frac{\sqrt{3}}{4}\times a^2 = \left(\frac{\sqrt{3}}{4}\times\frac{400}{3}\right)$ cm$^2 = \frac{100}{\sqrt{3}}$ cm^2.

194. Let the length of sides of the two triangles be a_1 and a_2 respectively and their altitudes be h_1 and h_2 respectively. Then,

$\frac{\frac{\sqrt{3}}{4}a_1^2}{\frac{\sqrt{3}}{4}a_2^2} = \frac{25}{36} \Rightarrow \left(\frac{a_1}{a_2}\right)^2 = \left(\frac{5}{6}\right)^2 \Rightarrow \frac{a_1}{a_2} = \frac{5}{6}.$

And, $\dfrac{\frac{1}{2}\times a_1\times h_1}{\frac{1}{2}\times a_2\times h_2}=\dfrac{25}{36}\Rightarrow\dfrac{5}{6}\times\dfrac{h_1}{h_2}=\dfrac{25}{36}\Rightarrow\dfrac{h_1}{h_2}=\dfrac{25}{36}\times\dfrac{5}{6}=\dfrac{5}{6}.$

195. Let each side of the triangle be a cm.

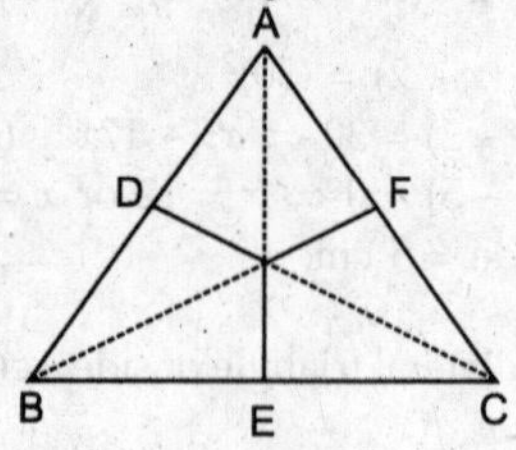

Then, area (ΔAOB) + ar (ΔBOC) + ar (ΔAOC) = ar (ΔABC)

$$\Rightarrow\frac{1}{2}\times a\times 6+\frac{1}{2}\times a\times 7+\frac{1}{2}\times a\times 8=\frac{\sqrt{3}}{4}a^2$$

$$\Rightarrow\frac{a}{2}(6+7+8)=\frac{\sqrt{3}}{4}a^2\Rightarrow a=\left(\frac{21}{2}\times\frac{4}{\sqrt{3}}\right)=14\sqrt{3}\text{ cm}.$$

196. Let the side of the triangle be a. Then,

$$a^2=\left(\frac{a}{2}\right)^2+x^2\ \Leftrightarrow\ \frac{3a^2}{4}=x^2\ \Leftrightarrow\ a^2=\frac{4x^2}{3}.$$

$$\therefore\quad \text{Area}=\frac{\sqrt{3}}{4}a^2=\frac{\sqrt{3}}{4}\times\frac{4}{3}x^2=\frac{x^2}{\sqrt{3}}=\frac{x^2\sqrt{3}}{3}.$$

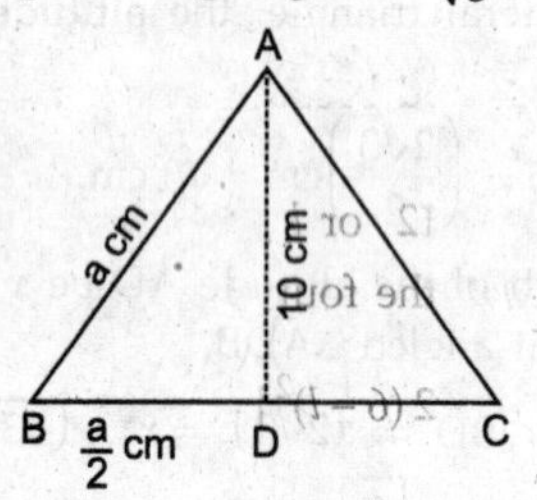

197. Let the length of side of the square be a units.

Then, $BE=EC=DF=FC=\dfrac{a}{2}$

$$AE=\sqrt{(AB)^2+(BE)^2}=\sqrt{a^2+\left(\frac{a}{2}\right)^2}$$

$$=\sqrt{a^2+\frac{a^2}{4}}=\sqrt{\frac{5a^2}{4}}=\frac{\sqrt{5}a}{2}.$$

Similarly, $AF=\dfrac{\sqrt{5}a}{2}.$

$$EF=\sqrt{(CE)^2+(CF)^2}=\sqrt{\left(\frac{a}{2}\right)^2+\left(\frac{a}{2}\right)^2}=\sqrt{\frac{2a^2}{4}}=\frac{a}{\sqrt{2}}.$$

$$EX=\frac{1}{2}EF=\frac{a}{2\sqrt{2}}.$$

$$AX=\sqrt{(AE)^2-(EX)^2}=\sqrt{\left(\frac{\sqrt{5}a}{2}\right)^2-\left(\frac{a}{2\sqrt{2}}\right)^2}$$

$$=\sqrt{\frac{5a^2}{4}-\frac{a^2}{8}}=\sqrt{\frac{9a^2}{8}}=\frac{3a}{2\sqrt{2}}.$$

$$\therefore\ \text{Area }(\Delta AEF)=\frac{1}{2}\times EF\times AX=\frac{1}{2}\times\frac{a}{\sqrt{2}}\times\frac{3a}{2\sqrt{2}}=\frac{3a^2}{8}.$$

Required ratio $=\dfrac{3a^2}{8}:a^2=3:8.$

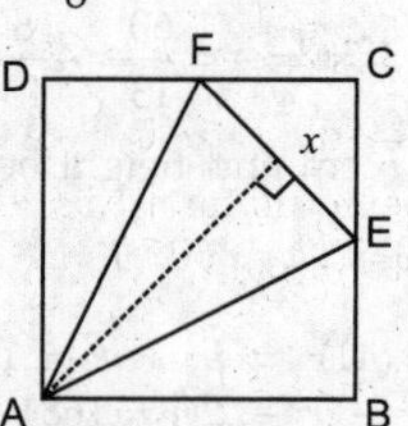

198. Area of a square with side a = a^2 sq. units.

Area of a triangle with base.

$= a = \left(\dfrac{1}{2}\times a\times h\right)$ sq. units

$\therefore\quad a^2=\dfrac{1}{2}\times a\times h\ \Leftrightarrow\ h=2a.$

Hence, the altitude of the triangle is $2a$.

199. Let the side of the square be a cm.

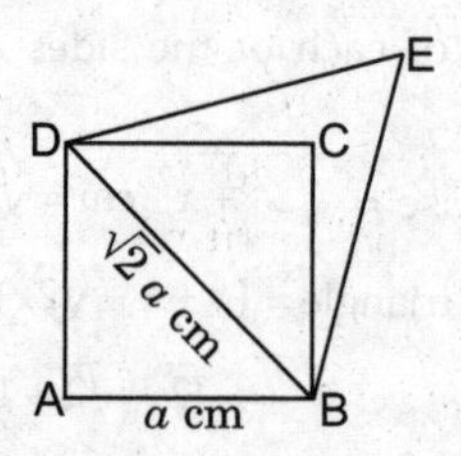

Then, the length of its diagonal = $\sqrt{2}\,a$ cm.

Area of equilateral triangle with side

$$\sqrt{2}a=\frac{\sqrt{3}}{4}\times(\sqrt{2}a)^2=\frac{\sqrt{3}a^2}{2}.$$

$\therefore$ Required ratio $=\dfrac{\sqrt{3}a^2}{2}:a^2=\sqrt{3}:2.$

200. Area of rectangle = lb sq. units.

Area of the triangle = $\dfrac{1}{2}lb$ sq. units.

$\therefore\quad$ Required ratio = $lb:\dfrac{1}{2}lb=2:1.$

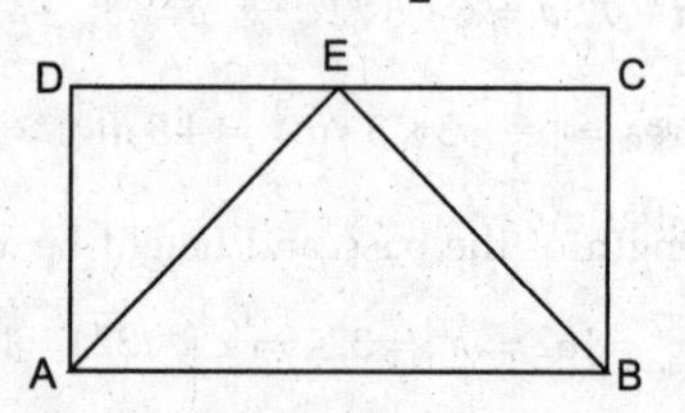

201. Let each side of the triangle be a cm and each side of the square be b cm.

Then, $X=\dfrac{\sqrt{3}}{4}a^2$ and $Y=b^2$, where $3a=4b$, *i.e.*, $b=\dfrac{3a}{4}.$

$\therefore\quad X=\dfrac{\sqrt{3}}{4}a^2$ and $Y=\dfrac{9a^2}{16}$ $\quad\left[\because\ b=\dfrac{3a}{4}\right]$

Now, $\dfrac{\sqrt{3}}{4}a^2=\dfrac{1.732}{4}a^2=0.433\,a^2$ and $\dfrac{9a^2}{16}=0.5625\,a^2.$

$\therefore\quad X < Y.$

202. Let the side of the square be a cm.

Then, its diagonal = $\sqrt{2}\,a$ cm.

Now, $\sqrt{2}\,a = 12\sqrt{2} \Rightarrow a = 12$ cm.

Perimeter of the square = $4a$ = 48 cm.

Perimeter of the equilateral triangle = 48 cm.

Each side of the triangle = 16 cm.

Area of the triangle = $\left(\frac{\sqrt{3}}{4}\times 16\times 16\right)\text{cm}^2 = (64\sqrt{3})\text{ cm}^2$.

203. $\frac{a}{b} = \frac{\frac{1}{2}x\times h_1}{\frac{1}{2}y\times h_2} \quad bxh_1 = ayh_2 \Leftrightarrow \frac{h_1}{h_2} = \frac{ay}{bx}$

$\left[\text{Ratio of areas} = \frac{a}{b}, \text{ Ratio of base} = x:y\right]$

Hence, $h_1 : h_2 = ay : bx$.

204. Let the sides of the triangle be $2x$, $3x$, $4x$ and their corresponding altitudes be h_1, h_2, h_3 respectively. Then,

$\frac{1}{2}\times 2x\times h_1 = \frac{1}{2}\times 3x\times h_2 = \frac{1}{2}\times 4x\times h_3$

$\Rightarrow xh_1 = \frac{3}{2}xh_2 = 2xh_3 = k(\text{say})$

$\Rightarrow h_1 = \frac{k}{x}, h_2 = \frac{2k}{2x}, h_3 = \frac{k}{2x}$.

$\therefore\ h_1 : h_2 : h_3 = \frac{k}{x} : \frac{2k}{3x} : \frac{k}{2x} = 1 : \frac{2}{3} : \frac{1}{2} = 6:4:3.$

205. Let the sides be x cm and (80% of x) cm = $\frac{4x}{5}$ cm.

Then, initial area

$= \frac{\sqrt{3}}{4}x^2$, final area = $\frac{\sqrt{3}}{4}\left(\frac{4x}{5}\right)^2 = \frac{16\sqrt{3}\,x^2}{100}$.

Decrease in area = $\left(\frac{\sqrt{3}}{4}x^2 - \frac{16\sqrt{3}}{100}x^2\right)\text{cm}^2 = \frac{9\sqrt{3}\,x^2}{100}\text{ cm}^2$.

Decrease% = $\left(\frac{9\sqrt{3}\,x^2}{100}\times\frac{4}{\sqrt{3}\,x^2}\times 100\right)\% = 36\%$.

206. Let initial base = b cm and initial height = h cm.

Then, initial area = $\left(\frac{1}{2}bh\right)\text{cm}^2$.

New base = (140% of b) cm = $\left(\frac{140b}{100}\right)$ cm = $\left(\frac{7b}{5}\right)$ cm.

New height = (60% of h) cm = $\left(\frac{60h}{100}\right)$ cm = $\left(\frac{3h}{5}\right)$ cm.

New area = $\left(\frac{1}{2}\times\frac{7b}{5}\times\frac{3h}{5}\right)\text{cm}^2 = \left(\frac{21}{50}bh\right)\text{cm}^2$.

Area decreased = $\left(\frac{1}{2}bh - \frac{21}{50}bh\right)\text{cm}^2 = \left(\frac{4}{50}bh\right)\text{cm}^2$.

Percentage decrease = $\left(\frac{4bh}{50}\times\frac{2}{bh}\times 100\right)\% = 16\%$.

207. $A_1 = \frac{\sqrt{3}}{2}a^2$ and $A_2 = \frac{\sqrt{3}}{2}(2a)^2 = 4\times\frac{\sqrt{3}}{2}a^2 = 4A_1$.

$\therefore$ K = 4.

208. Since vertical angles are equal and corresponding sides are proportional, the two triangles are similar. So, the ratio of their areas is equal to the ratio of the squares of their corresponding sides.

$\therefore$ Ratio of their areas = $\frac{(3x)^2}{(4x)^2} = \frac{9}{25} = 9:25$.

209. Original area = $\frac{1}{2}ab\sin\theta$.

New area = $\frac{1}{2}\times(2a)\times(2b)\sin\theta = 4\left(\frac{1}{2}ab\sin\theta\right)$

= 4 × original area.

210. Let $EF = x$ units. Then, $DF = 2x$ units.

$\frac{1}{2}\times EF\times DF = 5 \Rightarrow \frac{1}{2}\times x\times 2x = 5 \Rightarrow x^2 = 5 \Rightarrow x = \sqrt{5}$.

$\therefore DE = \sqrt{(DF)^2+(EF)^2} = \sqrt{(2\sqrt{5})^2+(\sqrt{5})^2} = \sqrt{25} = 5$ units

$\therefore AE = \sqrt{(DE)^2-(AD)^2} = \sqrt{5^2-4^2} = \sqrt{9} = 3$ units.

AB = 2AE = 6 units.

$\therefore$ Area of rect. ABCD = AB × AD

= (6 × 4) sq. units = 24 sq. units.

211. Let the length and breadth of the rectangle be l cm and b cm respectively.

Then, $2(l + b) = 12$ or $l + b = 6$ or $b = (6 - l)$.

Sum of areas of the four triangles

$= \frac{\sqrt{3}}{4}[2l^2 + 2(6-l)^2] = \frac{\sqrt{3}}{4}(4l^2 - 24l + 72)$

$= \sqrt{3}(l^2 - 6l + 18)$.

$\therefore\ \sqrt{3}(l^2-6l+18) = 10\sqrt{3} \Rightarrow l^2 - 6l + 18 = 10$

$\Rightarrow l^2 - 6l + 8 = 0 \Rightarrow (l-4)(l-2) = 0$

$\Rightarrow l = 4$ or $l = 2$.

Hence, length = 4 cm, breadth = 2 cm.

Area of rectangle = (4 × 2) cm² = 8 cm².

212. Area of the field = ar (ΔAFE) + ar (ΔAGB) + ar (ΔBGC) + ar (ΔDHC) + or (trap $DEFH$)

$= \left(\frac{1}{2}\times AF\times EF\right) + \left(\frac{1}{2}\times AG\times BG\right) + \left(\frac{1}{2}\times CG\times BG\right) + \left(\frac{1}{2}\times DH\times CH\right) + \left\{\frac{1}{2}\times(DH+EF)\times HF\right\}$

$= \left(\frac{1}{2}\times 50\times 30\right) + \left(\frac{1}{2}\times 80\times 50\right) + \left(\frac{1}{2}\times 70\times 50\right) + \left(\frac{1}{2}\times 20\times 30\right) + \left\{\frac{1}{2}\times(20+30)\times 70\right\}$

[$\because CG = (AC - AG) = (150 - 80)$ m = 70 m, $CH = (AC - AH)$ = (150 − 120) m = 30 m, $HF = (AH - AF) = (120 - 50)$ m = 70 m]

= (750 + 2000 + 1750 + 300 + 1750) m² = 6550 m².

213. Interchanging the distances to C and D, the field may be drawn as shown in the adjoining figure.

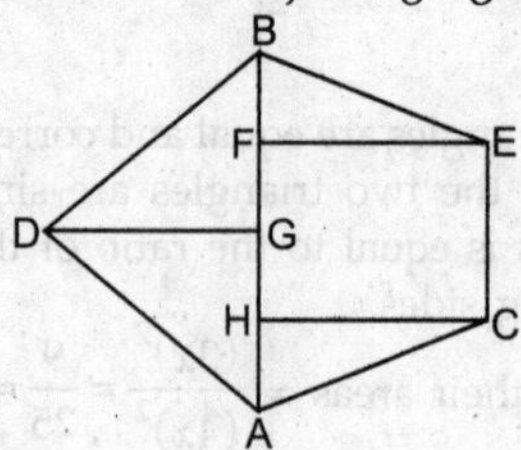

We have : $AB = 40$ m, $AF = 30$ m, $AG = 20$ m, $AH = 10$ m, $CH = 30$ m, $DG = 20$ m, $EF = 30$ m.

Area of the field = ar (ΔAHC) + ar (rect $CEFH$) + ar (ΔBFE) + ar (ΔBGD) + ar (ΔAGD)

$$= \left(\frac{1}{2}\times AH\times CH\right)+(CH\times FH)+\left(\frac{1}{2}\times BF\times EF\right)+\left(\frac{1}{2}\times BG\times DG\right)+\left(\frac{1}{2}\times AG\times DG\right)$$

$$= \left(\frac{1}{2}\times 10\times 30\right)+(30\times 20)+\left(\frac{1}{2}\times 10\times 30\right)+\left(\frac{1}{2}\times 20\times 20\right)+\left(\frac{1}{2}\times 20\times 20\right)$$

$= (150 + 600 + 150 + 200 + 200)\ m^2 = 1300\ m^2$.

214. The field may be drawn as shown in the adjoining figure.

We have: AB = 400 m, AF = 300 m, AG = 200 m, AH = 100 m, EF = 100 m, CH = 50 m, DG = x metres.

Area of the field

= ar (ΔAGD) + ar (ΔBGD) + ar (ΔBFE) + ar (trap $CEFH$) + ar (ΔAHC)

$$= \left(\frac{1}{2}\times AG\times GD\right)+\left(\frac{1}{2}\times BG\times GD\right)+\left(\frac{1}{2}\times BF\times EF\right)+\frac{1}{2}\times (EF+CH)\times FH+\left(\frac{1}{2}\times AH\times CH\right)$$

$$= \left(\frac{1}{2}\times 200\times x\right)+\left(\frac{1}{2}\times 200\times x\right)+\left(\frac{1}{2}\times 100\times 100\right)+\left\{\frac{1}{2}\times (100+50)\times 200\right\}+\left(\frac{1}{2}\times 100\times 50\right)$$

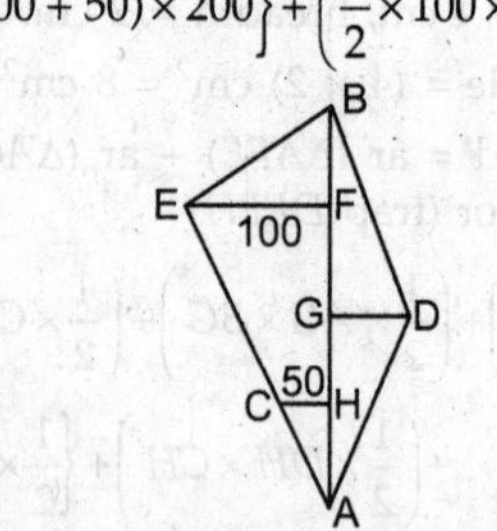

$= (100x + 100x + 5000 + 15000 + 2500)\ m^2$

$= (22500 + 200x)\ m^2$.

$\therefore$ $22500 + 200x = 27500 \Rightarrow 200x = 5000 \Rightarrow x = 25$ m.

215. Area of the field = (Base × Height) = $(150 \times 80)\ m^2 = 12000\ m^2$.

$\therefore$ Cost of watering = ₹(12000 × 0.50) = ₹ 6000.

216. Area of ||gm $ABCD$ = ($AB \times DH$) = ($AB \times BE$) = (7 × 6.5) $cm^2 = 45.5\ cm^2$.

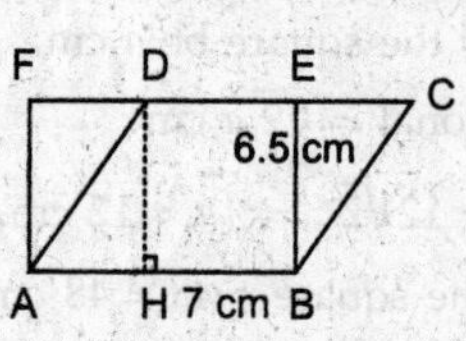

217. Let $ABCD$ be the rectangle and $ABEF$ be the parallelogram. Let $AB = 10$ cm.

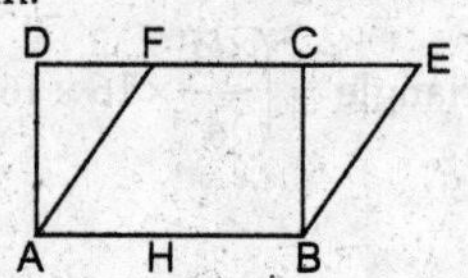

$2(AB + BC) = 36 \Rightarrow BC + 10 = 18 \Rightarrow BC = 8$ cm.

$\therefore$ Area of ||gm $ABEF$ = $(10 \times 8)\ cm^2 = 80\ cm^2$.

218. $10 \times 12 = 20 \times h \Rightarrow h = \frac{120}{60} = 6$ m.

219. Let $ABCD$ be the given ||gm.

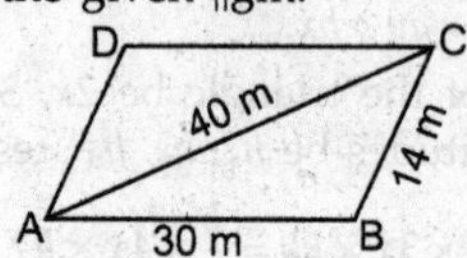

Area of ||gm $ABCD$ = 2 × (area of ΔABC).

Now, $a = 30$ m, $b = 14$ m, $c = 40$ m.

$\therefore$ $s = \frac{1}{2}(30+14+40)$ m = 42 m.

$\therefore$ Area of ΔABC = $\sqrt{s(s-a)(s-b)(s-c)}$

$= \sqrt{42\times 12\times 28\times 2}\ m^2 = 168\ m^2$.

Hence, area of || gm $ABCD$ = $(2 \times 168)\ m^2 = 336\ m^2$.

220. Let $ABCD$ be the given ||gm. Let $AC = 70$ cm. Draw $BL \perp AC$ and $DM \perp AC$.

Then, $DM = BL = 27$ cm.

Area of || gm ACBD = ar (ΔABC) + ar (ΔACD)

$$= \left[\left(\frac{1}{2}\times 70\times 27\right)+\left(\frac{1}{2}\times 70\times 27\right)\right] \text{ sq. cm} = 1890 \text{ sq. cm}.$$

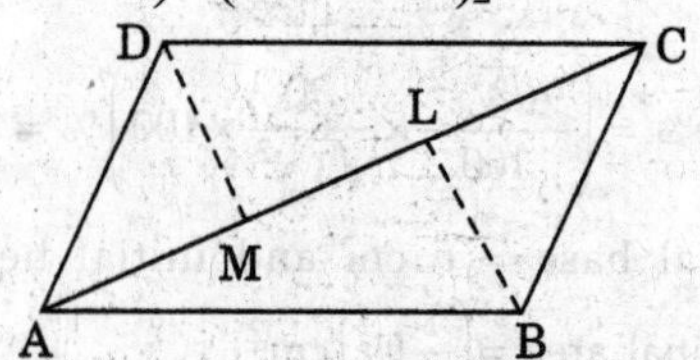

221. Let the altitude of the triangle be h_1 and base of each be b.

Then, $\frac{1}{2} \times b_1 \times h_1 = b \times h_2$, where $h_2 = 100$ m

$\Leftrightarrow h_1 = 2\ h_2 = (2 \times 100)$ m = 200 m.

222. Clearly, a parallelogram is formed as shown.

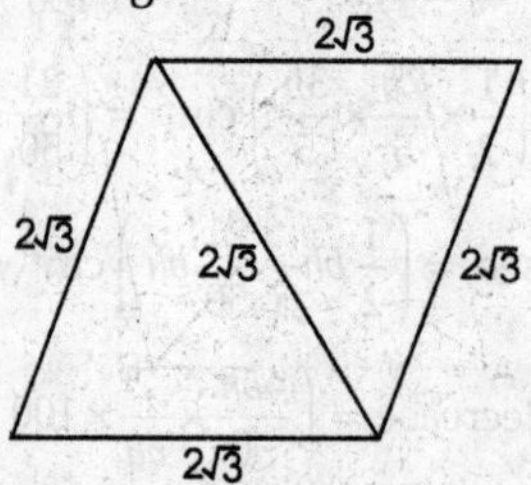

Area of the || gm so formed = Sum of areas of the two triangles = $\left[2\times\left\{\frac{\sqrt{3}}{4}\times(2\sqrt{3})^2\right\}\right]\text{cm}^2=\left(2\times\frac{\sqrt{3}}{4}\times12\right)\text{cm}^2$

$=6\sqrt{3}\text{ cm}^2.$

Let the length of the altitude be h cm.

Then, $2\sqrt{3}\,h=6\sqrt{3}\Rightarrow h=3$ cm.

223. Let each have base = b and height = h.

Then, P = $b\times h$, R = $b\times h$, T = $\frac{1}{2}\times b\times h$.

So, $P = R$, $P = 2T$ and $T = \frac{1}{2}$ R are all correct statements.

224. $\frac{1}{2}d_1\times d_2=150 \Leftrightarrow \frac{1}{2}\times10\times d_2=150 \Leftrightarrow d_2=30$ cm.

225. $\frac{1}{2}d_1\times 2d_1=25 \Leftrightarrow d_1^2=25 \Leftrightarrow d_1=5.$

∴ Sum of lengths of diagonals = (5 + 10) cm = 15 cm.

226. Perimeter of the rhombus = 56 m. Each side of the rhombus = $\frac{56}{4}$ m = 14 m.

Height of the rhombus = 5 m.

∴ Area = (14 × 5) m² = 70 m².

227. Area = $\frac{1}{2}d_1d_2=\left(\frac{1}{2}\times24\times10\right)\text{cm}^2=120\text{ cm}^2.$

$OA=\frac{1}{2}d_1=\left(\frac{1}{2}\times24\right)$ cm = 12 cm.

$OB=\frac{1}{2}d_2=\left(\frac{1}{2}\times10\right)$ cm = 5 cm.

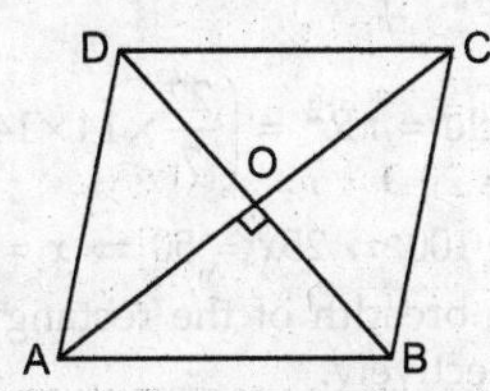

$AB^2 = OA^2 + OB^2 = (12)^2 + 52 = 169 \Leftrightarrow AB = 13$ cm.

∴ Perimeter = (13 × 4) cm = 52 cm.

228. $AB = 26$ cm and $AC = 48$ cm $\Rightarrow OA=\left(\frac{1}{2}\times48\right)$ cm = 24 cm.

$OB^2 = AB^2 - OA^2 = (26)^2 - (24)^2 = (26 + 24)(26 - 24) = 100$

$\Rightarrow OB = 50 \Rightarrow BD = 2 \times OB = (2 \times 50)$ cm = 100 cm.

∴ Area = $\frac{1}{2}\times AC\times BD=\left(\frac{1}{2}\times48\times100\right)$ cm = 2400 cm²

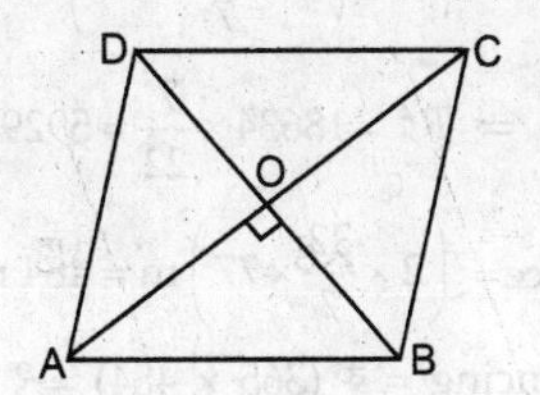

229. $\frac{1}{2}\times6\times d=24\Rightarrow d=\frac{24}{3}=8$ cm.

$OA = 4$ cm and $OB = 3$ cm.

∴ $AB=\sqrt{(OA)^2+(OB)^2}=\sqrt{4^2+3^2}=5$ cm.

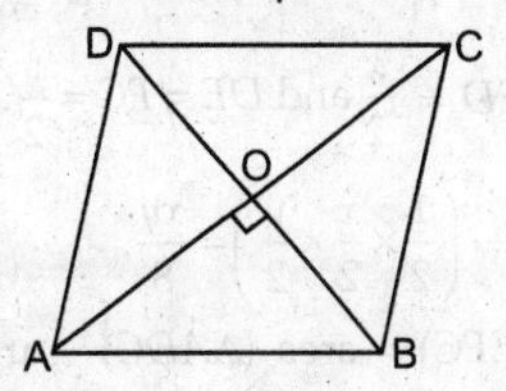

230. Let $AC = x$. Then, $BD = \frac{3}{4}x$.

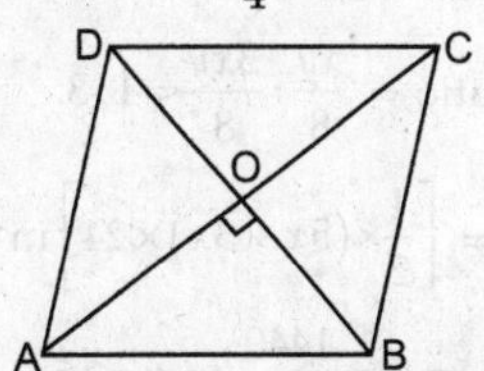

So, $OA=\frac{1}{2}AC=\frac{x}{2}$ and $OB=\frac{1}{2}BD=\frac{3}{8}x$.

$AB=\sqrt{(OA)^2+(OB)^2}=\sqrt{\left(\frac{x}{2}\right)^2+\left(\frac{3x}{8}\right)^2}$

$=\sqrt{\frac{x^2}{4}+\frac{9x^2}{64}}=\sqrt{\frac{25x^2}{64}}=\frac{5x}{8}.\ \frac{5x}{8}=20\Rightarrow x=\frac{20\times8}{5}=32$ m.

So, the length of diagonals are 32 m and 24 m.

∴ Area of the rhombus = $\left(\frac{1}{2}\times32\times24\right)\text{m}^2=384\text{ m}^2.$

231. $d_1=\left(\frac{80}{100}\times d_2\right)\Leftrightarrow d_1=\frac{4d_2}{5}$

Area of rhombus $=\frac{1}{2}d_1d_2=\left(\frac{1}{2}\times\frac{4d_2}{5}\times d_2\right)=\frac{2}{5}(d_2)^2.$

232. A square and a rhombus on the same base are equal in area.

233. Area of trapezium = $\left[\frac{1}{2}\times(1.5+2.5)\times6.5\right]\text{m}^2=13\text{ m}^2.$

234. Let the required distance be x cm.

Then, $\frac{1}{2}\times(6+10)\times x=32\Rightarrow x=4$ cm.

235. Let $ABCD$ be the given trapezium in which $AB \parallel CD$, E is the mid-point of AD, F is the mid-point of BC.

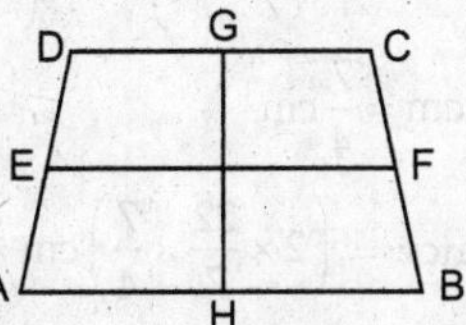

Then,

$EF=\frac{1}{2}(AB+CD)\Rightarrow AB+CD=2\,EF=(2\times4)\text{ cm}=8\text{ cm}.$

∴ Area of the trapezium = $\frac{1}{2}(AB+CD)\times GH$

$=\left(\frac{1}{2}\times8\times4\right)\text{cm}^2=16\text{ cm}^2.$

236. Let $AD = x$ and $DC = y$.

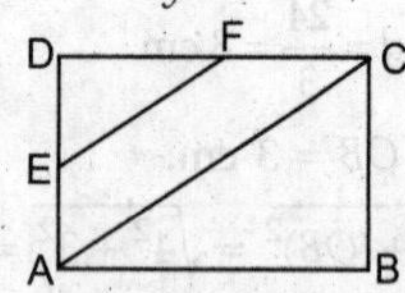

Then, $AE = ED = \frac{x}{2}$ and $DE = FC = \frac{y}{2}$.

area (ΔEDF) $= \left(\frac{1}{2} \times \frac{x}{2} \times \frac{y}{2}\right) = \frac{xy}{8}$.

area (trap. $AEFC$) = area (ΔADC) − area (ΔEDF)

$= \frac{xy}{2} - \frac{xy}{8} = \frac{3xy}{8}$.

$\therefore$ Required ratio $= \frac{xy}{8} : \frac{3xy}{8} = 1:3$.

237. Area of field $= \left[\frac{1}{2} \times (5x + 3x) \times 24\right] \text{m}^2 = (96x) \text{m}^2$.

$\therefore 96x = 1440 \Leftrightarrow x = \frac{1440}{96} \Leftrightarrow x = 15$.

Longer side of field = 5 × 15 = 75 m

238. $\frac{1}{2}$ (sum of parallel sides) × depth = Its area

$\Leftrightarrow \frac{1}{2}(12 + 8) \times d = 840 \Leftrightarrow d = 84$ m.

239. **(A)** Area $= \left(\frac{22}{7} \times 7 \times 7\right) \text{cm}^2 = 154 \text{ cm}^2$.

(B) Area = (12 × 10) cm^2 = 120 cm^2.

(C) Area = (12 × 12) cm^2 = 144 cm^2.

(D) Area = (14 × 11) cm^2 = 154 cm^2.

240. (*a*) Perimeter = (4 × 10) cm = 40 cm.

(*b*) Perimeter = 2(12 + 9) cm = 42 cm.

(*c*) Perimeter $= \left(2 \times \frac{22}{7} \times 7\right)$ cm = 44 cm.

(*d*) Perimeter = (4 × 9) cm = 36 cm.

241. (*a*) Side $= \sqrt{36}$ cm = 6 cm. Perimeter = (4 × 6) cm = 24 cm.

(*b*) Perimeter = (3 × 9) cm = 27 cm.

(*c*) Breadth $= \left(\frac{40}{10}\right)$ cm = 4 cm.

Perimeter = 2(10 + 4) cm = 28 cm.

(*d*) Perimeter $= \left(2 \times \frac{22}{7} \times 4\right) \text{cm} = \left(\frac{176}{7}\right) \text{cm} = 25.14$ cm.

242. Radius $= \frac{3.5}{2}$ cm $= \frac{7}{4}$ cm.

$\therefore$ Circumference $= \left(2 \times \frac{22}{7} \times \frac{7}{4}\right)$ cm = 11 cm.

243. Area of circle $= \left(\frac{22}{7} \times 14 \times 14\right) \text{cm}^2 = 616 \text{ cm}^2$.

Let the length of the rectangle be l cm.

Then, $22l = 616 \Rightarrow l = \frac{616}{22} = 28$ cm.

244. Required% $= \left[\frac{\pi \times (5)^2}{2\pi \times 5} \times 100\right]\% = 250\%$.

245. Speed = 12 km/hr $= \left(12 \times \frac{5}{18}\right)$ m/s $= \frac{10}{3}$ m/s.

Distance covered $= \left(20 \times 2 \times \frac{22}{7} \times 50\right)$ m $= \frac{44000}{7}$ m.

Time taken =

$\frac{\text{Distance}}{\text{Speed}} = \left(\frac{4400}{7} \times \frac{3}{10}\right) s = \left(\frac{4400 \times 3}{7} \times \frac{1}{60}\right) \text{min} = \frac{220}{7} \text{min}$

$= 31\frac{3}{7}$ min.

246. Area of the cut portion $= \left(4 \times \frac{22}{7} \times 5 \times 5\right) \text{cm}^2 = \left(\frac{2200}{7}\right) \text{cm}^2$.

Area of the uncut portion $= \left[\left(\frac{22}{7} \times 20 \times 20\right) - \frac{2200}{7}\right] \text{cm}^2$

$= \left(\frac{8800}{7} - \frac{2200}{7}\right) \text{cm}^2 = \left(\frac{6600}{7}\right) \text{cm}^2$.

$\therefore$ Required ratio $= \frac{6600}{7} : \frac{2200}{7} = 3:1$.

247. Area of the field grazed $= \left(\frac{22}{7} \times 14 \times 14\right)$ sq. ft = 616 sq. ft.

Number of days taken to graze the field

$= \frac{616}{100}$ days = 6 days (approx.).

248. $2\pi R = 2(l + b) \Leftrightarrow 2\pi R = 2(26 + 18)$ cm

$\Leftrightarrow R = \left(\frac{88}{2 \times 22} \times 7\right) = 14$ cm.

$\therefore$ Area of the circle $= \pi R^2 = \left(\frac{22}{7} \times 14 \times 14\right) \text{cm}^2 = 616 \text{ cm}^2$.

249. $2(14x + 11x) = 100 \Rightarrow 25x = 50 \Rightarrow x = 2$.

So, length and breadth of the rectangular field are 28 m and 22 m respectively.

Area of the circle = Area of the rectangular field = (28 × 22) m^2 = 616 m^2.

Let the radius of the circle be r meters.

Then, $\frac{22}{7} \times r^2 = 616 \Rightarrow r^2 = \frac{616 \times 7}{22} = 196 \Rightarrow r = 14$ m.

$\therefore$ Diameter = (2 × 14) m = 28 m.

250. $\pi R^2 = 24.64 \Leftrightarrow R^2 = \left(\frac{24.64}{22} \times 7\right) = 7.84 \Leftrightarrow R = \sqrt{7.84} = 2.8$ cm.

$\therefore$ Circumference $= \left(2 \times \frac{22}{7} \times 2.8\right)$ cm = 17.60 m.

251. $\pi R^2 = 18634 \Rightarrow R^2 = 18634 \times \frac{7}{22} = 5929 \Rightarrow R = 77$ m.

Circumference $= \left(2 \times \frac{22}{7} \times 77\right)$ m = 484 m.

$\therefore$ Cost of fencing = ₹ (365 × 484) = ₹ 176660.

252. $2\pi R = 396 \Rightarrow R = \frac{396 \times 7}{2 \times 22} = 63$ m.

Area $= \pi R^2 = \left(\frac{22}{7} \times 63 \times 63\right) m^2 = 12474\ m^2$.

253. $2\pi R = 1047.2 \Rightarrow R = \frac{1047.2 \times 7}{2 \times 22} = 166.6$ m.

$\therefore$ Area $= \pi R^2 = \left(\frac{22}{7} \times 166.6 \times 166.6\right) m^2 = 87231.76\ m^2$.

254. $2\pi R_1 = 132 \Rightarrow R_1 = \frac{132 \times 7}{2 \times 22} = 21$ m.

$2\pi R_2 = 176 \Rightarrow R_2 = \frac{176 \times 7}{2 \times 22} = 28$ m.

$\therefore$ Required difference $= \pi(R_2^2 - R_1^2) = \pi(R_2 + R_1)(R_2 - R_1)$

$= \left(\frac{22}{7} \times 49 \times 7\right) m^2 = 1078\ m^2$.

255. Circumference of the plot $= \left(\frac{3300}{15}\right)$ m $= 220$ m. $2\pi R = 220$

$\Rightarrow R = \frac{220 \times 7}{2 \times 22} = 35$ m.

Area of the plot $= \left(\frac{22}{7} \times 35 \times 35\right) m^2 = 3850\ m^2$.

$\therefore$ Cost of flooring = ₹ (3850 × 100) = ₹ 385000.

256. $2\pi R = \pi R^2 \Leftrightarrow R = 2 \Leftrightarrow 2R = 4$. Hence, diameter = 4.

257. $\pi R^2 = 7 \times (2\pi R) \Rightarrow R = 14$.

$\therefore$ Circumference $= \left(2 \times \frac{22}{7} \times 14\right)$ units = 88 units.

258. $2\pi R - R = 37 \Leftrightarrow \left(\frac{44}{7} - 1\right) R = 37 \Leftrightarrow R = 7$.

$\therefore$ Area of the circle $= \left(\frac{22}{7} \times 7 \times 7\right) cm^2 = 154\ cm^2$.

259. Let the radius of the new park be R m.

Then, $\pi R^2 = \pi \times 8^2 + \pi \times 6^2 = 100\pi \Rightarrow R^2 = 100$

$\Rightarrow R = 10$ m.

260. $\pi R_1^2 + \pi R_2^2 = \pi R_3^2 \Leftrightarrow R_1^2 + R_2^2 = R_3^2 \Leftrightarrow (9)^2 + R_2^2 = (15)^2$

$\Leftrightarrow R_2^2 = (15)^2 - (9)^2 = 144$

$\Leftrightarrow R_2 = 12$ cm.

261. We have : $R_1 + R_2 = 140$ ...(*i*)

And, $2\pi(R_1 - R_2) = 88 \Rightarrow R_1 - R_2 = \frac{88 \times 7}{2 \times 22} = 14$. ...(*ii*)

Adding (*i*) and (*ii*) we get : $2R_1 = 154$ or $R_1 = 77$.

Putting $R_1 = 77$ in (*i*) we get : $R_2 = 63$.

So, the diameters of the circles are 154 cm and 126 cm.

262. Let the height of the triangle be x cm.

Then, radius of the circle = (120 % of x) cm $= \left(\frac{6x}{5}\right)$ cm.

$\therefore \frac{1}{2} \times 36 \times x = \frac{22}{7} \times \frac{6x}{5} \times \frac{6x}{5} \Rightarrow x = \left(\frac{18 \times 7 \times 5 \times 5}{22 \times 6 \times 6}\right)$ cm.

So, radius of the circle $= \left[\frac{6}{5} \times \left(\frac{18 \times 7 \times 5 \times 5}{22 \times 6 \times 6}\right)\right]$ cm $= \left(\frac{105}{22}\right)$ cm.

$\therefore$ Area of the circle $= \left(\frac{22}{7} \times \frac{105}{22} \times \frac{105}{22}\right) cm^2 = \left(\frac{1575}{22}\right) cm^2$

$= 71.6\ cm^2 \approx 72\ cm^2$.

263. Let the radius of the pond be R metres.

Then, $\pi R^2 = 616 \Rightarrow R^2 = \frac{616 \times 7}{22} = 196 \Rightarrow R = 14$ m.

Radius of the stage $= \left(\frac{14}{2}\right)$ m $= 7$ m.

$\therefore$ Area where water is present

$= \pi(14^2 - 7^2) = \left(\frac{22}{7} \times 21 \times 7\right) m^2 = 462\ m^2$.

264. Side of the square $= \frac{44}{4}$ cm $= 11$ cm.

Area of the square $= (11 \times 11)\ cm^2 = 121\ cm^2$.

$2\pi R = 44 \Leftrightarrow 2 \times \frac{22}{7} \times R = 44 \Leftrightarrow R = 7$ cm.

Area of circle $= \pi R^2 = \left(\frac{22}{7} \times 7 \times 7\right) cm^2 = 154\ cm^2$.

$\therefore$ Area of the circle is larger by 33 cm^2.

265. Side of the square field $= \sqrt{12100}$ m $= 110$ m.

Perimeter of the circular field = Perimeter of the square field = (4 × 110) m = 440 m.

$2\pi R = 440 \Rightarrow R = \frac{440 \times 7}{2 \times 22} = 70$ m.

$\therefore$ Area of the circular field $= \left(\frac{22}{7} \times 70 \times 70\right) m^2 = 15400\ m^2$

266. Let the radius of the circle be R cm.

Then ,

$\pi R^2 = 39424 \Rightarrow R^2 = 39424 \times \frac{7}{22} = 12544 \Rightarrow R = 112$ cm.

Perimeter of the square = 112 cm.

Side of the square $= \left(\frac{112}{4}\right)$ cm $= 28$ cm.

$\therefore$ Area of the square = (28 × 28) cm^2 = 784 cm^2.

267. Length of wire $= 2\pi \times R = \left(2 \times \frac{22}{7} \times 56\right)$ cm $= 352$ cm.

Side of the square $= \frac{352}{4}$ cm $= 88$ cm.

Area of the square = (88 × 88) cm^2 = 7744 cm^2.

268. Area of the square = 407044 cm^2.

Side of the square $= \sqrt{407044}$ cm $= 638$ cm.

Circumference of circle = 638 cm.

Let the radius of the circle be R cm.

Then, $2\pi R = 638 \Rightarrow R = \frac{638 \times 7}{2 \times 22} = 101.5$ cm.

$\therefore$ Area of the circle $= \left(\frac{22}{7} \times 101.5 \times 101.5\right) cm^2 = 32378.5\ cm^2$.

269. Side of the square $= \sqrt{484}$ cm $= 22$ cm.

Perimeter of the square $= (22 \times 4)$ cm $= 88$ cm.

$2\pi R = 88 \Leftrightarrow 2 \times \frac{22}{7} \times R = 88 \Leftrightarrow R = \left(88 \times \frac{7}{44}\right) = 14$ cm.

$\therefore$ Required area $= \pi R^2 = \left(\frac{22}{7} \times 14 \times 14\right) \text{cm}^2 = 616 \text{ cm}^2$.

270. Length of wire $= 2\pi R = \left(2 \times \frac{22}{7} \times 21\right)$ cm $= 132$ cm.

Perimeter of rectangle $= 2(6x + 5x)$ cm $= 22x$ cm.

$\therefore$ $22x = 132 \Leftrightarrow x = 6$.

So, the sides of the rectangle are 36 cm and 30 cm.

$\therefore$ Area of the rectangle $= (36 \times 30) \text{ cm}^2 = 1080 \text{ cm}^2$.

271. Area of the flower bed $= [(100 \times 100) - 8614] \text{ m}^2$
$= 1386 \text{ m}^2$.

Let the radius of the circular flower bed be R metres.

Then, $\pi R^2 = 1386 \Rightarrow R^2 = \frac{1386 \times 7}{22} = 441 \Rightarrow R = 21$ m.

272. Total area of the field $= [(180 \times 120) + 40000] \text{ m}^2$
$= (21600 + 40000) \text{ m}^2 = 61600 \text{ m}^2$.

$\therefore$ $\pi R^2 = 61600 \Leftrightarrow R^2 = \left(61600 \times \frac{7}{22}\right) = (400 \times 7 \times 7)$ m

$\Leftrightarrow R = (20 \times 7)$ m $= 140$ m.

273. $\frac{\pi R_1^2}{\pi R_2^2} = \frac{4}{1} \Rightarrow \frac{R_1^2}{R_2^2} = \frac{4}{1} \Rightarrow \frac{R_1}{R_2} = \frac{2}{1}$.

274. $\frac{\pi R_1^2}{\pi R_2^2} = \frac{16}{49} \Leftrightarrow \frac{R_1^2}{(14 \times 14)} = \frac{16}{49}$

$\Leftrightarrow R_1^2 = \frac{14 \times 14 \times 16}{49}$

$\Leftrightarrow R_1 = \frac{14 \times 4}{7} = 8$ m.

275. Let the radii of the two circles be $3r$ and $2r$ respectively,

Then, required ratio $= \frac{2\pi(3r)}{2\pi(2r)} = \frac{3}{2} = 3:2$.

276. Let the radii of the two circles be r and $3r$ respectively.

Then, required ratio $= \frac{\pi r^2}{\pi(3r)^2} = \frac{\pi r^2}{9\pi r^2} = 1:9$.

277. $\frac{2\pi R_1}{2\pi R_2} = \frac{2}{3} \Rightarrow \frac{R_1}{R_2} = \frac{2}{3} \Rightarrow \frac{\pi R_1^2}{\pi R_2^2} = \left(\frac{2}{3}\right)^2 = \frac{4}{9}$.

278. Let the radius of the given circle be R cm and the side of the square be a cm.

Then, $2\pi R = 4a \Leftrightarrow \frac{R}{a} = \frac{2}{\pi}$.

Ratio of their areas $= \frac{\pi R^2}{a^2}$

$= \left(\pi \times \frac{4}{\pi^2}\right) = \left(\frac{4}{22} \times 7\right)$

$= \frac{14}{11} = 14:11$.

279. Let the area of each of the circle and the square be x sq.units.

Let the radius of the circle be r units and the side of the square be a unit.

Then, $\pi r^2 = x \Rightarrow r = \sqrt{\frac{x}{\pi}}$. And, $a^2 = x \Rightarrow a = \sqrt{x}$.

$\therefore$ Required ratio $= \frac{\sqrt{x}}{\sqrt{\frac{x}{\pi}}} = \sqrt{\pi}:1$.

280. Proceeding as in Q.279, we have:

Ratio of perimeters $= \frac{2\pi\sqrt{\frac{x}{\pi}}}{4\sqrt{x}} = \sqrt{\pi}:2$.

281. Distance covered in 1 revolution $= 2\pi R$

$= \left(2 \times \frac{22}{7} \times 0.63\right)$ m $= \frac{99}{25}$ m.

....

$= \left(\frac{99}{25} \times 500\right)$ m $= 1980$ m.

282. Distance covered in 1 revolution

$= \left(2 \times \frac{22}{7} \times \frac{56}{2}\right)$ cm $= 176$ cm.

Required number of revolutions

$= \left(\frac{1.1 \times 1000 \times 100}{176}\right) = 625$.

283. Distance covered in 1 revolution

$= \left(2 \times \frac{22}{7} \times 70\right)$ cm $= 440$ cm.

Number of revolutions made in 1 hr

$= \left(\frac{66 \times 1000 \times 100}{440}\right) = 15000$.

$\therefore$ Number of revolutions per minute $= \frac{15000}{60} = 250$.

284. Distance covered in 4 sec $= \left(\frac{30}{7} \times 7\right)$ m $= 30$ m.

Distance covered in 1 sec $= \frac{30}{4}$

Distance covered in 1 revolution $= \left(\frac{30}{4}\right)$ m $= \frac{15}{2}$ m.

$\therefore$ Required speed $= \left(\frac{15}{2}\right)$ m/s $= \left(\frac{15}{2} \times \frac{18}{5}\right)$ km/hr $= 27$ km/hr.

285. Distance covered in 5 sec $= \left(2 \times \frac{22}{7} \times 70 \times 10\right)$ cm

$= 4400$ cm $= 44$ m.

Distance covered in 1 sec $= \left(\frac{44}{5}\right)$ m $= 8.8$ m.

$\therefore$ Speed $= 8.8$ m/sec $= \left(8.8 \times \frac{18}{5}\right)$ km/hr

$= 31.68$ km/hr.

286. Distance covered in 1 revolution $= \left(2 \times \frac{22}{7} \times 35\right)$ cm = 220 cm.

Total distance covered by the wheel = (22 × 30) km = 660 km.

∴ Number of revolutions made by the wheel

$= \left(\frac{660 \times 1000 \times 100}{220}\right) = 300000.$

287. Let each wheel make x revolutions per sec.

Then, $\left[\left(2\pi \times \frac{7}{2} \times x\right) + (2\pi \times 7 \times x)\right] \times 10 = 1980$

$\Leftrightarrow \left(\frac{22}{7} \times 7 \times x\right) + \left(2 \times \frac{22}{7} \times 7 \times x\right) = 198$

$\Leftrightarrow 66x = 198 \Leftrightarrow x = 3.$

Distance moved by smaller wheel in 3 revolutions

$= \left(2 \times \frac{22}{7} \times \frac{7}{2} \times 3\right)$ cm = 66 cm.

∴ Speed of smaller wheel $= \frac{66}{3}$ cm/s = 22 cm/s.

288. Distance covered by smaller wheel in 1 revolution
$= (2\pi \times 15)$ cm $= (30\pi)$ cm.

Distance covered by larger wheel in 1 revolution
$= (2\pi \times 25)$ cm $= (50\pi)$ cm.

Let $k \times 30\pi = 15 \times 50\pi$. Then, $k = \left(\frac{15 \times 50\pi}{30\pi}\right) = 25.$

∴ Required number of revolutions = 25.

289. Required number of rotations

$= \frac{\text{Circumference of bigger ring}}{\text{Circumference of smaller ring}} = \frac{2 \times \pi \times 10}{2 \times \pi \times 2} = 5.$

290. Let the diameter of the wheel be d metres.

Distance covered in 1 revolution = (πd) m.

Distance covered in 113 revolutions = $(113\pi d)$ m.

$\therefore 113 \times \frac{22}{7} \times d = 226 \times 10$

$\Leftrightarrow d = \left(226 \times 10 \times \frac{7}{22} \times \frac{1}{113}\right) \text{m} = 6\frac{4}{11} \text{m}.$

291. Let the rear wheel make x revolutions. Then, the front wheel makes $(x + 5)$ revolutions.

$(x + 5) \times 40 = 48x \Rightarrow 8x = 200 \Rightarrow x = 25.$

Distance travelled by the cart = (48 × 25) ft = 1200 ft.

292. Circumference of the front wheel $= \left(2 \times \frac{22}{7} \times 14\right)$ cm = 88 cm.

Circumference of the rear wheel $= \left(2 \times \frac{22}{7} \times 21\right)$ cm = 132 cm.

Required distance = L.C.M. of 88 cm and 132 cm = 264 cm.

293. Time taken by front wheel to complete one revolution

$= \left(\frac{3.5}{15}\right)$ sec $= \frac{7}{30}$ sec.

Time taken by rear wheel to complete one revolution

$= \left(\frac{3}{15}\right)$ sec $= \frac{1}{5}$ sec.

∴ Required time $= \left[\text{L.C.M. of } \frac{7}{30} \text{ and } \frac{1}{5}\right]$ sec

$= \left(\frac{\text{L.C.M. of 7 and 1}}{\text{H.C.F. of 30 and 5}}\right)$ sec $= \frac{7}{5}$ sec = 1.4 sec.

294. Let the circumference of front wheel be x metres.

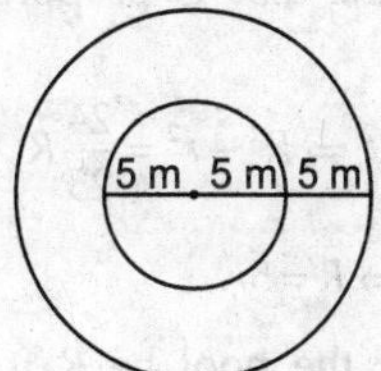

Then, circumference of rear wheel = $(x - 1)$ metres.

$\therefore \frac{600}{x} - \frac{600}{(x+1)} = 30 \Rightarrow \frac{1}{x(x+1)} = \frac{1}{20}$

$\Rightarrow x(x-1) = 20 \Rightarrow (x^2 + x - 20 = 0$

$\Rightarrow (x + 5)(x - 4) = 0 \Rightarrow x = 4\text{m}.$

295. Since the diameter is the longest chord of a circle, so maximum possible distance = (10 + 5) m = 15 m.

296. Radius of the ground = 17.5 m. Radius of inner circle
= (17.5 – 1.4) m = 16.1 m.

Area of the garden $= \pi \times [(17.5)^2 - (16.1)^2]\,\text{m}^2$

$= \left[\frac{22}{7} \times (17.5 + 16.1)(17.5 - 16.1)\right] \text{m}^2$

$= \left[\frac{22}{7} \times 33.6 \times 1.4\right] \text{m}^2 = 147.84\ \text{m}^2.$

297. Radius of the plot = 21 m.

Area of the path

$= \pi[(24.5)^2 - (21)^2]\,\text{m}^2 = [\pi(24.5 + 21)(24.5 - 21)]\,\text{m}^2$

$= \left(\frac{22}{7} \times 45.5 \times 3.5\right) \text{m}^2 = 500.5\ \text{m}^2.$

∴ Cost of gravelling = ₹ (500.5 × 4) = ₹ 2002.

298. Uncut area $= \pi(5^3 - 3^2)$ cm $= \left(\frac{22}{7} \times 8 \times 2\right) \text{cm}^2.$

Let the required radius be r cm.

Then, $\pi r^2 = \left(\frac{22}{7} \times 16\right) \Rightarrow r^2 = 16 \Rightarrow r = 4$ cm.

299. Let the radius of the ground be R metres.

Then, $2\pi R = 88 \Rightarrow R = \left(\frac{88 \times 7}{2 \times 22}\right) = 14$ m.

Area of land strip $= \pi[(14)^2 - (11)^2]\,\text{m}^2 = \left(\frac{22}{7} \times 25 \times 3\right) \text{m}^2$

$= \left(\frac{1650}{7}\right) \text{m}^2.$

∴ Cost of levelling = ₹ $\left(\frac{1650}{7} \times 7\right)$ = ₹ 1650.

300. $\pi R_1^2 = 616 \Leftrightarrow R_1^2 = \left(616 \times \frac{7}{22}\right) = 196 \Leftrightarrow R_1 = 14$ cm.

$\pi R_2^2 = 154 \Leftrightarrow R_2^2 = \left(154 \times \frac{7}{22}\right) = 49 \Leftrightarrow R_2 = 7$ cm.

Breadth of the ring = $(R_1 - R_2)$ cm = (14 – 7) cm = 7 cm.

301. Let the radii of the outer and inner circles be R and r respectively.

Then, $2\pi R - 2\pi r = 44 \Rightarrow 2\pi(R-r) = 44$

$$\Rightarrow (R-r) = \frac{44 \times 7}{22 \times 2} = 7.$$

302. Since weight of the disc is proportional to its area, we have:

$$\pi(R^2 - r^2) = \frac{24}{25}\pi R^2 \Rightarrow R^2 - r^2 = \frac{24}{25}R^2 \Rightarrow r^2 = \frac{1}{25}R^2$$

$$R^2 = 25r^2 \Rightarrow R = 5r.$$

303. Let the radius of the pool be R ft. Radius of the pool including the wall = $(R + 4)$ ft.

Area of the concrete wall

$= \pi[(R+4)^2 - R^2]$ sq. ft

$= \pi[(R+4+R)(R+4-R]$ sq. ft $= 8\pi\ (R+2)$ sq.ft.

$8\pi\ (R+2) = \frac{11}{25}\pi R^2$

$\Leftrightarrow 11R^2 = 200\ (R + 2$

$\Leftrightarrow 11R^2 - 200R - 400 = 0$

$\Leftrightarrow 11R^2 - 220R + 20R - 400 = 0$

$\Leftrightarrow 11R\ (R - 20) + 20\ (R - 20) = 0$

$\Leftrightarrow (R - 20)\ (11R + 20) = 0 \Leftrightarrow R = 20.$

$\Leftrightarrow$ Radius of the pool = 20 ft.

304. $\frac{2\pi R_1}{2\pi R_2} = \frac{23}{22} \Leftrightarrow \frac{R_1}{R_2} = \frac{23}{22} \Leftrightarrow R_1 = \frac{23}{22}R_2.$

Also, $R_1 - R_2 = 5$ m

$\Leftrightarrow \frac{23R_2}{22} - R_2 = 5 \Leftrightarrow R_2 = 110.$

$\Leftrightarrow$ Diameter of inner circle = (2×110) m = 220 m.

305. Let the radius of the given circle be R. Let the radii of the two inner circles be R_1 and R_2.

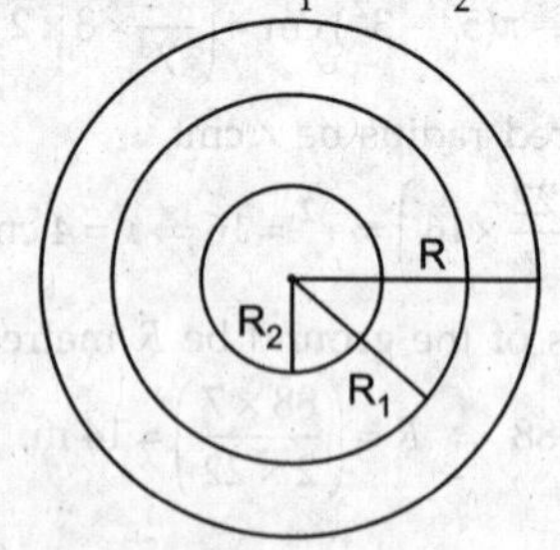

Then, $\pi(R_1^2 - R_2^2) = \pi R_2^2$

$\Rightarrow R_1^2 - R_2^2 = R_2^2$

$\Rightarrow R_1^2 = 2R_1^2 \Rightarrow \frac{R_2^2}{R_1^2} = \frac{1}{2} \Rightarrow \frac{R_2}{R_1} = \frac{1}{\sqrt{2}}.$

306. Let the original radius of the circle be R cm.

Then, $\pi[(R+1)^2 - R^2] = 22 \Rightarrow (2R+1) = \frac{22 \times 7}{22} = 7$

$$\Rightarrow 2R = 6 \Rightarrow R = 3 \text{ cm}.$$

307. Perimeter of rectangle = $[2(8 + 7)]$ cm = 30 cm.

Perimeter of square = (2×30) cm = 60 cm.

Side of the square = $\left(\frac{60}{4}\right)$ cm = 15 cm.

Radius of the semi-circle = $\left(\frac{15}{2}\right)$ cm.

$\therefore$ Circumference = $\left(\frac{22}{7} \times \frac{15}{2}\right)$ cm $= \left(\frac{165}{7}\right)$ cm = 23.57 cm.

308. Area of the semi circle

$$= \frac{1}{2}\pi R^2 = \left(\frac{1}{2} \times \frac{22}{7} \times 7 \times 7\right) \text{m}^2 = 77 \text{ m}^2.$$

309. Perimeter of window

$$= \pi R + 2R = \left(\frac{22}{7} \times \frac{63}{2} + 63\right) \text{cm} = (99 + 63) \text{ cm} = 162 \text{ cm}.$$

310. $\pi R = 33 \Rightarrow R = \left(\frac{33 \times 7}{22}\right) = \left(\frac{21}{2}\right)$ m.

$\therefore$ Required distance = $2R$ = 21 m.

311. Given :

$$= \pi R + 2R = 36 \Leftrightarrow (\pi + 2)R = 36 \Leftrightarrow R = \frac{36}{\left(\frac{22}{7} + 2\right)} \text{cm} = 7 \text{ cm}.$$

Required area = $\frac{\pi R^2}{2} = \left(\frac{22}{7} \times \frac{7 \times 7}{2}\right) \text{cm}^2 = 77 \text{ cm}^2.$

312. $\frac{\pi R^2}{2} = 11088 \Rightarrow R^2 = 11088 \times 2 \times \frac{7}{22} = 7056 \Rightarrow R = 84$ m.

$\therefore$ Perimeter = $\pi R + 2R = \left(\frac{22}{7} \times 84 + 2 \times 84\right)$ m = 432 m.

313. Length of each side of the square = $\sqrt{81}$ cm = 9 cm.

Length of wire = (9×4) cm = 36 cm.

$$\pi R + 2R = 36 \Leftrightarrow (\pi + 2)R = 36 \Leftrightarrow R = \frac{36}{\left(\frac{22}{7} + 2\right)} = 7 \text{cm}.$$

Area of the semicircle

$$= \frac{1}{2}\pi R^2 = \left(\frac{1}{2} \times \frac{22}{7} \times 7 \times 7\right) \text{cm}^2 = 77 \text{cm}^2.$$

314. Area of the shaded region

$$= \frac{1}{2}\pi\left(\frac{LM}{2}\right)^2 + \frac{1}{2}\pi\left(\frac{LN}{2}\right)^2 + \frac{1}{2}\pi\left(\frac{MN}{2}\right)^2$$

$$= \frac{1}{8}\pi\left[(LM)^2 + (LN)^2 + (MN)^2\right] = \frac{1}{8}\pi\,[2\,(MN)^2]$$

$$= \frac{1}{4}\pi\,(MN)^2 = \frac{1}{4}\pi x^2.$$

315. Area of the shaded portion = Area of semi-circle with AB as diameter + Area of semi-circle with BC as diameter + Area (ΔABC) – Area of semi-circle with AC as diameter

$$= \frac{1}{2}\pi\left(\frac{AB}{2}\right)^2 + \frac{1}{2}\pi\left(\frac{BC}{2}\right)^2 + 12 - \frac{1}{2}\pi\left(\frac{AC}{2}\right)^2$$

$$= \frac{1}{8}\pi\left[(AB)^2 + (BC)^2 - (AC)^2\right] + 12 = \frac{1}{8}\pi\,[(AC)^2 - (AC)^2] + 12$$

= 12 sq. units. $[\because (AB)^2 + (BC)^2 = (AC)^2]$

316. Perimeter of the shaded area = Sum of circumferences of semi-circles with OP, PQ and OQ as diameters.

$$= \pi\left(\frac{OP}{2}\right) + \pi\left(\frac{PQ}{2}\right) + \pi\left(\frac{OQ}{2}\right)$$

$$= [\pi(7+7+14)]\text{cm} = \left(\frac{22}{7}\times 28\right)\text{cm} = 88 \text{ cm}.$$

317. Let the length of the side of the square be x cm.

Then, radius of each semi circle $= \left(\frac{x}{2}\right)$ cm.

Total area $= \left[x^2 + \frac{\pi}{2}\left(\frac{x}{2}\right)^2 + \frac{\pi}{2}\left(\frac{x}{2}\right)^2\right]\text{cm}^2$

$$= \left(x^2 + \frac{\pi}{4}x^2\right)\text{cm}^2.$$

$$\therefore\ x^2 + \frac{\pi}{4}x^2 = 350 \Rightarrow x^2 + \frac{22x^2}{28} = 350$$

$$\Rightarrow x^2 + \frac{11x^2}{14} = 350$$

$$\Rightarrow \frac{25x^2}{14} = 350 \Rightarrow x^2 = \left(\frac{350\times 14}{25}\right) = 196$$

$$\Rightarrow x = 14 \text{ cm}.$$

318. Area of the shaded portion = (Sum of areas of 2 smaller semi-circles + Sum of areas of 2 bigger semi-circles) – Sum of areas of 2 smaller semi-circles

= Sum of areas of 2 bigger semi-circles

$$= \left(2\times\frac{\pi R^2}{2}\right)\text{sq. units} = (\pi R^2) \text{ sq. units}.$$

319. Required length = $2a$ + Sum of circumferences of 2 semi-circles of radius $r = 2a + 2\pi r = 2(a + \pi r)$.

320. Area of the shaded region = Area of the semi-circle with radius a units – Area of the triangle with base $2a$ units and height a units

$$= \left(\frac{\pi a^2}{2} - \frac{1}{2}\times 2a\times a\right)\text{sq. units}.$$

$$= \left(\frac{\pi a^2}{2} - a^2\right)\text{sq. units} = a^2\left(\frac{\pi}{2} - 1\right)\text{sq.units}$$

321. Area of the track = Area of the two rectangles + Area of the two semi-circular ring ends

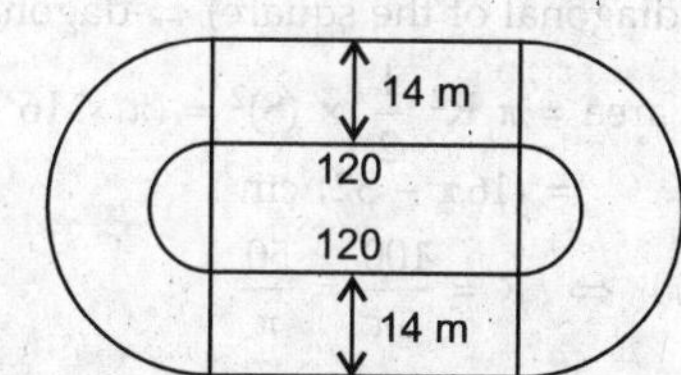

$$= \left[(2\times 120\times 14) + 2\times\frac{\pi}{2}\times\{(49)^2 - (35)^2\}\right]\text{m}^2$$

$$= \left[3360 + \frac{22}{7}\times(49+35)(49-35)\right]\text{m}^2$$

$$= \left(3360 + \frac{22}{7}\times 84\times 14\right)\text{m}^2 = (3360 + 3696)\text{ m}^2 = 7056 \text{ m}^2.$$

322. Let each side of the square be a cm and the radius of the semi-circle be r cm.

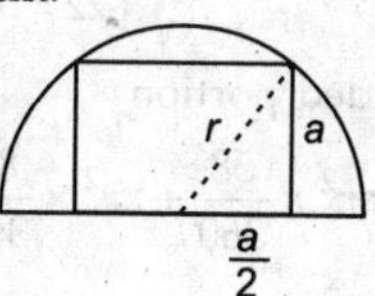

Then, $a^2 = 40 \text{ cm}^2$.

$$r^2 = a^2 + \left(\frac{a}{2}\right)^2 = a^2 + \frac{a^2}{4} = \frac{5a^2}{4} = \left(\frac{5\times 40}{4}\right) = 50.$$

$$\therefore \text{Area of the semi-circle} = \frac{\pi r^2}{2} = \left(\pi\times\frac{50}{2}\right)\text{cm}^2 - (25\pi)\text{cm}^2.$$

323. Let the radius of each of the circle and the semi-circle be r units.

Diagonal of the first square = $(2r)$ units.

Let the side of the second square be a units.

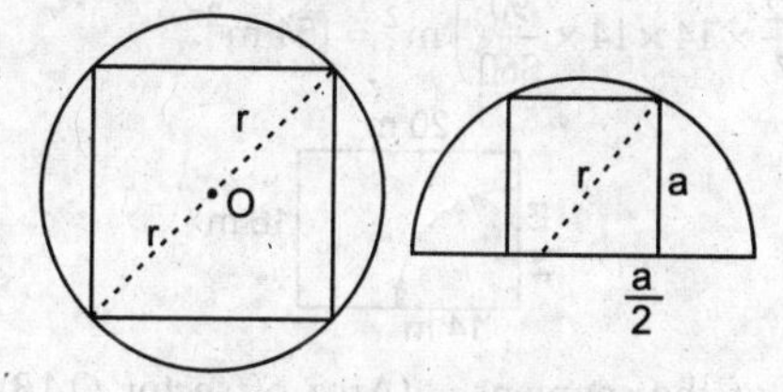

Then, $r^2 = a^2 + \left(\frac{a}{2}\right)^2 \Rightarrow r^2 = \frac{5a^2}{4} \Rightarrow a^2 = \frac{4r^2}{5}.$

$\therefore$ Ratio of the areas of the two squares

$$= \frac{\frac{1}{2}\times(2r)^2}{a^2} = \frac{2r^2}{\left(\frac{4r^2}{5}\right)} = \frac{5}{2} = 5:2.$$

324. Clearly, the radii of the semi-circular ends along the length and breadth are $\left(\frac{42}{2}\right)$ m and $\left(\frac{35}{2}\right)$ m. i.e. 21 m and 17.5 m respectively.

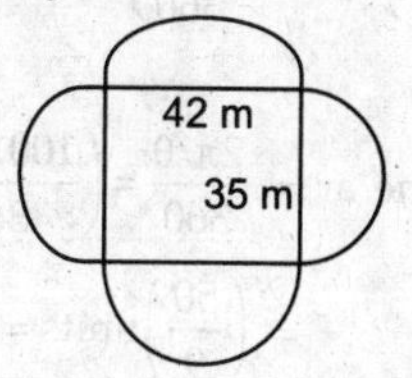

$\therefore$ Area of the total field = Area of rectangle with dimensions 42 m × 35 m + 2 × Area of semi-circle with radius 21 m + 2 × Area of semi-circle with radius 17.5 m

$$= \left(42\times 35 + 2\times\frac{22}{7}\times\frac{21\times 21}{2} + 2\times\frac{22}{7}\times\frac{17.5\times 17.5}{2}\right)\text{m}^2$$

$$= (1470 + 1386 + 962.5)\text{ m}^2 = 3818.5 \text{ m}^2.$$

325. Area of the sector

$$= \left(\frac{1}{2}\times \text{arc}\times R\right) = \left(\frac{1}{2}\times 3.5\times 5\right)\text{cm}^2 = 8.75 \text{ cm}^2.$$

326. Area of the sector

$$= \frac{\pi R^2\theta}{360} = \left(\frac{22}{7}\times 7\times 7\times\frac{108}{360}\right)\text{cm}^2 = 46.2 \text{ cm.}^2$$

327. $\frac{\pi R^2 \times 56}{360} = 17.6 \Rightarrow R^2 = \left(\frac{17.6 \times 360 \times 7}{22 \times 56}\right) = 36 \Rightarrow R = 6$ cm.

328. Area of the shaded portion

$$= \left(\pi r^2 \times \frac{42}{360} + \pi r^2 \times \frac{58}{360} + \pi r^2 \times \frac{80}{360}\right) \text{cm}^2$$

$$= \left[\frac{\pi r^2}{360}(42 + 58 + 80)\right] \text{cm}^2 = \left[\frac{22}{7} \times (\sqrt{7})^2 \times \frac{180}{360}\right] \text{cm}^2 = 11 \text{ cm}^2.$$

329. Angle traced by the minute hand in 5 minutes

$$= \left(\frac{360}{60} \times 5\right)^\circ = 30^\circ.$$

∴ Area of the sector

$$= \left(\frac{22}{7} \times 7 \times 7 \times \frac{30}{360}\right) \text{cm}^2 = 12.83 \text{ cm}^2.$$

330. Required area = Area of the quadrant with radius 14 m

$$= \left(\frac{22}{7} \times 14 \times 14 \times \frac{90}{360}\right) \text{m}^2 = 154 \text{ m}^2.$$

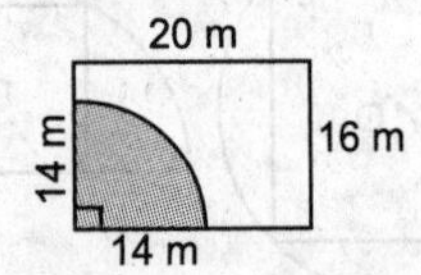

331. Area of the segment = (Area of sector OAB) – (Area of ΔOAB)

$$= \left(\frac{\pi r^2 \theta}{360^\circ} - \frac{1}{2} r^2 \sin\theta\right) = r^2 \left(\frac{\pi\theta}{360^\circ} - \frac{1}{2}\sin\theta\right)$$

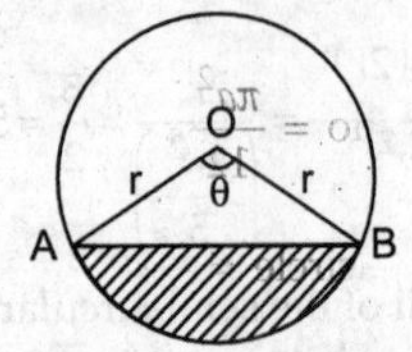

332. Length of the arc

$$= \frac{2\pi r\theta}{360} = \left(2 \times \frac{22}{7} \times 21 \times \frac{56}{360}\right) \text{cm} = \left(\frac{308}{15}\right) \text{cm} = 20.53 \text{ cm}.$$

333. $2\pi r = 100$.

So, length of the ar $= \frac{2\pi r\theta}{360} = \left(\frac{100 \times 20}{360}\right)$ units

$$= \left(\frac{50}{9}\right) \text{units} = 5.55 \text{ units}.$$

334. Side of the square $= \frac{120}{4}$ cm = 30 cm.

Radius of the required circle $= \left(\frac{1}{2} \times 30\right)$ cm = 15 cm.

....

= π× 2 2

$$= \left[\frac{22}{7} \times (15)^2\right] \text{cm}^2.$$

335. Radius of the requird circle $= \left(\frac{1}{2} \times 30\right)$ cm = 15 cm.

Area of the circle $= \left(\frac{22}{7} \times 7 \times 7\right) \text{cm}^2 = 154 \text{ cm}^2.$

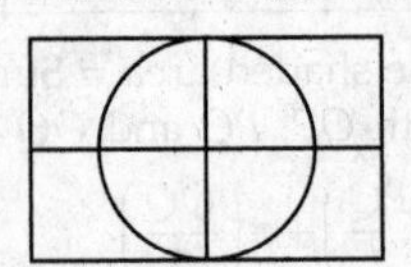

336. Diameter of the circle $= AC = \sqrt{(AB)^2 + (BC)^2}$

$$= \sqrt{8^2 + 6^2} \text{ cm} = \sqrt{100} \text{ cm} = 10 \text{ cm}.$$

Radius = 5 cm.

Required area = (Area of the circle) – (Area of the rectangle)

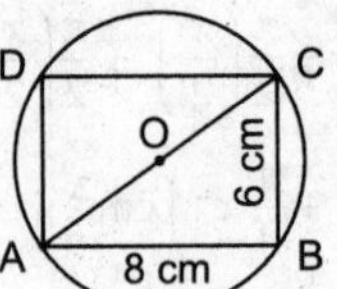

$$= \left[\left(\frac{22}{7} \times 5 \times 5\right) - (8 \times 6)\right] \text{cm}^2$$

$$= \left(\frac{550}{7} - 48\right) \text{cm}^2 = \left(\frac{214}{7}\right) \text{cm}^2 = 30.57 \text{ cm}^2 \approx 30.6 \text{ cm}^2.$$

337. Area of the rectangle = 32 cm². One side = 8 cm.

Other side $= \left(\frac{32}{8}\right)$ cm = 4 cm

∴ Diameter of the circle = Diagonal of the rectangle

$$= \sqrt{8^2 + 4^2} \text{ cm} = \sqrt{80} \text{ cm} = 4\sqrt{5} \text{ cm}.$$

338. $\pi R^2 = 220 \Leftrightarrow R^2 = \left(220 \times \frac{7}{22}\right) = 70.$

Now, $R = \frac{1}{2} \times (\text{diagonal}) \Leftrightarrow \text{diagonal} = 2R.$

Area of the seuare

$$= \frac{1}{2} \times (\text{diagonal})^2 = \left(\frac{1}{2} \times 4R^2\right) - 2R^2 = (2 \times 70) \text{ cm}^2 = 140 \text{ cm}^2.$$

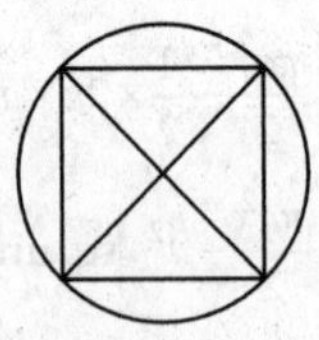

339. Given R = 4 cm.

$R = \frac{1}{2} \times$ (diagonal of the square) ⇔ diagonal = 2R = 8 cm

Required area = π R² $\frac{1}{2}$ × (8)² = (π × 16 – 32)

= (16π – 32) cm².

340. $2\pi R = 100 \Leftrightarrow R = \frac{100}{2\pi} = \frac{50}{\pi}.$

$$R = \frac{1}{2} \times \text{diagonal} \Leftrightarrow \text{diagonal} = 2R = \frac{2 \times 50}{\pi} = \frac{100}{\pi}.$$

$$\therefore \text{ Area of the square} = \frac{1}{2} \times (\text{diagonal})^2 = \frac{1}{2} \times \left(\frac{100}{\pi}\right)^2$$

$$\Leftrightarrow a^2 = \frac{1}{2} \times \left(\frac{100}{\pi}\right)^2 \Leftrightarrow a = \frac{1}{\sqrt{2}} \times \frac{100}{\pi} = \frac{50\sqrt{2}}{\pi} \text{ cm}.$$

341. Let r_1 and r_2 be the radii of the inscribed and circumscribed circles respectively.

Then, $r_1 = \frac{5}{2}$ cm.

$r_2 = \frac{1}{2} \times$ diagonal of the square $= \frac{1}{2} \times 5\sqrt{2} = \frac{5\sqrt{2}}{2}$ cm.

$\therefore$ Required ratio $= \dfrac{2\pi \times \frac{5\sqrt{2}}{2}}{2\pi \times \left(\frac{5}{2}\right)} = \sqrt{2}:1.$

342. Let the radius of the circle be r and the side of the square be a.

Then, diagonal of the square

$= 2r \Rightarrow \sqrt{2}\,a = 2r \Rightarrow a = \frac{2}{\sqrt{2}}\,r = \sqrt{2}r.$

Area of one shaded portion $= \frac{1}{4}\left[\pi r^2 - (\sqrt{2}r)^2\right] = \frac{1}{4}(\pi - 2)\,r^2.$

$\therefore \frac{1}{4}(\pi - 2)r^2 = \frac{4}{7} \Rightarrow \left(\frac{22}{7} - 2\right)r^2 = \frac{16}{7} \Rightarrow r^2 = \frac{16}{7} \times \frac{7}{8} \times 2$

$\Rightarrow r = \sqrt{2}.$

343. Let r_1 and r_2 be the radii of the incircle and circumcircle of a square respectively and let each side of the square be a.

Then, $r_1 = \frac{a}{2}$, $r_2 = \frac{1}{2} \times$ diagonal of the sequence

$= \frac{1}{2} \times \sqrt{2}a = \frac{\sqrt{2}a}{2}$ cm.

$\therefore$ Required ratio $= \dfrac{\pi \times \left(\frac{a}{2}\right)^2}{\pi \times \left(\frac{\sqrt{2}a}{2}\right)^2} = 1:2.$

344. Let the radius of the circle be r and the side of the circumscribed and inscribed squares be a_1 and a_2 respectively. Then, $a_1 = 2r$.

Diagonal of inscribed square

$= 2r \Rightarrow \sqrt{2}a_2 = 2r \Rightarrow a_2 = \frac{2r}{\sqrt{2}} = \sqrt{2}\,r.$

$\therefore$ Required ratio $= \frac{a_1^2}{a_2^2} = \frac{(2r)^2}{(\sqrt{2}r)^2} = \frac{4r^2}{2r^2} = 2:1.$

345. Radius of each circle = 2 units.

Area of the shaded region

= Area of the rectangle – Area of two circles

$= [(8 \times 4) - 2 \times \pi(2)^2]$ sq. units $= (32 - 8\pi)$ sq. units.

346. Side of square paper $= \sqrt{784}$ cm = 28 cm.

Radius of each circular plate $= \left(\frac{1}{4} \times 28\right)$ cm = 7 cm.

Circumference of each circular plate $= \left(2 \times \frac{22}{7} \times 7\right)$ cm

= 44 cm

347. Length of the fence $= 4\pi R$,

where $R = \frac{21}{2}$ m

$= \left(4 \times \frac{22}{7} \times \frac{21}{2}\right)$ m = 132 m.

Cost of fencing = ₹ $\left(132 \times \frac{25}{2}\right)$ = ₹ 1650.

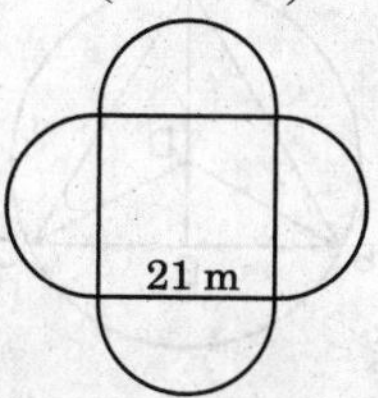

348. $\frac{a}{\sqrt{3}} = 8 \Rightarrow \frac{a}{2\sqrt{3}} = \frac{1}{2} \times 8 = 4$ cm.

$\left[\because \text{circum radius} = \frac{a}{\sqrt{3}}, \text{inradius} = \frac{a}{2\sqrt{3}}\right]$

349. Radius of incircle of an equilateral triangle $= \frac{a}{2\sqrt{3}}$.

Radius of circumcircle of an equilateral triangle $= \frac{a}{\sqrt{3}}$.

$\therefore$ Required ratio $= \frac{\pi a^2}{12} : \frac{\pi a^2}{3} = \frac{1}{12} : \frac{1}{3} = 1:4.$

350. Radius of circumcircle $= \frac{a}{\sqrt{3}} = \frac{12}{\sqrt{3}}$ cm $= 4\sqrt{3}$ cm.

351. Radius of incircle $= \frac{a}{2\sqrt{3}} = \frac{42}{2\sqrt{3}}$ cm $= 7\sqrt{3}$ cm.

Area of incircle $= \left(\frac{22}{7} \times 49 \times 3\right)$ cm² = 462 cm².

352. Radius of incircle $= \frac{a}{2\sqrt{3}}$.

Area of incircle $= \left(\frac{\pi \times a^2}{12}\right)$ cm².

$\therefore \frac{\pi a^2}{12} = 154 \Leftrightarrow a^2 = \frac{154 \times 12 \times 7}{22} \Leftrightarrow a = 14\sqrt{3}.$

$\therefore$ Perimeter of the triangle $= (3 \times 14\sqrt{3})$ cm

$= (42 \times 1.732)$ cm = 72.7 cm (approx.)

353. Side of equilateral triangle, $a = 4\sqrt{3}$ cm. Radius of circle,

$r = \frac{a}{\sqrt{3}} = \left(\frac{4\sqrt{3}}{\sqrt{3}}\right)$ cm = 4 cm.

Let each side of the square be x cm.

Then, $x = 2r = 8$ cm.

$\therefore$ Diagonal of the square

$= \sqrt{8^2 + 8^2}$ cm $= \sqrt{128}$ cm $= 8\sqrt{2}$ cm.

354. We have: $AE \perp BC$ and $AD = BD = CD = r$.

$AE = AD + DE = r + DE$.

In ΔBDC,

$BE = \sqrt{(BD)^2 - (DE)^2} = \sqrt{r^2 - (DE)^2} = \sqrt{(r - DE)(r + DE)}$.

$\therefore$ Area of the triangle $= \frac{1}{2} \times BC \times AE$

$= \frac{1}{2} \times 2BE \times AE = BE \times AE = \sqrt{(r - DE)(r + DE)}\ (r + DE)$

$= (r - DE)^{\frac{1}{2}} (r + DE)^{\frac{3}{2}}$.

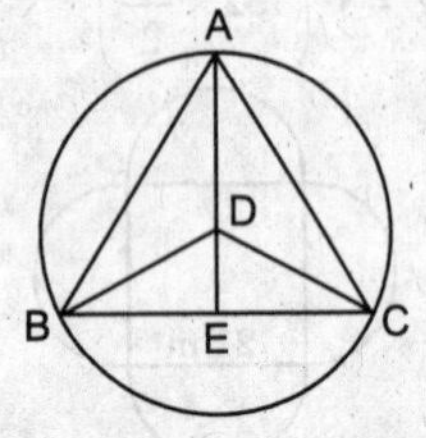

355. Let A, B and C denote the positions of the three boys. Then, $AB = BC = AC$.

So, ΔABC is equilateral.

Let the side of ΔABC be a.

Then, $\frac{a}{\sqrt{3}} = 5 \Rightarrow a = 5\sqrt{3}$.

$\therefore$ Required shortest distance $= 5\sqrt{3}$ m.

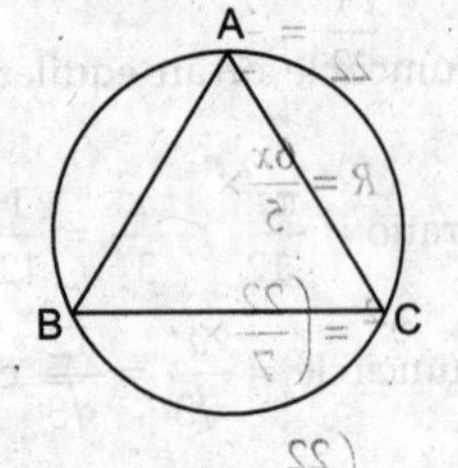

356. Radius, $r = 1$.

Let each side of the equilateral triangle be a.

Then, $\frac{a}{\sqrt{3}} = 1$ or $a = \sqrt{3}$.

$\therefore$ Area of the triangle

$= \frac{\sqrt{3}}{4} a^2 = \frac{\sqrt{3}}{4} \times (\sqrt{3})^2 = \frac{3\sqrt{3}}{4}$ sq. units.

357. We have : $a = 6$, $b = 11$, $c = 15$. $s = \frac{1}{2}(6 + 11 + 15) = 16$.

Area of the triangle, $\Delta = \sqrt{16 \times 10 \times 5 \times 1} = 20\sqrt{2}$ cm².

Radius of incircle $= \frac{\Delta}{s} = \frac{20\sqrt{2}}{16} = \frac{5\sqrt{2}}{4}$ cm.

358. $r = \frac{\text{Product of sides}}{4\Delta}$

$\Rightarrow \Delta = \frac{\text{Product of sides}}{4r} = \frac{196}{4 \times 2.5} = 19.6 \text{ cm}^2$.

359. $s = \frac{13 + 14 + 15}{2} = \frac{42}{2} = 21$.

$\therefore \Delta = \sqrt{21 \times 8 \times 7 \times 6} = (2 \times 3 \times 7) \text{ cm}^2 = 84 \text{ cm}^2$.

Radius of circle $= \left(\frac{13 \times 14 \times 15}{4 \times 84}\right) \text{cm}^2 = \left(\frac{65}{8}\right) \text{cm} = 8.125$ cm.

360. Let the radius of in circle be r cm.

Then, $2\pi r = 88 \Leftrightarrow r = \left(88 \times \frac{7}{22} \times \frac{1}{2}\right) = 14$.

Semi-perimeter, $s = \left(\frac{30}{2}\right)$ cm $= 15$ cm.

$\therefore$ Area of the triangle $= r \times s = (14 \times 15)$ cm² $= 210$ cm².

361. Radius $= \frac{\text{Area}}{\text{Semi-perimeter}} = \left(\text{Area} \times \frac{2}{\text{Area}}\right) = 2$.

362. Let the perimeter of each be a. Then,

side of the equilateral triangle $= \frac{a}{3}$;

side of the square $= \frac{a}{4}$;

radius of the circle $= \frac{a}{2\pi}$.

$T = \frac{\sqrt{3}}{4} \times \left(\frac{a}{3}\right)^2 = \frac{\sqrt{3}\, a^2}{36}$; $S = \left(\frac{a}{4}\right)^2 = \frac{a^2}{16}$; C_1

$\therefore$

$= \pi \times \left(\frac{a}{2\pi}\right)^2 = \frac{a^2}{4\pi} = \frac{7a^2}{88}$.

So, $C > S > T$.

363. Let the area of each be a. Then,

radius of the circle $= \frac{\sqrt{a}}{\pi}$; side of the square $= \sqrt{a}$;

side of the triangle $= \sqrt{\frac{a \times 4}{\sqrt{3}}}$.

Perimeter of the circle $= 2\pi\sqrt{\frac{a}{\pi}} = 2\sqrt{\pi a}$

$= 2\sqrt{3.14 \times a} = 2 \times 1.77\sqrt{a} = 3.54\sqrt{a}$.

Perimeter of the square $= 4\sqrt{a}$;

Perimeter of the triangle $= 3 \times \sqrt{\frac{4a}{1.732}} = 3 \times \sqrt{2.31a}$

$= 3 \times 1.52\sqrt{a} = 4.56\sqrt{a}$.

364. Required area $= \frac{1}{2} \times \text{base} \times \text{height} = \left(\frac{1}{2} \times 2r \times r\right) = r^2$.

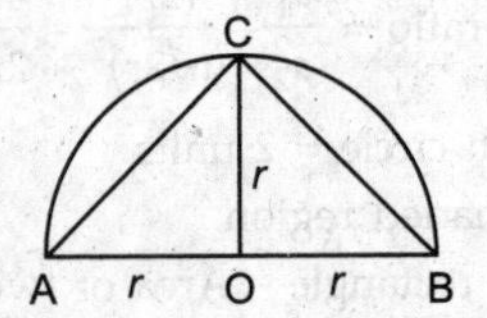

365. Required area $= \frac{\pi}{2} \times \left(\frac{AC}{2}\right)^2 = \frac{\pi}{2} \times \frac{AC^2}{4} = \frac{\pi}{2} \times \frac{AB^2 + BC^2}{4}$

$= \frac{\pi}{2} \times \left(\frac{AB^2}{4} + \frac{BC^2}{4}\right) = \frac{\pi}{2} \times \left(\frac{AB}{2}\right)^2 + \frac{\pi}{2} \times \left(\frac{BC}{2}\right)^2$

$= 81 + 36 = 117$ cm².

366. Let original radius be R cm.

Then, original circumference = $(2\pi R)$ cm.

New radius = (175% of R) cm = $\left(\frac{175}{100}\times R\right)$ cm = $\frac{7R}{4}$ cm.

New circumference = $\left(2\pi\times\frac{7R}{4}\right)$ cm = $\frac{7\pi R}{2}$ cm.

Increase in circumference = $\left(\frac{7\pi R}{2}-2\pi R\right)$ cm = $\frac{3\pi R}{2}$ cm.

Increase% = $\left(\frac{3\pi R}{2}\times\frac{1}{2\pi R}\times 100\right)\%$ = 75%.

367. Let the original and new radius of the balloon be r cm and R cm respectively.

Then, $2\pi r = 20 \Rightarrow r = \frac{20}{2\pi}$. And, $2\pi R = 25 \Rightarrow R = \frac{25}{2\pi}$.

$\therefore$ Required difference = $(R-r)=\left(\frac{25}{2\pi}-\frac{20}{2\pi}\right)=\frac{5}{2\pi}$.

368. Let original diameter be d metres.

Then, its circumference = (πd) metres.

Time taken to cover $(8\pi d)$ m = 40 min.

New diameter = $(10d)$ m.

Then, its circumference = $(\pi \times 10d)$ m.

$\therefore$ Time taken to go round it once

$= \left(\frac{40}{8\pi d}\times 10\pi d\right)$ m = 50 min.

369. Let the original radius be R cm.

New radius = $\left(\frac{106}{100}R\right)$ cm = $\left(\frac{53R}{50}\right)$ cm.

Original area = πR^2.

Increase in area $= \pi\left(\frac{53R}{50}\right)^2 - \pi R^2 = \pi R^2\left[\left(\frac{53}{50}\right)^2-1\right]$

$= \frac{\pi R^2\,[(53)^2-(50)^2]}{2500} = \frac{\pi R^2\,(103\times 3)}{2500}\ \text{m}^2.$

Increase% = $\left(\frac{\pi R^2\times 309}{2500}\times\frac{1}{\pi R^2}\times 100\right)\%$ = 12.36%.

370. Let the original radius be R. New radius = (100 + 200)% of R = 300% of R = $3R$.

Original area = πR^2; New area = $\pi \times (3R)^2 = 9\pi R^2$.

Increase in area = $(9\pi R^2 - \pi R^2) = 8\pi R^2$.

$\therefore$ Increase% = $\left(\frac{8\pi R^2}{\pi R^2}\times 100\right)\% = 800\%$.

371. Let the original radius be R cm.

New radius = (90% of R) cm = $\left(\frac{90}{100}\times R\right)$ cm = $\frac{9R}{10}$ cm.

Original area = πR^2.

Diminished area = $\left[\pi R^2 - \pi\left(\frac{9R}{10}\right)^2\right]$ cm^2

$= \left[\left(1-\frac{81}{100}\right)\pi R^2\right]$ cm^2 = $\left(\frac{19}{100}\pi R^2\right)$ cm^2.

Decrease% = $\left(\frac{19\pi R^2}{100}\times\frac{1}{\pi R^2}\times 100\right)\% = 19\%$.

372. Let the original radius be R. New radius = $2R$.

Original area = πR^2, New area = $\pi(2R)^2 = 4\pi R^2$. Increase in area = $(4\pi R^2 - \pi R^2) = 3\pi R^2$.

Increase% = $\left(\frac{3\pi R^2}{\pi R^2}\times 100\right)\% = 300\%$.

373. Let the original radius be R. New radius = $3R$.

Original circumference = $2\pi R$. New circumference = $2\pi(3R) = 6\pi R$.

$\therefore$ Required ratio = $\frac{6\pi R}{2\pi R} = 3$.

374. $2\pi R_1 = 4\pi$ and $2\pi R_2 = 8\pi \Rightarrow R_1 = 2$ and $R_2 = 4$

$\Rightarrow$ Original area = $(4\pi \times 2^2) = 16\pi$,

Increased area = $(4\pi \times 4^2) = 64\pi$.

Thus, the area quadruples.

375. Let the original circumference be x units. Then, new circumference = 120% of x = $\left(\frac{6x}{5}\right)$.

Let original radius = r and new radius = R.

$2\pi r = x \Rightarrow r = \frac{7x}{2\times 22} = \frac{7x}{44}$.

And, $2\pi R = \frac{6x}{5} \Rightarrow R = \frac{6x}{5}\times\frac{7}{2\times 22} = \frac{21x}{110}$

Original area = $\pi r^2 = \left(\frac{22}{7}\times\frac{7x}{44}\times\frac{7x}{44}\right) = \frac{7x^2}{88}$.

New area = $\pi R^2 = \left(\frac{22}{7}\times\frac{21x}{110}\times\frac{21x}{110}\right) = \frac{63x^2}{550}$

Increase in area = $\left(\frac{63x^2}{550}-\frac{7x^2}{88}\right) = \frac{77x^2}{2200}$.

$\therefore$ Increase% = $\left(\frac{77x^2}{2200}\times\frac{88}{7x^2}\times 100\right)\% = 44\%$.

376. Let the original circumference be x. Then, new circumference = 50% of x = $\frac{x}{2}$.

Let original radius = r and new radius = R.

$2\pi r = x \Rightarrow r = \frac{x\times 7}{2\times 22} = \frac{7x}{44}$.

$2\pi R = \frac{x}{2} \Rightarrow R = \frac{x}{2}\times\frac{7}{2\times 22} = \frac{7x}{88}$.

Original area = $\pi r^2 = \left(\frac{22}{7}\times\frac{7x}{44}\times\frac{7x}{44}\right) = \frac{7x^2}{88}$.

New area = $\pi R^2 = \left(\frac{22}{7}\times\frac{7x}{88}\times\frac{7x}{88}\right) = \frac{7x^2}{352}$.

Decrease in area = $\left(\frac{7x^2}{88}-\frac{7x^2}{352}\right) = \frac{21x^2}{352}$.

$\therefore$ Decrease% = $\left(\frac{21x^2}{352}\times\frac{88}{7x^2}\times 100\right)\% = 75\%$.

377. We have:

$$\text{Required area} = \frac{\pi r^2\theta_1}{360} + \frac{\pi r^2\theta_2}{360} + \frac{\pi r^2\theta_3}{360}$$

$$= \frac{\pi r^2}{360}(\theta_1 + \theta_2 + \theta_3)$$

$$= \frac{\pi r^2 \times 180}{360} = \frac{\pi r^2}{2}. \quad [\because \theta_1 + \theta_2 + \theta_3 = 180°]$$

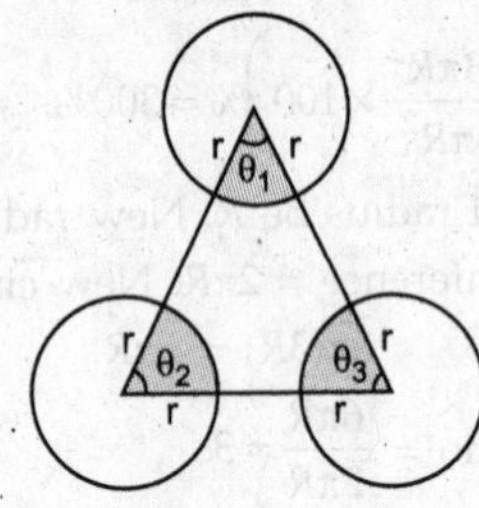

378. Required area

= (Area of an equilateral Δ of side 7 cm) – (3 × area of sector with θ = 60° and r = 3.5 cm)

$$= \left[\left(\frac{\sqrt{3}}{4} \times 7 \times 7\right) - \left(3 \times \frac{22}{7} \times 3.5 \times 3.5 \times \frac{60}{360}\right)\right] \text{cm}^2.$$

$$= \left(\frac{49\sqrt{3}}{4} - 11 \times 0.5 \times 3.5\right) \text{cm}^2$$

$$= (21.217 - 19.25)\ \text{cm}^2 = 1.967\ \text{cm}^2.$$

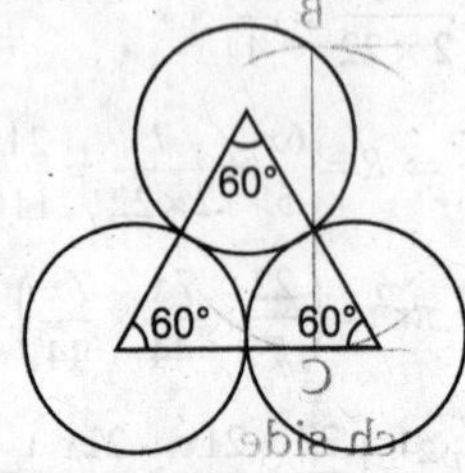

379. Required area = (Area of the square – Area of four quadrants each of radius a)

$$= \left[(2a)^2 - 4 \times \frac{1}{4} \times \frac{22}{7} \times a^2\right] \text{sq. units}$$

$$= \left(4a^2 - \frac{22}{7}a^2\right) \text{sq. units} = \left(\frac{6a^2}{7}\right) \text{sq. units}.$$

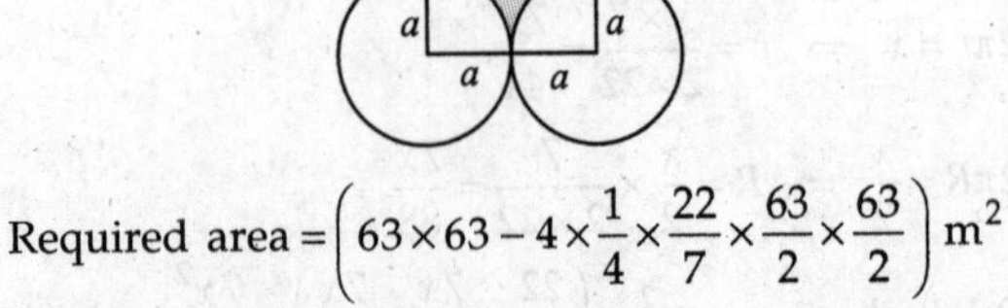

380. $\text{Required area} = \left(63 \times 63 - 4 \times \frac{1}{4} \times \frac{22}{7} \times \frac{63}{2} \times \frac{63}{2}\right) \text{m}^2$

$= 850.5\ \text{m}^2.$

381. Side of the square = $2r$.

Diagonal of the square = $2\sqrt{2}\,r$.

$\therefore$ Diameter of the inner circle = $(2\sqrt{2}\,r - 2r) = 2r(\sqrt{2} - 1)$

Radius of the inner circle = $r(\sqrt{2} - 1)$.

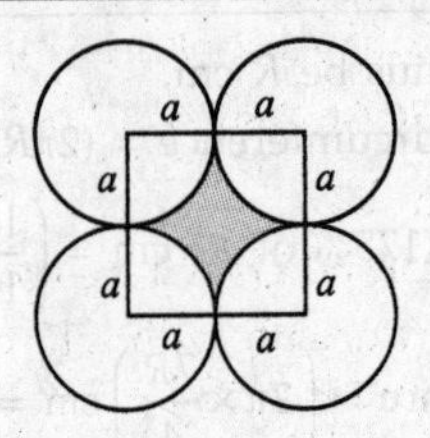

382. As discussed in Q. 379, we have :

$$\frac{6a^2}{7} = \frac{96}{7} \Rightarrow a^2 = \frac{96}{7} \times \frac{7}{6} = 16 \Rightarrow a = 4\ \text{cm}.$$

383. Let the diameter of the round fort be D.

Distance through the middle passage = D. Roundabout distance = $\frac{\pi D}{2}$.

Time taken to cover distance D = 14 min.

Time taken to cover distance

$$\frac{\pi D}{2} = \frac{14}{D} \times \frac{\pi D}{2} = 7\pi = \left(7 \times \frac{22}{7}\right) \text{min} = 22\ \text{min}.$$

$\therefore$ Required time difference = (22 – 14) min = 8 min.

384. Clearly, the longer diagonal of the kite is the diameter of the circle.

Also, $\angle ABC$ = 90° (angle in a semi-circle)

Let $AB = AD = 3x$ and $BC = CD = 4x$.

Then, $AC = \sqrt{AB^2 + BC^2} = 5x$.

Area of the kite = 2 × area (ΔABC)

$$= 2 \times \frac{1}{2} \times BC \times AB = 3x \times 4x = 12x^2.$$

$$\text{Area of the circle} = \pi r^2 = \left(\frac{22}{7} \times \frac{5x}{2} \times \frac{5x}{2}\right) = \frac{275}{14}x^2.$$

$$\text{Area wasted} = \left(\frac{275}{14}x^2 - 12x^2\right) = \frac{107}{14}x^2.$$

$$\text{Required percentage} = \left(\frac{107}{14} \times \frac{14}{275} \times 100\right)\% = 39\%.$$

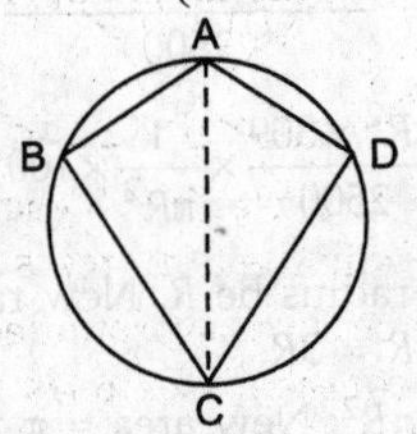

385. Area that can be grazed by the cow

= (Area of a circle with radius 8 cm) – (Area of a sector with r = 8 m and θ = 30°)

$$= \left(\pi \times 8^2 - \pi \times 8^2 \times \frac{30}{360}\right) \text{m}^2$$

$$= \left(64\pi - \frac{64\pi}{12}\right) \text{m}^2 = \left[64\pi\left(1 - \frac{1}{12}\right)\right] \text{m}^2$$

$$= \left(64\pi \times \frac{11}{12}\right) \text{m}^2 = \frac{176\pi}{3}\ \text{m}^2.$$

386. In ΔABC, $AB = AC \Rightarrow \angle ABC = \angle ACB = 75°$.

So, $\angle CBD = \angle BCE = (180° - 75°) = 105°$.

$BD = CE = 2$ m.

$\therefore$ Area that can be grazed by the cow

= [Area of a circle with radius 12 cm – Area of a sector with $r = 12$ m and $\theta = 30°$] + 2 × (Area of a sector with $r = 2$ m and $\theta = 105°$)

$$= \left[\left\{\pi \times (12)^2 - \pi \times (12)^2 \times \frac{30}{360}\right\} + 2\left(\pi \times 2^2 \times \frac{105}{360}\right)\right] m^2$$

$$= \left[(144\pi - 12\pi) + \frac{7}{3}\pi\right] m^2$$

$$= \left[\left(132 + 2\frac{1}{3}\right)\pi\right] m^2 = \left(134\frac{1}{3}\pi\right) m^2.$$

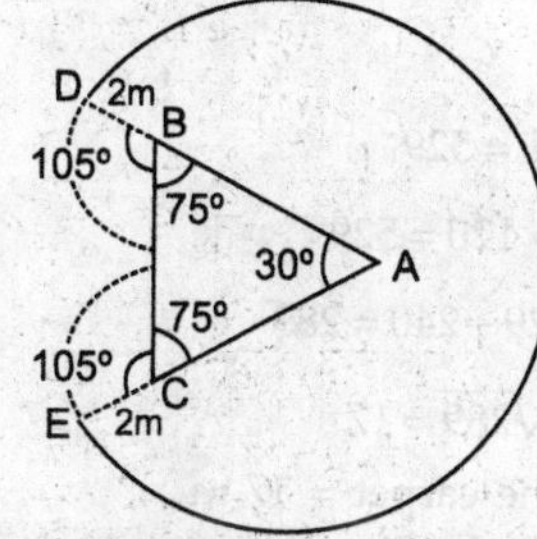

387. Clearly, radius of each circle = 1 cm.

Area of sector $OACBO$ = Area of sector $O'ADBO'$

$$= \left(\frac{1}{4} \times \pi \times 1^2\right) cm^2 = \left(\frac{\pi}{4}\right) cm^2.$$

Area of square $OAO'B = (1 \times 1)$ cm^2 = 1 cm^2.

$\therefore$ Required area = (Area of sector $OACBO$ + Area of sector $O'ADBO'$ – Area of square $OAO'B$)

$$= \left(\frac{\pi}{4} + \frac{\pi}{4} - 1\right) cm^2 = \left(\frac{\pi}{2} - 1\right) cm^2.$$

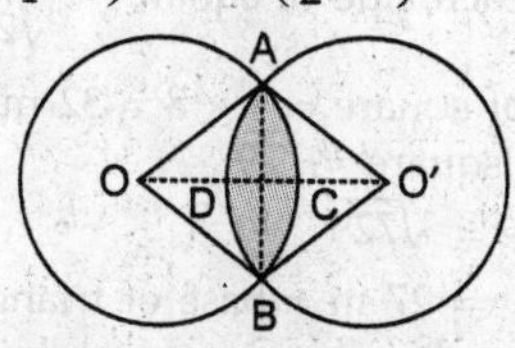

388. When 3 congruent circles touch each other externally, the triangle formed with their centres is an equilateral triangle. Hence, when a circle is surrounded by identical circles, centres of two consecutive circles make an angle of 60° with the central circle. Thus, six identical circles can surround a circle of equal radius.

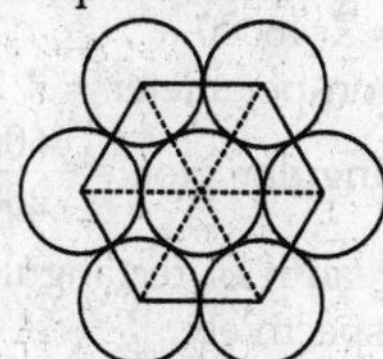

389. Distance moved by the skater in 44 sec

= Circumference of the circle = $\left(2 \times \frac{22}{7} \times 28\right)$ m = 176 m.

Speed of skater = $\left(\frac{176}{44}\right)$ m/sec = 4 m/sec.

Perimeter of hexagon = (6 × 48) m = 288 m.

$\therefore$ Required difference = $\left(\frac{288}{4}\right)$ sec = 72 sec.

390. Area of a hexagon = $\frac{6a^2}{4\tan 30°} = \left(\frac{6 \times 1^2}{4 \times \frac{1}{\sqrt{3}}}\right) cm^2$

$$= \left(\frac{6\sqrt{3}}{4}\right) cm^2 = \left(\frac{3\sqrt{3}}{2}\right) cm^2.$$

391. Required difference = $\frac{\pi \times (2a)^2}{4} = \frac{4\pi a^2}{4} = \pi a^2$.

392. Let AB be a side of the polygon and O be the centre of the circle.

Let $OM \perp AB$.

Perimeter = $2p \Rightarrow AB = \frac{2p}{n}$.

$\therefore$ Area of the polygon = n × area

$(\Delta OAB) = n \times \frac{1}{2} AB \times OM = n \times \frac{1}{2} \times \frac{2p}{n} \times r = pr.$

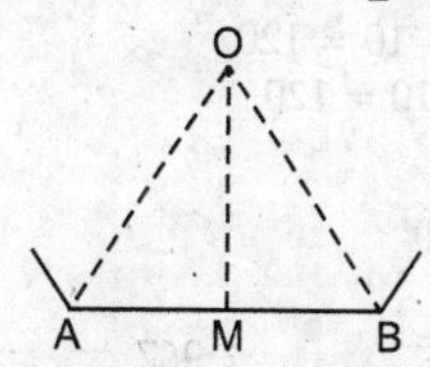

393.

A B D C
60°
60°

Let length of each side of square = 2π

According to the question,

$$\frac{\pi r^2}{2} + \frac{\pi r^2}{2} + 42 = \text{Area of square}$$

$$\Rightarrow \pi r^2 + 42 = 4r^2$$

$$\Rightarrow 4r^2 - \pi r^2 = 42$$

$$\Rightarrow r^2\left(4 - \frac{22}{7}\right) = 42$$

$$\Rightarrow r^2\left(\frac{28-22}{7}\right) = 42$$

$$\Rightarrow \frac{6r^2}{7} = 42$$

$$\Rightarrow r^2 = \frac{42 \times 7}{6}$$

$$\Rightarrow r^2 = 7 \times 7$$

$$\Rightarrow r = 7$$

$\therefore$ $2r$ = 14 cm

394. Given: Radius of a circle = 3cm

Area of circle = πr^2

$= \pi \times 3^2 = 9\pi$ sq. cm.

395. Given length and width of a square base plate of brass is x cm and 1 mm

Volume of the plate of square base = Area of base × height

$= x^2 \times \frac{1}{10} = \frac{x^2}{10}$ cu.cm.

According to the question.

$\frac{x^2}{10} \times 8.4 = 4725$

$\Rightarrow x^2 = \frac{4725 \times 10}{8.4} = 5625$

$\Rightarrow x = \sqrt{5625}$

$= 75$ cm

396. Let the length of rectangle be lm

And the breadth of the rectangle be b m

Then area of the rectangle = $l \times b$

$lb = 150\text{m}^2$ ....(i)

According to the question.

$(l-5)\times(b+2) = 150 - 30 = 120$

$(l-5)\times(b+2) = 120$ ... (ii)

$\Rightarrow lb - 5b + 2l - 10 = 120$

$150 - 5b + 2l - 10 = 120$

$5b - 2l = 20$

$\frac{5\times150}{l} - 2l^2 = 20l$

$2l^2 + 20l - 750 = 0$

$l^2 + 10l - 375 = 0$

$l(l+25) - 15(l+25) = 0$

$(l-15)(l+25) = 0$

On solving both equations we get,

$l = 15$m and $b = 10$m

side of square = length of rectangle (given)

So, the perimeter of the square = $4 \times l = 4 \times 15 = 60$m

397. Area of square = 4sq. units.

Side of square = $\sqrt{4} = 2$ units

Diagonal of square = $2\sqrt{2}$ units

Radius of the circle = $2\sqrt{2}$ units

$\therefore$ Area of circle = πr^2

$= \pi \times (2\sqrt{2})^2$

$= 8\pi$ sq. units.

398. Given:

$\Rightarrow \frac{\text{Circumference of circle}}{\text{Diameter of circle}} = \frac{22}{7}$

$\Rightarrow \frac{\text{Circumference of circle}}{\text{Twice of radius}} = \frac{22}{7}$

$\Rightarrow \frac{1\frac{4}{7}}{2r} = \frac{22}{7}$

$\Rightarrow \frac{\frac{11}{7}}{2r} = \frac{22}{7}$

$\Rightarrow \frac{11}{14r} = \frac{22}{7}$

$\Rightarrow 14r \times 22 = 11 \times 7$

$\Rightarrow r = \frac{11\times7}{14\times22} = \frac{1}{4}$ m

399.

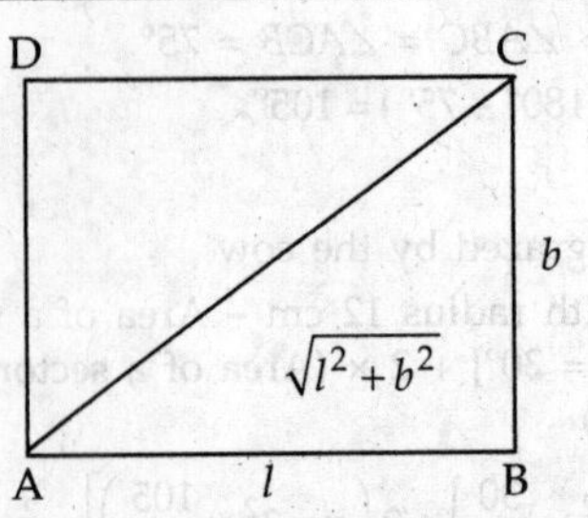

Let the length of carpet be l meter and breadth the b meter.

$\therefore$ Diagonal = $\sqrt{l^2+b^2}$ ....(i)

According to the question,

$lb = 120$ and $2(l + b) = 46$

$\Rightarrow l + b) = 23$

On squaring both sides.

$(l+b)^2 = 23^2$

$\Rightarrow l^2 + b^2 + 2lb = 529$

$\Rightarrow l^2 + b^2 + 2\times120 = 529$

$\Rightarrow l^2 + b^2 = 529 - 240 = 289$

$\therefore \sqrt{l^2+b^2} = \sqrt{289} = 17$

Diagonal of the carpet = 17 m

400. Radius and height of a right circular cylinder is 7cm and 20 cm respectively.

Total surface area of right circular cylinder = $2\pi rh + 2\pi r^2$

$= 2\pi r(h+r)$

$= 2\times\frac{22}{7}\times7(20+7)$

$= 2 \times 22 \times 27 = 1188$ sq. cm.

401. Height of triangle = perimeter of square

Diagonal of square = $8\sqrt{2}$ m

$\therefore$ Length of each side of square $= \frac{8\sqrt{2}}{\sqrt{2}} = 8$ m

$\therefore$ Perimeter of square = $4 \times 8 = 32$ m = Height

Area of other square = 729

Side of square = $\sqrt{729}$

= 27 m = base of triangle

$\therefore$ Area of triangle

$= \frac{1}{2} \times$ base × height

$= \frac{1}{2} \times 27 \times 32 = 432$ sq. m.

402. Total cost to construct a boundary wall around a rectangular plot = ₹ 46000

Rate of construction per meter = ₹ 200

Perimeter of rectangular plot $= \frac{46000}{200} = 230$ m

Let length and breadth of rectangular plot be 13 x meter and 10x meter respectively

$\therefore 2(13x + 10x) = 230$

$\Rightarrow 2\times23x = 230$

$\Rightarrow x = \frac{230}{2\times23} = 5$

$\therefore$ Length = $13 \times 5 = 65$ m

Breadth = 10 × 5 = 50 m
∴ Area of plot = 65 × 50
= 3250 sq. m^2

403. Let the radius of each circle be 'r' cm.

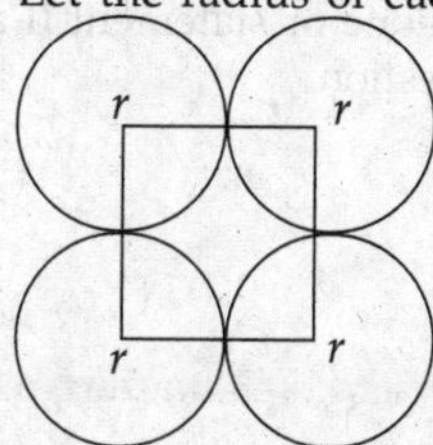

Then the side of the square will be '$2r$' cm
Area covered by the four circles in the square

$$= 4\times\frac{1}{4}\times\pi r^2 = \pi r^2 \text{cm}^2$$

Area of the square $=(2r)^2 = 4r^2\text{cm}^2$

Now, according to the question,
Remaining area of the square

$4r^2 - \pi r^2 = 168$

$r^2\left(4-\frac{22}{7}\right)=168$

$r^2\times(28-22)=168\times7$

$r^2 = \frac{168\times7}{6} = 28\times7 = 7\times4\times7$

∴ $r = \sqrt{7\times7\times4} = 7\times2 = 14$ cm.

404. Given length and breadth of courtyard is 25m long and 16 m respectively.
Area of courtyard = (25 × 16)sq. m^2 = 400 sq. m^2
Dimensions of bricks 20 cm by 10 cm

Area of the surface of brick $=\left(\frac{20\times10}{10000}\right)\text{m}^2$

∴ Number of bricks $= \dfrac{400}{\dfrac{20\times10}{10000}}$

$= \frac{400\times10000}{20\times10} = 20000$ bricks

405. Area of square = 3136 cm^2
Side of squared = $\sqrt{3136}$ = 56 cm
Perimeter of square = $4a$
= (4 × 56)cm= 224cm = Diameter of circle
∴ Circumference of circle = πd

$\frac{22}{7}\times224 = 704$ cm

406. Given base of triangle and its height is 15 cm and 12 cm respectively
Area of first triangle $= \frac{1}{2}\times$base × height

$= \frac{1}{2}\times15\times12$ = 90 sq. cm.

According to given information
Let height of triangle be h cm.
Area of new triangle = 180 sq. cm.
Base = 20 sq. cm.

$\Rightarrow 180 = \frac{1}{2}\times20\times h$

$\Rightarrow h = \frac{2\times180}{20} = 18$ cm.

407. Let each equal side of isosceles triangle be x cm
Perimeter of an isosceles triangle = 36cm

∴ $x+x+14=36$
$\Rightarrow 2x = 36 - 14 = 22$

$= x = \frac{22}{2} = 11$ cm.

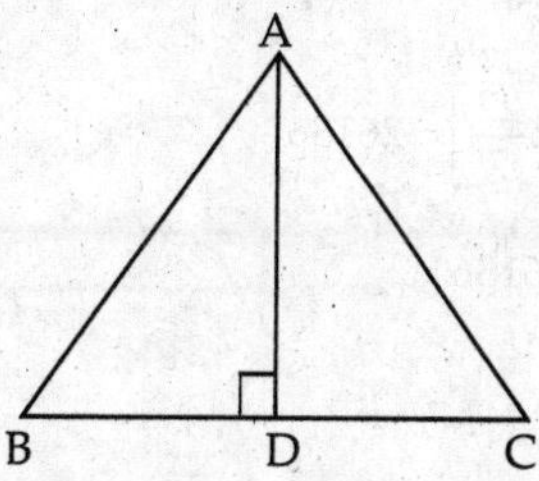

BD = DC = 7cm.
From ΔABD.
By using Pythagoras theorem

AD = $\sqrt{AB^2 - BD^2} = \sqrt{11^2-7^2}$

$= \sqrt{121-49} = \sqrt{72}$

$= 3\times2\sqrt{2}$

$6\sqrt{2}$ cm.

∴ Area of Δ ABC

$= \frac{1}{2}\times BC\times AD$

$= \frac{1}{2}\times14\times6\sqrt{2}$

$= 42\sqrt{2}$ sq. cm.

408. Radius of circle = 7cm
Given Area of rectangle = Area of circle = πr^2

$= \frac{22}{7}\times7\times7 = 154\text{cm}^2$

409. Each edges of cube = a cm
∴ Total surface area of cube = $6a^2$
$\Rightarrow 6a^2 = 864$

$\Rightarrow a^2 = \frac{864}{6} = 144$

$\Rightarrow a = \sqrt{144} = 12$ cm

∴ Volume of cube = a^3 cu.cm.
= (12 × 12 × 12) cu.cm.
= 1728 cu.cm.

410. Let the radius of circle be r cm and side of square be a cm.
Then circumference of circle
= $2\pi r$ and perimeter of square = $4a$

According to the question, $2\pi r = 4a\times\frac{110}{100}$

$\Rightarrow 2\pi r = \frac{44a}{10}$

$\Rightarrow r = \frac{44a}{2\pi\times10}$

$\Rightarrow r = \frac{11a}{5\pi}$

$\Rightarrow a = \frac{5\pi r}{11}$ ....(i)

Also, $\pi r^2 - a^2 = 216$

$\Rightarrow \pi r^2 - \frac{25\pi r^2}{121} = 216$ [from equation (i)]

$\Rightarrow \frac{121\pi r^2 - 25\pi r^2}{121} = 216$

$\Rightarrow r^2\left[121\pi - 25\pi^2\right] = 26136$

$\Rightarrow r^2\left[121 \times \frac{22}{7} - 25 \times \frac{22}{7} \times \frac{22}{7}\right] = 26136$

$\Rightarrow r^2\left[\frac{2662}{7} - \frac{12100}{49}\right] = 26136$

$\Rightarrow r^2\left[\frac{6534}{49}\right] = 26136$

$\Rightarrow r^2 = \frac{26136 \times 49}{6534} = 196$

$\Rightarrow r^2 = 196$

$\Rightarrow r = 14$ cm

$\therefore a = \frac{5\pi r}{11} = 5 \times \frac{22}{7} \times \frac{14}{11} = 20\text{cm}$

Hence, diagonal of square = $\sqrt{2}a = 20\sqrt{2}$ cm.

411.

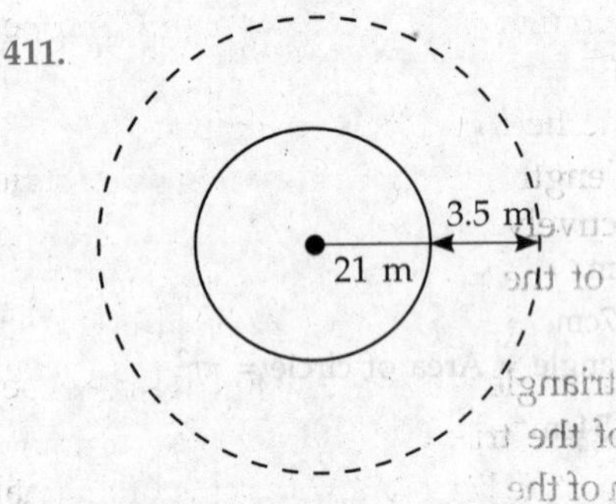

Diameter of park = 42 m

$\therefore$ Radius of park = r_1 = 21 m

Radius of park along with path = R_1= 21 + 3.5 = 24.5m

$\Rightarrow$ Area of path = $\pi(R_1)^2 - \pi(r_1)^2$

$\therefore$ Area of path

= Area of park alone with path – Area of park

$= \pi \times (24.5)^2 - \pi \times (21)^2 = \pi\left[(24.5)^2 - (21)^2\right]$

$= \pi[600.25 - 441] = \pi[15925] = \frac{159.25 \times 22}{7} = 500.5$ sq. m

Hence, cost of gravelling the path = 500.5 × 4 = ₹ 2002

412. Statement I

Perimeter of the circle = 88 cms

$\Rightarrow \quad 2\pi r = 88$

$r = \frac{88 \times 7}{22} \times \frac{1}{2}$

$\Rightarrow \quad r = 14$

Area of circle = πr^2

$= \frac{22}{7} \times 14 \times 14$

$= 616 \text{ cm}^2$

Statement II

Diameter of the circle = 28 cm

Radius of the circle = 14 cm

$\therefore$ Area of circle = πr^2

$= \frac{22}{7} \times 14 \times 14 = 616\text{cm}^2$

The data either in statement I alone or statement II alone are sufficient to answer the question.

Hence, option (c) is correct.

413.

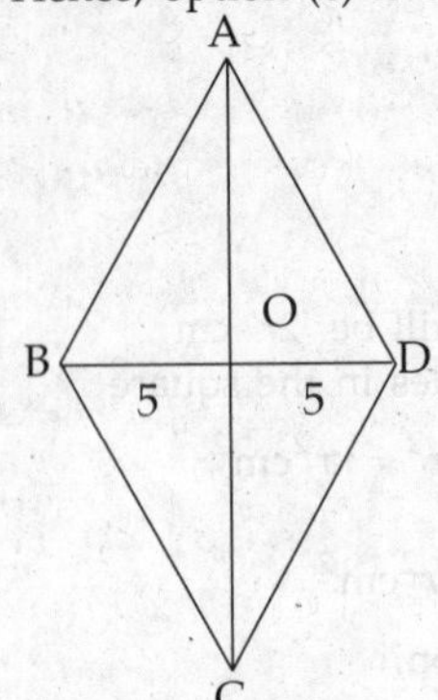

Side of a rhombus = 13cm

Diagonal of rhombus = 10cm

In ΔAOB

AO = $\sqrt{13^2 - 5^2} = \sqrt{169 - 25} = \sqrt{144} = 12$ cm.

$\Rightarrow$ AC = 24

Area of rhombus $= \frac{1}{2} \times d_1 \times d_2 = \frac{1}{2} \times 24 \times 10 = 120$ sq. cm.

414. Given length of the piece of wire = 84 cm

Length of the piece of wire = Circumference of circle

$= 2\pi r = 2 \times \frac{22}{7} \times 84 = 528$ cm.

Length of each side of square = a

$\therefore$ Perimeter of square = $4a$ = 528 cm

$\therefore$ Side of square = $\frac{528}{4}$ = 132 cm

415. Length of hall = 50 m

Breadth of hall = 45 m

Area of hall = (50 × 45) m

Maximum length of a square tiles

= HCF of 50 m and 45 m = 5 meter

Area of tiles = 5 × 5 = 25 sq. m.

$\therefore$ Number of tiles

$= \frac{50 \times 45}{25} = 90$ tiles

415. Side of square = a units

Side of hexagon = b units.

According to the question,

$4a = 6b$

$\Rightarrow \frac{a}{b} = \frac{6}{4} = \frac{3}{2}$

$\therefore \frac{\text{Area of hexagon}}{\text{Area of square}} = \frac{6 \times \frac{\sqrt{3}}{4} \times b^2}{a^2}$

$= \frac{6 \times \sqrt{3} \times 2 \times 2}{4 \times 3 \times 3}$

$= \frac{2\sqrt{3}}{3}$

Hence required ratio = $2\sqrt{3} : 3$

EXERCISE

(DATA SUFFICIENCY TYPE QUESTIONS)

Directions (*Questions 1 to 26*): ***Each of the questions given below consists of a sta tement and/or a question and two statements numbered I and II given below it. You have to decide whether the data provided in the statement(s) is/are sufficient to answer the question. Read both the statements and***

Give answer (a) if the data in Statement I alone are sufficient to answer the question, while the data in Statement II alone are not sufficient to answer the question;

Give answer (b) if the data in Statement II alone are sufficient to answer the question, while the data in Statement I alone are not sufficient to answer the question;

Give answer (c) if the data either in Statement I or in Statement II alone are sufficient to answer the question;

Give answer (d) if the data even in both Statements I and II together are not sufficient to answer the question;

Give answer (e) if the data in both Statements I and II together are necessary to answer the question.

1. What is the area of the rectangular plot ? **(Bank P.O., 2009)**
   I. The length of the plot is 375 metres.
   II. The length of the plot is thrice its breadth.
2. Is the perimeter of a certain rectangular park greater than 50 metres ?
   I. The two shorter sides of the park are each 15 metres long.
   II. The length of the park is 5 metres greater than the width of the park. **(N.I.F.T., 2007)**
3. What is the area of the square ? **(Bank P.O., 2008)**
   I. One side of the square is 21 cm.
   II. The perimeter of the square is 84 cm.
4. What is the area of the plot ?
   I. The perimeter of the plot is 208 metres.
   II. The length is more than the breadth by 4 metres.
5. The area of a playground is 1600 m^2. What is its perimeter ?
   I. It is a perfect square playground.
   II. It costs ₹ 3200 to put a fence around the playground at the rate of ₹ 20 per metre.
6. What is the area of the rectangle ?
   I. The ratio of the length and the breadth is 3 : 2.
   II. The area of the rectangle is 3.6 times its perimeter.
7. The area of a playground is 15400 square metres. What is its perimeter?
   I. It is a circular playground.
   II. It costs ₹ 30800 to clean the playground @ ₹ 2 per sq. ft. **(Bank P.O., 2007)**
8. What is the area of the circle ? **(Bank P.O., 2009)**
   I. Perimeter of the circle is 88 cm.
   II. Diameter of the circle is equal to the side of the square having area 784 sq. cm.
9. A rectangular field is 40 yards long. Find the area of the field. **(M.B.A., 2006)**
   I. A fence around the outside of the field is 140 yards long.
   II. The distance from one corner of the field to the opposite corner is 50 yards.
10. Area of a square is equal to the area of a circle. What is the circumference of the circle?
    I. The diagonal of the square is x inches.
    II. The side of the square is y inches.
11. The area of a rectangle is equal to the area of a right-angled triangle. What is the length of the rectangle?
    I. The base of the triangle is 40 cm.
    II. The height of the triangle is 50 cm.
12. What will be the cost of gardening a strip of land inside around a circular field, at the rate of ₹ 85 per sq. metre ?
    I. The area of the field is 1386 sq. metres.
    II. Breadth and length of the field are in the ratio of 3 : 5 respectively.
13. What is the area of the right-angled triangle? **(Bank Recruitment, 2009)**
    I. Height of the triangle is three-fourths of the base.
    II. Hypotenuse of the triangle is 5 metres.
14. What is the length of the line SQ which is the diagonal of a square as well as the diameter of a circle?
    I. All the four vertices of the square lie on the circumference of the circle.
    II. The numerical value of the area of the circle is twice the length of SQ.
15. What is the area of the rectangle ?
    I. The difference between the sides is 5 cm.
    II. The measure of its diagonal is 10 cm.
16. What is the area of the circle ?
    I. An arc of length 4 cm subtends an angle of 60° at the centre.
    II. A chord of length 5 cm subtends an angle of 90° at the centre.
17. What is the perimeter of a semi-circle? **(Bank P.O., 2010)**
    I. The radius of the semi-circle is equal to half the side of a square.
    II. The area of the square is 196 sq. cm.
18. What is the perimeter of the rectangle *ABCD*?
    I. Area of the circle is 38.5 sq. cm.
    II. $AB = 10$ cm.

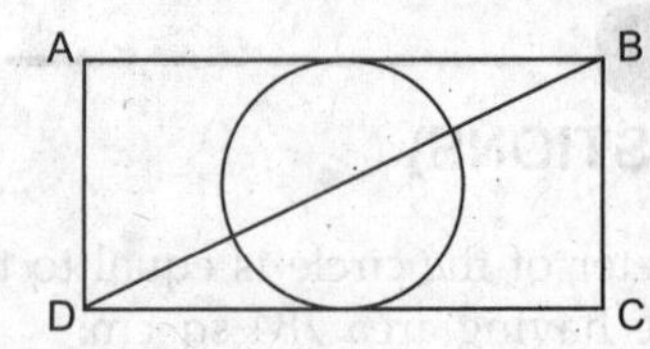

19. The area of a rectangle is equal to the area of a circle. What is the length of the rectangle ?

I. The radius of the circle is equal to the breadth of the rectangle.

II. The perimeter of the rectangle is 14 cm more than that of the circle.

20. Determine the perimeter of the square.

I. A circle is inscribed in the square.

II. The area of the circle is 36π.

21. What is the height of a right-angled triangle? **(M.A.T., 2005)**

I. The area of the right-angled triangle is equal to the area of a rectangle whose breadth is 12 cm.

II. The length of the rectangle is 18 cm.

22. Is the area of circular region X greater than the area of circular region Y ?

I. The circumference of X is greater than the circumference of circle Z and the circumference of Z is less than the circumference of Y.

II. The radius of X is greater that the radius of Y. **(N.I.F.T., 2007)**

23. What is the height of the triangle ?

I. The area of the triangle is 20 times its base.

II. The perimeter of the triangle is equal to the perimeter of a square of side 10 cm.

24. What will be the cost of painting the inner walls of a room if the rate of painting is ₹ 20 per square foot ?

I. Circumference of the floor is 44 feet.

II. The height of the wall of the room is 12 feet.

25. The diameter of the rear wheel of a vehicle is 1.2 m. What is the diameter of the front wheel?

I. Front wheel makes 240 revolutions while rear wheel makes 80.

II. In 240 revolutions, the front wheel covers a distance of $301\frac{5}{7}$ m.

26. There are two concentric circles C_2 and C_2 with radii r_1 and r_2. The circles are such that C_1 fully encloses C_1. Then, what is the radius of C_1 ?

I. The difference of their circumferences is k cm.

II. The difference of their areas is m sq. cm.

Directions (*Questions 27 to 36*): ***Each of the questions below consists of a question followed by three statements. You have to study the question and the statements and decide which of the statement(s) is/are necessary to answer the question.***

27. What is the area of rectangular field ?

I. The perimeter of the field is 110 metres.

II. The length is 5 metres more than the width.

III. The ratio between length and width is 6 : respectively.

(*a*) I and II only

(*b*) Any two of the three

(*c*) All I, II and III

(*d*) I, and either II or III only

(*e*) None of these

28. What is the area of the hall ?

I. Material cost of flooring per square metre i ₹ 2.50.

II. Labour cost of flooring the hall is ₹ 3500.

III. Total cost of flooring the hall is ₹ 14,500.

(*a*) I and II only (*b*) II and III only

(*c*) All I, II and III (*d*) Any two of the thre

(*e*) None of these

29. What is the area of the square? **(Bank P.O., 2006)**

I. Measure of diagonal of the square is given.

II. Measure of one side of the square is given.

III. Perimeter of the square is given.

(*a*) Only II (*b*) Only III

(*c*) Only I and III (*d*) Only II and III

(*e*) Any one of the three

30. What is the area of the right-angled triangle ? **(Bank P.O., 200**

I. Base of the triangle is X cm.

II. Height of the triangle is Y cm.

III. Hypotenuse of the triangle is Z cm.

(*a*) Only I and II (*b*) Only II

31. What is the length of the diagonal of the give rectangle?

I. The perimeter of the rectangle is 34 cm.

II. The difference between the length and breadt is 7 cm.

III. The length is 140% more than the breadth.

(*a*) Any two of the three (*b*) All I, II and III

(*c*) I, and either II or III (*d*) I and II only

(*e*) II and III only

32. What is the cost of flooring the rectangular hall ? **(M.A.T. 2006, R.B.I., 2002**

I. Length and breadth of the hall are in the respec tive ratio of 3 : 2.

II. Length of the hall is 48 m and cost of floorin is ₹ 85 per sq. m.

III. Perimeter of the hall is 160 m and cost of floorin is ₹ 85 per sq. m.

(*a*) I and II only

(*b*) II and III only

(*c*) III only

(*d*) I, and either II or III only
(*e*) Any two of the three

33. What is the area of a right-angled triangle ? **(M.A.T., 2007)**

I. The perimeter of the triangle is 30 cm.
II. The ratio between the base and the height of the triangle is 5 : 12.
III. The area of the triangle is equal to the area of a rectangle of length 10 cm.

(*a*) I and II only
(*b*) II and III only
(*c*) I and III only
(*d*) III, and either I or II only
(*e*) None of these

34. A path runs around a rectangular lawn. What is the width of the path ?

I. The length and breadth of the lawn are in the ratio of 3 : 1 respectively.
II. The width of the path is ten times the length of the lawn.
III. The cost of gravelling the path @ ₹ 50 per m^2 is ₹ 8832.

(*a*) All I, II and II (*b*) III, and either I or II
(*c*) I and III only (*d*) II and III only
(*e*) None of these

35. What is the area of the equilateral triangle ?

I. Length of the perpendicular from one of the vertices to the opposite side is x cm.
II. Length of each side of the triangle is y cm.
III. Perimeter of the triangle is z cm.

(*a*) Any one of the three (*b*) Any two of the three
(*c*) I and either II and III (*d*) All I, II and III
(*e*) Question cannot be answered even with information in all three statements

36. What is the area of the isosceles triangle ?

I. Perimeter of the isosceles triangle is 18 metres.
II. Base of the triangle is 8 metres.
III. Height of the triangle is 3 metres.

(*a*) I and II only
(*b*) II and III only
(*c*) I and III only
(*d*) II, and either I or III only
(*e*) Any two of the three

Directions (*Questions 37 to 41*): ***Each of the questions given below is followed by three statements. You have to study the question and all the three statements given to decide whether any information provided in the statement(s) is/are redundant and can be dispensed with while answering the given question.***

37. What will be the cost of painting the four walls of a room with length, width and height 5 metres, 3 metres and 8 metres respectively? The room has one door and one window.

I. Cost of painting per square metre is ₹ 25.
II. Area of window is 2.25 sq. metres which is half of the area of the door.
III. Area of the room is 15 sq. metres.

(*a*) I only
(*b*) II only
(*c*) III only
(*d*) II or III
(*e*) All are required to answer the question

38. What is the cost of painting the two adjacent walls of a hall at ₹ 5 per m^2 which has no windows or doors ?

I. The area of the hall is 24 sq. m.
II. The breadth, length and height of the hall are in the ratio of 4 : 6 : 5 respectively.
III. Area of one wall is 30 sq. m.

(*a*) I only
(*b*) II only
(*c*) III only
(*d*) Either I or III
(*e*) All I, II and III are required

39. What is the area of the given rectangle ?

I. Perimeter of the rectangle is 60 cm.
II. Breadth of the rectangle is 12 cm.
III. Sum of two adjacent sides is 30 cm.

(*a*) I only (*b*) II only
(*c*) III only (*d*) I and II only
(*e*) I or III only

40. What is the area of the given right-angled triangle?

I. Length of the hypotenuse is 5 cm.
II. Perimeter of the triangle is four times its base.
III. One of the angles of the triangle is 60°.

(*a*) II only
(*b*) III only
(*c*) II or III only
(*d*) II and III both
(*e*) Information given in all the three statements together is not sufficient to answer the question.

41. What is the height of the triangle whose area is equal to the area of a rectangle?

I. The ratio between the length and breadth of the rectangle is 3 : 2.
II. The base of the triangle is 16 cm.
III. The perimeter of the rectangle is 80 cm.

(*a*) Only I
(*b*) Only I or II
(*c*) Only III
(*d*) All I, II. and III together are required
(*e*) None of these

ANSWERS

1. (e)	2. (a)	3. (c)	4. (e)	5. (c)	6. (e)	7. (a)	8. (c)	9. (c)	10. (c)
11. (d)	12. (e)	13. (e)	14. (b)	15. (e)	16. (c)	17. (e)	18. (e)	19. (e)	20. (e)
21. (d)	22. (b)	23. (a)	24. (e)	25. (c)	26. (e)	27. (b)	28. (c)	29. (e)	30. (d)
31. (a)	32. (e)	33. (a)	34. (a)	35. (a)	36. (d)	37. (c)	38. (c)	39. (e)	40. (c)
41. (d)									

SOLUTIONS

1. I. Length = 375 m.

II. Breadth = $\left(\frac{1}{3} \times 375\right)$ m = 125 m.

$\therefore$ Area of the plot = (375×125) m^2 = 46875 m^2.

Thus, both I and II are required.

$\therefore$ Correct answer is *(e)*.

2. I. Since b = 15 m, So $l > 25$ m.

So, $(l + b) > 30$ m $\Rightarrow 2(l + b) > 60$ m.

$\therefore$ I alone gives the answer. Hence, correct answer is *(a)*.

3. I. Side = 21 cm $\Rightarrow$ Area = (side)^2 = 441 cm^2.

II. Perimeter = 84 cm $\Rightarrow$ Side = $\left(\frac{84}{4}\right)$ cm = 21 cm $\Rightarrow$ Area = (Side)^2 = 441 cm^2.

$\therefore$ Either I or II alone gives the answer. So, correct answer is *(c)*.

4. I. P = 208 m.

II. Let breadth = x metres. Then, length = $(x + 4)$ m.

$\therefore$ P = $[2\{x + (x + 4)\}]$ m = $(4x + 8)$ m.

Using both I and II, we have:

$4x + 8 = 208 \Rightarrow 4x = 200 \Rightarrow x = 50$.

Hence area = (50×54) m^2 = 2700 m^2.

Thus, both I and II are required.

$\therefore$ Correct answer is *(e)*.

5. Area = 1600 m^2.

I. Side = $\sqrt{1600}$ m = 40 m.

So, perimeter = (40×4) m = 160 m.

$\therefore$ I alone gives the answer.

II. Perimeter = $\frac{\text{Total cost}}{\text{Cost per metre}} = \frac{3200}{20}$ m = 160 m.

$\therefore$ II alone gives the answer.

$\therefore$ Correct answer is *(c)*.

6. I. Let $l = 3x$ metres and $b = 2x$ metres.

Then, area = $(6x^2)$ m^2.

II. Perimeter = $2(3x + 2x)$ m = $(10x)$ m.

$\therefore 6x^2 = 3.6 \times 10x \Leftrightarrow x = \frac{(3.6 \times 10)}{6} = 6$.

$\therefore$ l = 18 m and b = 12 m and so area can be obtained.

Thus, I and II together give the answer.

$\therefore$ Correct answer is *(e)*.

7. I. Since the playground is circular, we have :

$\pi r^2 = 15400 \Rightarrow r^2 = \frac{15400 \times 7}{22} = 4900 \Rightarrow r = 70$ m

$\Rightarrow$ Perimeter = $2\pi r = \left(2 \times \frac{22}{7} \times 70\right)$ m = 440 m.

II. Area = $\left(\frac{30800}{2}\right)$ m^2 = 15400 m^2.

Thus, I alone given the answer.

$\therefore$ Correct answer is *(a)*.

8. Let the radius of the circle be r.

I. Perimeter = $2\pi r = 88 \Rightarrow r = \left(\frac{88 \times 7}{2 \times 22}\right) = 14$ cm.

$\therefore$ Area = $\pi r^2 = \left(\frac{22}{7} \times 14 \times 14\right)$ cm^2 = 616 cm^2.

II. $2r$ = Side of the square = $\sqrt{784}$ cm = 28 cm $\Rightarrow r = 14$ cm.

$\therefore$ Area = $\pi r^2 = \left(\frac{22}{7} \times 14 \times 14\right)$ cm^2 = 616 cm^2.

So, either I alone or II alone gives the answer.

$\therefore$ Correct answer *(c)*.

9. I. l = 40 yards. Perimeter = 140 yards.

$2(l + b) = 140 \Rightarrow l + b = 70$

$\Rightarrow b = (70 - l) = 30$ yards.

Area of the field = (40×30) sq. yds = 1200 sq. yds.

II. l = 40 yards.

$l^2 + b^2 = (50)^2 \Rightarrow b^2 = 2500 - l^2 = 2500 - 1600 = 900$

$\Rightarrow b = 30$ yards.

Area of the field = (40×30) sq. yds = 1200 sq. yds.

So, either I alone or II alone gives the answer.

$\therefore$ Correct answer is *(c)*.

10. I. Area of the circle = Area of the square

$= \frac{1}{2}x^2$ sq. inches.

$\Rightarrow \pi r^2 = \frac{1}{2}x^2 \Rightarrow r = \sqrt{\frac{x^2}{2\pi}} = \frac{x}{\sqrt{2\pi}}$.

$\therefore$ Circumference of the circle = $2\pi r$, which can be obtained.

$\therefore$ I alone gives the answer.

II. Area of the circle = Area of the square = y^2 sq. inches

$\Rightarrow \pi r^2 = y^2 \Rightarrow r = \frac{y}{\sqrt{\pi}}$.

$\therefore$ Circumference of the circle = $2\pi r$, which can be obtained.

Thus, II alone gives the answer.

$\therefore$ Correct answer is (*c*).

11. Given : Area of rectangle = Area of a right-angled triangle

$\Rightarrow l \times b = \frac{1}{2} \times B \times H$

I. gives, B = 40 cm.

II. gives, H = 50 cm.

Thus, to find l, we need b also, which is not given.

$\therefore$ Given data is not sufficient to give the answer.

$\therefore$ Correct answer is (*d*).

12. I. $\pi R_1^2 = 1386 \Leftrightarrow R_1^2 = \left(1386 \times \frac{7}{22}\right) \Leftrightarrow R_1 = 21$ m.

II. R_2 = (21 – 1.4) m = 19.6 m.

$\therefore$ Area $= \pi (R_1^2 - R_2^2) = \frac{22}{7} \times [(21)^2 - (19.6)^2]$ m^2.

Thus, the required cost may be obtained.

$\therefore$ I and II together will give the answer.

$\therefore$ Correct answer is (*e*).

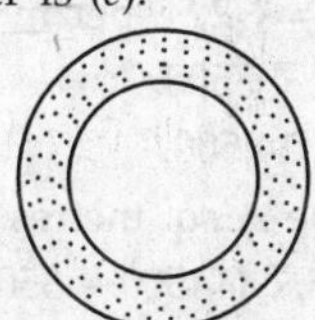

13. I. Let base = x , Then, height $= \frac{3}{4}x$.

II. Hypotenuse = 5 m.

Using both I and II, we have:

$$x^2 + \left(\frac{3}{4}x\right)^2 = 5^2 \Rightarrow x^2 = \frac{9}{16}x^2 + 25$$

$$\Rightarrow \frac{25x^2}{16} = 25 \Rightarrow x^2 = 16 \Rightarrow x = 4.$$

So, base 4 m, height = 3 m.

$\therefore$ Area $= \left(\frac{1}{2} \times 4 \times 3\right)$ m^2 = 6 m^2.

Thus, both I and II together give the answer.

$\therefore$ Correct answer is (*e*).

14. Let the length of SQ be x. Then, radius of the circle $= \frac{x}{2}$.

I. The fact given in the question can be inferred form the information given in I.

II. $\pi\left(\frac{x}{2}\right)^2 = 2x \Rightarrow \frac{\pi x^2}{4} = 2x$

$$\Rightarrow \pi x^2 = 8x \Rightarrow \pi x = 8 \Rightarrow x = \frac{8 \times 7}{22} = \frac{28}{11}.$$

Thus, II alone gives the answer.

$\therefore$ Correct answer is (*b*).

15. I. Let the sides be x cm and (x + 5) cm.

II. $d = \sqrt{(x+5)^2 + x^2}$

$\Leftrightarrow (x + 5)^2 + x^2 = (10)^2$

$\Leftrightarrow 2x^2 + 10x - 75 = 0$

$$\Leftrightarrow x = \frac{-10 \pm \sqrt{100+600}}{4} = \frac{-10+\sqrt{700}}{4}$$

$$= \frac{-10+10\sqrt{7}}{4} = \frac{-10+10\times 2.6}{4}.$$

Thus, sides and therefore area may be known.

Thus, both I and II are needed to get the answer.

$\therefore$ Correct answer is (*e*).

16. I. Length of arc $= \frac{2\pi R\theta}{360} \Leftrightarrow 4 = \left(\frac{2 \times \frac{22}{7} \times R \times 60}{360}\right)$.

This gives R and therefore, area of the circle = πR^2.

Thus, I only gives the answer.

II. $R^2 + R^2 = 5^2 \Leftrightarrow 2R^2 = 25 \Leftrightarrow R^2 = \frac{25}{2}$.

$\therefore$ Area of the circle $= \pi R^2 = \left(\frac{22}{7} \times \frac{25}{2}\right)$ sq. cm.

Thus, II only gives the answer.

$\therefore$ Correct answer is (*c*).

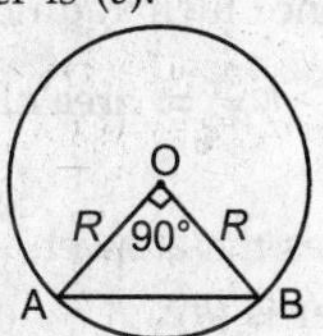

17. Let the radius of the semi-circle be r and the side of the square be a.

I. $r = \frac{a}{2}$.

II. $a = \sqrt{196}$ cm = 14 cm.

From I and II, we have : r = 7 cm.

$\therefore$ Perimeter of semi-circle = $\pi r + 2r$

$= \left(\frac{22}{7} \times 7 + 2 \times 7\right)$ cm = 36 cm.

Thus, both I and II are required.

$\therefore$ Correct answer is (*e*).

18. Let radius of the circle be r. Then, $BC = r$.

I. $\pi r^2 = 38.5 \Rightarrow r^2 = \frac{38.5 \times 7}{22} = 12.25 \Rightarrow r = 3.5.$

II. AB = 10 cm.

Using both I and II, we have: AB = 10 cm and BC = 3.5 cm.

$\therefore$ Perimeter = 2(10 + 3.5) cm = 27 cm.

Thus, both I and II together give the answer.

$\therefore$ Correct answer is (*e*).

19. Given : $l \times b = \pi R^2$. ...(*i*)

I. gives, $R = b$. ...(*ii*)

From (*i*) and (*ii*), we get $l = \frac{\pi R^2}{b} = \frac{\pi R^2}{R} = \pi R$. ...(*iii*)

II. gives, $2(l + b) = 2\pi R + 14$

$\Rightarrow l + b = \pi R + 7 \Rightarrow l + R = \pi R + 7$

$\Rightarrow l = \pi R - R + 7 \Rightarrow l = l - \frac{l}{\pi} + 7 \Rightarrow l = 7\pi.$

[Using (*iii*)]

Thus, I and II together give l. ∴ Correct answer is (*e*).

20. Let the radius of the circle be r and the side of the square be a.

I. Diameter of the circle = side of the square i.e. $2r = a$.

II. $\pi r^2 = 36\pi \Rightarrow r^2 = 36 \Rightarrow r = 6$.

Using both I and II, we have : $a = 12$ units.

∴ Perimeter of the square = (4 × 12) units= 48 units.

Thus, both I and II together give the answer.

∴ Correct answer is (*e*).

21. Using both I and II, we have:

Area of right-angled triangle = Area of rectangle = (18 × 12) cm² = 216 cm².

But, we can't find the height of the triangle unless the base is given.

Thus,. even both I and II together do not give the answer.

∴ Correct answer is (*d*).

22. I. From the given information, the circumference of circles x and y and hence their radii cannot be compared.

II. $r_X > r_Y \Rightarrow \pi r_X^2 > \pi r_Y^2 \Rightarrow$ area of circle $X >$ area of circle Y

Thus, II alone gives the answer.

∴ Correct answer is (*b*).

23. I. $A = 20 \times B \Rightarrow \frac{1}{2} \times B \times H = 20 \times B \Rightarrow H = 40$.

∴ I alone gives the answer.

II. gives, perimeter of the triangle = 40 cm.

This does not give the height of the triangle.

∴ Correct answer is (*a*).

24. I. Gives, $2\pi R = 44$.

II. Gives, $H = 12$.

∴ $A = 2\pi RH = (44 \times 12)$.

Cost of painting = ₹ (44 × 12 × 20).

Thus, I and II together give the answer.

∴ Correct answer is (*e*).

25. Let the radius of the front and rear wheels be r_1 and r_2 respectively.

Then, $r_2 = \left(\frac{1.2}{2}\right) \text{m} = 0.6 \text{ m}$.

I. $240 \times 2\pi r_1 = 80 \times 2\pi r_2$

$\Rightarrow 240\, r_1 = 80\, r_2 \Rightarrow 3\, r_1 = r_2$.

$\Rightarrow r_1 = \frac{r_2}{3} = \left(\frac{0.6}{3}\right) \text{m} = 0.2 \text{ m}$.

So, diameter of front wheel = (2 × 0.2) m = 0.4 m.

II. $240 \times 2\pi r_1 = 301\frac{5}{7} \Rightarrow r_1 = \left(\frac{2112}{7} \times \frac{7}{2 \times 22} \times \frac{1}{240}\right) = 0.2$ m.

So, diameter of front wheel = (2 × 0.2) m = 0.4 m.

Thus, either I alone or II alone gives the answer.

∴ Correct answer is (*c*).

26. I. $2\pi(r_1 - r_2) = k \Rightarrow r_1 - r_2 = \frac{k}{2\pi}$ ...(*i*)

II. $\pi(r_1^2 - r_2^2) = m \Rightarrow (r_1^2 - r_2^2) = \frac{m}{\pi} \Rightarrow (r_1 - r_2)(r_1 + r_2) = \frac{m}{\pi}$

$\Rightarrow (r_1 + r_2) = \frac{m}{\pi} \times \frac{2\pi}{k} = \frac{2m}{k}$ ...(*ii*)

Adding (*i*) and (*ii*) we get : $2r_1 = \frac{k}{2\pi} + \frac{2m}{k} = \frac{k^2 + 4m\pi}{2k\pi}$

$\Rightarrow r_1 = \frac{k^2 + 4m\pi}{4k\pi}$.

Thus, both I and II together give the answer.

∴ Correct answer is (*e*).

27. I. $2(l + b) = 110 \Rightarrow l + b = 55$.

II. $l = (b + 5) \Rightarrow l - b = 5$.

III. $\frac{l}{b} = \frac{5}{6} \Rightarrow 5l - 6b = 0$

These are three equations in l and b. We may solve them pairwise.

∴ Any two of the three will give the answer.

So Correct answer is (*b*).

28. I. Material cost = ₹ 2.50 per m².

II. Labour cost = ₹ 3500.

III. Total cost = ₹ 14,500.

Let the area be A sq. metres.

∴ Material cost = ₹ (14500 – 3500) = ₹ 11,000.

∴ $\frac{5A}{2} = 11000 \Leftrightarrow A = \left(\frac{11000 \times 2}{5}\right) = 4400\ m^2$.

Thus, all I, II and III are needed to get the answer.

∴ Correct answer is (*c*).

29. I. Area $= \frac{1}{2} \times (\text{diagonal})^2$.

II. Area = (Side)²

III. Area $= \left(\frac{\text{Perimeter}}{4}\right)^2$

Thus, only one of I, II and III gives the answer.

∴ Correct answer is (*e*).

30. Area of triangle $= \frac{1}{2} \times \text{Base} \times \text{Height}$.

The above formula can be used if we know any two of the base, height and hypotenuse of the triangle.

Thus, any two of the three, together give the answer.

∴ Correct answer is (*d*).

31. I. $2(l + b) = 34 \Rightarrow l + b = 17$ ...(*i*)

II. $(l - b) = 7$ ...(*ii*)

III. $l = (100 + 140)\%$ of b

$\Rightarrow l - \frac{240}{100} b = 0 \Rightarrow 100l - 240b = 0 \Rightarrow 5l - 12b = 0$ ...(*iii*)

These are 3 equations in l and b. We may solve them pairwise.

∴ Any two of the three will give the answer. So, Correct answer is (*a*).

32. I. Let $l = 3x$ metres and $b = 2x$ metres.

II. $l = 48$ m, Rate of flooring = ₹ 85 per m^2.

III. $2(l + b) = 160 \Leftrightarrow l + b = 80$,

Rate of flooring = ₹ 85 per m^2.

From **I** and **II**, we get $3x = 48 \Leftrightarrow x = 16$.

$\therefore$ $l = 48$ m, $b = 32$ m $\Rightarrow$ Area of floor = (48×32) m^2.

$\therefore$ Cost of flooring = ₹ $(48 \times 32 \times 85)$.

Thus, I and II give the answer.

From **II** and **III**, we get: $l = 48$ m, $b = (80 - 48)$ m = 32 m.

$\therefore$ Area of floor and cost of flooring is obtained.

Thus, II and III give the answer.

From **III** and **I**, we get: $3x + 2x = 80 \Leftrightarrow 5x = 80$

$\Leftrightarrow x = 16$.

$\therefore$ $l = (3 \times 16)$ m = 48 m and $b = (2 \times 16)$ m = 32 m.

$\therefore$ Area of floor and the cost of flooring is obtained.

Thus, III and I give the answer.

Hence, any two of the three will give the answer.

$\therefore$ Correct answer is (*e*).

33. From II, base : height = 5 : 12.

Let base = $5x$ and height = $12x$.

Then, hypotenuse = $\sqrt{(5x)^2 + (12x)^2} = 13x$.

From I, perimeter of the triangle = 30 cm.

$\therefore$ $5x + 12x + 13x = 30 \Leftrightarrow x = 1$.

So, base = $5x$ = 5 cm; height = $12x$ = 12 cm.

$\therefore$ Area = $\left(\frac{1}{2} \times 5 \times 12\right)$ cm^2 = 30 cm^2.

Thus, I and II together give the answer.

Clearly III is redundant, since the breadth of the rectangle is not given.

$\therefore$ Correct answer is (*a*).

34. III. Area of the path = $\frac{8832}{50}$ m^2 = $\frac{4416}{25}$ m^2.

II. Width of path = 10 × (length of the lawn).

I. Length = $3x$ metres and breadth = x metres.

Clearly, all the three will be required to find the width of the path.

$\therefore$ Correct answer is (*a*).

35. I. Let each side of the equilateral triangle be a cm.

Then, $a^2 - \left(\frac{a}{2}\right)^2 = x^2 \Rightarrow \frac{3a^2}{4} = x^2 \Rightarrow a^2 = \frac{4x^2}{3}$.

$\therefore$ Area of the triangle = $\left(\frac{\sqrt{3}}{4} \times \frac{4x^2}{3}\right) = \left(\frac{\sqrt{3}x^2}{3}\right)$ cm^2.

II. Area of the triangle = $\left(\frac{\sqrt{3}}{4} y^2\right)$ cm^2.

III. Each side of the triangle = $\left(\frac{z}{3}\right)$ cm.

$\therefore$ Area of the triangle = $\left[\frac{\sqrt{3}}{4} \times \left(\frac{z}{3}\right)^2\right]$ cm^2 = $\left(\frac{z^2}{12\sqrt{3}}\right)$ cm^2.

Thus, any one of I, II and III is sufficient to give the answer.

So, correct answer is (*a*).

36. II. Base = 8 m. **I.** Perimeter = 18 m. **III.** Height = 3 m.

From II and I, we get : $b = 8$ and $a + b + a = 18$ and so $a = 5$.

Thus, the three sides are 5 m, 5 m and 8 m. From this, the area can be found out.

From II and III, we get: Area = $\left(\frac{1}{2} \times 8 \times 3\right)$ m^2.

$\therefore$ Correct answer is (*d*).

37. Area of 4 walls = $[2(5 + 3) \times 8]$ m = 128 m^2.

II. Area to be painted

= $[128 - (2.25 + 2.25 \times 2)]$ m^2 = 121.25 m^2.

From **I** and **II**, we get : Cost of painting

= ₹ (121.25×25) = ₹ 3031.25.

Thus, only I and II are required while III is redundant.

$\therefore$ Correct answer is (*c*).

38. From II, let $l = 4x$, $b = 6x$ and $h = 5x$.

Then, area of the hall = $(24x^2)$ m^2.

From **I** Area of the hall = 24 m^2.

From II and I, we get $24x^2 = 24 \Leftrightarrow x = 1$.

$\therefore$ $l = 4$ m, $b = 6$ m and $h = 5$ m.

Thus, area of two adjacent walls = $[(l \times h) + (b \times h)]$ m^2 can be found out and so the cost of painting two adjacent walls may be found out.

Thus, III is redundant. $\therefore$ Correct answer is (*c*).

39. From **I** and **II**, we can find the length and breadth of the rectangle and therefore the area can be obtained. So, **III** is redundant.

Also, from **II** and **III**, we can find the length and breadth and therefore the area can be obtained. So, I is redundant.

$\therefore$ Correct answer is (*e*).

40. $\frac{BC}{AC} = \cos 60° = \frac{1}{2} \Rightarrow BC = \frac{5}{2}$ cm $[\because AC = 5 \text{ cm}]$

From **I** and **III**, we get :

$a = \frac{5}{2}$ cm, $b = 5$ cm and $\theta = 60°$.

$\therefore$ $A = \frac{1}{2} ab \sin C$ gives the area.

Thus, I and III give the result. So, II is redundant.

Again, **II** gives $a + b + c = 4a \Rightarrow b + c = 3a$

$\Rightarrow c = 3a - 5$ $[\because b = 5 \text{ from I}]$

$a^2 + (3a - 5)^2 = 25$. This gives a and therefore c.

Now, area of $\Delta ABC = \frac{1}{2} \times a \times c$, which can be obtained.

Thus I and II give the area. So, III is redundant.

$\therefore$ Correct answer is (*c*).

25 Volume and Surface Areas

IMPORTANT FORMULAE

I. Cuboid

Let length = l, breadth = b and height = h units. Then,

1. **Volume** = $(l \times b \times h)$ cubic units.
2. **Surface area** = $2(lb + bh + lh)$ sq. units.
3. **Diagonal** = $\sqrt{l^2 + b^2 + h^2}$ units.

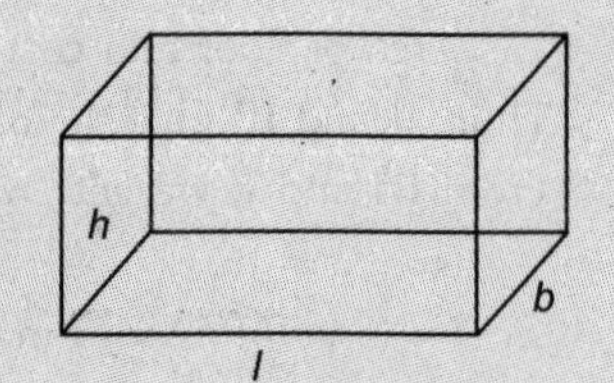

II. Cube

Let each edge of a cube be of length a. Then,

1. **Volume** = a^3 cubic units.
2. **Surface area** = $6a^2$ sq. units.
3. **Diagonal** = $\sqrt{3}\, a$ units.

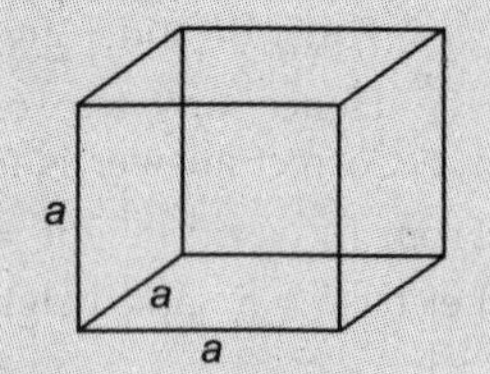

III. Cylinder

Let radius of base = r and Height (or length) = h. Then,

1. **Volume** = $(\pi r^2 h)$ cubic units.
2. **Curved surface area** = $(2\pi rh)$ sq. units.
3. **Total surface area** = $(2\pi rh + 2\pi r^2)$ sq. units
   $= 2\pi r(h + r)$ sq. units.

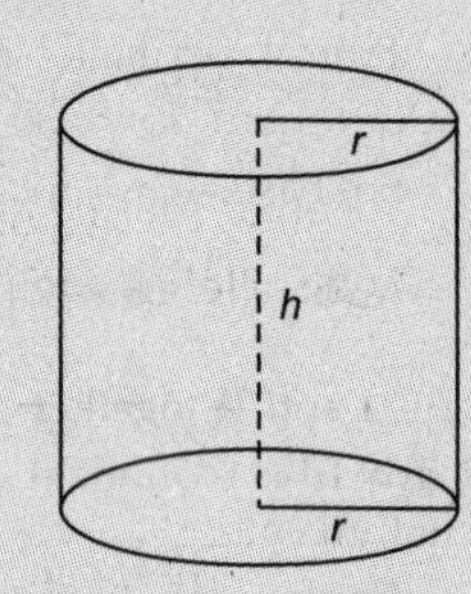

IV. Cone

Let radius of base = r and Height = h. Then,

1. **Slant height**, $l = \sqrt{h^2 + r^2}$ units.
2. **Volume** = $\left(\frac{1}{3}\pi r^2 h\right)$ cubic units.
3. **Curved surface area** = (πrl) sq. units.
4. **Total surface area** = $(\pi rl + \pi r^2)$ sq. units.

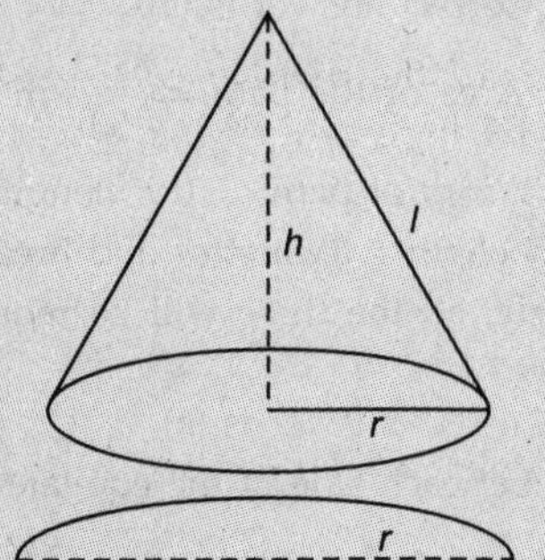

V. Frustum of a Cone

When a cone is cut by a plane parallel to the base of the cone then the portion between the plane and the base is called the frustum of the cone.

Let radius of base = R, radius of top = r, and height = h. Then,

1. **Volume** = $\frac{\pi h}{3}(R^2 + r^2 + Rr)$ cubic units.
2. **Slant height**, $l = \sqrt{(R - r)^2 + h^2}$ units.
3. **Lateral (or curved) surface area** = $\pi . l\,(R + r)$ sq. units.
4. **Total surface area** = $\pi\,[R^2 + r^2 + 1\,(R + r)]$ sq. units.

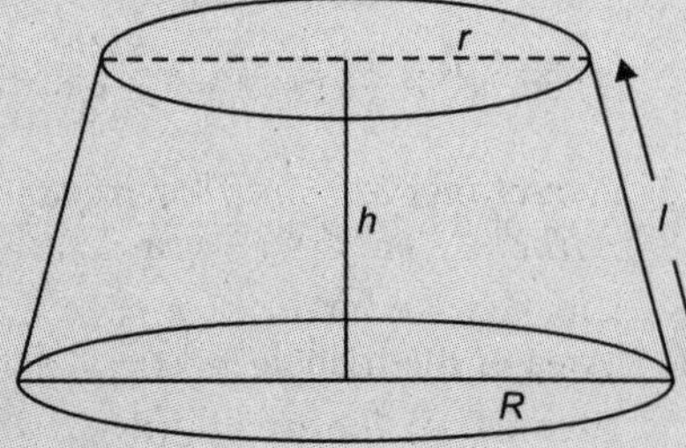

VI. Sphere

Let the radius of the sphere be r. Then,

1. **Volume** = $\left(\frac{4}{3}\pi r^3\right)$ cubic units.
2. **Surface area** = $(4\pi r^2)$ sq. units.

VII. Hemisphere

Let the radius of a hemisphere be r. Then,

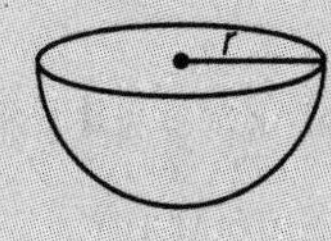

1. **Volume** = $\left(\frac{2}{3}\pi r^3\right)$ cubic units.
2. **Curved surface area** = $(2\pi r^2)$ sq. units.
3. **Total surface area** = $(3\pi r^2)$ sq. units.

VIII. Pyramid

1. **Volume** = $\frac{1}{3} \times$ area of base $\times$ height.
2. **Whole surface area** = Area of base + Area of each of the lateral faces

Remember : 1 litre = 1000 cm^3.

SOLVED EXAMPLES

Ex. 1. ***Find the volume and surface area of a cuboid 16 m long, 14 m broad and 7 m high.***

Sol. Volume = $(16 \times 14 \times 7)$ m^3 = 1568 m^3.

Surface area = $[2 (16 \times 14 + 14 \times 7 + 16 \times 7)]$ cm^2 = (2×434) cm^2 = 868 cm^2.

Ex. 2. ***A room is 12 metres long, 9 metres broad and 8 metres high. Find the length of the longest bamboo pole that can be placed in it.*** **(P.C.S., 2008)**

Sol. Length of the longest pole = Length of the diagonal of the room

$$= \sqrt{(12)^2 + 9^2 + 8^2} \text{ m} = \sqrt{289} \text{ m} = 17\text{m}.$$

Ex. 3. ***The volume of a wall, 5 times as high as it is broad and 8 times as long as it is high, is 12.8 cu. metres. Find the breadth of the wall.***

Sol. Let the breadth of the wall be x metres.

Then, Height = $5x$ metres and Length = $40x$ metres.

$$\therefore x \times 5x \times 40x = 12.8 \Leftrightarrow x^3 = \frac{12.8}{200} = \frac{128}{2000} = \frac{64}{1000}.$$

$$\text{So, } x = \frac{4}{10} \text{ m} = \left(\frac{4}{10} \times 100\right) \text{ cm} = 40 \text{ cm}.$$

Ex. 4. ***Find the number of bricks, each measuring 24 cm × 12 cm × 8 cm, required to construct a wall 24 m long, 8m high and 60 cm thick, if 10% of the wall is filled with mortar?*** **(M.B.A., 2010)**

Sol. Volume of the wall = $(2400 \times 800 \times 60)$ cu. cm.

Volume of bricks = 90% of the volume of the wall

$$= \left(\frac{90}{100} \times 2400 \times 800 \times 60\right) \text{ cu. cm.}$$

Volume of 1 brick = $(24 \times 12 \times 8)$ cu. cm.

$$\therefore \text{Number of bricks} = \left(\frac{90}{100} \times \frac{2400 \times 800 \times 60}{24 \times 12 \times 8}\right) = 45000.$$

Ex. 5. ***A rectangular sheet of paper, 10 cm long and 8 cm wide has squares of side 2 cm cut from each of its corners. The sheet is then folded to form a tray of depth 2 cm. Find the volume of this tray.*** **(R.R.B., 2006)**

Sol. Clearly, we have:

Length of the tray = $(10 - 2 \times 2)$ cm = 6 cm.

Breadth of the tray = $(8 - 2 \times 2)$ cm = 4 cm.

Depth of the tray = 2 cm.

$\therefore$ Volume of the tray = $(6 \times 4 \times 2)$ cm^3 = 48 cm^3.

Ex. 6. ***Water flows into a tank 200 m × 150 m through a rectangular pipe 1.5 m × 1.25 m @ 20 kmph. In what time (in minutes) will the water rise by 2 metres?***

Sol. Volume required in the tank = $(200 \times 150 \times 2)$ m^3 = 60000 m^3.

Length of water column flown in 1 min. = $\left(\frac{20 \times 1000}{60}\right)$ m = $\frac{1000}{3}$ m.

Volume flown per minute = $\left(1.5 \times 1.25 \times \frac{1000}{3}\right)$ m^3 = 625 m^3.

$\therefore$ Required time = $\left(\frac{60000}{625}\right)$ min. = 96 min.

Ex. 7. ***The dimensions of an open box are 50 cm, 40 cm and 23 cm. Its thickness is 3 cm. If 1 cubic cm of metal used in the box weighs 0.5 gms, find the weight of the box.***

Sol. Volume of the metal used in the box = External volume – Internal volume
= $[(50 \times 40 \times 23) - (44 \times 34 \times 20)]$ cm^3
= 16080 cm^3.

$\therefore$ Weight of the metal = $\left(\frac{16080 \times 0.5}{1000}\right)$ kg = 8.04 kg.

Ex. 8. ***The diagonal of a cube is $6\sqrt{3}$ cm. Find its volume and surface area.***

Sol. Let the edge of the cube be a.

$\therefore$ $\sqrt{3}\,a = 6\sqrt{3} \Rightarrow a = 6$.

So, Volume = $a^3 = (6 \times 6 \times 6)$ cm^3 = 216 cm^3.

Surface area = $6a^2 = (6 \times 6 \times 6)$ cm^2 = 216 cm^2.

Ex. 9. ***The surface area of a cube is 1734 sq. cm. Find its volume.***

Sol. Let the edge of the cube be a. Then,

$6a^2 = 1734 \Rightarrow a^2 = 289 \Rightarrow a = 17$ cm.

$\therefore$ Volume = $a^3 = (17)^3$ cm^3 = 4913 cm^3.

Ex. 10. ***A rectangular block 6 cm by 12 cm by 15 cm is cut up into an exact number of equal cubes. Find the least possible number of cubes.***

Sol. Volume of the block = $(6 \times 12 \times 15)$ cm^3 = 1080 cm^3.

Side of the largest cube = H.C.F. of 6 cm, 12 cm, 15 cm = 3 cm.

Volume of this cube = $(3 \times 3 \times 3)$ cm^3 = 27 cm^3.

Number of cubes = $\left(\frac{1080}{27}\right)$ = 40.

Ex. 11. ***A cube of edge 15 cm is immersed completely in a rectangular vessel containing water. If the dimensions of the base of vessel are 20 cm × 15 cm, find the rise in water level.*** **(R.R.B., 2003)**

Sol. Increase in volume = Volume of the cube = $(15 \times 15 \times 15)$ cm^3.

$\therefore$ Rise in water level = $\left(\frac{\text{Volume}}{\text{Area}}\right) = \left(\frac{15 \times 15 \times 15}{20 \times 15}\right)$ cm = 11.25 cm.

Ex. 12. ***Three solid cubes of sides 1 cm, 6 cm and 8 cm are melted to form a new cube. Find the surface area of the cube so formed.*** **(Bank P.O., 2009)**

Sol. Volume of new cube = $(1^3 + 6^3 + 8^3)$ cm^3 = 729 cm^3.

Edge of new cube = $\sqrt[3]{729}$ cm = 9 cm.

$\therefore$ Surface area of the new cube = $(6 \times 9 \times 9)$ cm^2 = 486 cm^2.

Ex. 13. ***If each edge of a cube is increased by 50%, find the percentage increase in its surface area.*** **(R.R.B., 2010)**

Sol. Let original length of each edge = a. Then, original surface area = $6a^2$.

New edge = (150% of a) = $\left(\frac{150}{100} a\right) = \frac{3a}{2}$.

New surface area = $6 \times \left(\frac{3a}{2}\right)^2 = \frac{27}{2} a^2$.

Increase percent in surface area = $\left(\frac{15}{2} a^2 \times \frac{1}{6a^2} \times 100\right)\%$ = 125%.

Ex. 14. ***Two cubes have their volumes in the ratio 1 : 27. Find the ratio of their surface areas.*** **(A.A.O. Exam, 2010)**

Sol. Let their edges be a and b. Then, $\frac{a^3}{b^3} = \frac{1}{27}$ or $\left(\frac{a}{b}\right)^3 = \left(\frac{1}{3}\right)^3$ or $\frac{a}{b} = \frac{1}{3}$.

$\therefore$ Ratio of their surface areas $= \frac{6a^2}{6b^2} = \frac{a^2}{b^2} = \left(\frac{a}{b}\right)^2 = \frac{1}{9}$, *i.e.,* $1:9$.

Ex. 15. ***Find the volume, curved surface area and the total surface area of a cylinder with diameter of base 7 cm and height 40 cm.***

Sol. Volume $= \pi r^2 h = \left(\frac{22}{7} \times \frac{7}{2} \times \frac{7}{2} \times 40\right) \text{ cm}^3 = 1540 \text{ cm}^3$.

Curved surface area $= 2\pi rh = \left(2 \times \frac{22}{7} \times \frac{7}{2} \times 40\right) \text{ cm}^2 = 880 \text{ cm}^2$.

Total surface area $= 2\pi rh + 2\pi r^2 = 2\pi r (h + r)$

$= \left[2 \times \frac{22}{7} \times \frac{7}{2} \times (40 + 3.5)\right] \text{ cm}^2 = 957 \text{ cm}^2$.

Ex. 16. ***If the capacity of a cylindrical tank is 1848 m³ and the diameter of its base is 14 m, then find the depth of the tank.***

Sol. Let the depth of the tank be h metres. Then,

$\pi \times (7)^2 \times h = 1848 \Leftrightarrow h = \left(1848 \times \frac{7}{22} \times \frac{1}{7 \times 7}\right) = 12$ m.

Ex. 17. ***2.2 cubic dm of lead is to be drawn into a cylindrical wire 0.50 cm in diameter. Find the length of the wire in metres.***

Sol. Let the length of the wire be h metres. Then,

$\pi \times \left(\frac{0.50}{2 \times 100}\right)^2 \times h = \frac{2.2}{1000} \Leftrightarrow h = \left(\frac{2.2}{1000} \times \frac{100 \times 100}{0.25 \times 0.25} \times \frac{7}{22}\right) = 112$ m.

Ex.18. ***How many iron rods, each of length 7 m and diameter 2 cm can be made out of 0.88 cubic metre of iron?***

Sol. Volume of 1 rod $= \left(\frac{22}{7} \times \frac{1}{100} \times \frac{1}{100} \times 7\right)$ cu. m $= \frac{11}{5000}$ cu. m.

Volume of iron = 0.88 cu. m.

Number of rods $= \left(0.88 \times \frac{5000}{11}\right) = 400$.

Ex. 19. ***A well with 14 m inside diameter is dug 10 m deep. Earth taken out of it has been evenly spread all around it to a width of 21 m to form an embankment. Find the height of the embankment.*** **(L.I.C.A.AO., 2007)**

Sol. Volume of earth dug out $= \left(\frac{22}{7} \times 7 \times 7 \times 10\right) \text{m}^3 = 1540 \text{ m}^3$.

Area of embankment $= \frac{22}{7} \times [(28)^2 - (7)^2] = \left(\frac{22}{7} \times 35 \times 21\right) \text{m}^2 = 2310 \text{ m}^2$.

$\therefore$ Height of embankment $= \left(\frac{\text{Volume}}{\text{Area}}\right) = \left(\frac{1540}{2310}\right) \text{m} = \frac{2}{3}$ m.

Ex. 20. ***The radii of the bases of two cylinders are in the ratio 3 : 5 and their heights are in the ratio 2 : 3. Find the ratio of their curved surface areas.*** **(C.P.O., 2007)**

Sol. Let the radii of the cylinders be $3x$, $5x$ and their heights be $2y$, $3y$ respectively.

Then, Ratio of their curved surface areas $= \frac{2\pi \times 3x \times 2y}{2\pi \times 5x \times 3y} = \frac{2}{5} = 2:5$.

Ex. 21. ***If 1 cubic cm of cast iron weighs 21 gms, then find the weight of a cast iron pipe of length 1 metre with a bore of 3 cm and in which thickness of the metal is 1 cm.***

Sol. Inner radius $= \left(\frac{3}{2}\right)$ cm $= 1.5$ cm,

Outer radius = (1.5 + 1) cm = 2.5 cm.

$\therefore$ Volume of iron = $[\pi \times (2.5)^2 \times 100 - \pi \times (1.5)^2 \times 100]$ cm^3

$= \frac{22}{7} \times 100 \times [(2.5)^2 - (1.5)^2]$ cm^3 $= \left(\frac{8800}{7}\right)$ cm^3.

$\therefore$ Weight of the pipe = $\left(\frac{8800}{7} \times \frac{21}{1000}\right)$ kg = 26.4 kg.

Ex. 22. ***Find the slant height, volume, curved surface area and the whole surface area of a cone of radius 21 cm and height 28 cm.***

Sol. Here, r = 21 cm and h = 28 cm.

$\therefore$ Slant height, $l = \sqrt{r^2 + h^2} = \sqrt{(21)^2 + (28)^2} = \sqrt{1225} = 35$ cm.

Volume = $\frac{1}{3}\pi r^2 h = \left(\frac{1}{3} \times \frac{22}{7} \times 21 \times 21 \times 28\right)$ cm^3 = 12936 cm^3.

Curved surface area = $\pi r l = \left(\frac{22}{7} \times 21 \times 35\right)$ cm^2 = 2310 cm^2.

Total surface area = $(\pi r l + \pi r^2) = \left(2310 + \frac{22}{7} \times 21 \times 21\right)$ cm^2 = 3696 cm^2.

Ex. 23. ***A conical tent is required to accommodate 5 persons and each person needs 16 cm² of space on the ground and 100 cubic metres of air to breathe. Find the vertical height of the tent.***

Sol. Let the radius of the base of the tent be r and the vertical height be h.

Then, area of the base = πr^2.

$\therefore \pi r^2 = 16 \times 5 = 80 \Rightarrow r^2 = \frac{80}{\pi}$.

Volume of the tent = $\frac{1}{3}\pi r^2 h = \frac{1}{3} \times \pi \times \frac{80}{\pi} \times h = \frac{80h}{3}$.

$\therefore \frac{80h}{3} = 100 \times 5 \Rightarrow 80h = 1500 \Rightarrow h = \frac{75}{4} = 18\frac{3}{4}$.

Hence, height of the tent = $18\frac{3}{4}$ m.

Ex. 24. ***How many metres of cloth 5 m wide will be required to make a conical tent, the radius of whose base is 7m and height is 24 m?*** **(M.A.T., 2006)**

Sol. Here, r = 7 m and h = 24 m.

So, $l = \sqrt{r^2 + h^2} = \sqrt{7^2 + (24)^2} = \sqrt{625} = 25$ m.

Area of canvas = $\pi r l = \left(\frac{22}{7} \times 7 \times 25\right)$ m^2 = 550 m^2.

$\therefore$ Length of canvas = $\left(\frac{\text{Area}}{\text{Width}}\right) = \left(\frac{550}{5}\right)$ m = 110 m.

Ex. 25. ***The heights of two right circular cones are in the ratio 1 : 2 and the perimeters of their bases are in the ratio 3 : 4. Find the ratio of their volumes.***

Sol. Let the radii of their bases be r and R and their heights be h and $2h$ respectively.

Then, $\frac{2\pi r}{2\pi R} = \frac{3}{4} \Rightarrow \frac{r}{R} = \frac{3}{4} \Rightarrow R = \frac{4}{3}r$.

$\therefore$ Ratio of volumes = $\frac{\frac{1}{3}\pi r^2 h}{\frac{1}{3}\pi\left(\frac{4}{3}r\right)^2 (2h)} = \frac{9}{32} = 9:32$.

Ex. 26. ***If the heights of two cones are in the ratio 7 : 3 and their diameters are in the ratio 6 : 7, what is the ratio of their volumes?*** **(M.B.A., 2009)**

Sol. Let the heights of the two cones be $7h$ and $3h$ and their radii be $6r$ and $7r$ respectively. Then,

$$\text{Ratio of their volumes} = \frac{\frac{1}{3} \times \pi \times (6r)^2 \times 7h}{\frac{1}{3} \times \pi \times (7r)^2 \times 3h} = \frac{36 \times 7}{49 \times 3} = \frac{12}{7}.$$

Hence, required ratio = 12 : 7.

Ex. 27. ***The radii of the bases of a cylinder and a cone are in the ratio of 3 : 4 and their heights are in the ratio 2 : 3. Find the ratio of their volumes.***

Sol. Let the radii of the cylinder and the cone be $3r$ and $4r$ and their heights be $2h$ and $3h$ respectively.

$$\therefore \frac{\text{Volume of cylinder}}{\text{Volume of cone}} = \frac{\pi \times (3r)^2 \times 2h}{\frac{1}{3}\pi \times (4r)^2 \times 3h} = \frac{9}{8} = 9 : 8.$$

Ex. 28. ***A conical vessel, whose internal radius is 12 cm and height 50 cm, is full of liquid. The contents are emptied into a cylindrical vessel with internal radius 10 cm. Find the height to which the liquid rises in the cylindrical vessel.***

Sol. Volume of the liquid in the cylindrical vessel

= Volume of the conical vessel

$$= \left(\frac{1}{3} \times \frac{22}{7} \times 12 \times 12 \times 50\right) \text{cm}^3 = \left(\frac{22 \times 4 \times 12 \times 50}{7}\right) \text{cm}^3.$$

Let the height of the liquid in the vessel be h.

Then, $\frac{22}{7} \times 10 \times 10 \times h = \frac{22 \times 4 \times 12 \times 50}{7}$ or $h = \left(\frac{4 \times 12 \times 50}{10 \times 10}\right) = 24$ cm.

Ex. 29. ***The radius and height of a right solid circular cone are r and h respectively. A conical cavity of radius $\frac{r}{2}$ and height $\frac{h}{2}$ is cut out of this cone. What is the whole surface area of the rest of the portion?***

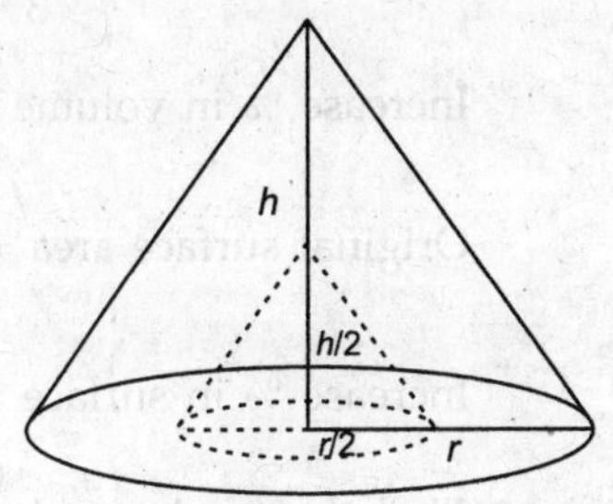

Sol. Clearly, required surface area = Total surface area of bigger cone + Curved surface area of smaller cone – Area of base of smaller cone

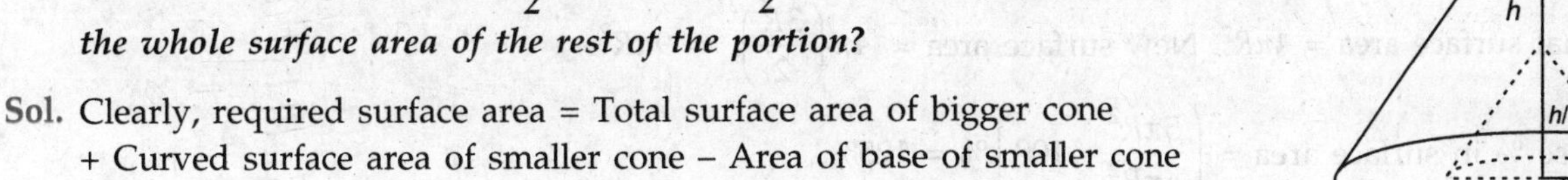

$$= \left[\left(\pi r\sqrt{r^2 + h^2} + \pi r^2\right) + \pi\left(\frac{r}{2}\right)\sqrt{\left(\frac{r}{2}\right)^2 + \left(\frac{h}{2}\right)^2} - \pi\left(\frac{r}{2}\right)^2\right]$$

$$= \pi r\sqrt{r^2 + h^2} + \pi r^2 + \frac{\pi r}{2}\sqrt{\frac{r^2 + h^2}{4}} - \frac{\pi r^2}{4}$$

$$= \pi r\sqrt{r^2 + h^2} + \pi r^2 + \frac{\pi r}{4}\sqrt{r^2 + h^2} - \frac{\pi r^2}{4}$$

True crocodile lizard

$$= \frac{4\pi r\sqrt{r^2 + h^2} + 4\pi r^2 + \pi r\sqrt{r^2 + h^2} - \pi r^2}{4}$$

$$= \frac{5\pi r\sqrt{r^2 + h^2} + 3\pi r^2}{4} = \frac{\pi r}{4}\left(5\sqrt{r^2 + h^2} + 3r\right).$$

Ex. 30. ***In a rocket shaped firecracker, explosive powder is to be filled up inside the metallic enclosure. The metallic enclosure is made up of a cylindrical base and conical top with the base of radius 8 cm. The ratio of height of cylinder and cone is 5 : 3. A cylindrical hole is drilled through the metal solid with height one-third the height of metal solid. What should be the radius of the hole, so that volume of the hole (in which gun powder is to be filled up) is half of the volume of metal after drilling?*** **(I.I.F.T., 2010)**

Sol. Let the height of cylinder and cone be $5x$ and $3x$ cm respectively.

Then, height of metal solid = $(5x + 3x)$ cm = $8x$ cm.

Height of hole = $\left(\frac{8x}{3}\right)$ cm.

Radius of cylinder = Radius of cone = 8 cm.

Let the radius of the hole be r cm.

Volume of metal solid after drilling

= Volume of cylinder + Volume of cone – Volume of hole

$$= \left(\pi \times 8^2 \times 5x + \frac{1}{3}\pi \times 8^2 \times 3x - \pi r^2 \times \frac{8x}{3}\right) cm^3 = \left(320\,\pi x + 64\pi x - \pi r^2 \cdot \frac{8x}{3}\right) cm^3 = \left(384\,\pi x - \pi r^2 \cdot \frac{8x}{3}\right) cm^3.$$

$$\therefore\ 384\pi x - \pi r^2 \cdot \frac{8x}{3} = 2\pi r^2 \cdot \frac{8x}{3} \Rightarrow 3\pi r^2 \cdot \frac{8x}{3} = 384\pi x \Rightarrow r^2 = \frac{384}{8} = 48.$$

$$\Rightarrow r = 4\sqrt{3} \text{ cm.}$$

Ex. 31. ***Find the volume and surface area of a sphere of radius 10.5 cm.***

Sol. Volume $= \frac{4}{3}\pi r^3 = \left(\frac{4}{3} \times \frac{22}{7} \times \frac{21}{2} \times \frac{21}{2} \times \frac{21}{2}\right) cm^3 = 4851 \text{ cm}^3.$

Surface area $= 4\pi r^2 = \left(4 \times \frac{22}{7} \times \frac{21}{2} \times \frac{21}{2}\right) cm^2 = 1386 \text{ cm}^2.$

Ex. 32. ***If the radius of a sphere is increased by 50%, find the increase percent in volume and the increase percent in the surface area.***

Sol. Let original radius = R.

Then, new radius $= \frac{150}{100} R = \frac{3R}{2}.$

Original volume $= \frac{4}{3}\pi R^3$, New volume $= \frac{4}{3}\pi\left(\frac{3R}{2}\right)^3 = \frac{9\pi R^3}{2}.$

Increase % in volume $= \left(\frac{19}{6}\pi R^3 \times \frac{3}{4\pi R^3} \times 100\right)\% = 237.5\%.$

Original surface area $= 4\pi R^2$. New surface area $= 4\pi\left(\frac{3R}{2}\right)^2 = 9\pi R^2.$

Increase % in surface area $= \left(\frac{5\pi R^2}{4\pi R^2} \times 100\right)\% = 125\%.$

Ex. 33. ***Find the number of lead balls, each 1 cm in diameter that can be made from a sphere of diameter 12 cm.***

Sol. Volume of larger sphere $= \left(\frac{4}{3}\pi \times 6 \times 6 \times 6\right) cm^3 = 288\pi \text{ cm}^3.$

Volume of 1 small lead ball $= \left(\frac{4}{3}\pi \times \frac{1}{2} \times \frac{1}{2} \times \frac{1}{2}\right) cm^3 = \frac{\pi}{6} \text{ cm}^3.$

$\therefore$ Number of lead balls $= \left(288\pi \times \frac{6}{\pi}\right) = 1728.$

Ex. 34. ***Three spheres of radii 3 cm, 4 cm and 5 cm are melted to form a new sphere. Find the radius of the new sphere.*** **(Hotel Management, 2010)**

Sol. Let the radius of the new sphere be r cm.

Then, Volume of new sphere = Sum of volumes of three spheres

$$\Rightarrow \frac{4}{3}\pi r^3 = \frac{4}{3}\pi \times 3^3 + \frac{4}{3}\pi \times 4^3 + \frac{4}{3}\pi \times 5^3$$

$$\Rightarrow r^3 = 3^3 + 4^3 + 5^3 = 27 + 64 + 125 = 216 \Rightarrow r = \sqrt[3]{216} = 6.$$

Hence, radius of new sphere = 6 cm.

Ex. 35. ***How many spherical bullets can be made out of a lead cylinder 28 cm high and with base radius 6 cm, each bullet being 1.5 cm in diameter?*** **(R.R.B., 2003)**

Sol. Volume of cylinder $= (\pi \times 6 \times 6 \times 28)$ cm^3

$= (36 \times 28)\ \pi$ cm^3.

Volume of each bullet $= \left(\frac{4}{3}\pi \times \frac{3}{4} \times \frac{3}{4} \times \frac{3}{4}\right) \text{cm}^3 = \frac{9\pi}{16} \text{cm}^3$.

Number of bullets $= \frac{\text{Volume of cylinder}}{\text{Volume of each bullet}} = \left[(36 \times 28)\pi \times \frac{16}{9\pi}\right] = 1792$.

Ex. 36. ***A copper sphere of diameter 18 cm is drawn into a wire of diameter 4 mm. Find the length of the wire.***

Sol. Volume of sphere $= \left(\frac{4}{3}\pi \times 9 \times 9 \times 9\right) \text{cm}^3 = 972\pi \text{ cm}^3$.

Volume of wire $= (\pi \times 0.2 \times 0.2 \times h) \text{ cm}^3$.

$\therefore 972\pi = \pi \times \frac{2}{10} \times \frac{2}{10} \times h \Rightarrow h = (972 \times 5 \times 5) \text{ cm} = \left(\frac{972 \times 5 \times 5}{100}\right) \text{m} = 243 \text{ m}$.

Ex. 37. ***Two metallic right circular cones having their heights 4.1 cm and 4.3 cm and the radii of their bases 2.1 cm each, have been melted together and recast into a sphere. Find the diameter of the sphere.***

Sol. Volume of sphere = Volume of 2 cones $= \left[\frac{1}{3}\pi \times (2.1)^2 \times 4.1 + \frac{1}{3}\pi \times (2.1)^2 \times 4.3\right] \text{cm}^3 = \frac{1}{3}\pi \times (2.1)^2 (8.4) \text{ cm}^3$.

Let the radius of the sphere be R.

$\therefore \frac{4}{3}\pi R^3 = \frac{1}{3}\pi (2.1)^3 \times 4$ or $R = 2.1$ cm.

Hence, diameter of the sphere = 4.2 cm.

Ex. 38. ***A cone and a sphere have equal radii and equal volumes. Find the ratio of the diameter of the sphere to the height of the cone.***

Sol. Let the radius of each be R and height of the cone be H.

Then, $\frac{4}{3}\pi R^3 = \frac{1}{3}\pi R^2 H$ or $\frac{R}{H} = \frac{1}{4}$ or $\frac{2R}{H} = \frac{2}{4} = \frac{1}{2}$. $\therefore$ Required ratio = 1 : 2.

Ex. 39. ***Find the volume, curved surface area and the total surface area of a hemisphere of radius 10.5 cm.***

Sol. Volume $= \frac{2}{3}\pi r^3 = \left(\frac{2}{3} \times \frac{22}{7} \times \frac{21}{2} \times \frac{21}{2} \times \frac{21}{2}\right) \text{cm}^3 = 2425.5 \text{ cm}^3$.

Curved surface area $= 2\pi r^2 = \left(2 \times \frac{22}{7} \times \frac{21}{2} \times \frac{21}{2}\right) \text{cm}^2 = 693 \text{ cm}^2$.

Total surface area $= 3\pi r^2 = \left(3 \times \frac{22}{7} \times \frac{21}{2} \times \frac{21}{2}\right) \text{cm}^2 = 1039.5 \text{ cm}^2$.

Ex. 40. ***A hemispherical bowl of internal radius 9 cm contains a liquid. This liquid is to be filled into cylindrical shaped small bottles of diameter 3 cm and height 4 cm. How many bottles will be needed to empty the bowl?***

Sol. Volume of bowl $= \left(\frac{2}{3}\pi \times 9 \times 9 \times 9\right) \text{cm}^3 = 486\pi \text{ cm}^3$.

Volume of 1 bottle $= \left(\pi \times \frac{3}{2} \times \frac{3}{2} \times 4\right) \text{cm}^3 = 9\pi \text{ cm}^3$.

Number of bottles $= \left(\frac{486\pi}{9\pi}\right) = 54$.

Ex. 41. ***A cone, a hemisphere and a cylinder stand on equal bases and have the same height. Find the ratio of their volumes.***

Sol. Let R be the radius of each.

Height of hemisphere = Its radius = R.

$\therefore$ Height of each = R.

Ratio of volumes $= \frac{1}{3}\pi R^2 \times R : \frac{2}{3}\pi R^3 : \pi R^2 \times R = 1 : 2 : 3$.

Ex. 42. ***A cylindrical container of radius 6 cm and height 15 cm is filled with ice-cream. The whole ice-cream has to be distributed to 10 children in equal cones with hemispherical tops. If the height of the conical portion is four times the radius of its base, then find the radius of the ice-cream cone.*** (M.A.T., 2007)

Sol. Volume of ice-cream in cylindrical container = $(\pi \times 6^2 \times 15)$ cm^3 = (540π) cm^3.

Let the radius of the base of the cone be r cm.

Then, height of the cone = $(4r)$ cm.

Volume of ice-cream in 10 cones with hemispherical tops = $\left[10\left\{\frac{1}{3}\pi r^2 \times 4r + \frac{2}{3}\pi r^3\right\}\right]$ cm^3 = $(20\pi r^3)$ cm^3.

$\therefore 20\pi r^3 = 540\pi \Rightarrow r^3 = \frac{540\pi}{20\pi} = 27 \Rightarrow r = 3.$

Hence, radius of ice-cream cone = 3 cm

EXERCISE

(OBJECTIVE TYPE QUESTIONS)

Directions : *Mark (✓) against the correct answer:*

1. A cuboid has .... edges. **(R.R.B., 2006)**
(a) 4 (b) 8
(c) 12 (d) 16

2. 1 litre is equal to
(a) 1 cu. cm (b) 10 cu. cm
(c) 100 cu. cm (d) 1000 cu. cm

3. A rectangular water tank is 8 m high, 6 m long and 2.5 m wide. How many litres of water can it hold? **(R.R.B., 2008)**
(a) 120 litres (b) 1200 litres
(c) 12000 litres (d) 120000 litres

4. The dimensions of a cuboid are 7cm, 11 cm and 13 cm. The total surface area is **(Teachers' Exam, 2011)**
(a) 311 cm^2 (b) 622 cm^2
(c) 1001 cm^2 (d) 2002 cm^2

5. A closed aquarium of dimensions 30 cm × 25 cm × 20 cm is made up entirely of glass plates held together with tapes. The total length of tape required to hold the plates together (ignore the overlapping tapes) is **(Hotel Management, 2009)**
(a) 75 cm (b) 120 cm
(c) 150 cm (d) 300 cm

6. The dimensions of a room are 15 m, 10 m and 8 m. The volume of a bag is 2.25 m^3. The maximum number of bags that can be a accommodated in the room is
(a) 531 (b) 533
(c) 535 (d) 550

7. A rectangular water reservoir contains 42000 litres of water. If the length of reservoir is 6 m and breadth of the reservoir is 3.5 m, then the depth of the reservoir will be **(R.R.B., 2006)**
(a) 2 m (b) 5 m
(c) 6 m (d) 8 m

8. A cistern 6 m long and 4 m wide contains water up to a depth of 1 m 25 cm. The total area of the wet surface is
(a) 49 m^2 (b) 50 m^2
(c) 53.5 m^2 (d) 55 m^2

9. A boat having a length 3 m and breadth 2 m is floating on a lake. The boat sinks by 1 cm when a man gets on it. The mass of man is
(a) 12 kg (b) 60 kg
(c) 72 kg (d) 96 kg

10. A water tank is 30 m long, 20 m wide and 12 m deep. It is made of iron sheet which is 3 m wide. The tank is open at the top. If the cost of the iron sheet is ₹ 10 per metre, then the total cost of the iron sheet required to build the tank is
(a) ₹ 6000 (b) ₹ 8000
(c) ₹ 9000 (d) ₹ 10000

11. Given that 1 cu. cm of marble weighs 25 gms, the weight of a marble block 28 cm in width and 5 cm thick is 112 kg. The length of the block is
(a) 26.5 cm (b) 32 cm
(c) 36 cm (d) 37.5 cm

12. Half cubic metre of gold sheet is extended by hammering so as to cover an area of 1 hectare. The thickness of the sheet is
(a) 0.0005 cm (b) 0.005 cm
(c) 0.05 cm (d) 0.5 cm

13. In a shower, 5 cm of rain falls. The volume of water that falls on 1.5 hectares of ground is :
(a) 75 cu. m (b) 750 cu. m
(c) 7500 cu. m (d) 75000 cu. m

14. The breadth of a room is twice its height and half its length. The volume of the room is 512 cu. m. The length of the room is **(N.M.A.T., 2007)**
(a) 16 m (b) 18 m
(c) 20 m (d) 32 m

15. The length of a cold storage is double its breadth. Its height is 3 metres. The area of its four walls (including the doors) is 108 m^2. Find its volume.
(a) 215 m^3 (b) 216 m^3
(c) 217 m^3 (d) 218 m^3

16. The length of a hall is 20 metres and the width is 16 metres. The sum of the areas of the floor and roof

is equal to the sum of the areas of the four walls. Find the volume of the hall.

(a) 2844.4 m^3 (b) 2866.8 m^3
(c) 2877.8 m^3 (d) 2899.8 m^3

17. If V be the volume and S be the surface area of a cuboid of dimensions a, b, c, then $\frac{1}{V}$ is equal to

(a) $\frac{S}{2}(a+b+c)$ (b) $\frac{2}{S}\left(\frac{1}{a}+\frac{1}{b}+\frac{1}{c}\right)$
(c) $\frac{2S}{a+b+c}$ (d) $2S\ (a+b+c)$

18. The volume of a rectangular block of stone is 10368 dm^3. Its dimensions are in the ratio of 3 : 2 : 1. If its entire surface is polished at 2 paise per dm^2, then the total cost will be

(a) ₹ 31.50 (b) ₹ 31.68
(c) ₹ 63 (d) ₹ 63.36

19. The dimensions of a rectangular box are in the ratio 2 : 3 : 4 and the difference between the cost of covering it with sheet of paper at the rate of ₹ 8 and ₹ 9.50 per square metre is ₹ 1248. Find the dimensions of the box in meters.

(a) 2 m, 12 m, 8 m (b) 4 m, 9 m, 16 m
(c) 8 m, 12 m, 16 m (d) None of these

20. It is required to construct a big rectangular hall to accommodate 500 persons, allowing 22.5 m^3 space per person. The height of the hall is to be kept at 7.5 m, while the total inner surface area of the walls must be 1200 sq. m. Then the length and breadth of the hall respectively are

(a) 40 m and 30 m (b) 45 m and 35 m
(c) 50 m and 30 m (d) 60 m and 20 m

21. A cuboidal water tank contains 216 litres of water. Its depth is $\frac{1}{3}$ of its length and breadth is $\frac{1}{2}$ of $\frac{1}{3}$ of the difference between length and depth. The length of the tank is (S.S.C., 2005)

(a) 2 dm (b) 6 dm
(c) 18 dm (d) 72 dm

22. The length of the longest rod that can be placed in a room of dimensions 10 m × 10 m × 5 m is (S.S.C., 2010)

(a) $15\sqrt{3}$ (b) 15
(c) $10\sqrt{2}$ (d) $5\sqrt{3}$

23. Find the length of the longest rod that can be placed in a room 16 m long, 12 m broad and $10\frac{2}{3}$ m high.

(a) $22\frac{1}{3}$ m (b) $22\frac{2}{3}$ m
(c) 23 m (d) 68 m

24. The volume of a rectangular solid is 210 cm^3 and the surface area is 214 cm^2. If the area of the base is 42 cm^2, then the edges of the rectangular solid are

(a) 3, 4 and 5 cm (b) 4, 5 and 6 cm
(c) 5, 6 and 7 cm (d) 6, 6 and 8 cm

25. How many bricks, each measuring 25 cm × 11.25 cm × 6 cm, will be needed to build a wall 8 m × 6 m × 22.5 cm? (M.A.T., 2008)

(a) 5600 (b) 6000
(c) 6400 (d) 7200

26. The number of bricks, each measuring 25 cm × 12.5 cm × 7.5 cm, required to construct a wall 6 m long, 5 m high and 0.5 m thick, while the mortar occupies 5% of the volume of the wall, is

(a) 3040 (b) 5740
(c) 6080 (d) 8120

27. 50 men took a dip in a water tank 40 m long and 20 m broad on a religious day. If the average displacement of water by a man is 4 m^3, then the rise in the water level in the tank will be :

(a) 20 cm (b) 25 cm
(c) 35 cm (d) 50 cm

28. A swimming bath is 24 m long and 15 m broad. When a number of men dive into the bath, the height of the water rises by 1 cm. If the average amount of water displaced by one of the men be 0.1 cu. m, how many men are there in the bath? (N.M.A.T., 2005)

(a) 32 (b) 36
(c) 42 (d) 46

29. A school room is to be built to accommodate 70 children so as to allow 2.2 m^2 of floor and 11 m^3 of space for each child. If the room be 14 metres long, what must be its breadth and height? (M.A.T., 2010)

(a) 11 m, 4 m (b) 11 m, 5 m
(c) 12 m, 5.5 m (d) 13 m, 6 m

30. A rectangular tank measuring 5 m × 4.5 m × 2.1 m is dug in the centre of the field measuring 13.5 m by 2.5 m. The earth dug out is evenly spread over the remaining portion of the field. How much is the level of the field raised? (M.A.T. 2005)

(a) 4 m (b) 4.1 m
(c) 4.2 m (d) 4.3 m

31. A plot of land in the form of a rectangle has dimensions 240 m × 180 m. A drainlet 10 m wide is dug all around it (outside) and the earth dug out is evenly spread over the plot, increasing its surface level by 25 cm. The depth of the drainlet is (M.A.T., 2006)

(a) 1.223 m (b) 1.225 m
(c) 1.227 m (d) 1.229 m

32. A cistern, open at the top, is to be lined with sheet of lead which weights 27 kg/m^2. The cistern is 4.5 m long and 3 m wide and holds 50 m^3. The weight of lead required is (M.A.T., 2009)

(a) 1660.5 kg (b) 1764.5 kg
(c) 1860.5 kg (d) 1864.5 kg

33. If a river 2.5 m deep and 45 m wide is flowing at the rate of 3.6 km per hour, then the amount of water that runs into the sea per minute is

(*a*) 6650 cu. m (*b*) 6750 cu. m
(*c*) 6850 cu. m (*d*) 6950 cu. m

34. A rectangular water tank is 80 m × 40 m. Water flows into it through a pipe 40 sq. cm at the opening at a speed of 10 km/hr. By how much, the water level will rise in the tank in half an hour?

(*a*) $\frac{3}{2}$ cm (*b*) $\frac{4}{9}$ cm
(*c*) $\frac{5}{8}$ cm (*d*) None of these

35. A rectangular tank is 225 m by 162 m at the base. With what speed must water flow into it through an aperture 60 cm by 45 cm so that the level may be raised 20 cm in 5 hours? **(M.A.T., 2006)**

(*a*) 5000 m/hr (*b*) 5200 m/hr
(*c*) 5400 m/hr (*d*) 5600 m/hr

36. The water in a rectangular reservoir having a base 80 m by 60 m is 6.5 m deep. In what time can the water be emptied by a pipe of which the cross-section is a square of side 20 cm, if the water runs through the pipe at the rate of 15 km per hour?

(*a*) 26 hrs (*b*) 42 hrs
(*c*) 52 hrs (*d*) 65 hrs

37. Rita and Meeta both are having lunch boxes of a cuboidal shape. Length and breadth of Rita's lunch box are 10% more than that of Meeta's lunch box, but the depth of Rita's lunch box is 20% less than that of Meeta's lunch box. The ratio of the capacity of Rita's lunch box to that of Meeta's lunch box is **(Hotel Management, 2010)**

(*a*) 11 : 15 (*b*) 15 : 11
(*c*) 121 : 125 (*d*) 125 : 121

38. The sum of the length, breadth and depth of a cuboid is 19 cm and its diagonal is $5\sqrt{5}$ cm. It surface area is

(*a*) 125 cm^2 (*b*) 236 cm^2
(*c*) 361 cm^2 (*d*) 486 cm^2

39. The sum of perimeters of the six faces of a cuboid is 72 cm and the total surface area of the cuboid is 16 cm^2. Find the longest possible length that can be kept inside the cuboid

(*a*) 5.2 cm (*b*) 7.8 cm
(*c*) 8.05 cm (*d*) 8.36 cm

40. A swimming pool 9 m wide and 12 m long is 1 m deep on the shallow side and 4 m deep on the deeper side. Its volume is :

(*a*) 208 m^3 (*b*) 270 m^3
(*c*) 360 m^3 (*d*) 408 m^3

41. Length of a rectangular solid is increased by 10% and breadth is decreased by 10%. Then the volume of the solid

(*a*) remains unchanged (*b*) decreases by 1%
(*c*) decreases by 10% (*d*) increases by 10%

42. The length, breadth and height of a cuboid are in the ratio 1 : 2 : 3. The length, breadth and height of the cuboid are increased by 100%, 200% and 200% respectively. Then the increase in the volume of the cuboid is

(*a*) 5 times (*b*) 6 times
(*c*) 12 times (*d*) 17 times

43. A rectangular piece of cardboard 18 cm × 24 cm is made into an open box by cutting a square of 5 cm side from each corner and building up the side. Find the volume of the box in cu. cm.

(*a*) 216 (*b*) 432
(*c*) 560 (*d*) None of these

44. An open box is made by cutting the congruent squares from the corners of a rectangular sheet of cardboard of dimensions 20 cm × 15 cm. If the side of each square is 2 cm, the total outer surface area of the box is **(Hotel Management, 2010)**

(*a*) 148 cm^2 (*b*) 284 cm^2
(*c*) 316 cm^2 (*d*) 460 cm^2

45. A closed box made of wood of uniform thickness has length, breadth and height 12 cm, 10 cm and 8 cm respectively. If the thickness of the wood is 1 cm, the inner surface area is **(E.S.T.C., 2006)**

(*a*) 264 cm^2 (*b*) 376 cm^2
(*c*) 456 cm^2 (*d*) 696 cm^2

46. A covered wooden box has the inner measures as 115 cm, 75 cm and 35 cm and the thickness of wood is 2.5 cm. Find the volume of the wood. **(M.B.A., 2008)**

(*a*) 81000 cu.cm (*b*) 81775 cu.cm
(*c*) 82125 cu.cm (*d*) None of these

47. The dimensions of an open box are 52 cm × 40 cm × 29 cm. Its thickness is 2 cm. If 1 cu. cm of metal used in the box weighs 0.5 gm, then the weight of the box is **(M.B.A., 2011)**

(*a*) 6.832 kg (*b*) 7.576 kg
(*c*) 7.76 kg (*d*) 8.56 kg

48. An open box is made of wood 3 cm thick. Its external dimensions are 1.46 m, 1.16 m and 8.3 dm. The cost of painting the inner surface of the box at 50 paise per 100 sq. cm is

(*a*) ₹ 138.50 (*b*) ₹ 277
(*c*) ₹ 415. 50 (*d*) ₹ 554

49. A cistern of capacity 8000 litres measures externally 3.3 m by 2.6 m by 1.1 m and its walls are 5 cm thick. The thickness of the bottom is

(*a*) 90 cm (*b*) 1 dm
(*c*) 1 m (*d*) 1.1 m

50. If a metallic cuboid weighs 16 kg, how much would a miniature cuboid of metal weigh, if all dimensions are reduced to one-fourth of the original?
(*a*) 0.25 kg (*b*) 0.50 kg
(*c*) 0.75 kg (*d*) 1 kg

51. A rectangular water tank is open at the top. Its capacity is 24 m^3. Its length and breadth are 4 m and 3 m respectively. Ignoring the thickness of the material used for building the tank, the total cost of painting the inner and outer surfaces of the tank at the rate of ₹ 10 per m^2 is **(M.B.A., 2006)**
(*a*) ₹ 400 (*b*) ₹ 500
(*c*) ₹ 600 (*d*) ₹ 800

52. If the areas of three adjacent faces of a cuboid are *x*, *y*, *z* respectively, then the volume of the cuboid is **(M.B.A. 2005, 2007)**
(*a*) xyz (*b*) $2xyz$
(*c*) $\sqrt{xyz}$ (*d*) $3\sqrt{xyz}$

53. If the areas of the three adjacent faces of a cuboidal box are 120 cm^2, 72 cm^2 and 60 cm^2 respectively, then find the volume of the box.
(*a*) 720 cm^3 (*b*) 864 cm^3
(*c*) 7200 cm^3 (*d*) $(72)^2$ cm^3

54. If the areas of three adjacent faces of a rectangular block are in the ratio of 2 : 3 : 4 and its volume is 9000 cu. cm; then the length of the shortest side is
(*a*) 10 cm (*b*) 15 cm
(*c*) 20 cm (*d*) 30 cm

55. The dimensions of a certain machine are 48″ × 30″ × 52″. If the size of the machine is increased proportionately until the sum of its dimensions equals 156″, what will be the increase in the shortest side? **(Campus Recruitment, 2009)**
(*a*) 4″ (*b*) 6″
(*c*) 8″ (*d*) 9″

56. If a metal slab of size 1 m × 20 cm × 1 cm is melted to another slab of 1 mm thickness and 1 m width, then the length of the new slab thus formed will be
(*a*) 200 cm (*b*) 400 cm
(*c*) 600 cm (*d*) 1000 cm

57. Rahul hired a contractor to dig a well of 10 metres length, 10 metres breadth and 10 metres depth for ₹ 40000. However, when the contractor was about to start the work, he changed his mind and asked him to get two wells dug, each with a length of 5 metres, breadth of 5 metres and depth of 5 metres. How much should Rahul pay to the contractor?
(*a*) ₹ 10000 (*b*) ₹ 20000
(*c*) ₹ 40000 (*d*) None of these

58. Each side of a cube measures 8 metres. What is the volume of the cube? **(P.C.S., 2008)**
(*a*) 72 cu. m (*b*) 144 cu. m
(*c*) 196 cu. m (*d*) None of these

59. The perimeter of one face of a cube is 20 cm. Its volume must be
(*a*) 125 cm^3 (*b*) 400 cm^3
(*c*) 1000 cm^3 (*d*) 8000 cm^3

60. Total surface area of a cube whose side is 0.5 cm is
(*a*) $\frac{1}{4}$ cm^2 (*b*) $\frac{1}{8}$ cm^2
(*c*) $\frac{3}{4}$ cm^2 (*d*) $\frac{3}{2}$ cm^2

61. The cost of the paint is ₹ 36.50 per kg. If 1 kg of paint covers 16 square feet, how much will it cost to paint outside of a cube having 8 feet each side?
(*a*) ₹ 692 (*b*) ₹ 768
(*c*) ₹ 876 (*d*) ₹ 972
(*e*) None of these

62. If the volume of a cube is 729 cm^3, then the surface area of the cube will be
(*a*) 456 cm^2 (*b*) 466 cm^2
(*c*) 476 cm^2 (*d*) 486 cm^2

63. The surface area of a cube is 150 cm^2. Its volume is **(E.S.I.C., 2006)**
(*a*) 64 cm^3 (*b*) 125 cm^3
(*c*) 150 cm^3 (*d*) 216 cm^3

64. The dimensions of a piece of iron in the shape of a cuboid are 270 cm × 100 cm × 64 cm. If it is melted and recast into a cube, then the surface area of the cube will be
(*a*) 14400 cm^2 (*b*) 44200 cm^2
(*c*) 57600 cm^2 (*d*) 86400 cm^2

65. The cost of painting the whole surface area of a cube at the rate of 13 paise per sq. cm is ₹ 343.98. Then the volume of the cube is :
(*a*) 8500 cm^3 (*b*) 9000 cm^3
(*c*) 9250 cm^3 (*d*) 9261 cm^3

66. An aluminium sheet 27 cm long, 8 cm broad and 1 cm thick is melted into a cube. The difference in the surface areas of the two solids would be **(M.B.A., 2008)**
(*a*) Nil (*b*) 284 cm^2
(*c*) 286 cm^2 (*d*) 296 cm^2

67. The length of an edge of a hollow cube open at one face is $\sqrt{3}$ metres. What is the length of the largest pole that it can accommodate?
(*a*) $\sqrt{3}$ m (*b*) 3 m
(*c*) $3\sqrt{3}$ m (*d*) $\frac{3}{\sqrt{3}}$ m

68. What is the volume of a cube (in cubic cm) whose diagonal measures $4\sqrt{3}$ cm?
(*a*) 8 (*b*) 16
(*c*) 27 (*d*) 64

69. If the total length of diagonals of a cube is 12 cm, then what is the total length of the edges of the cube? (C.D.S., 2005)
(a) $6\sqrt{3}$ cm (b) 12 cm
(c) 15 cm (d) $12\sqrt{3}$ cm

70. If the surface area of a cube is 13254 cm^2, then the length of its diagonal is
(a) $44\sqrt{3}$ cm (b) $45\sqrt{3}$ cm
(c) $46\sqrt{3}$ cm (d) $47\sqrt{3}$ cm

71. V_1, V_2, V_3 and V_4 are the volumes of four cubes of side lengths x cm, $2x$ cm, $3x$ cm and $4x$ cm respectively. Some statements regarding these volumes are given below
(1) $V_1 + V_2 + 2V_3 < V_4$
(2) $V_1 + 4V_2 + V_3 < V_4$
(3) $2(V_1 + V_3) + V_2 = V_4$
Which of these statements are correct?
(a) 1 and 2 (b) 2 and 3
(c) 1 and 3 (d) 1, 2 and 3

72. From a cube of side 8m, a square hole of 3m side is hollowed from end to end. What is the volume of the remaining solid? (R.R.B., 2006)
(a) 440 m^3 (b) 480 m^3
(c) 508 m^3 (d) 520 m^3

73. If the numbers representing volume and surface area of a cube are equal, then the length of the edge of the cube in terms of the unit of measurement will be
(a) 3 (b) 4
(c) 5 (d) 6

74. The volume of a cube is numerically equal to the sum of its edges. What is its total surface area in square units?
(a) 36 (b) 66
(c) 72 (d) 183

75. Except for one face of a given cube, identical cubes are glued through their faces to all the other faces of the given cube. If each side of the given cube measures 3 cm, then what is the total surface area of the solid body thus formed?
(a) 225 cm^2 (b) 234 cm^2
(c) 270 cm^2 (d) 279 cm^2

76. A solid cube just gets completely immersed in water when a 0.2 kg mass is placed on it. If the mass is removed, the cube is 2 cm above the water level. What is the length of each side of the cube? (P.C.S., 2009)
(a) 6 cm (b) 8 cm
(c) 10 cm (d) 12 cm

77. A cube of length 1 cm is taken out from a cube of length 8 cm. What is the weight of the remaining portion? (C.P.F., 2007)
(a) $\frac{7}{8}$ of the weight of the original cube
(b) $\frac{8}{9}$ of the weight of the original cube
(c) $\frac{63}{64}$ of the weight of the original cube
(d) $\frac{511}{512}$ of the weight of the original cube

78. How many cubes of 10 cm edge can be put in a cubical box of 1 m edge? (M.B.A., 2008)
(a) 10 (b) 100
(c) 1000 (d) 10000

79. A 4 cm cube is cut into 1 cm cubes. The total surface area of all the small cubes is (M.B.A., 2005)
(a) 24 cm^2 (b) 96 cm^2
(c) 384 cm^2 (d) None of these

80. A rectangular block with a volume of 250 cm^3 was sliced into two cubes of equal volume. How much greater (in sq. cm) is the combined surface area of the two cubes then the original surface area of the rectangular block?
(a) 48.64 (b) 50
(c) 56.25 (d) 84.67

81. A rectangular box measures internally 1.6 m long, 1 m broad and 60 cm deep. The number of cubical blocks each of edge 20 cm that can be packed inside the box is
(a) 30 (b) 53
(c) 60 (d) 120

82. How many cubes of 3 cm edge can be cut out of a cube of 18 cm edge?
(a) 36 (b) 216
(c) 218 (d) 432

83. Shobhraj takes a cube of 1 m edge-length and meticulously cuts smaller cubes, each of edge-length 1 mm from the parent cube. He joins these small cubes end-to-end. Thus, the total length of this 'cube-robe' will be
(a) 1 km (b) 10 km
(c) 100 km (d) 1000 km

84. How many small cubes, each of 96 cm surface area, can be formed from the material obtained by melting a larger cube of 384 cm surface area? (M.A.T., 2007)
(a) 5 (b) 8
(c) 800 (d) 8000

85. The volume of a cuboid is twice that of a cube. If the dimensions of the cuboid are 9 cm, 8 cm and 6 cm, the total surface area of the cube is (S.S.C., 2005)
(a) 72 cm^2 (b) 108 cm^2
(c) 216 cm^2 (d) 432 cm^2

86. A cuboidal block of 6 cm × 9 cm × 12 cm is cut up into an exact number of equal cubes. The least possible number of cubes will be

(a) 6 (b) 9
(c) 24 (d) 30

87. The size of a wooden block is $5 \times 10 \times 20$ cm. How many such blocks will be required to construct a solid wooden cube of minimum size?
(a) 6 (b) 8
(c) 12 (d) 16

88. An iron cube of side 10 cm is hammered into a rectangular sheet of thickness 0.5 cm. If the sides of the sheet are in the ratio 1 : 5, the sides are
(a) 10 cm, 50 cm (b) 20 cm, 100 cm
(c) 40 cm, 200 cm (d) None of these

89. A cube of white chalk is painted red, and then cut parallel to the sides to form two rectangular solids of equal volumes. What percent of the surface area of each of the new solids is not painted red?
(a) 15% (b) $16\frac{2}{3}\%$
(c) 20% (d) 25%

90. There is a cube of volume 216 cm^3. It is to be moulded into a cuboid having one edge equal to 6 cm. The number of ways that it can be done so that the edges have different integral values is
(a) 1 (b) 2
(c) 3 (d) 4

91. If three cubes of copper, each with an edge of 6 cm 8 cm and 10 cm respectively are melted to form a single cube, then the diagonal of the new cube will be
(a) 18 cm (b) 19 cm
(c) 19.5 cm (d) 20.8 cm

92. A larger cube is formed from the material obtained by melting three smaller cubes of 3, 4 and 5 cm side. The ratio of the total surface areas of the smaller cubes and the larger cube is (I.L.F.T., 2005)
(a) 2 : 1 (b) 3 : 2
(c) 25 : 18 (d) 27 : 20

93. Five equal cubes, each of side 5 cm, are placed adjacent to each other. The volume of the new solid formed will be
(a) 125 cm^3 (b) 625 cm^3
(c) 15525 cm^3 (d) None of these

94. If three equal cubes are placed adjacently in a row, then the ratio of the total surface area of the new cuboid to the sum of the surface areas of the three cubes will be (M.A.T., 2007)
(a) 1 : 3 (b) 2 : 3
(c) 5 : 9 (d) 7 : 9

95. Three cubes with sides in the ratio 3 : 4 : 5 are melted to form a single cube whose diagonal is $12\sqrt{3}$ cm. The sides of the cubes are
(a) 3 cm, 4 cm, 5 cm (b) 6 cm, 8 cm, 10 cm
(c) 9 cm, 12 cm, 15 cm (d) None of these

96. If the volumes of two cubes are in the ratio 27 : 1, the ratio of their edges is
(a) 1 : 3 (b) 1 : 27
(c) 3 : 1 (d) 27 : 1

97. The volumes of two cubes are in the ratio 8 : 27. The ratio of their surface areas is
(a) 2 : 3 (b) 4 : 9
(c) 12 : 9 (d) None of these

98. Two cubes have volumes in the ratio 1 : 27. Then the ratio of the area of the face of one of the cubes to that of the other is
(a) 1 : 3 (b) 1 : 6
(c) 1 : 9 (d) 1 : 12

99. If each edge of a cube is doubled, then its volume:
(a) is doubled (b) becomes 4 times
(c) becomes 6 times (d) becomes 8 times

100. By what percent the volume of a cube increases if the length of each edge was increased by 50%? (Bank P.O., 2011)
(a) 50% (b) 125%
(c) 237.5% (d) 273.5%

101. If each edge of a cube is increased by 25%, then the percentage increase in its surface area is :
(a) 25% (b) 48.75%
(c) 50% (d) 56.25%

102. A cube of edge 20 cm is completely immersed in a rectangular vessel containing water. If the dimensions of the base of the vessel are 20 cm by 40 cm, the rise in water level will be
(a) 2 cm (b) 8 cm
(c) 10 cm (d) 14 cm

103. A circular well with a diameter of 2 metres, is dug to a depth of 14 metres. What is the volume of the earth dug out? (S.S.C., 1999)
(a) 32 m^3 (b) 36 m^3
(c) 40 m^3 (d) 44 m^3

104. Find the cost of a cylinder of radius 14 m and height 3.5 m when the cost of its metal is ₹ 50 per cubic metre. (B.Ed Entrance, 2008)
(a) ₹ 100208 (b) ₹ 107800
(c) ₹ 10800 (d) ₹ 109800

105. If the radius and height of a right circular cylinder are 21 cm and 35 cm respectively, then the total surface area of the cylinder is
(a) 7092 sq cm (b) 7192 sq cm
(c) 7292 sq cm (d) 7392 sq cm

106. The capacity of a cylindrical tank is 246.4 litres. If the height is 4 metres, what is the diameter of the base?
(a) 1.4 m (b) 2.8 m
(c) 14 m (d) 28 m
(e) None of these

107. The volume of a right circular cylinder, 14 cm in height is equal to that of a cube whose edge is 11

cm. The radius of the base of the cylinder is (C.P.O., 2006)

(a) 5.2 cm (b) 5.5 cm
(c) 11 cm (d) 22 cm

108. Capacity of a cylindrical vessel is 25.872 litres. If the height of the cylinder is three times the radius of its base, what is the area of the base? (Bank P.O. 2007)

(a) 336 cm^2 (b) 616 cm^2
(c) 1232 cm^2 (d) Cannot be determined
(e) None of these

109. Two rectangular sheets of paper, each 30 cm × 18 cm are made into two right circular cylinders, one by rolling the paper along its length and the other along the breadth. The ratio of the volumes of the two cylinders, thus formed, is (M.B.A., 2006)

(a) 2 : 1 (b) 3 : 2
(c) 4 : 3 (d) 5 : 3

110. Three rectangles A_1, A_2 and A_3 have the same area. Their lengths a_1, a_2 and a_3 respectively are such that $a_1 < a_2 < a_3$. Cylinders C_1, C_2 and C_3 are formed from A_1, A_2 and A_3 respectively by joining the parallel sides along the breadth. Then

(a) C_1 will enclosed maximum volume
(b) C_2 will enclosed maximum volume
(c) C_3 will enclosed maximum volume
(d) Each of C_1, C_2 and C_3 will enclose equal volume

111. The volume of a right circular cylinder whose curved surface area is 2640 cm^2 and circumference of its base is 66 cm, is

(a) 3465 cm^3 (b) 7720 cm^3
(c) 13860 cm^3 (d) 55440 cm^3

112. A well has to be dug out that is to be 22.5 m deep and of diameter 7m. Find the cost of plastering the inner curved surface at ₹ 3 per sq. meter. (M.A.T., 2006; M.B.A., 2007)

(a) ₹ 1465 (b) ₹ 1475
(c) ₹ 1485 (d) ₹ 1495

113. The radius and height of a cylinder are in the ratio 5 : 7 and its volume is 4400 cm^3. Then its radius will be

(a) 4 cm (b) 5 cm
(c) 10 cm (d) 12 cm

114. The height of a right circular cylinder is 14 cm and its curved surface is 704 sq. cm. Then its volume is:

(a) 1408 cm^3 (b) 2816 cm^3
(c) 5632 cm^3 (d) 9856 cm^3

115. A closed metallic cylindrical box is 1.25 m high and its base radius is 35 cm. If the sheet metal costs ₹ 80 per m^2, the cost of the material used in the box is

(a) ₹ 281.60 (b) ₹ 290
(c) ₹ 340.50 (d) ₹ 500

116. The curved surface area of a right circular cylinder of base radius r is obtained by multiplying its volume by

(a) $2r$ (b) $\frac{2}{r}$
(c) $2r^2$ (d) $\frac{2}{r^2}$

117. The ratio of total surface area to lateral surface area of a cylinder whose radius is 20 cm and height 60 cm, is

(a) 2 : 1 (b) 3 : 2
(c) 4 : 3 (d) 5 : 3

118. Two cans have the same height equal to 21 cm. One can is cylindrical, the diameter of whose base is 10 cm. The other can has square base of side 10 cm. What is the difference in their capacities? (M.A.T., 2010)

(a) 250 cm^3 (b) 300 cm^3
(c) 350 cm^3 (d) 450 cm^3

119. The diameter of the base of a cylindrical drum is 35 dm and the height is 24 dm. It is full of kerosene. How many tins each of size 25 cm × 22 cm × 35 cm can be filled with kerosene from the drum?

(a) 120 (b) 600
(c) 1020 (d) 1200

120. The radius of the cylinder is half its height and area of the inner part is 616 sq. cms. Approximately how many litres of milk can it contain?

(a) 1.4 (b) 1.53
(c) 1.7 (d) 1.9
(e) 2.2

121. The sum of the radius of the base and the height of a solid cylinder is 37 metres. If the total surface area of the cylinder be 1628 sq. metres, its volume is

(a) 3180 m^3 (b) 4620 m^3
(c) 5240 m^3 (d) None of these

122. The curved surface area of a cylindrical pillar is 264 m^2 and its volume is 924 m^3. Find the ratio of its diameter to its height.

(a) 3 : 7 (b) 7 : 3
(c) 6 : 7 (d) 7 : 6

123. The height of a right circular cylinder is 6 m. If three times the sum of the areas of its two circular faces is twice the area of the curved surface, then the radius of its base is

(a) 1 m (b) 2 m
(c) 3 m (d) 4 m

124. The height of a closed cylinder of given volume and the minimum surface area is

(a) equal to its diameter (b) half of its diameter
(c) double of its diameter (d) None of these

125. If the radius of the base of a right circular cylinder is halved, keeping the height same, what is the ratio of the volume of the reduced cylinder to that of the original one? **(Hotel Management, 2005)**

(*a*) 1 : 2 (*b*) 1 : 4
(*c*) 1 : 8 (*d*) 8 : 1

126. The radii of the bases of two cylinders are in the ratio 3 : 4 and their heights are in the ratio 4 : 3. The ratio of their volumes is **(S.S.C., 2005)**

(*a*) 2 : 3 (*b*) 3 : 2
(*c*) 3 : 4 (*d*) 4 : 3

127. If the height of a cylinder is increased by 15 percent and the radius of its base is decreased by 10 percent then by what percent will its curved surface area change? **(S.S.C., 2006)**

(*a*) 3.5 percent decrease (*b*) 3.5 percent increase
(*c*) 5 percent decrease (*d*) 5 percent increase

128. If two cylinders of equal volumes have their heights in the ratio 2 : 3, then the ratio of their radii is **(Bank P.O., 2010)**

(*a*) $\sqrt{6} : \sqrt{3}$ (*b*) $\sqrt{5} : \sqrt{3}$
(*c*) 2 : 3 (*d*) $\sqrt{3} : \sqrt{2}$

129. *X* and *Y* are two cylinders of the same height. The base of *X* has diameter that is half the diameter of the base of *Y*. If the height of *X* is doubled, the volume of *X* becomes

(*a*) equal to the volume of *Y*
(*b*) double the volume of *Y*
(*c*) half the volume of *Y*
(*d*) greater than the volume of *Y*

130. The radius of a wire is decreased to one-third and its volume remains the same. The new length is how many times the original length?

(*a*) 1 time (*b*) 3 times
(*c*) 6 times (*d*) 9 times

131. If the radius of a cylinder is decreased by 50% and the height is increased by 50% to form a new cylinder, the volume will be decreased by

(*a*) 0% (*b*) 25%
(*c*) 62.5% (*d*) 75%

132. Diameter of a jar cylindrical in shape is increased by 25%. By what percent must the height be decreased so that there is no change in its volume?

(*a*) 10 (*b*) 25
(*c*) 36 (*d*) 50

(A.A.O. Exam, 2009)

133. A cylindrical tank of diameter 35 cm is full of water. If 11 litres of water is drawn off, the water level in the tank will drop by

(*a*) $10\frac{1}{2}$ cm (*b*) $11\frac{3}{7}$ cm
(*c*) $12\frac{6}{7}$ cm (*d*) 14 cm

134. A well with inner diameter 8 m is dug 14 m deep. Earth taken out of its has been evenly spread all around it to a width of 3 m to form an embankment. The height of the embankment will be **(G.B.O., 2007)**

(*a*) $4\frac{26}{33}$ m (*b*) $5\frac{26}{33}$ cm
(*c*) $6\frac{26}{33}$ cm (*d*) $7\frac{26}{33}$ cm

135. Water flows through a cylindrical pipe of internal diameter 7 cm at 2 m per second. If the pipe is always half full, then what is the volume of water (in litres) discharged in 10 minutes?

(*a*) 2310 (*b*) 3850
(*c*) 4620 (*d*) 9240

136. The radius of a cylindrical cistern is 10 metres and its height is 15 metres. Initially the cistern is empty. We start filling the cistern with water through a pipe whose diameter is 50 cm. Water is coming out of the pipe with a velocity of 5 m/sec. How many minutes will it take in filling the cistern with water? **(M.A.T., 2007)**

(*a*) 20 (*b*) 40
(*c*) 60 (*d*) 80

137. It is required to fix a pipe such that water flowing through it at a speed of 7 metres per minute fills a tank of capacity 440 cubic metres in 10 minutes. The inner radius of the pipe should be **(M.A.T., 2005)**

(*a*) $\sqrt{2}$ m (*b*) 2 m
(*c*) $\frac{1}{2}$ m (*d*) $\frac{1}{\sqrt{2}}$ m

138. Water flows out through a circular pipe whose internal diameter is 2 cm, at the rate of 6 metres per second into a cylindrical tank, the radius of whose base is 60 cm. By how much will the level of water rise in 30 minutes? **(M.A.T., 2006)**

(*a*) 2 m (*b*) 3 m
(*c*) 4 m (*d*) 5 m

139. Water is poured into an empty cylindrical tank at a constant rate for 5 minutes. After the water has been poured into the tank, the depth of the water is 7 feet. The radius of the tank is 100 feet. Which of the following is the best approximation for the rate at which the water was poured into the tank? **(M.B.A., 2006)**

(*a*) 140 cubic feet/sec (*b*) 440 cubic feet/sec
(*c*) 700 cubic feet/sec (*d*) 2200 cubic feet/sec

140. The number of circular pipes with an inside diameter of 1 inch which will carry the same amount of water as a pipe with an inside diameter of 6 inches is **(M.B.A., 2011)**

(*a*) 6π (*b*) 12
(*c*) 36 (*d*) 36π

141. Find the number of coins 1.5 cm in diameter and 0.2 cm thick, to be melted to form a right circular cylinder of height 10 cm and diameter 4.5 cm. **(M.A.T., 2005)**

(*a*) 430 (*b*) 440
(*c*) 450 (*d*) 460

142. Two cylindrical vessels with radii 15 cm and 10 cm and heights 35 cm and 15 cm respectively are filled with water. If this water is poured into a cylindrical vessel 15 cm in height, then the radius of the vessel is

(*a*) 17.5 cm (*b*) 18 cm
(*c*) 20 cm (*d*) 25 cm

143. 66 cubic centimetres of silver is drawn into a wire 1 mm in diameter. The length of the wire in metres will be

(*a*) 84 (*b*) 90
(*c*) 168 (*d*) 336

144. A copper rod of 1 cm diameter and 8 cm length is drawn into a wire of uniform diameter and 18 m length. The radius (in cm) of the wire is, **(S.S.C., 2005)**

(*a*) $\frac{1}{15}$ (*b*) $\frac{1}{30}$
(*c*) $\frac{2}{15}$ (*d*) 15

145. The diameter of a garden roller is 1.4 m and it is 2 m long. How much area will it cover in 5 revolutions?

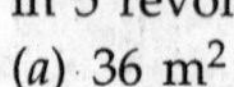

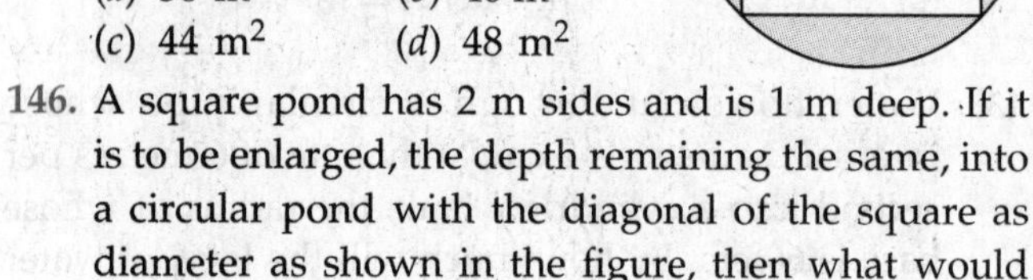

(*a*) 36 m^2 (*b*) 40 m^2
(*c*) 44 m^2 (*d*) 48 m^2

146. A square pond has 2 m sides and is 1 m deep. If it is to be enlarged, the depth remaining the same, into a circular pond with the diagonal of the square as diameter as shown in the figure, then what would be the volume of earth to be removed?

(*a*) $(2\pi - 2)$ m^3 (*b*) $(2\pi - 4)$ m^3
(*c*) $(4\pi - 2)$ m^3 (*d*) $(4\pi - 4)$ m^3

147. What part of a ditch, 48 metres long, 16.5 metres broad and 4 metres deep can be filled by the earth got by digging a cylindrical tunnel of diameter 4 metres and length 56 metres? **(S.S.C., 2007)**

(*a*) $\frac{1}{9}$ (*b*) $\frac{2}{9}$
(*c*) $\frac{7}{9}$ (*d*) $\frac{8}{9}$

148. Water is flowing at the rate of 5 km/hr through a cylindrical pipe of diameter 14 cm into a rectangular tank which is 50 m long and 44 m wide. Determine the time in which the level of water in the tank will rise by 7 cm. **(S.S.C., 2008)**

(*a*) 1 hour (*b*) $1\frac{1}{2}$ hours
(*c*) 2 hours (*d*) 3 hours

149. The trunk of a tree is a right cylinder 1.5 m in radius and 10 m high. The volume of the timber which remains when the trunk is trimmed just enough to reduce it to a rectangular parallelopiped on a square base is **(M.A.T. 2006)**

(*a*) 44 m^3 (*b*) 45 m^3
(*c*) 46 m^3 (*d*) 47 m^3

150. Rain water, which falls on a flat rectangular surface of length 6 m and breadth 4 m is transferred into a cylindrical vessel of internal radius 20 cm. What will be the height of water in the cylindrical vessel if a rainfall of 1 cm has fallen?

(*a*) 188 cm (*b*) 189 cm
(*c*) 190 cm (*d*) 191 cm

151. An iron pipe 20 cm long has exterior diameter equal to 25 cm. If the thickness of the pipe is 1 cm, then the whole surface of the pipe is **(M.A.T. 2007)**

(*a*) 3068 cm^2 (*b*) 3168 cm^2
(*c*) 3268 cm^2 (*d*) 3368 cm^2

152. A hollow garden roller 63 cm wide with a girth of 440 cm is made of iron 4 cm thick. The volume of the iron used is

(*a*) 54982 cm^3 (*b*) 56372 cm^3
(*c*) 57636 cm^3 (*d*) 58752 cm^3

153. A cylindrical tube open at both ends is made of metal. The internal diameter of the tube is 11.2 cm and its length is 21 cm. The metal everywhere is 0.4 cm thick. The volume of the metal is

(*a*) 280.52 cm^3 (*b*) 306.24 cm^3
(*c*) 310 cm^3 (*d*) 316 cm^3

154. What length of solid cylinder 2 cm in diameter must be taken to cast into a hollow cylinder of external diameter 12 cm, 0.25 cm thick and 15 cm long?

(*a*) 42.3215 cm (*b*) 44.0123 cm
(*c*) 44.0625 cm (*d*) 44.6023 cm

155. A hollow iron pipe is 21 cm long and its external diameter is 8 cm. If the thickness of the pipe is 1 cm and iron weighs 8 g/cm^3, then the weight of the pipe is

(*a*) 3.6 kg (*b*) 3.696 kg
(*c*) 36 kg (*d*) 36.9 kg

156. 1496 cm^3 of metal is used to cast a pipe of length 28 cm. If the internal radius of the pipe is 8 cm, the outer radius of the pipe is **(M.A.T., 2007)**

(*a*) 7 cm (*b*) 9 cm
(*c*) 10 cm (*d*) 12 cm

157. A milkman saves milk in two vessels, a cuboidal and the other a cylindrical one. The capacity of the cuboidal vessel is 20 litres more than the cylinddrical one. When 30 litres of milk is drawn from each of the two full vessels, the amount left in the cuboidal vessel is twice that left in the cylindrical vessel. The capacity (in litres) of the cuboidal vessel is **(I.L.F.T., 2005)**

(*a*) 30 (*b*) 50
(*c*) 70 (*d*) 130
(*e*) None of these

158. A circular cylinder can hold 61.6 c.c. of water. If the height of the cylinder is 40 cm and the outer diameter is 16 mm, then the thickness of the material of the cylinder is
(*a*) 0.2 mm (*b*) 0.3 mm
(*c*) 1 mm (*d*) 2 mm

159. Which one of the following figures will generate a cone when rotated about one of its straight edges?
(*a*) An equilateral triangle
(*b*) A sector of a circle
(*c*) A segment of a circle
(*d*) A right-angled triangle

160. The radius of the base and height of a cone are 3 cm and 5 cm respectively whereas the radius of the base and height of a cylinder are 2 cm and 4 cm respectively. The ratio of the volume of cone to that of the cylinder is
(*a*) 1 : 3 (*b*) 15 : 8
(*c*) 15 : 16 (*d*) 45 : 16

161. What is the weight of water contained in a conical vessel 21 cm deep and 16 cm in diameter? **(R.R.B., 2006)**
(*a*) 1.256 kg (*b*) 1.408 kg
(*c*) 2.480 kg (*d*) 3.875 kg

162. Find the slant height of the cone whose height is 4.8 cm and the diameter of base is 4 cm.
(*a*) 4.2 cm (*b*) 5.2 cm
(*c*) 6.2 cm (*d*) 7.2 cm

163. The curved surface of a right circular cone of height 84 cm and base diameter 70 cm is
(*a*) 1001 cm^2 (*b*) 9900 cm^2
(*c*) 10001 cm^2 (*d*) 10010 cm^2

164. The curved surface of a right circular cone of height 15 cm and base diameter 16 cm is
(*a*) 60π cm^2 (*b*) 68π cm^2
(*c*) 120π cm^2 (*d*) 136π cm^2

165. What is the total surface area of a right circular cone of height 14 cm and base radius 7 cm?
(*a*) 344.35 cm^2 (*b*) 462 cm^2
c) 498.35 cm^2 (*d*) None of these

166. A right triangle with sides 3 cm, 4 cm and 5 cm is rotated about the side of 3 cm to form a cone. The volume of the cone so formed is
(*a*) 12π cm^3 (*b*) 15π cm^3
(*c*) 16π cm^3 (*d*) 20π cm^3

167. The slant height of a right circular cone is 10 m and its height is 8 m. Find the area of its curved surface.
(*a*) 30π m^2 (*b*) 40π m^2
(*c*) 60π m^2 (*d*) 80π m^2

168. If a right circular cone of height 24 cm has a volume of 1232 cm^3, then the area of its curved surface is
(*a*) 154 cm^2 (*b*) 550 cm^2
(*c*) 704 cm^2 (*d*) 1254 cm^2

169. A conical tent is to accommodate 11 persons. Each person must have 4 sq. metres of the space on the ground and 20 cubic metres of air to breathe. The height of the cone is **(M.A.T., 2006)**
(*a*) 13 m (*b*) 14 m
(*c*) 15 m (*d*) 16 m

170. Area of the canvas cloth needed to erect a right conical tent of height 12 ft and circular base having circumference 10π ft is
(*a*) 60 sq ft (*b*) 65 sq ft
(*c*) 65π sq ft (*d*) 120π sq ft

171. The slant height of a conical mountain is 2.5 km and the area of its base is 1.54 km^2. The height of the mountain is
(*a*) 2.2 km (*b*) 2.4 km
(*c*) 3 km (*d*) 3.11 km

172. If the area of the base of a right circular cone is 3850 cm^2 and its height is 84 cm, then the curved surface area of the cone is
(*a*) 10001 cm^2 (*b*) 10010 cm^2
(*c*) 10100 cm^2 (*d*) 11000 cm^2

173. Volume of a right circular cone having base radius 70 cm and curved surface area 40040 cm^2 is
(*a*) 823400 cm^3 (*b*) 824000 cm^3
(*c*) 840000 cm^3 (*d*) 862400 cm^3

174. The radius and height of a right circular cone are in the ratio 3 : 4. If its volume is $301\frac{5}{7}$ cm^3, what is its slant height?
(*a*) 8 cm (*b*) 9 cm
(*c*) 10 cm (*d*) 12 cm

175. A vertical cone of volume V with vertex downwards is filled with water upto half of its height. The volume of the water is
(*a*) $\frac{V}{2}$ (*b*) $\frac{V}{4}$
(*c*) $\frac{V}{8}$ (*d*) $\frac{V}{16}$

176. A semicircular sheet of paper of diameter 28 cm is bent to cover the exterior surface of an open conical ice-cream cup. The depth of the ice-cream cup is **(M.A.T., 2006)**
(*a*) 8.12 cm (*b*) 10.12 cm
(*c*) 12.12 cm (*d*) 14.12 cm

177. The length of canvas 1.1 m wide required to build a conical tent of height 14 m and the floor area 346.5 sq. m is
(*a*) 490 m (*b*) 525 m
(*c*) 665 m (*d*) 860 m

178. If the height of a cone is doubled and its base diameter is trebled, then the ratio of the volume of the resultant cone to that of the original cone is
(*a*) 6 : 1 (*b*) 9 : 1
(*c*) 9 : 2 (*d*) 18 : 1

179. If both the radius and height of a right circular cone are increased by 20%, its volume will be increased by
(*a*) 20% (*b*) 40%
(*c*) 60% (*d*) 72.8%

180. If the height of a right circular cone is increased by 200% and the radius of the base is reduced by 50%, then the volume of the cone
(*a*) remains unaltered (*b*) decreases by 25%
(*c*) increases by 25% (*d*) increases by 50%

181. If the height of a cone be doubled and radius of base remains the same, then the ratio of the volume of the given cone to that of the second cone will be
(*a*) 1 : 2 (*b*) 2 : 1
(*c*) 1 : 8 (*d*) 8 : 1

182. If the height, curved surface area and the volume of a cone are h, c and v respectively, then $3\pi vh^3 - c^2h^2 + 9v^2$ will be equal to
(*a*) 0 (*b*) 1
(*c*) chv (*d*) v^2h

183. If the heights of two cones are in the ratio 7 : 3 and their diameters are in the ratio 6 : 7, what is the ratio of their volumes? **(M.B.A., 2009)**
(*a*) 3 : 7 (*b*) 4 : 7
(*c*) 5 : 7 (*d*) 12 : 7

184. The radii of two cones are in the ratio 2 : 1, their volumes are equal. Find the ratio of their heights.
(*a*) 1 : 8 (*b*) 1 : 4
(*c*) 2 : 1 (*d*) 4 : 1

185. If the ratio of volumes of two cones is 2 : 3 and the ratio of the radii of their bases is 1 : 2, then the ratio of their heights will be
(*a*) 3 : 4 (*b*) 4 : 3
(*c*) 3 : 8 (*d*) 8 : 3

186. Find the volume of the largest right circular cone that can be cut out from a cube whose edge is 9 cm.
(*a*) 170.93 cm^3 (*b*) 180.93 cm^3
(*c*) 190.93 cm^3 (*d*) 200.93 cm^3

187. A cone of height 7 cm and base radius 3 cm is carved from a rectangular block of wood 10 cm × 5 cm × 2 cm. The percentage of wood wasted is
(*a*) 34% (*b*) 46%
(*c*) 54% (*d*) 66%

188. A right circular cone and a right circular cylinder have equal base and equal height. If the radius of the base and the height are in the ratio 5 : 12, then the ratio of the total surface area of the cylinder to that of the cone is
(*a*) 3 : 1 (*b*) 13 : 9
(*c*) 17 : 9 (*d*) 34 : 9

189. A conical cavity is drilled in a circular cylinder of 15 cm height and 16 cm base diameter. The height and base diameter of the cone are the same as those of the cylinder. Determine the total surface area of the remaining solid.
(*a*) 215 π cm^2 (*b*) 376 π cm^2
(*c*) 440 π cm^2 (*d*) 542 π cm^2

190. The radius of the base and height of a metallic solid cylinder are r cm and 6 cm respectively. It is melted and recast into a solid cone of the same radius of base. The height of the cone is **(C.P.O., 2007)**
(*a*) 9 cm (*b*) 18 cm
(*c*) 27 cm (*d*) 54 cm

191. A solid metallic right circular cylinder of base diameter 16 cm and height 2 cm is melted and recast into a right circular cone of height three times that of the cylinder. Find the curved surface area of the cone. [Use π = 3.14] **(S.S.C., 2007)**
(*a*) 196.8 cm^2 (*b*) 228.4 cm^2
(*c*) 251.2 cm^2 (*d*) None of these

192. A right cylindrical vessel is full of water. How many right cones having the same radius and height as those of the right cylinder will be needed to store that water?
(*a*) 2 (*b*) 3
(*c*) 4 (*d*) 8

193. A solid metallic cylinder of base radius 3 cm and height 5 cm is melted to form cones, each of height 1 cm and base radius 1 mm. The number of cones is
(*a*) 450 (*b*) 1350
(*c*) 4500 (*d*) 13500

194. Ice cream completely filled in a cylinder of diameter 35 cm and height 32 cm is to be served by completely filling identical disposable cones of diameter 4 cm and height 7 cm. The maximum number of persons that can be served this way is
(*a*) 950 (*b*) 1000
(*c*) 1050 (*d*) 1100

195. A solid cylinder and a solid cone have equal base and equal height. If the radius and height be in the ratio of 4 : 3, the ratio of the total surface area of the cylinder to that of the cone is
(*a*) 10 : 9 (*b*) 11 : 9
(*c*) 12 : 9 (*d*) 14 : 9

196. Water flows at the rate of 10 metres per minute from a cylindrical pipe 5 mm in diameter. How long will it take to fill up a conical vessel whose diameter at the base is 40 cm and depth 24 cm?
(*a*) 48 min. 15 sec. (*b*) 51 min. 12 sec.
(*c*) 52 min. 1 sec. (*d*) 55 min.

197. A conical flask has base radius *a* cm and height *h* cm. it is completely filled with milk. The milk is poured into a cylindrical thermos flask whose base radius is *p* cm. What will be the height of the milk level in the flask?

(*a*) $\frac{a^2h}{3p^2}$ cm (*b*) $\frac{3hp^2}{a^2}$ cm

(*c*) $\frac{p^2}{3h^2}$ cm (*d*) $\frac{3a^2}{hp^2}$ cm

198. A solid cylindrical block of radius 12 cm and height 18 cm is mounted with a conical block of radius 12 cm and height 5 cm. The total lateral surface of the solid thus formed is

(*a*) 528 cm^2 (*b*) $1357\frac{5}{7}$ cm^2

(*c*) 1848 cm^2 (*d*) None of these

199. A tent is in the form of a right circular cylinder surmounted by a cone. The diameter of the cylinder is 24 m. The height of the cylindrical portion is 11 m while the vertex of the cone is 16 m above the ground. The area of the canvas required for the tent is **(M.A.T., 2006)**

(*a*) 1300 m^2 (*b*) 1310 m^2

(*c*) 1320 m^2 (*d*) 1330 m^2

200. A fountain having the shape of a right circular cone is fitted into a cylindrical tank of volume V so that the base of the tank coincides with the base of the cone and the height of the tank is the same as that of the cone. The volume of water in the tank, when it is completely filled with water from the fountain, is

(*a*) $\frac{V}{2}$ (*b*) $\frac{V}{3}$

(*c*) $\frac{V}{4}$ (*d*) $\frac{2V}{3}$

201. In a right circular cone, the radius of its base is 7 cm and its height is 24 cm. A cross-section is made through the mid-point of the height parallel to the base. The volume of the upper portion is **(S.S.C., 2006)**

(*a*) 154 cm^3 (*b*) 169 cm^3

(*c*) 800 cm^3 (*d*) 1078 cm^3

202. A right circular cone is divided into two portions by a plane parallel to the base and passing through a point which is $\frac{1}{3}$rd of the height from the top. The ratio of the volume of the smaller cone to that of the remaining frustum of the cone is

(*a*) 1 : 3 (*b*) 1 : 9

(*c*) 1 : 26 (*d*) 1 : 27

203. A bucket is in the form of a frustum of a cone and holds 28.490 litres of water. The radii of the top and bottom are 28 cm and 21 cm respectively. Find the height of the bucket.

(*a*) 15 cm (*b*) 20 cm

(*c*) 25 cm (*d*) 30 cm

204. A cone of height 10 cm and radius 5 cm is cut into two parts at half its height. The cut is given parallel to its circular base. What is the ratio of the curved surface area of the original cone and the curved surface area of the frustum?

(*a*) 3 : 1 (*b*) 3 : 2

(*c*) 4 : 1 (*d*) 4 : 3

205. A sphere, cylinder and cone of dimensions radius = *r* cm and height = 2*r* cm are made. Which one has the greatest volume?

(*a*) Cone (*b*) Sphere

(*c*) Cylinder (*d*) All have equal volume

206. Consider the volumes of the following **(Civil Services, 2002)**

1. A parallelopiped of length 5 cm, breadth 3 cm and height 4 cm
2. A cube of each side 4 cm
3. A cylinder of radius 3 cm and length 3 cm
4. A sphere of radius 3 cm

The volumes of these in the decreasing order is :

(*a*) 1, 2, 3, 4 (*b*) 1, 3, 2, 4

(*c*) 4, 2, 3, 1 (*d*) 4, 3, 2, 1

207. The volume of a sphere is $2145\frac{11}{21}$ cm^3. Its radius is equal to **(R.R.B., 2008)**

(*a*) 7 cm (*b*) 8 cm

(*c*) 9 cm (*d*) None of these

208. The volume of a sphere is 4851 cu. cm. Its curved surface area is

(*a*) 1386 cm^2 (*b*) 1625 cm^2

(*c*) 1716 cm^2 (*d*) 3087 cm^2

209. The curved surface area of a sphere is 5544 sq. cm. Its volume is

(*a*) 22176 cm^3 (*b*) 33951 cm^3

(*c*) 38808 cm^3 (*d*) 42304 cm^3

210. The volume of a sphere of radius *r* is obtained by multiplying its surface area by

(*a*) $\frac{4}{3}$ (*b*) $\frac{r}{3}$

(*c*) $\frac{4r}{3}$ (*d*) 3*r*

211. For a sphere of radius 10 cm, what percent of the numerical value of its volume would be the numerical value of the surface area?

(*a*) 24% (*b*) 26.5%

(*c*) 30% (*d*) 45%

212. If the volume of a sphere is divided by its surface area, the result is 27 cm. The radius of the sphere is

(*a*) 9 cm (*b*) 36 cm

(*c*) 54 cm (*d*) 81 cm

213. If the radii of two spheres are in the ratio 1 : 4, then their surface areas are in the ratio (C.P.O., 2007)

(*a*) 1 : 2 (*b*) 1 : 4
(*c*) 1 : 8 (*d*) 1 : 16

214. The radii of two spheres are in the ratio 3 : 2. Their volumes will be in the ratio (C.P.O., 2007)

(*a*) 9 : 4 (*b*) 8 : 27
(*c*) 27 : 8 (*d*) 3 : 2

215. Surface area of a sphere is 2464 cm^2. If its radius be doubled, then the surface area of the new sphere will be :

(*a*) 4928 cm^2 (*b*) 9856 cm^2
(*c*) 19712 cm^2 (*d*) Data insufficient

216. If the radius of a sphere is doubled, how many times does its volume become? (R.R.B., 2006, 2008)

(*a*) 2 times (*b*) 4 times
(*c*) 6 times (*d*) 8 times

217. If the radius of a sphere is increased by 2 cm, then its surface area increases by 352 cm^2. The radius of the sphere before the increase was

(*a*) 3 cm (*b*) 4 cm
(*c*) 5 cm (*d*) 6 cm

218. If the measured value of the radius is 1.5% larger, the percentage error (correct to one decimal place) made in calculating the volume of a sphere is

(*a*) 2.1 (*b*) 3.2
(*c*) 4.6 (*d*) 5.4

219. The volumes of two spheres are in the ratio of 64 : 27. The ratio of their surface areas is (Bank P.O., 2010)

(*a*) 1 : 2 (*b*) 2 : 3
(*c*) 9 : 16 (*d*) 16 : 9

220. If the surface areas of two spheres are in the ratio of 4 : 25, then the ratio of their volumes is (M.B.A., 2009)

(*a*) 4 : 25 (*b*) 25 : 4
(*c*) 125 : 8 (*d*) 8 : 125

221. If the volume and surface area of a sphere are numerically the same, then its radius is (C.P.O., 2006)

(*a*) 1 unit (*b*) 2 units
(*c*) 3 units (*d*) 4 units

222. If three metallic spheres of radii 6 cms, 8 cms and 10 cms are melted to form a single sphere, the diameter of the new sphere will be (Bank P.O., 2009)

(*a*) 12 cms (*b*) 24 cms
(*c*) 30 cms (*d*) 36 cms

223. A solid metallic sphere of radius 8 cm is melted and recast into spherical balls each of radius 2 cm. The number of spherical balls, thus obtained, is

(*a*) 16 (*b*) 48
(*c*) 64 (*d*) 82

224. A spherical ball of lead, 3 cm in diameter is melted and recast into three spherical balls. The diameter of two of these are 1.5 cm and 2 cm respectively. The diameter of the third ball is (M.A.T., 2005; 2009)

(*a*) 2.5 cm (*b*) 2.66 cm
(*c*) 3 cm (*d*) 3.5 cm

225. If a solid sphere of radius 10 cm is moulded into 8 spherical solid balls of equal radius, then the surface area of each ball is

(*a*) 50π cm^2 (*b*) 60π cm^2
(*c*) 75π cm^2 (*d*) 100π cm^2

226. A hollow spherical metallic ball has an external diameter 6 cm and is $\frac{1}{2}$ cm thick. The volume of metal used in the ball is

(*a*) $37\frac{2}{3}$ cm^3 (*b*) $40\frac{2}{3}$ cm^3
(*c*) $41\frac{2}{3}$ cm^3 (*d*) $47\frac{2}{3}$ cm^3

227. A solid piece of iron of dimensions 49 × 33 × 24 cm is moulded into a sphere. The radius of the sphere is

(*a*) 21 cm (*b*) 28 cm
(*c*) 35 cm (*d*) None of these

228. How many bullets can be made out of a cube of lead whose edge measures 22 cm, each bullet being 2 cm in diameter?

(*a*) 1347 (*b*) 2541
(*c*) 2662 (*d*) 5324

229. The volume of the largest sphere which can be carved out of a cube of side 6 cm is

(*a*) 113.14 cm^3 (*b*) 166 cm^3
(*c*) 179.66 cm^3 (*d*) 188.52 cm^3

230. How many lead shots each 3 mm in diameter can be made from a cuboid of dimensions 9 cm × 11 cm × 12 cm? (A.A.O. Exam, 2009)

(*a*) 7200 (*b*) 8400
(*c*) 72000 (*d*) 84000

231. A sphere and a cube have equal surface areas. The ratio of the volume of the sphere to that of the cube is (S.S.C., 2005; M.A.T., 2006)

(*a*) $\sqrt{\pi} : \sqrt{6}$ (*b*) $\sqrt{2} : \sqrt{\pi}$
(*c*) $\sqrt{\pi} : \sqrt{3}$ (*d*) $\sqrt{6} : \sqrt{\pi}$

232. The ratio of the volume of a cube to that of a sphere which will fit inside the cube is (M.A.T., 2010)

(*a*) $4 : \pi$ (*b*) $4 : 3\pi$
(*c*) $6 : \pi$ (*d*) $2 : \pi$

233. The volume of the largest possible cube that can be inscribed in a hollow spherical ball of radius *r* cm is (Hotel Management, 2009)

(a) $\frac{2}{\sqrt{3}}r^2$ (b) $\frac{4}{3}r^2$

(c) $\frac{8}{3\sqrt{3}}r^3$ (d) $\frac{1}{3\sqrt{3}}r^3$

234. A right circular cylinder and a sphere are of equal volumes and their radii are also equal. If h is the height of the cylinder and d, the diameter of the sphere, then **(S.S.C., 2007)**

(a) $h = d$ (b) $2h = d$

(c) $\frac{h}{3} = \frac{d}{2}$ (d) $\frac{h}{2} = \frac{d}{3}$

235. The surface area of a sphere is same as the curved surface area of a right circular cylinder whose height and diameter are 12 cm each. The radius of the sphere is

(a) 3 cm (b) 4 cm

(c) 6 cm (d) 12 cm

236. The diameter of the iron ball used for the shot-put game is 14 cm. It is melted and then a solid cylinder of height $2\frac{1}{3}$ cm is made. What will be the diameter of the base of the cylinder?

(a) 14 cm (b) $\frac{14}{3}$ cm

(c) 28 cm (d) $\frac{28}{3}$ cm

237. A solid metallic sphere of radius r is converted into a solid right circular cylinder of radius R. If the height of the cylinder is twice the radius of the sphere, then **(A.A.O. Exam, 2010)**

(a) $R = r$ (b) $R = r\sqrt{\frac{2}{3}}$

(c) $R = \sqrt{\frac{2r}{3}}$ (d) $R = \frac{2r}{3}$

238. The ratio of the volumes of a right circular cylinder and a sphere is 3 : 2. If the radius of the sphere is double the radius of the base of the cylinder, find the ratio of the total surface areas of the cylinder and the sphere. **(S.S.C., 2006)**

(a) 9 : 8 (b) 13 : 8

(c) 15 : 8 (d) 17 : 8

239. The volume of the greatest sphere that can be cut off from a cylindrical log of wood of base radius 1 cm and height 5 cm is

(a) $\frac{4}{3}\pi$ (b) $\frac{10}{3}\pi$

(c) 5π (d) $\frac{20}{3}\pi$

240. How many spherical bullets can be made out of a lead cylinder 15 cm high and with base radius 3 cm, each bullet being 5 mm in diameter?

(a) 6000 (b) 6480

(c) 7260 (d) 7800

241. A cylindrical rod of iron whose height is eight times its radius is melted and cast into spherical balls each of half the radius of the cylinder. The number of spherical balls is

(a) 12 (b) 16

(c) 24 (d) 48

242. A copper wire of length 36 m and diameter 2 mm is melted to form a sphere. The radius of the sphere (in cm) is **(M.B.A., 2008; S.S.C., 2010)**

(a) 2.5 (b) 3

(c) 3.5 (d) 4

243. The diameter of a sphere is 8 cm. It is melted and drawn into a wire of diameter 3 mm. The length of the wire is **(M.B.A., 2009)**

(a) 36.9 m (b) 37.9 m

(c) 38.9 m (d) 39.9 m

244. A cylindrical vessel of radius 4 cm contains water. A solid sphere of radius 3 cm is lowered into the water until it is completely immersed. The water level in the vessel will rise by :

(a) $\frac{2}{9}$ cm (b) $\frac{4}{9}$ cm

(c) $\frac{9}{4}$ cm (d) $\frac{9}{2}$ cm

245. The ratio of the surface area of a sphere and the curved surface area of the cylinder circumscribing the sphere is **(C.P.O., 2006)**

(a) 1 : 1 (b) 1 : 2

(c) 2 : 1 (d) 2 : 3

246. 12 spheres of the same size are made from melting a solid cylinder of 16 cm diameter and 2 cm height. The diameter of each sphere is

(a) $\sqrt{3}$ cm (b) 2 cm

(c) 3 cm (d) 4 cm

247. A spherical iron ball is dropped into a cylindrical vessel of base diameter 14 cm containing water. The water level is increased by $9\frac{1}{3}$ cm. What is radius of the ball?

(a) 3.5 cm (b) 7 cm

(c) 9 cm (d) 12 cm

248. If a hollow sphere of internal and external diameters 4 cm and 8 cm respectively is melted into a cylinder of base diameter 8 cm, then the height of the cylinder is

(a) 4 cm (b) $\frac{13}{3}$ cm

(c) $\frac{14}{3}$ cm (d) 5 cm

249. Each of the measures of the radius of the base of a cone and that of a sphere is 8 cm. Also, the volumes of these two solids are equal. The slant height of the cone is

(a) 34 cm (b) $34\sqrt{2}$ cm

(c) $4\sqrt{17}$ cm (d) $8\sqrt{17}$ cm

250. A metallic sphere of radius 5 cm is melted to make a cone with base of the same radius. What is the height of the cone? **(R.R.B., 2006)**

(a) 5 cm (b) 10 cm

(c) 15 cm (d) 20 cm

251. Some solid metallic right circular cones, each with radius of the base 3 cm and height 4 cm, are melted to form a solid sphere of radius 6 cm. The number of right circular cones is **(C.P.O., 2007)**

(a) 6 (b) 12

(c) 24 (d) 48

252. A metallic sphere of radius 10.5 cm is melted and recast into small right circular cones, each of base radius 3.5 cm and height 3 cm. The number of cones so formed is **(S.S.C., 2008)**

(a) 105 (b) 113

(c) 126 (d) 135

253. A cone of height 15 cm and base diameter 30 cm is carved out of a wooden sphere of radius 15 cm. The percentage of wood wasted is **(B.Ed Entrance, 2011)**

(a) 25% (b) 40%

(c) 50% (d) 75%

254. A metallic cone of radius 12 cm and height 24 cm is melted and made into spheres of radius 2 cm each. How many spheres are there?

(a) 108 (b) 120

(c) 144 (d) 180

255. In what ratio are the volumes of a cylinder, a cone and a sphere, if each has the same diameter and the same height?

(a) 1 : 3 : 2 (b) 2 : 3 : 1

(c) 3 : 1 : 2 (d) 3 : 2 : 1

256. If the diameter of a sphere is 6 m, its hemisphere will have a volume of **(R.R.B., 2007)**

(a) 18π (b) 36π

(c) 72π (d) None of these

257. The total surface area of a solid hemisphere of diameter 14 cm, is

(a) 308 cm^2 (b) 462 cm^2

(c) 1232 cm^2 (d) 1848 cm^2

258. Volume of a hemisphere is 19404 cu. cm. Its radius is

(a) 10.5 cm (b) 17.5 cm

(c) 21 cm (d) 42 cm

259. A hemispherical bowl is 176 cm round the brim. Supposing it to be half full, how many persons may be served from it in hemispherical glasses 4 cm in diameter at the top? **(M.A.T., 2009)**

(a) 1172 (b) 1272

(c) 1372 (d) 1472

260. The capacities of two hemispherical vessels are 6.4 litres and 21.6 litres. The areas of inner curved surfaces of the vessels will be in the ratio of

(a) $\sqrt{2} : \sqrt{3}$ (b) 2 : 3

(c) 4 : 9 (d) 16 : 81

261. A hemispherical bowl is made of steel 0.5 cm thick. The inside radius of the bowl is 4 cm. The volume of steel used in making the bowl is

(a) 55.83 cm^3 (b) 56.83 cm^3

(c) 57.83 cm^3 (d) 58.83 cm^3

262. The external and internal diameters of a hemispherical bowl are 10 cm and 8 cm respectively. What is the total surface area of the bowl?

(a) 257.7 cm^2 (b) 286 cm^2

(c) 292 cm^2 (d) 302 cm^2

263. A hemispherical bowl of internal radius 12 cm contains liquid. This liquid is to be filled into cylindrical container of diameter 4 cm and height 3 cm. The number of containers that is necessary to empty the bowl is **(Bank P.O., 2009)**

(a) 80 (b) 96

(c) 100 (d) 112

264. A hemispherical bowl is filled to the brim with a beverage. The contents of the bowl are transferred into a cylindrical vessel whose radius is 50% more than its height. If the diameter is same for both the bowl and the cylinder, the volume of the beverage in the cylindrical vessel is

(a) $66\frac{2}{3}\%$ (b) $78\frac{1}{2}\%$ (c) 100%

(d) More than 100% (*i.e.*, some liquid will be left in the bowl)

265. A water tank open at the top is hemispherical at the bottom and cylindrical above it. If radius of the hemisphere is 12 m and the total capacity of the tank is 3312π m^3, then the ratio of the surface areas of the hemispherical and the cylindrical portions is

(a) 1 : 1 (b) 3 : 5
(c) 4 : 5 (d) 6 : 5

266. If a cylindrical tower D metres in diameter and H metres high is capped with a semi-spherical dome, then the total visible surface of the tower will be

(a) $\frac{\pi D}{2}(2H + D)$ (b) $\frac{\pi D}{3}(H + 2D)$

(c) $\frac{\pi D}{2}\left(2H + \frac{D}{2}\right)$ (d) $\frac{\pi D}{3}\left(2H + \frac{D}{2}\right)$

267. The ratio of the volumes of a hemisphere and a cylinder circumscribing this hemisphere and having a common base is **(R.R.B., 2006)**

(a) 1 : 2 (b) 2 : 3
(c) 3 : 4 (d) 4 : 5

268. A metallic hemisphere is melted and recast in the shape of a cone with the same base radius (R) as that of the hemisphere. If H is the height of the cone, then

(a) $H = 2R$ (b) $H = 3R$
(c) $H = \sqrt{3}R$ (d) $H = \frac{2}{3}R$

269. A hemisphere of lead of radius 6 cm is cast into a right circular cone of height 75 cm. The radius of the base of the cone is

(a) 1.4 cm (b) 2 cm
(c) 2.4 cm (d) 4.2 cm

270. A hemisphere and a cone have equal bases. If their heights are also equal, then the ratio of their curved surfaces will be

(a) 1 : 2 (b) 2 : 1
(c) $1 : \sqrt{2}$ (d) $\sqrt{2} : 1$

271. If the radius of the base and height of a cylinder and cone are each equal to r, and the radius of a hemisphere is also equal to r, then the volumes of the cone, cylinder and hemisphere are in the ratio **(N.M.A.T., 2006)**

(a) 1 : 2 : 3 (b) 1 : 3 : 2
(c) 2 : 1 : 3 (d) 3 : 2 : 1

272. A solid body is made up of a cylinder of radius r and height r, a cone of base radius r and height r fixed to the cylinder's one base and a hemisphere of radius r to its other base. The total volume of the body (given $r = 2$) is

(a) 8π (b) 16π
(c) 32π (d) 64π

273. A solid cylinder of base radius 7 cm and height 24 cm is surmounted by a cone of the same radius and same vertical height. A hemisphere surmounts the cylinder at the other end. Surface area of the solid will be

(a) 527π cm^2 (b) 609π cm^2
(c) 707π cm^2 (d) 805π cm^2

274. A solid is in the form of a right circular cylinder with hemispherical ends. The total length of the solid is 35 cm. The diameter of the cylinder is $\frac{1}{4}$ of its height. The surface area of the solid is **(A.A.O. Exam, 2010)**

(a) 462 cm^2 (b) 693 cm^2
(c) 750 cm^2 (d) 770 cm^2

275. A sphere of maximum volume is cut out from a solid hemisphere of radius r. The ratio of the volume of the hemisphere to that of the cut out sphere is :

(a) 3 : 2 (b) 4 : 1
(c) 4 : 3 (d) 7 : 4

276. What is the volume in cubic cm of a pyramid whose area of the base is 25 sq cm and height 9 cm? **(R.R.B., 2006)**

(a) 60 (b) 75
(c) 90 (d) 105

277. If a regular square pyramid has a base of side 8 cm and height 30 cm, its volume is

(a) 120 cc (b) 240 cc
(c) 640 cc (d) 900 cc

278. The base of a pyramid is an equilateral triangle of side 1 m. If the height of the pyramid is 4 metres, then the volume is

(a) 0.550 m^3 (b) 0.577 m^3
(c) 0.678 m^3 (d) 0.750 m^3

279. A right pyramid is on a regular hexagonal base. Each side of the base is 10 m and the height is 60 m. The volume of the pyramid is

(a) 5000 m^3 (b) 5100 m^3
(c) 5195 m^3 (d) 5196 m^3

280. A pyramid has an equilateral triangle as its base of which each side is 1m. Its slant edge is 3 m. The whole surface area of the pyramid is equal to

(a) $\frac{\sqrt{3} + 2\sqrt{13}}{4}$ sq. m (b) $\frac{\sqrt{3} + 3\sqrt{13}}{4}$ sq. m

(c) $\frac{\sqrt{3}+3\sqrt{35}}{4}$ sq. m (d) $\frac{\sqrt{3}+2\sqrt{35}}{4}$ sq. m

281. A right pyramid has an equilateral triangular base of side 4 units. If the number of square units of its whole surface area is three times the number of cubic units of its volume, find its height.

(a) 3 units (b) 4 units
(c) 5 units (d) 6 units

282. Length of each edge of a regular tetrahedron is 1 cm. Its volume is **[SSC—CHSL (10+2) Exam, 2015]**

(a) $\frac{\sqrt{3}}{12}$ cm^3 (b) $\frac{1}{4}\sqrt{3}$ cm^3
(c) $\frac{\sqrt{2}}{6}$ cm^3 (d) $\frac{1}{12}\sqrt{2}$ cm^3

283. The volume of a right circular cone which is obtained from a wooden cube of edge 4.2 dm wasting minimum amount of wood is

[SSC—CHSL (10+2) Exam, 2015]

(a) 19404 dm^3 (b) 194.04 dm^3
(c) 19.404 dm^3 (d) 1940.4 dm^3

284. Base of a right prism is a rectangle, the ratio of whose length and breadth is 3 : 2. If the height of the prism is 12 cm and total surface area is 288 sq. cm the volume of the prism is

[SSC—CHSL (10+2) Exam, 2015]

(a) 291cm^3 (b) 288cm^3
(c) 290cm^3 (d) 286cm^3

285. The radius of a cylinder is 5m more than its height. If the curved surface area of the cylinder is 792m^2, what is the volume of the cylinder? (in m^3)

[IBPS—Bank Spl. Officers (IT) Exam, 2015]

(a) 5712 (b) 5244
(c) 5544 (d) 5306
(e) 5462

286. The radius of base and curved surface area of a right cylinder is '*r*' units and $4\pi rh$ square units respectively. The height of the cylinder is

[SSC—CHSL (10+2) Exam, 2015]

(a) $\frac{h}{2}$ units (b) *h* units
(c) 2*h* units (d) 4*h* units

287. A hemispherical bowl has 3.5cm radius. It is to be painted inside as well as outside. The cost of painting it at the rate of ₹ 5 per 10sq. cm will be

[SSC—CHSL (10+2) Exam, 2015]

(a) ₹ 77 (b) ₹ 100
(c) ₹ 175 (d) ₹ 50

288. If the volume and curved surfaces area of a cylinder are 616 m^3 and 352m^2 respectively, what is the total surface area of the cylinder (in m^2)

[IBPS—Bank PO/MT (Pre.) Exam, 2015]

(a) 429 (b) 419
(c) 435 (d) 421
(e) 417

289. The radius of a hemispherical bowls is 6cm. The capacity of the bowl is $\left(\text{Take } \pi=\frac{22}{7}\right)$

[SSC—CHSL (10+2) Exam, 2015]

(a) 495.51cm^3 (b) 452.57cm^3
(c) 345.53cm^3 (d) 422cm^3

290. Each side of a cube is decreased by 25%. Find the ratio of the volumes of the original cube and the resulting cube. **[SSC—CHSL (10+2) Exam, 2015]**

(a) 64 : 1 (b) 27 : 64
(c) 64 : 27 (d) 8 : 1

291. A hemisphere and a cone have equal bases. If their heights are also equal, then the ratio of their curved surfaces will be **[SSC—CHSL (10+2) Exam, 2015]**

(a) $\sqrt{2}:1$ (b) $1:\sqrt{2}$
(c) 2 : 1 (d) 1 : 2

292. The base of a right prism is a trapezium whose lengths of two parallels sides are 10 cm and 6cm and distance between them is 5 cm. If the heights of the prism is 8cm, its volume is

(a) 320 cm^3 (b) 300 cm^3
(c) 310 cm^3 (d) 300.5 cm^3

[SSC—CHSL (10+2) Exam, 2015]

293. The sum of the radius and the height of a cylinder is 19 m. The total surface area of the cylinder is 1672m^2, what is the volume of the cylinder? (in m^3)

[IBPS—Bank PO (Pre.) Exam, 2015]

(a) 3080 (b) 2940
(c) 3220 (d) 2660
(e) 2800

294. A solid piece of iron is in the form of a cuboid of dimensions (49cm × 33cm × 24cm) is melted and moulded to form a solid sphere. The radius of the sphere is

(a) 19cm (b) 21cm
(c) 23cm (d) 25cm

[DMRC—Train Operator (Station Controller) Exam, 2016]

295. A patient in a hospital is given soup daily in a cylindrical bowl of diameter 7 cm. If the bowl is filled with soup to a height of 4 cm, how much soup the hospital has to prepare daily to serve 250 patients? **[CLAT 2016]**

(a) 38L (b) 40L
(c) 39.5L (d) 35.5L

296. A sphere and a cube have same surface area. The ratio of squares of their volumes is **[CDS, 2016]**

(*a*) $6 : \pi$ (*b*) $5 : \pi$
(*c*) $3 : 5$ (*d*) $1 : 1$

297. The radius of a sphere is equal to the radius of the base of a right circular cone, and the volume of the sphere is double the volume of the cone. The ratio of the height of the cone to the radius of its base is **[CDS, 2016]**

(*a*) 2 : 1 (*b*) 1 : 2
(*c*) 2 : 3 (*d*) 3 : 2

298. A rectangular paper of 44 cm long and 6 cm wide is rolled to form a cylinder of height equal to width of the paper. The radius of the base of the cylinder so rolled is **[CDS, 2016]**

(*a*) 3.5 cm (*b*) 5 cm
(*c*) 7 cm (*d*) 14 cm

299. If three metallic spheres of radii 6 cm, 8 cm and 10 cm are melted to form a single sphere, then the diameter of the new sphere will be **[CDS, 2016]**

(*a*) 12 cm (*b*) 24 cm
(*c*) 30 cm (*d*) 36 cm

300. If the height of a right circular cone is increased by 200% and the radius of the base is reduced by 50%, then the volume of the cone **[CDS, 2016]**

(*a*) remains unaltered (*b*) decrease by 25%
(*c*) increase by 25% (*d*) increase by 50%

301. If the radius of a sphere is increased by 10%, then the volume will be increased by **[CDS, 2016]**

(*a*) 33.1% (*b*) 30%
(*c*) 50% (*d*) 10%

302. When a ball bounces, it rises to $\frac{2}{3}$ of the height from which it fell. If the ball is dropped from a height of 36 m, how high will it rise at the third bounce? **[CDS, 2016]**

(*a*) $10\frac{1}{3}$ m (*b*) $10\frac{2}{3}$ m
(*c*) $12\frac{1}{3}$ m (*d*) $12\frac{2}{3}$ m

303. A swimming pool 9m wide and 12m long and 1m deep on the shallow side and 4m deep on the deeper side. Its volume is
[DMRC—Customer Relations Assistant (CRA) Exam, 2016]

(*a*) 360 m^3 (*b*) 270 m^3
(*c*) 420 m^3 (*d*) None of these

304. A metal cube of edge 12 cm is melted and formed into three smaller cubes. If the edges of two smaller cubes are 6cm and 8cm, find the edges of the third smaller cube. **[DMRC—Jr. Engineer (Electrical) Exam 2016]**

(*a*) 8 cm (*b*) 10 cm
(*c*) 12 cm (*d*) None of these

ANSWERS

1. (c)	2. (d)	3. (d)	4. (b)	5. (d)	6. (b)	7. (a)	8. (a)	9. (b)	10. (a)
11. (b)	12. (b)	13. (b)	14. (a)	15. (b)	16. (a)	17. (b)	18. (d)	19. (c)	20. (c)
21. (c)	22. (b)	23. (b)	24. (c)	25. (c)	26. (c)	27. (b)	28. (b)	29. (b)	30. (c)
31. (c)	32. (d)	33. (b)	34. (c)	35. (c)	36. (c)	37. (c)	38. (b)	39. (c)	40. (b)
41. (b)	42. (d)	43. (c)	44. (b)	45. (b)	46. (c)	47. (a)	48. (b)	49. (b)	50. (a)
51. (d)	52. (c)	53. (a)	54. (b)	55. (b)	56. (a)	57. (a)	58. (d)	59. (a)	60. (d)
61. (c)	62. (d)	63. (b)	64. (d)	65. (d)	66. (c)	67. (b)	68. (d)	69. (c)	70. (d)
71. (d)	72. (a)	73. (d)	74. (c)	75. (b)	76. (c)	77. (d)	78. (c)	79. (c)	80. (b)
81. (d)	82. (b)	83. (d)	84. (b)	85. (c)	86. (c)	87. (b)	88. (b)	89. (d)	90. (d)
91. (d)	92. (c)	93. (b)	94. (d)	95. (b)	96. (c)	97. (b)	98. (c)	99. (d)	100. (c)
101. (d)	102. (c)	103. (d)	104. (b)	105. (d)	106. (d)	107. (b)	108. (b)	109. (d)	110. (c)
111. (c)	112. (c)	113. (c)	114. (b)	115. (a)	116. (b)	117. (c)	118. (d)	119. (d)	120. (b)
121. (b)	122. (b)	123. (d)	124. (a)	125. (b)	126. (c)	127. (b)	128. (d)	129. (c)	130. (d)
131. (c)	132. (c)	133. (b)	134. (c)	135. (c)	136. (d)	137. (a)	138. (b)	139. (c)	140. (c)
141. (c)	142. (d)	143. (a)	144. (b)	145. (c)	146. (b)	147. (b)	148. (c)	149. (b)	150. (d)
151. (b)	152. (d)	153. (b)	154. (c)	155. (b)	156. (b)	157. (c)	158. (c)	159. (d)	160. (c)
161. (b)	162. (b)	163. (d)	164. (d)	165. (c)	166. (a)	167. (c)	168. (b)	169. (c)	170. (c)
171. (b)	172. (b)	173. (d)	174. (c)	175. (c)	176. (c)	177. (b)	178. (d)	179. (d)	180. (b)

181. (a)	182. (a)	183. (d)	184. (b)	185. (d)	186. (c)	187. (a)	188. (c)	189. (c)	190. (b)
191. (c)	192. (b)	193. (d)	194. (c)	195. (d)	196. (b)	197. (a)	198. (d)	199. (c)	200. (d)
201. (a)	202. (c)	203. (a)	204. (d)	205. (c)	206. (d)	207. (b)	208. (a)	209. (c)	210. (b)
211. (c)	212. (d)	213. (d)	214. (c)	215. (b)	216. (d)	217. (d)	218. (c)	219. (d)	220. (d)
221. (c)	222. (b)	223. (c)	224. (a)	225. (d)	226. (d)	227. (a)	228. (b)	229. (a)	230. (d)
231. (d)	232. (c)	233. (c)	234. (d)	235. (c)	236. (c)	237. (b)	238. (d)	239. (a)	240. (b)
241. (d)	242. (b)	243. (b)	244. (c)	245. (a)	246. (d)	247. (b)	248. (c)	249. (d)	250. (d)
251. (c)	252. (c)	253. (d)	254. (a)	255. (c)	256. (a)	257. (b)	258. (c)	259. (c)	260. (c)
261. (b)	262. (b)	263. (b)	264. (c)	265. (c)	266. (a)	267. (b)	268. (a)	269. (c)	270. (d)
271. (b)	272. (b)	273. (b)	274. (d)	275. (b)	276. (b)	277. (c)	278. (b)	279. (d)	280. (c)
281. (b)	282. (d)	283. (c)	284. (b)	285. (c)	286. (c)	287. (a)	288. (a)	289. (b)	290. (c)
291. (a)	292. (a)	293. (a)	294. (b)	295. (d)	296. (a)	297. (a)	298. (c)	299. (b)	300. (b)
301. (a)	302. (b)	303. (b)	304. (b)						

SOLUTIONS

3. Volume of the tank $= (8 \times 100 \times 6 \times 100 \times 2.5 \times 100)$ cm^3 $= 120000000$ cm^3

$= \left(\frac{120000000}{1000}\right)$ litres $= 120000$ litres.

4. Surface area $= [2(7 \times 11 + 11 \times 13 + 7 \times 13)]$ cm^2

$= (2 \times 311)$ cm^2 $= 622$ cm^2.

5. Total length of tape required = Sum of lengths of edges $= (30 \times 4 + 25 \times 4 + 20 \times 3)$ cm $= 300$ cm.

6. Required number of bags =

$\frac{\text{Volume of the room}}{\text{Volume of each bag}} = \frac{15 \times 10 \times 8}{2.25} = 533.333 \approx 533.$

7. Volume of the reservoir = 42000 litres = 42 m^3.

Let the depth of the reservoir be h metres.

Then, $6 \times 3.5 \times h = 42$ or $h = \frac{42}{6 \times 3.5} = 2$ m.

8. Area of the wet surface $= [2(lb + bh + lh) - lb]$

$= 2(bh + lh) + lb$

$= [2(4 \times 1.25 + 6 \times 1.25) + 6 \times 4]$ m^2 $= 49$ m^2.

9. Volume of water displaced $= (3 \times 2 \times 0.01)$ m^3 $= 0.06$ m^3.

$\therefore$ Mass of man = Volume of water displaced × Density of water $= (0.06 \times 1000)$ kg $= 60$ kg.

10. Since the tank is open at the top, we have:

Area of sheet required = Surface area of the tank

$= lb + 2(bh + lh)$

$= [30 \times 20 + 2(20 \times 12 + 30 \times 12)]$ m^2 $= (600 + 1200)$ m^2 $= 1800$ m^2.

Length of sheet required $= \left(\frac{\text{Area}}{\text{Width}}\right) = \left(\frac{1800}{3}\right)$ m $= 600$ m.

$\therefore$ Cost of the sheet = ₹ (600×10) = ₹ 6000.

11. Let length = x cm. Then,

$x \times 28 \times 5 \times \frac{25}{1000} = 112 \Rightarrow x = \left(112 \times \frac{1000}{25} \times \frac{1}{28} \times \frac{1}{5}\right)$ cm $= 32$ cm.

12. Volume of gold $= \left(\frac{1}{2} \times 100 \times 100 \times 100\right)$ cm^3.

Area of sheet $= 10000$ m^2 $= (10000 \times 100 \times 100)$ cm^2.

$\therefore$ Thickness of the sheet =

$\left(\frac{1 \times 100 \times 100 \times 100}{2 \times 10000 \times 100 \times 100}\right)$ cm $= 0.005$ cm.

13. Area $= (1.5 \times 10000)$ m^2 $= 15000$ m^2. Depth $= \frac{5}{100}$ m $= \frac{1}{20}$ m.

$\therefore$ Volume = (Area × Depth) $= \left(15000 \times \frac{1}{20}\right)$ m^3 $= 750$ m^3.

14. Let the height of the room be x metres.

Then, breadth = $2x$ metres and length = $4x$ metres.

$\therefore$ Volume of the room $= (4x \times 2x \times x)$ m^3 $= (8x^3)$ m^3.

$8x^3 = 512 \Rightarrow x^3 = 64 \Rightarrow x = 4.$

Length of the room is 16 m.

15. Let the breadth be x metres. Then, length = $2x$ metres.

Area of 4 walls $= [2(2x + x) \times 3]$m^2 $= (18x)$ m^2.

$\therefore 18x = 108 \Rightarrow x = \frac{108}{18} = 6.$

So, length = 12 m, breadth = 6 m.

Volume $= (12 \times 6 \times 3)$ m^3 $= 216$ m^3.

16. Let the height of the hall be h metres.

Then, $2 \times 20 \times 16 = 2(20 + 16) \times h \Rightarrow 72h = 640$

$\Rightarrow h = \frac{640}{72} = \frac{80}{9}.$

$\therefore$ Volume of the hall

$= \left(20 \times 16 \times \frac{80}{9}\right)$ m^3 $= \left(\frac{25600}{9}\right)$ m^3 $= 2844.4$ m^3.

17. $V = abc.$

$S = 2(ab + bc + ca) = 2abc\left(\frac{1}{a} + \frac{1}{b} + \frac{1}{c}\right)$

$\Rightarrow S = 2V\left(\frac{1}{a}+\frac{1}{b}+\frac{1}{c}\right) \Rightarrow \frac{1}{V} = \frac{2}{S}\left(\frac{1}{a}+\frac{1}{b}+\frac{1}{c}\right)$.

18. Let the dimensions be $3x$, $2x$ and x respectively. Then, $3x \times 2x \times x = 10368 \Leftrightarrow x^3 = \left(\frac{10368}{6}\right) = 1728 \Leftrightarrow x = 12$.
So, the dimensions of the block are 36 dm, 24 dm and 12 dm.
Surface area $= [2(36 \times 24 + 24 \times 12 + 36 \times 12)]\ dm^2$
$= [2 \times 144 (6 + 2 + 3)]\ dm^2 = 3168\ dm^2$.
$\therefore$ Cost of polishing $= ₹\left(\frac{2 \times 3168}{100}\right) = ₹\ 63.36$.

19. Let the length, breadth and height of the box be $2x$, $3x$ and $4x$ respectively.
Then, surface area of the box $= 2[2x.3x + 3x.4x + 2x.4x]$
$= [2(6x^2 + 12x^2 + 8x^2)] = 52x^2$.
$\therefore 52x^2 = \frac{1248}{1.50} = 832 \Rightarrow x^2 = \frac{832}{52} = 16 \Rightarrow x = \sqrt{16} = 4$.
Hence, the dimensions of the box are 8 m, 12 m and 16 m.

20. Volume of the hall $= (500 \times 22.5)\ m^3 = 11250\ m^3$.
Let the length and breadth of the hall be l and b metres respectively.
Then, $l \times b \times h = 11250 \Rightarrow lb = \frac{11250}{7.5} = 1500$ ...(i)
And, $2(l + b) \times h = 1200 \Rightarrow 2(l + b) = \frac{1200}{7.5} = 160$
$\Rightarrow l + b = 80$ ...(ii)
Putting $b = (80 - l)$ in (i), we get:
$l(80 - l) = 1500 \Rightarrow l^2 - 80l + 1500 = 0 \Rightarrow (l - 30)(l - 50) = 0 \Rightarrow l = 50$.
Hence, length = 50 m, breadth = 30 m.

21. Let the length of the tank be x dm. Then, depth of the tank $= \frac{x}{3}$ dm.
Breadth of the tank
$= \left[\frac{1}{2} \text{ of } \frac{1}{3} \text{ of } \left(x - \frac{x}{3}\right)\right] dm = \left(\frac{1}{2} \times \frac{1}{3} \times \frac{2x}{3}\right) dm = \frac{x}{9}\ dm$.
$\therefore x \times \frac{x}{9} \times \frac{x}{3} = 216 \Rightarrow x^3 = 216 \times 27 \Rightarrow x = 6 \times 3 = 18$.

22. Required length $= \sqrt{(10)^2 + (10)^2 + (5)^2}\ m = \sqrt{225}\ m = 15\ m$.

23. Required length
$= \sqrt{(16)^2 + (12)^2 + \left(\frac{32}{3}\right)^2}\ m = \sqrt{256 + 144 + \frac{1024}{9}}\ m$
$= \sqrt{\frac{4624}{9}}\ m = \frac{68}{3}\ m = 22\frac{2}{3}\ m$.

24. Let l, b and h represent the lengths of the edges of the solid. Then, $l \times b = 42$ ...(i)
$lbh = 210 \Rightarrow h = \frac{210}{lb} = \frac{210}{42} \Rightarrow h = 5$.
Surface area $= 2(lb + bh + lh) = 2(42 + 5b + 5l)$
$= 84 + 10(l + b)$.
$\therefore 84 + 10(l + b) = 214 \Rightarrow l + b = 13$. ...(ii)
Putting $b = (13 - l)$ in (i), we get: $l(13 - l) = 42 \Rightarrow l^2 - 13l + 42 = 0 \Rightarrow (l - 6)(l - 7) = 0$
$\Rightarrow l = 7$.
Hence, length = 7 cm, breadth = 6 cm, height = 5 cm.

25. Number of bricks =
$\frac{\text{Volume of the wall}}{\text{Volume of 1 brick}} = \left(\frac{800 \times 600 \times 22.5}{25 \times 11.25 \times 6}\right) = 6400$.

26. Volume of the bricks = 95% of volume of wall
$= \left(\frac{95}{100} \times 600 \times 500 \times 50\right) cm^3$.
Volume of 1 brick $= (25 \times 12.5 \times 7.5)\ cm^3$.
$\therefore$ Number of bricks $= \left(\frac{95}{100} \times \frac{600 \times 500 \times 50}{25 \times 12.5 \times 7.5}\right) = 6080$.

27. Total volume of water displaced $= (4 \times 50)\ m^3 = 200\ m^3$.
$\therefore$ Rise in water level $= \left(\frac{200}{40 \times 20}\right) m = 0.25\ m = 25\ cm$.

28. Volume of water displaced $= \left(24 \times 15 \times \frac{1}{100}\right) m^3 = \frac{18}{5} m^3$.
Volume of water displaced by 1 man $= 0.1\ m^3$.
$\therefore$ Number of men $= \left(\frac{18/5}{0.1}\right) = \left(\frac{18}{5} \times 10\right) = 36$.

29. Let the breadth and height of the room be b and h metres respectively.
Then, area of the floor $= (14b)\ m^2$.
$\therefore 14b = 2.2 \times 70 \Rightarrow b = \frac{2.2 \times 70}{14} = 11$.
Volume of the room $= (14 \times 11 \times h)\ m^3 = (154h)\ m^3$.
$\therefore 154h = 11 \times 70 \Rightarrow h = \frac{11 \times 70}{154} = 5$.

30. Volume of earth dug out $= (5 \times 4.5 \times 2.1)\ m^3 = 47.25\ m^3$.
Area over which earth is spread $= (13.5 \times 2.5 - 5 \times 4.5)\ m^2 = (33.75 - 22.5)\ m^2 = 11.25\ m^2$.
$\therefore$ Rise in level $= \frac{\text{Volume}}{\text{Area}} = \left(\frac{47.25}{11.25}\right) m = 4.2\ m$.

31. Volume of earth dug out $= (240 \times 180 \times 0.25)\ m^3 = 10800\ m^3$.
Let the depth of the drainlet be h metres.
Then, volume of earth dug out
$= [\{(260 \times 200) - (240 \times 180)\}h]\ m^3 = (8800h)\ m^3$.
$\therefore 8800h = 10800 \Rightarrow h = \frac{10800}{8800} = \frac{27}{22} = 1.227\ m$.

32. Let the depth of the cistern be h metres.
Then, $4.5 \times 3 \times h = 50 \Rightarrow h = \frac{50}{13.5} = \frac{100}{27}$.
Area of sheet required $= lb + 2(bh + lh) = lb + 2h(l + b)$
$= \left[4.5 \times 3 + 2 \times \frac{100}{27}(4.5 + 3)\right] m^2$
$= \left(13.5 + \frac{200}{27} \times 7.5\right) m^2 = \left(\frac{27}{2} + \frac{500}{9}\right) m^2 = \frac{1243}{18} m^2$.
$\therefore$ Weight of lead $= \left(27 \times \frac{1243}{18}\right) kg = \left(\frac{3729}{2}\right) kg = 1864.5\ kg$.

33. Length of water column flown in 1 min

$= \left(\frac{3.6 \times 1000}{60}\right) \text{m} = 60 \text{ m}.$

$\therefore$ Volume flown per minute = $(60 \times 45 \times 2.5)$ m^3 = 6750 m^3.

34. Length of water column flown in 1 min.

$= \left(\frac{10 \times 1000}{60}\right) \text{m} = \frac{500}{3} \text{ m}.$

Volume flown per minute $= \left(\frac{500}{3} \times \frac{40}{100 \times 100}\right) \text{m}^3 = \frac{2}{3} \text{m}^3.$

Volume flown in half an hour $= \left(\frac{2}{3} \times 30\right) \text{m}^3 = 20 \text{ m}^3.$

$\therefore$ Rise in water level $= \left(\frac{20}{40 \times 80}\right) \text{m} = \left(\frac{1}{160} \times 100\right) \text{cm} = \frac{5}{8} \text{ cm}.$

35. Volume flown in 5 hours $= \left(225 \times 162 \times \frac{20}{100}\right) \text{m}^3 = 7290 \text{ m}^3.$

Volume flown in 1 hour $= \left(\frac{7290}{5}\right) \text{m}^3 = 1458 \text{ m}^3.$

$\therefore$ Required speed $= \left(\frac{1458}{0.60 \times 0.45}\right) \text{m/hr} = 5400 \text{ m/hr}.$

36. Volume of water in the reservoir = $(80 \times 60 \times 6.5)$ m^3 = 31200 m^3.

Volume of water flowing out per hour

$= \left(15000 \times \frac{20}{100} \times \frac{20}{100}\right) \text{m}^3 = 600 \text{ m}^3.$

$\therefore$ Total time taken to empty the tank $= \left(\frac{31200}{600}\right) \text{hrs} = 52 \text{ hrs}.$

37. Let l, b and h denote the length, breadth and depth of Meeta's lunch box.

Then, length of Rita's lunch box = 110% of $l = \frac{11l}{10}$.

breadth of Rita's lunch box = 110% of $b = \frac{11b}{10}$.

depth of Rita's lunch box = 80% of $h = \frac{4h}{5}$.

$\therefore$ Ratio of the capacities of Rita's and Meeta's lunch boxes $= \frac{11l}{10} \times \frac{11b}{10} \times \frac{4h}{5} : lbh = \frac{121}{125} : 1 = 121 : 125.$

38. $(l + b + h) = 19$ and

$\sqrt{l^2 + b^2 + h^2} = 5\sqrt{5}$ and so $(l^2 + b^2 + h^2) = 125.$

Now, $(l + b + h)^2 = 19^2 \Rightarrow (l^2 + b^2 + h^2) + 2(lb + bh + lh) = 361$

$\Rightarrow 2(lb + bh + lh) = (361 - 125) = 236.$

$\therefore$ Surface area = 236 cm^2.

39. Sum of perimeters of the six faces

$= 2[2(l + b) + 2(b + h) + 2(l + h)]$

$= 4(2l + 2b + 2h) = 8(l + b + h).$

Total surface area = = $2(lb + bh + lh)$.

$\therefore 8(l + b + h) = 72$ and $2(lb + bh + lh) = 16 \Rightarrow l + b + h = 9$ and $lb + bh + lh = 8$.

Now, $(l + b + h)^2 = l^2 + b^2 + h^2 + 2(lb + bh + lh)$

$\Rightarrow 9^2 = l^2 + b^2 + h^2 + 16 \Rightarrow l^2 + b^2 + h^2 = 81 - 16 = 65.$

Required length $= \sqrt{l^2 + b^2 + h^2} = \sqrt{65} = 8.05$ cm.

40. Volume

$= \left[12 \times 9 \times \left(\frac{1 + 4}{2}\right)\right] \text{m}^3 = (12 \times 9 \times 2.5) \text{ m}^3 = 270 \text{ m}^3.$

41. Let the original length, breadth and height of the solid be l, b and h respectively.

Original volume = (lbh) cu. units.

New length = 110% of $l = \frac{11l}{10}$.

New breadth = 90% of $b = \frac{9b}{10}$.

New volume $= \left(\frac{11l}{10} \times \frac{9b}{10} \times h\right)$ cu. units $= \left(\frac{99}{100} lbh\right)$ cu. units.

Decrease $= \left(lbh - \frac{99}{100} lbh\right) = \frac{lbh}{100}.$

$\therefore$ Decrease% $= \left(\frac{lbh}{100} \times \frac{1}{lbh} \times 100\right)\% = 1\%.$

42. Let the original length, breadth and height of the cuboid be x, $2x$ and $3x$ units respectively.

Then, original volume = $(x \times 2x \times 3x)$ cu. units = $6x^3$ cu. units.

New length = 200% of $x = 2x$,

New breadth = 300% of $2x = 6x$,

New height = 300% of $3x = 9x$.

$\therefore$ New volume = $(2x \times 6x \times 9x)$ cu. units

= $108\,x^3$ cu. units.

Increase in volume = $(108\,x^3 - 6x^3)$ cu. units

= $(102x^3)$ cu. units

$\therefore$ Required ratio $= \frac{102x^3}{6x^3} = 17.$

43. Clearly, l = (18 – 10) cm = 8 cm, b = (24 – 10) cm = 14 cm, h = 5 cm.

$\therefore$ Volume of the box = $(8 \times 14 \times 5)$ cm^3 = 560 cm^3.

44. Clearly, l = (20 – 4) cm = 16 cm, b = (15 – 4) cm = 11 cm, h = 2cm

$\therefore$ Outer surface area of the box = $[2(l + b) \times h] + lb$

= $[\{2(16 + 11) \times 2\} + 16 \times 11]$ cm^2

= $(108 + 176)$ cm^2 = 284 cm^2.

45. Internal length = (12 – 2) cm = 10 cm,

Internal breadth = (10 – 2) cm = 8 cm,

Internal height = (8 – 2) cm = 6 cm.

Inner surface area = $2[10 \times 8 + 8 \times 6 + 10 \times 6]$ cm^2

= (2×188) cm^2 = 376 cm^2.

46. The external measures of the box are (115 + 5) cm, (75 + 5) cm and (35 + 5) cm *i.e.*, 120 cm, 80 cm and 40 cm.

Volume of the wood = External volume – Internal volume

= $[(120 \times 80 \times 40) - (115 \times 75 \times 35)]$ cm^3

= $(384000 - 301875)$ cm^3 = 82125 cm^3.

47. Since the box is an open one, we have:

Internal length = (52 – 4) cm = 48 cm;

Internal breadth = (40 – 4) cm = 36 cm;

Internal depth = (29 – 2) cm = 27 cm.

Volume of the metal used in the box = External volume – Internal volume

= $[(52 \times 40 \times 29) - (48 \times 36 \times 27)]$ cm^3

$= (60320 - 46656)$ cm^3 = 13664 cm^3.

$\therefore$ Weight of the box = $\left(\frac{13664 \times 0.5}{1000}\right)$ kg = 6.832 kg.

48. Internal length = (146 – 6) cm = 140 cm.
Internal breadth = (116 – 6) cm = 110 cm.
Internal depth = (83 – 3) cm = 80 cm.
Area of inner surface = $[2(l + b) \times h] + lb$
$= [2(140 + 110) \times 80 + 140 \times 110]$ cm^2 = 55400 cm^2.

$\therefore$ Cost of painting = ₹$\left(\frac{1}{2} \times \frac{1}{100} \times 55400\right)$ = ₹ 277.

49. Let the thickness of the bottom be x cm.
Then, $[(330 - 10) \times (260 - 10) \times (110 - x)] = 8000 \times 1000$
$\Leftrightarrow 320 \times 250 \times (110 - x) = 8000 \times 1000$
$\Leftrightarrow (110 - x) = \frac{8000 \times 1000}{320 \times 250} = 100$
$\Leftrightarrow x = 10$ cm = 1 dm.

50. Let the dimensions of the bigger cuboid be x, y and z.
Then, Volume of the bigger cuboid = xyz.
Vlume of the miniature cuboid
$= \left(\frac{1}{4}x\right)\left(\frac{1}{4}y\right)\left(\frac{1}{4}z\right) = \frac{1}{64}xyz.$

$\therefore$ Weight of the miniature cuboid = $\left(\frac{1}{64} \times 16\right)$ kg = 0.25 kg.

51. Depth of the tank = $\left(\frac{24}{4 \times 3}\right)$ m = 2 m.

Since the tank is open and thickness of material is to be ignored, we have
Sum of inner and outer surfaces = $2[\{2(l + b) \times h\} + lb]$
$= 2[\{2(4 + 3) \times 2\} + 4 \times 3]$ m^2 = 80 m^2.
$\therefore$ Cost of painting = ₹ (80 × 10) = ₹ 800.

52. Let length = l, breadth = b, height = h. Then, $x = lb$, $y = bh$, $z = lh$.
Let V be the volume of the cuboid. Then, $V = lbh$.
$\therefore xyz = lb \times bh \times lh = (lbh)^2 = V^2$ or $V = \sqrt{xyz}$.

53. Let the length, breadth and height of the box be l, b and h respectively. Then,
Volume
$= lbh = \sqrt{(lbh)^2} = \sqrt{lb \times bh \times lh} = \sqrt{120 \times 72 \times 60} = 720 \text{ cm}^3.$

54. Let $lb = 2x$, $bh = 3x$ and $lh = 4x$.
Then, $24x^3 = (lbh)^2 = 9000 \times 9000 \Rightarrow x^3 = 375 \times 9000$
$\Rightarrow x = 150$.
So, $lb = 300$, $bh = 450$, $lh = 600$ and $lbh = 9000$.
$\therefore h = \frac{9000}{300} = 30, l = \frac{9000}{450} = 20$ and $b = \frac{9000}{600} = 15$.
Hence, shortest side = 15 cm.

55. Sum of original dimensions = 48 + 30 + 52 = 130.
Increase in sum = 156 – 130 = 26.
Since the dimensions have been increased proportionately,
so increase in shortest side = $\left(26 \times \frac{30}{130}\right)'' = 6''$.

56. Let the length of the new slab be x metres.
Then, $1 \times 0.20 \times 0.01 = x \times 0.001 \times 1 \Rightarrow x = \frac{0.002}{0.001} = 2.$
$\therefore$ Required length = 2 m = 200 cm.

57. Clearly, payment shall be made in proportion to the volume of earth dug.

$\frac{\text{Volume actually dug}}{\text{Volume to be dug as settled}} = \frac{2 \times (5 \times 5 \times 5)}{10 \times 10 \times 10} = \frac{1}{4}.$

$\therefore$ Payment to be made = $\frac{1}{4} \times 40000 = 10000.$

58. Volume of the cube = 8^3 cu. m = 512 cu. m

59. Edge of the cube = $\left(\frac{20}{4}\right)$ cm = 5 cm.

$\therefore$ Volume = (5 × 5 × 5) cm^3 = 125 cm^3.

60. Surface area = $\left[6 \times \left(\frac{1}{2}\right)^2\right]$ cm^2 = $\frac{3}{2}$ cm^2.

61. Surface area of the cube = (6×8^2) sq. ft. = 384 sq. ft.
Quantity of paint required = $\left(\frac{384}{16}\right)$ kg = 24 kg.
$\therefore$ Cost of painting = ₹ (36.50 × 24) = ₹ 876.

62. $a^3 = 729 \Rightarrow a = \sqrt[3]{729} = 9.$
$\therefore$ Surface area = $6a^2$ = (6 × 9 × 9) cm^2 = 486 cm^2.

63. $6a^2 = 150 \Rightarrow a^2 = 25 \Rightarrow a = 5$. $\therefore$ Volume = $a^3 = 5^3$ cm^3 = 125 cm^3.

64. Volume of the cube = (270 × 100 × 64) cm^3.
Edge of the cube =
$\sqrt[3]{270 \times 100 \times 64}$ cm = (3 × 10 × 4) cm = 120 cm.
$\therefore$ Surface area = (6 × 120 × 120) cm^2 = 86400 cm^2.

65. Surface area = $\left(\frac{34398}{13}\right)$ = 2646 cm^2.
$\therefore 6a^2 = 2646 \Rightarrow a^2 = 441 \Rightarrow a = 21.$
So, Volume = (21 × 21 × 21) cm^3 = 9261 cm^3.

66. Volume of cube = Volume of sheet = (27 × 8 × 1) cm^3 = 216 cm^3.
Edge of cube = $\sqrt[3]{216}$ cm = 6 cm.
Surface area of sheet= $2(lb + bh + lh) = 2$ (27 × 8 + 8 × 1 + 27 × 1) cm^2.
= (216 + 8 + 27) cm^2 = 502 cm^2.
Surface area of cube = $6a^2$ = (6 × 6^2) cm^2 = 216 cm^2.
$\therefore$ Required difference = (502 – 216) cm^2 = 286 cm^2.

67. Required length = Diagonal = $\sqrt{3}\,a = (\sqrt{3} \times \sqrt{3})$ m = 3 m.

68. $\sqrt{3}\,a = 4\sqrt{3} \Rightarrow a = 4.$
$\therefore$ Volume = (4 × 4 × 4) cm^3 = 64 cm^3.

69. Since a cube has 4 diagonals, we have: Length of a diagonal = $\left(\frac{12}{4}\right)$ cm = 3 cm.
Let the length of each edge of the cube be a cm.
Then, $\sqrt{3}a = 3$ or $a = \sqrt{3}$.
$\therefore$ Total length of the edges of the cube = $12\sqrt{3}$ cm.

70. $6a^2 = 13254 \Rightarrow a^2 = 2209 \Rightarrow a = \sqrt{2209} = 47.$
$\therefore$ Length of diagonal = $\sqrt{3}\,a = 47\sqrt{3}$ cm.

71. Clearly, we have:
$V_1 = x^3$, $V_2 = (2x)^3 = 8x^3$, $V_3 = (3x)^3 = 27x^3$,
$V_4 = (4x)^3 = 64x^3$.
(1) $V_1 + V_2 + 2V_3 = x^3 + 8x^3 + 2 \times 27x^3 = 63x^3 < V_4$.
(2) $V_1 + 4V_2 + V_3 = x^3 + 4 \times 8x^3 + 27x^3 = 60x^3 < V_4$.
(3) $2(V_1 + V_3) + V_2 = 2(x^3 + 27x^3) + 8x^3 = 64x^3 = V_4$.

72. Volume of the remaining solid = Volume of the cube − Volume of the cuboid cut out from it
$= [(8 \times 8 \times 8) - (3 \times 3 \times 8)]\ m^3 = (512 - 72)\ m^3 = 440\ m^3.$

73. $a^3 = 6a^2 \Rightarrow a = 6.$

74. $a^3 = 12a \Rightarrow a^2 = 12 \Rightarrow 6a^2 = (6 \times 12)$ sq. units $= 72$ sq. units.

75. Clearly, each of the 5 faces of the given cube are glued to a face of another cube.
∴ Total surface area of the solid $5 \times 5a^2 + a^2 = 26a^2$
$= (26 \times 3^2)\ cm^2 = 234\ cm^2.$

76. Let the length of each side of the cube be a cm.
Then, volume of the part of cube outside water = volume of the mass placed on it
$\Rightarrow 2a^2 = 0.2 \times 1000 = 200 \Rightarrow a^2 = 100 \Rightarrow a = 10.$

77. Volume of the bigger cube $= (8^3)\ cm^3 = 512\ cm^3.$
Volume of the cut-out cube $= (1^3)\ cm^3 = 1\ cm^3.$
Volume of the remaining portion $= (512 - 1)\ cm^3 = 511\ cm^3.$

$$\frac{\text{Weight of the remaining portion}}{\text{Weight of the original cube}} = \frac{511}{512}.$$

78. Number of cubes $= \left(\frac{100 \times 100 \times 100}{10 \times 10 \times 10}\right) = 1000.$

79. Number of small cubes formed $= \left(\frac{4 \times 4 \times 4}{1 \times 1 \times 1}\right) = 64.$
Total surface area of the small cubes $= [64 \times (6 \times 1^2)]\ cm^2 = 384\ cm^2.$

80. Clearly, when the rectangular block was cut into 2 identical cubes, two new faces were formed – one on each cube along the line of the cut. So, the difference in surface areas is equal to the surface area of the newly formed faces.
Volume of each cube $= \left(\frac{250}{2}\right) cm^3 = 125\ cm^3.$
Edge of each cube $= \sqrt[3]{125}\ cm = 5\ cm.$
Hence, difference in surface areas $= (2 \times 5^2)\ cm^2 = 50\ cm^2.$

81. Number of blocks $= \left(\frac{160 \times 100 \times 60}{20 \times 20 \times 20}\right) = 120.$

82. Number of cubes $= \left(\frac{18 \times 18 \times 18}{3 \times 3 \times 3}\right) = 216.$

83. Number of cubes formed $= \frac{10^3 \times 10^3 \times 10^3}{1 \times 1 \times 1} = 10^9.$
∴ Total length of cube-robe $= (1 \times 10^9)$ mm $= 10^9$ mm
$= \left(\frac{10^9}{10^6}\right) km = 10^3\ km = 1000\ km.$

84. Let the length of each edge of small cube be a_1 and that of large cube be a_2.
Then, $6a_1^2 = 96$ and $6a_2^2 = 384 \Rightarrow a_1^2 = 16$ and $a_2^2 = 64$
$\Rightarrow a_1 = 4$ and $a_2 = 8.$
∴ Number of cubes formed $= \frac{\text{Volume of larger cube}}{\text{Volume of smaller cube}}$
$= \left(\frac{8 \times 8 \times 8}{4 \times 4 \times 4}\right) = 8.$

85. Volume of the cuboid $= (9 \times 8 \times 6)\ cm^3 = 432\ cm^3.$
Volume of the cube $= \left(\frac{1}{2} \times 432\right) cm^3 = 216\ cm^3.$
$a^3 = 216 \Rightarrow a = \sqrt[3]{216} = 6 \Rightarrow 6a^2 = (6 \times 6^2) = 216.$

86. Volume of block $= (6 \times 9 \times 12)\ cm^3 = 648\ cm^3.$
Side of largest cube = H.C.F. of 6 cm, 9 cm, 12 cm = 3 cm.
Volume of this cube $= (3 \times 3 \times 3)$ cm $= 27\ cm^3.$
∴ Number of cubes $= \left(\frac{648}{27}\right) = 24.$

87. Side of smallest cube = L.C.M. of 5 cm, 10 cm, 20 cm = 20 cm.
Volume of the cube $= (20 \times 20 \times 20)\ cm^3 = 8000\ cm^3.$
Volume of the block $= (5 \times 10 \times 20)\ cm^3 = 1000\ cm^3.$
∴ Number of blocks $= \left(\frac{8000}{1000}\right) = 8.$

88. Let the sides of the sheet be x and $5x$. Then,
Volume of the sheet = Volume of the cube
$\Rightarrow x \times 5x \times \frac{1}{2} = 10 \times 10 \times 10 \Rightarrow 5x^2 = 2000 \Rightarrow x^2 = 400$
$\Rightarrow x = 20.$
∴ The sides are 20 cm and 100 cm.

89. Let the length of each edge of the cube be a.
Then, the dimensions of each of the two rectangular solids are a, a and $\frac{a}{2}$.
Surface area of each rectangular solid
$= 2\left[a \times a + a \times \frac{a}{2} + a \times \frac{a}{2}\right] = 4a^2.$
Surface area of unpainted face of each solid $= (a \times a) = a^2.$
∴ Required percentage $= \left(\frac{a^2}{4a^2} \times 100\right)\% = 25\%.$

90. Let the other two dimensions of the cuboid be a and b cm respectively.
Then, $6ab = 216$ or $ab = 36.$
The possible values of (a, b) are (1, 36), (2, 18), (3, 12) and (4, 9).

91. Volume of the new cube $= (6^3 + 8^3 + 10^3)\ cm^3 = 1728\ cm^3.$
Let the edge of the new cube be a cm.
∴ $a^3 = 1728 \Rightarrow a = 12.$
Hence, length of diagonal $= \sqrt{3}a = 12\sqrt{3}$ cm
$= (12 \times 1.732)$ cm $= 20.784$ cm ≈ 20.8 cm.

92. Volume of the larger cube $= (3^3 + 4^3 + 5^3)\ cm^3 = 216\ cm^3.$
Let the edge of the larger cube be a cm.
∴ $a^3 = 216 \Rightarrow a = 6.$
Required ratio $= \frac{6(3^2 + 4^2 + 5^2)}{6 \times 6^2} = \frac{6 \times 50}{6 \times 36} = \frac{25}{18}.$

93. The new solid formed is a cuboid of length 25 cm, breadth 5 cm and height 5 cm.
∴ Volume $= (25 \times 5 \times 5)\ cm^3 = 625\ cm^3.$

94. Let the length of each edge of each cube be a.
Then, the cuboid formed by placing 3 cubes adjacently has the dimensions $3a$, a and a.
Surface area of the cuboid $= 2\,[3a \times a + a \times a + 3a \times a] = 2\,(3a^2 + a^2 + 3a^2) = 14a^2.$
Sum of surface areas of 3 cubes $= (3 \times 6a^2) = 18a^2.$
∴ Required ratio $= 14a^2 : 18a^2 = 7 : 9.$

95. Let the sides of the three cubes be $3x$, $4x$ and $5x$.
Then, Volume of the new cube $= [(3x)^3 + (4x)^3 + (5x)^3] = 216x^3$.
Edge of the new cube $= (216x^3)^{1/3} = 6x$.
Diagonal of the new cube $= 6\sqrt{3}\,x$.
$\therefore\ 6\sqrt{3}\,x = 12\sqrt{3} \Rightarrow x = 2$.
So, the sides of the cubes are 6 cm, 8 cm and 10 cm.

96. Let their edges be a and b.
Then, $\frac{a^3}{b^3} = \frac{27}{1} \Leftrightarrow \left(\frac{a}{b}\right)^3 = \left(\frac{3}{1}\right)^3$
$\Leftrightarrow \frac{a}{b} = \frac{3}{1} \Leftrightarrow a : b = 3 : 1$.

97. Let their edges be a and b. Then,
$\frac{a^3}{b^3} = \frac{8}{27} \Leftrightarrow \left(\frac{a}{b}\right)^3 = \left(\frac{2}{3}\right)^3 \Leftrightarrow \frac{a}{b} = \frac{2}{3} \Leftrightarrow \frac{a^2}{b^2} = \frac{4}{9}$
$\Leftrightarrow \frac{6a^2}{6b^2} = \frac{4}{9}$.

98. Let their edges be a and b. Then,
$\frac{a^3}{b^3} = \frac{1}{27} \Leftrightarrow \left(\frac{a}{b}\right)^3 = \left(\frac{1}{3}\right)^3 \Leftrightarrow \frac{a}{b} = \frac{1}{3} \Leftrightarrow \frac{a^2}{b^2} = \frac{1}{9}$.

99. Let original edge $= a$. Then, volume $= a^3$.
New edge $= 2a$. So, new volume $= (2a)^3 = 8a^3$.
$\therefore$ Volume becomes 8 times.

100. Let original edge $= a$. Then, original volume $= a^3$.
New edge $= \frac{150}{100}a = \frac{3a}{2}$. New volume $= \left(\frac{3a}{2}\right)^3 = \frac{27a^3}{8}$.
Increase in volume $= \left(\frac{27a^3}{8} - a^3\right) = \frac{19a^3}{8}$.
$\therefore$ Increase% $= \left(\frac{19a^3}{8} \times \frac{1}{a^3} \times 100\right)\% = 237.5\%$.

101. Let original edge $= a$. The, surface area $= 6a^2$.
New edge $= \frac{125}{100}a = \frac{5a}{4}$.
New surface area $= 6 \times \left(\frac{5a}{4}\right)^2 = \frac{75a^2}{8}$.
Increase in surface area $= \left(\frac{75a^2}{8} - 6a^2\right) = \frac{27a^2}{8}$.
$\therefore$ Increase % $= \left(\frac{27a^2}{8} \times \frac{1}{6a^2} \times 100\right)\% = 56.25\%$.

102. Volume increased $= (20)^3$ cm^3 $= 8000$ cm^3.
$\therefore$ Rise in water level $= \left(\frac{8000}{20 \times 40}\right)$ cm $= 10$ cm.

103. Volume $= \pi r^2 h = \left(\frac{22}{7} \times 1 \times 1 \times 14\right)$ m^3 $= 44$ m^3.

104. Volume $= \pi r^2 h = \left(\frac{22}{7} \times 14 \times 14 \times 3.5\right)$ m^3 $= 2156$ m^3.
$\therefore$ Cost of the cylinder = ₹ (2156 × 50) = ₹ 107800.

105. Total surface area $= 2\pi r(h + r) = \left[2 \times \frac{22}{7} \times 21 \times (35 + 21)\right]$ cm^2
$= 7392$ cm^2.

106. Volume of the tank = 246.4 litres = 246400 cm^3.
Let the radius of the base be r cm. Then,
$\left(\frac{22}{7} \times r^2 \times 400\right) = 246400 \Leftrightarrow r^2 = \left(\frac{246400 \times 7}{22 \times 400}\right) = 196 \Leftrightarrow r = 14$.
$\therefore$ Diameter of the base $= 2r = 28$ cm.

107. Volume of the cylinder = Volume of the cube $= (11)^3$ cm^3 $= 1331$ cm^3.
Let the radius of the base be r cm. Then,
$\frac{22}{7} \times r^2 \times 14 = 1331 \Rightarrow r^2 = \frac{1331}{44} = \frac{121}{4} \Rightarrow r = \frac{11}{2} = 5.5$.

108. Volume of cylinder = 25.872 litres = (25.872 × 1000) cm^3 $= 25872$ cm^3.
Let the radius of the base of the cylinder be r cm. Then, height $= (3r)$ cm.
$\therefore\ \frac{22}{7} \times r^2 \times (3r) = 25872 \Rightarrow r^3 = \frac{25872 \times 7}{66} = 2744$
$\Rightarrow r = \sqrt[3]{2744} = 14$.
Hence, area of the base $= \pi r^2 = \left(\frac{22}{7} \times 14 \times 14\right)$ cm^2 $= 616$ cm^2.

109. Clearly, the cylinder formed by rolling the paper along its length has height 18 cm and circumference of base 30 cm *i.e.*,
$h = 18$ cm and $2\pi r = 30$ or $r = \frac{30}{2} \times \frac{7}{22} = \frac{105}{22}$.
$\therefore$ Volume $= \pi r^2 h = \left(\frac{22}{7} \times \frac{105}{22} \times \frac{105}{22} \times 18\right)$ cm^3 $= \frac{14175}{11}$ cm^3.
The cylinder formed by rolling the paper along its breadth has height 30 cm and circumference of base 18 cm *i.e.*
$h = 30$ cm and $2\pi r = 18$ or $r = \frac{18}{2} \times \frac{7}{22} = \frac{63}{22}$.
$\therefore$ Volume $= \pi r^2 h = \left(\frac{22}{7} \times \frac{63}{22} \times \frac{63}{22} \times 30\right)$ cm^3 $= \frac{8505}{11}$ cm^3.
Required ratio $= \frac{14175}{11} : \frac{8505}{11} = 5 : 3$.

110. Let the breadths of the rectangles A_1, A_2 and A_3 be b_1, b_2 and b_3 respectively. Since the rectangles have the same area and $a_1 < a_2 < a_3$, we have: $b_1 > b_2 > b_3$.
When the rectangles are folded to form cylinders, then their lengths a_1, a_2, a_3 determine the radii of the cylinders while their breadths b_1, b_2, b_3 form their heights.
Volume of cylinder $= \pi r^2 h$.
Clearly, the rectangle A_3 with length a_3 shall have maximum value of r^2 and hence C_3 has maximum volume.

111. $2\pi r = 66 \Rightarrow r = \left(66 \times \frac{1}{2} \times \frac{7}{22}\right) = \frac{21}{2}$ cm.
$\frac{2\pi rh}{2\pi r} = \left(\frac{2640}{66}\right) \Rightarrow h = 40$ cm.
$\therefore$ Volume $= \left(\frac{22}{7} \times \frac{21}{2} \times \frac{21}{2} \times 40\right)$ cm^3 $= 13860$ cm^3.

112. Curved surface area $= 2\pi rh = \left(2 \times \frac{22}{7} \times \frac{7}{2} \times 22.5\right)$ m^2
$= 495$ m^2.
$\therefore$ Cost of plastering = ₹ (495 × 3) = ₹ 1485.

113. Let the radius and height of the cylinder be $5x$ and $7x$ cm respectively.
Then, volume $= \pi r^2 h = \left[\frac{22}{7} \times (5x)^2 \times 7x\right]$ cm^3

$= (550\, x^3)\ \text{cm}^3$.

$\therefore\ 550\, x^3 = 4400 \Rightarrow x^3 = \dfrac{4400}{550} = 8 \Rightarrow x = \sqrt[3]{8} = 2.$

Hence, radius = (5 × 2) cm = 10 cm.

114. $\dfrac{2\pi rh}{h} = \dfrac{704}{14} \Rightarrow 2\pi r = \dfrac{704}{14}. \Rightarrow r = \left(\dfrac{704}{14} \times \dfrac{1}{2} \times \dfrac{7}{22}\right) = 8$ cm.

$\therefore$ Volume $= \left(\dfrac{22}{7} \times 8 \times 8 \times 14\right)\text{cm}^3 = 2816\ \text{cm}^3$

115. Total surface area

$= 2\pi r\,(h + r) = \left[2 \times \dfrac{22}{7} \times \dfrac{35}{100} \times (1.25 + 0.35)\right]\text{m}^2$

$= \left(2 \times \dfrac{22}{7} \times \dfrac{35}{100} \times \dfrac{16}{10}\right)\text{m}^2 = 3.52\ \text{m}^2.$

$\therefore$ Cost of the material = ₹ (3.52 × 80) = ₹ 281.60.

116. Curved surface area $= 2\pi rh = (\pi r^2 h) \cdot \dfrac{2}{r} = \left(\text{Volume} \times \dfrac{2}{r}\right).$

117. $\dfrac{\text{Total surface area}}{\text{Lateral surface area}} = \dfrac{2\pi rh + 2\pi r^2}{2\pi rh} = \dfrac{(h + r)}{h} = \dfrac{80}{60} = \dfrac{4}{3}.$

118. Difference in capacities = Volume of cuboidal can − Volume of cylindrical can

$= \left[(10 \times 10 \times 21) - \left(\dfrac{22}{7} \times 5 \times 5 \times 21\right)\right]\text{cm}^3$

$= (2100 - 1650)\ \text{cm}^3 = 450\ \text{cm}^3.$

119. Number of tins $= \dfrac{\text{Volume of the drum}}{\text{Volume of each tin}}$

$= \dfrac{\left(\dfrac{22}{7} \times \dfrac{35}{2} \times \dfrac{35}{2} \times 24\right)}{\left(\dfrac{25}{10} \times \dfrac{22}{10} \times \dfrac{35}{10}\right)} = 1200.$

120. It is given that $r = \dfrac{1}{2}h$ and $2\pi rh + \pi r^2 = 616\ \text{m}^2$

$\therefore\ 2\pi \times \dfrac{1}{2}h \times h + \pi \times \dfrac{1}{4}h^2 = 616$

$\Rightarrow \dfrac{5}{4} \times \dfrac{22}{7} \times h^2 = 616 \Rightarrow h^2 = \left(616 \times \dfrac{28}{110}\right) = \dfrac{28 \times 28}{5}.$

$\therefore$ Volume

$= \pi r^2 h = \dfrac{22}{7} \times \dfrac{1}{4}h^2 \times h = \dfrac{22}{7} \times \dfrac{1}{4} \times \dfrac{28 \times 28}{5} \times \dfrac{28}{\sqrt{5}}\ \text{cm}^3$

$= \left(\dfrac{22 \times 28 \times 28}{25} \times \sqrt{5}\right)\text{cm}^3 = \left(\dfrac{22 \times 28 \times 28 \times 2.23}{25 \times 1000}\right)$ litres

= 1.53 litres.

121. $(h + r) = 37$ and $2\pi r\,(h + r) = 1628$. $\therefore\ 2\pi r \times 37 = 1628$

or $r = \left(\dfrac{1628}{2 \times 37} \times \dfrac{7}{22}\right) = 7.$

So, $r = 7$ m and $h = 30$ m.

$\therefore$ Volume $= \left(\dfrac{22}{7} \times 7 \times 7 \times 30\right)\text{m}^3 = 4620\ \text{m}^3.$

122. $\dfrac{\pi r^2 h}{2\pi rh} = \dfrac{924}{264} \Rightarrow r = \left(\dfrac{924}{264} \times 2\right) = 7$ m. And, $2\pi rh = 264$

$\Rightarrow h = \left(264 \times \dfrac{7}{22} \times \dfrac{1}{2} \times \dfrac{1}{7}\right) = 6$ m.

$\therefore$ Required ratio $= \dfrac{2r}{h} = \dfrac{14}{6} = 7 : 3.$

123. $3 \times 2\pi r^2 = 2 \times 2\pi rh \Rightarrow 6r = 4h \Rightarrow r = \dfrac{2}{3}h = \left(\dfrac{2}{3} \times 6\right)$ m = 4m.

124. $V = \pi r^2 h$ and $S = 2\pi rh + 2\pi r^2 \Rightarrow S = 2\pi r\,(h + r),$

where $h = \dfrac{V}{\pi r^2} \Rightarrow S = 2\pi r\left(\dfrac{V}{\pi r^2} + r\right) = \dfrac{2V}{r} + 2\pi r^2$

$\Rightarrow \dfrac{dS}{dr} = \dfrac{-2V}{r^2} + 4\pi r$ and $\dfrac{d^2S}{dr^2} = \left(\dfrac{4V}{r^3} + 4\pi\right) > 0$

$\therefore$ S is minimum when $\dfrac{dS}{dr} = 0 \Leftrightarrow \dfrac{-2V}{r^2} + 4\pi r = 0 \Leftrightarrow V$

$= 2\pi r^3 \Leftrightarrow \pi r^2 h = 2\pi r^3 \Leftrightarrow h = 2r.$

125. Let original radius = R. Then, new radius $= \dfrac{R}{2}.$

$\dfrac{\text{Volume of reduced cylinder}}{\text{Volume of original cylinder}} = \dfrac{\pi \times \left(\dfrac{R}{2}\right)^2 \times h}{\pi \times R^2 \times h} = \dfrac{1}{4}.$

126. Let their radii be $3x$, $4x$ and heights be $4y$, $3y$.

Ratio of their volumes $= \dfrac{\pi \times (3x)^2 \times 4y}{\pi \times (4x)^2 \times 3y} = \dfrac{36}{48} = \dfrac{3}{4}.$

127. Let original height = h and original radius = r.

New height = 115% of $h = \dfrac{23h}{20}.$

New radius = 90% of $r = \dfrac{9r}{10}.$

Original curved surface area = $2\pi rh$.

New curved surface area $= \left(2\pi \times \dfrac{9r}{10} \times \dfrac{23h}{20}\right) = \dfrac{207}{200} \times 2\pi rh.$

Increase in curved surface area =

$\left(\dfrac{207}{200} \times 2\pi rh - 2\pi rh\right) = \dfrac{7}{200} \times 2\pi rh.$

$\therefore$ Increase% $= \left(\dfrac{7}{200} \times 2\pi rh \times \dfrac{1}{2\pi rh} \times 100\right)\% = 3.5\%.$

128. Let their heights be $2h$ and $3h$ and radii be r and R respectively. Then,

$\pi r^2(2h) = \pi R^2(3h) \Rightarrow \dfrac{r^2}{R^2} = \dfrac{3}{2} \Rightarrow \dfrac{r}{R} = \dfrac{\sqrt{3}}{\sqrt{2}}$ i.e. $\sqrt{3} : \sqrt{2}.$

129. Let the height of X and Y be h, and their radii be r and $2r$ respectively. Then,

Volume of X = $\pi r^2 h$ and Volume of Y = $\pi\,(2r)^2\,h = 4\pi r^2 h$.

New height of X = $2h$.

So, new volume of X

$= \pi r^2\,(2h) = 2\pi r^2 h = \dfrac{1}{2}(4\pi r^2 h) = \dfrac{1}{2} \times (\text{Volume of } Y).$

130. Let original radius = r and original length = h.

New radius $= \dfrac{r}{3}$ and let new length = H. Then,

$\pi r^2 h = \pi\left(\dfrac{r}{3}\right)^2 \times H$ or $H = 9H.$

131. Let original radius = r and original height = h. Original volume = $\pi r^2 h$.

New radius = 50% of $r = \frac{r}{2}$.

New height = 150% of $h = \frac{3h}{2}$.

New volume = $\pi\left(\frac{r}{2}\right)^2\left(\frac{3h}{2}\right) = \pi \times \frac{r^2}{4} \times \frac{3h}{2} = \frac{3}{8}\pi r^2 h$.

Decrease in volume $= \pi r^2 h - \frac{3}{8}\pi r^2 h = \frac{5}{8}\pi r^2 h$.

$\therefore$ Decrease% $= \left(\frac{5}{8}\pi r^2 h \times \frac{1}{\pi r^2 h} \times 100\right)\% = 62.5\%$.

132. Let original radius = r and original height = h.
Original volume = $\pi r^2 h$.

New radius = 125% of $r = \frac{5r}{4}$. Let new height = H.

Then, $\pi r^2 h = \pi\left(\frac{5r}{4}\right)^2 \times H$ or $H = \frac{16}{25}h$.

Decrease in height $= \left(h - \frac{16}{25}h\right) = \frac{9h}{25}$.

$\therefore$ Decrease% $= \left(\frac{9h}{25} \times \frac{1}{h} \times 100\right)\% = 36\%$.

133. Let the drop in the water level be h cm. Then,

$\frac{22}{7} \times \frac{35}{2} \times \frac{35}{2} \times h = 11000 \Leftrightarrow h = \left(\frac{11000 \times 7 \times 4}{22 \times 35 \times 35}\right)$ cm

$= \frac{80}{7}$ cm $= 11\frac{3}{7}$ cm.

134. Volume of earth dug out $= \left(\frac{22}{7} \times 4 \times 4 \times 14\right)$ m^3 = 704 m^3.

Area of embankment

$= \frac{22}{7} \times (7^2 - 4^2) = \left(\frac{22}{7} \times 11 \times 3\right)$ m$^2 = \frac{726}{7}$ m^3.

Height of embankment =

$\left(\frac{\text{Volume}}{\text{Area}}\right) = \left(\frac{704 \times 7}{726}\right)$ m $= \frac{224}{33}$ m $= 6\frac{26}{33}$ m.

135. Volume of water flown in 1 sec.

$= \left(\frac{22}{7} \times \frac{7}{2} \times \frac{7}{2} \times 200\right)$ cm^3 = 7700 cm^3.

Volume of water flown in 10 min.= (7700 × 60 × 10) cm^3

$= \left(\frac{7700 \times 60 \times 10}{1000}\right)$ litres = 4620 litres.

136. Volume of cistern = (π × 10^2 × 15) m^3 = 1500 π m^3.
Volume of water flowing through the pipe in 1 sec.
= (π × 0.25 × 0.25 × 5) m^3 = 0.3125 π m^3.

$\therefore$ Time taken to fill the cistern $= \left(\frac{1500\pi}{0.3125\pi}\right) = \left(\frac{1500 \times 10000}{3125}\right)$

$= 4800$ sec $= \left(\frac{4800}{60}\right)$ min = 80 min.

137. Let the inner radius of the pipe be r metres. Then,

Volume of water flowing through the pipe in 10 min

$= \left[\left(\frac{22}{7} \times r^2 \times 7\right) \times 10\right]$ m^3 = $(220r^2)$m^3.

$\therefore$ $220\,r^2 = 440 \Rightarrow r^2 = 2 \Rightarrow r = \sqrt{2}$ m.

138. Volume of water flown through the pipe in 30 min
= [(π × 0.01 × 0.01 × 6) × 30 × 60] m^3 = (1.08 π) m^3.
Let the rise in level of water be h metres.

Then, $\pi \times 0.6 \times 0.6 \times h = 1.08\,\pi \Rightarrow h = \left(\frac{1.08}{0.6 \times 0.6}\right) = 3$ m.

139. Volume of water flown into the tank in 5 min.

$= \left(\frac{22}{7} \times 100 \times 100 \times 7\right)$ cu. feet = 2220000 cu. feet.

$\therefore$ Rate of flow of water $= \left(\frac{220000}{5 \times 60}\right)$ cu. ft/sec = 733.3 cu. ft/sec $\approx$ 700 cu. ft/sec.

140. Let the length of each pipe be l inches.
Then, volume of water in thinner pipe

$= \left[\pi \times \left(\frac{1}{2}\right)^2 \times l\right]$ cu. inch $= \left(\frac{\pi l}{4}\right)$ cu. inch.

Volume of water in thicker pipe = (π × 3^2 × l) cu.inch
= $(9\pi l)$ cu.inch.

$\therefore$ Required number of pipes $= \frac{9\pi l}{\left(\frac{\pi l}{4}\right)} = 36$.

141. Volume of one coin $= \left(\frac{22}{7} \times \frac{75}{100} \times \frac{75}{100} \times \frac{2}{10}\right)$ cm^3 $= \frac{99}{280}$ cm^3.

Volume of larger cylinder $= \left(\frac{22}{7} \times \frac{9}{4} \times \frac{9}{4} \times 10\right)$ cm^3.

Number of coins $= \left(\frac{22}{7} \times \frac{9}{4} \times \frac{9}{4} \times 10 \times \frac{280}{99}\right) = 450$.

142. Let the radius of the vessel be R. Then,
$\pi R^2 \times 15 = \pi \times (15)^2 \times 35 + \pi \times (10)^2 \times 15 \Leftrightarrow \pi R^2 \times 15 = 9375\pi \Leftrightarrow R^2 = 625 \Leftrightarrow R = 25$ cm.

143. Let the length of the wire be h. Radius $= \frac{1}{2}$ mm $= \frac{1}{20}$ cm. Then,

$\frac{22}{7} \times \frac{1}{20} \times \frac{1}{20} \times h = 66 \Leftrightarrow h = \left(\frac{66 \times 20 \times 20 \times 7}{22}\right) = 8400$ cm = 84 m.

144. Volume of copper rod $= \left(\pi \times \frac{1}{2} \times \frac{1}{2} \times 8\right)$ cm^3 = 2π cm^3.
Let the radius of the wire be r cm.
Then, volume of wire = (πr^2 × 1800) cm^3 = 1800 πr^2 cm^3.

$\therefore$ $1800\,\pi r^2 = 2\pi \Rightarrow r^2 = \frac{2}{1800} = \frac{1}{900} \Rightarrow r = \sqrt{\frac{1}{900}} = \frac{1}{30}$.

145. Curved surface area of the roller

$= \left(2 \times \frac{22}{7} \times 0.7 \times 2\right)$ m^2 = 8.8 m^2.

$\therefore$ Area covered in 5 revolutions = (8.8 × 5) m^2 = 44 m^2.

146. Diagonal of the square $= \sqrt{2^2 + 2^2}$ m $= \sqrt{8}$ m $= 2\sqrt{2}$ m.

Diameter of circular pond = $2\sqrt{2}$ m. Radius of circular pond = $\sqrt{2}$ m.

Volume of circular pond $= \left[\pi \times (\sqrt{2})^2 \times 1\right]$ m^3 = (2π) m^3.

Volume of square pond = (2 × 2 × 1) m^3 = 4 m^3.

$\therefore$ Volume of earth to be removed = (2π – 4) m^3.

147. Volume of earth dug $= \left(\frac{22}{7} \times 2 \times 2 \times 56\right)$ m^3 = 704 m^3.

Volume of ditch = (48 × 16.5 × 4) m^3 = 3168 m^3.

$\therefore$ Required fraction $= \frac{704}{3168} = \frac{2}{9}$.

148. Volume of water flown into the tank
$= (50 \times 44 \times 0.07)\ m^3 = 154\ m^3$.
Volume of water flowing through the pipe in 1 hour
$= \left(\frac{22}{7} \times 0.07 \times 0.07 \times 5000\right) m^3 = 77 m^3$.
$\therefore$ Required time $= \left(\frac{154}{77}\right) = 2$ hrs.

149. Let the length of each side of the square base be x metres.
Then, $x^2 + x^2 = 3^2 \Rightarrow 2x^2 = 9$
$\Rightarrow x^2 = \frac{9}{2} \Rightarrow x = \frac{3}{\sqrt{2}}$.

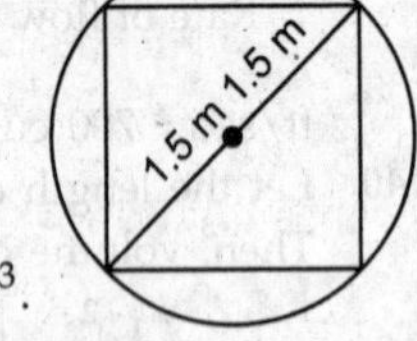

$\therefore$ Volume of parallelopiped
$= \left(\frac{3}{\sqrt{2}} \times \frac{3}{\sqrt{2}} \times 10\right) m^3 = \frac{90}{2} m^3 = 45\ m^3$.

150. Volume of rain water $= (600 \times 400 \times 1)\ cm^3 = 240000\ cm^3$.
Let the height of water in the cylindrical vessel be h cm.
Then, $\frac{22}{7} \times 20 \times 20 \times h = 240000 \Rightarrow h = \frac{240000 \times 7}{22 \times 20 \times 20} = \frac{2100}{11}$
$= 190.9$ cm ≈ 191 cm.

151. External radius, $R = \frac{25}{2}$ cm.
Internal radius, $r = \left(\frac{25}{2} - 1\right)$ cm $= \frac{23}{2}$ cm.
Length, $h = 20$ cm.
Whole surface area $= 2\pi Rh + 2\pi rh + 2\pi\ (R^2 - r^2) = 2\pi\ [(R + r)\ h + (R^2 - r^2)]$
$= 2 \times \frac{22}{7} \times \left[\left(\frac{25}{2} + \frac{23}{2}\right) \times 20 + \left(\frac{25}{2} + \frac{23}{2}\right)\left(\frac{25}{2} - \frac{23}{2}\right)\right]$
$= \left(2 \times \frac{22}{7} \times 504\right) cm^2 = 3168\ cm^2$.

152. Circumference of the girth $= 440$ cm.
$\therefore 2\pi R = 440 \Rightarrow R = \left(440 \times \frac{1}{2} \times \frac{7}{22}\right) = 70$ cm.
So, Outer radius $= 70$ cm.
Inner radius $= (70 - 4)$ cm $= 66$ cm.
Volume of iron $= \pi\ [(70)^2 - (66)^2] \times 63$
$= \left(\frac{22}{7} \times 136 \times 4 \times 63\right) cm^3 = 58752\ cm^3$.

153. Internal radius $= \left(\frac{11.2}{2}\right)$ cm $= 5.6$ cm,
External radius $= (5.6 + 0.4)$ cm $= 6$ cm.
Volume of metal
$= \left\{\frac{22}{7} \times [(6)^2 - (5.6)^2] \times 21\right\} cm^3 = (66 \times 11.6 \times 0.4)\ cm^3$
$= 306.24\ cm^3$.

154. External radius $= 6$ cm,
Internal radius $= (6 - 0.25)$ cm
$= 5.75$ cm.
Volume of material in hollow cylinder
$= \left\{\frac{22}{7} \times [(6)^2 - (5.75)^2] \times 15\right\} cm^3$
$= \left(\frac{22}{7} \times 11.75 \times 0.25 \times 15\right) cm^3$
$= \left(\frac{22}{7} \times \frac{1175}{100} \times \frac{25}{100} \times 15\right) cm^3 = \left(\frac{11 \times 705}{56}\right) cm^3$.
Let the length of solid cylinder be h. Then,
$\frac{22}{7} \times 1 \times 1 \times h = \left(\frac{11 \times 705}{56}\right) \Leftrightarrow h = \left(\frac{11 \times 705}{56} \times \frac{7}{22}\right)$ cm
$= 44.0625$ cm.

155. External radius $= 4$ cm, Internal radius $= 3$ cm.
Volume of iron
$= \left\{\frac{22}{7} \times [(4)^2 - (3)^2] \times 21\right\} cm^3 = \left(\frac{22}{7} \times 7 \times 1 \times 21\right) cm^3$
$= 462\ cm^3$.
$\therefore$ Weight of iron $= (462 \times 8)$ gm $= 3696$ gm $= 3.696$ kg.

156. Let the outer radius of the pipe be R cm.
Then, volume of metal used = External volume – Internal volume $= \pi R^2h - \pi r^2h = \pi h\ (R^2 - r^2)$
$= \frac{22}{7} \times 28 \times (R^2 - 8^2) = 88\ (R^2 - 64)$.
$\Rightarrow 88\ (R^2 - 64) = 1496 \Rightarrow R^2 - 64 = 17 \Rightarrow R^2 = 81$
$\Rightarrow R = 9$ cm.

157. Let the capacity of the cylindrical vessel be x litres.
Then, capacity of the cuboidal vessel $= (x + 20)$ litres.
$\therefore (x + 20) - 30 = 2(x - 30) \Rightarrow x - 10 = 2x - 60 \Rightarrow x = 50$.

158. Let the internal radius of the cylinder be x. Then,
$\frac{22}{7} \times r^2 \times 40 = \frac{616}{10} \Leftrightarrow r^2 = \left(\frac{616 \times 7}{10 \times 22 \times 40}\right) = 0.49$
$\Leftrightarrow r = 0.7$.
So, internal radius $= 0.7$ cm $= 7$ mm.
$\therefore$ Thickness $= (8 - 7)$ mm $= 1$ mm.

160. $\frac{\text{Volume of cone}}{\text{Volume of cylinder}} = \frac{\frac{1}{3} \times \pi \times (3)^2 \times 5}{\pi \times (2)^2 \times 4} = \frac{45}{48} = \frac{15}{16}$.

161. Volume of water $= \left(\frac{1}{3} \times \frac{22}{7} \times 8 \times 8 \times 21\right) cm^3 = 1408\ cm^3$
$= \left(\frac{1408}{1000}\right)$ kg $= 1.408$ kg.

162. Radius, $r = 2$ cm. Height, $h = 4.8$ cm.
$\therefore$ Slant height, $l = \sqrt{r^2 + h^2} = \sqrt{2^2 + (4.8)^2}$ cm
$= \sqrt{4 + 23.04}$ cm $= \sqrt{27.04}$ cm $= 5.2$ cm.

163. $h = 84$ cm, $r = 35$ cm.
So, $l = \sqrt{r^2 + h^2} = \sqrt{(35)^2 + (84)^2} = \sqrt{8281}$ cm $= 91$ cm.
$\therefore$ Curved surface area
$= \pi rl = \left(\frac{22}{7} \times 35 \times 91\right) cm^2 = 10010\ cm^2$.

164. $h = 15$ cm, $r = 8$ cm. So, $l = \sqrt{r^2 + h^2} = \sqrt{8^2 + (15)^2} = 17$ cm.
$\therefore$ Curved surface area $= \pi rl = (\pi \times 8 \times 17)\ cm^2$
$= 136\pi\ cm^2$.

165. $h = 14$ cm, $r = 7$ cm. So, $l = \sqrt{(7)^2 + (14)^2} = \sqrt{245} = 7\sqrt{5}$ cm.
$\therefore$ Total surface area $= \pi rl + \pi r^2$
$= \left(\frac{22}{7} \times 7 \times 7\sqrt{5} + \frac{22}{7} \times 7 \times 7\right) cm^2$

$= [154(\sqrt{5}+1)]\text{ cm}^2 = (154 \times 3.236)\text{ cm}^2 = 498.35\text{ cm}^2.$

166. Clearly, we have $r = 3$ cm and $h = 4$ cm.

$\therefore$ Volume $= \frac{1}{3}\pi r^2 h = \left(\frac{1}{3} \times \pi \times 3^2 \times 4\right)\text{ cm}^3 = 12\pi\text{ cm}^3.$

167. $l = 10$ m, $h = 8$ m. So, $r = \sqrt{l^2 - h^2} = \sqrt{(10)^2 - 8^2} = 6$ m.

$\therefore$ Curved surface area $= \pi rl = (\pi \times 6 \times 10)\text{ m}^2 = 60\pi\text{ m}^2.$

168. $\frac{1}{3} \times \frac{22}{7} \times r^2 \times 24 = 1232 \Leftrightarrow r^2 = \left(\frac{1232 \times 7 \times 3}{22 \times 24}\right) = 49$

$\Leftrightarrow r = 7.$

Now, $r = 7$ cm, $h = 24$ cm. So, $l = \sqrt{(7)^2 + (24)^2} = 25$ cm.

$\therefore$ Curved surface area $= \left(\frac{22}{7} \times 7 \times 25\right)\text{ cm}^2 = 550\text{ cm}^2.$

169. Let radius of base $= r$ and height $= h$.

Required floor area $= (4 \times 11)\text{ m}^2 = 44\text{ m}^2$. So, $\pi r^2 = 44$.

Required volume $= (20 \times 11)\text{ m}^3 = 220\text{ m}^3$.

So, $\frac{1}{3}\pi r^2 h = 220 \Rightarrow \frac{1}{3} \times 44 \times h = 220 \Rightarrow h = \frac{220 \times 3}{44} = 15$ m.

170. Let the radius of base be r ft. Then, $2\pi r = 10\pi$ or $r = 5$.

$l = \sqrt{r^2 + h^2} = \sqrt{5^2 + (12)^2} = \sqrt{169} = 13$ ft.

$\therefore$ Area of cloth $= \pi rl = (\pi \times 5 \times 13)$ sq ft $= 65\pi$ sq ft.

171. Let the radius of the base be r km. Then,

$\pi r^2 = 1.54 \Rightarrow r^2 = \left(\frac{1.54 \times 7}{22}\right) = 0.49 \Rightarrow r = 0.7$ km.

Now, $l = 2.5$ km, $r = 0.7$ km.

$\therefore h = \sqrt{(2.5)^2 - (0.7)^2}\text{ km} = \sqrt{6.25 - 0.49}\text{ km} = \sqrt{5.76}\text{ km}$

$= 2.4$ km.

So, height of the mountain $= 2.4$ km.

172. $\pi r^2 = 3850 \Rightarrow r^2 = \left(\frac{3850 \times 7}{22}\right) = 1225 \Rightarrow r = 35.$

Now, $r = 35$ cm, $h = 84$ cm.

So, $l = \sqrt{(35)^2 + (84)^2} = \sqrt{1225 + 7056} = \sqrt{8281} = 91$ cm.

$\therefore$ Curved surface area $= \left(\frac{22}{7} \times 35 \times 91\right)\text{ cm}^2 = 10010\text{ cm}^2.$

173. $\frac{22}{7} \times 70 \times l = 40040 \Rightarrow l = \left(\frac{40040 \times 7}{22 \times 70}\right) = 182.$

Now, $l = 182$ cm, $r = 70$ cm.

So, $h = \sqrt{(182)^2 - (70)^2} = \sqrt{252 \times 112} = 168$ cm.

$\therefore$ Volume $= \left(\frac{1}{3} \times \frac{22}{7} \times 70 \times 70 \times 168\right)\text{ cm}^3 = 862400\text{ cm}^3.$

174. Let the radius and height of the cone be $3x$ and $4x$ respectively. Then,

$\frac{1}{3} \times \frac{22}{7} \times (3x)^2 \times 4x = \frac{2112}{7} \Leftrightarrow \frac{264}{7}x^3 = \frac{2112}{7} \Leftrightarrow x^3 = \frac{2112}{64} = 8$

$\Leftrightarrow x = 2.$

$\therefore$ Radius $= 6$ cm, Height $= 8$ cm. Slant height

$= \sqrt{6^2 + 8^2}\text{ cm} = \sqrt{100}\text{ cm} = 10\text{cm}.$

175. Let the radius and height of the cone be r and h respectively.

Then, $V = \frac{1}{3}\pi r^2 h.$

Now, $\Delta AOB \sim \Delta COD$.

So, $\frac{OA}{OC} = \frac{AB}{CD} \Rightarrow \frac{h}{h/2} = \frac{r}{CD} \Rightarrow CD = \frac{r}{2}.$

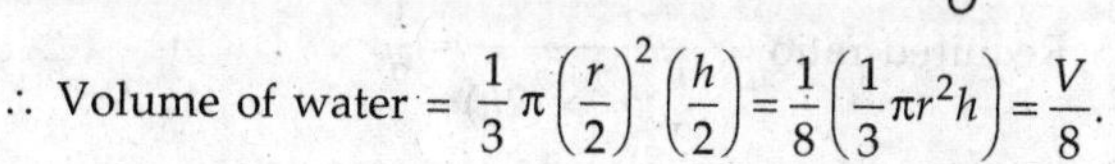

$\therefore$ Volume of water $= \frac{1}{3}\pi\left(\frac{r}{2}\right)^2\left(\frac{h}{2}\right) = \frac{1}{8}\left(\frac{1}{3}\pi r^2 h\right) = \frac{V}{8}.$

176. Slant height of the cup, l = Radius of sheet = 14 cm.

Circumference of the base = Circumference of the paper sheet $= \left(\frac{22}{7} \times 14\right)$ cm $= 44$ cm.

Let the radius of the base of the cone be r cm.

$\therefore 2\pi r = 44 \Rightarrow r = \frac{44 \times 7}{2 \times 22} = 7.$

Height, $h =$

$\sqrt{l^2 - r^2} = \sqrt{(14)^2 - 7^2} = \sqrt{147} = 7\sqrt{3}$ cm $= 12.12$ cm.

177. $\pi r^2 = 346.5 \Rightarrow r^2 = \left(346.5 \times \frac{7}{22}\right) = \frac{441}{4} \Rightarrow r = \frac{21}{2}.$

$\therefore l = \sqrt{r^2 + h^2} = \sqrt{\frac{441}{4} + (14)^2} = \sqrt{\frac{1225}{4}} = \frac{35}{2}.$

So, area of canvas needed =

$\pi rl = \left(\frac{22}{7} \times \frac{21}{2} \times \frac{35}{2}\right)\text{ m}^2 = \left(\frac{33 \times 35}{2}\right)\text{ m}^2.$

$\therefore$ Length of canvas $= \left(\frac{33 \times 35}{2 \times 1.1}\right)$ m $= 525$ m.

178. Let the original radius and height of the cone be r and h respectively.

Then, new radius $= 3r$ and new height $= 2h$.

$\therefore \frac{\text{New volume}}{\text{Original volume}} = \frac{\frac{1}{3} \times \pi \times (3r)^2 \times 3h}{\frac{1}{3} \times \pi \times r^2 \times h} = \frac{18}{1}.$

179. Let the original radius and height of the cone be r and h respectively.

Then, Original volume $= \frac{1}{3}\pi r^2 h.$

New radius $= \frac{120}{100} r = \frac{6}{5} r$, New height $= \frac{6}{5} h.$

New volume $= \frac{1}{3}\pi \times \left(\frac{6}{5} r\right)^2 \times \left(\frac{6}{5} h\right) = \frac{216}{125} \times \frac{1}{3}\pi r^2 h.$

Increase in volume $= \frac{91}{125} \times \frac{1}{3}\pi r^2 h.$

$\therefore$ Increase % $= \left(\frac{\frac{91}{125} \times \frac{1}{3}\pi r^2 h}{\frac{1}{3}\pi r^2 h} \times 100\right)\% = 72.8\%.$

180. Let the original radius and height of the cone be r and h respectively.

Then, original volume $= \frac{1}{3}\pi r^2 h.$

New radius = $\frac{r}{2}$ and new height = $3h$.

New volume = $\frac{1}{3} \times \pi \times \left(\frac{r}{2}\right)^2 \times 3h = \frac{3}{4} \times \frac{1}{3} \pi r^2 h.$

$\therefore$ Decrease % = $\left(\frac{\frac{1}{4} \times \frac{1}{3} \pi r^2 h}{\frac{1}{3} \pi r^2 h} \times 100 \right) \% = 25\%.$

181. Required ratio = $\frac{\frac{1}{3} \pi r^2 h}{\frac{1}{3} \pi r^2 \times (2h)} = \frac{1}{2}.$

182. Volume of the cone, $v = \frac{1}{3} \pi r^2 h.$

Curved surface area, $c = \pi r l = \pi r \sqrt{r^2 + h^2}$

$\Rightarrow c^2 = \pi^2 r^2 (r^2 + h^2).$

$\therefore 3\pi v h^3 - c^2 h^2 + 9v^2$

$= 3\pi \times \frac{1}{3} \pi r^2 h \times h^3 - \pi^2 r^2 (r^2 + h^2) h^2 + 9 \times \frac{1}{9} \pi^2 r^4 h^2$

$= \pi^2 r^2 h^4 - \pi^2 r^4 h^2 - \pi^2 r^2 h^4 + \pi^2 r^4 h^2 = 0.$

183. Let the heights of two cones be $7x$ and $3x$ and their radii be $6y$ and $7y$ respectively. Then,

Ratio of volumes = $\frac{\frac{1}{3} \pi \times (6y)^2 \times 7x}{\frac{1}{3} \pi \times (7y)^2 \times 3x} = \frac{36 \times 7}{49 \times 3} = \frac{12}{7}.$

184. Let their radii be $2x$, x and their heights be h and H respectively. Then,

$\frac{1}{3} \times \pi \times (2x)^2 \times h = \frac{1}{3} \times \pi \times x^2 \times H$ or $\frac{h}{H} = \frac{1}{4}.$

185. Let their radii be x and $2x$, and their heights be h and H respectively. Then,

$\frac{\frac{1}{3} \times \pi \times x^2 \times h}{\frac{1}{3} \times \pi \times (2x)^2 \times H} = \frac{2}{3}$ or $\frac{h}{H} = \frac{2}{3} \times 4 = \frac{8}{3}.$

186. Volume of the largest cone

= Volume of the cone with diameter of base 9 cm and height 9 cm.

$= \left(\frac{1}{3} \times \frac{22}{7} \times 4.5 \times 4.5 \times 9\right) \text{cm}^3 \left(\frac{1336.5}{7}\right) \text{cm}^3 = 190.93 \text{ cm}^3$

187. Volume of the block = $(10 \times 5 \times 2)$ cm³ = 100 cm³.

Volume of the cone carved out = $\left(\frac{1}{3} \times \frac{22}{7} \times 3 \times 3 \times 7\right) \text{cm}^3 = 66 \text{ cm}^3.$

$\therefore$ Wood wasted = $(100 - 66)\% = 34\%.$

188. Let their radius and height be $5x$ and $12x$ respectively.

Slant height of the cone, $l = \sqrt{(5x)^2 + (12x)^2} = 13x.$

$\frac{\text{Total surface area of cylinder}}{\text{Total surface area of cone}} = \frac{2\pi r (h + r)}{\pi r (l + r)} = \frac{2(h + r)}{(l + r)}$

$= \frac{2 \times (12x + 5x)}{(13x + 5x)} = \frac{34x}{18x} = \frac{17}{9}.$

189. Total surface area of the remaining solid = Curved surface area of the cylinder

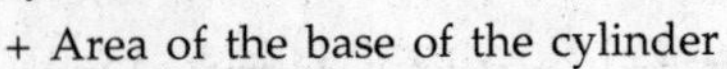

+ Area of the base of the cylinder

+ Curved surface area of the cone

$= 2\pi r h + \pi r^2 + \pi r \sqrt{r^2 + h^2}$

$= 2\pi \times 8 \times 15 + \pi \times 8^2 + \pi \times 8 \times \sqrt{8^2 + (15)^2}$

$= 240\pi + 64\pi + 136\pi = 440\pi$ sq. cm.

190. Let the height of the cone be h cm.

Then, $\pi \times r^2 \times 6 = \frac{1}{3} \times \pi \times r^2 \times h \Rightarrow h = 18$ cm.

191. Let the radius of the cone be r cm.

Then, $\pi \times 8^2 \times 2 = \frac{1}{3} \times \pi \times r^2 \times 6 \Rightarrow r = 8.$

Slant height, $l = \sqrt{r^2 + h^2} = \sqrt{8^2 + 6^2} = \sqrt{100} \text{ cm} = 10 \text{ cm}.$

Curved surface area of cone = $\pi r l = (3.14 \times 8 \times 10)$ cm² = 251.2 cm²

192. Let radius of each be r and height of each be h.

Then, number of cones needed

$= \frac{\text{Volume of cylinder}}{\text{Volume of 1 cone}} = \frac{\pi r^2 h}{\frac{1}{3} \pi r^2 h} = 3.$

193. Volume of cylinder = $(\pi \times 3 \times 3 \times 5)$ cm³ = 45π cm³.

Volume of 1 cone = $\left(\frac{1}{3} \pi \times \frac{1}{10} \times \frac{1}{10} \times 1\right) \text{cm}^3 = \frac{\pi}{300} \text{cm}^3.$

$\therefore$ Number of cones = $\left(45\pi \times \frac{300}{\pi}\right) = 13500.$

194. Volume of cylinder = $\left(\pi \times \frac{35}{2} \times \frac{35}{2} \times 32\right) \text{cm}^3 = 9800\,\pi \text{cm}^3.$

Volume of 1 cone = $\left(\frac{1}{3} \times \pi \times 2 \times 2 \times 7\right) \text{cm}^3 = \frac{28\pi}{3} \text{cm}^3.$

$\therefore$ Number of persons that can be served

$= \left(9800\pi \times \frac{3}{28\pi}\right) = 1050.$

195. Let the radius and height of the cone and the cylinder be $4x$ and $3x$ respectively.

Then, total surface area of cylinder

$= [2\pi (4x)(4x + 3x)]$ sq. units $= (8\pi x . 7x)$ sq. units.

$= (56\,\pi\, x^2)$ sq. units.

Slant height of cone, $l = \sqrt{(4x)^2 + (3x)^2} = \sqrt{25x^2} = 5x.$

Total surface area of cone = $\pi r (l + r) = \pi . 4x\ (5x + 4x)$

$= (36\pi\, x^2)$ sq. units

$\therefore$ Required ratio = $\frac{56\pi x^2}{36\pi x^2} = 14 : 9.$

196. Volume flown in conical vessel = $\frac{1}{3} \pi \times (20)^2 \times 24 = 3200\pi.$

Volume flown in 1 min. = $\left(\pi \times \frac{2.5}{10} \times \frac{2.5}{10} \times 1000\right) = 62.5\pi.$

$\therefore$ Time taken = $\left(\frac{3200\pi}{62.5\pi}\right) = 51$ min. 12 sec.

197. Volume of milk in conical flask = $\left(\frac{1}{3}\pi a^2 h\right)$ cm³.
Let the height of the milk in the cylindrical flask be x cm.
Then, volume of milk in cylindrical flask = $(\pi p^2 x)$ cm³.

$$\therefore \frac{1}{3}\pi a^2 h = \pi p^2 x \Rightarrow x = \frac{1}{3}\cdot\frac{\pi a^2 h}{\pi p^2} = \frac{a^2 h}{3p^2} \text{ cm.}$$

198. Slant height of the cone, $l = \sqrt{(12)^2 + (5)^2} = 13$ cm.
Lateral surface of the solid = Curved surface of cone + Curved surface of cylinder + Surface area of bottom
$= \pi rl + 2\pi rh + \pi r^2$, where h is the height of the cylinder

$$= \pi r\,(l + h + r) = \left[\frac{22}{7}\times 12\times(13+18+12)\right]\text{cm}^2$$

$$= \left(\frac{22}{7}\times 12\times 43\right)\text{cm}^2 = \left(\frac{11352}{7}\right)\text{cm}^2 = 1621\frac{5}{7}\text{ cm}^2.$$

199. Radius, $r = 12$ m.
Height of conical part, $h = (16 - 11)$ m = 5 m.
Slant height of conical part,
$l = \sqrt{r^2 + h^2} = \sqrt{(12)^2 + 5^2} = \sqrt{169} = 13$ m.
Height of cylindrical part, $H = 11$ m.
Area of canvas required = Curved surface area of cylinder + Curved surface area of cone
$= 2\pi rH + \pi rl$

$$= \left[\frac{22}{7}(2\times 12\times 11 + 12\times 13)\right]\text{m}^2$$

$$= \left[\frac{22}{7}(264+156)\right]\text{m}^2 = \left(\frac{22}{7}\times 420\right)\text{m}^2 = 1320 \text{ m}^2.$$

200. Let the radius and height of the tank be r and h respectively.
Then, $V = \pi r^2 h$.
$\therefore$ Volume of water in the tank = Vol. of cylinder − Vol. of cone

$$= \pi r^2 h - \frac{1}{3}\pi r^2 h = \frac{2}{3}\pi r^2 h = \frac{2}{3}V.$$

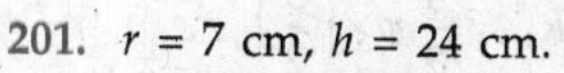

201. $r = 7$ cm, $h = 24$ cm.
Now, $\Delta AOB \sim \Delta COD$.

$$\text{So, } \frac{OA}{OC} = \frac{AB}{CD} \Rightarrow \frac{h}{h/2} = \frac{r}{CD} \Rightarrow CD = \frac{r}{2}.$$

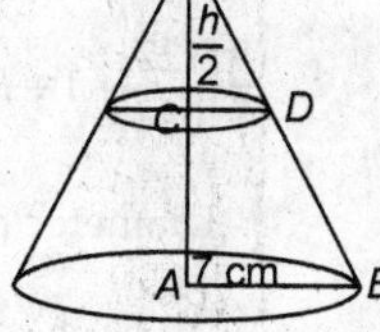

$\therefore$ Volume of upper portion

$$= \frac{1}{3}\pi\left(\frac{r}{2}\right)^2\left(\frac{h}{2}\right) = \left(\frac{1}{3}\times\frac{22}{7}\times\frac{7}{2}\times\frac{7}{2}\times 12\right)\text{cm}^3$$

$= 154$ cm³.

202. Let the radius and height of the cone be r and h respectively.
Then, $AB = r$, $OA = h$, $OC = \frac{h}{3}$.
Now, $\Delta AOB \sim \Delta COD$.

$$\therefore \frac{AB}{CD} = \frac{OA}{OC} \Rightarrow \frac{r}{CD} = \frac{h}{h/3} \Rightarrow CD = \frac{r}{3}.$$

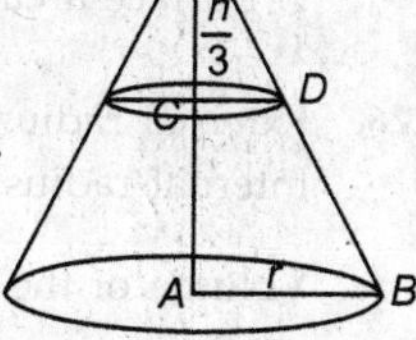

Volume of bigger cone = $\frac{1}{3}\pi r^2 h$.

Volume of smaller cone = $\frac{1}{3}\pi\left(\frac{r}{3}\right)^2\left(\frac{h}{3}\right) = \frac{1}{27}\left(\frac{1}{3}\pi r^2 h\right)$.

Volume of frustum = $\frac{1}{3}\pi r^2 h - \frac{1}{27}\left(\frac{1}{3}\pi r^2 h\right) = \frac{26}{27}\left(\frac{1}{3}\pi r^2 h\right)$.

Hence, required ratio = $\frac{1}{27}\left(\frac{1}{3}\pi r^2 h\right) : \frac{26}{27}\left(\frac{1}{3}\pi r^2 h\right) = 1 : 26.$

203. Volume of bucket = 28.490 litres = (28.490 × 1000) cm³ = 28490 cm³.
Let the height of the bucket be h cm.
We have : $r = 21$ cm, $R = 28$ cm.

$$\therefore \frac{\pi}{3}h\left[(28)^2 + (21)^2 + 28\times 21\right] = 28490$$

$$\Rightarrow h\,(784 + 441 + 588) = \frac{28490\times 21}{22}$$

$$\Rightarrow 1813\,h = 27195 \Rightarrow h = \frac{27195}{1813} = 15\text{cm}.$$

204. We have, $\Delta AOB \sim \Delta COD$.

$$\therefore \frac{AB}{CD} = \frac{OA}{OC} \Rightarrow \frac{5}{CD} = \frac{10}{5} \Rightarrow CD = \frac{5}{2}\text{cm}.$$

Curved surface area of the cone
$= \left[\pi\times 5\times\sqrt{5^2 + (10)^2}\right]\text{cm}^2$
$= 25\sqrt{5}\,\pi$ cm².

Curved surface area of the frustum

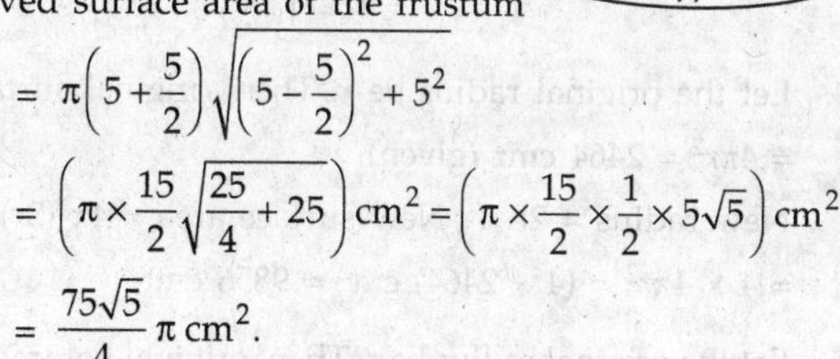

$$= \pi\left(5 + \frac{5}{2}\right)\sqrt{\left(5 - \frac{5}{2}\right)^2 + 5^2}$$

$$= \left(\pi\times\frac{15}{2}\sqrt{\frac{25}{4} + 25}\right)\text{cm}^2 = \left(\pi\times\frac{15}{2}\times\frac{1}{2}\times 5\sqrt{5}\right)\text{cm}^2$$

$$= \frac{75\sqrt{5}}{4}\pi\text{ cm}^2.$$

Hence, required ratio = $25\sqrt{5}\pi : \frac{75\sqrt{5}}{4}\pi = 4 : 3.$

205. Volume of sphere = $\left(\frac{4}{3}\pi r^3\right)$ cm³.
Volume of cylinder = $[\pi r^2.(2r)]$ cm³ = $(2\pi r^3)$ cm³.
Volume of cone = $\left[\frac{1}{3}\pi r^2\cdot(2r)\right]$ cm³ = $\left(\frac{2}{3}\pi r^3\right)$ cm³.
Clearly, cylinder has the greatest volume.

206. Volume of parallelopiped = (5 × 3 × 4) cm³ = 60 cm³.
Volume of cube = $(4)^3$ cm³ = 64 cm³.
Volume of cylinder = $\left(\frac{22}{7}\times 3\times 3\times 3\right)$ cm³ = 84.86 cm³.
Volume of sphere = $\left(\frac{4}{3}\times\frac{22}{7}\times 3\times 3\times 3\right)$ = 113.14 cm³.

207. $\frac{4}{3}\times\frac{22}{7}\times r^3 = \frac{45056}{21} \Rightarrow r^3 = \left(\frac{45056}{21}\times\frac{3}{4}\times\frac{7}{22}\right) = 512$

$$\Rightarrow r = \sqrt[3]{512} = 8 \text{ cm.}$$

208. $\frac{4}{3}\times\frac{22}{7}\times r^3 = 4851 \Rightarrow r^3 = \left(4851\times\frac{3}{4}\times\frac{7}{22}\right) = \left(\frac{21}{2}\right)^3$

$$\Rightarrow r = \frac{21}{2}.$$

$\therefore$ Curved surface area

$$= \left(4\times\frac{22}{7}\times\frac{21}{2}\times\frac{21}{2}\right)\text{cm}^2 = 1386 \text{ cm}^2.$$

209. $4\pi r^2 = 5544 \Rightarrow r^2 = \left(5544 \times \frac{1}{4} \times \frac{7}{22}\right) = 441 \Rightarrow r = 21.$

$\therefore$ Volume $= \left(\frac{4}{3} \times \frac{22}{7} \times 21 \times 21 \times 21\right) cm^3 = 38808 \ cm^3.$

210. Volume $= \frac{4}{3}\pi r^3 = \frac{r}{3}(4\pi r^2) = \frac{r}{3} \times$ Surface area.

211. Volume of the sphere $= \left[\frac{4}{3}\pi (10)^3\right] cm^3$. Surface area of the sphere $= [4\pi (10)^2] \ cm^2$.

$\therefore$ Required percentage $= \left[\frac{4\pi (10)^2}{\frac{4}{3}\pi (10)^3} \times 100\right]\% = 30\%.$

212. $\frac{\frac{4}{3}\pi r^3}{4\pi r^2} = 27 \Rightarrow r = 81$ cm.

213. Let the radii of the two spheres be r and $4r$ respectively.

Then, required ratio $= \frac{4\pi r^2}{4\pi (4r)^2} = \frac{r^2}{16r^2} = \frac{1}{16} = 1:16.$

214. Let the radii of the two spheres be $3r$ and $2r$ respectively.

Then, required ratio $= \frac{\frac{4}{3}\pi (3r)^3}{\frac{4}{3}\pi (2r)^3} = \frac{27}{8} = 27:8.$

215. Let the original radius be r. Then, original surface area $= 4\pi r^2 = 2464 \ cm^2$ (given).

New radius $= 2r$. $\therefore$ New surface area $= 4\pi (2r)^2$
$= 4 \times 4\pi r^2 = (4 \times 2464) \ cm^2 = 9856 \ cm^2.$

216. Let the original radius be r. Then, original volume $= \frac{4}{3}\pi r^3$.

New radius $= 2r$.

$\therefore$ New volume $= \frac{4}{3}\pi (2r)^3 = 8 \times \frac{4}{3}\pi r^3 = 8 \times$ original volume.

217. $4\pi (r+2)^2 - 4\pi r^2 = 352 \Leftrightarrow (r+2)^2 - r^2 = \left(352 \times \frac{7}{22} \times \frac{1}{4}\right) = 28.$

$\Leftrightarrow (r + 2 + r)(r + 2 - r) = 28 \Leftrightarrow 2r + 2 = 14$

$\Rightarrow r = \left(\frac{14}{2} - 1\right) = 6$ cm.

218. Let the correct radius be 100 cm.

Then, measured radius = 101.5 cm.

$\therefore$ Error in volume $= \frac{4}{3}\pi [(101.5)^3 - (100)^3] \ cm^3$

$= \frac{4}{3}\pi (1045678.375 - 1000000) \ cm^3$

$= \left(\frac{4}{3} \times \pi \times 45678.375\right) cm^3.$

$\therefore$ Error % $= \left\{\frac{\frac{4}{3}\pi (45678.375)}{\frac{4}{3}\pi (100 \times 100 \times 100)} \times 100\right\}\% = 4.56\%$

$= 4.6\%$ (app.).

219. Let their radii be R and r. Then,

$\frac{\frac{4}{3}\pi R^3}{\frac{4}{3}\pi r^3} = \frac{64}{27} \Rightarrow \left(\frac{R}{r}\right)^3 = \frac{64}{27} = \left(\frac{4}{3}\right)^3 \Rightarrow \frac{R}{r} = \frac{4}{3}.$

Ratio of surface areas $= \frac{4\pi R^2}{4\pi r^2} = \left(\frac{R}{r}\right)^2 = \left(\frac{4}{3}\right)^2 = \frac{16}{9}.$

220. Let their radii be R and r.

Then, $\frac{4\pi R^2}{4\pi r^2} = \frac{4}{25} \Rightarrow \left(\frac{R}{r}\right)^2 = \left(\frac{2}{5}\right)^2 \Rightarrow \frac{R}{r} = \frac{2}{5}.$

$\therefore$ Ratio of volumes $= \frac{\frac{4}{3}\pi R^3}{\frac{4}{3}\pi r^3} = \left(\frac{R}{r}\right)^3 = \left(\frac{2}{5}\right)^3 = \frac{8}{125}.$

221. $\frac{4}{3}\pi r^3 = 4\pi r^2 \Rightarrow r = 3.$

222. Volume of new sphere

$= \left[\frac{4}{3}\pi \times (6)^3 + \frac{4}{3}\pi \times (8)^3 + \frac{4}{3}\pi \times (10)^3\right] cm^3$

$= \left\{\frac{4}{3}\pi [(6)^3 + (8)^3 + (10)^3]\right\} cm^3$

$= \left(\frac{4}{3}\pi \times 1728\right) cm^3 = \left[\frac{4}{3}\pi \times (12)^3\right] cm^3.$

Let the radius of the new sphere be R.

Then, $\frac{4}{3}\pi R^3 = \frac{4}{3}\pi \times (12)^3 \Rightarrow R = 12$ cm.

$\therefore$ Diameter $= 2R = 24$ cm.

223. Volume of bigger sphere

$= \left[\frac{4}{3}\pi \times (8)^3\right] cm^3 = \left(\frac{4}{3}\pi \times 512\right) cm^3.$

Volume of 1 ball $= \left[\frac{4}{3}\pi \times (2)^3\right] cm^3 = \left(\frac{4}{3}\pi \times 8\right) cm^3.$

$\therefore$ Number of balls $= \frac{\frac{4}{3}\pi \times 512}{\frac{4}{3}\pi \times 8} = \frac{512}{8} = 64.$

224. Let the radius of the third ball be R cm. Then,

$\frac{4}{3}\pi \times \left(\frac{3}{4}\right)^3 + \frac{4}{3}\pi \times (1)^3 + \frac{4}{3}\pi \times R^3 = \frac{4}{3}\pi \times \left(\frac{3}{2}\right)^3$

$\Rightarrow \frac{27}{64} + 1 + R^3 = \frac{27}{8} \Rightarrow R^3 = \frac{125}{64} = \left(\frac{5}{4}\right)^3 \Rightarrow R = \frac{5}{4}.$

$\therefore$ Diameter of the third ball $= 2R = \frac{5}{2}$ cm $= 2.5$ cm.

225. Volume of each ball $= \frac{1}{8} \times \left(\frac{4}{3}\pi \times 10 \times 10 \times 10\right) cm^3.$

Let the radius of each ball be r cm.

Then, $\frac{4}{3}\pi r^3 = \frac{1}{8} \times \left(\frac{4}{3}\pi \times 10 \times 10 \times 10\right) \Rightarrow r^3 = \left(\frac{10}{2}\right)^3 = 5^3$

$\Rightarrow r = 5.$

$\therefore$ Surface area of each ball $= 4\pi r^2 = [4\pi \times (5)^2] \ cm^2 = (100 \ \pi) \ cm^2.$

226. External radius = 3 cm,
Internal radius = (3 – 0.5) cm = 2.5 cm.

Volume of the metal $= \left[\frac{4}{3} \times \frac{22}{7} \times \{(3)^3 - (2.5)^3\}\right] cm^3$

$= \left(\frac{4}{3} \times \frac{22}{7} \times \frac{91}{8}\right) cm^3 = \left(\frac{143}{3}\right) cm^3 = 47\frac{2}{3} \ cm^3.$

227. Volume of the solid = $(49 \times 33 \times 24)$ cm^3.
Let the radius of the sphere be r.

Then, $\frac{4}{3}\pi r^3 = (49 \times 33 \times 24) \Leftrightarrow r^3 = \left(\frac{49 \times 33 \times 24 \times 3 \times 7}{4 \times 22}\right)$

$= (21)^3 \Leftrightarrow r = 21.$

228. Number of bullets

$= \frac{\text{Volume of the cube}}{\text{Volume of 1 bullet}} = \left(\frac{22 \times 22 \times 22}{\frac{4}{3} \times \frac{22}{7} \times 1 \times 1 \times 1}\right) = 2541.$

229. Clearly, the largest sphere that can be carved out of a cube will have a diameter equal to the edge of the cube.

So, radius of the sphere $= \frac{6}{2} = 3$ cm.

$\therefore$ Volume of the sphere

$= \left(\frac{4}{3} \times \frac{22}{7} \times 3^3\right) \text{cm}^3 = \frac{792}{7} \text{cm}^3 = 113.14 \text{ cm}^3.$

230. Volume of each lead shot =

$\left[\frac{4}{3}\pi \times \left(\frac{0.3}{2}\right)^3\right] \text{cm}^3 = \left(\frac{4}{3} \times \frac{22}{7} \times \frac{27}{8000}\right) \text{cm}^3 = \frac{99}{7000} \text{cm}^3.$

$\therefore$ Number of lead shots $= \left(9 \times 11 \times 12 \times \frac{7000}{99}\right) = 84000.$

231. $4\pi R^2 = 6a^2 \Rightarrow \frac{R^2}{a^2} = \frac{3}{2\pi} \Rightarrow \frac{R}{a} = \frac{\sqrt{3}}{\sqrt{2\pi}}.$

$\frac{\text{Volume of sphere}}{\text{Volume of cube}} = \frac{\frac{4}{3}\pi R^3}{a^3} = \frac{4}{3}\pi \cdot \left(\frac{R}{a}\right)^3 = \frac{4}{3}\pi \cdot \frac{3\sqrt{3}}{2\pi\sqrt{2\pi}}$

$= \frac{2\sqrt{3}}{\sqrt{2\pi}} = \frac{\sqrt{12}}{\sqrt{2\pi}} = \frac{\sqrt{6}}{\sqrt{\pi}}$

232. Let the edge of the cube be a.
Then, volume of the cube = a^3.
Radius of the sphere = $(a/2)$.

Volume of the sphere $= \frac{4}{3}\pi\left(\frac{a}{2}\right)^3 = \frac{\pi a^3}{6}.$

$\therefore$ Required ratio $= a^3 : \frac{\pi a^3}{6} = 6 : \pi.$

233. Clearly, the diagonal of the largest possible cube will be equal to the diameter of the sphere.
Let the edge of the cube be a.

$\sqrt{3}a = 2r \Rightarrow a = \frac{2}{\sqrt{3}}r. \quad \therefore$ Volume $= a^3 = \left(\frac{2}{\sqrt{3}}r\right)^3 = \frac{8}{3\sqrt{3}}r^3.$

234. Let the radius of the sphere and that of the right circular cylinder be r.
Then, volume of the cylinder = $\pi r^2 h$.

Volume of the sphere $= \frac{4}{3}\pi r^3.$

$\therefore \pi r^2 h = \frac{4}{3}\pi r^3 \Rightarrow 3h = 4r \Rightarrow 3h = 2d \Rightarrow \frac{h}{2} = \frac{d}{3}.$

235. $4\pi R^2 = 2\pi \times 6 \times 12 \Rightarrow R^2 = \left(\frac{6 \times 12}{2}\right) = 36 \Rightarrow R = 6$ cm.

236. Let the radius of the cylinder be R.

Then, $\pi \times R^2 \times \frac{7}{3} = \frac{4}{3}\pi \times 7 \times 7 \times 7 \Rightarrow R^2$

$= \left(\frac{4 \times 7 \times 7 \times 7}{3} \times \frac{3}{7}\right) = 196 = (14)^2 \Rightarrow R = 14$ cm.

$\therefore$ Diameter = $2R$ = 28 cm.

237. Volume of the sphere = Volume of the cylinder

$\Rightarrow \frac{4}{3}\pi r^3 = \pi R^2 \cdot 2r \Rightarrow 2r^2 = 3R^2 \Rightarrow R^2 = \frac{2r^2}{3} \Rightarrow R = r\sqrt{\frac{2}{3}}.$

238. Let the radius of the cylinder be r. Then, radius of the sphere = $2r$.

$\frac{\text{Volume of cylinder}}{\text{Volume of sphere}} = \frac{3}{2} \Rightarrow \frac{\pi r^2 h}{\frac{4}{3}\pi(2r)^3} = \frac{3}{2} \Rightarrow \frac{h}{r} = 16 \Rightarrow h = 16r.$

$\therefore$ Required ratio $= \frac{\text{Total suface area of cylinder}}{\text{surface area of sphere}}$

$= \frac{2\pi r \cdot (16r) + 2\pi r^2}{4\pi(2r)^2} = \frac{34\pi r^2}{16\pi r^2} = \frac{17}{8}.$

239. Required volume = Volume of a sphere of radius 1 cm

$= \left(\frac{4}{3}\pi \times 1 \times 1 \times 1\right) \text{cm}^3 = \frac{4}{3}\pi \text{ cm}^3.$

240. Volume of cylinder = $\pi \times (3)^2 \times 15 = 135\pi$ cm^3.

Radius of 1 bullet $= \frac{5}{2}$ mm $= \frac{5}{20}$ cm $= \frac{1}{4}$ cm.

Volume of 1 bullet $= \left(\frac{4}{3}\pi \times \frac{1}{4} \times \frac{1}{4} \times \frac{1}{4}\right) \text{cm}^3 = \frac{\pi}{48} \text{cm}^3.$

$\therefore$ Number of bullets $= \left(135\pi \times \frac{48}{\pi}\right) = 6480.$

241. Let the radius of the cylindrical rod be r.
Then, height of the rod = $8r$ and radius of one ball $= \frac{r}{2}$.

$\therefore$ Number of balls $= \frac{\pi \times r^2 \times 8r}{\frac{4}{3}\pi \times \left(\frac{r}{2}\right)^3} = \left(\frac{8 \times 8 \times 3}{4}\right) = 48.$

242. Let the radius of the sphere be r cm. Then,

$\frac{4}{3}\pi r^3 = \pi \times (0.1)^2 \times 3600 \Rightarrow r^3 = 36 \times \frac{3}{4} = 27 \Rightarrow r = 3$ cm.

243. Let the length of the wire be h. Then,

$\pi \times \frac{3}{20} \times \frac{3}{20} \times h = \frac{4}{3}\pi \times 4 \times 4 \times 4$

$\Leftrightarrow h = \left(\frac{4 \times 4 \times 4 \times 4 \times 20 \times 20}{3 \times 3 \times 3}\right) \text{cm} = \left(\frac{102400}{27}\right) \text{cm}$

= 3792.5 cm = 37.9 m.

244. Let the rise in the water level be h cm.
Then,
$\pi \times 4 \times 4 \times h = \frac{4}{3}\pi \times 3 \times 3 \times 3 \Rightarrow h = \left(\frac{3 \times 3}{4}\right) = \frac{9}{4}$ cm.

245. Let the radius of the sphere be r. 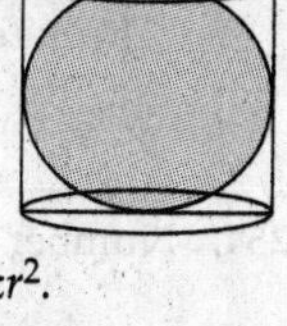
Then, radius of the cylinder = r.
height of the cylinder = $2r$.
Surface area of sphere = $4\pi r^2$.
Surface area of the cylinder = $2\pi r\,(2r) = 4\pi r^2$.
$\therefore$ Required ratio = $4\pi r^2 : 4\pi r^2 = 1 : 1$.

246. Let the radius of each sphere be r cm.

Then, Volume of 12 spheres = Volume of cylinder

$\Rightarrow 12\times\frac{4}{3}\pi\times r^3 = \pi\times8\times8\times2 \Rightarrow r^3 = \left(\frac{8\times8\times2\times3}{12\times4}\right)$

$\Rightarrow r = 2$ cm.

$\therefore$ Diameter of each sphere = $2r$ = 4 cm.

247. Let the radius of the ball be r cm.

Volume of ball = Volume of water displaced by it

$\therefore \frac{4}{3}\pi r^3 = \pi\times7\times7\times\frac{28}{3} \Rightarrow r^3 = 7^3 \Rightarrow r = 7$ cm.

248. Let the height of the cylinder be h cm.

Then, $\frac{4}{3}\pi[(4)^3 - (2)^3] = \pi\times4^2\times h$

$\Rightarrow \frac{4}{3}\times\pi\times56 = \pi\times16h \Rightarrow h = \frac{4\times56}{3\times16} = \frac{14}{3}$ cm.

249. Let the height of the cone be h cm.

Then, $\frac{1}{3}\pi\times8^2\times4 = \frac{4}{3}\pi\times8^3 \Rightarrow h = 32$ cm.

$\therefore$ Slant height, l =

$\sqrt{h^2 + r^2} = \sqrt{(32)^2 + 8^2} = \sqrt{1088} = 8\sqrt{17}$ cm.

250. Let the height of the cone be h cm.

Then, $\frac{4}{3}\pi\times5^3 = \frac{1}{3}\pi\times5^2\times h \Rightarrow h = 20$ cm.

251. Volume of sphere = $\left(\frac{4}{3}\pi\times6^3\right)$ cm^3 = $(288\,\pi)$ cm^3.

Volume of each cone = $\left(\frac{1}{3}\pi\times3^2\times4\right)$ cm^3 = (12π) cm^3.

$\therefore$ Number of cones = $\frac{288\pi}{12\pi} = 24$.

252. Volume of sphere

$= \left[\frac{4}{3}\pi\times(10.5)^3\right]$ cm^3 = $(4\pi\times10.5\times10.5\times3.5)$ cm^3.

Volume of each cone

$= \left[\frac{1}{3}\pi\times(3.5)^2\times3\right]$ cm^3 = $(\pi\times3.5\times3.5)$ cm^3.

$\therefore$ Number of cones formed = $\frac{4\pi\times10.5\times10.5\times3.5}{\pi\times3.5\times3.5} = 126$.

253. Volume of sphere = $\left(\frac{4}{3}\pi\times15\times15\times15\right)$ cm^3.

Volume of cone = $\left(\frac{1}{3}\pi\times15\times15\times15\right)$ cm^3.

Volume of wood wasted =

$\left[\left(\frac{4}{3}\pi\times15\times15\times15\right) - \left(\frac{1}{3}\pi\times15\times15\times15\right)\right]$ cm^3.

= $(\pi\times15\times15\times15)$ cm^3.

$\therefore$ Required percentage = $\left(\frac{\pi\times15\times15\times15}{\frac{4}{3}\pi\times15\times15\times15}\times100\right)\% = 75\%$.

254. Number of spheres = $\frac{\text{Volume of cone}}{\text{Volume of 1 sphere}}$

$= \frac{\frac{1}{3}\pi\times12\times12\times24}{\frac{4}{3}\pi\times2\times2\times2} = 108.$

255. Let radius = R and height = H.

Then, Ratio of their volumes

$= \pi R^2H : \frac{1}{3}\pi R^2H : \frac{4}{3}\pi R^3 = H : \frac{1}{3}H : \frac{4}{3}R$

$= H : \frac{1}{3}H : \frac{4}{3}\times\frac{H}{2} = 3:1:2.$ $\left[\text{In sphere, } H = 2R \text{ or } R = \frac{H}{2}\right]$

256. Volume of hemisphere = $\left(\frac{2}{3}\pi\times3\times3\times3\right)$ m^3 = (18π) m^3.

257. Total surface area = $3\pi R^2 = \left(3\times\frac{22}{7}\times7\times7\right)$ cm^2 = 462 cm^2.

258. Let the radius be R cm.

Then, $\frac{2}{3}\times\frac{22}{7}\times R^3 = 19404 \Leftrightarrow R^3 = \left(19404\times\frac{21}{44}\right) = (21)^3$

$\Leftrightarrow$ R = 21 cm.

259. Let the radius of the hemispherical bowl be r cm.

Then, $2\pi r = 176 \Rightarrow r = \frac{176\times7}{2\times22} = 28.$

Volume of liquid in the bowl = $\frac{1}{2}\times\left(\frac{2}{3}\times\pi\times28\times28\times28\right)$ cm^3

$= \left(\frac{2}{3}\times\pi\times14\times28\times28\right)$ cm^3.

Volume of 1 glass = $\left(\frac{2}{3}\times\pi\times2\times2\times2\right)$ cm^3.

$\therefore$ Required number of persons =

$\frac{\text{Volume of liquid in the bowl}}{\text{Volume of 1 glass}} = \left(\frac{14\times28\times28}{2\times2\times2}\right) = 1372.$

260. Let their radii be R and r. Then,

$\frac{\frac{2}{3}\pi R^3}{\frac{2}{3}\pi r^3} = \frac{6.4}{21.6} \Leftrightarrow \left(\frac{R}{r}\right)^3 = \frac{8}{27} = \left(\frac{2}{3}\right)^3 \Leftrightarrow \frac{R}{r} = \frac{2}{3}.$

$\therefore$ Ratio of curved surface areas = $\frac{2\pi R^2}{2\pi r^2} = \left(\frac{R}{r}\right)^2 = \frac{4}{9}.$

261. Internal radius = 4 cm; External radius = 4.5 cm.

Volume of steel used in making the bowl.

$= \left[\frac{2}{3}\times\frac{22}{7}\times\{(4.5)^3 - 4^3\}\right]$ cm^3 = $\left(\frac{2}{3}\times\frac{22}{7}\times27.125\right)$ cm^3

$= \left(\frac{2\times22\times3.875}{3}\right)$ cm^3 = $\left(\frac{170.5}{3}\right)$ cm^3 = 56.83 cm^3.

262. Internal radius, r = 4 cm; External radius, R = 5 cm.

Total surface area = $2\pi R^2 + 2\pi r^2 + \pi(R^2 - r^2)$

$= 3\pi R^2 + \pi r^2 = [\pi(3\times25 + 16)]$ cm^2.

$= \left(\frac{22}{7}\times91\right)$ cm^2 = 286 cm^2.

263. Volume of hemispherical bowl = $\left(\frac{2}{3}\times\pi\times12\times12\times12\right)$ cm^3.

Volume of 1 cylindrical container = $(\pi\times2\times2\times3)$ cm^3.

$\therefore$ Number of containers required = $\frac{2}{3}\times\frac{12\times12\times12}{2\times2\times3} = 96.$

264. Let the height of the vessel be x. Then, radius of the bowl $=$ radius of the vessel $= \frac{x}{2}$.

Volume of the bowl, $V_1 = \frac{2}{3}\pi\left(\frac{x}{2}\right)^3 = \frac{1}{12}\pi x^3$.

Volume of the vessel, $V_2 = \pi\left(\frac{x}{2}\right)^2 x = \frac{1}{4}\pi x^3$.

Since $V_2 > V_1$, so the vessel can contain 100% of the beverage filled in the bowl.

265. Let the height of the cylindrical part be h metres.

Volume of the tank = Volume of hemispherical part + Volume of cylindrical part

$= \left(\frac{2}{3}\times\pi\times 12\times 12\times 12 + \pi\times 12\times 12\times h\right)\text{m}^3$

$= \pi\,(1152 + 144\,h)\ \text{m}^3$

$\therefore \pi\,(1152 + 144\,h) = 3312\,\pi \Rightarrow 144\,h = 2160 \Rightarrow h = 15$ m.

So, ratio of surface areas $= \frac{2\pi r^2}{2\pi rh} = \frac{r}{h} = \frac{12}{15} = 4:5$.

266. Total visible surface area

= Curved surface area of cylinder + Curved surface area of hemisphere =

$\left[2\pi\times\frac{D}{2}\times H + 2\pi\times\left(\frac{D}{2}\right)^2\right]\text{m}^2 = \left(\pi DH + \frac{\pi D^2}{2}\right)\text{m}^2$

$= \left[\frac{\pi D}{2}(2H + D)\right]\text{m}^2.$

267. Let the radius of the hemisphere be r cm.

Then, radius of the cylinder = r cm.

height of the cylinder = r cm.

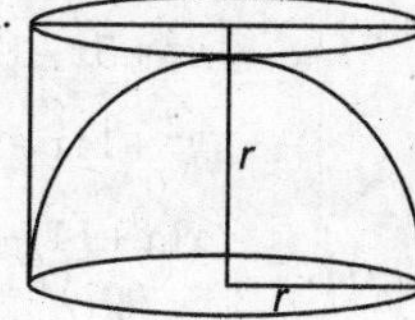

$\therefore$ Required ratio =

$\frac{\text{Volume of hemisphere}}{\text{Volume of cylinder}} = \frac{\frac{2}{3}\pi r^3}{\pi r^2\times r} = \frac{2}{3}.$

268. $\frac{2}{3}\pi R^3 = \frac{1}{3}\pi R^2 H \Rightarrow H = 2R.$

269. Let the radius of the cone be R cm.

Then, $\frac{1}{3}\pi\times R^2\times 75 = \frac{2}{3}\pi\times 6\times 6\times 6$

$\Leftrightarrow R^2 = \left(\frac{2\times 6\times 6\times 6}{75}\right) = \left(\frac{144}{25}\right) = \left(\frac{12}{5}\right)^2 \Leftrightarrow R = \frac{12}{5}\text{ cm} = 2.4\text{ cm}.$

270. Let the radius of each be R. Height of hemisphere, $H = R$.

So, height of cone = height of hemisphere = R.

Slant height of cone $= \sqrt{R^2 + R^2} = \sqrt{2}\,R$.

$\frac{\text{Curved surface area of hemisphere}}{\text{Curved surface area of cone}} = \frac{2\pi R^2}{\pi R\times\sqrt{2}\,R} = \sqrt{2}:1.$

271. Required ratio = Volume of cone : Volume of cylinder : Volume of hemisphere

$= \frac{1}{3}\pi r^2 r : \pi r^2 r : \frac{2}{3}\pi r^3 = \frac{1}{3}:1:\frac{2}{3} = 1:3:2.$

272. Total volume of the body

= Volume of the cylinder + Volume of the cone + Volume of the hemisphere

$= \pi r^2.r + \frac{1}{3}\pi r^2\cdot r + \frac{2}{3}\pi r^3 = 2\pi r^3 = 2\pi.\ (2)^3 = 16\pi.$

273. Surface area of the solid =

= Curved surface area of cone

+ Curved surface area of cylinder

+ Curved surface area of hemisphere

$= \left(\pi\times 7\times\sqrt{7^2 + (24)^2} + 2\pi\times 7\times 24 + 2\pi\times 7\times 7\right)\text{cm}^2$

$= (175\pi + 336\pi + 98\pi)\ \text{cm}^2 = (609\pi)\ \text{cm}^2.$

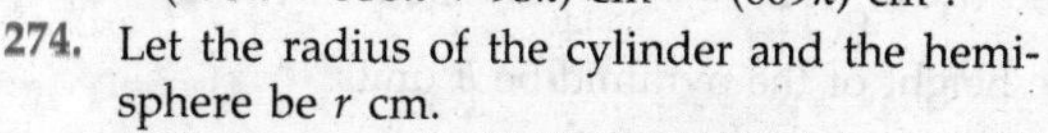

274. Let the radius of the cylinder and the hemisphere be r cm.

Diameter of the cylinder = $(2r)$ cm.

Height of the cylinder = $(4\times 2r)$ cm = $(8r)$ cm.

Total length of the solid = $(8r + r + r)$ cm = $(10r)$ cm.

$10r = 35 \Rightarrow r = 3.5$ cm.

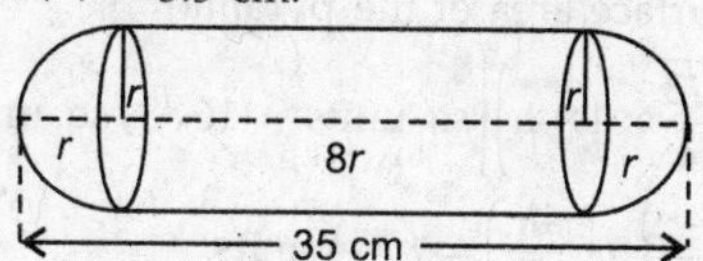

$\therefore$ Surface area of the solid

= Curved surface area of the cylinder + 2 × (curved surface area of the hemisphere)

$= \left(2\times\frac{22}{7}\times 3.5\times 28 + 2\times 2\times\frac{22}{7}\times 3.5\times 3.5\right)\text{cm}^2$

$= (616 + 154)\ \text{cm}^2 = 770\ \text{cm}^2.$

275. Volume of hemisphere $= \frac{2}{3}\pi r^3$.

Volume of biggest sphere = Volume of sphere with diameter $r = \frac{4}{3}\pi\left(\frac{r}{2}\right)^3 = \frac{1}{6}\pi r^3$.

$\therefore$ Required ratio $= \frac{\frac{2}{3}\pi r^3}{\frac{1}{6}\pi r^3} = \frac{4}{1}$ *i.e.* 4 : 1.

276. Volume of pyramid =

$\frac{1}{3}\times\text{area of base}\times\text{height} = \left(\frac{1}{3}\times 25\times 9\right)\text{cm}^3 = 75\ \text{cm}^3.$

277. Volume of pyramid $= \left(\frac{1}{3}\times 8^2\times 30\right)\text{cm}^3 = 640\ \text{cm}^3$.

or 640 CC

278. Area of the base $= \left(\frac{\sqrt{3}}{4}\times 1^2\right)\text{m}^2 = \frac{\sqrt{3}}{4}\text{m}^2.$

$\therefore$ Volume of pyramid $= \left(\frac{1}{3}\times\frac{\sqrt{3}}{4}\times 4\right)\text{m}^3 = \left(\frac{\sqrt{3}}{3}\right)\text{m}^3$

$= \left(\frac{1.732}{3}\right)\text{m}^3 = 0.577\ \text{m}^3.$

279. Area of hexagonal base $= \left[\frac{3\sqrt{3}}{2}\times(10)^2\right]\text{m}^2 = 150\sqrt{3}\ \text{m}^2.$

$\therefore$ Volume of pyramid $= \left(\frac{1}{3}\times 150\sqrt{3}\times 60\right)\text{m}^3 = 3000\sqrt{3}\ \text{m}^3$

$= (3000\times 1.732)\ \text{m}^3 = 5196\ \text{m}^3.$

280. Area of base $= \left(\frac{\sqrt{3}}{4}\times 1^2\right) m^2 = \frac{\sqrt{3}}{4} m^2.$

Clearly, the pyramid has 3 triangular faces each with sides 3 m, 3 m and 1 m.

So, area of each lateral face

$= \sqrt{\frac{7}{2}\times\left(\frac{7}{2}-3\right)\left(\frac{7}{2}-3\right)\left(\frac{7}{2}-1\right)} m^2 \quad \left[\because s = \frac{3+3+1}{2} = \frac{7}{2}\right].$

$= \sqrt{\frac{7}{2}\times\frac{1}{2}\times\frac{1}{2}\times\frac{5}{2}} m^2 = \frac{\sqrt{35}}{4} m^2.$

$\therefore$ Whole surface area of the pyramid

$= \left(\frac{\sqrt{3}}{4} + 3\times\frac{\sqrt{35}}{4}\right) m^2 = \frac{\sqrt{3}+3\sqrt{35}}{4} m^2.$

281. Let the height of the pyramid be h units.

Then, volume of the pyramid

$= \left[\frac{1}{3}\times\left(\frac{\sqrt{3}}{4}\times 4\times 4\right)\times h\right]$ cu. units $= \left(\frac{4h}{\sqrt{3}}\right)$ cu. units.

Whole surface area of the pyramid

$= \left[4\times\left(\frac{\sqrt{3}}{4}\times 4\times 4\right)\right]$ sq. units. $= (16\sqrt{3})$ sq. units

$\therefore 16\sqrt{3} = 3\times\left(\frac{4h}{\sqrt{3}}\right) \Rightarrow h = 4$ units.

282. Length of each edge of a regular tetrahedron $= 1$ cm

Volume of regular tetrahedron

$= \frac{a^3}{6\sqrt{2}}$ cm^3

$= \frac{1}{6\sqrt{2}} = \frac{\sqrt{2}}{6\sqrt{2}\times\sqrt{2}}$ cu.cm

$= \frac{\sqrt{2}}{12}$ cu.cm.

283.

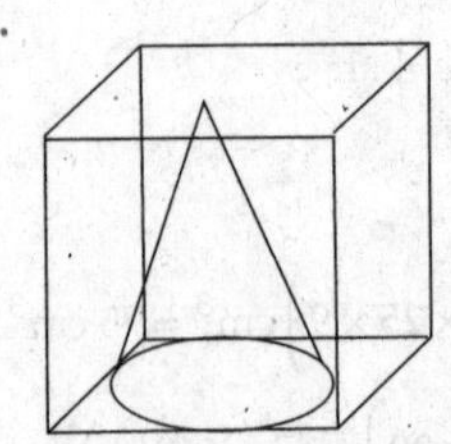

The volume of cone should be maximum.

$\therefore$ Radius of the base of cone

$= \frac{\text{Edge of cube}}{2} = \frac{4.2}{2} = 2.1$ dm.

Height of cone = Edge of cube = 4.2 dm.

$\therefore$ Volume of cone $= \frac{1}{3}\pi r^2 h$

$= \left(\frac{1}{3}\times\frac{22}{7}\times 2.1\times 2.1\times 4.2\right)$cu.dm.

$= 19.404$ cu.dm.

284. Let the length of base be $3a$ cm and breadth be $2a$ cm

Total surface area of prism

= [perimeter of base × height] + [2 × area of base]

$= [2(3a+2a)\times 12 + 2\times 3a\times 2a]$ sq. cm.

$= (120a + 12a^2)$ sq. cm.

According to the question,

$120a + 12a^2 = 288$

$\Rightarrow a^2 + 10a = 24$

$\Rightarrow a^2 + 10a - 24 = 0$

$\Rightarrow a^2 + 12a - 2a - 24 = 0$

$\Rightarrow a(a+12) - 2(a+12) = 0$

$\Rightarrow (a-2)(a+2) = 0$

$\Rightarrow a = 2$ because $a \neq -12$

$\therefore$ Volume of prism = Area of base × height

$= (3a\times 2a\times 12)$ cu. cm.

$= 72a^2 = (72\times 2\times 2)$ cu.cm.

$= 288$ cu.cm.

285. Let the height of the cylinder be x m.

Then, radius = $(x + 5)$m

Curved surface area of the cylinder = $2\pi rh$

Now, $2\pi(x+5)\times x = 792$

$2\times\frac{22}{7}\times(x^2+5x) = 792$

$x^2 + 5x = \frac{792\times 7}{44} = 126$

$\Rightarrow x^2 + 5x = 126$

$x^2 + 5x - 126 = 0$

$x^2 + 14x - 9x - 126 = 0$

$x(x+14) - 9(x+14) = 0$

$(x-9)(x+14) = 0$

$\therefore x = 9, -14$ (neglect negative value)

$\therefore$ Height of cylinder = 9m

$\therefore$ Radius of cylinder = 9 + 5 = 14m

Volume of cylinder = $\pi r^2 h$

$= \frac{22}{7}\times 14\times 14\times 9 = 5544 m^3$

286. Radius of base = r units

Curved surface area of a right cylinder = $4\pi rh$

Curved surface area of cylinder = $2\pi RH$

$\therefore$ According to the question, $2\pi rH = 4\pi rh$

$\Rightarrow$ Height of cylinder = $2h$ units

287. Radius of a hemispherical bowl = 3.5cm

Inner and outer surface areas of the bowl = $4\pi r^2$

$= 4\times\frac{22}{7}\times 3.5\times 3.5$

= 154 sq. cm.

Total cost of painting at the rate of ₹ 5 per 10 sq. cm.

$= 154\times\frac{5}{10}$ = ₹ 77

288. Volume of cylinder = $\pi r^2 h$

$\therefore$ Curved surface area of cylinder = $2\pi rh$

$\therefore \frac{\pi r^2 h}{2\pi rh} = \frac{616}{352}$

$\Rightarrow r = \frac{2 \times 616}{352} = 3.5$ m

$\therefore$ volume of cylinder = $\pi r^2 h$ = 616

$\Rightarrow \frac{22}{7} \times 3.5 \times 3.5 \times h = 616$

$\Rightarrow$ 11 × 3.5 × h = 616

$\Rightarrow h = \frac{616}{11 \times 3.5} = 16$

$\therefore$ Total surface area of the cylinder

$= 2\pi rh + 2\pi r^2$

$= 2\pi r(h + r)$

$= 2 \times \frac{22}{7} \times 3.5(16 + 3.5)$

$= 2 \times \frac{22}{7} \times 3.5(19.5)$

= 22 × 19.5 = 429 sq. m.

289. Radius of hemisphere bowl = 6cm

$\therefore$ Volume of hemisphere = $\frac{2}{3}\pi r^3 = \frac{2}{3} \times \frac{22}{7} \times 6 \times 6 \times 6$

$= \frac{9504}{21} = 452.57 \text{ cm}^3$

290. Let the side of cube = 10cm

$\therefore$ Original volume = 10 × 10 × 10 = 1000 cm^3

Now, side of new cube = 10 – 25% of 10 = 7.5cm

$\therefore$ New volume = 7.5 × 7.5 × 7.5 = 421.875cm^3

$\therefore$ Required Ratio = $\frac{1000}{421.875} = \frac{1000000}{421875} = \frac{64}{27}$ = 64 : 27

291.

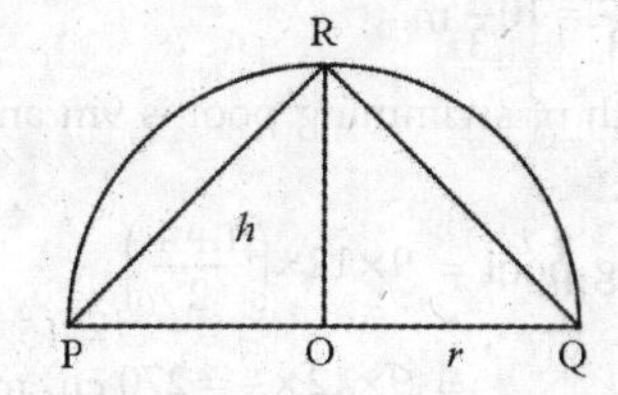

Let

OP = OQ = OR = r

$\therefore$ OR = h = r

$\therefore$ Curved surface area of the hemisphere = $2\pi r^2$

Curved surface area of a cone = πrl

Where $l = \sqrt{h^2 + r^2} = \sqrt{r^2 + r^2} = r\sqrt{2}$

$\therefore$ Required ratio = $\frac{2\pi r^2}{\pi rl} = \frac{2\pi r^2}{\pi r \cdot r\sqrt{2}}$

$= \frac{2}{\sqrt{2}} = \frac{2 \times \sqrt{2}}{\sqrt{2} \times \sqrt{2}} = \frac{2\sqrt{2}}{2} = \frac{\sqrt{2}}{2} = \frac{\sqrt{2}}{1} = \sqrt{2}:1$

292. Length of parallel sides of prism = 10cm and 6cm

Height of prism = 8cm

$\therefore$ Volume of prism = $\frac{1}{2}(10 + 6) \times 5 \times 8$

$= \frac{1}{2} \times 16 \times 5 \times 8 = 320 \text{ cm}^3$

293. Let the radius of the cylinder be r and height be h.

Then, $r + h = 19$ ....(i)

Again, total surface area of cylinder = ($2\pi rh + 2\pi r^2$)

Now, $2\pi r(h + r) = 1672$

Or, $2\pi r \times 19 = 1672$

Or $38\pi r = 1672$

$\therefore \pi r = \frac{1672}{38} = 44$ m

$\therefore r = \frac{44 \times 7}{22} = 14$

$\therefore$ Height = 19 – 14 = 5m

Volume of cylinder = $\pi r^2 h$

$= \frac{22}{7} \times 14 \times 14 \times 5$

= 22 × 2 × 14 × 5 = 3080m^3

294. Let radius of sphere be r cm.

$\therefore$ Volume of sphere = volume of cuboid

$\Rightarrow \frac{4}{3}\pi r^2 = L \times b \times h$

$\Rightarrow \frac{4}{3}\pi r^3 = 49 \times 33 \times 24$

$\Rightarrow \frac{4}{3} \times \frac{22}{7} \times r^3 = 49 \times 33 \times 24$

$\Rightarrow r^3 = \frac{49 \times 33 \times 24 \times 3 \times 7}{4 \times 22}$

$\Rightarrow r^3 = 9261$

$\therefore r = \sqrt[3]{9261} = \sqrt[3]{21 \times 21 \times 21} = 21$ cm.

295. Diameter of bowl = 7cm

$\therefore$ Radius of bowl = $\frac{2}{7}$ cm.

Height = 4cm

$\therefore$ Volume of cylindrical bowl = $\pi r^2 h$

$= \frac{22}{7} \times \frac{7}{2} \times \frac{7}{2} \times 4$ = 154 cu.cm

Hence, volume of soup for 250 patients = 154 × 250

= 38500 cm^3 = 38.5L.

296. Let the radius of the sphere be R and length of each side of the cube = a

Surface area of sphere = $4\pi R^2$

Surface area of a cube = $6a^2$

$\Rightarrow 4\pi r^2 = 6a^2$

$\Rightarrow \frac{R^2}{a^2} = \frac{6}{4\pi} = \frac{3}{2\pi}$

Radio of the square of the volumes

$= \frac{\left(\frac{4}{3}\pi R^3\right)^2}{(a^3)^2}$

$= \frac{16}{9}\left(\frac{\pi^2 \cdot R^6}{a^6}\right)$

$\Rightarrow \frac{16\pi^2}{9}\left(\frac{R^2}{a^2}\right)^3$

$= \frac{16}{9}\pi^2\left(\frac{3}{2\pi}\right)^3$

$= \frac{16}{9}\pi^2 \times \frac{27}{8\pi^3}$

$= \frac{16\times27}{9\times8\pi}$

$= \frac{6}{\pi} = 6:\pi$

297. Let the radius of cone and the sphere be R and the height of the cone be H.

Volume of sphere $= \frac{4}{3}\pi r^3$

Volume of cone $= \frac{1}{3}\pi r^2 h$

According to given information $= \frac{4}{3}\pi R^3 = 2\times\frac{1}{3}\pi R^2 H$

$\Rightarrow 4R = 2h$

$\Rightarrow \frac{H}{R} = \frac{4}{2} = 2:1$

298. Length of rectangle paper = circumference of the base of cylinder

If r is the radius of the cylinder $44 = 2\pi r$

$\Rightarrow r = \frac{44\times7}{2\times22} = 7$ cm.

299. Given Raddi of three metallic spheres be $r_1, r_2\ r_3$ are 6cm, 8cm and 10cm respectively.

Let the radius of the new sphere be R.

$\frac{4}{3}\pi R^3 = \frac{4}{3}\pi(r_1^3 + r_2^3 + r_3^3)$

$\frac{4}{3}\pi R^3 = \frac{4}{3}\pi(6^3 + 8^3 + 10^3)$

$R^3 = (216 + 512 + 1000) = 1728$

$\Rightarrow R = \sqrt[3]{12\times12\times12}$

$R = 12$

Diameter = 24cm

300. Let the radius of a right circular cone be R cm and height be H cm.

Volume of right circular cone $= \frac{1}{3}\pi R^2 H$ cu.cm.

When height of right circular cone is increased by 200% and radius of the base is reduced by 50%.

New volume $= \frac{1}{3}\pi\left(\frac{R}{2}\right)^2 \cdot 3H$

$= \frac{1}{3}\pi\frac{R^2 4}{4}\cdot 3H = \frac{\pi R^2 H}{4}$

Difference $= \pi R^2 H\left(\frac{1}{3} - \frac{1}{4}\right) = \frac{1}{12}\pi R^2 H$

Decrease percentage $= \frac{\frac{1}{12}\pi R^2 H}{\frac{1}{3}\pi R^2 H}\times100 = 25\%$

301. If R is the radius of sphere, volume of the sphere $= \frac{4}{3}\pi R^3$.

When radius of sphere is increased by 10%.

New volume $= \frac{4}{3}\pi(1.1R)^3$

$= \frac{4}{3}\pi R^3(1.331)$

Difference $= \frac{4}{3}\pi R^3(1.331) - \frac{4}{3}\pi R^3 = \frac{4}{3}\pi R^3(1.331 - 1)$

$= \frac{4}{3}\pi R^3(0.331)$

Increase% $= \frac{\frac{4}{3}\pi R^3(0.331)}{\frac{4}{3}\pi R^3}\times100 = 33.1\%$

302. Ball is dropped from the height of 36m when the ball will rise at the third bounce

Required height $= \frac{2}{3}\times\frac{2}{3}\times\frac{2}{3}\times36$

$= \frac{32}{3} = 10\frac{2}{3}$ m.

303. Given length of width of swimming pool is 9m and 12m respectively.

Volume of swimming pool $= 9\times12\times\left(\frac{1+4}{2}\right)$

$= 9\times12\times\frac{5}{2} = 270$ cu. meter.

304. Let Edge of third small cube be x cm

Volume of cube = (edge)^3

According to the question, $6^3 + 8^3 + x^3 = 12^3$

$\Rightarrow 216 + 512 + x^3 = 1728$

$x^3 = 1728 - 728 = 1000$

$\Rightarrow x = \sqrt[3]{1000} = 10$ cm

EXERCISE

(DATA SUFFICIENCY TYPE QUESTIONS)

Directions (*Questions 1 to 10*): ***Each of the questions given below consists of a statement and/or a question and two statements numbered I and II given below it. You have to decide whether the data provided in the statement(s) is/are sufficient to answer the given question. Read both the statements and***

Give answer (a) if the data in Statement I alone are sufficient to answer the question, while the data in Statement II alone are not sufficient to answer the question;

Give answer (b) if the data in Statement II alone are sufficient to answer the question, while the data in Statement I alone are not sufficient to answer the question;

Give answer (c) if the data either in Statement I or in Statement II alone are sufficient to answer the question;

Give answer (d) if the data even in both Statements I and II together are not sufficient to answer the question;

Give answer (e) if the data in both Statements I and II together are necessary to answer the question.

1. What is the weight of the iron beam?
   I. The beam is 9 m long, 40 cm wide and 20 cm high.
   II. Iron weighs 50 kg per cubic metre.
2. What is the volume of 32 metre high cylindrical tank?
   I. The area of its base is 154 m^2.
   II. The diameter of the base is 14 m.
3. What is the volume of a cube?
   I. The area of each face of the cube is 64 square metres.
   II. The length of one side of the cube is 8 metres.
4. How much cardboard will it take to make an open cubical box with no top?
   I. The area of the bottom of the box is 4 square meters.
   II. The volume of the box is 8 cubic metres.
5. What is the total cost of painting the inner surface of an open box at the rate of 50 paise per 100 sq. cm?
   I. The box is made of wood 3 cm thick.
   II. The external dimensions of the box are 50 cm, 40 cm and 23 cm.
6. What is the capacity of a cylindrical tank?
   I. Radius of the base is half of its height which is 28 metres.
   II. Area of the base is 616 sq. metres and its height is 28 metres.
7. What is the volume of the cylinder?
   I. Height is equal to the diameter.
   II. Perimeter of the base is 352 cm.
8. What will be the total cost of whitewashing the conical tomb at the rate of 80 paise per square metre?
   I. The diameter and the slant height of the tomb are 28 m and 50 m.
   II. The height of the tomb is 48 m and the area of its base is 616 sq. m.
9. What is the height of a circular cone?
   I. The area of that cone is equal to the area of a rectangle whose length is 33 cm.
   II. The area of the base of that cone is 154 sq. cm.
10. Is a given rectangular block, a cube?
    I. At least 2 faces of the rectangular block are squares.
    II. The volume of the block is 64.
11. A spherical ball of given radius x cm is melted and made into a right circular cylinder. What is the height of the cylinder?
    I. The volume of the cylinder is equal to the volume of the ball.
    II. The area of the base of the cylinder is given.
12. What is the ratio of the volume of the given right circular cone to the one obtained from it?
    I. The smaller cone is obtained by passing a plane parallel to the base and dividing the original height in the ratio 1 : 2.
    II. The height and the base of the new cone are one-third those of the original cone.

Directions (*Questions 13 to 16*): ***Each of the questions given below consists of a question followed by three statements. You have to study the question and the statements and decide which of the statement(s) is/are necessary to answer the question.***

13. What is the capacity of the cylindrical tank?
    I. The area of the base is 61,600 sq. cm.
    II. The height of the tank is 1.5 times the radius.
    III. The circumference of base is 880 cm.
    (*a*) Only I and II (*b*) Only II and III
    (*c*) Only I and III (*d*) Any two of the three
    (*e*) Only II and either I or III
14. What is the capacity of the cylindrical tank? **(Bank. P.O., 2008)**
    I. Radius of the base is half of its height.
    II. Area of the base is 616 square metres.
    III. Height of the cylinder is 28 metres.
    (*a*) Only I and II (*b*) Only II and III
    (*c*) Only I and III (*d*) All I, II and III
    (*e*) Any two of the three
15. A solid metallic cone is melted and recast into a sphere. What is the radius of the sphere?
    I. The radius of the base of the cone is 2.1 cm.
    II. The height of the cone is four times the radius of its base.
    III. The height of the cone is 8.4 cm.
    (*a*) Only I and II (*b*) Only II and III
    (*c*) Only I and III (*d*) Any two of the three
    (*e*) All I, II and III
16. What is the total surface area of the cone?
    I. The area of the base of the cone is 154 cm^2.
    II. The curved surface area of the cone is 550 cm^2.
    III. The volume of the cone is 1232 cm^3.
    (*a*) I, and either II or III (*b*) II, and either I or III
    (*c*) III, and either I or II (*d*) Any two of the three
    (*e*) None of these

ANSWERS

1. (e)	2. (c)	3. (c)	4. (c)	5. (e)	6. (c)	7. (e)	8. (c)	9. (d)	10. (d)
11. (b)	12. (c)	13. (e)	14. (e)	15. (d)	16. (a)				

SOLUTIONS

1. I. gives, $l = 9$ m, $b = \frac{40}{100}$ m $= \frac{2}{5}$ m and $h = \frac{20}{100}$ m $= \frac{1}{5}$ m.

This gives, volume
$= (l \times b \times h) = \left(9 \times \frac{2}{5} \times \frac{1}{5}\right) m^3 = \frac{18}{25} m^3.$

II. gives, weight of iron is 50 kg / m^3.

$\therefore$ Weight $= \left(\frac{18}{25} \times 50\right)$ kg $= 36$ kg.

Thus, both I and II are needed to get the answer.

$\therefore$ Correct answer is (e).

2. Given, height = 32 m.

I. gives, area of the base = 154 m^2.

$\therefore$ Volume = (area of the base × height)
$= (154 \times 32)\ m^3 = 4928\ m^3.$

Thus, I alone gives the answer.

II. gives, radius of the base = 7 m.

$\therefore$ Volume $= \pi r^2 h = \left(\frac{22}{7} \times 7 \times 7 \times 32\right) m^3 = 4928\ m^3.$

Thus, II alone gives the answer.

$\therefore$ Correct answer is (c).

3. Let each edge be a metres. Then,

I. $a^2 = 64 \Rightarrow a = 8$ m

$\Rightarrow$ Volume $= (8 \times 8 \times 8)\ m^3 = 512\ m^3.$

Thus, I alone gives the answer.

II. $a = 8$ m $\Rightarrow$ Volume $= (8 \times 8 \times 8)\ m^3 = 512\ m^3.$

Thus, II alone gives the answer.

$\therefore$ Correct answer is (c).

4. I. Let the length of each edge of the box be a metres. Then, $a^2 = 4 \Rightarrow a = 2$ m.

$\therefore$ Area of the cardboard needed
$= 5a^2 = (5 \times 2^2)\ m^2 = 20\ m^2.$

Thus, I alone gives the answer.

II. $a^3 = 8 \Rightarrow a = 2$ m.

$\therefore$ Required area $= 5a^2 = (5 \times 2^2)\ m^2 = 20\ m^2.$

Thus, II alone gives the answer. So, correct answer is (c).

5. I. gives, thickness of the wall of the box = 3 cm.

II. gives, Internal length = (50 – 6) cm = 44 cm,
Internal breadth = (40 – 6) = 34 cm,
Internal height = (23 – 3) cm = 20 cm.
Area to be painted = (area of 4 walls + area of floor) $= [2(l + b) \times h + (l \times b)]$
$= [2(44 + 34) \times 20 + (44 \times 34)]\ cm^2 = 4616\ cm^2.$

Cost of painting $= ₹\left(\frac{1}{2 \times 100} \times 4616\right) = ₹\ 23.08.$

Thus, both I and II are needed to get the answer.

$\therefore$ Correct answer is (e).

6. I. gives, $h = 28$ m and $r = 14$ cm.

$\therefore$ Capacity $= \pi r^2 h$, which can be obtained.

Thus, I alone gives the answer.

II. gives, $\pi r^2 = 616\ m^2$ and $h = 28$ m.

$\therefore$ Capacity $= (\pi r^2 \times h) = (616 \times 28)\ m^3.$

Thus, II alone gives the answer.

$\therefore$ Correct answer is (c).

7. I. gives, $h = 2r$.

II. gives, $2\pi r = 352 \Rightarrow r = \left(\frac{352}{2} \times \frac{7}{22}\right)$ cm $= 56$ cm.

From I and II, we have $r = 56$ cm,
$h = (2 \times 56)$ cm $= 112$ cm.

Thus, we can find the volume.

$\therefore$ Correct answer is (e).

8. I. gives, $r = 14$ m, $l = 50$ m.

$\therefore$ Curved surface $= \pi r l = \left(\frac{22}{7} \times 14 \times 50\right) m^2 = 2200\ m^2.$

Cost of whitewashing $= ₹\left(2200 \times \frac{80}{100}\right) = ₹\ 1760.$

Thus, I alone gives the answer.

II. gives, $h = 48$ m, $\pi r^2 = 616\ m^2$. These results give r and h and so l can be found out.

$\therefore$ Curved surface $= \pi r l$.

Thus, II alone gives the answer.

$\therefore$ Correct answer is (c).

9. II. gives the value of r.

But, in I, the breadth of rectangle is not given. So, we cannot find the surface area of the cone. Hence, the height of the cone cannot be determined.

$\therefore$ Correct answer is (d).

10. I. gives, any two of l, b, h are equal.

II. gives, $lbh = 64$.

From I and II, the values of l, b, h may be (1, 1, 64), (2, 2, 16), (4, 4, 4).

Thus, the block may be a cube or cuboid.

$\therefore$ Correct answer is (d).

11. Clearly, I is not needed, since it is evident from the given question.

From II, we get radius of the base of the cylinder.

Now, $\frac{4}{3}\pi x^3 = \pi r^2 h$ in which x and r are known.

$\therefore$ h can be determined.

$\therefore$ Correct answer is (*b*).

12. I. Let the radius and height of the bigger cone be r and h respectively and let its volume be V_1.

Then, radius of smaller cone $= \frac{r}{2}$. And, height of smaller cone $= \frac{h}{2}$.

Let the volume of the smaller cone be V_2. Then,

$$\frac{V_1}{V_2} = \frac{\frac{1}{3}\pi r^2 h}{\frac{1}{3}\pi\left(\frac{r}{2}\right)^2\left(\frac{h}{2}\right)} = \frac{8}{1}.$$

Thus, I alone gives the answer.

II. Let the radius and height of the bigger cone be r and h respectively and let its volume be V_1.

Then, radius of smaller cone $= \frac{r}{3}$. And, height of smaller cone $= \frac{h}{3}$.

Let the volume of the smaller cone be V_2. Then,

$$\frac{V_1}{V_2} = \frac{\frac{1}{3}\pi r^2 h}{\frac{1}{3}\pi\left(\frac{r}{3}\right)^2\left(\frac{h}{3}\right)} = \frac{27}{1}.$$

Thus, II alone gives the answer.

$\therefore$ Correct answer is (*c*).

13. Capacity $= \pi r^2 h$.

I. gives, $\pi r^2 = 61600$. This gives r.

II. gives, $h = 1.5\ r$.

Thus, I and II give the answer. Again,

III. gives $2\pi r = 880$. This gives r.

So, II and III also give the answer.

$\therefore$ Correct answer is (*e*).

14. I & II. $\pi r^2 = 616 \Rightarrow r^2 = \frac{616 \times 7}{22} = 196 \Rightarrow r = 14$ m.

So, $h = 28$ m.

$\therefore$ Capacity $= \left(\frac{22}{7} \times 14 \times 14 \times 28\right) m^3 = 17248\ m^3$.

II & III. $\pi r^2 = 616 \Rightarrow r = 14$ m. And, $h = 28$ m.

$\therefore$ Capacity $= \left(\frac{22}{7} \times 14 \times 14 \times 28\right) m^3 = 17248\ m^3$.

II & III. $h = 28$ m and $r = \frac{h}{2} = 14$ m.

$\therefore$ Capacity $= \left(\frac{22}{7} \times 14 \times 14 \times 28\right) m^3 = 17248\ m^3$.

Thus, any two of the three given statements are sufficient.

$\therefore$ Correct answer is (*e*).

15. $\frac{4}{3}\pi R^3 = \frac{1}{3}\pi r^2 h$.

Now r and h can be determined from any two of I, II and III. Thus, R can be calculated.

$\therefore$ Correct answer is (*d*).

16. Total surface area of the cone $= (\pi rl + \pi r^2)$ cm^2.

I. gives, $\pi r^2 = 154$. Thus, we can find r.

II. gives, $\pi rl = 550$.

From I and II we get the answer.

III. gives, $\frac{1}{3}\pi r^2 h = 1232$.

From I and III, we can find h and therefore, l. Hence the surface area can be determined.

$\therefore$ Correct answer is (*a*).

26 Races and Games of Skill

IMPORTANT FACTS

Race : *A contest of speed in running, riding, driving, sailing or rowing is called a race.*

Race Course : *The ground or path on which contests are made is called a race course.*

Starting Point : *The point from which a race begins is known as a starting point.*

Winning Point or Goal : *The point set to bound a race is called a winning point or a goal.*

Winner : *The person who first reaches the winning point is called a winner.*

Dead Heat Race : *If all the persons contesting a race reach the goal exactly at the same time, then the race is said to be a dead heat race.*

Start : Suppose A and B are two contestants in a race. If before the start of the race, A is at the starting point and B is ahead of A by 12 metres, then we say that 'A gives B, a start of 12 metres'.

To cover a race of 100 metres in this case, A will have to cover 100 metres while B will have to cover only (100 – 12) = 88 metres.

In a 100 m race, 'A can give B 12 m' or 'A can give B a start of 12 m' or 'A beats B by 12 m' means that while A runs 100 m, B runs (100 – 12) = 88 m.

Games : 'A game of 100, means that the person among the contestants who scores 100 points first is the winner'.

If A scores 100 points while B scores only 80 points, then we say that 'A can give B 20 points'.

SOLVED EXAMPLES

Ex. 1. ***In a km race, A beats B by 28 metres or 7 seconds. Then, find A's time over the course.***

Sol. Clearly, B covers 28 m in 7 seconds.

$\therefore$ B's time over the course $= \left(\frac{7}{28} \times 1000\right) \text{sec} = 250$ sec.

$\therefore$ A's time over the course

$= (250 - 7)$ sec $= 243$ sec $= 4$ min 3 sec.

Ex. 2. ***A runs $1\frac{3}{4}$ times as fast as B. If A gives B a start of 84 m, how far the winning post be so that A and B might reach it at the same time?***

Sol. $A : B = \frac{7}{4} : 1 = 7 : 4.$

Thus, in a race of 7 m, A gains 3 m over B.

3 m are gained by A in a race of 7 m.

84 m are gained by A in a race of $\left(\frac{7}{3} \times 84\right) \text{m} = 196 \text{m}.$

$\therefore$ Winning post must be 196 m away from the starting point.

Ex. 3. ***A can run 1 km in 3 min 10 sec and B can cover the same distance in 3 min 20 sec. By what distance can A beat B?*** **(Railways, 2005)**

Sol. A beats B by (200 – 190) sec = 10 sec.

Distance covered by B in 10 sec

$= \left(\frac{1000}{200} \times 10\right) \text{m} = 50 \text{m}.$

$\therefore$ A beats B by 50 m.

Ex. 4. ***In a 100 m race, A beats B by 25 m and B beats C by 4 m. In the same race, find the distance by which A beats C.***

Sol. $A : B = 100 : 75$ and $B : C = 100 : 96.$

$$\therefore A : C = \left(\frac{A}{B} \times \frac{B}{C}\right) = \left(\frac{100}{75} \times \frac{100}{96}\right) = \frac{100}{72} = 100 : 72.$$

A beats C by $(100 - 72)$ m = 28 m.

Ex. 5. ***In a 100 m race, A runs at 8 km per hour. If A gives B a start of 5 m and still beats him by 15 seconds, what is B's speed?***

Sol. Time taken by A to cover 100 m

$$= \left(\frac{60 \times 60}{8000} \times 100\right) \text{sec} = 45 \text{ sec}.$$

$\therefore$ B covers $(100 - 5)$ m

= 95 m in $(45 + 15)$ sec = 60 sec.

$$\therefore B\text{'s speed} = \left(\frac{95}{60}\right) \text{m/sec} = \left(\frac{95}{60} \times \frac{18}{5}\right) \text{km/hr} = \frac{57}{10} \text{km/hr} = 5.7 \text{ km/hr}.$$

Ex. 6. ***A, B and C are three contestants in a km race. If A can give B a start of 40 m and A can give C a start of 64 m, how many metres start can B give C?***

Sol. $A : B = 1000 : 960$ and $A : C = 1000 : 936.$

$$\frac{B}{C} = \left(\frac{B}{A} \times \frac{A}{C}\right) = \left(\frac{960}{1000} \times \frac{1000}{936}\right) = \frac{1000}{975} \Rightarrow B : C = 1000 : 975.$$

$\therefore$ B can give C a start of 25 m.

Ex. 7. ***In a 100 m race for children, A runs at 1.66 m/s. If A gives B a start of 4m and still beats him by 12 seconds, what is B's speed?*** **(C.P.O., 2007)**

Sol. Time taken by A to run 100 m

$$= \frac{100}{1.66} \text{sec} = \frac{100 \times 100}{166} \text{sec} = \frac{5000}{83} \text{sec}.$$

Time taken by B to run 96 m

$$= \left(\frac{5000}{83} + 12\right) \text{sec} = \frac{(5000 + 996)}{83} \text{sec} = \frac{5996}{83} \text{sec}.$$

B's speed

$$= \left(\frac{96 \times 83}{5996}\right) \text{m/sec} = \left(\frac{24 \times 83}{1499}\right) \text{m/s} = \frac{1992}{1499} \text{m/s}$$

= 1.328 m/s = 1.33 m/s.

Ex. 8. ***In a game of 80 points, A can give B 5 points and C 15 points. How many points B can give C in a game of 60?***

(*a*) 8 points (*b*) 10 points

(*c*) 20 points (*d*) 12 points

Sol. $A : B = 80 : 75$ and $A : C = 80 : 65$

$$\frac{B}{C} = \left(\frac{B}{A} \times \frac{A}{C}\right) = \left(\frac{75}{80} \times \frac{80}{65}\right) = \frac{15}{13} = \left(\frac{15 \times 4}{13 \times 4}\right) = \frac{60}{52}$$

$\Rightarrow B : C = 60 : 52.$

Hence, in a game of 60, B can give C 8 points.

EXERCISE
(OBJECTIVE TYPE QUESTIONS)

Directions: *Mark (√) against the correct answer in each of the following :*

1. In a 100 m race, *A* covers the whole distance in 36 seconds and *B* in 45 seconds. In this race, *A* beats *B* by
(*a*) 20 m (*b*) 25 m
(*c*) 22.5 m (*d*) 9 m

2. In a kilometre race, A beats B by 100 m and B beats C by 150 m. In the same race, by how many metres does A beat C? (M.B.A., 2004)
(*a*) 225 m (*b*) 235 m
(*c*) 240 m (*d*) 250 m

3. A can run 22.5 m while *B* runs 25 m. In a kilometre race, *B* beats A by (M.B.A., 2006)
(*a*) 100 m (*b*) $111\frac{1}{9}$ m
(*c*) 25 m (*d*) 50 m

4. In a kilometre race, *A*, *B* and *C* are three participants. *A* can give *B* a start of 50 m and C a start of 69 m. The start which *B* can allow *C*, is (S.S.C., 2006)
(*a*) 17 m (*b*) 18 m
(*c*) 19 m (*d*) 20 m

5. In a 1000 m race, *A* can beat *B* by 100 m. In a race of 400 m, *B* can beat *C* by 40 m. By how many metres will *A* beat *C* in a race of 500 m? (Railways, 2006)
(*a*) 85 m (*b*) 95 m
(*c*) 105 m (*d*) 115 m

6. In a 100 m race, *A* beats *B* by 10 m and *C* by 13 m. In a race of 180 m, *B* will beat *C* by
(*a*) 5.4 m (*b*) 4.5 m
(*c*) 5 m (*d*) 6 m

7. In a 200 m race, *A* can beat *B* by 31 m and *C* by 18 m. In a race of 350 m, *C* will beat *B* by:
(*a*) 22.75 m (*b*) 25 m
(*c*) 19.5 m (*d*) 13 m

8. In a race of 200 m, *B* can give a start of 10 m to *A* and *C* can give a start of 20 m to *B*. The start that *C* can give to *A* in the same race is (S.S.C., 2007)
(*a*) 27 m (*b*) 29 m
(*c*) 30 m (*d*) 25 m

9. In a 200 m race, A beats B by 35 m or 7 seconds. *A*'s time over the course is
(*a*) 40 sec (*b*) 47 sec
(*c*) 33 sec (*d*) None of these

10. In a 500 m race, the ratio of the speeds of two contestants *A* and *B* is 3 : 4. If A has a start of 140 m, then A wins by
(*a*) 60 m (*b*) 40 m
(*c*) 20 m (*d*) 10 m

11. A runs $1\frac{2}{3}$ times as fast as *B*. If *A* gives *B* a start of 80 m, how far must the winning post be so that *A* and *B* might reach it at the same time?
(*a*) 200 m (*b*) 300 m
(*c*) 270 m (*d*) 160 m

12. In a 100 m race, *A* can beat *B* by 25 m and *B* can beat *C* by 4 m. In the same race *A* can beat *C* by
(*a*) 21 m (*b*) 26 m
(*c*) 28 m (*d*) 29 m

13. *A* and *B* take part in a 100 m race. *A* runs at 5 km an hour. *A* gives *B* a start of 8 m and still beats him by 8 seconds. The speed of *B* is (Railways, 2007)
(*a*) 4.45 km/hr (*b*) 4.14 km/hr
(*c*) 4.15 km/hr (*d*) 4.25 km/hr

14. In a 400 m race, *A* gives *B* a start of 5 seconds and beats him by 15 m. In another race of 400 m, *A* beats *B* by $7\frac{1}{7}$ seconds. Their respective speeds are (M.A.T. 2009)
(*a*) 6 m/sec, 7 m/sec (*b*) 5 m/sec, 7 m/sec
(*c*) 8 m/sec, 7 m/sec (*d*) 9 m/sec, 7 m/sec

15. In a kilometre race, *A* beats *B* by 30 seconds and *B* beats *C* by 15 seconds. If *A* beats *C* by 180 m, the time taken by *A* to run 1 kilometre, is (S.S.C., 2006)
(*a*) 200 sec (*b*) 205 sec
(*c*) 210 sec (*d*) 250 sec

16. In a 800 metre race, *A* defeated *B* by 15 seconds. If *A*'s speed was 8 km/hr, the speed of B was (S.S.C., 2004)
(*a*) $\frac{16}{27}$ km/hr (*b*) $\frac{27}{16}$ km/hr
(*c*) $7\frac{17}{25}$ km/hr (*d*) $8\frac{17}{25}$ km/hr

17. *A* and *B* can cover a 200 m race in 22 seconds and 25 seconds respectively. When *A* finished the race, then *B* is at what distance from the finishing line?
(*a*) 24 m (*b*) 30 m
(*c*) 48 m (*d*) 54 m
(Railways, 2004)

18. In a game of 100 points, *A* can give *B* 20 points and *C* 28 points. Then, *B* can give *C*:
(*a*) 8 points (*b*) 10 points
(*c*) 14 points (*d*) 40 points

19. At a game of billiards, *A* can give *B* 15 points in 60 and *A* can give C 20 points in 60. How many points can *B* give *C* in a game of 90?
(*a*) 30 points (*b*) 20 points
(*c*) 10 points (*d*) 12 points

20. Four sisters Suvarna, Tara, Uma and Vibha are playing a game such that the loser doubles the money of each of the other players from her share. They played four games and each sister lost one game in alphabetical order. At the end of fourth game, each sister had ₹ 32. How much money did Suvarna start with?
(*a*) ₹ 60 (*b*) ₹ 34
(*c*) ₹ 66 (*d*) ₹ 28
[SSC—CGL (Tier I) Exam, 2012]

21. A team played 40 games in a season and won in 24 of them. What percent of games played did the team win?
(*a*) 70% (*b*) 40%
(*c*) 60% (*d*) 35%
(SSC—CGL (Tier I) Exam, 2012]

Directions (22 and 25): At the start of a game of cards, J and B together had four times as much money as T, while T and B together had three times as much as J. At the end of the evening, J and B together had three times as much money as T, while T and B together had twice as much as J, B lost ₹ 200.

22. What fraction of the total money did T have at the beginning of the game? **[SNAP, 2012]**
(*a*) 1/3 (*b*) 1/8
(*c*) 2/9 (*d*) 1/5

23. What fraction of the total money did J win/lose? **[SNAP, 2012]**
(*a*) Won 1/12 (*b*) Lost 1/6
(*c*) Lost 1/3 (*d*) Won 1/5

24. In racing over a distance *d* at uniform speed, A can beat B by 20 metres, B can beat C by 10 metres, and A can beat C by 28 metres. Then d, in metres, is **[GBO Exam, 2012]**
(*a*) 50 (*b*) 75
(*c*) 100 (*d*) 120

25. A runs $1\frac{2}{3}$ times as fast as B. If A gives B a start of 80m, how far must the winning post from the starting point be so that A and B might reach it at the same time? **[CDS Exam, 2016]**
(*a*) 200m (*b*) 300m
(*c*) 270m (*d*) 160m

ANSWERS

1. (*a*)	2. (*b*)	3. (*a*)	4. (*d*)	5. (*b*)	6. (*d*)	7. (*b*)	8. (*b*)	9. (*c*)	10. (*c*)
11. (*a*)	12. (*c*)	13. (*b*)	14. (*c*)	15. (*b*)	16. (*c*)	17. (*a*)	18. (*b*)	19. (*c*)	20. (*c*)
21. (*c*)	22. (*d*)	23. (*a*)	24. (*c*)	25. (*a*)					

SOLUTIONS

1. Clearly, *A* beats *B* by 9 seconds.

Distance covered by *B* in 9 sec. = $\left(\frac{100}{45} \times 9\right)$m = 20m.

∴ *A* beats *B* by 20 m.

2. *A* : *B* = 1000 : 900 and *B* : *C* = 1000 : 850.

$\frac{A}{C} = \frac{A}{B} \times \frac{B}{C} = \frac{1000}{900} \times \frac{1000}{850} = \frac{1000}{765} \Rightarrow A : C = 1000 : 765.$

∴ *A* beats C by (1000 – 765) m = 235 m.

3. $B : A = 25 : \frac{45}{2} = 50 : 45 = (50 \times 20) : (45 \times 20)$ = 1000 : 900.

∴ In a km race, *B* beats *A* by (1000 – 900) m = 100 m.

4. *A* : *B* : *C* = 1000 : (1000 – 50) : (1000 – 69)
= 1000 : 950 : 931.

In a 950 m race, *B* can give *C* a start of (950 – 931) m = 19 m.

In a 1000 m race, *B* can give *C* a start of $\left(\frac{19}{950} \times 1000\right)$m = 20 m.

5. *A* : *B* = 1000 : 900, *B* : *C* = 400 : 360 = 100 : 90 = 900 : 810
⇒ *A* : *B* : *C* = 1000 : 900 : 810 ⇒ *A* : *C* = 1000 : 810 = 500 : 405
⇒ In a 500 m race, A beats C by (500 – 405) m = 95 m.

6. *A*:*B*=100:90 and *A*:*C*=100:87 ⇒ $\frac{A}{B} = \frac{100}{90} = \frac{10}{9}$ and $\frac{A}{C} = \frac{100}{87}$

$\Rightarrow \frac{B}{C} = \left(\frac{B}{A} \times \frac{A}{C}\right) = \left(\frac{9}{10} \times \frac{100}{87}\right) = \frac{90}{87} = \frac{90 \times 2}{87 \times 2} = \frac{180}{174}$

⇒ B : C = 180 : 174

⇒ In a 180 m race, B beats C by (180 – 174) m = 6 m.

7. *A* : *B* = 200 : 169 and *A* : *C* = 200 : 182

$\Rightarrow \frac{C}{B} = \left(\frac{C}{A} \times \frac{A}{B}\right) = \left(\frac{182}{200} \times \frac{200}{190}\right) = \frac{182}{169}.$

When *C* covers 182 m, *B* covers = 169 m.

When *C* covers 350 m, *B* covers = $\left(\frac{169}{182} \times 350\right)$m = 325 m.

∴ *C* beats *B* by 25 m.

8. *B* : *A* = 200 : 190, *C* : *B* = 200 : 180

$\frac{C}{A} = \left(\frac{C}{B} \times \frac{B}{A}\right) = \left(\frac{200}{180} \times \frac{200}{190}\right) = \frac{200}{171}.$

∴ *C* can give to *A*, a start of (200 – 171) m = 29 m.

9. *B* covers 35 m in 7 seconds.

B covers 200 m in $\left(\frac{7}{35} \times 200\right)$sec = 40 sec.

Time taken by *A* = (40 – 7) sec = 33 sec.

10. To reach the winning post A has to cover
$= (500 - 140)$ m $= 360$ m.
While A covers 3 m, B covers 4 m.

While A covers 360 m, B covers $\left(\frac{4}{3}\times 360\right)\text{m} = 480\,\text{m}$.

Thus, when A reaches the winning post, B covers 480 m.
$\therefore$ A wins by $(500 - 480)$ m $= 20$ m.

11. Ratio of speeds of A and $B = \frac{5}{3}:1 = 5:3$.
Thus, in a race of 5 m, A gains 2 m over B.
2 m are gained by B in a race of 5 m.

80 m will be gained by B in a race of $\left(\frac{5}{2}\times 80\right)\text{m} = 200$ m.

$\therefore$ Winning post is 200 m away from the starting point

12. $A : B = 100 : 75$ and $B : C = 100 : 96$.

$$A : C = \left(\frac{A}{B}\times\frac{B}{C}\right) = \left(\frac{100}{75}\times\frac{100}{96}\right) = \frac{100}{72}.$$

$\therefore$ A beats C by $(100 - 72)$ m $= 28$ m.

13. A's speed $= 5$ km/hr $= \left(5\times\frac{5}{18}\right)\text{m/sec} = \frac{25}{18}\text{m/sec}$.

Time taken by A to cover 100 m $= \left(100\times\frac{18}{25}\right)$ sec $= 72$ sec.

Time taken by B to cover 92 m $= (72 + 8)$ sec $= 80$ sec.

B's speed $=$

$$\left(\frac{92}{80}\right)\text{m/sec} = \left(\frac{92}{80}\times\frac{18}{5}\right)\text{km/hr} = \frac{414}{100}\text{km/hr} = 4.14\,\text{km/hr}.$$

14. Suppose A covers 400 m in t sec. Then, B covers 385 m in $(t + 5)$ sec.

$\therefore$ B covers 400 m in $\left\{\frac{(t+5)}{385}\times 400\right\}\text{sec} = \frac{80(t+5)}{77}$ sec.

Also, B covers 400 m in $\left(t + 7\frac{1}{7}\right)\text{sec} = \frac{(7t+50)}{7}$ sec.

$\therefore$ $\frac{80(t+5)}{77} = \frac{7t+50}{7}$ $\Rightarrow 80(t + 5) = 11(7t + 50)$

$\Rightarrow (80t - 77t) = (550 - 400) \Rightarrow 3t = 150 \Rightarrow t = 50.$

$\therefore$ A's speed $=$

$\frac{400}{50}\text{m/sec} = 8\,\text{m/sec}$, B's speed $= \frac{385}{55}\text{m/sec} = 7\,\text{m/sec}$.

15. In a km race, suppose A takes t sec. Then, B takes $(t + 30)$ sec. and C takes $(t + 45)$ sec.
180 m is covered by C in 45 sec.

$\therefore$ 1000 m is covered by C in $\left(\frac{45}{180}\times 1000\right)\text{sec} = 250$ sec.

$\therefore$ A covers 1000 m in $(250 - 45)$ sec $= 205$ sec.

16. A's speed $= 8$ km/hr $= \left(8\times\frac{5}{18}\right)\text{m/sec} = \frac{20}{9}\text{m/sec}$.

Time taken by A to cover 800 m $= \left(800\times\frac{9}{20}\right)$ sec $= 360$ sec.

Time taken by B to cover 800 m $= (360 + 15)$ sec
$= 375$ sec.

Speed of

$$B = \frac{800}{375}\text{m/sec} = \left(\frac{800}{375}\times\frac{18}{5}\right)\text{km/hr} = \frac{192}{25}\text{km/hr} = 7\frac{17}{25}\text{km/hr}.$$

17. Distance covered by B in 25 sec $= 200$ m.

Distance covered by B in 22 sec. $= \left(\frac{200}{25}\times 22\right)\text{m} = 176\,\text{m}$.

$\therefore$ B was at a distance of $(200 - 176)$ m $= 24$ m from the finishing line.

18. $A : B = 100 : 80$ and $A : C = 100 : 72$.

$$\therefore\ \frac{B}{C} = \left(\frac{B}{A}\times\frac{A}{C}\right) = \left(\frac{80}{100}\times\frac{100}{72}\right) = \frac{10}{9}\times\frac{10}{10} = \frac{100}{90} = 100:90.$$

$\therefore$ B can give C 10 points.

19. $A : B = 60 : 45$ and $A : C = 60 : 40$

$$\therefore\ \frac{B}{C} = \left(\frac{B}{A}\times\frac{A}{C}\right) = \left(\frac{45}{60}\times\frac{60}{40}\right) = \frac{45}{40}\times\frac{2}{2} = \frac{90}{80} = 90:80.$$

$\therefore$ B can give C 10 points in a game of 90.

20.

End of	Suvarna	Tara	Uma	Vibha
4th Game	32	32	32	32
3rd Game	16	16	16	80
2nd Game	8	8	72	40
1st Game	4	68	36	20
Original Money	62	34	18	10

Suvarna starts with ₹ 66

21. Number of games played $= 40$
Number of won games $= 24$

Percentage of games played $= \frac{24}{40}\times 100 = 60\%$

Direction for Solution: (3 and 4)

J and B have 4 times as much as T. $\frac{1}{5}$ th.
So, T so total.
Similarly, J is 1/4th and so on.
Taking total as $60x$:
T has $12x$, J has $15x$ so B has $33x$
Finally T has $15x$, J has $20x$ so B has $25x$.

22. So T has 1/5th initially.

23. J won $5/60 = 1/12$

24. Let distance be $= x$ metre A runs $= x$ metre
B runs $= (x - 20)$ metres. B can beat C by 10 metres
C runs $= (x - 10)$ metres A can beat by C 28 metres
C runs $= (x - 28)$ metres B runs $= x - 20$

C runs $= \left(\frac{x-10}{x}\right)\times(x-20)$

'A' can beat C by 28 metre $x - \left[\frac{(x-10)(x-20)}{x}\right] = 28$

$x^2 - x^2 + 30x - 200 = 28x$ $30x - 200 = 28x$

$\Rightarrow 30x - 28x = 200$ $2x = 200$
$x = 100$ metres.

25. Let speed of B $= a$ m/s

Speed of A $= \frac{5}{3}a$ m/s

Let x be the distance $= \frac{x\times 3}{5a} = \frac{x-80}{a}$

$\Rightarrow 3x = 5x - 400$ $\Rightarrow 2x = 400$
$\Rightarrow x = 200$m

27 Calendar

IMPORTANT FACTS

We are supposed to find the day of the week on a given date.

For this, we use the concept of *odd days.*

I. Odd Days: In a given period, the number of days more than the complete weeks are called *odd days.*

II. Leap Year:

(*i*) Every year divisible by 4 is a leap year, if it is not a century.

(*ii*) Every 4th century is a leap year and no other century is a leap year.

Note : A leap year has 366 days.

Examples:

(*i*) Each of the years 1948, 2004, 1676 etc. is a leap year.

(*ii*) Each of the years 400, 800, 1200, 1600, 2000 etc. is a leap year.

(*iii*) None of the years 2001, 2002, 2003, 2005, 1800, 2100 is a leap year.

III. Ordinary Year:

The year which is not a leap year is called an ordinary year. An ordinary year has 365 days.

IV. Counting of Odd Days:

(*i*) 1 ordinary year = 365 days = (52 weeks + 1day).

$\therefore$ *1 ordinary year has 1 odd day.*

(*ii*) 1 leap year = 366 days = (52 weeks + 2 days).

$\therefore$ *1 leap year has 2 odd days.*

(*iii*) 100 years = 76 ordinary years + 24 leap years

$= (76 \times 1 + 24 \times 2)$ odd days = 124 odd days

= (17 weeks + 5 days) $\equiv$ 5 odd days.

$\therefore$ Number of odd days in 100 years = 5

Number of odd days in 200 years = $(5 \times 2) \equiv 3$ odd days

Number of odd days in 300 years = $(5 \times 3) \equiv 1$ odd day.

Number of odd days in 400 years = $(5 \times 4 + 1) \equiv 0$ odd day.

Similarly, each one of 800 years, 1200 years, 1600 years, 2000 years, etc. has 0 odd days.

V. Day of the Week Related to Odd Days:

No. of days	0	1	2	3	4	5	6
Day	Sun.	Mon.	Tues.	Wed.	Thurs.	Fri.	Sat.

SOLVED EXAMPLES

Ex. 1. ***What was the day of the week on 16th July, 1776?***

Sol. 16th July, 1776 = (1775 years + Period from 1.1.1776 to 16.7.1776)

Counting of odd days:

Number of odd days in 1600 years = 0

Number of odd days in 100 years = 5

75 years = 18 leap years + 57 ordinary years

$= (18 \times 2 + 57 \times 1)$ odd days = 93 odd days

= (13 weeks + 2 days) $\equiv$ 2 odd days

$\therefore$ 1775 years have

= (0 + 5 + 2) odd days = 7 odd days ≡ 0 odd day.

Jan.		Feb.		March		April		May		June		July	
(31	+	29	+	31	+	30	+	31	+	30	+	16)	= 198 days

198 days = (28 weeks + 2 days) ≡ 2 odd days.

∴ Total number of odd days = (0 + 2) = 2.

Hence, the required day is Tuesday.

Ex. 2. ***What was the day of the week on 15th August, 1947?***

Sol. 15th August, 1947 = (1946 years + Period from 1.1.1947 to 15.8.1947)

Odd days in 1600 years = 0

Odd days in 300 years = (5 × 3) = 15 ≡ 1

46 years = (11 leap years + 35 ordinary years)

= (11 × 2 + 35 × 1) odd days = 57 odd days

= (8 weeks + 1 day) ≡ 1 odd day.

∴ Odd days in 1946 years = (0 + 1+ 1) = 2.

Jan.		Feb.		March		April		May		June		July		Aug	
(31	+	28		31	+	30	+	31	+	30	+	31	+	15)	= 227 days

227 days = (32 weeks + 3 days) ≡ 3 odd days.

Total number of odd days = (2 + 3) = 5.

Hence, the required day is Friday.

Ex. 3. ***What was the day of the week on 4th June, 2002?***

Sol. 4th June, 2002 = (2001 years + Period from 1.1.2002 to 4.6.2002)

Odd days in 1600 years = 0

Odd days in 400 years = 0

Odd days in 1 ordinary year = 1

Odd days in 2001 years = (0 + 0 + 1) = 1

Jan.		Feb.		March		April		May		June	
(31	+	28	+	31	+	30	+	31	+	4)	= 155 days

= 22 weeks + 1 day ≡ 1 odd day

Total number of odd days = (1 + 1) = 2

∴ Required day is Tuesday.

Ex. 4. ***On what dates of March 2005 did Friday fall?***

Sol. First we find the day on 1.3.2005

1.3.2005 = (2004 years + Period from 1.1.2005 to 1.3.2005)

Odd days in 1600 years = 0 Odd days in 400 years = 0

4 years = (1 leap year + 3 ordinary years)

= (1 × 2 + 3 × 1) odd days = 5 odd days

Jan.		Feb.		March
(31	+	28	+	11)

= 60 days = (8 weeks + 4 days) ≡ 4 odd days.

Total number of odd days = (0 + 0 + 5 + 4) = 9 ≡ 2 odd days

∴ 1.3.2005 was Tuesday. So, Friday lies on 4.3.2005

Hence, Friday lies on 4th, 11th, 18th and 25th of March, 2005.

Ex. 5. ***Prove that the calendar for the year 2003 will serve for the year 2014.***

Sol. We must have same day on 1.1.2003 and 1.1.2014.

So, number of odd days between 31.12.2002 and 31.12.2013 must be 0.

This period has 3 leap years and 8 ordinary years.

Number of odd days = (3 × 2 + 8 × 1) = 14 ≡ 0 odd day

∴ Calendar for the year 2003 will serve for the year 2014.

EXERCISE

(OBJECTIVE TYPE QUESTIONS)

Directions: ***Mark (√) against the correct answer in each of the following:***

1. January 1, 2007 was Monday. What day of the week lies on Jan. 1, 2008?
   (*a*) Monday (*b*) Tuesday
   (*c*) Wednesday (*d*) Sunday
2. January 1, 2008 is Tuesday. What day of the week lies on Jan. 1, 2009?
   (*a*) Monday (*b*) Wednesday
   (*c*) Thursday (*d*) Sunday
3. On 8th Dec, 2007 Saturday falls. What day of the week was it on 8th Dec. 2006?
   (a) Sunday (*b*) Thursday
   (*c*) Tuesday (*d*) Friday
4. On 6th March, 2005 Monday falls. What was the day of the week on 6th March, 2004?
   (*a*) Sunday (*b*) Saturday
   (*c*) Tuesday (*d*) Wednesday
5. The calendar for the year 2007 will be the same for the year:
   (*a*) 2014 (*b*) 2016
   (*c*) 2017 (*d*) 2018
6. On what dates of April, 2001 did Wednesday fall?
   (*a*) 1st, 8th, 15th, 22nd, 29th
   (*b*) 2nd, 9th, 16th, 23rd, 30th
   (*c*) 3rd, 10th, 17th, 24th
   (*d*) 4th, 11th, 18th, 25th
7. What was the day of the week on 17th June, 1998?
   (*a*) Monday (*b*) Tuesday
   (*c*) Wednesday (*d*) Thursday
8. What was the day of the week on 28th May, 2006?
   (*a*) Thursday (*b*) Friday
   (*c*) Saturday (*d*) Sunday
9. What will be the day of the week on 15th August, 2010?
   (*a*) Sunday (*b*) Monday
   (*c*) Tuesday (*d*) Friday
10. Today is Monday. After 61 days, it will be
    (*a*) Wednesday (*b*) Saturday
    (*c*) Tuesday (*d*) Thursday
11. The last day of a century cannot be
    (*a*) Monday (*b*) Wednesday
    (*c*) Tuesday (*d*) Friday
12. Which of the following is not a leap year?
    (a) 700 (*b*) 800
    (c) 1200 (*d*) 2000
13. How many days are there in x weeks x days?
    (a) $7x^2$ (*b*) $8x$
    (*c*) $14x$ (*d*) 7
14. It was Sunday on Jan 1, 2006. What was the day of the week on Jan 1, 2010?
    (*a*) Sunday (*b*) Saturday
    (*c*) Friday (*d*) Wednesday
15. On 8th Feb, 2005 it was Tuesday. What was the day of the week on 8th Feb, 2004?
    (*a*) Tuesday (*b*) Monday
    (*c*) Sunday (*d*) Wednesday
16. For a certain month, the dates of three of the Sundays are even numbers. Then, the 15th of the that month falls on a **[SSC—CGL (Tier I) Exam, 2012]**
    (*a*) Thursday (*b*) Friday
    (*c*) Saturday (*d*) Sunday
17. What was the day of the week on 15 August, 1947?
    [DMRC— Customer Relationship Assistant (CRA) Exam, 2016]
    (*a*) Saturday (*b*) Friday
    (*c*) Thursday (*d*) Wednesday
18. The calendar for the year 2009 will be the same as that of the year
    [DMRC— Customer Relationship Assistant (CRA) Exam, 2016]
    (*a*) 2013 (*b*) 2014
    (*c*) 2015 (*d*) 2014

ANSWERS

1. (*b*)	2. (*c*)	3. (*d*)	4. (*b*)	5. (*d*)	6. (*d*)	7. (*c*)	8. (*d*)	9. (*a*)	10. (*b*)
11. (*c*)	12. (*a*)	13. (*b*)	14. (*c*)	15. (*c*)	16. (*c*)	17. (*b*)	18. (*c*)		

SOLUTIONS

1. The year 2007 is an ordinary year. So, it has 1 odd day.
   1st day of the year 2007 was Monday.
   1st day of the year 2008 will be 1 day beyond Monday.
   Hence, it will be Tuesday.
2. The year 2008 is a leap year. So, it has 2 odd days.
   1st day of the year 2008 is Tuesday (Given)
   So, 1st day of the year 2009 is 2 days beyond Tuesday.
   Hence, it will be Thursday.
3. The year 2006 is an ordinary year. So, it has 1 odd day.
   So, the day on 8th Dec, 2007 will be 1 day beyond the day on 8th Dec, 2006.
   But, 8th Dec, 2007 is Saturday.
   $\therefore$ 8th Dec, 2006 is Friday.
4. The year 2004 is a leap year. So, it has 2 odd days.
   $\therefore$ The day on 6th March, 2005 will be 2 days beyond the day on 6th March, 2004.
   But, 6th March, 2005 is Monday.
   $\therefore$ 6th March, 2004 is Saturday.
5. Count the number of odd days from the year 2007 onwards to get the sum equal to 0 odd day.

Year	2007	2008	2009	2010	2011	2012	2013	2014	2015	2016	2017
Odd day	1	2	1	1	1	2	1	1	1	2	1

   Sum = 14 odd days $\equiv$ 0 odd day.
   $\therefore$ Calendar for the year 2018 will be the same as for the year 2007.
6. We shall find the day on 1st April, 2001.
   1st April, 2001 = (2000 years + Period from 1.1.2001 to 1.4.2001)
   Odd days in 1600 years = 0
   Odd days in 400 years = 0

   Jan. Feb. March April
   (31 + 28 + 31 + 1) = 91 days $\equiv$ 0 odd days.

16. The dates of three of the Sundays are even number is 2, 9, 16, 23, 30.
    So, on 16th of that month = Sunday, 15th of that month falls on a Saturday
17. 15 August, 1947 means 1946 complete years + first 7 months upto July 1947 + 15 days of August 1947
    1600 years have 0 odd day.
    300 years have 1 odd day
    46 years have 11 leap years and 35 ordinary years
    = (11 × 2) + (35 × 1)
    = 22 + 35 = 57 odd days
    = 8 × 7 + 1 odd days
    = 8 weeks + 1 odd day
    Up to 1946 there are 1 + 1 = 2 odd days
    January 1947 $\Rightarrow$ 3 odd days
    February 1947 $\Rightarrow$ 0 odd days
    (1947 is a normal year)
    March 1947 $\Rightarrow$ 3 odd days
    April 1947 $\Rightarrow$ 2 odd days
    May 1947 $\Rightarrow$ 3 odd days
    June 1947 $\Rightarrow$ 2 odd days
    July 1947 $\Rightarrow$ 3 odd days
    Up to 15 August $\Rightarrow$ 15 odd days
    Total number of odd days up to 15 August 1947
    = 2 + 3 + 0 + 3 + 2 + 3 + 2 + 3 + 15 = 33 odd days.
    Hence, 15th August, 1947 was Friday.
18. 2008 was a leap year.
    A leap year has two odd days.
    Suppose year 2008 starts with a Monday.
    Then the first day of 2009 was Wednesday.
    Now,
    First day of 2010 $\Rightarrow$ Thursday
    First day of 2011 $\Rightarrow$ Friday
    First day of 2012 $\Rightarrow$ Saturday
    Because 2012 was a leap year
    First day of 2013 $\Rightarrow$ Monday
    First day of 2014 $\Rightarrow$ Tuesday
    First day of 2015 $\Rightarrow$ Wednesday
    Thus, the calendar for the year 2009 was the same as that of the year 2015.

28 Clocks

IMPORTANT FACTS

The face or dial of a watch is a circle whose circumference is divided into 60 equal parts, called minute spaces.

A clock has two hands, the smaller one is called the *hour hand* or *short hand* while the larger one is called the *minute hand* or *long hand*.

(*i*) In 60 minutes, the minute hand gains 55 minutes on the hour hand.

(*ii*) In every hour, both the hands coincide once.

(*iii*) The hands are in the same straight line when they are coincident or opposite to each other.

(*iv*) When the two hands are at right angles, they are 15 minute spaces apart.

(*v*) When the hands are in opposite directions, they are 30 minute spaces apart.

(*vi*) Angle traced by hour hand in 12 hrs = 360°.

(*vii*) Angle traced by minute hand in 60 min. = 360°.

Too Fast and Too Slow : *If a watch or a clock indicates 8.15, when the correct time is 8, it is said to be 15 minutes too fast.*

On the other hand, if it indicates 7.45, when the correct time is 8, it is said to be 15 minutes too slow.

Both the hands of a clock are together after every $65\frac{5}{11}$ min. So, if both the hands are meeting after an interval less than $65\frac{5}{11}$ min, the clock is running fast and if they meet after an interval greater than $65\frac{5}{11}$ min, the clock is running slow.

Interchange of Hands: Whenever the hands of the clock interchange positions (i.e., the minute hand takes the place of hour hand and the hour hand and takes the place of minute hand), the sum of the angles traced by hour hand and minute hand is 360°.

Suppose this happens after x minutes.

Angle traced by minute hand in x min = $(6x)°$.

Angle traced by hour hand in x min = $(0.5x)°$.

$\therefore\ 0.5x + 6x = 360 \Leftrightarrow 6.5x = 360 \Leftrightarrow x = \frac{3600}{65} = 55\frac{5}{13}$.

Thus, the hands of a clock interchange positions after every $55\frac{5}{13}$ minutes.

SOLVED EXAMPLES

Ex. 1. ***Find the angle between the hour hand and the minute hand of a clock when the time is 3.25.***

Sol. Angle traced by the hour hand in 12 hours = 360°.

Angle traced by it in 3 hrs 25 min., i.e.

$\frac{41}{12}$ hrs $= \left(\frac{360}{12} \times \frac{41}{12}\right)^\circ = 102\frac{1}{2}^\circ$.

Angle traced by minute hand in 60 min. = 360°.

Angle traced by it in 25 min. $= \left(\frac{360}{60} \times 25\right)^\circ = 150°$.

$\therefore$ Required angle $= \left(150° - 102\frac{1}{2}^\circ\right) = 47\frac{1}{2}^\circ$.

Ex. 2. ***At what time between 2 and 3 o'clock will the hands of a clock be together?***

Sol. At 2 o'clock, the hour hand is at 2 and the minute hand is at 12, i.e. they are 10 min. spaces apart.

To be together, the minute hand must gain 10 minutes over the hour hand.

Now, 55 minutes are gained by it in 60 min.

$\therefore$ 10 minutes will be gained in $\left(\frac{60}{55}\times 10\right)$ min. $= 10\frac{10}{11}$ min.

$\therefore$ The hands will coincide at $10\frac{10}{11}$ min. past 2.

Ex. 3. ***At what time between 4 and 5 o'clock will the hands of a clock be at right angle?***

Sol. At 4 o'clock, the minute hand will be 20 min. spaces behind the hour hand.

Now, when the two hands are at right angles, they are 15 min. spaces apart.

So, they are at right angles in following two cases.

Case I. *When minute hand is 15 min. spaces behind the hour hand :*

In this case min. hand will have to gain (20 – 15) = 5 minute spaces.

55 min. spaces are gained by it in 60 min.

5 min. spaces will be gained by it in $\left(\frac{60}{55}\times 5\right)$ min. $= 5\frac{5}{11}$ min.

$\therefore$ They are at right angles at $5\frac{5}{11}$ min. past 4.

Case II. *When the minute hand is 15 min. spaces ahead of the hour hand :*

To be in this position, the minute hand will have to gain (20 + 15) = 35 minute spaces.

55 min. spaces are gained in 60 min.

35 min. spaces are gained in

$\left(\frac{60}{55}\times 35\right)$ min. $= 38\frac{2}{11}$ min.

$\therefore$ They are at right angles at $38\frac{2}{11}$ min. past 4.

Ex. 4. ***Find at what time between 8 and 9 o'clock will the hands of a clock be in the same straight line but not together.***

Sol. At 8 o'clock, the hour hand is at 8 and the minute hand is at 12, i.e. the two hands are 20 min. spaces apart.

To be in the same straight line but not together they will be 30 minute spaces apart.

So, the minute hand will have to gain (30 – 20) = 10 minute spaces over the hour hand.

55 minute spaces are gained in 60 min.

10 minute spaces will be gained in $\left(\frac{60}{55}\times 10\right)$ min. $= 10\frac{10}{11}$ min.

$\therefore$ The hands will be in the same straight line but not together at $10\frac{10}{11}$ min. past 8.

Ex. 5. ***At what time between 5 and 6 o'clock are the hands of a clock 3 minutes apart?***

Sol. At 5 o'clock, the minute hand is 25 min. spaces behind the hour hand.

Case I. *Minute hand is 3 min. spaces behind the hour hand.*

In this case, the minute hand has to gain (25 – 3) = 22 minute spaces.

55 min. are gained in 60 min.

22 min. are gained in $\left(\frac{60}{55}\times 22\right)$ min. = 24 min.

$\therefore$ The hands will be 3 min. apart at 24 min. past 5.

Case II. *Minute hand is 3 min. spaces ahead of the hour hand.*

In this case, the minute hand has to gain (25 + 3) = 28 minute spaces.

55 min. are gained in 60 min.

28 min. are gained in $\left(\frac{60}{55}\times 28\right) = 31\frac{5}{11}$ min.

$\therefore$ The hands will be 3 min. apart at $31\frac{5}{11}$ min. past 5.

Ex. 6. ***The minute hand of a clock overtakes the hour hand at intervals of 65 minutes of the correct time. How much a day does the clock gain or lose?*** **(M.A.T., 2003)**

Sol. In a correct clock, the minute hand gains 55 min. spaces over the hour hand in 60 minutes.

To be together again, the minute hand must gain 60 minutes over the hour hand.

55 min. are gained in 60 min.

60 min. are gained in $\left(\frac{60}{55}\times 60\right)$ min. $= 65\frac{5}{11}$ min.

But, they are together after 65 min.

$\therefore$ Gain in 65 min. $= \left(65\frac{5}{11} - 65\right)$ min. $= \frac{5}{11}$ min.

Gain in 24 hours $= \left(\frac{5}{11}\times\frac{60\times 24}{65}\right)$ min. $= 10\frac{10}{43}$ min.

$\therefore$ The clock gains $10\frac{10}{43}$ minutes in 24 hours.

Ex. 7. ***A watch which gains uniformly, is 5 min. slow at 8 o'clock in the morning on Sunday and it is 5 min. 48 sec. fast at 8 p.m. on following Sunday. When was it correct?***

Sol. Time from 8 a.m. on Sunday to 8 p.m. on following Sunday = 7 days 12 hours = 180 hours.

$\therefore$ The watch gains $\left(5 + 5\frac{4}{5}\right)$ min. or $\frac{54}{5}$ min. in 180 hrs.

Now $\frac{54}{5}$ min. are gained in 180 hrs.

$\therefore$ 5 min. are gained in $\left(180\times\frac{5}{54}\times 5\right)$ hrs. = 83 hrs 20 min. = 3 days 11 hrs 20 min.

$\therefore$ Watch is correct 3 days 11 hrs 20 min. after 8 a.m. of Sunday.

$\therefore$ It will be correct at 20 min. past 7 p.m. on Wednesday.

Ex. 8. ***A clock is set right at 5 a.m. The clock loses 16 minutes in 24 hours. What will be the true time when the clock indicates 10 p.m. on 4th day?***

Sol. Time from 5 a.m. on a day to 10 p.m. on 4th day = 89 hours.

Now 23 hrs 44 min. of this clock = 24 hours of correct clock.

$\therefore$ $\frac{356}{15}$ hrs of this clock = 24 hours of correct clock.

89 hrs of this clock $= \left(24\times\frac{15}{356}\times 89\right)$ hrs of correct clock = 90 hrs of correct clock.

So, the correct time is 11 p.m.

Ex. 9. ***A clock is set right at 8 a.m. The clock gains 10 minutes in 24 hours. What will be the true time when the clock indicates 1 p.m. on the following day?***

Sol. Time from 8 a.m. on a day to 1 p.m. on the following day = 29 hours.

24 hours 10 min. of this clock = 24 hours of the correct clock.

$\frac{145}{6}$ hrs of this clock = 24 hrs of the correct clock.

29 hrs of this clock $= \left(24\times\frac{6}{145}\times 29\right)$ hrs of the correct clock

= 28 hrs 48 min. of correct clock.

$\therefore$ The correct time is 28 hrs 48 min. after 8 a.m. This is 48 min. past 12.

Ex. 10. ***Rohan leaves home between 7 a.m. and 8 a.m. and returns between 1 p.m. and 2 p.m. to find that the minute and hour hands have interchanged their positions. How long was Rohan out of the house?***

Sol. Clearly, the hands will interchange positions after crossing each other 6 times i.e. they together will make (6 + 1) or 7 complete revolutions.

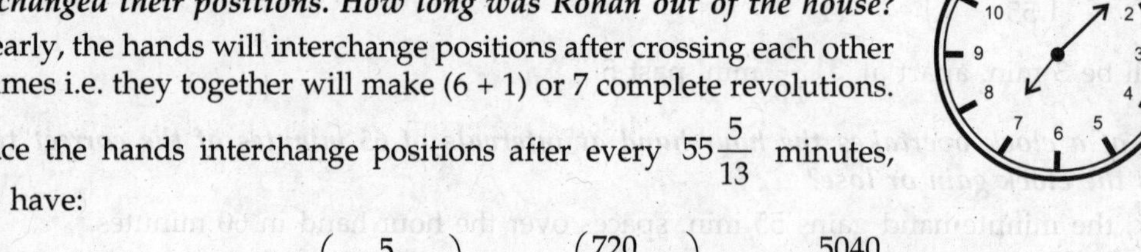

Since the hands interchange positions after every $55\frac{5}{13}$ minutes, we have:

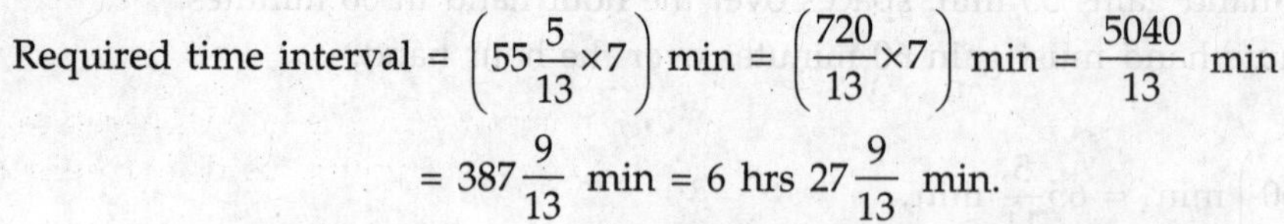

$$\text{Required time interval} = \left(55\frac{5}{13}\times 7\right)\text{ min} = \left(\frac{720}{13}\times 7\right)\text{ min} = \frac{5040}{13}\text{ min}$$

$$= 387\frac{9}{13}\text{ min} = 6\text{ hrs } 27\frac{9}{13}\text{ min.}$$

EXERCISE

(OBJECTIVE TYPE QUESTIONS)

Directions: ***Mark (✓) against the correct answer:***

1. London time is five and a half hours behind Delhi time. What time is it in London if it is 0.2.35 in Delhi? **(E.P.F.O.S.S.A., 2004)**
   (*a*) 07.05 (*b*) 08.05
   (*c*) 21.05 (*d*) 21.35

2. A bus leaves at 12.25 noon and reaches destination at 10.45 am. The duration of the journey is **(R.R.B., 2005)**
   (*a*) 22 hrs 20 min (*b*) 22 hrs 40 min
   (*c*) 24 hrs 20 min (*d*) 24 hrs 40 min

3. An accurate clock shows 80′ clock in the morning. Through how many degrees will the hour hand rotate when the clock shows 2O′ clock in the afternoon?
   (*a*) 144° (*b*) 150°
   (*c*) 168° (*d*) 180°

4. How many rotations will the hour hand of a clock complete in 72 hours? **(Bank Recruitment, 2006)**
   (*a*) 3 (*b*) 6
   (*c*) 9 (*d*) 12

5. Through what angle does the minute hand of a clock turn in 5 minutes? **(E.S.I.C., 2006)**
   (*a*) 30° (*b*) 32°
   (*c*) 35° (*d*) 36°

6. In an accurate clock, in a period of 2 hours 20 minutes the minute hand will move over
   (*a*) 140° (*b*) 320°
   (*c*) 520° (*d*) 840°

7. A clock is started at noon. By 10 minutes past 5, the hour hand has turned through
   (*a*) 145° (*b*) 150°
   (*c*) 155° (*d*) 160°

8. At 9:38 A.M, through how many degrees the hour hand of a clock moved since noon the previous day? **(SNAP, 2004)**
   (*a*) 323 (*b*) 612
   (*c*) 646 (*d*) 649

9. At 3.40, the hour hand and the minute hand of a clock form an angle of **(Hotel Management, 2004; Campus Recruitment, 2008)**
   (*a*) 120° (*b*) 125°
   (*c*) 130° (*d*) 135°

10. The angle between the minute hand and the hour hand of a clock when the time is 8.30, is **(R.R.B. 2006)**
    (*a*) 80° (*b*) 75°
    (*c*) 60° (*d*) 105°

11. The angle between the minute hand and the hour hand of a clock when the time is 4.20, is **(P.C.S., 2008)**
    (*a*) 0° (*b*) 10°
    (*c*) 5° (*d*) 20°

12. At what angle the hands of a clock are inclined at 15 minutes past 5? **(L.I.C.A.A.O., 2003)**
    (*a*) $58\frac{1}{2}°$ (*b*) 64°
    (*c*) $67\frac{1}{2}°$ (*d*) $72\frac{1}{2}°$

13. The reflex angle between the hands of a clock at 10.25 is
    (*a*) 180° (*b*) $192\frac{1}{2}°$
    (*c*) 195° (*d*) $197\frac{1}{2}°$

14. Match List I with List II and select the correct answer using the codes given below the lists:

List I (Time)		List II (Angle between hour hand and minute hand of a clock)	
A.	1.10 p.m.	1.	20°
B.	2.15 p.m.	2.	$22\frac{1}{2}°$
C.	8.40 p.m.	3.	24°
		4.	25°
		5.	30°

	A	B	C		A	B	C
(a)	4	2	1	(b)	4	3	2
(c)	5	2	1	(d)	4	3	2

15. An accurate clock shows the time as 3.00. After the hour hand has moved 135°, the time would be
(a) 6.30 (b) 7.30
(c) 8.00 (d) 9.30

16. What is the area of the face of a clock described by its minute hand between 9 a.m. and 9.35 a.m; if the minute hand is 10 cm long? (M.B.A., 2004)
(a) $36\frac{2}{3}$ cm² (b) $157\frac{1}{7}$ cm²
(c) $183\frac{1}{3}$ cm² (d) None of these

17. The hands of a clock are 10 cm and 7 cm respectively. The difference between the distance traversed by their extremities in 3 days 5 hours is (M.A.T., 2006)
(a) 4552.67 cm (b) 4555.67 cm
(c) 4557.67 cm (d) 4559.67 cm

18. The minute arm of a clock is 10 cm long. The number of minutes taken by the tip of the arm to travel a length of 10 cm is nearly equal to
(a) 5 (b) 10
(c) 15 (d) 20

19. At which time number of minutes elapsed since midnight is nine times the number of minutes before noon? (R.R.B., 2006)
(a) 8.30 a.m. (b) 6.56 a.m.
(c) 9.46 a.m. (d) 10.48 a.m.

20. How many times do the hands of a clock coincide in a day?
(a) 20 (b) 21
(c) 22 (d) 24

21. How many times in a day, the hands of a clock are straight? (I.I.F.T., 2005)
(a) 22 (b) 24
(c) 44 (d) 48

22. How many times are the hands of a clock at right angle in a day?
(a) 22 (b) 24
(c) 44 (d) 48

23. How many times in a day, are the hands of a clock in straight line but opposite in direction? (R.R.B., 2003)
(a) 20 (b) 22
(c) 24 (d) 48

24. How many times are the hour hand and the minute hand of a clock at right angles during their motion from 1.00 p.m. to 10.00 p.m.? (I.A.S., 2009)
(a) 9 (b) 10
(c) 18 (d) 20

25. A clock gains 5 minutes in one hour. Therefore, the angle traversed by the minute hand in 1 hour is
(a) 360° (b) 390°
(c) 390.5° (d) None of these

26. A clock strikes once at 1O' clock, twice at 2O' clock, thrice at 3O' clock and soon. What is the total number of strikings in a day? (R.R.B., 2006)
(a) 136 (b) 146
(c) 156 (d) 166

27. A wall-clock takes 9 seconds in tringing at 9O' clock. The time, it will take in tringing at 11O' clock, is (C.P.O., 2004)
(a) 10 seconds (b) 10.80 seconds
(c) 11 seconds (d) 11.25 seconds

28. If a clock strikes six times in 5 seconds, the number of strikes in 10 seconds is
(a) 8 (b) 9
(c) 10 (d) 11

29. In every 30 minutes the time of a watch increases by 3 minutes. After showing the correct time at 5 a.m; what time will the watch show after 6 hours?
(a) 10 : 54 a.m. (b) 11 : 30 a.m.
(c) 11 : 36 a.m. (d) 11 : 42 a.m.
(e) 11 : 38 p.m. (Bank P.O., 2009)

30. A watch becomes fast by 5 minutes everyday. By what percent does it become fast? (R.R.B., 2006)
(a) $\frac{5}{24}$% (b) $\frac{1}{12}$%
(c) 5% (d) $\frac{50}{144}$%

31. A clock goes slow from midnight by 5 minutes at the end of the first hour, by 10 minutes at the end of the second hour, by 15 minutes at the end of the third hour and so on. What will be the time by this clock after 6 hours? (S.S.C., 2002)
(a) 5.15 a.m. (b) 5.30 a.m.
(c) 6 a.m. (d) 6.30 a.m.

32. A watch goes fast by 15 minutes compared to the right time everyday. If it is corrected and set to the standard time at 12O' clock at noon, which of the following will be the time shown by it at 4 : 00 a.m. in the morning?
(a) 3 : 45 a.m. (b) 4 : 10 a.m.
(c) 4 : 15 a.m. (d) 4 : 30 a.m.

33. It is between 3 P.M. and 4 P.M. and the distance between the hour and the minute hand of clock is 18 minute spaces. What time does the clock show? (R.R.B., 2006)
(*a*) 3.12 P.M. (*b*) 3.27 P.M.
(*c*) 3.31 P.M. (*d*) 3.36 P.M.

34. At what time between 9 and 10 o'clock are the hands of a clock 23 minute spaces apart?
(*a*) 9 : 18 (*b*) 9 : 23
(*c*) 9 : 24 (*d*) 9 : 26

35. How much does a watch lose per day, if its hands coincide every 64 minutes? (M.B.A. 2004, 05, 06; G.B.O., 2007; Campus Recruitment, 2008, 2010)
(*a*) $32\frac{8}{11}$ min. (*b*) $36\frac{5}{11}$ min.
(*c*) 90 min. (*d*) 96 min.

36. At what time, in minutes, between 3 o'clock and 4 o'clock, both the needles will coincide each other? (R.R.B., 2002)
(*a*) $5\frac{1}{11}''$ past (*b*) $12\frac{4}{11}''$ past
(*c*) $13\frac{4}{11}''$ past (*d*) $16\frac{4}{11}''$ past

37. At what time between 9 and 10 o'clock will the hands of a watch be together?
(*a*) 45 min. past 9 (*b*) 50 min. past 9
(*c*) $49\frac{1}{11}$ min. past 9 (*d*) $48\frac{2}{11}$ min. past 9

38. At what time between 7 and 8 o'clock will the hands of a clock be in the same straight line but, not together? (A.A.O. Exam., 2003)
(*a*) 5 min. past 7 (*b*) $5\frac{2}{11}$ min. past 7
(*c*) $5\frac{3}{11}$ min. past 7 (*d*) $5\frac{5}{11}$ min. past 7

39. At what time between 4 and 5 o'clock will the hands of a watch point in opposite directions?
(*a*) 45 min. past 4 (*b*) 40 min. past 4
(*c*) $50\frac{4}{11}$ min. past 4 (*d*) $54\frac{6}{11}$ min. past 4

40. At what time between 5.30 and 6 will the hands of a clock be at right angles?
(*a*) $43\frac{5}{11}$ min. past 5 (*b*) $43\frac{7}{11}$ min. past 5
(*c*) 40 min. past 5 (*d*) 45 min. past 5

41. Henry started a trip into the country between 8 A.M. and 9 A.M. when the hands of clock were together. He arrived at his destination between 2 P.M. and 3 P.M. when the hands of the clock were exactly 180° apart. How long did he travel? (SNAP, 2004)
(*a*) 6 hours (*b*) 7 hours
(*c*) 9 hours (*d*) 11 hours

42. Imagine that your watch was correct at noon, but then it began to lose 30 minutes each hour. It now shows 4 p.m. but it stopped 5 hours ago. What is the correct time now? (M.B.A. 2004)
(*a*) 9.30 p.m. (*b*) 11 p.m.
(*c*) 1 a.m. (*d*) 1.30 a.m.

43. A mechanical grandfather clock is at present showing 7 hr 40 min 6 sec. Assuming that it loses 4 seconds in every hour, what time will it show after exactly $6\frac{1}{2}$ hours? (M.B.A. 2004)
(*a*) 14 hr 9 min 34 sec (*b*) 14 hr 9 min 40 sec
(*c*) 14 hr 10 min 6 sec (*d*) 14 hr 10 min 32 sec

44. I have two watches with a 12 hour cycle. One of them gains one minute a day and the other loses $1\frac{1}{2}$ minutes per day. If I set them both at the correct time, how long will it be before they again tell the correct time together?
(*a*) 288 days (*b*) 480 days
(*c*) 720 days (*d*) 1440 days

45. A watch is 1 minute slow at 1 p.m. on Tuesday and 2 minutes fast at 1 p.m. on Thursday. When did it show the correct time? (M.A.T. 2004)
(*a*) 1.00 a.m. on Wednesday
(*b*) 5.00 a.m. on Wednesday
(*c*) 1.00 p.m. on Wednesday
(*d*) 5.00 p.m. on Wednesday

46. A watch which gains uniformly is 2 minutes low at noon on Monday and is 4 min. 48 sec fast at 2 p.m. on the following Monday. When was it correct?
(*a*) 2 p.m. on Tuesday (*b*) 2 p.m. on Wednesday
(*c*) 3 p.m. on Thursday (*d*) 1 p.m. on Friday

47. A watch which gains 5 seconds in 3 minutes was set right at 7 a.m. In the afternoon of the same day, when the watch indicated quarter past 4 o'clock, the true time is
(*a*) $59\frac{7}{12}$ min. past 3 (*b*) 4 p.m.
(*c*) $58\frac{7}{11}$ min. past 3 (*d*) $2\frac{3}{11}$ min. past 4

48. Between 5 and 6, a lady looked at her watch and mistaking the hour hand for the minute hand, she thought that the time was 57 minutes earlier than the correct time. The correct time was (M.B.A. 2003)
(*a*) 12 minutes past 5 (*b*) 24 minutes past 5
(*c*) 36 minutes past 5 (*d*) 48 minutes past 5

49. How much does a watch lose per day if its hands coincide every 64 minutes?

[IDBI Bank Executive Officers Exam, 2012]

(*a*) 37 minutes (*b*) $32\frac{8}{11}$ minutes

(*c*) 31 minutes (*d*) None of these

50. Wall clock gains 2 minutes in 12 hours, while a table clock loses 2 minutes every 36 hours. Both are set right at 12 noon on Tuesday. The correct time when both show the same time next would be

[SSC—FCI Gr. III Exam, 2012]

(*a*) 12:30 at night, after 130 days

(*b*) 12 noon, after 135 days

(*c*) 1:30 at nights, after 130 days

(*d*) 12 midnight after 135 days

51. The angle between the hands of a clock when the time is 4:25 am is [CLAT, 2016]

(*a*) $13\frac{1}{2}°$ (*b*) $17\frac{1}{2}°$

(*c*) $14\frac{1}{2}°$ (*d*) $12\frac{1}{2}°$

52. At 8:30, the hour hand and the minute hand of clock form an angle of [CDS Exam, 2016]

(*a*) 80° (*b*) 75°

(*c*) 70° (*d*) 60°

53. A clock is displaying correct time at 9am on Monday. If the clock loses 12 minutes in 24 hours, then the actual time when the clock indicates 8:30pm on Wednesday of the same week is

[DMRC—Customer Relationship Assistant (CRA) Exam, 2016]

(*a*) 8 pm (*b*) 7 pm

(*c*) 9 pm (*d*) 8: 59 : 45 pm

54. There are two clocks, both set to show 10 pm on 21st January 2010. One clock gains 2 minutes in an hour and the other clock loses 5 minutes in an hour. Then by how many minutes do the two clocks differ at 4 pm on 22nd January 2010?

[DMRC—Customer Relationship Assistant (CRA) Exam, 2016]

(*a*) 126 minutes (*b*) 136 minutes

(*c*) 96 minutes (*d*) 106 minutes

ANSWERS

1. (*c*)	2. (*a*)	3. (*d*)	4. (*b*)	5. (*a*)	6. (*d*)	7. (*c*)	8. (*d*)	9. (*c*)	10. (*b*)
11. (*b*)	12. (*c*)	13. (*d*)	14. (*a*)	15. (*b*)	16. (*c*)	17. (*c*)	18. (*b*)	19. (*d*)	20. (*c*)
21. (*c*)	22. (*c*)	23. (*b*)	24. (*c*)	25. (*b*)	26. (*c*)	27. (*d*)	28. (*d*)	29. (*c*)	30. (*d*)
31. (*b*)	32. (*b*)	33. (*d*)	34. (*c*)	35. (*a*)	36. (*d*)	37. (*c*)	38. (*d*)	39. (*d*)	40. (*b*)
41. (*a*)	42. (*c*)	43. (*b*)	44. (*d*)	45. (*b*)	46. (*b*)	47. (*b*)	48. (*b*)	49. (*b*)	50. (*b*)
51. (*b*)	52. (*b*)	53. (*c*)	54. (*a*)						

SOLUTIONS

1. Clealy, time in London is 5 hrs 30 minutes behnd 2.35 a.m. which is 9.05 p.m. or 21.05 hrs.

2. Duration of the journey
= (Duration form 12.25 noon to midnight)
+ (Duration from 12.00 midnight to 10.45 a.m.)
= 11 hrs 35 min + 10 hrs 45 min = 22 hrs 20 min.

3. Angle traced by the hour hand in 6 hours
$= \left(\frac{360}{12}\times 6\right)^\circ = 180°.$

4. Number of rotations $= \frac{72}{12} = 6.$

5. Angle traced by the minute hand in 5 minutes
$= \left(\frac{360}{60}\times 5\right)^\circ = 30°.$

6. Angle traced by the minute hand in 2 hrs 20 min, i.e., 140 min $= \left(\frac{360}{60}\times 140\right)^\circ = 840°.$

7. Angle traced by the hour hand in 12 hrs = 360°.
Angle traced by the hour hand in 5 hrs 10 min, i.e., $\frac{31}{6}$ hrs $= \left(\frac{360}{12}\times\frac{31}{6}\right) = 155°.$

8. Time from 12 noon to 9 : 38 A.M. = 12 hrs + 9 hrs 38 min = 21 hrs 38 min.
$= 21\frac{38}{60}\text{ hrs} = 21\frac{19}{30}\text{ hrs} = \frac{649}{30}\text{ hrs}.$
Angle traced by the hour hand in 12 hrs = 360°.
Angle traced by the hour hand in
$\frac{649}{30}\text{ hrs} = \left(\frac{360}{12}\times\frac{649}{30}\right)^\circ = 649°.$

9. Angle traced by hour hand in 12 hrs. = 360°.
Angle traced by it in $\frac{11}{3}$ hrs $= \left(\frac{360}{12}\times\frac{11}{3}\right)^\circ = 110°.$
Angle traced by minute hand in 60 min. = 360°.
Angle traced by it in 40 min. $= \left(\frac{360}{60}\times 40\right)^\circ = 240°.$
∴ Required angle = (240 – 110)° = 130°.

10. Angle traced by hour hand in

$\frac{17}{2}$ hrs $= \left(\frac{360}{12} \times \frac{17}{2}\right)^\circ = 255°$.

Angle traced by min. hand in 30 min. $= \left(\frac{360}{60} \times 30\right)^\circ = 180°$.

$\therefore$ Required angle = (255 – 180)° = 75°.

11. Angle traced by hour hand in

$\frac{13}{3}$ hrs $= \left(\frac{360}{12} \times \frac{13}{3}\right)^\circ = 130°$.

Angle traced by min. hand in 20 min. $= \left(\frac{360}{60} \times 20\right)^\circ = 120°$.

$\therefore$ Required angle = (130 – 120)° = 10°.

12. Angle traced by hour hand in $\frac{21}{4}$ hrs $= \left(\frac{360}{12} \times \frac{21}{4}\right)^\circ = 157\frac{1}{2}^\circ$.

Angle traced by min. hand in 15 min. $= \left(\frac{360}{12} \times 15\right)^\circ = 90°$.

$\therefore$ Required angle $= \left(157\frac{1}{2}\right)^\circ - 90° = 67\frac{1}{2}^\circ$.

13. Angle traced by hour hand in

$\frac{125}{12}$ hrs $= \left(\frac{360}{12} \times \frac{125}{12}\right)^\circ = 312\frac{1}{2}^\circ$.

Angle traced by minute hand in 25 min $= \left(\frac{360}{60} \times 25°\right) = 150°$.

$\therefore$ Reflex angle = $360° - \left(312\frac{1}{2} - 150\right)^\circ = 360° - 162\frac{1}{2}^\circ$

$= 197\frac{1}{2}^\circ$.

14. (A) Angle traced by hour hand in $\frac{7}{6}$ hrs $= \left(\frac{360}{12} \times \frac{7}{6}\right)^\circ = 35°$.

Angle traced by minute hand in 10 min $= \left(\frac{360}{60} \times 10\right)^\circ = 60°$.

$\therefore$ Required angle = (60° – 35°) = 25°.

(B) Angle traced by hour hand in $\frac{9}{4}$ hrs $= \left(\frac{360}{12} \times \frac{9}{4}\right)^\circ = 67\frac{1}{2}^\circ$.

Angle traced by minute hand in 15 min $= \left(\frac{360}{60} \times 15\right)^\circ = 90°$.

$\therefore$ Required angle $= \left(90° - 67\frac{1}{2}^\circ\right) = 22\frac{1}{2}^\circ$.

(C) Angle traced by hour hand in $\frac{26}{3}$ hrs $= \left(\frac{360}{12} \times \frac{26}{3}\right)^\circ = 260°$.

Angle traced by minute hand in 40 min $= \left(\frac{360}{60} \times 40\right)^\circ = 240°$.

$\therefore$ Required angle = (260° – 240°) = 20°

15. Time taken by the hour hand to move 360° = 12 hours.

Time taken by the hour hand to move 135°

$= \left(\frac{12}{360} \times 135\right)$ hrs $= 4\frac{1}{2}$ hrs.

$\therefore$ Required time is $4\frac{1}{2}$ hrs ahead of 3.00, i.e., 7.30.

16. Angle swept by the minute hand in 35 min

$= \left(\frac{360}{60} \times 35\right)^\circ = 210°$.

$\therefore$ Required area = Area of a sector of a circle with radius 10 cm and central angle 210°

$= \frac{\pi r^2 \theta}{360} = \left(\frac{22}{7} \times 10 \times 10 \times \frac{210}{360}\right) \text{cm}^2 = \frac{550}{3} \text{cm}^2 = 183\frac{1}{3} \text{cm}^2$.

17. Number of rounds completed by the minute hand in 3 days 5 hrs = (3 × 24 + 5) = 77.

Number of rounds completed by the hour hand in 3 days 5 hrs $= \left(3 \times 2 + \frac{5}{12}\right) = 6\frac{5}{12}$.

$\therefore$ Difference between the distance traversed

$= \left[77 \times \left(2 \times \frac{22}{7} \times 10\right) - 6\frac{5}{12} \times \left(2 \times \frac{22}{7} \times 7\right)\right]$ cm

= (4840 – 282.33) cm = 4557.67 cm.

18. Distance covered by the arm tip in 1 round

$= \left(2 \times \frac{22}{7} \times 10\right)$ cm $= \frac{440}{7}$ cm.

Now, $\frac{440}{7}$ cm is covered in 60 min.

$\therefore$ 10 cm is covered in $\left(60 \times \frac{7}{440} \times 10\right)$ min

$= 9.54$ min ≈ 10 min.

19. Let the required time be x minutes after midnight.

Duration from 12 midnight to 12 noon

= 12 hrs = (12 × 60) min = 720 min.

So, $x = 9\,(720 - x) \Rightarrow 10x = 6480 \Rightarrow x = 648$.

Hence, required time = 648 min after midnight = 10 hrs 48 min after midnight = 10.48 a.m.

20. The hands of a clock coincide 11 times in every 12 hours (Since between 11 and 1, the coincide only once, i.e. at 12 o'clock).

$\therefore$ The hands coincide 22 times in a day.

21. In 12 hours, the hands coincide or are in opposite direction 22 times.

$\therefore$ In 24 hours, the hands coincide or are in opposite direction 44 times a day.

22. In 12 hours, they are at right angles 22 times.

$\therefore$ In 24 hours, they are at right angles 44 times.

23. The hands of a clock point in opposite directions (in the same straight line) 11 times in every 12 hours (Because between 5 and 7 they point in opposite directions at 6 o'clock only). So, in a day, the hands point in the opposite directions 22 times.

24. The duration from 1.00 p.m. to 10.00 p.m. is 9 hours and during each of these 9 hours the hands of the clock are at right angles twice.

So, required number = 9 × 2 = 18.

25. Clearly, the minute hand traverses 65 minutes in 1 hour.

$\therefore$ Required angle $= \left(\frac{360}{60} \times 65\right)^\circ = 390°$.

26. Total number of strikings = 2 (1 + 2 + 3 + ... + 12)

$= 2\times\frac{12\times13}{2} = 156.$

27. There are 8 intervals in 9 trings and 10 intervals in 11 trings.

Time duration of 8 intervals = 9 sec.

∴ Required time = Duration of 10 intervals

$= \left(\frac{9}{8}\times10\right)\text{sec} = 11.25 \text{ sec.}$

28. There are 5 intervals in 6 strikes.

Number of intervals in 5 seconds = 5. Number of intervals in 10 seconds = 10.

So, the clock will strike 11 times in 10 seconds.

29. Time gained in 1 hour = 6 min.

Time gained in 6 hours = (6 × 6) min = 36 min.

After 6 hours, the correct time is 11:00 a.m. and the watch will show 11:36 a.m.

30. Number of minutes in a day = (24 × 60) = 1440.

∴ Required percentage = $\left(\frac{5}{1440}\times100\right)\% = \frac{50}{144}\%.$

31. Time lost in 1 hour = 5 min.

Time lost in 6 hours = (5 × 6) min = 30 min.

After 6 hours, the correct time will be 6 a.m. and the clock will show 5.30 a.m.

32. Duration from 12 noon to 4:00 a.m. = 16 hours.

Time gained in 24 hours = 15 min.

Time gained in 16 hours = $\left(\frac{5}{24}\times16\right)\text{min} = 10 \text{ min.}$

Hence, time shown by the watch at 4 a.m. = 4:10 a.m.

33. At 3 o' clock, the minute hand is 15 min spaces behind the hour hand.

Thus, the minute hand has to gain (15 + 18) = 33 minute spaces.

55 min are gained in 60 min.

33 min are gained in $\left(\frac{60}{55}\times33\right) = 24 \text{ min.}$

∴ The hands will be 18 min spaces apart at 3:36 P.M.

34. At 9O' clock, the minute hand is 4 min. spaces behind the hour hand.

Thus, the minute hand has to gain (45 – 23)

= 22 min sapces.

5 min are gained in 60 min.

22 min are gained in $\left(\frac{60}{55}\times22\right) = 24 \text{ min.}$

∴ The hands will be 23 min spaces apart at 9:24.

35. 55 min. spaces are covered in 60 min.

60 min. spaces are covered in

$\left(\frac{60}{55}\times60\right)\text{min.} = 65\frac{5}{11}\text{ min.}$

Loss in 64 min. = $\left(65\frac{5}{11}-64\right) = \frac{16}{11}\text{ min.}$

Loss in 24 hrs = $\left(\frac{16}{11}\times\frac{1}{64}\times24\times60\right)\text{min.} = 32\frac{8}{11}\text{ min.}$

36. At 3 o'clock, the minute hand is 15 min. spaces apart from the hour hand.

To be coincident, it must gain 15 min. spaces.

55 min. are gained in 60 min.

15 min. are gained in $\left(\frac{60}{55}\times15\right)\text{min.} = 16\frac{4}{11}\text{ min.}$

∴ The hands are coincident at $16\frac{4}{11}$ min. past 3.

37. To be together between 9 and 10 o'clock, the minute hand has to gain 45 min. spaces.

55 min. spaces are gained in 60 min.

45 min. spaces are gained in $\left(\frac{60}{55}\times45\right)\text{min. or } 49\frac{1}{11}\text{ min.}$

∴ The hands are together at $49\frac{1}{11}$ min. past 9.

38. When the hands of the clock are in the same straight line but not together, they are 30 minute spaces apart.

At 7 o'clock, they are 25 min. spaces apart.

∴ Minute hand will have to gain only 5 min. spaces.

55 min. spaces are gained in 60 min.

5 min. spaces are gained in $\left(\frac{60}{55}\times5\right)\text{min} = 5\frac{5}{11}\text{ min.}$

∴ Required time = $5\frac{5}{11}$ min. past 7.

39. At 4 o'clock, the hands of the watch are 20 min. spaces apart.

To be in opposite directions, they must be 30 min. spaces apart.

∴ Minute hand will have to gain 50 min. spaces.

55 min. spaces are gained in 60 min.

50 min. spaces are gained in $\left(\frac{60}{55}\times50\right)\text{min. or } 54\frac{6}{11}\text{ min.}$

∴ Required time = $54\frac{6}{11}$ min. past 4.

40. At 5 o'clock, the hands are 25 min. spaces apart.

To be at right angles and that too between 5.30 and 6, the minute hand has to gain (25 + 15) = 40 min. spaces.

55 min. spaces are gained in 60 min.

40 min. spaces are gained in $\left(\frac{60}{55}\times40\right)\text{min.} = 43\frac{7}{11}\text{ min.}$

∴ Required time = $43\frac{7}{11}$ min. past 5.

41. To be together between 8 A.M. and 9 A.M, the minute hand has to gain 40 min spaces.

55 min. spaces are gained in 60 min.

40 min. spaces are gained in $\left(\frac{60}{55}\times40\right)\text{min} = 43\frac{7}{11}\text{ min.}$

So, Henry started his trip at $43\frac{7}{11}$ min past 8 A.M.

Now, to be 180° apart, the hands must be 30 min spaces apart.

At 2 P.M, they are 10 min spaces apart.

∴ The minute hand will have to gain (10 + 30) = 40 min spaces.

As calculated above, 40 min. spaces are gained in $43\frac{7}{11}$ min.

So, Henry's trip ended at $43\frac{7}{11}$ min past 2 P.M.

∴ Duration of travel = Duration from $43\frac{7}{11}$ min past 8 A.M. to $43\frac{7}{11}$ min past 2 P.M. = 6 hours.

42. The watch loses $\frac{1}{2}$ hour each hour. So, it must have taken 8 hours to show 4 p.m. from 12 noon. Thus, it stopped at 8 p.m.

So, the correct time is 5 hours ahead of 8 p.m., i.e., 1 a.m.

43. Time lost in $6\frac{1}{2}$ hours $= \left(6\frac{1}{2}\times 4\right)$ sec = 26 sec.

Correct time after $6\frac{1}{2}$ hours = 7 hr 40 min 6 sec + 6 hr 30 min = 14 hr 10 min 6 sec.

Time shown by the clock = 14 hr 10 min 6 sec – 26 sec = 14 hr 9 min 40 sec.

44. Clearly, the first watch will show the correct time when it has gained 12 hours i.e., (12 × 60) = 720 min and the secon watch will show the correct time when it has lost 720 min.

Time taken by first watch to gain 720 min = 720 days.

Time taken by second watch to gain 720 min $=\left(720\div 1\frac{1}{2}\right)\text{days}=\left(720\times\frac{2}{3}\text{ days}\right)=480$ days.

So the first watch shows correct time after every 720 days and the second wach after every 480 days.

∴ Time after which both the clocks will together tell the correct time = L.C.M. of 720 and 480 = 1440 days.

45. Time from 1 p.m. on Tuesday to 1 p.m. on Thursday = 48 hours.

So, the watch gains (1 + 2) min or 3 min in 48 hrs.

Now, 3 min are gained in 48 hrs.

So, 1 min is gained in $\left(\frac{48}{3}\right)$ = 16 hrs.

Thus, the watch showed the correct time 16 hrs. after 1 p.m. on Tuesday, i.e. 5 a.m. on Wednesday.

46. Time from 12 p.m. on Monday to 2 p.m. on the following Monday = 7 days 2 hours = 170 hours.

∴ The watch gains $\left(2+4\frac{4}{5}\right)$ min. or $\frac{34}{5}$ min. in 170 hrs.

Now, $\frac{34}{5}$ min. are gained in 170 hrs.

∴ 2 min. are gained in $\left(170\times\frac{5}{34}\times 2\right)$ hrs = 50 hrs.

∴ Watch is correct 2 days 2 hrs. after 12 p.m. on Monday *i.e.* it will be correct at 2 p.m. on Wednesday.

47. Time from 7 a.m. to 4.15 p.m. = 9 hrs 15 min. = $\frac{37}{4}$ hrs.

3 min. 5 sec. of this clock = 3 min. of the correct clock.

⇒ $\frac{37}{720}$ hrs of this clock = $\frac{1}{20}$ hrs of the correct clock

⇒ $\frac{37}{4}$ hrs of this clock

$=\left(\frac{1}{20}\times\frac{720}{37}\times\frac{37}{4}\right)$ hrs of the correct clock

= 9 hrs of the correct clock

∴ The correct time is 9 hrs after 7 a.m., i.e. 4 p.m.

48. Since the time read by the lady was 57 minutes earlier than the correct time, so the minute hand is (60 – 57) = 3 minute spaces behind the hour hand.

Now, at 5 o'clock, the minute hand is 25 minute spaces behind the hour hand.

To be 3 minute spaces behind, it must gain (25 – 3) = 22 minute spaces.

55 min spaces are gained in 60 min.

22 min spaces are gained in $\left(\frac{60}{55}\times 22\right)$ = 24 min.

Hence, the correct time was 24 minutes past 5.

49. 55 minutes spaces are covered in 60 minutes

60 minutes spaces are covered in $\left[\frac{60}{55}\times 60\right]$ minutes $=65\frac{5}{11}$ minutes

Loss in 64 minute = $65\frac{5}{11}-64=\frac{16}{11}$ minutes

Loss in 24 hours = $\left(\frac{16}{11}\times\frac{1}{64}\times 24\times 60\right)$ minutes $= 32\frac{8}{11}$ minutes

50. After 12 days, i.e., after 12 × 24 hours clock A will gain 48 minutes and will slow 12:48 noon.

After 12 days, i.e., after 12 × 24 hours clock B will loose 16 minutes and will show 11:44 am.

The two clocks will show the same time after 135 days

The time difference has to be 12 hours between then = 720 minutes.

A will gain 540 minutes in 135 days.

B will loose 180 minutes in 135 days Total 720 minutes.

Further if we consider only time then the problem becomes simpler

Total difference of minutes between the times shown by the clocks after 36 hours

⇒ $\frac{16}{3}$ minutes difference in 1 day

⇒ 12 × 60 minutes difference in $\frac{3}{16}\times 12\times 60=135$ days

51. Let angle between the hands of clock be x^o.

When the time is 4 : 25 a.m.

{Where M = minutes and H = hours}

Required angle = $30\left(\frac{M}{5}-H\right)-\frac{M}{2}$

$=30\left(\frac{25}{5}-4\right)-\frac{25}{2}=30\left(\frac{25-20}{5}\right)-\frac{25}{2}=30\left(\frac{5}{5}\right)-\frac{25}{2}=30-\frac{25}{2}$

$=\frac{60-25}{2}=\frac{35}{2}=17\frac{1}{2}^{o}$

52. In 1 hour, the hour hand's make the angle of 30°.

The hour hand make the angle of x^o in $8\frac{30}{60}$ hours.

$\Rightarrow x=\left(30\times 8\frac{1}{2}\right)^{o}$

$=\left(30\times\frac{17}{2}\right)=225^{o}$

The minute hand make the angle in 1 minute = 6°

Minute hand makes the angle in 30 minutes

= (6 × 30)° = 180°

Required angle = 255°–180° = 75°

53. Time interval from 9 am on Monday to 8 : 30 pm on Wednesday

$=(24\times 2.5)-0:30$ hours

= 60 – 0 : 30 hours

= 59 hours 30 minutes

$=59\frac{30}{60}=59\frac{1}{2}$

$=\frac{119}{2}$ hours

Also 24 hours – 12 minutes

= 23 hours 48 minutes

$=23+\frac{48}{60}=23\frac{4}{5}$ hours $=\frac{119}{5}$ hours

$\frac{119}{5}$ hours of this clock = 24 hours of the correct clock

$\therefore\ \frac{119}{2}$ hours of this clock $=\frac{24\times 5}{119}\times\frac{119}{2}=60$ hours

$\left(60-\frac{119}{2}\right)$hours

$=\frac{120-119}{2}$ hours $=\frac{1}{2}$ hours = 30 minutes

Hence, the correct time is 30 minutes after 8 : 30 pm. i.e. 9 pm.

54. One clock show 10pm. On 21st January 2010

One clock gains = 2 minutes

Other clock loses = 5 minutes

Time period between 10 pm and 4 pm = 18 hours

∴ Required difference = (2 × 18 + 5 × 18) minutes

= 126 minutes

29 Stocks and Shares

To start a big business or an industry, a large amount of money is needed. It is beyond the capacity of one or two persons to arrange such a huge amount. However, some persons associate together to form a company. They, then, draft a proposal, issue a prospectus (in the name of the company), explaining the plan of the project and invite the public to invest money in this project. They, thus, pool up the funds from the public, by assigning them ***shares*** of the company.

IMPORTANT FACTS AND FORMULAE

I. Stock-capital: *The total amount of money needed to run the company is called the* ***stock-capital.***

II. Shares or Stock: *The whole capital is divided into small units, called* ***shares*** *or* ***stock.***

For each investment, the company issues a *share-certificate*, showing the value of each share and the number of shares held by a person.

The person who subscribes in shares or stock is called a ***shareholder*** *or* ***stockholder.***

III. Dividend: *The annual profit distributed among shareholders is called* ***dividend.***

Dividend is paid annually as per share or as a percentage.

IV. Face Value: *The value of a share or stock printed on the share-certificate is called its* ***Face Value*** *or* ***Nominal Value*** *or* ***Par Value.***

V. Market Value: The stocks of different companies are sold and bought in the open market through brokers at stock-exchanges. A share (or stock) is said to be :

(*i*) ***At premium*** or ***Above par***, if its market value is more than its face value.

(*ii*) ***At par***, if its market value is the same as its face value.

(*iii*) ***At discount*** or ***Below par***, if its market value is less than its face value.

Thus, if a ₹ 100 stock is quoted at a premium of 16, then market value of the stock

= ₹ (100 + 16) = ₹ 116.

Likewise, if a ₹ 100 stock is quoted at a discount of 7, then market value of the stock

= ₹ (100 – 7) = ₹ 93.

VI. Brokerage: *The broker's charge is called* ***brokerage.***

(*i*) When stock is purchased, brokerage is added to the cost price.

(*ii*) When stock is sold, brokerage is subtracted from the selling price.

Remember:

(*i*) The face value of a share always remains the same.

(*ii*) The market value of a share changes from time to time.

(*iii*) Dividend is always paid on the face value of a share.

(*iv*) Number of shares held by a person

$$= \frac{\text{Total Investment}}{\text{Investment in 1 Share}} = \frac{\text{Total Income}}{\text{Income from 1 Share}} = \frac{\text{Total Face Value}}{\text{Face value of 1 Share}}.$$

Thus, by a ₹ 100, 9% stock at 120, we mean that :

(*i*) Face Value (N.V.) of stock = ₹ 100.

(*ii*) Market Value (M.V.) of stock = ₹ 120.

(*iii*) Annual dividend on 1 share = 9% of face value = 9% of ₹ 100 = ₹ 9.

(*iv*) An investment of ₹ 120 gives an annual income of ₹ 9.

(*v*) Rate of interest p.a. = Annual income from an investment of ₹ 100.

$$= \left(\frac{9}{120} \times 100\right)\% = 7\frac{1}{2}\%.$$

SOLVED EXAMPLES

Ex. 1. ***Find the cost of***

(i) ₹ 7200, 8% stock at 90 ***(ii) ₹ 4500, 8.5% stock at 4 premium***

(iii) ₹ 6400, 10% stock at 15 discount

Sol. *(i)* Cost of ₹ 100 stock = ₹ 90.

Cost of ₹ 7200 stock = ₹ $\left(\frac{90}{100} \times 7200\right)$ = ₹ 6480.

(ii) Cost of ₹ 100 stock = ₹ (100 + 4) = ₹ 104.

Cost of ₹ 4500 stock = ₹ $\left(\frac{104}{100} \times 4500\right)$ = ₹ 4680.

(iii) Cost of ₹ 100 stock = ₹ (100 – 15) = ₹ 85.

Cost of ₹ 6400 stock = ₹ $\left(\frac{85}{100} \times 6400\right)$ = ₹ 5440.

Ex. 2. ***Find the cash required to purchase ₹ 3200, $7\frac{1}{2}$% stock at 107 $\left(\text{brokerage } \frac{1}{2}\%\right)$.***

Sol. Cash required to purchase ₹ 100 stock = ₹ $\left(107 + \frac{1}{2}\right)$ = ₹ $\frac{215}{2}$.

Cash required to purchase ₹ 3200 stock = ₹ $\left(\frac{215}{2} \times \frac{1}{100} \times 3200\right)$ = ₹ 3440.

Ex. 3. ***Find the cash realised by selling ₹ 2440, 9.5% stock at 4 discount $\left(\text{brokerage } \frac{1}{4}\%\right)$.***

Sol. By selling ₹ 100 stock, cash realised = ₹ $\left[(100 - 4) - \frac{1}{4}\right]$ = ₹ $\frac{383}{4}$.

By selling ₹ 2400 stock, cash realised = ₹ $\left(\frac{383}{4} \times \frac{1}{100} \times 2400\right)$ = ₹ 2298.

Ex. 4. ***Find the annual income derived from ₹ 2500, 8% stock at 106.***

Sol. Income from ₹ 100 stock = ₹ 8.

Income from ₹ 2500 stock = ₹ $\left(\frac{8}{100} \times 2500\right)$ = ₹ 200.

Ex. 5. ***Find the annual income derived by investing ₹ 6800 in 10% stock at 136.***

Sol. By investing ₹ 136, income obtained = ₹ 10.

By investing ₹ 6800, income obtained = ₹ $\left(\frac{10}{136} \times 6800\right)$ = ₹ 500.

Ex. 6. ***Which is better investment? $7\frac{1}{2}$% stock at 105 or $6\frac{1}{2}$% stock at 94.***

Sol. Let the investment in each case be ₹ (105 × 94).

Case I : $7\frac{1}{2}$% stock at 105 :

On investing ₹ 105, income = ₹ $\frac{15}{2}$.

On investing ₹ (105 × 94), income = ₹ $\left(\frac{15}{2} \times \frac{1}{105} \times 105 \times 94\right)$ = ₹ 705.

Case II : $6\frac{1}{2}$% stock at 94 :

On investing ₹ 94, income = ₹ $\frac{13}{2}$.

On investing ₹ (105 × 94), income = ₹ $\left(\frac{13}{2} \times \frac{1}{94} \times 105 \times 94\right)$ = ₹ 682.50.

Clearly, the income from $7\frac{1}{2}$% stock at 105 is more.

Hence, the investment in $7\frac{1}{2}\%$ stock at 105 is better.

Ex. 7. ***Find the cost of 96 shares of ₹ 10 each at $\frac{3}{4}$ discount, brokerage being $\frac{1}{4}$ per share.***

Sol. Cost of 1 share = ₹ $\left[\left(10-\frac{3}{4}\right)+\frac{1}{4}\right]$ = ₹ $\frac{19}{2}$.

Cost of 96 shares = ₹ $\left(\frac{19}{2}\times 96\right)$ = ₹ 912.

Ex. 8. ***Chinmay invested 25%, 30% and 20% of his savings in buying shares of three different companies P, Q and R which declared dividends 10%, 12% and 15% respectively. If his total income on account of dividends be ₹ 5460, find the amount he invested in buying shares of the company Q.***

Sol. Let Chinmay's savings be ₹ x.
Then, amount invested in shares of company P = 25% of ₹ x;
amount invested in shares of company Q = 30% of ₹ x;
amount invested in shares of company R = 20% of ₹ x.
Total income = ₹ (10% of 25% of x + 12% of 30% of x + 15% of 20% of x)

$$= ₹\left(\frac{250}{10000}x+\frac{360}{10000}x+\frac{300}{10000}x\right) = ₹\frac{910}{10000}x.$$

$$\therefore \frac{910x}{10000} = 5460 \Rightarrow x = \frac{5460\times 10000}{910} = 60000.$$

Hence, amount invested in shares of company Q = 30% of ₹ 60000 = ₹ 18000.

Ex. 9. ***Find the income derived from 88 shares of ₹ 25 each at 5 premium, brokerage being $\frac{1}{4}$ per share and the rate of dividend being $7\frac{1}{2}\%$ per annum. Also, find the rate of interest on the investment.***

Sol. Cost of 1 share = ₹ $\left(25+5+\frac{1}{4}\right)$ = ₹ $\frac{121}{4}$.

Cost of 88 shares = ₹ $\left(\frac{121}{4}\times 88\right)$ = ₹ 2662.

$\therefore$ Investment made = ₹ 2662.
Face value of 88 shares = ₹ (88 × 25) = ₹ 2200.

Dividend on ₹ 100 = $\frac{15}{2}$. Dividend on ₹ 2200 = ₹ $\left(\frac{15}{2}\times\frac{1}{100}\times 2200\right)$ = ₹ 165.

$\therefore$ Income derived = ₹ 165.

Rate of interest on investment = $\left(\frac{165}{2662}\times 100\right)$ = 6.2%.

Ex. 10. ***Ravi invested ₹ 913 partly in 4% stock at ₹ 97 and partly in 5% stock at ₹ 107. If his income form both is equal, find the amount invested in each stock.*** **(R.R.B., 2006)**

Sol. Let the investment in 4% stock be ₹ x.
Then, investment in 5% stock = ₹ $(913 - x)$.

$$\frac{4}{97}\times x = \frac{5}{107}\times(913-x) \Leftrightarrow \frac{4}{97}x\,\frac{4565}{107}-\frac{5x}{107} \Leftrightarrow \frac{4x}{97}+\frac{5x}{107}=\frac{4565}{107}$$

$$\Leftrightarrow \frac{428x+485x}{97\times 107} = \frac{4565}{107} \Leftrightarrow 913x = \frac{4565}{107}\times 97\times 107$$

$$\Leftrightarrow x = \frac{4565\times 97}{913} = 485.$$

Hence, amount invested in 4% stock = ₹ 485.
And, amount invested in 5% stock = ₹ (913 − 485) = ₹ 428.

Ex. 11. ***A man buys ₹ 25 shares in a company which pays 9% dividend. The money invested is such that it gives 10% on investment. At what price did he buy the shares?*** (G.B.O., 2007)

Sol. Suppose he buys each share for ₹ x.

Then, $\left(25 \times \frac{9}{100}\right) = \left(x \times \frac{10}{100}\right)$ or $x = 22.50$.

$\therefore$ Cost of each share = ₹ 22.50.

Ex. 12. ***A man sells ₹ 5000, 12% stock at 156 and invests the proceeds partly in 8% stock at 90 and 9% stock at 108. He thereby increases his income by ₹ 70. How much of the proceeds were invested in each stock?*** (M.A.T., 2005)

Sol. S.P. of ₹ 5000 stock = ₹ $\left(\frac{156}{100} \times 5000\right)$ = ₹ 7800.

Income from this stock = ₹ $\left(\frac{12}{100} \times 5000\right)$ = ₹ 600.

Let investment in 8% stock be ₹ x and that in 9% stock = ₹ $(7800 - x)$.

$\therefore \left(x \times \frac{8}{90}\right) + (7800 - x) \times \frac{9}{108} = (600 + 70)$

$\Leftrightarrow \frac{4x}{45} + \frac{7800 - x}{12} = 670 \Leftrightarrow 16x + 117000 - 15x = (670 \times 180) \Leftrightarrow x = 3600.$

$\therefore$ Money invested in 8% stock at 90 = ₹ 3600.

Money invested in 9% at 108 = ₹ (7800 – 3600) = ₹ 4200.

EXERCISE

(OBJECTIVE TYPE QUESTIONS)

Directions: ***Mark (✓) against the correct answer:***

1. The cost price of a ₹ 100 stock at 4 discount, when brokerage is $\frac{1}{4}$% is
   (*a*) ₹ 95.75 (*b*) ₹ 96
   (*c*) ₹ 96.25 (*d*) ₹ 104.25

2. The cash realised on selling a 14% stock at ₹ 106.25, brokerage being $\frac{1}{4}$%, is
   (*a*) ₹ 105.50 (*b*) ₹ 106
   (*c*) ₹ 106.50 (*d*) ₹ 113.75

3. How many shares of market value ₹ 25 each can be purchased for ₹ 12750, brokerage being 2%?
   (*a*) 450 (*b*) 500
   (*c*) 550 (*d*) 600

4. A man invests in a 16% stock at 128. The interest obtained by him is
   (*a*) 8% (*b*) 12%
   (*c*) 12.5% (*d*) 16%

5. The income derived from a ₹ 100, 13% stock at ₹ 105, is
   (*a*) ₹ 5 (*b*) ₹ 8
   (*c*) ₹ 13 (*d*) ₹ 18

6. A wants to secure an annual income of ₹ 1500 by investing in 15% debentures of face value ₹ 100 each and available for ₹ 104 each. If the brokerage is 1%, then the sum of money he should invest is (M.A.T., 2002)
   (*a*) ₹ 10504 (*b*) ₹ 10784
   (*c*) ₹ 15000 (*d*) ₹ 19642

7. A man invested ₹ 4455 in ₹ 10 shares quoted at ₹ 8.25. If the rate of dividend be 12%, his annual income is : (G.B.O., 2007)
   (*a*) ₹ 207.40 (*b*) ₹ 534.60
   (*c*) ₹ 648 (*d*) ₹ 655.60

8. A man invested ₹ 14,400 in ₹ 100 shares of a company at 20% premium. If the company declares 5% dividend at the end of the year, then how much does he get? (R.R.B., 2008; Hotel Management, 2003)
   (*a*) ₹ 500 (*b*) ₹ 600
   (*c*) ₹ 650 (*d*) ₹ 720

9. A person has deposited ₹ 13200 in a bank which pays 14% interest. He withdraws the money and invests in ₹ 100 stock at ₹ 110 which pays a dividend of 15%. How much does he gain or lose? (M.A.T., 2004)
   (*a*) Loses ₹ 48 (*b*) Gains ₹ 48
   (*c*) Loses ₹ 132 (*d*) Gains ₹ 132

10. A 6% stock yields 8%. The market value of the stock is
(*a*) ₹ 48 (*b*) ₹ 75
(*c*) ₹ 96 (*d*) ₹ 133.33

11. A 9% stock yields 8%. The market value of the stock is
(*a*) ₹ 72 (*b*) ₹ 92
(*c*) ₹ 112.50 (*d*) ₹ 116.50

12. A 12% stock yielding 10% is quoted at
(*a*) ₹ 83.33 (*b*) ₹ 110
(*c*) ₹ 112 (*d*) ₹ 120

13. By investing ₹ 3450 in a $4\frac{1}{2}\%$ stock, a man obtains an income of ₹ 150. Find the market price of the stock. **(SCMHRD, 2002)**
(*a*) ₹ 103.50 (*b*) ₹ 105
(*c*) ₹ 107.50 (*d*) ₹ 110

14. To produce an annual income of ₹ 1200 from a 12% stock at 90, the amount of stock needed is
(*a*) ₹ 10,000 (*b*) ₹ 10,800
(*c*) ₹ 14,400 (*d*) ₹ 16,000

15. In order to obtain an income of ₹ 650 from 10% stock at ₹ 96, one must make an investment of
(*a*) ₹ 3100 (*b*) ₹ 6240
(*c*) ₹ 6500 (*d*) ₹ 9600

16. By investing in $16\frac{2}{3}\%$ stock at 64, one earns ₹ 1500. The investment made is
(*a*) ₹ 5640 (*b*) ₹ 5760
(*c*) ₹ 7500 (*d*) ₹ 9600

17. A man invested ₹ 1552 in a stock at 97 to obtain an income of ₹ 128. The dividend from the stock is
(*a*) 7.5% (*b*) 8%
(*c*) 9.7% (*d*) None of these

18. A man bought 20 shares of ₹ 50 at 5 discount, the rate of dividend being $13\frac{1}{2}\%$. The rate of interest obtained is :
(*a*) $12\frac{1}{2}\%$ (*b*) $13\frac{1}{2}\%$
(*c*) 15% (*d*) $16\frac{2}{3}\%$

19. At what price should I buy a share the value of which is ₹ 100, paying a dividend of 8% so that my yield is 11%? **(M.A.T., 2005)**
(*a*) ₹ 70 (*b*) ₹ 72.72
(*c*) ₹ 75 (*d*) ₹ 84

20. A man buys ₹ 50 shares in a company which pays 10% dividend. If the man gets 12.5% on his investment, at what price did he buy the shares? **(L.I.C.A.A.O., 2003)**
(*a*) ₹ 37.50 (*b*) ₹ 40
(*c*) ₹ 48 (*d*) ₹ 52

21. The market value of a 10.5% stock, in which an income of ₹ 756 is derived by investing ₹ 9000, brokerage being $\frac{1}{4}\%$, is
(*a*) ₹ 108.25 (*b*) ₹ 112.20
(*c*) ₹ 124.75 (*d*) ₹ 125.25

22. Sakshi invests a part of ₹ 12,000 in 12% stock at ₹ 120 and the remainder in 15% stock at ₹ 125. If his total dividend per annum is ₹ 1360, how much does he invest in 12% stock at ₹ 120?
(*a*) ₹ 4000 (*b*) ₹ 4500
(*c*) ₹ 5500 (*d*) ₹ 6000

23. ₹ 9800 are invested partly in 9% stock at 75 and 10% stock at 80 to have equal amount of incomes. The investment in 9% stock is
(*a*) ₹ 4800 (*b*) ₹ 5000
(*c*) ₹ 5400 (*d*) ₹ 5600

24. A person wants to invest ₹ 140000 in two types of bonds. The annual return is 12% on bond A and 16% on bond B. One of the conditions requires that the investment in bond B cannot be more than 40% of the investment in bond A. What is the maximum return he can get per year? **(S.S.C., 2002)**
(*a*) ₹ 15600 (*b*) ₹ 16800
(*c*) ₹ 19200 (*d*) ₹ 20800

25. A man invests some money partly in 9% stock at 96 and partly in 12% stock at 120. To obtain equal dividends from both, he must invest the money in the ratio
(*a*) 3 : 4 (*b*) 3 : 5
(*c*) 4 : 5 (*d*) 16 : 15

26. Which is better investment — 11% stock at 143 or $9\frac{3}{4}\%$ stock at 117?
(*a*) 11% stock at 143 (*b*) $9\frac{3}{4}\%$ stock at 117
(*c*) Both are equally good
(*d*) Cannot be compared, as the total mount of investment is not given

27. A person invests ₹ 5508 in 4% stock at 102. He afterwards sells out at 105 and reinvests in 5% stock at 126. What is the change in his income? **(I.I.F.T., 2005)**
(*a*) ₹ 7 (*b*) ₹ 9
(*c*) ₹ 10 (*d*) ₹ 20

28. A retired man sells out ₹ 7500 of a 10% stock at ₹ 105.50 and invests the proceeds in 14% stock at ₹ 124.50. What is the change in income if he pays a service charge of 0.5% of the face value on each transaction?
(*a*) ₹ 95 (*b*) ₹ 114
(*c*) ₹ 132 (*d*) None of these

29. Which is better investment, 12% stock at par with an income tax at the rate of 5 paise per rupee or

$14\frac{2}{7}\%$ stock at 120 free from income tax?

(*a*) 12% stock (*b*) $14\frac{2}{7}\%$ stock

(*c*) Both are equally good (*d*) Cannot be compared

30. A invested some money in 10% stock at 96. If B wants to invest in an equally good 12% stock, he must purchase a stock worth of :

(*a*) ₹ 80 (*b*) ₹ 115.20

(*c*) ₹ 120 (*d*) ₹ 125.40

ANSWERS

1. (*c*)	2. (*b*)	3. (*b*)	4. (*c*)	5. (*c*)	6. (*a*)	7. (*c*)	8. (*b*)	9. (*a*)	10. (*b*)
11. (*c*)	12. (*d*)	13. (*a*)	14. (*a*)	15. (*b*)	16. (*b*)	17. (*b*)	18. (*c*)	19. (*b*)	20. (*b*)
21. (*c*)	22. (*a*)	23. (*b*)	24. (*b*)	25. (*d*)	26. (*b*)	27. (*b*)	28. (*c*)	29. (*b*)	30. (*b*)

SOLUTIONS

1. C.P. = ₹ $\left(100 - 4 + \frac{1}{4}\right)$ = ₹ 96.25.

2. Cash realised = ₹ (106.25 – 0.25) = ₹ 106.

3. C.P. of each share = ₹ (25 + 2% of 25) = ₹ 25.50.

∴ Number of shares = $\left(\frac{12750}{25.50}\right)$ = 500.

4. By investing ₹ 128, income derived = ₹ 16.

By investing ₹ 100, income derived = ₹ $\left(\frac{16}{128} \times 100\right)$ = ₹ 12.5.

∴ Interest obtained = 12.5%.

5. Income on ₹ 100 stock = ₹ 13.

6. Income on each debenture = 15% of ₹ 100 = ₹ 15.

Number of debentures required = ₹ $\left(\frac{1500}{15}\right)$ = ₹ 100.

Cost of each debenture

= ₹ (104 + 1% of 104) = (104 + 1.04) = ₹ 105.04.

∴ Total investment = ₹ (105.04 × 100) = ₹ 10504.

7. Number of shares = $\left(\frac{4455}{8.25}\right)$ = 540.

Face value = ₹ (540 × 10) = ₹ 5400.

Annual income = ₹ $\left(\frac{12}{100} \times 5400\right)$ = ₹ 648.

8. Number of shares = $\left(\frac{14400}{120}\right)$ = 120.

Face value = ₹ (100 × 120) = ₹ 12000.

Annual income = ₹ $\left(\frac{5}{100} \times 12000\right)$ = ₹ 600.

9. Income from bank = 14% of ₹ 13200 = ₹ 1848.

Number of shares purchased = ₹ $\left(\frac{13200}{110}\right)$ = ₹ 120.

Income from stock

= (15% of ₹ 100) × 120 = ₹ (15 × 120) = ₹ 1800.

∴ Loss = ₹ (1848 – 1800) = ₹ 48.

10. For an income of ₹ 8, investment = ₹ 100.

For an income of ₹ 6, investment = ₹ $\left(\frac{100}{8} \times 6\right)$ = ₹ 75.

∴ Market value of ₹ 100 stock = ₹ 75.

11. To obtain ₹ 8, investment = ₹ 100.

To obtain ₹ 9, investment = ₹ $\left(\frac{100}{8} \times 9\right)$ = ₹ 112.50.

∴ Market value of ₹ 100 stock = ₹ 112.50.

12. To earn ₹ 10, money invested = ₹ 100.

To earn ₹ 12, money invested = ₹ $\left(\frac{100}{10} \times 12\right)$ = ₹ 120.

∴ Market value of ₹ 100 stock = ₹ 120.

13. To earn ₹ 150, investment = ₹ 3450.

To earn ₹ 4.50, investment = ₹ $\left(\frac{3450}{150} \times 4.50\right)$ = ₹ 103.50.

∴ Market value of ₹ 100 stock = ₹ 103.50.

14. For an income of ₹ 12, stock needed = ₹ 100.

For an income of ₹ 1200, stock needed

= ₹ $\left(\frac{100}{12} \times 1200\right)$ = ₹ 10,000.

15. To obtain ₹ 10, investment = ₹ 96.

To obtain ₹ 650, investment = ₹ $\left(\frac{96}{10} \times 650\right)$ = ₹ 6240.

16. To earn ₹ $\frac{50}{3}$, investment = ₹ 64.

To earn ₹ 1500, investment = ₹ $\left(64 \times \frac{3}{50} \times 1500\right)$ = ₹ 5760.

17. By investing ₹ 1552, income = ₹ 128.

By investing ₹ 97, income = ₹ $\left(\frac{128}{1552} \times 97\right)$ = ₹ 8.

∴ Dividend = 8%.

18. Investment = ₹ [20 × (50 – 5)] = ₹ 900.

Face value = ₹ (50 × 20) = ₹ 1000.

Dividend = ₹ $\left(\frac{27}{2} \times \frac{1000}{100}\right)$ = ₹ 135.

Interest obtained = $\left(\frac{135}{900} \times 100\right)$% = 15%.

19. Dividend on ₹ 100 = 8% of ₹ 100 = ₹ 8.

₹ 11 is an income on ₹ 100.

∴ ₹ 8 is an income on ₹ $\left(\frac{100}{11} \times 8\right)$ = ₹ 72.72.

20. Dividend on 1 share = ₹ $\left(\frac{10}{100} \times 50\right)$ = ₹ 5.

₹ 12.50 is an income on an investment of ₹ 100.

₹ 5 is an income on an investment of ₹ $\left(100 \times \frac{2}{25} \times 5\right)$ = ₹ 40.

∴ Cost of 1 share = ₹ 40.

21. For an income of ₹ 756, investment = ₹ 9000.

For an income of ₹ $\frac{21}{2}$, investment = ₹ $\left(\frac{9000}{756} \times \frac{21}{2}\right)$ = ₹ 125.

∴ For a ₹ 100 stock, investment = ₹ 125.

Market value of ₹ 100 stock = ₹ $\left(125 - \frac{1}{4}\right)$ = ₹ 124.75.

22. Let investment in 12% stock be ₹ x. Then, investment in 15% stock = ₹ $(12000 - x)$.

$\frac{12}{120} \times x + \frac{15}{125} \times (12000 - x) = 1360$

$\Leftrightarrow \frac{x}{10} + \frac{3}{25}(12000 - x) = 1360$

$\Leftrightarrow 5x + 72000 - 6x = 1360 \times 50 \Leftrightarrow x = 4000.$

23. Let the investment in 9% stock be ₹ x.

Then, investment in 10% stock = ₹ $(9800 - x)$.

$\frac{9}{75} \times x = \frac{10}{80} \times (9800 - x) \Leftrightarrow \frac{3x}{25} = \frac{9800 - x}{8}$

$\Leftrightarrow 24x = 9800 \times 25 - 25x$

$\Leftrightarrow 49x = 9800 \times 25 \Leftrightarrow x = 5000.$

24. Let the investment in Bond A be ₹ x. Then, investment in Bond B = ₹ $(140000 - x)$.

For maximum return, we have :

$140000 - x = 40\%$ of $x \Rightarrow 140000 - x = \frac{2}{5}x$

$\Rightarrow \frac{7}{5}x = 140000 \Rightarrow x = \frac{140000 \times 5}{7} = 100000.$

So, investment in Bond A = ₹ 100000;

Investment in Bond B = ₹ (140000 – 100000) = ₹ 40000.

∴ Maximum return = 12% of ₹ 100000 + 16% of ₹ 40000
= ₹ (12000 + 4800) = ₹ 16800.

25. For an income of ₹ 1 in 9% stock at 96,

Investment = ₹ $\left(\frac{96}{9}\right)$ = ₹ $\frac{32}{3}$.

For an income of ₹ 1 in 12% stock at 120, investment ₹ $\left(\frac{120}{12}\right)$ = ₹ 10.

∴ Ratio of investments = $\frac{32}{3}$: 10 = 32 : 30 = 16 : 15.

26. Let investment in each case be ₹ (143 × 117).

Income in 1st case = ₹ $\left(\frac{11}{143} \times 143 \times 117\right)$ = ₹ 1287.

Income in 2nd case = ₹ $\left(\frac{39}{4 \times 117} \times 143 \times 117\right)$ = ₹ 1394.25.

Clearly, $9\frac{3}{4}\%$ stock at 117 is better.

27. Number of shares purchased = $\frac{5508}{102} = 54$.

Income from each share = 4% of ₹ 100 = ₹ 4.

∴ Original income = ₹ (54 × 4) = ₹ 216.

Money incurred from sale of share
= ₹ (105 × 54) = ₹ 5670.

Number of new shares purchased = $\left(\frac{5670}{126}\right) = 45$.

New income = ₹ (45 × 5) = ₹ 225.

∴ Change in income = ₹ (225 – 216) = ₹ 9.

28. Number of shares sold = $\frac{7500}{100} = 75$.

Proceeds from sale of ₹ 7500 stock
= ₹ [(105.50 – 0.5) × 75] = ₹ 7875.

Number of new shares purchased

$= \left(\frac{7875}{124.50 + 0.50}\right) = \left(\frac{7875}{125}\right) = 63.$

Original income = 10% of ₹ 7500 = ₹ 750.

New income = 14% of ₹ 6300 = ₹ $\left(\frac{14}{100} \times 6300\right)$ = ₹ 882.

∴ Change in income = ₹ (882 – 750) = ₹ 132.

29. Let investment in each case = ₹ (100 × 120).

Income from 12% stock = ₹ $\left(\frac{12}{100} \times 100 \times 120\right)$ = ₹ 1440.

Net income = ₹ $\left(1440 - \frac{5}{100} \times 1440\right)$ = ₹ 1368.

Income from $14\frac{2}{7}\%$ stock = ₹ $\left(\frac{100}{7 \times 20} \times 100 \times 120\right)$
= ₹ 1428.57.

Clearly, $14\frac{2}{7}\%$ stock is better.

30. For an income of ₹ 10, investment = ₹ 96.

For an income of ₹ 12, investment

= ₹ $\left(\frac{96}{10} \times 12\right)$ = ₹ 115.20.

30 Permutations and Combinations

IMPORTANT FACTS AND FORMULAE

I. Factorial *n*: *Let n be a positive integer. Then, factorial n is denoted by $\lfloor n$ or $n!$, defined as $\lfloor n = n(n-1)(n-2)(n-3) \ldots 4 \cdot 3 \cdot 2 \cdot 1$.*

Ex. (*i*) $\lfloor 4 = (4 \times 3 \times 2 \times 1) = 24$. (*ii*) $\lfloor 5 = (5 \times 4 \times 3 \times 2 \times 1) = 120$.

Note: We define, $\lfloor 0 = 1$.

II. (*i*) **Permutations:** *The different arrangements of a given number of things by taking some or all at a time are called permutations.*

Ex.1. All permutations or arrangements made with the letters *a, b, c* by taking two at a time are (*ab, ba, ac, ca, bc, cb*).

Ex.2. All permutations made with the letters *a, b, c* by taking 3 at a time are (*abc, acb, bac, bca, cab, cba*).

(*ii*) ***Number of Permutations of n things, taking r at a time is given by:***

$$^nP_r = n(n-1)(n-2) \ldots (n-r+1) = \frac{\lfloor n}{\lfloor n-r}.$$

Ex. (*i*) $^8P_2 = (8 \times 7) = 56$. (*ii*) $^7P_3 = (7 \times 6 \times 5) = 210$.

(*iii*) ***Number of all permutations of n things, taking all at a time is $\lfloor n$.***

(*iv*) If there are *n* objects of which p_1 are alike of one kind; p_2 are alike of another kind; p_3 are alike of third kind and so on and p_r are alike of *r*th kind such that $(p_1 + p_2 + \ldots + p_r) = n$, then **number of permutations** $= \dfrac{\lfloor n}{\lfloor p_1 \cdot \lfloor p_2 \cdot \lfloor p_3 \cdot \ldots \lfloor p_r}$.

III. (*i*) **Combinations:** *Each of the different groups or selections which can be formed by taking some or all at a time, is called a combination.*

Ex. 1. *Out of three boys A, B, C we want to select two.*

The possible selections are (AB, BC, CA).

Note that AB and BA represent the same combination.

Ex. 2. *The only combination of three letters A, B, C taken all at a time is* **ABC**.

Ex. 3. *Various groups of two out of 4 persons A, B, C, D are AB, AC, AD, BC, BD, CD.*

Important Note: AB and BA are two different permutations.

But, they represent the same combination.

(*ii*) ***Number of all combinations of n things, taken r at a time, is***

$$^nC_r = \frac{\lfloor n}{(\lfloor r)(\lfloor n-r)} = \frac{n(n-1)(n-2) \ldots \text{to } r \text{ factors}}{\lfloor r}$$

(*iii*) $^nC_n = 1$ and $^nC_0 = 1$ (*iv*) $^nC_r = {^nC_{(n-r)}}$

Ex. (*i*) $^8C_3 = \dfrac{8 \times 7 \times 6}{3 \times 2 \times 1} = 56$. (*ii*) $^{16}C_{13} = {^{16}C_{(16-13)}} = {^{16}C_3} = \dfrac{16 \times 15 \times 14}{3 \times 2 \times 1} = 560$.

SOLVED EXAMPLES

Ex. 1. *Evaluate :* $\dfrac{\underline{|50}}{\underline{|48}}$.

Sol. $\dfrac{\underline{|50}}{\underline{|48}} = \dfrac{50 \times 49 \times \underline{|48}}{\underline{|48}} = (50 \times 49) = 2450.$

Ex. 2. *Evaluate :* (i) $^5P_5$ **(ii) $^{50}P_3$**

Sol. (i) $^5P_5 = \underline{|5} = (5 \times 4 \times 3 \times 2 \times 1) = 120.$

(ii) $^{50}P_3 = \dfrac{\underline{|50}}{\underline{|(50-3)}} = \dfrac{\underline{|50}}{\underline{|47}} = \dfrac{50 \times 49 \times 48 \times (\underline{|47})}{\underline{|47}} = (50 \times 49 \times 48) = 117600.$

Ex. 3. *Evaluate :* (i) $^{10}C_3$ **(ii) $^{100}C_{98}$** **(iii) $^{60}C_{60}$**

Sol. (i) $^{10}C_3 = \dfrac{10 \times 9 \times 8}{\underline{|3}} = \dfrac{10 \times 9 \times 8}{3 \times 2 \times 1} = 120.$

(ii) $^{100}C_{98} = {}^{100}C_{(100-98)} = {}^{100}C_2 = \dfrac{(100 \times 99)}{(2 \times 1)} = 4950.$

(iii) $^{60}C_{60} = 1 \quad [\because {}^nC_n = 1]$

Ex. 4. *In how many different ways can the letters of the word 'FIGHT' be arranged?* **(Bank P.O., 2008)**

Sol. The given word contains 5 different letters.

Required number of ways $= {}^5P_5 = \underline{|5} = (5 \times 4 \times 3 \times 2 \times 1) = 120.$

Ex. 5. *In how many different ways can the letters of the word 'PRESENT' be arranged?* **(Bank P.O., 2006)**

Sol. The word 'PRESENT' contains 7 letters, namely 2E and all other 5 are different.

$\therefore$ Required number of ways $= \dfrac{\underline{|7}}{\underline{|2}} = \dfrac{7 \times 6 \times 5 \times 4 \times 3 \times (\underline{|2})}{\underline{|2}} = 2520.$

Ex. 6. *How many arrangements can be made out of the letters of the word 'ENGINEERING'?*

Sol. The word 'ENGINEERING' contains 11 letters, namely 3E, 3N, 2G, 2I and 1R.

$\therefore$ Required number of ways $= \dfrac{\underline{|11}}{(\underline{|3})(\underline{|3})(\underline{|2})(\underline{|2})(\underline{|1})}$

$= \dfrac{11 \times 10 \times 9 \times 8 \times 7 \times 6 \times 5 \times 4 \times 3 \times 2 \times 1}{6 \times 6 \times 2 \times 2 \times 1}$

$= (11 \times 10 \times 7 \times 6 \times 5 \times 4 \times 3) = 277200.$

Ex. 7. *In how many different ways can the letters of the word 'DESIGN' be arranged so that the vowels are at the two ends?* **(Bank P.O., 2009)**

Sol. The given word 'DESIGN' contains 4 consonants and 2 vowels.

At the two ends the two vowels can be arranged in 2 ways.

Remaining 4 letters can be arranged in $\underline{|4} = (4 \times 3 \times 2 \times 1) = 24$ ways.

Total number of ways $= (24 \times 2) = 48.$

$\therefore$ Required number of ways $= 48.$

Ex. 8. *In how many different ways can the letters of the word 'DAUGHTER' be arranged so that the vowels always come together?*

Sol. The given word contains 8 different letters.

When the vowels AUE are taken together, we may treat them as 1 letter.

Then, the letters to be arranged are DGHTR (AUE)

The vowels can be arranged in $^6P_6 = \underline{|6} = 720$ ways.

The vowels AUE may be arranged in $\underline{|3} = 6$ ways.

Required number of ways $= (720 \times 6) = 4320$ ways.

Ex. 9. ***In how many different ways can the letters of the word 'DIRECTOR' be arranged so that the vowels are always together?***

Sol. In the given word, we treat the vowels IEO as 1 letter.

Thus, we have DRCTR (IEO).

This group has 6 letters in which R occurs 2 times and other are all different.

Number of ways of arranging these letters $= \frac{\lfloor 6}{\lfloor 2} = \frac{(6 \times 5 \times 4 \times 3 \times 2 \times 1)}{2} = 360.$

Now, 3 vowels can be arranged among themselves in $\lfloor 3 = 6$ ways.

$\therefore$ Required number of ways $= (360 \times 6) = 2160.$

Ex. 10. ***In how many different ways can the letters of the word 'DIGEST' be arranged so that the vowels are never together?*** **(Bank P.O., 2004)**

Sol. In the given word DIGEST, we take the vowels IE as one letter.

Then, we can write it as DGST (IE).

This word has 5 letters which can be arranged among themselves in

$\lfloor 5 = (5 \times 4 \times 3 \times 2 \times 1) = 120$ ways.

The letters of IE can be arranged in 2 ways.

$\therefore$ Number of ways of arranging the letters of given word with vowels together

$= (120 \times 2) = 240$ ways.

Number of ways of arranging all the letters of the given word

$= \lfloor 6 = (6 \times 5 \times 4 \times 3 \times 2 \times 1) = 720$ ways.

$\therefore$ Number of ways of arrangements so that the vowels are never together

$= (720 - 240) = 480.$

Ex. 11. ***In how many different ways can the letters of the word 'DETAIL' be arranged so that the vowels occupy only the odd positions?*** **(Bank P.O., 2002)**

Sol. There are 6 letters in the given word, out of which there are 3 consonants and 3 vowels.

Let us mark these positions as (1) (2) (3) (4) (5) (6).

Now, 3 vowels can be placed at any of 3 places, marked 1, 3, 5.

Number of these arrangements $= {}^3P_3 = \lfloor 3 = 6.$

Also, 3 consonants can be placed at the remaining 3 places.

Number of these arrangements $= {}^3P_3 = \lfloor 3 = 6.$

Total number of ways $= (6 \times 6) = 36.$

Ex. 12. ***In how many ways can a cricket eleven be chosen out of 14 players?***

Sol. Required number of ways $= {}^{14}C_{11} = {}^{14}C_{(14-11)} = {}^{14}C_3 = \frac{14 \times 13 \times 12}{3 \times 2 \times 1} = 364.$

Ex. 13. ***In how many ways, a committee of 6 members be selected from 7 men and 5 ladies, consisting of 4 men and 2 ladies?***

Sol. We have to select (4 men out of 7) and (2 ladies out of 5).

$\therefore$ Required number of ways $= {}^7C_4 \times {}^5C_2 = {}^7C_3 \times {}^5C_2 = \left(\frac{7 \times 6 \times 5}{3 \times 2 \times 1} \times \frac{5 \times 4}{2 \times 1}\right) = 350.$

EXERCISE

(OBJECTIVE TYPE QUESTIONS)

Directions: ***Mark (√) against the correct answer in each of the following:***

1. $({}^{75}P_2 - {}^{75}C_2) = ?$

(a) 0 (b) 75
(c) 150 (d) 2775
(e) 5550

2. In how many different ways can the letters of the word DISPLAY be arranged? **(Bank P.O., 2009)**

(a) 720 (b) 1440
(c) 2520 (d) 5040
(e) None of these

3. In how many different ways can the letters of the word SMART be arranged? **(Bank P.O., 2009)**
(*a*) 25 (*b*) 60
(*c*) 180 (*d*) 200
(*e*) None of these

4. In how many different ways can the letters of the word FORMULATE be arranged? **(Bank P.O., 2008)**
(*a*) 8100 (*b*) 40320
(*c*) 153420 (*d*) 362880
(*e*) None of these

5. In how many different ways can the letters of the word GAMBLE be arranged? **(Bank P.O., 2010)**
(*a*) 15 (*b*) 25
(*c*) 60 (*d*) 125
(*e*) None of these

6. In how many different ways can the letters of the word RIDDLED be arranged? **(Bank P.O., 2006)**
(*a*) 840 (*b*) 1680
(*c*) 2520 (*d*) 5040
(*e*) None of these

7. In how many different ways can the letters of the word CREATE be arranged? **(Bank P.O., 2011)**
(*a*) 25 (*b*) 36
(*c*) 360 (*d*) 720
(*e*) None of these

8. In how many different ways can the letters of the word TOTAL be arranged? **(Bank P.O., 2009)**
(*a*) 45 (*b*) 60
(*c*) 72 (*d*) 120
(*e*) None of these

9. In how many different ways can the letters of the word OFFICES be arranged? **(Bank P.O., 2010)**
(*a*) 2520 (*b*) 5040
(*c*) 1850 (*d*) 1680
(*e*) None of these

10. In how many different ways can the letters of the word BANANA be arranged?
(*a*) 60 (*b*) 120
(*c*) 360 (*d*) 720
(*e*) None of these

11. In how many different ways can the letters of the word WEDDING be arranged? **(Bank P.O., 2008)**
(*a*) 2500 (*b*) 2520
(*c*) 5000 (*d*) 5040
(*e*) None of these

12. In how many different ways can the letters of the word INCREASE be arranged? **(Bank P.O., 2009)**
(*a*) 40320 (*b*) 10080
(*c*) 20160 (*d*) 64
(*e*) None of these

13. In how many different ways can the letters of the word ABSENTEE be arranged? **(Bank P.O., 2006)**
(*a*) 512 (*b*) 6720
(*c*) 9740 (*d*) 40320
(*e*) None of these

14. In how many different ways can the letters of the word AWARE be arranged? **(Bank P.O., 2010)**
(*a*) 40 (*b*) 60
(*c*) 120 (*d*) 150
(*e*) None of these

15. In how many different ways can the letters of the word DAILY be arranged? **(Bank P.O., 2008)**
(*a*) 48 (*b*) 60
(*c*) 120 (*d*) 160
(*e*) None of these

16. In how many different ways can the letters of the word RUMOUR be arranged?
(*a*) 30 (*b*) 90
(*c*) 180 (*d*) 720
(*e*) None of these

17. In how many different ways can the letters of the word OPERATE be arranged? **(Bank P.O., 2009)**
(*a*) 360 (*b*) 720
(*c*) 5040 (*d*) 2520
(*e*) None of these

18. In how many different ways can the letters of the word PUNCTUAL be arranged? **(Bank P.O., 2009)**
(*a*) 64 (*b*) 960
(*c*) 20160 (*d*) 40320
(*e*) None of these

19. In how many different ways can the letters of the word CREAM be arranged? **(Bank P.O., 2008)**
(*a*) 25 (*b*) 120
(*c*) 260 (*d*) 480
(*e*) None of these

20. Out of 5 men and 3 women, a committee of three members is to be formed so that it has 1 woman and 2 men. In how many different ways can it be done? **(Bank P.O., 2009)**
(*a*) 10 (*b*) 20
(*c*) 23 (*d*) 30
(*e*) None of these

21. Out of 5 women and 4 men, a committee of three members is to be formed in such a way that at least one member is a woman. In how many different ways can it be done? **(Bank P.O., 2009)**
(*a*) 76 (*b*) 80
(*c*) 84 (*d*) 96
(*e*) None of these

22. A committee of 5 members is to be formed out of 3 trainees, 4 professors and 6 research associates. In how many different ways can this be done, if the committee should have 4 professors and 1 research associate or all 3 trainees and 2 professors? **(S.B.I. P.O., 2010)**

(*a*) 12 (*b*) 13
(*c*) 24 (*d*) 52
(*e*) None of these

23. A committee of 5 members is to be formed out of 3 trainees, 4 professors and 6 research associates. In how many different ways can this be done if the committee should have 2 trainees and 3 research associates? **(S.B.I. P.O., 2010)**

(*a*) 15 (*b*) 45
(*c*) 60 (*d*) 9
(*e*) None of these

24. In how many ways can a committee of 4 people be chosen out of 8 people? **(Bank P.O., 2007)**

(*a*) 32 (*b*) 70
(*c*) 110 (*d*) 126
(*e*) None of these

25. A committee of 5 members is to be formed by selecting out of 4 men and 5 women. In how many different ways the committee can be formed if it should have 2 men and 3 women? **(Bank P.O., 2005)**

(*a*) 16 (*b*) 36
(*c*) 45 (*d*) 60
(*e*) None of these

26. A committee of 5 members is to be formed by selecting out of 4 men and 5 women. In how many different ways the committee can be formed if it should have at least 1 man? **(Bank P.O., 2011)**

(*a*) 115 (*b*) 120
(*c*) 125 (*d*) 140
(*e*) None of these

27. In how many ways a committee consisting of 5 men and 6 women can be formed from 8 men and 10 women? **(Bank P.O., 2009)**

(*a*) 266 (*b*) 5040
(*c*) 11760 (*d*) 86400
(*e*) None of these

28. A select group of 4 is to be formed from 8 men and 6 women in such a way that the group must have at least 1 woman. In how many different ways can it be done? **(Bank P.O., 2005)**

(*a*) 364 (*b*) 728
(*c*) 931 (*d*) 1001
(*e*) None of these

29. From a group of 7 men and 6 women, 5 persons are to be selected to form a committee so that at least 3 men are there on the committee. In how many ways can it be done?

(*a*) 564 (*b*) 645
(*c*) 735 (*d*) 756
(*e*) None of these

30. A box contains 2 white, 3 black and 4 red balls. In how many ways can 3 balls be drawn from the box, if at least 1 black ball is to be included in the draw?

(*a*) 32 (*b*) 48
(*c*) 64 (*d*) 96
(*e*) None of these

31. In how many ways can a group of 5 men and 2 women be made out of a total of 7 men and 3 women?

(*a*) 45 (*b*) 63
(*c*) 90 (*d*) 126
(*e*) None of these

32. In how many different ways can the letters of the word ENGINEERING be arranged?

(*a*) 277200 (*b*) 92400
(*c*) 69300 (*d*) 23100
(*e*) None of these

33. In how many different ways can the letters of the word ALLAHABAD be arranged?

(*a*) 3780 (*b*) 1890
(*c*) 7560 (*d*) 2520
(*e*) None of these

34. In how many different ways can the letters of the word JUDGE be arranged in such a way that the vowels always come together?

(*a*) 48 (*b*) 120
(*c*) 124 (*d*) 160
(*e*) None of these

35. In how many different ways can the letters of the word AUCTION be arranged in such a way that the vowels always come together? **(Bank P.O., 2010)**

(*a*) 30 (*b*) 48
(*c*) 144 (*d*) 576
(*e*) None of these

36. In how many different ways can the letters of the word SOFTWARE be arranged in such a way that the vowels always come together? **(Bank P.O., 2009)**

(*a*) 120 (*b*) 360
(*c*) 1440 (*d*) 13440
(*e*) 4320

37. In how many different ways can the letters of the word OPTICAL be arranged in such a way that the vowels always come together?

(*a*) 120 (*b*) 720
(*c*) 2160 (*d*) 4320
(*e*) None of these

38. In how many different ways can the letters of the word BANKING be arranged in such a way that the vowels always come together? **(Bank P.O., 2009)**

(*a*) 120 (*b*) 240
(*c*) 360 (*d*) 540
(*e*) 720

39. In how many different ways can the letters of the word CAPITAL be arranged so that the vowels always come together? (Bank P.O. 2012)
(*a*) 120 (*b*) 360
(*c*) 720 (*d*) 840
(*e*) None of these

40. In how many ways can the letters of the word MATHEMATICS be arranged so that all the vowels always come together?
(*a*) 10080 (*b*) 120960
(*c*) 4989600 (*d*) 20160
(*e*) None of these

41. In how many different ways can the letters of the word CORPORATION be arranged so that the vowels always come together? (Bank P.O. 2011)
(*a*) 810 (*b*) 1440
(*c*) 2880 (*d*) 50400
(*e*) 5760

42. In how many different ways can the letters of the word MACHINE be arranged so that the vowels may occupy only the odd positions?
(*a*) 210 (*b*) 576
(*c*) 144 (*d*) 1728
(*e*) 3456

43. In how many different ways can the letters of the word EXTRA be arranged so that the vowels are never together?
(*a*) 120 (*b*) 48
(*c*) 72 (*d*) 168
(*e*) None of these

44. In an examination there are three multiple choice questions and each question has 4 choices. The number of ways in which a student can fail to get all answers correct is [MAT, 2012]
(*a*) 11 (*b*) 27
(*c*) 12 (*d*) 63

45. There are six teachers. Out of them two are primary teachers and two are secondary teachers. They are to stand in a row, so as the primary teachers, middle teachers and secondary teachers are always in a set. The number of ways in which they can do So, is [MAT, 2011]
(*a*) 52 (*b*) 48
(*c*) 34 (*d*) None of these

46. In how many different ways can the letters of the word 'BAKERY' be arranged? [SBI— Bank Clerical Exam, 2012]
(*a*) 2,400 (*b*) 2,005
(*c*) 720 (*d*) 5,040
(*e*) None of these

47. In how many different ways can the letters of the word 'TRANSPIRATION' be arranged so that the vowels always come together? [DMRC—Train Operator/Station Controller Exam, 2016]
(*a*) 2429500 (*b*) 1360800
(*c*) 1627800 (*d*) None of these

48. In how many ways can the letters of the word 'MOMENT' be arranged? [UPSSSC—Lower Subordinate (Pre.) Exam, 2016]
(*a*) 360 (*b*) 60
(*c*) 720 (*d*) 120

ANSWERS

1. (*d*)	2. (*d*)	3. (*e*)	4. (*d*)	5. (*e*)	6. (*a*)	7. (*c*)	8. (*b*)	9. (*a*)	10. (*a*)
11. (*b*)	12. (*c*)	13. (*b*)	14. (*b*)	15. (*c*)	16. (*c*)	17. (*d*)	18. (*c*)	19. (*b*)	20. (*d*)
21. (*b*)	22. (*e*)	23. (*c*)	24. (*b*)	25. (*d*)	26. (*c*)	27. (*c*)	28. (*c*)	29. (*a*)	30. (*c*)
31. (*b*)	32. (*a*)	33. (*c*)	34. (*a*)	35. (*d*)	36. (*e*)	37. (*b*)	38. (*e*)	39. (*b*)	40. (*b*)
41. (*d*)	42. (*b*)	43. (*c*)	44. (*d*)	45. (*b*)	46. (*c*)	47. (*b*)	48. (*a*)		

SOLUTIONS

1. $({}^{75}P_2 - {}^{75}C_2) = \left\{\frac{\underline{|75}}{\underline{|75-2}} - \frac{75 \times 74}{2}\right\} = \frac{\underline{|75}}{\underline{|73}} - (75 \times 37)$

$= \frac{75 \times 74 \times \underline{|73}}{\underline{|73}} - (75 \times 37)$

$= (75 \times 74 - 75 \times 37) = 75 \times 37 \times (2 - 1)$
$= (75 \times 37) = 2775.$

2. The given word contains 7 letters, all different.
∴ Required number of ways $= {}^7P_7 = \underline{|7}$
$= (7 \times 6 \times 5 \times 4 \times 3 \times 2 \times 1) = 5040.$

3. The given word contains 5 letters, all different.
∴ Required number of ways $= {}^5P_5 = \underline{|5}$
$= (5 \times 4 \times 3 \times 2 \times 1) = 120.$

4. The given word contains 9 letters, all different.

$\therefore$ Required number of ways $= {}^9P_9 = \underline{|9}$

$= (9 \times 8 \times 7 \times 6 \times 5 \times 4 \times 3 \times 2 \times 1) = 362880.$

5. The given word contains 6 letters, all different.

$\therefore$ Required number of ways $= {}^6P_6 = \underline{|6}$

$= (6 \times 5 \times 4 \times 3 \times 2 \times 1) = 720.$

6. The given word contains 7 letters of which D is taken 3 times.

$\therefore$ Required number of ways $= \dfrac{\underline{|7}}{\underline{|3}} = \dfrac{7 \times 6 \times 5 \times 4 \times \underline{|3}}{\underline{|3}}$

$= (7 \times 6 \times 5 \times 4) = 840.$

7. The given word contains 6 letters of which E is taken 2 times.

$\therefore$ Required number of ways $= \dfrac{\underline{|6}}{\underline{|2}} = \dfrac{6 \times 5 \times 4 \times 3 \times \underline{|2}}{\underline{|2}} = 360.$

8. The given word contains 5 letters of which T is taken 2 times.

$\therefore$ Required number of ways $= \dfrac{\underline{|5}}{\underline{|2}} = \dfrac{5 \times 4 \times 3 \times \underline{|2}}{\underline{|2}} = 60.$

9. The given word contains 7 letters of which F is taken 2 times.

$\therefore$ Required number of ways

$= \dfrac{\underline{|7}}{\underline{|2}} = \dfrac{7 \times 6 \times 5 \times 4 \times 3 \times 2 \times 1}{2 \times 1} = 2520.$

10. The given word contains 6 letters of which A is taken 3 times, N is taken 2 times and the rest are all different.

$\therefore$ Required number of ways

$= \dfrac{\underline{|6}}{\underline{|3}\,.\,\underline{|2}} = \dfrac{6 \times 5 \times 4 \times 3 \times 2 \times 1}{6 \times 2} = 60.$

11. The given word contains 7 letters of which D is taken 2 times.

$\therefore$ Required number of ways

$= \dfrac{\underline{|7}}{\underline{|2}} = \dfrac{7 \times 6 \times 5 \times 4 \times 3 \times 2 \times 1}{2 \times 1} = 2520.$

12. The given word contains 8 letters of which E is taken 2 times.

$\therefore$ Required number of ways

$= \dfrac{\underline{|8}}{\underline{|2}} = \dfrac{8 \times 7 \times 6 \times 5 \times 4 \times 3 \times 2 \times 1}{2} = 20160.$

13. The given word contains 8 letters of which E is taken 3 times.

$\therefore$ Required number of ways

$= \dfrac{\underline{|8}}{\underline{|3}} = \dfrac{8 \times 7 \times 6 \times 5 \times 4 \times 3 \times 2 \times 1}{6} = 6720.$

14. The given word contains 5 letters of which A is taken 2 times.

$\therefore$ Required number of ways $= \dfrac{\underline{|5}}{\underline{|2}} = \dfrac{5 \times 4 \times 3 \times 2 \times 1}{2} = 60.$

15. The given word contains 5 letters, all different.

$\therefore$ Required number of ways $= \underline{|5} = (5 \times 4 \times 3 \times 2 \times 1) = 120.$

16. The given word contains 6 letters out of which R is taken 2 times, U is taken 2 times and other letters are all different.

$\therefore$ Required number of ways

$= \dfrac{\underline{|6}}{\underline{|2} \cdot \underline{|2}} = \dfrac{6 \times 5 \times 4 \times 3 \times 2 \times 1}{2 \times 2} = 180.$

17. The given word contains 7 letters out of which E is taken 2 times and all other letters are different.

$\therefore$ Required number of ways

$= \dfrac{\underline{|7}}{\underline{|2}} = \dfrac{7 \times 6 \times 5 \times 4 \times 3 \times 2 \times 1}{2} = 2520.$

18. The given word contains 8 letters out of which U is taken 2 times and all other letters are different.

$\therefore$ Required number of ways

$= \dfrac{\underline{|8}}{\underline{|2}} = \dfrac{8 \times 7 \times 6 \times 5 \times 4 \times 3 \times 2 \times 1}{2} = 20160.$

19. The given word contains 5 letters, all different.

$\therefore$ Required number of ways $= \underline{|5} = (5 \times 4 \times 3 \times 2 \times 1) = 120.$

20. Required number of ways $= \left({}^3C_1 \times {}^5C_2\right) = 3 \times \dfrac{5 \times 4}{2 \times 1} = 30.$

21. Required number of ways $= ({}^5C_1 \times {}^4C_2) + ({}^5C_2 \times {}^4C_1) + ({}^5C_3)$

$= \left(5 \times \dfrac{4 \times 3}{2 \times 1}\right) + \left(\dfrac{5 \times 4}{2 \times 1} \times 4\right) + \left(\dfrac{5 \times 4 \times 3}{3 \times 2 \times 1}\right)$

$= (30 + 40 + 10) = 80.$

22. Required number of ways $= ({}^4C_4 \times {}^6C_1) + ({}^3C_3 \times {}^4C_2)$

$= (1 + 6) + \left(1 + \dfrac{4 \times 3}{2}\right) = (7 + 7) = 14.$

23. Required number of ways $= ({}^3C_2 \times {}^6C_3) = ({}^3C_1 \times {}^6C_3)$

$= \left(3 \times \dfrac{6 \times 5 \times 4}{3 \times 2 \times 1}\right) = 60.$

24. Required number of ways $= {}^8C_4 = \dfrac{8 \times 7 \times 6 \times 5}{4 \times 3 \times 2 \times 1} = 70.$

25. Required number of ways $= ({}^4C_2 \times {}^5C_3) = ({}^4C_2 \times {}^5C_2)$

$= \left(\dfrac{4 \times 3}{2 \times 1} \times \dfrac{5 \times 4}{2 \times 1}\right) = 60.$

26. The committee should have

(1 man, 4 women) or (2 men, 3 women) or (3 men, 2 women) or (4 men, 1 woman).

Required number of ways $= ({}^4C_1 \times {}^5C_4) + ({}^4C_2 \times {}^5C_3) + ({}^4C_3 \times {}^5C_2) + ({}^4C_6 \times {}^5C_1)$

$= ({}^4C_1 \times {}^5C_1) + ({}^4C_2 \times {}^5C_2) + ({}^4C_1 \times {}^5C_2) + ({}^4C_4 \times {}^5C_1)$

$= (4 \times 5) + \left(\dfrac{4 \times 3}{2 \times 1} \times \dfrac{5 \times 4}{2 \times 1}\right) + \left(4 \times \dfrac{5 \times 4}{2 \times 1}\right) + (1 \times 5)$

$= (20 + 60 + 40 + 5) = 125.$

27. Required number of ways $= ({}^8C_5 \times {}^{10}C_6) + ({}^8C_3 \times {}^{10}C_4)$

$= \dfrac{8 \times 7 \times 6}{\underline{|3}} \times \dfrac{10 \times 9 \times 8 \times 7}{\underline{|4}}$

$= \dfrac{8 \times 7 \times 6}{6} \times \dfrac{10 \times 9 \times 8 \times 7}{4 \times 3 \times 2 \times 1} = 11760.$

28. Required number of ways

$= ({}^6C_1 \times {}^8C_3) + ({}^6C_2 \times {}^8C_2) + ({}^6C_3 \times {}^8C_1) + ({}^6C_4 \times {}^8C_0)$

$= \left\{6\times\frac{8\times7\times6}{\lfloor 3}\right\} + \left(\frac{6\times5}{2\times1}\times\frac{8\times7}{2\times1}\right) + \left(\frac{6\times5\times4}{\lfloor 3}\times 8\right) + ({}^6C_2\times 1)$

$= \left\{6\times\frac{8\times7\times6}{3\times2\times1}\right\} + 420 + \left(\frac{6\times5\times4}{6}\times8\right)+\left(\frac{6\times5}{2\times1}\times1\right)$

$= (336 + 420 + 160 + 15) = 931.$

29. Required number of ways

$= ({}^7C_3\times{}^6C_2)+({}^7C_4\times{}^6C_1)+({}^7C_5\times{}^6C_0)$

$= \left\{\frac{7\times6\times5}{\lfloor 3}\times\frac{6\times5}{\lfloor 2}\right\}+({}^7C_3\times{}^6C_1)+({}^7C_2\times1)$

$= \left(\frac{7\times6\times5}{6}\times\frac{6\times5}{2\times1}\right)+\left(\frac{7\times6\times5}{3\times2\times1}\times6\right)+\left(\frac{7\times6}{2\times1}\times1\right)$

$= (525 + 210 + 21) = 756.$

30. We may have (1 black and 2 non-black) or (2 black and 1 non-black) or (3 black).

Required no. of ways $= ({}^3C_1\times{}^6C_2)+({}^3C_2\times{}^6C_1)+({}^3C_3)$

$= \left(3\times\frac{6\times5}{2\times1}\right)+\left(\frac{3\times2}{2\times1}\times6\right)+1 = (45 + 18 + 1) = 64.$

31. Required no. of ways

$= ({}^7C_5\times{}^3C_2) = ({}^7C_2\times{}^3C_1) = \frac{7\times6}{2\times1}\times3 = 63.$

32. The given word contains 11 letters, namely 3E, 3N, 2G, 2I and 1R.

$\therefore$ Required number of ways $= \frac{\lfloor 11}{(\lfloor 3)(\lfloor 3)(\lfloor 2)(\lfloor 2)(\lfloor 1)}$

$= \frac{11\times10\times9\times8\times7\times6\times5\times4\times3\times2\times1}{6\times6\times2\times2\times1}$

$= (11 \times 10 \times 9 \times 8 \times 7 \times 5) = 277200.$

33. The given word contains 9 letters, namely 4A, 2L, 1H, 1B and 1D.

$\therefore$ Required number of ways $= \frac{\lfloor 9}{(\lfloor 4)(\lfloor 2)(\lfloor 1)(\lfloor 1)(\lfloor 1)}$

$= \frac{9\times8\times7\times6\times5\times4\times3\times2\times1}{4\times3\times2\times1\times2} = 7560.$

34. The given word contains 5 different letters.

Keeping the vowels UE together, we suppose them as 1 letter.

Then, we have to arrange the letters JDG(UE).

Now, 4 letters can be arranged in $\lfloor 4 = 24$ ways.

The vowels (UE) can be arranged among themselves in 2 ways.

$\therefore$ Required no. of ways = (24 × 2) = 48.

35. The given word contains 7 different letters.

Keeping the vowels (AUIO) together, we take them as 1 letter.

Then, we have to arrange the letters CTN(AUIO).

Now, 4 letters can be arranged in $\lfloor 4$ = 24 ways.

The vowels (AUIO) can be arranged among themselves in $\lfloor 4$ = 24 ways.

$\therefore$ Required number of ways = (24 × 24) = 576.

36. The given word contains 8 different letters.

We keep the vowels (OAE) together and treat them as 1 letter.

Thus, we have to arrange the 6 letters SFTWR(OAE).

These can be arranged in $\lfloor 6$ = 720 ways.

The vowels (OAE) can be arranged among themselves in $\lfloor 3$ = 6 ways.

$\therefore$ Required number of ways = (720 × 6) = 4320.

37. The given word contains 7 different letters.

We keep the vowels (OIA) together and treat them as 1 letter.

Thus, we have to arrange the letters PTCL(OIA).

These can be arranged in $\lfloor 5$ = 120 ways.

The vowels (OIA) can be arranged among themselves in $\lfloor 3$ = 6 ways.

$\therefore$ Required number of ways = (120 × 6) = 720.

38. The given word contains 7 letters of which N is taken 2 times.

We keep the vowels (AI) together and treat them as 1 letter.

Thus, we have to arrange 6 letters BNKNG(AI) of which N occurs 2 times and the rest are different.

These can be arranged in $\frac{\lfloor 6}{\lfloor 2} = (6\times5\times4\times3) = 360$ ways.

Now 2 vowels (AI) can be arranged among themselves in 2 ways.

$\therefore$ Required number of ways = (360 × 2) = 720.

39. Keeping the vowels (AIA) together, we have CPTL (AIA).

We treat (AIA) as 1 letter.

Thus, we have to arrange 5 letters.

These can be arranged in $\lfloor 5 = (5\times4\times3\times2\times1)$ ways = 120 ways.

Now, (AIA) are 3 letters with 2A and 1I.

These can be arranged among themselves in $\frac{\lfloor 3}{\lfloor 2} = \frac{3\times2\times1}{2\times1} = 3$ ways.

$\therefore$ Required number of ways = (120 × 3) = 360.

40. Keeping the vowels (AEIA) together, we have MTHMTCS(AEAI).

Now, we have to arrange 8 letters, out of which we have 2M, 2T and the rest are all different.

Number of ways of arranging these letters

$= \frac{\lfloor 8}{\lfloor 2 . \lfloor 2} = \frac{8\times7\times6\times5\times4\times3\times2\times1}{2\times1\times2\times1} = 10080.$

Now, (AEAI) has 4 letters, out of which we have 2A, 1E and 1I.

Number of ways of arranging these letters

$= \frac{\lfloor 4}{\lfloor 2} = \frac{4\times3\times2\times1}{2} = 12.$

$\therefore$ Required number of ways = (10080 × 12) = 120960.

41. Keepting the vowels (OOAIO) together as one letter we have CRPRTN(OOAIO).

This has 7 letters, out of which we have 2R, 1C, 1P, 1T and 1N.

Number of ways of arranging these letters

$= \frac{\lfloor 7}{\lfloor 2} = \frac{7 \times 6 \times 5 \times 4 \times 3 \times 2 \times 1}{2 \times 1} = 2520.$

Now, (OOAIO) has 5 letters, out of which we have 3O, 1A and 1I.

Number of ways of arranging these letters

$= \frac{\lfloor 5}{\lfloor 3} = \frac{5 \times 4 \times 3 \times 2 \times 1}{3 \times 2 \times 1} = 20.$

$\therefore$ Required number of ways = $(2520 \times 20) = 50400$.

42. There are 7 letters in the given word, out of which there are 3 vowels and 4 consonants.

Let us mark the positions to be filled up as follows:

(1)(2)(3)(4)(5)(6)(7)

Now, 3 vowels can be placed at any of the three places out of four marked 1, 3, 5, 7.

Number of ways of arranging the vowels = $^4P_3$

$= (4 \times 3 \times 2) = 24$.

4 consonants at the remaining 4 positions may be arranged in $^4P_4 = \lfloor 4 = 24$ ways.

Required number of ways = $(24 \times 24) = 576$.

43. Taking the vowels (EA) as one letter, the given word has the letters XTR (EA), i.e., 4 letters.

These letters can be arranged in $\lfloor 4 = 24$ ways.

The letters *EA* may be arranged amongst themselves in 2 ways.

Number of arrangements having vowels together

$= (24 \times 2) = 48$ ways.

Total arrangements of all letters = $\lfloor 5 = (5 \times 4 \times 3 \times 2 \times 1) = 120$.

Number of arrangements not having vowels together

$= (120 - 48) = 72$.

44. Number of ways of attempting 1st, 2nd, 3rd questions are each.

Total number of ways = $4^3 = 4 \times 4 \times 4 = 64$

Number of ways, getting all correct answers = $1^3 = 1$

$\therefore$ Number of ways of not getting all answer correct

$= 64 - 1 = 63$

45. There are 2 primary teachers.

They can stand in a row in P(2, 2) = 2!

$= 2 \times 1$ ways = 2 ways

$\therefore$ Two middle teachers.

They can stand in a row in P(2, 2) = 2!

$= 2 \times 1 = 2$ ways

There are two secondary teachers.

They can stand in a row in

P(2, 2) = 2! = 2×1 = 2 ways

These three sets can be arranged themselves in 3!

Ways = $3 \times 2 \times 1$ = 6 ways

Hence, the required number of ways

$= 2 \times 2 \times 2 \times 6$ = 48 ways

46. The letters of the word 'BAKERY'' be arranged in 6! ways st.

$6! = 6 \times 5 \times 4 \times 3 \times 2 \times 1 = 720$

47. The word TRANSPIRATION has 13 letters in which each of T, R, A, N and I has come two time

We have to arrange TT RR NN PS (AA II O).

There are five vowels in the given words.

$\therefore$ we consider these give vowels as one letter.

$\therefore$ Required number of arrangements.

$= \frac{9! \times 5!}{2!2!2!2!2!}$

$= \frac{9 \times 8 \times 7 \times 6 \times 5 \times 4 \times 3 \times 2 \times 5 \times 4 \times 3 \times 2}{2 \times 2 \times 2 \times 2 \times 2}$

$= 1360800$

48. There are six letters in the given word MOMENT and letter 'M' has come twice.

$\therefore$ Required number of ways

$= \frac{6!}{2!} = \frac{6 \times 5 \times 4 \times 3 \times 2 \times 1}{2 \times 1} = 360$

31 Probability

IMPORTANT FACTS AND FORMULAE

I. Experiment: An operation which can produce some well-defined outcomes is called an experiment.

II. Random Experiment: An experiment in which all possible outcomes are known and the exact output cannot be predicted in advance, is called a random experiment.

Examples of Performing a Random Experiment:

(i) Rolling an unbiased dice

(ii) Tossing a fair coin

(iii) Drawing a card from a pack of well-shuffled cards

(iv) Picking up a ball of certain colour from a bag containing balls of different colours

Details :

(i) When we throw a coin, then either a Head (H) or a Tail (T) appears.

(ii) A dice is a solid cube, having 6 faces, marked 1, 2, 3, 4, 5, 6 respectively.

When we throw a die, the outcome is the number that appears on its upper face.

(iii) A pack of cards has 52 cards.

It has 13 cards of each suit, namely Spades, Clubs, Hearts and Diamonds.

Cards of spades and clubs are black cards.

Cards of hearts and diamonds are red cards.

There are 4 honours of each suit.

These are Aces, Kings, Queens and Jacks.

These are called face cards.

III. Sample Space: When we perform an experiment, then the set S of all possible outcomes is called the Sample Space.

Examples of Sample Spaces:

(i) In tossing a coin, S = {H, T}.

(ii) If two coins are tossed, then S = {HH, HT, TH, TT}.

(iii) In rolling a dice, we have, S = {1, 2, 3, 4, 5, 6}.

IV. Event : Any subset of a sample space is called an event.

V. Probability of Occurrence of an Event:

Let S be the sample space and let E be an event. Then, $E \subseteq S$.

$\therefore \quad P(E) = \dfrac{n(E)}{n(S)}$.

VI. Results on Probability:

(i) $P(S) = 1$ *(ii)* $0 \le P(E) \le 1$ *(iii)* $P(\phi) = 0$

(iv) For any events A and B, we have :

$P(A \cup B) = P(A) + P(B) - P(A \cap B)$

(v) If $\bar{A}$ denotes (not-A), then $P(\bar{A}) = 1 - P(A)$.

SOLVED EXAMPLES

Ex. 1. ***In a throw of a coin, find the probability of getting a head.***

Sol. Here $S = \{H, T\}$ and $E = \{H\}$.

$\therefore \quad P(E) = \dfrac{n(E)}{n(S)} = \dfrac{1}{2}$.

Ex. 2. ***Two unbiased coins are tossed. What is the probability of getting at most one head ?***

Sol. Here S = {HH, HT, TH, TT}.

Let E = event of getting at most one head.

$\therefore$ E = {TT, HT, TH}.

$\therefore$ $P(E) = \frac{n(E)}{n(S)} = \frac{3}{4}$.

Ex. 3. ***An unbiased die is tossed. Find the probability of getting a multiple of 3.***

Sol. Here S = {1, 2, 3, 4, 5, 6}.

Let E be the event of getting a multiple of 3.

Then, E = {3, 6}.

$\therefore$ $P(E) = \frac{n(E)}{n(S)} = \frac{2}{6} = \frac{1}{3}$.

Ex. 4. ***In a simultaneous throw of a pair of dice, find the probability of getting a total more than 7.***

Sol. Here, $n(S) = (6 \times 6) = 36$.

Let E = Event of getting a total more than 7

= {(2, 6), (3, 5), (3, 6), (4, 4), (4, 5), (4, 6), (5, 3), (5, 4), (5, 5), (5, 6), (6, 2), (6, 3), (6, 4), (6, 5), (6, 6)}.

$\therefore$ $P(E) = \frac{n(E)}{n(S)} = \frac{15}{36} = \frac{5}{12}$.

Ex. 5. ***A bag contains 6 white and 4 black balls. Two balls are drawn at random. Find the probability that they are of the same colour.***

Sol. Let S be the sample space. Then,

$n(s)$ = Number of ways of drawing 2 balls out of (6 + 4) = ${}^{10}C_2 = \frac{(10 \times 9)}{(2 \times 1)} = 45$.

Let E = Event of getting both balls of the same colour. Then,

$n(E)$ = Number of ways of drawing (2 balls out of 6) or (2 balls out of 4)

$= ({}^6C_2 + {}^4C_2) = \frac{(6 \times 5)}{(2 \times 1)} + \frac{(4 \times 3)}{(2 \times 1)} = (15 + 6) = 21$.

$\therefore$ $P(E) = \frac{n(E)}{n(S)} = \frac{21}{45} = \frac{7}{15}$.

Ex. 6. ***Two dice are thrown together. What is the probability that the sum of the numbers on the two faces is divisible by 4 or 6 ?***

Sol. Clearly, $n(S) = 6 \times 6 = 36$.

Let E be the event that the sum of the numbers on the two faces is divisible by 4 or 6. Then

E = {(1, 3), (1, 5), (2, 2), (2, 4), (2, 6), (3, 1), (3, 3), (3, 5), (4, 2), (4, 4), (5, 1), (5, 3), (6, 2), (6, 6)}

$\therefore$ $n(E) = 14$.

Hence, $P(E) = \frac{n(E)}{n(S)} = \frac{14}{36} = \frac{7}{18}$.

Ex. 7. ***Two cards are drawn at random from a pack of 52 cards. What is the probability that either both are black or both are queens ?***

Sol. We have $n(s) = {}^{52}C_2 = \frac{(52 \times 51)}{(2 \times 1)} = 1326$.

Let A = event of getting both black cards;

B = event of getting both queens.

$\therefore$ $A \cap B$ = event of getting queens of black cards.

$\therefore$ $n(A) = {}^{26}C_2 = \frac{(26 \times 25)}{(2 \times 1)} = 325$, $n(B) = {}^4C_2 = \frac{(4 \times 3)}{(2 \times 1)} = 6$ and $n(A \cap B) = {}^2C_2 = 1$.

$\therefore$ $P(A) = \frac{n(A)}{n(S)} = \frac{325}{1326}$; $P(B) = \frac{n(B)}{n(S)} = \frac{6}{1326}$ and $P(A \cap B) = \frac{n(A \cap B)}{n(S)} = \frac{1}{1326}$.

$\therefore$ $P(A \cup B) = P(A) + P(B) - P(A \cap B) = \left(\frac{325}{1326} + \frac{6}{1326} - \frac{1}{1326}\right) = \frac{330}{1326} = \frac{55}{221}$.

EXERCISE
(OBJECTIVE TYPE QUESTIONS)

Directions: ***Mark (✓) against the correct answer:***

1. In a simultaneous throw of two coins, the probability of getting at least one head is

(a) $\frac{1}{2}$ (b) $\frac{1}{3}$ (c) $\frac{2}{3}$ (d) $\frac{3}{4}$

2. Three unbiased coins are tossed. What is the probability of getting at least 2 heads?

(a) $\frac{1}{4}$ (b) $\frac{1}{2}$ (c) $\frac{1}{3}$ (d) $\frac{1}{8}$

3. Three unbiased coins are tossed. What is the probability of getting at most two heads?

(a) $\frac{3}{4}$ (b) $\frac{1}{4}$ (c) $\frac{3}{8}$ (d) $\frac{7}{8}$

4. In a single throw of a die, what is the probability of getting a number greater than 4 ?

(a) $\frac{1}{2}$ (b) $\frac{1}{3}$ (c) $\frac{2}{3}$ (d) $\frac{1}{4}$

5. In a simultaneous throw of two dice, what is the probability of getting a total of 7 ?

(a) $\frac{1}{6}$ (b) $\frac{1}{4}$ (c) $\frac{2}{3}$ (d) $\frac{3}{4}$

6. What is the probability of getting a sum 9 from two throws of a dice ?

(a) $\frac{1}{6}$ (b) $\frac{1}{8}$ (c) $\frac{1}{9}$ (d) $\frac{1}{12}$

7. In a simultaneous throw of two dice, what is the probability of getting a doublet?

(a) $\frac{1}{6}$ (b) $\frac{1}{4}$ (c) $\frac{2}{3}$ (d) $\frac{3}{7}$

8. In a simultaneous throw of two dice, what is the probability of getting a total of 10 or 11 ?

(a) $\frac{1}{4}$ (b) $\frac{1}{6}$ (c) $\frac{7}{12}$ (d) $\frac{5}{36}$

9. Two dice are thrown simultaneously. What is the probability of getting two numbers whose product is even ?

(a) $\frac{1}{2}$ (b) $\frac{3}{4}$ (c) $\frac{3}{8}$ (d) $\frac{5}{16}$

10. Tickets numbered 1 to 20 are mixed up and then a ticket is drawn at random. What is the probability that the ticket drawn bears a number which is a multiple of 3 ?

(a) $\frac{3}{10}$ (b) $\frac{3}{20}$ (c) $\frac{2}{5}$ (d) $\frac{1}{2}$

11. Tickets numbered 1 to 20 are mixed up and then a ticket is drawn at random. What is the probability that the ticket drawn has a number which is a multiple of 3 or 5?

(a) $\frac{1}{2}$ (b) $\frac{2}{5}$ (c) $\frac{8}{15}$ (d) $\frac{9}{20}$

12. In a lottery, there are 10 prizes and 25 blanks. A lottery is drawn at random. What is the probability of getting a prize ?

(a) $\frac{1}{10}$ (b) $\frac{2}{5}$ (c) $\frac{2}{7}$ (d) $\frac{5}{7}$

13. One card is drawn at random from a pack of 52 cards. What is the probability that the card drawn is a face card ?

(a) $\frac{1}{13}$ (b) $\frac{4}{13}$ (c) $\frac{1}{4}$ (d) $\frac{9}{52}$

14. A card is drawn from a pack of 52 cards. The probability of getting a queen of club or a king of heart is

(a) $\frac{1}{13}$ (b) $\frac{2}{13}$

(c) $\frac{1}{26}$ (d) $\frac{1}{52}$

15. One card is drawn from a pack of 52 cards. What is the probability that the card drawn is either a red card or a king ?

(a) $\frac{1}{2}$ (b) $\frac{6}{13}$

(c) $\frac{7}{13}$ (d) $\frac{27}{52}$

16. From a pack of 52 cards, one card is drawn at random. What is the probability that the card drawn is a ten or a spade ?

(a) $\frac{4}{13}$ (b) $\frac{1}{4}$

(c) $\frac{1}{13}$ (d) $\frac{1}{26}$

17. The probability that a card drawn from a pack of 52 cards will be a diamond or a king, is

(a) $\frac{2}{13}$ (b) $\frac{4}{13}$

(c) $\frac{1}{13}$ (d) $\frac{1}{52}$

18. From a pack of 52 cards, two cards are drawn together at random. What is the probability of both the cards being kings ?

(a) $\frac{1}{15}$ (b) $\frac{25}{57}$

(c) $\frac{35}{256}$ (d) $\frac{1}{221}$

19. Two cards are drawn together from a pack of 52 cards. The probability that one is a spade and one is a heart, is

(a) $\frac{3}{20}$ (b) $\frac{29}{34}$

(c) $\frac{47}{100}$ (d) $\frac{13}{102}$

20. Two cards are drawn from a pack of 52 cards. The probability that either both are red or both are kings, is

(a) $\frac{7}{13}$ (b) $\frac{3}{26}$

(c) $\frac{63}{221}$ (d) $\frac{55}{221}$

21. A bag contains 6 black and 8 white balls. One ball is drawn at random. What is the probability that the ball drawn is white ?

(a) $\frac{3}{4}$ (b) $\frac{4}{7}$

(c) $\frac{1}{8}$ (d) $\frac{3}{7}$

(e) None of these

22. In a box, there are 8 red, 7 blue and 6 green balls. One ball is picked up randomly. What is the probability that it is neither red nor green ?

(a) $\frac{2}{3}$ (b) $\frac{3}{4}$

(c) $\frac{7}{19}$ (d) $\frac{8}{21}$

(e) $\frac{9}{21}$

23. A box contains 4 red, 5 green and 6 white balls. A ball is drawn at random from the box. What is the probability that the ball drawn is either red or green?

(a) $\frac{2}{5}$ (b) $\frac{3}{5}$

(c) $\frac{1}{5}$ (d) $\frac{7}{15}$

(e) None of these

24. A basket contains 4 red, 5 blue and 3 green marbles. If 2 marbles are drawn atrandom from the basket, what is the probability that both are red? **(S.B.I. P.O., 2010)**

(a) $\frac{3}{7}$ (b) $\frac{1}{2}$

(c) $\frac{1}{11}$ (d) $\frac{1}{6}$

(e) None of these

25. An urn contains 6 red, 4 blue, 2 green and 3 yellow marbles. If two marbles are drawn at random from the urn, what is the probability that both are red? **(S.B.I. P.O., 2010)**

(a) $\frac{1}{6}$ (b) $\frac{1}{7}$

(c) $\frac{2}{15}$ (d) $\frac{2}{5}$

(e) None of these

26. A basket contains 6 blue, 2 red, 4 green and 3 yellow balls. If three balls are picked up at random, what is the probability that none is yellow? **(Bank P.O., 2009)**

(a) $\frac{3}{455}$ (b) $\frac{1}{5}$

(c) $\frac{4}{5}$ (d) $\frac{44}{91}$

(e) None of these

27. An urn contains 6 red, 4 blue, 2 green and 3 yellow marbles. If three marbles are picked up at random, what is the probability that 2 are blue and 1 is yellow? **(S.B.I. P.O., 2010)**

(*a*) $\frac{3}{91}$ (*b*) $\frac{1}{5}$

(*c*) $\frac{18}{455}$ (*d*) $\frac{7}{15}$

(*e*) None of these

28. An urn contains 6 red, 4 blue, 2 green and 3 yellow marbles. If four marbles are picked up at random, what is the probability that 1 is green, 2 are blue and 1 is red ? **(S.B.I. P.O., 2011)**

(*a*) $\frac{13}{35}$ (*b*) $\frac{24}{455}$

(*c*) $\frac{11}{15}$ (*d*) $\frac{1}{13}$

(*e*) None of these

29. An urn contains 6 red, 4 blue, 2 green and 3 yellow marbles. If two marbles are picked up at random, what is the probability that either both are green or both are yellow? **(Bank P.O., 2010)**

(*a*) $\frac{5}{91}$ (*b*) $\frac{1}{35}$

(*c*) $\frac{1}{3}$ (*d*) $\frac{4}{105}$

(*e*) None of these

30. A basket contains 6 blue, 2 red, 4 green and 3 yellow balls. If four balls are picked up at random, what is the probability that 2 are red and 2 are green ? **(Bank P.O., 2009)**

(*a*) $\frac{4}{15}$ (*b*) $\frac{5}{27}$

(*c*) $\frac{1}{3}$ (*d*) $\frac{2}{455}$

(*e*) None of these

31. A basket contains 4 red, 5 blue and 3 green marbles. If three marbles are picked up at random what is the probability that at least one is blue? **(S.B.I. P.O., 2010)**

(*a*) $\frac{7}{12}$ (*b*) $\frac{37}{44}$

(*c*) $\frac{5}{12}$ (*d*) $\frac{7}{44}$

(*e*) None of these

32. An urn contains 6 red, 4 blue, 2 green and 3 yellow marbles. If 4 marbles are picked up at random, what is the probability that at least one of them is blue? **(S.B.I. P.O., 2010)**

(*a*) $\frac{4}{15}$ (*b*) $\frac{69}{91}$

(*c*) $\frac{11}{15}$ (*d*) $\frac{22}{91}$

(*e*) None of these

33. A basket contains 6 blue, 2 red, 4 green and 3 yellow balls. If 5 balls are picked up at random, what is the probability that at least one is blue? **(Bank P.O., 2009)**

(*a*) $\frac{137}{143}$ (*b*) $\frac{18}{455}$

(*c*) $\frac{9}{91}$ (*d*) $\frac{2}{5}$

(*e*) None of these

34. An urn contains 2 red, 3 green and 2 blue balls. If 2 balls are drawn at random, find the probability that no ball is blue. **(Railways, 2006)**

(*a*) $\frac{5}{7}$ (*b*) $\frac{10}{21}$

(*c*) $\frac{2}{7}$ (*d*) $\frac{11}{21}$

(*e*) None of these

35. A box contains 10 black and 10 white balls. What is the probability of drawing 2 balls of the same colour?

(*a*) $\frac{9}{19}$ (*b*) $\frac{9}{38}$

(*c*) $\frac{10}{19}$ (*d*) $\frac{5}{19}$

(*e*) None of these

36. A box contains 20 electric bulbs, out of which 4 are defective. Two balls are chosen at random from this box. The probability that at least one of them is defective, is

(*a*) $\frac{4}{19}$ (*b*) $\frac{7}{19}$

(*c*) $\frac{12}{19}$ (*d*) $\frac{21}{95}$

(*e*) None of these

37. In a class, there are 15 boys and 10 girls. Three students are selected at random. The probability that the selected students are 2 boys and 1 girl, is:

(*a*) $\frac{21}{46}$ (*b*) $\frac{25}{117}$

(*c*) $\frac{1}{50}$ (*d*) $\frac{3}{25}$

(*e*) None of these

38. Four persons are chosen at random from a group of 3 men, 2 women and 4 children. The chance that exactly 2 of them are children, is

(*a*) $\frac{1}{9}$ (*b*) $\frac{1}{5}$

(c) $\frac{1}{12}$ (d) $\frac{10}{21}$

(e) None of these

39. Two dice are tossed. The probability that the total score is a prime number is

(a) $\frac{1}{6}$ (b) $\frac{1}{2}$

(c) $\frac{5}{12}$ (d) $\frac{7}{9}$

(e) None of these

40. In a class, 30% of the students offered English, 20% offered Hindi and 10% offered both. If a student is selected at random, what is the probability that he has offered English or Hindi ?

(a) $\frac{2}{5}$ (b) $\frac{3}{5}$

(c) $\frac{3}{4}$ (d) $\frac{3}{10}$

(e) None of these

41. A man and his wife appear in an interview for two vacancies in the same post. The probability of husband's selection is $\frac{1}{7}$ and the probability of wife's selection is $\frac{1}{5}$. What is the probability that only one of them is selected ?

(a) $\frac{4}{5}$ (b) $\frac{2}{7}$

(c) $\frac{4}{7}$ (d) $\frac{8}{15}$

(e) None of these

42. A speaks truth in 75% cases and B in 80% of the cases. In what percentage of cases are they likely to contradict each other, in narrating the same incident?

(a) 5% (b) 15%

(c) 35% (d) 45%

(e) None of these

43. A speaks truth in 60% cases and B speaks truth in 70% cases. The probability that they will say the same thing while describing a single event, is **(Railways, 2006)**

(a) 0.54 (b) 0.56

(c) 0.68 (d) 0.94

(e) None of these

44. A committee of 3 members is to be selected out of 3 men and 2 women. What is the probability that the committee has at least 1 woman? **(Bank P.O. ,2008)**

(a) $\frac{1}{10}$ (b) $\frac{9}{20}$

(c) $\frac{1}{20}$ (d) $\frac{9}{10}$

(e) None of these

45. A bag contains 3 blue, 2 green and 5 red balls. If four balls are picked at random, what is the probability that two are green and two are blue?

[DMRC—Customer Relationship Assistant (CRA) Exam, 2016]

(a) $\frac{1}{18}$ (b) $\frac{1}{70}$

(c) $\frac{3}{5}$ (d) $\frac{1}{2}$

46. Dev can hit a target 3 times in 6 shots Pawan can hit the target 2 times in 6 shots and Lakhan can hit the target 4 times in 4 shots. What is the probability that at least 2 shots hit the target

[DMRC—Customer Relationship Assistant (CRA) Exam, 2016]

(a) $\frac{2}{3}$ (b) $\frac{1}{3}$

(c) $\frac{1}{2}$ (d) None of these

47. A bag contains 10 mangoes out of which 4 are taken out together. If one of them is found to be good, the probability that other is also good is

[DMRC—Train Operator (Station Controller) Exam, 2016]

(a) $\frac{1}{3}$ (b) $\frac{8}{15}$

(c) $\frac{5}{18}$ (d) $\frac{2}{3}$

48. A bag contains 4 red, 5 yellow and 6 pink balls. Two balls are drawn at random. What is the probability that none of the balls drawn are yellow?

[IBPS—Bank PO/MT (Pre.) Exam, 2015]

(a) $\frac{1}{7}$ (b) $\frac{3}{7}$

(c) $\frac{2}{7}$ (d) $\frac{5}{14}$ (e) $\frac{9}{14}$

49. A bag contains 6 red balls 11 yellow balls and 5 pink balls. If two balls are drawn at random from the bag. One after another what is the probability that the first ball is red and second ball is yellow.

[IBPS—Bank PO (Pre.) Exam, 2015]

(a) $\frac{1}{14}$ (b) $\frac{2}{7}$

(c) $\frac{5}{7}$ (d) $\frac{3}{14}$

(e) None of these

50. A bag contains 4 red balls, 6 blue balls and 8 pink balls. One ball is drawn at random and replace with 3 pink balls. A probability that the first ball drawn was either red or blue in colour and the second ball drawn was pink in colour?

[CET—(Maharashtra (MBA) Exam, 2016]

(a) 12/21 (b) 13/17

(c) 11/30 (d) 13/18

(e) None of these

ANSWERS

1. (d)	2. (b)	3. (d)	4. (b)	5. (a)	6. (c)	7. (a)	8. (d)	9. (b)	10. (a)
11. (d)	12. (c)	13. (b)	14. (c)	15. (c)	16. (a)	17. (b)	18. (d)	19. (d)	20. (d)
21. (b)	22. (d)	23. (b)	24. (c)	25. (b)	26. (d)	27. (c)	28. (b)	29. (d)	30. (d)
31. (b)	32. (b)	33. (a)	34. (b)	35. (a)	36. (b)	37. (a)	38. (d)	39. (c)	40. (a)
41. (b)	42. (c)	43. (a)	44. (d)	45. (b)	46. (a)	47. (a)	48. (b)	49. (b)	50. (e)

SOLUTIONS

1. Here S = {HH, HT, TH, TT}.

Let E = event of getting at least one head = {HT, TH, HH}.

$\therefore \quad P(E) = \frac{n(E)}{n(S)} = \frac{3}{4}.$

2. Here S = {TTT, TTH, THT, HTT, THH, HTH, HHT, HHH}.

Let E = event of getting at least two heads = {THH, HTH, HHT, HHH}.

$\therefore \quad P(E) = \frac{n(E)}{n(S)} = \frac{4}{8} = \frac{1}{2}.$

3. Here S = {TTT, TTH, THT, HTT, THH, HTH, HHT, HHH}.

Let E = event of getting at most two heads.

Then, E = {TTT, TTH, THT, HTT, THH, HTH, HHT}.

$\therefore \quad P(E) = \frac{n(E)}{n(S)} = \frac{7}{8}.$

4. When a die is thrown, we have S = {1, 2, 3, 4, 5, 6}.

Let E = event of getting a number greater than 4 = {5, 6}.

$\therefore \quad P(E) = \frac{n(E)}{n(S)} = \frac{2}{6} = \frac{1}{3}.$

5. We know that in a simultaneous throw of two dice, n (S) = 6 × 6 = 36.

Let E = event of getting a total of 7 = {(1, 6), (2, 5), (3, 4), (4, 3), (5, 2), (6, 1)}.

$\therefore \quad P(E) = \frac{n(E)}{n(S)} = \frac{6}{36} = \frac{1}{6}.$

6. In two throws of a die, n (S) = (6 × 6) = 36.

Let E = event of getting a sum 9 = {(3, 6), (4, 5), (5, 4), (6, 3)}.

$\therefore \quad P(E) = \frac{n(E)}{n(S)} = \frac{4}{36} = \frac{1}{9}.$

7. In a simultaneous throw of two dice, n (S) = (6 × 6) = 36.

Let E = event of getting a doublet = {(1, 1), (2, 2), (3, 3), (4, 4), (5, 5), (6, 6)}.

$\therefore \quad P(E) = \frac{n(E)}{n(S)} = \frac{6}{36} = \frac{1}{6}.$

8. In a simultaneous throw of two dice, we have n (S) = (6 × 6) = 36.

Let E = event of getting a total of 10 or 11 = {(4, 6), (5, 5), (6, 4), (5, 6), (6, 5)}.

$\therefore \quad P(E) = \frac{n(E)}{n(S)} = \frac{5}{36}.$

9. In a simultaneous throw of two dice, we have n (S) = (6 × 6) = 36.

Let E = event of getting two numbers whose product is even.

Then, E = {(1, 2), (1, 4), (1, 6), (2, 1), (2, 2), (2, 3), (2, 4), (2, 5), (2, 6), (3, 2), (3, 4), (3, 6), (4, 1), (4, 2), (4, 3), (4, 4), (4, 5), (4, 6), (5, 2), (5, 4), (5, 6), (6, 1), (6, 2), (6, 3), (6, 4), (6, 5), (6, 6)}.

$\therefore \quad n(E) = 27.$

$\therefore \quad P(E) = \frac{n(E)}{n(S)} = \frac{27}{36} = \frac{3}{4}.$

10. Here, S = {1, 2, 3, 4, ..., 19, 20}.

Let E = event of getting a multiple of 3 = {3, 6, 9, 12, 15, 18}.

$\therefore \quad P(E) = \frac{n(E)}{n(S)} = \frac{6}{20} = \frac{3}{10}.$

11. Here, S = {1, 2, 3, 4, ..., 19, 20}.

Let E = event of getting a multiple of 3 or 5 = {3, 6, 9, 12, 15, 18, 5, 10, 20}.

$\therefore \quad P(E) = \frac{n(E)}{n(S)} = \frac{9}{20}.$

12. P (getting a prize) $= \frac{10}{(10+25)} = \frac{10}{35} = \frac{2}{7}.$

13. Clearly, there are 52 cards, out of which there are 16 face cards.

$\therefore$ P (getting a face card) $= \frac{16}{52} = \frac{4}{13}.$

14. Here, n (S) = 52.

Let E = event of getting a queen of club or a king of heart.

Then, n (E) = 2.

$\therefore \quad P(E) = \frac{n(E)}{n(S)} = \frac{2}{52} = \frac{1}{26}.$

15. Here, n (S) = 52.

There are 26 red cards (including 2 kings) and there are 2 more kings.

Let E = event of getting a red card or a king.

Then, n (E) = 28.

$\therefore \quad P(E) = \frac{n(E)}{n(S)} = \frac{28}{52} = \frac{7}{13}.$

16. Here, $n(S) = 52$.
There are 13 spades (including one ten) and there are 3 more tens.
Let E = event of getting a ten or a spade.
Then, $n(E) = (13 + 3) = 16$.
$\therefore \quad P(E) = \frac{n(E)}{n(S)} = \frac{16}{52} = \frac{4}{13}$.

17. Here, $n(S) = 52$.
There are 13 cards of diamond (including one king) and there are 3 more kings.
Let E = event of getting a diamond or a king.
Then, $n(E) = (13 + 3) = 16$.
$\therefore \quad P(E) = \frac{n(E)}{n(S)} = \frac{16}{52} = \frac{4}{13}$.

18. Let S be the sample space.
Then, $n(S) = {}^{52}C_2 = \frac{(52 \times 51)}{(2 \times 1)} = 1326$.
Let E = event of getting 2 kings out of 4.
$\therefore \quad n(E) = {}^4C_2 = \frac{(4 \times 3)}{(2 \times 1)} = 6$.
$\therefore \quad P(E) = \frac{n(E)}{n(S)} = \frac{6}{1326} = \frac{1}{221}$.

19. Let S be the sample space.
Then, $n(S) = {}^{52}C_2 = \frac{(52 \times 51)}{(2 \times 1)} = 1326$.
Let E = event of getting 1 spade and 1 heart.
$\therefore \quad n(E)$ = number of ways of choosing 1 spade out of 13 and 1 heart out of 13
$= ({}^{13}C_1 \times {}^{13}C_1) = (13 \times 13) = 169$.
$\therefore \quad P(E) = \frac{n(E)}{n(S)} = \frac{169}{1326} = \frac{13}{102}$.

20. Clearly, $n(S) = {}^{52}C_2 = \frac{(52 \times 51)}{2} = 1326$.
Let E_1 = event of getting both red cards,
E_2 = event of getting both kings.
Then, $E_1 \cap E_2$ = event of getting 2 kings of red cards.
$\therefore n(E_1) = {}^{26}C_2 = \frac{(26 \times 25)}{(2 \times 1)} = 325; n(E_2) = {}^4C_2 = \frac{(4 \times 3)}{(2 \times 1)} = 6;$
$n(E_1 \cap E_2) = 2C_2 = 1$
$\therefore \quad P(E_1) = \frac{n(E_1)}{n(S)} = \frac{325}{1326}; P(E_2) = \frac{n(E_2)}{n(S)} = \frac{6}{1326};$
$P(E_1 \cup E_2) = \frac{1}{1326}$
$\therefore \quad P$ (both red or both kings) $= P(E_1 \cup E_2) = P(E_1) + P(E_2) - P(E_1 \cap E_2)$
$= \left(\frac{325}{1326} + \frac{6}{1326} - \frac{1}{1326}\right) = \frac{330}{1326} = \frac{55}{221}$.

21. Total number of balls $= (6 + 8) = 14$.
Number of white balls = 8.
$P(\text{drawing a white ball}) = \frac{8}{14} = \frac{4}{7}$.

22. Total number of balls $= (8 + 7 + 6) = 21$.
Let E = Event that the ball drawn is neither red nor green
= Event that the ball drawn is red.
$\therefore \quad n(E) = 8$.
$\therefore \quad P(E) = \frac{8}{21}$.

23. Total number of balls $= (4 + 5 + 6) = 15$.
$P(\text{drawing a red ball or a green ball}) = P(\text{red}) + P(\text{green})$
$= \left(\frac{4}{15} + \frac{5}{15}\right) = \frac{9}{15} = \frac{3}{5}$.

24. Total number of balls $= (4 + 5 + 3) = 12$.
Let E be the event of drawing 2 red balls.
Then, $n(E) = {}^4C_2 = \frac{4 \times 3}{2 \times 1} = 6$.
Also, $n(S) = {}^{12}C_2 = \frac{12 \times 11}{2 \times 1} = 66$.
$\therefore P(E) = \frac{n(E)}{n(S)} = \frac{6}{66} = \frac{1}{11}$.

25. Total number of balls $= (6 + 4 + 2 + 3) = 15$.
Let E be the event of drawing 2 red balls.
Then, $n(E) = {}^6C_2 = \frac{6 \times 5}{2 \times 1} = 15$.
Also, $n(S) = {}^{15}C_2 = \frac{15 \times 14}{2 \times 1} = 105$.
$\therefore \quad P(E) = \frac{n(E)}{n(S)} = \frac{15}{105} = \frac{1}{7}$.

26. Total number of balls $= (6 + 2 + 4 + 3) = 15$.
Let E be the event of drawing 3 non-yellow balls.
Then, $n(E) = {}^{12}C_3 = \frac{12 \times 11 \times 10}{3 \times 2 \times 1} = 220$.
Also, $n(S) = {}^{15}C_3 = \frac{15 \times 14 \times 13}{3 \times 2 \times 1} = 455$.
$\therefore \quad P(E) = \frac{n(E)}{n(S)} = \frac{220}{455} = \frac{44}{91}$.

27. Total number of marbles $= (6 + 4 + 2 + 3) = 15$.
Let E be the event of drawing 2 blue and 1 yellow marble.
Then, $n(E) = ({}^4C_2 \times {}^3C_1) = \frac{4 \times 3}{2 \times 1} \times 3 = 18$.
Also, $n(S) = {}^{15}C_3 = \frac{15 \times 14 \times 13}{3 \times 2 \times 1} = 455$.
$\therefore \quad P(E) = \frac{n(E)}{n(S)} = \frac{18}{455}$.

28. Total number of marbles $= (6 + 4 + 2 + 3) = 15$.
Let E be the event of drawing 1 green, 2 blue and 1 red marble.
Then, $n(E) = ({}^2C_1 \times {}^4C_2 \times {}^6C_1) = 2 \times \frac{4 \times 3}{2 \times 1} \times 6 = 72$.
And, $n(S) = {}^{15}C_4 = \frac{15 \times 14 \times 13 \times 12}{4 \times 3 \times 2 \times 1} = 1365$.
$\therefore \quad P(E) = \frac{n(E)}{n(S)} = \frac{72}{1365} = \frac{24}{455}$.

29. Total number of marbles = (6 + 4 + 2 + 3) = 15.
Let E be the event of drawing 2 marbles such that either both are green or both are yellow.
Then, $n(E) = ({}^2C_1 + {}^3C_2) = (1 + {}^3C_1) = (1 + 3) = 4$. And, $n(S) = {}^{15}C_2 = \frac{15 \times 14}{2 \times 1} = 105$.

$\therefore \ P(E) = \frac{n(E)}{n(S)} = \frac{4}{105}$.

30. Total number of balls = (6 + 2 + 4 + 3) = 15.
Let E be the event of drawing 4 balls such that 2 are red and 2 are green.

Then, $n(E) = ({}^2C_2 \times {}^4C_2) = \left(1 \times \frac{4 \times 3}{2 \times 1}\right) = 6$.

And, $n(S) = {}^{15}C_4 = \frac{15 \times 14 \times 13 \times 12}{4 \times 3 \times 2 \times 1} = 1365$.

$\therefore \ P(E) = \frac{n(E)}{n(S)} = \frac{6}{1365} = \frac{2}{455}$.

31. Total number of marbles = (4 + 5 + 3) = 12.
Let E be the event of drawing 3 marbles such that none is blue.
Then, $n(E)$ = number of ways of drawing 3 marbles out of 7 $= {}^7C_3 = \frac{7 \times 6 \times 5}{3 \times 2 \times 1} = 35$.

And, $n(S) = {}^{12}C_3 = \frac{12 \times 11 \times 10}{3 \times 2 \times 1} = 220$.

$\therefore \ P(E) = \frac{n(E)}{n(S)} = \frac{35}{220} = \frac{7}{44}$.

Required probability $= 1 - P(E) = \left(1 - \frac{7}{44}\right) = \frac{37}{44}$.

32. Total number of marbles = (6 + 4 + 2 + 3) = 15.
Let E be the event of drawing 4 marbles such that none is blue.
Then, $n(E)$ = number of ways of drawing 4 marbles out of 11 non-blue

$= {}^{11}C_4 = \frac{11 \times 10 \times 9 \times 8}{4 \times 3 \times 2 \times 1} = 330$.

And, $n(S) = {}^{15}C_4 = \frac{15 \times 14 \times 13 \times 12}{4 \times 3 \times 2 \times 1} = 1365$.

$\therefore \ P(E) = P(E) = \frac{n(E)}{n(S)} = \frac{330}{1365} = \frac{22}{91}$.

$\therefore$ Required probability $= \left(1 - \frac{22}{91}\right) = \frac{69}{91}$.

33. Total number of balls = (6 + 2 + 4 + 3) = 15.
Let E be the event of drawing 5 balls out of 9 non-blue balls

$= {}^9C_5 = {}^9C_{(9-5)} = {}^9C_4 = \frac{9 \times 8 \times 7 \times 6}{4 \times 3 \times 2 \times 1} = 126$.

And, $n(S) = {}^{15}C_5 = \frac{15 \times 14 \times 13 \times 12 \times 11}{5 \times 4 \times 3 \times 2 \times 1} = 3003$.

$\therefore \ P(E) = \frac{n(E)}{n(S)} = \frac{126}{3003} = \frac{6}{143}$.

$\therefore$ Required probability $= \left(1 - \frac{6}{143}\right) = \frac{137}{143}$.

34. Total number of balls = (2 + 3 + 2) = 7.
Let E be the event of drawing 2 non-blue balls.

Then, $n(E) = {}^5C_2 = \frac{5 \times 4}{2 \times 1} = 10$.

And, $n(S) = {}^7C_2 = \frac{7 \times 6}{2 \times 1} = 21$.

$\therefore \ P(E) = \frac{n(E)}{n(S)} = \frac{10}{21}$.

35. Total number of balls = (10 + 10) = 20.
Let E be the event of drawing 2 balls of the same colour.
$n(E)$ = number of ways of drawing 2 black balls or 2 white balls

$n(E) = ({}^{10}C_2 + {}^{10}C_2) = 2 \times {}^{10}C_2 = 2 \times \frac{10 \times 9}{2 \times 1} = 90$.

$n(S)$ = number of ways of drawing 2 balls out of 20

$= {}^{20}C_2 = \frac{20 \times 19}{2 \times 1} = 190$.

$\therefore \ P(E) = \frac{n(E)}{n(S)} = \frac{90}{190} = \frac{9}{19}$.

36. P(none is defective) $= \frac{{}^{16}C_2}{{}^{20}C_2} = \left(\frac{16 \times 15}{2 \times 1} \times \frac{2 \times 1}{20 \times 19}\right) = \frac{12}{19}$.

P(at least 1 is defective) $= \left(1 - \frac{12}{19}\right) = \frac{7}{19}$.

37. Let S be the sample space and let E be the event of selecting 2 boys and 1 girl.
Then, $n(S)$ = number of ways of selecting 3 students out of 25 $= {}^{25}C_3 = \frac{25 \times 24 \times 23}{3 \times 2 \times 1} = 2300$.

And, $n(E) = ({}^{15}C_2 \times {}^{10}C_1) = \left(\frac{15 \times 14}{2 \times 1} \times 10\right) = 1050$.

$\therefore \ P(E) = \frac{n(E)}{n(S)} = \frac{1050}{2300} = \frac{21}{46}$.

38. $n(S)$ = number of ways of choosing 4 persons out of 9

$= {}^9C_4 = \frac{9 \times 8 \times 7 \times 6}{4 \times 3 \times 2 \times 1} = 126$.

$n(E)$ = Number of ways of choosing 2 children out of 4 and 2 persons out of (3 + 2) persons

$n(E) = ({}^4C_2 \times {}^5C_2) = \left(\frac{4 \times 3}{2 \times 1} \times \frac{5 \times 4}{2 \times 1}\right) = 60$.

$\therefore \ P(E) = \frac{n(E)}{n(S)} = \frac{60}{126} = \frac{10}{21}$.

39. Clearly, $n(S) = (6 \times 6) = 36$.
Let E be the event that the sum is a prime number. Then, $n(E) = \{(1, 1), (1, 2), (1, 4), (1, 6), (2, 1), (2, 3), (2, 5), (3, 2), (3, 4), (4, 1), (4, 3), (5, 2), (5, 6), (6, 1), (6, 5)\}$

$\therefore \ n(E) = 15$.

$\therefore \quad P(E) = \frac{n(E)}{n(S)} = \frac{15}{36} = \frac{5}{12}$.

40. $P(E) = \frac{30}{100} = \frac{3}{10}, P(H) = \frac{20}{100} = \frac{1}{5}$ and $P(E \cap H) = \frac{10}{100} = \frac{1}{10}$.

$P(E \text{ or } H) = P(E \cup H)$

$= P(E) + P(H) - P(E \cap H) = \left(\frac{3}{10} + \frac{1}{5} - \frac{1}{10}\right) = \frac{4}{10} = \frac{2}{5}$.

41. Let E_1 = Event that the husband is selected and E_2 = Event that the wife is selected. Then,

$P(E_1) = \frac{1}{7}$ and $P(E_2) = \frac{1}{5}$.

$\therefore \quad P(\bar{E}_1) = \left(1 - \frac{1}{7}\right) = \frac{6}{7}$ and $P(\bar{E}_2) = \left(1 - \frac{1}{5}\right) = \frac{4}{5}$.

$\therefore$ Required probability = $P[(A \text{ and not } B) \text{ or } (B \text{ and not } A)]$

$= P\left[(E_1 \cap \bar{E}_2) \text{ or } (E_2 \cap \bar{E}_1)\right]$

$= P\left[(E_1 \cap \bar{E}_2) + P(E_2 \cap \bar{E}_1)\right]$

$= P(E_1).P(\bar{E}_2) + P(E_2).P(\bar{E}_1) = \left(\frac{1}{7} \times \frac{4}{5}\right) + \left(\frac{1}{5} \times \frac{6}{7}\right) = \frac{10}{35} = \frac{2}{7}$.

42. Let E_1 = Event that A speaks the truth and E_2 = Event that B speaks the truth. Then,

$P(E_1) = \frac{75}{100} = \frac{3}{4}, P(E_2) = \frac{80}{100} = \frac{4}{5}, P(\bar{E}_1) = \left(1 - \frac{3}{4}\right)$

$= \frac{1}{4}, P(\bar{E}_2) = \left(1 - \frac{4}{5}\right) = \frac{1}{5}$.

P(A and B contradict each other)

= P[(A speaks the truth and B tells a lie) or (A tells a lie and B speaks the truth)]

$= P\left[(E_1 \cap \bar{E}_2) \text{ or } (\bar{E}_1 \cap E_2)\right] = P(E_1 \cap \bar{E}_2) + P(\bar{E}_1 \cap E_2)$

$= P(E_1).P(\bar{E}_2) + P(\bar{E}_1).P(E_2)$

$= \left(\frac{3}{4} \times \frac{1}{5}\right) + \left(\frac{1}{4} \times \frac{4}{5}\right) = \left(\frac{3}{20} + \frac{1}{5}\right) = \frac{7}{20}$

$= \left(\frac{7}{20} \times 100\right)\% = 35\%$.

43. Let E_1 = Event that A speaks the truth and E_2 = Event that B speaks the truth.

Then, $P(E_1) = \frac{60}{100} = \frac{3}{5}, P(E_2) = \frac{70}{100} = \frac{7}{10}, P(\bar{E}_1)$

$= \left(1 - \frac{3}{5}\right) = \frac{2}{5}, P(\bar{E}_2) = \left(1 - \frac{7}{10}\right) = \frac{3}{10}$.

P(A and B say the same thing)

= P[(A speaks the truth and B speaks the truth) or (A tells a lie and B tells a lie)]

$= P\left[(E_1 \cap E_2) \text{ or } (\bar{E}_1 \cap \bar{E}_2)\right] = P(E_1 \cap E_2) + P(\bar{E}_1 \cap \bar{E}_2)$

$= P(E_1).P(E_2) + P(\bar{E}_1).P(\bar{E}_2)$

$= \left(\frac{3}{5} \times \frac{7}{10}\right) + \left(\frac{2}{5} \times \frac{3}{10}\right) = \frac{27}{50} = 0.54$.

44. Total number of persons = (3 + 2) = 5.

$\therefore \quad n(S) = {}^5C_3 = {}^5C_2 = \frac{5 \times 4}{2 \times 1} = 10$.

Let E be the event of selecting 3 members having at least 1 woman

Then, $n(E) = n$[(1 woman and 2 men) or (2 women and 1 man)]

= n(1 woman and 2 men) + n(2 women and 1 man)

$= ({}^2C_1 \times {}^3C_1) + ({}^2C_2 \times {}^3C_1) = ({}^2C_1 \times {}^3C_1) + (1 \times {}^3C_1)$

$= (2 \times 3) + (1 \times 3) = (6 + 3) = 9$.

$\therefore \quad P(E) = \frac{n(E)}{n(S)} = \frac{9}{10}$.

45. Number of blue balls = 3 balls

Number of green balls = 2 balls

Number of red balls = 5 balls

Total balls in the bag = 3 + 2 + 5 = 10

Total possible outcomes = Selection of 4 balls out of 10 balls = ${}^{10}C_4 = \frac{10!}{4!\times(10-4)!} = \frac{10\times9\times8\times7}{1\times2\times3\times4} = 210$

Favorable outcomes = (selection of 2 green balls out of 2 balls) × (selection of 2 balls out of 3 blue balls)

$= {}^2C_2 \times {}^3C_2$

= 1 × 3 = 3

$\therefore$ Required probability $= \frac{\text{Favorable out comes}}{\text{Total possible outcomes}}$

$= \frac{3}{210} = \frac{1}{70}$

46. Probability of hitting the target:

Dev can hit target $\Rightarrow \frac{3}{6} = \frac{1}{2}$, Lakhan can hit target $= \frac{4}{4} = 1$

Pawan can hit target $= \frac{2}{6} = \frac{1}{3}$

Required probability that at least 2 shorts hit target

$= \frac{1}{2} \times \frac{2}{3} + \frac{1}{2} \times \frac{1}{3} + \frac{1}{2} \times \frac{1}{3}$

$= \frac{1}{3} + \frac{1}{6} + \frac{1}{6} = \frac{4}{6} = \frac{2}{3}$

47. Out of 10 mangoes, 4 mangoes are rotten

$\therefore$ Required probability $= \frac{{}^6C_2}{{}^{10}C_2} = \frac{\frac{6!}{2!(6-2)!}}{\frac{10!}{2!(10-2)!}} = \frac{\frac{6!}{2!4!}}{\frac{10!}{2!\times8!}}$

$= \frac{\frac{6\times5}{1\times2}}{\frac{10\times9}{1\times2}} = \frac{6\times5}{10\times9} = \frac{1}{3}$

48. Number of red balls = 4

Number of yellow ball = 5

Number of pink ball = 6

Total number of balls = 4 + 5 + 6 = 15

Total possible outcomes = selection of 2 balls out of 15 balls = ${}^{15}C_2 = \frac{15!}{2!(15-2)!} = \frac{15!}{2!\times13!} = \frac{15\times14}{1\times2} = 105$

Total favourable outcomes = selection of 2 balls out of 4 orange and 6 pink balls.

$$^{10}C_2 = \frac{10!}{2!(10-2)!} = \frac{10!}{2!8!} = \frac{10\times 9}{1\times 2} = 45$$

$\therefore$ Required probability = $\frac{45}{105} = \frac{3}{7}$

49. Number of red balls = 6
Number of yellow ball = 11
Number of pink balls = 5
Total number of balls = 6 + 11 + 5 = 22

Total possible outcomes = $n(E) = {}^{22}C_2 = \frac{22!}{2!(22-2)!} = \frac{22!}{2\times 20!}$

$= \frac{22\times 21}{2\times 1} = 231$

Number of favourable outcomes

$= n(s) = {}^{6}C_1 \times {}^{11}C_1 = 6\times 11 = 66$

Required probability = $\frac{n(E)}{n(S)} = \frac{66}{231} = \frac{2}{7}$

50. Number of Red balls = 4
Number of Blue balls = 6
Number of Pink balls = 8
Total number of balls = 4 + 6 + 8 = 18
Required probability

$= \frac{4}{18}\times\frac{11}{20} + \frac{6}{18}\times\frac{11}{20}$

$= \frac{11}{20}\left[\left(\frac{4}{18}+\frac{6}{18}\right)\right]$

$= \frac{11}{20}\times\frac{10}{18} = \frac{11}{36}$

32 True Discount

IMPORTANT CONCEPTS

Suppose a man has to pay ₹ 156 after 4 years and the rate of interest is 14% per annum. Clearly, ₹ 100 at 14% will amount to ₹ 156 in 4 years. So, the payment of ₹ 100 now will clear off the debt of ₹ 156 due 4 years hence. We say that :

Sum due = ₹ 156 due 4 years hence;

Present Worth (P.W.) = ₹ 100;

True Discount (T.D.) = ₹ (156 – 100) = ₹ 56 = (Sum due) – (P.W.).

We define : ***T.D. = Interest on P.W.***

Amount = (P.W.) + (T.D.).

Interest is reckoned on P.W. and true discount is reckoned on the amount.

IMPORTANT FORMULAE

Let rate = R% per annum and Time = T years. Then,

I. $\text{P.W.} = \dfrac{100 \times \text{Amount}}{100 + (R \times T)} = \dfrac{100 \times \text{T.D.}}{R \times T}$ II. $\text{T.D.} = \dfrac{(\text{P.W.}) \times R \times T}{100} = \dfrac{\text{Amount} \times R \times T}{100 + (R \times T)}$

III. $\text{Sum} = \dfrac{(\text{S.I.}) \times (\text{T.D.})}{(\text{S.I.}) - (\text{T.D.})}$ IV. (S.I.) – (T.D.) = S.I. on T.D.

V. When the sum is put at compound interest, then $\text{P.W.} = \dfrac{\text{Amount}}{\left(1 + \dfrac{R}{100}\right)^T}$.

SOLVED EXAMPLES

Ex. 1. ***Find the present worth of ₹ 930 due 3 years hence at 8% per annum. Also find the discount.***

Sol. $\text{P.W.} = \dfrac{100 \times \text{Amount}}{100 + (R \times T)} = ₹\left[\dfrac{100 \times 930}{100 + (8 \times 3)}\right] = ₹\left(\dfrac{100 \times 930}{124}\right) = ₹\, 750.$

T.D. = (Amount) – (P.W.) = ₹ (930 – 750) = ₹ 180.

Ex. 2. ***The true discount on a bill due 9 months hence at 12% per annum is ₹ 540. Find the amount of the bill and its present worth.***

Sol. Let amount be ₹ x. Then,

$$\frac{x \times R \times T}{100 + (R \times T)} = \text{T.D.} \Rightarrow \frac{x \times 12 \times \frac{3}{4}}{100 + \left(12 \times \frac{3}{4}\right)} = 540 \Rightarrow x = \left(\frac{540 \times 109}{9}\right) = ₹\, 6540.$$

∴ Amount = ₹ 6540.

P.W. = ₹ (6540 – 540) = ₹ 6000.

Ex. 3. ***The true discount on a certain sum of money due 3 years hence is ₹ 250 and the simple interest on the same sum for the same time and at the same rate is ₹ 375. Find the sum and the rate percent.***

Sol. T.D. = ₹ 250 and S.I. = ₹ 375.

$\therefore$ Sum due $= \dfrac{\text{S.I.} \times \text{T.D.}}{(\text{S.I.}) - (\text{T.D.})} = ₹\left(\dfrac{375 \times 250}{375 - 250}\right) = ₹\,750.$

Rate $= \left(\dfrac{100 \times 375}{750 \times 3}\right)\% = 16\dfrac{2}{3}\%.$

Ex. 4. ***The difference between the simple interest and true discount on a certain sum of money for 6 months at $12\frac{1}{2}\%$ per annum is ₹ 25. Find the sum.***

Sol. Let the sum be ₹ x. Then,

T.D. $= \dfrac{x \times \frac{25}{2} \times \frac{1}{2}}{100 + \left(\frac{25}{2} \times \frac{1}{2}\right)} = \left(x \times \dfrac{25}{4} \times \dfrac{4}{425}\right) = \dfrac{x}{17}.$

S.I. $= \left(x \times \dfrac{25}{2} \times \dfrac{1}{2} \times \dfrac{1}{100}\right) = \dfrac{x}{16}.$

$\therefore \dfrac{x}{16} - \dfrac{x}{17} = 25 \Rightarrow 17x - 16x = 25 \times 16 \times 17 \Rightarrow x = 6800.$

Hence, sum due = ₹ 6800.

Ex. 5. ***A bill falls due in 1 year. The creditor agrees to accept immediate payment of the half and to defer the payment of the other half for 2 years. By this arrangement he gains ₹ 40. What is the amount of the bill, if the money be worth $12\frac{1}{2}\%$?***

Sol. Let the sum be ₹ x. Then,

$$\left[\frac{x}{2} + \frac{\frac{x}{2} \times 100}{100 + \left(\frac{25}{2} \times 2\right)}\right] - \frac{x \times 100}{100 + \left(\frac{25}{2} \times 1\right)} = 40 \Rightarrow \frac{x}{2} + \frac{2x}{5} - \frac{8x}{9} = 40 \Rightarrow x = 3600.$$

$\therefore$ Amount of the bill = ₹ 3600.

EXERCISE

(OBJECTIVE TYPE QUESTIONS)

Directions: ***Mark (✓) against the correct answer:***

1. The present worth of ₹ 2310 due $2\frac{1}{2}$ years hence, the rate of interest being 15% per annum, is
   (a) ₹ 1750 (b) ₹ 1680
   (c) ₹ 1840 (d) ₹ 1443.75
2. If the true discount on a sum due 2 years hence at 14% per annum be ₹ 168, the sum due is
   (a) ₹ 768 (b) ₹ 968
   (c) ₹ 1960 (d) ₹ 2400
3. The true discount on ₹ 2562 due 4 months hence is ₹ 122. The rate percent is
   (a) 12% (b) $13\frac{1}{3}\%$
   (c) 15% (d) 14%
4. The true discount on ₹ 1760 due after a certain time at 12% per annum is ₹ 160. The time after which it is due is
   (a) 6 months (b) 8 months
   (c) 9 months (d) 10 months
5. The true discount on a bill due 9 months hence at 16% per annum is ₹ 189. The amount of the bill is
   (a) ₹ 1386 (b) ₹ 1764
   (c) ₹ 1575 (d) ₹ 2268
6. The interest on ₹ 750 for 2 years is the same as the true discount on ₹ 960 due 2 years hence. If the rate of interest is the same in both cases, it is
   (a) 12% (b) 14%
   (c) 15% (d) $16\frac{2}{3}\%$

7. The simple interest and the true discount on a certain sum for a given time and at a given rate are ₹ 85 and ₹ 80 respectively. The sum is
(*a*) ₹ 1800 (*b*) ₹ 1450
(*c*) ₹ 1360 (*d*) ₹ 6800

8. If ₹ 10 be allowed as true discount on a bill of ₹ 110 due at the end of a certain time, then the discount allowed on the same sum due at the end of double the time is
(*a*) ₹ 20 (*b*) ₹ 21.81
(*c*) ₹ 22 (*d*) ₹ 18.33

9. A man wants to sell his scooter. There are two offers, one at ₹ 12,000 cash and the other at a credit of ₹ 12,880 to be paid after 8 months, money being at 18% per annum. Which is the better offer?
(*a*) ₹ 12,000 in cash (*b*) ₹ 12,880 at credit
(*c*) Both are equally good

10. Goods were bought for ₹ 600 and sold the same day for ₹ 688.50 at a credit of 9 months and thus gaining 2%. The rate of interest per annum is
(*a*) $16\frac{2}{3}\%$ (*b*) $14\frac{1}{2}\%$
(*c*) $13\frac{1}{3}\%$ (*d*) 15%

11. The present worth of ₹ 1404 due in two equal half-yearly instalments at 8% per annum simple interest is
(*a*) ₹ 1325 (*b*) ₹ 1300
(*c*) ₹ 1350 (*d*) ₹ 1500

12. A trader owes a merchant ₹ 10,028 due 1 year hence. The trader wants to settle the account after 3 months. If the rate of interest is 12% per annum, how much cash should he pay?
(*a*) ₹ 9025.20 (*b*) ₹ 9200
(*c*) ₹ 9600 (*d*) ₹ 9560

13. A man buys a watch for ₹ 1950 in cash and sells it for ₹ 2200 at a credit of 1 year. If the rate of interest is 10% per annum, the man
(*a*) gains ₹ 55 (*b*) gains ₹ 50
(*c*) loses ₹ 30 (*d*) gains ₹ 30

14. A man purchased a cow for ₹ 3000 and sold it the same day for ₹ 3600, allowing the buyer a credit of 2 years. If the rate of interest be 10% per annum, then the man has a gain of
(*a*) 0% (*b*) 5%
(*c*) 7.5% (*d*) 10%

15. A owes B, ₹ 1573 payable $1\frac{1}{2}$ years hence. Also B owes A, ₹ 1444.50 payable 6 months hence. If they want to settle the account forthwith, keeping 14% as the rate of interest, then who should pay and how much? **(M.A.T. 2006; G.B.O., 2007)**
(*a*) A, ₹ 28.50 (*b*) B, ₹ 37.50
(*c*) A, ₹ 50 (*d*) B, ₹ 50

16. A has to pay ₹ 220 to B after 1 year. B asks A to pay ₹ 110 in cash and defer the payment of ₹ 110 for 2 years. A agrees to it. If the rate of interest be 10% per annum, in this mode of payment
(*a*) There is no gain or loss to any one
(*b*) A gains ₹ 7.34 (*c*) A loses ₹ 7.34
(*d*) A gains ₹ 11

17. ₹ 20 is the true discount on ₹ 260 due after a certain time. What will be the true discount on the same sum due after half of the former time, the rate of interest being the same?
(*a*) ₹ 10 (*b*) ₹ 10.40
(*c*) ₹ 15.20 (*d*) ₹ 13

18. The true discount on a certain sum of money due $2\frac{2}{3}$ years hence, is ₹ 150 and the simple interest on the same sum for the same time and at the same rate is ₹ 200. Interest rate per annum is **[MAT, 2011]**
(*a*) 10% (*b*) 12%
(*c*) $12\frac{1}{2}\%$ (*d*) $8\frac{1}{2}\%$

19. ₹ 20 is the true discount on ₹ 260 due after a certain time. What will be the true discount on the same sum due after half of the former time, the rate of interest being the same? **[MAT, 2011]**
(*a*) ₹ 15.20 (*b*) ₹ 10.40
(*c*) ₹ 10.83 (*d*) ₹ 13

20. The total discount on ₹ 1860 due after a certain time at 5% is ₹ 60. Find the time after which it is due **[SSC—CHSL (10+2) Exam, 2015]**
(*a*) 9 months (*b*) 10 months
(*c*) 7 months (*d*) 8 months

21. The difference between simple interest and the true discount on ₹ 2400 due 4 years hence at 5% per annum simple interest is **[SSC—CHSL (10+2) Exam, 2015]**
(*a*) ₹ 70 (*b*) ₹ 30
(*c*) ₹ 50 (*d*) ₹ 80

ANSWERS

1. (*b*)	2. (*a*)	3. (*c*)	4. (*d*)	5. (*b*)	6. (*b*)	7. (*c*)	8. (*d*)	9. (*a*)	10. (*a*)
11. (*a*)	12. (*b*)	13. (*b*)	14. (*a*)	15. (*d*)	16. (*b*)	17. (*b*)	18. (*c*)	19. (*b*)	20. (*d*)
21. (*d*)									

SOLUTIONS

1. P.W. = ₹ $\left[\frac{100\times 2310}{100+\left(15\times\frac{5}{2}\right)}\right]$ = ₹ 1680.

2. P.W. = $\frac{100\times \text{T.D.}}{R\times T}=\frac{100\times 168}{14\times 2}=600$.

∴ Sum = (P.W. + T.D.) = ₹ (600 + 168) = ₹ 768.

3. P.W. = ₹ (2562 – 122) = ₹ 2440.

∴ S.I. on ₹ 2440 for 4 months = ₹ 122.

∴ Rate = $\left(\frac{100\times 122}{2440\times\frac{1}{3}}\right)\%=15\%$.

4. P.W. = ₹ (1760 – 160) = ₹ 1600.

∴ S.I. on ₹ 1600 at 12% = ₹ 160.

∴ Time = $\left(\frac{100\times 160}{1600\times 12}\right)=\frac{5}{6}$ years $=\left(\frac{5}{6}\times 12\right)$ months = 10 minutes.

5. Let P.W. be ₹ x.

Then, S.I. on ₹ x at 16% for 9 months = ₹ 189.

∴ $x\times 16\times\frac{9}{12}\times\frac{1}{100}=189$ or $x = 1575$.

∴ P.W. = ₹ 1575.

∴ Sum due = P.W. + T.D. = ₹ (1575 + 189) = ₹ 1764.

6. S.I. on ₹ 750 = T.D. on ₹ 960.

This means P.W. of ₹ 960 due 2 years hence is ₹ 750.

∴ T.D. = ₹ (960 – 750) = ₹ 210.

Thus, S.I. on ₹ 750 for 2 years is ₹ 210.

∴ Rate = $\left(\frac{100\times 210}{750\times 2}\right)\%=14\%$.

7. Sum = $\frac{\text{S.I.}\times\text{T.D.}}{(\text{S.I.})-(\text{T.D.})}=\frac{85\times 80}{(85-80)}$ = ₹ 1360.

8. S.I. on ₹ (110 – 10) for a certain time = ₹ 10.

S.I. on ₹ 100 for double the time = ₹ 20.

T.D. on ₹ 120 = ₹ (120 – 100) = ₹ 20.

T.D. on ₹ 110 = ₹ $\left(\frac{20}{120}\times 110\right)$ = ₹ 18.33.

9. P.W. of ₹ 12,880 due 8 months hence

= ₹ $\left[\frac{12880\times 100}{100+\left(18\times\frac{8}{12}\right)}\right]$ = ₹ $\left(\frac{12880\times 100}{112}\right)$ = ₹ 11500.

Clearly, ₹ 12,000 in cash is a better offer.

10. S.P = 102% of ₹ 600 = ₹ $\left(\frac{102}{100}\times 600\right)$ = ₹ 612.

Now, P.W. = ₹ 612 and sum = ₹ 688.50.

∴ T.D. = ₹ (688.50 – 612) = ₹ 76.50.

Thus, S.I. on ₹ 612 for 9 months is ₹ 76.50.

∴ Rate = $\left(\frac{100\times 76.50}{612\times\frac{3}{4}}\right)\%=16\frac{2}{3}\%$.

11. Required sum = P.W. of ₹ 702 due 6 months hence + P.W. of ₹ 702 due 1 year hence

= ₹ $\left[\left(\frac{100\times 702}{100+8\times\frac{1}{2}}\right)+\left(\frac{100\times 702}{100+(8\times 1)}\right)\right]$ = ₹ (675 + 650)

= ₹ 1325.

12. Required money = P.W. of ₹ 10028 due 9 months hence

= ₹ $\left[\frac{10028\times 100}{100+\left(12\times\frac{9}{12}\right)}\right]$ = ₹ 9200.

13. S.P. = P.W. of ₹ 2200 due 1 year hence

= ₹ $\left[\frac{2200\times 100}{100+(10\times 1)}\right]$ = ₹ 2000.

∴ Gain = ₹ (2000 – 1950) = ₹ 50.

14. C.P. = ₹ 3000.

S.P. = ₹ $\left[\frac{3600\times 100}{100+(10\times 2)}\right]$ = ₹ 3000.

Gain = 0%.

15. A owes = P.W. of ₹ 1573 due $\frac{3}{2}$ years hence

= ₹ $\left[\frac{1573\times 100}{100+\left(14\times\frac{3}{2}\right)}\right]$ = ₹ $\left(\frac{1573\times 100}{121}\right)$ = ₹ 1300.

B owes = P.W. of ₹ 1444.50 due 6 months hence

= ₹ $\left[\frac{1444.50\times 100}{100+\left(14\times\frac{1}{2}\right)}\right]$ = ₹ $\left(\frac{1444.50\times 100}{107}\right)$ = ₹ 1350.

∴ B must pay ₹ 50 to A.

16. A has to pay = P.W. of ₹ 220 due 1 year hence

= ₹ $\left[\frac{220\times 100}{100+(10\times 1)}\right]$ = ₹ 200.

A actually pays = ₹ 110 + P.W. of ₹ 110 due 2 years hence

= $\left[110+\frac{110\times 100}{100+(10\times 2)}\right]$ = ₹ 192.66.

∴ A gains = ₹ (200 – 192.66) = ₹ 7.34.

17. S.I. on ₹ (260 – 20) for a given time = ₹ 20.

S.I. on ₹ 240 for half the time = ₹ 10.

T.D. on ₹ 250 = ₹ 10.

∴ T.D. on ₹ 260 = ₹ $\left(\frac{10}{250}\times 260\right)$ = ₹ 10.40.

18. TD = ₹ 150 and SI = ₹ 200

Sum due = $\frac{SI \times TD}{(SI)-(TD)}$

$= ₹\left(\frac{200 \times 150}{200-150}\right) = ₹\ 600$

Rate = $\left(\frac{100 \times 200}{600 \times \frac{8}{3}}\right)\%$

$= \left(\frac{20000}{1600}\right)\%$

$= \left(\frac{200}{16}\right)\%$

$= 12\frac{1}{2}\%$

19. SI on ₹ (260 – 20) for a given time = ₹ 20

SI on ₹ 240 for half the time = ₹ 20

TD on ₹ 250 = ₹ 10

TD on ₹ 260 = $\frac{10}{250} \times 260$ = ₹ 10.40

20. Here, A = 1860, R = 5%

TD = 60

$\therefore\ TD = \frac{A \times R \times T}{100 + R \times T}$

$\Rightarrow\ 60 = \frac{1860 \times 5 \times T}{100 + 5T}$

$\Rightarrow$ 6000 + 300T = 9300T

$\Rightarrow$ 6000 = 9300T – 300T

$\Rightarrow$ 6000 = 9000T

$\Rightarrow\ T = \frac{6000}{9000}$

$\Rightarrow\ T = \frac{2}{3}$ year

$\Rightarrow\ T = \frac{2}{3} \times 12 = 8$ months

21. Given A = 2400, R = 5%, T = 4 year

$\therefore\ TD = \frac{A \times R \times T}{100 + R \times T}$

$= \frac{2400 \times 4 \times 5}{100 + 20}$ = ₹ 400

$\therefore\ SI - TD = \frac{TD \times R \times T}{100}$

$= \frac{400 \times 5 \times 4}{100}$ = ₹ 80

33 Banker's Discount

IMPORTANT CONCEPTS

I. **Banker's Discount** : Suppose a merchant A buys goods worth, say ₹ 10,000 from another merchant B at a credit of say 5 months. Then, B prepares a bill, called the bill of exchange. A signs this bill and allows B to withdraw the amount from his bank account after exactly 5 months.

The date exactly after 5 months is called *nominally due date.* Three days (known as *grace days*) are added to it to get a date, known as *legally due date.*

Suppose B wants to have the money before the legally due date. Then he can have the money from the banker or a broker, who deducts S.I. on the face value (i.e., ₹ 10,000 in this case) for the period from the date on which the bill was discounted (*i.e.,* paid by the banker) and the legally due date. This amount is known as ***Banker's Discount* (B.D.)**

Thus, **B.D.** *is the S.I. on the face value for the period from the date on which the bill was discounted and the legally due date.*

II. **Banker's Gain (B.G.) = (B.D.) – (T.D.)** *for the unexpired time.*

Note : When the date of the bill is not given, grace days are not to be added.

IMPORTANT FORMULAE

1. B.D. = S.I. on bill for unexpired time.

2. $\text{B.G.} = (\text{B.D.}) - (\text{T.D.}) = \text{S.I. on T.D.} = \dfrac{(\text{T.D.})^2}{\text{P.W.}}$.

3. $\text{T.D.} = \sqrt{\text{P.W.} \times \text{B.G.}}$

4. $\text{T.D.} = \left(\dfrac{\text{Amount} \times \text{Rate} \times \text{Time}}{100}\right)$.

5. $\text{T.D.} = \left[\dfrac{\text{Amount} \times \text{Rate} \times \text{Time}}{100 + (\text{Rate} \times \text{Time})}\right]$.

6. $\text{Amount} = \left(\dfrac{\text{B.D.} \times \text{T.D.}}{\text{B.D.} - \text{T.D.}}\right)$.

7. $\text{T.D.} = \left(\dfrac{\text{B.G.} \times 100}{\text{Rate} \times \text{Time}}\right)$.

SOLVED EXAMPLES

Ex. 1. ***A bill for ₹ 6000 is drawn on July 14 at 5 months. It is discounted on 5th October at 10%. Find the banker's discount, true discount, banker's gain and the money that the holder of the bill receives.***

Sol. Face value of the bill = ₹ 6000.

Date on which the bill was drawn = July 14 at 5 months.

Nominally due date = December 14. Legally due date = December 17.

Date on which the bill was discounted = October 5.

Unexpired time : Oct. + Nov. + Dec.

$26 + 30 + 17 = 73 \text{ days} = \dfrac{1}{5} \text{ year}.$

$\therefore \quad \text{B.D.} = \text{S.I. on ₹ 6000 for } \dfrac{1}{5} \text{ year} = ₹\left(6000 \times 10 \times \dfrac{1}{5} \times \dfrac{1}{100}\right) = ₹\ 120.$

$$\text{T.D.} = ₹\left[\frac{6000 \times 10 \times \frac{1}{5}}{100 + \left(10 \times \frac{1}{5}\right)}\right] = ₹\left(\frac{12000}{102}\right) = ₹\,117.64.$$

$\therefore$ B.G. = (B.D.) – (T.D.) = ₹ (120 – 117.64) = ₹ 2.36.

Money received by the holder of the bill = ₹ (6000 – 120) = ₹ 5880.

Ex. 2. ***If the true discount on a certain sum due 6 months hence at 15% is ₹ 120, what is the banker's discount on the same sum for the same time and at the same rate?***

Sol. B.G. = S.I. on T.D. = $₹\left(120 \times 15 \times \frac{1}{2} \times \frac{1}{100}\right) = ₹\,9.$

$\therefore$ (B.D.) – (T.D.) = ₹ 9.

$\therefore$ B.D. = ₹ (120 + 9) = ₹ 129.

Ex. 3. ***The banker's discount on ₹ 1800 at 12% per annum is equal to the true discount on ₹ 1872 for the same time at the same rate. Find the time.***

Sol. S.I. on ₹ 1800 = T.D. on ₹ 1872.

$\therefore$ P.W. of ₹ 1872 is ₹ 1800.

$\therefore$ ₹ 72 is S.I. on ₹ 1800 at 12%.

$\therefore$ Time = $\left(\frac{100 \times 72}{12 \times 1800}\right)$ year $= \frac{1}{3}$ year = 4 months.

Ex. 4. ***The banker's discount and the true discount on a sum of money due 8 months hence are ₹ 120 and ₹ 110 respectively. Find the sum and the rate percent.***

Sol. Sum = $\left(\frac{\text{B.D.} \times \text{T.D.}}{\text{B.D.} - \text{T.D.}}\right) = ₹\left(\frac{120 \times 110}{120 - 110}\right) = ₹\,1320.$

Since B.D. is S.I. on sum due, so S.I. on ₹ 1320 for 8 months is ₹ 120.

$\therefore$ Rate = $\left(\frac{100 \times 120}{1320 \times \frac{2}{3}}\right)\% = 13\frac{7}{11}\%.$

Ex. 5. ***The present worth of a bill due sometime hence is ₹ 1100 and the true discount on the bill is ₹ 110. Find the banker's discount and the banker's gain.***

Sol. T.D. = $\sqrt{\text{P.W.} \times \text{B.G.}}$

$\therefore$ B.G. = $\frac{(\text{T.D.})^2}{\text{P.W.}} = ₹\left(\frac{110 \times 110}{1100}\right) = ₹\,11.$

$\therefore$ B.D. = (T.D. + B.G.) = ₹ (110 + 11) = ₹ 121.

Ex. 6. ***The banker's discount on ₹ 1650 due a certain time hence is ₹ 165. Find the true discount and the banker's gain.***

Sol. Sum = $\frac{\text{B.D.} \times \text{T.D.}}{\text{B.D.} - \text{T.D.}} = \frac{\text{B.D.} \times \text{T.D.}}{\text{B.G.}}.$

$\therefore \frac{\text{T.D.}}{\text{B.G.}} = \frac{\text{Sum}}{\text{B.D.}} = \frac{1650}{165} = \frac{10}{1}.$

Thus, if B.G. is Re 1, T.D. = ₹ 10.

If B.D. is ₹ 11, T.D. = ₹ 10. If B.D. is ₹ 165, T.D. = $₹\left(\frac{10}{11} \times 165\right) = ₹\,150.$

And, B.G. = ₹ (165 – 150) = ₹ 15.

Ex. 7. ***What rate percent does a man get for his money when in discounting a bill due 10 months hence, he deducts 10% of the amount of the bill?***

Sol. Let, amount of the bill = ₹ 100. Money deducted = ₹ 10.

Money received by the holder of the bill = ₹ (100 – 10) = ₹ 90.

∴ S.I. on ₹ 90 for 10 months = ₹ 10.

∴ Rate = $\left(\dfrac{100 \times 10}{90 \times \dfrac{10}{12}}\right)\% = 13\dfrac{1}{3}\%$.

EXERCISE

(OBJECTIVE TYPE QUESTIONS)

Directions: ***Mark (✓) against the correct answer:***

1. The true discount on a bill of ₹ 540 is ₹ 90. The banker's discount is
   (*a*) ₹ 60 (*b*) ₹ 108
   (*c*) ₹ 110 (*d*) ₹ 112
2. The present worth of a certain bill due sometime hence is ₹ 800 and the true discount is ₹ 36. The banker's discount is
   (*a*) ₹ 37 (*b*) ₹ 37.62
   (*c*) ₹ 34.38 (*d*) ₹ 38.98
3. The present worth of a certain sum due sometime hence is ₹ 1600 and the true discount is ₹ 160. The banker's gain is
   (*a*) ₹ 20 (*b*) ₹ 24
   (*c*) ₹ 16 (*d*) ₹ 12
4. The banker's gain of a certain sum due 2 years hence at 10% per annum is ₹ 24. The present worth is
   (*a*) ₹ 480 (*b*) ₹ 520
   (*c*) ₹ 600 (*d*) ₹ 960
5. The banker's gain on a bill due 1 year hence at 12% per annum is ₹ 6. The true discount is
   (*a*) ₹ 72 (*b*) ₹ 36
   (*c*) ₹ 54 (*d*) ₹ 50
6. The banker's discount on a bill due 4 months hence at 15% is ₹ 420. The true discount is
   (*a*) ₹ 400 (*b*) ₹ 360
   (*c*) ₹ 480 (*d*) ₹ 320
7. The banker's gain on a sum due 3 years hence at 12% per annum is ₹ 270. The banker's discount is
   (*a*) ₹ 960 (*b*) ₹ 840
   (*c*) ₹ 1020 (*d*) ₹ 760
8. The present worth of a sum due sometime hence is ₹ 576 and the banker's gain is ₹ 16. The true discount is
   (*a*) ₹ 36 (*b*) ₹ 72
   (*c*) ₹ 48 (*d*) ₹ 96
9. The banker's discount on ₹ 1600 at 15% per annum is the same as true discount on ₹ 1680 for the same time and at the same rate. The time is
   (*a*) 3 months (*b*) 4 months
   (*c*) 6 months (*d*) 8 months
10. The banker's discount on a sum of money for $1\frac{1}{2}$ years is ₹ 558 and the true discount on the same sum for 2 years is ₹ 600. The rate percent is
    (*a*) 10% (*b*) 13%
    (*c*) 12% (*d*) 15%
11. The banker's discount of a certain sum of money is ₹ 72 and the true discount on the same sum for the same time is ₹ 60. The sum due is
    (*a*) ₹ 360 (*b*) ₹ 432
    (*c*) ₹ 540 (*d*) ₹ 1080
12. The banker's discount on a certain sum due 2 years hence is $\frac{11}{10}$ of the true discount. The rate percent is **(M.A.T., 2005)**
    (*a*) 11% (*b*) 10%
    (*c*) 5% (*d*) 5.5%
13. The banker's gain on a certain sum due $1\frac{1}{2}$ years hence is $\frac{3}{25}$ of the banker's discount. The rate percent is :
    (*a*) $5\frac{1}{5}\%$ (*b*) $9\frac{1}{9}\%$
    (*c*) $8\frac{1}{8}\%$ (*d*) $6\frac{1}{6}\%$

ANSWERS

1. (*b*)	2. (*b*)	3. (*c*)	4. (*c*)	5. (*d*)	6. (*a*)	7. (*c*)	8. (*d*)	9. (*b*)	10. (*c*)
11. (*a*)	12. (*c*)	13. (*b*)							

SOLUTIONS

1. P.W. = ₹ (540 – 90) = ₹ 450.

$\therefore$ S.I. on ₹ 450 = ₹ 90.

S.I. on ₹ 540 = ₹ $\left(\frac{90}{450}\times 540\right)$ = ₹ 108.

$\therefore$ B.D. = ₹ 108.

2. B.G. = $\frac{(\text{T.D.})^2}{\text{P.W.}}$ = ₹ $\left(\frac{36\times 36}{800}\right)$ = ₹ 1.62.

$\therefore$ B.D. = (T.D. + B.G.) = ₹ (36 + 1.62) = ₹ 37.62.

3. B.G. = $\frac{(\text{T.D.})^2}{\text{P.W.}}$ = ₹ $\left(\frac{160\times 160}{1600}\right)$ = ₹ 16.

4. T.D. = $\left(\frac{\text{B.G.}\times 100}{\text{Rate}\times\text{Time}}\right)$ = ₹ $\left(\frac{24\times 100}{10\times 2}\right)$ = ₹ 120.

$\therefore$ P.W. = $\frac{100\times\text{T.D.}}{\text{Rate}\times\text{Time}}$ = ₹ $\left(\frac{100\times 120}{10\times 2}\right)$ = ₹ 600.

5. T.D. = $\frac{\text{B.G.}\times 100}{\text{R}\times\text{T}}$ = ₹ $\left(\frac{6\times 100}{12\times 1}\right)$ = ₹ 50.

6. T.D. = $\frac{\text{B.D.}\times 100}{100+(\text{R}\times\text{T})}$ = ₹ $\left[\frac{420\times 100}{100+\left(15\times\frac{1}{3}\right)}\right]$

= ₹ $\left(\frac{420\times 100}{105}\right)$ = ₹ 400.

7. T.D. = $\left(\frac{\text{B.G.}\times 100}{\text{R}\times\text{T}}\right)$ = ₹ $\left(\frac{270\times 100}{12\times 3}\right)$ = ₹ 750.

$\therefore$ B.D. = ₹ (750 + 270) = ₹ 1020.

8. T.D. = $\sqrt{\text{P.W.}\times\text{B.G.}} = \sqrt{576\times 16} = 96.$

9. S.I. on ₹ 1600 = T.D. on ₹ 1680.

$\therefore$ ₹ 1600 is the P.W. of ₹ 1680, *i.e.*,

₹ 80 is S.I. on ₹ 1600 at 15%.

$\therefore$ Time = $\left(\frac{100\times 80}{1600\times 15}\right)$ year = $\frac{1}{3}$ year = 4 months.

10. B.D. for $\frac{3}{2}$ years = ₹ 558. B.D. for 2 years

= ₹ $\left(558\times\frac{2}{3}\times 2\right)$ = ₹ 744.

T.D. for 2 years = ₹ 600.

$\therefore$ Sum = $\frac{\text{B.D.}\times\text{T.D.}}{\text{B.D.}-\text{T.D.}}$ = ₹ $\left(\frac{744\times 600}{144}\right)$ = ₹ 3100.

Thus, ₹ 744 is S.I. on ₹ 3100 for 2 years.

$\therefore$ Rate = $\left(\frac{100\times 744}{3100\times 2}\right)\% = 12\%.$

11. Sum = $\frac{\text{B.D.}\times\text{T.D.}}{\text{B.D.}-\text{T.D.}}$ = ₹ $\left(\frac{72\times 60}{72-60}\right)$ = ₹ $\left(\frac{72\times 60}{12}\right)$ = ₹ 360.

12. Let T.D. be ₹ 1. Then, B.D. = ₹ $\frac{11}{10}$ = ₹ 1.10.

$\therefore$ Sum = ₹ $\left(\frac{1.10\times 1}{1.10-1}\right)$ = ₹ $\left(\frac{110}{10}\right)$ = ₹ 11.

$\therefore$ S.I. on ₹ 11 for 2 years is ₹ 1.10.

$\therefore$ Rate = $\left(\frac{100\times 1.10}{11\times 2}\right)\% = 5\%.$

13. Let, B.D. = ₹ 1. Then, B.G. = ₹ $\frac{3}{25}$.

$\therefore$ T.D. = (B.D. – B.G.) = ₹ $\left(1-\frac{3}{25}\right)$ = ₹ $\frac{22}{25}$.

Sum = $\left(\frac{1\times\frac{22}{25}}{1-\frac{22}{25}}\right)$ = ₹ $\frac{22}{3}$.

S.I. on ₹ $\frac{22}{3}$ for $1\frac{1}{2}$ years is ₹ 1.

$\therefore$ Rate = $\left(\frac{100\times 1}{\frac{22}{3}\times\frac{3}{2}}\right)\% = 9\frac{1}{9}\%.$

34 Heights and Distances

IMPORTANT FACTS AND FORMULAE

I. We already know that:

In a right angled ΔOAB, where $\angle BOA = \theta$,

(*i*) $\sin\theta = \dfrac{\text{Perpendicular}}{\text{Hypotenuse}} = \dfrac{AB}{OB}$;

(*ii*) $\cos\theta = \dfrac{\text{Base}}{\text{Hypotenuse}} = \dfrac{OA}{OB}$;

(*iii*) $\tan\theta = \dfrac{\text{Perpendicular}}{\text{Base}} = \dfrac{AB}{OA}$;

(*iv*) $\text{cosec}\,\theta = \dfrac{1}{\sin\theta} = \dfrac{OB}{AB}$;

(*v*) $\sec\theta = \dfrac{1}{\cos\theta} = \dfrac{OB}{OA}$;

(*vi*) $\cot\theta = \dfrac{1}{\tan\theta} = \dfrac{OA}{AB}$.

II. Trigonometrical Identities:

(*i*) $\sin^2\theta + \cos^2\theta = 1$. (*ii*) $1 + \tan^2\theta = \sec^2\theta$. (*iii*) $1 + \cot^2\theta = \text{cosec}^2\,\theta$.

III. Values of T-ratios:

θ	$0°$	$(\pi/6)$ $30°$	$(\pi/4)$ $45°$	$(\pi/3)$ $60°$	$(\pi/2)$ $90°$
$\sin\theta$	0	$\frac{1}{2}$	$\frac{1}{\sqrt{2}}$	$\frac{\sqrt{3}}{2}$	1
$\cos\theta$	1	$\frac{\sqrt{3}}{2}$	$\frac{1}{\sqrt{2}}$	$\frac{1}{2}$	0
$\tan\theta$	0	$\frac{1}{\sqrt{3}}$	1	$\sqrt{3}$	not defined

IV. Angle of Elevation: Suppose a man from a point O looks up at an object P, placed above the level of his eye. Then, the angle which the line of sight makes with the horizontal through O, is called the angle of elevation of P as seen from O.

$\therefore$ Angle of elevation of P from O = $\angle AOP$.

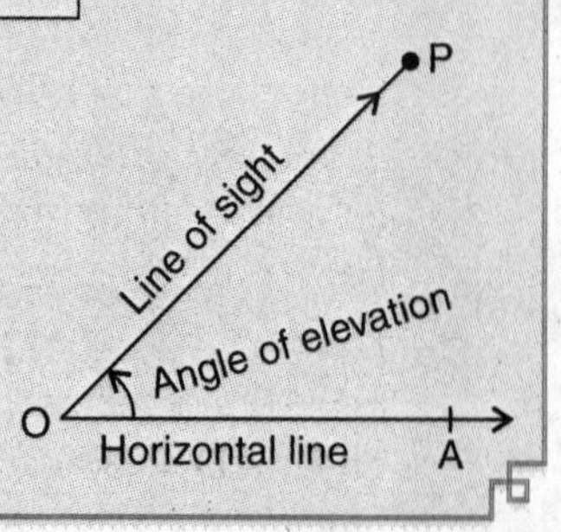

V. Angle of Depression: Suppose a man from a point O looks down at an object P, placed below the level of his eye, then the angle which the line of sight makes with the horizontal through O, is called the angle of depression of P as seen from O.

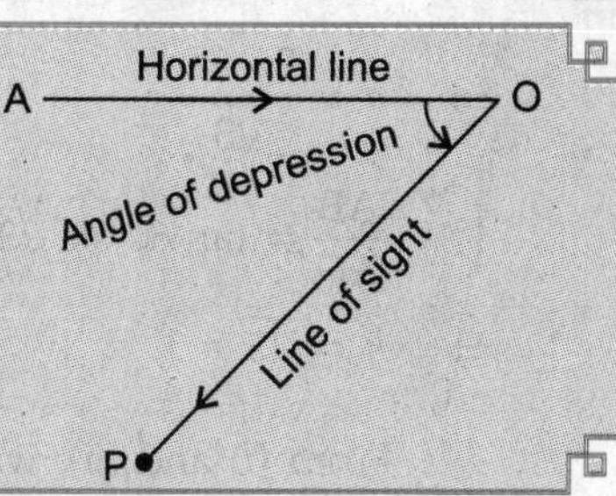

SOLVED EXAMPLES

Ex. 1. ***If the height of a pole is $2\sqrt{3}$ metres and the length of its shadow is 2 metres, find the angle of elevation of the sun.***

Sol. Let AB be the pole and AC be its shadow.

Let angle of elevation, $\angle ACB = \theta$.

Then, $AB = 2\sqrt{3}$ m, $AC = 2$ m.

$$\tan\theta = \frac{AB}{AC} = \frac{2\sqrt{3}}{2} = \sqrt{3} \Rightarrow \theta = 60°.$$

So, the angle of elevation is 60°.

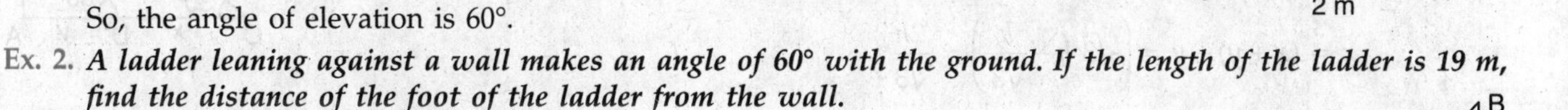

Ex. 2. ***A ladder leaning against a wall makes an angle of 60° with the ground. If the length of the ladder is 19 m, find the distance of the foot of the ladder from the wall.***

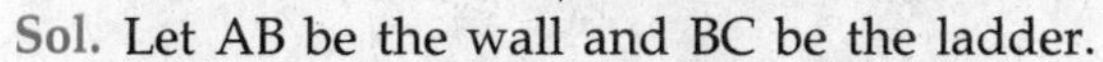

Sol. Let AB be the wall and BC be the ladder.

Then, $\angle ACB = 60°$ and $BC = 19$ m.

Let $AC = x$ metres

$$\frac{AC}{BC} = \cos 60° \Rightarrow \frac{x}{19} = \frac{1}{2} \Rightarrow x = \frac{19}{2} = 9.5.$$

$\therefore$ Distance of the foot of the ladder from the wall = 9.5 m.

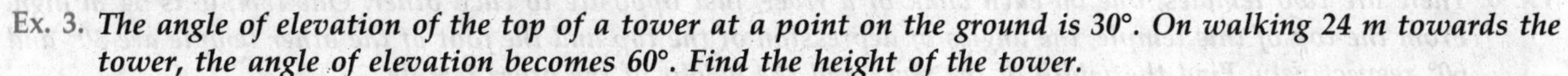

Ex. 3. ***The angle of elevation of the top of a tower at a point on the ground is 30°. On walking 24 m towards the tower, the angle of elevation becomes 60°. Find the height of the tower.***

Sol. Let AB be the tower and C and D be the points of observation. Then,

$$\frac{AB}{AD} = \tan 60° = \sqrt{3} \Rightarrow AD = \frac{AB}{\sqrt{3}} = \frac{h}{\sqrt{3}}.$$

$$\frac{AB}{AC} = \tan 30° = \frac{1}{\sqrt{3}} \Rightarrow AC = AB \times \sqrt{3} = h\sqrt{3}.$$

$$CD = (AC - AD) = \left(h\sqrt{3} - \frac{h}{\sqrt{3}}\right).$$

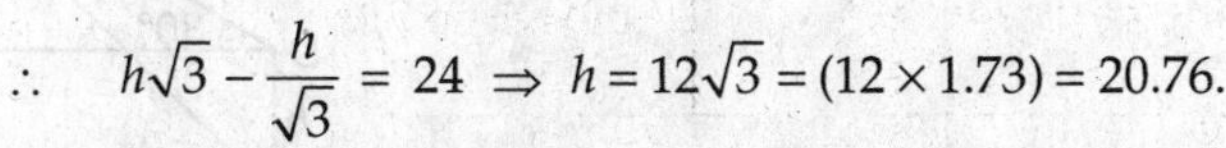

$$\therefore \quad h\sqrt{3} - \frac{h}{\sqrt{3}} = 24 \Rightarrow h = 12\sqrt{3} = (12 \times 1.73) = 20.76.$$

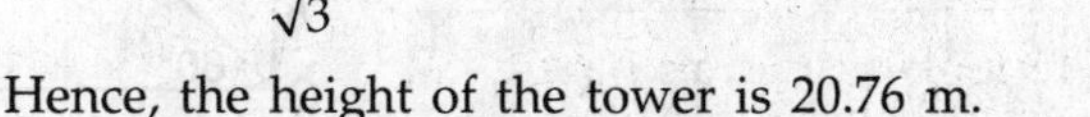

Hence, the height of the tower is 20.76 m.

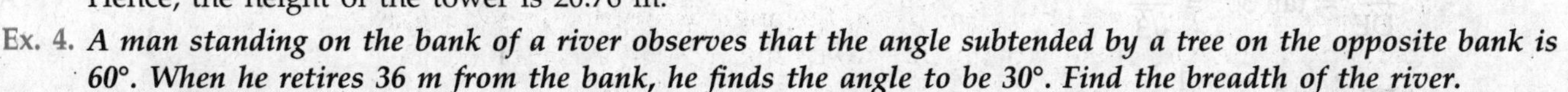

Ex. 4. ***A man standing on the bank of a river observes that the angle subtended by a tree on the opposite bank is 60°. When he retires 36 m from the bank, he finds the angle to be 30°. Find the breadth of the river.***

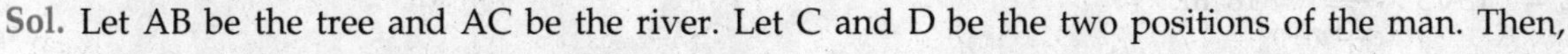

Sol. Let AB be the tree and AC be the river. Let C and D be the two positions of the man. Then,

$\angle ACB = 60°$, $\angle ADB = 30°$ and $CD = 36$ m.

Let $AB = h$ metres and $AC = x$ metres.

Then, $AD = (36 + x)$ metres.

$$\frac{AB}{AD} = \tan 30° = \frac{1}{\sqrt{3}} \Rightarrow \frac{h}{36 + x} = \frac{1}{\sqrt{3}}$$

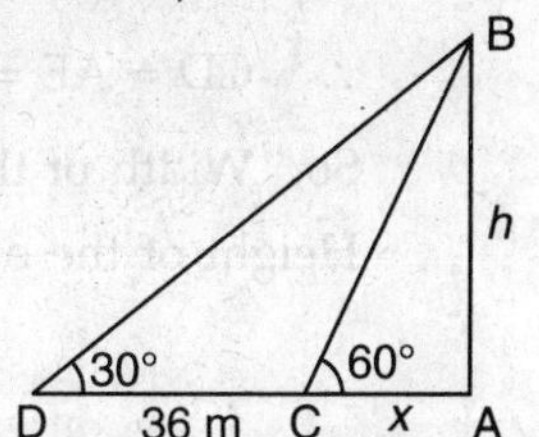

$\Rightarrow \quad h = \dfrac{36 + x}{\sqrt{3}}$ ...(*i*)

$\dfrac{AB}{AC} = \tan 60° = \sqrt{3} \Rightarrow \dfrac{h}{x} = \sqrt{3}$

$\Rightarrow \quad h = \sqrt{3}\, x$ ...(*ii*)

From (*i*) and (*ii*), we get : $\dfrac{36 + x}{\sqrt{3}} = \sqrt{3}\, x \Rightarrow x = 18$ m.

So, the breadth of the river = 18 m.

Ex. 5. ***A man on the top of a tower, standing on the seashore, finds that a boat coming towards him takes 10 minutes for the angle of depression to change from 30° to 60°. Find the time taken by the boat to reach the shore from this position.***

Sol. Let AB be the tower and C and D be the two positions of the boat.

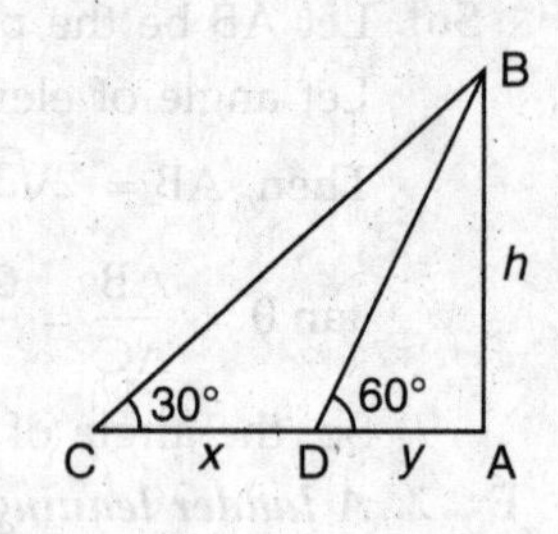

Let AB = h, CD = x and AD = y. $\dfrac{h}{y} = \tan 60° = \sqrt{3} \Rightarrow y = \dfrac{h}{\sqrt{3}}$.

$\dfrac{h}{x + y} = \tan 30° = \dfrac{1}{\sqrt{3}} \Rightarrow x + y = \sqrt{3}\, h.$

$\therefore x = (x + y) - y = \left(\sqrt{3}\, h - \dfrac{h}{\sqrt{3}}\right) = \dfrac{2h}{\sqrt{3}}$

Now, $\dfrac{2h}{\sqrt{3}}$ is covered in 10 min.

$\therefore \quad \dfrac{h}{\sqrt{3}}$ will be covered in $\left(10 \times \dfrac{\sqrt{3}}{2h} \times \dfrac{h}{\sqrt{3}}\right) = 5$ min.

Hence, required time = 5 minutes.

Ex. 6. ***There are two temples, one on each bank of a river, just opposite to each other. One temple is 54 m high. From the top of this temple, the angles of depression of the top and the foot of the other temple are 30° and 60° respectively. Find the width of the river and the height of the other temple.***

Sol. Let AB and CD be the two temples and AC be the river.

Then, AB = 54 m.

Let AC = x metres and CD = h metres. ∠ACB = 60°, ∠EDB = 30°.

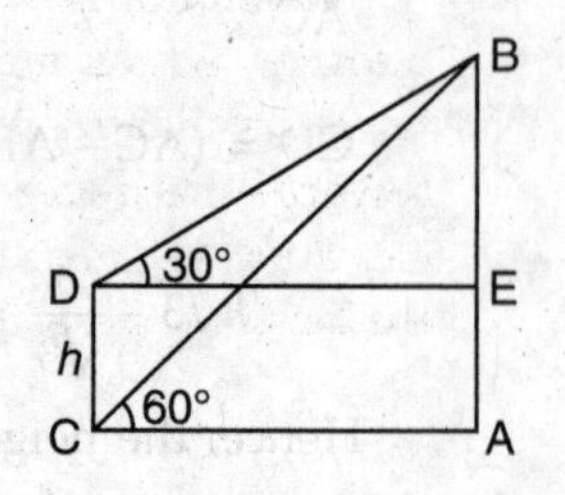

$\dfrac{AB}{AC} = \tan 60° = \sqrt{3}$

$\Rightarrow \quad AC = \dfrac{AB}{\sqrt{3}} = \dfrac{54}{\sqrt{3}} = \left(\dfrac{54}{\sqrt{3}} \times \dfrac{\sqrt{3}}{\sqrt{3}}\right) = 18\sqrt{3}$ m.

DE = AC = $18\sqrt{3}$ m.

$\dfrac{BE}{DE} = \tan 30° = \dfrac{1}{\sqrt{3}}$

$\Rightarrow \quad BE = \left(18\sqrt{3} \times \dfrac{1}{\sqrt{3}}\right) = 18$ m.

$\therefore \quad$ CD = AE = AB – BE = (54 – 18) m = 36 m.

So, Width of the river = AC = $18\sqrt{3}$ m = (18 × 1.73) m = 31.14 m.

Height of the other temple = CD = 18 m.

EXERCISE

(OBJECTIVE TYPE QUESTIONS)

Directions: ***Mark (✓) against the correct answer:***

1. The angle of elevation of the sun, when the length of the shadow of a tree is $\sqrt{3}$ times the height of the tree, is **(R.R.B., 2008)**

   (*a*) 30° (*b*) 45°
   (*c*) 60° (*d*) 90°

2. From a point P on a level ground, the angle of elevation of the top of a tower is 30°. If the tower is 100 m high, the distance of point P from the foot of the tower is **(R.R.B., 2006)**

   (*a*) 149 m (*b*) 156 m
   (*c*) 173 m (*d*) 200 m

3. The angle of elevation of a ladder leaning against a wall is 60° and the foot of the ladder is 4.6 m away from the wall. The length of the ladder is :

   (*a*) 2.3 m (*b*) 4.6 m
   (*c*) 7.8 m (*d*) 9.2 m

4. An observer 1.6 m tall is $20\sqrt{3}$ m away from a tower. The angle of elevation from his eye to the top of the tower is 30°. The height of the tower is :

   (*a*) 21.6 m (*b*) 23.2 m
   (*c*) 24.72 m (*d*) None of these

5. Two ships are sailing in the sea on the two sides of a lighthouse. The angles of elevation of the top of the lighthouse as observed from the two ships are 30° and 45° respectively. If the lighthouse is 100 m high, the distance between the two ships is

   (*a*) 173 m (*b*) 200 m
   (*c*) 273 m (*d*) 300 m

6. A man standing at a point P is watching the top of a tower, which makes an angle of elevation of 30° with the man's eye. The man walks some distance towards the tower to watch its top and the angle of elevation becomes 60°. What is the distance between the base of the tower and the point P? **(Bank P.O., 2007)**

   (*a*) $4\sqrt{3}$ units (*b*) 8 units
   (*c*) 12 units (*d*) Data inadequate
   (*e*) None of these

7. The angle of elevation of the top of a tower from a certain point is 30°. If the observer moves 20 m towards the tower, the angle of elevation of the top of the tower increases by 15°. The height of the tower is **(S.S.C., 2005)**

   (*a*) 17.3 m (*b*) 21.9 m
   (*c*) 27.3 m (*d*) 30 m

8. A man is watching from the top of a tower a boat speeding away from the tower. The boat makes an angle of depression of 45° with the man's eye when at a distance of 60 metres from the tower. After 5 seconds, the angle of depression becomes 30°. What is the approximate speed of the boat, assuming that it is running in still water?

   (*a*) 32 kmph (*b*) 36 kmph
   (*c*) 38 kmph (*d*) 40 kmph
   (*e*) 42 kmph

9. On the same side of a tower, two objects are located. Observed from the top of the tower, their angles of depression are 45° and 60°. If the height of the tower is 150 m, the distance between the objects is

   (*a*) 63.5 m (*b*) 76.9 m
   (*c*) 86.7 m (*d*) 90 m

10. A man on the top of a vertical observation tower observes a car moving at a uniform speed coming directly towards it. If it takes 12 minutes for the angle of depression to change from 30° to 45°, how soon after this will the car reach the observation tower? **(R.R.B., 2008)**

    (*a*) 14 min. 35 sec. (*b*) 15 min. 49 sec.
    (*c*) 16 min. 23 sec. (*d*) 18 min. 5 sec.

11. The top of a 15 metre high tower makes an angle of elevation of 60° with the bottom of an electric pole and angle of elevation of 30° with the top of the pole. What is the height of the electric pole? **(R.R.B., 2009)**

    (*a*) 5 metres (*b*) 8 metres
    (*c*) 10 metres (*d*) 12 metres
    (*e*) None of these

12. The angle of depression of a point situated at a distance of 70m from the base of a tower is 60°. The height of the tower is **[SSC—CHSL (10+2) Exam, 2015]**

    (*a*) $35\sqrt{3}$ m (*b*) $70\sqrt{3}$ m
    (*c*) $\frac{70\sqrt{3}}{3}$ m (*d*) 70 m

13. *TF* is a tower with *F* on the ground. The angle of elevation of *T* from *A* is $x°$ such that $\tan x° = \frac{2}{5}$ and AF = 200m. The angle of elevation of *T* from a nearer point *B* is $y°$ with BF = 80m. The value of $y°$ is **[SSC—CHSL (10+2) Exam, 2015]**

    (*a*) 75° (*b*) 45°
    (*c*) 60° (*d*) 30°

14. A boy is standing at the top of the tower and another boy is at the ground at some distance from the foot of the tower, then the angle of elevation and depression between the boys when both look at each other will be [CLAT, 2016]

(*a*) Equal
(*b*) Angle of elevation will be greater
(*c*) Cannot be predicted for relation
(*d*) Angle of depression will be greater

15. The angles of elevation of the top of a tower from two points P and Q at distances m^2 and n^2 respectively, from the base and in the same straight line with it are complementary. The height of the tower is [CDS, 2016]

(*a*) $(mn)^{1/2}$ (*b*) $mn^{1/2}$
(*c*) $m^{1/2}n$ (*d*) mn

16. The angle of elevation of a cloud from a point 200 m above a lake is 30° and the angle of depression of its reflection in the lake is 60°. The height of the cloud is [CDS, 2016]

(*a*) 200 m (*b*) 300 m
(*c*) 400 m (*d*) 600 m

17. From the top of a tower, the angles of depression of two objects P and Q (situated on the ground on the same side of the tower) separated at a distance of $(3-\sqrt{3})$ m are 45° and 60° respectively. The height of the tower is [CDS, 2016]

(*a*) 200 m (*b*) 250 m
(*c*) 300 m (*d*) None of these

18. If a 30 m ladder is placed against a 15 m wall such that it just reaches the top of the wall, then the elevation of the wall is equal to
[DMRC—Customer Relationship Assistant (CRA) Exam, 2016]

(*a*) 45° (*b*) 30°
(*c*) 60° (*d*) 50°

ANSWERS

1. (*a*)	2. (*c*)	3. (*d*)	4. (*a*)	5. (*c*)	6. (*d*)	7. (*c*)	8. (*a*)	9. (*a*)	10. (*c*)
11. (*c*)	12. (*b*)	13. (*b*)	14. (*a*)	15. (*d*)	16. (*a*)	17. (*c*)	18. (*a*)		

SOLUTIONS

1. Let AB be the tree and AC be its shadow.
Let $\angle ACB = \theta$.

Then, $\dfrac{AC}{AB} = \sqrt{3}$

$\Rightarrow \cot\theta = \sqrt{3} \Rightarrow \theta = 30°$.

2. Let AB be the tower.
Then, $\angle APB = 30°$ and AB = 100 m.

$\dfrac{AB}{AP} = \tan 30° = \dfrac{1}{\sqrt{3}}$

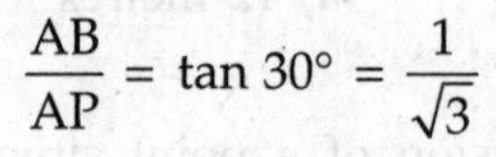

$\Rightarrow AP = (AB \times \sqrt{3})$

$= 100\sqrt{3}$ m.

$= (100 \times 1.73)$ m = 173 m.

3. Let AB be the wall and BC be the ladder.
Then, $\angle ACB = 60°$ and AC = 4.6 m.

$\dfrac{AC}{BC} = \cos 60° = \dfrac{1}{2}$

$\Rightarrow BC = 2 \times AC = (2 \times 4.6)$ m
$= 9.2$ m.

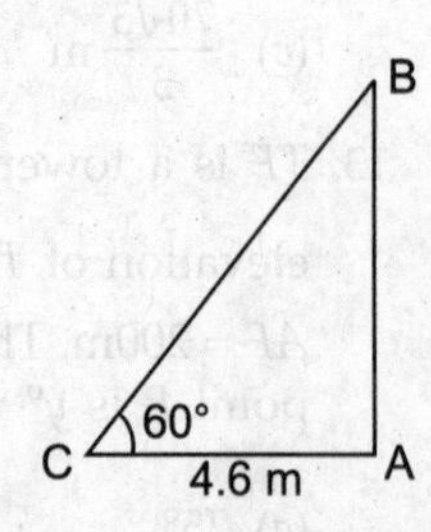

4. Let AB be the observer and CD be the tower.
Draw $BE \perp CD$.
Then, CE = AB = 1.6 m,
$BE = AC = 20\sqrt{3}$ m.

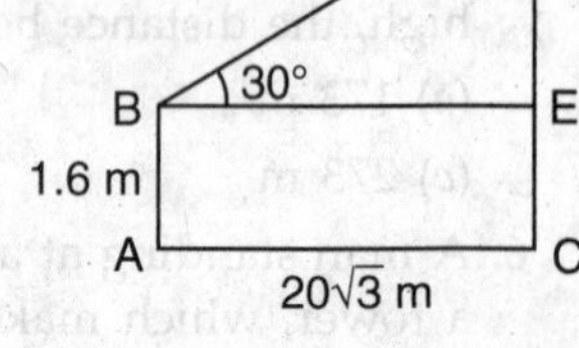

$\dfrac{DE}{BE} = \tan 30° = \dfrac{1}{\sqrt{3}}$

$\Rightarrow DE = \dfrac{20\sqrt{3}}{\sqrt{3}}$ m = 20 m.

$\therefore$ CD = CE + DE = (1.6 + 20) m = 21.6 m.

5. Let AB be the lighthouse and C and D be the positions of the ships.
Then, AB = 100 m, $\angle ACB = 30°$ and $\angle ADB = 45°$.

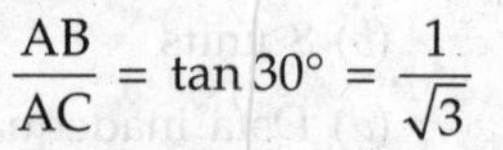

$\dfrac{AB}{AC} = \tan 30° = \dfrac{1}{\sqrt{3}}$

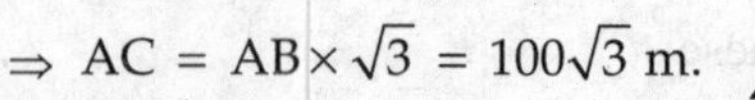

$\Rightarrow AC = AB \times \sqrt{3} = 100\sqrt{3}$ m.

$\dfrac{AB}{AD} = \tan 45° = 1$

$\Rightarrow AD = AB = 100$ m.

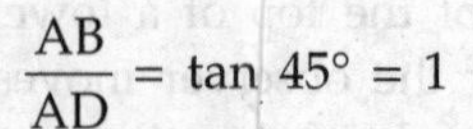

$\therefore CD = (AC + AD) = (100\sqrt{3} + 100)$ m

$= 100(\sqrt{3} + 1)$ m $= (100 \times 2.73)$ m = 273 m.

6. One of AB, AD and CD must have been given.
So, the data is inadequate.

7. Let AB be the tower and C and D be the points of observation.
Then, $\angle ACB = 30°$, $\angle ADB = 45°$ and CD = 20 m.
Let AB = h.

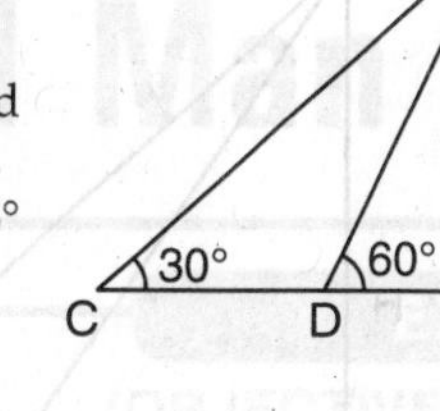

Then, $\frac{AB}{AC} = \tan 30° = \frac{1}{\sqrt{3}}$

$\Rightarrow$ $AC = AB \times \sqrt{3} = h\sqrt{3}$.

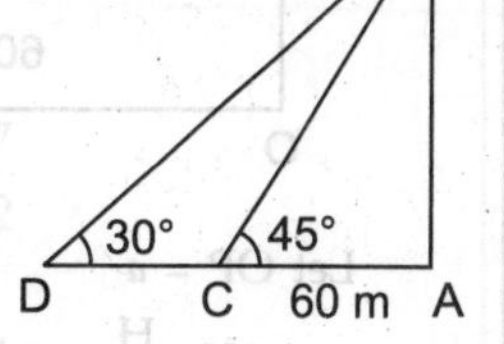

And, $\frac{AB}{AD} = \tan 45° = 1$

$\Rightarrow$ AD = AB = h.

CD = 20 $\Rightarrow$ (AC – AD) = 20 $\Rightarrow$ $h\sqrt{3} - h = 20$.

$\therefore \quad h = \frac{20}{(\sqrt{3}-1)} \times \frac{(\sqrt{3}+1)}{(\sqrt{3}+1)}$

$= 10(\sqrt{3}+1)$ m $= (10 \times 2.73)$ m $= 27.3$ m.

8. Let AB be the tower and C and D be the two positions of the boats.
Then, $\angle ACB = 45°$, $\angle ADB = 30°$ and AC = 60 m.
Let AB = h.

Then, $\frac{AB}{AC} = \tan 45° = 1$

$\Rightarrow$ AB = AC $\Rightarrow$ h = 60 m.

And, $\frac{AB}{AD} = \tan 30° = \frac{1}{\sqrt{3}}$

$\Rightarrow$ $AD = (AB \times \sqrt{3}) = 60\sqrt{3}$ m.

$\therefore \quad CD = (AD - AC) = 60(\sqrt{3}-1)$ m.

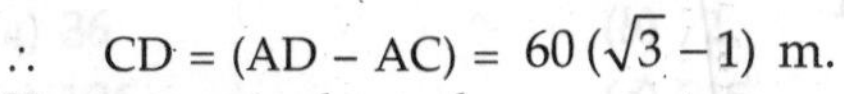

Hence, required speed

$= \left[\frac{60(\sqrt{3}-1)}{5}\right]$ m/s $= (12 \times 0.73)$ m/s

$= \left(12 \times 0.73 \times \frac{18}{5}\right)$ km/hr

$= 31.5$ km/hr ≈ 32 km/hr.

9. Let AB be the tower and C and D be the objects.
Then, AB = 150 m, $\angle ACB = 45°$ and $\angle ADB = 60°$.

$\frac{AB}{AD} = \tan 60° = \sqrt{3}$

$\Rightarrow$ $AD = \frac{AB}{\sqrt{3}} = \frac{150}{\sqrt{3}}$ m.

$\frac{AB}{AC} = \tan 45° = 1$

$\Rightarrow$ AC = AB = 150 m.

$\therefore$ CD = (AC – AD)

$= \left(150 - \frac{150}{\sqrt{3}}\right)$ m $= \left[\frac{150(\sqrt{3}-1)}{\sqrt{3}} \times \frac{\sqrt{3}}{\sqrt{3}}\right]$ m

$= 50(3-\sqrt{3})$ m $= (50 \times 1.27)$ m $= 63.5$ m.

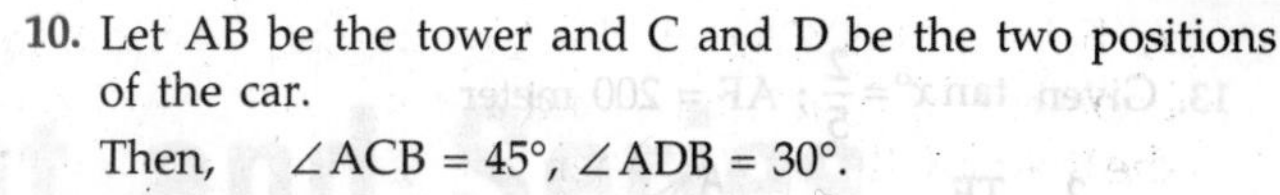

10. Let AB be the tower and C and D be the two positions of the car.
Then, $\angle ACB = 45°$, $\angle ADB = 30°$.
Let AB = h, CD = x and AC = y.

$\frac{AB}{AC} = \tan 45° = 1 \Rightarrow \frac{h}{y} = 1 \Rightarrow y = h.$

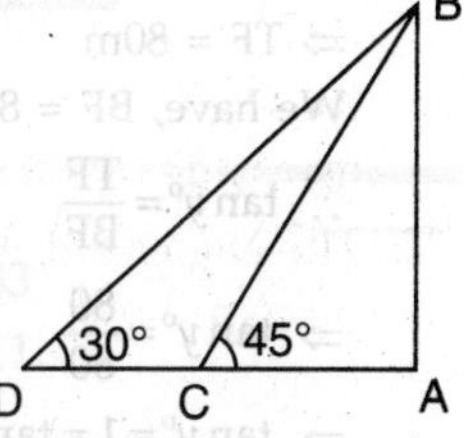

$\frac{AB}{AD} = \tan 30° = \frac{1}{\sqrt{3}}$

$\Rightarrow \frac{h}{x+y} = \frac{1}{\sqrt{3}}$

$\Rightarrow x + y = \sqrt{3}\,h.$

$\therefore \; x = (x+y) - y = \sqrt{3}\,h - h = h(\sqrt{3}-1).$

Now, $h(\sqrt{3}-1)$ is covered in 12 min.

So, h will be covered in $\left[\frac{12}{h(\sqrt{3}-1)} \times h\right] = \frac{12}{(\sqrt{3}-1)}$ min.

$= \left(\frac{1200}{73}\right)$ min. $\approx$ 16 min. 23 sec.

11. Let AB be the tower and CD be the electric pole.
Then, $\angle ACB = 60°$, $\angle EDB = 30°$ and AB = 15 m.
Let CD = h. Then, BE = (AB – AE) = (AB – CD) = (15 – h).

$\frac{AB}{AC} = \tan 60° = \sqrt{3} \Rightarrow AC = \frac{AB}{\sqrt{3}} = \frac{15}{\sqrt{3}}.$

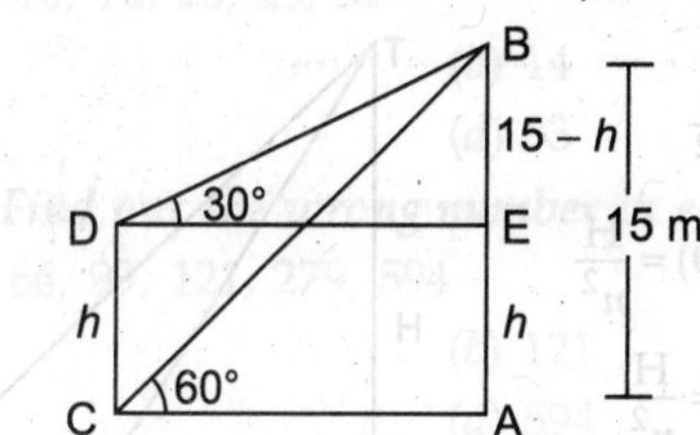

And, $\frac{BE}{DE} = \tan 30° = \frac{1}{\sqrt{3}}$

$\Rightarrow$ $DE = (BE \times \sqrt{3}) = \sqrt{3}(15-h).$

$AC = DE \Rightarrow \frac{15}{\sqrt{3}} = \sqrt{3}(15-h)$

$\Rightarrow 3h = (45-15) \Rightarrow h = 10$ m.

12. Length of the tower AB = h meter
$\angle DAC = \angle ACB = 60°$
BC = 70 meter
In ΔABC,

$\tan 60° = \frac{AB}{BC}$

$\Rightarrow \sqrt{3} = \frac{h}{70}$

$\Rightarrow h = 70\sqrt{3}$ meter.

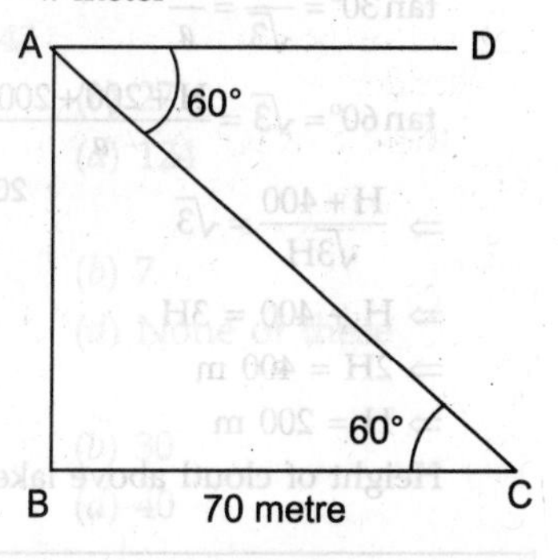

82. 1, 2, 8, 33, 148, 760, 4626
(*a*) 2 (*b*) 8
(*c*) 33 (*d*) 148
(*e*) 760

83. 3, 8, 18, 46, 100, 210, 432
(*a*) 8 (*b*) 18
(*c*) 46 (*d*) 100
(*e*) 210

84. 789, 645, 545, 481, 440, 429, 425
(*a*) 645 (*b*) 545
(*c*) 481 (*d*) 440
(*e*) 429

85. 1050, 510, 242, 106, 46, 16, 3
(*a*) 510 (*b*) 242
(*c*) 106 (*d*) 46
(*e*) 16

86. 5, 8, 20, 42, 124, 246, 736
(*a*) 8 (*b*) 20
(*c*) 42 (*d*) 124
(*e*) 246

87. 2, 3, 6, 15, 52.5, 157.5, 630
(*a*) 3 (*b*) 6
(*c*) 15 (*d*) 52.5
(*e*) 157.5

88. 888, 440, 216, 104, 48, 22, 6
(*a*) 440 (*b*) 216
(*c*) 104 (*d*) 48
(*e*) 22

89. 4, 5, 15, 49, 201, 1011, 6073
(*a*) 5 (*b*) 15
(*c*) 49 (*d*) 201
(*e*) 1011

90. Complete the following series.
9, 11, 15, 23, 39, ?
[DMRC—Customer Relationship Assistant (CRA) Exam, 2016]
(a) 71 (b) 64
(c) 42 (d) 56

91. Find out the wrong number in a given series.
644, 328, 164, 84, 44, 24, 14
[UPSSC—Lower Subordinate (Pre.) Exam, 2016]
(a) 328 (b) 164
(c) 84 (d) 44

Direction: ***In the following number series only one number is wrong. Find out the wrong number.***

92. 18000, 3600, 720, 144.2, 28.8, 5.76
[DMRC—Train Operator (Station controller), Exam 2016]
(a) 5.76 (b) 720
(c) 144.2 (d) 28.8

93. What will be come in place of number ? in the following series?
155 151 144 132 133?
[IBPS Bank PO/MT (Pre.) Exam, 2015]
(a) 89 (b) 71
(c) 85 (d) 92
(e) 60

94. What will be come in place of question mark in the given series.
264 262 271 243 308 ?
[IBPS—Bank PO (Pre) Exam, 2015]
(a) 216 (b) 163
(c) 194 (d) 205
(e) 182

Direction: ***What will come in the place of the question mark (?) in the following number series?***
[SBI—Jr. Associates (Pre.) Exam, 2016]

95. 48, 23, ?, 4.25, 1.125
(a) 10.5 (b) 10
(c) 2.5 (d) 11
(e) None of these

Direction: ***In these question, a number series is given. Only one number is wrong which doesn't fit in the series. Find out the wrong number.***

96. 13 6 8 13.5 29 75 228
[CET—Maharashtra (MBA) Exam, 2016]
(a) 75 (b) 29
(c) 5 (d) 6
(e) 8

ANSWERS

1. (*d*)	2. (*c*)	3. (*c*)	4. (*b*)	5. (*a*)	6. (*d*)	7. (*b*)	8. (*c*)	9. (*c*)	10. (*b*)
11. (*b*)	12. (*b*)	13. (*a*)	14. (*b*)	15. (*d*)	16. (*b*)	17. (*b*)	18. (*d*)	19. (*c*)	20. (*c*)
21. (*b*)	22. (*a*)	23. (*c*)	24. (*d*)	25. (*a*)	26. (*d*)	27. (*d*)	28. (*a*)	29. (*a*)	30. (*b*)
31. (*b*)	32. (*a*)	33. (*b*)	34. (*d*)	35. (*c*)	36. (*c*)	37. (*b*)	38. (*b*)	39. (*c*)	40. (*d*)
41. (*b*)	42. (*a*)	43. (*c*)	44. (*b*)	45. (*a*)	46. (*a*)	47. (*c*)	48. (*b*)	49. (*c*)	50. (*a*)
51. (*c*)	52. (*b*)	53. (*b*)	54. (*b*)	55. (*b*)	56. (*b*)	57. (*b*)	58. (*b*)	59. (*c*)	60. (*c*)
61. (*e*)	62. (*d*)	63. (*c*)	64. (*d*)	65. (*b*)	66. (*c*)	67. (*e*)	68. (*d*)	69. (*c*)	70. (*b*)
71. (*b*)	72. (*c*)	73. (*c*)	74. (*e*)	75. (*e*)	76. (*c*)	77. (*d*)	78. (*e*)	79. (*b*)	80. (*a*)
81. (*a*)	82. (*e*)	83. (*b*)	84. (*d*)	85. (*c*)	86. (*b*)	87. (*d*)	88. (*e*)	89. (*a*)	90. (*a*)
91. (*a*)	92. (*c*)	93. (*c*)	94. (*e*)	95. (*a*)	96. (*d*)				

SOLUTIONS

1. Each of the numbers except 12, is a prime number.
2. Each of the numbers except 21, is an even number.
3. Each of the numbers except 14, is an odd number.
4. Each of the given numbers except 23, is a perfect square.
5. Each of the numbers except 28, is a multiple of 3.
6. Each of the numbers except 81, is a prime number.
7. Each of the numbers except 72, is a perfect square.
8. Each of the numbers except 54, is a multiple of 5.
9. The pattern is $1^2, 2^2, 3^2, 4^2, 5^2, 6^2, 7^2$. But, instead of 5^2, it is 20, which is to be turned out.
10. The pattern is $2^3, 3^3, 4^3, 5^3, 6^3, 7^3$. But, 100 is not a perfect cube.
11. The pattern is 1^2, $1^2 + 2^2$, $1^2 + 2^2 + 3^2$, $1^2 + 2^2 + 3^2 + 4^2$, $1^2 + 2^2 + 3^2 + 4^2 + 5^2$, $1^2 + 2^2 + 3^2 + 4^2 + 5^2 + 6^2$. But, 50 is not of this pattern.
12. In each number except 427, the middle digit is the sum of the other two.
13. In each number except 751, the difference of third and first digit is the middle one.
14. In each number except 383, the product of first and third digits is the middle one.
15. The pattern is $x^2 + 1$, where $x = 1, 2, 3, 4, 5, 6, 7, 8$ etc. But, 64 is out of pattern.
16. The pattern is $x^2 + 3$, where $x = 4, 5, 6, 7, 8, 9$ etc. But, 102 is out of pattern.
17. Sum of the digits in each number, except 324 is 10.
18. Pattern is 1st × 2nd = 3rd; 2nd × 3rd = 4th; 3rd × 4th = 5th. But, 4th × 5th = 50 × 500 = 25000 ≠ 5000 = 6th.
19. 2nd = (1st + 1); 3rd = (2nd + 2); 4th = (3rd + 3); 5th = (4th + 4). But, 18 = 6th ≠ 5th + 5 = 14 + 5 = 19.
20. Each number except 279 is a multiple of 11.
21. The terms are alternately multiplied by 1.5 and divided by 3. However, 18.5 does not satisfy it.
22. Alternately 23 is added and 17 is subtracted from the terms. So, 634 is wrong.
23. The terms are successively divided by 12, 10, 8, 6, ... etc. So, 24 is wrong.
24. The numbers are $1^3, 2^3, 3^3, 4^3$ etc. So, 124 is wrong; it must have been 5^3 *i.e.*, 125.
25. Terms at odd places are 5, 6, 7, 8 etc. and each term at even place is 16. So, 9 is wrong.
26. The difference between two successive terms from the beginning are 7, 5, 7, 5, 7, 5. So, 40 is wrong.
27. The numbers are 7 × 8, 8 × 9, 9 × 10, 10 × 11, 11 × 12, 12 × 13. So, 150 is wrong.
28. Go on adding 5, 8, 11, 14, 17, 20. So, the number 47 is wrong and must be replaced by 46.
29. The numbers are squares of odd natural numbers, starting from 5 upto 15. So, 36 is wrong.
30. Add $1^2, 2^2, 3^2, 4^2, 5^2, 6^2$. So, 91 is wrong.
31. Subtract 1, 3, 5, 7, 9, 11 from successive numbers. So, 34 is wrong.
32. Subtract 20, 25, 30, 35, 40, 45 from successive numbers. So, 0 is wrong.
33. Each number is a composite number except 11.
34. Prime numbers 2, 3, 5, 7, 11, 13 are to be added successively. So, 165 is wrong.
35. Each number is the square of a composite number except 190.
36. Prime numbers 2, 3, 5, 7, 11, 13 have successively been subtracted. So, 100 is wrong. It must be (108 – 11) i.e., 97.
37. The pattern is 1 × 3, 2 × 5, 3 × 7, 4 × 9, 5 × 11, 6 × 13, 7 × 15 etc.
38. Double the number and add 1 to it, to get the next number. So, 160 is wrong.
39. Alternately, we add 4 and double the next. So, 132 is wrong. It must be (68 × 2) i.e., 136.
40. The numbers are cubes of primes i.e., $2^3, 3^3, 5^3, 7^3, 11^3$. Clearly, none is wrong.
41. Each number is the preceding number multiplied by – 2. So, the required number is – 128.
42. Numbers are alternately multiplied by 2 and increased by 3. So, the missing number = 61 × 2 = 122.
43. Numbers are $1^2, 2^2, 3^2, 4^2, 5^2, 6^2, 7^2$. So, the next number is $8^2 = 64$.
44. Numbers are $1^3, 2^3, 3^3, 4^3, 5^3, 6^3$. So, the missing number is $7^3 = 343$.
45. Numbers are all primes. The next prime is 43.
46. Each number is twice the preceding one with 1 added or subtracted alternately. So, the next number is (2 × 261 + 1) = 523.
47. There are two series, beginning respectively with 3 and 7. In one 3 is added and in another 2 is subtracted. The next number is 1 – 2 = – 1.
48. Each number is double the preceding one plus 1. So, the next number is (255 × 2) + 1 = 511.
49. The pattern is 1 × 2, 2 × 3, 3 × 4, 4 × 5, 5 × 6, 6 × 7, 7 × 8. So, the next number is 8 × 9 = 72.
50. Numbers are alternately multiplied by 3 and divided by 2. So, the next number = 54 ÷ 2 = 27.
51. Each number is 15 multiplied by a prime number i.e., 15 × 11, 15 × 13, 15 × 17, 15 × 19, 15 × 23. So, the next number is 15 × 29 = 435.
52. Numbers are $(2^3 - 1), (3^3 - 1), (4^3 - 1), (5^3 - 1), (6^3 - 1), (7^3 - 1)$ etc. So, the next number is $(8^3 - 1) = (512 - 1) = 511$.

53. Go on multiplying the given numbers by 2, 3, 4, 5, 6. So, the correct next number is 1440.

54. There are two series (8, 11, 14, 17, 20) and (7, 12, 17, 22) increasing by 3 and 5 respectively.

55. There are two series (10, 13, 16, 19) and (5, 10, 20, 40), one increasing by 3 and the other multiplied by 2.

56. Each previous number is multiplied by 2.

57. Alternately, we add 5 and subtract 7.

58. Alternately, we add 3 and subtract 1.

59. Second number is one more than twice the first; third number is one less than twice the second; fourth number is one more than twice the third; fifth number is one less than the fourth. Therefore, the sixth number is one more than twice the fifth.
So, the missing number is 75.

60. The difference between consecutive terms are respectively 5, 7, 9, 11 and 13.
So, 34 is a wrong number.

61. $2 = (1^3 + 1)$; $9 = (2^3 + 1)$; $28 = (3^3 + 1)$; $65 = (4^3 + 1)$; $125 = (5^3 + 1)$; $216 \neq (6^3 + 1)$ and $344 = (7^3 + 1)$.
So, 216 is a wrong number.

62. Multiply each term by 3 to obtain the next term.
Hence, 30 is a wrong number.

63. Go on subtracting prime numbers, 19, 17, 13, 11, 7, 5 from the numbers to get the next number.
So, 88 is wrong.

64. Go on subtracting 24, 21, 18, 15, 12, 9 from the numbers to get the next number.
Clearly, 128 is wrong.

65. Go on multiplying with 1, 2, 3, 4, 5, 6 to get the next number. So, 96 is wrong.

66. Go on dividing by 4 to get the next number.
So, 200 is wrong.

67. Go on adding 7, 9, 11, 13, 15, 17, 19 respectively to obtain the next number.
So, 135 is wrong.

68. Let the given numbers be A, B, C, D, E, F, G. Then, A, A × 1, B × 2 + 2, C × 3 + 3, D × 4 + 4, E × 5 + 5, F × 6 + 6 are the required numbers.
Clearly, 228 is wrong.

69. Go on multiplying the number by 2 and adding 1 to it to get the next number.
So, 27 is wrong.

70. Go on adding 7, 9, 11, 13, 15, 17 respectively to obtain the next number.
So, 33 is wrong.

71. Go on dividing by 6, 5, 4, 3, 2, 1 respectively to obtain the next number.
Clearly, 92 is wrong.

72. Go on subtracting 3 and dividing the result by 2 to obtain the next number.
Clearly, 46 is wrong.

73. Go on multiplying 2 and adding 1 to get the next number.
So, 39 is wrong.

74. A × 2 + 1, B × 3 + 1, C × 2 + 1, D × 3 + 1 and so on.
So, 356 is wrong.

75. Numbers must be $(14)^2$, $(13)^2$, $(11)^2$, $(10)^2$, $(9)^2$, $(8)^2$.
So, 80 is wrong.

76. Each even term of the series is obtained by multiplying the previous term by 2.
2nd term = (1st term) × 2 = 6 × 2 = 12;
4th term = (3rd term) × 2 = 48 × 2 = 96;
6th term = (5th term) × 2 = 384 × 2 = 768.
∴ 4th term should be 96 instead of 100.

77. 2nd term = (1st term) × 3 – 4 = 10 × 3 – 4 = 26;
3rd term = (2nd term) × 3 – 4 = 26 × 3 – 4 = 74;
4th term = (3rd term) × 3 – 4 = 74 × 3 – 4 = 218;
5th term = (4th term) × 3 – 4 = 218 × 3 – 4 = 650.
∴ 5th term must be 650 instead of 654.

78. 2nd term = (1st term) × 1 + 1 = 15 × 1 + 1 = 16;
3rd term = (2nd term) × 2 + 2 = 16 × 2 + 2 = 34;
4th term = (3rd term) × 3 + 3 = 34 × 3 + 3 = 105;
5th term = (4th term) × 4 + 4 = 105 × 4 + 4 = 424;
6th term = (5th term) × 5 + 5 = 425 × 5 + 5 = 2125.
∴ 6th term should be 2125 instead of 2124.

79. 7th term = (8th term) × 2 + 1 = 20 × 2 + 1 = 41;
6th term = (7th term) × 2 + 2 = 41 × 2 + 2 = 84;
5th term = (6th term) × 2 + 3 = 84 × 2 + 3 = 171;
4th term = (5th term) × 2 + 4 = 171 × 2 + 4 = 346.
∴ 4th term should be 346 instead of 347.

80. 2nd term = (1st term) + 2^2 = 32 + 4 = 36;
3rd term = (2nd term) + 3^2 = 36 + 9 = 45;
4th term = (3rd term) + 4^2 = 45 + 16 = 61;
5th term = (4th term) + 5^2 = 61 + 25 = 86.
∴ 3rd term should be 45 instead of 41.

81. There are two sequences (3, 9, 67.5, 810) and (4, 22.5, 202.5).
Pattern is : (1st term × 3), (2nd term × 7.5), (3rd term × 12) for the first sequence and (1st term × 5), (2nd term × 9) and so on for the second sequence.

82. 2nd term = (1st term × 1 + 1^2) = 1 × 1 + 1^2 = 2;
3rd term = (2nd term × 2 + 2^2) = 2 × 2 + 2^2 = 8;
4th term = (3rd term × 3 + 3^2) = 8 × 3 + 3^2 = 33;
5th term = (4th term × 4 + 4^2) = 33 × 4 + 4^2 = 148;
6th term = (5th term × 5 + 5^2) = 148 × 5 + 5^2 = 765.
∴ 760 is wrong.

83. 2nd term = (1st term × 2 + 2) = 3 × 2 + 2 = 8;
3rd term = (2nd term × 2 + 4) = 8 × 2 + 4 = 20;
4th term = (3rd term × 2 + 6) = 20 × 2 + 6 = 46;
5th term = (4th term × 2 + 8) = 46 × 2 + 8 = 100 and so on.
∴ 18 is wrong.

84. 2nd term = 1st term – $(12)^2$ = 789 – 144 = 645;
3rd term = (2nd term) – $(10)^2$ = 645 – 100 = 545;
4th term = (3rd term) – $(8)^2$ = 545 – 64 = 481;

5th term = (4th term) – $(6)^2$ = 481 – 36 = 445.

∴ 440 is wrong.

85. $2\text{nd term} = (\text{Ist term} - 30) \div 2 = \left(\frac{1050-30}{2}\right) = 10.$

$3\text{rd term} = (2\text{nd term} - 26) \div 2 = \left(\frac{510-26}{2}\right) = 242;$

$4\text{th term} = (3\text{rd term} - 22) \div \left(\frac{242-22}{2}\right) = 110.$

∴ 106 is wrong.

86. 2nd term = (1st term × 2 – 2) = (5 × 2 – 2) = 8;

3rd term = (2nd term × 3 – 2) = (8 × 3 – 2) = 22;

4th term = (3rd term × 2 – 2) = (22 × 2 – 2) = 42;

5th term = (4th term × 3 – 2) = (42 × 3 – 2) = 124 and so on.

∴ 20 is wrong.

87. 2nd term = (1st term × 1.5) = 2 × 1.5 = 3;

3rd term = (2nd term × 2) = 3 × 2 = 6;

4th term = (3rd term × 2.5) = 6 × 2.5 = 15;

5th term = (4th term × 3) = 15 × 3 = 45.

∴ 52.5 is wrong.

88. $2\text{nd term} = \left(\frac{1\text{st term} - 8}{2}\right) = \left(\frac{888-8}{2}\right) = 440;$

$3\text{rd term} = \left(\frac{2\text{nd term} - 8}{2}\right) = \left(\frac{440-8}{2}\right) = 216;$

$4\text{th term} = \left(\frac{3\text{rd term} - 8}{2}\right) = \left(\frac{216-8}{2}\right) = 104;$

$5\text{th term} = \left(\frac{4\text{th term} - 8}{2}\right) = \left(\frac{104-8}{2}\right) = 48;$

$6\text{th term} = \left(\frac{5\text{th term} - 8}{2}\right) = \left(\frac{48-8}{2}\right) = 20.$

∴ 22 is wrong.

89. 2nd term = (1st term × 1 + 2) = (4 × 1 + 2) = 6;

3rd term = (2nd term × 2 + 3) = (6 × 2 + 3) = 15;

4th term = (3rd term × 3 + 4) = (15 × 3 + 4) = 49;

5th term = (4th term × 4 + 5) = (49 × 4 + 5) = 210 and so on.

∴ 5 is wrong.

90. 9 + 2 = 11

11 + 4 = 15

15 + 8 = 23

23 + 16 = 39

39 + 32 = $\boxed{71}$

⇒ ? = 71

91. 644 – 320 = 324 ≠ $\boxed{328}$

324 – 160 = 164

164 – 80 = 84

84 – 40 = 44

44 – 20 = 24

24 – 10 = 14

Hence 328 is wrong number, correct number is 328.

92. The patter is followed by

18000 ÷ 5 = 3600

3600 ÷ 5 = 720

720 ÷ 5 = 144 ≠ $\boxed{144.2}$

144 ÷ 5 = 28.8

28.8 ÷ 5 = 5.76

Hence, 144.2 wrong number and correct number is 144.

93. The pattern is followed by

155 – 4 = 151

151 – 7 = 144 $\{\because 7 = 4 + 3\}$

144 – 12 = 132 $\{\because 12 = 7 + 5\}$

132 – 19 = 113 $\{\because 19 = 12 + 7\}$

113 – 28 = 85 $\{\because 28 = 19 + 9\}$

Hence ? = 85

94. The series followed by following rule:

$-(1^3+1); +(2^3+1); -(3^3+1); +(4^3+1); -(5^3+1)....$

$264 - (1^3+1) = 264 - 2 = 262$

$262 + (2^3+1) = 262 + 9 = 271$

$271 - (3^3+1) = 271 - 28 = 243$

$243 + (4^3+1) = 243 + 65 = 308$

$308 - (5^3+1) = 308 - 126 = 182$

95. 48, 23, ?, 4.25, 1.125

It follows by $2x + 2$ series from R.H.S.

⇒ $(1.125) \times 2 + 2 = 4.25$

4.25 × 2 + 2 = 10.5

10.5 × 2 + 2 = 23

23 × 2 + 2 = 48

⇒ ? = 10.5

96. The patter is followed by

13 × 0.5 + 0.5 = 7 ≠ $\boxed{6}$

7 × 1 + 1 = 8

8 × 1.5 + 1.5 = 13.5

13.5 × 2 + 2 = 29

29 × 2.5 + 2.5 = 75

75 × 3 + 3 = 228

Hence, 6 is wrong number and correct number is 7.

Section–II

Data Interpretation

36 Tabulation

This section consists of questions based on the data regarding common disciplines such as *Production over a period of few years in a factory; Imports; Exports; Salary of employees in a factory; Number of students in a college in various faculties etc.* These data are in the form of a table. This table is followed by certain questions based on the information given in the table and the candidate is required to answer those questions.

The horizontal lines in a table are called its *rows,* the vertical lines are called *columns* and the distinctive heads are known as *captions.* The units of measurements are given with the captions.

EXERCISE – I

Ex. 1. Directions (*Questions 1 to 5*): *Study the given table carefully and answer the questions that follow :*

Number of candidates appeared and qualified for a test (in hundreds) in 6 different years from 5 different zones. **(Bank P.O., 2011)**

Year	P		Q		R		S		T	
	App.	Qual.	App.	Qual.	App.	Qual.	App.	Qual.	App.	Qual.
2005	3.2	2.5	3.5	1.4	3.8	2.2	4.2	2.4	6.2	2.6
2006	4.6	3.4	6.9	4.2	6.9	4.4	7.4	3.3	6.2	4.8
2007	6.5	4.9	7.7	4.5	5.9	4.8	8.3	5.6	6.4	4.2
2008	7.4	5.7	5.4	3.4	7.2	3.2	9.3	6.4	7.8	6.2
2009	8.8	4.8	6.6	5.2	8.6	6.8	11.4	5.2	9.9	6.9
2010	9.2	5.6	10.6	6.4	10.3	7.4	14.2	11.4	11.8	9.4

Note: Here App. means Appeared and Qual. means Qualified.

1. In which years was in zones the difference between the appeared candidates and qualified candidates the second lowest ?

   (*a*) 2005 (*b*) 2007 (*c*) 2008 (*d*) 2009 (*e*) 2010

2. The number of candidates who qualified the test from zone R in the year 2010 was approximately what percentage of the number of candidates who appeared from zone *Q* in the year 2008 ?

   (*a*) 152 (*b*) 147 (*c*) 142 (*d*) 132 (*e*) 137

3. What was the average number of candidates appeared from zone *T* over all the years together ?

   (*a*) 810 (*b*) 815 (*c*) 825 (*d*) 805 (*e*) 820

4. What was the ratio of the number of candidates appeared from zone *P* in the year 2005 to the number of candidates qualified from zone *S* in the year 2007 ?

   (*a*) 4 : 7 (*b*) 4 : 9 (*c*) 9 : 4 (*d*) 8 : 13 (*e*) None of these

5. From which zone was the total number of candidates who qualified the test, the second highest in the year ?

   (*a*) *P* (*b*) *Q* (*c*) *R* (*d*) *S* (*e*) *T*

Ex. 2. Directions (*Questions 6 to 10*): *Study the following table carefully and answer the questions that follow:*

(Bank P.O., 2011)

Semester Fees (In ₹ thousands) For Five Different Courses In 6 Different Years

Years	Course				
	B.Tech	M.Sc.	B.Ed.	M.Phil	Diploma
2005	11.5	5.8	7.5	4.7	1.8
2006	14.5	6.4	11.6	5.8	3.2
2007	20.0	10.2	13.9	8.6	4.8
2008	22.2	14.6	15.8	12.7	5.6
2009	35.8	17.7	18.5	25.1	12.5
2010	50.7	20.9	22.6	18.9	14.9

6. What was the approximate per cent increase in the semester fees of B.Ed course in the year 2007 as compared to the previous year ?
(*a*) 26 % (*b*) 30 % (*c*) 20 % (*d*) 16 % (*e*) 10 %

7. What was the average semester fee charged for M.Sc. course over all the years together ?
(*a*) ₹ 12700 (*b*) ₹ 12600 (*c*) ₹ 12060 (*d*) ₹ 12070 (*e*) ₹ 13140

8. What was the difference between the total semester fee charged for Diploma course over the years together and the fee charged for B.Tech Course in the year 2009 ?
(*a*) ₹ 8500 (*b*) ₹ 8000 (*c*) ₹ 6500 (*d*) ₹ 7000 (*e*) None of these

9. The semester fee charged for M.Phil course in the year 2008 was approximately what percentage of the semester fee charged for M.Sc course in the year 2009 ?
(*a*) 67 (*b*) 84 (*c*) 80 (*d*) 76 (*e*) 72

10. What was the total semester fee charged for all the courses together in the year 2006 ?
(*a*) ₹ 42500 (*b*) ₹ 41500 (*c*) ₹ 41600 (*d*) ₹ 42200 (*e*) none of these

Ex. 3. Directions (*Questions 11 to 15*): *Study the following table carefully and answer the questions given below:*

Number (N) of Candidates (In lakhs) Appearing For An Entrance Examination From Six Different States And The Percentage (P) of Candidates Clearing the Same Over the Years **(Bank P.O., 2010)**

STATE →	A		B		C		D		E		F	
YEAR ↓	N	P	N	P	N	P	N	P	N	P	N	P
2004	1.23	42	1.04	51	1.11	32	1.32	24	1.23	36	1.33	31
2005	1.05	43	1.12	62	1.07	47	1.15	49	1.18	55	1.24	24
2006	2.04	38	1.48	32	1.08	28	1.96	35	1.42	49	1.58	26
2007	1.98	41	2.07	43	1.19	30	1.88	46	1.36	47	1.79	29
2008	1.66	53	1.81	50	1.56	42	1.83	60	1.73	57	1.86	34
2009	1.57	39	1.73	36	1.64	52	2.01	56	1.69	55	1.95	37

11. What is the ratio of the total number of candidates clearing the entrance examination from State B in the year 2004 to that of those clearing the entrance examination from State C in the same year ?
(*a*) 221 : 148 (*b*) 218 : 143 (*c*) 148 : 221 (*d*) 143 : 218 (*e*) None of these

12. In which year did the highest number of candidates clear the entrance exam from State *D* ?
(*a*) 2008 (*b*) 2006 (*c*) 2009 (*d*) 2007 (*e*) None of these

13. What is the number of candidates not clearing the entrance exam from State A in the year 2007 ?
(*a*) 186820 (*b*) 11682 (*c*) 1868200 (*d*) 116820 (*e*) None of these

14. What is the total number of candidates clearing the entrance examination from States E and F together in the year 2006 ?
(*a*) 16160 (*b*) 110660 (*c*) 11066 (*d*) 1106600 (*e*) None of these

15. What is the average number of candidates appearing for the entrance exam from State D in the years 2007, 2008 and 2009 together ?

(*a*) $1907\frac{2}{3}$ (*b*) $18666\frac{1}{3}$ (*c*) $1866\frac{1}{3}$ (*d*) $190666\frac{2}{3}$ (*e*) None of these

Ex. 4. Directions (*Questions 16 to 20*): *Study the following table carefully and answer the questions that follow:*

(Bank P.O., 2010)

Number of Candidates (in lakhs) Appearing In an Entrance Examination From Six Different Cities

City	A	B	C	D	E	F
Number of candidates	1.25	3.14	1.08	2.27	1.85	2.73

Ratio of Candidates Passing And Failing Within the City

City	Ratio of Passing and Failing
A	7 : 3
B	5 : 3
C	4 : 5
D	1 : 3
E	3 : 2
F	7 : 5

16. What is the ratio of the number of candidates failing the exam from City D to that of those failing the exam from City A ?

(*a*) 289 : 42 (*b*) 42 : 289 (*c*) 227 : 50 (*d*) 50 : 227 (*e*) None of these

17. The number of candidates appearing for the exam from City C is what per cent of the number of candidates appearing for the exam from City B ? (rounded off to nearest integer)

(*a*) 27 % (*b*) 34 % (*c*) 42 % (*d*) 21 % (*e*) 38 %

18. The number of candidates passing the examination from City F is what per cent of the total number of candidates appearing from all the cities together ? (rounded off to two digits after the decimal)

(*a*) 12.93% (*b*) 14.46% (*c*) 10.84% (*d*) 11.37% (*e*) None of these

19. Which city has the highest number of students failing the entrance exam ?

(*a*) F (*b*) C (*c*) B (*d*) D (*e*) None of these

20. What is the number of candidates passing the exam from City E ?

(*a*) 13000 (*b*) 1110000 (*c*) 113000 (*d*) 11000 (*e*) None of these

Ex. 5. Directions (*Questions 21 to 25*): *Study the table given below and answer the questions that follow:*

(Bank P.O., 2009)

Total Number of Employees in Different Departments of an Organization and Percentage of Females and Males

Department	Total No. of Employees	Percentage of Females	Percentage of Males
IT	840	45	55
Accounts	220	35	65
Production	900	23	77
HR	360	65	35
Marketing	450	44	56
Customer service	540	40	60

21. What is the respective ratio of the number of females in Production department to the number of females in the Marketing department ?

(*a*) 22 : 23 (*b*) 35 : 33 (*c*) 23 : 22 (*d*) 33 : 35 (*e*) None of these

22. What is the ratio of the number of females in the HR and Accounts departments together to the number of males in the same departments together?
(a) 311 : 269 (b) 268 : 319 (c) 269 : 311 (d) 319 : 268 (e) None of these

23. What is the total number of employees in all the departments together?
(a) 3260 (b) 3310 (c) 3140 (d) 3020 (e) None of these

24. The total number of employees in the HR department forms approximately what per cent of the total number of employees in the Accounts department?
(a) 149% (b) 178% (c) 157% (d) 164% (e) 137%

25. What is the total number of males in the IT and Customer Service departments together?
(a) 687 (b) 678 (c) 768 (d) 876 (e) None of these

ANSWERS

1. (b)	2. (e)	3. (d)	4. (a)	5. (e)	6. (c)	7. (b)	8. (d)	9. (e)	10. (b)
11. (a)	12. (c)	13. (d)	14. (b)	15. (d)	16. (c)	17. (b)	18. (a)	19. (d)	20. (e)
21. (c)	22. (a)	23. (b)	24. (d)	25. (e)					

SOLUTIONS

1. In zone S, the difference between the appeared candidates and the qualified candidates in various years is given below:
$2005 \rightarrow (4.2 - 2.4) = 1.8$, $2006 \rightarrow (7.4 - 3.3) = 4.1$, $2007 \rightarrow (8.3 - 5.6) = 2.7$.
$2008 \rightarrow (9.3 - 6.4) = 2.9$, $2009 \rightarrow (11.4 - 5.2) = 6.2$, $2010 \rightarrow (14.2 - 11.4) = 2.8$
It was lowest in 2005 and second lowest in 2007.

2. Required percentage
$$= \left(\frac{7.4}{5.4} \times 100\right)\% = \frac{3700}{27}\% = 137\%.$$

3. Average number of candidates appeared from T all over the years
$$= \frac{(6.2 + 6.2 + 6.4 + 7.8 + 9.9 + 11.8) \times 100}{6}$$
$$= \frac{(48.3 \times 100)}{6} = \frac{4830}{6} = 805.$$

4. Required ratio $= \frac{3.2}{5.6} = \frac{32}{56} = \frac{4}{7} = 4:7.$

5. Total number of candidates who qualified the test in 2009 and 2010 from various zones are :
$P \rightarrow (4.8 + 5.6) = 10.4$, $Q \rightarrow (5.2 + 6.4) = 11.6$, $R \rightarrow (6.8 + 7.4) = 14.2$,
$S \rightarrow (5.2 + 11.4) = 16.6$, $T \rightarrow (6.9 + 9.4) = 16.3$
It was highest from zone S and second highest from zone T.

6. Percent increase in semester fees of B.Ed in the year 2007 as compared to 2006
$$= \left[\frac{(13.9 - 11.6)}{11.6} \times 100\right]\%$$
$$= \left(\frac{2.3}{11.6} \times 100\right)\% = \frac{2300}{116}\%$$
$$= \frac{575}{29}\% = 19.8\% \simeq 20\% \text{ (nearly)}.$$

7. Average semester fee for M.Sc. course over the given years
$$= ₹\, \frac{(5.8 + 6.4 + 10.2 + 14.6 + 17.7 + 20.9) \times 1000}{6}$$
$$= ₹\left(\frac{75.6 \times 1000}{6}\right) = ₹\left(\frac{75600}{6}\right) = ₹12600.$$

8. Required difference
$= ₹\ \{(1.8 + 3.2 + 4.8 + 5.6 + 12.5 + 14.9) \times 1000 - (35.8 \times 1000)\}$
$= ₹\ [(42.8 \times 1000) - (35.8 \times 1000)] = ₹\ (7 \times 1000)$
$= ₹\ 7000.$

9. Required percentage
$$= \left\{\frac{(12.7 \times 1000)}{(17.7 \times 1000)} \times 100\right\}\% = \left(\frac{127}{177} \times 100\right)\%$$
$$= \frac{12700}{177}\% = 71.75\% = 72\% \text{ (approx).}$$

10. Total semester fee for all the courses in 2006
$= ₹\ (14.5 + 6.4 + 11.6 + 5.8 + 3.2) \times 1000$
$= ₹\ (41.5 \times 1000) = ₹\ 41500.$

11. Required ratio
$$= \frac{(1.04 \text{ lakhs} \times 51\%)}{(1.11 \text{ lakhs} \times 32\%)} = \left(\frac{1.04 \times 51}{1.11 \times 32}\right)$$
$$= \left(\frac{104 \times 51}{111 \times 32}\right) = \left(\frac{13 \times 17}{37 \times 4}\right) = \frac{221}{148} = 221:148.$$

12. Number of candidates clearing the exam from State D in
$$2008 \rightarrow \left(1.83 \times \frac{60}{100}\right) \text{lakhs} = \frac{(1.83 \times 3)}{5} \text{ lakhs}$$
$$= \frac{5.49}{5} \text{ lakhs} = 1.10 \text{ lakhs}.$$
$$2009 \rightarrow \left(2.01 \times \frac{56}{100}\right) \text{lakhs} = \left(\frac{2.01 \times 14}{25}\right) \text{lakhs}$$

$= \frac{28.14}{25}$ lakhs = 1.12 lakhs.

In rest of the years it is clearly less. So, it is maximum in the year 2009.

13. Number of candidates not clearing the exam from State A in 2007

$= [1.98 \times (100 - 41)\%]$ lakhs $= \left(1.98 \times \frac{59}{100}\right)$ lakhs

$= \left(\frac{116.82}{100} \times 100000\right) = 116820.$

14. Number of candidates clearing the exam from States E and F together in 2006

$= \left(1.42 \text{ lakhs} \times \frac{49}{100}\right) + \left(1.58 \text{ lakhs} \times \frac{26}{100}\right)$

$= \frac{(1.42 \times 49) + (1.58 \times 26)}{100}$ lakhs

$= \frac{(69.58 + 41.08)}{100}$ lakhs

$= \frac{110.66}{100} \times 100000 = 110660.$

15. Average number of candidates appearing from State D in 2007, 2008, 2009

$= \frac{(1.88 + 1.83 + 2.01)}{3}$ lakhs $= \frac{5.72}{3}$ lakhs

$= \left(\frac{5.72 \times 100000}{3}\right) = \frac{572000}{3} = 190666\frac{2}{3}.$

16. Number of candidates failing from city D

$= \left(\frac{3}{4} \times 2.27 \times 100000\right)$

$= \left(\frac{3}{4} \times \frac{227}{100} \times 100000\right) = (227 \times 750).$

Number of candidates failing from city A

$= \left(\frac{3}{10} \times 1.25 \times 100000\right)$

$= \left(\frac{3}{10} \times \frac{125}{100} \times 100000\right) = (300 \times 125).$

Required ratio $= \frac{227 \times 750}{300 \times 125} = \frac{227}{50} = 227 : 50.$

17. Number of candidates from city C

$= (1.08 \times 100000) = 108000.$

Number of candidates from city B

$= (3.14 \times 100000) = 314000.$

Required percentage $= \left(\frac{108000}{314000} \times 100\right)\%$

$= \left(\frac{108}{314} \times 100\right)\% = \left(\frac{54}{157} \times 100\right)\%$

$= \frac{5400}{157}\% = 34.39\% \approx 34\%.$

18. Total number of candidates from all the 5 cities

$= [(1.25 + 3.14 + 1.08 + 2.27 + 1.85 + 2.73) \times 100000]$

$= (12.32 \times 100000) = 1232000.$

Number of candidates passing the exam from City F

$= \left(\frac{7}{12} \times 2.73 \times 100000\right) = \left(\frac{7 \times 273 \times 1000}{12}\right)$

$= (7 \times 91 \times 250) = 159250.$

Required percentage $= \left(\frac{159250}{1232000} \times 100\right)\%$

$= \left(\frac{15925}{1232}\right)\% = 12.926 \approx 12.93\%.$

19. Number of failures from different cities:

$A \rightarrow \left(1.25 \times 100000 \times \frac{3}{10}\right) = 37500;$

$B \rightarrow \left(3.14 \times 100000 \times \frac{3}{8}\right) = \left(\frac{314000 \times 3}{8}\right) = 117750;$

$C \rightarrow \left(1.08 \times 100000 \times \frac{5}{9}\right) = \left(108000 \times \frac{5}{9}\right) = 60000;$

$D \rightarrow \left(2.27 \times 100000 \times \frac{3}{4}\right) = \left(227000 \times \frac{3}{4}\right) = 170250;$

$E \rightarrow \left(1.85 \times 100000 \times \frac{2}{5}\right) = \left(185000 \times \frac{2}{5}\right) = 74000;$

$F \rightarrow \left(2.73 \times 100000 \times \frac{5}{12}\right) = \left(273000 \times \frac{5}{12}\right) = 113750.$

So, the maximum number of failures are from City D.

20. Number of candidates passing the exam from City E

$= \left(1.85 \times 100000 \times \frac{3}{5}\right) = \left(185000 \times \frac{3}{5}\right)$

$= (37000 \times 3) = 111000.$

21. Number of females in Production : Number of females in Marketing

$= \left(900 \times \frac{23}{100}\right) : \left(450 \times \frac{44}{100}\right) = 207 : 198 = 23 : 22.$

22. (Number of females in HR and Accounts) : (Number of males in HR and Accounts)

$= \left\{\left(\frac{65}{100} \times 360\right) + \left(\frac{35}{100} \times 220\right)\right\} : \left\{\left(\frac{35}{100} \times 360\right) + \left(\frac{65}{100} \times 220\right)\right\}$

$= (234 + 77) : (126 + 143) = 311 : 269.$

23. Total number of employees in all the departments

$= (840 + 220 + 900 + 360 + 450 + 540) = 3310.$

24. Required percentage $= \left(\frac{360}{220} \times 100\right)\% = 163.6\% \approx 164\%.$

25. Total number of males in IT and Customer service

$= \left(840 \times \frac{55}{100}\right) + \left(540 \times \frac{60}{100}\right) = (462 + 324) = 786.$

EXERCISE – II

Directions (*Questions 1 to 5*): *Study the table carefully to answer the questions that follow:* (Bank P.O., 2011)

Number of Boys and Girls (in Hundreds) in Six Different Years in 5 Different Schools

School →	A		B		C		D		E	
Years ↓	Boys	Girls	Boys	Girls	Boys	Girls	Boys	Girls	Boys	Girls
2005	3.3	3.6	5.2	3.1	5.5	4.5	2.4	1.4	6.5	6.6
2006	6.6	4.2	4.9	2.2	6.9	3.3	4.4	2.3	5.5	3.6
2007	9.3	6.9	4.7	4.2	5.8	4.9	6.4	3.3	2.7	2.4
2008	5.4	9.6	6.3	5.4	6.6	5.2	5.3	5.4	5.4	5.7
2009	8.4	12.9	7.5	5.9	8.7	6.6	12.1	5.2	6.8	6.5
2010	12.3	14.4	9.8	4.4	11.7	4.2	12.2	9.4	10.8	12.7

1. What is the approximate percentage decrease in the number of boys in School *D* in the year 2008 as compared to that in the previous year ?
(*a*) 17% (*b*) 12% (*c*) 9% (*d*) 5% (*e*) 23%

2. The number of girls in School *B* in the year 2009 is approximately what per cent of the total number of students in School *E* in the year 2006 ?
(*a*) 46% (*b*) 52% (*c*) 70% (*d*) 58% (*e*) 65%

3. What is the average number of girls in School *A* in all the years taken together ?
(*a*) 760 (*b*) 800 (*c*) 860 (*d*) 600 (*e*) None of these

4. What is the ratio of the number of boys in School C in the year 2009 to the number of girls in School A in the year 2009 ?
(*a*) 29 : 41 (*b*) 36 : 11 (*c*) 29 : 43 (*d*) 36 : 13 (*e*) None of these

5. In which year is the total number of students the third highest in School *E* ?
(*a*) 2006 (*b*) 2007 (*c*) 2008 (*d*) 2005 (*e*) 2010

Directions (*Questions 6 to 10*): *Study the following information and answer the questions that follow :* (*Bank P.O., 2012*)

The graph given below represents the production (in tonnes) and sales (in tonnes) of Company A from 2006 to 2011.

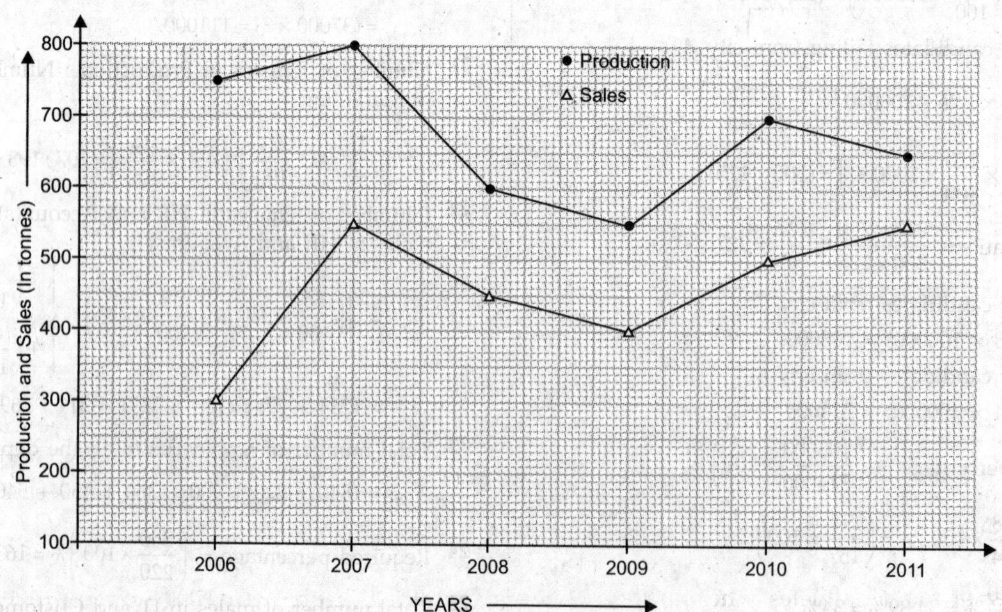

Production and Sales of Company *A* during 6 years

The table given below represents the ratio of the production (in tonnes) of Company A to the production (in tonnes) of Company B, and the ratio of sales (in tonnes) of Company A to the sales (in tonnes) of Company B.

Year	Production (A : B)	Sales (A : B)
2006	5 : 4	2 : 3
2007	8 : 7	11 : 12
2008	3 : 4	9 : 14
2009	11 : 12	4 : 5
2010	14 : 13	10 : 9
2011	13 : 14	1 : 1

6. What is the approximate percentage increase in the production of Company *A* (in tonnes) from the year 2009 to the production of Company *A* (in tonnes) in the year 2010 ?
(*a*) 18 % (*b*) 38 % (*c*) 23 % (*d*) 27 % (*e*) 32 %
7. The sales of Company *A* in the year 2009 was approximately what per cent of the production of Company *A* in the same year ?
(*a*) 65 % (*b*) 73 % (*c*) 79 % (*d*) 83 % (*e*) 69 %
8. What is the average production of Company *B* (in tonnes) from the year 2006 to the year 2011?
(*a*) 574 (*b*) 649 (*c*) 675 (*d*) 593 (*e*) 618
9. What is the ratio of the total production (in tonnes) of Company *A* to the total sales (in tonnes) of Company *A* ?
(*a*) 81 : 64 (*b*) 64 : 55 (*c*) 71 : 81 (*d*) 71 : 55 (*e*) 81 : 55
10. What is the ratio of production of Company *B* (in tonnes) in the year 2006 to production of Company *B* (in tonnes) in the year 2008 ?
(*a*) 2 : 5 (*b*) 4 : 5 (*c*) 3 : 4 (*d*) 3 : 5 (*e*) 1 : 4

Directions (*Questions 11 to 15*): *Study the table given below carefully and answer the questions that follow :*

(Bank P.O. 2011)

Number of Athletes (In Hundred) Who Participated In a Sports Event From 5 Different Countries Over The Years

M → Male & F → Female

Countries →	A		B		C		D		E	
Years ↓	M	F	M	F	M	F	M	F	M	F
2005	4.4	3.3	6.3	4.2	4.5	3.1	5.6	4.1	4.7	2.1
2006	6.6	4.2	8.4	6.2	6.9	3.3	8.4	6.3	7.8	5.2
2007	4.6	1.8	7.4	4.8	4.8	2.8	9.3	7.3	8.7	6.5
2008	9.6	4.9	11.4	8.4	6.6	4.2	12.6	9.4	8.9	5.8
2009	11.8	6.4	10.6	5.2	7.9	6.3	14.4	10.2	11.8	9.2
2010	8.2	5.2	6.4	7.2	10.8	6.9	15.6	12.1	13.6	9.8

11. In which of the following years was the total number of participants (athletes) the second highest from Country C ?
(*a*) 2005 (*b*) 2006 (*c*) 2007 (*d*) 2008 (*e*) None of these
12. What was the average number of female athletes who participated from Country *B* over all the years together?
(*a*) 1200 (*b*) 400 (*c*) 600 (*d*) 1800 (*e*) 3600
13. What was the approximate percentage decrease in the number of male athletes who participated from Country C in the year 2007 as compared to the previous year ?
(*a*) 21% (*b*) 30% (*c*) 35% (*d*) 39% (*e*) 25%
14. The number of female athletes who participated from Country *E* in the year 2009 was approximately what percentage of the total number of athletes who participated from Country *B* in the year 2008 ?
(*a*) 40% (*b*) 46% (*c*) 50% (*d*) 56% (*e*) 60%

15. In which of the following countries is the difference between the number of male and female participants second highest in the year 2006?
(a) A (b) B (c) C (d) D (e) E

Directions (*Questions 16 to 20*): ***Study the following table and answer the questions that are given below:***
Expenditure of a Company (In Lakh Rupees) Per Annum Over The Given Years

Items of Expenditure / Year ↓	Salary	Fuel and Transport	Bonus	Interest on Loans	Taxes
2007	288	98	3.00	23.4	83
2008	342	112	2.52	32.5	108
2009	324	101	3.84	41.6	74
2010	336	133	3.68	36.4	88
2011	420	142	3.96	49.4	98

16. The ratio between the total expenditure on Taxes for all the years and the total expenditure on Fuel and Transport for all the years respectively, is approximately :
(a) 4 : 7 (b) 10 : 13 (c) 5 : 6 (d) 5 : 8 (e) 2 : 3

17. The total expenditure of the company over these items during the year 2009 is
(a) ₹ 544.44 lakhs (b) ₹ 501.11 lakhs (c) ₹ 446.46 lakhs (d) ₹ 478.87 lakhs (e) ₹ 612.13 lakhs

18. What is the average amount of interest per year which the company had to pay during this period ?
(a) ₹ 32.43 lakhs (b) ₹ 33.72 lakhs (c) ₹ 34.18 lakhs (d) ₹ 35.69 lakhs (e) ₹ 36.66 lakhs

19. Total expenditure on all these items in 2007 was approximately what per cent of the total expenditure in 2011 ?
(a) 62 % (b) 66 % (c) 69 % (d) 71 % (e) 73 %

20. The total amount of bonus paid by the company during the given period is approximately what per cent of the total amount of salary paid during this period ?
(a) 0.1 % (b) 0.5 % (c) 1 % (d) 1.25 % (e) 1.11 %

Directions (*Questions 21 to 26*): ***Study the following table and answer the questions based on it :***
Number of Candidates Appeared, Qualified And Selected In a Competitive Examination From 5 States Delhi; H.P.; U.P.; Punjab and Haryana Over The Years 2007 To 2011

Year	Delhi			H.P.			U.P.			Punjab			Haryana		
	App.	Qual.	Sel.	App.	Qual.	Sel.	App.	Qual.	Sel.	App.	Qual.	Sel.	App.	Qual.	Sel.
2007	8000	850	94	7800	810	82	7500	720	78	8200	680	85	6400	700	75
2008	4800	500	48	7500	800	65	5600	620	85	6800	600	70	7100	650	75
2009	7500	640	82	7400	560	70	4800	400	48	6500	525	65	5200	350	55
2010	9500	850	90	8800	920	86	7000	650	70	7800	720	84	6400	540	60
2011	9000	800	70	7200	850	75	8500	950	80	5700	485	60	4500	600	75

21. In the year 2007, which state had the lowest percentage of candidates selected over the candidates appeared ?
(a) Delhi (b) H.P. (c) U.P. (d) Punjab (e) Haryana

22. The percentage of candidates qualified from Punjab over those appeared from Punjab is highest in the year :
(a) 2007 (b) 2008 (c) 2009 (d) 2010 (e) 2011

23. The percentage of candidates selected from U.P. over those qualified from U.P. is highest in the year :
(a) 2007 (b) 2008 (c) 2009 (d) 2010 (e) 2011

24. The number of candidates selected from Haryana during the period under review is approximately what percent of the number selected from Delhi during this period ?
(a) 79.5% (b) 81% (c) 84.5% (d) 88.5% (e) 92.5%

25. For which state the average number of candidates selected over the years is the maximum ?
(a) Delhi (b) H.P. (c) U.P. (d) Punjab (e) Haryana

26. What is the approximate percentage of total number of candidates selected to the total number of candidates qualified for all the five states together during the year 2009 ?
(a) 10% (b) 11% (c) 12% (d) 13% (e) 14%

Directions (*Questions 27 to 31*): ***The following table gives the percentage of marks obtained by 7 students in 6 different subjects in an examination. Study the table and answer the questions based on it.*** (Bank P.O. 2003)

Note: ***The numbers in the brackets give the maximum marks in each subject.***

Student \ Subjects (Max. Marks)	Maths (150)	Chemistry (130)	Physics (120)	Geography (100)	History (60)	Computer Science (40)
Ayush	90	50	90	60	70	80
Aman	100	80	80	40	80	70
Sajal	90	60	70	70	90	70
Rohit	80	65	80	80	60	60
Muskan	80	65	85	95	50	90
Tanvi	70	75	65	85	40	60
Tarun	65	35	50	77	80	80

27. What was the aggregate of marks obtained by Sajal in all the six subjects ?
(a) 409 (b) 419 (c) 429 (d) 439 (e) 449

28. What is the overall percentage of Tarun ?
(a) 52.5% (b) 55% (c) 60% (d) 63% (e) 64.5%

29. What are the average marks obtained by all the seven students in Physics ? (rounded off to two digits after decimal)
(a) 77.26 (b) 89.14 (c) 91.37 (d) 96.11 (e) 103.21

30. The number of students who obtained 60% and above marks in all the subjects is :
(a) 1 (b) 2 (c) 3 (d) None (e) None of these

31. In which subject is the overall percentage the best ?
(a) History (b) Maths (c) Physics (d) Chemistry (e) Geography

Directions (*Questions 32 to 35*): ***The following table gives the percentage distribution of population of five states, P, Q, R, S and T on the basis of poverty line and also on the basis of sex. Study the table and answer the questions based on it.***

State	Percentage of Population below Poverty line	Proportion of Males and Females	
		Below Poverty line	Above Poverty Line
		M : F	M : F
P	35	5 : 6	6 : 7
Q	25	3 : 5	4 : 5
R	24	1 : 2	2 : 3
S	19	3 : 2	4 : 3
T	15	5 : 3	3 : 2

32. What will be the number of females above poverty line in the State S if it is known that the population of State S is 7 million ?
(a) 3 million (b) 2.43 million (c) 1.33 million (d) 5.7 million (e) 1.61 million

33. If the male population above poverty line for State R is 1.9 million, then the total population of State R is :
(a) 4.5 million (b) 4.85 million (c) 5.35 million (d) 6.25 million (e) 7.6 million

34. What will be the male population above poverty line for State P if the female population below poverty line for State P is 2.1 million ?
(a) 2.1 million (b) 2.3 million (c) 2.7 million (d) 3.3 million (e) 3.4 million

35. If the population of males below poverty line for State Q is 2.4 million and that for State T is 6 million, then the total populations of states Q and T are in the ratio :
(a) 1 : 3 (b) 2 : 5 (c) 3 : 7 (d) 4 : 9 (e) 5 : 12

ANSWERS

1. (a)	2. (e)	3. (c)	4. (c)	5. (d)	6. (d)	7. (b)	8. (c)	9. (e)	10. (c)
11. (e)	12. (c)	13. (b)	14. (b)	15. (e)	16. (b)	17. (a)	18. (e)	19. (c)	20. (c)
21. (d)	22. (d)	23. (b)	24. (d)	25. (a)	26. (d)	27. (e)	28. (c)	29. (b)	30. (b)
31. (b)	32. (b)	33. (d)	34. (d)	35. (b)					

SOLUTIONS

1. Number of boys in School *D* in 2007

$= (6.4 \times 100) = 640.$

Number of boys in School *D* in 2008

$= (5.3 \times 100) = 530.$

Decrease % $= \left(\frac{110}{640} \times 100\right)\% = \frac{275}{16}\% = 17.1\% \simeq 17\%.$

2. Number of girls in School *B* in 2009

$= (5.9 \times 100) = 590.$

Total number of students in School *E* in 2006

$= (5.5 + 3.6) \times 100 = (9.1 \times 100) = 910.$

Required % $= \left(\frac{590}{910} \times 100\right)\% = \frac{5900}{91}\%$

$= 64.8\% \simeq 65\%$ (nearly).

3. Average number of girls in School *A* over the years

$= \frac{(3.6 + 4.2 + 6.9 + 9.6 + 12.9 + 14.4) \times 100}{6}$

$= \left(\frac{51.6 \times 100}{6}\right) = \frac{5160}{6} = 860.$

4. (Number of boys in C in 2009) : (Number of girls in *A* in 2009)

$= (8.7 \times 100) : (12.9 \times 100)$

$= \frac{870}{1290} = \frac{29}{43} = 29 : 43.$

5. Total number of students in School *E* in various years:

2005 → $(6.5 + 6.6) \times 100$

$= 1310$, 2006 → $(5.5 + 3.6) \times 100 = 910$,

2007 → $(2.7 + 2.4) \times 100$

$= 510$, 2008 → $(5.4 + 5.7) \times 100 = 1110$,

2009 → $(6.8 + 6.5) \times 100$

$= 1330$, 2010 → $(10.8 + 12.7) \times 100 = 2350.$

It is highest in 2010, 2nd highest in 2009 and third highest in 2005.

6. Production of *A* in 2009 = 550 tonnes.

Production of *A* in 2010 = 700 tonnes.

Increase % $= \left(\frac{150}{550} \times 100\right)\% = \frac{300}{11}\% = 27.2\% \simeq 27\%.$

7. Sales of *A* in 2009 = 400 tonnes

Production of *A* in 2009 = 550 tonnes

Required percentage

$= \left(\frac{400}{550} \times 100\right)\% = \frac{800}{11}\% = 72.7\% \simeq 73\%.$

8. Total production of *B* from 2006 to 2011

$= \left[\left(750 \times \frac{4}{5}\right) + \left(800 \times \frac{7}{8}\right) + \left(600 \times \frac{4}{3}\right) + \left(550 \times \frac{12}{11}\right) + \left(700 \times \frac{13}{14}\right) + \left(650 \times \frac{14}{13}\right)\right]$ tonnes

$= (600 + 700 + 800 + 600 + 650 + 700)$ tonnes

$= 4050$ tonnes.

∴ Average production $= \frac{4050}{6}$ tonnes = 675 tonnes.

9. (Total production of *A*) : (Total sales of *A*)

$= (750 + 800 + 600 + 550 + 700 + 650)$

$: (300 + 550 + 450 + 400 + 500 + 550)$

$= 4050 : 2750 = \frac{4050}{2750} = \frac{81}{55} = 81 : 55.$

10. Production of *B* in 2006

$= \left(750 \times \frac{4}{5}\right)$ tonnes = 600 tonnes.

Production of B in 2008

$= \left(600 \times \frac{4}{3}\right)$ tonnes = 800 tonnes.

Required ratio = 600 : 800 = 3 : 4

11. Total number of athletes from C in various years:

2005 → (4.5 + 3.1) × 100 = (7.6 × 100) = 760;
2006 → (6.9 + 3.3) × 100 = 10.2 × 100 = 1020;
2007 → (4.8 + 2.8) × 100 = (7.6 × 100) = 760;
2008 → (6.6 + 4.2) × 100 = 10.8 × 100 = 1080;
2009 → (7.9 + 6.3) × 100 = 14.2 × 100 = 1420;
2010 → (10.8 + 6.9) × 100 = 17.7 × 100 = 1770.

It was second highest in 2009. So, the correct answer is (*e*).

12. Average number of female athletes from B over all the years

$$= \frac{(4.2 + 6.2 + 4.8 + 8.4 + 5.2 + 7.2) \times 100}{6} = \frac{3600}{6} = 600.$$

13. Number of male athletes in 2006 from C

= (6.9 × 100) = 690.

Number of male athletes in 2007 from C

= (4.8 × 100) = 480.

$$\text{Decrease } \% = \left\{\frac{(690 - 480)}{690} \times 100\right\}\% = \left(\frac{210}{690} \times 100\right)$$

$$= \frac{700}{23}\% = 30.4\% \simeq 30\% \text{ (nearly)}.$$

14. Number of female athletes from E in 2009

= (9.2 × 100) = 920.

Total number of athletes from B in 2008

= (11.4 + 8.4) × 100 = 19.8 × 100 = 1980.

Let 920 = x % of 1980. Then,

$$\frac{x}{100} \times 1980 = 920 \Rightarrow x = \left(\frac{920 \times 100}{1980}\right)$$

$$= \frac{4600}{99}\% = 46.46\% \simeq 46\%.$$

15. In 2006, the difference between males and females in various countries was

A → (6.6 – 4.2) × 100 = (2.4 × 100) = 240;
B → (8.4 – 6.2) × 100 = 2.2 × 100 = 220;
C → (6.9 – 3.3) × 100 = (3.6 × 100) = 360;
D → (8.4 – 6.3) × 100 = 2.1 × 100 = 210;
E → (7.8 – 5.2) × 100 = (2.6 × 100) = 260.

It was second highest in E.

16. Total expenditure on Taxes

= ₹ (83 + 108 + 74 + 88 + 98) lakh
= ₹ 451 lakh.

Total expenditure on Fuel and Transport

= ₹ (98 + 112 + 101 + 133 + 142) lakh.
= ₹ 586 lakh.

$$\text{Required ratio} = \frac{451}{586} = \frac{1}{1.3} = \frac{10}{13} = 10 : 13 \text{ (approx.)}.$$

17. Total expenditure during 2009

= ₹ (324 + 101 + 3.84 + 41.6 + 74) lakh
= ₹ 544.44 lakh.

18. Total amount of interest paid during the period

= ₹ (23.4 + 32.5 + 41.6 + 36.4 + 49.4) lakhs
= ₹ 183.3 lakh

Average amount of interest paid per year

$= ₹\left(\frac{183.3}{5}\right)$ lakh = ₹ 36.66 lakh.

19. Total expenditure in 2007

= ₹ (288 + 98 + 3.00 + 23.4 + 83) lakh
= ₹ 495.4 lakh

Total expenditure in 2011

= ₹ (420 + 142 + 3.96 + 49.4 + 98) lakh
= ₹ 713.36 lakh.

Let 495.4 = x % of ₹ 713.36.

Then,

$$\frac{x}{100} \times 713.36 = 495.4$$

$$\Rightarrow x = \left(\frac{495.40}{713.36} \times 100\right) = \left(\frac{12385}{17834} \times 100\right) = 69.4\% \simeq 69\%.$$

20. Total amount of bonus paid

= ₹ (3 + 2.52 + 3.84 + 3.68 + 3.96) lakh
= ₹ 17 lakh.

Total amount of salary paid

= ₹ (288 + 342 + 324 + 336 + 420) lakh
= ₹ 170 lakh.

$$\text{Required } \% = \left(\frac{17}{1710} \times 100\right)\% = \frac{170}{171}\% = 0.99\% \simeq 1\%.$$

21. Percentage of candidates selected over the candidates appeared in 2007 from various states :

Delhi → $\left(\frac{94}{8000} \times 100\right)\% = \frac{47}{40}\% = 1.175\%;$

H.P. → $\left(\frac{82}{7800} \times 100\right)\% = \frac{41}{39}\% = 1.051\%;$

U.P. → $\left(\frac{78}{7500} \times 100\right)\% = \frac{26}{25}\% = 1.040\%;$

Punjab → $\left(\frac{85}{8200} \times 100\right)\% = 1.037\%;$

Haryana → $\left(\frac{75}{6400} \times 100\right)\% = 1.172\%.$

Clearly, this percentage is lowest for Punjab.

22. The percentages of those qualified from Punjab over those appeared from Punjab during different years are :

2007 → $\left(\frac{680}{8200} \times 100\right)\% = \frac{340}{41}\% = 8.29\%;$

2008 → $\left(\frac{600}{6800} \times 100\right)\% = \frac{150}{17}\% = 8.82\%;$

2009 → $\left(\frac{525}{6500} \times 100\right)\% = \frac{105}{13}\% = 8.08\%;$

$2010 \rightarrow \left(\frac{720}{7800} \times 100\right)\% = 9.23\%;$

$2011 = \left(\frac{485}{5700} \times 100\right)\% = 8.50\%.$

Clearly, this percentage is maximum in 2010.

23. The percentage of candidates selected from U.P. over those qualified from U.P. during different years :

$2007 \rightarrow \left(\frac{78}{720} \times 100\right)\% = 10.83\%$

$2008 \rightarrow \left(\frac{85}{620} \times 100\right)\% = 13.71\%;$

$2009 \rightarrow \left(\frac{48}{400} \times 100\right)\% = 12\%;$

$2010 \rightarrow \left(\frac{70}{650} \times 100\right)\% = 10.77\%;$

$2011 \rightarrow \left(\frac{80}{950} \times 100\right)\% = \frac{169}{19}\% = 8.42\%.$

Clearly, this percentage is highest in 2008.

24. Required percentage

$= \left\{\frac{(75+75+55+60+75)}{(94+48+82+90+70)} \times 100\right\}\%$

$= \left(\frac{340}{384} \times 100\right)\% = \left(\frac{85 \times 100}{96}\right)\%$

$= \left(\frac{85 \times 25}{24}\right)\% = \frac{2125}{24}\% = 88.5\%.$

25. Average number of candidates per year from various states are

Delhi $\rightarrow \frac{(94+48+82+90+70)}{5} = \frac{384}{5} = 76.8;$

H.P. $\rightarrow \frac{(82+65+70+86+75)}{5} = \frac{378}{5} = 75.6;$

U.P. $\rightarrow \frac{(78+85+48+70+80)}{5} = \frac{361}{5} = 72.2;$

Punjab $\rightarrow \frac{(85+70+65+84+60)}{5} = \frac{364}{5} = 72.8;$

Haryana $\rightarrow \frac{(75+75+55+60+75)}{5} = \frac{340}{5} = 68.$

Clearly, this average is maximum for Delhi.

26. Required percentage

$= \left\{\frac{(82+70+48+65+55)}{(640+560+400+525+350)} \times 100\right\}\%$

$= \left(\frac{320}{2475} \times 100\right)\% = \frac{1280}{99}\% = 12.92\% \approx 13\%.$

27. Aggregate marks obtained by Sajal

= (90% of 150) + (60% of 130) + (70% of 120) + (70% of 100) + (90% of 60) + (70% of 40)

= (135 + 78 + 84 + 70 + 54 + 28) = 449.

28. Aggregate marks obtained by Tarun

= (65% of 150) + (35% of 130) + (50% of 120) + (77% of 100) + (80% of 60) + (80% of 40)

= (97.5 + 45.5 + 60 + 77 + 48 + 32) = 360.

Total maximum marks of all the 6 subjects

= (150 + 130 + 120 + 100 + 60 + 40) = 600.

Overall percentage of Tarun

$= \left(\frac{360}{600} \times 100\right)\% = 60\%.$

29. Total marks obtained in Physics by all the 7 students

= (90% of 120) + (80% of 120) + (70% of 120) + (80% of 120) + (85 % of 120) + (65 % of 120)+ (50 % of 120)

= (108 + 96 + 84 + 96 + 102 + 78 + 60) = 624.

∴ Average marks obtained by them in Physics

$= \frac{624}{7} = 89.14.$

30. From the given table it is clear that Sajal and Rohit obtained 60% or more marks in each of the 6 subjects.

31. For each subject, we find the overall percentage as under:

(*i*) Maths $= \left[\frac{1}{7} \times (90+100+90+80+80+70+65)\right]\%$

$= \left[\frac{1}{7} \times (575)\right]\% = 82.14\%.$

(*ii*) Chemistry

$= \left[\frac{1}{7} \times (50+80+60+65+65+75+35)\right]\%$

$= \left[\frac{1}{7} \times (430)\right]\% = 61.43\%.$

(*iii*) Physics

$= \left[\frac{1}{7} \times (90+80+70+80+85+65+50)\right]\%$

$= \left[\frac{1}{7} \times (520)\right]\% = 74.29\%.$

(*iv*) Geography

$= \left[\frac{1}{7} \times (60+40+70+80+95+85+77)\right]\%$

$= \left[\frac{1}{7} \times (507)\right]\% = 72.43\%.$

(*v*) History $= \left[\frac{1}{7} \times (70+80+90+60+50+40+80)\right]\%$

$= \left[\frac{1}{7} \times (470)\right]\% = 67.14\%.$

(*vi*) Computer Science

$= \left[\frac{1}{7} \times (80+70+70+60+90+60+80)\right]\%$

$= \left[\frac{1}{7} \times (510)\right]\% = 72.86\%.$

Clearly, this percentage is highest for Maths.

32. Total population of State S = 7 million.

∴ Population above poverty line

= [(100 − 19)% of 7] million

= (81% of 7) million = 5.67 million.

And so, the number of females above poverty line in State

S = $\left(\frac{3}{7}\times 5.67\right)$ million = 2.43 million.

33. Let the total population of State R be x million.

Then, population of State R above poverty line

= [(100 – 24)% of x] million

= $\left(\frac{76}{100}\times x\right)$ million.

And so, male population of State R above poverty line =

$\left[\frac{2}{5}\times\left(\frac{76}{100}\times x\right)\right]$ million.

But, it is given that male population of State R above poverty line = 1.9 million.

$\therefore \quad \frac{2}{5}\times\left(\frac{76}{100}\times x\right)=1.9 \Rightarrow x=\frac{5\times 100\times 1.9}{76\times 2}=6.25.$

$\therefore$ Total population of State R = 6.25 million.

34. Female population below poverty line for State P = 2.1 million.

Let the male population below poverty line for State P be x million.

Then 5 : 6 = $x:2.1 \Rightarrow \frac{x}{2.1}=\frac{5}{6}\Rightarrow x=\frac{2.1\times 5}{6}=1.75.$

$\therefore$ Population below poverty line for State P = (2.1 + 1.75) million = 3.85 million.

Let the population above poverty line for State P be y million.

Since, 35% of the total population of State P is below poverty line, therefore, 65% of the total population of State P is above poverty line. So, the ratio of population below poverty line to that above poverty line for State P is 35 : 65.

$\therefore \quad 35:65=3.85:y \Rightarrow y=\frac{65\times 3.85}{35}=7.15.$

$\therefore$ Population above poverty line for State P = 7.15 million and so, male population above poverty line for State

P = $\left(\frac{6}{13}\times 7.15\right)$ million = 3.3 million.

35. For State Q:

Male population below poverty line = 2.4 million.

Let the female population below poverty line be x million.

Then, 3 : 5 = 2.4 : x

$\Rightarrow x=\frac{5\times 2.4}{3}=4.$

$\therefore$ Total population below poverty line

= (2.4 + 4) = 6.4 million.

Let the total population of Q be p. Then,

25% of p = 6.4 million

$\Rightarrow \quad \frac{25}{100}\times p=6.4 \Rightarrow p=(6.4\times 4)=25.6$ million.

For State T:

Male population below poverty line = 6 million.

Let the female population below poverty line be y million.

Then, 5 : 3 = 6 : $y \Rightarrow y=\frac{3\times 6}{5}=3.6.$

$\therefore$ Total population below poverty line

= (6 + 3.6) = 9.6 million.

Let the total population of State T be q. Then,

15% of q = 9.6 million

$\Rightarrow \quad \frac{15}{100}\times q=9.6 \Rightarrow q=\left(9.6\times\frac{20}{3}\right)=64$ million.

$\therefore \quad$ Required ratio = $\frac{p}{q}=\frac{25.6}{64}=0.4=\frac{4}{10}=\frac{2}{5}=2:5.$

EXERCISE – III

Directions (*Questions 1 to 5*): *Study the table and answer the given questions.*

Months	Gross Revenue	Amount Allocated for Commission	Amount Allocated for discount and offer	Net Revenue
March	₹ 360000	₹ 31200	—	—
April	₹ 320000	₹ 28000	₹ 16000	—
May	—	—	₹ 36000	₹ 336000
June	—	₹ 42000	₹ 30200	₹ 330000
July	—	₹ 00	₹ 28000	₹ 362000

Note: I. Net revenue = Gross revenue – Amount allocated for commission – amount allocated for discount and others.

II. Few values are missing in the table (indicated by–). A candidate is expected to calculate the missing value, It is required to answer the given question on the basis of the given data and the information.

1. In July, if 40% of the Gross revenue of the magazine was collected from advertisement, what was the amount of Gross revenue collected from advertisement in that particular month?

[IBPS—RRB (Off. Gr. 'B') Exam, 2015]

(*a*) ₹ 148000 (*b*) ₹ 164000 (*c*) ₹ 144000 (*d*) ₹ 172000 (*e*) ₹ 156000

2. In March, if Net revenue of the magazine was 85% of its Gross revenue, what was the amount allocated for discount and others? [IBPS—RRB (Off. Gr. 'B') Exam, 2015]

(*a*) ₹ 23200 (*b*) ₹ 24200 (*c*) ₹ 22400 (*d*) ₹ 22800 (*e*) ₹ 21600

3. Amount allocated for commission in March is what percent less than the amount allocated for commission in July? [IBPS—RRB (Off. Gr. 'B') Exam, 2015]

(*a*) 24% (*b*) 18% (*c*) 28% (*d*) 32% (*e*) 22%

4. What is the difference between Net revenue of the magazine in April and its Gross revenue in June? [IBPS—RRB (Off. Gr. 'B') Exam, 2015]

(*a*) ₹ 132000 (*b*) ₹ 126000 (*c*) ₹ 118000 (*d*) ₹ 124000 (*e*) ₹ 136000

5. In May, the respective ratio of amount allocated for commission and amount allocated for discount and others was 4 : 3. What was the Gross revenue of the magazine in May? [IBPS—RRB (Off. Gr. 'B') Exam, 2015]

(*a*) ₹ 424000 (*b*) ₹ 440000 (*c*) ₹ 380000 (*d*) ₹ 420000 (*e*) ₹ 430000

Directions (*Questions 6 to 10*): *Refer to the table and answer the questions that follow:*

Data related to performance of 6 batsmen in a tournament:

Name of the batsman	Number of matches played in the tournament	Average runs scored in the tournament	Total balls faces in the tournament	Strike Rate
A	8	—	—	129.6
B	20	81	—	—
C	—	38	400	114
D	—	—	—	72
E	28	55	1280	—
F	—	—	—	66

Note: (i) Strike rate = (Total runs scored/Total balls faced) × 100

(ii) All the given batsmen could bat in all the given matches played by them.

(iii) Few values are missing in the table (indicated by –) A candidate is expected to calculate the missing value, if it is required to answer the given question, on the basis of the given data and information.

6. The respective ratio between total number of balls faced by D and that by F in the tournament is 3 : 4. Total number of runs scored by F in the tournament is what percent more than the total runs scored by D in the tournament? [RBI Gr. 'B' (Phase – I) Exam, 2015]

(*a*) $22\frac{2}{9}$ (*b*) $32\frac{4}{9}$ (*c*) $18\frac{8}{9}$ (*d*) $24\frac{4}{9}$ (*e*) $28\frac{2}{9}$

7. If the runs scored by E in last 3 matches of the tournament are not considered, his average runs scored in the tournament will decrease by 9. If the runs scored by E in the 26th and 27th match are below 128 and no two scores among these 3 scores are equal, what are the minimum possible runs scored by E in the 28th match? [RBI Gr. 'B' (Phase – I) Exam, 2015]

(*a*) 137 (*b*) 135 (*c*) 141 (*d*) 120.31 (*e*) 139

8. In the tournament, the total number of balls faced by batsman A is 74 less than the total number of runs scored by him. What is the average run scored by batsman A in the tournament? [RBI Gr. 'B' (Phase – I) Exam, 2015]

(*a*) 42.5 (*b*) 39.5 (*c*) 38 (*d*) 44 (*e*) 40.5

9. Batsman B faced equal number of balls in first 10 matches he played in the tournament and last 10 matches he played in the tournament. If his strike rate in first 10 matches and last 10 matches of the tournament are 120 and 158 respectively, what is the total number of balls faced by him in the tournament? [RBI Gr. 'B' (Phase – I) Exam, 2015]

(*a*) 1150 (*b*) 1400 (*c*) 1200 (*d*) 1446.42 (*e*) 1500

10. What is the number of matches played by batsman C in the tournament? **[RBI Gr. 'B' (Phase – I) Exam, 2015]**

(*a*) 10 (*b*) 16 (*c*) 12 (*d*) 18 (*e*) 8

Directions (*Questions 11 to 15*): *Study the table carefully and answer the given questions.*

Total exports of six countries over five years (in ₹ crore)

Years → / Country ↓	1998	1999	2000	2001	2002
P	20	40	60	45	90
Q	30	25	15	50	100
R	50	55	70	90	65
S	45	60	20	15	25
T	60	50	55	100	110
U	24	40	60	75	120

Note: Profit = Exports – Imports

11. What was the profit of all the countries together in the year 2002 if the total imports of all the countries together was ₹ 385 crore? **[IBPS—Bank Spl. Officer (IT) Exam, 2015]**

(*a*) ₹ 125 crore (*b*) ₹ 160 crore (*c*) ₹ 280 crore (*d*) ₹ 240 crore (*e*) ₹ 200 crore

12. If the ratio of export to import in country S and country U is 1 : 2 and 4 : 1 in the year 1998, then what is the total import of country U and S together in that particular years? (In ₹ crore) **[IBPS—Bank Spl. Officer (IT) Exam, 2015]**

(*a*) 52 (*b*) 92 (*c*) 96 (*d*) 65 (*e*) 44

13. If the export of country P in the year 2003 is 20% more than the total export of country Q in 2001 and the export of country T in 2000 together, then what was the profit of P in the year 2003 if its import was ₹ 92 crore for that year? (in ₹ crore) **[IBPS—Bank Spl. Officer (IT) Exam, 2015]**

(*a*) 10 (*b*) 58 (*c*) 22 (*d*) 46 (*e*) 34

14. By what per cent is the average export of country T over all the given years more than the average export of country R over all the given years? **[IBPS—Bank Spl. Officer (IT) Exam, 2015]**

(*a*) $13\frac{7}{11}\%$ (*b*) $9\frac{1}{11}\%$ (*c*) $13\frac{5}{7}\%$ (*d*) $4\frac{7}{11}\%$ (*e*) $12\frac{1}{7}\%$

15. What is the percentage increase in the export of all the countries together during the year 1999 to 2001? (rounded off to two digits after decimal) **[IBPS—Bank Spl. Officer (IT) Exam, 2015]**

(*a*) 88.99% (*b*) 72.39% (*c*) 38.89% (*d*) 62.89% (*e*) 40.60%

Directions (*Questions 16 to 20*): *Study the table carefully and answer the given questions.*

Number of pages printed by 5 printers during 5 days

Printers / Days	A	B	C	D	E
Monday	139	147	211	141	184
Tuesday	141	189	164	189	151
Wednesday	115	141	159	156	136
Thursday	89	223	120	147	113
Friday	187	93	257	160	124

16. What is the respective ratio between total number of pages printed by printer B on Wednesday and Thursday together and total number of pages printed by printer C on Monday and Friday together?

[United India Insurance Co. Ltd. Assistant (Online) Exam, 2015]

(*a*) 7 : 9 (*b*) 9 : 11 (*c*) 11 : 13 (*d*) 7 : 11 (*e*) 9 : 11

17. What is the difference between total number of pages printed by printers C and D together on Tuesday and total number of pages printed by printers A and E together on Thursday?

[United India Insurance Co. Ltd. Assistant (Online) Exam, 2015]

(*a*) 153 (*b*) 149 (*c*) 161 (*d*) 151 (*e*) 157

18. The number of pages printed by printer A on Wednesday is what percent of the number of pages printed by printer D on Friday?

[United India Insurance Co. Ltd. Assistant (Online) Exam, 2015]

(*a*) $65\frac{1}{8}$ (*b*) $69\frac{1}{4}$ (*c*) $71\frac{7}{8}$ (*d*) $75\frac{3}{8}$ (*e*) $65\frac{1}{4}$

19. What is the average number of pages printed by printer B on Monday, Tuesday and Friday?

[United India Insurance Co. Ltd. Assistant (Online) Exam, 2015]

(*a*) 138 (*b*) 143 (*c*) 151 (*d*) 139 (*e*) 147

20. The number of pages printed by printer E on Monday is what percent more than the number of pages printed by printer C on Thursday?

[United India Insurance Co. Ltd. Assistant (Online) Exam, 2015]

(*a*) $60\frac{1}{3}$ (*b*) $51\frac{2}{3}$ (*c*) $45\frac{2}{3}$ (*d*) $53\frac{1}{3}$ (*e*) $55\frac{1}{3}$

Directions (*Questions 21 to 25*): ***Study the table carefully and answer the given question:***

Publishing Houses	Number of Books Published	Ratio of Academic and Non-academic Books	Percentage of Books distributed	Number of distributors in publishing house
M	28200	7 : 3	81	17
N	32200	5 : 9	74	23
O	29700	6 : 5	92	18
P	31200	8 : 5	86	24
Q	33800	7 : 6	79	25
R	35700	11 : 6	82	21
S	37800	5 : 13	89	24

21. What is the difference between the number of academic books published by publishing house M and P?

[IDBI Bank (Executive Officer's) Exam, 2015]

(*a*) 450 (*b*) 640 (*c*) 540 (*d*) 504 (*e*) None of these

22. How many books were given to each distributor by publisher Q if each publisher gets equal number of books?

[IDBI Bank (Executive Officer's) Exam, 2015]

(*a*) 1806 (*b*) 1068 (*c*) 1608 (*d*) 1308 (*e*) None of these

23. What is the average number of non-academic books published by publishers R and S?

[IDBI Bank (Executive Officer's) Exam, 2015]

(*a*) 18750 (*b*) 18850 (*c*) 19950 (*d*) 18950 (*e*) 19990

24. If the total number of books published by publishers P, Q and R is increased by 30% and the total number of books published by remaining publishers be decreased by 20%, what will be the new average of books published by all the publishers?

[IDBI Bank (Executive Officer's) Exam, 2015]

(*a*) 33418 (*b*) 33318 (*c*) 32518 (*d*) 33618 (*e*) None of these

25. What is the total number of books distributed by publishers O and Q?

[IDBI Bank (Executive Officer's) Exam, 2015]

(*a*) 26702 (*b*) 27324 (*c*) 55026 (*d*) 54026 (*e*) None of these

ANSWERS

1. (d)	2. (d)	3. (e)	4. (b)	5. (d)	6. (a)	7. (d)	8. (e)	9. (a)	10. (c)
11. (a)	12. (c)	13. (e)	14. (a)	15. (c)	16. (a)	17. (d)	18. (c)	19. (b)	20. (d)
21. (c)	22. (b)	23. (c)	24. (b)	25. (d)					

SOLUTIONS

1. Gross revenue of July collected from advertisement
= 362000 +28000 + 40000
= 390000 + 40000 = 430000
Gross revenue collected from advertisement
$= 430000 \times \frac{40}{100} = 4300 \times 40 =$ ₹172000

2. In March,
Net revenue $= 360000 \times \frac{85}{100} = 306000$
$\therefore$ Amount allocated for discount and others.
$= 360000 - 306000 - 31200 = 54000 - 31200 = \because 22800$

3. Amount collected for commission in March = 31200
Amount collected for commission in July = 40000
Required percentage $= \frac{8800}{40000} \times 100 = 22\%$

4. Net revenue in April = 320000 – 44000 = ₹ 276000
Gross revenue in June = 330000 + 72000 = ₹ 402000
Required difference = 402000 – 276000 = ₹ 126000

5. In May, ratio of amount allocated for commission and Amount allocated for discount = 4 : 3
In May, amount allocated for commission = 4 × 12000 and 3 × 12000
Amount allocated for discount = 48000 and 36000
$\because$ Gross revenue in May net revenue + amount allocated for commission = 336000 + 84000 = ₹ 420000

6. Let the total number of balls faces by D = $3x$ and the total number of balls faced by F = $4x$. According to the question, the total number of runs made by D.
$$= \frac{72 \times 3x}{100} = \frac{216x}{100}$$
The total number of runs made by F
$$= \frac{66 \times 4x}{100} = \frac{264x}{100}$$
The more runs made by F as compare to D
$$\frac{264x}{100} - \frac{216x}{100} \times \frac{48x}{100}$$
So, the percentage of more runs
$$\frac{\frac{48x}{100}}{\frac{216x}{100}} \times 100 - \frac{48x}{100} \times \frac{100}{216x} \times 100 = \frac{200}{9} = 22\frac{2}{9}$$

7. Total runs scored by batsman E = 28 × 55
The strike rate of E.
$$= \frac{\text{Total runs scored}}{\text{Total balls faced}} \times 100$$
$$= \frac{28 \times 55}{1280} \times 100 = 120.3125$$

8. Let the total number of runs scored by a batsman = x
Since given that strike rate, according to the question,
$$129.6 = \frac{x}{x-74} \times 100$$
$$129.6x - 129.6 \times 74 = 100x$$
$$x = \frac{129.6 \times 74}{29.6} = 324$$
So, the average run scored by the batsman A
$$= \frac{324}{8} = 40.5$$

9 Combined Strike rate of 20 matches $= \frac{120+158}{2} = 139$
Total balls faced
$$= \frac{\text{Total runs scored}}{\text{Strike rate}} \times 100 = \frac{20 \times 81}{139} \times 100 = 1165.43 \approx 1150$$

10. The number of matches played by batsman C
The total runs scored
$$\frac{\text{Total runs made by C}}{\text{Average runs scored}}$$
The total runs scored $= \frac{\text{Strike rate} \times \text{total ball faced}}{100}$
$$= \frac{114 \times 400}{100} = 456$$
So, the number of matches played by batsman C
$$= \frac{456}{38} = 12$$

11. Total import of all countries together in 2002
= ₹ 385 crore
Now, in 2002 total export of all companies together
= 90 + 100 + 65 + 25 + 110 + 120 = 510 crore
Total profit in 2002 = 510 – 385 = 125 crore

12. Import of company S in the year
1998 $= \frac{45 \times 2}{1} =$ ₹ 90 crore
Import of company U in the year 1998
$= 24 \times \frac{1}{4}$ ₹ 6 crore
Total import of company U and S together in 1998
= ₹ (90 + 6) = ₹ 96 crore

13. Total export of country Q in 2001 = ₹50 crore.
Total export of country T in 2000 = ₹55 crore
Total export = 50 + 55 = ₹ 105 crore

Now, total export of country P in 2003 = $\frac{105\times120}{100}$

= ₹ 126 crore

Total import of country P in 2003 = ₹ 92 crore

Profit = 126 – 92 = ₹ 34 crore

14. Total export of country T

= 60 + 50 + 55 + 110 + 110 = 376

Average export of Country T = $\frac{375}{5}$ = ₹ 75 crore

Total export of country R = 50 + 55 + 70 + 90 + 65 = 330

Average export of Country R = $\frac{330}{5}$ = ₹ 66 crore

Required% $\frac{75-66}{66}\times100=\frac{9}{66}\times100=\frac{150}{11}\%=13\frac{7}{11}\%$

15. Total export of all countries together in 1999

= 40 + 25 + 55 + 60 + 50 + 40 = ₹ 270 crore

Total export of all countries together in 2001

= 45 + 50 + 90 + 15 + 100 + 75 = ₹ 375 crore

Required % increase

$=\frac{375-270}{270}\times100=\frac{105}{11}\times100=\frac{350}{9}\%=38.88\%\approx38.89\%$

16. Total number of pages printed by printer B on Wednesday and Thursday = 141 + 223 = 364

Total number of pages printed by printer C on Monday and Friday = 211 + 257 = 468

Required Ratio = 364 : 468 = 7 : 9

17. Total number of pages printed by printer C and D together on Tuesday = 164 + 189 = 353

Total number of pages printed by printer A and E together on Thursday = 89 + 113 = 202

Required difference

= 353 – 202 = 151

18. Number of pages printed by printer A on Wednesday = 115

Number of pages printed by printer D on Friday = 160

Required percent = $\frac{115}{160}\times100=\frac{575}{8}=71\frac{7}{8}$

19. Total number of pages printed by printer B on Monday, Tuesday and Friday

= 147 + 189 + 93 = 429

Required average = $\frac{429}{3}=143$

20. Number of pages printed by Printer E on Monday = 184

Number of pages printed by printer C on Thursday = 120

Required percent = $\frac{184-120}{120}\times100$

$=\frac{6400}{120}=\frac{160}{3}=53\frac{1}{2}\%$

21. Difference between numbers of books published by publishing house M and P.

$\frac{7}{10}\times28200-\frac{8}{12}\times31200$

= 19740 – 19200 = 540

22. Each publisher get equal number books

$=\frac{79}{100}\times\frac{33800}{25}=1068$

23. The number of non-academic books published by publisher R and S.

$\frac{6}{17}\times35700+\frac{13}{18}\times37800$

= 12600 + 27300 = 39900

The average number of nonacademic books published by Published R and S = $\frac{39900}{2}$ = 19950

24. $\frac{100700\times\frac{130}{100}+127900\times\frac{80}{100}}{7}=\frac{233230}{7}=33318$

25. Total number of books distributed by Publisher O

$=\frac{92}{100}\times29700=27324$

Total number of books distributed by publishers Q

$=\frac{79}{100}+33800=26702$

Total number of books = 27324 + 26702 = 54026

37 Bar Graphs

EXERCISE – I

Directions (*Questions 1–5*): ***Study the following bar-graph carefully and answer the questions given below:***

(S.S.C., 2012)

Export of Pearls (in crores of rupees)

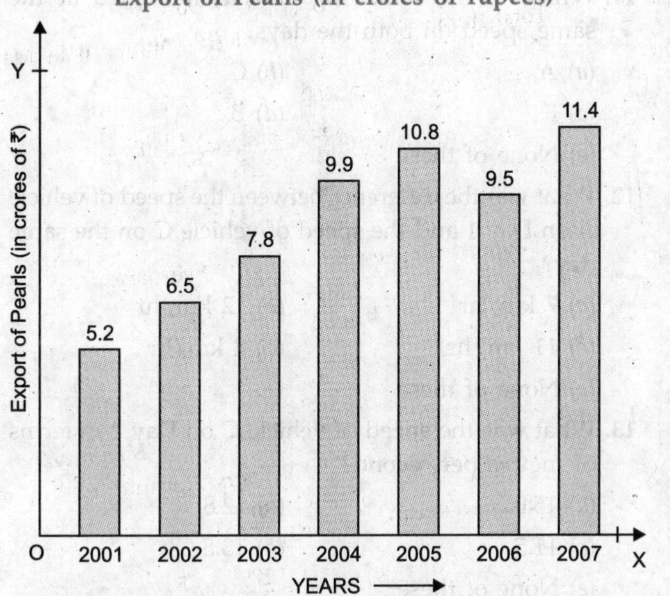

1. The average export of pearls for the given period (in crores ₹) was

(*a*) 8.7 (*b*) 8.73
(*c*) 9.73 (*d*) 8.85

2. In which year was there maximum percentage increase in export of pearls to that in the previous year?

(*a*) 2002 (*b*) 2007
(*c*) 2005 (*d*) 2004

3. In how many years was the export above average for the given period?

(*a*) 2 (*b*) 4
(*c*) 5 (*d*) 3

4. In which of the following pairs of years was the average export of pearls around ₹ 9 crores?

(*a*) 2002 and 2003 (*b*) 2003 and 2004
(*c*) 2004 and 2005 (*d*) 2005 and 2006

5. What was the percentage increase in export from 2006 to 2007?

(*a*) $16\frac{2}{3}\%$ (*b*) 19%
(*c*) 20%t (*d*) $33\frac{1}{3}\%$

Directions (*Questions 6–10*): ***Study the following pie-chart and bar diagram and answer the following questions***

(Bank P.O., 2011)

Percentage-wise Distribution of students in 6 Different Schools. Total number of students = 6000.

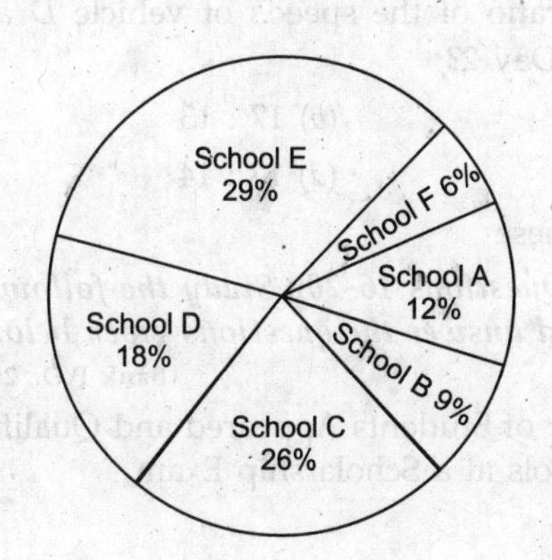

Number of Boys in Each School Out of 6000 Students

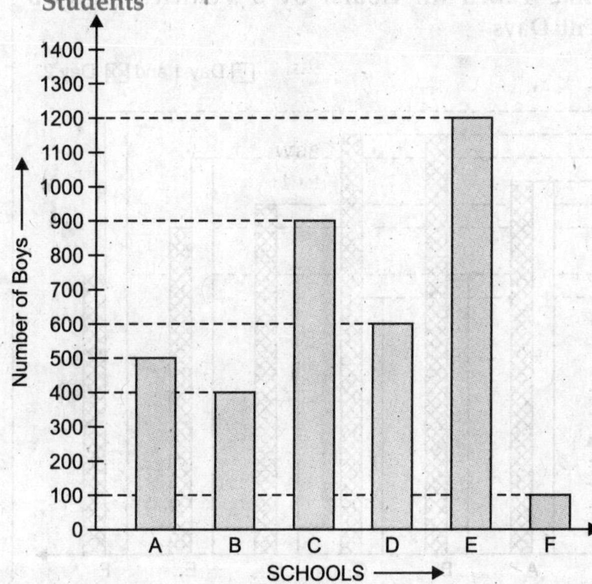

6. What is the sum of the number of girls in School C, the number of girls in School E and the number of boys in School D together ?
(*a*) 1700 (*b*) 1900
(*c*) 1600 (*d*) 1800
(*e*) None of these

7. What is the ratio of the number of boys in School C, the number of girls in School B and the total number of students in School E?
(*a*) 45 : 7 : 97 (*b*) 43 : 9 : 97
(*c*) 45 : 7 : 87 (*d*) 43 : 9 : 87
(*e*) None of these

8. What is the difference between the total number of students in School *F* and the number of boys in School *E* ?
(*a*) 820 (*b*) 860
(*c*) 880 (*d*) 900
(*e*) None of these

9. In which of the following schools is the total number of students equal to the number of girls in School E ?
(*a*) A (*b*) B
(*c*) C (*d*) D
(*e*) F

10. The number of girls in School A is approximately what percentage of the total number of students in School B ?
(*a*) 55 (*b*) 50
(*c*) 35 (*d*) 45
(*e*) 40

Directions (*Questions 11–15*): *Study the following bar graph and the table carefully and answer the questions given below:* **(Bank P.O., 2012)**

Time Taken (in Hours) by 6 Vehicles on Two Different Days

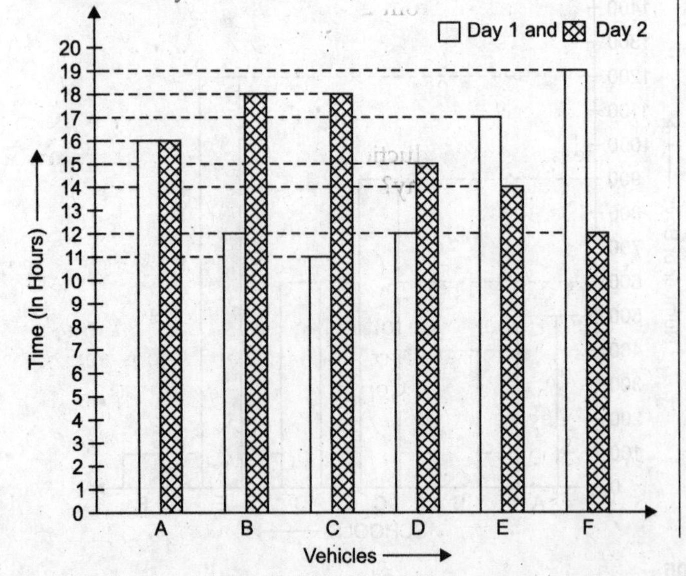

Distance Covered (in km) by 6 Vehicles on Each day

Vehicle	Day 1	Day 2
A	832	864
B	516	774
C	693	810
D	552	765
E	935	546
F	703	636

11. Which of the following vehicles travelled at the same speed on both the days?
(*a*) A (*b*) C
(*c*) F (*d*) B
(*e*) None of these

12. What was the difference between the speed of vehicle *A* on Day 1 and the speed of vehicle C on the same day?
(*a*) 7 km/hr (*b*) 12 km/hr
(*c*) 11 km/hr (*d*) 8 km/hr
(*e*) None of these

13. What was the speed of vehicle C on Day 2 in terms of metres per second?
(*a*) 15.3 (*b*) 12.8
(*c*) 11.5 (*d*) 13.8
(*e*) None of these

14. The distance travelled by vehicle *F* on Day 2 was approximately what per cent of the distance travelled by it on Day 1?
(*a*) 80% (*b*) 65%
(*c*) 85% (*d*) 95%
(*e*) 90%

15. What is the ratio of the speeds of vehicle *D* and vehicle *E* on Day 2?
(*a*) 15 : 13 (*b*) 17 : 13
(*c*) 13 : 11 (*d*) 17 : 14
(*e*) None of these

Directions (*Questions 16–20*): *Study the following graph carefully and answer the questions given below:* **(Bank P.O., 2011)**

Total Number of Students Appeared and Qualified from Various Schools at a Scholarship Exam

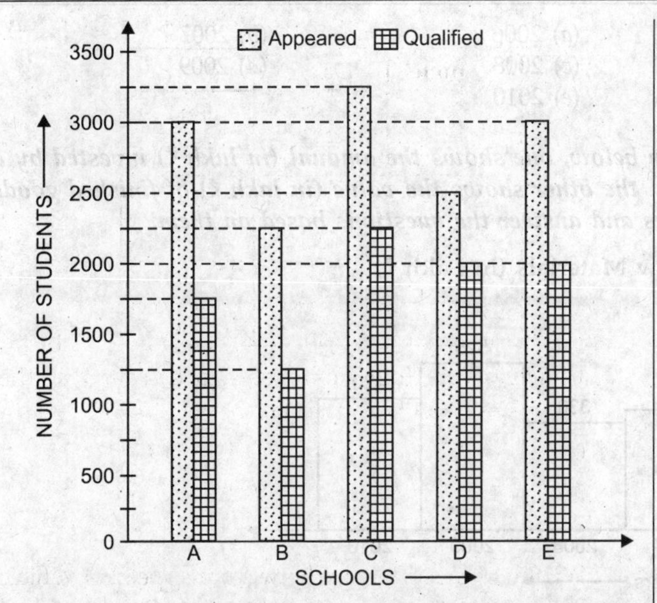

16. The average number of students qualified in the examination from Schools C and D is what percent of the average number of students appeared for the examination from the same schools? (rounded off to 2 digits after decimal)

(*a*) 58.62 (*b*) 73.91
(*c*) 62.58 (*d*) 58.96
(*e*) None of these

17. What is the ratio of the number of students appeared to the number of students qualified at the scholarship exam from School C ?

(*a*) 7 : 12 (*b*) 6 : 5
(*c*) 9 : 13 (*d*) 9 : 10
(*e*) None of these

18. What is the ratio of the number of students qualified in the scholarship examination from School A and the number of students qualified in the examination from School B?

(*a*) 8 : 3 (*b*) 5 : 7
(*c*) 7 : 3 (*d*) 7 : 5
(*e*) None of these

19. The number of students appeared for the scholarship exam from School D is approximately what percent of the total number of students appeared for the exam from all the schools together ?

(*a*) 12 (*b*) 24
(*c*) 29 (*d*) 18
(*e*) 8

20. What is the difference between the average number of students appeared in the scholarship exam from all the given schools and the average number of students qualified from all the schools together?

(*a*) 950 (*b*) 1100
(*c*) 990 (*d*) 1020
(*e*) None of these

Directions (*Questions 21–26*): ***The bar graph given below gives the data of the production of paper (in lakh tonnes) by three different companies X, Y and Z over last 5 years. Study the graph carefully and answer the questions that follow.***

Production of Paper (in lakh tons) By Companies X, Y and Z over the Years

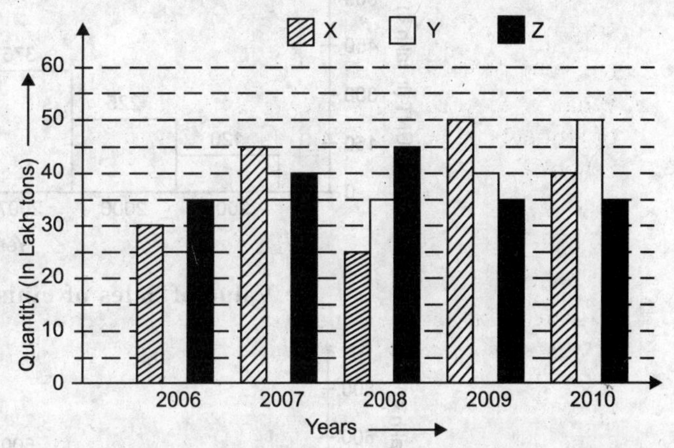

21. What is the difference between the production of Company Z in 2008 and Company Y in 2006?

(*a*) 2 lakh tons (*b*) 20 lakh tons
(*c*) 20 thousand tons (*d*) 200 lakh tons
(*e*) None of these

22. What is the ratio of the average production of Company X during the period 2008-2010 to the average production of Company Y during the same period?

(*a*) 1 : 1 (*b*) 15 : 17
(*c*) 23 : 25 (*d*) 27 : 29
(*e*) None of these

23. What is the percentage increase in the production of Company Y from 2006 to 2009?

(*a*) 30% (*b*) 45%
(*c*) 50% (*d*) 60%
(*e*) 75%

24. The average production for 5 years was maximum for which company?

(*a*) X (*b*) Y
(*c*) Z (*d*) X and Y both
(*e*) X and Z both

25. For which of the following years, the percentage rise or fall in production from the previous year is the maximum for Company Y?

(*a*) 2007 (*b*) 2008
(*c*) 2009 (*d*) 2010
(*e*) 2007 and 2010

26. In which year was the percentage of production of Company Z to the production of Company Y, the maximum?
(*a*) 2006 (*b*) 2007
(*c*) 2008 (*d*) 2009
(*e*) 2010

Directions (*Questions 27–31*): ***Out of the bar graphs given below, one shows the amount (in lakh ₹) invested by a company in purchasing raw materials over the years and the other shows the value (in lakh ₹) of finished goods sold by the company over the years. Study the bar graphs and answer the questions based on them.***

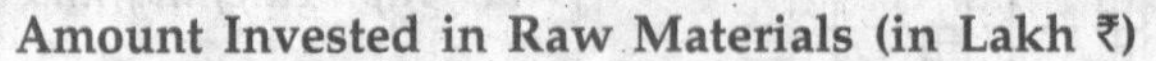
Amount Invested in Raw Materials (in Lakh ₹)

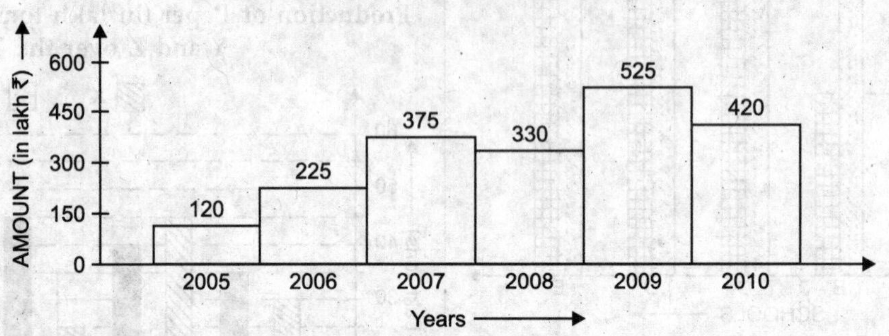

Value of Sales of Finishes Goods (in Lakh ₹)

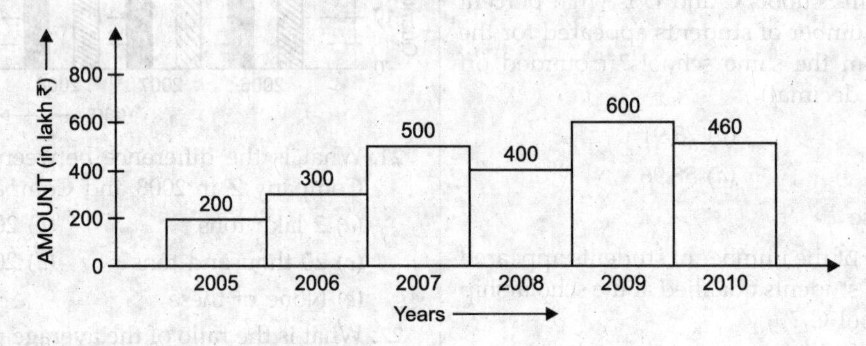

27. In which years, there is maximum percentage increase in the amount invested in raw materials as compared to the previous year?
(*a*) 2006 (*b*) 2007
(*c*) 2008 (*d*) 2009
(*e*) 2010

28. In which year, the percentage change (compared to previous year) in the investment on raw materials is the same as that in the value of sales of finished goods?
(*a*) 2006 (*b*) 2007
(*c*) 2008 (*d*) 2009
(*e*) 2010

29. What was the difference between the average amount invested in raw materials during the given period and the average value of sales of finished goods during this period?
(*a*) ₹ 62.5 lakhs (*b*) ₹ 68.5 lakhs
(*c*) ₹ 71.5 lakhs (*d*) ₹ 77.5 lakhs
(*e*) ₹ 83.5 lakhs

30. The value of sales of finished goods in 2009 was approximately what percent of the average amount invested in raw materials in the years 2007, 2008 and 2009?
(*a*) 33% (*b*) 37%
(*c*) 45% (*d*) 49%
(*e*) 53%

31. The maximum difference between the amount invested in raw materials and the value of sales of finished goods was during the year
(*a*) 2005 (*b*) 2006
(*c*) 2007 (*d*) 2008
(*e*) 2009

ANSWERS

1. (b)	2. (d)	3. (b)	4. (b)	5. (c)	6. (d)	7. (c)	8. (e)	9. (b)	10. (e)
11. (d)	12. (c)	13. (e)	14. (e)	15. (b)	16. (b)	17. (e)	18. (e)	19. (d)	20. (a)
21. (b)	22. (c)	23. (d)	24. (e)	25. (a)	28. (b)	29. (d)	30. (d)	31. (c)	

SOLUTIONS

Questions (1–5):

1. Average export of pearls over the period

$= ₹\left\{\frac{1}{7}(5.2+6.5+7.8+9.9+10.8+9.5+11.4)\right\}$ crores

$= ₹\left(\frac{61.1}{7}\right)$ crores $=$ ₹ (8.728) crores $=$ ₹ 8.73 crores.

2. Increase % in various years:

$2002 \to \left\{\frac{(6.5-5.2)}{5.2}\times 100\right\}\% = \left(\frac{1.3}{5.2}\times 100\right)\%$

$= \left(\frac{13}{52}\times 100\right)\% = 25\%.$

$2003 \to \left\{\frac{(7.8-6.5)}{6.5}\times 100\right\}\% = \left(\frac{1.3}{6.5}\times 100\right)\%$

$= \left(\frac{13}{65}\times 100\right)\% = 20\%.$

$2004 \to \left\{\frac{(9.9-7.8)}{7.8}\times 100\right\}\% = \left(\frac{2.1}{7.8}\times 100\right)\%$

$= \left(\frac{21}{78}\times 100\right)\% = \frac{350}{13}\% = 26.9\%.$

$2005 \to \left\{\frac{(10.8-9.9)}{9.9}\times 100\right\}\% = \left(\frac{0.9}{9.9}\times 100\right)\%$

$= \left(\frac{9}{99}\times 100\right)\% = \frac{100}{9}\% = 11.1\%.$

$2007 \to \left\{\frac{(11.4-9.5)}{9.5}\times 100\right\}\% = \left(\frac{1.9}{9.5}\times 100\right)\%$

$= \left(\frac{19}{95}\times 100\right)\% = 20\%.$

Clearly, the maximum increase was in 2004.

3. Average export during the given period $=$ ₹ 8.73 crores.

It was above average in 2004, 05, 06 and 07, i.e. in 4 years.

4. Average export in 2003 and 2004

$= ₹\ \frac{(7.8+9.9)}{2}$ crores

$= ₹\left(\frac{17.7}{2}\right)$ crores

$=$ ₹ 8.85 crores $=$ ₹ 9 crores (nearly).

5. Percentage increase in export from 2006 to 2007

$= \left\{\frac{(11.4-9.5)}{9.5}\times 100\right\}\% = \left(\frac{1.9}{9.5}\times 100\right)\%$

$= \left(\frac{19}{95}\times 100\right)\% = 20\%.$

Questions (6–10):

Number of students in:

$A \to \left(\frac{12}{100}\times 6000\right) = 720;\ B \to \left(\frac{9}{100}\times 6000\right) = 540;$

$C \to \left(\frac{26}{100}\times 6000\right) = 1560;\ D \to \left(\frac{18}{100}\times 6000\right) = 1080;$

$E \to \left(\frac{29}{100}\times 6000\right) = 1740;$

$F \to \left(\frac{6}{100}\times 6000\right) = 360.$

Number of boys in :

A → 500, B → 400, C → 900, D → 600, E → 1200, F → 100.

Number of girls in:

A → (720 – 500) = 220; B → (540 – 400) = 140; C → (1560 – 900) = 660;

D → (1080 – 600) = 480; E → (1740 – 1200) = 540; F → (360 – 100) = 260.

6. Required sum = (660 + 540 + 600) = 1800.

7. Required ratio = 900 : 140 : 1740 = 90 : 14 : 174 = 45 : 7 : 87.

8. (Number of boys in E) – (Number of students in F) = (1200 – 100) = 1100.

9. Number of girls in School E = 540 = Total number of students in B.

10. Let (Number of girls in A) be x% of number of students in B. Then,

$220 = \frac{x}{100}\times 540 \Rightarrow x = \left(\frac{220\times 100}{540}\right)$

$= \frac{1100}{27} = 40.7 \simeq 40\%$ (nearly).

Questions (11–15):

Speeds of vehicles on Day 1:

$A \to \frac{832}{16}$ km/hr = 52 km/hr;

$B \to \frac{516}{12}$ km/hr = 43 km/hr;

$C \to \frac{693}{11}$ km/hr = 63 km/hr;

$D \to \frac{552}{12}$ km/hr = 46 km/hr;

$E \to \frac{935}{17}$ km/hr = 55 km/hr;

$F \to \frac{703}{19}$ km/hr = 37 km/hr.

Speeds of vehicles on Day 2:

$A \rightarrow \frac{864}{16}$ km/hr = 54 km/hr;

$B \rightarrow \frac{774}{18}$ km/hr = 43 km/hr;

$C \rightarrow \frac{810}{18}$ km/hr = 45 km/hr;

$D \rightarrow \frac{765}{15}$ km/hr = 51 km/hr;

$E \rightarrow \frac{546}{14}$ km/hr = 39 km/hr;

$F \rightarrow \frac{636}{12}$ km/hr = 53 km/hr.

11. Clearly *B* travelled at the same speed on both the days.

12. Difference between the speed of A on Day 1 and speed of C on Day 1

$= (63 - 52)$ km/hr = 11 km/hr.

13. Speed of C on Day 2 = 45 km/hr

$= \left(45 \times \frac{5}{18}\right) \text{m/sec} = \frac{25}{2} \text{m/s} = 12.5 \text{ m/s}.$

14. Required% $= \left(\frac{636}{703} \times 100\right)\% = \frac{63600}{703}\% = 90.46\% \simeq 90\%.$

15. Required ratio

$= \frac{\text{Speed of D on Day 2}}{\text{Speed of E on Day 2}} = \frac{51}{39} = \frac{17}{13} = 17:13.$

Questions (16–20):

16. Average number of students qualified from C and D

$= \frac{1}{2}(2250 + 2000) = \frac{4250}{2} = 2125.$

Average number of students appeared from C and D

$= \frac{1}{2}(3250 + 2500) = \frac{5750}{2} = 2875.$

Required% $= \left(\frac{2125}{2875} \times 100\right)\% = \left(\frac{85}{115} \times 100\right)\%$

$= \left(\frac{1700}{23}\right)\% = 73.91\%.$

17. (Number of students appeared from C): (Number of students qualified from C) $= \frac{3250}{2250} = \frac{13}{9} = 13:9.$

18. (Number of students qualified from *A*): (Number of students qualified from B) $= \frac{1750}{1250} = \frac{7}{5} = 7:5.$

19. Required%

$= \left\{\frac{2500}{(3000 + 2250 + 3250 + 2500 + 3000)} \times 100\right\}\%$

$= \left(\frac{2500}{14000} \times 100\right)\% = \frac{125}{7}\% = 18\%$ (nearly).

20. Average number of students appeared from all the schools

$= \frac{1}{5}(3000 + 2250 + 3250 + 2500 + 3000)$

$= \frac{14000}{5} = 2800.$

Average number of students qualified from all the schools

$= \frac{1}{5}(1750 + 1250 + 2250 + 2000 + 2000)$

$= \frac{9250}{5} = 1850.$

Required difference = (2800 − 1850) = 950.

Questions (21–26):

21. Required difference

= (45 − 25) lakh tons = 20 lakh tons.

22. Average production of X during 2008 to 2010

$= \frac{1}{3} \times (25 + 50 + 40)$ lakh tons $= \left(\frac{115}{3}\right)$ lakh tons.

Average production of Y during 2008 to 2010

$= \frac{1}{3} \times (35 + 40 + 50)$ lakh tons $= \left(\frac{125}{3}\right)$ lakh tons.

$\therefore$ Required ratio $= \left(\frac{115}{3} \times \frac{3}{125}\right) = \frac{23}{25} = 23:25.$

23. Percentage increase in production of Y from 2006 to 2009

$= \left\{\frac{(40 - 25)}{25} \times 100\right\}\% = \left(\frac{15}{25} \times 100\right)\% = 60\%.$

24. Average production (in lakh tons) in 5 years for various companies are:

$X \rightarrow \frac{1}{5} \times (30 + 45 + 25 + 50 + 40) = \left(\frac{1}{5} \times 190\right) = 38;$

$Y \rightarrow \frac{1}{5} \times (25 + 35 + 35 + 40 + 50) = \left(\frac{1}{5} \times 185\right) = 37;$

$Z \rightarrow \frac{1}{5} \times (35 + 40 + 45 + 35 + 35) = \left(\frac{1}{5} \times 190\right) = 38.$

Clearly, it is maximum for X and Z both.

25. Percentage change (rise or fall) in production of *Y* in comparison to previous year, for different years is:

$2007 \rightarrow \left\{\frac{(35 - 25)}{25} \times 100\right\}\% = \left(\frac{10 \times 100}{25}\right)\% = 40\%;$

2008 → No change, i.e. 0%;

$2009 \rightarrow \left\{\frac{(40 - 35)}{35} \times 100\right\}\% = \left(\frac{5}{35} \times 100\right)\%$

$= \frac{100}{7}\% = 14.3\%;$

$2010 \rightarrow \left\{\frac{(50 - 40)}{40} \times 100\right\}\% = \left(\frac{10}{40} \times 100\right)\% = 25\%.$

So, it is maximum in 2007.

26. Percentage production of Z to production of Y in various years:

$2006 \rightarrow \left(\frac{35}{25} \times 100\right)\% = (35 \times 4)\% = 140\%;$

$2007 \rightarrow \left(\frac{40}{35} \times 100\right)\% = \frac{800}{7}\% = 114.3\%;$

$2008 \rightarrow \left(\frac{45}{35} \times 100\right)\% = \frac{900}{7}\% = 128.57\%;$

$$2009 \rightarrow \left(\frac{35}{40} \times 100\right)\% = \frac{175}{2}\% = 87.5\%;$$

$$2010 \rightarrow \left(\frac{35}{50} \times 100\right)\% = 70\%.$$

Clearly, this percentage was maximum in 2010.

Questions (27–31):

27. The percentage increase in amount invested in raw-materials as compared to previous year for different years are:

$$2006 \rightarrow \left\{\frac{(225-120)}{120} \times 100\right\}\% = \left(\frac{105}{120} \times 100\right)\% = \frac{175}{2}\%$$

$$= 87.5\%$$

$$2007 \rightarrow \left\{\frac{(375-225)}{225} \times 100\right\}\%$$

$$= \left(\frac{150}{225} \times 100\right)\% = \frac{200}{3}\% = 66.67\%;$$

In 2008, there is a decrease.

$$2009 \rightarrow \left\{\frac{(525-330)}{330} \times 100\right\}\%$$

$$= \left(\frac{195}{330} \times 100\right)\% = \frac{650}{11}\% = 59.09\%.$$

In 2010, there is a decrease.

So, the maximum percentage increase in investment is in the year 2006.

28. The percentage change in the amount invested in raw-materials and in the value of sales of finished goods for different years are:

Year	Percentage change in Amount invested in raw-material	Percentage change in value of sales of finished goods
2006	$\left[\frac{(225-120)}{120} \times 100\right]\% = 87.5\%$	$\left[\frac{(300-200)}{200} \times 100\right]\% = 50\%$
2007	$\left[\frac{(375-225)}{225} \times 100\right]\% = 66.67\%$	$\left[\frac{(500-300)}{300} \times 100\right]\% = 66.67\%$
2008	$\left[\frac{(330-375)}{375} \times 100\right]\% - 12\%$	$\left[\frac{(400-500)}{500} \times 100\right]\% = -20\%$
2009	$\left[\frac{(525-330)}{330} \times 100\right]\% = 59.09\%$	$\left[\frac{(600-400)}{400} \times 100\right]\% = 50\%$
2010	$\left[\frac{(420-525)}{525} \times 100\right]\% = -20\%$	$\left[\frac{(460-600)}{600} \times 100\right]\% = -23.33\%.$

Thus, the percentage difference is same during the year 2007.

29. Required difference

$$= \left[₹\left(\frac{200+300+500+400+600+460}{6}\right) - ₹\left(\frac{120+225+375+330+525+420}{6}\right)\right] \text{lakh}$$

$$= \left\{₹\left(\frac{2460}{6}\right) - ₹\left(\frac{1995}{6}\right)\right\} \text{lakh}$$

$$= ₹\,(410 - 332.5) \text{ lakh} = ₹\,77.5 \text{ lakh.}$$

30. Required percentage

$$= \left\{\frac{600}{(375+330+525)} \times 100\right\}\% = \left(\frac{600}{1230} \times 100\right)\%$$

$$= \left(\frac{2000}{41}\right)\% = 48.78\% \simeq 49\%.$$

31. (Amount spent on Raw Material) – (Value of sales of finished goods) for various years are :

2005 → ₹ (200 – 120) lakh = ₹ 80 lakh.

2006 → ₹ (300 – 225) lakh = ₹ 75 lakh.

2007 → ₹ (500 – 375) lakh = ₹ 125 lakh.

2008 → ₹ (400 – 330) lakh = ₹ 70 lakh.

2009 → ₹ (600 – 525) lakh = ₹ 75 lakh.

2010 → ₹ (460 – 420) lakh = ₹ 40 lakh.

Clearly, the maximum difference was during the year 2007.

EXERCISE – II

Directions (*Questions* 1–5): ***Study the following bargraph and answer the questions given below:***

Production of Fertilizers by a Company (in 10000 tonnes) Over the Years

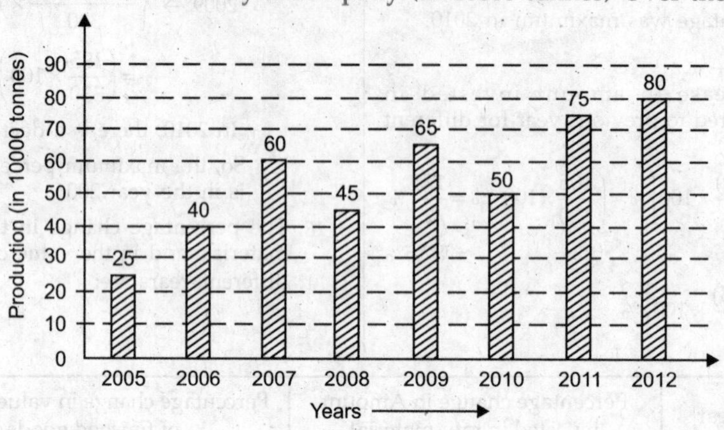

1. In how many of the given years was the production of fertilizers more than the average production of the given years?
(*a*) 1 (*b*) 2
(*c*) 3 (*d*) 4
(*e*) 5

2. The average production of 2006 and 2007 was exactly equal to the average production of which of the following pairs of years?
(*a*) 2010 and 2011 (*b*) 2009 and 2010
(*c*) 2008 and 2010 (*d*) 2005 and 2009
(*e*) 2005 and 2011

3. What was the percentage decline in the production of fertilizers from 2007 to 2008?
(*a*) $33\frac{1}{3}\%$ (*b*) 30%
(*c*) 25% (*d*) 21%
(*e*) 20%

4. In which year was the percentage increase in production as compared to the previous year, the maximum?
(*a*) 2012 (*b*) 2011
(*c*) 2009 (*d*) 2007
(*e*) 2006

5. What was the percentage increase in production of fertilizers in 2012 compared to that in 2005?
(*a*) 320% (*b*) 300%
(*c*) 220% (*d*) 200%
(*e*) 150%

Directions (*Questions* 6–10): ***The bar graph given below shows the percentage distribution of total expenditure of a company under various expense heads during a year. Study the graph carefully and answer the questions that follow:***

Percentage Distribution of Total Expenditure of a Company

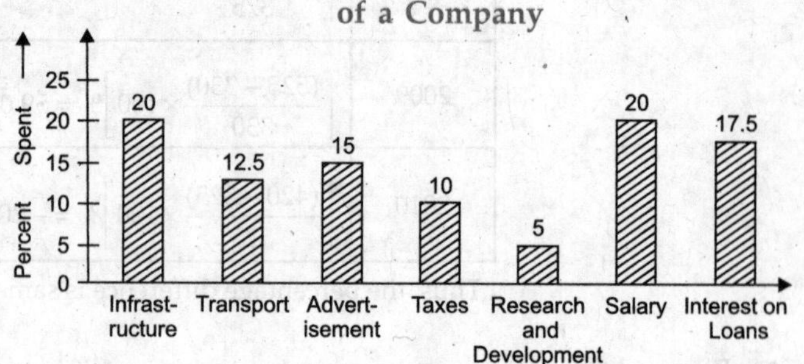

6. The expenditure on the Interest on Loans is by what percent more than the expenditure on Transport?
(*a*) 5% (*b*) 10%
(*c*) 20% (*d*) 30%
(*e*) 40%

7. What is the ratio of the total expenditure on Infrastructure and Transport to the total expenditure on Taxes and Interest on Loans?
(*a*) 5 : 4 (*b*) 8 : 7
(*c*) 9 : 7 (*d*) 13 : 11
(*e*) Cannot be determined

8. If the expenditure on Advertisement is ₹ 2.10 crores, then the difference between the expenditures on Transport and Taxes is:
(*a*) ₹ 1.25 crores (*b*) ₹ 95 lakhs
(*c*) ₹ 65 lakhs (*d*) ₹ 35 lakhs
(*e*) ₹ 25 lakhs

9. The total expenditure of the company is how many times the expediture on Research and Development?
(a) 27 (b) 20
(c) 18 (d) 8
(e) 5

10. If the Interest on Loans amounted to ₹ 2.45 crores, then the total expenditure on Advertisement, Taxes and Research and Development is:
(a) ₹ 7 crores (b) ₹ 5.4 crores
(c) ₹ 4.2 cores (d) ₹ 3 crores
(e) ₹ 2.4 crores

Directions (*Questions 11–15*): ***Study the following pie-chart and bar graph and answer the questions that follow:*** (Bank P.O. , 2011)

Percentage Wise Distribution of Teachers in 6 Districts

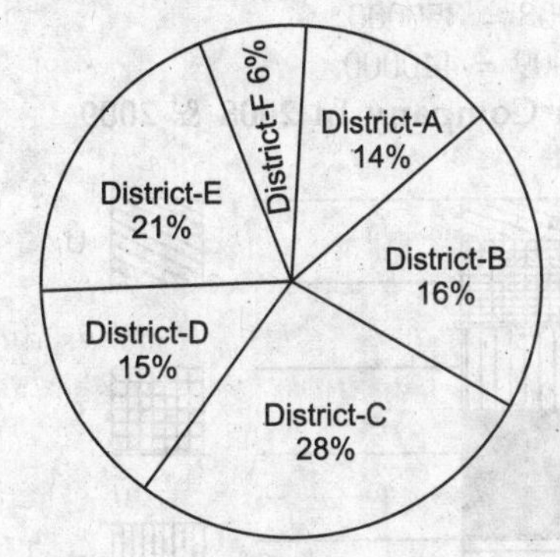

Number of Males In Each District Out of 4500 Teachers

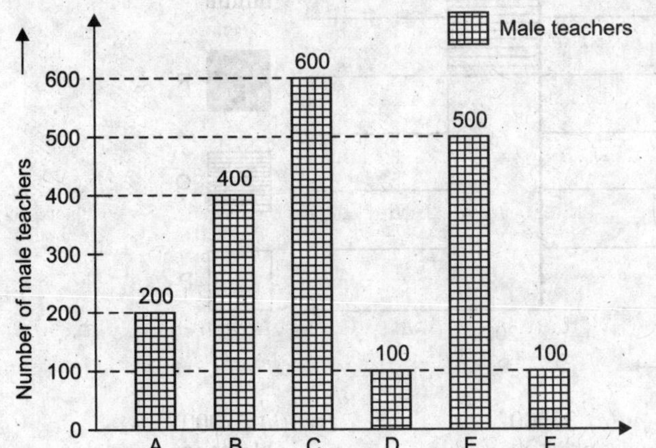

11. What is the total number of male teachers in District F, female teachers in District C and female teachers in District B together?
(a) 1080 (b) 1120
(c) 1180 (d) 1020
(e) None of these

12. The number of female teachers in District D is approximately what per cent of the total number of teachers (both male & female) in District A?
(a) 70 (b) 75
(c) 80 (d) 95
(e) 90

13. In which district is the number of male teachers more than the number of female teachers?
(a) B only (b) D only
(c) Both B and E (d) Both E and F
(e) None of these

14. What is the difference between the number of female teachers in District F and the total number of teachers (both male and female) in District E?
(a) 625 (b) 775
(c) 675 (d) 725
(e) None of these

15. What is the ratio of the number of male teachers in District C to the number of female teachers in District B?
(a) 11 : 15 (b) 15 : 11
(c) 15 : 8 (d) 30 : 13
(e) None of these

Directions (*Questions 16–20*): ***Study the following graph carefully and answer the questions that follow:*** (Bank P.O., 2011)

No. of Students (in thousands) who opted for Three Different Specializations during the Given Five Years in a University

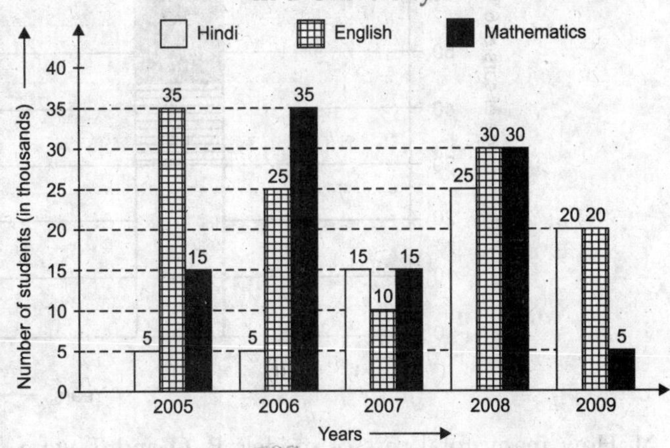

16. Out of the total number of students who opted for the given three subjects in the year 2009, 38% were girls. How many boys opted for Mathematics in the same year?
(a) 1322 (b) 1332
(c) 1312 (d) Cannot be determined
(e) None of these

17. If the total number of students in the university in the year 2007 was 455030, the total number of students who opted for the given three subjects was approximately what percent of the total students?
(a) 19 (b) 9
(c) 12 (d) 5
(e) 23

18. What is the total number of students who opted for Hindi and Mathematics in the years 2006, 2007 and 2009 together?

(*a*) 97000 (*b*) 93000
(*c*) 85000 (*d*) 96000
(*e*) None of these

19. The total number of students who opted for Mathematics in the years 2005 and 2008 together is approximately what percent of the total number of students who opted for all three subjects in the same years?

(*a*) 38 (*b*) 28
(*c*) 42 (*d*) 32
(*e*) 48

20. What is the ratio of the number of students who opted for English in the years 2006 and 2008 together to the number of students who opted for Hindi in the years 2005 and 2009 together?

(*a*) 11 : 5 (*b*) 12 : 7
(*c*) 11 : 7 (*d*) 12 : 5
(*e*) None of these

Directions (*Questions 21–25*): ***The bar-graph given below shows the percentage distribution of the total production of a car manufacturing company into various models over two years. Study the graph carefully and answer the questions that follow.***

Total number of cars produced in 2008 = 350000.
Total Number of cars produced in 2009 = 440000.

Percentage of 6 Types of Cars Manufactured By a Company In 2008 & 2009

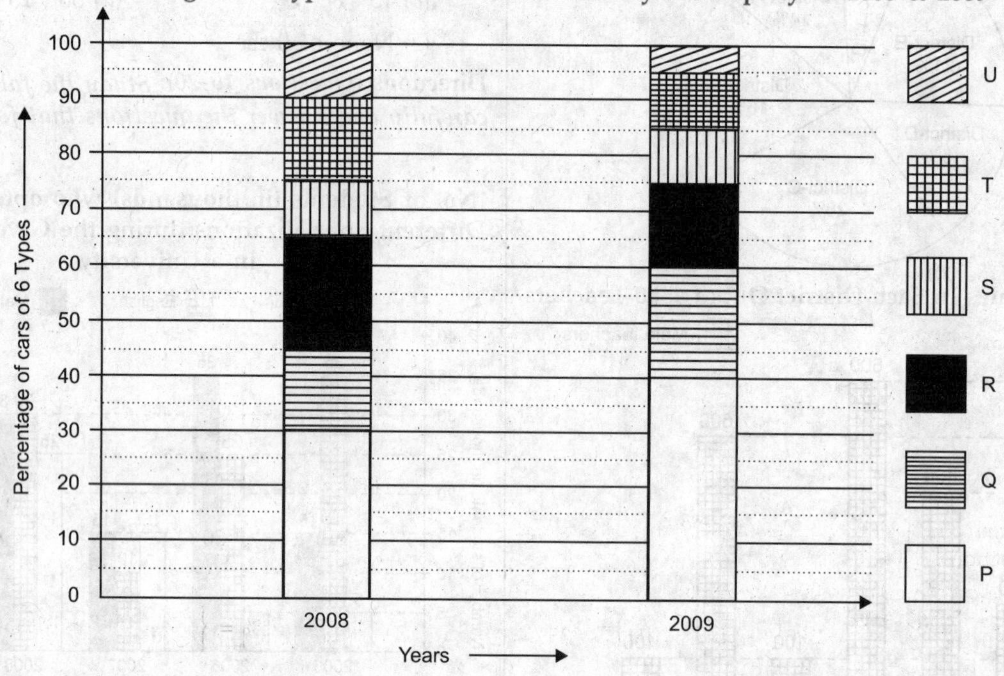

21. How many total cars of models P, Q and T were manufactured in the year 2008?

(*a*) 245000 (*b*) 227500
(*c*) 210000 (*d*) 192500
(*e*) 157500

22. For which model the percentage rise/fall in production was minimum from 2008 to 2009?

(*a*) Q (*b*) R
(*c*) S (*d*) T
(*e*) U

23. What was the difference in the number of *Q* type cars produced in 2008 and that produced in 2009?

(*a*) 35500 (*b*) 27000
(*c*) 22500 (*d*) 17500
(*e*) 16000

24. If the percentage production of *P* type cars in 2009 be the same as in 2008, then the number of *P* type cars produced in 2009 would have been:

(*a*) 140000 (*b*) 132000
(*c*) 117000 (*d*) 105000
(*e*) 97000

25. If 85% of the *S* type cars produced in each year were sold by the company, how many *S* type cars remained unsold?

(*a*) 7650 (*b*) 9350
(*c*) 11850 (*d*) 12250
(*e*) 13350

ANSWERS

1. (d)	2. (e)	3. (c)	4. (e)	5. (c)	6. (e)	7. (d)	8. (d)	9. (b)	10. (c)
11. (a)	12. (e)	13. (c)	14. (b)	15. (c)	16. (d)	17. (b)	18. (e)	19. (d)	20. (a)
21. (c)	22. (b)	23. (a)	24. (b)	25. (c)					

SOLUTIONS

Questions (1–5):

1. Average production (in 10000 tonnes) over the given years

$$= \frac{(25+40+60+45+65+50+75+80)}{8}$$

$$= \frac{440}{8} = 55.$$

Clearly, the productions during 2007, 2009, 2011 and 2012 are more than the average production. These are 4 years.

2. Average production (in 10000 tonnes) during 2006 and 2007

$$= \frac{(40+60)}{2} = \frac{100}{2} = 50.$$

Average production (in 10000 tonnes) during:

(2010 and 2011) $\rightarrow \frac{(50+75)}{2} = \frac{125}{2} = 62.5;$

(2009 and 2010) $\rightarrow \frac{(65+50)}{2} = \frac{115}{2} = 57.5;$

(2008 and 2010) $\rightarrow \frac{(45+50)}{2} = \frac{95}{2} = 47.5;$

(2005 and 2009) $\rightarrow \frac{(25+65)}{2} = \frac{90}{2} = 45;$

(2005 and 2011) $\rightarrow \frac{(25+75)}{2} = \frac{100}{2} = 50.$

∴ Average production of 2006 and 2007 = Average production of 2005 and 2011.

3. Decline percentage from 2007 to 2008

$$= \left\{\frac{(60-45)}{60}\times 100\right\}\% = \left(\frac{15}{60}\times 100\right)\% = 25\%.$$

4. Percentage increase in a year compared to previous year:

2006 $\rightarrow \left\{\frac{(40-25)}{25}\times 100\right\}\% = \left(\frac{15}{25}\times 100\right)\% = 60\%;$

2007 $\rightarrow \left\{\frac{(60-40)}{40}\times 100\right\}\%$

$$= \left(\frac{20}{40}\times 100\right)\% = 50\%;$$

In 2008, there is decrease in production.

2009 $\rightarrow \left\{\frac{(65-45)}{45}\times 100\right\}\%$

$$= \left(\frac{20}{45}\times 100\right)\% = \frac{400}{9}\% = 44.44\%;$$

In 2010, there is a decrease in production.

2011 $\rightarrow \left\{\frac{(75-50)}{50}\times 100\right\}\% = \left(\frac{25}{50}\times 100\right)\% = 50\%;$

2012 $\rightarrow \left\{\frac{(80-75)}{75}\times 100\right\}\%$

$$= \left(\frac{5}{75}\times 100\right)\% = \frac{20}{3}\% = 6.67\%.$$

Clearly, maximum percentage increase is in the year 2006.

5. Percentage increase in production in 2012 compared to 2005

$$= \left\{\frac{(80-25)}{25}\times 100\right\}\% = \left(\frac{55}{25}\times 100\right)\% = 220\%.$$

Questions (6–10):

6. Let the total expenditure be ₹ x. Then,

Expenditure on Interest on Loans

$$= (17.5\% \text{ of ₹ } x) = ₹\left(\frac{175x}{1000}\right).$$

Expenditure on Transport

$$= (12.5\% \text{ of ₹ } x) = ₹\left(\frac{125x}{1000}\right).$$

$$\text{Difference} = ₹\left(\frac{175x}{1000} - \frac{125x}{1000}\right) = ₹\frac{(175x - 125x)}{1000}$$

$$= ₹\frac{50x}{1000} = ₹\frac{x}{20}$$

$$\therefore \text{ Required\%} = \left\{\frac{x}{20}\times\frac{1000}{125x}\times 100\right\}\% = 40\%.$$

7. Let the total expenditure be ₹ x. Then

Total expenditure on Infrastructure and Transport

$$= \{(20 + 12.5)\% \text{ of ₹ } x\}$$

$$= ₹\left(\frac{32.5\times x}{100}\right) = ₹\left(\frac{325x}{1000}\right).$$

Total expenditure on Taxes and Interest on Loans

$$= \{(10 + 17.5)\% \text{ of ₹ } x\}$$

$$= ₹\left(\frac{27.5\times x}{100}\right) = ₹\left(\frac{275x}{1000}\right).$$

$$\therefore \text{ Required ratio} = \frac{325x}{1000} : \frac{275x}{1000} = 13:11.$$

8. Let the total expenditure be ₹x crores. Then

15% of x = 2.10

$\Rightarrow \frac{15 \times x}{100} = 2.10 \Rightarrow 15x = (2.10 \times 100)$

$\Rightarrow 15x = 210$

$\Rightarrow x = \frac{210}{15} = 14.$

∴ Total expenditure = ₹ 14 crores.

(Expenditure on Transport) – (Expenditure on Taxes)

= ₹ {(12.5 – 10)% of 14 crores}

$= ₹\left(\frac{2.5}{100} \times 14\right)$ crores

$= ₹\frac{35}{100}$ crores

$= ₹\left(\frac{35}{100} \times 100 \text{ lakhs}\right) = ₹\ 35$ lakh.

9. Let the total expenditure (in crores) be ₹ x. Then,

Expenditure on Research & Development

= ₹(5% of x)

$= ₹\frac{5x}{100} = ₹\frac{x}{20}.$

(Total Expenditure): (Expenditure on Research and Development)

$= x : \frac{x}{20} = 20\,x : x = 20 : 1.$

∴ Total Expenditure = 20 times the expenditure on Research & Development.

10. Let the total expenditure be ₹x crores.

Then, 17.5% of x = 2.45

$\Rightarrow \frac{17.5x}{100} = 2.45 \Rightarrow x = \frac{2.45 \times 100}{17.5} = \frac{2450}{175} \Rightarrow x = 14.$

∴ Total expenditure = ₹ 14 crores.

Expenditure on Advertisement,
Taxes, Research and Development

= [(15 + 10 + 5)% of ₹ 14 crores]

$= ₹\left(\frac{30}{100} \times 14\right)$ crores

= ₹ 4.2 crores.

Questions (11–15):

Total number of teachers in :

$A \rightarrow \left(\frac{14}{100} \times 4500\right) = 630;$

$B \rightarrow \left(\frac{16}{100} \times 4500\right) = 720;$

$C \rightarrow \left(\frac{28}{100} \times 4500\right) = 1260;$

$D \rightarrow \left(\frac{15}{100} \times 4500\right) = 675;$

$E \rightarrow \left(\frac{21}{100} \times 4500\right) = 945;$

$F \rightarrow \left(\frac{6}{100} \times 4500\right) = 270.$

	A	B	C	D	E	F
Males	200	400	600	100	500	100
Females	430	320	660	575	445	170

11. Total number of male teachers in F, female teachers in C and female teachers in B

= (100 + 660 + 320) = 1080.

12. Female teachers in D = 575.

Total number of teachers in A

= (200 + 430) = 630.

Required percentage $= \left(\frac{575}{630} \times 100\right)\%$

$= \frac{5750}{63}\% = 91.2\% \simeq 90\%.$

13. Clearly, the number of male teachers is more than the number of female teachers in *B* and *E*.

14. Number of female teachers in *F* = 170

Total number of teachers in *E* = (500 + 445) = 945.

Required difference = (945 – 170) = 775.

15. Number of male teachers in C : Number of female teachers in B = 600 : 320 = 15 : 8.

Questions (16–20):

16. Number of students who opted for the given three subjects in the year 2009 is (20000 + 20000 + 5000) = 45000.

Number of girls = 38% of 45000

$= \left(45000 \times \frac{38}{100}\right) = 17100.$

Out of these, the number of boys who opt for Mathematics cannot be found.

17. In 2007, we have :

Total number of students = 455030.

Number of those choosing the given three subjects = (15000 + 10000 + 15000) = 40000.

Required percentage $= \left(\frac{40000}{455030} \times 100\right)\%$

$= 8.79\% \simeq 9\%.$

18. Number of students who opt Hindi and Mathematics in 2006, 2007 and 2009.

= [(5 + 35) + (15 + 15)

+ (20 + 5)] thousands = 95000.

19. Number of students opting Mathematics in 2005 and 2008 = (15000 + 30000) = 45000.

Number of students opting for these three subjects in 2005 and 2008

= [(5 + 35 + 15) + (25 + 30 + 30)] thousands

= (55000 + 85000) = 140000.

$$\text{Required\%} = \left(\frac{45000}{140000} \times 100\right)\% = \frac{225}{7}\% = 32\% \text{ (nearly).}$$

20. Ratio of the number who opted for English in 2006 and 2008 to the number who opted for Hindi in 2005 and 2009

= (25 + 30) : (5 + 20) = 55 : 25 = 11 : 5.

Questions (21–25):

Number of cars of different models produced in 2008 out of 350000 :

$$P = 30\% \text{ of } 350000 = \left(350000 \times \frac{30}{100}\right) = 105000;$$

$$Q = (45 - 30)\% \text{ of } 350000 = \left(350000 \times \frac{15}{100}\right) = 52500;$$

$$R = (65 - 45)\% \text{ of } 350000 = \left(350000 \times \frac{20}{100}\right) = 70000;$$

$$S = (75 - 65)\% \text{ of } 350000 = \left(350000 \times \frac{10}{100}\right) = 35000;$$

$$T = (90 - 75)\% \text{ of } 35000 = \left(350000 \times \frac{15}{100}\right) = 52500;$$

$$U = (100 - 90)\% \text{ of } 350000 = \left(350000 \times \frac{10}{100}\right) = 35000.$$

Number of cars of different types produced in 2009 out of 440000:

$$P \rightarrow (40\% \text{ of } 440000) = \left(440000 \times \frac{40}{100}\right) = 176000;$$

$$Q \rightarrow (60 - 40)\% \text{ of } 440000 = \left(440000 \times \frac{20}{100}\right) = 88000;$$

$$R \rightarrow (75 - 60)\% \text{ of } 440000 = \left(440000 \times \frac{15}{100}\right) = 66000;$$

$$S \rightarrow (85 - 75)\% \text{ of } 440000 = \left(440000 \times \frac{10}{100}\right) = 44000;$$

$$T \rightarrow (95 - 85)\% \text{ of } 440000 = \left(440000 \times \frac{10}{100}\right) = 44000;$$

$$U \rightarrow (100 - 95)\% \text{ of } 440000 = \left(440000 \times \frac{5}{100}\right) = 22000.$$

21. Total number of cars of models *P*, *Q* and *T* produced in 2008

= (105000 + 52500 + 52500) = 210000.

22. Percentage change (rise or fall) in production from 2008 to 2009 is:

$$P \rightarrow \left\{\frac{(176 - 105)}{105} \times 100\right\}\%$$

$$= \left(\frac{71 \times 20}{21}\right)\% = \frac{1420}{21}\% = 67.6\% \text{ (Rise)}$$

$$Q \rightarrow \left\{\frac{(88 - 52.5)}{52.5} \times 100\right\}\% = \left(\frac{355}{525} \times 100\right)\%$$

$$= \left(\frac{71 \times 20}{21}\right)\% = \frac{1420}{21}\% = 67.6\% \text{ (Rise)}$$

$$R \rightarrow \left\{\frac{(70 - 66)}{70} \times 100\right\}\%$$

$$= \left(\frac{4}{70} \times 100\right)\% = \frac{40}{7}\% = 5.7\% \text{ (Fall)}$$

$$S \rightarrow \left\{\frac{(44 - 35)}{35} \times 100\right\}\%$$

$$= \left(\frac{9 \times 100}{35}\right)\% = \frac{180}{7}\% = 25.7\% \text{ (Rise)}$$

$$T \rightarrow \left\{\frac{(525 - 440)}{525} \times 100\right\}\% = \left(\frac{85 \times 100}{525}\right)\%$$

$$= \left(\frac{85 \times 4}{21}\right)\% = \frac{340}{21}\% = 16.2\% \text{ (Fall)}$$

$$U \rightarrow \left\{\frac{(35 - 22)}{35} \times 100\right\}\% = \left(\frac{13 \times 100}{35}\right)\%$$

$$= \left(\frac{13 \times 20}{7}\right)\% = \frac{260}{7}\% = 37.1\% \text{ (Fall)}$$

Clearly, minimum rise/fall percentage is in case of R.

23. Difference of production of Q in 2008 and 2009

= (88000 − 52500) = 35500.

24. Let the percentage production of P in 2009

= percentage production of *P* in 2008 = 30%.

Then, Production of P in 2009 = 30% of 440000

$$= \left(\frac{30}{100} \times 440000\right) = 132000.$$

25. Number of *S* type cars remained unsold in 2008 and 2009

= 15% of 35000) + (15% of 44000)

$$= \left(35000 \times \frac{15}{100}\right) + \left(44000 \times \frac{15}{100}\right)$$

$$= (5250 + 6600) = 11850.$$

EXERCISE – III

Directions (*Questions* 1–5): ***The following chart represents Demand and Production for 5 companies ABCDE. On the basis of the graph answer the questions.***

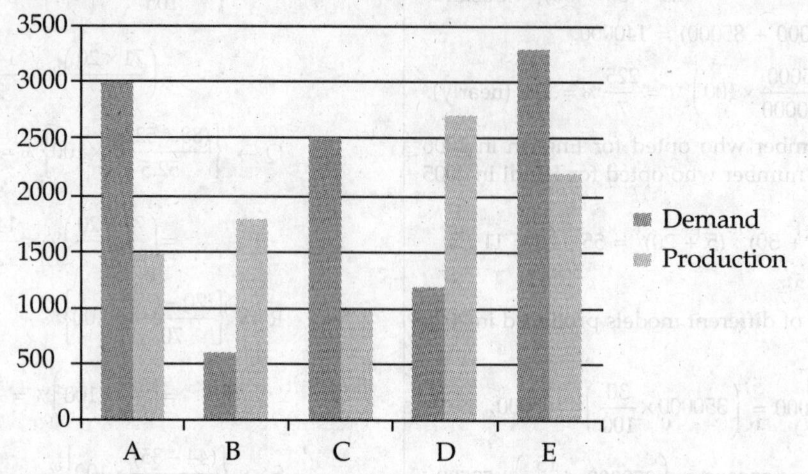

1. If company A desires to meet the demand by purchasing surplus production of company, then the most suitable company is
[SSC—CHSL (10+2) Exam, 2015]
(*a*) C (*b*) D
(*c*) E (*d*) B

2. If x% of demand for company C equals demand for company B, then x equals.
[SSC—CHSL (10+2) Exam, 2015]
(*a*) 24 (*b*) 20
(*c*) 60 (*d*) 4

3. If the production of company D is *h* times of the production of company A. Then *h* equals:
[SSC—CHSL (10+2) Exam, 2015]
(*a*) 1.5 (*b*) 2.5
(*c*) 1.2 (*d*) 1.8

4. The difference between average demand and average production of the five companies taken together is
[SSC—CHSL (10+2) Exam, 2015]
(*a*) 400 (*b*) 280
(*c*) 130 (*d*) 620

5. The ratio of the number of companies having more demand to those having more production than production than demand is
[SSC—CHSL (10+2) Exam, 2015]
(*a*) 4 : 1 (*b*) 2 : 2
(*c*) 3 : 2 (*d*) 2 : 3

Directions (*Questions* 6–10): ***The bar graph given below shows the sales of books (in thousand number from six branches of a publishing company during two consecutive years 2000 and 2001. Sales of books (in thousands numbers) from six branches B1, B2, B3, B4, B5 and B6 of a publishing company in 2000 and 2001.***

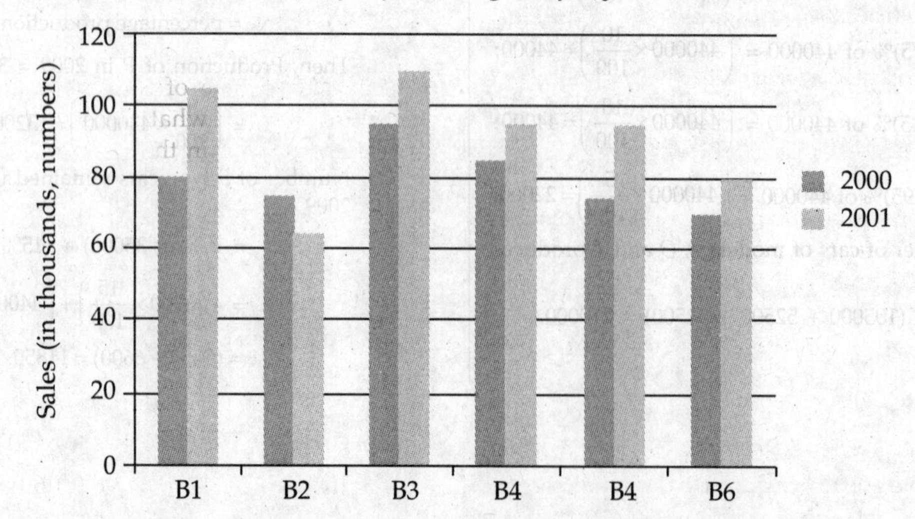

BAR GRAPH

6. What is the ratio of the total sales of branch ... both years to the total sales of branch B4 ... years?

[RBI Gr. 'B' (Phase—I) E...

(*a*) 4 : 5 (*b*) 10 : 1
(*c*) 7 : 9 (*d*) 8 : 5

7. Total sales of branch B6 for both the ye... percent of the total sales of branch B3 ... ears is what ... for both the ...

[RBI Gr. 'B' (Phas... e—I) Exam, 2015]

... (*b*) 80.23
(*d*) 85.7

... average sales of branches B1, ... is the average sales of branches ... in 2000?

[RBI Gr. 'B' (Phase—I) Exam, 2015]

... n B2 for ... for both ... xam, 2015]

(*a*) 45% (*b*) 82.5
(*c*) 90.6 (*d*) 87.5

9. What is the average sales of all the branches (in thousands numbers) for the years 2000?

[RBI Gr. 'B' (Phase—I) Exam, 2015]

(*a*) 73 (*b*) 80
(*c*) 83 (*d*) 85

10. Total sales branches B1, B3 and B5 together for both the years (in thousands numbers) is?

[RBI Gr. 'B' (Phase—I) Exam, 2015]

(*a*) 250 (*b*) 315
(*c*) 560 (*d*) 435

(Questions 11–15): ***Study the following graph carefully to answer the questions that follow:***

Monthly income (₹ in thousands) of three different persons in six different years

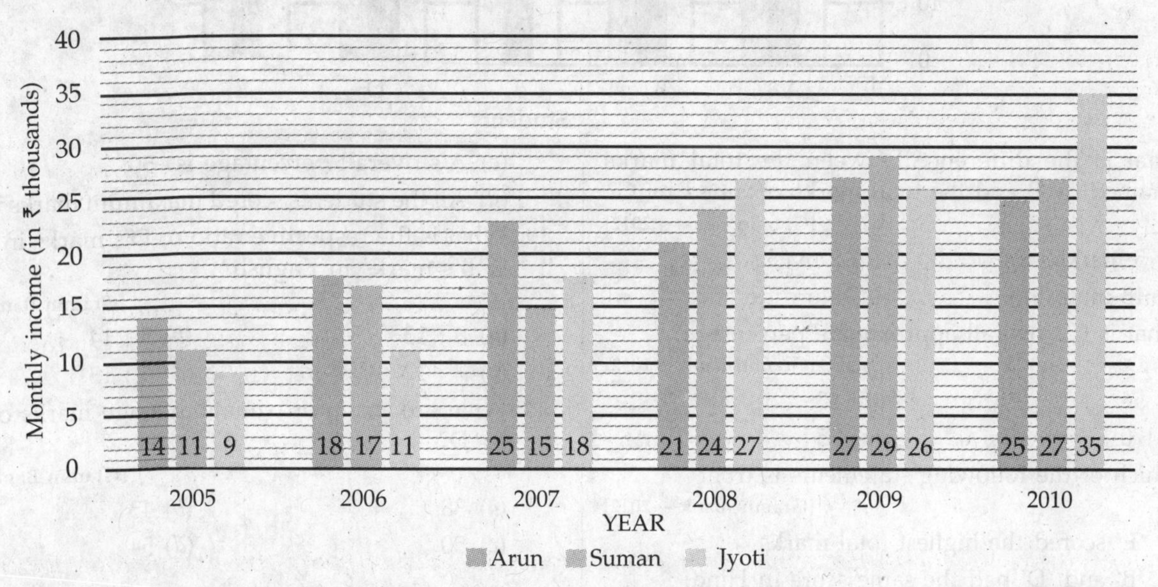

11. What was the difference between the total monthly salary of Arun in all the years together and Suman's monthly income in the year 2007?

[IBPS—Bank Clerical Exam, 2012]

(*a*) ₹ 1.24 lakhs (*b*) ₹ 1.14 lakhs
(*c*) ₹ 11.4 lakhs (*d*) ₹ 12.4 lakhs

12. What is the respective ratio between Arun's monthly income in the year 2006, Suman's monthly income in the year 2007 and Jyoti's monthly income in the year 2005?

[IBPS—Bank Clerical Exam, 2012]

(*a*) 6 : 3 : 5 (*b*) 5 : 6 : 4
(*c*) 5 : 4 : 7 (*d*) None of these

13. In which year was the difference between Jyoti's monthly income and Arun's monthly income second highest?

[IBPS—Bank Clerical Exam, 2012]

(*a*) 2005 (*b*) 2006
(*c*) 2007 (*d*) 2009

14. Monthly income of Suman in the year 2009 was approximately what percentage of the monthly income of Jyoti in the year 2010?

[IBPS—Bank Clerical Exam, 2012]

(*a*) 72 (*b*) 89
(*c*) 83 (*d*) 67

15. What was the percentage increase in the monthly income of Jyoti in the year 2008 as compared to previous year?

[IBPS—Bank Clerical Exam, 2012]

(*a*) 50 (*b*) 150
(*c*) 160 (*d*) 60

Direction (*Questions* 16–20): ***Study the following graph carefully and answer the questions given below:***

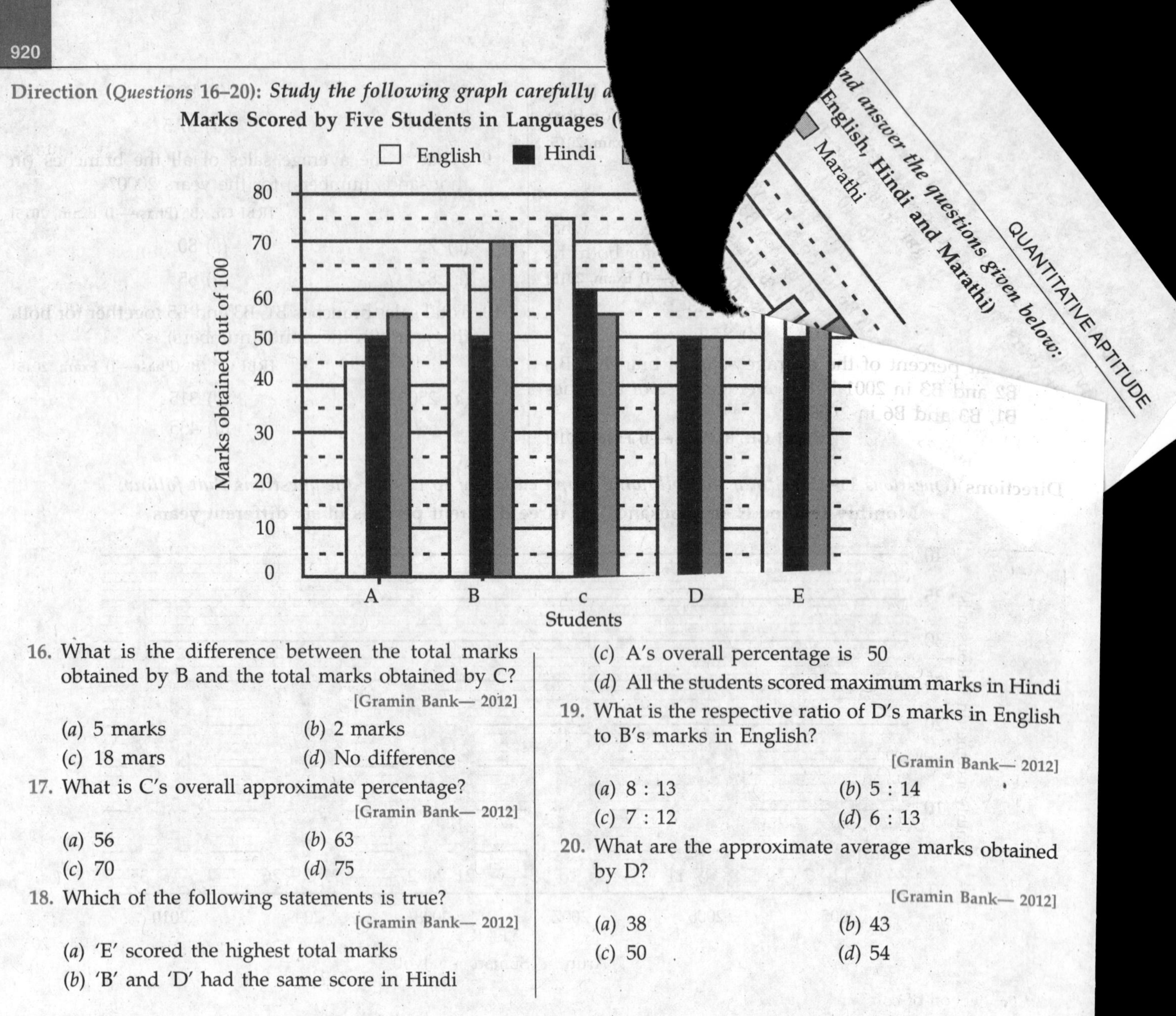

16. What is the difference between the total marks obtained by B and the total marks obtained by C? **[Gramin Bank— 2012]**

(*a*) 5 marks (*b*) 2 marks
(*c*) 18 mars (*d*) No difference

17. What is C's overall approximate percentage? **[Gramin Bank— 2012]**

(*a*) 56 (*b*) 63
(*c*) 70 (*d*) 75

18. Which of the following statements is true? **[Gramin Bank— 2012]**

(*a*) 'E' scored the highest total marks
(*b*) 'B' and 'D' had the same score in Hindi
(*c*) A's overall percentage is 50
(*d*) All the students scored maximum marks in Hindi

19. What is the respective ratio of D's marks in English to B's marks in English? **[Gramin Bank— 2012]**

(*a*) 8 : 13 (*b*) 5 : 14
(*c*) 7 : 12 (*d*) 6 : 13

20. What are the approximate average marks obtained by D? **[Gramin Bank— 2012]**

(*a*) 38 (*b*) 43
(*c*) 50 (*d*) 54

Directions (*Questions* 21–25): ***Study the bar chart given below and answer the following questions:***

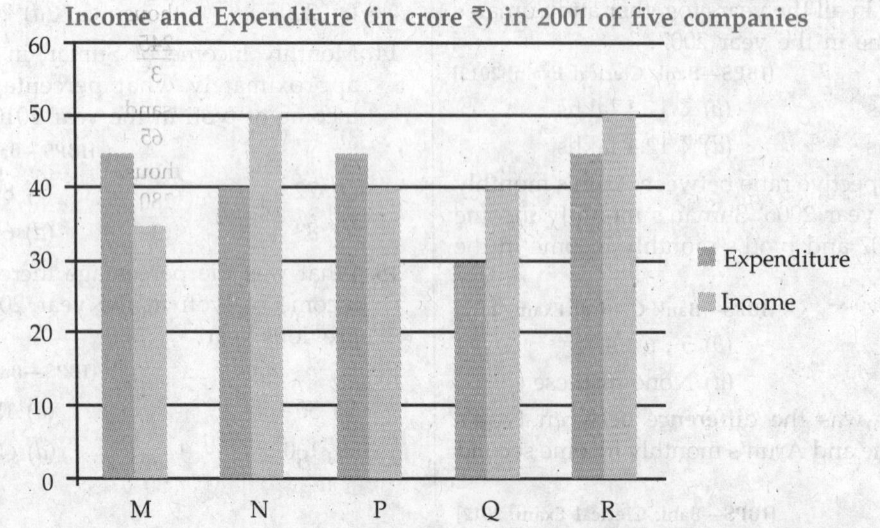

21. In 2001, the approximate percentage of profit/loss of all the five companies taken together is equal to
[SSC—CHSL (10 + 2) Exam, 2015]

(a) 6.88% loss (b) 4.65% profit
(c) 6.48% profit (d) 4% loss

22. If the income of company Q in 2001 was 10% more than that in 2000 and the company had earned a profit of 20% in 2000, then its expenditure in 2000 (in crore ₹) was
[SSC—CHSL (10 + 2) Exam, 2015]

(a) 34.34 (b) 28.28
(c) 29.09 (d) 32.32

23. The company earning the maximum percentage of profit in the year 2001 is
[SSC—CHSL (10 + 2) Exam, 2015]

(a) Q (b) M
(c) N (d) P

24. The companies M and N together had a percentage of profit/loss of
[SSC—CHSL (10 + 2) Exam, 2015]

(a) No loss and no profit (b) 12% loss
(c) 10% loss (d) 10% profit

25. For company R if the expenditure had increased by 20% in the year 2001 from the year 2000 and the company had earned profit of 10% in 2000, the company's income in 2000 was (in crore ₹)
[SSC—CHSL (10 + 2) Exam, 2015]

(a) 41.67 (b) 35.75
(c) 37.25 (d) 38.5

ANSWERS

1. (d)	2. (a)	3. (d)	4. (b)	5. (c)	6. (c)	7. (a)	8. (d)	9. (b)	10. (c)
11. (b)	12. (d)	13. (b)	14. (c)	15. (a)	16. (a)	17. (b)	18. (c)	19. (a)	20. (b)
21. (c)	22. (d)	23. (a)	24. (a)	25. (a)					

SOLUTIONS

1. Difference between demand and production of company A = 3000 − 1500 = 1500
Difference between production and demand of company D = 2700 − 1200 = 1500

2. Given x% of demand for company C = Demand for company B

$$\Rightarrow \frac{2500 \times x}{100} = 600$$

$$\Rightarrow 25x = 600$$

$$\Rightarrow x = \frac{600}{25} = 24$$

3. Production of company D = 2700
Production of company A = 1500

$$h = \frac{\text{Production of company D}}{\text{Product of company A}}$$

$$= \frac{2700}{1500} = \frac{9}{5} = 1.8$$

4. Total production of the five companies
= 1500 + 1800 + 1000 + 2700 + 2200 = 9200
Total demand of the five companies
= 3000 + 600 + 2500 + 1200 + 3300 = 10600
Required difference

$$= \frac{1}{5}(10600 - 9200)$$

$$= \frac{1}{5} \times 1400 = 280$$

5. Number of companies having more demand than production = 3
Number of companies having more production than demand = 2
Required ratio = 3 : 2

6. $$\text{Required ratio} = \frac{\text{Total Sales of branch B2 for both years}}{\text{Total Sales of branch B4 for both years}}$$

$$= \frac{75+65}{85+95} = \frac{140}{180} = \frac{7}{9}$$

7. Total sales of branch B6 for both years = 70 + 80 = 150
Total sales of branch B3 for both years = 95 + 110 = 205

$$\text{Required percentage } \frac{150}{205} \times 100 = 73.7\%$$

8. Total sales (in thousands numbers) of branches B1, B3 and B6 in 200 = 80 + 95 + 70 = 245
Average sales (in thousands number) of branches B1, B3 and B6 in 2000 = $\frac{245}{3}$
Total sales (in thousands number) of branches B1, B2 and B3 in 2001 = 105 + 65 + 110 = 280
Average sales (in thousands number) of branches B1, B2 and B3 in 2001 = $\frac{280}{3}$

$$\text{So, required percentage} = \frac{\frac{245}{3}}{\frac{280}{3}} \times 100\%$$

$$= \frac{245}{280} \times 100 = 87.5\%$$

9. Total sales of all the six branches (in thousand numbers) for the year 2000 = 80 + 75 + 95 + 85 + 75 + 70 = 480

Average sales of all the six branches (in thousand numbers) for the year 2000 = $\frac{480}{8} = 80$

10. Total safes of branches B1, B3 and B5 for both the years (in thousands numbers)
= (80 + 105) + (95 + 110) + (75 + 95) = 560

11. Total monthly salary of Arun in all the years
= 14000 + 18000 + 23000 + 21000 + 27000 + 25000
= ₹ 1,28,000
Monthly salary of Suman in the year 2007 = Rs 15000
Difference between their Salary
= 128000 – 15000 = Rs 1.13 Lakh

12.

In year 2006 Arun's salary	In year 2007 Suman's salary	In year 2005 Jyoti's salary
18000	15000	9000
18	15	9
6	5	3

13.

Year	Arun's Income	Jyoti's Income	Difference
2005	14000	9000	5000
2006	18000	11000	7000
2007	23000	18000	5000
2008	21000	27000	6000
2009	27000	26000	1000
2010	25000	35000	10,000

In 2006 difference between Jyoti's monthly income and Arun's monthly income second highest.

14. Monthly income of Suman in year 2009 = Rs 29000
Monthly income of Jyoti in year 2010 = Rs 35000
$= \frac{29000}{3500} \times 100 = 82.85 \approx 83\%$

15. Joyti's income in 2008 = Rs 27000
Joyti's income in 2007 = Rs 18000
Increase percentage $= \frac{2700 - 1800}{18000} \times 100$
$= \frac{9000}{18000} \times 100 = 50\%$

16. Total marks obtain by C = 75 + 60 + 55 = 190
Total marks obtain by B = 65 + 50 +70 = 185
Difference = 190 – 185 = 5 marks

17. Total marks of C = 190
Maximum marks = 300
Percentage $= \frac{190}{300} \times 100 = 63.3 \approx 63\%$

18. By observation and solving method A's overall percentage is 50

19. D's marks: B's marks
40 : 65
8 : 13

20. Total marks of D in three subjects = 140
Number of subjects = 3
Average $= \frac{140}{3} = 46.6 \approx 47$

21. Total income of all the five companies
= ₹ (35 + 50 + 40 + 40 + 50) crores = ₹ 215 crores
Total expenditure of all the five companies
= ₹ (45 + 40 + 45 + 30 + 45) crores
= ₹ 205 crores
∴ Profit percent
$= \left(\frac{\text{Income} - \text{Expenditure}}{\text{Expenditure}}\right) \times 100$
$= \frac{215 - 205}{205} \times 100$
$= \frac{1000}{205} = 4.88\%$

22. Income of company Q in 2000 $= \frac{100}{110} \times 140 = ₹\ \frac{400}{11}$ crores
If expenditure in 2000 be ₹ x crores.
Profit % $= \left(\frac{\text{Income} - \text{Expenditure}}{\text{Expenditure}}\right) \times 100$
$= \frac{\frac{400}{11} - x}{x}$
$\Rightarrow \frac{20}{100} = \frac{1}{5} = \frac{400 - 11x}{11x}$
$\Rightarrow 5 \times 400 - 55x = 11x$
$\Rightarrow 66x = 2000$
$\Rightarrow x = \frac{2000}{66}$
= ₹ 30.30 crores

23. From bar diagram
Profit percent of company Q.
$= \frac{40 - 30}{30} \times 100$
$= \frac{100}{3} = 33\frac{1}{3}\%$

24. Total income of companies M and N
= ₹ (35 + 50) crores
= ₹ 85 crores
Total expenditure
= ₹ (45 + 40) crores
= ₹ 85 crores
Hence, the companies M and N had no loss and no profit

25. Expenditure of company R in 2000 $= \frac{45 \times 100}{120}$
= ₹ 37.5 crore
Let the income of company in 2000 be ₹ x crores
$\therefore 10 = \frac{x - 37.5}{37.5} \times 100$
$\Rightarrow x = 37.5 = \frac{37. \times 10}{100}$
$\Rightarrow x = 37.5 = 3.75$
$\Rightarrow x - 37.5 = 3.75$
⇒ ₹ 41.25 crores

38 Pie Chart

EXERCISE – I

Ex 1. (***Questions 1 to 4***): ***Study the following pie-chart carefully and answer the questions given below:*** (Bank P.O., 2011)

Cost Estimated by a Family in Renovation of their House

Grills 10%
Architect's Fees 11%
Interior Decoration 19%
Curtains 10%
Painting 15%
Miscellaneous 8%
Furniture 13%
Flooring 14%

Total Estimated Cost = ₹ 120000

1. What is the difference in the amount estimated by the family on interior decoration and that on architect's fees ?
(*a*) ₹ 10000
(*b*) ₹ 9500
(*c*) ₹ 7200
(*d*) ₹ 9000
(*e*) None of these

2. Other than getting the discount of 12 % on the estimated cost of furniture and the actual miscellaneous expenditure being ₹ 10200 instead of the estimated one, the family's estimated cost is correct. What is the total amount spent by the family in renovating its house?
(*a*) ₹ 116728 (*b*) ₹ 115926
(*c*) ₹ 119500 (*d*) ₹ 116500
(*e*) None of these

3. What is the cost estimated by the family on painting and flooring together ?
(*a*) ₹ 36500 (*b*) ₹ 34800
(*c*) ₹ 36000 (*d*) ₹ 34500
(*e*) None of these

4. The family gets a discount on furniture and pays 12% less than the estimated cost on furniture. What is the amount spent on furniture ?
(*a*) ₹ 13200 (*b*) ₹ 14526
(*c*) ₹ 13526 (*d*) ₹ 13728
(*e*) None of these

Ex. (***Questions 5–9***): ***Study the following pie-chart and table carefully and answer the questions given below:*** (Bank P.O., 2012)

Percentagewise Distribution of the Number of Mobile Phones Sold by a Shopkeeper During Six Months

Ratio of mobile phones sold of company A & company B

December 16%
July 17%
November 12%
October 8%
August 22%
September 25%

Total number of mobile phones sold = 45000

Month	Ratio (A : B)
July	8 : 7
August	4 : 5
September	3 : 2
October	7 : 5
November	7 : 8
December	7 : 9

5. What is the ratio of the number of mobile phones sold of Company B during July to those sold during December of the same company?
(*a*) 119 : 145 (*b*) 116 : 135
(*c*) 119 : 135 (*d*) 119 : 130
(*e*) None of these

6. If 35 % of the mobile phones sold by Company A during November were sold at a discount, how many mobile phones of Company A were sold without a discount, during that month?
(*a*) 882 (*b*) 1635
(*c*) 1638 (*d*) 885
(*e*) None of these

7. If the shopkeeper earned a profit of ₹ 433 on each mobile phone sold of Company *B* during October, what was his total profit earned on the mobile phones of that company during the same month ?
(*a*) ₹ 649900 (*b*) ₹ 645900
(*c*) ₹ 649400 (*d*) ₹ 649500
(*e*) None of these

8. The number of mobile phones sold of Company A during July is approximately what per cent of the number of mobile phones sold of Company A during December?
(*a*) 110 (*b*) 140
(*c*) 150 (*d*) 105
(*e*) 130

9. What is the total number of mobile phones sold of Company B during August and September together?
(*a*) 10000 (*b*) 15000
(*c*) 10500 (*d*) 9500
(*e*) None of these

Ex 3. (*Questions 10–14*): *Study the following pie-chart and the table given below it carefully to answer the questions given below:* **(Bank P.O., 2010)**

Percentage-wise distribution of lecturers in 6 different subjects in a university total number of lecturers : 1600

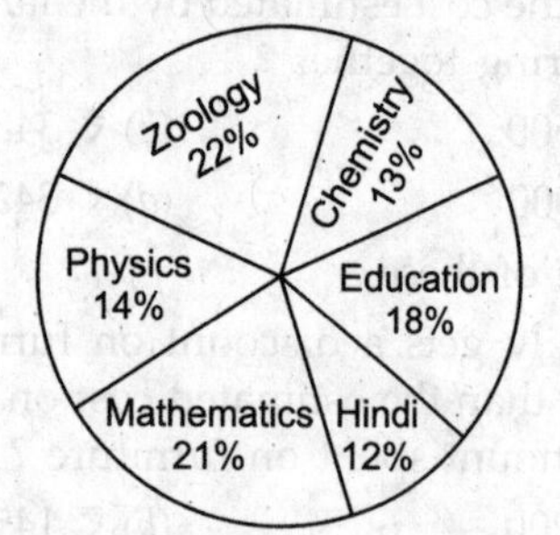

Ratio of male to female lectures

Lecturers	Males : Females
Mathematics	3 : 4
Education	5 : 3
Hindi	1 : 3
Chemistry	1 : 7
Physics	9 : 5
Zoology	7 : 9

10. Total number of lecturers (both male and female) in Hindi is approximately what per cent of the total number of female lectures in Mathematics and Chemistry together?
(*a*) 58 (*b*) 43
(*c*) 47 (*d*) 51
(*e*) 50

11. What is the difference between the total number of lecturers (both male and female) is Zoology and the total number of male lecturers in Chemistry and Education together?
(*a*) 192 (*b*) 182
(*c*) 146 (*d*) 136
(*e*) None of these

12. What is the difference between the number of female lecturers in Zoology and the number of male lecturers in Hindi?
(*a*) 156 (*b*) 160
(*c*) 150 (*d*) 153
(*e*) None of these

13. What is the total number of male lecturers in the university?
(*a*) 696 (*b*) 702
(*c*) 712 (*d*) 668
(*e*) None of these

14. What is the ratio of the number of female lecturers in Physics to the number of male lecturers in Mathematics ?
(*a*) 5 : 9 (*b*) 2 : 9
(*c*) 3 : 7 (*d*) 5 : 3
(*e*) None of these

Ex 4. (*Questions 15–19*): *The pie-chart shown below gives the distribution of land in a village under various food crops. Study the pie-chart carefully and answer the questions that follow:*

Distribution of areas (in acres) under various food crops

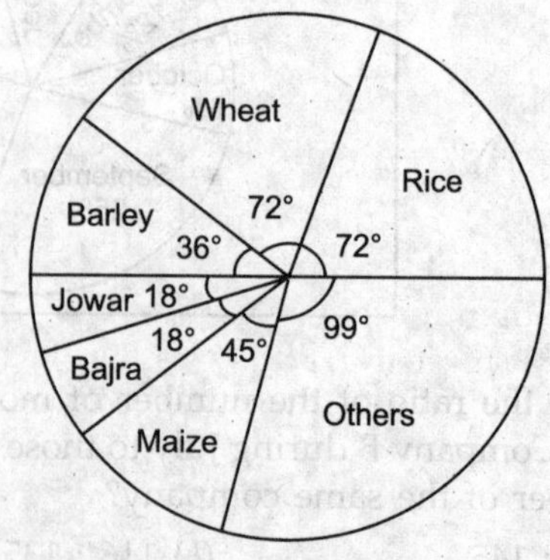

15. Which combination of three crops contribute to 50% of the total area under the food crops?
(*a*) Wheat, Barley and Jowar
(*b*) Rice, Wheat and Jowar

(c) Rice, Wheat and Barley
(d) Bajra, Maize and Rice

16. If the total area under jowar was 1.5 million acres, then what was the area (in million acres) under rice ?
(a) 6 (b) 7.5
(c) 9 (d) 4.5

17. If the production of wheat is 6 times that of barley, then what is the ratio between the yield per acre of wheat and barley?
(a) 3 : 2 (b) 3 : 1
(c) 12 : 1 (d) 2 : 3

18. If the yield per acre of rice was 50% more than that of barley, then the production of barley is what percent of that of rice?
(a) 30% (b) $33\frac{1}{3}\%$
(c) 35% (d) 36%

19. If the total area goes up by 5%, and the area under wheat production goes up by 12%, then what will be the angle for wheat in the new pie-chart?
(a) 62.4° (b) 76.8°
(c) 80.6° (d) 84.2°

Ex 5. ***(Questions 20–24): The following pie-charts show the distribution of students of graduate and post-graduate levels in 7 different Institutes : M, N, P, Q, R, S and T in a town. Study the pie-charts carefully and answer the questions given below:***

Distribution of students at graduate and post-graduate levels in seven institutes — *m, n, p, q, r, s* and *t*

Total Number of Students of Graduate Level = 27300

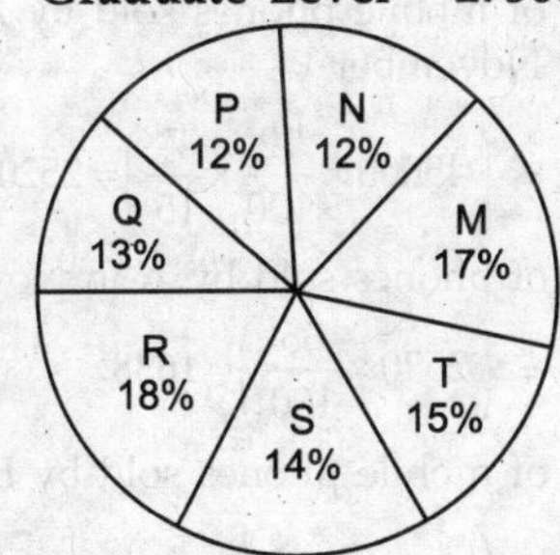

Total Number of Students of Post-Graduate Level = 24700

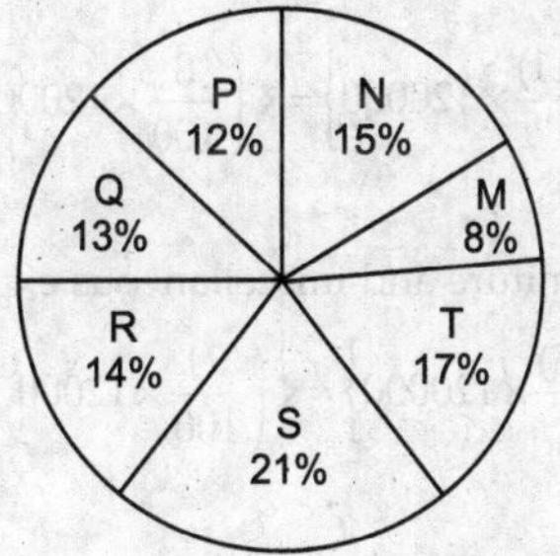

20. How many students of institutes *M* and *S* are studying at graduate level?
(a) 7516 (b) 8463
(c) 9127 (d) 9404

21. Total number of students studying at post-graduate level from institutes *N* and *P* is
(a) 5601 (b) 5944
(c) 6669 (d) 7004

22. What is the total number of graduate and post-graduate level students in institute *R*?
(a) 8320 (b) 7916
(c) 9116 (d) 8372

24. What is the ratio between the number of students studying at post-graduate and graduate levels respectively from institute *S*?
(a) 14 : 19 (b) 19 : 21
(c) 17 : 21 (d) 19 : 14

24. What is the ratio between the number of students studying at post-graduate level from institute *S* and the number of students studying at graduate level from institute *Q*?
(a) 13 : 19 (b) 21 : 13
(c) 13 : 8 (d) 19 : 13

Ex 6. ***(Questions 25–29): Study the following pie-diagrams carefully and answer the questions given below:***

Percentage Composition of Human Body

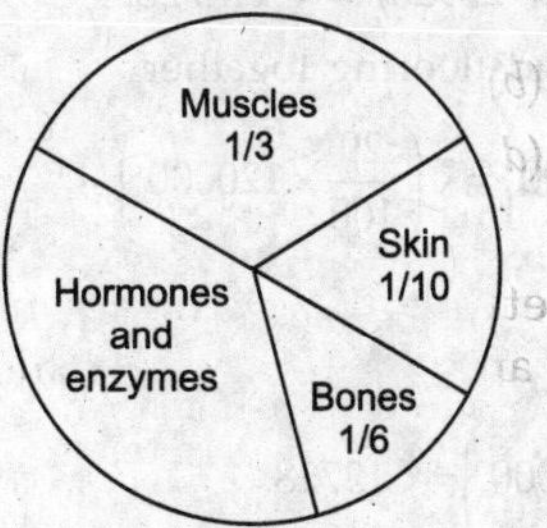

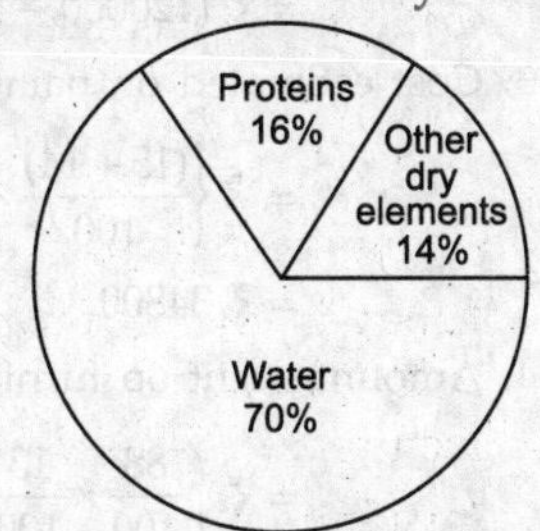

25. In the human body, what part is made of neither bones nor skin ?
(a) $\frac{1}{40}$ (b) $\frac{3}{80}$
(c) $\frac{2}{5}$ (d) None of these

26. What is the ratio of the distribution of proteins in the muscles to that of the distribution of proteins in the bones?
(*a*) 1 : 18 (*b*) 1 : 2
(*c*) 2 : 1 (*d*) 18 : 1

27. What will be the quantity of water in the body of a person weighing 50 kg?
(*a*) 20 kg (*b*) 35 kg
(*c*) 41 kg (*d*) 42.5 kg

28. What percent of the total weight of human body is equivalent to the weight of the proteins in skin in human body?
(*a*) 0.016 (*b*) 1.6
(*c*) 0.16 (*d*) Data inadequate

29. To show the distribution of proteins and other dry elements in the human body, the arc of the circle should subtend at the centre an angle of
(*a*) 54° (*b*) 126°
(*c*) 108° (*d*) 252°

ANSWERS

1. (*e*)	2. (*e*)	3. (*b*)	4. (*d*)	5. (*c*)	6. (*c*)	7. (*d*)	8. (*e*)	9. (*a*)	10. (*d*)
11. (*c*)	12. (*c*)	13. (*a*)	14. (*a*)	15. (*c*)	16. (*a*)	17. (*b*)	18. (*b*)	19. (*b*)	20. (*b*)
21. (*c*)	22. (*d*)	23. (*d*)	24. (*d*)	25. (*d*)	26. (*c*)	27. (*b*)	28. (*b*)	29. (*c*)	

SOLUTIONS

1. Required difference

$= ₹ \left\{\frac{(19-11)}{100}\times 120000\right\} = ₹\left(\frac{8}{100}\times 120000\right)$

= ₹ 9600.

2. Estimated cost of furniture and miscellaneous expenditure

$= ₹\left\{\frac{(13+8)}{100}\times 120000\right\} = ₹\left(\frac{21}{100}\times 120000\right)$

= ₹ 25200.

Actual cost of furniture

$= ₹\left(\frac{88}{100}\times\frac{13}{100}\times 120000\right) = ₹\,13728.$

Actual cost of furniture and miscellaneous expenditure
= ₹ (13728 + 10200) = ₹ 23928.

Total amount spent in renovating the house
= ₹ (120000 − 25200 + 23928) = ₹ 118728.

3. Cost estimated on painting and flooring together

$= ₹\left\{\frac{(15+14)}{100}\times 120000\right\} = ₹\left(\frac{29}{100}\times 120000\right)$

= ₹ 34800.

4. Amount spent on furniture

$= ₹\left(\frac{88}{100}\times\frac{13}{100}\times 120000\right) = ₹\,13728.$

5. No. of mobile phones sold by B during July

$= \left(45000\times\frac{17}{100}\times\frac{7}{15}\right) = 3570.$

No. of mobile phones sold by B during December

$= \left(45000\times\frac{16}{100}\times\frac{9}{16}\right) = 4050.$

Required ratio $= \frac{3570}{4050} = \frac{119}{135} = 119:135.$

6. No. of mobile phones sold by A during November

$= \left(45000\times\frac{12}{100}\times\frac{7}{15}\right) = 2520.$

No. of phones sold by A in November without discount

$= \left(2520\times\frac{65}{100}\right) = 1638.$

7. No. of mobile phones sold by B during October

$= \left(45000\times\frac{8}{100}\times\frac{5}{12}\right) = 1500.$

Required profit = ₹ (1500 × 433) = ₹ 649500.

8. No. of mobile phones sold by A during July

$= \left(45000\times\frac{17}{100}\times\frac{8}{15}\right) = 4080.$

No. of mobile phones sold by A during December

$= \left(45000\times\frac{16}{100}\times\frac{7}{16}\right) = 3150.$

Let 4080 = x % of 3150.

Then, $\frac{x}{100}\times 3150 = 4080$

$\Rightarrow\ x = \left(\frac{4080\times 2}{63}\right) = 129.5 \simeq 130.$

Required percentage = 130%.

9. Mobile phones of B sold during August

$= \left(45000\times\frac{22}{100}\times\frac{5}{9}\right) = 5500.$

Mobile phones of B sold during September

$= \left(45000\times\frac{25}{100}\times\frac{2}{5}\right) = 4500.$

Required number of phones sold = (5500 + 4500)
= 10000.

Direction (*Questions 10–29*):

Number of lecturers in various subjects are:

Chemistry $\rightarrow \left(\frac{13}{100}\times 1600\right) = 208$;

Education $\rightarrow \left(\frac{18}{100}\times 1600\right) = 288$;

Hindi $\rightarrow \left(\frac{12}{100}\times 1600\right) = 192$;

Mathematics $\rightarrow \left(\frac{21}{100}\times 1600\right) = 336$;

Physics $\rightarrow \left(\frac{14}{100}\times 1600\right) = 224$;

Zoology $\rightarrow \left(\frac{22}{100}\times 1600\right) = 352$.

Subjects	Number of males	Number of females
Chemistry	$\left(208\times\frac{1}{8}\right) = 26$	$(208 - 26) = 182$
Education	$\left(288\times\frac{5}{8}\right) = 180$	$(288 - 180) = 108$
Hindi	$\left(192\times\frac{1}{4}\right) = 48$	$(192 - 48) = 144$
Mathematics	$\left(336\times\frac{3}{7}\right) = 144$	$(336 - 144) = 192$
Physics	$\left(224\times\frac{9}{14}\right) = 144$	$(224 - 144) = 80$
Zoology	$\left(352\times\frac{7}{16}\right) = 154$	$(352 - 154) = 198$

10. Required % $= \left\{\frac{192}{192+182}\times 100\right\}\% = \left(\frac{192}{374}\times 100\right)\%$

$= \frac{9600}{187}\% = 51.3\% \simeq 51\%$.

11. Required difference $= 352 - (26 + 180)$

$= 352 - 206 = 146$.

12. Required difference $= (198 - 48) = 150$.

13. Total number of male lecturers in the university

$= (26 + 180 + 48 + 144 + 144 + 154) = 696$.

14. Required ratio $= 80 : 144 = 5 : 9$.

15. For 50% of the total area, the sum of the central angles must be 180°.

For the given combinations, the sum of the central angles are :

(*a*) (Wheat + Barley + Jowar)

$\rightarrow (72^\circ + 36^\circ + 18^\circ) = 126^\circ$.

(*b*) (Rice + Wheat + Jowar)

$\rightarrow (72^\circ + 72^\circ + 18^\circ) = 162^\circ$.

(*c*) (Rice + Wheat + Barley)

$\rightarrow (72^\circ + 72^\circ + 36^\circ) = 180^\circ$.

16. Let the total area be A million acres. Then,

Area under Jowar $= \left(\frac{18}{360}\times A\right) = \frac{A}{20}$.

Area under Rice $= \left(\frac{72}{360}\times A\right) = \frac{A}{5}$.

$\frac{A}{20} = 1.5$ million acres $\Rightarrow A = (1.5\times 20)$

$= ....$

$\therefore$ Area under rice

$= \left(\frac{1}{5}\times 30\right)$ million acres $= 6$ million acres.

17. Area under wheat

$= \frac{72A}{360} = \frac{A}{5}$, Area under barley $= \frac{36A}{360} = \frac{A}{10}$.

Let the production of barley be y tons.

Then, production of wheat $= 6y$ tons.

Yield of wheat per acre $= \frac{6y}{(A/5)} = \frac{30y}{A}$.

Yield of barley per acre $= \frac{y}{(A/10)} = \frac{10y}{A}$.

Required ratio $= \frac{30y}{A} : \frac{10y}{A} = 3:1$.

18. Area under rice $= \frac{72A}{360} = \frac{A}{5}$,

Area under barley $= \frac{36A}{360} = \frac{A}{10}$

Let the yield of barley per acre be x tons.

Then yield of rice per acre $= \frac{150x}{100}$ tons $= \frac{3x}{2}$ tons.

Required % $= \left\{\frac{\left(x\times\frac{A}{10}\right)}{\frac{3x}{2}\times\frac{A}{5}}\times 100\right\}\% = \frac{100}{3}\% = 33\frac{1}{3}\%$.

19. Let the total area be A acres.

Then, new total area $= \frac{105A}{100} = \frac{21A}{20}$.

Area under wheat $= \frac{72A}{360} = \frac{A}{5}$.

New area under wheat $= \left(\frac{112}{100}\times\frac{A}{5}\right) = \frac{28A}{125}$.

Angle for wheat

$= \left\{\frac{\left(\frac{28A}{125}\right)}{\left(\frac{21A}{20}\right)}\times 360^\circ\right\} = \left(\frac{28A}{125}\times\frac{20}{21A}\times 360\right)^\circ$

$= \left(\frac{384}{5}\right)^\circ = 76.8^\circ$.

20. Students of institute M at graduate level
$= 17\%$ of $27300 = 4641$.
Students of institute S at graduate level
$= 14\%$ of $27300 = 3822$.
$\therefore$ Total number of students at graduate level in institutes M and $S = 4641 + 3822 = 8463$.

21. Required number $= (15\% \text{ of } 24700) + (12\% \text{ of } 24700)$
$= 3705 + 2964 = 6669$.

22. Required number $= (18\% \text{ of } 27300) + (14\% \text{ of } 24700)$
$= 4914 + 3458 = 8372$.

23. Required ratio
$$= \frac{(21\% \text{ of } 24700)}{(14\% \text{ of } 27300)} = \frac{21 \times 24700}{14 \times 27300} = \frac{19}{14} = 19:14.$$

24. Required ratio
$$= \frac{(21\% \text{ of } 24700)}{(13\% \text{ of } 27300)} = \frac{21 \times 24700}{13 \times 27300} = \frac{19}{13} = 19:13.$$

25. Part of the body made of neither bones nor skin
$$= 1 - \left(\frac{1}{6} + \frac{1}{10}\right) = \frac{11}{15}.$$

26. Required ratio $= \dfrac{16\% \text{ of } \frac{1}{3}}{16\% \text{ of } \frac{1}{6}} = \dfrac{6}{3} = \dfrac{2}{1} = 2:1.$

27. Quantity of water in the body of a person weighing 50 kg $= (70\% \text{ of } 50 \text{ kg}) = 35$ kg.

28. Let the body weight be x kg.
Then, Weight of skin protein in the body
$$= \left\{16\% \text{ of } \left(\frac{1}{10} \text{ of } x\right)\right\} \text{kg} = \left(\frac{16}{100} \times \frac{1}{10} \times x\right) \text{kg}$$
$$= \frac{2x}{125} \text{ kg.}$$
$\therefore$ Required percentage
$$= \left\{\left(\frac{2x}{125}\right) \times \frac{1}{x} \times 100\right\}\% = \frac{8}{5}\% = 1.6\%.$$

29. Percentage of proteins and other dry elements in the body $= (16\% + 14\%) = 30\%$.
Required central angle $= \left(\dfrac{30}{100} \times 360\right)^\circ = 108^\circ$.

EXERCISE – II

Directions (*Questions 1-5*): *Study the pie-chart given below carefully and answer the questions that follow.*
(Bank P.O., 2009)

Percentage-wise break up of students in terms of specialization in M.B.A.

Total Number of students = 8000

HR 14%
IB 19%
IT 17%
IR 16%
Marketing 22%
Finance 12%

1. What is the total number of students having specialisation in IR, Marketing and IT ?
(*a*) 4640
(*b*) 4080
(*c*) 4260
(*d*) 4400
(*e*) None of these

2. Students having IB as specialisation forms approximately what percent of students having Marketing as specialisation ?
(*a*) 116 (*b*) 86
(*c*) 124 (*d*) 74
(*e*) 66

3. What is the total number of students having IB as specialisation ?
(*a*) 1520 (*b*) 1280
(*c*) 1360 (*d*) 1120
(*e*) None of these

4. What is the ratio of the students having Finance as specialisation to students having HR as specialisation?
(*a*) 11 : 19 (*b*) 18 : 13
(*c*) 6 : 7 (*d*) 4 : 7
(*e*) None of these

5. Students having IR as specialisation forms approximately what percent of students having HR as specialisation ?
(*a*) 87 (*b*) 106
(*c*) 76 (*d*) 62
(*e*) 114

Directions (*Questions 6–10*): *The circle-graph given below shows the spending of a state on various sports during a particular year. Study the graph carefully and answer the given questions.*

Hockey 63°
Football 54°
Others 27°
Golf 36°
Tennis 45°
Basket Ball 54°
Cricket 81°

6. What percent of the total spendings is spent on Tennis ?
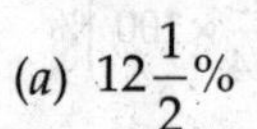
(*a*) $12\frac{1}{2}\%$
(*b*) $22\frac{1}{2}\%$
(*c*) 25%
(*d*) 45%

7. How much percent more is spent on Hockey than that on Golf ?

(*a*) 27% (*b*) 35%
(*c*) 37.5% (*d*) 75%

8. How much percent less is spent on Football than that on Cricket ?
(*a*) $22\frac{2}{9}\%$ (*b*) 27%
(*c*) $33\frac{1}{3}\%$ (*d*) $37\frac{1}{2}\%$

9. If the total amount spent on sports during the year was ₹ 2 crores, the amount spent on Cricket and Hockey together was

(a) ₹ 800000 (b) ₹ 8000000
(c) ₹ 12000000 (d) ₹ 16000000

10. If the total amount spent on sports during the year be ₹ 18000000, the amount spent on Basketball exceeds that on Tennis by

(a) ₹ 450000 (b) ₹ 460000
(c) ₹ 475000 (d) None of these

Directions (*Questions 11–15*): *Study the following pie-graphs carefully and answer the questions given below.*

Distribution of Candidates Enrolled For M.B.A. Entrance Examination And Those Who Passed In Different Institutes : P, Q, R, S, T, V and X.

Candidates Enrolled = 8550

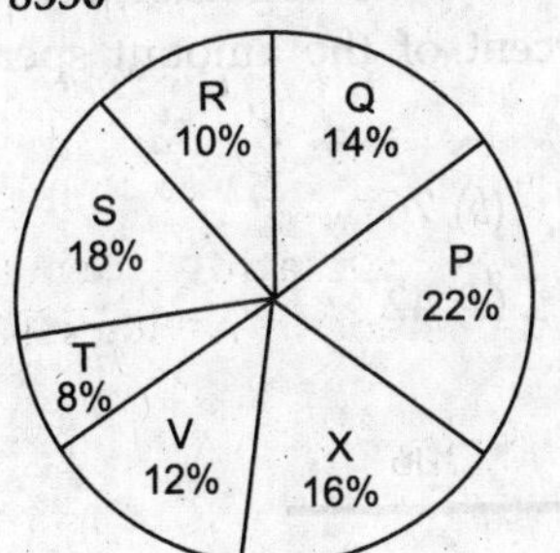

Candidates Who Passed = 5700

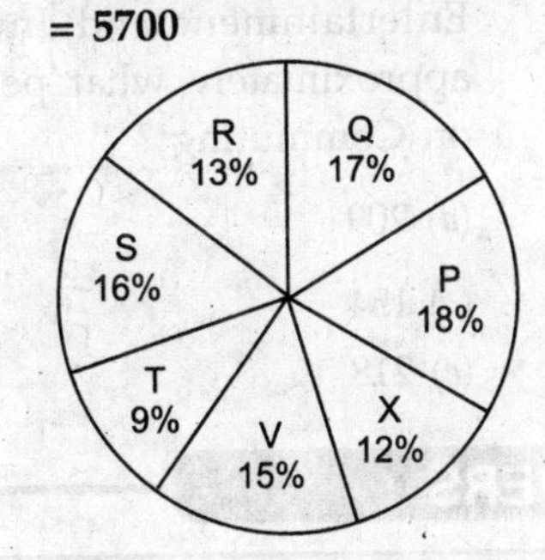

11. What percentage of candidates passed the Exam from institute T out of the total number of candidates enrolled from the same institute ?

(a) 50% (b) 62.5%
(c) 75% (d) 80%

12. What is the ratio of candidates passed to the candidates enrolled from institute P ?

(a) 9 : 11 (b) 14 : 17
(c) 6 : 11 (d) 9 : 17

13. What is the percentage of candidates passed to the candidates enrolled for institutes Q and R together ?

(a) 68% (b) 83%
(c) 74% (d) 65%

14. Which institute has the highest percentage of candidates passed to the candidates enrolled ?

(a) Q (b) R
(c) V (d) T

15. The number of candidates passed from institutes S and P together exceeds the number of candidates enrolled from institutes T and R together by :

(a) 228 (b) 279
(c) 399 (d) 407

Directions (*Questions 16–20*): *Study the following pie-charts carefully and answer the questions that follow:* **(Bank P.O., 2009)**

Percentage of Students Enrolled In Different Streams In a College Total Number of students = 3500

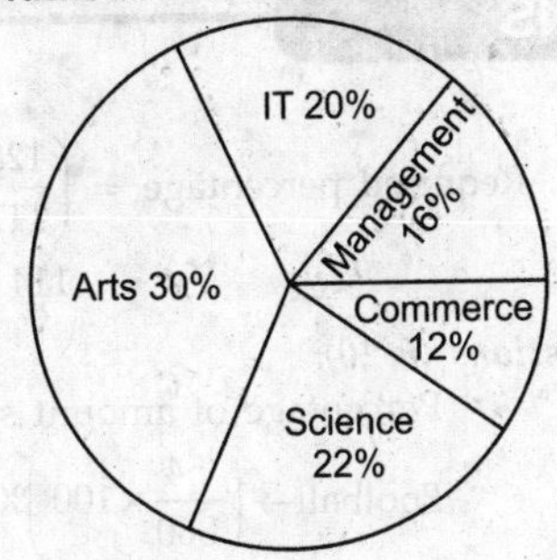

Percentage Break-up of Girls Enrolled In These Streams Out of The Total Students Total Number of Girls = 1500

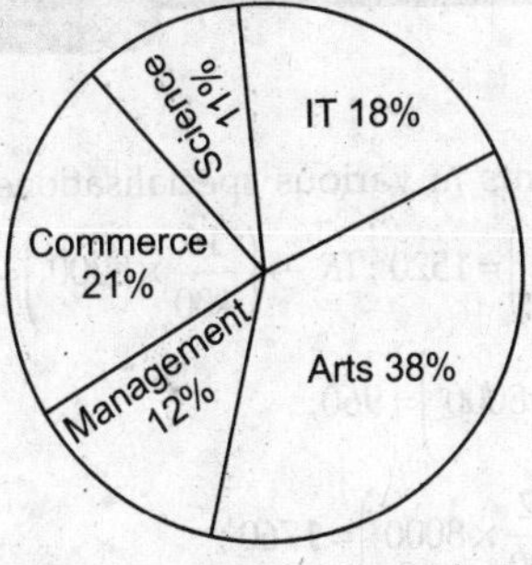

16. What is the total number of boys enrolled in Management and IT together ?

(a) 1050 (b) 810
(c) 1120 (d) 980
(e) None of these

17. What is the ratio of the number of girls enrolled in Arts to the number of boys enrolled in Science ?

(a) 14 : 23 (b) 2 : 3
(c) 114 : 121 (d) 53 : 65
(e) None of these

18. What is the total number of girls enrolled in Science and Commerce together ?

(a) 450 (b) 495
(c) 345 (d) 480
(e) None of these

19. If 20% of the girls enrolled in Science change their stream to Management, then what will be the new number of Management students altogether ?

(a) 593 (b) 733
(c) 453 (d) 1003
(e) None of these

20. The number of girls enrolled in Arts, Science and Commerce forms what percent of total number of students in the College ?

(*a*) 25 (*b*) 40

(*c*) 60 (*d*) 75

(*e*) None of these

Directions (*Questions 21–24*): ***Study the following pie-chart carefully and answer the questions that follow:***

(Bank P.O., 2008)

Degreewise Break-up of Expenditure of a Family In a Month

Total Amount Spent In a Month = ₹ 45800.

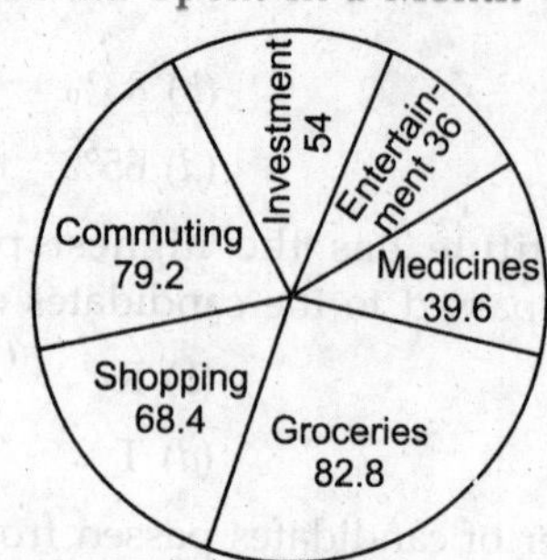

21. What is the amount spent by the family on commuting ?

(*a*) ₹ 10076 (*b*) ₹ 10534

(*c*) ₹ 6870 (*d*) ₹ 8702

(*e*) None of these

22. What is the ratio of the amount spent by the family on Medicine to the amount spent on Groceries ?

(*a*) 1 : 2 (*b*) 13 : 21

(*c*) 3 : 5 (*d*) 11 : 23

(*e*) None of these

23. What is the total amount spent by the family on Entertainment and Shopping together?

(*a*) ₹ 9618 (*b*) ₹ 13282

(*c*) ₹ 13740 (*d*) ₹ 11908

(*e*) None of these

24. The total amount spent by the family on Groceries, Entertainment and Investments together forms approximately what percent of the amount spent on Commuting ?

(*a*) 209 (*b*) 76

(*c*) 154 (*d*) 42

(*e*) 218

ANSWERS

1. (*d*)	2. (*b*)	3. (*a*)	4. (*c*)	5. (*e*)	6. (*a*)	7. (*d*)	8. (*c*)	9. (*b*)	10. (*d*)
11. (*c*)	12. (*c*)	13. (*b*)	14. (*b*)	15. (*c*)	16. (*b*)	17. (*c*)	18. (*d*)	19. (*a*)	20. (*e*)
21. (*a*)	22. (*d*)	23. (*b*)	24. (*e*)						

SOLUTIONS

Questions (1–5):

Number of students in various specialisations:

$IB \rightarrow \left(\frac{19}{100} \times 8000\right) = 1520$; $IR \rightarrow \left(\frac{16}{100} \times 8000\right) = 1280$;

Finance $\rightarrow \left(\frac{12}{100} \times 8000\right) = 960$;

Marketing $\rightarrow \left(\frac{22}{100} \times 8000\right) = 1760$;

$IT \rightarrow \left(\frac{17}{100} \times 8000\right) = 1360$; $HR \rightarrow \left(\frac{14}{100} \times 8000\right) = 1120$.

1. Required number of students = (1280 + 1760 + 1360) = 4400.

2. Required percentage $= \left(\frac{1520}{1760} \times 100\right)\% = \frac{950}{11}\%$

$= 86.36\% \approx 86\%$ (approx.)

3. Number of those having *IB* as specialisation = 1520.

4. Required ratio = Finance : $HR = \frac{960}{1120} = \frac{6}{7} = 6:7$.

5. Required percentage $= \left(\frac{1280}{1120} \times 100\right)\% = \frac{800}{7}\%$

$= 114.28\% \approx 114\%$ (approx.)

Questions (6–10):

Percentage of amount spent on various sports:

Football $\rightarrow \left(\frac{54}{360} \times 100\right)\% = 15\%$;

Hockey $\rightarrow \left(\frac{63}{360} \times 100\right)\% = 17.5\%$;

Cricket $\rightarrow \left(\frac{81}{360} \times 100\right)\% = 22.5\%$;

Basketball $\rightarrow \left(\frac{54}{360} \times 100\right)\% = 15\%$;

Tennis $\rightarrow \left(\frac{45}{360} \times 100\right)\% = 12.5\%$;

Golf $\rightarrow \left(\frac{36}{360} \times 100\right)\% = 10\%$;

Others → $\left(\frac{27}{360}\times 100\right)\% = 7.5\%$.

6. Percentage of money spent on Tennis = $12\frac{1}{2}\%$.

7. Let the total amount spent be ₹ 100. Then,
Money spent on Hockey = ₹ 17.50
and that on Golf = ₹ 10.
Difference = ₹ (17.50 – 10) = ₹ 7.50.

Required % = $\left(\frac{15}{2\times 10}\times 100\right)\% = 75\%$.

8. Let the total amount spent be ₹ 100. Then,
Money spent on Football = ₹ 15
and that on Cricket = ₹ 22.50.

Difference = ₹ (22.50 – 15) = ₹ 7.50 = ₹ $\frac{15}{2}$.

Required % = $\left(\frac{15}{2}\times\frac{2}{45}\times 100\right)\% = 33\frac{1}{3}\%$.

9. Total amount spent on sports = ₹ 20000000.
Amount spent on Cricket and Hockey
= (22.5 + 17.5)% = 40%
= ₹ $\left(20000000 \times \frac{40}{100}\right)$ = ₹ 8000000.

10. (Amount spent on Basketball) – (Amount spent on Tennis)
= (15 – 12.5)% of ₹ 18000000
= ₹ $\left(\frac{2.5}{100}\times 18000000\right)$ = ₹ 450000.

Questions (11–15):

Candidates enrolled in:

P → $\left(\frac{22}{100}\times 8550\right) = 1881$; Q → $\left(\frac{14}{100}\times 8550\right) = 1197$;

R → $\left(\frac{10}{100}\times 8550\right) = 855$;

S → $\left(\frac{18}{100}\times 8550\right) = 1539$; T → $\left(\frac{8}{100}\times 8550\right) = 684$;

V → $\left(\frac{12}{100}\times 8550\right) = 1026$;

X → $\left(\frac{16}{100}\times 8550\right) = 1368$.

Candidates passed in

P → $\left(\frac{18}{100}\times 5700\right) = 1026$, Q → $\left(\frac{17}{100}\times 5700\right) = 969$;

R → $\left(\frac{13}{100}\times 5700\right) = 741$;

S → $\left(\frac{16}{100}\times 5700\right) = 912$, T → $\left(\frac{9}{100}\times 5700\right) = 513$;

V → $\left(\frac{15}{100}\times 5700\right) = 855$;

X → $\left(\frac{12}{100}\times 5700\right) = 684$.

11. Required pass percentage = $\left(\frac{513}{684}\times 100\right)\% = 75\%$.

12. Required ratio = $\frac{1026}{1881} = \frac{114}{209} = \frac{6}{11} = 6:11$.

13. Required percentage for Q and R

$= \left\{\frac{(969+741)}{(1197+855)}\times 100\right\}\%$

$= \left(\frac{1710}{2052}\times 100\right)\% = \frac{250}{3}\% = 83\%$ (nearly).

14. Required percentage :

$P \rightarrow \left(\frac{1026}{1881}\times 100\right)\% = 54.6\%$;

$Q \rightarrow \left(\frac{969}{1197}\times 100\right)\% = 80.95\%$;

$R \rightarrow \left(\frac{741}{855}\times 100\right)\% = 86.7\%$;

$S \rightarrow \left(\frac{912}{1539}\times 100\right)\% = 59.25\%$;

$T \rightarrow \left(\frac{513}{684}\times 100\right)\% = 75\%$,

$V \rightarrow \left(\frac{855}{1026}\times 100\right)\% = 83.33\%$;

X → $\left(\frac{684}{1368}\times 100\right)\% = 50\%$.

This is highest for the institute R.

15. (Candidates passed from S and P) – (Candidates enrolled from T and R)
= (912 + 1026) – (684 + 855)
= (1938 – 1539) = 399.

Questions (16–20):

Number of students enrolled in various streams:

IT → $\left(\frac{20}{100}\times 3500\right) = 700$;

Arts → $\left(\frac{30}{100}\times 3500\right) = 1050$;

Science → $\left(\frac{22}{100}\times 3500\right) = 770$;

Commerce → $\left(\frac{12}{100}\times 3500\right) = 420$;

Management → $\left(\frac{16}{100}\times 3500\right) = 560$.

Number of girls enrolled in various streams :

IT → $\left(\frac{18}{100}\times 1500\right) = 270$,

Arts → $\left(\frac{38}{100}\times 1500\right) = 570$;

Science → $\left(\frac{11}{100}\times 1500\right) = 165$;

Commerce → $\left(\frac{21}{100}\times 1500\right) = 315$;

Management $\rightarrow \left(\frac{12}{100} \times 1500\right) = 180.$

16. Total number of boys enrolled in Management and *IT* together

$= (560 - 180) + (700 - 270)$

$= (380 + 430) = 810.$

17. (Number of girls enrolled in Arts): (Number of boys enrolled in Science)

$= 570 : (770 - 165) = 570 : 605$

$= \frac{570}{605} = \frac{114}{121} = 114:121.$

18. Total number of girls enrolled in Science and Commerce together

$= (165 + 315) = 480.$

19. Number of Management students already enrolled = 560.

New required number $= 560 + \left(\frac{20}{100} \times 165\right)$

$= (560 + 33) = 593.$

20. Number of girls enrolled in Arts, Science and Commerce $= (570 + 165 + 315) = 1050.$

Required percentage $= \left(\frac{1050}{3500} \times 100\right)\% = 30\%.$

Questions (21–24):

Percentage Break-up of expenditure is:

Investments $\rightarrow \left(\frac{54}{360} \times 100\right)\% = 15\%;$

Commuting $\rightarrow \left(\frac{79.2}{360} \times 100\right)\% = 22\,\%;$

Shopping $\rightarrow \left(\frac{68.4}{360} \times 100\right)\% = 19\%;$

Groceries $\rightarrow \left(\frac{82.8}{360} \times 100\right)\% = 23\%;$

Medicines $\rightarrow \left(\frac{39.6}{360} \times 100\right)\% = 11\%,$

Entertainment $\rightarrow \left(\frac{36}{360} \times 100\right)\% = 10\%.$

21. Amount spent on Commuting $= ₹\ (45800 \times \frac{22}{100})$

$= ₹\ 10076.$

22. (Amount spent on Medicine) : (Amount spent on Groceries)

$= ₹\left(45800 \times \frac{11}{100}\right) : ₹\left(45800 \times \frac{23}{100}\right) = 11:23.$

23. Amount spent on Entertainment and Shopping

$= ₹\left\{45800 \times \frac{(10+19)}{100}\right\} = ₹\left(45800 \times \frac{29}{100}\right)$

$= ₹\ 13282.$

24. Amount spent on Groceries, Entertainment and Investments

$= ₹\left\{45800 \times \frac{(23+10+15)}{100}\right\} = ₹\left(45800 \times \frac{48}{100}\right)$

Amount spent on Commuting $= ₹\left(45800 \times \frac{22}{100}\right)$

Required % $= \left\{\frac{45800 \times \frac{48}{100}}{45800 \times \frac{22}{100}} \times 100\right\}\% = \frac{2400}{11}\%$

$= 218.18\% \simeq 218\%.$

EXERCISE – III

Directions (*Questions 1-5*): *Refer to the pie-charts and answer the given questions.*

Distribution of total number of Dell Laptops Sold by 5 Stores

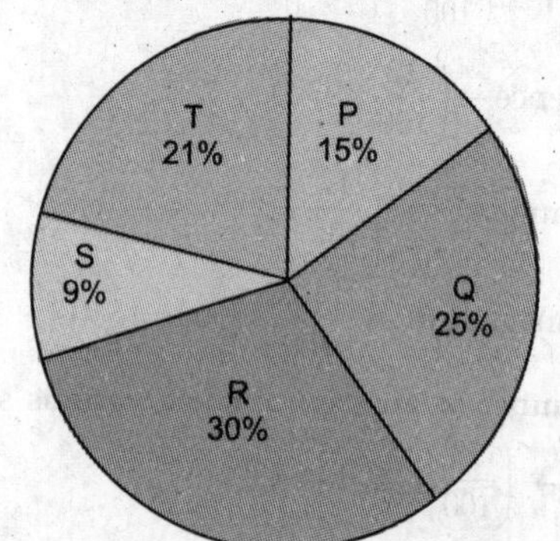

Total Number : 2400

Distribution of Number of Laptops (both Dell and Lenovo) Sold by 5 Stores in 2011

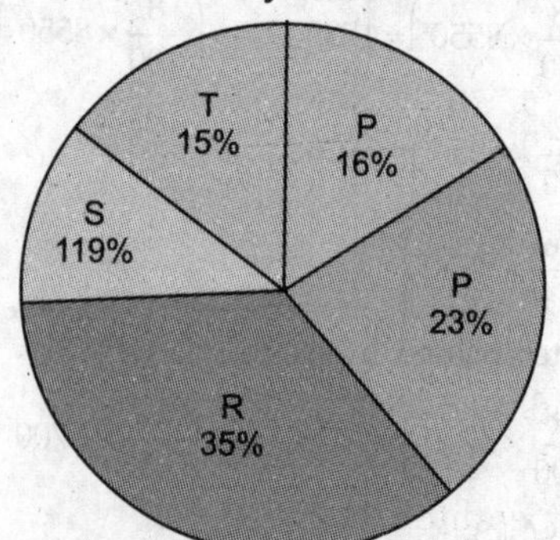

Total Number : 4500

1. What is the average number of Dell Laptops sold by stores P, R and S together?

[IBPS—RRB (Officer's Gr. "B' Exam, 2015]

(*a*) 424 (*b*) 432

(*c*) 428 (*d*) 454

2. What is the central angle corresponding to number of Dell laptops sold by store S?

[IBPS—RRB (Officer's Gr. "B' Exam, 2015]

(a) 29.4° (b) 38.6°
(c) 36.2° (d) 32.4°

3. Number of Dell laptops sold by store Q is approximately what percent of the number of the number of laptops (both Dell and Lenovo) sold by store R?

[IBPS—RRB (Officer's Gr. "B' Exam, 2015]

(a) 28% (b) 45%
(c) 50% (d) 38%

4. What is the difference between number of laptops (both Dell and Lenovo) sold by store Q and total number of Lenovo laptops sold by store R and S together?

[IBPS—RRB (Officer's Gr. "B' Exam, 2015]

(a) 185 (b) 99
(c) 91 (d) 119

5. Number of Dell laptops sold by store T is what percent more than the number of laptops sold by store P?

[IBPS—RRB (Officer's Gr. "B' Exam, 2015]

(a) 30% (b) 45%
(c) 40% (d) 42.5%

Directions (*Questions 6–9*): *Study the pie chart and answer the given questions.*

The total expenditure of a company for a particular month is ₹ 60000. The various heads of expenditure I to IV are indicated in a pie chart given below. These heads are:

I. Raw materials
II. Conveyance
III. Electricity
IV. Overhead expenses

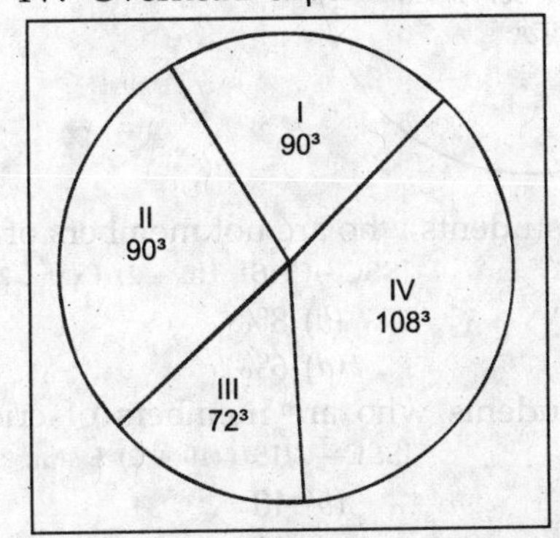

6. Total expenditure on conveyance is

[SSC—CHSL (10+2) Exam, 2015]

(a) ₹ 12,000 (b) ₹ 15,000
(c) ₹ 20,000 (d) ₹ 10,000

7. What percentage of total expenditure is on electricity?

[SSC—CHSL (10+2) Exam, 2015]

(a) 23% (b) 25%
(c) 30% (d) 20%

8. What is the amount spent on overhead expenses?

[SSC—CHSL (10+2) Exam, 2015]

(a) ₹ 12,000 (b) ₹ 15,000
(c) ₹ 18,000 (d) ₹ 10,000

9. What percentage of total expenditure is on raw materials?

[SSC—CHSL (10+2) Exam, 2015]

(a) 25% (b) 30%
(c) 60% (d) 23%

Directions (*Questions 10-14*): *Refer to the pie charts and answer the given questions.*

Distribution of total number of members (both male and female) in 5 health clubs in 2011

Total number : 6300

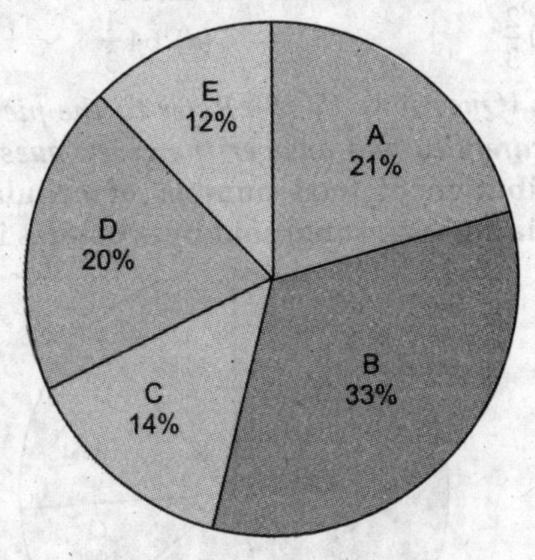

Distribution of total number of male members in 5 health clubs in 2011

Total number: 3600

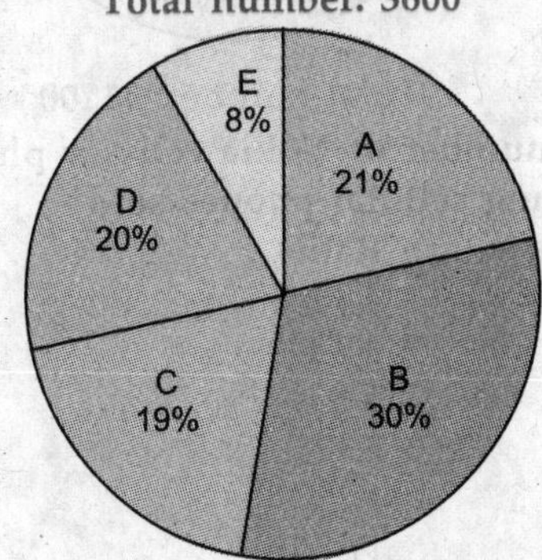

10. What is the central angle corresponding to number of male and female in health club D and E?

[RBI Gr. 'B' (Phase—I) Exam, 2015]

(a) 115.2° (b) 125.5°
(c) 210.25° (d) 155.5°

11. What is the average number of female members in health clubs A, B and C?

[RBI Gr. 'B' (Phase—I) Exam, 2015]

(a) 564 (b) 572
(c) 568 (d) 548

12. Number of male members in health clubs, A and C is what percentage less than the number of both

male and female members of health club B and C in 2011? [RBI Gr. 'B' (Phase—I) Exam, 2015]

(*a*) 69 (*b*) 51.36
(*c*) 72 (*d*) 42.21

13. What is the central angle corresponding to number of both male and female in health club B? [RBI Gr. 'B' (Phase—I) Exam, 2015]

(*a*) 118.8° (*b*) 112.6°
(*c*) 124.8° (*d*) 116.4°

14. Number of female members in health club E is what percent less than number of male members in health club B? [RBI Gr. 'B' (Phase—I) Exam, 2015]

(*a*) $56\frac{2}{3}$ (*b*) $54\frac{1}{2}$
(*c*) $60\frac{2}{3}$ (*d*) $64\frac{1}{3}$

Directions (*Questions 15–19*): *Refer to the pie-chart and the table carefully and answer the given questions.*

Distribution of total number of cellular phones (both Nokia and Samsung) sold by six stores in October

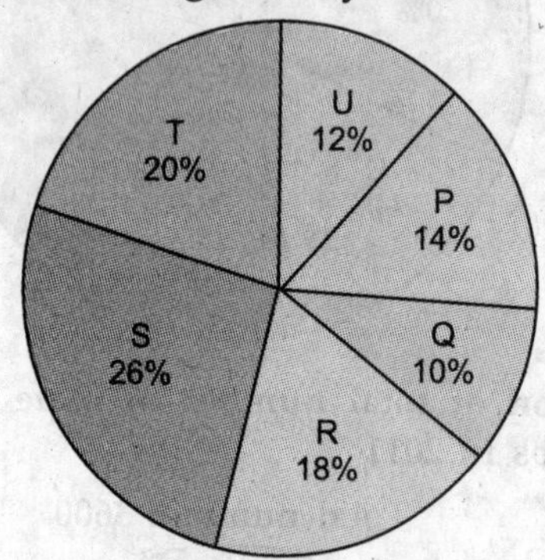

Total number: 11200

Ratio of the number of Nokia cellular phones sold to that of Samsung cellular phones sold

Store	Ratio
P	4 : 3
Q	3 : 1
R	5 : 4
S	7 : 6
T	1 : 4
U	11 : 10

15. What is the average of Nokia cellular phones sold by store P, R, S and T together? [IBPS—Bank Spl. Officer (IT) Exam, 2015]

(*a*) 1008 (*b*) 1048
(*c*) 984 (*d*) 1006

16. The number of Nokia cellular phones sold by store R is what per cent more than that of Samsung cellular phones sold by store P and Q together? [IBPS—Bank Spl. Officer (IT) Exam, 2015]

(*a*) $23\frac{1}{17}\%$ (*b*) $19\frac{5}{17}\%$
(*c*) $18\frac{3}{17}\%$ (*d*) $20\frac{3}{17}\%$

17. What is the central angles corresponding to the total number of cellular phones (both Nokia and Samsung) sold by store S? [IBPS—Bank Spl. Officer (IT) Exam, 2015]

(*a*) 99.2° (*b*) 93.6°
(*c*) 105.6° (*d*) 97.4°

18. What is the ratio of the number of Nokia cellular phones sold by store S to the Samsung cellular phones sold by store T and U together? [IBPS—Bank Spl. Officer (IT) Exam, 2015]

(*a*) 43 : 72 (*b*) 49 : 76
(*c*) 43 : 76 (*d*) 49 : 72

19. The total number of cellular phones (both Nokia and Samsung) sold by store Q increased by 15% from October to November and the same of cellular phones sold by store T increased by 5% from October to November. What was the total number of cellular phones sold by store Q and T together in November? [IBPS—Bank Spl. Officer (IT) Exam, 2015]

(*a*) 3540 (*b*) 3720
(*c*) 3640 (*d*) 3420

Directions (*Questions 20–23*): *Study the Pie chart carefully and answer the questions.*

Student of a College

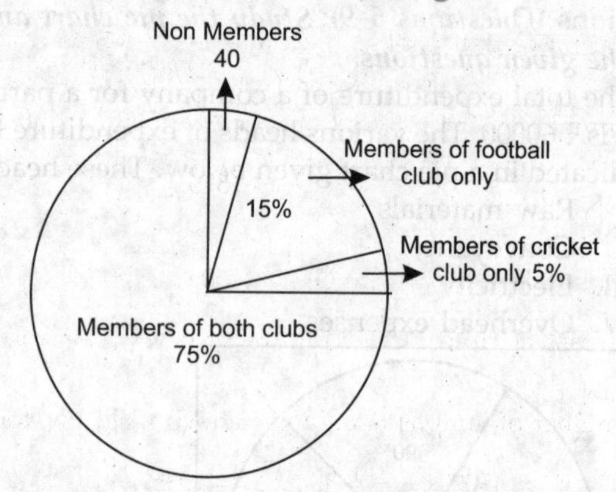

20. Percentage of students who are not members of any club is [SSC—CHSL (10 + 2) Exam, 2015]

(*a*) 5% (*b*) 8%
(*c*) 10% (*d*) 6%

21. Number of students who are members of cricket club only [SSC—CHSL (10 + 2) Exam, 2015]

(*a*) 35 (*b*) 40
(*c*) 42 (*d*) 41

22. Ratio of members of cricket club only and football club only respectively is [SSC—CHSL (10 + 2) Exam, 2015]

(*a*) 1 : 3 (*b*) 2 : 1
(*c*) 1 : 2 (*d*) 3 : 1

23. The number of students who are members of both the clubs is [SSC—CHSL (10 + 2) Exam, 2015]

(*a*) 500 (*b*) 650
(*c*) 550 (*d*) 600

ANSWERS

1. (b)	2. (d)	3. (d)	4. (b)	5. (c)	6. (b)	7. (d)	8. (c)	9. (a)	10. (a)
11. (a)	12. (b)	13. (a)	14. (a)	15. (a)	16. (d)	17. (b)	18. (b)	19. (c)	20. (a)
21. (b)	22. (a)	23. (d)							

SOLUTIONS

1. Percent of Dell Laptops sold by P, R and S together
$= 15\% + 30\% + 9\% = 54\%$
Total Dell Laptops sold by, P, R and S together
$= 2400 \times \frac{54}{100} = 1296$
$\therefore$ Average $= \frac{1296}{3} = 432$

2. Dell laptops sold by store S = 9%
Central angle corresponding to number of Dell Laptops sold by store S.
$= \frac{9}{100} \times 360 = 32.4\%$

3. Percent of Dell Laptops sold by Store Q = 25%
Total number of Dell laptops sold by store Q
$= 2400 \times \frac{25}{100} = 600$
Percent of Dell Laptops Dell and Lenovo Sold by store R = 35
Number of laptops (Dell and Lenovo) sold by store R
$= 4500 \times \frac{35}{100} = 1575$
Required percentage $= \frac{600}{1575} \times 100 = 38.095 \approx 38\%$

4. Percent of laptops (Dell and Lenovo) sold by store Q = 23%
Number of laptops (Dell and Lenovo) sold by store Q.
$= 4500 \times \frac{23}{100} = 45 \times 23 = 1035$
Percent of Laptops (Dell and Lenovo) sold by R and S together = 35% + 11% = 46%
Now, total number of laptops (Lenovo and Dell) sold by R and S together $= 4500 \times \frac{46}{100} = 2070$
Percent of laptops sold by R and S together
$= 30\% + 9\% = 39\%$
Number of Dell laptops sold by R and S together
$= 2400 \times \frac{39}{100} = 936$
Number of Lenovo laptops = 2070 − 936 = 1134
= 2070 − 850 = 1220
Required difference = 1134 − 1034 = 99

5. Number of Dell laptops sold by store
$T = 2400 \times \frac{21}{100} = 504$
Number of laptops sold by store $P = 2400 \times \frac{15}{100} = 360$
Required percentage $= \frac{504 - 360}{360} \times 100 = 40\%$

6. Corresponding angle for conveyance = 90°
$\because 360° \equiv$ ₹ 60000
$\therefore$ Total expenditure on conveyance $= \frac{90}{360} \times 6000$
= ₹ 15000

7. Corresponding angle for expenditure on electricity = 72°
$\because 360° \equiv 100\%$
$\therefore$ Total expenditure on electricity $= \frac{72}{360} \times 100 = 20\%$

8. Corresponding angle for overhead expenses = 108°
$\because 360° \equiv$ ₹ 60000
Amount spent on Overhead expenses
$= \frac{108}{360} \times 60000 =$ ₹ 18000

9. Corresponding angle for raw materials = 90°
$\because 360° \equiv 100\%$
Percentage of raw material $= \frac{90}{360} \times 100 = 25\%$

10. Percentage of male and female members in health club D and E = 20% + 12% = 32%
The central angles corresponding to number of male and female in health club D and E.
$= 360 \times 32\% = \frac{260 \times 32}{100} = 115.2°$

11. The number of female members in health clubs A, B and C
$\frac{6300 \times 68}{100} - \frac{3600 \times 72}{100} = 4284 - 2592 = 1692$
Average number of female number in health cube A, B and C $= \frac{1692}{3} = 564$

12. Number of male members in health clubs A and C
$= \frac{3600 \times 40}{100} = 1440$

Number of male and female members in health clubs B and C = 6300 × 47% = 2961

Number of male members in health club A and C percent less than the number of both male and female members of health club B and C = $\frac{2961-1440}{2961}$ × 100 = 51.36%

13. Percentage of both male and female members in health club B = 33%

The central angles corresponding to number of male and female in health club B = $\frac{360}{100}$ × 33 = 118.8°

14. Number of male and female members in Health club E

= 6300 × $\frac{12}{100}$ = 756

Number of male members in health club

E = $\frac{2600\times8}{100}$ 288

Number of female members in health club

E = 756 – 288 = 468

The number of male members in health club B

= $\frac{3600\times30}{100}$ = 1080

Required less percentage = $\frac{1080-468}{1080}\times100$

= $\frac{612}{1080}\times100 = 56\frac{2}{3}$

Solution (15 to 19)

Store	Nokia cellular Phones	Samsung Cellular Phones	Total number of cellular phone
P	896	672	1568
Q	840	280	1120
R	1120	896	2016
S	1568	1344	2912
T	448	1792	2240
U	704	640	1344

15. Total Nokia Phone sold by stores P, R, S and T = 896 + 1120 + 1568 = 448 = 4032

∵ Required average = $\frac{4032}{4}$ = 1008

16. Number of Nokia phones sold by Store R = 1120

Number of Samsung phones sold by store P and Q together = 672 + 280 = 952

∵ Required percentage = $\frac{1120-952}{952}\times100$

= $\frac{16800}{952}\% = \frac{300}{17}\% = 17\frac{11}{17}\%$ more

17. Percentage of caller phones (both Nokia and Samsung) sold by Store S = 26%

Required central angle = $\frac{26}{100}\times360 = 93.6°$

18. Number of Nokia phones sold by Store S = 1568

Number of Samsung phones sold by Store T and U together = 1792 + 640 = 2432

∵ Required Ratio = $\frac{1568}{2432} = \frac{49}{76}$ = 49 : 76

19. Number of cellular phones (both Nokia and Samsung) sold by store Q in October = 11200 × $\frac{10}{100}$ = 1120

∵ Number of cellular phones (both Nokia and Samsung) sold by store Q in November = 1120 × $\frac{115}{100}$ = 1288

Number of cellular phones (both Nokia and Samsung) sold by Store T in October = 11200 × $\frac{20}{100}$ = 2240

∵ Number of cellular phones (both Nokia and Samsung) sold by Store T in Number = 2240 × $\frac{105}{100}$ = 2352

∵ Total number of cellular phones (both Nokia and Samsung) sold by Q and T Together in November = 1288 + 2352 = 3640

Solution (20 to 23)

20. Percentage of students who are members of any club = 75 + 15 + 5 = 95%

Percentage of students who are not members of any club = 100 – 95% = 5%

21. Number of students who are not members of any club = 40 = 5%

Percentage of members of cricket club only = 5%

Number of members of cricket club only = 40

22. Percentage of member of cricket club only = 5%

Percentage of member of football club only = 15%

Required ratio

= 5 : 15 = 1 : 3

23. Let total number of students of a college be x

Non members students = 40

∴ 5% of x = 40

⇒ $\frac{x\times5}{100}$ = 40

⇒ $x = \frac{100\times40}{5}$ = 800

Percentage of members of both club = 75%

Number of members of both club = $\frac{75\times800}{100}$ = 75 × 8 = 600

39 Line Graphs

EXERCISE - I

Directions *(Question 1-5)*: ***Study the following line graph carefully and answer the questions given below:***

(Bank P.O., 2011)

Number of Students Appearing For Aptitude Test From Various Towns (In Thousands)

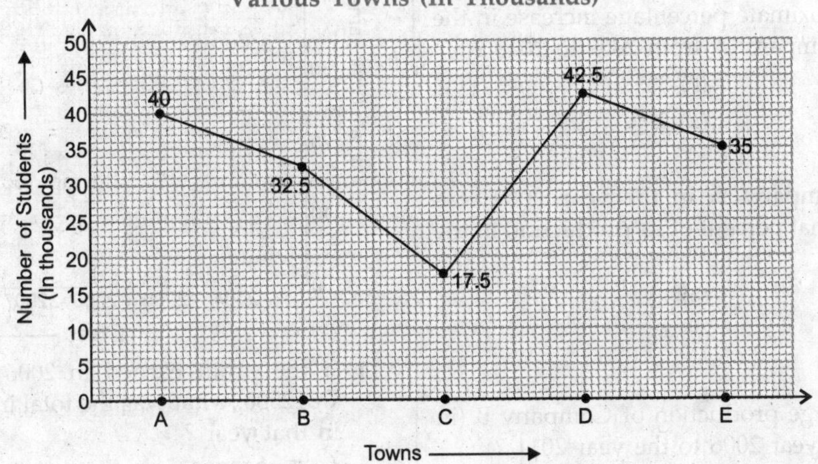

1. What is the ratio of the number of students appearing for the Aptitude Test from Town *B* to that from Town A?
   (*a*) 3 : 4 (*b*) 13 : 16
   (*c*) 11 : 16 (*d*) 2 : 3
   (*e*) None of these
2. What is the average number of students appearing for the Aptitude Test from all the towns together ?
   (*a*) 33500 (*b*) 3350
   (*c*) 17500 (*d*) 33.5(*e*) None of these
3. The number of students appearing for the Aptitude Test from Town E is approximately what per cent of the total number of students appearing for the Aptitude Test from all the towns together ?
   (*a*) 15 (*b*) 17
   (*c*) 19 (*d*) 21
   (*e*) 23
4. What is the ratio of the number of students appearing for the Aptitude Test from Towns C and D together to the number of students appearing for the Aptitude Test from Towns A, D and E together?
   (*a*) 11 : 13 (*b*) 20 : 43
   (*c*) 20 : 47 (*d*) 37 : 20
   (*e*) None of these
5. The number of students appearing for the Aptitude Test from Town D is approximately what percentage of the number of students appearing for the Aptitude Test from Town C ?
   (*a*) 243 (*b*) 413
   (*c*) 134 (*d*) 341
   (*e*) 143

Directions *(Questions 6–10)*: ***Study the following graph and answer the questions that follow:***

(Bank P.O., 2012)

Production (in tonnes) and Sales (in tonnes) of Company A from 2006 to 2011

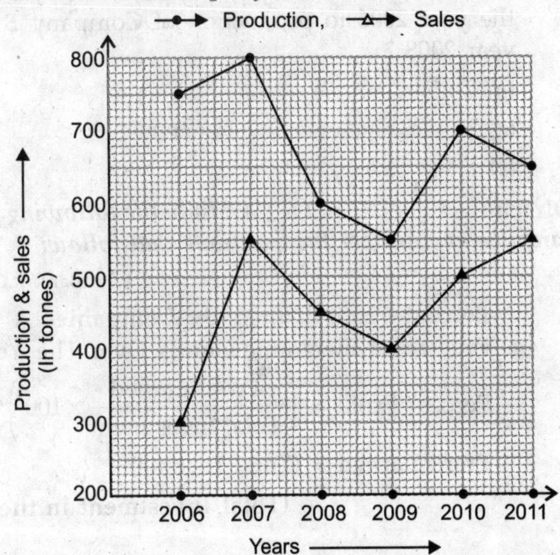

The table given below represents the ratio of the production (in tonnes) of Company A to the production (in tonnes) of Company B and ratio of sales of Company A and Company B.

Year	Production (A : B)	Sales (A : B)
2006	5 : 4	2 : 3
2007	8 : 7	11 : 12
2008	3 : 4	9 : 14
2009	11 : 12	4 : 5
2010	14 : 13	10 : 9
2011	13 : 14	1 : 1

6. What is the approximate percentage increase in the production of Company A from 2009 to 2010 ?
   (a) 18% (b) 38%
   (c) 23% (d) 27%
   (e) 32%

7. The sales of Company A in the year 2009 was approximately what percent of its production in the same year?
   (a) 65% (b) 73%
   (c) 79% (d) 83%
   (e) 69%

8. What is the average production of Company B (in tonnes) from the year 2006 to the year 2011 ?
   (a) 574 (b) 649
   (c) 675 (d) 593
   (e) 618

9. What is the ratio of the total production of Company *A* to the total sales of Company *A* ?
   (a) 81 : 64 (b) 64 : 55
   (c) 71 : 81 (d) 71 : 55
   (e) 81 : 55

10. What is the ratio of production of Company *B* in the year 2006 to production of Company *B* in the year 2008 ?
    (a) 2 : 5 (b) 4 : 5
    (c) 3 : 4 (d) 3 : 5
    (e) 1 : 4

Directions ***(Questions 11–18): Study the following graphs carefully and answer the questions that follow:***

(Bank P.O., 2011)

Percent Profit Earned By Companies *A* and *B* Producing Electronic Goods Over The Years.

$$\text{Percent Profit} = \left(\frac{\text{Profit Earned}}{\text{Total Investment}} \times 100\right)\%$$

Profit Earned = (Total Income) – (Total Investment in the Year)

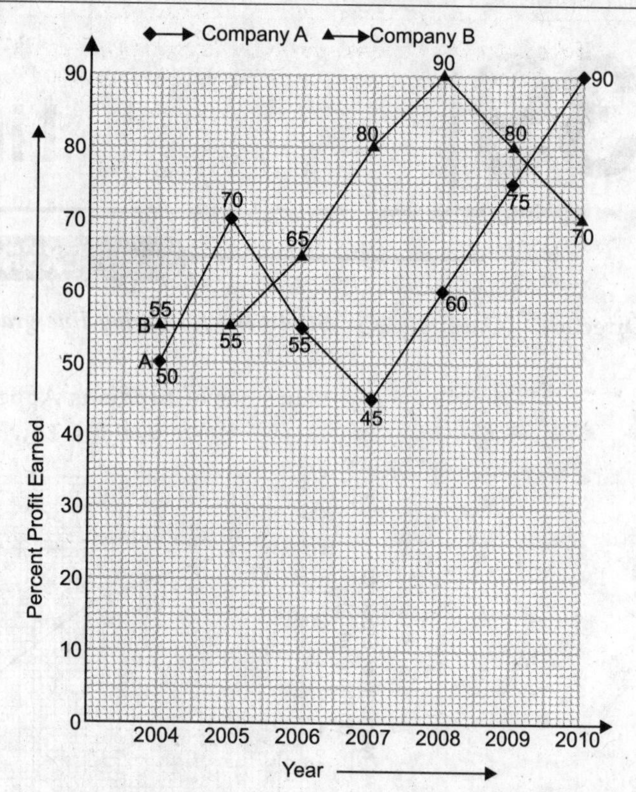

11. If the profit earned in 2006 by Company B was ₹ 812500, what was the total income of the company in that year ?
    (a) ₹ 1250000 (b) ₹ 2062500
    (c) ₹ 1650000 (d) 1825000
    (e) None of these

12. If the amounts invested by the two companies in 2005 were equal, what was the ratio of the total income of Company A to that of B on 2005 ?
    (a) 31 : 33 (b) 33 : 31
    (c) 34 : 31 (d) 14 : 11
    (e) None of these

13. If the total amount invested by the two companies in 2009 was ₹ 27 lakh, while the amount invested by Company B was 50% of the amount invested by Company A, what was the total profit earned by the two companies together ?
    (a) ₹ 21.15 lakh (b) ₹ 20.70 lakh
    (c) ₹ 18.70 lakh (d) ₹ 20.15 lakh
    (e) None of these

14. If the income of Company A in 2007 and that in 2008 were equal and the amount invested in 2007 was ₹ 12 lakh, what was the amount invested in 2008 ?
    (a) ₹ 1087500 (b) ₹ 1085700
    (c) ₹ 1245000 (d) ₹ 1285000
    (e) None of these

15. If the amount of profit earned by Company A in 2006 was ₹ 10.12 lakh, what was the total investment ?

(*a*) ₹ 13.8 lakh (*b*) ₹ 14.9 lakh
(*c*) ₹ 15.4 lakh (*d*) ₹ 14.2 lakh
(*e*) None of these

16. If the amount invested by Company B in 2004 is ₹ 12 lakh and income of 2004 is equal to the investment in 2005, what is the amount of profit earned in 2005 by Company B ?

(*a*) ₹ 6.6 lakh (*b*) ₹ 18.6 lakh
(*c*) ₹ 10.23 lakh (*d*) ₹ 9.6 lakh
(*e*) None of these

17. If the investments of Company *A* in 2007 and 2008 were equal, what is the difference between the profits earned in the two years if the income in 2008 was ₹ 24 lakh ?

(*a*) ₹ 2.25 lakh (*b*) ₹ 3.6 lakh
(*c*) ₹ 1.8 lakh (*d*) ₹ 2.6 lakh
(*e*) None of these

18. If each of the companies *A* and *B* invested ₹ 25 lakh in 2010, what was the average profit earned by the two companies ?

(*a*) ₹ 18 lakh (*b*) ₹ 22.5 lakh
(*c*) ₹ 17.5 lakh (*d*) ₹ 20 lakh
(*e*) None of these

Directions (*Questions 19–23*): ***Study the following graph carefully and answer the questions that follow:***

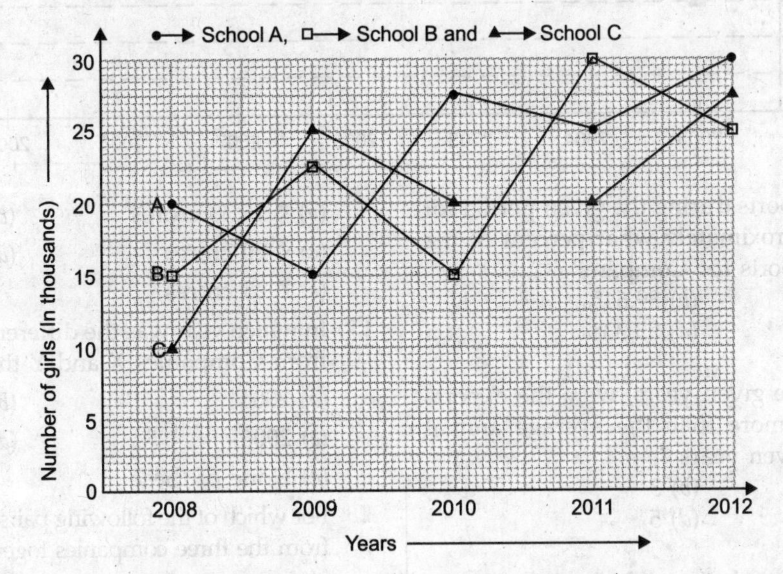

19. What was the ratio between the number of girls enrolled in School C in the year 2011 and the total number of girls enrolled in School A and School B together in the same year ?

(*a*) 11 : 3 (*b*) 3 : 11
(*c*) 4 : 11 (*d*) 4 : 7
(*e*) None of these

20. In which school was the difference between the number of girls enrolled in the years 2012 and 2008 minimum ?

(*a*) Only School A
(*b*) Only School B
(*c*) Only School C
(*d*) Both School A and School B
(*e*) Both School A and School C

21. What was the approximate average number of girls enrolled in the year 2010 in all the three schools together ?

(*a*) 20800 (*b*) 2300
(*c*) 20000 (*d*) 22500
(*e*) 21600

22. Total number of girls enrolled in all the three schools in the year 2008 was what percentage of the number of girls enrolled in School C in the year 2011 ?

(*a*) 44.4 % (*b*) 225%
(*c*) 165% (*d*) 240%
(*e*) None of these

23. In which year was the total number of girls enrolled in all the three schools together second highest ?

(*a*) 2008 (*b*) 2009
(*c*) 2010 (*d*) 2011
(*e*) 2012

Directions (*Questions 24-28*): *Study the following graphs and answer the questions given below which are based on these graphs.*

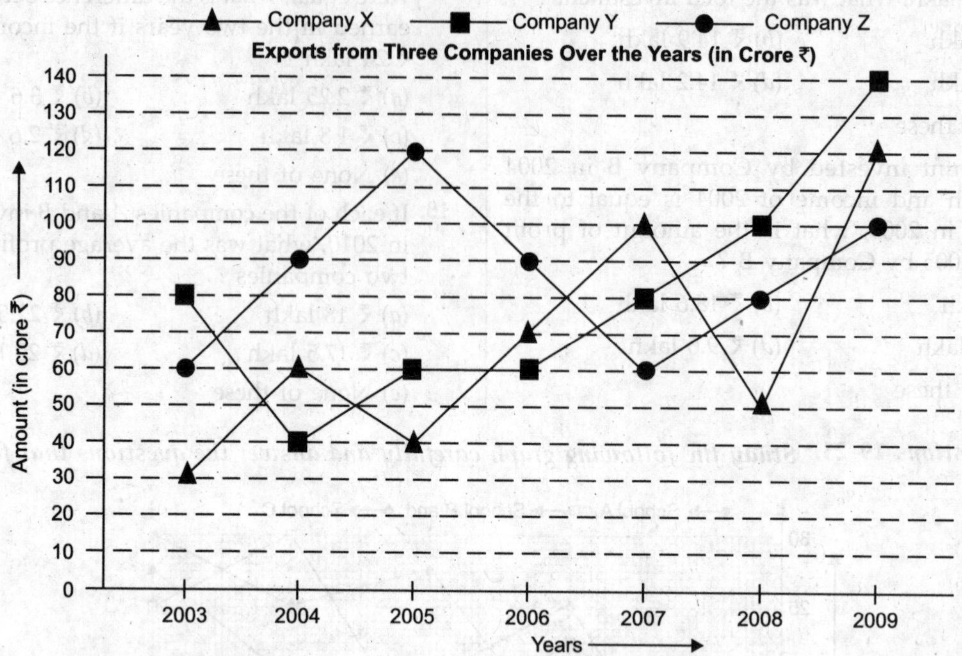

24. Average annual exports during the given period for Company Y is approximately what percent of the average annual exports for Company Z ?

(*a*) 87.12% (*b*) 89.64%
(*c*) 91.21% (*d*) 93.33%
(*e*) 95.15%

25. In how many of the given years, were the exports from Company Z more than the average annual exports over the given years ?

(*a*) 2 (*b*) 3
(*c*) 4 (*d*) 5
(*e*) 6

26. What was the difference between the average exports of the three companies in 2003 and the average exports in 2008 ?

(*a*) ₹ 15.33 crores (*b*) ₹ 18.67 crores
(*c*) ₹ 20 crores (*d*) ₹ 22 : 17 crores
(*e*) ₹ 25 crores

27. In which year was the difference between the exports from Companies X and Y the minimum ?

(*a*) 2004 (*b*) 2005
(*c*) 2006 (*d*) 2007
(*e*) None of these

28. For which of the following pairs of years the total exports from the three companies together are equal ?

(*a*) 2005 and 2008 (*b*) 2006 and 2008
(*c*) 2007 and 2008 (*d*) 2005 and 2006
(*e*) 2003 and 2004

The amount of exports of X, Y, Z (In crore ₹) in various years are:

	Export (in crore ₹)						
Year →	2003	2004	2005	2006	2007	2008	2009
X	30	60	40	70	100	50	120
Y	80	40	60	60	80	100	140
X	60	90	120	90	60	80	100

ANSWERS

1. (*b*)	2. (*a*)	3. (*d*)	4. (*e*)	5. (*a*)	6. (*a*)	7. (*b*)	8. (*c*)	9. (*e*)	10. (*c*)
11. (*b*)	12. (*c*)	13. (*b*)	14. (*a*)	15. (*e*)	16. (*c*)	17. (*a*)	18. (*d*)	19. (*c*)	20. (*d*)
21. (*a*)	22. (*b*)	23. (*d*)	24. (*d*)	25. (*c*)	26. (*c*)	27. (*c*)	28. (*d*)		

SOLUTIONS

1. Ratio of number of students from Town B to that from Town A

$= \frac{32.5 \times 1000}{40 \times 1000} = \frac{325}{400} = \frac{13}{16} = 13:16.$

2. Average number of students appearing in Aptitude Test from all towns

$= \frac{(40 + 32.5 + 17.5 + 42.5 + 35) \times 1000}{5}$

$= \frac{167.5 \times 1000}{5}$

$= (33.5 \times 1000) = 33500.$

3. Required % $= \left\{\frac{35 \times 1000}{167.5 \times 1000} \times 100\right\}\%$

$= \left(\frac{350 \times 100}{1675}\right)\% = \frac{1400}{67}\%$

$= 20.89\% \simeq 21\%$ (nearly).

4. (Students from Towns C and D) : (Students from Towns A, D and E)

$= \frac{(17.5 + 42.5) \times 1000}{(40 + 42.5 + 35) \times 1000}$

$= \frac{60}{117.5} = \frac{600}{1175} = \frac{24}{47} = 24:47.$

5. Required prcentage

$= \left(\frac{42.5 \times 1000}{17.5 \times 1000} \times 100\right)\%$

$= \left(\frac{425}{175} \times 100\right)\% = \left(\frac{425 \times 4}{7}\right)\%$

$= \frac{1700}{7}\% = 242.85\% \simeq 243\%$ (nearly).

6. Percentage increase in production of A from 2009 to 2010

$= \left\{\frac{(700 - 550)}{550} \times 100\right\}\%$

$= \left(\frac{150}{550} \times 100\right)\% = \frac{300}{11}\%$

$= 27.2\% \simeq 27\%$ (approx.)

7. Required % $= \left(\frac{400}{550} \times 100\right)\% = \frac{800}{11}\%$

$= 72.7\% \simeq 73\%$ (approx.)

8. Average production of Company B from 2006 to 2011

$= \frac{1}{6} \times \left[\left(\frac{4}{5} \times 750\right) + \left(\frac{7}{8} \times 800\right) + \left(\frac{4}{3} \times 600\right) + \left(\frac{12}{11} \times 550\right) + \left(\frac{13}{14} \times 700\right) + \left(\frac{14}{13} \times 650\right)\right]$ tonners

$= \frac{1}{6}(600 + 700 + 800 + 600 + 650 + 700)$ tonnes

$= \frac{4050}{6}$ tonnes $= 675$ tonnes.

9. Total production of Company A

= (750 + 800 + 600 + 550 + 700 + 650) tonnes

= 4050 tonnes.

Total sales of Company A

= (300 + 550 + 450 + 400 + 500 + 550) tonnes

= 2750 tonnes.

Required ratio = 4050 : 2750 $= \frac{4050}{2750} = \frac{81}{55} = 81:55.$

10. Production of Company B in 2006

$= \left(\frac{4}{5} \text{ of } 750\right)$ tonnes $= 600$ tonnes.

Production of Company B in 2008

$= \left(\frac{4}{3} \text{ of } 600\right)$ tonnes = 800 tonnes.

Required ratio = 600 : 800 = 3 : 4.

11. Investment in 2006

$= ₹\left(\frac{100}{65} \times 812500\right) = ₹(100 \times 12500)$

$= ₹1250000.$

Total income of *B* in 2006

= (Investment) + (Profit)

= ₹(1250000 + 812500) = ₹ 2062500.

12. Let the investment of each in 2005 be ₹ x. Then

(Income of A) : (Income of B)

= ₹ (x + 70% of x) : ₹ (x + 55% of x) [∵ Income = (Investment) + (Profit)]

$= \left(x + \frac{70x}{100}\right) : \left(x + \frac{55x}{100}\right)$

$= \left(x + \frac{7x}{10}\right) : \left(x + \frac{11x}{20}\right)$

$= \frac{17x}{10} : \frac{31x}{20} = 34:31.$

13. Let the investment of *A* in 2009 be ₹ x. Then,

Investment of B = 50% of ₹ x = ₹ $\left(x \times \frac{50}{100}\right) = ₹\left(\frac{x}{2}\right).$

$\therefore \left(x + \frac{x}{2}\right) = 27$ lakh

$\Rightarrow \frac{3x}{2} = 27$ lakh

$\Rightarrow x = \left(27 \times \frac{2}{3}\right)$ lakh = 18 lakh.

∴ Investment of A in 2009 = ₹ 18 lakh and investment of B = ₹ 9 lakh.

Profit of A = ₹ $\left(18 \text{ lakh} \times \frac{75}{100}\right) = ₹\,13.50$ lakh.

Profit of B = ₹ $\left(9 \text{ lakh} \times \frac{80}{100}\right) = ₹\,7.20$ lakh.

Total profit of A and B = ₹ (13.50 + 7.20) lakh

= ₹ 20.70 lakh.

14. Investment of A in 2007

$= ₹\ 12$ lakh and profit % = 45%.

Income of A in 2007 $= ₹\left(\frac{145}{100}\times 12 \text{ lakh}\right) = ₹\ 17.4$ lakh.

Amount invested by A in 2008 $= ₹\left(\frac{100}{160}\times 17.4 \text{ lakh}\right)$

$= ₹\ (10.875 \times 100000) = ₹\ 1087500.$

15. Let the investment of A in 2006 be ₹ x. Then,

Profit = 55% of ₹ $x = ₹\left(x\times\frac{55}{100}\right) = ₹\left(\frac{11x}{20}\right)$.

$\therefore \quad \frac{11x}{20} = 10.12 \text{ lakh} = 10.12\times 100000 = 1012000$

$\Rightarrow \quad x = \left(1012000\times\frac{20}{11}\right) = 1840000 = 18.4 \text{ lakh}$

$\Rightarrow$ Investment of A in 2006 = 18.4 lakh.

16. Investment of B in 2004 = 12 lakh.

Income of B in 2004 $= ₹\left(\frac{155}{100}\times 12 \text{ lakh}\right) = ₹\ (18.6 \text{ lakh})$.

Profit earned in 2005 $= ₹\left(\frac{55}{100}\times 18.6 \text{ lakh}\right)$

$= ₹\left(\frac{11}{10}\times 9.3 \text{ lakh}\right)$

$= ₹\ 10.23$ lakh.

17. Let the investment of A in 2008 be ₹ x. Then,

$\left(\frac{160}{100}\times x\right) = 24 \text{ lakh} \Rightarrow x = \left(24\times\frac{5}{8}\right) \text{lakh} = 15 \text{ lakh.}$

$\therefore$ Investment of A in 2008 = 15 lakh.

Profit of A in 2008

$= ₹\ (24 - 15)$ lakh $= ₹\ 9$ lakh.

Investment of A in 2007

= Investment of A in 2008 = ₹ (15 lakh).

Profit of A in 2007 $= ₹\left(\frac{45}{100}\times 15 \text{ lakh}\right)$

$= ₹\frac{27}{4} \text{ lakh} = ₹\ 6.75 \text{ lakh.}$

Difference between the profits of A in 2007 and 2008

$= ₹\ (9 - 6.75)$ lakh $= ₹\ 2.25$ lakh.

18. Average profit of A and B in 2010

$= \frac{1}{2}\times\left[\left(\frac{90}{100}\times 25 \text{ lakh}\right)+\left(\frac{70}{100}\times 25 \text{ lakh}\right)\right]$

$= \frac{1}{2}\times\left(\frac{45}{2}+\frac{35}{2}\right)\text{lakh} = \frac{80}{4} \text{ lakh} = 20 \text{ lakh.}$

19. Required ratio = 20000 : (25000 + 30000)

= 20000 : 55000 = 20 : 55 = 4 : 11.

20. Difference between the number of girls enrolled in 2012 and 2008 (in thousands) :

A → (30 − 20) = 10 ; B → (25 − 15)

= 10 ; C → (27.5 − 10) = 17.5

So, it was minimum in both A and B.

21. Required average

$= \frac{1}{3}(27.5 + 15 + 20)$ thousands

$= \left(\frac{62.5}{3}\times 1000\right) = \frac{62500}{3}$

$= 20833 \approx 20800$ (approx.)

22. Required percentage $= \left\{\frac{(20+15+10)\times 1000}{20\times 1000}\times 100\right\}\%$

$= \left\{\frac{45}{20}\times 100\right\}\% = 225\%.$

23. Total number of girls enrolled in all the three schools in various years (in thousands) :

2008 → (20 + 15 + 10) = 45 ;

2009 → (15 + 22.5 + 25) = 62.5;

2010 → (27.5 + 15 + 20) = 62.5 ;

2011 → (25 + 30 + 20) = 75;

2012 → (30 + 25 + 27.5) = 82.5.

Clearly, it was second highest in 2011.

24. Average annual export of Y during the given period (in crore ₹) :

$= \frac{1}{7}(80 + 40 + 60 + 60 + 80 + 100 + 140)$

$= \frac{560}{7} = 80.$

Average annual export of Z during the given period (In crore ₹)

$= \frac{1}{7}(60 + 90 + 120 + 90 + 60 + 80 + 100) = \frac{600}{7}.$

Required percentage $= \left\{\frac{80}{\left(\frac{600}{7}\right)}\times 100\right\}\%$

$= \left(\frac{80\times 7\times 100}{600}\right)\% = \frac{280}{3}\% = 93.33\%.$

25. Average annual export of Z (in crore ₹)

$= ₹\left(\frac{600}{7}\right)$ crores $= ₹\ 85.71$ crores.

From the graph it follows that the export of z was more than the average during the years 2004, 2005, 2006 and 2009. i.e. during four years.

26. Average export of X, Y and Z in 2003

$= ₹\left\{\frac{1}{3}(30 + 80 + 60) \text{ crores}\right\} = ₹\left(\frac{170}{3}\right)$ crores.

Average export of X, Y and Z in 2008

$= ₹\left\{\frac{1}{3}(50 + 100 + 80)\right\}$ crores $= ₹\left(\frac{230}{3}\right)$ crores.

Required difference $= ₹\left(\frac{230}{3}-\frac{170}{3}\right)$ crores

$= ₹\left(\frac{60}{3}\right)$ crores $= ₹\ 20$ crores.

27. Difference between the exports of X and Y (In crore ₹):

2003 → (80 − 30) = 50 ;

2004 → (60 − 40) = 20 ;

2005 → (60 − 40) = 20 ;

2006 → (70 − 60) = 10 ;

2007 → (100 − 80) = 20 ;

2008 → (100 – 50) = 50 ;
2009 → (140 – 120) = 20.
This is minimum in the year 2006.

28. Total exports of X, Y, Z (in crore ₹) are:
2003 → (30 + 80 + 60) = 170 ;
2004 → (60 + 40 + 90) = 190 ;
2005 → (40 + 60 + 120) = 220 ;
2006 → (70 + 60 + 90) = 220 ;
2007 → (100 + 80 + 60) = 240 ;
2008 → (50 + 100 + 80) = 230 ;
2009 → (120 + 140 + 100) = 360.
The total export of X, Y, Z remains the same during 2005 and 2006.

EXERCISE – II

Directions (Questions 1–5): The following linegraph gives the percent profit earned by two companies X and Y during the period 2006 – 2011. Study the line graph and answer the questions that are based on it.

Percentage Profit Earned by Companies X and Y over Given Years

Profit or Loss % = $\left\{\dfrac{(\text{Income}) - (\text{Expenditure})}{(\text{Expenditure})} \times 100\right\}$

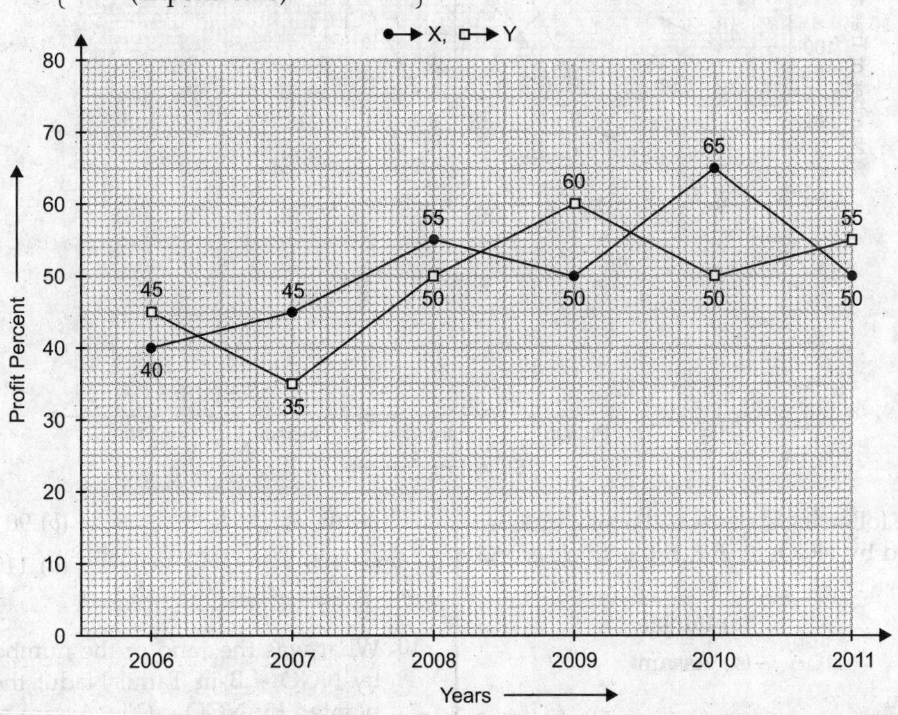

1. If the expenditure of Company Y in 2007 was ₹ 220 crores, what was its income in that year ?
(*a*) ₹ 312 crores (*b*) ₹ 297 crores
(*c*) ₹ 283 crores (*d*) ₹ 275 crores
(*e*) ₹ 261 crores

2. If the incomes of the two companies were equal in 2009, what was the ratio of expenditure of Company X to that of Company Y in that year ?
(*a*) 6 : 5 (*b*) 5 : 6
(*c*) 11 : 6 (*d*) 16 : 15
(*e*) 15 : 16

3. The incomes of the Companies X and Y in 2010 were in the ratio 3 : 4 respectively. What was the respective ratio of their expenditures in 2010 ?
(*a*) 7 : 22 (*b*) 14 : 19
(*c*) 15 : 22 (*d*) 27 : 35
(*e*) 33 : 40

4. If the expenditures of Companies X and Y in 2006 were equal and the total income of the two companies in that year be ₹ 342 crores, what was the total profit of the two companies together in that year ? Profit = (Income) – (Expenditure)
(*a*) ₹ 240 crores (*b*) ₹ 171 crores
(*c*) ₹ 120 crores (*d*) ₹ 102 crores
(*e*) None of these

5. The expenditure of Company X in the year 2008 was ₹ 200 crores and the income of this company in the same year was the same as its expenditure in 2011. The income of Company X in 2011 was :
(*a*) ₹ 465 crores (*b*) ₹ 385 crores
(*c*) ₹ 335 crores (*d*) ₹ 295 crores
(*e*) ₹ 255 crores

Directions *(Questions 6–10)*: ***Study the following graph carefully and answer the questions that follow.*** **(Bank P.O., 2011)**

Number of Trees Planted by Three Different NGOs A, B and C in Five Different States

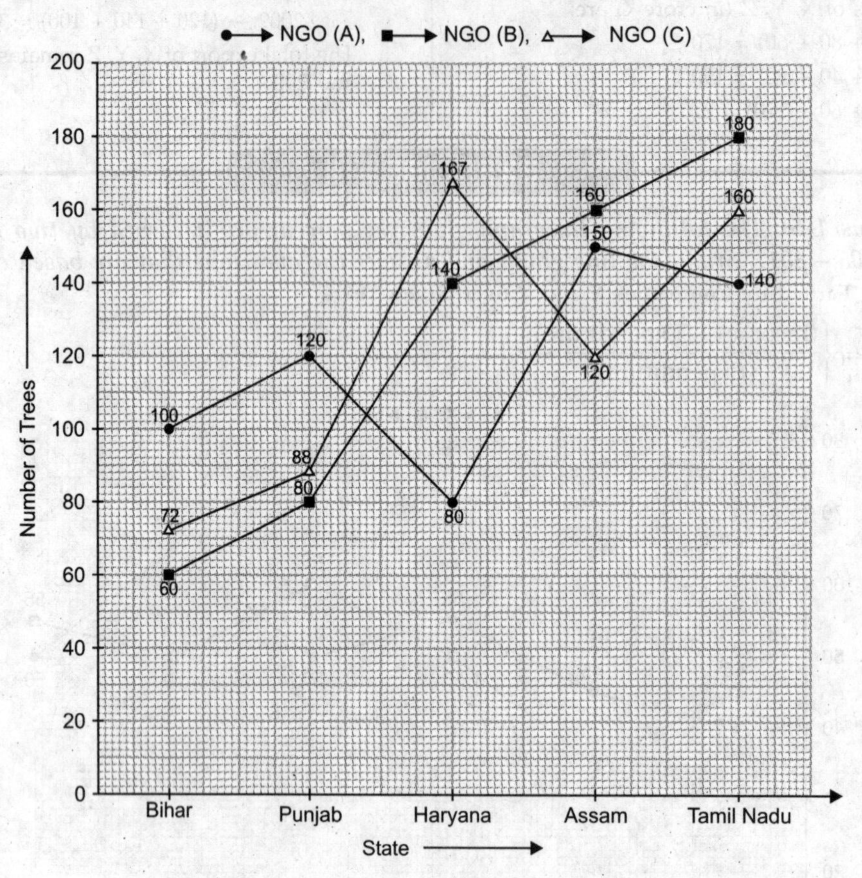

6. In which of the following states was the total number of trees planted by NGOs A and B together second lowest ?
   (*a*) Bihar (*b*) Punjab
   (*c*) Haryana (*d*) Assam
   (*e*) Tamil Nadu

7. What was the difference between the trees planted by NGO – A in Haryana and those planted by NGO – C in Tamil Nadu ?
   (*a*) 90 (*b*) 60
   (*c*) 120 (*d*) 160
   (*e*) None of these

8. What was the average number of trees planted in Haryana by all the NGOs together ?
   (*a*) 420 (*b*) 140
   (*c*) 120 (*d*) 390
   (*e*) None of these

9. The total number of trees planted by NGOs A and B together in Bihar was approximately what percentage of the total number of trees planted by NGOs B and C together in Punjab ?
   (*a*) 85 (*b*) 90
   (*c*) 105 (*d*) 110
   (*e*) 95

10. What was the ratio of the number of trees planted by NGO – B in Tamil Nadu, the number of trees planted by NGO – C in Assam and the number of trees planted by NGO – *A* in Assam ?
   (*a*) 5 : 3 : 6 (*b*) 5 : 6 : 3
   (*c*) 6 : 4 : 5 (*d*) 6 : 5 : 3
   (*e*) None of these

Directions *(Questions 11–15)*: ***The following line-graph gives the ratio of the amounts of imports by a company to the amount of exports from that company over the period from 2005 to 2011.*** **(Bank P.O., 2011)**

The questions given below are based on this graph.

11. In how many of the given years were the exports more than the imports ?
   (*a*) 1 (*b*) 2
   (*c*) 3 (*d*) 4
   (*e*) None of these

12. The imports were minimum proportionate to the exports of the company in which of the following years ?
(*a*) 2005 (*b*) 2006
(*c*) 2007 (*d*) 2010
(*e*) 2011

13. If the imports of the company in 2006 be ₹ 272 crores, the exports from the company in the same year was:
(*a*) ₹ 370 crores (*b*) ₹ 320 crores
(*c*) ₹ 280 crores (*d*) ₹ 275 crores
(*e*) ₹ 264 crores

Ratio of Values of Imports to Exports by a Company Over the Years

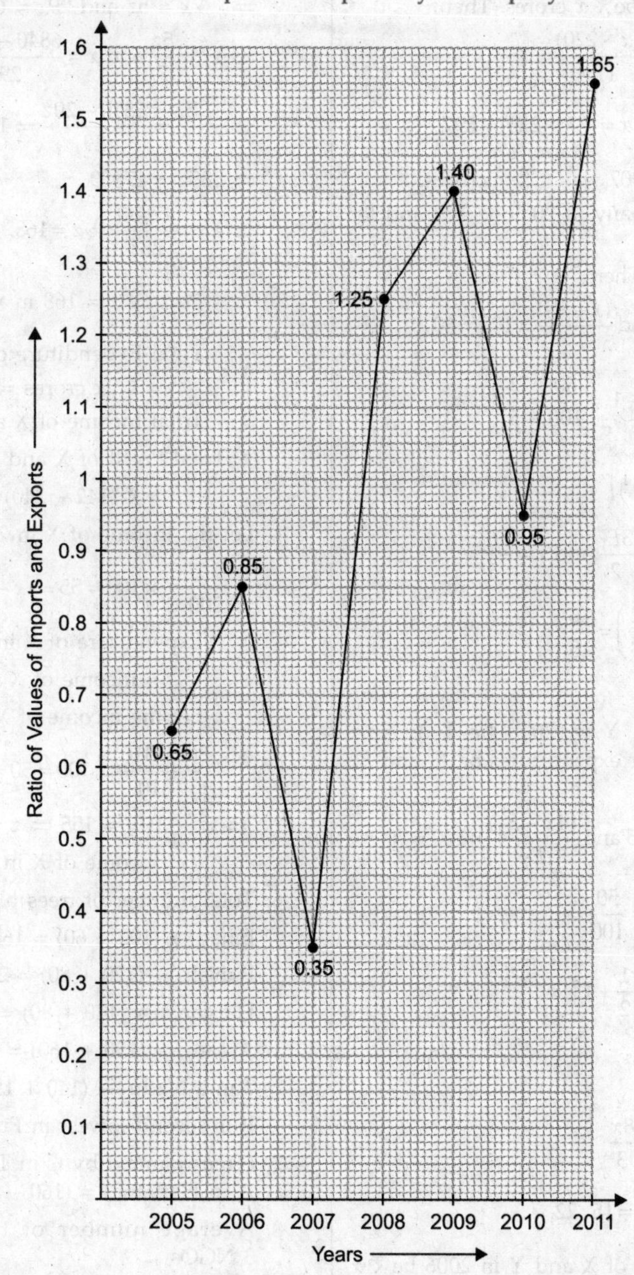

14. What was the percentage increase in imports from 2007 to 2008 ?
(*a*) 72% (*b*) 56%
(*c*) 28% (*d*) None of these
(*e*) Data inadequate

15. If the imports in 2008 was ₹ 250 crores and the total exports in the years 2008 and 2009 together was ₹ 500 crores, then the imports in 2009 was
(*a*) ₹ 250 crores (*b*) ₹ 300 crores
(*c*) ₹ 357 crores (*d*) ₹ 420 crores
(*e*) None of these

ANSWERS

1. (b)	2. (d)	3. (c)	4. (d)	5. (a)	6. (b)	7. (e)	8. (e)	9. (e)	10. (c)
11. (d)	12. (c)	13. (b)	14. (e)	15. (d)					

SOLUTIONS

1. Let the income of Y in 2007 be ₹ x crores. Then,

$$\frac{(x-220)}{220}\times 100 = 35 \Rightarrow \frac{5(x-220)}{11} = 35$$

$$\Leftrightarrow (x-220) = \frac{35\times 11}{5} = 77 \Rightarrow x = (77+220) = 297.$$

Hence, the income of Y in 2007 was ₹ 297 crores.

2. Let the income of each company in 2009 be ₹ x and let their expenditures be E_1 and E_2 respectively. Then,

$$\frac{(x-E_1)}{E_1}\times 100 = 50 \text{ and } \frac{(x-E_2)}{E_2}\times 100 = 60$$

$$\Rightarrow \frac{x}{E_1} - 1 = \frac{50}{100} = \frac{1}{2} \text{ and } \frac{x}{E_2} - 1 = \frac{60}{100} = \frac{3}{5}$$

$$\Rightarrow \frac{x}{E_1} = \left(\frac{1}{2}+1\right) \text{ and } \frac{x}{E_2} = \left(\frac{3}{5}+1\right)$$

$$\Rightarrow \frac{x}{E_1} = \frac{3}{2} \text{ and } \frac{x}{E_2} = \frac{8}{5} \Rightarrow x = \frac{3E_1}{2} \text{ and } x = \frac{8E_2}{5}$$

$$\Rightarrow \frac{3E_1}{2} = \frac{8E_2}{5} \Rightarrow \frac{E_1}{E_2} = \left(\frac{8}{5}\times\frac{2}{3}\right) = \frac{16}{15}$$

$$\Rightarrow E_1 : E_2 = 16 : 15.$$

3. Let the incomes of X and Y in 2010 be ₹ $3x$ and ₹ $4x$ respectively and let their expenditures be E_1 and E_2 respectively.

$$\text{Then, } \frac{(3x-E_1)}{E_1}\times 100 = 65 \text{ and } \frac{(4x-E_2)}{E_2}\times 100 = 50$$

$$\Rightarrow \frac{3x}{E_1} - 1 = \frac{65}{100} \text{ and } \frac{4x}{E_2} - 1 = \frac{50}{100}$$

$$\Rightarrow \frac{3x}{E_1} = \left(\frac{13}{20}+1\right) \text{ and } \frac{4x}{E_2} = \left(\frac{1}{2}+1\right)$$

$$\Rightarrow \frac{3x}{E_1} = \frac{33}{20} \text{ and } \frac{4x}{E_2} = \frac{3}{2}$$

$$\Rightarrow E_1 = \frac{60x}{33} = \frac{20x}{11} \text{ and } E_2 = \frac{8x}{3}$$

$$\Rightarrow E_1 : E_2 = \frac{20x}{11} : \frac{8x}{3} = 60 : 88 = 15 : 22.$$

4. Let the expenditures of each of X and Y in 2006 be ₹ x crores and let the income of X in 2006 be ₹ z crores.

Then, income of Y in 2006 = ₹ $(342 - z)$ crores.

$$\therefore \frac{(z-x)}{x}\times 100 = 40 \text{ and } \frac{\{(342-z)-x\}}{x}\times 100 = 45$$

$$\Rightarrow \frac{(z-x)}{x} = \frac{40}{100} = \frac{2}{5} \text{ and } \frac{(342-z-x)}{x} = \frac{45}{100} = \frac{9}{20}$$

$$\Rightarrow 5z - 5x = 2x \text{ and } 6840 - 20z - 20x = 9x$$

$$\Rightarrow 7x = 5z \text{ and } 29x = 6840 - 20z$$

$$\Rightarrow x = \frac{5z}{7} \text{ and } x = \frac{6840-20z}{29}$$

$$\Rightarrow \frac{5z}{7} = \frac{6840-20z}{29} \Rightarrow 145z = 47880 - 140z$$

$$\Rightarrow 285z = 47880$$

$$\Rightarrow z = \frac{47880}{285} \Rightarrow z = 168.$$

Putting $z = 168$ in $x = \frac{5z}{7}$, we get $x = \frac{5\times 168}{7} = 120.$

∴ Total Expenditure of X and Y in 2006 = ₹ $2x$ crores = ₹ 240 crores.

Total Income of X and Y in 2006 = ₹ 342 crores.

∴ Total Profit of X and Y in 2006 = ₹ (342 – 240) crores = ₹ 102 crores.

5. Let the income of X in 2008 be ₹ x crores. Then,

$$\frac{(x-200)}{200}\times 100 = 55 \Rightarrow x - 200 = 110 \Rightarrow x = 310.$$

∴ Expenditure of X in 2011 = Income of X in 2008 = ₹ 310 cores.

Let the income of X in 2011 be ₹ z crores. Then,

$$\frac{(z-310)}{310}\times 100 = 50 \Rightarrow \frac{(z-310)}{310} = \frac{50}{100} = \frac{1}{2}$$

$$\Rightarrow (z - 310) = 155 \Rightarrow z = 465.$$

∴ Income of X in 2011 = ₹ 465 crores.

6. Total number of trees planted by A and B in :

Bihar → (100 + 60) = 160 ;

Punjab → (120 + 80) = 200 ;

Haryana → (140 + 80) = 220 ;

Assam → (150 + 160) = 310 ;

Tamil Nadu → (140 + 180) = 320.

It is second lowest in Punjab.

7. (Trees planted by C in Tamil Nadu) – (Trees planted by A in Haryana) = (160 – 80) = 80.

8. Average number of trees planted in Haryana by 3 NGOs

$$= \frac{1}{3}(80+140+167) = \frac{387}{3} = 129.$$

9. Required% $= \left\{\frac{(100+60)}{(80+88)}\times 100\right\}\%$

$$= \left(\frac{160}{168}\times 100\right)\%$$

$= \frac{2000}{21} = 95\%$ (approx.)

10. Required ratio = 180 : 120 : 150 = 6 : 4 : 5.

11. Clearly, Export > Import only when $\frac{\text{Import}}{\text{Export}} < 1$.

From the graph it is clear that the above ratio is less than 1 in the years 2005, 2006, 2007 and 2010.

Thus (Imports : Exports) < 1 in four years.

12. The imports are minimum proportionate to exports means (value of import) : (value of export) should have minimum value.

Clearly, this ratio has a minimum value of 0.35 in 2007.

13. From graph, we find that the ratio of value of import to the value of export in 2006 is 0.85.

Let the value of export in 2006 be ₹ x crores. Then,

$$\frac{272}{x} = 0.85 \Rightarrow x = \frac{272}{0.85} = \left(\frac{272 \times 100}{85}\right) = 320.$$

Hence, the value of exports in 2006 was ₹ 320 crores.

14. The graph gives only the ratio of value of imports and that of exports. In order to find the percentage increase in imports from 2007 to 2008, we require the value of import or that of export during these years.

So, we cannot find the percentage increase in imports. Hence, the data is inadequate to answer the question.

15. Let the value of export in 2008 be ₹ x crores.

Then, the value of export in 2009 = ₹ $(500 - x)$ crores.

$$\frac{250}{x} = 1.25 \Rightarrow x = \frac{250}{1.25} = \left(\frac{250 \times 100}{125}\right) = 200.$$

$\therefore$ Export in 2008 = ₹ 200 crores.

Export in 2009 = ₹ (500 − 200) crores = ₹ 300 crores.

Let the value of import in 2009 be ₹ y crores.

Then,

$$\frac{y}{300} = 1.40 \Rightarrow y = (1.40 \times 300) = \left(\frac{140}{100} \times 300\right) = 420.$$

Hence, the value of import in 2009 was ₹ 420 crores.

EXERCISE – III

Directions (*Questions 1-5*): *Refer to the graph and answer the given questions*

Data Related to Number of Calories Burned by Two Individuals (A and B) on Treadmill During 5 Days

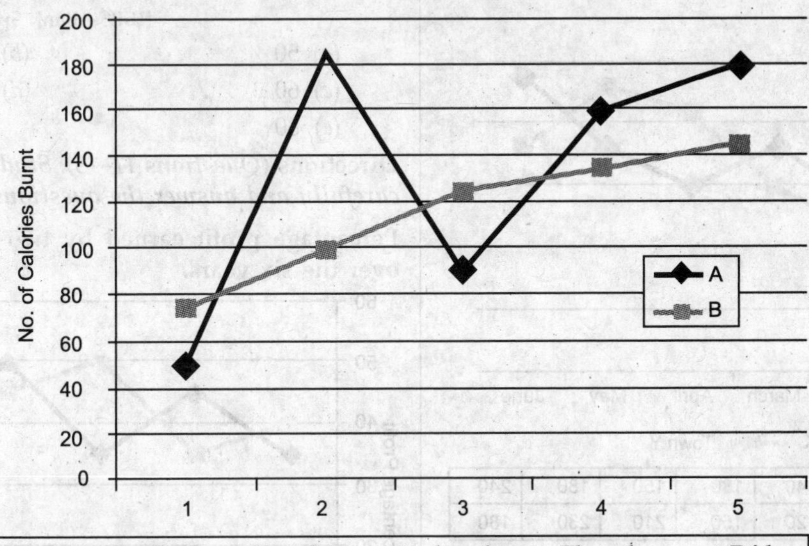

	Monday	Tuesday	Wednesday	Thursday	Friday
A	50	185	90	160	180
B	75	100	125	135	145

1. What is the respective ratio of total number of calories burned by A and B together on Wednesday and the by the same individuals together on Tuesday?

[IBPS—RRB (Off. Gr. 'B') Exam, 2015]

(*a*) 45 : 59 (*b*) 43 : 57

(*c*) 41 : 57 (*d*) 43 : 61

(*e*) 47 : 61

2. If the number of calories burned by A and B increased by 10% and 20% respectively from Friday to Saturday, what was the total number of calories burned by them together on Saturday?

[IBPS—RRB (Off. Gr. 'B') Exam, 2015]

(*a*) 378 (*b*) 372

(*c*) 368 (*d*) 384

(*e*) 364

3. What is the total number of calories burned by A on Tuesday, Wednesday and Thursday together?

[IBPS—RRB (Off. Gr. 'B') Exam, 2015]

(*a*) 425 (*b*) 440
(*c*) 430 (*d*) 445
(*e*) 435

4. If the average number of calories burned by B on Thursday, Friday and Saturday together is 125, what was the number of calories burned by B on Saturday?

[IBPS—RRB (Off. Gr. 'B') Exam, 2015]

(*a*) 110 (*b*) 95
(*c*) 115 (*d*) 90
(*e*) 105

5. Number of calories burned by B increased by what percent from Monday to Thursday?

[IBPS—RRB (Off. Gr. 'B') Exam, 2015]

(*a*) 80% (*b*) 60%
(*c*) 70% (*d*) 75%
(*e*) 65%

Directions (*Questions 6–10*): *Refer to the graph and answer the given questions:*

Number of watches of 'PQR' brand sold in Town X and Y in 6 different Months

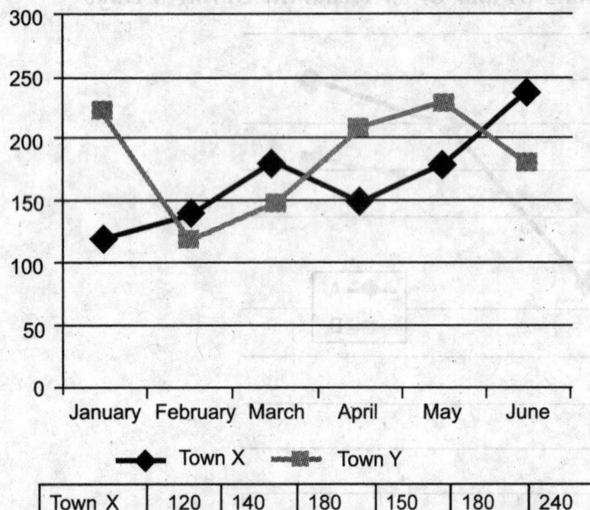

Town X	120	140	180	150	180	240
Town Y	220	120	150	210	230	180

6. What is the average number of watches sold in Town X in January, February, March and June?

[IBPS—Bank Spl. Officer (IT) Exam, 2015]

(*a*) 180 (*b*) 190
(*c*) 175 (*d*) 170
(*e*) 185

7. The number of watches sold in Town Y in April is what per cent more than the number of watches sold in Town X in the same month?

[IBPS—Bank Spl. Officer (IT) Exam, 2015]

(*a*) 42% (*b*) 40%
(*c*) 30% (*d*) 50%
(*e*) 38%

8. The number of watches sold in Town Y increased by what per cent from February to May?

[IBPS—Bank Spl. Officer (IT) Exam, 2015]

(*a*) 96% (*b*) $92\frac{1}{3}\%$
(*c*) 97% (*d*) $91\frac{2}{3}\%$
(*e*) $95\frac{2}{3}\%$

9. The number of watches sold in Town X in July was 10% more than the number of watches sold in the same town in May. What is the ratio of the number of watches sold in July to that sold in January in the same town?

[IBPS—Bank Spl. Officer (IT) Exam, 2015]

(*a*) 34 : 23 (*b*) 32 : 25
(*c*) 31 : 20 (*d*) 33 : 23
(*e*) 33 : 20

10. What is the difference between the total number of watches sold in both the towns together in June and the total number of watches sold in both the towns together in March?

[IBPS—Bank Spl. Officer (IT) Exam, 2015]

(*a*) 50 (*b*) 90
(*c*) 60 (*d*) 70
(*e*) 80

Directions (*Questions 11–15*): *Study the following graph carefully and answer the questions given below it.*

Percentage profit earned by two companies A and B over the six years.

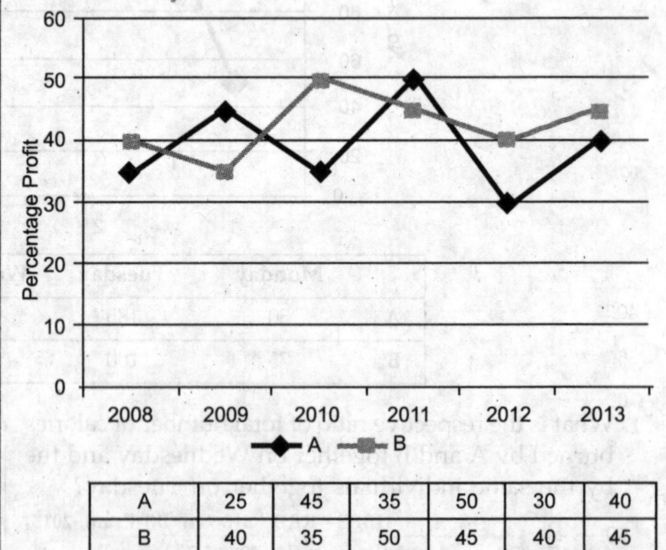

A	25	45	35	50	30	40
B	40	35	50	45	40	45

11. Expenditure of company B in 2009 and 2010 are ₹ 12 lakhs and ₹ 14.5 lakhs respectively. What was the total income of company B in 2009 and 2010 together (in lakh rupees)?

[IDBI Bank (Executive Officer's) Exam, 2015]

(*a*) 39.75 (*b*) 37.95
(*c*) 38.75 (*d*) 38.55
(*e*) None of these

12. Ratio of expenditures of company A and B in 2012 was 3 : 4 respectively. What was the respective ratio of their incomes in 2012?

[IDBI Bank (Executive Officer's) Exam, 2015]

(*a*) 21 : 26 (*b*) 13 : 14
(*c*) 14 : 13 (*d*) 26 : 21
(*e*) None of these

13. Total expenditure of company A in all the years together was 82.5 lakhs. What was the total income of the company A in all the years together?

[IDBI Bank (Executive Officer's) Exam, 2015]

(*a*) 1.23 crores (*b*) 98.75 crores
(*c*) 99.85 crores (*d*) Cannot be determined
(*e*) None of these

14. If the expenditure of company A and B in 2013 were equal and the total incomes of the two companies was ₹ 5.7 lakhs. What was the total expenditure of the two companies in 2013?

[IDBI Bank (Executive Officer's) Exam, 2015]

(*a*) 4 lakhs (*b*) 2 lakhs
(*c*) 4.2 lakhs (*d*) Cannot be determined
(*e*) None of these

15. If the income of company B in 2010 and 2011 were in the ratio of 2 : 3 respectively, what was the respective ratio of expenditures of that company in these two years?

[IDBI Bank (Executive Officer's) Exam, 2015]

(*a*) 20 : 29 (*b*) 9 : 10
(*c*) 29 : 45 (*d*) 10 : 29
(*e*) None of these

Directions ***(Questions 16–20): Refer to the graph and answer the given questions:***

Data related to the number of projects handled by two companies A and B over 5 years.

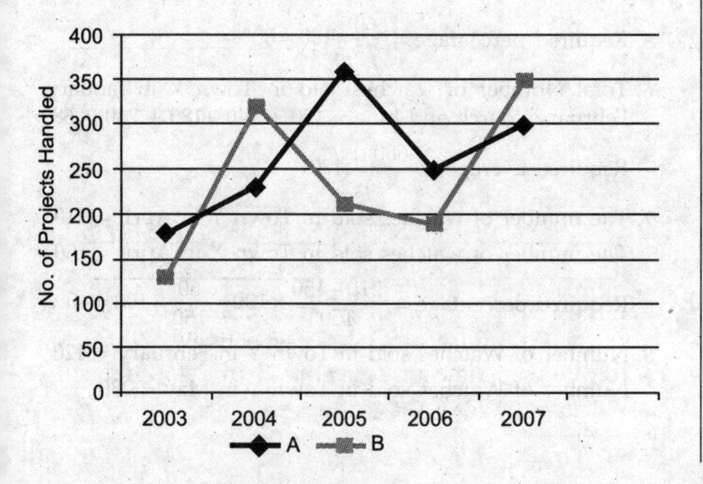

16. Out of the total number of projects handled by Company A in 2005 and 2006 together, 20% were governmental projects. What was the total number of governmental projects handled by Company A in 2005 and 2006 together?

[IBPS—RRBs (Off. Gr. 'B') Exam, 2015]

(*a*) 108 (*b*) 132
(*c*) 128 (*d*) 116
(*e*) 122

17. The projects handled by a company can be broadly classified into two types: governmental projects and non-governmental projects. If the average number of non-governmental projects handled by the same company B in 2003 and 2004 Is 127. What is the total number of governmental projects handled by the same company in 2003 and 2004 together?

[IBPS—RRBs (Off. Gr. 'B') Exam, 2015]

(*a*) 204 (*b*) 188
(*c*) 192 (*d*) 196
(*e*) 212

18. The number of projects handled by Company B decreased by what per cent from 2004 to 2006?

[IBPS—RRBs (Off. Gr. 'B') Exam, 2015]

(*a*) $35\frac{5}{8}$ (*b*) $30\frac{7}{8}$
(*c*) $50\frac{3}{8}$ (*d*) $45\frac{3}{8}$
(*e*) $40\frac{5}{8}$

19. If the number of projects handled by company A increased by 20% from 2007 to 2008 and by 5% from 2008 to 2009, what was the number of projects handled by Company A in 2009?

[IBPS—RRBs (Off. Gr. 'B') Exam, 2015]

(*a*) 378 (*b*) 372
(*c*) 384 (*d*) 396
(*e*) 368

20. What is the difference between the total number of projects handled by company A in 2003 and 2004 together and the total number of projects handled by Company B in 2005 and 2007 together?

[IBPS—RRBs (Off. Gr. 'B') Exam, 2015]

(*a*) 120 (*b*) 150
(*c*) 130 (*d*) 180
(*e*) 170

Directions ***(Questions 21–25): Read the graph and answer the given questions.***

Number of visas issued by Country 'XYZ' for Country A and Country B in 6 different months.

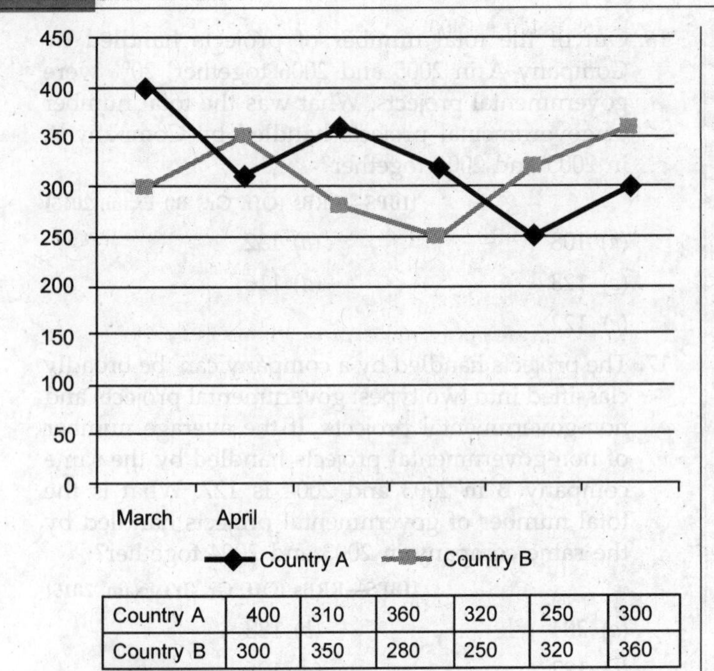

Country A	400	310	360	320	250	300
Country B	300	350	280	250	320	360

21. What is the difference between the total number of visas issued for Country A and Country B together in April and the total number of visas issued for both the countries together in June?

[IBPS Bank PO/MT CWE-V (Pre.) Exam, 2015]

(*a*) 90 (*b*) 70
(*c*) 110 (*d*) 100
(*e*) 80

22. What is the average number of visas issued for Country B in March, May, July and August?

[IBPS Bank PO/MT CWE-V (Pre.) Exam, 2015]

(*a*) 315 (*b*) 310
(*c*) 320 (*d*) 335
(*e*) 325

23. The number of visas issued for Country A in March decreased by 20% from the previous month. What is the respective ratio between the number of visas issued for Country A in February and the number of visas issued for the same country in May?

[IBPS Bank PO/MT CWE-V (Pre.) Exam, 2015]

(*a*) 25 : 13 (*b*) 25 : 18
(*c*) 26 : 13 (*d*) 24 : 13
(*e*) 26 : 15

24. The number of visas issued for Country A decreased by what percent from May to July?

[IBPS Bank PO/MT CWE-V (Pre.) Exam, 2015]

(*a*) $35\frac{1}{3}$ (*b*) 33
(*c*) $30\frac{9}{5}$ (*d*) $32\frac{2}{3}$
(*e*) $32\frac{4}{9}$

25. The number of visas issued for Country B in March is what percent less than the number of visas issued for Country A in June?

[IBPS Bank PO/MT CWE-V (Pre.) Exam, 2015]

(*a*) 8.5 (*b*) 7.75
(*c*) 4.25 (*d*) 6.25
(*e*) 5.75

ANSWERS

1. (*b*)	2. (*b*)	3. (*e*)	4. (*b*)	5. (*a*)	6. (*d*)	7. (*b*)	8. (*d*)	9. (*e*)	10. (*b*)
11. (*b*)	12. (*e*)	13. (*d*)	14. (*a*)	15. (*c*)	16. (*e*)	17. (*d*)	18. (*e*)	19. (*a*)	20. (*b*)
21. (*a*)	22. (*a*)	23. (*b*)	24. (*c*)	25. (*d*)					

SOLUTIONS

1. Total number of calories burnt by A and B together on Wednesday = 90 + 125 = 215
Total number of calories burnt by A and B together on Tuesday = 185 + 100 = 285
Required ratio = 215 : 285 = 43 : 57

2. Total number of calories burnt on Saturday
$=180 \times \frac{110}{100} + 145 \times \frac{120}{100}$
= 198 + 174 = 372

3. Total number of calories burnt by
A = 185 + 90 + 160 = 435

4. Average calories = 125 Total calories = 3 × 125 = 375
Number of calories burnt on Saturday = 375 – 280 = 95

5. Required percentage = $\frac{60}{75}\times 100 = 80\%$

6. Total Number of watches sold in Town X in January, February, March and June = 120 + 140 +180 + 240 = 680
Required average = $\frac{680}{4} = 170$

7. The number of watches sold in Town Y in April = 210
The number of watches sold in Town X in April = 150
Required percentage = $\frac{210-150}{150}\times 100 = \frac{60}{150}\times 100 = 40\%$

8. Number of Watches sold in Town Y in February = 120
Number of Watches sold in Town Y in May = 230

Required percentage increase

$= \frac{230-120}{120} \times 100 = \frac{110}{120} \times 100 = \frac{110 \times 5}{6}$

$= \frac{275}{3} = 91\frac{2}{3}\%$

9. Number of watches sold in Town X in the month of May = 180

Number of watches sold in Town X in the month of July

$= \frac{180 \times 110}{100} = 198$

Number of watches sold in Town X in the month of January = 120

$\therefore$ Required ratio $= \frac{198}{120} = \frac{33}{20} = 33:20$

10. Total number of watches sold in both the towns together in the month of June = 240 + 180 = 420

Total number of watches sold in both the towns together in March = 180 + 150 = 330

Required difference = 420 − 330 = 90

11. Profit percent earned by company B in 2009 = 35%

Profit percent earned by company B in 2010 = 50%

Expenditure of company B in 2009 = 12 lakhs

Expenditure of company B in 2010 = 14.5 lakhs

Income of company B in 2009 = 35% = $\frac{I-E}{E} \times 100$

$\Rightarrow 35 = \frac{(I - 12 \text{ lakh})}{12 \text{ lakh}} \times 100$

$\Rightarrow$ (35 × 12) Lakh = 100I − 1200 lakh

$\Rightarrow$ 420 lakh = 100I − 1200 lakh

$\Rightarrow$ I = 16.20 lakh

Income of company B in 2009 = 50% = $\frac{I-E}{E} \times 100$

$\Rightarrow 50 = \frac{I - 14.5 \text{ lakh}}{14.5 \text{ lakh}} \times 100$

$\Rightarrow$ (50 × 14.5) lakh = 100I − 14.50 lakh

$\Rightarrow$ 2175 = (100) I $\Rightarrow$ I = 21.75 lakhs

So, total income of company B in 2009 and 2010

= 16.2 + 21.75

= ₹ 37.95 Lakhs

12. For company A, In 2012

$P\% = \frac{I-E}{E} \times 100$

$\Rightarrow 30 = \frac{I-3}{3} \times 100$

$\Rightarrow 90 = 100\,I - 300$

$\Rightarrow \frac{390}{100} = I$

$\Rightarrow I = 3.9$

For company B, in 2012

$P\% = \frac{I-E}{E} \times 100$

$40 = v$

$\Rightarrow 160 = 100\,I - 400$

$\Rightarrow \frac{560}{100} = I$

$\Rightarrow I = 5.6$

Then required ratio $= \frac{3.9}{5.6} = \frac{39}{56}$

13. Solution cannot be determined because profit percentage of company A in all the years are not given.

14. Let the income of company A in 2013 = x

Let the income of company B in 2013 = $(5.7 - x)$

Expenditure of company A = Expenditure of Company B = E $\frac{40}{100} = \frac{x-E}{E} \times 100$

$\frac{x}{E} = 1.4$ .... (i) and $\frac{45}{100} = \frac{(5.7-x)-E}{E}$

$\Rightarrow \frac{5.7-x}{E} = 14.5$ ...(ii)

Divide equation (ii) by (i) we get

$\Rightarrow \frac{5.7-x}{E} \times \frac{E}{x} = \frac{145}{140}$

$\Rightarrow \frac{5.7x}{x} = \frac{145}{140}$

$\Rightarrow 5.7 \times 140 - 140x = 145x$

$\Rightarrow 798 = 285x$

$\Rightarrow x = 2.8$ lakhs

$\because \frac{x}{E} = 1.4$

E = 2 lakhs

Total expenditure of two companies

= (2 + 2) = 4 lakhs

15. In 2010, $50 = \frac{2-E_1}{E_1} \times 100$

$\Rightarrow 50\,E_1 = 200 - 100\,E_1$

$\Rightarrow 150\,E_1 = 200$

$\Rightarrow E_1 = \frac{4}{3}$

In 2011, $45 = \frac{(3-E_2)}{E_2} \times 100$

$\Rightarrow 45\,E_2 = 300 - 100\,E_2$

$\Rightarrow 145\,E_2 = 300$

$\Rightarrow E_2 = \frac{300}{145}$

Then, $\frac{E_1}{E_2} = \frac{4}{3} \times \frac{145}{300}$

$\Rightarrow \frac{E_1}{E_2} = \frac{29}{35}$

16. Number of governmental projects handled by company A in 2005 and 2006 together = 360 + 250 = 610

Number of Governmental projects handled by company A in 2005 and 2006 together = 20% of 610 = $\frac{20 \times 610}{100} = 122$

17. Average number of non-governmental projects handled by company B = 127

Number of Non-Governmental projects handled by Company B in 2003 and 2004 is = 127 × 2 = 254

Number of Governmental projects handled by Company B in 2003 and 2004 together

= 130 + 320 − 254 = 40 − 254 = 196

18. Number of projects handled by Company B in 2004 = 320

Number of projects handled by Company B in 2006 = 190

Required decrease percentage = $\frac{320-190}{320}\times 100$

$= \frac{130}{320}\times 100 = \frac{1300}{32}\% = \frac{325}{8}$

$= 40\frac{5}{8}\%$ decrease

19. Number of projects handled by company A in 2008

= 120% of 300 = $\frac{120\times 300}{100} = 360$

Number of projects handled by Company A in 2009

= 105% of 360 = $\frac{105\times 360}{100} = 378$

20. The number of projects handled by company A in 2003 and 2004 together = 180 + 230 = 410

The number of projects handled by company B in 2005 and 2007 together = 210 + 350 = 560

Required difference = 560 − 410 = 150

21. Visas issued for country A and country B in April

= 310 + 350 = 660

Visas issued for country A and country B in June

= 320 + 250 = 570

Required difference

= 660 − 570 = 90

22. Total number of visas issued for country B in March May, July and August

= 300 + 280 + 320 + 360 = 1260

Required average = $\frac{300+280+320+360}{4}$

$= \frac{1260}{4} = 315$

23. Number of visas for country A in February

$= \frac{400\times 100}{80} = 500$

∴ Required ratio = 500 : 360

= 25 : 18

24. Number of visas issued for country A in May = 360

Number of visas issued for country A in July = 250

Percentage decrease = $\frac{360-250}{360}\times 100$

$= \frac{1100}{36} = \frac{275}{9} = 30\frac{5}{9}\%$

25. Number of visas issued for country B in March = 300

Number of visas issued for country A in June = 320

Required percent = $\frac{320-300}{320}\times 100$